RHS PLANT FINDER 2006-2007

Devised by Chris Philip
and Realised by Tony Lord

Consultant Editor
Tony Lord

RHS Editors
James Armitage Janet Cubey
Neil Lancaster Christopher Whitehouse

Compiler
Judith Merrick

A Dorling Kindersley Book

London, New York, Munich, Melbourne, Delhi

Published by
Dorling Kindersley Ltd
80 Strand, London WC2R 0RL
A Penguin company

First edition April 1987
Twentieth edition April 2006

British Library Cataloguing Publication Data.
A Catalogue record for this book is available from the British Library.

ISBN 1 4053 1455 9

Compiled by
The Royal Horticultural Society
80 Vincent Square,
London SW1P 2PE
Registered charity no: 222879

www.rhs.org.uk

Royal Horticultural Society

Illustrations by Sarah Young
Maps by Alan Cooper

Produced for Dorling Kindersley Ltd by
COOLING BROWN
Printed and bound in England by Clays Ltd, St Ives Plc

The Compiler and the Editors of the *RHS Plant Finder* have taken every care, in the time available, to check all the information supplied to them by the nurseries concerned. Nevertheless, in a work of this kind, containing as it does hundreds of thousands of separate computer encodings, errors and omissions will, inevitably, occur. Neither the RHS, the Publisher nor the Editors can accept responsibility for any consequences that may arise from such errors.

If you find mistakes we hope that you will let us know so that the matter can be corrected in the next edition.

Contents

INTRODUCTION

The *RHS Plant Finder* exists to put enthusiastic gardeners in touch with suppliers of plants. The book is divided into two related sections – PLANTS and NURSERIES. PLANTS includes an A–Z Plant Directory of some 73,000 plant names, against which are listed a series of nursery codes. These codes point the reader to the full nursery details contained in the NURSERIES section towards the back of the book.

The *RHS Plant Finder* is comprehensively updated every year and provides the plant lover with the richest source of suppliers known to us, whether you are looking for plants locally, shopping from your armchair or touring the country in search of the rare and unusual.

NEW IN THIS EDITION

This year's essay looks at the topical subject of plant conservation and has been drawn together by Dr Janet Cubey, RHS Principal Botanist. The RHS and NCCPG will be holding a joint conference on this subject in April 2006.

In this edition of the ***RHS Plant Finder***, revision to plant names has been concentrated in the genera *Hydrangea*, *Syringa* and *Sorbus*. Sharp-eyed readers may also notice some additional classification codes in the genus *Dahlia*, noteably for the increasily popular double-orchid and single-orchid (also known as star) dahlias. The genus *Acis* has also been recognised by the RHS Advisory Panel on Nomenclature and Taxonomy, following increasing evidence in the literature, as being distinct from *Leucojum* and therefore appears in this edition for the first time.

As you will see from the entries in the NURSERY DETAILS BY CODE many nurseries do not now publish a printed catalogue but produce an online version only. This is a growing trend, fuelled by the cost of printing a full catalogue.

It is important to remember when ordering that many of the nurseries listed in the book are small, family-run, businesses that propagate their own material. They cannot therefore guarantee to hold large stocks of the plants they list. Many will, however, propagate to order.

AVAILABLE FROM THE COMPILER

APPLICATION FOR ENTRY

Nurseries appearing in the *RHS Plant Finder* for the first time this year are printed in bold type in the *Nursery Index by Name* starting on p.910.

If you wish your nursery to be considered for inclusion in the next edition of the *RHS Plant Finder* (2007-2008), please write for details to the Compiler at the address below.

PLANTS LAST LISTED IN EARLIER EDITIONS

Plants cease to be listed for a variety of reasons. For more information turn to *How to Use the Plant Directory* on p.18.

A listing of the 34,000 or so plants listed in earlier editions, but for which we currently have no known supplier, is available from the Compiler. Please send a self-addressed A4 envelope stamped with £1.10 stamps. This is also available in electronic format.

LISTS OF NURSERIES FOR PLANTS WITH MORE THAN 30 SUPPLIERS

To prevent the book from becoming too big, we do not print the nursery codes where more than 30 nurseries offer the same plant. The plant is then listed as having "More than 30 suppliers". This is detailed more fully in *How to Use the Plant Directory* on p.18.

If any readers have difficulty in finding such a plant, we will be pleased to send a full list of all the nurseries that we have on file as stockists. All such enquiries must include the full name of the plant being sought, as shown in the *RHS Plant Finder*, together with an A5 size SAE. For more than one plant, please send an A4 1st class SAE.

The above may all be obtained from:
The Compiler, *RHS Plant Finder*, RHS Garden Wisley, Woking, Surrey GU23 6QB
Email: plantfinder@rhs.org.uk

THE RHS PLANT FINDER ONLINE

The *RHS Plant Finder* is available on the Internet. Visit the Royal Horticultural Society's website **www.rhs.org.uk** and search the *RHS Plant Finder* database online.

TO AVOID DISAPPOINTMENT, WE SUGGEST THAT YOU ALWAYS

check with the nursery before visiting or ordering and always use the current edition of the book.

ACKNOWLEDGMENTS

Judith Merrick, assisted by Saiqa Hussain and Patty Boardman, compiled this year's edition, whilst Richard Sanford managed the editing of the plant names on the database. Rupert Wilson and Graham Hawkes administered the Horticultural Database using the BG-BASE ™ Collection Management Software from which the book is produced.

We would like to acknowledge the help of Simon Maughan, RHS Publications, London, John David, RHS Head of Botany, Kerry Walter of BG-BASE (UK) Ltd., Max Phillips of Strange Software Ltd. and Alan Cooper, who produces the nursery maps.

There have been further staff changes in the Botany Department at Wisley this year, with the retirement of Diana Miller as Keeper of the Herbarium. We should like to take this opportunity to thank her for the help and information she has given us over the years. We are pleased that Christopher Whitehouse has now taken over as Keeper of the Herbarium and we are exceedingly grateful to him for continuing to play a very active editing role, alongside James Armitage and Neil Lancaster, during this ***RHS Plant Finder*** season.

Once again this year we are indebted to our colleagues on the RHS Advisory Panel on Nomenclature and Taxonomy, along with the RHS International Registrars all of whom have provided much valuable guidance and information. Scores of nurseries have sent helpful information about plants which has proved immensely useful in verifying some of the most obscure names, as well as suggesting corrections to existing entries. Some of these suggested corrections remain to be checked and entered in our next edition and we are grateful for your patience while information is checked and processed, though those that contravene the Codes of Nomenclature may have to be rejected. We are grateful, too, to our regular correspondents.

Cistus	R. Page ('97, '99 & '02)
Clematis	V. Matthews, International Registrar, RHS ('00–'06)
Cotoneaster	Jeanette Fryer, NCCPG Collection Holder ('99)
Dahlia	R. Hedge, RHS Wisley ('96–'00 & '02)
Dianthus	Dr A.C. Leslie, International Registrar, RHS Wisley ('91–'00 & '02)
Erica	Dr E.C. Nelson, International Registrar
Geranium	D.X. Victor, International Registrar ('03)
Hebe	Mrs J. Hewitt ('94–'99)
Ilex	Ms S. Andrews ('92–'98)
Iris	Mrs J. Hewitt ('95–'99, '02 & '05)
Jovibarba & *Sempervivum*	P.J. Mitchell, International Registrar, Sempervivum Society ('98)
Lavandula	Ms S. Andrews ('02, '03 & '05)
Lilium	Dr A.C. Leslie, International Registrar, RHS Wisley ('91–'00 & '02)
Liriope	Dr P.R. Fantz ('99)
Meconopsis	Dr E. Stevens ('02, '03 & '05)
Narcissus	Mrs S. Kington, International Registrar, RHS ('91–'00 & '02)
Ophiopogon	Dr P.R. Fantz ('99)
Rhododendron	Dr A.C. Leslie, International Registrar, RHS Wisley ('91–'00 & '02)
Sorbus	Dr H. McAllister ('01)
Thymus	Mrs M. Easter ('03–'06)

To all these, as well as to the many readers and nurseries who have also made comments and suggestions, we are once again extremely grateful.

Tony Lord, Consultant Editor, and Janet Cubey, RHS Principal Botanist, February 2006

CONSERVATION AND THE ENVIRONMENT

As the ***RHS Plant Finder*** demonstrates, gardens in Britain have been greatly enriched by the diversity of plants introduced to cultivation from abroad. Whilst the vast majority of those introduced have enhanced our gardens, a few have proved to be highly invasive and to threaten native habitats. Once such plants are established it is very difficult, costly and potentially damaging to native eco-systems to eradicate or control the invasive "alien" species. Gardeners can help by choosing not to buy or distribute non-native invasive plants and by taking steps to prevent them escaping into the wild and by disposing of them in a responsible way.

The top seven invasive non-native species are no longer listed in the *RHS Plant Finder*. Any cultivars or varieties of them that are listed are believed to be less invasive than the species themselves. These seven plants are:

Azolla filiculoides - fairy fern
Crassula helmsii - New Zealand pygmy weed
Fallopia japonica - Japanese knotweed
Heracleum mantegazzianum - giant hogweed
Hydrocotyle ranunculoides - floating pennywort
Impatiens glandulifera - Himalayan balsam
Myriophyllum aquaticum - parrot's feather

Bringing plants back from abroad

Travelling can be a great source of inspiration for gardeners and often provides an introduction to new and interesting plants. Anyone thinking of bringing plants back into Britain from overseas must realise, however, that this is a complex matter. Various regulations are in force which apply to amateur gardeners as well as to commercial nurseries. The penalties for breaking these can be serious.

Some of the most important regulatory bodies are listed below.

Plant Health regulations are in place to control the spread of pests and diseases. Plants are divided into the categories of prohibited, controlled and unrestricted, but there are also limits that vary according to the part of the world you are travelling from. For full details contact the Plant Health division of DEFRA, or visit www.defra.gov.uk/planth/ph.htm
DEFRA has produced a leaflet that summarises the Horticultural Code of Practice. This is available online at www.defra.gov.uk or by phoning the helpline on 08459 335577.

The Convention on International Trade in Endangered Species (CITES) affects the transport of animal and plant material across international boundaries. Its aim is to prevent exploitative trade and thereby to prevent harm and the ultimate extinction of wild populations. Export and import licences are required for any plants listed on the CITES Appendices. A broad range of plants is covered in these Appendices, including *Cactaceae* and *Orchidaceae* and, although species are mentioned in the convention title, the restrictions cover all cultivars and hybrids too. Details of the plants listed in the Appendices can be found on the CITES website, www.ukcites.gov.uk/intro/cites_species.htm, or in the leaflets detailed below.

The Convention on Biological Diversity (CBD or the "Rio Convention") recognises the property rights of individual countries in relation to their own biodiversity. It exists to enable access to that biodiversity, but equally to ensure the sharing of any benefit derived from it. Export permits are required for plant material taken from the country of origin, with prior informed consent being gained for any uses that the material will be used for in the future.
Further information on the Convention can be found on the CBD website, www.biodiv.org.

If you would like to read more about these subjects, *Conservation and Environment Guidelines* leaflets are available on request from the RHS. Please write to the Compiler at the address given on page 4 enclosing an A4 SAE, or find them online at www.rhs.org.uk/publications. Leaflets are also available on a wider range of subjects, with topics including:

Peat and the gardener
Potentially harmful garden plants
The use of limestone in horticulture
Trees and timber products
Wild and endangered plants in cultivation
Wildlife in gardens

EXTENDED GLOSSARY

This glossary combines some of the helpful introductory sections from older editions in an alphabetical listing. A fuller, more discursive account of plant names, *Guide to Plant Names,* and a detailed guide to the typography of plant names, *Recommended Style for Printing Plant Names,* are both available as RHS Advisory Leaflets. To request a copy of either please send an A4 SAE to The Compiler at the contact address given on page 4.

ADVISORY PANEL ON NOMENCLATURE AND TAXONOMY

This Panel advises the RHS on individual problems of nomenclature regarding plants in cultivation and, in particular, use of names in the *RHS Horticultural Database*, reflected in the annual publication of the *RHS Plant Finder*.

The aim is always to make the plant names in the *RHS Plant Finder* as consistent, reliable and stable as possible and acceptable to gardeners and botanists alike, not only in the British Isles but around the world. Recent proposals to change or correct names are examined with the aim of creating a balance between the stability of well-known names and botanical and taxonomic correctness. In some cases the Panel feels that the conflicting views on the names of some groups of plants will not easily be resolved. The Panel's policy is then to wait and review the situation once a more obvious consensus is reached, rather than rush to rename plants only to have to change them again when opinions have shifted.

The Panel is chaired by Dr Alan Leslie (RHS) with Dr Janet Cubey (RHS) (Vice-Chair) and includes: Dr Crinan Alexander (RBGE), Susyn Andrews, Chris Brickell, Dr James Compton, Dr John David (RHS), Mike Grant (RHS Publications), Dr Stephen Jury (University of Reading), Sabina Knees, Dr Tony Lord, Julian Shaw (RHS) & Adrian Whiteley, with Dr Christopher Whitehouse (RHS) as Secretary.

AUTHORITIES

In order that plant names can be used with precision throughout the scientific world, the name of the person who coined the name of a plant species (its author, or authority) is added to the plant name. Usually this information is irrelevant to gardeners, except in cases where the same name has been given to two different plants or a name is commonly misapplied. Although only one usage is correct, both may be encountered in books, so indicating the author is the only way to be certain about which plant is being referred to. This can happen equally with cultivars. Authors' names, where it is appropriate to cite them, appear in a smaller typeface after the species or cultivar name to which they refer and are abbreviated following Brummitt and Powell's *Authors of Plant Names*.

♀ AWARD OF GARDEN MERIT

The Award of Garden Merit (AGM) is intended to be of practical value to the ordinary gardener and is therefore awarded only after a period of assessment by the Society's Standing and Joint Committees. An AGM plant:

- must be available
- must be of outstanding excellence for garden decoration or use
- must be of good constitution
- must not require highly specialist growing conditions or care
- must not be particularly susceptible to any pest or disease
- must not be subject to an unreasonable degree of reversion

The AGM symbol is cited in conjunction with the **hardiness** rating. The RHS publication *AGM Plants 2006–07* gives the full list of AGM plants. Copies can be ordered from RHS Enterprises on (01483) 211320. Information about AGM plants is also available on the RHS website at www.rhs.org.uk.

BOTANICAL NAMES

The aim of the botanical naming system is to provide each different plant with a single, unique, universal name. The basic unit of plant classification is the species. Species that share a number of significant characteristics are grouped together to form a genus (plural **genera**). The name of a species is made up of two elements; the name of the genus followed by the specific epithet, for example, *Narcissus romieuxii.*

Variation within a species can be recognised by division into subspecies (usually abbreviated to subsp.), varietas (or variety abbreviated to var.) and forma (or form abbreviated to f.). Whilst it is unusual for a plant to have all of these, it is possible, as in this example, *Narcissus romieuxii* subsp. *albidus* var. *zaianicus* f. *lutescens*.

The botanical elements are always given in italics, with only the genus taking an initial capital letter. The rank indications are never in italics. In instances where the rank is not known it is necessary to form an invalid construction by quoting a second epithet without a rank. This is an unsatisfactory situation, but requires considerable research to resolve.

CLASSIFICATION OF GENERA

Genera that include a large number of species or with many cultivars are often subdivided into informal horticultural classifications or more formal Cultivar Groups, each based on a particular characteristic or combination of characteristics. Colour of flower or fruit and shape of flower are common examples and, with fruit, whether a cultivar is grown for culinary or dessert purposes. How such groups are named differs from genus to genus.

To help users of the *RHS Plant Finder* find the plants they want, the classifications used within cultivated genera are listed using codes and plants are marked with the appropriate code in brackets after its name in the Plant Directory. To find the explanation of each code, simply look it up under the genus concerned in the **Classification of Genera** starting on p.28. The codes relating to edible fruits are also listed here, but these apply across several genera.

COLLECTORS' REFERENCES

Abbreviations (usually with numbers) following a plant name refer to the collector(s) of the plant. These abbreviations are expanded, with a collector's name or expedition title, in the section **Collectors' References** starting on p.20.

A collector's reference may indicate a new, as yet unnamed range of variation within a species. The inclusion of collectors' references in the *RHS Plant Finder* supports the book's role in sourcing unusual plants.

The Convention on Biological Diversity calls for conservation of biodiversity, its sustainable use and the fair and equitable sharing of any derived benefits. Since its adoption in 1993, collectors are required to have prior informed consent from the country of origin for the acquisition and commercialisation of collected material.

COMMON NAMES

In a work such as this, it is necessary to refer to plants by their botanical names for the sake of universal comprehension and clarity. However, at the same time we recognise that with fruit and vegetables most people are more familiar with their common names than their botanical ones. Cross-references are therefore given from common to botanical names for fruit, vegetables and the commoner culinary herbs throughout the Plant Directory.

CULTIVAR

Literally meaning cultivated variety, cultivar names are given to denote variation within species and that generated by hybridisation, in cultivation. To make them easily distinguishable from botanical names, they are not printed in italics and are enclosed in single quotation marks. Cultivar names coined since 1959 should follow the rules of the International Code of Nomenclature for Cultivated Plants (**ICNCP**).

DESCRIPTIVE TERMS

Terms that appear after the main part of the plant name are shown in a smaller font to distinguish them. These descriptive elements give extra information about the plant and may include the **collector's reference**, **authority**, or what colour it is. For example, *Fritillaria thessala* SBEL 443, *Penstemon* 'Sour Grapes' M. Fish, *Lobelia tupa* dark orange.

FAMILIES

Genera are grouped into larger groups of related plants called families. Most family names, with the exception of eight familiar names, end with the same group of letters, *-aceae*. While it is still acceptable to use these eight exceptions, the modern trend adopted in the *RHS Plant Finder* is to use alternative names with *–aceae* endings. The families concerned are *Compositae* (*Asteraceae*), *Cruciferae* (*Brassicaceae*), *Gramineae* (*Poaceae*), *Guttiferae* (*Clusiaceae*), *Labiatae* (*Lamiaceae*), *Leguminosae* (split here into *Caesalpiniaceae*, *Mimosaceae* and *Papilionaceae*), *Palmae* (*Arecaceae*) and *Umbelliferae* (*Apiceae*). Also the traditionally large family *Liliaceae* is split into a number of smaller, more natural, families that as yet may be unfamiliar to readers.
Apart from these exceptions we follow Brumitt's *Vascular Plant Families and Genera* for our family names.

GENUS (plural – GENERA)

Genera used in the *RHS Plant Finder* are almost always those given in Brummitt's *Vascular Plant Families and Genera*. For spellings and genders of generic names, Greuter's *Names in Current Use for Extant Plant Genera* has also been consulted. See **Botanical Names**.

GREX

Within orchids, hybrids of the same parentage, regardless of how alike they are, are given a grex name. Individuals can be selected, given cultivar names and propagated vegetatively. For example, *Pleione* Versailles gx 'Bucklebury', where Versailles is the grex name and 'Bucklebury' is a selected **cultivar**.

GROUP

This is a collective name for a group of cultivars within a genus with similar characteristics. The word Group is always included and, where cited with a cultivar name, it is enclosed in brackets, for example, *Actaea simplex* (Atropurpurea Group) 'Brunette', where 'Brunette' is a distinct cultivar in a group of purple-leaved cultivars.

Another example of a Group is *Rhododendron polycladum* Scintillans Group. In this case *Rhododendron scintillans* was a species that is now botanically 'sunk' within *R. polycladum*, but it is still recognised horticulturally as a Group.

Group names are also used for swarms of hybrids with the same parentage, for example, *Rhododendron* Polar Bear Group. These were formerly treated as **grex** names, a term now used only for orchids. A single clone from the Group may be given the same cultivar name, for example, *Rhododendron* 'Polar Bear'.

HARDINESS

Hardiness ratings are shown for **Award of Garden Merit** plants. The categories used are as follows:

H1 = plants requiring heated glass in the British Isles
H2 = plants requiring unheated glass in the British Isles
H3 = plants hardy outside in some regions of the British Isles or in particular situations, or which, while usually grown outside in summer, need frost-free protection in winter (eg. dahlias)
H4 = plants hardy throughout the British Isles
H1-2, H2-3, H3-4 = plants intermediate between the two ratings given
H1+3 = requiring heated glass; may be grown outside in summer

HYBRIDS

Some species, when grown together, in the wild or in cultivation, are found to interbreed and form hybrids. In some instances a hybrid name is coined, for example hybrids between *Primula hirsuta* and *P. minima* are given the name *Primula* × *forsteri*, the multiplication sign indicating hybrid origin. Hybrid formulae that quote the parentage of the hybrid are used where a unique name has not been coined, for example *Rhododendron calophytum* × *R. praevernum*. Hybrids between different genera are also possible, for example × *Mahoberberis* is the name given to hybrids between *Mahonia* and *Berberis*.

There are also a few special-case hybrids called graft hybrids, where the tissues of two plants are physically rather than genetically mixed. These are indicated by an addition rather than a multiplication sign, so *Laburnum* + *Cytisus* becomes +*Laburnocytisus*.

ICNCP

The ICNCP is the International Code of Nomenclature for Cultivated Plants. First published in 1959, the most recent edition was published in 2004.

Cultivar names that do not conform to this Code, and for which there is no valid alternative, are flagged I (for invalid). This code states that the minimum requirement is for a cultivar name to be given in conjunction with the name of the genus. However, in the ***RHS Plant Finder*** we choose to give as full a name as possible to give the gardener and botanist more information about the plant.

NOTES ON NOMENCLATURE AND IDENTIFICATION

The **Notes on Nomenclature and Identification**, starting on p.23, give further information for names that are complex or may be confusing. See also **Advisory Panel on Nomenclature and Taxonomy**.

PLANT BREEDERS' RIGHTS

Plants covered by an *active* grant of Plant Breeders' Rights (PBR) are indicated throughout the Plant Directory. Grants indicated are those awarded by both UK and EU Plant Variety Rights offices. Because grants can both come into force and lapse at any time, this book can only aim to represent the situation at one point in time, but it is hoped that this will act as a useful guide to growers and gardeners. UK grants represent the position as of the end of December 2005 and EU grants as of the end of October 2005. We do not give any indication where PBR grants may be pending.

To obtain PBR protection, a new plant must be registered and pass tests for distinctness, uniformity and stability under an approved name. This approved name, under the rules of the **ICNCP**, established by a legal process, has to be regarded as the cultivar name. Increasingly however, these approved names are a code or "nonsense" name and are therefore often unpronounceable and meaningless, so the plants are given other names designed to attract sales when they are released. These secondary names are often referred to as selling names but are officially termed **trade designations**.

For further information on UK PBR contact:

Mr R Greenaway
Plant Variety Rights Office, White House Lane, Huntingdon Road, Cambridge CB3 0LF
Tel: (01223) 342396
Fax: (01223) 342386.
Website: www.defra.gov.uk/planth/pvs/default.htm

For details of plants covered by EU Community Rights contact the Community Plant Variety Office (CPVO):

Office Communautaire des Variétés Végétales, PO Box 62141, 3 Boulevard Maréchal Foch, F-49021 Angers, Cedex 02, France
Tel: 00 33 (02) 41 25 64 00
Fax: 00 33 (02) 41 25 64 10
Website: www.cpvo.eu.int

The *RHS Plant Finder* takes no responsibility for ensuring that nurseries selling plants with PBR are licensed to do so.

Reverse Synonyms

It is likely that users of this book will come across names in certain genera that they did not expect to find. This may be because species have been transferred from another genus (or **genera**). In the list of **Reverse Synonyms** on p.33, the name on the left-hand side is that of an accepted genus to which species have been transferred from the genus on the right. Sometimes all species will have been transferred, but in many cases only a few will be affected. Consulting **Reverse Synonyms** enables users to find the genera from which species have been transferred. Where the right-hand genus is found in the Plant Directory, the movement of species becomes clear through the cross-references in the nursery code column.

Selling Names

See **Trade Designations**

Series

With seed-raised plants and some popular vegetatively-propagated plants, especially bedding plants and pot plants such as *Petunia* or *Impatiens*, Series have become increasingly popular. A Series contains a number of similar cultivars, but differs from a **Group** in that it is a marketing device, with cultivars added to create a range of flower colours in plants of similar habit. Individual colour elements within a species may be represented by slightly different cultivars over the years. Series names are styled similarly to **Groups**.

Species

See under **Botanical Names**

Subspecies

See under **Botanical Names**

Synonyms

Although the ideal is for each species or cultivar to have only one name, anyone dealing with plants soon comes across a situation where one plant has received two or more names, or two plants have received the same name. In each case, only one name and application, for reasons of precision and stability, can be regarded as correct. Additional names are known as synonyms. Further information on synonyms and why plants change names is available in *Guide to Plant Names*. See the introduction to this glossary for details of how to request a copy.

See also **Reverse Synonyms**.

Trade Designations

A **trade designation** is the name used to market a plant when the cultivar name is considered unsuitable for selling purposes. It is styled in a different typeface and without single quotation marks.

In the case of **Plant Breeders' Rights** it is a legal requirement for the cultivar name to appear with the trade designation on a label at the point of sale. Most plants are sold under only one trade designation, but some, especially roses, are sold under a number of names, particularly when cultivars are introduced from other countries. Usually, the correct cultivar name is the only way to ensure that the same plant is not bought unwittingly under two or more different trade designations. The *RHS Plant Finder* follows the recommendations of the **ICNCP** when dealing with trade designations and PBR. These are always to quote the cultivar name and trade designation together and to style the trade designation in a different typeface, without single quotation marks.

Translations

When a cultivar name is translated from the language of first publication, the translation is regarded as a **trade designation** and styled accordingly. We endeavour to recognise the original cultivar name in every case and to give an English translation where it is in general use.

VARIEGATED PLANTS

Following a suggestion from the Variegated Plant Group of the Hardy Plant Society, a (v) is cited after those plants which are "variegated". The dividing line between variegation and less distinct colour marking is necessarily arbitrary and plants with light veins, pale, silver or dark zones, or leaves flushed in paler colours, are not shown as being variegated unless there is an absolutely sharp distinction between paler and darker zones.

For further details of the Variegated Plant Group, please write to:

Jerry Webb, Esq.,
17 Heron Way, Minster Heights,
Ilminster TA19 0BX

VARIETY

See under **Botanical Names** and **Cultivar**

'The question of nomenclature is always a vexed one. The only thing certain is, that it is impossible to please everyone.'

W.J. BEAN – PREFACE TO FIRST EDITION OF *Trees & Shrubs Hardy in the British Isles*

PLANT CONSERVATION

Plant Conservation – two words that are often heard, but what image do they conjure up for you?

- The conservation of our native British flora in its natural habitats or in our gardens
- The conservation of plants from around the world in their native habitats or in gardens throughout the world
- The conservation of rare cultivars of plants in our gardens
- The conservation of an individual plant of historical or cultural importance.

In reality, plant conservation embraces all of these and more.

In 1978, the RHS held a conference looking at *The Practical Role of Gardens in the Conservation of Rare and Threatened Plants*, which resulted in the creation of the National Council for the Conservation of Plants & Gardens (NCCPG) and led to the establishment of the National Plant Collection scheme.

Since then the global environment, in relation to conservation of plants and the movement of plant genetic resources, has changed fundamentally, setting new challenges for plant conservation today. So in April 2006, the RHS and the NCCPG are holding a joint conference, *Growing Heritage – Garden Plants and Conservation*, which will aim to build upon what has already been achieved, to raise awareness of the importance of cultivated plants and the responsible use of wild-collected material in gardens, and to agree on an action plan for the conservation of plants in gardens in the future.

In summary, the five key objectives of the conference, focusing on knowledge, education, strategy, enhancing diversity and best practice, are:

- To improve and share information about cultivated plants and their conservation
- To promote the role of gardeners and gardens in plant conservation
- To increase resources for cultivated plant conservation
- To help plant collectors and the nursery trade work with biodiversity regulation
- To use and develop genetic resources for horticulture responsibly.

For further information about these objectives and to see the Action Plan resulting from the discussions at this conference, please visit the *Growing Heritage* website, www.growingheritage.org.uk

---

Conservation stories

These can help to highlight the importance and diversity of plant conservation activities. In preparation for the conference we have been gathering conservation stories together. The following is a selection. If you would like to add a story to our growing collection, then please do get in touch at growingheritage@rhs.org.uk.

Cosmos atrosanguineus

This is an attractive, popular, chocolate-scented garden plant, but is believed to be extinct in the wild. It was first discovered in Mexico in the 1860s, and has remained in cultivation ever since, gaining an RHS Award of Merit for Exhibition in 1938. It has not, however, been re-discovered in the wild, although plants are now being re-introduced from micropropagated material at the Royal Botanic Gardens, Kew.

Until recently, all the plants in cultivation were thought to be a single clone that was self-incompatible and therefore did not set seed. A fertile form called 'Pinot Noir' has now been introduced to cultivation from New Zealand and is protected in most countries by Plant Breeders' Rights.

Cosmos atrosanguineus is widely available, but the cultivar 'Pinot Noir' has not yet made it into the *RHS Plant Finder* – maybe next year?

***Dianthus* (Malmaison)**

Malmaison carnations, with their distinctive fragrance of cloves, were popular from the 1860s until the First World War. The combined effect of the reduction of staff in estate gardens and a virus affecting the plants meant that by the end of the 20th century the flowers were nearly lost to cultivation.

National Plant Collection holder Jim Marshall rediscovered some Malmaison carnations in the Scottish gardens of Sir George Taylor. These included 'Souvenir de la Malmaison', 'Princess of Wales', 'Duchess of Westminster' and 'Thora'. Bulked up by micropropagation and virus-reduced, Marshall's Malmaisons now produce rooted cuttings for the retail trade, resulting in a number of prominent gardens growing them again. These cultivars are all listed in the *RHS Plant Finder*.

Brodie Daffodils

Daffodils did not become popular garden plants until the end of the 19th century. In 1880 the nurseryman Peter Barr grew about 500 varieties; by 1907 the RHS had published a list of 1,400 names and the next edition of the Daffodil Register is expected to contain some 24,000.

This explosion of cultivars is largely the result of painstaking hybridisation carried out by a relatively small number of enthusiasts. One of the greatest of these was Major Ian Brodie of Brodie, the 24th Laird.

Between 1899 and 1942, Brodie raised tens of thousands of daffodil seedlings in the walled garden at Brodie Castle. His daffodil breeding was completed with military precision. His collection was planted in regular, well-labelled lines, each cross made was recorded meticulously in a notebook, often with notes on the weather and the resulting seed-set and number of seedlings raised. He deemed only 370 of the seedlings he raised to be worthy of naming, although a further 70 were named by nurserymen or fellow enthusiasts to whom he had passed on numbered stocks.

By the time the National Trust for Scotland acquired Brodie Castle in 1978, only a small number of the daffodils could be recognised with any certainty within the grounds. Only a handful of Brodie daffodils have remained in commerce: 'Coverack Perfection', 'Hexameter', 'Samaria', 'Swansdown', 'Tain', 'White Butterfly', and possibly 'Kilmorack'. Indeed, it is likely that some of the Brodie cultivars were never distributed commercially and so are now probably extinct.

However, over the past 20 years about 100 stocks have been identified and they are still coming to light, some in Australia, with leads still being pursued in the United States. It is thought that some may still survive in the UK, for example 'Cameronian', 'Gallipoli', 'Lovat Scout' or 'Sulva' in an old soldier's garden; 'Aida', 'Mozart' or 'Musician' in a musicologist's; and perhaps 'Helston', 'Penzance', 'Perth' or 'Windsor' may still be found in the places for which they were named.

Daffodils are usually naturalised in mixed, unlabelled collections. However, they have an advantage over many rare garden plants in that they can persist despite neglect. Therefore it may be enough simply to have an old planting list of cultivars to be able to find missing ones. For example, 'Silver Salver' was found recently by simply searching through a large collection where it had been recorded as growing *circa* 1956.

The Brodie daffodils have been sent to other National Trust gardens, and some stocks, of whose names we can be confident, have bulked up enough to allow them to be sold to visitors to Brodie Castle. Each sale includes a certificate, part of which is a return slip so the purchaser can register that they have a particular stock. In this way the dispersed collection is being registered, which will help to ensure that the Brodie cultivars will never again risk being lost to cultivation.

The Lorton Yew Tree

In High Lorton in Cumbria stands a particular yew tree, which most people wouldn't look at twice; yet it has great local significance. It is thought that it is the yew tree referred to in the writings of the Quaker George Fox in 1653, and it is certainly the tree that was visited in 1804 by William and Dorothy Wordsworth and which inspired his poem *Yew Trees*, which begins "There is a Yew-tree, pride of Lorton Vale, Which to this day stands single, in the midst Of its own darkness …".

In 2004, to celebrate the bicentenary of the Wordsworths' visit to the tree, a book commemorating the tree and its history in literature was published by the local history society and a vegetatively propagated plant was established in another area of the village.

***Leucanthemum* × *superbum* 'Fiona Coghill'**

Whilst undertaking research for her National Plant Collection of *Leucanthemum* × *superbum*, Lady Hagart-Alexander of Ballochmyle became particularly interested in a cultivar by the name of 'Fiona Coghill'. The plant had originally been raised nearby in Kilmacolm, Ayrshire, by Jimmy Whittock and named after his granddaughter. The catalogue description of 'large, fully double flowers' did not help much with identification, but further details describing 'the whiteness of the petals accented by the small, greenish centre' did distinguish the flower as being unusual.

Further enquiries after this cultivar in Scotland were unsuccessful, so Lady Hagart-Alexander continued her search in Ireland, where Slieve Donard had first marketed the plant in the 1960s. Eventually, Reg Maxwell of Belfast Botanic Garden made contact with Philip Woods, who had been in charge of the propagation of 'Fiona Coghill' whilst working for Slieve Donard. Attracted by the plant, Mr Woods had grown it in his own garden and, as a result, nearly seven years after starting her quest, an offset was obtained by Lady Hagart-Alexander to grow on in her National Plant Collection.

Now this cultivar is commercially available once more and listed in the *RHS Plant Finder*.

Ramosmania rodriguesii

The café marron is a highly decorative plant that can flower continuously for many months, with creamy-white flowers all along the branches. It is also a critically endangered Rodrigues endemic that had been thought lost, but a single specimen was then discovered in the early 1980s. Cuttings were flown to the Royal Botanic Gardens, Kew in a joint conservation project with IUCN and the Mauritian Forestry Commission. After propagation problems, cuttings were eventually rooted, with some being sent back to Mauritius.

More recently the self-incompatibility mechanisms have been successfully bypassed, and fruits with viable seeds have been produced. Seeds have been placed in the Millennium Seed Bank at Wakehurst Place to help prevent extinction in the longer term. Other seeds have been germinated in vitro to enable mass production of plants from a wider gene pool. Some of these will be re-introduced to Rodrigues.

Araucaria araucana

It is said that the plant-collector Archibald Menzies, who served as naturalist on Captain Vancouver's HMS *Discovery* during his voyage round the world in 1790, was dining with the Governor of Chile one night when he noticed some unusual nuts on the table and put a few in his pocket. Some of them sprouted on the voyage home, and he returned to England with five plants of *Araucaria araucana*, the monkey puzzle tree, one of which survived at Kew till 1892.

Perhaps the most famous tree of its native land, it is estimated to be 200 million years old, on the basis of fossil records. The seed forms a staple food of the Pehuenche Indians and is also sold in local Chilean markets. Each tree has a high seed yield and they are easily harvested, but the trees have a very slow rate of growth and, grown from seed, it can take up to 40 years before the next generation of seed is produced. The monkey puzzle tree is dioecious, and it is not possible to tell whether it is male or female until it flowers.

The native habitat of *Araucaria araucana* is now threatened and has been decreasing in size. The International Conifer Conservation Programme has introduced more diversity into the collections within the UK and Europe in recent years, to act as a larger gene pool resource for the future.

***Impatiens* 'Ray of Hope'**

Impatiens gordonii is a rare and threatened native of the Seychelles, and there are said to be no more than 120 plants left in the wild. *I.* 'Ray of Hope', a hybrid between *I. gordonii* and *I. walleriana*, was raised and is being sold by the Eden Project. £1 from each plant sold goes back to the Seychelles to help protect their rare and endangered plants, including *I. gordonii*, in its natural habitat.

Janet Cubey
February 2006

With grateful thanks to other members of the Growing Heritage Conference Steering Group for collating some of the plant stories.

SYMBOLS AND ABBREVIATIONS

SYMBOLS APPEARING TO THE LEFT OF THE NAME

*	Name not validated. Not listed in the appropriate International Registration Authority checklist nor in works cited in the Bibliography. For fuller discussion see p.7
I	Invalid name. See *International Code of Botanical Nomenclature 2000* and *International Code of Nomenclature for Cultivated Plants 2004*. For fuller discussion see p.7
N	Refer to Notes on Nomenclature and Identification on p.23
§	Plant listed elsewhere in the Plant Directory under a synonym
×	Hybrid genus
+	Graft hybrid genus

SYMBOLS APPEARING TO THE RIGHT OF THE NAME

✿	National Council for the Conservation of Plants and Gardens (NCCPG) National Plant Collection® exists for all or part of this genus. Provisional Collections appear in brackets. Full details of the NCCPG Plant Collections are found in the *National Plant Collections® Directory 2005* available from: www.nccpg.com or NCCPG, RHS Garden, Wisley, Woking, Surrey GU23 6QP
♀H4	The Royal Horticultural Society's Award of Garden Merit, see p.7
(d)	double-flowered
(F)	Fruit
(f)	female
(m)	male
(v)	variegated plant, see p.11
PBR	Plant Breeders Rights see p.9
new	New plant entry in this edition

For abbreviations relating to individual genera see **Classification of Genera** p.28
For **Collectors' References** see p.20
For symbols used in the **Nurseries** section see p.784

SYMBOLS AND ABBREVIATIONS USED AS PART OF THE NAME

×	hybrid species
aff.	affinis (allied to)
agg.	aggregate, a single name used to cover a group of very similar plants, regarded by some as separate species
ambig.	ambiguous, a name used by two authors for different plants and where it is unclear which is being offered
cl.	clone
cv(s)	cultivar(s)
f.	forma (botanical form)
gx	grex
sp.	species
subsp.	subspecies
subvar.	subvarietas (botanical subvariety)
var.	varietas (botanical variety)

IT IS NOT WITHIN THE REMIT OF THIS BOOK TO CHECK
that nurseries are applying the right names to the right plants or to ensure nurseries selling plants with Plant Breeders' Rights are licensed to do so.

Please, never use an old edition

RHS PLANT TRIALS BULLETINS

RHS Plant Trials Bulletins are full colour A4 booklets that provide information for both the professional and keen amateur gardener on specific plant groups.

Each year the results of some of the RHS Plant Trials are published as bulletins. These list, illustrate and describe the plants that have been given the Award of Garden Merit 🏆 during the trial. Background botanical and cultivation information is also included as are useful selection tables, comparing the different entries in the trial.

Currently the following twelve bulletins are available:

Canna
Delphinium
Hardy Fuchsias
Hardy Geraniums (Stage 1)
Hardy Lavender
Hyacinthaceae (Little Blue Bulbs)
Miscanthus
Perennial Yellow Daisies
Salad Potatoes
Shrubby Potentilla
Silver Saxifrage
Spiraea

If you would like a copy of any of these, please contact:
The Trials Office, RHS Garden Wisley, Woking, Surrey GU23 6QB. Please enclose an A4 SAE and a cheque for £2.50 per copy (a donation towards costs) made out to the Royal Horticultural Society.

To view the RHS Plant Trials Bulletins online, please visit
www.rhs.org.uk/plants/trials_bulletins.asp

PLANTS

WHATEVER PLANT YOU ARE LOOKING FOR, MAYBE AN OLD FAVOURITE OR A MORE UNUSUAL CULTIVAR, SEARCH HERE FOR A LIST OF THE SUPPLIERS THAT ARE CLOSEST TO YOU.

How to Use the Plant Directory

Nursery Codes

Look up the plant you require in the alphabetical Plant Directory. Against each plant you will find one or more four-letter codes, for example LLin, each code represents one nursery offering that plant. The first letter of each code indicates the main area of the country in which the nursery is situated. For this geographical key, refer to the **Nursery Codes and Symbols** on p.792.

Turn to the **Nursery Details by Code** starting on p.796 where, in alphabetical order of codes, you will find details of each nursery which offers the plant in question. If you wish to visit any nursery, you may find its location on one of the maps (following p.919). Please note, however, that not all nurseries, especially mail order only nurseries, choose to be shown on the maps. For a fuller explanation of how to use the nursery listings please turn to p.793. **Always check that the nursery you select has the plant in stock before you set out.**

Plants with more than 30 Suppliers

In some cases, against the plant name you will see the term 'more than 30 suppliers' instead of a nursery code. If we were to include every plant listed by all nurseries, the *RHS Plant Finder* would become unmanageably bulky. We therefore ask nurseries to restrict their entries to those plants that are not already well represented. As a result, if more than 30 nurseries offer any plant the Directory gives no nursery codes and the plant is listed instead as having 'more than 30 suppliers'. You should have little difficulty in locating these in local nurseries or garden centres. However, if you are unable to find such plants, we will be pleased to send a full list of all the nurseries that we have on file as stockists. To obtain a list, please see the Introduction on p.4.

Finding Fruit, Vegetables and Herbs

You will need to search for these by their botanical names. Common names are cross-referenced to their botanical names in the Plant Directory.

If you have Difficulty Finding your Plant

If you cannot immediately find the plant you seek, look through the various species of the genus. You may be using an incomplete name. The problem is most likely to arise in very large genera such as *Phlox* where there are a number of possible species, each with a large number of cultivars. A search through the whole genus may well bring success. Please note that, for space reasons, the following are not listed in the Plant Directory: annuals, orchids, except hardy terrestrial orchids; cacti, except hardy cacti.

Cross-references

It may be that the plant name you seek is a synonym. Our intention is to list nursery codes only against the correct botanical name. Where you find a synonym you will be cross-referred to the correct name. Occasionally you may find that the correct botanical name to which you have been referred is not listed. This is because it was last listed in an earlier edition as explained below.

Plants Last Listed in Earlier Editions

It may be that the plant you are seeking has no known suppliers and is thus not listed.

The loss of a plant name from the Directory may arise for a number of reasons – the supplier may have gone out of business, or may not have responded to our latest questionnaire and has therefore been removed from the book. Such plants may well be still available but we have no current knowledge of their whereabouts. Alternatively, some plants may have been misnamed by nurseries in previous editions, but are now appearing under their correct name.

To obtain a listing of plants last listed in earlier editions please see the Introduction on p.4.

Please, never use an old edition

USING THE PLANT DIRECTORY

The main purpose of the Plant Directory is to help the reader correctly identify the plant they seek and find its stockist. Each nursery has a unique identification code which appears to the right of the plant name. Turn to **Nursery Details by Code** (p.796) for the address, opening times and other details of the nursery. The first letter of each nursery code denotes its geographical region.

Turn to the map on p.792 to find your region code and then identify the nurseries in your area.

Another purpose of the Directory is to provide more information about the plant through the symbols and other information. For example, if it has an alternative names, is new to this edition or has received the RHS Award of Garden Merit.

Euonymus (*Celastraceae*)

	B&L 12543	EPla EWes
	B&SWJ 4457	WPGP
	CC 4522	CPLG
	alatus 🏆H4	More than 30 suppliers
	- B&SWJ 8794	WCru
	- var. ***apterus***	EPfP
	- Chicago Fire	see *E. alatus* 'Timber Creek'
	- 'Ciliodentatus'	see *E. alatus* 'Compactus'
§	- 'Compactus' 🏆H4	More than 30 suppliers
§	- 'Fire Ball'	EPfP
	- Little Moses = 'Odom'	MBlu
*	- 'Macrophyllus'	EPfP
	- 'Rudy Haag'	CPMA EPfP
	- 'Select'	see *E. alatus* 'Fire Ball'
	- 'Silver Cloud' **new**	EPfP
§	- 'Timber Creek'	CPMA EPfP MBlu MBri NLar
	americanus	EPfP GIBF MBlu NLar
	- 'Evergreen' **new**	EPfP
	- narrow-leaved	EPfP NLar
	atropurpureus	EPfP
	'Benkomoki' **new**	MGos
	bungeanus	CMCN EPfP EPla NLar
	- 'Dart's Pride'	CPMA EPfP NLar
	- 'Fireflame'	EPfP NLar
*	- var. ***mongolicus***	EPfP
	- 'Pendulus'	EPfP MBlu SIFN
	- var. ***semipersistens***	CPMA EPla
	carnosus	EPfP NLar
	'Copper Wire'	EMil SPoG
	cornutus var. ***quinquecornutus***	CPMA EPfP LPan MBlu NBhm NLar SIFN SPoG WPGP WPat
	'Den Haag'	EPfP MBri
	echinatus	EPfP EPla
	- BL&M 306	SLon
	europaeus	More than 30 suppliers
	- f. ***albus***	CPMA CTho EPfP LTwo NLar
	- 'Atropurpureus'	CMCN CTho EPfP MBlu MBri NLar SIFN
	- 'Atrorubens'	CPMA
	- 'Aucubifolius' (v)	EPfP
*	- 'Aureus'	CNat
	- 'Brilliant' **new**	EPfP
*	- f. ***bulgaricus***	EPfP
	- 'Chrysophyllus'	EPfP MBlu NLar
	- 'Howard'	EPfP
	- var. ***intermedius***	ENot EPfP MAsh MBlu NLar
	- 'Miss Pinkie'	CEnd CMCN
	- 'Pumilis' **new**	EPfP
	- 'Red Cascade' 🏆H4	More than 30 suppliers
	- 'Scarlet Wonder'	CPMA EPfP MBri NLar
	- 'Thornhayes'	CTho EPfP
I	- 'Variegatus' **new**	EPfP
	farreri	see *E. nanus*
	fimbriatus	EPfP
	fortunei Blondy = 'Interbolwi'PBR (v)	More than 30 suppliers

ABBREVIATIONS
To save space a dash indicates that the previous heading is repeated. If written out in full the name would be Euonymus alatus *'Fire Ball'.*

NEW
Plant new to this edition.

DESCRIPTIVE TERM
See p.8.

SYMBOLS TO THE LEFT OF THE NAME
Provides information about the name of the plant. See p.15 for the key.

SYMBOLS TO THE RIGHT OF THE NAME
Tells you more about the plant itself, e.g. (v) *indicates that the plant is variegated,* (F) *= fruit. See p.15 for the key.*

SELLING NAMES
See p.10.

🏆H4
This plant has received the RHS Award of Garden Merit. See p.7.

CROSS-REFERENCES
Directs you to the correct name of the plant and the nursery codes. See p.18.

NURSERY CODE
A unique code identifying each nursery. Turn to p.796 for details of the nurseries.

MORE THAN 30 SUPPLIERS
Indicates that more than 30 Plant Finder nurseries supply the plant, and it may be available locally. See p.18.

PBR
Plant Breeders' Rights. See p.9.

SUPPLEMENTARY KEYS TO THE DIRECTORY

COLLECTORS' REFERENCES

Abbreviations following a plant name, refer to the collector(s) of the plant. These abbreviations are expanded below, with a collector's name or expedition title. For a fuller explanation, see p.8.

A&JW	A. & J. Watson
A&L	Ala, A.; Lancaster, Roy
AB&S	Archibald, James; Blanchard, John W; Salmon, M.
AC	Clark, Alan J.
AC&H	Apold, J.; Cox, Peter; Hutchison, Peter
AC&W	Albury; Cheese, M.; Watson, J.M.
ACE	AGS Expedition to China (1994)
ACL	Leslie, Alan C.
AER	Robinson, Allen
AGS/ES	AGS Expedition to Sikkim (1983)
AGSJ	AGS Expedition to Japan (1988)
Airth	Airth, Murray
Akagi	Akagi Botanical Garden
AL&JS	Sharman, Joseph L.; Leslie, Alan C.
ARG	Argent, G.C.G.
B	Blanchard, John
B L.	Beer, Len
B&L	Brickell, Christopher D.; Leslie, Alan C.
B&M & BM	Brickell, Christopher D.; Mathew, Brian
B&S	Bird P. & Salmon M.
B&SWJ	Wynn-Jones, Bleddyn; Wynn-Jones, Susan
B&V	Burras, K. & Vosa, C.G.
BB	Bartholomew, B.
BC	Chudziak, W.
BC&W	Beckett; Cheese, M.; Watson, J.M.
Beavis	Beavis, Derek S.
Berry	Berry, P.
Berry & Brako	Berry, P. & Brako, Lois
BKBlount	Blount, B.K.
BL&M	University of Bangor Expedition to NE Nepal
BM	Mathew, Brian F.
BM&W	Binns, David L.; Mason, M.; Wright, A.
BOA	Boardman, P.
Breedlove	Breedlove, D.
BR	Rushbrooke, Ben
BS	Smith, Basil
BSBE	Bowles Scholarship Botanical Expedition (1963)
BSSS	Crûg Expedition, Jordan (1991)
Bu	Bubert, S.
Burtt	Burtt, Brian L.
C	Cole, Desmond T.
C&C	Cox, P.A. & Cox, K.N.E.
C&Cu	Cox, K.N.E. & Cubey, J.
C&H	Cox, Peter; Hutchison, Peter
C&K	Chamberlain & Knott
C&R	Christian & Roderick
C&S	Clark, Alan; Sinclair, Ian W.J.
C&V	K.N.E. Cox & S. Vergera
C&W	Cheese, M.; Watson, J.M.
CC	Chadwell, Christopher
CC&H	Chamberlain, David F.; Cox, Peter; Hutchison, P.
CC&McK	Chadwell, Christopher; McKelvie, A.
CC&MR	Chadwell, Christopher; Ramsay
CCH&H	Chamberlain, D.F.; Cox, P.; Hutchison, P.; Hootman, S.
CCH&H	Chamberlain, Cox, Hootman & Hutchison
CD&R	Compton, J.; D'Arcy, J.; Rix, E.M.
CDB	Brickell, Christopher D.
CDC	Coode, Mark J.E.; Dockrill, Alexander
CDC&C	Compton, D'Arcy, Christopher & Coke
CDPR	Compton, D'Arcy, Pope & Rix
CE&H	Christian, P.J.; Elliott; Hoog
CEE	Chengdu Edinburgh Expedition China 1991
CGW	Grey-Wilson, Christopher
CH&M	Cox, P.; Hutchison, P.; Maxwell-MacDonald, D.
CHP&W	Kashmir Botanical Expedition
CL	Lovell, Chris
CLD	Chungtien, Lijiang & Dali Exped. China (1990)
CM&W	Cheese M., Mitchel J. & Watson, J.
CN&W	Clark; Neilson; Wilson
CNDS	Nelson, C. & Sayers D.
Cooper	Cooper, R.E.

Cox Cox, Peter A.
CPC Cobblewood Plant Collection
CPN Compton, James
CSE Cyclamen Society Expedition (1990)
CT Teune, Carla
Dahl Dahl, Sally
DBG Denver Botanic Garden, Colorado
DC Cheshire, David
DF Fox, D.
DJH Hinkley, Dan
DJHC Hinkley China
DM Millais, David
Doleshy Doleshy, F.L.
DS&T Drake, Sharman J.; Thompson
DWD Rose, D.
DZ Zummell, D.
ECN Nelson, E. Charles
EDHCH Hammond, Eric D.
EGM Millais, T.
EKB Balls, Edward K.
EM East Malling Research Station
EMAK Edinburgh Makalu Expedition (1991)
EMR Rix, E.Martyn
EN Needham, Edward F.
ENF Fuller, E. Nigel
ETE Edinburgh Taiwan Expedition (1993)
ETOT Kirkham, T.S.; Flanagan, Mark
F Forrest, G.
F&M Fernandez & Mendoza, Mexico
F&W Watson, J.; Flores, A.
Farrer Farrer, Reginald
FK Kinmonth, Fergus W.
FMB Bailey, F.M.
G Gardner, Martin F.
G&K Gardner, Martin F.; Knees, Sabina G.
G&P Gardner, Martin F.; Page, Christopher N.
GDJ Dumont, Gerard
GG Gusman, G.
GS Sherriff, George
Green Green, D.
Guitt Guittoneau, G.G.
Guiz Guizhou Expedition (1985)
GWJ Goddard, Sally; Wynne-Jones, Bleddyn & Susan
G-W&P Grey-Wilson, Christopher; Phillips
H Huggins, Paul
H&B Hilliard, Olive M.; Burtt, Brian L.
H&D Howick, C.; Darby
H&M Howick, Charles; McNamara, William A.
H&W Hedge, Ian C.; Wendelbo, Per W.
Harry Smith Smith, K.A.Harry
Hartside Hartside Nursery
HCM Heronswood Expedition to Chile (1998)
HECC Hutchison, Evans, Cox, P., Cox, K.
HH&K Hannay, S&S & Kingsbury, N
HLMS Springate, L.S.
HM&S Halliwell, B., Mason, D. & Smallcombe
HOA Hoog, Anton
Hummel Hummel, D.
HW&E Wendelbo, Per; Hedge, I.; Ekberg, L.
HWEL Hirst, J.Michael; Webster, D.
HWJ Crûg Heronswood Joint Expedition
HWJCM Crûg Heronswood Expedition
HWJK Crûg Heronswood Expedition, East Nepal (2002)
HZ Zetterlund, Henrik
ICE Instituto de Investigaciónes Ecológicas Chiloé & RBGE
IDS International Dendrological Society
ISI Int. Succulent Introductions
J&JA Archibald, James; Archibald, Jennifer
J. Jurasek Jurasek, J.
JCA Archibald, James
JE Jack Elliott
JJ Jackson, J.
JJ&JH Halda, J.; Halda, J.
JJH Halda, Joseph J.
JLS Sharman, J.L.
JM-MK Mahr, J.; Kammerlander, M.
JMT Mann Taylor, J.
JN Nielson, Jens
JR Russell, J.
JRM Marr, John
JW Watson, J.M.
K Kirkpatrick, George
K&LG Gillanders, Kenneth; Gillanders, L.
K&Mc Kirkpatrick, George; McBeath, Ronald J.D.
K&P Josef Kopec, Milan Prasil
K&T Kurashige, Y.; Tsukie, S.
KC Cox, Kenneth
KEKE Kew/Edinburgh Kanchenjunga Expedition (1989)
KGB Kunming/Gothenburg Botanical Expedition (1993)
KM Marsh, K.
KR Rushforth, K.D.
KRW Wooster, K.R. (distributed after his death by Kath Dryden)
KW Kingdon-Ward, F.
L Lancaster, C. Roy
L&S Ludlow, Francis; Sherriff, George
LA Long Ashton Research Station clonal selection scheme
LB Bird P., Salmon, M.
LEG Lesotho Edinburgh/Gothenburg Expedition (1997)
Lismore Lismore Nursery, Breeder's Number
LM&S Leslie, Mattern & Sharman
LP Palmer, W.J.L.
LS&E Ludlow, Frank; Sherriff, George; Elliott, E. E.
LS&H Ludlow, Frank; Sherriff, George; Hicks, J. H.

LS&T	Ludlow, Frank; Sherriff, George; Taylor, George
M&PS	Mike & Polly Stone
M&T	Mathew; Tomlinson
Mac&W	McPhail & Watson
McB	McBeath, R.J.D.
McLaren	McLaren, H.D.
MDM	Myers, Michael D.
MECC	Scottish Rock Garden Club, Nepal (1997)
MESE	Alpine Garden Society Expedition, Greece 1999
MF	Foster, Maurice
MH	Heasman, Matthew T.
MK	Kammerlander, Michael
MP	Pavelka, Mojmir
MPF	Frankis, M.P.
MS	Salmon, M.
MS&CL	Salmon, M.; Lovell, C.
MSF	Fillan, M.S.
NJM	Macer, N.J.
NNS	Ratko, Ron
NS	Turland, Nick
NVFDE	Northern Vietnam First Darwin Expedition
Og	Ogisu, Mikinori
P&C	Paterson, David S.; Clarke, Sidney
P&W	Polastri; Watson, J. M.
PB	Bird, Peter
PC&H	Pattison, G.; Catt, P.; Hickson, M.
PD	Davis, Peter H.
PF	Furse, Paul
PJC	Christian, Paul J.
PJC&AH	P.J. Christian & A. Hogg
PNMK	Nicholls, P.; Kammerlander, M.
Polunin	Polunin, Oleg
Pras	Prasil, M.
PS&W	Polunin, Oleg; Sykes, William; Williams, John
PW	Wharton, Peter
R	Rock, J.F.C.
RB	Brown, R.
RBS	Brown, Ray, Sakharin Island
RCB/Arg	Brown, Robert, Argentina, (2002)
RCB/Eq	Brown, Robert, Ecuador, (1988)
RCB/TQ	Brown, Robert, Turkey (2001)
RH	Hancock, R.
RMRP	Rocky Mountain Rare Plants, Denver, Colorado
RS	Suckow, Reinhart
RSC	Richard Somer Cocks
RV	Richard Valder
RWJ	Crûg Farm-Rickards Ferns Expedition to Taiwan (2003)
S&B	Blanchard, J.W.; Salmon, M.
S&F	Salmon, M. & Fillan, M.
S&L	Sinclair, Ian W.J.; Long, David G.
S&SH	Sheilah and Spencer Hannay
Sandham	Sandham, John
SB&L	Salmon, Bird and Lovell
SBEC	Sino-British Expedition to Cangshan
SBEL	Sino-British Lijiang Expedition
SBQE	Sino-British Expedition to Quinghai
Sch	Schilling, Anthony D.
SD	Sashal Dayal
SDR	Rankin, Stella; Rankin, David
SEH	Hootman, Steve
SEP	Swedish Expedition to Pakistan
SF	Forde, P.
SG	Salmon, M. & Guy, P.
SH	Hannay, Spencer
Sich	Simmons, Erskine, Howick & Mcnamara
SLIZE	Swedish-Lithuanian-Iranian Zagros Expedition to Iran (May 1988)
SOJA	Kew / Quarryhill Expedition to Southern Japan
SS&W	Stainton, J.D.Adam; Sykes, William; Williams, John
SSNY	Sino-Scottish Expedition to NW Yunnan (1992)
T	Taylor, Nigel P.
T&K	Taylor, Nigel P.; Knees, Sabina
TH	Hudson, T.
TS&BC	Smythe, T and Cherry, B
TSS	Spring Smyth, T.L.M.
TW	Tony Weston
USDAPI	US Department of Agriculture Plant Index Number
USDAPQ	US Dept. of Agriculture Plant Quarantine Number
USNA	United States National Arboretum
VHH	Vernon H. Heywood
W	Wilson, Ernest H.
WM	McLewin, William
Woods	Woods, Patrick J.B.
Wr	Wraight, David & Anke
Yu	Yu, Tse-tsun

NOTES ON NOMENCLATURE AND IDENTIFICATION

These notes refer to plants in the Plant Directory that are marked with a 'N' to the left of the name. 'Bean Supplement' refers to W.J. Bean *Trees & Shrubs Hardy in the British Isles* (Supplement to the 8th edition) edited by D L Clarke 1988.

***Acer davidii* 'Ernest Wilson' and *A. davidii* 'George Forrest'**
These cultivars should be grafted in order to retain the characteristics of the original clones. However, many plants offered under these names are seed-raised.

***Acer palmatum* 'Sango-kaku'/ 'Senkaki'**
Two or more clones are offered under these names. *A. palmatum* 'Eddisbury' is similar with brighter coral stems.

***Achillea ptarmica* The Pearl Group/ *A. ptarmica* (The Pearl Group) 'Boule de Neige' / *A. ptarmica* (The Pearl Group) 'The Pearl'**
In the recent trial of achilleas at Wisley, only one of the several stocks submitted as 'The Pearl' matched the original appearance of this plant according to Graham Stuart Thomas, this being from Wisley's own stock. At rather less than 60cm (2ft), this needed little support, being the shortest of the plants bearing this name, with slightly grey, not glossy dark green, leaves and a non-invasive habit. This has been designated as the type for this cultivar and only this clone should bear the cultivar name 'The Pearl'. The Pearl Group covers all other double-flowered clones of this species, including seed-raised plants which are markedly inferior, sometimes scarcely double, often invasive and usually needing careful staking. It has been claimed that 'The Pearl' was a re-naming of Lemoine's 'Boule de Neige' but not all authorities agree: all plants submitted to the Wisley trial as 'Boule de Neige' were different from each other, not the same clone as Wisley's 'The Pearl' and referrable to The Pearl Group.

Anemone magellanica
According to *The European Garden Flora*, this is a variant of the very variable *A. multifida*.

***Anemone nemorosa* 'Alba Plena'**
This name is used for several double white forms including *A. nemorosa* 'Flore Pleno' and *A. nemorosa* 'Vestal'.

***Artemisia granatensis* misapplied**
Possibly a variant of *A. absinthium*.

***Artemisia ludoviciana* var. *latiloba* / *A. ludoviciana* 'Valerie Finnis'**
Leaves of the former are glabrous at maturity, those of the latter are not.

***Artemisia stelleriana* 'Boughton Silver'**
This was thought to be the first validly published name for this plant, 'Silver Brocade' having been published earlier but invalidly in an undated publication. However, an earlier valid publication for the cultivar name 'Mori' has subsequently been found for the same plant. A proposal to conserve 'Boughton Silver' has been tabled because of its more widespread use.

***Aster amellus* Violet Queen**
It is probable that more than one cultivar is sold under this name.

Aster dumosus
Many of the asters listed under *A. novi-belgii* contain varying amounts of *A. dumosus* blood in their parentage. It is not possible to allocate these to one species or the other and they are therefore listed under *A. novi-belgii*.

***Aster × frikartii* 'Mönch'**
The true plant is very rare in British gardens. Most plants are another form of *A. × frikartii*, usually 'Wunder von Stäfa'.

Aster novi-belgii
See note under *A. dumosus*. *A. laevis* is also involved in the parentage of most cultivars.

Azara paraguayensis
This is an unpublished name for what seems to be a hybrid between *A. serrata* and *A. lanceolata*.

***Berberis buxifolia* 'Nana'/ 'Pygmaea'**
See explanation in Bean Supplement.

***Berberis stenophylla* 'Lemon Queen'**
This sport from 'Pink Pearl' was first named in 1982. The same mutation occurred again and was named 'Cream Showers'. The older name has priority.

Betula utilis* var. *jacquemontii
Plants are often the clones *B. utilis* var. *jacquemontii* 'Inverleith' or *B. utilis* var. *jacquemontii* 'Doorenbos'

Brachyscome
Originally published as *Brachyscome* by Cassini who later revised his spelling to *Brachycome*. The original spelling has been internationally adopted.

***Calamagrostis × acutiflora* 'Karl Foerster'**
C. × *acutiflora* 'Stricta' differs in being 15cm taller, 10-15 days earlier flowering with a less fluffy inflorescence.

Caltha polypetala
This name is often applied to a large-flowered variant of C. *palustris*. The true species has more (7-10) petals.

***Camassia leichtlinii* 'Alba'**
The true cultivar has blueish-white, not cream flowers.

Camassia leichtlinii **'Plena'**
This has starry, transparent green-white flowers; creamy-white 'Semiplena' is sometimes offered under this name.

Camellia japonica **'Campbellii'**
This name is used for five cultivars including 'Margherita Coleoni' but applies correctly to Guichard's 1894 cultivar, single to semi-double full rose pink.

Campanula lactiflora **'Alba'**
This refers to the pure white flowered clone, not to blueish- or greyish-white flowered plants, nor to seed-raised plants.

Carex morrowii **'Variegata'**
C. oshimensis 'Evergold' is sometimes sold under this name.

Carya illinoinensis
The correct spelling of this name is discussed in *Baileya*, **10**(1) (1962).

Cassinia retorta
Now included within *C. leptophylla*. A valid infraspecific epithet has yet to be published.

Ceanothus **'Italian Skies'**
Many plants under this name are not true to name.

Chamaecyparis lawsoniana **'Columnaris Glauca'**
Plants under this name might be *C. lawsoniana* 'Columnaris' or a new invalidly named cultivar.

Chamaecyparis pisifera **'Squarrosa Argentea'**
There are two plants of this name, one (valid) with variegated foliage, the other (invalid) with silvery foliage.

Chrysanthemum **'Anastasia Variegated'**
Despite its name, this seems to be derived from 'Mei-kyo', not 'Anastasia'.

Clematis chrysocoma
The true *C. chrysocoma* is a non-climbing erect plant with dense yellow down on the young growth, still uncommon in cultivation.

Clematis montana
This name should be used for the typical white-flowered variety only. Pink-flowered variants are referable to *C. montana* var. *rubens*.

Clematis **'Victoria'**
Raised by Cripps (1867). There is also a Latvian cultivar of this name with petals with a central white bar in the collection of Janis Ruplēns and probably, though not certainly, of his own raising.

Colchicum **'Autumn Queen'**
Entries here might refer to the slightly different *C.* 'Prinses Astrid'.

Cornus **'Norman Hadden'**
See note in Bean Supplement, p.184.

Cotoneaster dammeri
Plants sold under this name are usually *C. dammeri* 'Major'.

Cotoneaster frigidus **'Cornubia'**
According to Hylmø this cultivar, like all other variants of this species, is fully deciduous. Several evergreen cotoneasters are also grown under this name, most are clones of *C.* × *watereri* or *C. salicifolius*.

Crataegus coccinea
C. intricata, *C. pedicellata* and *C. biltmoreana* are occasionally supplied under this name.

Crocus cartwrightianus **'Albus'**
The plant offered is the true cultivar and not *C. hadriaticus*.

Dianthus fringed pink
D. 'Old Fringed Pink' and *D.* 'Old Fringed White' are also sometimes sold under this name.

Dianthus **'Musgrave's Pink' (p)**
This is the registered name of this white-flowered cultivar.

Elymus magellanicus
Although this is a valid name, Roger Grounds has suggested that many plants might belong to a different, perhaps unnamed species.

Epilobium glabellum **misapplied**
Plants under this name are not *E. glabellum* but are close to *E. wilsonii* Petrie or perhaps a hybrid of it.

Erodium glandulosum
Plants under this name are often hybrids.

Erodium guttatum
Doubtfully in commerce; plants under this name are usually *E. heteradenum, E. cheilanthifolium* or hybrids.

Erysimum cheiri **'Baden-Powell'**
Plant of uncertain origin differing from *E. cheiri* 'Harpur Crewe' only in its shorter stature.

Fagus sylvatica **Cuprea Group/Atropurpurea Group**
It is desirable to provide a name, Cuprea Group, for less richly coloured forms, used in historic landscapes before the purple clones appeared.

Fagus sylvatica **'Pendula'**
This name refers to the Knap Hill clone, the most common weeping form in English gardens. Other clones occur, particularly in Cornwall and Ireland.

Fuchsia loxensis
For a comparison of the true species with the hybrids 'Speciosa' and 'Loxensis' commonly grown under this name, see Boullemier's Check List (2nd ed.) p.268.

Gentiana cachemirica
Most plants sold are not true to type.

Geum **'Borisii'**
This name refers to cultivars of *G. coccineum* Sibthorp & Smith, especially *G.* 'Werner Arends' and not to *G.* × *borisii* Kelleper.

Halimium alyssoides **and** *H. halimifolium*
Plants under these names are sometimes *H.* × *pauanum* or *H.* × *santae*.

Hebe **'C.P. Raffill'**
See note in Bean Supplement, p.265.

Hebe **'Carl Teschner'**
See note in Bean Supplement, p.264.

Hebe glaucophylla
A green reversion of the hybrid *H.* 'Glaucophylla Variegata' is often sold under this name.

***Hedera helix* 'Caenwoodiana' / 'Pedata'**
Some authorities consider these to be distinct cultivars while others think them different morphological forms of the same unstable clone.

***Hedera helix* 'Oro di Bogliasco'**
Priority between this name and 'Jubiläum Goldherz' and 'Goldheart' has yet to be finally resolved.

***Helleborus* × *hybridus* / *H. orientalis* misapplied**
The name *H.* × *hybridus* for acaulescent hellebore hybrids does not seem to follow the *International Code of Botanical Nomenclature* Article H.3.2 requiring one of the parent species to be designated and does not seem to have been typified, contrary to Article 7 of the Code. However, the illustration accompanying the original description in Vilmorin's *Blumengärtnerei* 3(1): 27 (1894) shows that one parent of the cross must have been *H. guttatus*, now treated as part of *H. orientalis*. Taking this illustration as the type for this hybrid species makes it possible to retain *H.* × *hybridus* formally as a hybrid binomial (rather than *H. hybridus* as in a previous edition), as the Code's requirement to distinguish one parent is now met.

***Hemerocallis fulva* 'Kwanso', 'Kwanso Variegata', 'Flore Pleno' and 'Green Kwanso'**
For a discussion of these plants see *The Plantsman*, 7(2).

***Heuchera micrantha* var. *diversifolia* 'Palace Purple'**
This cultivar name refers only to plants with deep purple-red foliage. Seed-raised plants of inferior colouring should not be offered under this name.

Hosta montana
This name refers only to plants long grown in Europe, which differ from *H. elata.*

***Hydrangea macrophylla* Teller Series**
This is used both as a descriptive common name for Lacecap hydrangeas (German *teller* = plate, referring to the more or less flat inflorescence) and for the series of hybrids raised by Wädenswil in Switzerland bearing German names of birds. It is not generally possible to link a hydrangea described by the series name plus a colour description (e.g. Teller Blau, Teller Rosa, Teller Rot) to a single cultivar.

Hypericum fragile
The true *H. fragile* is probably not available from British nurseries.

***Hypericum* 'Gemo'**
Either a selection of *H. prolificum* or *H. prolificum* × *H. densiflorum.*

Ilex* × *altaclerensis
The argument for this spelling is given by Susyn Andrews, *The Plantsman*, 5(2) and is not superceded by the more recent comments in the Supplement to Bean's Trees and Shrubs.

Iris
Apart from those noted below, cultivar names marked 'N' are not registered. The majority of those marked 'I' have been previously used for a different cultivar.

***Iris histrioides* 'Major'**
Two clones are offered under this name, the true one pale blue with darker spotting on the falls, the incorrect one violet-blue with almost horizontal falls.

Juniperus* × *media
This name is illegitimate if applied to hybrids of *J. chinensis* × *J. sabina*, having been previously used for a different hybrid (P.A. Schmidt, *IDS Yearbook 1993*, 47-48). Because of its importance to gardeners, a proposal to conserve its present use was tabled but subsequently rejected.

Lavandula spica
This name is classed as a name to be rejected (*nomen rejiciendum*) by the *International Code of Botanical Nomenclature.*

Lavatera olbia* and *L. thuringiaca
Although *L. olbia* is usually shrubby and *L. thuringiaca* usually herbaceous, both species are very variable. Cultivars formally ascribed to one species or the other have been shown to be hybrids and are referable to the recently-named hybrid species *L.* × *clementii.*

***Lobelia* 'Russian Princess'**
This name, originally for a pink-flowered, green-leaved cultivar, is now generally applied to a purple-flowered, dark-leaved cultivar that seems to lack a valid name.

***Lonicera periclymenum* 'Serotina'**
See note in Bean Supplement, p.315.

Lonicera sempervirens* f. *sulphurea
Plants in the British Isles usually a yellow-flowered form of *L. periclymenum.*

***Malus domestica* 'Dummellor's Seedling'**
The phonetic spelling 'Dumelow's Seedling' contravenes the ICBN ruling on orthography, i.e. that, except for intentional latinizations, commemorative names should be based on the original spelling of the person's name (Article 60.11). The spelling adopted here is that used on the gravestone of the raiser in Leicestershire.

***Meconopsis* Fertile Blue Group**
This Group comprises seed-raised and intrinsically perennial tall blue poppies of as yet indeterminate origin (i.e. fertile forms other than the species *M. betonicifolia*, *M. grandis* and *M. simplicifolia*). The only cultivar so far established is *M.* 'Lingholm' (syns 'Blue Ice' and 'Correnie'). The bulk of seed-

raised plants in cultivation and offered for sale are very likely to be *M.* 'Lingholm', although sometimes poorly selected. Many of these plants are currently being distributed erroneously as *M.* × *sheldonii* and as *M. grandis.*

***Meconopsis* George Sherriff Group**
This Group comprises a number of sterile (almost invariably) clones of large blue poppies previously (and erroneously) known collectively as *M. grandis* GS600.

***Meconopsis grandis* ambig.**
See note under *M.* Fertile Blue Group. The true species has been recently reintroduced into cultivation in the British Isles but is still rarely offered.

***Meconopsis* Infertile Blue Group**
This Group comprises long-established sterile (almost invariably) clones of large blue poppies other than George Sherriff Group and often given the epithet × *sheldonii.*

***Meconopsis* × *sheldonii* ambig.**
See notes for *M.* Fertile Blue Group and *M.* Infertile Blue Group.

***Melissa officinalis* 'Variegata'**
The true cultivar of this name had leaves striped with white.

***Nemesia caerulea* 'Joan Wilder'**
The lavender blue clone 'Joan Wilder', described and illustrated in *The Hardy Plant,* 14(1), 11-14, does not come true from seed; it may only be propagated from cuttings.

***Osmanthus heterophyllus* 'Gulftide'**
Probably correctly *O.* × *fortunei* 'Gulftide'.

***Papaver orientale* agg.**
Plants listed as *P. orientale* agg. (i.e. aggregate) or as one of its cultivars may be *P. orientale* L., *P. pseudo-orientale* or *P. bracteatum* or hybrids between them.

***Pelargonium* 'Lass o' Gowrie'**
The American plant of this name has pointed, not rounded leaf lobes.

Pelargonium quercifolium
Plants under this name are mainly hybrids. The true species has pointed, not rounded leaf lobes.

***Penstemon* 'Taoensis'**
This name for a small-flowered cultivar or hybrid of *P. isophyllus* originally appeared as 'Taoense' but must be corrected to agree in gender with *Penstemon* (masculine). Presumably an invalid name (published in Latin form since 1958), it is not synonymous with *P. crandallii* subsp. *glabrescens* var. *taosensis.*

Pernettya
Botanists now consider that *Pernettya* (fruit a berry) is not separable from *Gaultheria* (fruit a capsule) because in some species the fruit is intermediate between a berry and a capsule. For a fuller explanation see D. Middleton, *The Plantsman,* 12(3).

***Picea pungens* 'Glauca Pendula'**
This name is used for several different glaucous cultivars.

Pinus ayacahuite
P. ayacahuite var. *veitchii* (syn. *P. veitchii)* is occasionally sold under this name.

***Pinus nigra* 'Cebennensis Nana'**
A doubtful name, possibly a synonym for *P. nigra* 'Nana'.

Polemonium archibaldiae
Usually sterile with lavender-blue flowers. A self-fertile white-flowered plant is sometimes sold under this name.

***Prunus laurocerasus* 'Castlewellan'**
We are grateful to Dr Charles Nelson for informing us that the name 'Marbled White' is not valid because although it has priority of publication it does not have the approval of the originator who asked for it to be called 'Castlewellan'.

Prunus serrulata* var. *pubescens
See note in Bean Supplement, p.398.

***Prunus* × *subhirtella* 'Rosea'**
Might be *P. pendula* var. *ascendens* 'Rosea', *P. pendula* 'Pendula Rosea', or *P.* × *subhirtella* 'Autumnalis Rosea'.

Rheum* × *cultorum
The name *R.* × *cultorum* was published without adequate description and must be abandoned in favour of the validly published *R.* × *hybridum.*

***Rhododendron* (azaleas)**
All names marked 'N', except for the following, refer to more than one cultivar.

***Rhododendron* 'Hinomayo'**
This name is based on a faulty transliteration (should be 'Hinamoyo') but the spelling 'Hinomayo' is retained in the interests of stability.

Rhus typhina
Linnaeus published both *R. typhina* and *R. hirta* as names for the same species. Though *R. hirta* has priority, it has been proposed that the name *R. typhina* should be conserved.

Rosa gentiliana
Plants under this name are usually the cultivar 'Polyantha Grandiflora' but might otherwise be *R. multiflora* 'Wilsonii', *R. multiflora* var. *cathayensis, R. henryi* or another hybrid.

***Rosa* 'Gros Choux de Hollande' hort. (Bb)**
It is doubtful if this name is correctly applied.

***Rosa* 'Jacques Cartier' hort.**
For a discussion on the correct identity of this rose see *Heritage Rose Foundation News,* Oct. 1989 & Jan. 1990.

***Rosa* 'Kazanlik'**
For a discussion on the correct identity of this rose see *Heritage Roses,* Nov. 1991.

***Rosa* Sweetheart**
This is not the same as the Sweetheart Rose, a common name for *R.* 'Cécile Brünner'.

Rosa wichurana
This is the correct spelling according to the ICBN 1994 Article 60.11 (which enforces Recommendation 60C.1c) and not *wichuraiana* for this rose commemorating Max Wichura.

***Rubus fruticosus* L. agg.**
Though some cultivated blackberries do belong to *Rubus fruticosus* L. *sensu stricto,* others are more correctly ascribed to other species of *Rubus* section *Glandulosus* (including *R. armeniacus, R. laciniatus* or *R. ulmifolius)* or are hybrids of species within this section. Because it is almost impossible to ascribe every cultivar to a single species or hybrid, they are listed under *R. fruticosus* L. agg. (i.e. aggregate) for convenience.

Salvia microphylla* var. *neurepia
The type of this variety is referable to the typical variety, *S. microphylla* var. *microphylla.*

***Salvia officinalis* 'Aurea'**
S. officinalis var. *aurea* is a rare variant of the common sage with leaves entirely of gold. It is represented in cultivation by the cultivar 'Kew Gold'. The plant usually offered as *S. officinalis* 'Aurea' is the gold variegated sage *S. officinalis* 'Icterina'.

***Sambucus nigra* 'Aurea'**
Plants under this name are usually not *S. nigra.*

Sedum nevii
The true species is not in cultivation. Plants under this name are usually either *S. glaucophyllum* or occasionally *S. beyrichianum.*

***Skimmia japonica* 'Foremanii'**
The true cultivar, which belongs to *S. japonica* Rogersii Group, is believed to be lost to cultivation. Plants offered under this name are usually *S. japonica* 'Veitchii'.

***Spiraea japonica* 'Shirobana'**
Shirobana-shimotsuke is the common name for *S. japonica* var. *albiflora.* Shirobana means white-flowered and does not apply to the two-coloured form.

Staphylea holocarpa* var. *rosea
This botanical variety has woolly leaves. The cultivar 'Rosea', with which it is often confused, does not.

Stewartia ovata* var. *grandiflora.
Most, possibly all, plants available from British nurseries under this name are not true to name but are derived from the improved Nymans form.

***Thymus* Coccineus Group**
Thymes under this have dark crimson (RHS 78A) flowers whereas those of 'Alan Bloom' are purplish-pink (RHS 78C).

***Thymus serpyllum* cultivars**
Most cultivars are probably correctly cultivars of *T. polytrichus* or hybrids though they will remain listed under *T. serpyllum* pending further research.

***Thymus* 'Silver Posie'**
The cultivar name 'Silver Posie' is applied to several different plants, not all of them *T. vulgaris.*

***Tricyrtis* Hototogisu**
This is the common name applied generally to all Japanese *Tricyrtis* and specifically to *T. hirta.*

Tricyrtis macropoda
This name has been used for at least five different species.

Uncinia rubra
This name is also misapplied to *U. egmontiana* and *U. uncinata.*

Verbena
Entries marked (G) are considered by some botanists to belong to a separate genus, *Glandularia.*

***Verbena* 'Kemerton'**
Origin unknown, not from Kemerton.

***Viburnum opulus* 'Fructu Luteo'**
See note below.

***Viburnum opulus* 'Xanthocarpum'**
Some entries under this name might be the less compact *V. opulus* 'Fructu Luteo'.

Viburnum plicatum
Entries may include the 'snowball' form, *V. plicatum* f. *plicatum* (syn. *V. plicatum* 'Sterile'), as well as the 'lacecap' form, *V. plicatum* f. *tomentosum.*

Viola labradorica
See Note in *The Garden,* **110(2)**: 96.

***Wisteria floribunda* 'Violacea Plena' and *W.f.* 'Yae-kokuryū'**
We are grateful to Yoko Otsuki, who has established through Engei Kyokai (the Horticultural Society of Japan) that there are two different double selections of *Wisteria floribunda.* 'Violacea Plena' has double lavender/lilac flowers, while 'Yae-kokuryū' has more ragged and tightly double flowers with purple/indigo centres. Each is distinctive but it is probable that both are confused in the British nursery trade. 'Yae-fuji' might be an earlier name for 'Violacea Plena' or a Group name covering a range of doubles but, as *fuji* is the Japanese common name for the species, would not be a valid name under ICNCP.

CLASSIFICATION OF GENERA

Genera including a large number of species, or with many cultivars, are often subdivided into informal horticultural classifications, or formal cultivar groups in the case of *Clematis* and *Tulipa*. The breeding of new cultivars is sometimes limited to hybrids between closely-related species, thus for *Saxifraga* and *Primula*, the cultivars are allocated to the sections given in the infrageneric treatments cited. Please turn to p.8 for a fuller explanation.

ACTINIDIA

(s-p) Self-pollinating

BEGONIA

(C) Cane-like
(R) Rex Cultorum
(S) Semperflorens Cultorum
(T) × *tuberhybrida* (Tuberous)

CHRYSANTHEMUM

(By the National Chrysanthemum Society)
(1) Indoor Large (Exhibition)
(2) Indoor Medium (Exhibition)
(3a) Indoor Incurved: Large-flowered
(3b) Indoor Incurved: Medium-flowered
(3c) Indoor Incurved: Small-flowered
(4a) Indoor Reflexed: Large-flowered
(4b) Indoor Reflexed: Medium-flowered
(4c) Indoor Reflexed: Small-flowered
(5a) Indoor Intermediate: Large-flowered
(5b) Indoor Intermediate: Medium-flowered
(5c) Indoor Intermediate: Small-flowered
(6a) Indoor Anemone: Large-flowered
(6b) Indoor Anemone: Medium-flowered
(6c) Indoor Anemone: Small-flowered
(7a) Indoor Single: Large-flowered
(7b) Indoor Single: Medium-flowered
(7c) Indoor Single: Small-flowered
(8a) Indoor True Pompon
(8b) Indoor Semi-pompon
(9a) Indoor Spray: Anemone
(9b) Indoor Spray: Pompon
(9c) Indoor Spray: Reflexed
(9d) Indoor Spray: Single
(9e) Indoor Spray: Intermediate
(9f) Indoor Spray: Spider, Quill, Spoon or Any Other Type
(10a) Indoor, Spider
(10b) Indoor, Quill
(10c) Indoor, Spoon
(11) Any Other Indoor Type
(12a) Indoor, Charm
(12b) Indoor, Cascade
(13a) October-flowering Incurved: Large-flowered
(13b) October-flowering Incurved: Medium-flowered
(13c) October-flowering Incurved: Small-flowered
(14a) October-flowering Reflexed: Large-flowered
(14b) October-flowering Reflexed: Medium-flowered
(14c) October-flowering Reflexed: Small-flowered
(15a) October-flowering Intermediate: Large-flowered
(15b) October-flowering Intermediate: Medium-flowered
(15c) October-flowered Intermediate: Small-flowered
(16) October-flowering Large
(17a) October-flowering Single: Large-flowered
(17b) October-flowering Single: Medium-flowered
(17c) October-flowering Single: Small-flowered
(18a) October-flowering Pompon: True Pompon
(18b) October-flowering Pompon: Semi-pompon
(19a) October-flowering Spray: Anemone
(19b) October-flowering Spray: Pompon
(19c) October-flowering Spray: Reflexed
(19d) October-flowering Spray: Single
(19e) October-flowering Spray: Intermediate
(19f) October-flowering Spray: Spider, Quill, Spoon or Any Other Type
(20) Any Other October-flowering Type
(22a) Charm: Anemone
(22b) Charm: Pompon
(22c) Charm: Reflexed
(22d) Charm: Single
(22e) Charm: Intermediate
(22f) Charm: Spider, Quill, Spoon or Any Other Type
(23a) Early-flowering Outdoor Incurved: Large-flowered
(23b) Early-flowering Outdoor Incurved: Medium-flowered
(23c) Early-flowering Outdoor Incurved: Small-flowered
(24a) Early-flowering Outdoor Reflexed:

	Large-flowered
(24b)	Early-flowering Outdoor Reflexed: Medium-flowered
(24c)	Early-flowering Outdoor Reflexed: Small-flowered
(25a)	Early-flowering Outdoor Intermediate: Large-flowered
(25b)	Early-flowering Outdoor Intermediate: Medium-flowered
(25c)	Early-flowering Outdoor Intermediate: Small-flowered
(26a)	Early-flowering Outdoor Anemone: Large-flowered
(26b)	Early-flowering Outdoor Anemone: Medium-flowered
(27a)	Early-flowering Outdoor Single: Large-flowered
(27b)	Early-flowering Outdoor Single: Medium-flowered
(28a)	Early-flowering Outdoor Pompon: True Pompon
(28b)	Early-flowering Outdoor Pompon: Semi-pompon
(29a)	Early-flowering Outdoor Spray: Anemone
(29b)	Early-flowering Outdoor Spray: Pompon
(29c)	Early-flowering Outdoor Spray: Reflexed
(29d)	Early-flowering Outdoor Spray: Single
(29e)	Early-flowering Outdoor Spray: Intermediate
(29f)	Early-flowering Outdoor Spray: Spider, Quill, Spoon or Any Other Type
(29K)	Early-flowering Outdoor Spray: Korean
(29Rub)	Early-flowering Outdoor Spray: Rubellum
(30)	Any Other Early-flowering Outdoor Type

CLEMATIS

(Cultivar Groups as per Matthews, V. (2002) *The International Clematis Register & Checklist 2002*, RHS, London.)

(A)	Atragene Group
(Ar)	Armandii Group
(C)	Cirrhosa Group
(EL)	Early Large-flowered Group
(F)	Flammula Group
(Fo)	Forsteri Group
(H)	Heracleifolia Group
(I)	Integrifolia Group
(LL)	Late Large-flowered Group
(M)	Montana Group
(T)	Texensis Group
(Ta)	Tangutica Group
(V)	Viorna Group
(Vb)	Vitalba Group
(Vt)	Viticella Group

DAHLIA

(By the National Dahlia Society with corresponding numerical classification according to the RHS's International Register)

(Sin)	1 Single
(Anem)	2 Anemone-flowered
(Col)	3 Collerette
(WL)	4 Waterlily (unassigned)
(LWL)	4B Waterlily, Large
(MWL)	4C Waterlily, Medium
(SWL)	4D Waterlily, Small
(MinWL)	4E Waterlily, Miniature
(D)	5 Decorative (unassigned)
(GD)	5A Decorative, Giant
(LD)	5B Decorative, Large
(MD)	5C Decorative, Medium
(SD)	5D Decorative, Small
(MinD)	5E Decorative, Miniature
(SBa)	6A Small Ball
(MinBa)	6B Miniature Ball
(Pom)	7 Pompon
(C)	8 Cactus (unassigned)
(GC)	8A Cactus, Giant
(LC)	8B Cactus, Large
(MC)	8C Cactus, Medium
(SC)	8D Cactus, Small
(MinC)	8E Cactus, Miniature
(S-c)	9 Semi-cactus (unassigned)
(GS-c)	9A Semi-cactus, Giant
(LS-c)	9B Semi-cactus, Large
(MS-c)	9C Semi-cactus, Medium
(SS-c)	9D Semi-cactus, Small
(MinS-c)	9E Semi-cactus, Miniature
(Misc)	10 Miscellaneous
(Fim)	11 Fimbriated
(SinO)	12 Single Orchid (Star)
(DblO)	13 Double Orchid
(B)	Botanical
(DwB)	Dwarf Bedding
(Lil)	Lilliput (in combination)

DIANTHUS

(By the RHS)

(b)	Carnation, border
(M)	Carnation, Malmaison
(pf)	Carnation, perpetual-flowering
(p)	Pink
(p,a)	Pink, annual

FRUIT

(B)	Black (*Vitis*), Blackcurrant (*Ribes*)
(Ball)	Ballerina (*Malus*)
(C)	Culinary (*Malus, Prunus, Pyrus, Ribes*)
(Cider)	Cider (*Malus*)
(D)	Dessert (*Malus, Prunus, Pyrus, Ribes*)
(F)	Fruit
(G)	Glasshouse (*Vitis*)
(O)	Outdoor (*Vitis*)
(P)	Pinkcurrant (*Ribes*)
(Perry)	Perry (*Pyrus*)
(R)	Red (*Vitis*), Redcurrant (*Ribes*)
(S)	Seedless (*Citrus, Vitis*)
(W)	White (*Vitis*), Whitecurrant (*Ribes*)

GLADIOLUS

(B)	Butterfly
(E)	Exotic
(G)	Giant
(L)	Large
(M)	Medium
(Min)	Miniature
(N)	Nanus
(P)	Primulinus
(S)	Small
(Tub)	Tubergenii

HYDRANGEA MACROPHYLLA

(H)	Hortensia
(L)	Lacecap

IRIS

(By the American Iris Society)

(AB)	Arilbred
(BB)	Border Bearded
(Cal-Sib)	Series *Californicae* × Series *Sibiricae*
(CH)	Californian Hybrid
(DB)	Dwarf Bearded (not assigned)
(Dut)	Dutch
(IB)	Intermediate Bearded
(La)	Louisiana Hybrid
(MDB)	Miniature Dwarf Bearded
(MTB)	Miniature Tall Bearded
(SDB)	Standard Dwarf Bearded
(Sino-Sib)	Series *Sibiricae*, chromosome number 2n=40
(Spuria)	Spuria
(TB)	Tall Bearded

LILIUM

(Classification according to *The International Lily Register* (ed. 3, 1982) with amendments from Supp. 10 (1992), RHS)

(I)	Early-flowering Asiatic Hybrids derived from *L. amabile, L. bulbiferum, L. cernuum, L. concolor, L. davidii, L.* × *hollandicum, L. lancifolium, L. leichtlinii, L.* × *maculatum* and *L. pumilum*
(Ia)	Upright flowers, borne singly or in an umbel
(Ib)	Outward-facing flowers
(Ic)	Pendant flowers
(II)	Hybrids of Martagon type, one parent having been a form of *L. hansonii* or *L. martagon*
(III)	Hybrids from *L. candidum, L. chalcedonicum* and other related European species (excluding *L. martagon*)
(IV)	Hybrids of American species
(V)	Hybrids derived from *L. formosanum* and *L. longiflorum*
(VI)	Hybrid Trumpet Lilies and Aurelian hybrids from Asiatic species, including *L. henryi* but excluding those from *L. auratum, L. japonicum, L. rubellum* and *L. speciosum*.
(VIa)	Plants with trumpet-shaped flowers
(VIb)	Plants with bowl-shaped flowers
(VIc)	Plants with flat flowers (or only the tips recurved)
(VId)	Plants with recurved flowers
(VII)	Hybrids of Far Eastern species as *L auratum, L. japonicum, L. rubellum* and *L. speciosum* (Oriental Hybrids)
(VIIa)	Plants with trumpet-shaped flowers
(VIIb)	Plants with bowl-shaped flowers
(VIIc)	Plants with flat flowers
(VIId)	Plants with recurved flowers
(VIII)	All hybrids not in another division
(IX)	All species and their varieties and forms

MALUS *SEE* FRUIT

NARCISSUS

(By the RHS, revised 1998)

(1)	Trumpet
(2)	Large-cupped
(3)	Small-cupped
(4)	Double
(5)	Triandrus
(6)	Cyclamineus
(7)	Jonquilla and Apodanthus
(8)	Tazetta
(9)	Poeticus
(10)	Bulbocodium
(11a)	Split-corona: Collar

(11b)	Split-corona: Papillon
(12)	Miscellaneous
(13)	Species

NYMPHAEA

(H)	Hardy
(D)	Day-blooming
(N)	Night-blooming
(T)	Tropical

PAEONIA

(S)	Shrubby

PELARGONIUM

(A)	Angel
(C)	Coloured Foliage (in combination)
(Ca)	Cactus (in combination)
(d)	Double (in combination)
(Dec)	Decorative
(Dw)	Dwarf
(DwI)	Dwarf Ivy-leaved
(Fr)	Frutetorum
(I)	Ivy-leaved
(Min)	Miniature
(MinI)	Miniature Ivy-leaved
(R)	Regal
(Sc)	Scented-leaved
(St)	Stellar (in combination)
(T)	Tulip (in combination)
(U)	Unique
(Z)	Zonal

PRIMULA

(Classification by Section as per Richards. J. (2002) *Primula* (2nd edition). Batsford, London)

(Ag)	*Auganthus*
(Al)	*Aleuritia*
(Am)	*Amethystinae*
(Ar)	*Armerina*
(Au)	*Auricula*
(A)	Alpine Auricula
(B)	Border Auricula
(S)	Show Auricula
(St)	Striped Auricula
(Bu)	*Bullatae*
(Ca)	*Capitatae*
(Cf)	*Cordifoliae*
(Ch)	*Chartaceae*
(Co)	*Cortusoides*
(Cr)	*Carolinella*
(Cu)	*Cuneifoliae*
(Cy)	*Crystallophlomis*
(Da)	*Davidii*
(De)	*Denticulatae*
(Dr)	*Dryadifoliae*
(F)	*Fedtschenkoanae*
(G)	*Glabrae*
(Ma)	*Malvaceae*
(Mi)	*Minutissimae*
(Mo)	*Monocarpicae*
(Mu)	*Muscarioides*
(Ob)	*Obconicolisteri*
(Or)	*Oreophlomis*
(Pa)	*Parryi*
(Pe)	*Petiolares*
(Pf)	*Proliferae*
(Pi)	*Pinnatae*
(Pr)	*Primula*
(Poly)	Polyanthus
(Prim)	Primrose
(Pu)	*Pulchellae*
(Py)	*Pycnoloba*
(R)	*Reinii*
(Si)	*Sikkimenses*
(So)	*Soldanelloides*
(Sp)	*Sphondylia*
(Sr)	*Sredinskya*
(Su)	*Suffrutescentes*
(Y)	*Yunnannenses*

PRUNUS *SEE* FRUIT

PYRUS *SEE* FRUIT

RHODODENDRON

(A)	Azalea (deciduous, species or unclassified hybrid)
(Ad)	Azaleodendron
(EA)	Evergreen azalea
(G)	Ghent azalea (deciduous)
(K)	Knap Hill or Exbury azalea (deciduous)
(M)	Mollis azalea (deciduous)
(O)	Occidentalis azalea (deciduous)
(R)	Rustica azalea (deciduous)
(V)	Vireya rhododendron
(Vs)	Viscosa azalea (deciduous)

RIBES *SEE* FRUIT

ROSA

(A)	Alba
(Bb)	Bourbon
(Bs)	Boursault
(Ce)	Centifolia
(Ch)	China
(Cl)	Climbing (in combination)

(D)	Damask
(DPo)	Damask Portland
(F)	Floribunda or Cluster-flowered
(G)	Gallica
(Ga)	Garnette
(GC)	Ground Cover
(HM)	Hybrid Musk
(HP)	Hybrid Perpetual
(HT)	Hybrid Tea or Large-flowered
(Min)	Miniature
(Mo)	Moss (in combination)
(N)	Noisette
(Patio)	Patio, Miniature Floribunda or Dwarf Cluster-flowered
(Poly)	Polyantha
(PiH)	Pimpinellifolia hybrid (Hybrid Scots Briar)
(Ra)	Rambler
(RH)	Rubiginosa hybrid (Hybrid Sweet Briar)
(Ru)	Rugosa
(S)	Shrub
(T)	Tea

SAXIFRAGA

(Classification by Section from Gornall, R.J. (1987). *Botanical Journal of the Linnean Society*, 95(4): 273-292)

(1)	*Ciliatae*
(2)	*Cymbalaria*
(3)	*Merkianae*
(4)	*Micranthes*
(5)	*Irregulares*
(6)	*Heterisia*
(7)	*Porphyrion*
(8)	*Ligulatae*
(9)	*Xanthizoon*
(10)	*Trachyphyllum*
(11)	*Gymnopera*
(12)	*Cotylea*
(13)	*Odontophyllae*
(14)	*Mesogyne*
(15)	*Saxifraga*

TULIPA

(Classification by Cultivar Group from *Classified List and International Register of Tulip Names* by Koninklijke Algemeene Vereening voor Bloembollenculture 1996)

(1)	Single Early Group
(2)	Double Early Group
(3)	Triumph Group
(4)	Darwinhybrid Group
(5)	Single Late Group (including Darwin Group and Cottage Group)
(6)	Lily-flowered Group
(7)	Fringed Group
(8)	Viridiflora Group
(9)	Rembrandt Group
(10)	Parrot Group
(11)	Double Late Group
(12)	Kaufmanniana Group
(13)	Fosteriana Group
(14)	Greigii Group
(15)	Miscellaneous

VERBENA

(G)	Species and hybrids considered by some botanists to belong to the separate genus *Glandularia*.

VIOLA

(C)	Cornuta Hybrid
(dVt)	Double Violet
(ExVa)	Exhibition Viola
(FP)	Fancy Pansy
(PVt)	Parma Violet
(SP)	Show Pansy
(T)	Tricolor
(Va)	Viola
(Vt)	Violet
(Vtta)	Violetta

VITIS *SEE* FRUIT

Reverse Synonyms

The following list of reverse synonyms is intended to help users find from which genus an unfamiliar plant name has been cross-referred. For a fuller explanation see p.10.

Abelmoschus – Hibiscus
Abutilon – Corynabutilon
Acacia – Racosperma
Acca – Feijoa
× *Achicodonia – Eucodonia*
Achillea – Anthemis
Achillea – Tanacetum
Acinos – Calamintha
Acinos – Clinopodium
Acinos – Micromeria
Acmella – Spilanthes
Actaea – Cimicifuga
Actaea – Souliea
Aethionema – Eunomia
Agapetes – Pentapterygium
Agarista – Leucothoe
Agastache – Cedronella
Agathosma – Barosma
Agave – Manfreda
Agrostis – Eragrostis
Aichryson – Aeonium
Ajania – Chrysanthemum
Ajania – Dendranthema
Ajania – Eupatorium
Albizia – Acacia
Alcea – Althaea
Allardia – Waldheimia
Allocasuarina – Casuarina
Aloysia – Lippia
Althaea – Malva
Alyogyne – Anisodontea
Alyogyne – Hibiscus
Alyssum – Ptilotrichum
× *Amarygia – Amaryllis*
Amaryllis – Brunsvigia
Amomyrtus – Myrtus
Amsonia – Rhazya
Anacamptis – Orchis
Anaphalis – Gnaphalium
Anchusa – Lycopsis
Androsace – Douglasia
Androstoma – Cyathodes
Anemanthele – Oryzopsis
Anemanthele – Stipa
Anemone – Eriocapitella
Anisodontea – Malvastrum
Anisodus – Scopolia
Anomatheca – Freesia
Anomatheca – Lapeirousia
Anredera – Boussingaultia
Antirrhinum – Asarina
Aphanes – Alchemilla
Apium – Apium × *Petroselinum*
Arctanthemum – Chrysanthemum
Arctostaphylos – Arbutus
Arctotis – Venidium
Arctotis – × *Venidioarctotis*
Arenga – Didymosperma
Argyranthemum – Anthemis
Argyranthemum – Chrysanthemum
Armoracia – Cochlearia
Arnoglossum – Cacalia
Arundinaria – Pseudosasa
Asarina – Antirrhinum
Asarum – Hexastylis
Asparagus – Myrsiphyllum
Asparagus – Smilax
Asperula – Galium
Asphodeline – Asphodelus
Asplenium – Camptosorus
Asplenium – Ceterach
Asplenium – Phyllitis
Asplenium – Scolopendrium
Aster – Crinitaria
Aster – Doellingeria
Aster – Erigeron
Aster – Microglossa
Aster – Symphyotrichum
Astilboides – Rodgersia
Asyneuma – Campanula
Athanasia – Hymenolepis
Atropanthe – Scopolia
Aurinia – Alyssum
Austrocedrus – Libocedrus
Austromyrtus – Myrtus
Azorella – Bolax
Azorina – Campanula

Bambusa – Arundinaria
Bashania – Arundinaria
Bassia – Kochia
Beaucarnea – Nolina
Bellevalia – Muscari
Bellis – Erigeron
Bignonia – Campsis
Blechnum – Lomaria
Blepharocalyx – Temu
Bolax – Azorella
Bolboschoenus – Scirpus
Bonia – Indocalamus
Borago – Anchusa
Bothriochloa – Andropogon
Bouteloua – Chondrosum
Boykinia – Telesonix
Brachyglottis – Senecio
Brimeura – Hyacinthus
Brodiaea – Triteleia
Brugmansia – Datura
Brunnera – Anchusa
Buglossoides – Lithospermum
Bulbine – Bulbinopsis

Cacalia – Adenostyles
Calamagrostis – Stipa
Calamintha – Clinopodium
Calamintha – Thymus
Calibrachoa – Petunia
Callisia – Phyodina
Callisia – Tradescantia
Calocedrus – Libocedrus
Calomeria – Humea
Caloscordum – Nothoscordum
Calylophus – Oenothera
Calytrix – Lhotzkya
Camellia – Thea
Campanula – Campanula × *Symphyandra*
Campanula – Symphyandra
Cardamine – Dentaria
Carpobrotus – Lampranthus
Cassiope – Harrimanella
Cedronella – Agastache
Centaurium – Erythraea
Centella – Hydrocotyle
Centranthus – Kentranthus
Centranthus – Valeriana
Cephalaria – Scabiosa
Ceratostigma – Plumbago
Chaenomeles – Cydonia
Chaenorhinum – Linaria
Chamaecytisus – Cytisus
Chamaedaphne – Cassandra
Chamaemelum – Anthemis
Chamerion – Chamaenerion
Chamerion – Epilobium
Chasmanthium – Uniola
Cheilanthes – Notholaena
Chiastophyllum – Cotyledon
Chimonobambusa – Arundinaria
Chimonobambusa – Qiongzhuea
Chionohebe - Parahebe
Chionohebe – Pygmea
× *Chionoscilla – Scilla*
Chlorophytum – Diuranthera

Chromolaena – Eupatorium
Chrysanthemum – Dendranthema
Chrysopsis – Heterotheca
Cicerbita – Lactuca
Cissus – Ampelopsis
Cissus – Parthenocissus
× *Citrofortunella – Citrus*
Clarkia – Eucharidium
Clarkia – Godetia
Clavinodum – Arundinaria
Claytonia – Calandrinia
Claytonia – Montia
Clematis – Atragene
Clematis – Clematopsis
Cleyera – Eurya
Clinopodium – Calamintha
Clytostoma – Bignonia
Clytostoma – Pandorea
Cnicus – Carduus
Conoclinium – Eupatorium
Codonopsis – Campanumoea
Consolida – Delphinium
Cordyline – Dracaena
Cornus – Chamaepericlymenum
Cornus – Dendrobenthamia
Coronilla – Securigera
Cortaderia – Gynerium
Corydalis - Capnoides
Corydalis – Fumaria
Corydalis – Pseudofumaria
Cosmos – Bidens
Cotinus – Rhus
Cotula – Leptinella
Crassula – Rochea
Crassula – Sedum
Crassula – Tillaea
Cremanthodium – Ligularia
Crinodendron – Tricuspidaria
Crocosmia – Antholyza
Crocosmia – Curtonus
Crocosmia – Montbretia
Cruciata – Galium
Ctenanthe – Calathea
Ctenanthe – Stromanthe
× *Cupressocyparis – Chamaecyparis*
× *Cupressocyparis -* × *Cuprocyparis*
Cupressus – Chamaecyparis
Cyclosorus – Pneumatopteris
Cymbalaria – Linaria
Cymophyllus – Carex
Cyperus – Mariscus
Cypripedium – Criogenes
Cyrtanthus – Anoiganthus
Cyrtanthus – Vallota
Cyrtomium – Phanerophlebia
Cyrtomium – Polystichum
Cytisus – Argyrocytisus
Cytisus – Genista
Cytisus – Lembotropis
Cytisus – Spartocytisus

Daboecia – Menziesia
Dacrycarpus – Podocarpus
Dactylorhiza – Orchis
Dalea – Petalostemon
Danae – Ruscus
Darmera – Peltiphyllum
Datura – Brugmansia
Davallia – Humata
Delairea – Senecio
Delosperma – Lampranthus
Delosperma – Mesembryanthemum
Desmodium – Lespedeza
Deuterocohnia – Abromeitiella
Dicentra – Corydalis
Dichelostemma – Brodiaea
Dicliptera – Barleria
Dicliptera – Justicia
Diervilla – Weigela
Dietes – Moraea
Diplazium – Athyrium
Dipogon – Dolichos
Disporopsis – Polygonatum
Dracaena – Pleomele
Dracunculus – Arum
Dregea – Wattakaka
Drepanostachyum – Bambusa
Drepanostachyum – Chimonobambusa
Drepanostachyum – Gelidocalamus
Drepanostachyum – Thamnocalamus
Drimys – Tasmannia
Duchesnea – Fragaria
Dypsis – Chrysalidocarpus
Dypsis – Neodypsis

Echeveria – Cotyledon
Echinacea – Rudbeckia
Echinospartum – Genista
Edraianthus – Wahlenbergia
Egeria – Elodea
Elatostema – Pellionia
Eleutherococcus – Acanthopanax
Elliottia – Botryostege
Elliottia – Cladothamnus
Elymus – Agropyron
Elymus – Leymus
Ensete – Musa
Epipremnum – Philodendron
Epipremnum – Scindapsus
Episcia – Alsobia
Eranthis – Aconitum
Eremophila – Myoporum
Erepsia - Semnanthe
Erigeron – Haplopappus
Erysimum – Cheiranthus
Eucalyptus – Corymbia
Eupatorium – Ageratina
Eupatorium – Ayapana
Eupatorium – Bartlettina
Euphorbia – Poinsettia
Euryops – Senecio
Eustachys – Chloris
Eustoma – Lisianthus

Fallopia – Bilderdykia
Fallopia – Polygonum
Fallopia – Reynoutria
Farfugium – Ligularia
Fargesia – Arundinaria
Fargesia – Borinda
Fargesia – Semiarundinaria
Fargesia – Sinarundinaria
Fargesia – Thamnocalamus
Fatsia – Aralia
Felicia – Agathaea
Felicia – Aster
Fibigia – Farsetia
Filipendula – Spiraea
Foeniculum – Ferula
Fortunella – Citrus

Galium – Asperula
Gaultheria – Chiogenes
Gaultheria – Pernettya
Gaultheria – × *Gaulnettya*
Gelasine – Sisyrinchium
Genista – Chamaespartium
Genista – Cytisus
Genista – Echinospartum
Genista – Teline
Gethyum – Ancrumia
Geum – Sieversia
Gladiolus – Acidanthera
Gladiolus – Anomalesia
Gladiolus – Homoglossum
Gladiolus – Petamenes
Glebionis – Chrysanthemum
Glebionis – Xanthophthalmum
Glechoma – Nepeta
Gloxinia – Seemannia
Gomphocarpus – Asclepias
Gomphocarpus – Asclepias
Goniolimon – Limonium
Graptopetalum – Sedum
Graptopetalum – Tacitus
Greenovia – Sempervivum
Gymnadenia – Nigritella
Gymnospermium – Leontice

Habranthus – Zephyranthes
Hacquetia – Dondia
× *Halimiocistus – Cistus*

× Halimiocistus – Halimium
Halimione – Atriplex
Halimium – Cistus
Halimium – Helianthemum
Halimium – × Halimiocistus
Halocarpus – Dacrydium
Hanabusaya – Symphyandra
Hedychium – Brachychilum
Helianthella – Helianthus
Helianthemum – Cistus
Helianthus – Coreopsis
Helianthus – Heliopsis
Helichrysum – Gnaphalium
Helicodiceros – Dracunculus
Helictotrichon – Avena
Helictotrichon – Avenula
Hepatica – Anemone
Herbertia – Alophia
Hermodactylus – Iris
Heterocentron – Schizocentron
Heteromeles – Photinia
Heterotheca – Chrysopsis
× Heucherella – Heuchera
× Heucherella – Tiarella
Hibbertia – Candollea
Hieracium – Andryala
Himalayacalamus – Arundinaria
Himalayacalamus – Chimonobambusa
Himalayacalamus – Drepanostachyum
Himalayacalamus – Drepanostachyum
Himalayacalamus – Thamnocalamus
Hippocrepis – Coronilla
Hippolytia – Achillea
Hippolytia – Tanacetum
Hoheria – Plagianthus
Homalocladium – Muehlenbeckia
Howea – Kentia
Hyacinthoides – Endymion
Hyacinthoides – Scilla
Hylomecon – Chelidonium
Hymenocallis – Elisena
Hymenocallis – Ismene
Hymenoxys – Dugaldia
Hymenoxys – Helenium
Hyophorbe – Mascarena
Hypoxis – Rhodohypoxis

Incarvillea – Amphicome
Indocalamus – Sasa
Iochroma – Acnistus
Iochroma – Cestrum
Iochroma – Dunalia
Ipheion – Tristagma
Ipheion – Triteleia
Ipomoea – Calonyction
Ipomoea – Mina
Ipomoea – Pharbitis
Ipomopsis – Gilia
Ischyrolepis – Restio
Isolepis – Scirpus
Isotoma – Laurentia
Isotoma – Solenopsis

Jamesbrittenia – Sutera
Jeffersonia – Plagiorhegma
Jovibarba – Sempervivum
Juncus – Scirpus
Jurinea – Jurinella
Justicia – Beloperone
Justicia - Duvernoia
Justicia – Jacobinia
Justicia – Libonia

Kalanchoe – Bryophyllum
Kalanchoe – Kitchingia
Kalimeris – Aster
Kalimeris – Asteromoea
Kalimeris – Boltonia
Kalopanax – Acanthopax
Kalopanax – Eleutherococcus
Keckiella - Penstemon
Keckiella – Penstemon
Kitagawia – Peucedanum
Knautia – Scabiosa
Kniphofia – Tritoma
Kohleria – Isoloma
Krascheninnikovia – Ceratoides
Kunzea – Leptospermum

Lablab – Dolichos
Lagarosiphon – Elodea
Lagarostrobos – Dacrydium
Lamium – Galeobdolon
Lamium – Lamiastrum
Lampranthus – Mesembryanthemum
Lavatera – Malva
Ledebouria – Scilla
× Ledodendron – Rhododendron
Ledum – Rhododendron
Leontodon – Microseris
Lepechinia – Sphacele
Lepidothamnus – Dacrydium
Leptecophylla – Cyathodes
Leptinella – Cotula
Leptodactylon – Gilia
Leucanthemella – Chrysanthemum
Leucanthemella – Leucanthemum
Leucanthemopsis – Chrysanthemum
Leucanthemum – Chrysanthemum
Leucocoryne – Beauverdia
Leucophyta – Calocephalus
Leucopogon – Cyathodes
Leucopogon – Styphelia
× Leucoraoulia – Raoulia
× Leucoraoulia – Raoulia × Leucogenes
Leymus – Elymus
Ligularia – Senecio
Ligustrum – Parasyringa
Lilium – Nomocharis
Limonium – Statice
Linanthus – Linanthastrum
Lindelofia – Adelocaryum
Lindera – Parabenzoin
Lindernia – Ilysanthes
Liriope – Ophiopogon
Lithodora – Lithospermum
Lobelia – Monopsis
Lophomyrtus – Myrtus
Lophospermum – Asarina
Lophospermum – Maurandya
Lotus – Dorycnium
Lotus – Tetragonolobus
Ludwigia – Jussiaea
Luma – Myrtus
× Lycene – Lychnis
Lychnis – Agrostemma
Lychnis – Silene
Lychnis – Viscaria
Lycianthes – Solanum
Lytocaryum – Cocos
Lytocaryum – Microcoelum

Macfadyena – Bignonia
Macfadyena – Doxantha
Machaeranthera – Xylorhiza
Machaerina – Baumea
Mackaya – Asystasia
Macleaya – Bocconia
Maclura - Cudrania
Macropiper – Piper
Magnolia – Parakmeria
Mahonia – Berberis
Maianthemum – Smilacina
Mandevilla – Dipladenia
Mandragora – Atropa
Marrubium – Ballota
Matricaria – Tripleurospermum
Maurandella – Asarina
Maurandya – Asarina
Melanoselinum – Thapsia
Melicytus – Hymenanthera
Melinis – Rhynchelytrum
Mentha – Preslia
Merremia – Ipomoea
Mimulus – Diplacus
Minuartia – Arenaria
Moltkia – Lithodora
Moltkia – Lithospermum

Morina – Acanthocalyx
Morina – Acanthocalyx
Mukdenia – Aceriphyllum
Muscari – Hyacinthus
Muscari – Leopoldia
Muscari – Muscarimia
Muscari – Pseudomuscari
Myrteola – Myrtus

Naiocrene – Claytonia
Naiocrene – Montia
Nectaroscordum – Allium
Nematanthus – Hypocyrta
Nemesia – Diascia × *Linaria*
Neolitsea – Litsea
Neopaxia – Claytonia
Neopaxia – Montia
Neoregelia – Nidularium
Nepeta – Dracocephalum
× *Niduregelia – Guzmania*
Nipponanthemum – Chrysanthemum
Nipponanthemum – Leucanthemum
Nolina – Beaucarnea
Nymphoides – Villarsia

Ochagavia – Fascicularia
Oemleria – Osmaronia
Oenothera – Chamissonia
Olsynium – Sisyrinchium
Onixotis – Dipidax
Onoclea – Matteuccia
Ophiopogon – Convallaria
Orchis – Anacamptis
Orchis – Dactylorhiza
Oreopteris – Thelypteris
Orostachys – Sedum
Oscularia – Lampranthus
Osmanthus – Phillyrea
Osmanthus – × *Osmarea*
Othonna – Hertia
Othonna – Othonnopsis
Ozothamhus – Helichrysum

Pachyphragma – Cardamine
Pachyphragma – Thlaspi
Pachystegia - Olearia
Packera – Senecio
Paederota – Veronica
Pallenis – Asteriscus
Papaver – Meconopsis
Parahebe – Derwentia
Parahebe – Hebe
Parahebe – Veronica
Paraserianthes – Albizia
Paris – Daiswa
Parthenocissus – Ampelopsis
Parthenocissus – Vitis
Passiflora – Tetrapathaea
Paxistima – Pachystema
Pecteilis – Habenaria
Pelargonium – Geranium
Peltoboykinia – Boykinia
Penstemon – Chelone
Penstemon – Nothochelone
Penstemon – Pennellianthus
Pentaglottis – Anchusa
Pericallis – Senecio
Persea – Machilus
Persicaria – Aconogonon
Persicaria – Bistorta
Persicaria – Polygonum
Persicaria – Tovara
Petrocoptis – Lychnis
Petrophytum – Spiraea
Petrorhagia – Tunica
Petroselinum – Carum
Phegopteris – Thelypteris
Phoenicaulis – Parrya
Photinia – Stransvaesia
Photinia – × *Stravinia*
Phuopsis – Crucianella
Phyla – Lippia
Phymatosorus – Microsorum
Phymosia – Sphaeralcea
Physoplexis – Phyteuma
Physostegia – Dracocephalum
Pieris – Arcterica
Pilosella – Hieracium
Platycladus – Thuja
Plecostachys – Helichrysum
Plectranthus – Coleus
Plectranthus – Solenostemon
Pleioblastus – Arundinaria
Pleioblastus – Sasa
Podophyllum – Dysosma
Podranea – Tecoma
Polygonum – Persicaria
Polypodium – Phlebodium
Polyscias – Nothopanax
Poncirus – Aegle
Potentilla – Comarum
Pratia – Lobelia
Prenanthes – Nabalus
Pritzelago – Hutchinsia
Prumnopitys – Podocarpus
Prunus – Amygdalus
Pseudocydonia – Chaenomeles
Pseudogynoxys – Senecio
Pseudopanax – Metapanax
Pseudopanax – Neopanax
Pseudosasa – Arundinaria
Pseudotsuga – Tsuga
Pseudowintera – Drimys
Pterocephalus – Scabiosa
Pteryxia - Cymopterus
Ptilostemon – Cirsium
Pulicaria – Inula
Pulsatilla – Anemone
Purshia – Cowania
Puschkinia – Scilla
Pyrrocoma – Aster
Pyrrocoma – Haplopappus

Reineckea – Liriope
Retama – Genista
Retama – Lygos
Rhamnus – Frangula
Rhapis – Chamaerops
Rhodanthe – Helipterum
Rhodanthemum – Argyranthemum
Rhodanthemum – Chrysanthemopsis
Rhodanthemum – Chrysanthemum
Rhodanthemum – Leucanthemopsis
Rhodanthemum – Leucanthemum
Rhodanthemum – Pyrethropsis
Rhodiola – Clementsia
Rhodiola – Rosularia
Rhodiola – Sedum
Rhododendron – Azalea
Rhododendron – Azaleodendron
Rhododendron – Rhodora
Rhododendron – Therorhodion
Rhododendron – Tsusiophyllum
Rhodophiala – Hippeastrum
× *Rhodoxis – Hypoxis* × *Rhodohypoxis*
× *Rhodoxis – Rhodohypoxis*
Rhus – Toxicodendron
Rhyncospora – Dichromena
Rosularia – Cotyledon
Rosularia – Sempervivella
Rothmannia – Gardenia
Ruellia – Dipteracanthus

Saccharum – Erianthus
Sagina – Minuartia
Sanguisorba – Dendriopoterium
Sanguisorba – Poterium
Sasa – Arundinaria
Sasaella – Arundinaria
Sasaella – Pleioblastus
Sasaella – Sasa
Sauromatum – Arum
Scadoxus – Haemanthus
Schefflera – Brassaia
Schefflera – Dizygotheca
Schefflera – Heptapleurum
Schizachyrium – Andropogon
Schizostachyum – Arundinaria
Schizostachyum – Thamnocalamus
Schizostylis – Hesperantha

Schoenoplectus – Scirpus
Scilla – Oncostema
Scirpoides – Scirpus
Sedum – Hylotelephium
Sedum – Sedastrum
Semiaquilegia – Aquilegia
Semiaquilegia – Paraquilegia
Semiarundinaria – Arundinaria
Semiarundinaria – Oligostachyum
Senecio – Cineraria
Senecio – Kleinia
Senecio – Ligularia
Senna – Cassia
Seriphidium – Artemisia
Shortia – Schizocodon
Sibbaldiopsis – Potentilla
Silene – Lychnis
Silene – Melandrium
Silene – Saponaria
Sinacalia – Ligularia
Sinacalia – Senecio
Sinningia – Gesneria
Sinningia – Rechsteineria
Sinobambusa – Pleioblastus
Sinobambusa – Pseudosasa
Siphocranion – Chamaesphacos
Sisymbrium – Hesperis
Sisyrinchium – Phaiophleps
Smallanthus – Polymnia
Solanum – Lycianthes
Soleirolia – Helxine
Solenostemon – Coleus
× *Solidaster – Aster*
× *Solidaster – Solidago*
Sorbaria – Spiraea
Sparaxis – Synnotia
Sphaeralcea – Iliamna
Sphaeromeria – Tanacetum
Spirodela – Lemna
Stachys – Betonica
Stemmacantha – Centaurea
Stemmacantha – Leuzea
Stenomesson – Urceolina
Stewartia – Stuartia
Stipa – Achnatherum
Stipa – Agrostis
Stipa – Calamagrostis
Stipa – Lasiagrostis
Stipa – Nassella
Strobilanthes – Parachampionella
Strobilanthes – Pteracanthus
Succisa – Scabiosa
Sutera – Bacopa
Syagrus – Arecastrum
Syagrus – Cocos
Syncarpha - Helipterum
Syzygium – Caryophyllus

Talbotia – Vellozia
Tanacetum – Achillea
Tanacetum – Balsamita
Tanacetum – Chrysanthemum
Tanacetum – Matricaria
Tanacetum – Pyrethrum
Tanacetum – Spathipappus
Tecoma – Tecomaria
Telekia – Buphthalmum
Tetradium – Euodia
Tetraneuris - Actinella
Tetraneuris – Actinella
Tetraneuris – Hymenoxys
Tetrapanax – Fatsia
Thamnocalamus – Arundinaria
Thlaspi – Hutchinsia
Thlaspi – Noccaea
Thlaspi – Vania
Thuja – Thujopsis
Thymus – Origanum
Tiarella – × *Heucherella*
Tonestus – Haplopappus
Toona – Cedrela
Trachelium – Diosphaera
Trachycarpus – Chamaerops
Tradescantia – Rhoeo
Tradescantia – Setcreasea
Tradescantia – Zebrina
Trichopetalum – Anthericum
Tripetaleia – Elliottia
Tripogandra – Tradescantia
Tristaniopsis – Tristania
Triteleia – Brodiaea
Tritonia – Crocosmia
Tritonia – Montbretia
Trochiscanthes – Angelica
Tropaeolum – Nasturtium hort.
Tulipa – Amana
Tupistra – Campylandra
Tutcheria – Pyrenaria
Tweedia – Oxypetalum

Ugni – Myrtus
Utricularia – Polypompholyx
Uvularia – Oakesiella

Vaccaria – Melandrium
Vaccinium – Oxycoccus
Verbascum – Celsia
Verbascum – × *Celsioverbascum*
Verbena – Glandularia
Verbena – Lippia
Veronicastrum – Veronica
Vigna – Phaseolus
Viola – Erpetion
Vitaliana – Androsace
Vitaliana – Douglasia

Wedelia – Zexmenia
Weigela – Diervilla
Weigela – Macrodiervilla

Xanthorhiza – Zanthorhiza
Xerochrysum – Bracteantha
Xerochrysum – Helichrysum

Yushania – Arundinaria
Yushania – Sinarundinaria
Yushania – Thamnocalamus

Zantedeschia – Calla
Zauschneria – Epilobium
Zephyranthes – × *Cooperanthes*
Zephyranthes – Cooperia

THE PLANT DIRECTORY

A

Abelia ✿ (*Caprifoliaceae*)

	biflora	NLar
	chinensis misapplied	see *A.* x *grandiflora*
§	***chinensis*** R.Br.	EBee ECre EPfP MAsh SDnm SEND SMer SPer SPla SPoG SRms WBod WFar WHCG WLeb WPat WTel
§	***dielsii***	CPLG
	'Edward Goucher'	CBcs CDoC CMac CWSG EBee ECrN ELan EPfP LBMP LPan LRHS LSRN MGos MRav NBir NHol SEND SPer SPlb SRGP SWvt WFar WPat WSHC
	engleriana	CPle EBee ECrN EPfP MBri NLar WFar
	floribunda ♀H3	CBcs CDul CMac CPLG CPle CSBt CSam CWib EBee ECre ELan EPfP IDee LBMP LRHS NLar SDnm SPer SPoG SSpi WAbe WBod WFar WGob WPat WPic WSHC
§	x ***grandiflora*** ♀H4	More than 30 suppliers
	- 'Aurea'	see *A.* x *grandiflora* 'Gold Spot'
	- 'Compacta'	LRHS WFar
	- Confetti = 'Conti'PBR (v)	More than 30 suppliers
	- dwarf	CDoC
§	- 'Francis Mason' (v)	More than 30 suppliers
§	- 'Gold Spot'	CBcs CDoC CWSG EPfP MGos MWat WBrE WGob WRHF WWeb
	- 'Gold Strike'	see *A.* x *grandiflora* 'Gold Spot'
	- 'Goldsport'	see *A.* x *grandiflora* 'Gold Spot'
	- 'Hopleys'PBR (v)	CBcs CDoC CMac CSBt EBee EPfP LHop LRHS MAsh MGos SBra SLim SPoG WFar WGob WLeb
	- 'Panache' (v)	MGos MRav
	- 'Prostrate White'	MAsh
	- 'Sherwoodii'	CWSG WFar WPat
	- 'Sunrise'PBR (v)	CDoC CSBt ELan ENot EPfP EQua ERas LRHS NCGa NLar SBod SBra SHBN SLim SLon SPer SPla SPoG
	- 'Tanya'	WSPU
	- 'Variegata'	see *A.* x *grandiflora* 'Francis Mason'
	mosanensis	CMCN MBri NLar
	rupestris misapplied	see *A.* x *grandiflora*
	rupestris Lindl.	see *A. chinensis* R.Br.
	schumannii ♀H4	More than 30 suppliers
	- 'Saxon Gold'PBR	NEgg SLim SPoG
	spathulata	WFar
	triflora	CAbP CPLG CPle CWib EBee ECre EPfP LAst LHop LRHS MMuc NLar SLon WFar
	zanderi	see *A. dielsii*

Abeliophyllum (*Oleaceae*)

	distichum	More than 30 suppliers
	- Roseum Group	CBcs CDoC CPLG CPMA EBee ELan EPfP EWTr GBuc LAst LHop LRHS MAsh MGos MRav NSti SHBN SLon SPer SPoG WFar

Abelmoschus (*Malvaceae*)

§	***manihot***	EWin

Abies ✿ (*Pinaceae*)

	alba	CDul LCon LLin MBar NWea WMou
	- 'Compacta'	CKen
	- 'King's Dwarf'	CKen
	- 'Microphylla'	CKen
	- 'Münsterland'	CKen NLar
	- 'Nana' misapplied	see *Picea glauca* 'Nana'
	- 'Nana' ambig.	CKen
	- 'Pendula'	ECho
	- 'Schwarzwald'	NLar
	amabilis	LCon
	- 'Spreading Star'	LCon
	arizonica	see *A. lasiocarpa* var. *arizonica*
	x ***arnoldiana***	MBar NLar
	- 'Cyrille'	MBlu
	balsamea	CDul LCon LLin NWea WMou
	- Hudsonia Group ♀H4	CDoC CKen CMac ECho EHul IMGH LCon LLin LRHS MBar NDlv NHol NLar NMen SLim SPoG WEve
	- 'Jamie'	CKen NLar
	- 'Le Feber'	CKen
	- 'Nana'	CKen CRob ECho EHul EOrn LCon LLin LRHS MAsh NLar WFar
	- var. ***phanerolepis*** 'Bear Swamp'	CKen NLar
	- 'Piccolo'	CKen ECho EHul IMGH NLar SLim SPoG WFar WGor
	- 'Prostrata'	ECho EHul LLin LRHS WEve
	- 'Renswoude'	CKen
	- 'Tyler Blue'	CKen
	- 'Verkade's Prostrate'	CKen
	borisii-regis	LCon
*	- 'Pendula'	CKen
	brachyphylla dwarf	see *A. homolepis* 'Prostrata'
	cephalonica	LCon NWea
I	- 'Compacta' **new**	SPoG
	- 'Greg's Broom'	CKen ECho
§	- 'Meyer's Dwarf'	CDoC EBrs ECho EHul LCon LLin LRHS MBar NLar SCoo SLim SPoG WEve
	- 'Nana'	see *A. cephalonica* 'Meyer's Dwarf'
	chensiensis	LCon
	concolor ♀H4	CBcs CDul CTho EHul EMac EWTr GWCH LCon LPan MBar NWea
	- 'Archer's Dwarf'	CKen ECho LCon MGos NLar SLim
	- 'Argentea' Niemetz, 1903	CKen ECho LCon
	- 'Aurea'	MGos
	- 'Birthday Broom'	CKen NLar
	- 'Blue Cloak' **new**	NLar
	- 'Blue Sapphire'	CKen
	- 'Blue Spreader'	CKen MGos
§	- 'Compacta' ♀H4	CDoC CKen EBrs ECho EOrn LCon LLin LRHS MAsh MBar MGos NEgg NLar SCoo SLim SPoG WEve WFar
	- 'Fagerhult'	CKen NLar
	- 'Gable's Weeping'	CKen
	- 'Glauca'	see *A. concolor* Violacea Group

	– 'Glauca Compacta'	see *A. concolor* 'Compacta'
	– 'Hillier Broom'	see *A. concolor* 'Hillier's Dwarf'
§	– 'Hillier's Dwarf'	CKen
	– 'Husky Pup'	CKen
	– Lowiana Group	LCon
	– – 'Creamy'	CKen
	– 'Masonic Broom'	CKen NLar
	– 'Mike Stearn'	CKen NLar
	– 'Mora'	CKen
	– 'Ostrov nad Ohri'	CKen
	– 'Piggelmee'	CKen ECho LLin NLar SLim
	– 'Scooter'	CKen NLar
	– 'Sherwood's Blue'	ECho
*	– 'Swift's Silver'	LCon LRHS WBVN WEve
§	– Violacea Group	CDoC CKen ECho LCon LLin MAsh MBar MBri MGos SCoo SLim WEve WFar
	– 'Wattez Prostrate'	ECho NLar SCoo SLim WFar
	– 'Wattezii'	CKen ECho LCon LLin
	– 'Wintergold'	CKen EBrs ECho MGos NLar WEve
	delavayi	CMCN LCon MGos NWea
	– SDR 2569	GKev
	– SDR 3269	GKev
	– 'Major Neishe'	ECho
I	– 'Nana'	CKen
	– 'Nana Headfort'	see *A. fargesii* 'Headfort'
	fargesii	LCon NLar
§	– 'Headfort'	LCon MBar
	forrestii	CKen
	– var. ***ferreana*** SF 95168	ISea
	– – SF 95226	ISea
	fraseri	CTri MBar NWea SCoo WMou
	– 'Blue Bonnet'	CKen
	– 'Raul's Dwarf'	CKen ECho
	grandis	CBcs CDul EMac LCon LLin LRav MBar NWea SCoo SHBN WMou
	– 'Compacta'	CKen
	– 'Van Dedem's Dwarf'	CKen NLar
	holophylla	LCon NLar NWea
	homolepis	CDul LCon NLar
§	– 'Prostrata'	CKen
	koreana	More than 30 suppliers
	– 'Alpin Star'	CKen
	– 'Aurea'	see *A. koreana* 'Flava'
	– 'Blaue Zwo'	CKen ECho MAsh NLar
	– 'Blauer Eskimo'	CKen LCon MBlu NLar SLim
	– 'Blauer Pfiff'	CKen ECho NLar
	– 'Blinsham Gold'	CKen
	– 'Blue Emperor'	CKen NLar
	– 'Blue Magic'	CKen NLar
	– 'Blue 'n' Silver'	ECho LLin NLar WEve
	– 'Bonsai Blue'	NLar
	– 'Cis'	CDHC CKen ECho NLar SCoo SLim
	– 'Compact Dwarf'	ECho EPot LLin MAsh MBar MGos NLar WEve
	– 'Crystal Globe'	CKen ECho LCon NLar
	– 'Dark Hill' **new**	NLar
	– 'Doni Tajuso'	CKen
§	– 'Flava'	CKen ECho IMGH LLin MBar MGos NLar SCoo WEve
	– 'Frosty'	NLar SLim
	– 'Gait'	CKen ECho NLar
	– 'Golden Dream'	CKen ECho
	– 'Golden Glow'	NLar WFar
	– 'Green Carpet'	CKen NLar SLim
	– 'Grübele' witches' broom	CKen
	– 'Inverleith'	CKen
	– 'Knospenkönigin'	NLar
	– 'Kohout'	CKen ECho NLar
	– 'Lippetal'	CKen ECho
	– 'Luminetta'	CKen ECho MGos NLar SLim
	– 'Nadelkissen'	CKen ECho
	– 'Nisbet'	ECho IMGH LLin SCoo SLim WEve WGor
	– 'Oberon'	CKen CRob ECho EHul LCon MAsh NLar SLim
	– 'Piccolo'	CKen ECho
	– 'Pinocchio'	CKen ECho
	– 'Prostrata'	see *A. koreana* 'Prostrate Beauty'
§	– 'Prostrate Beauty'	ECho EOrn LLin SPoG WEve WFar WGor
	– 'Schneestern'	NLar
	– 'Silberkugel'	CKen ECho SLim
	– 'Silberlocke' $\mathbb{Y}^{H4}$	CDoC CKen CRob EBrs ECho LBee LCon LLin LPan LRHS MBar MBlu MBri MGos NBea NEgg NLar SCoo SLim SPer SPoG WEve WFar WOrn
	– 'Silbermavers'	CKen
	– 'Silberperl'	CKen ECho LCon NLar
	– 'Silberschmelze'	ECho LLin
	– 'Silver Show'	CKen
	– 'Taiga'	NLar
	– 'Threave'	CKen
	– 'Tundra'	NLar
	– 'Winter Goldtip'	ECho LLin WEve
	lasiocarpa	CDul LCon NWea
§	– var. ***arizonica***	CDul ECGP
	– – 'Argentea'	NWea
	– – 'Compacta' Hornibr. $\mathbb{Y}^{H4}$	CDoC CKen CMac EBrs ECho EHul ELan LBee LCon LLin LRHS MAsh MBar MBri MGos SCoo SHBN SLim SPoG WFar WGor
	– – 'Kenwith Blue'	CKen ECho LLin MGos NLar WFar
	– 'Compacta' Beissn.	ECho WFar
	– 'Day Creek'	CKen
	– 'Duflon'	CKen
	– 'Glauca'	see *A. lasiocarpa* var. *arizonica* 'Argentea'
	– 'Green Globe'	CKen ECho LLin MBar NLar WEve
	– 'Joe's Alpine' **new**	CKen
*	– 'King's Blue'	CKen
	– 'Logan Pass'	CKen NLar
	– 'Mulligan's Dwarf'	CKen ECho
	– 'Prickly Pete'	CKen
	– 'Roger Watson'	WEve
	– 'Toenisvorst'	CKen
	magnifica	LCon NWea
I	– 'Nana'	CKen NEgg NLar
	– witches' broom	CKen
	nobilis	see *A. procera*
	nordmanniana $\mathbb{Y}^{H4}$	CDul CTri EHul EMac EPfP LBuc LCon LPan MBar MGos NWea SHBN SPer WEve WMou
	– 'Arne's Dwarf'	CKen
	– 'Barabits' Compact'	ECho LLin MBar MGos NLar
	– 'Barabits' Gold'	ECho LLin
	– 'Barabits' Spreader'	CKen ECho LLin
	– subsp. ***equi-trojani***	LCon NWea
	– – 'Archer'	CKen
	– 'Golden Spreader' $\mathbb{Y}^{H4}$	CDoC CKen EBrs ECho EOrn LBee LCon LLin LRHS MAsh MBar MBri MGos NLar SCoo SLim SPoG WEve WFar
	– 'Hasselt'	CKen
	– 'Jakobsen'	CKen
	– 'Pendula'	LPan
	– 'Silberspitze'	CKen
	numidica	LPan
	– 'Glauca'	CKen LCon LLin
	– 'Lawrenceville'	ECho
I	– 'Pendula'	LCon
	pindrow	ECho LCon
	pinsapo	LCon LRHS MBar SEND
	– 'Aurea'	CKen EBrs ECho LCon LLin MGos NLar SLim WEve WFar
I	– 'Aurea Nana'	CKen
	– 'Fastigiata'	MPkF
	– 'Glauca' $\mathbb{Y}^{H4}$	CDoC CKen CTho ECho EHul ELan LCon LLin LPan MBar MBlu

		NLar SCoo SLim SPoG WEve WMou
	– 'Hamondii'	CKen
I	– 'Horstmann'	CKen ECho LCon LLin NLar WEve
	– 'Kelleriis'	ECho LCon
	– 'Pendula'	ECho LCon MGos MPkF NLar WEve
	– 'Quicksilver'	CKen
§	***procera*** ♀H4	CBcs CDoC CDul EHul EMac LCon MBar NWea WBVN WEve WMou
	– 'Bizarro'	NLar
	– 'Blaue Hexe'	CKen ECho NLar SLim SPoG WFar
	– Glauca Group	CDoC CMac CTho ECho LCon LLin LPan LRHS MAsh MBar MBlu MBri MGos SHBN WEve WFar WGer WOrn
	– 'Glauca Prostrata'	CRob ECho LBee LCon LPan LRHS MBar MGos SCoo WEve WFar
	– 'La Graciosa' **new**	NLar
	– 'Noble's Dwarf'	ECho
	– 'Obrighofen'	NLar
	– 'Seattle Mount' **new**	NLar
	– 'Sherwoodii'	CKen ECho
	recurvata	LCon NLar
	Rosemoor hybrid	CKen
	veitchii	CBcs CDul LCon NWea
	– 'Heddergott'	CKen ECho LCon MGos NLar SLim
	– 'Heine'	CKen
I	– 'Pendula'	CKen
	– 'Rumburg'	CKen

Abromeitiella (*Bromeliaceae*)

	brevifolia ♀H1	EPem WCot

Abrotanella (*Asteraceae*)

	sp.	ECho ITim

Abutilon ✿ (*Malvaceae*)

	'Amsterdam'	ERea
	'Ashford Red'	CBcs CPLG SKHP SOWG WKif
*	'Benary's Giant'	CPLG EAro
	'Boule de Neige'	CHal SOWG
	'Canary Bird' ♀H2	CBcs CCCN CHEx CHal MLan
	'Canary Bird' misapplied	see *A.* 'Golden Fleece'
	'Cannington Carol' (v) ♀H2	CCCN EWin SRGP
	'Cannington Peter' (v) ♀H2	CCCN
	'Cannington Sally' (v)	EWin MLan SRGP
	'Cannington Sonia' (v)	ERea
	'Cerise Queen'	NPri
	'Cloth of Gold'	SOWG
	'Cynthia Pike' (v)	LRHS SRms
§	'Golden Fleece'	ERea
	'Hinton Seedling'	CCCN CRHN
	x ***hybridum*** hort. apricot-flowered	CHEx
	– red-flowered	CHEx
	indicum	CPLG IDee
	'Jacqueline Morris'	LRHS MAsh SPoG SSta
	'Kentish Belle' ♀H2-3	CBcs CCCN CDoC CHEx CHal CMHG CMac CRHN EBee ECGP ECot ELan ELon EPfP LSRN NPal SBra SCoo SPer SPlb WFar
I	'Kentish Belle Variegatum' (v)	ELan
	'Marion' ♀H2	CHrt CRHN LRHS SOWG SPoG WCot
	'Master Michael'	CMac ERea
	megapotamicum ♀H3	CBcs CBrm CCCN CHEx CMHG CPLG CRHN CSBt CTri EBee ELan EPfP EPla EShb GQui LRHS MAsh MGos MLan MRav SOWG SPer SPoG SRms WBod WFar WSHC XPep
	– 'Compactum'	ENot
	– 'Variegatum' (v)	CBcs CBrm CCCN CPLG CSBt ELan EPfP GQui LRHS MAsh MGos SBod SOWG SPer SPoG SWvt WFar
	– 'Wakehurst'	see *A.* 'Wakehurst'
	– 'Wisley Red'	CRHN
	x ***milleri*** hort. ♀H2	CMac CPLG CRHN ERea MLan WWlt
	– 'Variegatum' (v)	CHEx CMac CPLG EWin LRHS SEND
	'Nabob' ♀H2	CCCN CDoC CHal CHrt CRHN ERea LRHS MLan SOWG SPoG
	'Orange Vein'	CHal EShb
	'Patrick Synge'	CCCN CMHG CPle EShb SOWG SPhx
	pictum	CHal ERea
	– 'Thompsonii' (v)	CHEx CHal ERea EShb MJnS WDyG
	'Pink Lady'	CHal ERea EShb
	'Red Bells'	EPla
	'Savitzii' (v) ♀H2	CHal SOWG SRms
	sellowianum var. ***marmoratum***	ERea
	'Simcox White'	CCCN
	'Souvenir de Bonn' (v) ♀H2	CHal EShb MLan SAga WCot
	x ***suntense***	CCCN CMHG CPLG CSBt EPfP ERas ERea GKev LHyd LRHS LSou MJnS NPer SChF SOWG WAbe WBod WHil
	– 'Jermyns' ♀H3	EPfP LRHS MBri MFOX SCoo SLon SPoG SSpi WFar
	– 'Violetta'	CEnd CHEx MAvo
	– white-flowered	EMan
	theophrasti	MSal
	variegated, salmon (v)	LAst
	'Victory'	SKHP
	vitifolium	CBcs CCCN ECot EMan EPfP EQua IDee MGos MHer NBid NEgg NLar SPer WHil WKif
	– var. ***album***	CBcs CDul CPLG EMan EPfP LHyd MLan MWgw SEND SPer SSpi WBor WFar WSHC WSpi
	– 'Buckland'	CGHE CHll
	– 'Simcox White'	WEas
	– 'Tennant's Gold' **new**	LBuc
	– 'Tennant's White' ♀H3	CAbP CCCN EPfP ERea LRHS MBri
	– 'Veronica Tennant' ♀H3	CPLG ERea SAga WKif
§	'Wakehurst'	WCot
	'Westfield Bronze'	CRHN

Acacia ✿ (*Mimosaceae*)

	acinacea	SPlb
	adunca	SPlb
	alpina	WCel
	armata	see *A. paradoxa*
	baileyana ♀H2	CBcs CGHE CSBt CTrG ECot ELan EMil EPfP ERea IClo ISea LRHS MGos MPRe SCoo SEND SOWG SPer SPlb SPoG SWvt WFar WPat
	– var. ***aurea***	SPlb
	– 'Purpurea' ♀H2	CAbb CBcs CCCN CDoC CEnd CKno EBee EMil EPfP LHop MBri MGos MLan MPRe SCoo SMad SPlb SWvt WCot WFar WPGP WPat
	boormanii	WCel
	brachybotrya **new**	CDTJ
	cultriformis	CTrC
	cyanophylla	see *A. saligna*
	dealbata ♀H2	More than 30 suppliers
	– 'Gaulois Astier'	MPRe
	– subsp. ***subalpina***	WCel WPGP
	drummondii subsp. ***elegans*** **new**	SSpi
	Exeter hybrid	CSBt

	filicifolia	WCel
	fimbriata	CRHN
	floribunda 'Lisette'	EPfP
	frigescens	WCel
	julibrissin	see *Albizia julibrissin*
	juniperina	see *A. ulicifolia*
	karroo	CArn CCCN CPLG SKHP XPep
	kybeanensis	EBee WCel WPGP
	longifolia	CBcs CCCN CDTJ EBee EPfP IClo SEND SPer SRms WGer
	- subsp. ***sophorae***	CCCN GGar
	macradenia	SPlb
	mearnsii	WCel
	melanoxylon	CDTJ CTrC GGar ISea WCel WHer
	motteana	ECot
	mucronata	CTrC EShb
	obliquinervia	WCel
§	***paradoxa*** ♀^{H2}	WPat
	pataczekii	CWSG ENot EPfP ERea EWes LRHS SKHP
	pendula	IDee
	podalyriifolia	CDoC EBee SPlb
	pravissima ♀$^{H2-3}$	More than 30 suppliers
	- 'Bushwalk Baby' new	SOWG
	retinodes ♀^{H2}	CBcs CCCN CDoC CPLG CRHN CTrC EBee EPfP ERea LRav MTPN SEND SLim WCFE
	riceana	CCCN CPLG CTrG IDee LRav
	rubida	EBee IDee LRav MGos MPRe SPlb WCel
§	***saligna***	CDTJ EBee SBLw
	sentis	see *A. victoriae*
	spectabilis	SPlb
	suaveolens	SPlb
§	***ulicifolia***	CPLG CSBt CTrG
	verticillata	CBcs CCCN CDTJ CHll CTrG EBee GGar MTPN SOWG
	- riverine	CTrC SKHP
§	***victoriae***	ERea

Acaena (*Rosaceae*)

	adscendens misapplied	see *A. affinis*, *A. magellanica* subsp. *magellanica*, *A. saccaticupula* 'Blue Haze'
	adscendens Vahl	see *A. magellanica* subsp. *laevigata*
	adscendens ambig. 'Glauca'	EMan NBir SBla
§	***affinis***	EBee ECha SDix
	anserinifolia misapplied	see *A. novae-zelandiae*
§	***anserinifolia*** (Forst. & Forst. f.) Druce	ECha GGar NHol
	buchananii	CSpe CTri EBee ECho EDAr EGoo EPot GAbr GGar MLLN MWgw NBro NLar SRms SSvw STre WFar WPer
	caerulea hort.	see *A. caesiiglauca*
§	***caesiiglauca***	CTri EBee EDAr GAbr GGar MLHP NBid SBla SGar WEas WPer
	fissistipula	EDAr WHer WMoo
	glaucophylla	see *A. magellanica* subsp. *magellanica*
	inermis	MLLN SPlb
	- 'Purpurea'	CBrm ECha EDAr EGoo EShb GAbr GGar NLar SIng SPlb WHoo WMoo WPtf
	macrocephala	EBee
§	***magellanica*** subsp. ***laevigata***	GGar
§	- subsp. ***magellanica***	EBee EDAr
	microphylla ♀^{H4}	CSam CTri EAlp EBee ECho GAbr GGar LBee LRHS MFOX NLar NMen SHFr SIng SPlb SRms WFar
	- Copper Carpet	see *A. microphylla* 'Kupferteppich'
	- 'Glauca'	see *A. caesiiglauca*
§	- 'Kupferteppich'	CBrm EBee ECho EDAr EMan ETod GAbr GGar MBri MRav MWgw NBir NLar NVic SBch WMoo WPat WPer
	- 'Pulchella'	EMan LRHS
	minor var. ***antartica*** new	GBin
	myriophylla	EBee ECho EDAr
§	***novae-zelandiae***	CTri EBee GGar SDix WMoo WPer
	ovalifolia	EBee ECho
	'Pewter'	see *A. saccaticupula* 'Blue Haze'
	pinnatifida	EDAr NBro WCot
	poeppigiana	EBee
	profundeincisa	see *A. anserinifolia* (Forst. & Forst. f.) Druce
	'Purple Carpet'	see *A. microphylla* 'Kupferteppich'
	'Purple Haze'	CSpe
	saccaticupula	EDAr MWgw NLar
§	- 'Blue Haze'	CGrW CMea EBee ECha ECho EDAr EPot GGar LRHS MLLN MRav NVic SIng SPer SPlb SRms WFar WHoo WMoo
	sanguisorbae	see *A. anserinifolia* (Forst. & Forst. f.) Druce
	splendens new	SIng
	viridior	see *A. anserinifolia* (Forst. & Forst. f.) Druce

Acalypha (*Euphorbiaceae*)

	hispaniolae ♀^{H1}	CKob ERea
	hispida ♀^{H1}	LRHS MBri
	pendula	see *A. reptans*
§	***reptans***	CHal SPet

Acanthocalyx see *Morina*

Acantholimon (*Plumbaginaceae*)

	androsaceum	see *A. ulicinum*
	glumaceum	WPat
§	***ulicinum***	ECho EPot WAbe

Acanthopanax see *Eleutherococcus*

	ricinifolius	see *Kalopanax septemlobus*

Acanthus ✿ (*Acanthaceae*)

	balcanicus misapplied	see *A. hungaricus*
	caroli-alexandri	EMon IPot MAvo MSte WHil
	dioscoridis	EGle EMon MAvo SMHy WSel
	- var. ***perringii***	CDes EBee ECha GBin LHop MAvo NChi WCot WFar WHil WPGP WSHC WSel
	hirsutus	CFis EMar EMon LPio NBre SPav WCot WHil
	- f. ***roseus***	WFar
	- subsp. ***syriacus***	EBee EHrv EMon MSte NBre NLar WCot WHil WLin WViv
	- - JCA 106.500	SPhx
	'Hollande du Nort' new	EBee
§	***hungaricus***	CArn CBcs CBrm CHar CHid EBee ECha ECtt EGle ELan EMar EMon EShb LBMP LRHS MPop MRav MSte NCGa NChi NLar SDix SPav SPer SWat WCot WFar WHil WMnd WSel
	- AL&JS 90097YU	EMon WPrP
	- MESE 561	EPPr
	longifolius	see *A. hungaricus*
	mollis	More than 30 suppliers
	- 'Feilding Gold'	see *A. mollis* 'Hollard's Gold'
	- 'Fielding Gold'	see *A. mollis* 'Hollard's Gold'
	- free-flowering	MSte WHil
§	- 'Hollard's Gold'	More than 30 suppliers
	- 'Jefalba'	see *A. mollis* (Latifolius Group) 'Rue Ledan'
	- Latifolius Group	EBee ECrN EMan EPfP LRHS MRav MSte SPer SRms WHil WHoo WTin

§	- - 'Rue Ledan'	CBct EBee EMon IPot LPio MAvo MSte NLar SPhx WCot WFar WHil WSel WTin
	- - 'Sjaak'	EBee
	sennii	SMad SPhx WHil WSHC
	spinosus L. ♀H4	More than 30 suppliers
	- Ferguson's form	WCot WHil
	- 'Lady Moore' (v)	EMon IBlr IPot MCCP NLar SBch WCot WHil
	- 'Royal Haughty'	MSte WHil
	- Spinosissimus Group	CBct CMHG ECha EHrv ELan EMan EMon LEdu LPio MCCP MRav NChi SAga SMad SPhx SWat WCot WFar WHil WMnd WTin
	'Summer Beauty'	EWTr LHop LPio MAvo MBri MSte NBre NLar NPro WCot WCra WFar WGer WHil

Acca (*Myrtaceae*)

	sp.	SBLw SWvt WBod
	sellowiana (F)	More than 30 suppliers
	- 'Apollo' (F)	ERea
	- 'Coolidge' (F)	ERea
	- 'Mammoth' (F)	CBcs CCCN ERea
	- 'Triumph' (F)	CBcs CCCN ERea
	- 'Variegata' (F/v)	ELan LAst

Acer ✿ (*Aceraceae*)

	HWJK 2040 from Nepal	WCru
	acuminatum	WNor
	albopurpurascens	WPGP
	argutum	IMGH WCwm WNor
	barbinerve	CMCN EPfP WNor
	buergerianum	CDul CMCN CMen CPMA IArd LRHS MBlu MBri MMuc MPkF NLar SBLw SCoo STre WCwm WGer WNor
	- 'Goshiki-kaede' (v)	CPMA
	- 'Integrifolium'	see *A. buergerianum* 'Subintegrum'
	- 'Mino-yatsubusa'	MPkF
	- 'Miyasama-yatsubusa'	MPkF
	- 'Naruto'	CMCN MPkF
§	- 'Subintegrum'	CMCN
*	- 'Variegatum' (v)	CMCN
	calcaratum	CDul CMCN
	campbellii B&SWJ 7685	WCru
*	- var. ***fansipanense*** B&SWJ 8270	WCru
	- - HWJ 569	WCru
§	- subsp. ***flabellatum*** B&SWJ 8057	WCru
	- - var. ***yunnanense***	CBcs CDoC EBee ECrN IMGH NPen WCwm WHCr
	- subsp. ***sinense***	see *A. sinense*
	- subsp. ***wilsonii***	see *A. wilsonii*
	campestre ♀H4	More than 30 suppliers
	- 'Carnival' (v)	CBcs CDul CEnd CMCN CPMA CWib EBee ECrN EMil LRHS MAsh MBlu MBri MPkF NHol NLar SMad SPer SPoG SPur SWvt WMou WPGP
	- 'Commodore'	LPan
	- 'Elsrijk'	CCVT CLnd EBee SBLw SCoo
	- 'Evelyn'	see *A. campestre* 'Queen Elizabeth'
	- 'Evenly Red'	MBlu
	- 'Pendulum'	CEnd ECrN
	- 'Postelense'	CEnd CMCN CPMA MBlu MGos MPkF
	- 'Pulverulentum' (v)	CDoC CEnd CMCN CPMA MGos SSta
§	- 'Queen Elizabeth'	CCVT MGos
	- 'Red Shine'	MGos
	- 'Royal Ruby'	CWSG MGos SSta WFar
*	- 'Ruby Glow'	CDoC CEnd ECrN
	- 'Schwerinii'	CDul
I	- 'Silver Celebration' (v)	CPMA
	- 'William Caldwell'	CEnd CTho ECrN
	capillipes ♀H4	CBcs CCVT CDul CLnd CMCN CSam CTho CWib EBee ECrN EMui ENot LCro LRHS MAsh MBar MGos NBea NWea SBLw SPer STre WFar WHCr WNor WOrn WPGP WPat
	- 'Candy Stripe'	see *A.* x *conspicuum* 'Candy Stripe'
	- 'Gimborn'	WPGP
	- 'Honey Dew'	NLar
	- var. ***morifolium***	see *A. morifolium*
	cappadocicum	CDul CMCN CSam ECrN MLan NPen NWea SBLw WNor
	- 'Aureum' ♀H4	More than 30 suppliers
	- subsp. ***divergens***	MPkF
	- var. ***mono***	see *A. pictum*
	- 'Rubrum' ♀H4	CBcs CDul CLnd CMCN EBee ECrN EPfP LAst LBuc LPan LRHS MBlu MBri MGos MRav SBLw SLim SPer WFar WHer WOrn
	- subsp. ***sinicum***	CEnd EPfP GBin WFar WPGP
	- - GWJ 9360	WCru
	- - var. ***tricaudatum***	CPLG WPGP
	carpinifolium	CBcs CBrd CMCN EWTr IArd MPkF NLar WCwm WNor
	catalpifolium	see *A. longipes* subsp. *catalpifolium*
§	***caudatifolium***	CMCN WCwm WPGP
	- B&SWJ 3531	WCru
	- B&SWJ 6734	WCru
§	***caudatum*** GWJ 9279	WCru
	- subsp. ***ukurunduense***	CMCN MPkF WNor
	cinnamomifolium	see *A. coriaceifolium*
	circinatum	CBcs CDoC CDul CLnd CMCN CPMA CSam ECrN EPfP EShb EWTr LRHS MBlu MBri MLan MPkF NBea NLar NPen NWea SCoo SHBN SSta WFar WNor
	- B&SWJ 9565	WCru
	- 'Little Gem'	CPMA
	- 'Little Joe'	CPMA
	- 'Monroe'	MPkF
	- 'Pacific Fire'	CPMA
	- 'Sunglow'	NLar
	circinatum x ***palmatum***	SIFN
	cissifolium	CBcs CDoC CLnd CMCN EPfP IArd LRHS MBri NLar WNor
	x ***conspicuum*** 'Candy Stripe'	CLnd CPMA NLar SIFN SLim SSpi SSta
	- 'Elephant's Ear'	CPMA EPfP NLar
	- 'Mozart' **new**	SHBN
I	- 'Phoenix'	CEnd CMCN CPMA EPfP MAsh MBlu NLar SIFN SSpi WPat
	- 'Silver Ghost'	MGos MPkF
§	- 'Silver Vein'	CDoC CDul CEnd CMCN CPMA EBee ECrN EPfP LRHS MGos MWea SIFN SPur SSpi SSta WPGP
§	***coriaceifolium***	WNor
	crataegifolium	CMCN WNor
	- 'Meuri-keade-no-fuiri' (v)	MPkF
	- 'Meuri-no-ôfu' (v)	MPkF
	- 'Veitchii' (v)	CDoC CMCN CPMA EPfP MBlu MBri MPkF NLar SIFN SSpi
	creticum L., non F. Schmidt.	see *A. sempervirens*
	dasycarpum	see *A. saccharinum*
	davidii	CAbP CBcs CCVT CDoC CDul CLnd CMCN CMHG CSBt CSam CTrG ECrN ITim LPan LRHS MBar MGos MRav NBea NHol SBLw SHBN SLim SPer WBVN WFar WNor WOrn WPat
	- B&SWJ 8183	WCru
§	- 'Canton'	MPkF
	- 'Cantonspark'	see *A. davidii* 'Canton'

N	- 'Ernest Wilson'	CBcs CMCN EBee MBlu NEgg NLar
N	- 'George Forrest' ♀H4	CBcs CCVT CDoC CDul CMCN CTho EBee ECrN ELan EMil EPfP LPan LRHS MBlu MBri MDun NBea NEgg NWea SBLw SBod SEND SHBN SLim SPer SPoG WFar WOrn
	- 'Hagelunie'	MPkF
	- 'Karmen'	CGHE CLnd CPMA EBee MPkF SIFN WPGP
	- 'Madeline Spitta'	CMCN CPMA MBlu MPkF SIFN
	- 'Rosalie'	EPfP MBlu MBri
	- 'Serpentine' ♀H4	CBcs CDoC CMCN CPMA CTho EBee EPfP EPla MAsh MBlu MBri NEgg NLar SIFN SSpi SSta WFar WOrn WPGP
	- 'Silver Vein'	see *A.* x *conspicuum* 'Silver Vein'
	distylum	WCwm
	divergens	CMCN
	elegantulum	CDoC LTwo WCwm WNor WPGP
	erianthum	CLnd NPen WHCr WNor
	fabri	CBcs CDul CMCN WNor
	flabellatum	see *A. campbellii* subsp. *flabellatum*
	forrestii	CMCN EPfP NBea NHol WCwm WNor
	- 'Alice'	CBcs CDul CEnd CLnd CMCN CPMA SIFN SSta
§	- 'Sirene'	CPMA
§	- 'Sparkling'	CPMA
	x ***freemanii***	CMCN
	- 'Armstrong'	SBLw WFar
	- Autumn Blaze = 'Jeffersred'	CBcs CCVT CDoC CDul CMCN EPfP LRHS MBlu MGos SBLw SCoo SMad WFar WPat
	- Autumn Fantasy = 'Dtr 102'	MBlu SCoo SIFN
	- Celebration = 'Celzam'	MGos WFar
	- 'Elegant'	SBLw
	- 'Indian Summer'	see *A.* x *freemanii* 'Morgan'
§	- 'Morgan'	CEnd CPMA SIFN
	fulvescens	see *A. longipes*
	ginnala	see *A. tataricum* subsp. *ginnala*
	glabrum	WNor
	globosum	see *A. platanoides* 'Globosum'
	grandidentatum	see *A. saccharum* subsp. *grandidentatum*
	griseum ♀H4	More than 30 suppliers
	grosseri	CDul CMCN CTri GGar
	- var. ***hersii*** ♀H4	CBcs CCVT CDoC CDul CLnd CPLG CWib EBee ECrN ENot EPfP EPla LRHS MAsh MBri MRav NBea NWea SBLw SPer SWvt WBVN WCwm WFar WGer WHCr WNor WOrn WPGP WPat
	- 'Leiden'	EPfP MBlu
	heldreichii	CMCN EPfP
	henryi	CDul CLnd CMCN EPfP NLar WCwm WNor
	hookeri	CMCN
	hyrcanum	CMCN
	japonicum	CMCN LRHS MBar SSta WHCr WNor
	- B&SWJ 5950	WCru
§	- 'Aconitifolium' ♀H4	More than 30 suppliers
	- 'Ao-jutan' new	CPMA
	- 'Attaryi'	CMCN MPkF
	- 'Aureum'	see *A. shirasawanum* 'Aureum'
	- 'Ezo-no-momiji'	see *A. shirasawanum* 'Ezo-no-momiji'
	- 'Filicifolium'	see *A. japonicum* 'Aconitifolium'
	- 'Green Cascade'	CBcs CBdw CEnd CMCN CPMA ECho MPkF NLar SIFN SPoG WPGP WPat
	- 'Kalmthout' new	CBdw
	- 'King's Copse'	LPan
	- 'Laciniatum'	see *A. japonicum* 'Aconitifolium'
	- f. ***microphyllum***	see *A. shirasawanum* 'Microphyllum'
§	- 'Mikasa-yama'	LRHS
	- 'Ogurayama'	see *A. shirasawanum* 'Ogurayama'
	- 'Ō-isami'	CMCN EPfP LRHS MPkF SIFN
	- 'Ō-taki'	CPMA ECho
	- 'Vitifolium' ♀H4	CBcs CDoC CEnd CMCN CPMA CSBt ECho ELan EPfP LPan LRHS MBlu MBri MGos MPkF NBea NEgg NLar NPal SIFN SPer SPoG SSpi SSta WPGP WPat
	kawakamii	see *A. caudatifolium*
	laevigatum	CMCN
	laxiflorum	EBee EPla
	- HWJK 2240	WCru
	leucoderme	see *A. saccharum* subsp. *leucoderme*
	lobelii Bunge	see *A. turkestanicum*
	lobelii Tenore	CLnd WPGP
§	***longipes***	CMCN
	- Sich 731	WPGP
§	- subsp. ***catalpifolium***	CMCN
	macrophyllum	CDul CMCN CTho EPfP IDee LHyd
	mandschuricum	CBcs EPfP MBri MPkF WCwm WNor
§	***maximowiczianum***	CBcs CMCN CSam CTho MPkF WFar WNor
	maximowiczii	ECrN MPkF WHCr WNor
	metcalfii	WNor
	micranthum	CDoC CEnd CGHE CMCN EBee EPfP GGar IMGH LTwo MBlu MBri MPkF NLar SHGN SIFN SSpi WCwm WNor WPGP
	miyabei	MPkF
	mono	see *A. pictum*
	monspessulanum	CDul CMCN SEND XPep
§	***morifolium***	EBee MPkF
	morrisonense	see *A. caudatifolium*
	negundo	CCVT CDul CLnd CMCN CWib ECrN NWea SBLw WNor
	- IDS 2000	WHCr
	- 'Argenteovariegatum'	see *A. negundo* 'Variegatum'
	- 'Auratum'	CMCN MBar SBLw
	- 'Aureomarginatum' (v)	ECrN LAst LBuc WOrn
	- 'Aureovariegatum' (v)	CBcs MBar
	- subsp. ***californicum***	WNor
§	- 'Elegans' (v)	CDul CEnd CLnd CMCN ECrN EPfP LRHS NHol SCoo SHBN SPer WFar
	- 'Elegantissimum'	see *A. negundo* 'Elegans'
	- 'Flamingo' (v)	More than 30 suppliers
	- 'Kelly's Gold'	CBcs CLnd CWSG ECho LRHS MAsh MBri MGos NPro SCoo SLim SPoG WFar WHar WOrn
	- subsp. ***mexicanum*** F&M 48 new	WPGP
§	- 'Variegatum' (v)	CBcs CLnd ECrN LAst LRHS SBLw SPer WFar
	- var. ***violaceum***	CBcs CEnd CMCN
	- 'Winter Lightning'	LPan
	nikoense	see *A. maximowiczianum*
	oblongum	CDul CMCN WPGP
	- HWJK 2422	WCru
	oliverianum	EBee EPfP WNor WPGP
	- subsp. ***formosanum*** B&SWJ 6773	WCru
	- - B&SWJ 6797	WCru
	opalus	CMCN
	orientale	see *A. sempervirens*
	orizabense new	EBee
	Pacific Sunset = 'Warrenred'	LRHS

	palmatum	More than 30 suppliers
	- 'Abigail Rose' (v)	CBdw
§	- 'Aka-shigitatsu-sawa'	CBcs CMCN CMac CMen CPMA ECho LMil LRHS MGos MPkF NLar SIFN SPer SVil WBod WFar WHar
	- 'Akane'	CBdw CMen ECho MPkF
	- 'Akebono'	CBdw CPMA
	- 'Akegarasu'	CMen ECho NLar
	- 'Alpenweiss' **new**	CPMA
	- 'Alpine Sunrise'	CBdw
	- 'Alpine Surprise'	CPMA
	- 'Amagi-shigure'	CBdw CPMA
	- 'Aoba-jo'	CMen CPMA ECho MPkF NLar
	- 'Ao-kanzashi' (v)	CBdw MPkF
	- 'Aoshime-no-uchi'	see *A. palmatum* 'Shinobuga-oka'
	- 'Aoyagi'	CEnd CMCN CMen CPMA ECho EPfP LAst LMil LRHS MAsh MBri MGos NHol SIFN WFoF
§	- 'Arakawa'	CEnd CMCN CMen ECho MPkF SIFN
	- 'Arakawa-ukon'	CPMA
	- 'Aratama'	CBdw CPMA MGos SCoo WBod WPat
	- 'Ariake-nomura'	CMen MPkF
	- 'Asahi-zuru' (v)	CBcs CBdw CDoC CMCN CMen CPMA EBee ECho LPan LRHS MAsh MBri MGos MPkF NHol NLar SPer SVil WFar WFoF WHar WPat
	- 'Ashurst Wood'	SIFN
	- 'Atrolineare'	CMen ECho MPkF NBPN NBea NLar WPat
	- 'Atropurpureum'	CBcs CBrm CCVT CDul CMen CSBt CTho CTri CWCL CWib EBee ECrN EMui LAst LCro LSRN MDun MGos MSwo NEgg SHBN SLon STre SWvt WBVN WBod WHCr
	- f. ***atropurpureum***	CBcs CDoC CEnd CWSG EBee ECho EPfP EWTr LBuc LHyd LRHS MBar MGos NBea NBlu NHol NWea SHBN SPer SReu WCFE WFar WHar WPat
	- 'Atropurpureum Novum'	MPkF
	- 'Atsugama'	CBdw
	- 'Attraction'	CMCN
	- 'Aureum'	CBdw CMCN CMen CWib ECho EPfP LRHS MAsh MBlu MGos MPkF NLar SBod SIFN SSpi WFar
	- Autumn Glory Group	CEnd CMen CPMA ECho
	- 'Autumn Red'	ECho LPan LRHS
*	- 'Autumn Showers'	CEnd CPMA
	- 'Azuma-murasaki'	CMen CPMA ECho MPkF NLar
	- 'Beni-chidori'	CMen ECho
	- 'Beni-gasa'	CPMA
	- 'Beni-hime'	CPMA MPkF
	- 'Beni-hoshi'	CBdw WPat
	- 'Beni-kagami'	CEnd CMCN CPMA EPfP LRHS MBlu NBPN NBea NLar
	- 'Beni-kawa'	CBdw CMen CPMA ECho LMil MPkF SIFN SPur SSpi WPat
	- 'Beni-komachi'	CBcs CEnd CMCN CMac CMen CPMA ECho EPfP LMil LRHS MAsh MBri MGos MPkF NLar SIFN SVil WHar
	- 'Beni-maiko'	CBdw CEnd CMCN CMen CPMA CWib ECho EPfP LBuc LMil LRHS MBri MGos MPkF MWea NLar SCoo SIFN WBVN WBod WHar WPGP WPat
	- 'Beni-musume' **new**	CBdw
	- 'Beni-otake'	CBdw CLnd CMCN CMen CPMA ECho EPfP LMil LRHS MBri MGos MPkF NLar SIFN SVil WPat
	- 'Beni-schichihenge' (v)	CBcs CBdw CEnd CMCN CMen CPMA CWGN ECho EPfP LRHS MAsh MBri MGos MPkF NHol SCoo SIFN SPoG SVil WBod WPGP WPat
	- 'Beni-shi-en'	CBdw CPMA NLar
	- 'Beni-shigitatsu-sawa'	see *A. palmatum* 'Aka Shigitatsusawa'
	- 'Beni-tsukasa' (v)	CBdw CEnd CMen CPMA ECho LMil LRHS MPkF SIFN SSpi SSta WPGP
	- 'Beni-ubi-gohon'	CPMA MPkF NLar
	- 'Beni-zuru'	CBdw
	- 'Bloodgood' ♀H4	More than 30 suppliers
	- 'Bonfire' misapplied	see *A. palmatum* 'Seigai'
	- 'Bonfire' ambig.	CPMA LRHS
	- 'Bonnie Bergman'	CPMA
	- 'Boskoop Glory'	ECho
	- 'Brandt's Dwarf'	CBdw MPkF WPat
	- 'Burgundy Lace' ♀H4	CBcs CDoC CEnd CMCN CMen CPMA CWib ECho EMac EMil LPan LRHS LSRN MAsh MBlu MBri MGos MPkF NHol SCoo SIFN SPer WBod WFar WHar WOrn WPGP WPat
	- 'Butterfly' (v)	CBcs CDoC CEnd CMCN CMen CPMA CWCL CWGN CWSG CWib ECho EPfP LAst LCro LMil LPan LRHS LSRN MBar MGos NHol SCoo SHBN SLim SMad SPer SPoG SSta WBod WFar
	- 'Calico'	CBdw CPMA
	- 'Carlis Corner'	CPMA
	- 'Carminium'	see *A. palmatum* 'Corallinum'
	- 'Chikuma-no'	MPkF
	- 'Chirimen-nishiki' (v)	CMCN MPkF
	- 'Chishio'	see *A. palmatum* 'Shishio'
	- 'Chishio Improved'	see *A. palmatum* 'Shishio Improved'
	- 'Chishio-hime'	CBdw
	- 'Chitose-yama' ♀H4	CEnd CMCN CMen CPMA CWCL CWib EBee ECho EPfP LRHS MBar MBri MGos MLan MPkF MRav NEgg NLar SCoo SIFN SLim SSpi SSta WBod WFar WPat
§	- 'Chiyo-hime'	CBdw
	- 'Coonara Pygmy'	CBdw CMCN CMen CPMA ECho LRHS MGos MPkF NLar SBod SCoo WFar WPat
	- 'Coral Pink'	CBdw CPMA ECho MPkF
§	- 'Corallinum'	CEnd CMCN CMen CPMA ECho MPkF NLar WPat
	- var. ***coreanum***	CMCN LMil SIFN WNor
	- - B&SWJ 4474	WCru
	- - B&SWJ 8606	WCru
	- - 'Korean Gem'	CPMA ECho
	- 'Crimson Carol'	CBdw
	- 'Crimson Prince'	CBcs ECho EMac ENot MBri MPkF SBod SCoo SVil
	- 'Crippsii'	CBcs CDoC CMen ECho EMil LRHS MBri MGos MPkF SCoo WFar WPat
	- 'Demi-sec'	CBdw CMen
	- 'Deshōjō'	CBdw CMCN CMen ECho LPan MBar MBlu MGos MLan MPkF NHol NLar SCoo SHBN
	- 'Deshōjō-nishiki'	CBdw
	- 'Diana'	CMen MPkF NLar
	- 'Diane Verkade'	CBdw
	- var. ***dissectum*** ♀H4	More than 30 suppliers
	- - 'Ao-shidare'	CBdw CPMA
	- - 'Ariadne' (v)	CBdw CPMA CWib MBri MGos MPkF NLar SCoo SIFN WPat
	- - 'Autumn Fire'	CBdw CPMA
	- - 'Baby Lace'	CBdw CPMA NLar
	- - 'Balcombe Green'	SIFN
	- - 'Baldsmith'	CBdw CPMA MGos WPat
	- - 'Barrie Bergman'	CBdw CPMA

	- - 'Beni-fushigi'	CBdw MPkF NLar WPat
	- - 'Beni-shidare Tricolor' (v)	CBdw CMen NLar
	- - 'Beni-shidare Variegated' (v)	CMCN CPMA ECho
	- - 'Beni-tsukasa-shidare'	CBdw
	- - 'Berrima Bridge'	CBdw CPMA
	- - 'Bewley's Red'	CBdw CPMA
	- - 'Brocade'	CBdw CMCN MPkF WPat
	- - 'Bronzewing'	CPMA
	- - 'Chantilly Lace'	CBdw CPMA ECho
	- - 'Chelwood'	SIFN
	- - 'Crimson Queen' $\mathbb{Y}^{H4}$	More than 30 suppliers
	- - Dissectum Atropurpureum Group	CBcs CCVT CPMA CTri CWCL ELan EPfP LCro LHyd LRHS MAsh MGan MGos NBea NHol NWea SCoo SHBN SLim SReu SSpi SSta WFar WHCr WOrn
	- - 'Dissectum Flavescens'	CBdw CEnd CMac CPMA ECho MBlu
§	- - 'Dissectum Nigrum'	CPMA CTri CWCL CWSG ECho LRHS MAsh MPkF NBPN NBea NBee NHol SSpi WPat
	- - 'Dissectum Palmatifidum'	CDoC CLnd ECho EQua LRHS MPkF SCoo SPer SVil WFar WPat
	- - 'Dissectum Rubrifolium'	ECho
§	- - 'Dissectum Variegatum' (v)	CBcs CPMA EPfP LRHS MPkF
	- - Dissectum Viride Group	CBcs CMCN CMen CPMA CSBt CWSG ECho ELan EMui ENot EPfP LMil LPan LRHS MAsh MGan MGos MSwo NBea NBlu NEgg SBod SLim SPer SPla SSta WFar WOrn
	- - 'Doctor Baker'	CBdw
	- - 'Ellen'	CBdw CPMA WPat
	- - 'Emerald Lace'	CPMA MBlu NLar
	- - 'Felice'	CBdw CPMA MPkF WPat
	- - 'Filigree' (v)	CBdw CMCN CMen CPMA ECho EPfP LMil LRHS MAsh MGos MPkF NLar SIFN SSpi WPGP WPat
	- - 'Garnet' $\mathbb{Y}^{H4}$	More than 30 suppliers
	- - 'Goshiki-shidare' (v)	CEnd CMen CPMA ECho MPkF
	- - 'Green Globe'	CBdw LPan LRHS NLar
	- - 'Green Hornet'	CPMA
	- - 'Green Lace'	LPan MPkF
	- - 'Green Mist'	CBdw CPMA WPat
	- - 'Hanzel'	WPat
	- - 'Inaba-shidare' $\mathbb{Y}^{H4}$	More than 30 suppliers
I	- - 'Kawaii'	CPMA
	- - 'Kiri-nishiki'	CMen CPMA ECho MPkF NLar
	- - 'Lemon Chiffon'	CBdw
*	- - 'Lionheart'	CBdw CDoC CPMA ECho EMac EMil LPan LRHS MBri MGos MPkF NLar SBod SCoo SPer WFar WHar WPat
	- - 'Mioun'	CBdw
	- - 'Octopus'	CBdw CPMA
	- - 'Orangeola'	CBdw CEnd CPMA ECho MAsh MGos MPkF NHol NLar SCoo SIFN WPat
	- - 'Ornatum'	CDoC CDul CMCN CMen CWib ECho EPfP IMGH LMil LPan MBar MGos MPkF MRav NBea NBlu NEgg SCoo SHBN WFar WGer WHCr WHar
	- - 'Otto's Dissectum'	CBdw CPMA
	- - 'Pendulum Julian'	CMCN MPkF SBod SIFN
	- - 'Pink Ballerina' (v)	CPMA
	- - 'Pink Filigree'	CBdw LPan MPkF
	- - 'Raraflora'	CBdw CPMA
	- - 'Red Autumn Lace'	CBdw LPan WPat
	- - 'Red Dragon'	CDoC CMen CPMA ECho ECrN EQua LPan LRHS MPkF NLar WHar WPat
	- - 'Red Feather'	CPMA
	- - 'Red Filigree Lace'	CBdw CEnd CMCN CMen CPMA CWGN ECho EPfP MBlu MGos NHol SIFN WPat
	- - 'Red Select'	ECho MPkF
	- - 'Red Strata' **new**	CBdw
	- - 'Rilas Red'	CBdw
	- - 'Seiryū' $\mathbb{Y}^{H4}$	More than 30 suppliers
§	- - 'Shōjō-shidare'	CBdw CDul CEnd CPMA ECho LRHS NLar
	- - 'Spring Delight'	CBdw NLar
	- - 'Sumi-shidare'	CBdw
	- - 'Sunset'	CBdw CPMA EMui MPkF WPat
	- - 'Tamukeyama'	CLnd CMCN CMen CPMA EBee ECho ELan EMac ENot LMil LPan LRHS MGos MPkF NLar SBod SCoo SLau SVil WFar WPat
	- - 'Toyama-nishiki' (v)	CMCN CMen ECho SIFN WPat
	- - 'Tumukeyama'	CBcs
	- - 'Waterfall'	CMCN CPMA ECho
	- - 'Watnong'	CBdw CPMA
	- - 'Zaaling'	CPMA ECho
	- 'Doctor Tilt'	WPat
	- 'Dormansland'	LMil SCoo SIFN
	- 'Dragon's Fire'	CBdw EMui
	- 'Eddisbury'	CEnd CMen CPMA MPkF NBea NLar SSta WBod WOrn WPat
	- 'Edna Bergman'	CPMA
	- 'Effegi'	see *A. palmatum* 'Fireglow'
	- 'Eimini'	CBdw MPkF WPat
	- 'Elegans'	CMen ECho EPfP MPkF NLar SIFN
	- Emperor 1 = 'Wolff'	MPkF WPat
	- 'Englishtown'	CBdw WPat
	- 'Enkan'	CBdw CPMA MBri MPkF NLar WPat
	- 'Eono-momiji'	CMen
	- 'Ever Red'	see *A. palmatum* var. *dissectum* 'Dissectum Nigrum'
	- 'Fall's Fire'	CBdw CPMA
	- 'Fascination'	CBdw CPMA
	- 'Filigree Rouge'	CBdw
	- 'Fior d'Arancio'	CPMA NBea NLar
§	- 'Fireglow'	CBcs CDoC CEnd CLnd CMCN CMen CPMA CSBt CWib ECho EMil LPan LRHS MBlu MBri MGos MPkF NBea NEgg NLar SCoo SIFN WFar WHar WPGP WPat
	- 'First Ghost'	CBdw CPMA
	- 'Fjellheim'	CPMA MPkF
	- 'Frederici Guglielmi'	see *A. palmatum* var. *dissectum* 'Dissectum Variegatum'
	- 'Fūhjin'	CBdw
	- 'Garyū'	MPkF
	- 'Gassho'	CBdw
	- 'Geisha'	CBdw CPMA MGos MPkF
	- 'Gekkō-nishiki'	CBdw
	- 'Germaine's Gyration'	CBdw CPMA
	- 'Glowing Embers'	WPat
	- 'Golden Pond'	CBdw CPMA
	- 'Goshiki-kotohime' (v)	CMCN CPMA MPkF
	- 'Goten-nomura'	CBdw
	- 'Green Star'	CBdw
	- 'Green Trompenburg'	CMCN CMen ECho MGos MPkF NLar SIFN
§	- 'Hagoromo'	CDoC CMen ECho MPkF SCoo WFar
	- 'Hanami-nishiki'	ECho MPkF WPat
	- 'Harusame' (v)	MPkF
	- 'Hatsukoi' (v)	CBdw
	- 'Hazeroino' (v)	MPkF
	- 'Heartbeat'	CBdw CPMA
	- var. ***heptalobum***	CMCN
§	- 'Heptalobum Elegans'	CMCN LRHS MBlu SSpi
	- 'Heptalobum Elegans Purpureum'	see *A. palmatum* 'Hessei'

- 'Herbstfeuer' CPMA MPkF
§ - 'Hessei' CEnd CMCN ECho LRHS MBlu NBea NLar
- 'Higasayama' (v) CBcs CEnd CMCN CMen CPMA ECho LRHS MAsh MGos MPkF NHol SCoo SIFN WHar WPGP WPat
- 'Hino-tori-nishiki' CMen
- 'Hi-no-tsukasa' CBdw
- 'Hōgyoku' CMCN CPMA MPkF
- 'Hondoshi' CBdw
- 'Hooftman A' **new** CBdw
- 'Hoshi-kuzu' CBdw MPkF
- 'Hubbs Red Willow' **new** CBdw
- 'Ibo-nishiki' CMen MPkF SIFN
- 'Ichigyōji' CEnd CMCN CMen CPMA ECho LMil LRHS SChF SIFN WPGP WPat
- 'Improved Shishio' see *A. palmatum* 'Shishio Improved'
- 'Inazuma' CBcs CDoC CMCN CMen CPMA ECho EPfP LRHS MPkF NBPN NLar SBod SCoo SLau WFar WPat
- 'Irish Lace' CBdw CPMA
- 'Issai-nishiki' ECho MPkF
* - 'Issai-nishiki-kawazu' MPkF
- 'Itami-nishiki' CBdw
- 'Jane' MPkF
- 'Japanese Sunrise' CPMA MPkF
- 'Jerre Schwartz' MGos WPat
- 'Jirō-shidare' CBdw CPMA EPfP LRHS MPkF NLar SIFN
- 'Julia D.' **new** NLar
- 'Junihitoe' see *A. shirasawanum* 'Junihitoe'
- 'Kaba' CMen MPkF
- 'Kagero' (v) MBri MPkF WFar
§ - 'Kagiri-nishiki' (v) CBcs CDul CMCN CMen CPMA CWSG ECho LRHS MPkF NEgg NHol NLar SIFN WFar WNor
- 'Kamagata' CBdw CEnd CMCN CMen CPMA ECho EPfP LMil LRHS MAsh MBri MGos MPkF NHol NLar SCoo SIFN SPer SVil WPGP WPat
- 'Kandy Kitchen' CPMA MGos MPkF
- 'Karaori-nishiki' (v) CMen ECho MBlu MPkF NLar
- 'Karasugawa' (v) CBdw CMen CPMA ECho MGos MPkF NLar
- 'Kasagiyama' CBdw CEnd CMCN CMen CPMA ECho LMil LRHS MPkF NBea NLar SIFN WBod WPGP
- 'Kasen-nishiki' CBdw CMen ECho MPkF
- 'Kashima' CEnd CMCN CMen CPMA ECho MBNS MPkF NLar WFar
- 'Kashima-yatsubusa' CBdw
- 'Katja' CMen WPat
- 'Katsura' ♀H4 More than 30 suppliers
- 'Ki-hachijō' CMCN CMen CPMA ECho EPfP MBri NLar WPat
- 'Kingsville Variegated' (v) CBdw
- 'Kinran' CMCN CMen ECho LRHS MPkF
- 'Kinshi' CBdw CEnd CMCN CMen CPMA ECho EPfP LRHS MPkF NBea NHol SIFN SSta WPat
- 'Kiyohime' CBdw CDoC CMCN CMen ECho MBlu MPkF NBea WFar WPat
- 'Koba-shōjō' CBdw
- 'Ko-chidori' CBdw
- 'Kogane-nishiki' ECho
- 'Kogane-sakae' CPMA
- 'Kokobunji-nishiki' (v) CBdw
- 'Komache-hime' CBdw CMen CPMA ECho WPat
* - 'Komaru' NLar
- 'Komon-nishiki' (v) CBdw CMen CPMA ECho
- 'Koriba' CBdw CPMA MPkF NLar
§ - 'Koshimino' CPMA
- 'Kotohime' CBdw CMCN CMen CPMA MBri MPkF NLar SCoo SIFN
- 'Koto-ito-komachi' CBdw CMen CPMA ECho MPkF NLar WPat
- 'Koto-maru' MPkF
- 'Koto-no-ito' CBdw CMCN MBri MGos MPkF NLar WHar WPat
- 'Koya-san' CBdw CMen MPkF
- 'Koyō-ao-shidare' CBdw
- 'Krazy Krinkle' CPMA
- 'Kurabu-yama' CMCN CMen MPkF
- 'Kurui-jishi' CBdw MGos MPkF SIFN WPat
- 'Kyra' CMen MPkF
- 'Lemon Lime Lace' CBdw CPMA
- 'Linearilobum' CDoC ECho EPfP LHyd LMil LRHS MBlu MGos MPkF NBea NHol NLar SCoo WFar WHar WNor WPat
- 'Linearilobum Atropurpureum' LRHS NBea WNor
- 'Lin-ling' LMil SIFN
- 'Little Princess' see *A. palmatum* 'Chiyo-hime'
- 'Lozita' WPat
- 'Lutescens' ECho MPkF
- 'Lydia' MPkF
- 'Maiko' CMen ECho MPkF
- 'Mama' CMen ECho
- 'Manyō-no-sato' (v) CBdw
- 'Mapi-no-machihime' CBdw CEnd CMCN CMen CPMA ECho ELan LMil LRHS MAsh MBri MGos MPkF NHol SIFN WPGP WPat
- 'Marakumo' MPkF
- 'Mardi Gras' CPMA
- 'Masamurasaki' WPat
- 'Masukagami' (v) CEnd CPMA MPkF
- 'Matsuga-e' (v) CMen ECho MPkF
- 'Matsukaze' CMCN CMen CPMA ECho SIFN
- 'Meihō-nishiki' CBdw CPMA
- 'Melanie' CPMA SIFN
- 'Meoto' CBdw
- 'Midori-no-teiboku' CBdw
- 'Mikasayama' see *A. japonicum* 'Mikasa-yama'
- 'Mikawa-yatsubusa' CBdw CMCN CMen CPMA ECho LRHS MGos MPkF NBhm NLar SVil WPat
- 'Mimaye' CPMA
- 'Mirte' CPMA MPkF SIFN WFar WPat
- 'Mischa' CBdw
- 'Misty Moon' CBdw
- 'Mitsuba-yama' CBdw
- 'Mizuho-beni' CMen CPMA ECho
- 'Mizu-kuguri' CMCN MPkF NLar
- 'Momenshide' CBdw
- 'Momoiro-koya-san' CBdw CPMA MPkF WPat
- 'Mon Papa' CPMA
- 'Monzukushi' CPMA MPkF
- 'Moonfire' CMCN CPMA EPfP LMil LRHS MAsh MPkF NLar SIFN SPoG WPat
- 'Mr Sun' CPMA
* - 'Muncaster' LMil SIFN
- 'Murasaki-hime' MPkF
- 'Murasaki-kiyohime' CBdw CEnd CMCN CMen CPMA ECho MPkF WPat
- 'Murasaki-shikibu' CBdw
- 'Mure-hibari' CMCN CPMA MPkF SIFN
- 'Murogawa' CPMA ECho
- 'Nanase-gawa' MPkF
- 'Nicholsonii' CMCN CTri ECho EPfP LMil MPkF NLar SIFN WFar WPat
- 'Nigrum' ♀H4 CMCN ECho LPan SHBN WPat
- 'Nishiki-gasane' (v) MPkF
§ - 'Nishiki-gawa' CBdw CEnd CMCN CMen CPMA ECho MPkF WPGP
- 'Nishiki-momiji' CMen
- 'Nomura' CMen CPMA
- 'Nomurishidare' misapplied see *A. palmatum* var. *dissectum* 'Shōjō-shidare'

	- 'Nomurishidare' Wada	SSpi
	- 'Nuresagi'	CBdw CEnd CPMA
	- 'Ōgi-nagashi' (v)	CBdw
	- 'Ōgon-sarasa'	CPMA MPkF
	- 'Ojishi'	CMen MPkF
	- 'Ō-kagami'	CBcs CDoC CEnd CMen CPMA ECho LMil LRHS MPkF NLar SCoo SIFN WPGP
	- 'Okukuji-nishiki'	CBdw CPMA
	- 'Okushimo'	CBdw CEnd CMCN CMen CPMA ECho LRHS MBri MPkF NHol NLar WPGP WPat
	- 'Omato'	CMen CPMA MPkF SIFN WFar
	- 'Omurayama'	CBcs CDoC CEnd CMCN CMen CPMA ECho ENot EPfP LRHS MGos MPkF NBhm NLar SCoo SPer SSta SVil WFar WPat
	- 'Orange Dream'	More than 30 suppliers
	- 'Oregon Sunset'	CBdw MPkF WPat
	- 'Oridono-nishiki' (v)	CBcs CDul CEnd CMCN CMen CPMA ECho ELan ENot EPfP LMil LRHS MAsh MBar MBlu MGos MPkF NEgg SCoo SIFN SPer SSta WBod WFar WHar WOrn
	- 'Ori-zuru'	CBdw
	- 'Ōsakazuki' ♀H4	More than 30 suppliers
	- 'Ōshio-beni'	CPMA ECho
	- 'Ōshū-shidare'	CBdw CMen CPMA ECho EPfP MPkF WFar
	- 'Oto-hime'	CPMA ECho MPkF
	- 'Otome-zakura'	CMCN CMen CPMA ECho MPkF WPat
	- 'Peaches and Cream' (v)	CBcs CBdw CPMA ECho MPkF NLar SPer WPat
	- 'Peve Dave' **new**	NLar
	- 'Peve Multicolor'	CBdw CPMA MGos MPkF NLar
	- 'Phoenix'	CBdw MPkF
	- 'Pine Bark Maple'	see *A. palmatum* 'Nishiki-gawa'
	- 'Pixie'	CBdw CMCN CPMA MPkF NLar WPat
	- 'Princetown Gold' **new**	MAsh
	- var. ***pubescens*** B&SWJ 6886	WCru
	- 'Pung-kil'	CBdw MPkF
	- 'Purple Ghost'	CBdw
	- 'Red Baron'	CPMA
	- 'Red Cloud'	CBdw NLar
	- 'Red Embers' **new**	CWib
	- 'Red Emperor'	NLar
	- 'Red Flash'	LPan WPat
	- 'Red Jonas'	NBPN WPat
	- 'Red Pygmy' ♀H4	More than 30 suppliers
	- 'Red Shadow'	SIFN
	- 'Red Spider'	CPMA
	- 'Red Wood'	CDoC CPMA ECho MBri MPkF SBod SCoo SLau SPer SVil WPat
	- 'Reticulatum'	see *A. palmatum* 'Shigitatsu-sawa'
	- 'Ribesifolium'	see *A. palmatum* 'Shishigashira'
	- 'Rising Sun'	CPMA
	- 'Rokugatsu-en-nishiki'	CBdw WPat
	- 'Roseomarginatum'	see *A. palmatum* 'Kagiri-nishiki'
	- 'Roseum Ornatum'	CBdw
	- 'Rough Bark Maple'	see *A. palmatum* 'Arakawa'
	- 'Royle'	CBdw CPMA
	- 'Rubrum'	CMen ECho
I	- 'Rubrum Kaiser'	CPMA ECho
	- 'Ruby Star'	CPMA NLar
	- 'Ryuto' **new**	CBdw
	- 'Ryuzu'	CPMA MPkF WPat
	- 'Sagara-nishiki' (v)	CBdw CEnd CMen CPMA ECho
	- 'Saint Jean'	CBdw
	- 'Samidare'	CPMA EPfP MPkF NLar
	- 'Sandra'	CMen MPkF
N	- 'Sango-kaku' ♀H4	More than 30 suppliers
	- 'Saoshika'	CMCN CMen CPMA ECho MPkF

	- 'Sa-otome'	CMen ECho MPkF
	- 'Satsuki-beni'	ECho
	- 'Sawa-chidori'	CBdw
	- 'Sazanami'	CEnd CPMA ECho MPkF NBea NLar WNor WPGP WPat
	- 'Scolopendriifolium'	CDoC LMil MPkF SCoo SLau WFar WPat
§	- 'Seigai'	CPMA MPkF
	- 'Seigen'	CBdw CEnd CMCN CMen CPMA ECho MPkF WPGP
I	- 'Seigen Aureum'	CPMA
	- 'Seiun-kaku'	CBdw CMen CPMA MBri WPat
	- 'Sekimori'	CBdw CPMA SIFN
	- 'Sekka-yatsubusa'	CMCN CMen ECho
	- 'Senkaki'	see *A. palmatum* 'Sango-kaku'
	- 'Septemlobum Elegans'	see *A. palmatum* 'Heptalobum Elegans'
	- 'Septemlobum Purpureum'	see *A. palmatum* 'Hessei'
	- 'Sessilifolium' dwarf	see *A. palmatum* 'Hagoromo'
	- 'Sessilifolium' tall	see *A. palmatum* 'Koshimino'
	- 'Shaina'	CBcs CDoC CEnd CMen CPMA CWib ECho LPan LRHS MBri MGos MPkF NBhm SBod SCoo SVil WFar WHar
	- 'Sharp's Pygmy'	CBdw CPMA ECho MPkF WPat
	- 'Sherwood Flame'	CMCN CPMA CWib ECho LRHS MAsh MBlu MGos MPkF NLar SCoo WFar WPat
	- 'Shichigosan'	CMen
	- 'Shidava Gold'	CBdw CPMA SIFN
	- 'Shi-en'	MPkF
	- 'Shigarami'	CPMA MPkF
	- 'Shigi-no-hoshi'	CBdw
§	- 'Shigitatsu-sawa' (v)	CBcs CBdw CEnd CMCN CMen CPMA ECho EMil LPan LRHS MGos MPkF NBea NLar SHBN SIFN
	- 'Shigure-bato'	CMCN CPMA MPkF
	- 'Shigurezome'	CMCN MPkF
	- 'Shikageori-nishiki'	CMen CPMA ECho LRHS MPkF
	- 'Shime-no-uchi'	CMCN CPMA LMil MPkF SIFN
	- 'Shindeshōjō'	More than 30 suppliers
§	- 'Shinobuga-oka'	CMCN CMen CPMA ECho MPkF SCoo SLau
	- 'Shinonome'	CPMA MPkF
	- 'Shiro-fu-nishiki'	CBdw
§	- 'Shishigashira'	CDoC CMCN CMen CPMA EBee ECho EPfP LMil LRHS MBar MBlu MBri MDun MGos MPkF NBea NLar SCoo SIFN WBod WFar WPat
	- 'Shishigashira-no-yatsubusa'	CBdw
§	- 'Shishio'	CBcs CMCN CMen ECho LAst LHyd LRHS MPkF SSpi SVil WPat
§	- 'Shishio Improved'	CBdw CEnd CMCN CPMA CTho CWSG ECho EPfP MAsh MBlu MGos MPkF NBhm NLar SIFN SPur STre SWvt WBod WHar
	- 'Shōjō'	CMCN CPMA WFar
	- 'Shōjō-no-mai'	CBdw
	- 'Shōjō-nomura'	CAbP CEnd CMen CPMA LRHS MGos MPkF NBea NLar WPGP WPat
	- 'Sister Ghost'	CBdw CPMA
	- 'Skeeter's Broom'	CBcs CBdw CDoC ECho LRHS MBri MGos MPkF NBPN SBod SCoo SIFN SVil WPat
*	- 'Sode-nishiki'	CBdw CPMA MPkF NLar
	- 'Stella Rossa'	CBdw CEnd CPMA LPan LRHS MBlu MPkF NBea NLar WPat
	- 'Suminagashi'	CBcs CDoC CMCN CMen ECho ENot LMil LRHS MBri MGos MPkF NBPN NLar SBod SChF SCoo SIFN SLau SPer SVil WBod WPat

I	- 'Summer Gold'	LPan
*	- 'Sunago' **new**	NLar
	- 'Suruga-nishiki' (v)	CBdw
	- 'Susan'	MPkF
	- 'Taiyō-nishiki'	CBdw CPMA MPkF
	- 'Takinogawa'	LRHS
	- 'Tamahime'	CMCN CMen CPMA ECho SIFN
	- 'Tana'	CBdw CMCN CPMA EPfP MPkF SIFN WFar WPat
	- 'Tarō-yama'	CBdw CPMA WPat
	- 'Tatsuta'	ECho MPkF WHar
	- 'Taylor'^{PBR} (v)	MPkF NLar SCoo
	- 'Tennyo-no-hoshi'	ECho MPkF NLar
	- 'Tiger Rose'	CBdw CPMA
	- 'Tiny Tim'	CBdw CPMA
	- 'Trompenburg' 𝕐^{H4}	More than 30 suppliers
	- 'Tsuchigumo'	CMCN CMen CPMA ECho MPkF NLar
	- 'Tsukubane'	WPat
	- 'Tsukushigata'	CMCN
	- 'Tsuma-beni'	CBdw CMCN CMen CPMA EPfP LRHS MPkF
	- 'Tsuma-gaki'	CBdw CMCN CMen CPMA ECho EPfP MBri MGos MPkF WPat
	- 'Tsuri-nishiki'	CBdw CPMA ECho NLar
	- 'Ueno-homare'	CBdw MPkF SCoo WPat
	- 'Ueno-yama'	CBcs CBdw CPMA MGos MPkF
	- 'Ukigumo' (v)	CBcs CBdw CEnd CLnd CMCN CMen CPMA CSBt CWSG CWib ECho ELan EMil LMil LRHS MBlu MBri MGos MPkF NHol SBod SCoo SIFN SPer SPoG SSta WFar WPat
	- 'Ukon'	CBdw CMCN CMen CPMA ECho EMil LMil MBri MPkF SBod SCoo SVil
	- 'Umegae'	CPMA
	- 'Uncle Ghost' **new**	CPMA
	- 'Usu-midori'	CPMA
	- 'Utsu-semi'	CPMA MPkF SIFN
	- 'Van der Akker'	CPMA
	- 'Vanderhoss Red'	ECho
	- 'Vens Red'	WPat
	- 'Versicolor' (v)	CBdw CEnd CMCN CPMA SHBN
	- 'Vic Broom'	CBdw
	- 'Vic Pink'	CBdw CPMA WPat
	- 'Villa Taranto'	CBcs CBdw CDoC CEnd CMCN CMen CPMA ECho EPfP LMil LRHS MAsh MBlu MBri MGos MPkF NBea NHol NLar SCoo SIFN SSpi SSta SVil WHar WPGP WPat
	- 'Volubile'	CMCN CMen ECho EPfP
	- 'Wabito'	CMCN CPMA ECho MPkF
	- 'Waka-midori'	ECho
	- 'Waka-momiji' (v)	CBdw CPMA
	- 'Wakehurst Pink' (v)	CMCN MPkF WPat
	- 'Wendy'	CMen CPMA MPkF NLar WPat
	- 'Wetumpka Red'	CPMA
	- 'Wilson's Pink Dwarf'	CBdw CEnd CMen CPMA CWib ECho EPfP MBri MGos MPkF NLar SCoo WGer WPat
	- 'Winter Flame'	CBdw CPMA MAsh NLar WHar WPat
	- 'Wolff's Broom'	CBdw WPat
	- 'Wou-nishiki'	CBdw CMCN CMen ECho MPkF
	- 'Yana-gawa'	CMen ECho
	- 'Yasemin'	CBdw CMen CPMA MPkF NLar SIFN
	- 'Yezo-nishiki'	CBdw CMCN CMen LRHS MPkF WFar
	- 'Yūba e'	MPkF WFar WPat
	- 'Yūgure'	MPkF NLar WFar
	papilio	see *A. caudatum*
	paxii	CMCN
	pectinatum 'Sirene'	see *A. forrestii* 'Sirene'
	- 'Sparkling'	see *A. forrestii* 'Sparkling'
	pensylvanicum 𝕐^{H4}	CBcs CCVT CDul CLnd CMCN CSam CTho EBee ECrN ELan EPfP EWTr LPan LRHS MBri MGos MRav NBee NBlu NHol NWea SBLw SHBN SLim SPer SSpi WFar WHCr WNor WOrn
	- 'Erythrocladum'	CEnd CMCN CPMA EPfP LRHS MAsh MBri NBea NHol NLar SLim SPur SSpi SSta WFar
	pentaphyllum	CMCN LRHS SIFN SSpi
*	***phlebanthum*** B&SWJ 9751 **new**	WCru
§	***pictum***	CMCN WNor
	- subsp. ***okamotoanum***	CMCN WPGP
	- - B&SWJ 8516	WCru
	- 'Shufu-nishiki'	CMCN
	- 'Usugomo'	WPat
	platanoides 𝕐^{H4}	CBcs CCVT CDoC CDul CLnd CMCN CTri CWib EBee ECrN EMac EPfP GAbr LBuc MGos MSwo NBee NWea SBLw SPer STre WFar WHar WMou WNor
	- 'Cleveland'	CBcs
	- 'Columnare'	CDul CLnd CMCN CWib ECrN SBLw SCoo WOrn
	- 'Crimson King' 𝕐^{H4}	More than 30 suppliers
	- 'Crimson Sentry'	CDoC CDul CEnd CLnd CMCN CWib EBee ECrN ENot EPfP IArd LAst LBuc LCro LPan MAsh MBlu MBri MGos MLan MRav NBee SCoo SLim SPoG WFar WHar
	- 'Cucullatum'	CMCN
	- 'Deborah'	CBcs CTho LPan SBLw SCoo WOrn
	- 'Drummondii' (v)	More than 30 suppliers
	- 'Emerald Queen'	CLnd CWib ECrN SBLw SHBN
	- 'Faassen's Black'	CPMA SBLw
§	- 'Globosum'	CLnd CMCN EBee ECrN LBuc LCro LPan SBLw SWvt
	- 'Goldsworth Purple'	CDul CLnd
	- 'Laciniatum'	CEnd CMCN ECrN
	- 'Lorbergii'	see *A. platanoides* 'Palmatifidum'
	- 'Marit'	WPat
§	- 'Palmatifidum'	CLnd
	- Princeton Gold = 'Prigo'^{PBR}	CDoC ECrN ELan ENot LPan LRHS MGos SCoo SPoG
	- 'Red Lace' **new**	WOrn
	- 'Reitenbachii'	CDul
	- 'Royal Red'	CBcs CDul CWib EBee ECrN ENot LPan MRav NBPN NLar SCoo
	- 'Schwedleri' 𝕐^{H4}	CDul CMCN ECrN EPfP MGos NWea SBLw
	- 'Tharandt'	CMCN
	- 'Walderseei'	CLnd
	pseudoplatanus	CBcs CCVT CDul CLnd CMCN CSBt CTri ECrN EMac LBuc LPan MBar MGos NBee NWea SBLw SPer WFar WHar WMou
§	- 'Atropurpureum'	CDoC CDul CLnd EWTr NBee NWea SBLw WHar
	- 'Brilliantissimum' 𝕐^{H4}	More than 30 suppliers
	- 'Corstorphinense'	CMCN
	- 'Erectum'	WFar
	- 'Leopoldii' misapplied	see *A. pseudoplatanus* f. *variegatum*
	- 'Prinz Handjéry'	CBcs CDul CEnd CLnd CMCN CTri CWib LPan LRHS MAsh MBar MGos NHol NWea SBLw SIFN SPer SPoG SSpi WHar
	- f. ***purpureum***	LAst SEND
	- 'Spaethii' misapplied	see *A. pseudoplatanus* 'Atropurpureum'
	- 'Sunshine'	ENot
§	- f. ***variegatum*** (v)	NEgg
	- - 'Esk Sunset' (v)	CBcs CDul ECho ENot LRHS MBri MGos MPkF NLar

- - 'Leopoldii' ambig. (v)	CBcs CDul CLnd CMCN EBee ECrN ELan LAst LPan NBee SBLw SCoo SEND SHBN SPer SWvt WFar WOrn
- - 'Leopoldii' Vervaene (v)	SCrf
- - 'Nizetii' (v)	CMCN LRHS SBLw
- - 'Simon-Louis Frères' (v)	CCVT CDul CEnd CLnd CMCN CWSG CWib EBee ECrN EMui LAst LPan LRHS MAsh MBar MBri MDun MGos NBee SCrf SIFN SPer SWvt WFar WFoF WHar WOrn
- 'Worleei'	see *A. pseudoplatanus* 'Worley'
§ - 'Worley'	CBcs CDul CLnd CMCN CSBt CTri EBee ECrN LRHS MAsh MBar MRav NBee NWea SBLw SCrf SEND SHBN SLim SPer WHar WOrn
pseudosieboldianum	CMCN IDee MBlu WNor
- B&SWJ 8746	WCru
- var. ***microsieboldianum*** B&SWJ 8766	WCru
pubipalmatum	WNor
pycnanthum	EPfP
robustum	WNor
rubescens	CPMA WPGP
- B&SWJ 6735	WCru
- variegated seedlings (v)	CPMA WPGP
rubrum	More than 30 suppliers
- 'Autumn Spire' **new**	CPMA
- 'Bowhall'	CMCN
- 'Brandywine'	MBri
- 'Candy Ice' (v)	CPMA
- 'Columnare'	CMCN EPfP
- 'Embers' **new**	CPMA
- 'Firedance' **new**	CPMA
- 'Northwood' **new**	CPMA
- 'October Glory' ♀H4	More than 30 suppliers
- Red Sunset = 'Franksred'	CDoC CDul CEnd CMCN CPMA CTho EBee EPfP LPan LRHS MBlu NLar SCoo SIFN SMad SSta WPGP
- 'Scanlon'	CBcs CDoC CDul CEnd CMCN CPMA CTho EBee ECho EPfP LAst LPan MBlu SBLw SPer WOrn
- 'Schlesingeri'	CEnd CLnd CMCN CMac CPMA EPfP
- 'Somerset'	CPMA MBri
- 'Sun Valley'	CPMA
- 'Tilford'	SIFN SSta
§ ***rufinerve*** ♀H4	CBcs CCVT CDoC CDul CLnd CMCN CTho CTri EBee ECrN EPfP EPla LCro LRHS MBri NBea NWea SBLw SCoo SPer WBVN WGer WNor WOrn WPGP
- 'Albolimbatum'	see *A. rufinerve* 'Hatsuyuki'
- 'Albomarginatum'	see *A. rufinerve* 'Hatsuyuki'
- 'Erythrocladum'	CPMA
§ - 'Hatsuyuki' (v)	CDoC CDul CEnd CMCN CPMA SIFN WPGP
- 'Winter Gold'	CPMA CTho LRHS NLar SIFN SPur SSpi
§ ***saccharinum***	CBcs CCVT CDoC CDul CLnd CMCN CTri CWib EBee ECrN ELan EMac EPfP MGos MLan NBee NPen NWea SBLw SCoo SHBN SPer WFar WHar WNor
- 'Born's Gracious'	CPMA EMil
- 'Fastigiatum'	see *A. saccharinum* f. *pyramidale*
- f. ***laciniatum***	CMCN EBee LAst LRHS MBlu MGos MMuc SPer
- 'Laciniatum Wieri'	CDul CMCN CTho EBee ECrN LAst LPan SBLw
- f. ***lutescens***	CDul CMCN CTho MBlu SBLw
§ - f. ***pyramidale***	CDoC CLnd CMCN EBee ECrN SBLw
saccharum	CAgr CBcs CDoC CDul CLnd CMCN CTho ECrN EPfP MBlu MLan NWea SBLw SHBN SPer WNor
- 'Adirondak'	CPMA
- 'Arrowhead'	CPMA
- subsp. ***barbatum***	see *A. saccharum* subsp. *floridanum*
- 'Brocade'	CPMA MPkF
- 'Caddo'	CPMA
- 'Fiddlers Creek'	CPMA
§ - subsp. ***floridanum***	CMCN
§ - subsp. ***grandidentatum***	CMCN NLar
- 'Green Mountain'	CPMA LPan
- 'Legacy'	LPan
§ - subsp. ***leucoderme***	CMCN
- 'Majesty'	CPMA
- subsp. ***nigrum***	CMCN
- - 'Greencolumn'	CPMA
- - 'Monumentale'	CMCN
- 'Sugar Cone'	CPMA
§ ***sempervirens***	CGHE CMCN LEdu WPGP
'Sensu'	CPMA
serrulatum B&SWJ 6760	WCru
shirasawanum	CMCN WNor
§ - 'Aureum' ♀H4	More than 30 suppliers
- 'Autumn Moon'	CBcs CBdw CPMA EPfP MBri MPkF NLar SCoo
§ - 'Ezo-no-momiji'	CMCN CMen CPMA MPkF NLar
- 'Johin'	CPMA
- 'Jordan'	LPan NLar
§ - 'Jûnihitoe'	WNor
- 'Lovett'	CPMA
§ - 'Microphyllum'	CMCN ECho MPkF WNor
§ - 'Ogurayama'	CBdw CPMA ECho
- 'Palmatifolium'	CBdw CMCN CPMA SIFN
- 'Susanne'	CPMA
- var. ***tenuifolium***	WNor
sieboldianum	CMCN CMen CTri ECho ECrN EPfP SSpi WHCr WHar WNor WPat
- 'Sode-no-uchi'	CMCN CMen SIFN
'Silver Cardinal' (v)	CBcs CDoC CDul CEnd CMCN CPMA EBee EPfP MBlu MBri MGos MPkF NBhm NLar SPoG WHar
'Silver Vein'	see *A.* x *conspicuum* 'Silver Vein'
§ ***sinense***	SSpi WCwm WNor
spicatum	EPfP NLar WNor
§ ***stachyophyllum***	GQui
§ ***sterculiaceum***	CMCN EBee WPGP
- subsp. ***franchetii***	NLar
takesimense	MBri WCru
- B&SWJ 8500	WCru
tataricum	CMCN MBri
§ - subsp. ***ginnala***	CBcs CDul CLnd CMCN CTri CWSG ECrN EMac EPfP EWTr LRav MGos NBea NPal NWea SBLw SHBN SLim SPer WCwm WNor WPat
- - 'Flame'	CPMA CWSG EBee ECrN ELan EPfP MGos NLar NPen SPoG
tegmentosum	CMCN CPMA EPfP LPan MBlu MBri WNor
- B&SWJ 8421	WCru
- subsp. ***glaucorufinerve***	see *A. rufinerve*
tetramerum	see *A. stachyophyllum*
trautvetteri	CMCN EPfP WNor
triflorum ♀H4	CBcs CMCN CPMA CTho EPfP IMGH LPan LRHS MBri NBea NLar SSpi WFar
truncatum	CMCN MPkF WNor
- 'Akikaze-nishiki' (v)	CPMA MPkF
tschonoskii	GQui WNor
- subsp. ***koreanum***	CTho MPkF WNor
§ ***turkestanicum***	CMCN EBee WFar
velutinum	CMCN

	– var. ***vanvolxemii***	WPGP
	villosum	see *A. sterculiaceum*
	'White Tigress'	CTho MBlu WPGP
§	***wilsonii***	CDul CSam WNor
	x ***zoeschense***	CMCN
	– 'Annae'	CPMA MAsh NHol SBLw

Aceriphyllum see *Mukdenia*

x *Achicodonia* (*Gesneriaceae*)

	'Dark Velvet'	WDib

Achillea (*Asteraceae*)

	ageratifolia ♀H4	EBla ECho ECtt LBee MTho NBre NLar SRms WFar
	– subsp. ***serbica***	XPep
§	***ageratum***	CArn CHby CPrp CWan ELau GPoy MHer MNHC MSal NGHP NPri NTHB SIde SRms WGwG WHer WJek WPer
	– 'W.B. Childs'	CSli CSpe ECha EGle ELan GBuc MArl MCot MNrw NDov SHar WCot WEas
	'Alabaster'	CDes CSli EBee GBuc NBHF NDov SPhx
	Anthea = 'Anblo'PBR	CKno CWCL EBee EBla EBrs EGle EWsh GMaP GSki LPio LRHS MBri MLLN MRav MSte NChi NCob NLar SPer SRGP SRkn SRms WAul WFar XPep
§	'Apfelblüte'	CPrp CSBt CSli CTca CWCL EBee EBla ECha ECtt EGle ELan GSki LRHS LSRN MRav MWgw NCGa NDov NGdn NHol SPer WCAu WFar WMnd WPer
	Appleblossom	see *A.* 'Apfelblüte'
	'Apricot Beauty'	CSli CTca EBee ECtt GMaP GQue LSRN MBri NHol NPro SSvw
	argentea misapplied	see *A. clavennae*, *A. umbellata*
	argentea Lamarck	see *Tanacetum argenteum*
I	***argentifolia*** hort. **new**	EAlp
	aurea	see *A. chrysocoma*
	'Bahama'	EPPr GBin GQue MAvo NBre NBro WWeb
	'Belle Epoque' ♀H4	CDes CSli EBee MAvo NBHF
	'Bloodstone'	CSli EBee ECtt EShb EWes EWsh MRav NBHF WOut
	'Breckland Bouquet'	EWes
	'Breckland Ruby'	EWes
	'Brilliant'	LRHS WWeb
	'Caroline'	LRHS WWeb
	cartilaginea	CSli EPPr NBHF NBre SPav WFar WMoo
	– 'Silver Spray'	EBee GQue NBre NLar SDnm SPav WPtf
	'Christine's Pink' ♀H4	CKno CSli EPPr EShb MAvo NBHF
§	***chrysocoma***	ECho WMoo WTel XPep
	– 'Grandiflora'	CHar ECha ELan EMar MFOX NGdn
§	***clavennae***	ECho ECtt LPio MLLN SAga SBla SRms WAbe WCot WFar
	'Clotted Cream' **new**	MBnl
	clypeolata Sibth. & Sm.	CAby CSam EBee EPPr EShb LHop LPio MBri NBre NLar SPlb SRms WOut WPer
	coarctata	NBir WPer XPep
	'Coronation Gold' ♀H4	CDoC CPrp CSam CTca CWCL EBee EBla ECtt ELan ENot EPfP ERou GMac GSki LAst LRHS MBri MNFA MRav MWat NChi SAga WCAu WCot WEas WFar XPep
	'Credo' ♀H4	CSli EBee EBla ECha ECtt EGle EMon EPfP EWTr GBuc LAst LPio LRHS MLLN MNFA MRav MSte MWgw NCGa NGdn NHol NRnb SMad SPer SPla WMnd WWlt
	crithmifolia	XPep
	decolorans	see *A. ageratum*
	erba-rotta	WPer
	– subsp. ***moschata***	ECho NBro
§	'Fanal'	More than 30 suppliers
	'Faust'	CAby CDes CHar CKno CSli CWoW EBla ELon NBHF SMrm STes WPGP WPrP
	'Feuerland'	CSam CSli CTca CWCL EBee EBla ECha ECtt EPfP ERou LRHS MAvo MLLN MNFA MRav NBir NCGa NDov NGdn NSti SMad SPer SWat WCAu WCot WFar WHil WPer WWeb
	filipendulina	NSti SWal WHrl
	– 'Cloth of Gold' ♀H4	More than 30 suppliers
	– 'Gold Plate' ♀H4	More than 30 suppliers
	– 'Parker's Variety' ♀H4	EBee GQue MLan NBre WFar WOut
	Flowers of Sulphur	see *A.* 'Schwefelblüte'
	'Forncett Beauty'	CSli NBHF WHil
	'Forncett Bride'	CSli NBHF NBre NDov WHil
	'Forncett Candy'	CSli NBHF NDov
	'Forncett Citrus'	CAby CSli EBee NBHF NBre WPGP
	'Forncett Fletton'	CFir CMHG CSli CWCL EBee EGle EMar EPPr EPfP EShb GBri IPot LHop MAvo MBnl MNFA MNrw MRav NBHF NCob NGdn NHol SAga STes WCAu WHil WPtf WTMC WWlt
	'Forncett Ivory'	CSli MSte NBHF NBre WHil
	fraasii	MDKP
	'Gartenzwerg' **new**	EMon
	glaberrima hybrid	EMan WCot
	'Gloria Jean'	SHar
	'Gold and Grey'	CSli
	'Goldstar'	EBee NBPC NDov WFar
	grandifolia misapplied	see *Tanacetum macrophyllum* (Waldst. & Kit.) Sch.Bip.
§	***grandifolia*** Friv.	CElw CFwr COIW CSam EBee EGle GBuc MRav MSte NBro SMad SPer SSvw WAul WBor WFar WHer WHil WMnd WMoo WOld
	'Great Expectations'	see *A.* 'Hoffnung'
	'Grey and Gold'	SMrm
	'Hannelore Pahl'	NBre
	'Hartington White'	GBuc MWgw
	'Heidi' ♀H4	CCVN CSli CTca CWoW GBri
	'Hella Glashoff' ♀H4	CDes CMea CSli EBee ECho ECtt EGle EGoo EPPr GBin MWea NCGa NDov WCot WHoo WWeb
§	'Hoffnung'	CPrp CSli CTca CWCL EBee EBla ECtt EGle EMan ERou GSki LRHS MBri MRav NPro SPer WCAu WMnd WPer
	'Huteri'	CLyd EAlp EAro EBee EBla ECho ECtt EDAr EGoo EPfP EPot LBee LRHS MAvo MHer MRav SPoG WEas WFar
	'Inca Gold'	CTca EBee EBla ECha ECtt EGle EHrv EMan EPPr EShb GBuc GQue LRHS MRav NBro NCGa NCob NGdn NHol NPro SAga SPav WTMC
	'Jacqueline'	EBee EWll
	'Joey'	MAvo NRnb WHil
	'Judity'	LRHS WWeb
	x ***kellereri***	NLar XPep
	'King Alfred'	LAst MWea
	x ***kolbiana***	EMan LSou NHol NMen SRms WLin
§	– 'Weston'	NBre
§	'Lachsschönheit' ♀H4	More than 30 suppliers

	Name	Suppliers
	x ***lewisii***	NMen
	- 'King Edward' $\mathbb{Y}^{H4}$	CSam EAlp ECha ECho EDAr EPfP GBin GMaP LPio LRHS NBir SAga SBla SIng SPoG WFar
	ligustica	WCot
	'Lucky Break' $\mathbb{Y}^{H4}$	EBla ECha SDix SMHy
	macrophylla	NBre
	'Marie Ann'	CWCL EBee ECtt ERou GBri GQue LPio MAvo MBnl MLLN NBPC NBhm NLar NPro NSti SPhx SSvw
	'Marmalade'	CSli CTca LSou NDov WMnd WPGP
	'Martina' $\mathbb{Y}^{H4}$	CDoC CKno CMMP CPrp CSli CTca EBee ECtt EGle EPPr EPfP GAbr GBuc GSki IPot LAst LHop LRHS MBnl MLLN MNFA MRav MSte NCGa NDov NGdn NHol NOrc NPro SRGP
	'McVities'	CSli CWCL EBee ECtt EPPr GMaP LEdu MBnl MLLN NCGa NPro SDnm SPav STes WCAu WCra WHil WMnd WTin
	millefolium	CArn COld CWan ELau EUnu GPoy GWCH MNHC NLan NMir NSco SECG SPlb WHer WJek WSFF WSel XPep
	- 'Bright Cerise'	WFar
	- 'Carla Hussey'	WFar
	- 'Cassis'	CSpe CTca EAro GQue LDai NBre NEgg SDnm SPav WFar WOut WRHF
§	- 'Cerise Queen'	More than 30 suppliers
	- 'Christel'	CCVN CDes CSli CTca EBee EWes GBin MAvo
	- 'Christine'	CTca GBin NBre
	- 'Colorado'	CSam CWCL EAro GAbr NBre NChi NHol NRnb SPav WFar WHrl
	- dark red	CSli
	- 'Debutante'	WHil
	- 'Excel' **new**	EBee
	- 'Fire King'	CElw CHal
	- 'Harlekin'	EBee
	- 'Kelwayi' $\mathbb{Y}^{H4}$	CSli
	- Kirschkönigin	see *A. millefolium* 'Cerise Queen'
	- 'Lansdorferglut' $\mathbb{Y}^{H4}$	CKno CSli CTca EPPr LRHS MBri MRav NDov NPro SPhx
	- 'Lavender Beauty'	see *A. millefolium* 'Lilac Beauty'
	- 'Lemon Curd'	LDai
§	- 'Lilac Beauty'	CBgR CHar CMHG COlW CSli ECha EHrv ELon EPPr ERou EWTr GMaP GSki IPot LCro LRHS LSRN MRav NBir NGHP NHol NPri NSti SPav WFar WHoo WPer XPep
*	- 'Lilac Queen'	CSli MArl
	- 'Lollypop'	LDai
	- 'Oertels Rose'	WFar
	- 'Paprika'	More than 30 suppliers
*	- 'Pastel Shades'	IFoB WMoo
	- 'Raspberry Ripple'	GBin
	- 'Red Beauty'	CMHG CSli CWCL EBee ERou LRHS LSou NBro SBch SMad SRms SWat XPep
	- 'Red Velvet'	More than 30 suppliers
	- 'Rougham Beauty'	CSli
	- 'Rougham Cream'	CSli
	- 'Rougham White'	CSli
	- 'Ruby Port'	NPri WFar
	- 'Salmon Pink'	WFar
	- 'Salmon Queen'	NGHP NHol WCra
	- 'Sammetriese'	CAby CBgR CSli EGle GBuc LRHS MNrw MSte NCGa SMad WCAu WCot WFar WHoo WTin
	- 'Schneetaler'	GBin
	- 'Serenade'	EBee EBla WFar
	- 'Summer Berries'	NBHF WRHF

	Name	Suppliers
	- 'Summertime'	LAst SBod SPav
	- 'Tickled Pink'	WPer
	- 'White Beauty'	SPoG
	- 'White Queen'	EBee EMar LBMP WPer
	- 'Yellowstone'	EWes LAst LDai WCra
	'Mondpagode' $\mathbb{Y}^{H4}$	CHar CMHG CPrp CSli EBee ECGP EGle LRHS LSRN MAvo MBNS MNFA MRav MSte MWgw NCGa NGdn NPro SMHy SPhx WPtf
*	'Moonbeam'	EBla
	'Moonshine' $\mathbb{Y}^{H3}$	More than 30 suppliers
	'Moonwalker'	CAbP EAro EBee MBri MLLN MWrn NBre NGBl SIde SPav WFar WPer
	nobilis	XPep
	- subsp. ***neilreichii***	CSli CSpe EBee EBla EGoo EHrv EWTr GBri LRHS MAvo MLLN MNFA NSti SPer WCot WHal WPrP WTin
	'Nostalgia'	EBee
	odorata	EBee XPep
	'Old Brocade'	CSli EBee EShb NBre NDov NGby SPhx WPGP WPtf
	'Old Rose' **new**	MAvo MBnl
	'Peardrop'	NBre
	'Peter Davis'	see *Hippolytia herderi*
	pindicola subsp. ***integrifolia***	EWes
	'Pink Lady'	EBee EBla MBri SPoG
	'Pink Temptation'	MAvo WHil
	pink-flowered, from Santa Cruz Island	CKno
	'Pretty Belinda' **new**	EBee ERou IPot NBPC SHBN WBor WWlt
	'Pretty Flamingo' **new**	WOut
	'Prospero'	CMea WCot WCra
	ptarmica	CArn CBre ELau EMFW MHer MSal NMir NPri SHBN SIde SPer
*	- 'Ballerina'	MWrn NBre NDov NGdn NLar
	- Innocence	see *A. ptarmica* 'Unschuld'
	- 'Major'	GMaP NBre
	- 'Nana Compacta'	CSli CSpe EBee EBla ECha EMan IGor LRHS MLLN NBir SPlb SPoG WCFE WFar WHil WWlt
	- 'Perry's White'	CBcs CBre EBee ECha EGle LRHS MNFA MNrw NGHP NGdn NHol SRGP WCot
	- 'Stephanie Cohen'	see *A. sibirica* 'Stephanie Cohen'
N	- The Pearl Group seed-raised (d)	CTri ECha ELan GMaP NPri NVic SPlb SPoG SWat WFar WMoo WPer WTin
N	- - 'Boule de Neige' (clonal) (d)	CHal EBee EPfP GSki MBri MRav MWgw NBre NCob NPer NSti SPer SPet SPla WFar
N	- - 'The Pearl' (clonal) (d) $\mathbb{Y}^{H4}$	CDes CSBt EBee EPfP ERou IFoB LBMP LCro LHop MLHP MRav MSte MWat NBPC NBid NBir NBro NEgg NGHP SRms SWal WBor WBrk WCAu WCot WEas WFar WHer WHil WSFF
§	- 'Unschuld'	NBir
	- 'Weihenstephan' **new**	EBee
	'Rose Madder'	More than 30 suppliers
	'Rougham Bright Star'	CSli
	'Rougham Salmon'	CSli CTca
	'Sally'	NBre
	Salmon Beauty	see *A.* 'Lachsschönheit'
	'Sandstone'	see *A.* 'Wesersandstein'
§	'Schwefelblüte'	MRav NBir SBch
	'Schwellenburg'	CDes CHar CSli EBee NBre WPGP
	sibirica	CBgR SRGP
	- var. ***camschatica*** 'Love Parade'	CSli CTca EBee ECtt EMan EPfP GMac GSki LRHS MBri MEHN MGol MNFA MNHC MRav NBPC NEgg NGdn NSti SPad SPer SRGP SSvw WFar WMoo

§	– 'Stephanie Cohen'	CPrp EBee ECtt EGle EMan ERou GBin MLLN MSte NBhm NGdn WCot WFar WTMC
	'Stephanie'	EBee EPPr EWes NBre
	'Summer Glory'	NCob
	Summer Pastels Group	CBrm CHrt EMil LRHS NBir NBlu NHol NOrc NRnb SPav SPoG SRms SWal SWat WFar WHil WWeb
	'Summerwine' ♀H4	More than 30 suppliers
	'Sunbeam'	WWeb
I	'Taygetea'	CSam CSli CTca EBee EBla ELan EMan EPfP EShb MNFA MSte MWgw SDix SPer WCAu WFar WKif WPer WSHC
	'Terracotta'	More than 30 suppliers
	'The Beacon'	see *A.* 'Fanal'
	tomentosa ♀H4	CTri ECha ECho ECtt EPfP
§	– 'Aurea'	EBla ECho ELau NBre NBro SRms
	– 'Maynard's Gold'	see *A. tomentosa* 'Aurea'
§	***umbellata***	EBee GBri WBrk WCot XPep
	– 'Weston'	see *A.* x *kolbiana* 'Weston'
	'Walther Funcke'	More than 30 suppliers
§	'Wesersandstein'	CDes CFir CHar CKno CSli CTca CWCL EBee ECtt EPPr ERou EShb GMaP LRHS MAvo MBnl MBri MLLN NBir NCGa NHol NPro SAga SBod STes WCot WFar WHoo WPer WTin
	'Wilczekii'	NBre NChi SRms
	'Yellowstone'	MBri SMer WWeb

x *Achimenantha* (*Gesneriaceae*)

'Inferno' ♀H1	EABi WDib
'Tyche' **new**	EABi

Achimenes (*Gesneriaceae*)

'Ambroise Verschaffelt' ♀H1	EABi LAma WDib
'Blue David' **new**	EABi
'Blue Sparkles' **new**	EBrs
'Boy David' **new**	EABi
'Cattleya'	LAma
'Charity' **new**	WDib
'Clouded Yellow'	EABi
'Coral Cameo Mix' **new**	EABi
'Crummock Water'	WDib
'Donna' **new**	EABi
'Dot'	EABi
erecta	WDib
'Extravaganza' **new**	WDib
grandiflora 'Robert Dressler' **new**	EABi
'Harry Williams'	LAma WDib
'Hilda Michelssen' ♀H1	WDib
'Jennifer Goode'	EABi
'Jubilee Gem'	EABi
'Just Divine' **new**	EABi
'Little Beauty'	SWal WDib
longiflora	EABi
– 'Margarita' **new**	EABi
'Luneberg' **new**	EABi
'Maxima'	LAma
'Mozelle' **new**	EABi
'Orange Delight'	WDib
(Palette Series) 'Palette Mix Lilac' **new**	EABi
– 'Palette Mix Purple Dwarf' **new**	EABi
– 'Palette Mix Red Dwarf' **new**	EABi
– 'Palette Mix Salmon' **new**	EABi
– 'Palette Mix White' **new**	EABi
– 'Palette Red Mix' **new**	EABi
'Patens Major'	WDib
'Peach Blossom'	EBrs LAma
'Pearly Queen'	EABi
'Pink Beauty'	EABi
'Platinum' **new**	EABi
I 'Purple Hybrid' **new**	EABi
'Purple King'	SWal
'Red Giant'	EABi
'Rose Dream' **new**	EABi
'Stan's Delight' (d) ♀H1	EABi WDib
'Summer Sunset' **new**	EABi
'Tarantella'	EABi WDib
'Teresa'	EABi
(Tetra Series) 'Tetra Klaus Neubner' **new**	EABi
– 'Tetra Orange Glow' **new**	EABi
– 'Tetra Verschaffelt' **new**	EABi
– 'Tetra Wine Red Charm' **new**	EABi
'Trailing Yellow' **new**	EABi
'Vivid'	EABi
'Wetterflow's Triumph'	EABi WDib
'Yellow Beauty' **new**	WDib

Achlys (*Berberidaceae*)

californica	IBlr
japonica	EBee WCru
triphylla	GGar IBlr WCru

Achnatherum see *Stipa*

Achyranthes (*Amaranthaceae*)

bidentata	CArn MSal

Acidanthera see *Gladiolus*

Acinos (*Lamiaceae*)

§	***alpinus***	CArn CBrm CHFP CPBP EAlp EAro EBee EDAr EMan EPot LTwo NLar NOrc SBch SBla SHGN WJek
§	***arvensis***	EUnu MHer MSal
§	***corsicus***	NLAp NMen NWCA WHoo WPat

Aciphylla (*Apiaceae*)

aurea	GCrs LTwo NLar NWCA SMad SPlb
glaucescens	ECou GCrs NLar SMad
hectorii	EMan
kirkii	EMan
pinnatifida	GCrs GGar
squarrosa	CTrC WThu
subflabellata	EBee ECou

Acis (*Amaryllidaceae*)

§	***autumnalis*** ♀H4	More than 30 suppliers
	– 'Cobb's Variety'	WCot
	– var. ***oporantha***	CSsd ERos MSte
	– var. ***pulchella***	EBrs ECho ERos
§	***longifolia***	ECho ERos
	nicaeensis ♀H2-3	CGra CHHB CLyd CPBP CStu EBrs EBur ECho ERos ITim LRHS MAsh MTho SCnR WAbe WCot
§	***rosea***	CLyd EBur ERos NMen NWCA SCnR WAbe
§	***tingitana***	EBrs ECho WCot
§	***trichophylla***	EBrs ECho SCnR WCot
	– f. ***purpurascens***	EBrs ECho WCot
§	***valentina***	CPBP EBrs ECho EPot SCnR SRot WCot

Acmella (*Asteraceae*)

§	***oleracea***	CArn EUnu MSal SCoo

Acmena (*Myrtaceae*)

smithii	EShb

Acnistus (*Solanaceae*)

australis	see *Iochroma australe*

Acoelorraphe (*Acanthaceae*)

wrightii	EAmu

Acoelorrhaphe (*Arecaceae*)

sp.	LPal

Aconitum (*Ranunculaceae*)

ACE 1449	GBuc
B&SWJ 2954 from Nepal	WCru
B&SWJ 8488 from Korea **new**	WCru
CC 4914	MGol
CNDS 036 from Burma	WCru
GWJ 9393 from northern India	WCru
- GWJ 9417	WCru
alboviolaceum var. ***albiflorum*** B&SWJ 4105	WCru
- - B&SWJ 8444	WCru
anglicum	see *A. napellus* subsp. *napellus* Anglicum Group
anthora	NBHF
arcuatum B&SWJ 774	WCru
austroyunnanense	EBee
- BWJ 7902	WCru
autumnale misapplied	see *A. carmichaelii* Wilsonii Group
autumnale ambig.	NBir
autumnale Rchb.	see *A. fischeri* Rchb.
x ***bicolor***	see *A.* x *cammarum* 'Bicolor'
* 'Blue Opal'	CDes EBee ECtt EWes
'Blue Sceptre'	EBee EGle GBin LDai MBNS MBri NLar NMoo WAul WSel
'Bressingham Spire' ♀H4	More than 30 suppliers
§ x ***cammarum*** 'Bicolor' ♀H4	More than 30 suppliers
- 'Grandiflorum Album'	CAby ERou MSte SPhx
§ ***carmichaelii***	CArn CMea EBee EMan GSki LLWP LRHS MBri NBro NOrc SPet SRms WBod WCot WFar WHoo WMoo WSel WTin
- Arendsii Group **new**	ECtt
- 'Arendsii' ♀H4	More than 30 suppliers
- 'Blue Bishop'	LSou
- 'Pink Sensation'	EBee ECtt EGle ERou LTwo MBNS NBPC NBre NDov NGHP NSti SMrm WCAu WHil WSpi
- 'Royal Flush'PBR	CFir CMil EGle GCai MBNS MBri MLLN NCob NEgg NGdn NLar SPoG WCot WKif WWeb
- var. ***truppelianum*** HWJ 732	WCru
§ - Wilsonii Group	CAby EBee EMar GGar LRHS MCot MLLN MRav MSte MWat MWgw NDov SBch SPhx WFar WPGP WPer WSel
- - 'Barker's Variety'	CFir CKno CPou EGle EMan EPfP EWTr GBuc GMac LPio NCGa NDov NHol NLar NSti WCot WSHC
- - 'Kelmscott' ♀H4	ECtt EGle EMon EWes GMac MCot MRav MSte SAga SDix SMHy WFar WRHF
- - 'Spätlese'	CAbP EBee ECtt EGle EMan EMar EMon GAbr GSki LHop MEHN MLLN MNFA MSte MWgw NBHF NBir NDov NEgg NGdn SAga SMHy SPer STes WCot WCra WLin WWlt
- - 'The Grim Reaper'	EMon SSvw
chasmanthum	EBee WCot
chiisanense B&SWJ 4446 **new**	WCru
chuianum **new**	EBee
cilicicum	see *Eranthis hyemalis* Cilicica Group
'Cloudy' **new**	EKen NBPC NGdn SPer
compactum	see *A. napellus* subsp. *vulgare*
'Eleonara'	CFir EBee EGle EMan EMar EPPr EPfP ERou EWes GBuc GCra LHop MAvo MBri MLLN NGHP NGdn NLar NMoo NSti SPer SSvw WFar WMoo
elwesii	EBee NBre
episcopale	WCru WFar
aff. ***episcopale***	LPio WSHC
-CLD 1426	GBuc WFar
ferox	EBee ELon EWes GBin MLLN
- HWJK 2217	WCru
fischeri misapplied	see *A. carmichaelii*
§ ***fischeri*** Rchb.	CSpe CWib NMoo
fukutomei	NBre
- B&SWJ 337	GBin WCru
- var. ***formosanum***	LEdu
- - B&SWJ 3057	WCru
fukutomei x ***japonicum*** subsp. ***subcuneatum*** **new**	EBee
gammiei GWJ 9418	WCru
grossedentatum **new**	GBin
helmsleyanum **new**	CWGN
§ ***hemsleyanum***	CBgR CPrp CRHN EBee EPfP GCra GKev MDun MHar MWgw NBid NCGa NChi NGHP SGar SMad WBrE WCot WCru WFar WHoo
- dark blue	CMea
hyemale	see *Eranthis hyemalis*
incisofidum **new**	EBee
'Ivorine'	More than 30 suppliers
jaluense B&SWJ 8741	WCru
japonicum	GAbr WFar
* - var. ***hakonense*** **new**	EBee
- subsp. ***subcuneatum*** B&SWJ 6228	WCru
krylovii **new**	WCot
laciniatum GWJ 9254 **new**	WCru
lamarckii	see *A. lycoctonum* subsp. *neapolitanum*
longecassidatum B&SWJ 4277	WCru
- B&SWJ 8486	WCru
lycoctonum	MGol NLar SRms WBVN WCAu WCot
- 'Dark Eyes'	CAbP CFir EBee EGle LSou MBNS NCob NDov SPoG WCot WGwG
- 'Graupe' **new**	WCot
- 'Langhuso' **new**	WCot
§ - subsp. ***lycoctonum***	MSal SRms
- subsp. ***moldavicum***	EBee
§ - subsp. ***neapolitanum***	CBod EBee ECtt EGle ELan EMan EMar EPfP GMaP GSki MLLN NGHP NGdn NLar SWat WBor WFar WHil WSpi
- 'Russian Yellow' **new**	GBin
§ - subsp. ***vulparia***	CArn CPrp CSam EBee ECha EDAr EMar GKev GMac GPoy LPio MNFA MRav MSal NDov SWal WAul WCot WEas WPer WSel
nagarum BWJ 7644 **new**	WCru
napellus	CArn CDWL CMHG CSpe EBee ECtt ELau EMar GAbr GGar GPoy GSki LAst LCro LEdu MWat NGHP SPoG SRms SWat WBVN WBor WHoo WMoo WSel WShi
- 'Albiflorus'	see *A. napellus* subsp. *vulgare* 'Albidum'
- 'Bergfürst'	CAby EGle MBri NDov SMHy SPhx
- 'Blue Valley'	EBee EGle EPfP EQua EWes NPro WFar

	- 'Carneum'	see *A. napellus* subsp. *vulgare* 'Carneum'
	- 'Gletschereis'	GBin
§	- subsp. ***napellus*** Anglicum Group	CSev CWan EBee GBuc MGol MSal MSte NEgg NLar NSti SMac WCot WPen
	- 'Rubellum'	CDWL EBee EGle ELan ENot EPfP ERou GGar LAst NBPC NBir NBro NOrc NPri SPoG WBor WMnd WMoo WPnP WSpi
	- 'Schneewittchen'	EBee SSvw
	- 'Sphere's Variety'	NOrc
§	- subsp. ***vulgare*** 'Albidum'	More than 30 suppliers
§	- - 'Carneum'	EGle EMan GCra MLLN NChi WHer WKif WLin WSel
	napiforme	EBee SAga WPGP WPnP
	- B&SWJ 943	SMeo WCru
	neapolitanum	see *A. lycoctonum* subsp. *neapolitanum*
	'Newry Blue'	CMea CSam ELan EMon ERou GBuc NBHF NBir NEgg NHol NLar SRms WFar WPer
	orientale misapplied	see *A. lycoctonum* subsp. *vulparia*
	orientale ambig.	NPro
	paniculatum	MBri NBre WCot
	- 'Roseum'	MBNS WFar
	piepunense new	GKev
	'Pink Sensation'[PBR]	CFir ECtt EPfP GQue IPot LPio NLar
	proliferum B&SWJ 4107	WCru
	pseudohuiliense new	EBee
	pseudolaeve	SPhx
	- B&SWJ 8663	WCru
	pyrenaicum	see *A. lycoctonum* subsp. *neapolitanum*
	ranunculifolium	see *A. lycoctonum* subsp. *neapolitanum*
	sczukinii	EMon
	seoulense B&SWJ 694	WCru
	- B&SWJ 864	WCru
	septentrionale	see *A. lycoctonum* subsp. *lycoctonum*
	'Spark's Variety' ♀H4	More than 30 suppliers
	spicatum GWJ 9418	WCru
	'Stainless Steel'	More than 30 suppliers
	subcuneatum new	EBee
	x ***tubergenii***	see *Eranthis hyemalis* Tubergenii Group
	uchiyamai	NLar
	- B&SWJ 1005	WCru
	- B&SWJ 1216	ELon WCru
	- B&SWJ 4446	WCru
	variegatum (v)	NGdn
	volubile misapplied	see *A. hemsleyanum*
	volubile Pall.	NTHB
	vulparia	see *A. lycoctonum* subsp. *vulparia*
	'Wu To Di'	EBee GKev
	yamazakii	WCru

Aconogonon see *Persicaria*

Acorus ✿ (*Acoraceae*)

	calamus	CArn CBen CDWL CWat EHon ELau EMFW GPoy LCro MCCP MGol MSal NBlu NPer SPer SWat WHer
	- 'Argenteostriatus' (v)	CBen CWat EBee ECha ECtt EHon EMFW EPfP NBlu NOrc SWat WMAq
*	***christophii***	EBee ELon EPPr EWes SApp WMoo
	gramineus	ELau MLan MNHC NPer SWat WHer WMoo WTin
	- 'Golden Delight'	CKno
	- 'Golden Edge' (v)	EPPr WMoo
	- 'Hakuro-nishiki' (v)	CEnd CStu EBee ECtt EHul ENot EOrn EPPr EPot GBuc GKev LCro MBar MCCP MGos MMoz MWgw NBid NHol SAga SHBN SPoG SRms SRot SWvt WMoo
	- 'Licorice'	EBee EPPr EWin MDKP MSal NHol WLeb WMoo WPnP
	- 'Masamune' (v)	EBee EPla GBin LLWG NHol SApp WMoo WTin
	- 'Minimus Aureus'	CBgR CBre
	- 'Oborozuki' misapplied	see *A. gramineus* 'Ogon'
	- 'Oborozuki' (v)	CKno CStu EBee EPla WPrP
§	- 'Ogon' (v)	More than 30 suppliers
	- var. ***pusillus***	EBee EPla NBro
	- 'Variegatus' (v)	More than 30 suppliers
	- 'Yodo-no-yuki' (v)	EBee EPla
	'Intermedius'	NPer

Acradenia (*Rutaceae*)

	frankliniae	CBcs CCCN CMHG CPle CPne CTrC CTrG GGar IArd IDee LRHS SEND SSpi WFar WPGP WSHC

Actaea (*Ranunculaceae*)

	alba misapplied	see *A. pachypoda*, *A. rubra* f. *neglecta*
	arizonica	CLAP EBee WCru
	asiatica	CDes CLAP EBee WPGP
	- B&SWJ 616	WCru
	- B&SWJ 6351 from Japan new	WCru
	- B&SWJ 8694 from Korea new	WCru
	- BWJ 8174 from China	WCru
	biternata	CLAP MSte
	- B&SWJ 5591	WCru
§	***cimicifuga***	CDes CLAP EBee GPoy MSte
	- B&SWJ 2657	WCru
§	***cordifolia***	EBee EMan GBin GMaP LBMP MLLN MSal WCru
	- 'Blickfang'	CLAP
	dahurica	EBee MGol MSal NLar SBla SWat
	- B&SWJ 8426	WCru
	- B&SWJ 8573	WCru
	- B&SWJ 8653	GEdr
	elata	EBee
	erythrocarpa	see *A. rubra*
	europaea	EBee SPhx WCru
	frigida B&SWJ 2966	WCru
	heracleifolia	GSki
	- B&SWJ 8843	WCru
§	***japonica***	CLAP CMea EBee LEdu NCGa WCot WFar
	- B&SWJ 5828	WCru
	- var. ***acutiloba***	EBee
	- - B&SWJ 6257	WCru
	- compact	GBin
	- - B&SWJ 8758A	WCru
	mairei	WCru
	- BWJ 7635	WCru
	- BWJ 7939	WCru
§	***matsumurae*** 'Elstead Variety' ♀H4	GBin MBri MRav NBre
	- 'Frau Herms'	CLAP
	- 'White Pearl'	More than 30 suppliers
§	***pachypoda*** ♀H4	COld CPom EBee ECGP ECha ELan GBuc GPoy IGor ITer MSal MSte NBid NCGa NLar NMen WBVN WCru
	- f. ***rubrocarpa***	EBee ELan
§	***podocarpa***	MSal SPlb SRms
§	***racemosa*** ♀H4	CArn COld CSam EBee ELan EPfP ERou GPoy LEdu LFur MHer MLLN MSal NBid NGdn NSti SPer WCAu WCot WFar WMnd

§ ***rubra*** ♀H4	CHid CMHG EBee ECha ELan GAbr GBuc GGar GKev MRav MSte NBid SMad WCru WEas WFar WPGP
- B&SWJ 9555	WCru
- ***alba***	see *A. pachypoda*, *A. rubra* f. *neglecta*
§ - f. ***neglecta***	CDes EBee GBuc GEdr GGar NLar SMad WCru
simplex	CSam EBee ECha EWTr GCra GSki LRHS NPri SWat
- B&SWJ 8664	WCru
§ - Atropurpurea Group	More than 30 suppliers
- - 'Bernard Mitchell'	CFir
- - 'Black Negligee'	NBhm
- - 'Brunette' ♀H4	More than 30 suppliers
- - 'Hillside Black Beauty'	CBgR CLAP CSpe EBee ECtt EGle ELan ERou GMaP IBal IPot LHop MEHN MLLN MNrw NBPC NBir NCGa NCob NDov SMad SPoG WCAu WCot
- - 'James Compton'	More than 30 suppliers
- 'Mountain Wave'	CLAP EBee WFar
- 'Pink Spike'	More than 30 suppliers
§ - 'Prichard's Giant'	CLAP ECha GBin GBuc MBri MRav MSte NEgg SPhx WFar
- ***ramosa***	see *A. simplex* 'Prichard's Giant'
- 'Scimitar'	SMeo
- 'Silver Axe'	NBre
spicata	COld EBee GBin GBuc GCra GEdr GPoy ITer MSal MSte NLar WCru
- from England	WCru
- var. ***rubra***	see *A. rubra*
taiwanensis	CLAP
- B&SWJ 343	CLAP
- B&SWJ 3413	WCru
- RWJ 9996	WCru
yesoensis	CFir
- B&SWJ 6355	WCru
yunnanensis ACE 1880	GBuc

Actinella see *Tetraneuris*

Actinidia (*Actinidiaceae*)

BWJ 8161 from China	WCru
arguta (f/F)	CAgr EMui NLar WPGP
- (m)	EMui SHBN
- B&SWJ 569	WCru
- 'Issai' (s-p/F)	CBcs CCCN EPfP ERea LBuc MGos NLar
- 'Kiwai Vert' (f/F)	CAgr
- LL #1 (m)	CAgr
- LL#2 (f/F)	CAgr
- LL#3 (m)	CAgr
- 'Weiki'	MGos
callosa var. ***ephippioidea*** B&SWJ 1790	WCru
- var. ***formosana*** B&SWJ 3806	WCru
chinensis misapplied	see *A. deliciosa*
§ ***deliciosa***	CPLG ERom MGos SLon WBVN WSHC
- (f/F)	MRav SHBN
- (m)	LCro
- 'Atlas' (m)	CAgr ECrN MPRe NLar
* - 'Boskoop'	MWat
- 'Hayward' (f/F)	CAgr CBcs CDoC CHEx EBee ECrN ELan EMil EMui EPfP ERea LCro LRHS MPRe NLar NPal SDea SHBN SPer SWvt WCru WFar
- 'Jenny' (s-p/F)	CAgr CSut CTri ECrN EMui LAst LBuc LRHS MAsh MBri MCoo MGos MLan SDea SKee SLim SLon SPoG
- 'Solo'	CDoC MPRe
- 'Tomuri' (m)	CBcs CDoC CHEx EBee ELan EMil EMui EPfP ERea LCro LRHS NLar NPal SHBN SPer SWvt WCru
hypoleuca B&SWJ 5942	WCru
kolomikta ♀H4	More than 30 suppliers
- (m)	CAgr MBlu NScw
- B&SWJ 4243	WCru
- 'Tomoko' (F)	WCru
- 'Yazuaki' (m)	WCru
latifolia B&SWJ 3563	WCru
petelotii HWJ 628	WCru
pilosula	CBcs CPLG CSPN CWGN EBee EPfP EWld ISea LEdu LHop MAsh MBri MGos SCoo SLon WCru WPGP WPat WSHC
polygama (F)	EWld IArd IDee
- B&SWJ 5444	WCru
- B&SWJ 8525 from Korea	WCru
- B&SWJ 8923 from Japan	WCru
purpurea (f/F)	CAgr
rubricaulis B&SWJ 3111	WCru
rufa B&SWJ 3525	WCru
aff. ***strigosa*** HWJK 2367	WCru
tetramera B&SWJ 3564	WCru

Actinotus (*Apiaceae*)

helianthi	EMan

Adansonia (*Bombacaceae*)

gregorii	SPlb

Adelocaryum see *Lindelofia*

Adenia (*Passifloraceae*)

glauca	LToo
spinosa	LToo

Adenium (*Apocynaceae*)

obesum ♀H1	LToo
- subsp. ***boehmianum***	LToo

Adenocarpus (*Papilionaceae*)

decorticans	SPlb

Adenophora (*Campanulaceae*)

BWJ 7696 from China	WCru
'Afterglow'	see *Campanula rapunculoides* 'Afterglow'
asiatica	see *Hanabusaya asiatica*
aurita	CFir CMdw CMea MLLN NCGa NChi WPrP
axilliflora	NSfd
bulleyana	CDMG CHar EBee EGle ELan EMan EWTr GBuc LRHS MWgw NBid NChi NRnb NSfd SDnm SPav SPet SPlb WCot WFar WPer WTMC
* ***campanulata***	WPer
coelestis	EBee EMan NBre NRnb NSfd SPhx
- ACE 2455	GBuc
- B&SWJ 7998	WCru
confusa	CPLG EMan LBBr LDai LHop MDKP MWea NBre NSfd SAga SPav WFar WHer WSHC
* ***cymerae***	LDai NRnb NSfd
divaricata	EMan WFoF
forrestii	NBre NEgg WFar
grandiflora B&SWJ 8555	WCru
himalayana	GBri WPer
jasionifolia new	EBee
- BWJ 7946	WCru
khasiana	CFir GMac LDai LTwo MDKP NLar NRnb NSfd WPrP WPtf
koreana	EBee NBre NSfd SPav
kurilensis	WTMC
lamarkii B&SWJ 8738 new	WCru

latifolia misapplied	see *A. pereskiifolia*
latifolia Fischer	CWan NBir WFar
liliifolia	CWoW ECtt ELan EMan MNFA NBPC NCGa NPer NRnb NSfd NSti SMad SPav SPet WFar WHal WTin
morrisonensis RWJ 10008	WCru
§ ***nikoensis***	GKev NBid NRnb NSfd
§ – var. ***stenophylla***	NBre WCot
nipponica	see *A. nikoensis* var. *stenophylla*
§ ***pereskiifolia***	CWan EWes NBre NEgg NSfd SEND SHar SPlb WCot WFar WPer
polyantha	CHar EBee EHrv GAbr GBuc MWea NLar NSfd SBod SRms WFar
polymorpha	see *A. nikoensis*
potaninii	CFir EBee EHrv ELan EMan GBuc NCGa NEgg NRnb NSfd NSti SGar SPav SPoG WFar WHal WPtf
– pale-flowered	EHrv WHal
remotiflora B&SWJ 8562	WCru
stricta subsp. ***sessilifolia***	GBuc NBre NEgg SPla
sublata	NRnb NSfd WFar
takedae	NRnb
– var. ***howozana***	LBBr LHop MLHP NRnb WPrP
taquetii	EBee NEgg
– B&SWJ 1303	WCru
tashiroi	CMHG CPrp ECtt EPfP GBuc NLar NPro NRnb NSfd
triphylla	EBee NBir SPav WFar
– RBS 0204	CStu
– var. ***hakusanensis***	EBee NBre
– var. ***japonica***	LDai NRnb
– – B&SWJ 8835	WCru
uehatae B&SWJ 126	WCru

Adenostyles see *Cacalia*

alpina	see *Cacalia hastata*

Adiantum ✿ (*Adiantaceae*)

§ ***aleuticum*** 🏆H4	CBcs CLAP EFer ELan EMon MAvo NBid NBro NHol WAbe WFib WPGP WRic WTMC
– 'Imbricatum'	CBcs CLAP ECha MGos MPes NHol NLar NMyG SPla SRms WFar WFib WRic
§ – 'Japonicum'	CLAP CMil ELan MAvo NBir NHol SBla SRms WFar WHal WPGP
– 'Laciniatum'	SRms
– 'Miss Sharples'	CDTJ CLAP CMil ELan LRHS MAsh MGos MPes MWgw NEgg NLar SPoG SRms WFar WRic
§ – 'Subpumilum' 🏆H4	CLAP CWsd MRav SRms WAbe WFib WRic
capillus-veneris	CHEx MMHG SChr WCot WFib WRic
cuneatum	see *A. raddianum*
fulvum new	WRic
hispidulum	CCCN LRHS SRms WRic
– 'Bronze Venus'	CCCN
pedatum misapplied	see *A. aleuticum*
pedatum ambig.	CWsd
pedatum L. 🏆H4	CBcs CHEx CLAP ECha EFer ELan EPfP GEdr GMaP MAsh MAvo MBri MMoz NHol NMoo NVic SApp SDix SPer SSpi SWat WFar WPGP WTMC
– Asiatic form	see *A. aleuticum* 'Japonicum'
– 'Japonicum'	see *A. aleuticum* 'Japonicum'
– 'Roseum'	see *A. aleuticum* 'Japonicum'
– var. ***subpumilum***	see *A. aleuticum* 'Subpumilum'
pubescens	MBri WRic
§ ***raddianum*** 🏆H2	CHal
– 'Fragrans'	see *A. raddianum* 'Fragrantissimum'
§ – 'Fragrantissimum'	MBri
– 'Fritz Lüthi' 🏆H2	CHal MBri
– 'Micropinnulum'	WRic
– 'Monocolor'	MBri
venustum 🏆H4	CGHE CHEx CLAP CWsd EFer EGle EMon EPot LBBr MAsh MAvo NVic SDix SHFr SRms SSpi SWat WCot WEas WFar WFib WHal WIvy WPGP WRic

Adina (*Rubiaceae*)

rubella	NLar

Adlumia (*Papaveraceae*)

fungosa	CSpe

Adonis (*Ranunculaceae*)

amurensis misapplied	see *A.* 'Fukujukai', *A. multiflora*
amurensis ambig.	CMea EPot LAma LTwo SCnR WCot WLin
– 'Pleniflora'	see *A. multiflora* 'Sandanzaki'
brevistyla	CPom EBee GBuc
'Fukujukai'	ECha GEdr MBri WFar WWst
§ ***multiflora***	EBee
§ – 'Sandanzaki' (d)	EPot EWes NLar SBod WCot WFar
sutchuenensis	EBee
vernalis	EBee GEdr GPoy NLar NSla SBla WBVN

Adoxa (*Adoxaceae*)

moschatellina	CRWN NMen WHer WPnP WSFF WShi

Adromischus (*Crassulaceae*)

cooperi	EPem WCot WEas
cristatus	EPem
subdistichus	EPem

Aechmea (*Bromeliaceae*)

sp.	XBlo
caudata var. ***variegata*** new	CHEx
distichantha var. ***schlumbergeri***	CFir
fasciata 🏆H1	LRHS MBri XBlo
ramosa	XBlo
victoriana	XBlo

Aegle (*Rutaceae*)

sepiaria	see *Poncirus trifoliata*

Aegopodium (*Apiaceae*)

podagraria 'Bengt'	EMon
– 'Dangerous' (v)	CHid CNat
– gold-margined (v)	EMon EPPr
– 'Variegatum' (v)	CDoC EBee ECha ECrN EDAr EHrv EMar EMon EPPr EPla GMaP LHop LRHS MBar MBri MRav MWgw NBid NPri NSti NVic SMac SPer SPoG WCAu WCFE WCot WCra WHil WMoo

Aeonium (*Crassulaceae*)

arboreum 🏆H1	CAbb CDTJ CHEx EPem EShb LPio MWya NPal WRos
– 'Albovariegatum' (v) new	LPio
– 'Atropurpureum' 🏆H1	CHEx CSpe EAmu EPem EPfP ERea EShb MBri MLan NPer SEND SWal WCot
– green-leaved	SEND
I – 'Magnificum'	EBee EPfP EShb EWin EWll SAPC SArc
– 'Variegatum' (v)	EShb NPer
balsamiferum	CAbb CCCN CHEx CSpe CTrC EBee EPfP EWin SAPC SArc SChr WCot
'Black Cap'	CCCN

	'Blush'	EBee EWin MAvo
	'Blushing Beauty'	LRHS
	canariense	CBrP CCCN CHEx LPio
	- var. ***palmense***	EBee EWin
§	- var. ***subplanum***	CTrC
	castello-paivae	EBee EShb EWin
	'Cristata Sunburst' new	WCot
	cuneatum	MLan SChr SEND SPet
	decorum	SEND
*	- 'Variegatum' (v)	CBow LPio WCot
	'Dinner Plate'	CHEx
	'Dinner Plate' x ***haworthii***	CHEx
	x ***domesticum***	see *Aichryson* x *domesticum*
	goochiae	CBow EBee EWin
	haworthii ♀H1	CAbb CArn CBrP CHEx CHal LPio SBHP SEND
	- 'Variegatum' (v)	EBee EShb EWin LPio SChr
	lindleyi	SChr
	- var. ***viscatum***	EBee EWin
*	***multiflora***	EWin
*	- 'Variegata' (v)	EBee EWin
	nobile	CBrP
	percarneum	EShb
	simsii	CHal EBee EWin
	- variegated (v)	EPem EShb
	subplanum	see *A. canariense* var. *subplanum*
	tabuliforme ♀H1	CAbb CCCN CSpe EPem EShb
	- 'Cristatum'	EPem
	urbicum	CHEx
	'Zwartkop' ♀H1	More than 30 suppliers

Aeschynanthus (*Gesneriaceae*)

	'Big Apple'	CHal LRHS WDib
	Black Pagoda Group	LRHS WDib
	'Fire Wheel'	LRHS WDib
	hildebrandii	WDib
	'Holiday Bells'	WDib
	'Hot Flash'	CSpe LRHS WDib
	'Little Tiger'	LRHS
	longicalyx	LRHS WDib
§	***longicaulis*** ♀H1	LRHS WDib
	marmoratus	see *A. longicaulis*
	'Mona'	MBri
	radicans ♀H1	LRHS MBri WDib
	'Scooby Doo'	WDib
	speciosus ♀H1	CHal EShb LRHS WDib

Aesculus ✿ (*Hippocastanaceae*)

	arguta	see *A. glabra* var. *arguta*
	x ***arnoldiana***	CDul CMCN
	- 'Autumn Splendor'	EPfP
§	x ***bushii***	CMCN CTho MGos NLar
	californica	CBcs CMCN EBee EPfP ERod SSpi WPGP
	- 'Blue Haze'	SSpi
	x ***carnea***	CDul CTri ELan MBar SBLw
	- 'Aureomarginata' (v)	CTho ERod LTwo SMad WPat
	- 'Briotii' ♀H4	More than 30 suppliers
	- 'Marginata' (v)	MBlu
	- 'Plantierensis'	CDul ECrN MBlu SBLw
*	- 'Variegata' (v)	CBcs CDul CMCN MGos
	chinensis	CMCN
	'Dallimorei' (graft-chimaera)	CTho SMad WPat
	flava ♀H4	CCVT CMCN CTho EBee ECrN EPfP ISea LPan NWea SBLw SHBN SLim SSpi WFar WPGP
	- f. ***vestita***	CDoC CDul MBlu
	georgiana	see *A. sylvatica*
	glabra	CDul CMCN CTho EGFP
§	- var. ***arguta***	CMCN
	- 'Autumn Blaze'	EPfP MBri SMad
	- 'October Red'	EPfP MBlu MBri WPGP
	glaucescens	see *A.* x *neglecta*
	hippocastanum ♀H4	More than 30 suppliers
§	- 'Baumannii' (d) ♀H4	CDoC CDul CLnd EBee ECrN EPfP ERod LPan MGos MSwo NWea SBLw SHBN SPer WFar
	- 'Digitata'	CDul CMCN SBLw
	- 'Flore Pleno'	see *A. hippocastanum* 'Baumannii'
	- 'Hampton Court Gold'	CBcs CDoC CDul CMCN NBhm
	- 'Honiton Gold'	CTho
	- 'Laciniata'	CBcs CDul CMCN ERod IArd MBlu NLar SMad
	- 'Monstrosa'	MBri SMad
	- 'Pyramidalis'	CDul SBLw
	- 'Wisselink'	CDul CLnd CMCN ECrN MBlu
	indica	CDul CHEx CLnd CMCN CTho EBee ECrN ELan EMil EPfP GGGa IArd ISea SHBN SSpi WPGP
	- 'Sydney Pearce' ♀H4	CDoC CDul CEnd CMCN ERod MBlu MBri MGos NLar SMad SSpi WPGP
	x ***marylandica***	CDul
	x ***mississippiensis***	see *A.* x *bushii*
	x ***mutabilis*** 'Harbisonii'	NLar
	- 'Induta'	CLnd CMCN EBee EPfP IArd MBlu MBri NLar NSti SDix SMad SSpi WFar
§	- 'Penduliflora'	CDul CEnd CTho EPfP MBlu
§	x ***neglecta***	CLnd CMCN
	- 'Autumn Fire'	MBlu MBri
	- 'Erythroblastos' ♀H4	CBcs CDoC CDul CEnd CLnd CMCN EBee EPfP ERod MAsh MBlu MBri NLar SCoo SHBN SLim SMad SSpi SSta WPGP WPat
	parviflora ♀H4	CBcs CDul CLnd CMCN CTri EBee ECrN ELan EPfP EWTr IDee LPan LRHS MBar MBlu MBri MGos MLan MRav NBea NBlu NEgg SLPl SLim SMad SPer SSpi WFar WOrn WPGP
§	***pavia*** ♀H4	CBcs CDul CLnd CMCN CTho EPfP MBri SSpi WCru
	- 'Atrosanguinea'	CDul CEnd CLnd CMCN EBee EPfP ERod IDee MBlu NPal SMad
	- var. ***discolor***	SBLw
	- - 'Koehnei'	CDul CMCN MBlu NLar
	- 'Penduliflora'	see *A.* x *mutabilis* 'Penduliflora'
	- 'Purple Spring'	MBlu MBri
	- 'Rosea Nana'	CMCN WPat
	splendens	see *A. pavia*
§	***sylvatica***	CMCN CTho MBri
	turbinata	CBcs CDul CLnd CMCN ISea SSpi
	- var. ***pubescens***	WPGP
	wilsonii	CDul CTho WPGP

Aethionema (*Brassicaceae*)

I	***antitaurii*** new	EDAr
	armenum	GKev
	coridifolium	WPer
§	***grandiflorum*** ♀H4	GEdr GKev NBro SRms WFar WPer WRHF
	- Pulchellum Group ♀H4	CSpe GKev
	iberideum	MDKP SRms
*	***kotschyi*** hort.	ECho EDAr NMen SBla WAbe
	membranaceum	ECho EDAr NHol WFar
	oppositifolium	CLyd WHoo
	pulchellum	see *A. grandiflorum*
	schistosum	LTwo WAbe
	spicatum	WFar
	'Warley Rose' ♀H4	CLyd EAlp ECho ELan EPot GMaP LHop LRHS NLAp NMen SIng SRms WFar WPat
	'Warley Ruber'	CPBP NBir NMen SBla WAbe WFar

Aextoxicon (*Aextoxicaceae*)

	punctatum	CMCN

Afrocarpus (*Podocarpaceae*)

	falcatus	CTrC ECou GGar

Agalinis (*Scrophulariaceae*)

	linariodes	EMan

Agapanthus ✿ (*Alliaceae*)

	'Aberdeen'	CPne XPde
	'Adonis'	CPrp IBal IBlr
	'African Moon'	CPne
§	***africanus*** 🏆H1	CAbb CElw COlW CWib EBee ECho EHrv EPfP GSki LCro LEdu LPan LRHS MNHC NBlu SAPC SArc SBod SPav SPer SSwd SWat WBor WBrE WFar WPer XPep
	- 'Albus' 🏆H1	CBcs CDoC CTca EBee EBrs ECho EMan EPfP GSki IFoB LCro LRHS NBlu SBod SEND SMeo SPav SPer WGwG WPer XPep
	'Albatross'	CPne ECha
	'Albus' ambig.	CAvo CPLG GMaP LPan MGos MHer MWat SAga SHom
I	'Albus Nanus'	ECho LPan
	'Amsterdam'	CPen NHoy XPde
	'Angela'	CPne XPde
	'Anthea'	CPne XPde
	'Aphrodite'	IBlr
	'Apple Court'	XPde
	'Aquamarine'	CAvo CFFs SBch
	'Arctic Star'	CPLG CPne GSki XPde
	Ardernei hybrid	CAvo CDes CPne CPrp EBee ECha ECtt EWTr EWes GMac GQue IBal IBlr LFur LPio LSou MBNS MBnl MBri MSte NEgg SAga SRos STes WBor WCFE WCot WGwG WPGP XPde
§	'Argenteus Vittatus' (v) 🏆H1	CDes CPen CPrp ELan EPfP MBNS NHoy NOrc WSPU
	'Atlas'	IBlr
	'Aureovittatus' (v) **new**	NHoy
	'Baby Blue'	see *A.* 'Blue Baby'
	'Back in Black'	CHFP CPne CSpe EBee EPfP ERou EWes IBal IPot LPio MBNS NBPC NBPN NChi NCob NLar NOrc SHBN SPoG
	'Ballyrogan'	IBlr
	'Balmoral' **new**	CPne
	'Bangor Blue'	IBal IBlr
	'Basutoland'	LRHS
	'Beatrice'	CPne XPde
	'Beeches Dwarf'	CPne EBee ELan NHoy
	'Ben Hope'	GBuc IBal IBlr NHoy SDnm SPav WCot XPde
	'Beth Chatto'	see *A. campanulatus* 'Albovittatus'
	'Bethlehem Star'	CBgR CPne GSki SRos
	'Bianco'	XPde
	'Bicton Bell'	CPne IBlr
	'Big Blue'	EBee
	'Black Pantha'	More than 30 suppliers
§	'Blue Baby'	CAbb CCCN CLyd CPen CPrp CRez EBee ELan ELon IBal IBlr LCro LRHS NHoy SMrm WFar WThu XPde
	'Blue Bird'	CPne XPde
	'Blue Boy'	XPde
	'Blue Brush'	CPne CSBt EBee EMil ENor NHoy SCoo SEND SPoG
	'Blue Cascade'	IBlr
	'Blue Companion'	CPne CPrp IBlr NHoy
	'Blue Diamond' ambig.	EHrv NHoy SRos
	'Blue Dot'	EBee
	'Blue Formality'	IBal IBlr
	'Blue Giant'	CBcs CCVN CPen CPrp EBee ELan EPfP ERea IBlr LCro LRHS MBri MNFA MPop MSte NEgg NGby NHoy SAga SWat WCFE WFar WPGP WSpi
	'Blue Globe'	CMMP ERou GMaP STes WCAu WHil WTMC
	'Blue Gown'	CPne CSam
	'Blue Haze'	SRos XPde
	'Blue Heaven' PBR	CPne EBee EWTr
	'Blue Ice' **new**	CPne
	'Blue Imp'	CPne GBuc GSki IBlr LRHS NHol SApp
	'Blue Lakes' **new**	XPde
	'Blue Méoni'	XPde
	'Blue Moon'	CPen EBee ECha IBal IBlr LBBr LRHS NHoy WCot
	'Blue Nile'	CPne XPde
	'Blue Prince'	CPen CPrp EBee LBuc MBNS NHoy
	'Blue Ribbon'	CPne XPde
I	'Blue Skies' Dunlop	IBlr
	'Blue Skies' ambig.	CBcs GSki NCGa NHoy SWat XPde
	'Blue Skies' from New Zealand	WTMC
	'Blue Spear' **new**	CPen
	'Blue Triumphator'	CPne CTca EBee EBrs EPfP EWTr EWll GMaP IBlr LRHS MPop NGby NHoy NScw SBod SMeo SMrm XPde
	'Blue Umbrella' **new**	EBee NHoy
	'Blue Velvet'	CPne XPde
	'Bressingham Blue'	CPne CPrp CTri EBee EBrs ECho EWes IBal IBlr IFoB LRHS MRav MSte NHoy NVic SWat WGer XPde
	'Bressingham Bounty'	EBrs
	'Bressingham White'	CPne EBee ECtt EHrv EMan LEdu LRHS MRav NCGa NHoy SWat XPde
	'Bristol'	XPde
	'Buckingham Palace'	CDes CPne CPrp EBee ECho GAbr IBal IBlr NHoy WCot WPGP XPde
	'Cally Blue'	GAbr
	'Cambridge'	CPne XPde
	campanulatus	CPLG CPrp CWCL EBee ECho ELan EPfP GGar GSki IBal IBlr IGor ITim LPio LRHS MRav NCob NHoy SWat WAbe WCot WFar WPGP XPep
	- var. ***albidus***	CDes CPne CWCL EBee ECha ECho ELan ENot EPfP GKev IBlr LHop LPio LRHS MNFA MRav MSte MWgw NGdn NHol NHoy NSti NVic SPer WFar WHoo WPGP XPde
§	- 'Albovittatus'	CSam ECho EWTr LPio NHoy
	- 'Albus Nanus'	see *A.* 'Albus Nanus'
	- 'Beth Chatto' (v)	CPrp IBal
	- bright blue	CWCL
	- 'Buckland'	IBlr
	- 'Cobalt Blue'	ECha LCro NHoy
	- 'Isis'	CFir CPne CPrp CSam CTri CWCL EBee EBla EBrs ECha GBuc GSki IBal IBlr LRHS NCGa SRos
	- 'Oxford Blue'	CPen CPrp GBri GBuc IBal IBlr LRHS NHoy SRos WPGP XPde
	- subsp. ***patens*** 🏆H3	CPrp EBla EMan EPfP GBin GBri GBuc IBal LPio SWat WPGP
	- - deep blue-flowered	CFir CPrp IBlr LRHS
	- 'Profusion'	CWCL EBee EBrs ECha IBal IBlr LRHS NHoy SRos WFar XPde
	- 'Slieve Donard Variety'	see *A.* 'Slieve Donard'
	- variegated (v)	EBee EBla ECha NPer
	- 'Wedgwood Blue'	CPrp EBrs IBal IBlr SRos XPde
	- 'Wendy'	CPne CPrp IBal IBlr XPde
	- 'White Hope'	IBal IBlr SRos
	'Carefree'	CPrp
	'Castle of Mey'	CPne CPrp EBee GAbr GBuc IBlr LFur LPio MTho NHoy SPav SRos WPGP XPde

	'Catharina'	CPne XPde
§	***caulescens*** ♀H1	EBee EBrs GBuc IBlr IGor WBrE WPGP XPde
	- subsp. ***angustifolius***	CPne EBee IBlr WCot XPep
	- subsp. ***caulescens***	CPne IBlr SWat
	'Cedric Morris'	IBlr LPio NHoy SRos XPde
	'Chandra'	IBlr
	'Charlotte'	XPde
	'Cherry Holley'	CPne SRos
	'Clarence House'	CPne CPrp XPde
	coddii	CPLG CPne EWes IBlr WCot WHil XPde
	'Columba'	CPen CPne CPrp CTca LAma LDai NHoy XPde
	comptonii	see *A. praecox* subsp. *minimus*
	'Cool Blue' **new**	CPne
	'Cornish Sky' **new**	CPne
	'Crystal Drop'	CPne SWat
	'Dainty Lady' **new**	NHoy
	Danube	see *A.* 'Donau'
	'Dark Star'	EBee WFar
	'Dartmoor'	CPne
	'Davos' **new**	CPne
	'Dawn Star'	XPde
	'Debbie'	XPde
	'Delft'	CPrp IBal IBlr
	'Density'	IBlr
	'Devon Dawn'	CPne
	'Diana' **new**	XPde
	'Dnjepr'	GSki XPde
	'Dokter Brouwer'	CPen EBee GSki MDKP NHoy SKHP WGwG XPde
§	'Donau'	CDoC CPen CPne EBee EBrs NBir NHoy SMrm SWat WFar XPde
	'Dorothy Kate'	CPne
	'Double Diamond' **new**	CPen
	'Dublin' **new**	CPne
	'Duivenbrugge Blue' **new**	CPne XPde
	'Duivenbrugge White'	XPde
	dyeri	see *A. inapertus* subsp. *intermedius*
	'Ed Carman' (v)	WCot
	'Elisabeth'	CPne
	'Enigma' **new**	CPne LRHS NHoy
	'Ethel's Joy'	CPen
	'Eve'	EBee IBlr XPde
	'Evening Star'	CPne ECha GSki LRHS XPde
	'Exmoor'	CPne
	'Far Horizon'	CPne
	'Fast Track' **new**	WCot
	'Findlay's Blue'	GBuc WPGP
	'Flanders Giant' **new**	XPde
	'Gayle's Lilac'	CBcs CElw CPne CPrp CSam CWGN EBee ECtt EGle ELan EMil GSki IBal LPio LRHS MAvo MLLN MRav NBPC NCGa NCob NHoy NSti SApp SDnm SPav SPoG WBrk WCot WGer
	'Gem'	CPne
	'Getty White'	GBin
I	'Giganteus Albus' **new**	XPde
	'Glacier Stream'	CCVN CPen EBee EHrv GSki NHoy WSpi
	'Glen Avon'	CAbb CFir CPne CPrp EBee EMil IBal LCro NBPC NHoy NLar SApp SCoo WSpi XPde
	'Golden Rule' (v)	CBow CDes CFir CPne CPrp EBee GBuc IBal IBlr MAvo WPGP XPde
	'Goldfinger' (v) **new**	CPne
	'Harvest Blue'	CPne
§	Headbourne hybrids	More than 30 suppliers
	'Heavenly Blue'	CPne
	'Helen'	IBlr
	'Holbeach'	CPen CPne XPde
	'Holbrook'	CSam
	'Hydon Mist'	XPde
	'Ice Blue Star'	CPne SRos
	'Ice Lolly'	CPen EBee
	inapertus	CPLG CPrp EWes GSki IGor LPio MHer SMHy SMad SWat WCot WLin WPGP XPep
	- dwarf	IBlr
	- subsp. ***hollandii***	CAvo CPne CPom IBlr MSte NHoy SBla SKHP SWat WCot
	- - 'Zealot'	IBlr
	- subsp. ***inapertus***	ERea IBlr SWat WCot
I	- - 'Albus'	IBlr
	- - 'Cyan'	IBlr
	- - 'White' **new**	CPne
	- 'Indigo Cascade'	SWat
§	- subsp. ***intermedius***	CPne CPrp EBee IBlr SKHP SWat WCot
	- 'Midnight Cascade'	SWat
	- subsp. ***parviflorus***	CPne IBlr
	- subsp. ***pendulus***	CAby CDes CFir CPne EBee EBrs IBlr WPGP
	- - 'Graskop'	CPne IBlr
	- - 'Violet Dusk'	IBlr
	- 'Purple Cloud'	see *A.* 'Purple Cloud'
	'Innocence'	IBlr
I	'Intermedius' van Tubergen	CPne EBee
	'Intermedius' Leichtlin **new**	XPde
	'Jack Elliott'	SMHy
	'Jack's Blue'	More than 30 suppliers
	'Jersey Giant'	NHoy XPde
	'Jodie'	CPne XPde
	'Johanna'	CPne XPde
	'Jolanda'	CPne
	'Kew White'	SDix
	'Kingston Blue'	CMea CPne CPrp EBee EBla ECha EHrv IBal IBlr LRHS LSou MLLN NHoy SRGP WFar WPrP WSHC XPde
	'Kirstenbosch' **new**	CPne
	'Kirsty'	CPne
	'Kobold'	CPne EGle NHoy SBod WFar
	'Lady Edith'	IBlr
§	'Lady Grey'	IBlr
	'Lady Moore'	EGle IBlr IGor SMHy XPde
	'Latent Blue'	IBlr
	'Lavender Haze' **new**	EBee NHoy
	'Leicester'	EBee XPde
	'Lilac Bells'	CPne
	'Lilac Mist' **new**	EBee
	'Lilac Time'	CPne EBee IBlr XPde
	'Lilliput'	More than 30 suppliers
	'Limoges' **new**	XPde
	'Little Diamond'	SPoG
	'Little White' **new**	ENot
	'Loch Hope' ♀H3	CAbb CCtw CDoC CPne CPrp EBee EBrs EGle EMan GAbr GGar GSki IBal IGor LAst MFOX MLLN MSte NCob NHoy SApp SPav SPer SRos SVil WCot WHoo WPnn WSpi XPde
	'Lorna' **new**	CPne
	'Lowland Nursery' **new**	XPde
	'Luly'	CPne XPde
	'Lydenburg'	IBlr
	'Lyn Valley' **new**	CPne
	'Mabel Grey'	see *A.* 'Lady Grey'
	'Magnifico'	IBlr
	'Majorie'	CPne
	'Malaga' **new**	XPde
	'Marcus'	CPne
	'Mariètte'	CPen CPne EBee XPde
	'Marjorie'	CWCL SApp XPde
	'Martine'	CPne
	'Meibont' (v)	CPne WCot
	'Mercury'	CPne IBlr

	'Middleburg' new	CPne
	Midknight Blue = 'Monmid' new	NHoy
	'Midnight'	EWes SAga WSHC
	'Midnight Blue' P. Wood	IBlr
	'Midnight Blue' ambig.	ECha ELan GBuc GSki IBal IGor MSte SPav WFar
§	'Midnight Star'	More than 30 suppliers
	'Miniature Blue'	SWat
	mixed seedlings	CPen CPne ENot EPfP IBal MGos NOrc SRos
	mixed whites	WCFE
	'Montreal'	XPde
*	'Mooreanus' misapplied	EBee EPfP IBlr WPGP XPde
	'Morning Star'	CPne GSki SRos
	'Mount Stewart'	IBal IBlr
	'Navy Blue'	see *A.* 'Midnight Star'
	'New Love'	EBee
	'Newa' new	XPde
	'Nikki'	CPne
	'Norman Hadden'	IBlr
	nutans	see *A. caulescens*
	- 'Polar White' new	NHoy
	'Nyx'	IBlr
	'NZ Blue' new	XPde
	'NZ White' new	XPde
	'Offenham Cream' new	WCot
	'Oslo'	CPne NHoy XPde
	'Oxbridge'	IBlr
	Palmer's hybrids	see *A.* Headbourne hybrids
	'Paris'	CPen XPde
	'Patent Blue'	CPrp IBal IBlr
	'Penelope Palmer'	IBal IBlr
	'Penny Slade'	SAga SRos XPde
	'Peter Pan' ambig.	More than 30 suppliers
	'Peter Pan American'	GKev
	'Phantom'	CPne IBlr XPde
	'Pinchbeck'	CPne XPde
	'Pinky' new	XPde
	'Pinocchio'	CPen CWib ECho GSki NHol XPde
	'Plas Merdyn Blue'	IBal IBlr
	'Plas Merdyn White'	CFir IBal IBlr NHoy XPde
	'Podge Mill'	CWCL IBlr XPde
	'Polar Ice'	CFir CPen CPne EBee ERea GBin GSki IBlr LRHS WFar WHil XPde
	'Porcelain'	IBlr
	praecox	CPrp EBee EShb GAbr IBlr NHoy
	- 'Blue Storm' new	LBuc
	- 'Dwarf White'	see *A.* white dwarf hybrids
	- 'Flore Pleno' (d)	CDes CDoC CPne CPrp EBee ECha EHrv ELan EMon IBal IBlr MBNS NBPC NCob NGdn NHoy NLar SPoG WCot WFar WKif WPGP WPrP XPde
	- 'Floribundus'	ECtt SWat
	- 'Maximus Albus'	CPou ENot IBal IBlr WBrE
§	- subsp. ***minimus***	CAvo CBrm CElw CPne CPou EBee GSki IBlr LPio NHoy SWat WCot
	- - 'Adelaide'	EBee SWat
	- - blue-flowered	SWat
	- - white-flowered	CPne SWat
	- 'Neptune'	IBlr
§	- subsp. ***orientalis***	CCCN CPne CSut EHrv ERea GGar GSki IBlr NPal SWat WPic XPep
	- - var. ***albiflorus***	CDes CPne CPou CSut EBee GSki LAst NHoy SMad XPde
	- - 'Weaver'	CPne WHil
	- subsp. ***praecox***	IBlr IGor
	- - azure-flowered	SWat
	- - 'Variegatus'	see *A.* 'Argenteus Vittatus'
	- 'Saturn'	IBlr
	- Slieve Donard form	IBlr
	- 'Storms River'	SWat XPep
	- 'Uranus'	IBlr
	- 'Venus'	IBlr
	- 'Vittatus' (v)	ERea MAvo NHoy WCot WFar
	'Premier'	CPrp EBee EBrs IBal IBlr SRos WPGP
	'Princess Margaret' new	CPne
	'Proteus'	EBee XPde
§	'Purple Cloud'	More than 30 suppliers
	'Purple Haze' new	CWGN
	'Purple Star'	EBee
	'Queen Anne'	NHoy
	'Queen Elizabeth The Queen Mother'	CPne CPrp
	'Raveningham Hall'	XPde
	'Regal Beauty' new	CPne EBee ENor NHoy SPoG
	'Rhone'	CPne IBlr XPde
	rich blue-flowered	XPde
	'Rosemary'	CPne XPde
	'Rosewarne'	CCCN CKno CPne CPrp EBee IBal IBlr NHoy XPde
	'Rotterdam'	CPen NHoy XPde
	'Royal Blue'	CHar CPne CWCL GBuc GMaP MSte NHol NHoy WSpi
	'Royal Lodge' new	XPde
	'Royal Purple'	XPde
	'Saint Pauls Waldenbury' new	CPne
	'San Gabriel' (v)	XPde
	'Sandringham'	CDes CPne EBee EWes IBlr WPGP XPde
	'Sapphire'	CPLG IBal IBlr XPde
	'Sarah'PBR new	CKno
	'Sea Coral'	CCCN CFir CPne CPrp EBee GGar IBal NHoy SHom
	'Sea Foam'	CPen CPne CPrp IBal MBNS MSte NLar WSpi XPde
	'Sea Mist'	CCCN CPne EBee EMil IBal WSpi
	'Sea Spray'	CCCN CPne EBee EMil IBal NHoy XPde
	'Septemberhemel'	CPen XPde
	'Sevilla'	XPde
	'Silver Baby'	CAbb CPen CPne MNrw MSte NHoy SRos
	'Silver Jubilee' new	XPde
	'Silver Mist'	CPne EBee IBlr XPde
	Silver Moon = 'Notfred'PBR (v)	CBow EBee EHrv ELan EMan ENot EPfP LBuc LFur LSou MGos NCob NHoy SPer SPoG WCot XPde
	'Silver Sceptre'	IBlr
	silver variegated (v)	SMrm
	'Sky'	CAbb CPne CWGN EBee ENor IBlr LBuc LCro MSte
	'Sky Rocket'	CPne IBlr
	'Sky Star'	CPne XPde
§	'Slieve Donard'	IBlr WFar
	'Sneeuwwitje'	XPde
	'Snow Cloud'	CAbb CPne CSBt EBee ELon NHoy WSpi XPde
	'Snow Pixie'	CAbb CPne CSBt CSpe CWGN EBee LSRN NHoy
	'Snow Princess'	CPen CPne IBal LBuc
	'Snowball'	CAby CBcs CDoC COIW CPne CPrp EBee ECho EMil GAbr IBal LSou MSte NBPC NHoy SPhx SVil WSpi XPde
	'Snowdrops'	CAbb CPne CPrp EBee EGle EHrv EPyc EWll GAbr GBuc GSki IBal LAst LHop MLLN MNrw MSte NCob NEgg SApp SBla SBod SDnm SPav SPer SPla SPoG WCot WFar
	'Snowstorm'PBR new	LBuc
	'Snowy Owl'	EBee
	'Southern Star' new	CPne
	'Spokes'	IBlr
	'Starburst'	IBlr

	'Stéphanie'	CPne XPde
	'Stéphanie Charm'	CPen XPde
	'Storm Cloud' (d)	CFir
	'Storm Cloud' Reads	see *A.* 'Purple Cloud'
	'Streamline'	More than 30 suppliers
	'Summer Clouds'	CPne EBee IBal LRHS MBNS NHoy
	'Summer Skies'	CPne IBal LRHS NHoy SRos
	'Summer Snow'	CPne
	'Sunfield'	CChe CPen CPrp EBee GBin GBuc GSki LAma LRHS NLar NPer WGer XPde
	'Super Star'	CPne XPde
I	'Supreme'	IBlr
	'Suzan'	XPde
	'Sylvine'	CPen XPde
	'Tall Boy'	IBlr
	'Tarka'	CPne
	'Taw Valley'	CPne
	'Thorn' **new**	CPne
	'Thumbelina'	CAbb CPne CSpe EBee NHoy
	'Timaru'	More than 30 suppliers
	'Tinkerbell' (v)	More than 30 suppliers
	'Tiny Tim'	EBee GSki
	'Titan'	IBlr
	'Torbay'	CPne CPrp EBee ECtt GSki IBlr MBNS NCGa NHol SBla SRos XPde
	Tresco hybrid	CHEx
	'Tresco Select'	NHoy
	'Trudy' **new**	XPde
	'Twilight'	IBlr
	umbellatus L'Hérit.	see *A. africanus*
	umbellatus Redouté	see *A. praecox* subsp. *orientalis*
	'Underway'	EWes IBlr XPde
	'Velvet Night' **new**	CPen
	'Virginia'	XPde
	'White Dwarf'	see *A.* white dwarf hybrids
§	white dwarf hybrids	CPen EBee ECha EMan EPfP LRHS NBre WFar
	'White Heaven'PBR	CKno CPne EBee
	'White Ice'	CBcs CPne SApp WSpi
	'White Orb' **new**	EBee ENor NHoy SPoG
	'White Star'	XPde
	'White Starlet'	NHoy XPde
	'White Superior'	CMMP CPne CSpe ERou GMaP LAst NCGa SHBN SPet STes WCAu WTMC
	'White Triumphator'	WCot
	'White Umbrella'	WPrP
	white-flowered	CHEx GGar NCob
	'Whitney'PBR	IBlr
	'Wholesome' **new**	IBal
	'Windlebrooke'	CPne EBee ECha XPde
	'Windsor Castle'	CPen CPrp IBal IBlr XPde
	'Windsor Grey'	CDes CDoC CPrp EBee IBal IBlr LFur LSou MAvo NCob SKHP WCot WGwG WPGP XPde
	'Winsome'	IBlr
	'Winter Sky' **new**	CPne XPde
	'Wolga'	CPne
	'Wolkberg' Kirstenbosch	IBlr
	'Yellow Tips' **new**	CPne
	'Yolande'	LAma
	'Yves Klein'	IBlr
	'Zachary'	CPne
	'Zella Thomas'	CPne EBee LHyd XPde

Agapetes (*Ericaceae*)

	'Ludgvan Cross' ♀H1-2	CCCN SAga WPic
	serpens ♀H1	CCCN CHEx CWib EShb SAga SLon WPic
	- 'Scarlet Elf'	CCCN SKHP
	smithiana var. ***major***	GGGa

Agarista (*Ericaceae*)

§	***populifolia***	WFar

Agastache (*Lamiaceae*)

	Acapulco Purple = 'Kiegapur'PBR **new**	LHop
	'After Eight'PBR **new**	EBee
	anethiodora	see *A. foeniculum* (Pursh) Kuntze
	anisata	see *A. foeniculum* (Pursh) Kuntze
	'Apricot Sunrise'	MNHC
	aurantiaca	EAro LHop NLar SPhx WHil WLin
	- 'Apricot Sprite'	CFis CWCL EAro EBee EWin LDai NHol SDnm SPav SPoG WFar WGwG WHil WWeb
	'Black Adder'	CKno CSpe EBee EBla EKen EWTr EWes GQue LCro LHop LPio LRHS MBri MCot NCob NDov NLar SCoo SSvw WSpi WWlt
	'Blue Fortune' ♀H3-4	CBcs EBee ECha ECtt EMan ENot EPfP GBri IBal LCro LPio LRHS MBri MLLN NCGa NDov NMoo SMer SMrm SPer SSvw WFar WHlf WWeb
	breviflora	SWal
§	***cana***	EAro ECtt EMan LDai MLLN SPhx WFar
	- 'Cinnabar Rose'	NBir WFar
	- 'Purple Pygmy'	EBee ECtt EShb
	'Firebird'	CWCL EBee EBla ECtt EHrv ELan IBal LHop LRHS LSRN MBri MNrw NBir NCGa NDov NGdn SAga SBla SGar SMrm SPer SPla SRkn SWat SWvt WAul WCAu WFar WHil
	foeniculum misapplied	see *A. rugosa*
§	***foeniculum*** (Pursh) Kuntze	CArn CChe CMea CPrp CWan EBee ECha ELan ELau GMaP GPoy LRHS MHer MNHC MRav NDov NGHP SPav SPhx SRms WCAu WFar WPer XPep
	- 'Alabaster'	CBcs EAro EBee EGoo ELau EShb LRHS SBch SPhx
	- 'Alba'	MLLN NBre NGHP SHDw SPav WFar
*	'Fragrant Delight'	SRms
	'Globetrotter'	LHop SAga SPhx
	'Glowing Embers'	ECtt EPfP LRHS
	'Hazy Days'	EAro EBee LSou SPhx WHil
	'Heather Queen'	SRkn
§	***mexicana***	EAro EUnu LDai LPio LSou MSal MWea SDnm SMHy SMrm SPav WJek
	- 'Champagne'	MWea
	- 'Marchant's Pink'	SMHy
	- 'Mauve Beauty'	EBee LSou
	- 'Red Fortune'PBR	CPrp EBee EBla ENot LBuc LHop NCGa
	- 'Rosea'	see *A. cana*
*	- 'Toronjil Morado'	LHop
	nepetoides	CArn EAro EMan EPPr EUnu MSal NLar NSti SDnm SPav SSvw
	occidentalis	EMan
	'Painted Lady'	CSpe EBee ECtt EWin LCro LPio MNrw SAga SBch SMrm SPhx
	pallidiflora var. ***neomexicana*** 'Lavender Haze'	EBee
	palmeri	EAro EMan LHop
	'Phoenix'	SMHy
	'Pink Panther'	ECtt EMan LHop
	'Pink Pearl'	WWeb
	'Pink Pop'	EAro EBee ECGP SPhx WHil
	pringlei	EAro SWat WMoo
	'Purple Candle'	EBee EWes SPla
	'Purple Haze'	NDov SPhx
§	***rugosa***	CAgr CArn CFir ELau EUnu GPoy LRHS MLLN MNHC MSal SDnm SMeo SPav SPhx SWat WJek WMoo WPer WSel XPep

- B&SWJ 4187 from Korea	WCru
- f. ***albiflora***	NBre SDnm WCAu WLin
- - 'Liquorice White'	CPrp EBee LRHS MWgw NBre NLar SPav SPer SWat
- 'Golden Jubilee'	CSam CSpe CWCL EAro EBee EBla ECha EGoo ELon EMan ENot EWin GAbr LDai LHop LPio LRHS LSou MBri MCCP MHar NDov NHol NLar SPhx SPoG WMoo
- 'Honey Bee Blue'	LRHS NHol
- 'Korean Zest'	EGoo WCru
- 'Liquorice Blue'	CKno EAro EBla ECrN LRHS MLan MWgw NBid NEgg NGdn NLar NOrc SDnm SGar SPad SPav SPer SPhx SWat WFar WMoo WPer
- pink-flowered	CEnt
rupestris	CMdw CSpe EAro EBee EMan LHop NLar SPhx SPur WKif
- 'Apache Sunset'	CBow LEdu MBri NTHB SDnm SGar SPav SPlb WHal WPtf
'Serpentine'	EBee NDov SPhx SSvw
'Spicy'	ECha MSte
'Tangerine Dreams' 🏆H3	EAro EBee EBla ECtt EMan EWin LRHS MWgw NCob SAga SBla SCoo SPhx
'Tutti-frutti'	EBee ECtt EHrv EMan LDai LHop SDnm SPav
urticifolia	CArn CSpe LRHS MSal NBre
- 'Alba'	CSpe EAro EBee NBre NLar WPer
- 'Liquorice'	CTca EBee SAga WFar

Agathaea see *Felicia*

Agathis (*Araucariaceae*)

australis	CDoC LCon LLin

Agathosma (*Rutaceae*)

ovata	CCCN
- 'Igoda'	EShb

Agave ✿ (*Agavaceae*)

albicans	MAga
albomarginata	CDTJ MAga
amaniensis	MAga
americana 🏆H1	More than 30 suppliers
- var. ***expansa***	MAga
- 'Marginata' (v) 🏆H3-4	CBrP CDTJ CHal CHll IBlr MAga MPRe SDnm SSwd
- 'Mediopicta' misapplied	see *A. americana* 'Mediopicta Alba'
- 'Mediopicta' (v) 🏆H1	CDTJ CHEx MAvo SAPC SArc STop WEas
§ - 'Mediopicta Alba' (v) 🏆H1	CBrP CDTJ EAmu MAga SChr
- 'Mediopicta Aurea' (v) new	MAga
- var. ***oaxacensis***	MAga
- subsp. ***protoamericana***	MAga
- 'Striata' (v)	EShb MAga
- 'Variegata' (v) 🏆H1	More than 30 suppliers
angustiarum	MAga
angustifolia	MAga
asperrima	CDTJ EPem MPRe
§ - subsp. ***maderensis***	MAga
- subsp. ***potosiensis***	MAga
§ - subsp. ***zarcensis***	MAga
attenuata	CAbb CBrP CHEx CTrC EAmu EWll LRHS MAga SAPC SArc
attenuata x ***shawii*** new	MAga
boldinghiana	MAga
bracteosa	CCCN EPem MAga MPRe SChr
brittoniana new	MAga
cantala	MAga
capensis	MAga
§ ***celsii***	CBrP CHEx CTrC EShb MAga SAPC SArc SChr
cerulata subsp. ***nelsonii***	MAga
chiapensis	MAga
chrysantha	CCCN CTrC EBee MAga SChr WLeb
chrysoglossa	MAga
colorata	CCCN CDTJ
- dwarf	MAga
cupreata	MAga
dasylirioides new	MAga
datylio new	MAga
decipiens	MAga
- dwarf	MAga
delamateri	MAga
deserti	CBrP WCot
- subsp. ***simplex*** variegated (v)	MAga
difformis	MAga
durangensis	MAga
eggersiana new	MAga
ensifera	MAga
evadens new	MAga
felgeri	CDTJ MAga
ferdinandi-regis	see *A. scabra* x *victoriae-reginae*
ferox	CBrP CDTJ CTrC CWil EWll LCro MPRe
filifera 🏆H1	CBcs CCCN CDTJ CHEx EPem MAga SChr
- 'Compacta' new	MAga
- subsp. ***microceps*** ISI 1184	MAga
flexispina	MAga
fourcroydes	MAga MPRe
franzosinii	MAga
funkiana	MAga
- blue-leaved new	MAga
geminiflora	CBcs CCCN CDTJ EPem EShb MAga WCot
gentryi new	MAga
ghiesbreghtii	MAga MPRe
gigantea	see *Furcraea foetida*
gigantensis	MAga
x ***glomeruliflora***	MAga
goldmaniana	MAga
x ***gracilipes***	MAga
guadalajarana new	CDTJ MAga
- dwarf	MAga
- 'Trelease'	MPRe
guiengola	MAga
havardiana	CTrC MAga
- dwarf	MAga
hiemiflora	MAga
horrida	MAga SChr
- 'Perotensis'	EShb
hurteri new	MAga
inaequidens	MAga
karwinskii	MAga
kerchovei	EPem MAga
§ ***lechuguilla***	MAga SChr
lechuguilla x ***lophantha***	MAga
lechuguilla x ***victoria-reginae*** new	MAga
lophantha	CDTJ MAga WCot
- var. ***caerulescens***	see *A. lechuguilla*
lurida Aiton	MAga MPRe
macroacantha	CDTJ MAga
mapisaga new	MAga
maximilliana new	MAga
- 'Katharinae' new	MAga
missionum from The Virgin Islands	MAga
mitis	see *A. celsii*
montana F&M 221	WPGP
multifilifera	MAga
neglecta	MAga
neomexicana	CCCN EPem IDee MAga
nizandensis	CHEx MAga

obscura	CDTJ
ocahui	MAga
- var. ***longifolia***	MAga
ornithobroma	MAga
oroensis	MAga
pachycentra new	MAga
palmeri	CBct CCCN CTrC EPem MAga SChr
panamana	see *A. vivipara* var. *vivipara*
parrasana	MAga
- dwarf	MAga
parryi	CDTJ CDoC CTrC EAmu EBee EPem EWll GKev IDee LEdu MAga SChr WLeb WPGP
- var. ***couesii***	see *A. parryi* var. *parryi*
- var. ***huachucensis***	CDTJ
§ - var. ***parryi***	CBrP CDTJ CFir EPem MAga MPRe
parvidentata	MAga
- blue-leaved new	MAga
parviflora 𝕐H1	MAga SChr
- subsp. ***flexiflora***	MAga
- - dwarf	MAga
x ***peacockii***	MAga
pedunculifera new	MAga
pelona	MAga
polianthiflora	MAga
polyacantha	MAga
- var. ***xalapensis***	MAga MPRe
potatorum 𝕐H1	SChr
- var. ***potatorum***	MAga
- var. ***verschaffeltii***	EPem MPRe
- - dwarf	MAga
promantorii	MAga
pumila new	MAga
pygmaea	see *A. seemanniana*
rhodacantha	MAga
salmiana	EAmu MAga
- var. ***angustifolia*** new	MAga
- subsp. ***crassispina***	MAga
- subsp. ***salmiana*** var. ***ferox***	MAga SAPC SArc SChr
- - variegated (v)	MAga
scabra	CBct CCCN EBee EPem MAga
- subsp. ***maderensis***	see *A. asperrima* subsp. *maderensis*
- subsp. ***zarcensis***	see *A. asperrima* subsp. *zarcensis*
§ ***scabra*** x ***victoriae-reginae***	SChr
scaposa	MAga
schidigera	CBrP MAga WCot
schottii	CDTJ MAga
- var. ***treleasei***	MAga
sebastiana	MAga
§ ***seemanniana***	MAga
shawii	MAga
shrevei subsp. ***matapensis***	MAga
sisalana	MAga
I - f. ***armata***	MAga
sobria	MAga
- subsp. ***sobria***	MAga
striata	CTrC EPem IDee XPep
- subsp. ***falcata*** new	MAga
* - ***rubra***	CDTJ
stricta 𝕐H1	CCCN CDTJ MAga MPRe
- dwarf	CBrP MAga
- 'Nana' new	CDTJ EPem
- 'Nana' blue-leaved new	MAga
stringens	MAga
subsimplex	MAga
tecta	MAga
tenuifolia new	MAga
tequilana blue-leaved	MAga
- green-leaved	MAga
thomasae	MAga
titanota	MAga
toumeyana	EPem MAga SChr
- var. ***bella***	CDTJ MAga
triangularis	MAga
underwoodii new	MAga
utahensis 𝕐H1	EPem MAga SEND
- var. ***discreta***	MAga
- dwarf	MAga
- var. ***eborispina***	MAga
- subsp. ***kaibabensis***	EPem
- var. ***nevadensis***	EPem MAga
victoriae-reginae 𝕐H1	CBrP CCCN CDTJ CTrC EPem EShb EWll MAga SWal WCot
- dwarf	MAga
- variegated (v)	SChr
-f. ***ornata*** new	MAga
vilmoriniana	EPem MAga
vivipara	MAga
- var. ***letonae***	MAga
- 'Marginata'	MAga
- var. ***nivea***	MAga
- var. ***sargentii***	MAga
§ - var. ***vivipara***	MAga
vizcainoensis	MAga
warelliana	MAga
weberi	MAga
wendtii new	MAga
wercklei	MAga
x ***winteriana***	MAga
xylonacantha	EPem MAga SChr
yuccifolia	MAga
zebra	MAga

Ageratina see *Eupatorium*

Ageratum (*Asteraceae*)

corymbosum	CHll CSpe

Aglaomorpha (*Polypodiaceae*)

coronans new	MPes WRic

Aglaonema (*Araceae*)

crispum 'Marie'	MBri
'Silver Queen' 𝕐H1	MBri

Agonis (*Myrtaceae*)

flexuosa	CTrC

Agrimonia (*Rosaceae*)

eupatoria	CArn COld CRWN ELau GPoy MHer MNHC NMir SECG SIde SWat WHer
* - var. ***alba***	NBre NLar
- 'Topas'	ELau
grandiflora	EBee NBre
gryposepala	EBee
odorata misapplied	see *A. procera*
odorata (L.) Mill.	see *A. repens*
pilosa	CArn EBee MSal
§ ***procera***	NEgg
§ ***repens***	MSal WMoo

Agropyron (*Poaceae*)

glaucum	see *Elymus hispidus*
magellanicum	see *Elymus magellanicus*
pubiflorum	see *Elymus magellanicus*
scabrum	see *Elymus scabrus*

Agrostemma (*Caryophyllaceae*)

coronaria	see *Lychnis coronaria*
githago	CEnt GWCH MWgw

Agrostis (*Poaceae*)

calamagrostis	see *Stipa calamagrostis*
§ ***canina*** 'Silver Needles' (v)	CBre EHul EMan EWes MMoz NBir NHol WFar WRos

	'Lago Lago'	EBee
	nebulosa	CKno EGoo

Aichryson (*Crassulaceae*)

§	x ***domesticum***	CHal EBee EWin SEND
	- 'Variegatum' (v) 🏆^{H1}	CHal EBak EWin WCot
	tortuosum	CFee

Ailanthus (*Simaroubaceae*)

§	***altissima***	CBcs CCVT CDul CHEx CLnd CPLG CTho EBee ECrN EMil EPfP EWTr LAst LPan MBlu NBlu NEgg SAPC SArc SBLw SCoo SDnm SPer SPlb SWvt WBVN WNor
	- var. ***tanakae*** B&SWJ 6777	WCru
	glandulosa	see *A. altissima*

Ainsliaea (*Asteraceae*)

	acerifolia B&SWJ 4795	WCru
	- B&SWJ 6059	WCru
	fragrans var. ***integrifolia***	WPtf

Aiphanes (*Arecaceae*)

	aculeata	LPal

Ajania (*Asteraceae*)

§	***pacifica***	CHal EBee EMan SMer SPoG WHer XPep
	tibetica JJH 9308103	NWCA

Ajuga (*Lamiaceae*)

	ciliata var. ***villosior***	CFir GBin WHil WOut
	genevensis	EBee EPPr EShb WOut WWeb
	- 'Tottenham'	WOut
	incisa 'Bikun' (v)	EBee ENot EWes
	- 'Blue Enigma'	CLAP EBee EWes SMac WOVN
	- 'Blue Ensign' **new**	LDai
	'Little Court Pink'	LBuc LRHS
	metallica hort.	see *A. pyramidalis*
	'Monmotaro San'	EMan
	'Pink Spires'	NCot
§	***pyramidalis***	CFee EBee ECho WHer
	- 'Metallica Crispa'	CBct CBow CRez CStu EBee ECho EMan EPPr EWes LAst LRHS MBNS NLar SBch SMer SPoG SRms SSvw SWvt WFar WWeb
	reptans	CRWN CTri EBee ECtt ELau EWTr GKev GPoy MHer MNHC MSal NMir NSco SGar WFar
	- f. ***albiflora*** 'Alba'	CArn CWan ECtt EMan EPfP GGar MNrw MRav NBro NSti SRms WCAu WFar WMoo
	- - 'Schneekerze'	EBee
	- - 'Silver Shadow'	WTin
	- 'Arctic Fox' (v)	CCVN CMil CTca CWCL CWGN EBee ECho ECtt EHrv GBuc LHop MNrw MRav NEgg NPri NRya SAga SWvt WBrk WCot WFar WHer
	- 'Argentea'	see *A. reptans* 'Variegata'
§	- 'Atropurpurea'	CBcs CHrt CStu CTca EBee ECha ECho ELan EMFW ENot EPfP GGar LBMP LCro LRHS MLHP NBlu NHol NVic SPer SPlb SRms SWvt WBrE WBrk WFar WWeb
	- Black Scallop = 'Binblasca'	CBct CHFP CHVG CHid EBee ECtt EKen EPPr ETod EWin LBMP LRHS MBNS MBnl MMHG NDov NHol
	- 'Braunherz'	More than 30 suppliers
	- 'Brean Down'	CNat
	- 'Burgundy Glow' (v)	More than 30 suppliers
§	- 'Catlin's Giant' 🏆^{H4}	More than 30 suppliers
	- 'Chocolate Chip'	see *A. reptans* 'Valfredda'
	- 'Delight' (v)	ECho ECot WEas
	- 'Ebony'	EBee LSRN WBrE
	- 'Ermine' (v)	MNrw MTPN SAga
	- 'Flisteridge'	CNat
	- 'Golden Beauty'	EBee ECtt EPPr EWes EWin
	- 'Grey Lady'	GBuc
	- 'Harlequin' (v)	SWvt WBrE
	- 'John Pierpoint'	LBuc SHar WCot
	- 'Jumbo'	see *A. reptans* 'Jungle Beauty'
§	- 'Jungle Beauty'	CSev EBee EMan EPfP EWTr LSou MRav NCob WCAu WFar WHen
	- 'Little Pink Court'	EBee
	- 'Macrophylla'	see *A. reptans* 'Catlin's Giant'
§	- 'Multicolor' (v)	CArn CBcs CChe CHEx EBee ECho ELan GGar LBMP LHop MAvo MBar NHol SBod SPer SPlb SPoG SRms SWal SWvt WFar WMoo WTel
	- 'Palisander'	EBee GSki LRHS MBNS NLar
I	- 'Pat's Selection' (v)	EMan
	- 'Pink Elf'	CBre CChe CMHG ECho EMan MRav NBro SBch SWat WFar WLin
	- 'Pink Splendour'	CBre NBre NChi
	- 'Pink Surprise'	CHid ECha ECtt EPfP GBuc LAst LRHS MHer MLHP NRya SSvw WFar WGwG WMoo WTMC
	- 'Purple Torch'	WEas WOut WTMC
	- 'Purpurea'	see *A. reptans* 'Atropurpurea'
	- 'Rainbow'	see *A. reptans* 'Multicolor'
	- 'Rosea'	WMoo
	- 'Silver Queen'	EBee
	- 'Tricolor'	see *A. reptans* 'Multicolor'
§	- 'Valfredda'	CEnt EAlp EBee ECho ECtt EMan EShb EWin GBin GGar LAst LRHS LSou NEgg NLar NPro SHar SPoG WCot WGwG WOut WWeb
	- 'Vanilla Chip' (v)	EBee
§	- 'Variegata' (v)	CBct EBee ECho ECtt EPfP EShb LBMP LHop MHer MNHC NBid NPri SBod SPer SPet SPoG SRms SWat WEas WFar WLin

Akebia (*Lardizabalaceae*)

	longeracemosa	CBcs LEdu MBri NLar SKHP WCot
	- B&SWJ 3606	WCru
	x ***pentaphylla***	EBee ELan EPfP LEdu LRHS MAsh SBra SPer WSHC
	- B&SWJ 2829	WCru
	quinata	More than 30 suppliers
	- B&SWJ 4425	WCru
	- 'Alba'	CBcs CSPN CWGN WPat
	- 'Amethyst'	MWea
	- 'Amethyst Glow'	EBee EPfP LRHS MBri SPer SPoG
	- cream-flowered	EBee EPfP ERea LRHS MWea SBra SPer SPoG SSta SWvt WCru WPGP
	- variegated (v)	CBcs CBow LTwo WCru WPat
	- 'White Chocolate'	WCru
	trifoliata	CBcs CHEx EBee EPfP LBuc LRHS SLim
	- B&SWJ 2829	WCru
	- B&SWJ 5063	WCru
	- 'Amethyst'	SBra

Alangium (*Alangiaceae*)

	chinense	CBcs EPla WBVN
	platanifolium	CAbP CPLG MBlu MBri NLar WPGP
	- var. ***macrophyllum***	WPGP
	- var. ***platanifolium***	NLar

Albizia (*Mimosaceae*)

	distachya	see *Paraserianthes lophantha*
§	***julibrissin***	CArn CDTJ CTrC EAmu EWin IDee LAst LPan LRHS MGol MJnS SBLw SHFr SPlb
	- Ombrella = 'Boubri'^{PBR}	LPan LRHS SBLw SCoo
	- f. ***rosea*** 🏆$^{H2-3}$	More than 30 suppliers
	- 'Rouge de Tuiliere' **new**	EMil

- 'Rouge d'Été' **new**	EBee
lophantha	see *Paraserianthes lophantha*

Albuca (*Hyacinthaceae*)

from Lesotho	WAbe
altissima	CStu EBee
angolensis **new**	CPou WHil
aurea	WHil
* ***batliana***	ECho
batteniana	CFir EBee EBrs ECho ERea
canadensis	CStu WHil
clanwilliamigloria	WHil WPrP
'Dirk Wallace'	CPLG
fastigiata **new**	WHil
- f. ***floribunda*** **new**	WCot
fragrans **new**	WHil
humilis	CDes CPLG CStu EBee ECho NMen WAbe WCot WPrP
juncifolia	EBee
maxima	CPou WCot WHil
nelsonii	CAvo EBee EBrs ERea LRHS WPGP
rupestris	WCot WHil
setosa	WHil
shawii	CAvo CDes CFFs CPou CPrp CStu EBee EBla EBrs ECho EMan EMar EMil ERos MHer MWgw NCGa NSla SAga SBch SBla SPad SPet SPoG SSvw WAbe WHil WPGP WPrP
trichophylla	WCot

Alcea (*Malvaceae*)

'Apple Blossom' (d)	NBHF
'Arabian Nights'	MBri NBHF SPav
'Blackcurrant Whirl'	NBHF SPav
ficifolia	GCra GMac LSou MCCP SDnm SPav WMoo
'Happy Lights'	CWib
'Peaches and Cream'	NRnb
'Peaches 'n' Dreams'	CWib EBee MBri NGBl NRnb WRHF
§ ***rosea***	CHrt EUnu GWCH LAst WFar XPep
- Chater's Double Group (d)	CWib ECtt ENot EPfP MBri MLan MWat SRms WRHF
- - pink (d)	ECtt EPfP NPri SPer
- - purple (d) **new**	EPfP
- - red (d)	ECtt NPri
- - salmon pink (d)	EPfP
- - scarlet (d) **new**	EPfP
- - violet (d)	SPer
- - white (d)	EPfP NPri SPer
- - yellow (d)	ECtt EPfP NPri SPer
- 'Crème de Cassis'	EPfP MWat NGBl NRnb SPav WRHF
- double apricot-flowered (d)	NBHF
- double pink-flowered (d)	MHer
- double red-flowered (d)	MHer
- double rose-flowered (d)	EBee SPer
- double scarlet-flowered (d)	SPer SPla
- double white-flowered (d)	MHer
- double yellow-flowered (d)	EBee MHer
- 'Lemon Light'	LHop
- 'Nigra'	CArn CMea CSpe EBee EGoo EHrv EPfP LAst LCro LHop LRHS LSRN MHer MSte MWat MWgw NGBl NGdn NPri SGar SMad SPer WCAu WFar XPep
- single-flowered	ENot MWat MWgw
- single pink-flowered	LRHS
- Summer Carnival Group	CWib LAst SRms WGor
§ ***rugosa***	CMea ECha EMan EMar GKev LHop LRHS MBri MSte MWgw SPav WPGP

Alcea x *Althaea* (*Malvaceae*)

'Parkallee' (d)	CSpe EBee ECtt EMan EMon GBin GBri LCro LDai MAvo MBNS MCCP SPhx WCot
'Parkfrieden' (d)	CSpe ECtt EMan EMon SPhx WCot
'Parkrondell' (d)	CBgR ECha ECtt EMan EMon GBri LBuc MAsh MBNS NCot SPoG WCot

Alchemilla ✿ (*Rosaceae*)

abyssinica	EBee ECho WHrl
alpina misapplied	see *A. conjuncta*, *A. plicatula*
alpina ambig.	EOHP
alpina L.	CEnt CFee CMea EBla ECho ECrN EPfP LBMP LEdu LRHS MRav NChi NGHP NMir SBch SIng SPet SRms SWat WFar WKif WMoo WPer
aroanica	EBee EBla
arvensis	see *Aphanes arvensis*
§ ***conjuncta***	More than 30 suppliers
elisabethae	EBla ECGP EMon
ellenbeckii	CFee CMCo EBee EBla ECho EDAr EPfP EWsh GGar LAst MHar MTho MWgw NChi SWat WFar WHen WPGP WPat
epipsila	CFwr EBee EShb EWes MSte NLar SPhx WPer
erythropoda ♀^{H4}	More than 30 suppliers
faeroensis	CMCo WPer WPtf WWFP
- var. ***pumila***	EBla GEdr MAvo NMen
filicaulis 'Minima'	CNat
§ ***fulgens***	EWTr LEdu
glaucescens	CNat EBla
hoppeana misapplied	see *A. plicatula*
iniquiformis	EBee WPGP
lapeyrousei	EBee EBla EPPr
mollis ♀^{H4}	More than 30 suppliers
* - 'Robusta'	ECha EPla SEND SPlb SWat WFar WMoo WPnP
- 'Thriller'	EBee EWin IBal WSpi WWeb
monticola	WPer
'Mr Poland's Variety'	see *A. venosa*
pedata **new**	NChi
pentaphylla	EBee EBla
§ ***plicatula***	WPer
psilomischa	EMon
pumila	NBre
saxatilis	IFoB WPer
speciosa	EBee
splendens misapplied	see *A. fulgens*
straminea	EBee MRav NBre
§ ***venosa***	EBee SPer
aff. ***venosa***	EPla
vetteri	EBee EBla WHrl
vulgaris misapplied	see *A. xanthochlora*
§ ***xanthochlora***	CArn EBee GPoy MSal NBre NLar NSco SRms WFar WHer WPer

Aldrovanda (*Droseraceae*)

vesiculosa	EFEx

alecost see *Tanacetum balsamita*

Alectryon (*Sapindaceae*)

excelsus	CBcs

Alisma (*Alismataceae*)

plantago-aquatica	CBen CDWL EHon EMFW NPer NSco SWat WFar WMAq WPnP
- var. ***parviflorum***	CBen CDWL SPlb SWat WMAq

Alkanna (Boraginaceae)

	tinctoria	MSal
	- HH&K 345	CMdw

Allamanda (Apocynaceae)

§	***blanchetii***	SOWG
	cathartica	ERea LRHS MBri MJnS
	- 'Birthe'	MBri
	- 'Cherry Red'	MJnS
	- 'Halley's Comet'	SOWG
	- 'Hendersonii' ♀H1	LRHS
	'Cherries Jubilee'	SOWG
	'Jamaican Sunset'	MJnS SOWG
	neriifolia	see *A. schottii*
§	***schottii*** ♀H1	LRHS SOWG
	violacea	see *A. blanchetii*

Alliaria (Brassicaceae)

	petiolata	CArn GPoy NLan SECG WHer WSFF

Allium ✿ (Alliaceae)

	aciphyllum	EBee
§	***acuminatum***	CPom EBee ECho GBin GSki NBir NMen
I	- 'Album'	ECho
	aflatunense misapplied	see *A. hollandicum*
	aflatunense ambig.	IBal
	aflatunense B. Fedtsch.	EMon LHop SApp
I	- 'Alba' **new**	CBgR EBrs
	'Akbulak'	EBee ECho LAma MSte
	albopilosum	see *A. cristophii*
	altissimum 'Goliath'	CGrW CTca EBee EBrs ERou LRHS WCot
	amabile	see *A. mairei* var. *amabile*
	ampeloprasum	EBee EBrs ECha ECho LAma NGHP WHer WShi
	- var. ***babingtonii***	CAgr CArn CNat GPoy ILis LEdu MLLN WHer WShi
§	- 'Elephant'	CArn
	amphibolum	EBee EBrs ECho EHrv
	amplectens	EBee EBrs ECho
§	***angulosum***	CAvo CMea EBee EBrs ECho LAma SMrm WCot
	angustitepalum	see *A. jesdianum* subsp. *angustitepalum*
	atropurpureum	CAby CBgR EBee EBrs ECha EHrv ELan EMon EPfP ERCP LAma LEdu LRHS MLLN MMHG SPhx WRHF
	atropurpureum x ***schubertii*** **new**	LRHS
	azureum	see *A. caeruleum*
	'Beau Regard' ♀H4	CTca CWCL EBee EBrs ERou LAma
	beesianum hort.	see *A. cyaneum*
	beesianum W.W. Smith	CLyd GCrs GEdr NBir NRya NWCA SBla SMeo
	- CD&R 95 from Sichuan, China	SMHy
	- 'Album' **new**	EBrs
	blandum	see *A. carolinianum*
	bolanderi	EBee GCrs
	bucharicum	ERos
	bulgaricum	see *Nectaroscordum siculum* subsp. *bulgaricum*
§	***caeruleum*** ♀H4	More than 30 suppliers
	- ***azureum***	see *A. caeruleum*
	caesium ♀H4	EBrs
	callimischon subsp. ***callimischon***	EBrs ECho
	- subsp. ***haemostictum***	CBgR EBrs ECho NMen SBla
	canadense	CArn EBee SHar
§	***carinatum***	ECho
§	- subsp. ***pulchellum*** ♀H4	CArn CAvo CBgR CBrm CHar CMea EBee EBrs ECha ECho EGle EPot ERou LAma LHop LLWP MHer MNFA MNrw MTho NMen SHFr SPhx SSvw WBor WHil WPer
	- - f. ***album*** ♀H4	CAvo CBgR CPom CSWP EBee EBrs ECha ECho EGle EMon EPot ERos ERou LEdu LLWP MNrw NChi NMen SBch SPhx WBor WCot WHil
	- - 'Tubergen'	ECho
§	***carolinianum***	GCrs MGol WCot
	cepa Aggregatum Group	GPoy ILis
	- 'Kew White'	WCot
	- 'Perutile'	CArn CHby GPoy ILis LEdu MHer
	- Proliferum Group	CArn CBod CHby CPrp CSev CWan GPoy ILis LEdu MHer MNHC NGHP SIde WGwG WHer WJek WSel
	- var. ***viviparum***	EBrs ECho LAma
	cernuum	More than 30 suppliers
§	- 'Hidcote' ♀H4	CSam EMon MSte WBVN WKif
	- 'Major'	see *A. cernuum* 'Hidcote'
	- pink-flowered	EBrs GSki SIng
	cirrhosum	see *A. carinatum* subsp. *pulchellum*
	cowanii	see *A. neapolitanum* Cowanii Group
	crenulatum	EBee EBrs ECho GCrs
§	***cristophii*** ♀H4	More than 30 suppliers
	cupanii	EBrs ECho
§	***cyaneum*** ♀H4	CGra CLyd CPBP CPom EBrs ECho ERos GCrs GEdr LBee LRHS NChi NMen NRya SBla WAbe WCot
	cyathophorum	ECho GCrs NWCA
§	- var. ***farreri***	CArn CBgR CBre EBee EBrs ECho EPot ERos GCrs GEdr GSki LBee LEdu LLWP LRHS MLHP MRav MSte NChi NRya SBch WBVN WCot WPrP
	darwasicum	ECho
	delicatulum	EBee
	diabaloense **new**	WCot
	dichlamydeum	ERos
§	***drummondii***	CPom ECho ERos
	'Early Emperor'	CWCL
	elatum	see *A. macleanii*
	ericetorum	ERos WCot
	eusperma	ECho LAma
	falcifolium	EBee EBrs ECho EPot LAma LRHS NMen WCot
	farreri	see *A. cyathophorum* var. *farreri*
	fasciculatum	EBee ECho LAma
	fetisowii	EBee
	fimbriatum	ECho
	'Firmament'	CAvo CFFs CMea EBee EBrs ECha ECho EMon ERou IHer IPot LAma LRHS MSte SPhx WCot
	fistulosum	CArn CHby CWan EBee EBrs ELau GPoy GSki ILis LAma LEdu MHer MNHC NGHP NHol NPri SIde WGwG WPer
	- red-flowered	CPrp NGHP
	- 'Red Welsh'	CAgr ILis WJek
	flavum ♀H4	CAby CArn CAvo CFFs CPom CTca ECha ECho EGle GSki IFoB LAma MRav SBch SHBN WBVN WGor WGwG
§	- 'Blue Leaf'	EBee ECho ERos MLLN NBir
	- subsp. ***flavum***	CMea EBee EBrs ECho ERou LEdu MMHG MNrw
	- - var. ***minus***	EBee ECho MTho NWCA
	- 'Glaucum'	see *A. flavum* 'Blue Leaf'
	- var. ***nanum***	EBrs ECho EPot GCrs GEdr
	- subsp. ***tauricum***	EBee EBrs ECho SPhx
	forrestii	EBee GBin GCrs GKev MDKP
	geyeri	EBee ECho GCrs WCot

	giganteum ♀H4	More than 30 suppliers
	'Gladiator' ♀H4	CFir CTca CWCL EBee EBrs ECtt EMon ERou LAma LRHS MLLN MNrw MRav MSte NOrc SPad SPer SPet SPhx
	glaucum	see *A. senescens* subsp. *montanum* var. *glaucum*
	'Globemaster' ♀H4	CAvo CFFs CFir CMea CWCL EBee EBrs ECho EHrv ELan EPfP ERCP ERou IBal LAma LCro LEdu LRHS MBri MMHG MSte NBPC SMeo SPer SPhx WCot WCra WFar WHal
	globosum	ECho
	'Globus'	CTca EBee EBrs ERou LAma LRHS
	goodingii	CPom EBee EBrs ECho GCrs GMaP
	'Guna'	LRHS
	guttatum subsp. ***dalmaticum***	EBee
	- subsp. ***sardoum***	ECho
	haematochiton	WCot
	'Hair'	see *A. vineale* 'Hair'
	heldreichii	EBee EBrs ECho
*	***hirtifolium*** var. ***album***	EBee EBrs ECho LAma
	'His Excellency'	CFir EBee EBrs ECho ERou LAma LRHS MSte
§	***hollandicum*** ♀H4	More than 30 suppliers
	- 'Purple Sensation' ♀H4	More than 30 suppliers
	hookeri ACE 2430	EPot WCot
	- var. ***muliense***	GEdr
	humile	WCot
	hyalinum	EBrs
	- pink-flowered	EBee WCot WPrP
§	***insubricum*** ♀H4	EBrs ECho ERos GCrs LEdu NBir NMen WAbe
	jajlae	see *A. rotundum* subsp. *jajlae*
	jesdianum	ECho EMon
§	- subsp. ***angustitepalum***	EBee EBrs LRHS
	- 'Michael Hoog'	see *A. rosenorum* 'Michael H. Hoog'
	- 'Purple King'	CMdw EBee EBrs ECho ERou LAma LRHS MNrw MSte
	- white-flowered	EBee EBrs ECho ERou
	kansuense	see *A. sikkimense*
	karataviense ♀H3	More than 30 suppliers
	- 'Ivory Queen'	CMea CTca EBee EBrs ECha ECho ECtt EMar EMon EPfP GKev IBal LAma LCro LRHS MNFA MSte MWgw NMRc SPlb WAul WFar
	kharputense	EBee
	komarovianum	see *A. thunbergii*
	lacunosum var. ***davisiae*** new	WCot
	- var. ***lacunosum*** new	WCot
	ledebourianum	EBrs ECho
	lenkoranicum	EBee EBrs ECho LRHS
	libani	WPer
	'Lucy Ball'	EBee EBrs ECtt EMon EPot ERou LAma LRHS MLLN MSte NBir NLar SPhx
§	***macleanii***	CArn EBee EBrs ECho LAma LRHS
	macranthum	EBee EBrs ECho GEdr MSte WCot
	mairei	CLyd EBee EBrs ECho ERos LHop LLWP LRHS MBar NMen NRya WTin
§	- var. ***amabile***	CLyd EBee ERos GCrs GEdr LBee NChi NLAp NRya NSla NWCA
	'Mars'	see *A. stipitatum* 'Mars'
	maximowiczii	EBee EBrs ECho
	moly	CArn CWCL EBee EBrs ECho EPfP GSki IFoB LAma MBri MRav NBPC NGHP NRya SRms WBor WCot WTin
	- 'Jeannine' ♀H4	CMea CTca EBee EBrs ECho EPot GAbr LAma MLLN MNFA SPhx
	'Mont Blanc'	CMea EBee EBrs ELan ERou GBin IPot LAma
	'Mount Everest'	see *A. stipitatum* 'Mount Everest'
	multibulbosum	see *A. nigrum*
	murrayanum misapplied	see *A. unifolium*
	murrayanum Reg.	see *A. acuminatum*
	narcissiflorum misapplied	see *A. insubricum*
§	***narcissiflorum*** Villars	ECho GCrs LEdu WCot
	neapolitanum	CAgr CArn EBee ECho EPot LAma LBee LRHS MBri NWCA SPer SRms WGwG WHil
§	- Cowanii Group	CTca EBee EBrs ECho EHrv SWal WCot
	- 'Grandiflorum'	CSam EBee EBrs ECho LRHS MLLN SPhx WBrE
	nevskianum	CTca EBee EBrs ECho LAma LRHS
§	***nigrum***	CArn CAvo CFFs CTca EBee EBrs ECho EHrv EMon EPot EShb LAma LRHS MLLN MRav NBir WCot
	nutans	CBod EBee EBrs ECho EMar EUnu EWin LAma LEdu MHer NGHP SHDw WHal WJek
	nuttallii	see *A. drummondii*
§	***obliquum***	CArn CMil EBee EBrs ECha ECho EGle GSki LRHS MSte WCot WTin
	odorum L.	see *A. ramosum* L.
	oleraceum	WHer
§	***oreophilum***	CArn CAvo CFFs CMea CSam CTca EBee EBrs ECha ECho ECtt EHrv EPfP GSki LAma LRHS MLLN MWat NRya NWCA SPer SRms WBor WCot WHoo WLin WTin
	- 'Samur' new	LRHS
§	- 'Zwanenburg' ♀H4	ECho EPot NMen WCot
	ostrowskianum	see *A. oreophilum*
	ovalifolium new	EBee
	- var. ***leuconeurum***	WCot
	paepalanthoides new	EBee
	pallens	CBre CWsd NBir
§	***paniculatum***	EBrs SCnR
	paradoxum	EBee LEdu NBir
	- var. ***normale***	CBgR CDes EBee EBrs ECho EMan EMon EPot NMen WCot
	pedemontanum	see *A. narcissiflorum* Villars
	peninsulare	CPBP
	'Pinball Wizard' new	EBee
	platycaule	WCot
	plummerae new	EBee EBrs ECho
	plurifoliatum	EBee ECho LAma
	polyphyllum	see *A. carolinianum*
	prattii new	EBee
	pulchellum	see *A. carinatum* subsp. *pulchellum*
	'Purple Giant'	ERCP
	'Purple Pride'	SPhx
	pyrenaicum misapplied	see *A. angulosum*
	pyrenaicum Costa & Vayreda	ELan
	ramosum Jacquin	see *A. obliquum*
§	***ramosum*** L.	EBee EBrs ECho LAma LEdu NBre NCob NGHP WPer
	'Renaissance' new	ERCP
	'Rien Poortvliet'	CArn EBee LAma
	robustum new	EBrs
	rosenbachianum misapplied	see *A. stipitatum*
	rosenbachianum Regel	CArn CMdw EBee EMon EPot ERou LAma MLLN
	- 'Akbulak'	EBrs ECho LRHS MSte
	- 'Album'	EBee EBrs ECha ECho EPot ERou LAma LRHS MLLN WCot
	- 'Purple King'	ECho LRHS
	- 'Shing'	EBee EBrs LAma LRHS
§	***rosenorum*** 'Michael H. Hoog'	EBee EBrs ECho ERou LAma LRHS WCot

	roseum	CArn CMea CPBP EBee EBrs ECho ECtt ERos LAma LLWP LRav MDKP NCGa
	rotundum **new**	LRHS
§	- subsp. ***jajlae***	EBee ECho LLWP LRHS
	'Round and Purple'	EBee EBrs
	rubellum	ERos
	rubens	CWCL
	sarawschanicum	EBee ECho
	- 'Chinoro'	EBrs ECho LRHS
	sativum	CArn MHer MNHC SIde WSel
	- 'Albigensian Wight' **new**	NGHP
	- 'Arno' ♀H4	CPrp
	- 'Cristo' ♀H4	CPrp
	- 'Elephant'	see *A. ampeloprasum* 'Elephant'
	- golden	GPoy
	- 'Iberian Wight'	NGHP
	- 'Mediterranean Wight'	NGHP
	- var. ***ophioscorodon***	EBee ECho GPoy ILis LAma
	- - 'Early White' ♀H4	NGHP
	- - 'Purple Wight'	NGHP
	- 'Solent White' ♀H4	NGHP
	- 'Sprint'	CPrp
	saxatile	EBee EBrs ECho ERos
	schmitzii	EMon
	schoenoprasum	More than 30 suppliers
	- f. ***albiflorum***	CArn CBgR CPbn CPrp CSWP EBrs ECha ECrN GMaP LEdu MHer MSte NBir NCGa NHol SIde SSvw WEas WHer
	- 'Black Isle Blush'	CPbn GPoy MHer SMHy
	- 'Corsican White'	EMon LEdu
	- fine-leaved	ELau
	- 'Forescate'	CBgR CBod CPrp EBee EBla EBrs ECha EWes GSki LAma LAst LHop LRHS MLLN MRav SBch SIde SPet SPla SSvw WHil
	- 'Forncett Forescate'	CBgR
	- 'Grolau'	EUnu
	- medium-leaved	ELau
	- 'Netherbyres Dwarf'	CArn
	- 'Pink Perfection'	GPoy MHer SMHy
	- 'Polyphant'	CBre
	- 'Shepherds' Crooks'	WThu
	- var. ***sibiricum***	GGar SDix WSel WShi
	- 'Silver Chimes'	CDes CWan EBee MRav SBch SHDw
	- thick-leaved	NPri
	schubertii	More than 30 suppliers
	scorodoprasum	CAgr SIde WJek
	- subsp. ***jajlae***	see *A. rotundum* subsp. *jajlae*
	- subsp. ***scorodoprasum***	EBrs LAma LEdu
	senescens	CArn CTri EBee ECGP ECho ERos EWsh LAma MRav NChi SApp SBch SBla SIng SRms SSvw WTin
	- var. ***calcareum***	CPLG EBee
	- giant	EMon
§	- subsp. ***montanum***	CSpe EBla ECha ECho EGoo EPot LAma LEdu LPio NBre NMen SDix SIng SMHy WAbe WCot WMoo
§	- - var. ***glaucum***	CArn CBgR CLyd CMea CPBP CPom CPrp CSpe CSsd EBee EBla EBrs ECha EPla GEdr LEdu LPio MNFA NRya SAga SIng SMeo SPet WCot WPer WRos WTin
	- subsp. ***senescens***	EBee EBrs EMon LEdu LPio MLLN WPrP
	sibthorpianum	see *A. paniculatum*
	siculum	see *Nectaroscordum siculum*
	sieheanum	EBee
§	***sikkimense***	CSsd CWCL EBee EBla ECho ERos GCrs GEdr LBee MDKP NCGa NSla SBla SPet SPla SSvw WCot WPer WPrP
	'Silver Spring' **new**	ERCP
	songpanicum	EBee
	sphaerocephalon	More than 30 suppliers
	splendens	EBee EBrs ECho ERos
	stellatum	LRHS WGwG
	stellerianum	WPer
	- var. ***kurilense***	CLyd WThu
§	***stipitatum***	EBrs EMon ERCP LAma LRHS SPhx WCot WHil
	- 'Album'	CArn EBee EBrs EMon EPot
	- 'Glory of Pamir'	LRHS
§	- 'Mars'	CFir EBee EBrs ERou LRHS MLLN NLar
§	- 'Mount Everest'	CArn CAvo CFFs CFir CTca EBee EBrs ECho EMon EPot ERou EShb GMaP LAma LRHS MLLN MSte MWgw NBPC NCGa SPhx WShi
§	- 'Violet Beauty'	CWCL EBee ERou LAma LRHS SMeo SPhx WCot
§	- 'White Giant'	EBee EBrs ERou MSte SMeo SPhx
	stracheyi	WCot
	strictum Ledeb.	see *A. szovitsii*
	subhirsutum	CLyd EBee
	subvillosum	ERos WCot
	'Summer Beauty'	see *A. senescens* subsp. *montanum*
	'Sweet Discovery'	EBee EBrs ECho ERou LAma
§	***szovitsii***	EBee
	textile	ERos
§	***thunbergii*** ♀H4	EBee ECho GCrs NBir NDlv NRya
	- 'Nanum'	CPom CSsd
	- 'Ozawa'	EBee LBee NMen SBla SIng WCot
	tibeticum	see *A. sikkimense*
*	***tournefortii***	EBee ECho
	triquetrum	CStu CTca EBee EBrs ECho ELan ELau EPfP EPot GGar IBlr ILis LAma LBMP LEdu NBir NSti SIng SPhx WCot WHer WLin WMoo
	tuberosum	More than 30 suppliers
	- B&SWJ 8881	WCru
	- purple/mauve-flowered	CHby ELau GWCH
	tubiflorum	EBee ECho
§	***unifolium*** ♀H4	CArn CAvo CBgR CFFs CMea CPom CSam CTca EBee EBrs ECho EPfP EPot GKev LAma LHop LRHS MLLN MNHC MNrw MRav NBir SGar SPhx WAbe WBrE WCot WFar WLin WPer
	ursinum	CArn CBgR CHby CWan EBee EBrs ECho EOHP GPoy LAma MNHC MWat NGHP NMir NTHB WAul WFar WHen WJek WPtf WShi
	'Valerie Finnis'	CPBP EBee ECho SAga SBla
	victorialis	EBrs ECho
	- 'Cantabria' ARMEH 7827 **new**	EBee
	vineale	CArn EBee NMir WHer
§	- 'Hair'	CAby EBrs ECho EMan EPfP ITer LAma LRHS MBri SMad WHil WRos WTMC
	violaceum	see *A. carinatum*
	'Violet Beauty'	see *A. stipitatum* 'Violet Beauty'
	virgunculae	CPBP EBee SBla SCnR WAbe
	wallichii	CLyd EBee EBrs ECho EMon GBin GMaP MBNS MGol NBir NChi WCot WTin
	- ACE 2458	WCot
	- plum-flowered	GEdr
	- purple-flowered	GEdr
	'White Giant'	see *A. stipitatum* 'White Giant'
	'World Cup'	LRHS
	zaprjagajevii	LEdu WCot
	zebdanense	EBee EBrs ECho ERos LAma LRHS

Allocasuarina (*Casuarinaceae*)

	diminuta **new**	EShb

monilifera	ECou
nana	IDee
zephyrea	CTrC

almond see *Prunus dulcis*

Alnus ✿ (*Betulaceae*)

cordata ♀H4	CBcs CCVT CDoC CDul CLnd CMCN CSBt CSto CTho CTri EBee ECrN ELan EMac EPfP LBuc MGos NBee NEgg NWea SBLw SHBN SPer SPlb SSta WFar WMou WOrn
cremastogyne	NLar
crispa	see *A. viridis* subsp. *crispa*
fauriei from Niigata, Japan	CSto
firma	CDul CMCN IDee
- var. ***sieboldiana***	see *A. sieboldiana*
glutinosa	CBcs CCVT CDoC CDul CLnd CRWN CSBt CTri EBee ECrN EMac EPfP EWTr LBuc MGos NBee NBlu NWea SBLw SHBN SHFr SPer WMou WOrn
- from Corsica	CSto
- 'Aurea'	CDul CEnd CLnd CTho CWib ECrN MBlu MDun MGos SBLw SPer
- var. ***barbata***	CSto
- 'Imperialis' ♀H4	CCVT CDoC CDul CEnd CPMA CTho EBee ECrN ELan EPfP EWTr IMGH LBuc LPan LRHS MBlu MBri MDun NBee NPal NWea SBLw SPer SPoG WOrn
- 'Laciniata'	CDoC CDul CTho ECrN MBlu MDun MGos NBlu SBLw WFar
hirsuta	CMCN CSto
incana	CDoC CDul CLnd CMCN CWib EBee ECrN EMac LBuc MBar MGos MMuc NPen NWea SBLw SHBN SPer WMou
- 'Aurea'	CBcs CDul CEnd CLnd CTho EBee ECrN ELan EMil EPfP ERas IArd LPan LRHS MBar MBlu MBri MGos NPal NWea SBLw SHBN SPer SPoG WOrn WPat
- 'Laciniata'	CTho LPan MGos SBLw SCoo WFar
- 'Pendula'	CTho SBLw
japonica	CLnd CSto NLar
lanata	WHCr
maximowiczii	CSto NLar
nepalensis	WCwm
nitida	CMCN CSto IDee
oregana	see *A. rubra*
pendula new	CSto
rhombifolia	CMCN
§ ***rubra***	CAgr CCVT CDoC CDul CLnd CMCN CPLG ECrN ELan EMac NWea SBLw WMou
- 'Pinnatifida'	see *A. rubra* f. *pinnatisecta*
§ - f. ***pinnatisecta***	CMCN CTho
§ ***rugosa***	CMCN
serrulata	see *A. rugosa*
§ ***sieboldiana***	CSto
sinuata	see *A. viridis* subsp. *sinuata*
x ***spaethii***	CDoC CTho MBri SBLw
subcordata	CLnd CSto
viridis	CAgr CMCN CSto ECrN NWea SBLw
§ - subsp. ***crispa***	CSto
- - var. ***mollis***	CMCN
§ - subsp. ***sinuata***	CAgr

Alocasia ✿ (*Araceae*)

x ***amazonica*** ♀H1	ERea LRHS MBri XBlo
'Calidora'	MJnS
cucullata	CFir
gageana	CDTJ CKob EAmu
macrorrhiza	CDTJ CKob EAmu MJnS
- 'Variegata' (v) ♀H1	MJnS
odora	EAmu XBlo
- from Yunnan new	MJnS
plumbea	XBlo
'Portodora'	EAmu MJnS
wentii	CDTJ EAmu

Aloe (*Aloaceae*)

aculeata	EShb
alooides new	CAbb
arborescens	CAbb CBct CBrP CDTJ CHEx CTrC EShb EWll SChr
- yellow-flowered	CTrC
aristata ♀H1	CAbb CHEx CHal EPem MBri SAPC SArc SChr SEND SWvt WGwG WHer
barbadensis	see *A. vera*
barberae	CAbb CCCN EShb
brevifolia ♀H1	CAbb CBrP EShb SAPC SArc
broomii	CAbb CCCN CDTJ EPfP SChr
camperi 'Maculata'	SChr
ciliaris	ERea EShb SChr
comptonii	EShb
cooperi	CAbb CCCN EShb
dawei	EPem
dichotoma	CAbb EShb
distans	SEND
dumetorum	EPem
ecklonis	CAbb CCCN CDTJ CTrC SChr SPlb
excelsa	SChr
ferox	CAbb CBrP CCCN CDTJ CTrC EPem EShb EUnu GPoy MSal SChr SEND SWal
fosteri	CDTJ
greatheadii	CTrC SChr
- var. ***davyana***	CCtw
humilis	CBrP CTrC EPem SChr
juvenna	EPem
littoralis	EPem
maculata	CDTJ CHEx CTrC
marlothii	CAbb CCCN EPem EShb
microstigma	CAbb CBct CCCN SChr
mitriformis	CBrP EPfP LCro SChr SEND
mutabilis	CHEx CTrC SChr
plicatilis	CAbb CCCN CDTJ CTrC EShb
polyphylla	WPGP
pratensis	CCCN CFir CPLG SChr SPlb
prinslooi	EPem
ramosissima	EShb
reitzii	CBct CTrC SPlb
speciosa	CAbb EShb
x ***spinosissima***	SChr
striata	CAbb CCCN EPem EShb SChr XPep
striatula	CAbb CBrP CDTJ CGHE CHEx CTrC EAmu EBee EShb IBlr LPJP SAPC SArc SBHP SChr WCot WGer WPGP XPep
- var. ***caesia***	IBlr
succotrina	CAbb
thraskii	CAbb
variegata (v) ♀H1	EShb SWvt WEas
§ ***vera*** ♀H1	CArn CCCN CDoC CHby COld CSpe ELau EOHP EPem ERea EShb EUnu GPoy ILis MNHC MSal NPer NPri NScw SBch SIde SWal WCot WHer

Alonsoa (*Scrophulariaceae*)

'Bright Spark'	CSpe
meridionalis	WWeb
- 'Rebel' new	LSou NPri
- 'Shell Pink'	WWeb

	'Pink Beauty'	CSpe
	unilabiata	CSpe
	warscewiczii	CEnt CHll ELan NBlu SHFr
	- pale-flowered	see *A. warscewiczii* 'Peachy-keen'
§	- 'Peachy-keen'	CSpe

Alopecurus (*Poaceae*)

	alpinus	see *A. borealis*
§	***borealis***	LRHS MMoz
	- subsp. ***glaucus***	CBrm CSpe EAlp EBee ELan EPPr GBin NSti SPer
	geniculatus	CRWN
	lanatus	NBea
	pratensis	NOrc XIsg
	- 'Aureovariegatus' (v)	CWan EBee EPPr EPla GMaP GSki LLWG MBar MBnl MBri MMoz MSte MWgw NBPC NBid NHol SApp SLim SPer WFar WMoo XIsg
	- 'Aureus'	ECha GBin LRHS MRav NBro NSti SPlb WFar
	- 'No Overtaking' (v)	EPPr XIsg

Alophia (*Iridaceae*)

	drummondii	ERos
	lahue	see *Herbertia lahue*

Aloysia (*Verbenaceae*)

	chamaedrifolia	CPle XPep
	citriodora	see *A. triphylla*
	gratissima **new**	EOHP
§	***triphylla*** ♀H2	More than 30 suppliers

Alpinia (*Zingiberaceae*)

	B&SWJ 3775	CKob WPGP
	formosana	LEdu
	japonica	CKob CPLG LEdu MSal
	- B&SWJ 8889	WCru
	malaccensis	CKob
	nutans misapplied	see *A. zerumbet*
	officinarum	CArn
	purpurata	MJnS
	- pink-flowered	MJnS
	speciosa	see *A. zerumbet*
§	***zerumbet***	MJnS
	- 'Variegata' (v)	CKob EAmu EShb MJnS XBlo

Alsobia see *Episcia*

Alstroemeria (*Alstroemeriaceae*)

	'Aimi'	LRHS MBri SBai SWal SWvt WFar WViv
	'Angelina'	LRHS SBai SPer SWvt
	angustifolia	GCrs
	'Apollo' ♀H4	LRHS MBNS MBri MNrw NBre SBai SPer SWvt WViv
	aurantiaca	see *A. aurea*
§	***aurea***	CTri EPfP EWin GGar MRav MWrn NLar SRms WMoo WSHC
	- 'Dover Orange'	CBod EPfP IGor LRHS NEgg SCoo SPoG
	- 'Lutea'	EBrs EWll LRHS NBre SPlb
	- 'Orange King'	CBod EBee EBrs ELan EPfP EWll LRHS NLar WCot
	'Blushing Bride'	CBcs EMar MBNS MBri SBai SPer SWvt WViv WWlt
	'Bonanza'	SBai SPer
	brasiliensis	CWsd EBee EShb LHop MNrw NChi WCot WSHC
	Butterfly hybrids	SWal
	'Candy Floss' **new**	EBee
	'Charm'	LRHS WFar
	'Coronet' ♀H4	LRHS MBNS WCra WViv
	'Dandy Candy'	EBrs NLar
	diluta subsp. ***chrysantha*** F&W 8700	WCot
	Doctor Salter's hybrids	ECGP LTwo MWgw NSla SRms
	'Elvira'	EMar SBai SPer
	'Evening Song'	EMar LRHS MBNS SBai SPer SWal SWvt
	aff. ***exserens***	WCot
	'Firefly'	LRHS
	'Flaming Star'	CBcs EMar MBri SBai WCot WViv
	'Fortune'	LRHS
	'Frances' (v)	CAvo
	'Freedom'	EBee LAst SPoG WGwG
	'Friendship' ♀H4	CBcs EMar NBre SBai SWal SWvt WViv
	garaventae	NLar WCot
	gayana	WCot
	'Gloria'	MBNS SWvt WViv
	'Glory of the Andes' (v)	CWGN EMan EMar NLar
	'Golden Delight'	LRHS MBri SBai SPer SPla WViv
	'Golden Queen'	WFar
§	H.R.H. Princess Alice = 'Staverpi' ♀H2	WFar
	haemantha	EBrs MDKP
	hookeri	ECho NLar SCnR
	- subsp. ***cummingiana***	LTwo WCot
	Inca Adore = 'Koadore' **new**	WViv
	'Inca Blaze'	WViv
	Inca Devotion = 'Konevotio' **new**	WViv
	'Inca Dream'	WViv
	Inca Exotica = 'Koexotica'	MGos WViv
	Inca Glow = 'Koglow'PBR	MGos WViv
	Inca Ice = 'Koice'	MGos WViv
	'Inca Moonlight'	WViv
	Inca Obsession = 'Koobsion'	WViv
	Inca Pulse = 'Konpulse' **new**	WViv
	Inca Serin = 'Koserin'	WViv
	Inca Tropic = 'Kotrop'	MGos WViv
	Isabella = 'Stalis'	WCra
	ligtu hybrids	CAvo CBcs CFFs CSBt EBrs ECha ELan EPfP IFoB LAst LHop LRHS MDun MNrw NPer NVic SPoG SRms SWal SWvt WBVN WBrE WFar WHoo
	- var. ***ligtu***	SPhx WCot
	'Lilac Wonder'	EBee NBhm
	'Little Eleanor'	EBee GBin LRHS WCot WFar WViv
	'Little Miss Charlotte'	LRHS WFar WViv
	'Little Miss Christina'	MBNS SBai SWvt WViv
	'Little Miss Isabel'	SBai WViv
	'Little Miss Matilda'	WViv
	'Little Miss Natalie' **new**	WViv
	'Little Miss Olivia'	WViv
	'Little Miss Rosalind'	MBNS SBai SWvt WViv
	'Little Miss Rosanna'	LRHS SWal WViv
	'Little Miss Sophie'	MBNS SBai SWvt WViv
	'Little Miss Tara'	MBNS SWvt WViv
	'Little Miss Veronica'	MBNS SBai WViv
	'Lucinda'	CBcs LRHS MBri SBai SPer SWvt WViv
	magnifica	WCot
	- subsp. ***magnifica***	WCot
	'Marina'	LRHS MBNS
	'Marissa'	GMaP LRHS
	'Mars'	LRHS SWal
	Meyer hybrids	MTho
	'Moulin Rouge'	MBNS MBri NLar SBai WViv
	'Orange Gem' ♀H4	LRHS MBNS WFar WViv
	'Orange Glory' ♀H4	GMaP IArd LRHS MBNS MBri SPla SWvt WFar WViv WWlt
	'Oriana'	SBai SWvt WViv
	pallida	CPBP
	- JCA 2.028.500	WCot
§	***paupercula***	WCot
	pelegrina	EBrs ECho LTwo MTho WCot

- 'Alba' ELan
- 'Rosea' ELan
'Perfect Blue' WViv
philippii WCot
'Phoenix' (v) CFir EBee EMar LRHS SBai SPla SWvt WCot WViv
'Pink Perfection' LRHS NLar
'Polka' EBee EMar LRHS MBNS WViv
presliana RB 94103 WCot
- subsp. ***australis*** CPou
- subsp. ***presliana*** WCot
Princess Aiko = 'Zapriko' PBR EBee SBai SPla
Princess Alice see *A.* H.R.H. Princess Alice
Princess Angela = 'Staprilan'PBR CBcs MBNS NLar SBai SCoo
Princess Anouska = 'Zaprinous' SBai
Princess Beatrix = 'Stadoran' WFar
Princess Camilla = 'Stapricamil' CBcs SBai
Princess Daniela = 'Stapridani'PBR SCoo SPoG
Princess Ella = 'Staprirange'PBR NLar SBai
Princess Isabella = 'Zapribel' SBai
Princess Ivana = 'Staprivane'PBR NLar SPoG
Princess Juliana = 'Staterpa' SPla SPoG
Princess Leyla = 'Stapriley'PBR CBcs MBNS SBai
'Princess Margaret' NLar
Princess Marilene = 'Staprilene'PBR MBNS SBai
Princess Monica = 'Staprimon'PBR MBNS SPla SPoG
Princess Oxana = 'Staprioxa'PBR NLar SCoo
Princess Paola = 'Stapripal'PBR MBNS SCoo SPla
Princess Ragna see *A.* Princess Stephanie = 'Stapirag'
Princess Sarah = 'Stalicamp' EBee MBNS
Princess Sissi = 'Staprisis'PBR SPoG
§ Princess Sophia = 'Stajello' SPoG
§ Princess Stephanie = 'Stapirag' NLar SPla
Princess Susana = 'Staprisusa'PBR NLar SCoo
Princess VictoriaPBR see *A.* 'Victoria'
Princess Zavina = 'Staprivina'PBR CBcs CFir MBNS NLar SBai
§ ***psittacina*** CAvo CGHE CHar CHll CSam CSev CStu EBee EBla ECha ECho EHrv ELan EPfP EPla GBuc GCra IFoB LAst LHop MDun MHer MSte NChi SWal WFar WPGP WSHC WTin
- 'Mona Lisa' EShb EWll LTwo NLar WCot WViv
§ - 'Royal Star' (v) EBee EBla ELan ELon EMan EMon ENot EPPr EPfP EPla LRHS MRav NLar WCot WFar WHil WHoo WPrP WSHC
- variegated see *A. psittacina* 'Royal Star'
pulchella Sims see *A. psittacina*
pulchra LTwo
'Purple Rain' EMar MBri MNrw SBai SWvt WViv
pygmaea MTho
'Red Beauty' GMaP LRHS MBNS MBri NBir SBai SPer SPlb SWvt WCot
'Red Beauty' (v) see *A.* 'Spitfire'
'Red Elf' LRHS MBNS NBre SWvt WFar WViv
'Regina'PBR see *A.* 'Victoria'
'Rhubarb and Custard' **new** EBee
'Rosy Wonder' NMoo
'Selina' GBin LRHS MBNS NBre SWal WFar WViv
'Serenade' EMar SBai WViv
'Short Purple' CDes
'Solent Candy' WFar
'Solent Crest' WFar
'Solent Dawn' WFar
'Solent Pride' WFar
'Solent Wings' WFar
'Sovereign' MDKP
§ 'Spitfire' (v) MBri SBai SWvt WViv
'Spring Delight' (v) EMan WCot
'Strawberry Lace' **new** EBee
'Sunrise' WWlt
'Sunstar' GMaP LRHS
'Sweet Laura'PBR LTwo NLar NOrc NPri SPoG
'Tanya' **new** WViv
'Tessa' EBee LRHS MBNS MBri NBre SBai WCot WViv
'Turkish Delight' **new** EBee
'Verona' LRHS
§ 'Victoria'PBR WFar
violacea see *A. paupercula*
'White Apollo' EBee SPla
'Yellow Friendship' ♀H4 LRHS MBNS NLar SPlb SWvt WCra WFar WViv
Yellow King see *A.* Princess Sophia
'Yellow Queen' WFar

Alternanthera (*Amaranthaceae*)

dentata 'Purple Knight' **new** EShb

Althaea (*Malvaceae*)

armeniaca EBee EMon GMac MGol NLar WCot
cannabina CAby CFir CSpe ELan EMon GBri GQui MGol WBor WHal WHoo WHrl WKif WOld WSHC XPep
officinalis CArn CPrp CSev CWan ELan EMon GMac GPoy ILis MHer MNHC MSal SECG SIde WGwG WPer WSpi XPep
- ***alba*** EBee LSou NLar WHer
§ - 'Romney Marsh' EBee EDAr EWll MRav NCot SMad WFar WKif WSHC
rosea see *Alcea rosea*
rugosostellulata see *Alcea rugosa*

Altingia (*Hamamelidaceae*)

gracilipes WPGP

x *Alworthia* (*Aloaceae*)

'Black Gem' CBct EBee EShb EWll SKHP SPoG

Alyogyne (*Malvaceae*)

hakeifolia CSpe ECou
- 'Elle Maree' ECou ERea LRHS SOWG
- 'Melissa Anne' ECou LRHS SOWG
§ ***huegelii*** EBee ECou EMan ERas SPoG WDyG
- 'Lavender Lass' **new** ECou
- 'Santa Cruz' CCCN CHll CMdw CPLG CSpe EMil ERea LHop SMad SOWG WPGP WRos

Alyssoides (*Brassicaceae*)

utriculata GAbr WPer

Alyssum (*Brassicaceae*)

argenteum misapplied	see *A. murale*
corymbosum	see *Aurinia corymbosa*
idaeum	LRHS
montanum	CArn ECha ECho NBir NBlu SPlb SRms WMoo
§ - 'Berggold'	CHrt ECho EPfP LRHS LRav
- Mountain Gold	see *A. montanum* 'Berggold'
§ ***murale***	NLar
oxycarpum	EPot SBla WAbe
saxatile	see *Aurinia saxatilis*
- 'Citrinum'	see *Aurinia saxatilis* 'Citrina'
scardicum	LTwo
serpyllifolium	NWCA
sinuatum	see *Aurinia sinuata*
spinosum	WFar WLin XPep
§ - 'Roseum' ♀H4	CSpe CTri ECha ELan EPot GMaP LBee LRHS MLHP NLAp NMen NWCA SBla WAbe WCot WPer
* - 'Roseum Variegatum' new	EPot
- 'Strawberries and Cream'	SBla WAbe WFar
tortuosum	LSou WMoo
wulfenianum	GAbr LTwo NEgg NLar STre

Amana see *Tulipa*

Amaranthus (*Amaranthaceae*)

hypochondriacus 'Pygmy Torch' ♀H3	CSpe
* ***multiflora*** new	EBee

x *Amarcrinum* (*Amaryllidaceae*)

'Dorothy Hannibal'	WCot
memoria-corsii	CPrp CTca ECho
- 'Howardii'	CFir EBee EBrs ECho EMan EShb LEdu LPio LRHS WCot

x *Amarine* (*Amaryllidaceae*)

tubergenii	CAvo
- 'Zwanenburg'	CAby EBee WCot

x *Amarygia* (*Amaryllidaceae*)

§ ***parkeri*** 'Alba'	CAvo EBee EBrs ECho EMan LPio MSte WCot
- 'Rosea' new	EBrs

Amaryllis ✿ (*Amaryllidaceae*)

§ ***belladonna*** ♀H2-3	CAby CBcs CBgR CHEx CPne CStu CTca CWsd EBrs ECho EMan EMon EPfP EShb LAma LEdu LRHS MBri MSte NCGa SChr SDnm SPav SPer WCot WGer
- 'Bloemfontein'	CAvo
- 'Cape Town'	EMon
- 'Hathor'	EBee
- 'Johannesburg'	CAvo EMon LRHS WCot
- 'Kimberley'	CPne EMon
- 'Major'	CAvo
- 'Parkeri Alba'	see x *Amarygia parkeri* 'Alba'
- 'Purpurea'	EBee EBrs EMon WCot
- white-flowered	EBee ECho WCot
- 'Windhoek'	CAvo

Amberboa (*Asteraceae*)

§ ***moschata*** new	WCot

Ambrosina (*Araceae*)

bassii	EBrs

Amelanchier ✿ (*Rosaceae*)

alnifolia	EPla MGol
- 'Forestburg' new	MBri
- 'Obelisk'PBR	CAbP CDul EBee LBuc LTwo MAsh MBri MGos NLar SCoo SPoG SSta
§ - var. ***pumila***	GSki LHop MSte SSta WNor WTin
- 'Smokey'	CDul EMil
§ ***arborea***	CPle SRms WNor
bartramiana	CTho SSta
- 'Eskimo'	EBee NLar
canadensis K. Koch	see *A. lamarckii*
canadensis Sieb. & Zucc.	see *A. arborea*
canadensis ambig.	ISea WBod
canadensis (L.) Medik.	More than 30 suppliers
denticulata F&M 176 new	WPGP
x ***grandiflora*** 'Autumn Brilliance'	CDul CEnd LRHS MAsh NHol NLar
- 'Ballerina' ♀H4	More than 30 suppliers
- 'Princess Diana'	NLar
- 'Robin Hill'	CBcs CWSG EBee ECrN LBuc LPan LRHS MBlu MGos MRav NEgg NLar SBLw SCoo SHBN SLim SMad WFar
- 'Rubescens'	CDul CEnd EBee LPan LRHS SLon
'La Paloma'	CWSG MAsh MBri SCoo SPoG
laevis	CBcs CDul CTri EPfP LPan LRHS MGos NLar SPer STre WGor
- 'Cumulus'	MAsh MBri NLar
- 'Prince Charles'	MBri NLar
- 'R.J. Hilton'	MBri MLan SCoo
- 'Snow Cloud'	CDoC
- 'Snowflakes'	CDoC CEnd CWSG EBee LRHS MAsh MDun MGos MLan NHol SLim SPoG SPur
§ ***lamarckii*** ♀H4	More than 30 suppliers
ovalis misapplied	see *A. spicata*
ovalis Medik.	SPlb XPep
- 'Edelweiss'	CEnd CPMA EBee LPan MBlu MGos NEgg NLar SCoo
- 'Helvetia'	CEnd WEas
pumila	see *A. alnifolia* var. *pumila*
spicata	ECrN

Amicia (*Papilionaceae*)

zygomeris	CHEx CHll CMdw CPLG CPle CPom CSpe EMan EWes GBuc IBal MCot SBHP SMad SMrm WCot WSHC

Ammi (*Apiaceae*)

majus	CArn CBre EMan MCot MSal SDix
visnaga	CArn CSpe CWCL EUnu MSal WHal

Ammocharis (*Amaryllidaceae*)

coranica	WCot

Ammophila (*Poaceae*)

arenaria	CBig CRWN GFor GQui XIsg
breviligulata	GBin

Amomum (*Zingiberaceae*)

dealbatum	CKob
subulatum	CKob

Amomyrtus (*Myrtaceae*)

§ ***luma***	CDoC CHEx CPLG CPrp CTrG CTri ELan GQui IDee SArc WFar WPic

Amorpha (*Papilionaceae*)

canescens	CBcs EMan MBri MWea NSti SKHP WBVN WSHC
fruticosa	CAgr CBcs CPle EWTr LEdu LRav MBlu MBri MGol NLar SPlb WSHC
herbacea	NLar
ouachitensis	NLar
paniculata	NLar

Amorphophallus ✿ (*Araceae*)

albus	CKob ITer LEdu WCot

bankokensis new	EBee
bulbifer	CDTJ CDes CKob EAmu EBee EBrs ITer LAma LEdu LRHS WPGP
dunnii	CKob
henryi	CKob
kerrii	CExc EBee
konjac	CDTJ CDes CExc CGHE CHEx CHHB CKob CStu EBee LEdu SKHP WCot WPGP
nepalensis	CKob EBrs ITer
paeoniifolius	MJnS
rivieri	EBee EBrs
stipitatus	CAby WCot
tonkinensis	CKob

Ampelocalamus (*Poaceae*)

scandens	CGHE EPla WPGP

Ampelocissus (*Vitaceae*)

sikkimensis HWJK 2066	WCru

Ampelodesmos (*Poaceae*)

mauritanica	CBig CFwr CHrt CKno COIW CSam EBee ECha EPPr EShb EWes GFor LRav MGol NLar SEND SMHy SMad SPlb WCot XIsg XPep

Ampelopsis (*Vitaceae*)

aconitifolia	EBee MGos NLar SBra WSPU
- 'Chinese Lace'	EBee LRHS NLar SBra WPGP
§ ***brevipedunculata***	CBcs CRHN ECrN ELan LHop SCoo SGar SLim SPer WFar
- 'Citrulloides'	WCru
§ - var. ***maximowiczii*** 'Elegans'	CBcs CHEx CMac CRHN CWib EBee ELan ENot EPfP EShb LAst LHop LRHS MBar MGos MRav MSwo NBlu NBro SAga SBra SHBN SPer SPla SPoG SWvt WCot WPat WSHC
delavayana	MWea
glandulosa var. ***brevipedunculata***	see *A. brevipedunculata*
- - 'Tricolor'	see *A. brevipedunculata* var. *maximowiczii* 'Elegans'
- var. ***hancei*** B&SWJ 3855	WCru
henryana	see *Parthenocissus henryana*
megalophylla	CBcs CHEx EBee ELan EPfP EShb IDee LRHS MBlu MBri NCGa NLar SPer WBVN WCru WFar WNor WOVN
sempervirens hort. ex Veitch	see *Cissus striata*
tricuspidata 'Veitchii'	see *Parthenocissus tricuspidata* 'Veitchii'

Amphicome see *Incarvillea*

Amsonia (*Apocynaceae*)

ciliata	CFee CFir ELan MGol SPhx WFar WPer
hubrichtii	CAby CEnt CMdw CPom EBee EBrs ECha EGle EPPr GBuc GMac LHop MGol MSte NDov SMad SPhx WCot WHoo
illustris	CEnt CPom EBee GMac LRHS MGol MSte NDov SHar WPer WTin
§ ***orientalis***	More than 30 suppliers
tabernaemontana	More than 30 suppliers
- var. ***salicifolia***	CAby CEnt EBee EGle GSki LRHS MSte NDov SPhx WAbb WCAu WRos WTin

Amygdalus see *Prunus*

Anacamptis (*Orchidaceae*)

§ ***laxiflora***	NLAp SHdy
§ ***morio***	NLAp SHdy
pyramidalis	EFEx NLAp SHdy WHer

Anacyclus (*Asteraceae*)

pyrethrum	GPoy
- var. ***depressus***	CTri EBee ECho ECtt ELan EPfP GMaP LRHS NTHB NVic NWCA SBla SIng SPet SPlb WCFE WFar WHoo WPer
- - 'Garden Gnome'	CTri ECho EWin NTHB SRms WFar
- - 'Silberkissen'	EDAr

Anagallis (*Primulaceae*)

arvensis	MHer MSal
monellii ♀H4	SBla
- Blue Compact = 'Wesanacomp' new	LSou SVil
- subsp. ***linifolia*** 'Blue Light'	CSpe
- 'Skylover'	CCCN LAst LSou SAga SPet
- 'Sunrise'	LAst SBla
tenella	EAlp SAga
- 'Studland'	CEnt EPot GAbr NWCA SBla SIng SPoG WAbe

Anagyris (*Papilionaceae*)

foetida	XPep

Ananas (*Bromeliaceae*)

comosus (F)	CCCN LRHS
- var. ***variegatus*** (v)	CKob MBri

Anaphalioides (*Asteraceae*)

bellidioides	CTri ECha GGar LRHS WCru

Anaphalis (*Asteraceae*)

alpicola	EPot NMen
margaritacea	CBcs CSBt EBee ECha ECrN ECtt EWTr GMaP MLLN NBid SMer SRms WFar WMoo WPtf
- var. ***cinnamomea***	WEas
§ - 'Neuschnee'	CTri CWan EBee MWgw NBre NGdn NMir NPri SPla WFar WPer
- New Snow	see *A. margaritacea* 'Neuschnee'
- var. ***yedoensis*** ♀H4	CTri EBee ECot EGle MCot MLHP NBre NEgg SDix SGar SPer SPoG WBrE WCAu WTin
§ ***nepalensis*** var. ***monocephala***	ELan EMon NBre NSti WCAu
nubigena	see *A. nepalensis* var. *monocephala*
sinica 'Moon's Silver'	EBee
transnokoensis	EBee EWes
§ ***trinervis***	CPLG
triplinervis ♀H4	CHrt CTca EBee ELan ENot EPPr EPfP GAbr GGar GKev GMaP MBri MHer MLLN MRav NBid NBir NBro NSti NVic SPer SPoG SRms SWat WBor WCAu WCot WFar WHoo WMoo
- CC 1620	WCot
- 'Silberregen' new	EBee
§ - 'Sommerschnee' ♀H4	EBee ECha ECot ECtt EGle EPfP ERou LBMP LRHS MBri MCot MNFA MRav NEgg SPer WMnd WPer
- Summer Snow	see *A. triplinervis* 'Sommerschnee'

Anarrhinum (*Scrophulariaceae*)

bellidifolium	SPet

Anchusa (*Boraginaceae*)

angustissima	see *A. leptophylla* subsp. *incana*
§ ***azurea***	CTca EUnu MGol NRnb WPer XPep

- 'Dropmore'	CTri EBee ELan EPfP LAst LBMP LRHS MGol MNHC NBPC NEgg NOrc SPav SRms SSth WPer
- 'Feltham Pride'	CMdw CSBt EBee GKev GMaP MSte NRnb NScw SPav SRms SWvt WFar WHoo WPGP WPer WWeb
- 'Little John'	ECot ERou SRms WTel
- 'Loddon Royalist' ♀H4	More than 30 suppliers
- 'Opal'	EBee ECot EPfP ETod LRHS MPop MWat NCGa NEgg SBch SPla SPoG WCAu
- 'Royal Blue'	LRHS
caespitosa misapplied	see *A. leptophylla* subsp. *incana*
capensis	EBee
- 'Blue Angel'	LRHS MNHC SWvt WFar WWeb
cespitosa Lam.	ECho ELan EWes LTwo SBla WAbe
italica	see *A. azurea*
laxiflora	see *Borago pygmaea*
§ ***leptophylla*** subsp. ***incana***	NEgg SBch
- - F&W 9550	MDKP
- 'Sapphire Blue'	NBHF
myosotidiflora	see *Brunnera macrophylla*
officinalis	CArn EUnu MSal SPav
sempervirens	see *Pentaglottis sempervirens*

Ancylostemon (*Gesneriaceae*)

convexus B&SWJ 6624	WCru

Andrachne (*Euphorbiaceae*)

colchica	WCot

Andrographis (*Acanthaceae*)

paniculata new	CArn

Andromeda (*Ericaceae*)

glaucophylla	CBrm MBar
polifolia	CMHG ECho GCrs GKev WFar
- 'Alba'	ECho GBin LRHS MAsh MBar NLAp NRya SBod SPer SPlb SPoG SWvt WFar
- 'Blue Ice'	CWib ELan EPfP LRHS MAsh MBri NHar NLAp NLar NMen SPer SPoG SSpi WAbe WFar WPat
- 'Compacta' ♀H4	CDoC CWib EBee ECho EPfP GCrs LRHS MBar MBri NHol NMen SPer SPoG SRms SWvt WGwG WSHC
- 'Compacta Alba' ♀H4	ECho
- 'Grandiflora'	ECho GBin GEdr GGar LRHS MAsh SBod
- 'Kirigamine'	LRHS MAsh
- 'Macrophylla' ♀H4	ECho GBin GCrs GEdr NHar WPat
- 'Minima'	WThu
- 'Nana'	CSBt ELan EPfP LRHS MAsh NMen
- 'Nikko'	CWib NHol
- 'Shibutsu'	NMen

Andropogon (*Poaceae*)

gerardii	CBig CKno CRWN EBee ECha EHul EPPr EPla EWsh GFor LEdu LRav SApp SMad WDyG XIsg
ischaemum	see *Bothriochloa ischaemum*
saccharoides	EBee LRav
scoparius	see *Schizachyrium scoparium*
virginicus	CBig GFor

Androsace (*Primulaceae*)

CD&R 2477 from China	WCru
albana	GKev
alpina	CGra WAbe
baltistanica	WAbe
barbulata	CStu WAbe
bisulca var. ***aurata*** SDR 2922	GKev
bulleyana	CStu WAbe
caduca	WAbe
carnea	CPBP ECho GKev
- ***alba***	EPot NWCA WLin
- subsp. ***brigantiaca***	CPBP GKev ITim NLAp NSla NWCA WAbe WHoo
- var. ***halleri***	see *A. carnea* subsp. *rosea*
- subsp. ***laggeri*** ♀H4	ECho EPot GCrs LTwo NLAp NSla WAbe
- - 'Andorra'	NLAp
§ - subsp. ***rosea*** ♀H4	NWCA
carnea x ***pyrenaica***	ECho EPot NMen WAbe
chamaejasme	ECho
ciliata	WAbe
cylindrica	CPBP GCrs GKev ITim LRHS NLAp NMen WAbe WFar
cylindrica x ***hirtella***	ECho ITim LRHS WAbe
cylindrica x ***hirtella***, ENF strain	WAbe
delavayi	WAbe
geraniifolia	CPLG EBee ECha MFOX SRms WCru WLin
globifera	EPot WAbe
gracilis PB 99/20	EPot
halleri	see *A. carnea* subsp. *rosea*
hedraeantha	CLyd ITim NLAp NRya NSla WAbe
himalaica	CPBP EPot GEdr NMen SBla
hirtella	CPBP ITim NLAp NMen WAbe
* ***idahoensis***	EPot WAbe
incana	WAbe
jacquemontii	see *A. villosa* var. *jacquemontii*
lactea	WAbe
laevigata	NMen SBla WAbe
- from Columbia River Gorge, USA	WAbe
- var. ***ciliolata***	NLAp NWCA SBla WLin
- - NNS 00-263	SBla
- - NNS 030-242	SBla
- 'Gothenburg'	WAbe
- 'Saddle Mount' new	WAbe
lanuginosa ♀H4	CLyd CMea ECho EPot NMen NWCA SBla SRms WAbe
limprichtii	see *A. sarmentosa* var. *watkinsii*
x ***marpensis***	EPot WAbe
mathildae	ITim WAbe
microphylla	see *A. mucronifolia* G. Watt
'Millstream'	CPBP
§ ***mollis***	CPBP
montana	WAbe
mucronifolia misapplied	see *A. sempervivoides*
§ ***mucronifolia*** G. Watt	EPot WAbe
mucronifolia x ***sempervivoides***	EAlp EPot
muscoidea	WAbe
- 'Breviscapa'	EPot SBla
- f. ***longiscapa***	WAbe
- Schacht's form	GCrs SBla WAbe
nivalis	WAbe
- 'Chumstick Form' new	CGra
- var. ***nivalis*** new	CGra
- - NNS 00-268	NWCA
ochotensis new	WAbe
primuloides	see *A. studiosorum*
pubescens	CGra ITim LRHS LTwo NMen
pyrenaica	ECho GKev ITim LRHS NLAp NMen SIng WAbe
rigida	NLAp WAbe
- KGB 168	EPot
robusta	GCrs
- subsp. ***purpurea***	WAbe
rotundifolia	EBee GEdr GKev WCru
sarmentosa misapplied	see *A. studiosorum*
sarmentosa ambig.	EAlp
sarmentosa Wall.	SRms WHoo
- from Namche, Nepal	WAbe
- Galmont's form	see *A. studiosorum* 'Salmon's Variety'

	- 'Sherriffii'	CFee EPot GEdr SIng SRms WHoo
§	- var. ***watkinsii***	EPot NMen
	- var. ***yunnanensis*** misapplied	see *A. studiosorum*
	- var. ***yunnanensis*** Knuth	see *A. mollis*
	selago	WAbe
§	***sempervivoides*** ♀H4	CLyd ECha ECho EDAr EPot GKev GMaP LHop LRHS NDlv NHol NLAp NMen NWCA SBla SPlb SRms WAbe WHoo WLin WPat
	- 'Greystone'	EPot NMen
	- 'Susan Joan' (v)	CPBP EPot GEdr GKev SBla WAbe
	septentrionalis 'Stardust'	ECho
	sericea	WAbe
	spinulifera	GKev
	strigillosa	WAbe
§	***studiosorum*** ♀H4	ECho GAbr GEdr GKev
	- 'Chumbyi'	GEdr LTwo NHol NLAp NWCA SBla SIng SRms WPat
	- 'Doksa'	CPBP EPot GCrs GKev NLAp SBla WAbe WPat
§	- 'Salmon's Variety'	CMea CTri ECho NRya WAbe
	tapete	WAbe
	- ACE 1725	EPot
	vandellii	CPBP ITim WAbe
	villosa var. ***arachnoidea***	CPBP
§	- var. ***jacquemontii***	CPBP NHar NWCA SBla
	- - lilac-flowered	CPBP EPot WAbe
	- - pink-flowered	EPot NLAp WAbe
	vitaliana	see *Vitaliana primuliflora*
	watkinsii	see *A. sarmentosa* var. *watkinsii*
	yargongensis	WAbe
	zambalensis	WAbe

Andryala (*Asteraceae*)

	agardhii	WLin WPat
	lanata	see *Hieracium lanatum*

Anemanthele (*Poaceae*)

§	***lessoniana*** ♀H4	More than 30 suppliers
	- 'Autumn Tints'	EPPr
	- 'Gold Hue'	EAlp

Anemarrhena (*Anthericaceae*)

	asphodeloides	CArn MSal WCot

Anemone ✿ (*Ranunculaceae*)

	B&SWJ 6716 from Taiwan	WCru
	aconitifolia Michx.	see *A. narcissiflora*
	aconitifolia ambig.	CSpe
	altaica	GAbr MSal NEgg NLar NSum SRms WBVN
	amurensis	EBee EBla
	apennina ♀H4	CAvo CLAP ECha GEdr IBlr WTin
	- var. ***albiflora***	CAvo CDes CFwr CLAP EBee EBrs ECha EPot ERos GEdr IBlr LRHS MAvo MSte NDov SMeo WCot WPnP
	- 'Ballyrogan Park'	IBlr
	- double-flowered (d)	EBee EBla ECha IBlr NDov SBla WCru
	- 'Petrovac'	CLAP EBrs EPot IBlr WCot
	baicalensis	EShb EWll
	baldensis	EBee ECho EDAr GCrs LBee LRHS NBre NOak SRms
	- SDR 3570	GKev
	barbulata	CLAP EWes GBuc NLar SPhx WBVN WSHC
	begoniifolia **new**	EBee
	blanda ♀H4	CPLG CWCL EBrs IHer LAma LBMP LHop MBri MNHC NBlu NChi SEND SWal WBVN WBor WFar WShi
	- blue shades	CSam CTca EBrs ECGP ECho EPfP EWTr GEdr GKev GMaP IGor LRHS SMeo SPer SPhx SWal WLin WRHF
	- 'Blue Star'	ECho
	- blue-flowered	CAvo CFFs CMea CTri ELan ENot EPot GAbr LAma LBMP LRHS MBri MNFA MWgw SMrm SPoG SRms WCra WFar
	- 'Charmer'	EBrs ECho EPot LHop NMen WHil
	- 'Ingramii'	WCot
	- 'Pink Charmer'	ECho ENot
	- 'Pink Star'	CTca EBrs ECho LAma LRHS MWgw NBir WLin
	- 'Radar' ♀H4	CAvo CFFs CMea EBrs ECho EPot ERCP LAma MNrw NBir WAbe
	- var. ***rosea*** ♀H4	EBrs ECho ELan EPfP LAma MLLN SPer SPoG WFar
	- 'Violet Star'	CMdw EBrs ECho EPot LRHS SMeo SPhx
	- 'White Splendour' ♀H4	More than 30 suppliers
	blue-flowered from China **new**	CDes
	canadensis	CHar CMea CPMA EBee EPPr GAbr GBuc GKev MNFA MNrw MSte NCGa NEgg NSum WBVN WCot
	caroliniana	EBee ECho GAbr GBuc GCrs LRHS NEgg WCru
	chapaensis HWJ 631	WCru
	coronaria 'Bicolor'	EBrs
	- De Caen Group	EBrs EPfP LAma LHop SPoG SWal WCra WFar
§	- - 'Die Braut'	EBrs EPfP LBMP LRHS NBir SMeo SPer WFar
	- - 'His Excellency'	see *A. coronaria* (De Caen Group) 'Hollandia'
§	- - 'Hollandia'	EBrs LBMP LRHS SMeo SPer
	- - 'Mister Fokker'	CTca EBrs LAma LBMP LRHS SPer WCra WFar
	- - The Bride	see *A. coronaria* (De Caen Group) 'Die Braut'
	- - 'The Governor'	CTca EBrs SWal WFar
	- Jerusalem hybrids	WFar
	- Saint Bridgid Group (d)	EBrs EPfP LAma MBri SPet WFar
	- - 'Lord Lieutenant' (d)	EBrs NBir SMeo WFar
	- - 'Mary Seton' (d) **new**	LRHS
	- - 'Mount Everest' (d)	EBrs NBir
	- - 'Saint Bridgid' (d) **new**	EBrs
	- - 'The Admiral' (d)	EBrs NBir SWal WFar
	- 'Sylphide' (Mona Lisa Series)	EBrs LBMP LRHS NBir SMeo SPer WCra WFar
	crinita	GBuc WBVN WLin
	cylindrica	CMHG CSam MDKP MNrw NBre NLar
	decapetala	NChi NRnb WLin
	demissa	GBuc GKev NBid NRya WCot
	- BWJ 7785	WCru
	- SDR 3307	EBee GKev
	dichotoma	SSvw
	drummondii	GKev GSki NChi WBVN WWeb
	elongata B&SWJ 2975	WCru
	eranthoides	CLAP EBee EBrs ECho
	fasciculata	see *A. narcissiflora*
	flaccida	CAby CDes CLAP EBee EHrv GBuc GMac LRHS MSte SPhx WCot WCru WFar WHal WSHC
	x ***fulgens***	ECha
	- 'Multipetala'	CSpe EBrs SBla WCot
	globosa	see *A. multifida* Poir.
	'Green Apples'	EKen
	'Guernica'	ECho EWes GBuc NRnb WBVN
	'Hatakeyama Double' (d)	CMdw
	'Hatakeyama Single'	CDes CMdw
	hepatica	see *Hepatica nobilis*
§	***hortensis***	NBre SBla SPhx
	- subsp. ***heldreichii***	CDes SBla

§	***hupehensis***	CPLG EWll GCrs GMaP IGor LRHS NOrc NPen WBod WFar
	- BWJ 8190	WCru
	- f. ***alba***	CDes CLAP CMil CSpe EBee EBla WCot WPGP WWeb
§	- 'Bowles' Pink' Υ^{H4}	CElw CPLG EBee EPPr IGor MAvo MWat SPet WBrk WCru WPGP WTin
	- 'Crispa'	see *A.* x *hybrida* 'Lady Gilmour' Wolley-Dod
	- 'Eugenie'	EBee GBuc GSki IPot LRHS MBNS NBir NHol SRGP
	- 'Hadspen Abundance' Υ^{H4}	More than 30 suppliers
	- 'Hadspen Red'	WFar
	- var. ***japonica***	CBrm CPou NCob
	- - B&SWJ 4886	WCru
	- - 'Bodnant Burgundy'	CDes CPrp EBee ECtt EGle WCAu WPGP
§	- - 'Bressingham Glow'	CMHG CPLG EBee ECtt EGle ELan EPfP EPot ERou GSki LHop LRHS MBri MNrw MRav MWgw NBir NHol NOrc NVic SHBN SPer SPet SWat WAbb WBrk WCAu WFar WMnd
§	- - 'Pamina' Υ^{H4}	More than 30 suppliers
	- - Prince Henry	see *A. hupehensis* var. *japonica* 'Prinz Heinrich'
§	- - 'Prinz Heinrich' Υ^{H4}	More than 30 suppliers
§	- - 'Rotkäppchen'	CPar EBee EBla ECtt EGle EMan GBin GMac LBMP LSou MAvo MRav NGby NHol NSti SMrm WCot WWeb
	- 'Ouvertüre'	CDes EBee MAvo WPGP
	- 'Praecox'	CMea EBee EBla EHrv EPfP GBri GBuc GSki LRHS MAvo MBNS MNFA NBir NCGa NGdn NHol NPri NSti SPoG SWvt WAbb WHal WHil WMnd WWeb
	- 'September Charm'	see *A.* x *hybrida* 'September Charm'
	- 'Splendens'	CMHG EBee ENot EWTr GBuc LAst LCro LHop LRHS MRav NEgg SPoG SPur SWal SWvt WAbb WFar WHal
	- 'Superba'	WKif
§	x ***hybrida***	MWat MWrn NChi NCob SGar WCru WFar WMoo
	- 'Alba Dura'	see *A. tomentosa* 'Albadura'
	- 'Alba' misapplied (UK)	see *A.* x *hybrida* 'Honorine Jobert'
	- 'Albert Schweitzer'	see *A.* x *hybrida* 'Elegans'
	- 'Andrea Atkinson'	More than 30 suppliers
	- 'Bowles' Pink'	see *A. hupehensis* 'Bowles' Pink'
	- 'Bressingham Glow'	see *A. hupehensis* var. *japonica* 'Bressingham Glow'
	- 'Coupe d'Argent'	EBee NBre
§	- 'Elegans' Υ^{H4}	CWCL EBee ECtt GMaP MRav NBPC NBir SWat WCru WHil WHoo WSpi
§	- 'Géante des Blanches'	CHar IGor LRHS MBri SMrm WFar WHoo
§	- 'Honorine Jobert' Υ^{H4}	More than 30 suppliers
§	- 'Königin Charlotte' Υ^{H4}	More than 30 suppliers
	- 'Kriemhilde'	EBee GBin
	- 'Lady Gilmour' misapplied	see *A.* x *hybrida* 'Montrose'
§	- 'Lady Gilmour' Wolley-Dod	CBgR CSpe EBee ECha ECtt EGle EHrv EPfP ERou EWTr GCra GMac LEdu LRHS MAvo MBri MRav NBPC NBir NCGa NChi NGdn SAga SHBN SPoG SRGP WCru WFar
	- 'Loreley'	CMea CPrp EBee GBuc MBNS MSte MWat NCGa SPet
	- 'Luise Uhink'	CPou IGor LCro NBir WEas
	- 'Margarete' Kayser & Seibert	COIW CPLG EBee EPPr IBlr LAst LRHS MBri MWat SMrm WCot WCru WFar
	- 'Max Vogel'	see *A.* x *hybrida* 'Elegans'
	- 'Monterosa'	see *A.* x *hybrida* 'Montrose'
§	- 'Montrose'	CPar CPou CSpe EBee EHrv EWes GMaP LRHS NBir NEgg SRms SWat WBor WFar
	- 'Pamina'	see *A. hupehensis* var. *japonica* 'Pamina'
	- Prince Henry	see *A. hupehensis* var. *japonica* 'Prinz Heinrich'
	- 'Prinz Heinrich'	see *A. hupehensis* var. *japonica* 'Prinz Heinrich'
	- 'Profusion'	CTri LBuc LRHS NBlu SHBN WHal
	- Queen Charlotte	see *A.* x *hybrida* 'Königin Charlotte'
	- 'Richard Ahrens'	EBee ECtt EGle ERou GBuc GMaP IBlr LHop LRHS MLHP MNFA NHol NOrc SAga SMeo SPla SRGP SWat WCAu WCru WFar WMnd WWeb
§	- 'Robustissima'	CSpe EBee ECtt EPfP ERou GBuc GMaP LLWP LRHS LSRN MGos MRav MSte MWgw NBir NCob NGdn NPri NSti SHBN SPer SPla SWat SWvt WAbb WAul WCAu WFar WMnd WMoo
	- 'Rosenschale'	CFwr EBee EGle LRHS MBri NCGa WCru WFar
	- 'Rotkäppchen'	see *A. hupehensis* var. *japonica* 'Rotkäppchen'
§	- 'September Charm' Υ^{H4}	More than 30 suppliers
	- 'Serenade'	CChe CPar EBee ECtt EPfP ERou EWTr LRHS MBri MLLN MRav NBir NCGa NEgg NRnb SHBN SPad SPoG SRkn SSvw WCAu WCot WFar WHil WHoo WMoo
	- Tourbillon	see *A.* x *hybrida* 'Whirlwind'
§	- 'Whirlwind'	More than 30 suppliers
	- 'White Queen'	see *A.* x *hybrida* 'Géante des Blanches'
	- Wirbelwind	see *A.* x *hybrida* 'Whirlwind'
	japonica	see *A.* x *hybrida*, *A. hupehensis*
	keiskeana	EBee GEdr WCru
	laceratoincisa new	EBee
§	x ***lesseri***	CFir CSpe EBee ECha ECho ECtt EDAr EHrv ELan GKev MHer NChi NEgg SBla SGar SPhx SRms WFar WHoo
	leveillei	More than 30 suppliers
	- BWJ 7919	WCru
§	x ***lipsiensis***	More than 30 suppliers
	- 'Pallida' Υ^{H4}	CPMA CWsd EBee EBla ECho ERos GBuc GCrs GEdr GKev IGor LLWP MAvo MNFA SBla WAbe WCot WHil
	lyallii	EBee GBuc WBrE
N	***magellanica*** hort. ex Wehrh.	see *A. multifida* Poir.
	matsudae B&SWJ 1452 new	WCru
	- 'Taiwan's Tiny Treasure' new	WCru
	mexicana B&SWJ 8414	WCru
	multifida misapplied, red-flowered	see *A.* x *lesseri*
§	***multifida*** Poir.	More than 30 suppliers
	- RCB/Arg RA-F-5	WCot
	- 'Major'	CFir CHar CMea CSpe EPfP LRHS NCob NPro NWCA SBla SPhx WBVN WFar
	- pink-flowered	GBuc LBMP
*	- 'Rubra'	CBgR CBrm CPrp EBee EDAr EHrv EPfP EWll GAbr GBuc LRHS MAvo MBNS MNFA MNrw NBPC NBir

		NDlv NEgg NWCA SPet SPoG WLin WWeb
	- yellow-flowered **new**	NSum
§	***narcissiflora***	EHrv GBuc IGor NBir NBre NChi WLin
	- var. ***citrina***	CWan CWsd
	nemorosa ♀H4	More than 30 suppliers
N	- 'Alba Plena' (d)	CSWP CSam EBee EBla EBrs ECha ECho EPPr ERos GBuc GEdr GGar GMac LRHS MTho NMen SIng WAbb WCru WEas WFar WHil WPnP
	- 'Allenii' ♀H4	EBee EBrs ECha ECho ELon ERos GBuc GEdr GMaP ITim MAvo MNFA MRav NMen NRya SBla SIng SMac WAbe WCot WCru WHil WPGP WPnP
	- 'Amy Doncaster'	CLAP
	- 'Atrocaerulea'	CLAP GBuc IBlr NLar WCru WHil
	- 'Atrorosea' **new**	EBee
	- 'Bill Baker's Pink'	CDes CLAP MAvo
	- 'Blue Beauty'	CLAP CPMA CPom EBee ELon ERos GBuc GMaP IBlr MAvo NMen SBch WAbe WCru WHil
	- 'Blue Bonnet'	CElw CPom CStu ECho GBuc IGor ITim MAvo MNrw WCot
	- 'Blue Eyes' (d)	CAby CDes CElw CLAP EBee EBla ECha EGle GBuc GCrs GEdr GMaP IBlr IGor ITim MAvo MSte NBir NDov NMen SBla WAbe WCot WCru WPGP
	- 'Blue Queen'	CStu GAbr GBuc
	- 'Bowles' Purple'	CPMA CPom CStu EBee EBrs ECho EPot GBuc GMaP IBlr MAvo MNrw NDov NHar NLAp NMyG NRya SBla SIng SPoG WCot WCru WFar WIvy WPGP WPtf WTin
	- 'Bracteata'	ECho EHrv ERos GEdr NDov NMen
	- 'Bracteata Pleniflora' (d)	CBow CLAP CStu EBee EBla EBrs ECha ECho EGle GBuc GMaP IBlr IGor LHop MAvo MNFA MNrw NBir NMen WAbe WCot WCru WFar WHal
	- 'Buckland'	CDes CFwr CLAP CWsd EBee EHrv EPfP IBlr SKHP WCru
	- 'Cedric's Pink'	CLAP CPMA EBee EPPr ERos IBlr IGor LTwo MNrw WCru
	- 'Celestial'	EBee EBla ECho EPPr GBuc
	- 'Danica'	EBee
	- 'Dee Day'	CLAP CWsd EBee ECha EHrv GBuc MAvo MNrw NDov SCnR WAbe WCru
	- 'Evelyn Meadows' ♀H4 **new**	SBla
	- 'Flore Pleno' (d)	CAby EBee EBla ECho GAbr NBir NDov NMen WHil WPGP
	- 'Frühlingsfee' **new**	NLar
	- 'Gerda Ramusen'	CLAP ECho LTwo
	- 'Glenroy Blush'	WAbe
	- 'Green Fingers'	CAby CHHB CLAP EBla ECho EHrv EPPr GBuc GEdr GMaP IGor ITim MAvo MNrw NDov NGby SCnR WAbe WCot WCru WIvy
	- 'Hannah Gubbay'	CLAP GBuc IBlr IGor MAvo MNrw MSte SIng WAbe
	- 'Hilda'	EBee EBrs ECho EGle EPot ERos GBuc GEdr IPot MAvo MNFA MNrw NDlv NDov NLAp NMen NRya NSla WAbe WCru WHil
	- 'Ice and Fire'	SSvw
	- 'Jack Brownless'	CLAP ITim WCot
	- 'Kentish Pink'	GBuc GCrs GMaP
	- 'Knightshayes Vestal' (d)	CLAP EBee MRav NHol WCot WCru WIvy

	- 'Lady Doneraile'	CDes CLAP CWsd EBee ECha GBuc ITim NBir NLar SSvw WCru WFar
	- 'Leeds' Variety'	CLAP EGle GCrs GMaP GMac IGor ITim MAvo MNrw MTho NDov NMen NSla SBla WCot WHil
	- 'Lismore Blue'	EBee EPot
	- 'Lismore Pink'	EHrv GBuc GEdr
	- 'Lychette'	CAby CAvo EBee ECha ECho EGle EHrv EPot GAbr GBuc IBlr ITim LPio MAvo NDov NSla NWCA SHar SPhx WAbe WCot WCru WHil WLin
	- 'Martin'	CStu
	- 'Mart's Blue'	GBuc
	- 'Monstrosa'	CBgR CHHB EBee EBrs ECho EPot GBuc SSvw WCot
	- 'New Pink'	CLAP CPom EBee IBlr
	- 'Parlez Vous'	CWsd EBee EGle EHrv EPPr GEdr LPio MAvo MNrw NDov NMen SCnR SKHP SMHy WCru
	- 'Pentre Pink'	EPot IBlr MAvo MNrw MSSP MTho WBVN WCru WIvy
	- 'Picos Pink'	EHrv GBuc NDov SCnR
	- 'Pink Carpet'	GBuc GEdr
	- pink-flowered	CLAP SPhx WCru
	- red-flowered	CStu
	- 'Robinsoniana' ♀H4	More than 30 suppliers
	- 'Rosea'	CHHB CLAP CStu EBrs ECho EPot GEdr GMac MNFA WAbe WCru WHil
	- 'Royal Blue'	More than 30 suppliers
	- 'Super Allenii' **new**	EBee
	- 'Tinney's Blush'	CLAP EBee SBla
	- 'Tomas'	EBee GBin GEdr MAvo NHar
	- 'Vestal' (d) ♀H4	More than 30 suppliers
	- 'Virescens' ♀H4	CAby CAvo CLAP CStu CWCL EBee ECha ECho EGle EHrv ELon EPPr ERos GAbr GBuc GCrs GEdr GMaP MAvo NDov NHar NSla NWCA SMHy WAbe WHal WIvy WPGP
	- 'Viridiflora'	CFwr CLAP ECho EGle EPfP GAbr GBuc LHop MNrw MRav MTho NBir NSti WCot WCru WFar WHil WSHC
	- 'Westwell Pink'	CAby CDes CLAP CSpe EBee LTwo MAvo MSSP MSte WCot WPGP
	- 'Wilks' Giant'	CLAP ITim MAvo WCru
	- 'Wilks' White'	CLAP EBee EBla EGle GEdr LBuc NSla WCru
	- 'Wyatt's Pink'	CLAP CWsd ELon GBuc ITim MAvo NCGa NSla WAbe WCru WPnP WTin
	- 'Yerda Ramusem'	EBee ECho EPPr
	nemorosa x ***ranunculoides***	see *A.* x *lipsiensis*
	obtusiloba	CLAP GBuc GCrs MTho SBla SRms WAbe
	- CLD 1549	GEdr
	- ***alba***	GMac SBla WAbe
	- var. ***polysepala***	GEdr
I	- 'Sulphurea'	CDes GEdr NMen
	- yellow-flowered	GBuc SBla WAbe
	palmata	CFwr CHFP CLAP EBee EDAr LDai MDKP MWea NBre SKHP SMad WCru WRos
	parviflora	GBuc
	patens	see *Pulsatilla patens*
	pavonina	CSpe EBee ECha ERos MAsh MBri MSSP MTho NBir SBla SPoG SRot
	- 'Chapeau de Cardinal'	SBla
	- 'Grecian Sunset'	CDes MAsh WPGP
	- lilac-flowered **new**	CDes
	- var. ***ocellata***	SAga

- pink-flowered **new**	CDes
polyanthes	EBee LRHS WCot
- HWJK 2337	WCru
prattii	CLAP EBee GEdr WHal
pseudoaltaica	EBee GEdr WCot WCru WWst
- pale blue-flowered	CLAP
pulsatilla	see *Pulsatilla vulgaris*
quinquefolia	CLAP WAbe WCot
raddeana	EBee EBrs ECho
ranunculoides ♀^{H4}	More than 30 suppliers
- 'Frank Waley'	WCot
* - ***laciniata***	CLAP GBuc MSte NMen WCot
- 'Pleniflora' (d)	CAvo CFwr CHHB CLAP EBla EBrs ECha ECho EHrv EMan GCrs GMaP MRav NLar NMen SBla WCot WFar WIvy
- subsp. ***ranunculoides*** **new**	EBrs GKev
- 'Semi Plena' **new**	CHHB EBrs
- subsp. ***wockeana***	CDes EBee ECho
riparia	see *A. virginiana* var. *alba*
rivularis	More than 30 suppliers
- BWJ 7611	WCru
- CC 4587	MGol
- CC 4588	MGol
- CLD 573	CDes WLin
- GWJ 9391	WCru
rockii **new**	GEdr
rupicola	EBee GMac NBir SBla
x ***seemannii***	see *A.* x *lipsiensis*
smithiana	CExc
stellata	see *A. hortensis*
sulphurea	see *Pulsatilla alpina* subsp. *apiifolia*
sylvestris	More than 30 suppliers
- 'Elise Fellmann' (d)	CLAP GBuc IGor WCot
- 'Flore Pleno' (d)	CDes CLAP EBee WCot
- 'Macrantha'	CDes CLAP CPrp EBee EMan EPfP GAbr GMac LAst NBPC WBrE WPGP WPrP
tetrasepala	CLAP EBee WCot WPGP
§ ***tomentosa***	EBee ECha EMan GGar GKev GSki IGor LBMP LRHS NBre SDix SPoG SRms SWat WBVN WFar WTMC WWeb
§ - 'Albadura'	EBee GSki NBre
- 'Robustissima'	see *A.* x *hybrida* 'Robustissima'
- 'September Glanz' **new**	EBee
trifolia	CAby CDes ECha EMan EPPr ERos GBuc GMac NBid NDov SCnR SRms WCot WPGP WPat
- pink-flowered	CLAP EBee MSte WFar
- 'Semiplena' (d)	CAby CDes EBee WCot
trullifolia	EBee EPPr EPfP GAbr GBin GCra GCrs GEdr GGar GKev GMaP GMac LAst LRHS MMHG MRav NSla SBla WRos
- ***alba***	GMac
- var. ***coelestina***	CDes GBuc NBir
- var. ***linearis*** **new**	EBee GMac
umbrosa **new**	EBee
vernalis	see *Pulsatilla vernalis*
virginiana	CSpe EBee EPPr EShb EWll GAbr LDai MDKP MFOX MSte MWea NBid NRnb WBVN WFar WHil WOut
§ - var. ***alba***	EBee EKen NLar NSti WBVN WPrP WPtf WTMC
vitifolia misapplied	see *A. tomentosa*
vitifolia DC.	WLin
- B&SWJ 2320	WCru
- B&SWJ 8202 from Vietnam	WCru
- GWJ 9434	WCru
- HWJK 2044	WCru

Anemonella (*Ranunculaceae*)

thalictroides	CBct CElw CFir CFwr CLAP CTca EBee ECho EFEx EHrv EPot GCrs GEdr GGar GSki ITim LAma LPio MAvo NCGa NDov NHar NMen NRya NWCA SBla WAbe WCru WFar WPrP
- 'Alba Plena' (d)	ECho GBuc
- 'Amelia'	CLAP GCrs GEdr NHar SCnR WAbe
- 'Betty Blake' (d)	EPot GCrs GEdr NHar
- 'Cameo'	CLAP EFEx EPot GEdr MAvo NHar SCnR WCru WWst
- 'Charlotte'	NHar
- 'Double Green' (d)	CLAP EFEx GEdr
- 'Flore Pleno' (d)	GCrs
- 'Full Double White' (d)	EFEx GEdr
- 'Green Hurricane' (d)	EFEx EPot GEdr ITim WWst
- 'Jade Feather'	CElw CGra SBla
- f. ***rosea***	CElw CLAP CPom CWCL EPot GBuc MAvo SMHy WAbe WCru WPrP
- - double pink-flowered (d)	SBla
- - 'Oscar Schoaf' (d)	CLAP EBee EPot GBuc GEdr ITim WAbe WWst
- - semi-double pink-flowered (d)	CElw CLAP EHrv MAvo NLar WWst
- semi-double white-flowered (d)	CElw CLAP EHrv GBuc NMen SBla WCot
- 'Tairin'	GEdr WWst
- 'White Bells'	NHar
- white-flowered **new**	WSpi

Anemonopsis (*Ranunculaceae*)

macrophylla	CDes CElw CLAP CWsd ECha EPot GBuc GCrs GEdr GMac IGor MNrw MSte MTho NLar SPhx WAbe WCru WLin WSHC
- 'White Swan' **new**	WCru

Anemopsis (*Saururaceae*)

californica	CDes EBee EMan EWes IFoB LLWG NLar WCru WPGP

Anethum (*Apiaceae*)

graveolens	CArn GPoy LRHS MHer MNHC SECG SIde SWal WPer WSel
- 'Dukat'	CSev ELau NGHP

angelica see *Angelica archangelica*

Angelica (*Apiaceae*)

B&SWJ 10345 from Guatemala **new**	WCru
acutiloba	CSpe EBee EMan EWll MHer MLLN NDov NGHP NLar NSti WCot WFar
archangelica	More than 30 suppliers
- 'Corinne Tremaine' (v)	CWan EMan NGHP NSti NTHB
atropurpurea	CArn CBct EBee ECtt EMan EMar EShb EWll GWWP ITer MHer MNrw MRav NCGa NDov NGHP NLar SWat WCAu WCot WFar WJek WMnd
'Coconut Ice'	ITer
dahurica	CArn EBee EUnu MSal
- B&SWJ 8603	WCru
decurrens	EBee
decursiva	MSal NDov WCot
- B&SWJ 5746	WCru
'Ebony'	CMea MCot MDKP SMad
florentii	CDes WPGP
gigas	More than 30 suppliers
- B&SWJ 4170	WCru
hispanica	see *A. pachycarpa*
japonica B&SWJ 8816a	WCru

montana	see *A. sylvestris*
morii RWJ 9802 new	WCru
§ ***pachycarpa***	More than 30 suppliers
pubescens	MSte NDov SPhx
- B&SWJ 5593	WCru
- var. ***matsumurae*** B&SWJ 6387	WCru
sachalinensis	EBee
sinensis	GPoy
'Summer Delight'	see *Ligusticum scoticum*
§ ***sylvestris***	CAgr CArn CHrt CRWN NGHP NSco NTHB WSel
* - 'Purpurea'	CKno CSpe CWsd EBee EWes SBch SDnm WPGP
- 'Vicar's Mead'	EBee EMan IPot LCro LHop LSRN MDKP MLLN NBPN NBid NCGa NChi NDov NGHP NLar NSti SPhx SPoG SRkn WPtf WSHC WSel
taiwaniana	CArn CRez CWan EBee ELan ITer NGHP NLar SGar SWat
ursina	MDKP
- RBS 0205	WBVN

Angelonia (*Scrophulariaceae*)

(Angelface Series) Angelface Blue = 'Anzwei'PBR	CSpe SVil
- Angelface Blue Bicolour = 'Anstern'	LAst SVil
'Stella Gem'	LRHS

Anigozanthos (*Haemodoraceae*)

'Big Red'	SOWG
(Bush Gems Series) 'Bush Eclipse'	SOWG
- 'Bush Haze'	SOWG
flavidus	CHEx CTrC ECre EOHP MBri MNHC SOWG SPlb
- 'Illusion'	CCCN
- 'Opal'	CCCN MNHC
- 'Orange Cross' new	SOWG
- 'Pearl'	CCCN
- 'Splendour'	CCCN MNHC
- yellow	WBrE
humilis Lindl. ♀H1	SOWG
manglesii ♀H1	CHEx SOWG SPlb WDyG
- 'Bush Dawn' (Bush Gems Series)	SOWG
'Regal Claw'	SOWG
'Royal Cheer'	SOWG

anise see *Pimpinella anisum*

Anisodontea (*Malvaceae*)

§ ***capensis***	CBcs CCCN EBee ELan EMan ERea LAst MAsh MBNS NBir SAga SBod SChF SLim SMrm SOWG SRkn SRms SWvt WDyG XPep
- 'Tara's Pink'	CSpe EBee EWes IFoB MAsh MBNS SAga SMrm SPhx
elegans	LHop
'Elegant Lady'	GFai
huegelii	see *Alyogyne huegelii*
x ***hypomadara*** misapplied	see *A. capensis*
§ x ***hypomadara*** (Sprague) D.M. Bates	ECtt SRms
julii	SPlb
malvastroides	XPep
scabrosa	CChe XPep

Anisodus (*Solanaceae*)

carnioliciodes BWJ 7501	WCru
§ ***luridus***	EDAr EWld MSal

Annona (*Annonaceae*)

cherimola (F)	CCCN MPRe XBlo

Anoiganthus see *Cyrtanthus*

Anomalesia see *Gladiolus*

Anomatheca (*Iridaceae*)

cruenta	see *A. laxa*
grandiflora	CHll CPLG ECho ERos
§ ***laxa*** ♀H2-3	More than 30 suppliers
- var. ***alba*** ♀H2-3	CPLG CPom CRHN CSpe CStu ECho EDif EHrv ELan ERos EShb IBal ITim MTho MWea NMen SBch WAbe WBrk WCFE
- ***albomaculata***	LRHS
- blue-flowered	CRHN ECho ERos WAbe
- 'Joan Evans'	CPom CRHN CStu ECho ECtt ELan ERos LTwo NDlv NMen NWCA SHom SRms WAbe WBrk WHrl
- red-spotted	CPLG ECho EDif ITim SGar
- ***viridiflora***	ECho
viridis	CPLG CPou EBee ECho ERos LRHS WBrk WPGP

Anopterus (*Escalloniaceae*)

glandulosus	IBlr WPGP WSHC

Anredera (*Basellaceae*)

§ ***cordifolia***	CRHN EBrs ECho EShb LEdu LRHS

Antennaria (*Asteraceae*)

aprica	see *A. parvifolia*
dioica	CArn CEnt CTri EDAr GAbr GPoy MHer NBlu SPlb SRms WFar
- 'Alba'	EDAr WFar
- 'Alex Duguid'	GCrs GMaP LBee LRHS NLAp SBla
- 'Aprica'	see *A. parvifolia*
§ - var. ***hyperborea***	ECGP
- 'Minima'	ECho NBro NMen SIng WAbe
- 'Nyewoods Variety'	NLAp
- red-flowered	ECho
- var. ***rosea***	see *A. rosea*
* - 'Rubra'	CTri ECha ECho EDAr GBin LRHS MHer NMen NWCA SBla WDyG
- ***tomentosa***	see *A. dioica* var. *hyperborea*
'Joy'	SBla
macrophylla hort.	see *A. microphylla*
§ ***microphylla***	CBrm ECho MBar SRms WEas WPat
neglecta	ECho
§ ***parvifolia***	CTri ECho MBar NLar NPri SRms WPer
- var. ***rosea***	see *A. microphylla*
plantaginifolia	EBee
'Red Wonder'	CMea NLar
§ ***rosea*** ♀H4	ECho NHol NLAp NMen NVic SPlb SRms WFar

Anthemis ✿ (*Asteraceae*)

from Turkey	EWes LLWP
§ 'Beauty of Grallagh'	ECtt ERou GBuc GMac IGor MAvo MDKP NCGa SDix WBor WSpi
carpatica	NBro
- 'Karpatenschnee'	CRez EBee NBre
§ ***cretica*** subsp. ***cretica***	CLyd NWCA
'Daisy Bee' new	EBee ENot
frutescens hort. & Siebert & Voss.	see *Argyranthemum frutescens*
'Grallagh Gold'	EBee EBla ECha ECtt EMon EWes LDai MBri MRav MWat NPer SPhx WFar WSpi WTel
'Grallagh Gold' misapplied, orange-yellow	see *A.* 'Beauty of Grallagh'
§ ***marschalliana***	CPBP EAlp EBee ECha ECho EDAr EPot LBee LRHS MSte SMrm SPlb
montana	see *A. cretica* subsp. *cretica*

nobilis	see *Chamaemelum nobile*
punctata subsp. ***cupaniana*** ♀H3-4	More than 30 suppliers
- - 'Nana'	EMon NPer SHar
rudolphiana	see *A. marschalliana*
sancti-johannis	CBgR CWib EBee EBla ERou IGor LDai MBri MNHC MSal MWgw NPer SDix SMad SPer SPoG SRms WFar WMoo WPer
'Sauce Béarnaise'	GCra WMnd
Susanna Mitchell = 'Blomit'	CHar EBee EBla ECtt EMan EPfP ERou EShb EWll GMaP GMac LRHS MAvo MLHP MNrw NBir NCob NDov SMrm WCAu WMnd WSHC WSpi WTin WWeb XPep
'Tetworth'	EBee EBla ECha ECtt EHrv ELan EMan EMon EWin GBuc MAvo MBNS MRav MSte NCGa NOrc SMad WFar WPer
tinctoria	CArn CHby EAro EBee ELau EMon GPoy LRHS MHer MNHC NPer SPet SWvt WAbe WJek
- from Judaea	EMon
- 'Alba'	NBre WHen WPer
* - 'Compacta'	EWes NBre NCob NGdn
- dwarf	EBee EBla EWin MAvo SBla SBri WFar
- 'E.C. Buxton'	More than 30 suppliers
- 'Eva'	EBee EMon LRHS NBre NCob NDov NLar WEas
I - 'Golden Rays'	EBee EWin MDKP NPro SDix
- 'Kelwayi'	CEnt CPrp CSBt CTri EBee EPfP ERou EShb GMaP LCro LRHS MBNS MBri NBPC NBro NCob NPer SPer SPla SPoG SRms WFar WHen WMoo WPer
- 'Lemon Maid'	CFir GBin NBre NCob SMrm
- 'Pride of Grallagh'	see *A.* 'Beauty of Grallagh'
- 'Sauce Hollandaise'	More than 30 suppliers
- subsp. ***tinctoria***	EMon
- 'Wargrave Variety'	More than 30 suppliers
'Tinpenny Sparkle' **new**	WCot WTin
triumfettii	NPer
tuberculata	EMan NChi
'White Water'	WAbe WFar

Anthericum (*Anthericaceae*)

algeriense	see *A. liliago*
baeticum	ERos
* ***fistulosum***	GSki
§ ***liliago***	CAby EBee ECho ELan ERos GMaP GMac GSki LHop MAvo MLLN MRav MSte MWgw NCGa SPer WPer
- 'Major' ♀H4	CAvo CDes EBee ECha ECho EHrv GBuc IGor MLHP NBre SPhx WPGP
ramosum	CSpe EBee EBrs ECha ECho ELan EMan EPot ERos EWes GKev GSki MBrN MLLN NBid NBir NCGa NEgg NWCA SMrm SPhx WLin WPer
- ***plumosum***	see *Trichopetalum plumosum*
saundersiae	CPLG CPne SHom
undulatum	ERos

Antholyza (*Iridaceae*)

coccinea	see *Crocosmia paniculata*
x ***crocosmioides***	see *Crocosmia* x *crocosmioides*
paniculata	see *Crocosmia paniculata*

Anthoxanthum (*Poaceae*)

odoratum	CArn CBig CRWN GPoy XIsg

Anthriscus (*Apiaceae*)

cerefolium	CArn CSev GPoy ILis MDun MHer MNHC SECG WJek WSel
sylvestris	CArn NSco
- 'Broadleas Blush'	CNat
- 'Kabir'	CNat
- 'Ravenswing'	More than 30 suppliers

Anthurium (*Araceae*)

amazonicum	MBri
andraeanum ♀H1	MBri
- 'Glowing Pink'	XBlo
- 'Red Heart'	XBlo
andreanum 'Tivolo' **new**	XBlo
'Aztec'	XBlo
'Caribo' **new**	XBlo
crenatum	XBlo
'Crimson'	XBlo
'Magenta'	XBlo
'Octavia' **new**	XBlo
'Pico Bello' **new**	XBlo
'Porcelaine White'	XBlo
scherzerianum ♀H1	MBri

Anthyllis (*Papilionaceae*)

barba-jovis	CSpe XPep
hermanniae	XPep
- 'Compacta'	see *A. hermanniae* 'Minor'
§ - 'Minor'	EPot NLar NMen WLin
montana	SBla
- subsp. ***atropurpurea***	LRHS
- 'Rubra' ♀H4	ECho EPot EWes LHop LTwo NMen
vulneraria	CFee ECho EWin NMir NRya NSco SECG WSFF
- subsp. ***atlantis***	GKev
- var. ***coccinea***	CHar CSam CSpe CSsd EBee GAbr GGar GKev MAvo MCCP MLLN MSte MTho NLar NSla NWCA SGar SPet WAbe WBVN WCFE WFar WHal

Antigonon (*Polygonaceae*)

leptopus	MJnS SOWG

Antirrhinum (*Scrophulariaceae*)

asarina	see *Asarina procumbens*
braun-blanquetii	CHal EBee EMan ERou EShb EWin MLLN NLar WCot WHil WPtf WRHF
'Candy Stripe'	ECtt EMan LSou
Chandelier Primrose Vein = 'Yaprim'	LSou
Chandelier Rose Pink = 'Yarob'	LSou
Chandelier Yellow = 'Yahit' **new**	LSou
glutinosum	see *A. hispanicum* subsp. *hispanicum*
graniticum	EBee
§ ***hispanicum***	NBir
- 'Avalanche'	CHal ECtt EMan EWin SPet
§ - subsp. ***hispanicum***	CSam SRot XPep
- - 'Roseum'	CMea CPom CSpe EMan SBHP SPet
latifolium	XPep
'Lipstick Orange' **new**	LAst
Luminaire Yellow = 'Balumyell'PBR (Luminaire Series)	NPri
majus	XPep
- 'Black Prince'	CSpe ECtt EMan EShb LHop LSou SAga
- 'Candy Snap'PBR (v)	LSou SPoG

- 'Magic Purple Eye' (Magic Series) new	LAst
- 'Night and Day'	CSpe SAga
molle	CPom CSpe ECtt GKev MCot MSte NBir NPer NWCA SChF SRot WAbe
- pink	CSWP MSte WAbe
Peachy = 'Yawed' (Crocodile Series) new	LSou
I 'Pendula Lampion Appleblossom'	LSou
I 'Pendula Lampion Salmon/Orange'	LSou
pulverulentum	LHop MArl SAga
Rich Ruby = 'Yaby' new	LAst
Ruby = 'Yactred' (Crocodile Series) new	LSou
sempervirens	EMan EWin SAga WAbe
siculum	EBee WMoo

añu see *Tropaeolum tuberosum*

Aphanes (*Rosaceae*)

§ ***arvensis***	MSal

Aphelandra (*Acanthaceae*)

squarrosa	CHal LRHS MBri
I - 'Citrina'	XBlo

Aphyllanthes (*Aphyllanthaceae*)

monspeliensis	CFee EBee ECho SBla

Apios (*Papilionaceae*)

§ ***americana***	CAgr CMdw CPom CWan EBee EBrs ECho EMon GBin ITer LEdu LFur NBir NLar NSti WBVN WCot WCru WSHC
tuberosa	see *A. americana*

Apium (*Apiaceae*)

graveolens	CArn CBgR CBod CPrp CWan ELau GPoy MHer MNHC MSal SIde WJek
- (Secalinum Group) 'Par-cel'	MHer NGHP

Apium x *Petroselinum* (*Apiaceae*)

hybrid	see *A. graveolens* Secalinum Group

Apocynum (*Apocynaceae*)

cannabinum	CArn COld GPoy MGol MSal

Aponogeton (*Aponogetonaceae*)

distachyos	CDWL CWat EHon EMFW EPfP NPer SCoo SWat WFar WMAq WPnP

apple see *Malus domestica*

apricot see *Prunus armeniaca*

Aptenia (*Aizoaceae*)

cordifolia ♀H1-2	CCCN CSev LRav NPer SChr SDnm SEND SPet XPep
- 'Variegata' (v)	CCCN EWin LAst MRav

Aquilegia ✿ (*Ranunculaceae*)

akitensis misapplied	see *A. flabellata* var. *pumila*
* ***alba variegata*** (v)	ECho WEas
alpina	CMea CPrp EBee ECho ECtt EPfP GEdr LCro MHer MLan MNHC MRav MWgw SPer SPet SRms WFar WHen WMoo WPer WRHF
- 'Alba'	CMMP NOak
amaliae	see *A. ottonis* subsp. *amaliae*
amurensis	CLAP
'Anja' (v)	WCot
'Apple Blossom'	GKev LSou
aragonensis	see *A. pyrenaica*
§ ***atrata***	CLAP CPou EBee ECho EDAr MDKP MHar MWea NBre NEgg SBch SMHy WBVN WHil WPer
atrovinosa	SPad
aurea misapplied	see *A. vulgaris* golden-leaved
barnebyi	NEgg
bertolonii ♀H4	ECho GCrs GKev LHop LRHS NDlv NMen NRya SBla SRms WAbe WHoo
Biedermeier Group	ECho LRHS MBNS NOrc NRnb SPoG WFar WPer
'Blue Berry'	WLin WPat
'Blue Jay' (Songbird Series)	ENot LBuc NPri SPer SWvt
'Blue Star' (Star Series)	CSam EBee ELan EPfP LRHS WHil WPer
'Bluebird' (Songbird Series) ♀H2	NPer
buergeriana	MDKP NChi NEgg STes WPer
- 'Calimero'	CHFP CPLG CSsd MDKP MSte NLar
- var. ***oxysepala***	see *A. oxysepala*
'Bunting' (Songbird Series) ♀H2	EWll NLar WFar
'Burnished Rose'	NRnb WHil
canadensis ♀H4	CLAP CMHG CPom CSpe EBee EDAr ELan GKev GQue LBMP MNFA MSte NBid NBir NBro NEgg NOak SGar SIng SRms SWal WPer
- SDR 1068	GKev
- 'Corbett'	CLAP GBuc MDKP WHil
- 'Little Lanterns'	CBgR CEnt CLAP CSam CWCL EBee EPPr GKev LBMP MBri MDKP MPop MSte NLar NSum SVil WFar WWeb
- 'Nana'	GBuc MDKP MWea WPat WThu
'Cardinal' (Songbird Series)	EWll MBri NLar NPri SPer WFar
cazorlensis	see *A. pyrenaica* subsp. *cazorlensis*
chaplinei	NBir NEgg SBch SBla
chrysantha	CBgR CHrt CSam CWan EBee EWTr GBuc GKev MLLN MNFA NBre NOak SRms WAbe WBrE WEas WLin WPer
I - 'Flore Pleno' (d)	MDKP NEgg
- 'Yellow Queen'	COIW CPLG CWCL EBee EGoo EPfP EShb GGar GMaP LBMP LHop MAvo MDKP NBre NLar NMoo NRnb SPhx SPla SPur SSvw SWal WCFE WHil WWFP
clematiflora	see *A. vulgaris* var. *stellata*
Clementine Series new	LBuc
coerulea ♀H4	MDKP SRms WLin
- 'Himmelblau'	EBee EGoo NBre
- 'Mrs Nicholls'	WSpi
'Colorado' (State Series)	EWll
'Crimson Star'	EBee ENot EPfP MDKP SPer SPur WMoo
'Debutante'	EBee LLWP MDKP MWea WGwG
desertorum	CPom MDKP
dinarica	WLin
discolor	EPot LHop LTwo NEgg NMen NRnb WLin WPat
'Double Chocolate'	LRHS
'Double Rubies' (d)	GCra NRnb SHar
'Dove' (Songbird Series) ♀H2	EWll MBri MHer NLar NPri SHar SPer SWat WFar
I 'Dragonfly'	CBcs CWib EPfP GAbr LBMP MNHC NBlu NBre NMir SPer SPet SPoG SPur WFar WRHF
ecalcarata	see *Semiaquilegia ecalcarata*
einseleana	EBee NEgg

elegantula	GCrs NEgg
'Firewheel'	see *A. vulgaris* var. *stellata* 'Firewheel'
flabellata ♀H4	GCra GGar NEgg NLAp WAbe WKif WPat WPer
- f. ***alba***	CTri ECho ELan NEgg NWCA WEas
* - - 'White Angel'	NHol WPer
- - 'White Jewel' (Jewel Series)	GKev SPla
- 'Blue Angel'	CBcs NHol WPer
- Cameo Series	CBrm EWll LBMP WFar WGor WHil
- - 'Cameo Blue and White'	CWib ECho MWat WFar
- - 'Cameo Blue'	ECho
- - 'Cameo Blush'	WFar
- - 'Cameo Pink and White'	ECho MHer WFar
- - 'Cameo Rose'	NBir
- Jewel Series	ECho SPet WPer
- - 'Blue Jewel'	ECho SPla
- - 'Pink Jewel'	SPla
- 'Ministar'	ECho EPfP LRHS MBNS MHer NBlu NCGa NVic SRot WBrE WFar WHil WPer
- 'Nana Alba'	see *A. flabellata* var. *pumila* f. *alba*
§ - var. ***pumila*** ♀H4	CSam CWCL ECha ECho EPfP GAbr GKev LHop MAvo MDKP NEgg NLAp SIng WFar WHil WPat WPer
§ - - f. ***alba*** ♀H4	ECha ECho GEdr GKev LBee LHop LRHS MBNS MSte SIng SRms WHil
- - 'Flore Pleno'	ECho
- - f. ***kurilensis***	MSte
- 'Vermont' (State Series)	CHFP
flavescens	WPer
formosa	CMea EBee ECho GGar LBMP MDKP NChi NEgg NPri NWCA WGwG WKif WPer
- var. ***truncata***	GBuc MLLN
§ ***fragrans***	CDMG CHar CHrt CLAP COIW CPom EBee EWTr GEdr GKev LBMP MTho MWat NEgg NOak NRnb NWCA SBla STes WGwG WHoo WPnP
- white-flowered	ELan
glandulosa	EBee NDlv NEgg NLar WEas
glauca	see *A. fragrans*
'Golden Guiness'	WPnP
'Goldfinch' (Songbird Series)	EWll NBir NPri SPer
grahamii	SBla
grata	MDKP NRnb
Harbutt's hybrids	ERou
'Hensol Harebell' ♀H4	CSWP EBee GBuc SHar SRms WPtf WSpi
'Ice Blue'	WCot
'Irish Elegance'	EGoo
japonica	see *A. flabellata* var. *pumila*
'Jenny'	NPri
jonesii	CGra CPBP
jonesii* x *saximontana	GKev
karelinii	NEgg
'Koralle'	CSam MDKP NBre NRnb WFar WHil
'Kristall'	EBee ERou EShb LCro MDKP NBre NOak NRnb SSvw STes WHil
laramiensis	CGra CPBP NEgg NWCA WAbe
'Lavender and White'	see *A.* 'Nuthatch'
'Little Plum'	WHil
longissima ♀H4	CHar CMea CSam EShb GBuc ILad MDKP MHer MLLN MWea NEgg NRnb SBla SHar WEas WGwG WHoo WLin WPen

'Louisiana' (State Series) ♀H2	CHFP
'Magpie'	see *A. vulgaris* 'William Guiness'
'Maxi'	MDKP NBre WHil
McKana Group	CTri ELan ENot EPfP GMaP LAst LBMP LHop LRHS MLHP MNHC MWgw NEgg NGdn NOak NRnb NVic SPer SPlb SPoG SRms WBVN WMnd WWlt
'Milk and Honey'	CBre EBee LBMP MRav NRnb STes
moorcroftiana	EBee NEgg
- CC 1371	WCra
Mrs Scott-Elliot hybrids	CSBt GAbr LHop MLan NEgg SGar SPer SPet WFar WRHF WWlt
Music Series ♀H4	SRms
nigricans	see *A. atrata*
§ 'Nuthatch' (Songbird Series)	NEgg
olympica	EBee EWes NEgg SKHP WPer
'Oranges and Lemons'	EDAr LSou
Origami Series	GAbr WFar
- 'Origami Yellow' ♀H3-4 **new**	CHFP
ottonis	LHop
§ - subsp. ***amaliae***	GEdr NEgg WAbe
§ ***oxysepala***	CPLG EBee NEgg WCru
- B&SWJ 4775	WCru
'Purple Emperor' PBR	LRHS SPoG
§ ***pyrenaica***	EBee GKev WAbe WLin
§ - subsp. ***cazorlensis***	NEgg
'Red Hobbit'	CBrm CSpe EBee ENot GAbr GGar GKev IBal ITim LRHS MAvo MDKP NBPC NBre NWCA WBrE WFar WHoo WRHF
'Red Star' (Star Series)	EBee ECho EPfP ERou SHar WHil WPer
'Robin' (Songbird Series)	ENot EWll NPri SWat WFar
rockii	CHFP CLAP CSam EBee GKev LHop MDKP MSte NEgg WHil
- B&SWJ 7965	WCru
- SDR 1680	GKev
'Roman Bronze'	see *Aquilegia* x *Semiaquilegia*, 'Roman Bronze'
'Rose Queen'	CSam MAvo MDKP NBre SSvw WHil WHoo
saximontana	CGra GKev ITim NLar NWCA WPer
§ 'Schneekönigin'	ENot GMaP WPer
scopulorum	CGra EPot NEgg SBla WAbe
shockleyi	GBuc
sibirica	SBla WPer
'Silver Queen'	ELan MDKP
'Simone's White'	EBee
skinneri	CDMG CHrt CPLG CSpe EBee EShb LHop MBNS MWat NCGa NEgg NRnb SPoG STes WCra WHil WMnd WMoo WRos WSpi
- 'Tequila Sunrise'	CWib EWsh SBra SPoG WPer
Snow Queen	see *A.* 'Schneekönigin'
Songbird Series	COIW MLLN NEgg NPri SWat WFar
'Spitfire' **new**	LBuc
'Spring Magic Blue and White' (Spring Magic Series)	LBuc NNor
stellata	see *A. vulgaris* var. *stellata*
'Stoulton Blue'	EBee WSPU WSpi
'Sunburst Ruby'	EDAr ITer LHop MBri MDKP MWat NEgg NOak NPro SPoG WMoo
'Sweet Lemon Drops'	GWWP LSou NRnb SPoG STes WHil
'Sweet Rainbows' (d)	LSou
'Tequila Sunrise' **new**	EKen
triternata	NEgg NWCA

	'Virginia' (State Series)	CHFP
	viridiflora	CHar CHrt CLAP CPom EBee ECrN GBuc ITer MAvo MHer NChi NRnb SBla SGar SMHy SPoG WCot WCru WEas WFar WGwG WHil WPGP WPer WPrP
	- 'Chocolate Soldier' **new**	CEnt SBra
	vulgaris	CArn CMHG CRWN EPfP GPoy LLWP NBro NSco SGar SPlb WCAu WMoo WPer WShi WTin
	- 'Adelaide Addison'	EBee ECha GBri GBuc MFOX NEgg WEas WFar WHoo
	- var. ***alba***	CMea EBee LCro LLWP MNFA WCAu
	- 'Altrosa'	NBre
*	- 'Anemoniflora'	WSpi
	- 'Aureovariegata'	see *A. vulgaris* Vervaeneana Group
	- ***clematiflora***	see *A. vulgaris* var. *stellata*
	- var. ***flore-pleno*** (d)	LLWP WHen WPer
	- - black-flowered (d)	WCot
	- - 'Blue Bonnet' (d)	ERou WHil
	- - blue-flowered (d)	WCot
	- - Dorothy Series (d)	GBuc LHop
	- - 'Double Pleat' blue/ white-flowered (d)	CWCL WPer
	- - 'Double Pleat' pink/ white-flowered (d)	NGdn WPer
	- - 'Jane Hollow' (d)	CPou
	- - pale blue-flowered (d)	LLWP NRnb
	- - 'Pink Bonnet' (d)	WFar
	- - pink-flowered (d)	GGar
	- - purple-flowered (d)	LLWP
	- - red-flowered (d)	GGar
	- - 'Strawberry Ice Cream' (d)	GBri LBMP NBro WBrE
	- - (Tower Series) 'Tower Light Blue' (d)	EGoo SAga
	- - - 'Tower White' (d)	EGoo
*	- - 'White Bonnet' (d)	SRos
	- - white-flowered (d)	LLWP
§	- golden-leaved	ECho WOut
	- Grandmother's Garden Group	EWll
	- 'Heidi'	EBee NBre
	- 'Magda'	WBrE
	- 'Magpie'	see *A. vulgaris* 'William Guiness'
	- 'Mellow Yellow'	ECtt GBuc GCra GKev ILad MBNS MDKP NRnb WHil WMoo WPer WRos
	- Munstead White	see *A. vulgaris* 'Nivea'
§	- 'Nivea' ♀H4	CPou CSam ECha LAst NChi SPoG
	- 'Pink Spurless'	see *A. vulgaris* var. *stellata* pink-flowered
	- (Pom Pom Series) 'Pom Pom Crimson'	NBro WCot
	- - 'Pom Pom Violet' (Pom Pom Series)	WSpi
§	- var. ***stellata***	CHrt ELan EPot EWsh GBuc LEdu MBNS NBro NEgg WBVN WMoo WPer WWeb
	- - Barlow Series (d)	WFar WRHF
	- - - 'Black Barlow' (d)	More than 30 suppliers
	- - - 'Blue Barlow' (d)	CBgR CHFP CSpe EBee ECtt EShb GMaP IBal LCro LSRN NBre SPad SPer SPhx WMnd WPer WRHF WWeb
	- - - 'Christa Barlow' (d)	EBee IBal LBMP LRHS MDKP NBre WWeb
	- - - 'Nora Barlow' (d) ♀H4	More than 30 suppliers
	- - - 'Rose Barlow' (d)	CBgR IBal SPad WHen WMnd WRHF WWeb
	- - - 'White Barlow' (Barlow Series) (d)	CPLG
	- - 'Crimson Shower'	WBrE
§	- - 'Firewheel'	LBMP WMoo
	- - 'Gisela Powell'	EBee MBNS
	- - 'Greenapples' (d)	CBre EBee EWll GCra GKev NRnb SMHy SPad WCot
*	- - 'Iceberg'	WSpi
§	- - pink-flowered	LLWP NSti
	- - purple-flowered	LLWP
	- - red-flowered	ELan LLWP
	- - 'Royal Purple' (d)	EDAr LSou MBNS NBro NCGa SPoG WBVN
	- - 'Ruby Port' (d)	CAby CElw CHFP EBee EGoo EPyc EShb GGar GKev GMaP IBal LBMP LCro LSRN MNrw NChi NPri SPer SPhx SPla SPoG SSvw STes WFar WPrP
	- - 'Ruby Port' crimped (d)	NDov WPnP
	- - 'Sunlight White' (d)	SWat WPer
§	- - white-flowered	CSpe GCra LHop NBro WFar
	- variegated foliage	see *A. vulgaris* Vervaeneana Group
§	- Vervaeneana Group (v)	CMHG CSam CWCL ECha ECtt EMar ENot EPfP ERou EWll EWsh IBal MNrw NBir NBre NEgg NOak NPer SPer SPla SPlb SPoG SRms SWat WFar WHoo WMoo WRos
	- - 'Graeme Iddon' (v)	GBuc
	- - 'Woodside'	see *A. vulgaris* Vervaeneana Group
	- - 'Woodside Blue' (v)	ECtt EGoo MFOX NHol NRnb WOut
	- - 'Woodside Pink' (v)	MGos MWgw
	- - 'Woodside Red' (v)	NRnb
	- - 'Woodside White' (v)	CGrW GKev MFOX NBir NRnb WBrk WOut
	- 'Westfaeld'	NOak
	- 'White Spurless'	see *A. vulgaris* var. *stellata* white-flowered
§	- 'William Guiness'	More than 30 suppliers
	- 'William Guiness Doubles' (d)	EShb WMoo
	'White Star' (Star Series)	EBee EPfP ERou LAst MRav WHil WPer
	Winky Series	MAvo
	- 'Winky Blue-White'	NBre NLar NPri WCFE WFar WHil WWeb
	- 'Winky Pink'	NLar
	- 'Winky Purple-White'	NBre WFar WWeb
	- 'Winky Red-White'	IBal MBNS NBre NPri SWvt WFar WHil WWeb
	- 'Winky Rose-Rose'	MBNS NBre
	yabeana	CDMG EBee EGoo GGar GKev MHer

Aquilegia x *Semiaquilegia* (*Ranunculaceae*)

	hybrid, blue	WCru
§	'Roman Bronze'	EBee EDAr ILad ITer LSou NEgg NOak

Arabis (*Brassicaceae*)

	aculeolata NNS 01-28	EPPr
	albida	see *A. alpina* subsp. *caucasica*
	alpina	NEgg SPlb
§	- subsp. ***caucasica***	ECho NBlu WFar
	- - 'Corfe Castle'	ECho ECtt
	- - 'Douler Angevine' (v)	LSou NPri SPoG
§	- - 'Flore Pleno' (d) ♀H4	CTri CWCL ECha ECho ECtt ELan GAbr GMaP MTho SIng SRms WBrk WEas WFar WHoo
	- - 'Pink Pearl'	ECho NBlu
	- - 'Pinkie'	ECho WRHF
	- - 'Rosea'	NBir NBlu NPri SRms WFar WMoo
§	- - 'Schneehaube' ♀H4	CTri CWib ECho ECtt EPfP EShb GMaP MBar NBlu NMir NPri SPoG SRms WMoo
	- - 'Snow White'	ECho
	- - Snowcap	see *A. alpina* subsp. *caucasica* 'Schneehaube'

	- - 'Snowdrop'	MRav NPri WFar
	- - 'Variegata' (v)	ECho ECtt ELan EPot GMaP LBee LHop MBri MHer NEgg NPri SPoG SRms WEas WFar
	- 'Revolution'	WCot
	androsacea	CStu EPot SRms
	x ***arendsii*** 'Compinkie'	ECtt SPlb SRms
	- 'Rosabella' (v)	EAlp
	blepharophylla	EPfP SIng SPet WCot
§	- 'Frühlingszauber' ♀H4	CWib NBir NBlu NPri SPoG SRms WFar
	- Spring Charm	see *A. blepharophylla* 'Frühlingszauber'
	bryoides	LRHS NMen
	caucasica	see *A. alpina* subsp. *caucasica*
	- 'Plena'	see *A. alpina* subsp. *caucasica* 'Flore Pleno'
	cypria	LSou
	double white-flowered (d)	CFee
	'Doulier Anguine'	EPot
	ferdinandi-coburgi	ECho WEas WRHF
	- 'Aureovariegata' (v)	CMea CTri ECho ECtt EDAr SPet SWvt
	- 'Old Gold'	ECho EDAr EPfP EPot LAst LBee LRHS MBar MHer NEgg NHol NPri SBla SPoG SRms SSvw SWvt WCFE WFar WHoo WRHF
	- 'Variegata'	see *A. procurrens* 'Variegata'
	glabra	WPer
§	***procurrens*** 'Variegata' (v) ♀H4	CTri ECha ECho ECtt ELan EPfP EPot EWes LBee LEdu LRHS MBar MHer MWgw NPri SBla SHFr SHGN SPlb SRms WTel
§	***scabra***	CNat
	Snow Cap	see *A. alpina* subsp. *caucasica* 'Schneehaube'
	stricta	see *A. scabra*
	'Tu Tu'	NLar

Arachniodes (*Dryopteridaceae*)

simplicior	CCCN LRHS WCot WRic
standishii	WRic

Araiostegia (*Davalliaceae*)

hymenophylloides	WCot

Aralia ✿ (*Araliaceae*)

	CD&R 2289 from China	WCru
	EDHCH 9720 from China	WCru
	armata B&SWJ 3137	WCru
	- RWJ 10060	WCru
	bipinnata B&SWJ 6719	WCru
	- RWJ 10101	WCru
	cachemirica	CDTJ CDes EWes NBid NLar SDix SMad SPlb WHal WPGP
	- CC 4578	MGol
	californica	COld EBee EPPr GPoy LEdu MSal MSte NLar SDix WCru
	chapaensis HWJ 723	WCru
	chinensis misapplied	see *A. elata*
	chinensis L.	CAgr MSal WBVN
	- BWJ 8102	WCru
	continentalis	EBee EPPr LEdu NLar WCot
	- B&SWJ 4152	WCru
	- B&SWJ 8524	WCru
	cordata	EBee EWes GAbr LEdu MSal NEgg NLar
	- B&SWJ 5511	WCru
	decaisneana B&SWJ 3588	WCru
	- RWJ 9910	WCru
§	***elata*** ♀H4	CBcs CDoC CDul CHEx CHll CLnd CMCo CPLG CTrG EBee ECrN ELan EPfP EWTr LPan LRHS MBlu MGos NBea NBlu SAPC SArc SPer SPoG WFar WNor WOrn WSpi
	- B&SWJ 5480	WCru
	- 'Albomarginata'	see *A. elata* 'Variegata'
	- 'Aureovariegata' (v)	CBcs CDoC ELan EPfP EWes MBlu NLar NMoo NPal WOrn WPat
	- 'Golden Umbrella' (v)	CDoC CPen NLar
	- 'Silver Umbrella'	CDoC CDul CPen EPfP MGos NLar
§	- 'Variegata' (v) ♀H4	CBcs CDoC CDul ELan EPfP MBlu MGos NLar NMoo NPal SHBN SPoG WCot WPat
	foliolosa B&SWJ 8360	WCru
	nudicaulis	GPoy
	papyrifera	see *Tetrapanax papyrifer*
	racemosa	CArn EBee GPoy LEdu MLLN MNrw MSal MSte MWgw NLar SRms WFar
	- B&SWJ 9570	WCru
	sieboldii	see *Fatsia japonica*
	spinosa	IClo MBlu NLar WHer
	stipulata	NLar WPGP

Araucaria (*Araucariaceae*)

	angustifolia	ECho LCon WPGP
§	***araucana***	More than 30 suppliers
	bidwillii	LCon
	columnaris	LCon
	cunninghamii	ECho LCon
	excelsa misapplied	see *A. heterophylla*
§	***heterophylla*** ♀H1	CCCN CDoC EShb LCon LRHS MBri SAPC SArc WNor
	imbricata	see *A. araucana*

Araujia (*Asclepiadaceae*)

sericifera	CHEx CMac CPLG CRHN CSpe CTrG EMil EShb GQui SDnm SGar SPav WBor WFoF WSHC WSpi XPep

Arbutus ✿ (*Ericaceae*)

andrachne	EPfP XPep
x ***andrachnoides*** ♀H4	CAbP CBcs CDul CPMA CTri ELan EPfP LRHS MAsh MWya SAPC SArc SBra SDnm SMad SPer SReu SSpi SSta WHCG WPGP WPat WSpi XPep
glandulosa	see *Arctostaphylos glandulosa*
'Marina'	CAbP CDoC CDul CEnd CPMA CSam EBee ELan EPfP LHop LRHS MAsh MBlu MWya SEND SMad SPer SPoG SReu SSpi SSta SWvt WFar WPGP WPat
menziesii ♀H3	CBcs CDoC CEnd CMCN CTho EBee ECrN EPfP LRHS MAsh MGos NLar NPen SLon SMad SPer SPoG SSpi WFar WOrn WPGP
unedo ♀H4	More than 30 suppliers
- 'Atlantic'	ECrN IArd LCro LPan LRHS MGos SPoG SWvt WGer WPat
- 'Compacta'	CBcs CDoC EBee LPan LRHS MAsh MGos SWvt XPep
- 'Elfin King'	ELan EPfP LHop LRHS MAsh SDnm SPoG SSta SWvt
- 'Quercifolia'	CPMA ELan EPfP NLar SDnm SReu SSta WBod WPat
- f. ***rubra*** ♀H4	More than 30 suppliers

Archontophoenix (*Arecaceae*)

alexandrae	EAmu LPal
cunninghamiana ♀H1	CBrP EAmu LPal

Arctanthemum (*Asteraceae*)

§	***arcticum***	CKno EBee ECha NBre
	- 'Roseum'	EBee GBin
	- 'Schwefelglanz'	EBee NCGa

Arcterica see *Pieris*

Arctium (*Asteraceae*)

lappa	CArn GPoy MHer MNHC MSal NMir SIde WHer
- 'Takinogawa Long' **new**	EUnu
minus	MSal NSco

Arctostaphylos (*Ericaceae*)

§ ***glandulosa***	SAPC SArc
x ***media*** 'Wood's Red'	MBar WFar
myrtifolia	MBar
stanfordiana C&H 105	GGGa
uva-ursi	CArn GPoy MBar NBlu NLar NMen SHBN SLon SPlb SSta WBod
- 'Massachusetts'	EBee LRHS MAsh NLar
- 'Snowcap'	MAsh NHol
- 'Vancouver Jade'	CDoC EBee LRHS LSRN MAsh MBar MBri SCoo SPer SPoG SReu SRms SSta SWvt WWeb

Arctotheca (*Asteraceae*)

calendula	XPep

Arctotis (*Asteraceae*)

adpressa	CPBP
Hannah = 'Archnah'PBR	CHVG CSpe LSou SVil
Hayley = 'Archley'PBR	CCCN LAst LSou SPoG SVil
x ***hybrida*** hort. 'Apricot'	CCCN CHEx EShb EWin LAst MLan SAga SMrm
- 'Bacchus'	SAga
- 'China Rose'	SAga SMrm
- cream-flowered	CHEx SAga
- 'Flame' 🏆H1+3	CAby CCCN EShb EWin LAst MBNS MLan SAga SCoo SMrm WEas WHlf
- 'Lydie'	CWCL
* - 'Mahogany' 🏆H1+3	CAby EShb LSou MBNS SAga WHlf
- 'Red Devil'	CCCN CHEx EWin LAst MBNS MLan SAga SCoo SMrm SPoG SVil
- 'Wine'	CCCN CHEx EWin LAst LSou MBNS MLan SCoo SMrm SRkn SVil
'Prostrate Raspberry'	CSpe SAga

Ardisia (*Myrsinaceae*)

crenata	LRHS MBri
japonica B&SWJ 3809	WCru
- var. ***angusta***	WCot
- 'Miyo-nishiki' (v)	WCot
maclurei B&SWJ 3772	LRHS

Areca (*Arecaceae*)

catechu	MBri
concinna	LPal
triandra **new**	XBlo
vestiaria	LPal

Arecastrum see *Syagrus*

Arenaria (*Caryophyllaceae*)

balearica	CWCL EAlp ECho EWes LBee LEdu LRHS SIng SPlb SRms WDyG
capillaris **new**	CTri
festucoides	ITim NLAp
globiflora **new**	WLin
hookeri	WLin
ledebouriana	EDAr GEdr NLar SBla WAbe
magellanica	see *Colobanthus quitensis*
montana 🏆H4	More than 30 suppliers
- 'Avalanche'	MFOX
pinifolia	see *Minuartia circassica*
purpurascens	EAlp ECho EDAr EWes NMen SBla SRms SRot WFar
- 'Elliott's Variety'	WPat
recurva	see *Minuartia recurva*
serpyllifolia **new**	EDAr
tetraquetra	NLAp
- subsp. ***amabilis***	EPot MBar NMen NSla SIng
tmolea	NMen
verna	see *Minuartia verna*

Arenga (*Arecaceae*)

engleri	EAmu LPal

Argemone (*Papaveraceae*)

grandiflora	SBch SPav
mexicana	ELan SPav
pleiacantha	SPav

Argyranthemum ✿ (*Asteraceae*)

'Anastasia'	MAJR
'Apricot Surprise'	see *A.* 'Peach Cheeks'
'Beth'	MAJR
'Blanche' (Courtyard Series)	MAJR
Blazer Primrose = 'Supanova' (Daisy Crazy Series)	MAJR
§ 'Blizzard' (d)	MAJR
Blushing Rose = 'Supaellie' (Daisy Crazy Series)	MAJR
'Bofinger'	MAJR
Boston yellow daisy	see *A. callichrysum*
'Bridesmaid'	CCCN MAJR
Bright Carmine = 'Supalight'PBR (Daisy Crazy Series)	MAJR
broussonetii	MAJR
Butterfly = 'Ulyssis' 🏆H1+3	EWin GCra MAJR WGor
§ ***callichrysum***	MAJR
'Camilla Ponticelli'	MAJR
canariense hort.	see *A. frutescens* subsp. *canariae*
'Champagne'	MAJR
'Cheek's Peach'	see *A.* 'Peach Cheeks'
Cherry Love (Daisy Crazy Series)	CCCN MAJR
'Christy Bell'	MAJR
* ***compactum***	MAJR
'Comtesse de Chambord'	MAJR SPet
'Cornish Gold' 🏆H1+3	CBcs CCCN LSou MAJR
coronopifolium	MAJR XPep
'Donington Hero' 🏆H1+3	MAJR MHom
double white-flowered (d)	EWin MAJR
'Edelweiss' (d)	MAJR MHom WHen
'Flamingo'	see *Rhodanthemum gayanum*
§ ***foeniculaceum*** misapplied	CTri ELan WHen WKif
§ ***foeniculaceum*** (Willd.) Webb & Sch.Bip.	CHal MAJR
- pink-flowered	see *A.* 'Petite Pink'
§ - 'Royal Haze' 🏆H1+3	CCCN CHll MAJR NPer
'Frosty'	MAJR MBNS
§ ***frutescens***	CHEx MAJR
- Blazer Rose = 'Supaglow'PBR (Daisy Crazy Series)	MAJR
§ - subsp. ***canariae*** 🏆H1+3	CCCN ECtt MAJR
- 'Ella'PBR	MAJR
- 'Gretel'	MAJR
- Gypsy Rose = 'M9/18d'	CCCN LSou SVil
- 'Henriette'PBR	MAJR
- Molimba Duplo Pearl = 'Argydupea' **new**	MAJR
- subsp. ***succulentum***	MAJR
- - 'Margaret Lynch'	MAJR
'Fuji Sundance'	MAJR
'George'	MAJR
'Gill's Pink'	CCCN ECtt MAJR MHom WPnn
'Golden Treasure'	MAJR
gracile	CHll
- 'Chelsea Girl' 🏆H1+3	CCCN CHEx COlW ECtt MAJR MCot MHom MLan WKif WPnn

	'Guernsey Pink'	MAJR MHom
	'Harvest Snow'	LAst MBNS
	'Icknield Jubilee'	MAJR
	'Icknield Lemon Ice' **new**	MAJR
	'Icknield Pink'	MAJR
	'Icknield Surprise'	MAJR
	'Icknield Sylvia'	MAJR
	'Icknield Yellow'	MAJR
	'Jamaica Primrose' ♕H1+3	CHEx CSpe CTri ECtt MAJR MHar SDix WHen WPnn
	'Jamaica Snowstorm'	see *A.* 'Snow Storm'
	'Julieanne'	LAst MAJR
	'Lemon Chiffon'	MAJR
	'Lemon Delight'	CHal LAst MAJR
	'Lemon Meringue' (d)	CCCN MAJR
	'Lemon Soufflé'	MAJR
	lemsii	MAJR
§	'Levada Cream' ♕H1+3	MAJR MHom
	'Libby Brett'	MAJR
	'Lilliput'	MAJR
	(Madeira Series) Madeira Madelana = 'Ohmadmade'PBR	SVil
	- Madeira Santana = 'Ohmadsant'	SVil
	- Madeira São Martinho = 'Ohmadsaom'	SVil
	- Madeira São Vicente = 'Ohmadsavi'PBR **new**	MAJR
§	***maderense*** ♕H1+3	CHll MAJR
	- pale-flowered	MAJR
	'Maja Bofinger'	EWin
	'Mary Cheek' (d) ♕H1+3	CCCN EWin MAJR SPet SRGP WHoo
	'Mary Wootton' (d)	ECtt MAJR MHom
	mawii	see *Rhodanthemum gayanum*
	'Mike's Pink'	MAJR
	'Millennium Star'	MAJR
	'Mini-snowflake'	see *A.* 'Blizzard'
§	'Mrs F. Sander' (d)	MAJR MCot
	'Nevada Cream'	see *A.* 'Levada Cream'
	ochroleucum	see *A. maderense*
§	'Peach Cheeks' (d)	CCCN MAJR
§	'Petite Pink' ♕H1+3	CCCN ECtt EWin LAst MAJR MHom WHen
	Ping-Pong = 'Innping' (d)	CBcs CCCN
	'Pink Australian' (d)	CCCN MAJR MHom
	'Pink Delight'	see *A.* 'Petite Pink'
	'Pink Pixie'	MAJR
	Pink Wonder = 'Supalily' (Daisy Crazy Series)	MAJR
	pinnatifidium subsp. ***succulentum***	MAJR
	Polly = 'Innpolly' **new**	SVil
	'Powder Puff' (d)	ECtt MAJR
	'Primrose Petite'PBR (Courtyard Series)	MAJR SVil
	prostrate double pink-flowered (d)	MAJR
	'Qinta White' (d) ♕H1+3	MAJR
	'Rising Sun'	MAJR
	'Rosa Dwarf'	MAJR
	'Royal Haze'	see *A. foeniculaceum* 'Royal Haze'
	'Saimi'	MAJR
	'Silver Leaf'	MAJR
	'Silver Queen'	see *A. foeniculaceum* misapplied
§	'Snow Storm' ♕H1+3	LAst MAJR MHom WPnn
	'Snowball'	MAJR
	'Snowflake' misapplied	see *A.* 'Mrs F. Sander'
	'Snowflake' (d)	WHen
	'Starlight'	MAJR
	'Sugar and Ice'PBR	CCCN MAJR
	'Sugar Baby'PBR	CCCN MAJR
	Sugar Cheer = 'Cobeer' **new**	MAJR
	'Sugar Lace'	MAJR
	Sultan's Lemon (Daisy Crazy Series)	MAJR
	Sultan's Pride = 'Cosupri' (Daisy Crazy Series)	MAJR
	'Summer Angel' (d)	MAJR
	'Summer Eyes'	MAJR
	'Summer Melody'PBR (d)	CBrm CCCN CSpe MAJR SMrm
	'Summer Pink'PBR	CCCN LAst LSou MAJR WGor
	'Summer Stars Pink' (Daisy Crazy Series) (d)	MAJR
	'Summertime'	MAJR
	Summit Pink = 'Cobsing' PBR (Daisy Crazy Series) **new**	MAJR
	'Sweety'	MAJR WPnn
	'Tony Holmes'	MAJR
	'Tweeny'	MAJR
	'Tweety'	MAJR
	'Vancouver' (d) ♕H1+3	CCCN CHll CWCL ECtt EShb EWin LAst MAJR MHom SBHP SEND SPet
	Vanilla Ripple = 'Supabright' (Daisy Crazy Series)	MAJR
	'Vara'	EWin
*	'Vera'	CCCN MAJR
	'Wellwood Park'	CCCN
	'Weymouth Pink'	MAJR
	'Weymouth Surprise'	MAJR
	White Blush = 'Supamorni' (Daisy Crazy Series)	MAJR
	White Crystal = 'Supagem' (Daisy Crazy Series)	MAJR
	'White Spider'	CCCN ELan MAJR MHom
	'White Star' (d)	MAJR
	'Whiteknights' ♕H1+3	MAJR
	'Yellow Australian' (d)	CCCN MAJR

Argyreia (*Convolvulaceae*)

nervosa	MGol

Argyrocytisus see *Cytisus*

Arisaema (*Araceae*)

	ACE 2408	GBuc
	B&L 12160	MGol
	B&L 12161	MGol
	C&H 7026	NMen
	CC 3203	CPLG
	CC 4462	MGol
	CC 4593	MGol
	CC 4595	MGol
	CC 4686	MGol
	CC 4688	MGol
	CC 4898	MGol
	CC 4899	MGol
	CC 4900	MGol
	CC 4901	MGol
	CC 4902	MGol
	CC 4903	MGol
	CC 4904	MGol
	CC 4905	MGol
	CC 5200	MGol
	Chen Yi 14	WCot
	Chen Yi 35	MLul
	Chen Yi 38	MLul WCot
	Chen Yi 41	WCot
	amurense	CLAP CStu EBee ECho EPot GBuc GGar GKev ITer LAma LFur MLLN WCot WFar WPnP
	- B&SWJ 947	WCru
§	- subsp. ***robustum***	CStu ECho LFur NMen WWst
*	***angustatum*** var. ***amurense***	LAma NLAp

- var. ***peninsulae***	EBee
- var. ***serratum***	see *A. serratum*
asperatum	EBee LAma MLul
bathycoleum	CHHB EBee
biauriculatum	see *A. wattii*
brachyspathum	see *A. heterophyllum*
brevipes	CFwr EBee NLAp
candidissimum ΨH4	More than 30 suppliers
- green-flowered	WCot
- pink-flowered **new**	MLul
- white-flowered	CHHB EBee GEdr LAma MLul WCot
ciliatum	CDes CPom CSpe CStu EBee EBla GBuc GEdr ITer LAma LFur MGol MLLN MLul MNrw NLar SRot WCot WIvy WSHC
- var. ***liubaense***	CFwr CGHE CKob CLAP CWsd EBee EPfP GEdr ITer MGol WPGP
- - CT 369	SCnR SKHP WCot
* ***coenobialis***	EBee MLul WCot
concinnum	CFir CKob CStu EBee EBrs EPot GBin LAma MGol MLul NLar WPnP
- GG 94152	WCot
- 'Sikkim'	MGol
consanguineum	CAby CDes CFwr CGHE CHEx CKob CLAP CMea CPLG EBee EBrs EPfP GBuc GCrs GEdr GGar GKev ITer LAma LFur MGol MLul MTho NHar NMen SGar SMad WCot WHil WPGP
- B&SWJ 071	WCru
- CC 3635	WCot
- GG 92112	WCot
- PJ 277	WCot
- SDR 2850	GKev
- SDR 3214	GKev
- 'J. Balis'	WCot
- subsp. ***kelung-insulare*** B&SWJ 256	WCru
- marble-leaf red	MGol WCot
- 'Qinling'	MGol WCot
- silver-centred-leaf red	ITer
costatum	CHEx CKob CLAP CPom EBee EBrs ECho EPot GBuc GEdr ITer LAma MLul NMen WCot WPGP
- CC 2924	WCot
- CC 3237	ITer WRos
dahaiense	LAma MLul
decipiens	EBee
dilatatum	EBee ITer LAma MLul WCot
dracontium	CLAP EBee EBrs ECho LAma NLar NMen
du-bois-reymondiae	LAma
echinatum	EBee
elephas	EBee LAma MLul WWst
engleri	CKob MLul
- GG 98173	WCot
erubescens	CPom CStu EBee EPot ERos MLul NLar WBVN WCot
- marbled-leaved **new**	GEdr
aff. ***erubescens*** **new**	WCot
exappendiculatum	CDes EBee WPGP
fargesii	CHHB CLAP EBee EBrs ECho EPot GEdr LAma MLul WCot WWst
flavum	CDes CGHE CHHB CKob CLAP CMea CStu CWCL EBee EBrs EPfP EPot GBuc GCrs GKev GWWP ITer ITim LAma LFur MLul MTho NHar NMen WBVN WCot WPGP
- CC 1782	WCot
- CC 3946	MGol
- subsp. ***abbreviatum***	MGol WCot
- - GG 84193	WWst
* - ***minus***	NWCA
- tall	CLAP ECho

- subsp. ***tibeticum***	EBee
formosanum B&SWJ 280	WCru
- B&SWJ 390	CPou WCot
- var. ***bicolorifolium*** B&SWJ 3528	WCru
- f. ***stenophyllum*** B&SWJ 1477	WCru
§ ***franchetianum***	CHHB EBee GEdr ITer LAma MGol MLul WCot
fraternum	WCot WWst
- CC 465	WCot
galeatum	EBee ECho EPot LAma MGol MLul WCot
grapsospadix **new**	EBee
§ ***griffithii***	EBee EBrs ECho EPot ERCP GGar ITer LAma LFur MLul NMyG SKHP WCru WPnP
- 'Numbuq'	GCra
- var. ***pradhanii***	ITer MLul
handelii	CPom EBee
helleborifolium	see *A. tortuosum*
§ ***heterophyllum***	CHHB EBee GEdr
- 'Baguo'	WCot
inkiangense	EBee LAma
- var. ***maculatum***	EBee
intermedium	EBee EBrs ECho GEdr GGar LAma MLul MNrw NMen SKHP
- CC 3102	WCot
- GG 96283	WCot
- var. ***biflagellatum*** PB 022	WCot
iyoanum	WCru
- subsp. ***nakaianum***	GEdr WWst
jacquemontii	CLAP EBee EBla EBrs ECho GBuc GCrs GEdr GGar GKev NLar NMen WCot WPGP
- CC 4598	MGol
- GG 88172	WCot
- GG 94120	WCot
aff. ***jacquemontii*** MECCN 29	NMen
- MECCN 76	NMen
japonicum Komarov	see *A. serratum*
jinshajiangense	EBee LAma MLul
kiushianum	EFEx GEdr LAma WCot WWst
leschenaultii	LAma WWst
lichiangense	GEdr LAma WCot
§ ***lobatum***	CHHB EBee LAma LFur MLul
maximowiczii	GEdr
meleagris	EBee LAma MLul
multisectum	CFir EBee
negishii	GEdr WCru
§ ***nepenthoides***	CKob EBee EBrs ECho EHrv EPot GEdr LAma LFur MGol MLul MNrw NMyG WPnP
ochraceum	see *A. nepenthoides*
omeiense	NLar
onoticum	see *A. lobatum*
polyphyllum B&SWJ 3904	WCru
propinquum	CLAP CPom EBee EBrs ECho EPot GGar ITer LAma MGol MLul NMen SKHP WCot WCru
purpureogaleatum	see *A. franchetianum*
rhizomatum	EBee LAma WCot
rhombiforme	EBee LAma MLul WCot WWst
ringens misapplied	see *A. amurense* subsp. *robustum*
ringens (Thunberg) Schott	CDes EBee EFEx EPot GKev LAma MGol MLul WWst
- f. ***praecox*** B&SWJ 1515	WCru
- f. ***sieboldii***	EBrs
- - B&SWJ 551	WCru
robustum	see *A. amurense* subsp. *robustum*
saxatile	CHHB EBee LAma MLul WCot WWst
sazensoo	GEdr LAma WWst

§ ***serratum***	CDes EBee EBrs ECho LAma MGol MNrw WCot WPGP
sikokianum	CKob EBee EBrs ECho EFEx EHrv EPot GEdr LAma LFur MGol MLul WCru
- var. ***henryanum***	EBee
- var. ***serratum***	CFir
speciosum	CHEx CKob CPLG EBee EBrs ECho ELan EPot GBuc GEdr GGar GSki IHer LAma MGol MLul NMen SPlb WFar WPnP
- B&SWJ 2403	WCru
- CC 3100	WCot
* - var. ***magnificum***	EBee EHrv MLul
* - var. ***sikkimense***	LAma
taiwanense	CFwr CLAP CPom GEdr SKHP WCot
- B&SWJ 269	WCru
- B&SWJ 356	CPou
- var. ***brevipedunculatum*** B&SWJ 1859	WCru
- f. ***cinereum*** B&SWJ 19121	WCru
- silver-leaved	WCot
tashiroi	GEdr WWst
ternatipartitum	GEdr WWst
- B&SWJ 5790	WCru
thunbergii	CPom EFEx WCot
- subsp. ***autumnale*** B&SWJ 1425	WCru
- subsp. ***urashima***	CLAP EBee EBrs EFEx GEdr LAma LFur MLul WWst
§ ***tortuosum***	CArn CKob CLAP EBee EBrs ECho ERos GBin GCrs GEdr GGar IHer ITer LAma LFur MLul MNrw MTho NLar NWCA WAbe WCot WPGP WPnP
- CC 1452	CPou
- GG 85320	ITer
- from high altitude	GBuc NMen
- var. ***helleborifolium*** CC 3641	WCot
tosaense	GEdr WWst
triphyllum	CLAP CPom EBee EBrs ECho EPot GEdr GGar GKev GSki ITer LAma MSal MTho NWCA SMad WFar WPGP WPnP
- subsp. ***stewardsonii***	EBee EBrs GCrs GGar ITer NMen WWst
- subsp. ***triphyllum*** var. ***atrorubens***	CLAP
§ ***utile***	EBee EBrs ECho ITer LAma MLul WPnP
- CC 3101	WCot
verrucosum	see *A. griffithii*
- var. ***utile***	see *A. utile*
§ ***wattii***	EBee LAma MLul
yamatense subsp. ***sugimotoi***	LAma
- - B&SWJ 5092	WCru
yunnanense	CLAP EBee LAma MGol WCot

Arisarum (*Araceae*)

proboscideum	More than 30 suppliers
- MS 958	EMar
vulgare	ECho
* - f. ***maculatum***	ECho
- subsp. ***simorrhinum***	CStu EBla EBrs ECho WCot
- subsp. ***vulgare***	EBee WCot WHal

Aristea (*Iridaceae*)

confusa	SWat
ecklonii	CAby CBod CHEx CPLG CPou CTrC EBee EMan EShb GGar GSki IGor SChr SWat WCot WDyG WOut WPic
ensifolia	CMdw MWea WPrP WSHC
grandis	CFir WCot
§ ***major***	CAbb CCtw CHII CPen CTrC EMan GSki
- pink-flowered	CAbb CDes WPGP
spiralis	SWat
thyrsiflora	see *A. major*

Aristida (*Poaceae*)

purpurea	LRav

Aristolochia ✿ (*Aristolochiaceae*)

baetica	CArn CPLG SKHP WPGP
californica	LEdu
chilensis	CCCN
clematitis	CArn EBee EBrs ECho GPoy LEdu MSal
contorta	EBee
delavayi	CHEx
durior	see *A. macrophylla*
elegans	see *A. littoralis*
fimbriata	CStu ITer
gigantea	CCCN CHII CSpe
grandiflora	CCCN
griffithii B&SWJ 2118	WCru
heterophylla	see *A. kaempferi* f. *heterophylla*
kaempferi B&SWJ 293	WCru
§ - f. ***heterophylla*** B&SWJ 3109	WCru
x ***kewensis*** new	CCCN
§ ***littoralis*** ♀H1	LRHS SOWG
§ ***macrophylla***	CBcs CHEx EBee EShb MBri MRav NPal SHBN SLim WSpi
manshuriensis B&SWJ 962	WCru
moupinensis BWJ 8181 new	WCru
onoei B&SWJ 4960	WCru
paucinervis	WCru
pearcei	CCCN
sempervirens	CStu WSHC
sipho	see *A. macrophylla*
tomentosa	IDee

Aristotelia (*Elaeocarpaceae*)

§ ***chilensis***	LEdu
- 'Variegata' (v)	CCCN CWib EBee GQui IDee SEND SPlb
fruticosa (f)	ECou
- (m)	ECou
- black-fruited (f)	ECou
- white-fruited (f)	ECou
macqui	see *A. chilensis*
peduncularis	CPLG
serrata	ECou
- (f)	ECou
- (m)	ECou

Armeria (*Plumbaginaceae*)

§ ***alliacea***	CSpe ECha EPPr MWgw
- f. ***leucantha***	SRms WMoo
Bees' hybrids	SRms WMoo
'Bees' Ruby'	WPer
'Bloodgood'	ECho
'Brutus'	CDes
caespitosa	see *A. juniperifolia*
- 'Bevan's Variety'	see *A. juniperifolia* 'Bevan's Variety'
canescens new	WLin
euscadiensis	CSpe EMon
§ ***girardii***	EPot
Joystick Series	ECho NVic
- 'Joystick Lilac Shades'	CBrm EShb LBMP NLar

	- 'Joystick Pink' **new**	SWal
	- 'Joystick Red'	CBrm EShb GGar SBri
	- 'Joystick White'	EGoo EShb NLar
§	***juniperifolia*** ♀H4	CLyd CMea CPBP ECho EDAr ELan EPfP GMaP LBee LRHS NMen NVic NWCA SIng SPoG SRms
	- 'Alba'	CMea ECho EDAr ELan EPfP EPot GBin NMen NPri NRya SIng SPoG SRms WAbe WFar WHoo WLin WThu
§	- 'Bevan's Variety' ♀H4	EAlp ECha ECho ECtt ELan EPfP EPot GGar GMaP LRHS MLHP MWat NLAp NMen NPri NRya SBla SPoG SRms SRot WAbe WFar WHoo WLin WPat
	- 'Brookside'	EPot
	- dark-flowered	EWes SBla WAbe
	- rose-flowered	ITim
	- spiny, dwarf	EPot NLAp
§	***maritima***	CArn ECho EPfP LAst LRHS MBar MNHC SECG SPet WCFE WFar WGwG WMoo XPep
	- 'Alba'	More than 30 suppliers
	- 'Bloodstone'	CTri ECho ECot ELan MWat SPoG
	- 'Corsica'	CTri EPot MBNS NBir NRya SMer WFar XPep
	- Düsseldorf Pride	see *A. maritima* 'Düsseldorfer Stolz'
§	- 'Düsseldorfer Stolz'	CElw EAlp ECha ECho ECtt EDAr ELan EPfP EPot GGar GKev GMaP ITim LHop LRHS MLHP NEgg NLAp NMen NPri SPoG WPat
	- 'Laucheana'	SHGN WHoo WMoo
*	- 'Pink Lusitanica'	ECho
I	- 'Rubrifolia'	More than 30 suppliers
	- 'Ruby Glow'	CTri LBuc
	- 'Splendens'	CBcs CHrt COIW CTri ECho EDAr EMil EPfP GGar GMaP GWCH LAst LBMP MHer NBlu NMir NNor NPri NRya NVic SBch SPoG SWal WFar WMoo WPer
	- 'Splendens Alba' **new**	EDAr
	- 'Vindictive' ♀H4	CMea CTri EPfP
	morisii	SBch
	'Nifty Thrifty' (v)	CBod CMea CTri EAlp EBee ECho ENot EWes EWin LRHS MBnl MHer NLAp NRya SCoo SIde SPoG SRot WFar WPat WWFP
	'Ornament'	ECtt LRav SHGN SPoG WHen
	plantaginea	see *A. alliacea*
	pseudarmeria	CHrt ELan EPfP MLan NBlu
	- 'Drumstick Red'	ECho WPer
	- 'Drumstick White'	WPer
	- hybrids	CTri ELan NMir SPad
	pungens	EBee
	setacea	see *A. girardii*
	tweedyi	EAlp
	'Vesuvius' **new**	SIng
	vulgaris	see *A. maritima*
	welwitschii	IFoB SRms
	'Westacre Beauty'	EWes

Armoracia (*Brassicaceae*)

§	***rusticana***	CArn CBod COld CPrp CSev CTri ELau EUnu GPoy ILis MBri MHer MNHC MSal NPer NPri NTHB SIde WGwG WHer WJek WSel WSpi
	- 'Variegata' (v)	CPrp ELau EMan EMon ITer LHop LRHS MAvo NSti SMad SPla WMoo WSel

Arnebia (*Boraginaceae*)

	echioides	see *A. pulchra*
	longiflora	see *A. pulchra*
§	***pulchra***	SBla

Arnica (*Asteraceae*)

	angustifolia subsp. ***alpina***	SRms
	- subsp. ***iljinii***	EBee NBir
	chamissonis Less.	CHby CHrt CWan EBee MNHC MSal NBre NLar WHil WJek WPer
	chamissonis Schmidt	see *A. sachalinensis*
	longifolia	NBre NEgg
	montana	CArn CSam EUnu GPoy MHer MLan MNHC SRms SWat WPer
	- yellow-flowered	MLan
§	***sachalinensis***	NBre
	- RBS 0206	EPPr MGol
	unalaschkensis	EBee

Aronia (*Rosaceae*)

	arbutifolia	CBcs CDul CTri EPfP EPla LSRN MBlu MGan NBlu SHBN SLon SPer WBod WOrn
	- 'Erecta'	EBee ECrN ELan EPfP GBin LHop MBNS MBlu MBri MWea NLar SLPl SMac SPoG SRms SSpi WFar
	melanocarpa	CAgr CBgR CDul CMCN CMHG CWib ELan EPfP LEdu LRHS MAsh MBar MBlu MRav SPer SSpi WFar WHCG
	- 'Autumn Magic'	CBcs CDoC CPMA EBee EPfP LAst LRHS MAsh MBlu NMyG SCoo SLPl
	- var. ***grandifolia***	CPMA
	- 'Hugin'	CAgr CPMA
	x ***prunifolia***	CAgr CDoC CDul CMHG EBee EWTr LEdu SPer WHCG
	- 'Aron' (F)	CPMA
	- 'Brilliant'	CDoC CTri EBee LAst LRHS SCoo SPur
	- 'Nero' (F)	CAgr
	- 'Serina' (F)	CPMA EBee
	- 'Viking' (F)	CAgr CPMA EBee ECrN EPfP LBuc MBlu NScw SPoG

Aronia x *Sorbus* (*Rosaceae*)

§	'Burka'	WPat

Arrhenatherum (*Poaceae*)

	elatius var. ***bulbosum***	NNor WFar
	- - 'Variegatum' (v)	CSpe EAlp EBee ELan ENot GBin GMaP LEdu LRHS MMoz MWgw NBid NHol NOrc SHFr SWal WFar WMoo WPer XIsg

Artemisia ✿ (*Asteraceae*)

	RBS 0207	EPPr
	from Taiwan	WHer
§	***abrotanum*** ♀H4	More than 30 suppliers
	absinthium	CArn CPbn CSev CWan EEls ELau EUnu GPoy MBar MHer MLLN MNHC NSti NTHB SAdn SECG SIde SPer SWat WPer XPep
*	- 'Argentea'	XPep
	- 'Corinne Tremaine' (v)	WHer
	- 'Lambrook Giant'	EEls
	- 'Lambrook Mist' ♀H3-4	CSev EBee EBla EEls ELan EPfP GBri GMaP GMac LRHS MRav MWgw NBre NCiC SBch SWat WCAu WMnd
	- 'Lambrook Silver' ♀H4	CArn CBcs CPLG CPrp CSam EBee ECha EEls EGle EHrv EPfP ERou LHop LRHS MHer MRav NBro SHBN SLim SPer SWat SWvt WFar WMnd WPer XPep
	- 'Silver Ghost'	EEls
*	- 'Variegata' (v)	CBcs EBla
	afra	CArn EBee EEls EMan EWin XPep

§	***alba***	CSev EEls EMan EMon EOHP GPoy ILis MHer MSal NSti SIde SMad WPer XPep
§	- 'Canescens' 🏆H4	CArn CSam CTri EBee ECha ECtt EEls EGle EHrv EPfP GMaP LAst LBMP LRHS MHer MRav SDix SPer SPoG SWvt WAul WCFE WCot WFar WHCG WMnd WPer
	annua	EEls MSal SIde WJek
	anomala	EEls
	arborescens 🏆H3	CArn CMHG ECrN EEls EWin SDix SDry SPer WHer XPep
	- 'Brass Band'	see *A.* 'Powis Castle'
	- 'Faith Raven'	CArn EBee EEls ERou GBin GBuc WFar
	- 'Little Mice'	EBee EEls WGwG
	- 'Porquerolles'	EAro EEls XPep
	arctica	EEls
	argyi	EEls
§	***armeniaca***	ECho EEls XPep
	assoana	see *A. caucasica*
	atrata	EEls
	barrelieri	EEls
	brachyloba	MLLN
	caerulescens	see *Seriphidium caerulescens*
	californica	EEls XPep
	- 'Canyon Gray'	EEls
	campestris subsp. ***borealis***	EEls WSel
	- subsp. ***campestris***	EEls XPep
	- subsp. ***glutinosa***	XPep
	- subsp. ***maritima***	EEls XPep
	- - from Wales	EEls
	camphorata	see *A. alba*
	cana	see *Seriphidium canum*
	canariensis	see *A. thuscula*
	canescens misapplied	see *A. alba* 'Canescens'
	canescens Willd.	see *A. armeniaca*
	capillaris	EEls MSal XPep
§	***caucasica*** 🏆H3-4	EBee ECho EEls EWes MBrN MHer SBla SChF SPhx SRms SRot WEas WJek WPer XPep
	- ***caucasica***	EEls WFar
	chamaemelifolia	CArn EBee EEls IGor MHer NBre WJek XPep
	cretacea	see *Seriphidium nutans*
	discolor Dougl. ex Besser	see *A. michauxiana*
	douglasiana	EEls
	- 'Valerie Finnis'	see *A. ludoviciana* 'Valerie Finnis'
	dracunculus	ECha GAbr MBar MNHC MRav NBlu NVic SPlb WBrk WFar WPer
	- French	CArn CBod CHby CHrt CSev EEls ELau EUnu GPoy GWCH LEdu MHer NGHP NPri SBch SIde WGwG WSel XPep
	- Russian	CArn CWan EEls EUnu XPep
	ferganensis	see *Seriphidium ferganense*
	filifolia	EEls XPep
	fragrans Willd.	see *Seriphidium fragrans*
	frigida 🏆H3-4	EEls WHCG XPep
	genipi	EEls MSal
	glacialis	ECha EEls XPep
	gmelinii	EBee EEls
	gnaphalodes	see *A. ludoviciana*
	gorgonum	EBee EEls EWes
	herba-alba	EAro EEls XPep
	'Huntington'	EEls WFar
	kawakamii B&SWJ 088	EEls WCru
	kitadakensis	EEls
	- 'Guizhou'	see *A. lactiflora* Guizhou Group
	laciniata	EEls
	lactiflora 🏆H4	CPrp EBee ECha ECtt EEls ELan ERou EWTr GMaP MRav NGdn NOrc SDix SPer SRms WFar WMoo WTin
	- dark	see *A. lactiflora* Guizhou Group
	- 'Elfenbein'	EBee GBin LHop
§	- Guizhou Group	More than 30 suppliers
	- 'Jim Russell'	CBow CDes CElw EBee EWes NBre NDov SPhx
	- ***purpurea***	see *A. lactiflora* Guizhou Group
	- 'Variegata'	see *A. vulgaris* 'Variegata'
	- 'Weisses Wunder'	EBee
	lagocephala	EEls EMan LSou
	lanata Willd. non Lam.	see *A. caucasica*
	laxa	see *A. umbelliformis*
	longifolia	XPep
§	***ludoviciana***	EEls ELan ERou IFoB MEHN MRav MWat NBid NOak NOrc NPer SBch SGar SRms WBVN WCFE
N	- var. ***latifolia***	see *A. ludoviciana* subsp. *ludoviciana* var. *latiloba*
	- subsp. ***ludoviciana*** var. ***incompta***	EBee ECha EEls EGle EMan MRav
§	- - var. ***latiloba***	EEls GBuc LHop LRHS MRav NBro NOak NSti SBch SWvt WCot WEas WHoo WPer
	- subsp. ***mexicana*** var. ***albula***	EEls WFar
	- 'Silver Queen' 🏆H4	More than 30 suppliers
N	- 'Valerie Finnis' 🏆H4	More than 30 suppliers
	manshurica	EMan LSou
	maritima	see *Seriphidium maritimum*
§	***michauxiana***	EBee EEls NSti WHer
	molinieri	EEls XPep
	mutellina	see *A. umbelliformis*
	niitakayamensis	EEls EOHP XPep
	nitida	EEls
	nutans	see *Seriphidium nutans*
	palmeri hort.	see *A. ludoviciana*
	pamirica	EEls
	aff. ***parviflora***	EBee
	- CLD 1531	EEls
	pedemontana	see *A. caucasica*
	pontica	CArn EBee ECha ECrN EEls ELan EShb GMaP GPoy LRHS MBNS MHer MNFA MRav MWgw NBro NSti SDix SMer SPer SSvw WFar WHoo WPer XPep
§	'Powis Castle' 🏆H3	More than 30 suppliers
	princeps	CArn EEls MSal SIde
	procera Willd.	see *A. abrotanum*
	purshiana	see *A. ludoviciana*
	pycnocephala new	EEls
	- 'David's Choice'	EEls SMad
	ramosa	EEls
	'Rosenschleier'	CAby EBee EMon EPPr EWes GBin NBre NCGa SPhx WFar WPGP WTin
	rutifolia	EEls
	sachalinensis	EEls WOut
	schmidtiana 🏆H4	ECha ECot EEls EMan MWat NLAp NOrc SRms
	- 'Nana' 🏆H4	More than 30 suppliers
	selengensis	EEls
	splendens misapplied	see *A. alba* 'Canescens'
	splendens Willd.	EEls ELan SPhx WEas
	- var. ***brachyphylla*** new	MAsh
	stelleriana	ECha EDAr EEls EShb EWTr GKev IFoB LHop MHer MWgw NBro NSti SPer SRms WCAu WEas XPep
	- RBS 0207	EEls GKev NLar
N	- 'Boughton Silver'	CHrt EBee ECtt EEls EGle EGoo ELan EPfP GBri GGar GMaP GMac LDai LRHS MAsh MRav SPer SRms SWvt WFar WMnd XPep
N	- 'Mori'	see *A. stelleriana* 'Boughton Silver'
	- 'Nana'	EEls EMan SWvt
	- 'Prostrata'	see *A. stelleriana* 'Boughton Silver'
	- 'Silver Brocade'	see *A. stelleriana* 'Boughton Silver'

	suksdorfii	EBee
	taurica	EEls
§	***thuscula***	EEls
	tridentata	see *Seriphidium tridentatum*
§	***umbelliformis***	EEls
	vallesiaca	see *Seriphidium vallesiacum*
	verlotiorum	EEls
	vulgaris L.	CAgr CArn CPrp EEls ELau GPoy GWCH MGol MHer MNHC WHer
	- 'Cragg-Barber Eye' (v)	EBee EEls EWin GSki NBid NPro SAga WHer
	- 'Crispa'	LSou
	- 'Obelisk'	EEls
	- Oriental Limelight = 'Janlim' (v)	COlW CPLG EBee ECtt EDAr EEls EPfP EUnu EWTr LEdu LHop LRHS MCCP MWgw NBir NEgg NOrc NPri SHar SPoG SWal SWvt WCAu WFar WHer WJek
	- 'Peddar's Gold' (v)	EBee EWin
§	- 'Variegata' (v)	CEnt EBee EEls NBir NSti SMad WFar WHer WMoo WPer
	x ***wurzellii***	EEls

Arthrocnemum (*Chenopodiaceae*)

	glaucum	XPep

Arthropodium (*Anthericaceae*)

	candidum	CStu EBee EBrs ECha ECho ECou GEdr ITim NWCA SHBN SRot WFar WPer WPtf
	- 'Capri'	EBee
	- ***maculatum***	GEdr LEdu SPlb WHil
	- ***purpureum***	CBcs CPLG EBee EMan EWll GBri GGar NLAp WFar WPGP
*	***carlesii***	CDes
	cirratum	CHEx ECou GGar IDee LEdu MLan SBch WSHC
	- 'Matapouri Bay'	CAbP CBcs CHEx EBee EMil ERea EWld WPGP
	milleflorum	GGar

Arthrostylidium (*Poaceae*)

	naibuense	CGHE EBee WPGP

Arum (*Araceae*)

	alpinum	see *A. cylindraceum*
	'Chameleon'	CDes EMan EMar EMon LFur MNrw MSte MTho NBir NLar SMad SPer WCot WCru WFar WHil WPGP WTin
§	***concinnatum***	CStu EBrs EPot SChr SHar SKHP WCot WPrP
	- JCA	CStu
	- black-spotted	EBee EMar
	- variegated (V) **new**	WCot
	concinnatum x ***cyrenaicum*** **new**	EBrs GKev
	cornutum	see *Sauromatum venosum*
	creticum	CArn CFir CSpe CWsd EBee ECha EMan EMar GBuc GSki ITer MNrw MRav MTho SCnR SDix SRot WBor WCot
	- MS 696	MNrw
	- FCC form	EBrs ECho SBla WCot WPGP
	- 'Marmaris White'	SCnR WCot
	- white-spathed	MNrw MTho
	- yellow-spathed	NBir WFar WIvy
	creticum x ***italicum***	MDKP WCot WFar
§	***cylindraceum*** **new**	EBrs ECho NLar
	cyrenaicum	CStu EBee ECho LEdu MNrw MTho SKHP WCot WPGP
	- from Crete	ECho WCot
	dioscoridis	CDes CStu EBrs ECho EWes GKev MTho NLar WCot
	- JCA 195.197	WCot
	- MS&CL 524	ITer
	- var. ***cyprium***	EBee EBrs ECho ITer
§	- var. ***dioscoridis***	EBee ERos ITer LFur WCot
	- - JCA 195200	WPrP
	- var. ***liepoldtii***	see *A. dioscoridis* var. *dioscoridis*
	- var. ***smithii***	see *A. dioscoridis* var. *dioscoridis*
	dracunculus	see *Dracunculus vulgaris*
	elongatum	EBee EBrs WCot
	hygrophilum	EBrs
	idaeum	EBrs
	italicum	CArn CLAP ECho GAbr GKev LAma MTho MWat NBPC NLar SBod SEND SWat WCot WFar WPnP WSHC WShi
	- subsp. ***albispathum***	CDes CHid CStu EBee ECho EDAr EMon WCot WFar WPGP
	- black-spotted	SCnR WFar
	- giant **new**	SBla WHil
	- 'Green Marble'	CBct WFar
	- subsp. ***italicum***	CBct EBee EBrs ECho EPla EShb GKev LFur NWCA WBrk
	- - 'Bill Baker'	EMon WFar
	- - 'Cyclops' EAF 7701	CHid MNrw WCot
§	- - 'Marmoratum' ♀H4	More than 30 suppliers
	- - 'Sparkler'	WCot
	- - 'Spotted Jack'	LFur MNrw NBre WCot WCru
	- - 'Tiny'	CFir EMon SCnR
§	- - 'White Winter'	CElw EBee ECGP EMon GBuc WCot WSPU
	- 'Nancy Lindsay'	EMar EMon
	- subsp. ***neglectum***	SChr WFar
	- - 'Miss Janay Hall' (v)	EBee EWes LFur LTwo WCot
	- 'Pictum'	see *A. italicum* subsp. *italicum* 'Marmoratum'
	- 'Splish Splash' **new**	CAvo CBow
	jacquemontii	ECho
	korolkowii	WCot
	maculatum	CArn CRWN EBrs EPot GKev GPoy LAma MHer MRav MSal NLar NMyG WHer WShi
	- 'Painted Lady' (v)	WCot
	- 'Pleddel'	MRav WCot
	- Tar Spot Group	CNat
	nickelii	see *A. concinnatum*
§	***nigrum***	EBrs ECho EWes WCot WGwG
	orientale	EPot WCot
	- subsp. ***amoenum***	MNrw
	petteri misapplied	see *A. nigrum*
	pictum	CDes CLAP CPLG EBee EBrs ECho ERos EWes GEdr LFur WCot WWst
	- 'Primrose Warburg' **new**	SBla
	- 'Taff's Form'	see *A. italicum* subsp. *italicum* 'White Winter'
	purpureospathum	CPom EBee EBrs WCot WPGP WWst
	rupicola var. ***rupicola***	WWst
	- var. ***virescens***	WCot
	sintenisii	EBee WCot
	'Streaked Spectre'	EMon

Aruncus ✿ (*Rosaceae*)

	AGSJ 214	NHol
	aethusifolius ♀H4	More than 30 suppliers
	- 'Little Gem'	ECho WCru
	asiaticus	EBla
	- B&SWJ 8624	WCru
	dioicus	More than 30 suppliers
§	- (m) ♀H4	CDoC ECha ELan EPla GSki MBNS MRav MWgw NBro NHol NSti SGar SMad SPer SRms SWal SWat WFar WMoo WPer
	- var. ***acuminatus***	EBee
	- Child of Two Worlds	see *A. dioicus* 'Zweiweltenkind'
	- 'Glasnevin'	CSev ECtt MRav WFar
	- var. ***kamtschaticus***	EBee EWes MCCP MGos NBre NHol NLar WPnP

- - AGSJ 238	NHol
- - RBS 0208	MGol MHar NGdn WBVN
- 'Kneiffii'	More than 30 suppliers
§ - 'Zweiweltenkind'	CEnt CRez EBee EBla EHrv GSki LCro NBre NLar SMad WCot
'Horatio'	EBee EBla EMon GBin IPot SMeo SPhx WCot
'Johannifest'	CDes EBee EBla EMon GBin LBBr
'Noble Spirit'	CEnt EBee EBla EPPr MNHC MWrn NGdn NLar SCoo SWal WWeb
'Perlehuhn'	EMon
plumosus	see *A. dioicus*
sinensis	EBla EShb NBre WFar
sylvestris	see *A. dioicus*
'Woldemar Meier'	EBee EBla EMon GBin

Arundinaria ✿ (*Poaceae*)

amabilis	see *Pseudosasa amabilis* (McClure) Keng f.
anceps	see *Yushania anceps*
angustifolia	see *Pleioblastus chino* 'Murakamianus'
auricoma	see *Pleioblastus viridistriatus*
chino	see *Pleioblastus chino*
disticha	see *Pleioblastus pygmaeus* 'Distichus'
falconeri	see *Himalayacalamus falconeri*
fargesii	see *Bashania fargesii*
fastuosa	see *Semiarundinaria fastuosa*
fortunei	see *Pleioblastus variegatus*
funghomii	see *Schizostachyum funghomii*
§ ***gigantea***	MWht SDry
- subsp. ***tecta***	CBcs MGos
hindsii	see *Pleioblastus hindsii*
hookeriana misapplied	see *Himalayacalamus falconeri* 'Damarapa'
hookeriana Munro	see *Himalayacalamus hookerianus*
humilis	see *Pleioblastus humilis*
japonica	see *Pseudosasa japonica*
jaunsarensis	see *Yushania anceps*
maling	see *Yushania maling*
marmorea	see *Chimonobambusa marmorea*
murielae	see *Fargesia murielae*
nitida	see *Fargesia nitida*
oedogonata	see *Clavinodum oedogonatum*
palmata	see *Sasa palmata*
pumila	see *Pleioblastus argenteostriatus* f. *pumilus*
pygmaea	see *Pleioblastus pygmaeus*
quadrangularis	see *Chimonobambusa quadrangularis*
simonii	see *Pleioblastus simonii*
spathiflora	see *Thamnocalamus spathiflorus*
tessellata	see *Thamnocalamus tessellatus*
vagans	see *Sasaella ramosa*
variegata	see *Pleioblastus variegatus*
veitchii	see *Sasa veitchii*
viridistriata	see *Pleioblastus viridistriatus*
'Wang Tsai'	see *Bambusa multiplex* 'Floribunda'

Arundo (*Poaceae*)

donax	More than 30 suppliers
I - 'Aureovariegata'	CDTJ IPot MDKP
- 'Golden Chain'	CKno EAlp EBee EPPr EWes SMad
- 'Macrophylla'	CBig CGHE CKno EPPr ETod LEdu LPJP SApp WPGP
- 'Variegata'	see *A. donax* var. *versicolor*
§ - var. ***versicolor*** (v)	More than 30 suppliers
- yellow-variegated (v)	CDes EShb SEND SPoG
formosana	CKno CMCo EBee EPPr XIsg
- 'Golden Showers'	WPnP
pliniana	EPla WPGP

Asarina (*Scrophulariaceae*)

antirrhiniflora	see *Maurandella antirrhiniflora*
barclayana	see *Maurandya barclayana*
erubescens	see *Lophospermum erubescens*
hispanica	see *Antirrhinum hispanicum*
lophantha	see *Lophospermum scandens*
lophospermum	see *Lophospermum scandens*
§ ***procumbens***	CDMG CEnt CMea CStu CTri EBee ECho EPfP GAbr GKev MNFA MTho NRya SGar SHFr SIng SRms WFar WGwG WPer
'Victoria Falls'	see *Maurandya* 'Victoria Falls'

Asarum ✿ (*Aristolochiaceae*)

Chen Yi 5	WCot
albomaculatum B&SWJ 1726	WCru
arifolium	CDes CLAP EHrv NLar
asaroides	CKob WWst
asperum	EBee EPot
campaniflorum	CLAP ECho EHrv LAma MLul WCru WWst
canadense	CArn CBct EBee ECho EHrv EPPr EPot ERos GPoy GSki LRHS MSal NLar WCru
caudatum	CAvo CDes CHEx CLAP CStu EBee EBrs ECha ECho EMon EPPr GBuc ITer LEdu NBro NLar NSti NWCA SRms WCot WCru WFar WPGP WSpi
- white-flowered	CDes CLAP EHrv
caudigerum	EBee MLul
- B&SWJ 1517	WCru
caulescens	CHHB CLAP EBee ECho EHrv EPPr LAma LEdu MLul WCru WWst
- B&SWJ 5886	WCru
costatum	CLAP
crispulatum new	EBee
debile	EBee
delavayi	CKob EBee EHrv LAma MLul WCot WCru
epigynum B&SWJ 3443	WCru
- 'Silver Web'	CLAP WCru
europaeum	More than 30 suppliers
fauriei	WCru
forbesii	EBee ECho EHrv MLul NLar WCot WWst
fukienense new	EBee
geophilum	EBee MLul
hartwegii	CLAP EBee EBrs EHrv GBuc GGar ITer NLar WCot WCru WPGP
- NNS 00-74	EPPr
- NNS 00-78	WCot
- NNS 01-35	GKev
heterotropoides	EBee
hypogynum B&SWJ 3628	WCru
infrapurpureum	WCot
- B&SWJ 1994	WCru
kumageanum	WCot
lemmonii	EMan LEdu WCru
leptophyllum B&SWJ 1983	WCru
longirhizomatosum	EBee MLul WCru
macranthum	WCot
- B&SWJ 1691	WCru
maculatum B&SWJ 1114	WCru
magnificum	CHHB CKob CLAP EBee EHrv LAma MLul WCru WWst
maximum	CFwr CHHB CKob CLAP CSpe EBee EBrs ECho EHrv ERCP LAma MLul NMen WCot WCru
- 'Silver Panda' new	EBee EHrv LSou SPoG
naniflorum 'Eco Decor'	CLAP EBee EHrv GEdr GMac GSki LAst LSou MBNS NLar NMyG WCot

petelotii B&SWJ 9706 **new**	WCru
pulchellum	EHrv WCot WCru WWst
rigescens	EBee EHrv EPot
sakawanum	EBee
shuttleworthii	CLAP NLar
sieboldii	CLAP WCru
splendens	More than 30 suppliers
taipingshanianum B&SWJ 1688	WCot WCru
taitonense	WWst
takaoi	CKob

Asclepias (*Asclepiadaceae*)

asperula subsp. ***capricornu***	CArn
'Cinderella'	EBee LBuc SSvw
curassavica	CCCN CHrt CSev EShb NBre SHFr SPav WRos
incarnata	CAgr CEnt CPom EBee ELan EPau ERou IFoB MRav NBre SPav SPlb WPer WTMC
- 'Alba'	ELan EMon MMuc
- 'Ice Ballet'	CPrp EBee ELan ERou EShb IFoB LHop LRHS MCCP NBPC NBre NEgg NTHB SAga SPoG SWat WPer
- 'Soulmate'	EBee ELan EPfP EWll LRav MLLN MMHG NBPC NBre NGdn NTHB SPad SPoG
physocarpa	see *Gomphocarpus physocarpus*
purpurascens	CArn EMon NEgg
speciosa	CAgr EMon NBre NLar WAul
sullivantii	NBre SPav
syriaca	CAgr CArn CPom EBee MSal NBre SPav
tuberosa	CAgr CArn CBcs CWib EBee EBrs EMan EShb GPoy LHop MHer MNrw MPop MSal NEgg SMad SPet SPoG
- Gay Butterflies Group	NBre NEgg NGdn SMrm
verticillata	NBre
viridiflora **new**	LRav

Asimina (*Annonaceae*)

triloba (F)	CBcs MBlu MBri MGol NLar SPlb WNor
- 'Davis' (F)	CAgr
- 'Sunflowers' **new**	CCCN

Askidiosperma (*Restionaceae*)

chartaceum	CTrC
esterhuyseniae	WNor

Asparagus (*Asparagaceae*)

asparagoides 🏆H1	ERea EShb SEND
§ - 'Myrtifolius'	CHal
crassicladus	EShb
densiflorus 'Mazeppa'	EShb
- 'Myersii' 🏆H1	CHal ERea EShb SEND SRms
- Sprengeri Group 🏆H1	CHal LRHS MBri
- - 'Variegatus'	EShb
denudatus	EShb
falcatus	EShb SEND
filicinus var. ***giraldii***	WCot
officinalis	MNHC SEND WFar WOut
* - 'Amarus' **new**	EMui
- 'Backlim' 🏆H4	ECrN EMil EMui
- 'Butler'	SDea
- 'Cito' (m)	LRHS SDea
- 'Connover's Colossal' 🏆H4	CWan ECrN ENot
- 'Dariana'	SDea
- 'Eros' **new**	EMui
- 'Franklim'	WFar
- 'Gijnlim' 🏆H4	ECrN EMil EMui NBlu SDea WHil
- 'Grolim' PBR **new**	EMil
- 'Guelph Millennium' **new**	EMui
- 'Jersey Giant' (m)	EMui
- 'Pacific Purple' **new**	EMui
- 'Purple Jumbo'	EBee ECrN
plumosus	see *A. setaceus*
pseudoscaber 'Spitzenschleier'	EBee EMan EShb MAvo
retrofractus	EShb WPGP
scandens	EShb
schoberioides	LEdu
§ ***setaceus*** 🏆H1	CHal EShb LRHS MBri
- 'Pyramidalis' 🏆H1	MBri
suaveolens	EShb
tenuifolius	EMon
verticillatus	SRms
virgatus	EShb WPGP

Asperula (*Rubiaceae*)

§ ***arcadiensis*** 🏆H3	ECho SBla WAbe
aristata subsp. ***scabra***	CSpe EBee ECha ELan EMan EMon
- subsp. ***thessala***	see *A. sintenisii*
boissieri	ECho
cyanchica	MSal
daphneola	ECho EWes SBla WAbe
gussonei	CMea CStu ECho EPot GCrs LRHS MWat NLAp NMen NWCA SBla WAbe WPat
lilaciflora	ECho
- var. ***caespitosa***	see *A. lilaciflora* subsp. *lilaciflora*
§ - subsp. ***lilaciflora***	CLyd CPBP ECho NMen
nitida	ECho
- subsp. ***puberula***	see *A. sintenisii*
odorata	see *Galium odoratum*
orientalis	WPGP
scutellaris	EBee
§ ***sintenisii*** 🏆H2-3	CLyd CMea CPBP ECho EPot LRHS NMen SBla WAbe WHoo WThu
suberosa misapplied	see *A. arcadiensis*
suberosa Sibth. & Sm.	ECho
taurina subsp. ***caucasica***	CPLG EBee NLar NSti
tinctoria	CArn EOHP GPoy MHer MSal SRms

Asphodeline (*Asphodelaceae*)

RCB/TQ C-2	WCot
Cally Hybrids **new**	EDAr
damascena	CPBP EBee
liburnica	CAvo EBee ECha ELan EMan ERos ERou GAbr GSki MRav NEgg SEND SSvw WCAu WCot WFar WHal WPer
§ ***lutea***	More than 30 suppliers
§ - 'Gelbkerze'	EBee NBre SPoG
- Yellow Candle	see *A. lutea* 'Gelbkerze'
taurica	ECho NBre WLin WPer

Asphodelus (*Asphodelaceae*)

acaulis	ECho SCnR WAbe WCot
§ ***aestivus***	EBee EMan GAbr GSki MFOX MRav SSvw SWat WCot WPer
albus	CArn CSpe EBee ECha EPPr EPyc GBuc GSki IFoB NBid SPer SPlb SRms WAul WPen WPer
asiaticus **new**	EBee
cerasiferus	see *A. ramosus*
fistulosus	MMHG NBir WPrP XPep
lusitanicus	see *A. ramosus*
luteus	see *Asphodeline lutea*
microcarpus	see *A. aestivus*
§ ***ramosus***	CAby CBrm CMdw CPar EBee ECho EMan GSki MGol MNrw MTho NEgg SMrm WBVN WCot WPer XPep

Aspidistra (*Convallariaceae*)

from China	WCot
attenuata	CKob
- B&SWJ 377	WCru
caespitosa 'Jade Ribbons'	IBlr WCot
'China Star'	CKob EBee IBlr WCot
'China Sun'	CKob WCot
daibuensis	CKob IBlr
- B&SWJ 312b	WCru
elatior ŸH1	CBct CHEx CHal CKob EBak EBee EShb IBlr LRHS MBri NLar NPal NScw SAPC SArc SEND SMad STre WCot
- 'Akebono' (v)	WCot
- 'Asahi' (v)	IBlr WCot
- 'Hoshi-zora' (v)	IBlr WCot
- 'Milky Way' (v)	CAby CBct CBow CHid EBee EShb EWin IBlr MTho SEND WCot
- 'Okame' (v)	WCot
- 'Variegata' (v) ŸH1	CBct CHEx CHal CKob ERea EShb IBlr IFoB MTho NBir WCot
- 'Variegata Exotica' new	XBlo
leshanensis (v)	IBlr
linearifolia 'Leopard'	IBlr WCot
longiloba	WCot
lurida	CBct EBee ERea IBlr
- 'Amanogawa' (v)	IBlr
- 'Fuji-no-mine' (v)	IBlr
- 'Irish Mist' (v)	IBlr
minutiflora	WCot
omeiensis new	WCot
punctata new	IBlr
saxicola 'Uan Fat Lady'	CKob WCru
sichuanensis new	WCot
typica	IBlr
urceolata new	IBlr
zongbayi new	WCot

Asplenium ✿ (*Aspleniaceae*)

adiantum-nigrum	SRms
australe 'Redondo' new	WFib
bulbiferum ŸH1-2	CDTJ CPLG CTrC ERea EShb WFib
bulbiferum x ***oblongifolium***	WRic
§ ***ceterach***	CLAP EBee EFer LRHS NMyG SRms WAbe WFib WHer WRic
csikii var. ***trogyense***	WAbe
dareoides	SRot WAbe
x ***ebenoides***	LRHS WRic
fontanum	WAbe
friesiorum new	SKHP
lyallii new	WRic
'Maori Princess'	WFib
nidus ŸH1	MBri
oblongifolium	CTrC WRic
obovatum subsp. ***lanceolatum*** new	WRic
ruprechtii new	WRic
ruta-muraria	EFer NHol SRms
§ ***scolopendrium*** ŸH4	More than 30 suppliers
- 'Angustatum'	More than 30 suppliers
- 'Apple Court' new	CLAP
- 'Capitatum'	MDun
* - 'Circinatum'	WPGP
- 'Conglomeratum'	SRms
- Crispum Group	CBgR CLAP CSBt EFer ELan MRav NHol SApp SRms SRot WAbe WFib WPGP WPtf
- - 'Golden Queen'	CLAP
- 'Crispum Bolton's Nobile' ŸH4	WFib WPGP
- Crispum Cristatum Group	CLAP NVic
- Crispum Fimbriatum Group	CLAP GQui
- Cristatum Group	More than 30 suppliers
- Fimbriatum Group	CLAP WRic
- 'Furcatum'	CFwr CLAP CPrp GEdr MAsh NEgg WRic
- 'Kaye's Lacerated' ŸH4	CLAP EFer ELan WFib WRic
- Laceratum Group	CLAP SRms
- Marginatum Group	EFer SWat WPGP
- - 'Irregulare'	SRms
- 'Muricatum'	CFwr CLAP ELan GBin MRav NBid NHol SRms WFib WTin
- 'Ramocristatum'	CLAP
- Ramomarginatum Group	CLAP ELan SRms WAbe WFar WRic
- 'Sagittatocristatum'	SRms WPGP
- (Sagittatocristatum Group) 'Apple Court'	CBgR
- 'Sagittato-projectum Sclater'	WFib
* - 'Sagittatum'	SRms
- 'Stagshorn'	SRms
- Undulatum Group	CBgR CLAP EBee ECha EPfP MAsh MPes NBir NEgg NMyG NSti SPla SRms SWat WIvy WPnP WRic
- Undulatum Cristatum Group	CLAP NDlv
septentrionale	SRms
trichomanes ŸH4	More than 30 suppliers
- Cristatum Group	SRms
- Incisum Group	CLAP CWCL LRHS MAvo NOrc SRms
- 'Ramocristatum'	WAbe
viride	SRms

Astartea (*Myrtaceae*)

fascicularis	CPLG

Astelia (*Asteliaceae*)

alpina	IBlr
banksii	CBcs CDoC CPen CTrC EBee ECou GGar IBal LRHS MBri WCot WDyG WGer
§ ***chathamica*** ŸH3	More than 30 suppliers
- 'Silver Spear'	see *A. chathamica*
cunninghamii	see *A. solandri*
fragrans	CSpe ECou GGar IBlr LEdu WCot WDyG
fragrans x ***chathamica*** new	ECou
graminea	IBlr
grandis	CTrC IBlr LEdu
nervosa	CAbb CTrC ECou IBlr LEdu SAPC SArc WCot WPat WPic
- 'Bronze Giant'	IBlr
- 'Westland'	CAbb CBcs CBod CDoC CPen CTrC EBee EMan EMil IBlr LEdu LRHS MBri MGos MRav SPoG WCot WLeb WPic
nivicola 'Red Gem'	LEdu
petriei	IBlr
§ ***solandri***	CHEx IBlr
trinervia	IBlr

Aster ✿ (*Asteraceae*)

acris	see *A. sedifolius*
acuminatus	EShb
alpinus ŸH4	CTri EAlp ECho EPfP GKev MWgw NEgg SBla SRms WFar WPer
- var. ***albus***	EBee EMil EPfP GKev NBre NBro SRGP WPer WWeb
- Dark Beauty	see *A. alpinus* 'Dunkle Schöne'
- var. ***dolomiticus***	GKev
§ - 'Dunkle Schöne'	CHrt ECho LDai MHar NBre NVic SRGP SRms WFar WPer WWeb
- 'Goliath'	ECho MMHG NBre NBro SPlb WFar WWeb

	- 'Happy End'	CMMP ECho EMil LDai NBre NBro NLar SRGP SRms WFar WWeb
	- 'Märchenland' (d)	CPBP NBre
	- 'Pinkie'	CSam EBee NBre NHol NLar SMad WLin WWeb
	- 'Trimix'	ECho GAbr NBir SRms WFar
	- violet-flowered	WPer
	- 'White Beauty'	SRms
*	- 'Wolfii'	SRms WFar
	amelloides	see *Felicia amelloides*
	amellus	LSou SPer WMoo
	- 'Blue King'	EBee EWsh MLLN SWvt WCAu
	- 'Breslau'	EBee
	- 'Brilliant'	EBee EBla ECtt EGle EMan LAst LSou MAvo MBNS MLLN MNFA MRav MWat NEgg SPer SRGP WIvy WOld
	- 'Butzemann'	EBee GBin
	- 'Forncett Flourish'	WOld WOut
	- 'Framfieldii' ♀H4	WFar WOld
	- 'Gründer'	WHil WOld
	- 'Jacqueline Genebrier' ♀H4	CHar EGle WCot WIvy WSHC
	- 'Joseph Lakin'	WFar
	- 'King George' ♀H4	More than 30 suppliers
	- 'Kobold'	WFar
	- 'Lac de Genève'	LCro MRav NLar WCot WFar WOld
	- 'Lady Hindlip'	WFar
	- 'Louise'	MBrN
	- 'Mira'	GBin
	- 'Moerheim Gem'	WIvy
	- 'Nocturne'	ERou WCot WIvy WOld
	- Pink Zenith	see *A. amellus* 'Rosa Erfüllung'
§	- 'Rosa Erfüllung'	CPrp EBee EBla ECtt ELon EPfP ERou EShb GBuc GMaP LHop MNFA MRav NDov NEgg SPet SPla SRGP SWvt WCot WMnd WOld WPer
	- 'Rotfeuer'	NGby
	- 'Rudolph Goethe'	EBee EMil EPyc ERou LAst LRHS MLLN MRav MSte NRnb NVic SHBN SMer SRGP WCAu WFar WMoo WOld
	- 'September Glow'	EGle
	- 'Silbersee'	EMon NDov
	- 'Sonia'	EBee ECha EGle MRav NGby NLar
	- 'Sonora'	CPrp ECGP EGle ENot ERou LHop MSte NBre NChi NDov SAga SRGP WKif WOld
	- 'Sternkugel'	GMac WOld
	- 'Ultramarine'	WFar
	- 'Vanity'	GBuc WOld
§	- 'Veilchenkönigin' ♀H4	More than 30 suppliers
N	- Violet Queen	see *A. amellus* 'Veilchenkönigin'
	- 'Weltfriede'	WOld
	'Anja's Choice'	EBee EMon EPPr EWsh MAvo NBre WCot WOld
	asper	see *A. bakerianus*
	asperulus	CWsd EBrs EPPr MBri MFOX NDov SBla SMeo SPhx
	'Bahamas'	ENot MBri SGar
§	***bakerianus***	NBir WFar
	'Barbados'	ENot MBri
	capensis 'Variegatus'	see *Felicia amelloides* variegated
§	***carolinianus***	EShb
	'Cassandra'	WOld
	ciliolatus 'Bigwig'	EBee
	'Claudia'	SRGP
	'Climax' misapplied	see *A. laevis* 'Calliope', *A. laevis* 'Arcturus'
	'Climax' ambig.	CBnk CElw GBuc MRav NBid NRnb NSti SAga SMrm SPhx
	'Climax' Vicary Gibbs	WOld
	coelestis	see *Felicia amelloides*
	coloradoensis	CGra CPBP NSla SBla
	'Connecticut Snow Flurry'	see *A. ericoides* f. *prostratus* 'Snow Flurry'
	'Coombe Fishacre' ♀H4	CHrt COlW CPrp EBee EPPr ERou GBuc MAvo MRav MSte NBre SAga SPla SPoG SSvw WCot WFar WOld WTin
	cordifolius	WFar WHil
	- 'Chieftain' ♀H4	CAby IGor MNFA MNrw SAga SPhx WIvy WOld
	- 'Elegans'	EBee IGor MBri MNFA MSte NSti WIvy WMnd WMoo WOld
	- 'Ideal'	EBee GMac NLar WOld WPer
	- 'Silver Queen'	WHil WOld
	- 'Silver Spray'	CPrp EBee ECtt ERou GMaP GMac MHom MLLN MNFA MWat NBre SRGP WOld WPer
	- 'Sweet Lavender' ♀H4	CWsd ERou GMac WMoo WOld
	corymbosus	see *A. divaricatus*
	'Cotswold Gem'	WCot WOld
§	'Dark Pink Star'	WOld
	'Deep Pink Star'	see *A.* 'Dark Pink Star'
	delavayi	EBee
	diffusus	see *A. lateriflorus*
	diplostephioides	CFis CMdw EBee EDAr EMan EPPr EShb NBre NDov NHol NLar SGar SPhx SPlb WAul WPtf
§	***divaricatus***	More than 30 suppliers
§	- 'Eastern Star'	NCGa WBVN WCot WOld
	- Raiche form	see *A. divaricatus* 'Eastern Star'
	drummondii	EBee
N	***dumosus***	CPLG WFar WPer
	- 'Biteliness'	NBre NLar
	- Sapphire = 'Kiesapphire'	CBow NPri
	ericoides	EShb NBre NOrc WFar XPep
	- 'Blue Star' ♀H4	CPrp CSam EBrs GBuc IGor LRHS MFOX MLLN MSte NBPC NBid NLar SHGN SPer SPoG WBor WCAu WCot WMnd WOld
	- 'Brimstone' ♀H4	EPPr IGor MRav NBre WOld
	- 'Cinderella'	COlW CPrp GBuc GMac NSti WOld
	- 'Cirylle'	MLLN NBre
	- 'Constance'	WOld
	- 'Enchantress'	ERou
	- 'Erlkönig'	EBee EMan EPPr LAst LRHS MRav MSte MWgw NCGa NGdn NLar SPla SWat WMnd WOld WPer
	- 'Esther'	CPrp EBee ECha EGle ELan ERou MSte SDix WOld
	- 'Golden Spray' ♀H4	EBee GMaP NLar NSti SPer WFar WMnd WOld WOut
	- 'Herbstmyrte'	MLLN
	- 'Hon. Edith Gibbs'	WOld
	- 'Hon. Vicary Gibbs'	see *A.* 'Hon. Vicary Gibbs'
	- 'Monte Cassino'	see *A. pilosus* var. *pringlei* 'Monte Cassino'
	- 'Pink Cloud' ♀H4	More than 30 suppliers
	- f. ***prostratus***	EBee EMon EPot SGar SHGN WFar
§	- - 'Snow Flurry' ♀H4	CBgR CMea CSam EBee ECha ECtt IGor MAvo MLLN MNFA MNrw SDix SPhx SPla SRGP WCAu WCot WEas WMnd WOld WOut
	- 'Rosy Veil'	CKno GMac IGor MHom NBir NGdn
	- 'Schneegitter'	MLLN MSte WCot WFar WOld
	- 'Schneetanne'	NBre NRnb
	- 'Sulphurea'	MWat
	- 'Vimmer's Delight'	WCot
	- 'White Heather'	CPrp IGor MNFA NLar WIvy WMnd WOld WPer WRHF
	- 'Yvette Richardson'	CWsd MHom MSte SMHy WOld
	falcatus	EBee
	- var. ***commutatus***	WCot
	'Fanny's Fall'	see *A. oblongifolius* 'Fanny's'
§	***flaccidus***	WRos

	foliaceus	EBee WHil
	- from Montana	EPPr
	x ***frikartii***	CPrp EBee EGle ELan EPfP ERou EShb LAst MRav SAga SHBN SRms SWvt WEas WMnd WOld WSHC
	- 'Eiger'	WOld
	- 'Flora's Delight'	WOld
	- 'Jungfrau'	CFis COIW CWGN EBee ERou GMaP LPio MRav MSte NLar SPhx WOld WSHC
N	- 'Mönch' Υ^{H4}	More than 30 suppliers
	- Wonder of Stafa	see *A.* x *frikartii* 'Wunder von Stäfa'
§	- 'Wunder von Stäfa' Υ^{H4}	CEnd CKno CPLG EBee ECtt ELan ELon EMan EPfP GBuc GMaP IPot LHop LPio LRHS MAvo MBNS MNFA MRav NBlu NLar WCot WMnd WOld WPGP
	glaucodes	EBee
	hayatae B&SWJ 8790	WCru
	'Herfstweelde'	CPrp EBee EMon GBuc LRHS MAvo MSte NCGa SMad WFar WOld
	x ***herveyi***	EBla EMan EMon LRHS SPhx WOld
	himalaicus	EShb SRms
*	'Hittlemaar'	WHil
§	'Hon. Vicary Gibbs' (*ericoides* hybrid)	MNFA MSte WOld WOut
	hybridus luteus	see x *Solidaster luteus*
	'Kylie' Υ^{H4}	CPrp EMon EPPr ERou GBuc GMac IGor MHom MSte NCGa SPhx SRGP WBor WCot WFar WHil WOld WTin
	laevis	EBee MSte NBre NLar WTin
	- 'Arcturus'	CFir MHom MLLN MSte NBre NCGa NRnb NSti SSvw WCot WFar WWlt
§	- 'Calliope'	CElw CKno CMea CSam CWan EBee ECtt GMaP LPio MAvo MHom MWat NOak NSti SAga SBri SMad SMrm SPhx WBor WBrk WEas WFar WHoo WIvy WKif WOld
	- var. ***geyeri***	MAvo MHar MHom MNrw
	- 'Nightshade'	WOld
	lanceolatus Willd.	WCot
	lanceolatus Kuntze	see *Pyrrocoma lanceolata*
	- 'Edwin Beckett'	CBre EMan MHom WOld
§	***lateriflorus***	CPLG EBee EWin WOld WPer
	- 'Bleke Bet'	WCot WOld
	- 'Buck's Fizz'	CHrt EBee ELan NLar WOld
	- 'Chloe'	NCGa
	- 'Datschi'	WFar
	- 'Delight'	MLLN
	- var. ***horizontalis*** Υ^{H4}	More than 30 suppliers
	- 'Jan'	WOld
	- 'Lady in Black'	More than 30 suppliers
	- 'Lovely'	EBee LRHS MLLN NBre NCGa NNor NRnb
	- 'Prince'	More than 30 suppliers
	laterifolius 'Snow Flurry'	see *A. ericoides* f. *prostratus* 'Snow Flurry'
§	***linosyris***	EBee EWes GBin NBre NLar WHer WOld
	- 'Goldilocks'	see *A. linosyris*
	'Little Carlow' (*cordifolius* hybrid) Υ^{H4}	More than 30 suppliers
	'Little Dorrit' (*cordifolius* hybrid)	EWsh MAvo MLLN WOld
	macrophyllus	CPou ELan EMon LRHS NLar WOld
	- 'Albus'	EBee EMon EPPr GBin WFar WIvy WOld
	- 'Twilight'	CHVG CSam EBee ECha ECtt EGle ELan EPfP EPla LBBr LBMP LLWP MLLN MNFA MSte NDov NSti SDix SRGP WCAu WCot WHil WIvy WMnd WOld
	'Midget'	NRnb
	mongolicus	see *Kalimeris mongolica*
	natalensis	see *Felicia rosulata*
	'Noreen' **new**	MAvo
	novae-angliae	CArn ELau NBPC NBre WOld
	- 'Alex Deamon'	WOld
	- 'Andenken an Alma Pötschke'	More than 30 suppliers
	- 'Andenken an Paul Gerber'	EBee EMon ERou MAvo MHom MNrw NGby WBrk WOld
	- 'Annabelle de Chazal'	WOld
	- Autumn Snow	see *A. novae-angliae* 'Herbstschnee'
	- 'Barr's Blue'	EBee ECtt EMon ERou EWsh GCra LRHS MAvo MBNS MSte MWat NLar SRms WBrk WCAu WFar WMoo WOld
	- 'Barr's Pink'	CBcs CBre EBee ECtt EMon ERou MBnl MHer MHom MLHP MRav MWat NLar SEND WBrk WCAu WFar WHrl WOld WPer WSFF
*	- 'Barr's Purple'	ECtt WOld
	- 'Barr's Violet'	EGle EPPr MAvo MHom SRms WBrk WCot WHal WHoo WHrl WMoo WOld WPer WTin
	- 'Bishop Colenso'	NBre
	- 'Christopher Harbutt'	EGle ERou NPro SRGP WOld
	- 'Colwall Constellation' **new**	WOld
	- 'Colwall Galaxy'	WOld
	- 'Colwall Orbit'	WOld
	- 'Crimson Beauty'	EMon EPPr GMac MAvo MHom MNFA MSte MWat WBrk WOld
	- 'Dwarf Alma Pötschke'	LCro
	- 'Eric Palmer'	ERou
	- 'Evensong'	WOld
	- 'Harrington's Pink' Υ^{H4}	More than 30 suppliers
	- 'Helen Picton'	WOld
§	- 'Herbstschnee'	CPrp EBee ECtt EHrv EMon EPfP ERou LEdu MBnl MHom MNFA MRav MSte MWat NSti SPet SPoG SRGP WBor WBrk WFar WHil WMnd WMoo WOld WPer WTin
	- 'James Ritchie'	WHoo WOld
	- 'John Davies'	WOld
	- 'Lachsglut'	MAvo WCot
	- 'Lou Williams'	WOld
I	- 'Lucida'	WBrk WHal WOld
	- 'Lye End Beauty'	CKno ECtt EGle EMon EPyc ERou LLWP LRHS MAvo MHom MNFA MRav MSte MWat WCot WHoo WMoo WOld WTin
	- 'Marina Wolkonsky'	EBee EWes WCot WOld
	- 'Millennium Star'	MSte WOld
	- 'Miss K.E. Mash'	ERou MHom SRGP WBrk WOld
	- 'Mrs S.T. Wright'	CTri ECtt EGle EMon ERou MBrN MHom MNFA MSte SRGP WFar WOld
	- 'Mrs S.W. Stern'	WOld
	- 'Pink Parfait'	EBrs ECtt GMac NBre NGdn WCot WOld
	- 'Pink Victor'	CTri EPPr SEND WCra WMoo
	- 'Primrose Upward'	CAby EWsh MSte WBrk WCot WOld
	- 'Purple Cloud'	EMon ERou LHop MHer MHom MNFA MWat MWgw NBre NGdn WBrk WHal WOld
I	- 'Purple Dome'	More than 30 suppliers
	- 'Quinton Menzies'	MSte WOld
	- 'Red Cloud'	NBre WOld
	- 'Rosa Sieger' Υ^{H4}	CBre CPrp ECtt EGle EMon ERou GMac MAvo MHom MSte NGdn SPhx WBor WBrk WHil WOld

	- 'Rose Williams'	WOld
	- 'Roter Stern'	ECtt ERou
	- 'Rubinschatz'	EBee MHom MSte NBre WOld
	- 'Rudelsburg'	EMon ERou
	- 'Sayer's Croft'	EGle EMon ERou MHom MWat NBre WBrk WCot WHil WHoo WOld WTin
	- September Ruby	see *A. novae-angliae* 'Septemberrubin'
§	- 'Septemberrubin'	CAby CMea CSsd EBee ECtt EMon ERou EWsh IFoB LHop MHer MHom MNFA MRav MSte NEgg NSti SMer SPhx SRGP WFar WMoo WOld WPnP WPrP
	- 'Treasure'	CBre EMon NBre WMoo WOld
	- 'Violetta'	CMea EBrs ECtt EGle EMon LSou MAvo MHom MNFA MSte MWea SPhx WBrk WFar WHoo WOld WTin
	- 'W. Bowman'	WOld
	- 'Wow'	NBre SMrm
N	***novi-belgii***	GWCH NSco WHer
	- 'Ada Ballard'	CBnk EBee ERou LDai LRHS NBre NGdn NRnb SPer SPet SPoG SRGP WOld
	- 'Albanian'	CBnk WOld
	- 'Alderman Vokes'	WOld
	- 'Alex Norman'	CBnk WOld
	- 'Algar's Pride'	CBnk CHrt ECtt ERou NRnb WOld
	- 'Alice Haslam'	CBnk EBee ECtt ERou GBri MCCP NOrc NPri NRnb SPoG SPur SRGP WOld WPer
	- 'Angela' **new**	CBnk
	- 'Anita Ballard'	CBnk WOld
	- 'Anita Webb'	CBnk GBri NBir NOak NRnb WOld
	- 'Anneke'	EBee SRGP WWeb
	- 'Apollo'	CBnk NBre NLar NPri WOld
	- 'Apple Blossom'	CBnk WOld
	- 'Arctic'	CBnk
	- 'Audrey'	CBnk CEnt EBee ECho ECtt ERou GMaP LRHS MBnl MLLN MWgw NCGa NGdn NOrc SPla SRGP STes WFar WOld WTel
	- 'Autumn Beauty'	CBnk WOld
	- 'Autumn Days'	CBnk WOld
	- 'Autumn Glory'	CBnk ERou WOld
	- 'Autumn Rose'	CBnk WOld
	- 'Baby Climax'	CBnk WOld
	- 'Beauty of Colwall'	CBnk WOld
	- 'Beechwood Challenger'	CBnk NRnb WOld
	- 'Beechwood Charm'	CBnk CWsd WOld
	- 'Beechwood Rival'	CBnk CTri EBee MSte NRnb
	- 'Beechwood Supreme'	CBnk ERou NRnb WOld
	- 'Beth' **new**	CBnk
	- 'Bewunderung'	NRnb WOld
	- 'Blandie'	CBnk CTri EBee MSte SRGP WCAu WOld
	- 'Blauglut'	CBnk WOld
	- 'Blue Baby'	CBnk WPer
	- 'Blue Bouquet'	CBnk CTri SRms WOld
	- 'Blue Boy'	MAvo WBrk WOld
	- 'Blue Danube'	CBgR CBnk WOld
	- 'Blue Eyes'	CAby CBnk CElw EMon SAga WOld
	- 'Blue Gown'	CBnk CMdw NRnb WOld WOut
	- 'Blue Lagoon'	CBgR CBnk CMea ELan MBnl MBri NOrc NRnb SPoG SRGP WBor WOld
	- 'Blue Patrol'	CBnk ERou NRnb WOld
	- 'Blue Radiance'	CBnk WOld
	- 'Blue Whirl'	WOld
	- 'Bonanza'	WOld WTel
	- 'Boningale Blue'	CBnk WOld
	- 'Boningale White'	CBnk ERou WOld
	- 'Bridesmaid'	CBnk WOld
	- 'Bridgette'	NBPC
	- 'Bright Eyes'	ERou SRGP
	- 'Brightest and Best'	CBnk WOld
	- 'Cameo'	CBnk WOld
	- 'Cantab'	CBnk WOld
	- 'Cantonese Queen' (v)	EPPr
	- 'Carlingcott'	CBnk ERou WOld
	- 'Carnival'	CBnk CMMP EBee ECtt LDai MMHG NEgg NOrc SPer SRGP WOld
	- 'Cecily'	CBnk WOld
	- 'Charles Wilson'	CBnk WOld
	- 'Chatterbox'	CBgR CBnk COlW CPrp EBee EPfP LRHS MRav MWat NLar SRms WOld
	- 'Chelwood'	CBnk WOld
	- 'Chequers'	CBnk CBrm CMMP EBee ECot MSte SRGP WOld
	- 'Christina'	see *A. novi-belgii* 'Kristina'
	- 'Christine Soanes'	CBnk NRnb WOld
	- 'Cliff Lewis'	CBnk ERou NRnb WOld
	- 'Climax Albus'	see *A.* 'White Climax'
	- 'Cloudy Blue'	CBnk NRnb WOld
	- 'Colonel F.R. Durham'	NRnb
	- 'Coombe Delight'	CBnk NRnb
	- 'Coombe Gladys'	CBnk ERou NRnb WOld
	- 'Coombe Joy'	ERou NRnb WOld
	- 'Coombe Margaret'	CBnk ERou WOld WOut
	- 'Coombe Pink'	CBnk ERou NRnb
	- 'Coombe Queen'	WOld
	- 'Coombe Radiance'	CBnk MSte WOld
	- 'Coombe Ronald'	CBnk MWat WOld
	- 'Coombe Rosemary'	CBnk ECtt ERou LRHS NLar WBor WOld
	- 'Coombe Violet'	CBnk MWat WOld
	- 'Countess of Dudley'	CBnk WOld WPer
	- 'Court Herald'	CBnk WOld
	- 'Crimson Brocade'	CAby CBnk EBee LCro MRav NLar SPhx SPoG SRGP WOld
	- 'Dandy'	CBnk EBee ECot ELan NBir NGdn SPoG SRGP WFar WOld
	- 'Daniela'	CBnk WBrk WOld
	- 'Daphne Anne'	WOld
	- 'Dauerblau'	CBnk WOld
	- 'Davey's True Blue'	CBnk CTri LCro MSte WOld
	- 'David Murray'	CBnk WOld
	- 'Dazzler'	CBnk CWsd WOld
	- 'Destiny'	WOld
	- 'Diana'	CBnk EWsh WOld
	- 'Diana Watts'	CBnk ERou NRnb WOld
	- 'Dietgard'	CBnk NRnb WOld
	- 'Dolly'	CBnk NBir WOld
	- 'Dora Chiswell' **new**	CBnk WOld
	- 'Dusky Maid'	CBnk WBor WOld
	- 'Elizabeth'	CAby CBnk CElw WOld
	- 'Elizabeth Bright'	CBnk WOld
	- 'Elizabeth Hutton'	CBnk ERou WOld
	- 'Elsie Dale'	CBnk WOld
	- 'Elta'	CBnk WOld
	- 'Erica'	CBnk CElw ERou MWat NRnb WOld
	- 'Ernest Ballard'	CBnk WOld
	- 'Eva'	CBnk WOld
	- 'Eventide'	CBcs CBnk CElw CTri ENot SPer SPhx WOld WRHF
	- 'Fair Lady'	CBnk MWat WOld
	- 'Faith'	CBnk WOld
	- 'Farncombe Lilac'	CBnk EBrs
	- 'Farrington'	WOld
	- 'Fellowship' $\mathbb{Y}^{H4}$	CAby CBnk CDes CFir EBee ERou MAvo MBri MSte MWat SAga SHar SPhx SRGP SRms WBrk WCot WHil WOld WTel
	- 'Flamingo'	CBnk
	- 'Fontaine'	WOld

	- 'Freda Ballard'	CBgR CBnk ECtt EWll GMaP MBnl MWat NGdn SRGP WCAu WOld
	- 'Freya'	CBnk WOld WSHC
	- 'Fuldatal'	CBnk WOld WOut
	- 'Gayborder Blue'	WOld
	- 'Gayborder Royal'	CBnk CFir WOld
	- 'Glory of Colwall'	CBnk WOld
	- 'Goliath'	CBnk WOld
	- 'Grey Lady'	CBnk WOld
	- 'Guardsman'	CBnk WOld
	- 'Gulliver'	CBnk WOld
	- 'Gurney Slade'	CBnk ERou NRnb WOld
	- 'Harrison's Blue'	CBnk ERou NBre NRnb SAga SPhx WBrk WOld WPer
	- 'Heinz Richard'	CBnk CMMP COlW EBee ECha LBMP MSte NBir NBre NEgg NGdn SBch SPet SRGP WOld
	- 'Helen'	CBnk WOld
	- 'Helen Ballard'	CBnk LCro NBre NRnb WBrk WOld
	- 'Herbstgruss vom Bresserhof'	EWTr NBre NRnb
	- 'Herbstpurzel'	CBnk WOld
	- 'Hilda Ballard'	CBnk NBre NRnb WOld
	- 'Ilse Brensell'	CBnk MSte WOld
	- 'Irene'	CBnk WOld
	- 'Isabel Allen'	WOld
	- 'Janet Watts'	CBnk ERou WOld
	- 'Jean'	CBnk MWat WOld
	- 'Jean Gyte'	WOld
	- 'Jeanette' **new**	CBnk WOld
	- 'Jenny'	More than 30 suppliers
	- 'Jollity'	CBnk WOld
	- 'Julia'	CBnk MAvo WOld
	- 'Karminkuppel'	NBre NRnb WOld
	- 'Kassel'	CBnk WOld
	- 'King of the Belgians'	WOld
	- 'King's College'	WOld
§	- 'Kristina'	CBnk COlW ECha ERou LRHS MBri MRav SPet SPoG WCot WOld WOut WTel
	- 'Lady Evelyn Drummond'	WOld
	- 'Lady Frances'	CBnk WOld
	- 'Lady in Blue'	More than 30 suppliers
	- 'Lady Paget'	WOld
	- 'Lassie'	CBnk CElw LLWP MWat SBri WCot WOld
	- 'Lavender Dream'	CBnk WOld
	- 'Lawrence Chiswell'	CBnk WOld
	- 'Lilac Time'	CBnk WLin WOld
	- 'Lisa Dawn'	CBnk WOld
	- 'Little Boy Blue'	CBnk ERou NBre NRnb SHBN WOld
	- 'Little Man in Blue'	CBnk WOld
	- 'Little Pink Beauty'	CBnk CEnt COlW CPrp EBee ECtt ELan ERou LHop LRHS MBNS MRav NBid NEgg NGdn NVic SPer SRGP STes WFar WOld
	- 'Little Pink Lady'	CBnk WOld
	- 'Little Pink Pyramid'	CBnk NRnb SRms
	- 'Little Red Boy'	CBnk WOld
	- 'Little Treasure'	CBnk WOld
	- 'Lucy'	CBnk WOld
	- 'Madge Cato'	CBnk WOld
	- 'Malvern Queen' **new**	CBnk
	- 'Mammoth'	NRnb WOld
	- 'Margaret Rose'	CBnk WOld
	- 'Margery Bennett'	CBnk GBri WOld
	- 'Marie Ballard'	CBcs CBnk CSBt EBee EPfP ERou GMaP MBri MRav MWat NGdn NOrc NPer SHBN SMer SPer SPoG SRGP SRms SWat WBrk WCAu WOld WPer WTMC
	- 'Marie's Pretty Please'	WOld
	- 'Marjorie'	CBnk NRnb SPoG WOld
	- 'Marjorie Tilbury'	ERou
	- 'Marjory Ballard'	CBnk WOld
*	- 'Mark Ballard'	NBre NRnb
	- 'Martonie'	WOld WPer
	- 'Mary' **new**	CBnk
	- 'Mary Ann Neil'	CBnk WOld
	- 'Mary Deane'	CBnk MSte WOld WPer
	- 'Mauve Magic'	CBnk WOld
	- 'Melbourne Belle'	CBnk NRnb WOld
	- 'Melbourne Magnet'	CBnk WOld
	- 'Michael Watts'	WOld
	- 'Midget' **new**	CBnk
	- 'Mistress Quickly'	CBnk ERou GBri MCot WOld
	- 'Mount Everest'	CBnk ERou SPhx WOld WPer
	- 'Mrs Leo Hunter'	CBnk NRnb WOld
	- 'Nesthäkchen'	ECho WOld
	- 'Newton's Pink'	CBnk
	- 'Niobe'	CBnk SPoG
	- 'Nobilis'	WOld
	- 'Norman's Jubilee'	CBnk EBee ERou NBir NRnb WOld
	- 'Nursteed Charm'	CBnk WOld
	- 'Oktoberschneekuppel'	ERou LRHS NRnb WOld
	- 'Orlando'	CBnk NRnb WOld
	- 'Pamela'	CBnk ERou WOld
	- 'Patricia Ballard'	CBcs CBnk CElw CPrp CSBt GCra GMaP MBri MWat NLar NPer SPer SPoG SRGP WCAu WFar WOld WPer
	- 'Peace'	CBnk ERou WOld
	- 'Percy Thrower'	CBnk NRnb WOld
	- 'Peter Chiswell'	CBnk WOld
	- 'Peter Harrison'	CBnk GMaP GMac NBir WOld WPer
	- 'Peter Pan'	CBnk CStu LSou WOld
	- 'Picture'	NBre NRnb WOld
	- 'Pink Gown'	WOld
	- 'Pink Lace'	CBnk ERou MBNS MLLN WOld WPer
	- 'Pink Pyramid'	NRnb WOld
	- 'Plenty'	CBnk MBri NRnb WOld
	- 'Porzellan'	CElw CMMP COlW EBee ECtt EGoo EMar MAvo NCGa NEgg NGdn SRGP WCot
	- 'Pride of Colwall'	CBnk ERou NRnb WBrk
	- 'Priory Blush'	CBnk SPhx WOld
	- 'Professor Anton Kippenberg'	CBnk CEnt EBee EPfP ERou GMaP LLWP LRHS MBri MHer MRav NBre NRnb SPer SRGP WOld WTel
	- 'Prosperity'	CBnk NBre NRnb WOld
*	- 'Prunella'	NRnb WOld
	- 'Purple Dome'	CBnk ECha LCro LSRN MCCP NEgg NMoo SHar SPhx WOld WOut
	- 'Queen Mary'	CBnk ERou WOld
	- 'Queen of Colwall'	CBnk WOld
	- 'Ralph Picton'	CBnk WOld
	- 'Raspberry Ripple'	CBnk ECot ERou WOld
	- 'Rector'	see *A. novi-belgii* 'The Rector'
	- 'Red Robin'	MWat
	- 'Red Sunset'	CBnk SRms WOld
	- 'Rembrandt'	ECtt EWll LDai NGdn SRGP
	- 'Remembrance'	CBnk NRnb WBrk WOld
	- 'Reverend Vincent Dale'	WOld
	- 'Richness'	CBnk NRnb SAga WOld
	- 'Robin Adair'	WOld
	- 'Roland Smith'	WOld
	- 'Rose Bonnet'	CBnk CSBt MWat SHBN SPlb
	- 'Rose Bouquet'	WOld
	- 'Roseanne' **new**	CBnk
	- 'Rosebud'	CBnk WBrk WOld
	- 'Rosemarie Sallmann'	NRnb
	- 'Rosenwichtel'	CBnk EMar MBri MWgw NCGa NLar NRnb WBrk WOld
	- 'Royal Ruby'	CBnk EBee EBrs ECtt LIMB WOld
	- 'Royal Velvet'	NRnb WOld

- 'Royal Violet'	NPri
- 'Rozika'	CBnk WOld
- 'Rufus'	CBnk WOld
- 'Sailor Boy'	CBnk EBee ERou NRnb WOld
- 'Saint Egwyn'	CBnk WOld
- 'Sam Banham'	CBnk WOld
- 'Sandford White Swan'	CBnk ERou GBuc MHom WBrk WEas WPer
- 'Sapphire'	SVil
- 'Sarah Ballard'	CBnk ERou MBnl MBri SRGP WOld
§ - 'Schneekissen'	CBnk CPrp CStu EBee ECho ECtt EGoo EPfP GMaP MHer MWgw NEgg NPri SPer SPoG SRGP STes SWvt WFar WOld
- 'Schöne von Dietlikon'	CBnk CKno WOld
- 'Schoolgirl'	CBnk NRnb WOld
- 'Sheena'	CBnk SRGP WOld
- 'Silberblaukissen'	GBin
§ - 'Silberteppich'	GMac
- Silver Carpet	see *A. novi-belgii* 'Silberteppich'
- 'Sir Edward Elgar' **new**	CBnk
- Snow Cushion	see *A. novi-belgii* 'Schneekissen'
- 'Snowdrift'	CBnk WOld
- 'Snowsprite'	CBcs CBnk CSBt ELan EPfP MWat NLar NOrc NPro SRGP SWat WBrk WOld
- 'Sonata'	ERou GMaP NRnb WOld
- 'Sophia'	CBnk NRnb WBrk WOld
- 'Starlight'	CBnk EBee ECho ENot ERou LSou MBNS NMoo SPoG WBor WFar WOld WRHF
- 'Steinebrück'	WOld
- 'Sterling Silver'	CBnk WOld
- 'Sunset'	WOld
- 'Susan'	ERou WOld
- 'Sweet Briar'	CBnk CElw WOld
- 'Tapestry'	CBnk WOld
- 'Terry's Pride'	CBnk WOld
- 'The Archbishop'	CBnk ECtt WOld
- 'The Bishop'	WOld
- 'The Cardinal'	CBnk ERou WOld
- 'The Choristers'	WOld
- 'The Dean'	CBnk ERou WOld
§ - 'The Rector'	CBnk WOld
- 'The Sexton'	CBnk ERou WOld
- 'Thundercloud'	CBnk NRnb WBrk WOld
- 'Timsbury'	CBnk CWsd NRnb WBrk WOld
- 'Tony'	CBnk WOld
- 'Tovarich'	CBnk WOld
- 'Trudi Ann'	CBnk NBir WOld
- 'Twinkle'	CBnk NEgg WOld
- 'Victor'	CBnk WOld
- 'Vignem'	NSti
- 'Violet Lady'	CBnk WOld
- 'Violetta'	LCro
- 'Waterperry'	CBnk MWat
- 'Weisses Wunder'	WOld WOut
- 'White Ladies'	CAby CBcs CBnk ECtt ERou GCra GMaP LLWP MWat NLar NOrc SPer SPoG SRGP
- 'White Swan'	CAby ECtt EPPr NRnb SPhx WOld
- 'White Wings'	CBnk WOld
- 'Winston S. Churchill'	CBnk CMMP COlW CTri EBee ELan EPfP ERou GMaP LRHS MWat SHBN SPer SPlb SPoG SRGP WOld WPnP WSpi
oblongifolius	WOld
§ - 'Fanny's'	CPrp EBee EBla ECtt LBMP MNFA SPet SRGP WCAu WCot WFar WOld
'Ochtendgloren' (*pringlei* hybrid) ♀H4	CPrp EBee EGle EMon EPPr EWes GBuc LBBr MAvo MNFA MNrw MSte NCGa SMrm WCAu WCot WFar WHal WOld WOut
Octoberlight	see *A.* 'Oktoberlicht'

§ 'Oktoberlicht'	EMon EPPr WOld
oolentangiensis	EBee
'Orchidee'	EBee ECtt EWes
'Orpheus' **new**	EMon
pappei	see *Felicia amoena*
'Pearl Star'	WOld
petiolatus	see *Felicia petiolata*
'Photograph' ♀H4	ECtt EPPr EWes MAvo MHom MSte SMrm WFar WIvy WMnd WOld
§ ***pilosus*** var. ***demotus*** ♀H4	EBee ECha EWes MLLN MRav MSte WFar WOld WTin
§ - var. ***pringlei*** 'Monte Cassino' ♀H4	CBgR CHid CSBt EBee EBla ECtt EPfP ERou LHop LRHS MBNS MLLN MRav MWat NBPC NCGa SMer SPav SPer SPhx SRGP WCAu WFar WOld
- - 'October Glory'	CMdw WFar
- - 'Phoebe'	WOld
- - 'Pink Cushion'	CMHG WCot
'Pink Cassino'	WCAu
'Pink Star'	CMea ECtt GMac MNFA MRav MWat NSti SBch SPhx WBrk WFar WHoo WOld WTin
'Pixie Dark Eye' (*ericoides* hybrid)	WCot
'Pixie Red Eye' (*ericoides* hybrid)	WCot
'Plowden's Pink'	WOld
'Prairie Lavender'	WOld
'Prairie Pink'	WOld
'Prairie Violet'	WOld
prenanthoides from Pennsylvania, USA **new**	EPPr
'Primrose Path'	WCot
§ ***ptarmicoides***	CSam EBee EBla EMon MLLN NBre SPhx WOld WPer
puniceus	NBre
purdomii	see *A. flaccidus*
pyrenaeus 'Lutetia'	CSam EBee ECha EMan GAbr GBuc GMaP MHom MNFA MSte MWgw NCGa NDov NLar SBla SRGP WCAu WCot WFar WHil WOld
radula	EBee EMan EMon MAvo MNrw NBre NLar NSti WOld WSHC
'Ringdove' (*ericoides* hybrid) ♀H4	CPrp EBee EBla ECGP ECtt EPfP ERou GMac LRHS MHom MNFA MNrw NSti SRGP STes WCAu WCot WIvy WOld
'Rosa Star'	WOld
rotundifolius 'Variegatus'	see *Felicia amelloides* variegated
rugulosus 'Asrugo'	EBee
x ***salignus***	WOld
- Scottish form	WOld
'Samoa'	ENot
§ ***scaber***	EBee WCot WPGP
scandens	see *A. carolinianus*
schreberi	EBee EPPr MHar MHom MLLN NBre NCGa WCot WOld
§ ***sedifolius***	EBee ELan EMan LPio LRHS MDKP MSte MWat NBid NDov SDix SPla WCot WFar WHil WMnd WOld WPer
- 'Nanus'	CPLG CSam ELan ENot ERou MLLN MRav MSte NBir NLar SPer WCot WFar WHil WMnd WOld WOut WSpi WTin
- 'Snow Flurries'	see *A. ericoides* f. *prostratus* 'Snow Flurry'
§ ***sibiricus***	EShb NBre NLar
'Snow Flurry'	see *A. ericoides* f. *prostratus* 'Snow Flurry'
'Snow Star'	WOld
souliei	EBee
- B&SWJ 7655	WCru
spathulifolius	NBir

spectabilis	WOld
stracheyi	EDAr
subcaeruleus	see *A. tongolensis*
'Sungal'^{PBR}	ERou
'Sunhelene'	WCot
'Sunmarie'	ERou
Sunplum = 'Danasplum'^{PBR}	ECtt ERou
'Sunqueen'	WCot
'Sunrio'	ERou
'Sunspring'	ERou
tataricus 'Jindai'	WCot WFar
thomsonii	WFar WOld
- 'Nanus'	CAby CMdw GMaP MCot MSte NBid NDov SAga SPhx WCot WFar WOld WSHC WSpi
tibeticus	see *A. flaccidus*
Tonga = 'Dasfour'	ENot
§ ***tongolensis***	EPfP SRms WFar WWFP
- 'Berggarten'	CHar LDai MBri NMoo SPoG WAbe WFar WWeb
- 'Dunkleviolette'	GBuc NBro SRms
- 'Lavender Star'	GBuc
- 'Napsbury'	CDes EBee ERou MBri WPGP WRHF
- 'Wartburgstern'	CPrp EBee EPfP NGdn STes WCFE WFar WPer
tradescantii misapplied	see *A. pilosus* var. *demotus*
tradescantii L.	EBee ELan EMan MBNS MBnl MRav MWgw NBre NHol NSti SMad WBrk WCot WOld WTin
trinervius subsp. ***ageratoides***	CPou WFar WOld
- - 'Asran'	EBee EMon EWes LSou SHGN SSvw WFar WOld
- - 'Stardust' **new**	MSte
- var. ***harae***	SSvw WOld
tripolium	WHer
'Triumph'	LBBr WCot
turbinellus misapplied Υ^{H4}	CAby CKno CSam CWsd EBee EMan EMon EPfP GBuc LBBr MBNS MSte SDix SMHy SPhx WCot WFar WHoo WOld WPtf WTin
turbinellus Lindl.	EPPr
- hybrid	CWsd WWeb
umbellatus	CBre CWsd EMon EPPr GBin LCro MNFA MWea NBre NCGa NLar NSti SRms WCot WOld WPrP WTin
* ***verticallis*** **new**	EMon
vimineus Lam.	see *A. lateriflorus*
- 'Ptarmicoides'	see *A. ptarmicoides*
§ 'White Climax'	CAby MSte SPhx WBrk WCot
'Wood's Pink' **new**	WSpi
yunnanensis	WSHC
'Yvonne'	CBre

Asteranthera (*Gesneriaceae*)

ovata	CGHE CPLG EBee GGGa GGar LSou MAsh NCGa SKHP SPoG WAbe WBod WCru WPGP WPrP WSHC

Asteriscus (*Asteraceae*)

'Gold Coin'	see *Pallenis maritima*
maritimus	see *Pallenis maritima*

Asteromoea (*Asteraceae*)

mongolica	see *Kalimeris mongolica*
pinnatifida	see *Kalimeris pinnatifida*

Asteropyrum (*Ranunculaceae*)

cavaleriei	EBee GEdr WCru

Asterotrichion (*Malvaceae*)

discolor	ECou

Astilbe ✿ (*Saxifragaceae*)

'Alive and Kicking' **new**	MBnl MBri
'America'	CMHG ECtt GBri
'Amethyst' (x *arendsii*)	CMHG EMFW GSki LRHS MRav NBir NBlu NBre SApp SMac SPer SRGP WCAu WFar WHoo WMoo
'Angel Wings' **new**	NPro
'Anita Pfeifer' (x *arendsii*)	CMHG GBin LRHS WFar WPnP
'Aphrodite' (*simplicifolia* hybrid)	CBcs CWCL LAst MDKP MLHP NBre NEgg NGdn NHol NPro SMac WBrE WGor
x ***arendsii***	CBrm ECho IFoB NBre SPet WMoo WPer
- 'Reinland' **new**	CWat
astilboides	CMHG NHol SWvt
'Atrorosea' (*simplicifolia* hybrid)	NCot SRms
'Avalanche'	CSBt GAbr GBin MBNS NHol WMnd
Bella Group (x *arendsii*)	NBre WMnd
'Bergkristall' (x *arendsii*)	CMHG
'Betsy Cuperus' (*thunbergii* hybrid)	CMHG EBee LRHS MRav MSte NBre SApp SRGP WCAu
biternata	EBee EMon
'Bonn' (*japonica* hybrid)	CWCL CWat NBlu SCoo SRms
§ 'Brautschleier' (x *arendsii*) Υ^{H4}	CBgR CMHG CMMP CMac CPrp CTri ECtt EPfP GCra LAst NGdn NLar NPri SRGP WPnP WPtf
'Bremen' (*japonica* hybrid)	CMHG CMMP GBin NHol
'Bressingham Beauty' (x *arendsii*)	CMHG CPrp CSam ECtt ELan EMFW ENot EPfP ERou GMaP LCro LRHS MRav MWrn NEgg NGdn NHol NPro SMer SPer SWvt WFar WMoo
Bridal Veil (x *arendsii*)	see *A.* 'Brautschleier'
§ 'Bronce Elegans' (*simplicifolia* hybrid) Υ^{H4}	CMHG EBee ECha ENot EPfP GBin GBuc GMaP GSki LAst LRHS MDun MRav NHol NOrc NPro SMac SMer SPer WCAu WFar WMoo
'Bronze Sprite' (*simplicifolia* hybrid)	ECho WFar
'Bronzlaub' (x *arendsii*)	CRez GBin
* ***bumalda*** 'Bronze Pygmy'	EBee EWTr NHol STes
'Bumalda' (x *arendsii*)	CBcs CFir CFwr CRez CWCL ENot GMaP GSki LLWG LRHS MWgw NChi NDlv NGdn NMyG NOrc NPro SPlb WFar WMoo
'Burgunderrot' (x *arendsii*) **new**	CWCL ERou MBri
'Carnea' (*simplicifolia* hybrid)	CMHG
'Catherine Deneuve'	see *A.* 'Federsee'
'Cattleya Dunkel' (x *arendsii*)	CMHG WFar
'Cattleya' (x *arendsii*)	CMHG CSam ECha GBri MBnl NBPC NLar NMoo WFar WMoo
'Ceres' (x *arendsii*)	CMHG NHol
'Cherry Ripe'	see *A.* 'Feuer'
chinensis	CMHG ECho EShb GSki IBlr LRHS NBre WSHC WWeb
- B&SWJ 8178	WCru
- 'Brokat'	GBin
- 'Christian'	GBin
- var. ***davidii***	CMHG GSki
- - B&SWJ 8583	WCru
- - B&SWJ 8645	WCru
- 'Finale'	CHar ECho EMFW NCGa NHol NPro SPer WFar WLin
- 'Frankentroll'	CMHG
- 'Intermezzo'	GMaP
§ - var. ***pumila*** Υ^{H4}	More than 30 suppliers
- - 'Serenade'	CMac EMil GSki LRHS MBri NGdn WFar

- 'Purple Glory' CMHG
- 'Purpurkerze' CBgR EWTr GBin GMaP LDai MBNS MBri MNrw NBPC NBro NGdn WBor
- 'Spätsommer' CMHG
- var. ***taquetii*** CMac EBee NBre NSti SRms
- - Purple Lance see *A. chinensis* var. *taquetii* 'Purpurlanze'
§ - - 'Purpurlanze' CKno CMHG ECha ECtt EMFW EMan EMon EPPr GCra LLWP LSRN MRav MWat MWgw NBid NBir NDov NGdn NHol NPro SPhx SPoG WCAu WFar WMoo
§ - - 'Superba' ♀H4 CMHG CMac CPLG CTri ECha EPfP GGar MCCP MLHP MLLN MSte NBro NGdn NHol SDix SPer SPoG SRms STes WEas WFar WMoo WPGP
- 'Troll' GBin
- 'Veronica Klose' CMHG EBee GBin NLar NPro WCAu
- 'Vision in Pink'PBR CWCL ERou NBhm
- 'Vision in Red'PBR CBgR CWCL CWat ERou GBin GGar MBNS MBnl MBri MNrw NBhm NLar NMyG WBor
- 'Visions' CMHG CMac CWCL EBee ECho ENot GBin GQue LRHS MBNS MBnl MBri MSte NBro NGdn NMyG NPro STes WFar WLin

Cologne see *A.* 'Köln'
'Crimson Feather' see *A.* 'Gloria Purpurea'
x ***crispa*** ECho IBlr WFar
- 'Gnom' EMFW NHar
- 'Lilliput' CBcs CRez GBin GBri GEdr GGar LRHS NDlv NHar NLar NPro NRya
§ - 'Perkeo' ♀H4 CBcs CBrm ECha ECho ELan EPfP GCrs GEdr GGar GMaP GSki IMGH LHop LRHS MDun MSte NBir NCGa NEgg NHar NLar NMen NPro NSla SPoG SRms WAul WBVN WFar WMoo
- 'Peter Pan' see *A.* x *crispa* 'Perkeo'
- 'Snow Queen' LRHS NBir NHar NMen NPro WFar
'Darwin's Dream' NLar NPri WFar
'Darwin's Favourite' (x *arendsii*) CWCL
'Deutschland' (*japonica* hybrid) CBcs CHVG CMHG ECtt EPfP ERou GMaP GSki LLWG LRHS MBNS MRav MWgw NBir NHol NVic SAga SPer SPla SPoG SRms STes SWat WAbe WAul WBVN WEas WFar WHoo WMoo
§ 'Diamant' (x *arendsii*) CMHG ERou EShb LRHS MWrn NGdn NHol WFar
Diamond (x *arendsii*) see *A.* 'Diamant'
'Drayton Glory' (x *arendsii*) see *A.* x *rosea* 'Peach Blossom'
'Dunkellachs' (*simplicifolia* hybrid) CBgR NMyG WAbe WFar
'Dutch Treat' (*japonica* hybrid) (v) CMea
'Düsseldorf' (*japonica* hybrid) CMHG CSam CWCL LLWG NHol
'Eden's Odysseus' EBee GBin NHol
'Elegans' (*simplicifolia* hybrid) CMHG WFar
Elizabeth Bloom = 'Eliblo'PBR (x *arendsii*) CHVG EBee GSki LLWG LRHS MRav NHol SVil WFar
'Elizabeth' (*japonica* hybrid) CMHG EBee
§ 'Ellie van Veen' (x *arendsii*) CMHG CWCL ERou GBin MAvo MBri NBhm NGdn NHol WPtf
'Ellie' (x *arendsii*) see *A.* 'Ellie van Veen'
'Else Schluck' (x *arendsii*) ECha
'Erica' (x *arendsii*) CMHG CTri EWll LRHS MBri MRav NPro WFar WMoo
'Etna' (*japonica* hybrid) CBcs CMHG CRez CSam EBee ERou GBri GSki LLWG MWrn NGdn NHol NLar NPro SRms WPnP
'Europa' (*japonica* hybrid) CMHG CMac CSBt ECtt EMFW GBin LHop MRav NEgg NOak SPla SPoG WFar WMoo
'Fanal' (x *arendsii*) ♀H4 More than 30 suppliers
'Fata Morgana' (x *arendsii* hybrid) CMHG
§ 'Federsee' (x *arendsii*) CBcs CDWL CHVG CMHG ECha ELan EMil EPyc LLWG LRHS MBNS NBPC NBre NBro NGdn NPro SPer WFar
§ 'Feuer' (x *arendsii*) CMCo CMHG CMMP CMac CPrp ELan EPfP GBuc LBMP LLWG LRHS MWgw NBid NGdn NHol NOrc NPro NVic SPer WBor WMoo
Fire see *A.* 'Feuer'
'Flamingo'PBR (x *arendsii*) GBin MAvo MBNS MBnl
'Gertrud Brix' (x *arendsii*) CBcs CWat NBir NGdn NPro SPla
§ ***glaberrima*** NBid NHol NMen
§ - var. ***saxatilis*** ♀H4 CLyd EBee EPfP GBin GGar IMGH LSou NHar NSla SPla WAbe WHal WThu
- ***saxosa*** see *A. glaberrima* var. *saxatilis*
- - ***minor*** see *A. glaberrima* var. *saxatilis*
* ***glaberrima*** x 'Saxosa' NHar
'Gladstone' (x *arendsii*) see *A.* 'W.E. Gladstone'
§ 'Gloria Purpurea' (x *arendsii*) CDWL CMHG LRHS NHol NMoo NMyG SRGP WMoo
'Gloria' (x *arendsii*) CMHG CMac CTri LRHS MRav WFar
Glow (x *arendsii*) see *A.* 'Glut'
§ 'Glut' (x *arendsii*) CMHG CWCL ECtt GBin LBBr LRHS MAvo NGdn NHol NMyG SRms WFar
'Granat' (x *arendsii*) CMHG CMMP CMac EMFW LLWG NBir NBre NHol NPro WMoo
* Grande Group (x *arendsii*) NBre
grandis CMHG WHer
'Grete Püngel' (x *arendsii*) ECha GBri MLLN WFar
'Harmony' (x *arendsii*) CMHG
'Heart and Soul'PBR **new** MBnl MBri
'Hennie Graafland' (*simplicifolia* hybrid) CBcs CChe CMHG CWCL EMil GAbr GBin LCro MBNS NCGa NLar NPro WLin
'Holden Clough' (*japonica* hybrid) NHol
Hyacinth (x *arendsii*) see *A.* 'Hyazinth'
§ 'Hyazinth' (x *arendsii*) CMHG CPLG CPrp EMFW ERou GMaP GSki LBMP LLWG LRHS LSou NGdn NHol NPro SPoG WFar
'Inshriach Pink' (*simplicifolia* hybrid) CBcs CCVN CMHG CPrp ELan EMFW GBin GCrs LRHS MBri NBir NHar NHol NOak SAga SBch SHGN WFar WHal WLin
'Irrlicht' (x *arendsii*) CMHG CSBt ELan EMFW EPfP EPla EShb GGar LHop LLWG LRHS NHol SMac SPer SWat WAul WPnP
japonica CPLG
* - 'Pumila' NGdn WBrE
- var. ***terrestris*** see *A. glaberrima*
'Jo Ophorst' (*davidii* hybrid) CMHG GSki LRHS MRav NGdn NHol NLar NPro SPer SRGP WFar
'Jump and Jive'PBR GGar NCGa
'Koblenz' (*japonica* hybrid) CMHG CWCL MDKP NMyG
§ 'Köln' (*japonica* hybrid) CMHG CWat GBin NMyG WFar
koreana GGar WCot
- B&SWJ 8611 WCru
- B&SWJ 8680 WCru
'Kriemhilde' CMHG
'Kvele' (x *arendsii*) CMHG WFar WMoo
§ 'Lachskönigin' (x *arendsii*) CMHG

	'Lilli Goos' (x *arendsii*)	CMHG GBin
	'Lollipop'	GBin MBNS MBnl MBri NBhm NPro WBor
	longicarpa B&SWJ 6711	WCru
	'Maggie Daley'	CMMP EBee LAst MBri NBro NPro SRGP WMoo WWeb
	'Mainz' (*japonica* hybrid)	CHVG CMHG ELan EMil
	'Mars' (x *arendsii*)	CMHG
	microphylla	CMHG CPLG NHol
	- pink-flowered	CMHG NHol
	'Moerheimii' (*thunbergii* hybrid)	CMHG
	'Moerheim's Glory' (x *arendsii*)	CMMP GBin LAst NBre NGdn
	'Mont Blanc' (x *arendsii*)	CMHG
	'Montgomery' (*japonica* hybrid)	CMHG CWCL ERou GAbr GBin LLWG LRHS LSRN MBNS MBri MRav MWat NBro NGdn NHol SBch SPad SRGP WBVN WFar
	'Obergärtner Jürgens' (x *arendsii*)	CMMP GBin
	Ostrich Plume	see *A.* 'Straussenfeder'
	'Paul Gaärder' (x *arendsii*)	CMHG
	'Peaches and Cream'	EBee LRHS MMHG MRav NBro NLar WPnP
	'Peter Barrow' (*glaberrima* hybrid)	GBin SRms
	'Pink Lightening'PBR (*simplicifolia* hybrid)	CBow CWCL EBee ERou EShb MAvo MBNS MBnl NBPC NBhm NLar NOrc SMrm WBor
	Pink Pearl (x *arendsii*)	see *A.* 'Rosa Perle'
	'Poschka'	CFir NPro
I	'Poschka Alba'	CFir NMyG NPro
	'Professor van der Wielen' (*thunbergii* hybrid)	CMHG CMil EBee EMon GGar LAst MSte NHol SDix SPer SRms WCAu WFar WSpi
	pumila	see *A. chinensis* var. *pumila*
*	'Queen'	ECho
	'Radius'	CBgR CMMP EBee GBin NGdn WPnP
	Red Light (x *arendsii*)	see *A.* 'Rotlicht'
	'Red Sentinel' (*japonica* hybrid)	CBcs CMMP CWCL CWat EMFW EMil ERou GBin GMaP LAst LLWG NBro NCGa NGdn NHol NPro SMrm SPoG WBor WFar WWeb
	'Rheinland' (*japonica* hybrid) ♀H4	CBcs CMHG CMMP CWCL EPfP LLWG NPri SPoG STes WCAu WEas WFar WHoo WPnP
	'Rhythm and Blues'PBR	GBin WWeb
	rivularis	CMHG GBin WCot
	- CC 4547	MGol
	- GWJ 9366	WCru
	- var. ***myriantha***	NBre
	- - BWJ 8076a	WCru
§	'Rosa Perle' (x *arendsii*)	CMHG CSam NHol
§	x ***rosea*** 'Peach Blossom'	CBcs CHVG CMHG CMMP GBuc NBir NEgg NHol NPro SPoG WFar WHoo WMoo WWeb
	- 'Queen Alexandra'	WFar
	'Rosea' (*simplicifolia* hybrid)	NHol WFar
	Rosemary Bloom = 'Rosblo'	EBee NHol
	'Rot Straussenfeder' (x *arendsii*)	GBin
§	'Rotlicht' (x *arendsii*)	CMHG ECot LLWG NHol NMyG NPro WFar WGor
	Salmon Queen (x *arendsii*)	see *A.* 'Lachskönigin'
	'Salmonea' (*simplicifolia* hybrid)	CMHG
	'Saxosa'	see *A. glaberrima* var. *saxatilis*
	Showstar Group (x *arendsii*)	LRHS NBre NPen SPoG WRHF
	simplicifolia ♀H4	WFar
	- 'Alba'	CMHG GBin NEgg NPro
	- Bronze Elegance	see *A.* 'Bronce Elegans'
	- 'Darwin's Snow Sprite'	CMac ECho GBin MBri MSte NHol NLar NPri WFar
	- 'Jacqueline'	EBee ECho NHol NLar WFar
*	- 'Nana Alba'	NPro
	- 'Praecox'	NEgg
	- 'Praecox Alba'	CMCo CWan EBee ENot GBin NEgg SMac
	- 'Sheila Haxton'	NHar
	'Snowdrift' (x *arendsii*)	CBrm CMHG CWat EPla GMaP GSki LBMP LLWG LRHS MAvo MBNS MDKP MWat NBir NCGa NOak NOrc NPro SPer SWat WFar
	'Solferino' (x *arendsii*)	CMHG
	'Spartan' (x *arendsii*)	see *A.* 'Rotlicht'
	'Spinell' (x *arendsii*)	CWCL MDun NMRc NOrc WFar WPnP
	'Sprite' (*simplicifolia* hybrid) ♀H4	More than 30 suppliers
	'Stand and Deliver' new	MBnl MBri
§	'Straussenfeder' (*thunbergii* hybrid) ♀H4	CBcs CDWL CMHG CTri EPfP EPla GMaP LAst LBMP LHop LRHS NBid NBir NBro NHol NOrc SMac SPer SPla SPoG WAul WCAu WFar WMoo WPnP WPtf
	'Sugar Plum' (*simplicifolia* hybrid)	EBee LAst NGdn
	'Superba'	see *A. chinensis* var. *taquetii* 'Superba'
	thunbergii	CEnt CPLG
	- var. ***hachijoensis***	EBee
	- - B&SWJ 5622	WCru
	- var. ***terrestris*** B&SWJ 6125	WCru
	'Touch of Pink'PBR (*simplicifolia* hybrid)	ERou
	'Venus' (x *arendsii*)	CBrm CDWL CHar CSam ECha ECtt EMFW EWTr GGar GMaP MSte NHol NOrc NVic SPer SRGP SWat WFar WMoo
	'Vesuvius' (*japonica* hybrid)	CBcs CDWL MDKP NBlu NBro NEgg NSti WLin
§	'W.E. Gladstone' (*japonica* hybrid)	CWat GSki MSte NBlu NHol NPro WAbe WGor
	'Walküre' (x *arendsii*)	CMHG
	'Walter Bitner'	GBin LLWG LRHS MBNS NHol SRGP SVil
	'Washington' (*japonica* hybrid)	CBcs EBee LAst MDKP NGdn
§	'Weisse Gloria' (x *arendsii*)	CHVG CMHG CMac CTca ECha ERou GBuc NBPC NBro NEgg NHol NMyG NOrc SPad SRGP WBor WMoo WTin
	White Gloria (x *arendsii*)	see *A.* 'Weisse Gloria'
	'White Queen' (x *arendsii*)	NHol
	'White Wings'PBR (*simplicifolia* hybrid)	NLar
	'William Reeves' (x *arendsii*)	CMHG NHol
	'Willie Buchanan' (*simplicifolia* hybrid)	CBcs CMHG CPrp ECtt GAbr GKev GMaP GSki LRHS MBar NEgg NHar NHol NMen SApp SIng SPer SPla SRms WAbe WFar WMoo
	'Zuster Theresa' (x *arendsii*)	CBgR CMHG EBee MBNS NBPC NBro SMrm SRGP WFar

Astilboides (*Saxifragaceae*)

§	***tabularis***	More than 30 suppliers

Astragalus (*Papilionaceae*)

	arnotianus	CPBP
	canadensis	EMan SPhx
	candelarius	SPhx
	glycyphyllos	CArn EBee

lusitanicus	LRav
membranaceus	CArn ELau MSal
- var. ***mongholicus***	MSal

Astrantia ✿ (*Apiaceae*)

bavarica	CCge EBee EMan EMar MDKP WFar WOut
'Bloody Mary'	CBgR GBin IBal MBNS MWea NBPC NGdn NLar NRnb NSti SHBN SPer
'Buckland'	More than 30 suppliers
carniolica	EMon EPyc GSki NEgg WTel
- ***major***	see *A. major*
- var. ***rubra***	see *A. carniolica* 'Rubra'
§ - 'Rubra'	CBcs EBee GKev MNFA MWrn NBre SMHy WHal WSHC
- 'Variegata'	see *A. major* 'Sunningdale Variegated'
'Dark Shiny Eyes'	CKno EBee IBal LCro NBhm NCGa NLar
'Hadspen Blood'	More than 30 suppliers
Harptree hybrid	CHar
'Helen'	NLar WCra
helleborifolia misapplied	see *A. maxima*
'Madeleine' **new**	NBhm
'Magnum Blush'	NBhm
§ ***major***	More than 30 suppliers
- 'Abbey Road'[PBR]	EBee EBla ENot LHop MBNS MWrn NLar SPoG WAul
* - ***alba***	CBcs CMHG CPrp CWCL EBee EBla ECha EGle EHrv EMon GMac GSki IBal LCro MBnl MNFA MWgw MWrn NBir NGdn NPer WMnd WWeb
- 'Ann Cann'	CBct
- 'Berendien Stam'	CCge EBee EMon
- subsp. ***biebersteinii***	CCge EBee EBla EMon NBir NBre
- 'Bo-Ann'	CWCL EBla EMan ERou IBal MAvo MBNS MBri NCob NLar NSti SHBN WAul
- 'Celtic Star'	EBee EBla ELan ERou GBuc GSki LHop MBnl NCGa NCob NEgg NGdn NMyG SPla SPoG WCAu WCot WTMC
- 'Claret'	More than 30 suppliers
- 'Côte d'Azur'	CBct
- 'Cyril James'	CBct
- 'Dulcie Scott'	WOut
- dwarf	WFar
- 'Gill Richardson'	CKno CLAP CPrp EBee EBla ECGP ECha EMar EPPr ERas EShb IPot LRHS LSRN MAvo MBnl MNFA MRav MWgw NBre NCob NDov NGdn NHol NOrc SPoG
- 'Greenfingers'	EBee EWes
- 'Gwaun Valley'	WFar
- 'Hillview Red'	CCge CElw EBee
- subsp. ***involucrata***	EBee EBla EHrv GSki LCro LRHS SWat WFar
- - 'Barrister'	CBct CSam EMon GBuc NLar WFar WOut WPGP
- - 'Canneman'	CBct EBee EBla EMon EWes MBnl NSti SMeo SMrm SPhx WCAu WCot WFar
- - 'Jumble Hole' **new**	NDov
- - 'Margery Fish'	see *A. major* subsp. *involucrata* 'Shaggy'
- - 'Moira Reid'	CBct CKno CLAP CMil EBee EBla ECGP ELan EMan GBri IPot LRHS LSRN MAvo MNFA MRav NBro NCob NDov SHar SRGP WFar
- - 'Orlando'	EBee EMon
§ - - 'Shaggy' 🏆H4	More than 30 suppliers
- 'Jade Lady'	WFar
- 'Lars'	More than 30 suppliers
- 'Little Snowstar'	EHrv IBal
- 'Maureen'	NOak
- 'Montelolor'	WFar
- 'Paper Moon'	WFar
- 'Primadonna'	CBct CCge CKno EBee EBla EHrv EMan ERou EWsh GSki MBNS MNFA MWrn NHol NLar SPlb WFar WHlf WPer WSpi
- 'Roma'[PBR]	More than 30 suppliers
- 'Rosa Lee'	CWCL EBee EMan IBal MWrn NCob NLar WAul
- var. ***rosea***	CBre COlW CPrp EBee EBla EDAr EHrv EPfP GKev GSki IBal LCro LHop LRHS LSRN MRav MWat MWrn NDlv NGdn NOak NSti SAga SPer SPla WCAu WCru WFar WMoo
- - George's form	CKno CPrp CSam EBee EBla EMan EMar EPPr IPot LAst LLWG LSRN MAvo MWrn NCob NHol
- 'Rosensinfonie'	CPLG EBee EBla GMaP GSki MNFA MWrn NBro NGdn NOak NPro WFar WMnd WOut
§ - 'Rubra'	More than 30 suppliers
- 'Ruby Cloud'	CBct CCge CHid EBee EBla EDAr EHrv EMan GSki IBal MNrw MRav MWrn NBro NGdn NLar NRnb NSti WFar WFoF WHlf WLin WMnd WSpi
- 'Ruby Wedding'	More than 30 suppliers
- 'Silver Glow'	EBee IBal LFur NGdn NMyG SHBN SPer WFar
- 'Starburst'	WFar
- 'Sue Barnes' (v)	EMon
§ - 'Sunningdale Variegated' (v) 🏆H4	More than 30 suppliers
- 'Titoki Point'	EBee MAvo WCot
- 'Variegata'	see *A. major* 'Sunningdale Variegated'
§ ***maxima*** 🏆H4	More than 30 suppliers
- 'Mark Fenwick'	NBir
* - ***rosea***	CWCL EBla ECtt MDKP NBir NEgg NGdn SAga
minor	CPrp CTca WCru
'Moulin Rouge'	More than 30 suppliers
'Queen's Children' **new**	NBhm
'Rainbow'	NLar
rubra	see *A. major* 'Rubra'
'Snow Star'[PBR]	CWCL CWib EBee EHrv GBin IPot LCro MAvo MBnl MBri MWrn
'Temptation Star' **new**	NLar
'Warren Hills'	EBla MWrn

Astrodaucus (*Apiaceae*)

orientalis **new**	SPhx

Asyneuma (*Campanulaceae*)

canescens	CDMG CEnt ELan EMan LSou MBNS NBre NSfd SGar
limonifolium	CPom SBla
§ ***prenanthoides***	NSfd
pulvinatum	CPBP SIng WAbe

Asystasia (*Acanthaceae*)

bella	see *Mackaya bella*
§ ***gangetica***	CSev EShb
violacea	see *A. gangetica*

Athamanta (*Apiaceae*)

turbith subsp. ***haynaldii***	EBee

Athanasia (*Asteraceae*)

§ ***parviflora***	SPlb

Atherosperma (*Monimiaceae*)

moschatum	CBcs CHll WSHC

Athrotaxis (*Cupressaceae*)

	cupressoides	CDoC CDul CKen LCon MBar WThu
	laxifolia	CDoC CKen EMil LCon MBar WThu
	selaginoides	CDoC CDul CTrG

Athyrium ✿ (*Woodsiaceae*)

	'Branford Beauty'	CCCN CDes CLAP LRHS WRic
	'Branford Rambler'	CLAP CRez WRic
	filix-femina 🏆H4	More than 30 suppliers
	- var. ***angustum*** 'Lady in Red'	CCCN CDes CElw CLAP CRez EBee LTwo MAvo MBri MGos NBid NLar SPad SPoG WRic
*	- ***congestum cristatum***	CLAP WFib
	- 'Corymbiferum'	GQui SRms
	- 'Crispum Grandiceps Kaye'	SRms
	- Cristatum Group	CLAP EFer ELan EMon MMoz SWat WAbe
§	- Cruciatum Group	CBgR CFwr CLAP EBee ELan EMon MMoz NHol SPer SRms WCot WFib WMoo WPtf WRic
	- 'Fieldii'	CLAP SRms
	- 'Frizelliae' 🏆H4	More than 30 suppliers
	- 'Frizelliae Capitatum'	CLAP WFib WPGP
	- 'Frizelliae Cristatum'	SRms
	- 'Grandiceps'	CLAP SRms
	- 'Minutissimum'	CBgR CDes CGHE CLAP EBee ECha ELan EMon MMoz WPGP
*	- 'Nudicaule'	SRms
	- 'Percristatum'	EMon
	- Plumosum Group	CLAP CWsd GBri GQui WAbe WFib
*	- 'Plumosum Aureum'	NBhm
	- 'Plumosum Axminster'	CLAP EFer EWsh
	- 'Plumosum Cristatum'	CLAP
	- 'Plumosum Divaricatum'	SRms
	- 'Plumosum Druery'	CLAP CWsd
	- Red Stem	see *A. filix-femina* 'Rotstiel'
§	- 'Rotstiel'	CFwr CLAP LRHS MMoz MPes WFar WMoo WPnP WRic
	- 'Vernoniae' 🏆H4	CLAP CWCL EBee ELan EMon EWsh MAsh NHol WRic
	- 'Vernoniae Cristatum'	CLAP NHol WFib
	- 'Victoriae'	CCCN CDes CFwr CPrp CWCL EKen GEdr GMaP MAsh MPes MWgw NBid NHol
	- Victoriae Group	see *A. filix-femina* Cruciatum Group
	'Ghost'	CCCN CDes CLAP CRez LRHS MAvo MGos NLar WPat WRic
	goeringianum 'Pictum'	see *A. niponicum* var. *pictum*
	niponicum	WHal
	- f. ***metallicum***	see *A. niponicum* var. *pictum*
§	- var. ***pictum*** 🏆H3	More than 30 suppliers
	- - 'Apple Court'	CCCN CRez WRic
	- - 'Burgundy Glow' **new**	CBow
	- - 'Burgundy Lace'	CBcs CLAP ERou MPop SJoo SPoG WPtf
*	- - 'Cristatoflabellatum'	CLAP ELan EMon SBla
	- - 'Red Beauty'	CFwr CLAP CRez EBee EPfP GAbr GBin MAvo MPes WCot WPnP
	- - 'Silver Falls'	CBcs CCVN CElw CLAP EPot ERou EShb LAst MAvo MBNS MBnl NCob NMyG WCot WHal WPnP
	- - 'Soul Mate'	CLAP
	- - 'Ursula's Red'	CBcs CBrm CCVN CElw CEnd CFwr CLAP CTrC EBee EPot ERou EShb GBin GKev IBal LAst LHop LSou MBNS MSte NBid NBir NMoo NMyG SMrm SPer SPoG WCot WMoo WPat
	- - 'Wildwood Twist'	CLAP
	otophorum 🏆H4	CRez EMon NBid NHol SRms WIvy WPGP WRic
	- var. ***okanum***	More than 30 suppliers
	vidalii	CFwr CLAP CRez EBee MPes NLar WFib WRic

Atractylodes (*Asteraceae*)

	japonica	EFEx
	macrocephala	CArn EFEx

Atragene see *Clematis*

Atriplex (*Chenopodiaceae*)

	canescens	NLar XPep
	cinerea	GGar
	halimus	CArn CBcs CDul ECha EPPr MBlu MBri MRav MWat NLar SLon SPlb SWat WCot WHer WKif WPat WSHC WTin XPep
	hortensis var. ***rubra***	CArn CEnt CSpe ELan LSou MHer MNHC NDov NGHP SIde WCot WEas WJek
	nummularia	XPep
	portulacoides	see *Halimione portulacoides*

Atropa (*Solanaceae*)

	acuminata **new**	EUnu
	bella-donna	CArn GPoy MGol MSal WTin
	- var. ***lutea***	EUnu MSal
	mandragora	see *Mandragora officinarum*

Atropanthe (*Solanaceae*)

§	***sinensis***	MSal

Aubrieta ✿ (*Brassicaceae*)

	albomarginata	see *A.* 'Argenteovariegata'
	'Alix Brett'	CMea CPBP ECho LRHS SPoG
	'April Joy' (d)	ECho ECot
§	'Argenteovariegata' (v) 🏆H4	ECho ELan SBla WAbe WHoo
	'Astolat' (v)	ECho ECtt NSla SBla SRms WAbe WEas
§	'Aureovariegata' (v) 🏆H4	CMea ECho ECtt ELan LRHS MHer NPer NWCA SBla WAbe WFar WRHF
	'Belisha Beacon'	ECho MBri
	Blaue Schönheit	see *A.* 'Blue Beauty'
§	'Blue Beauty'	CHVG WRHF
*	'Blue Mist'	ECho
§	'Bob Saunders' (d)	CMea ECho ECtt LTwo
	'Bonfire'	ECho
	'Bressingham Pink' (d) 🏆H4	ECho ECtt ELan EPfP LRHS SPoG
	'Bressingham Red'	ECho LRHS SIng SPoG
	'Campbellii'	ECho
	'Carnival'	NEgg
	Cascade Series	NEgg
	- 'Blue Cascade'	ECtt EPfP IBal NBlu NNor SPlb SPoG WGor
	- 'Lilac Cascade'	SPoG
	- 'Purple Cascade'	CTri CWib ECtt EPfP IBal LRHS NBlu SPlb SPoG SRms WGor
	- 'Red Cascade' 🏆H4	CTri CWib ECtt EPfP NBlu NNor SPlb SPoG
	'Crimson Queen'	ECho
	'Dantra'	ECho
	deltoidea 'Nana Variegata' (v)	CMea ECtt EPot WGor
	- 'Tauricola'	ECho
	- Variegata Group (v)	ECtt LRHS NSla WFar
	'Doctor Mules' 🏆H4	CSpe ECho LRHS SRms
	'Doctor Mules Variegata' (v)	CTri EAlp ECho ECtt EPfP LAst MHer NEgg NPri SPoG SWvt WFar
	'Eila' (d) **new**	STre
	'Elsa Lancaster'	EPot NMen NSla

§ 'Frühlingszauber' SRms WGor
glabrescens WAbe
- MESE 536 EPot
'Gloriosa' ECho
'Godstone' ECho
'Golden Carpet' ECho
'Golden King' see *A.* 'Aureovariegata'
gracilis WAbe
* 'Graeca' NPri
'Greencourt Purple' ♀H4 ECho ELan MHer MWat
'Gurgedyke' ECho SRms
'Hamburger Stadtpark' EAlp ECho EDAr
'Hemswell Purity'[PBR] see *A.* 'Snow Maiden'
'Hendersonii' SRms
'J.S. Baker' SRms
'Joy' (d) ECho ECtt LTwo NSla
'Kitte' ECho EPfP LAst NLar SPoG
'Leichtlinii' ECho NLar
'Lemon and Lime' ECho
'Little Gem' ECho
macedonica EAlp EPot
'Magician' ECho WCFE
'Mars' ECho
'Maurice Prichard' ECho ECtt
'Mrs Lloyd Edwards' ECho
'Mrs Rodewald' ♀H4 ECho SRms
'Novalis Blue' SRms
'Oakington Lavender' ECho
parviflora CStu
'Pike's Variegated' (v) ECho
pinardii NSla
'Purple Charm' SRms
'Red Carpet' ECho ELan EPot LRHS MAvo MHer SIng SPoG SRms
'Red Carpet Variegated' (v) CMea ECho
'Rose Queen' CMea CPBP LRHS SAga SMrm
Royal Series ♀H4 COlW
- 'Royal Blue' EPfP LRHS NEgg WFar WMoo
- 'Royal Lavender' WFar
- 'Royal Lilac' WFar
- 'Royal Red' EPfP NPri SRms WFar WGor WMoo
- 'Royal Rose' WFar
- 'Royal Violet' CTri LRHS NHol NPri WFar WPer
'Schofield's Double' see *A.* 'Bob Saunders'
'Silberrand' ECha ECtt EPot NSla
§ 'Snow Maiden'[PBR] ECho ECtt LRHS SPoG
'Somerfield Silver' MBar NPri
'Somerford Lime' (v) ECtt MBar NPri
Spring Charm see *A.* 'Frühlingszauber'
'Swan Red' (v) EPot LAst LIMB NPro NSla SPoG WAbe WFar
thessala CPBP
'Toby Saunders' ECho
'Triumphante' ECho ECtt LRHS LTwo
'Wanda' ECho
'Whitewell Gem' ECho SRms WMoo

Aucuba ✿ (*Aucubaceae*)

japonica (f) SMer
- (m) ENot SReu
- var. **borealis** **new** EMil
- 'Crassifolia' (m) EPla EQua SAPC SArc
- 'Crotonifolia' (f/v) ♀H4 More than 30 suppliers
- 'Crotonifolia' (m/v) CTca MAsh NBlu SRms
- 'Dentata' CHEx
- 'Golden King' (m/v) ♀H4 CDoC CMac CSBt CWib EBee ELan ENot EPfP LRHS MAsh MGos MWat NLar SLim SPla SPoG WFar WWeb
- 'Golden Spangles' (f/v) CBcs CDoC CHEx EBee ECot ERas NLar SWvt
- 'Goldstrike' (v) EBee
- 'Hillieri' (f) EPla EQua
- f. **longifolia** ♀H4 CMac NLar SAPC SArc SDix WCru
- - 'Lance Leaf' (m) EPla EQua SLon
- - 'Salicifolia' (f) CHEx EPla LAst MRav NLar SLon SPla WCru WFar WPGP
- 'Maculata' misapplied see *A. japonica* 'Variegata'
- 'Marmorata' EPla LRHS
- 'Nana Rotundifolia' (f) EPla
- Pepper Pot = 'Shilpot' SSta
- 'Pepperpot' (m/v) CHEx EPfP MAsh SPoG
- 'Picturata' (m/v) CBow CDul CHEx CMac CSBt EBee ELan LRHS MAsh MGan MGos MRav NEgg NHol SHBN SLim SPoG WFar
- 'Rozannie' (f/m) ♀H4 CBcs CDoC CDul CEnd CSBt EBee ECrN ELan ENot EPfP EPla LAst LPan LRHS LSRN MAsh MBlu MGos MRav MWat NEgg SLim SMac SPer SPla SPoG SReu SWvt WFar
- 'Speckles' GSki NLar
- 'Sulphurea Marginata' (f/v) CBcs CBow CMac CTri EBee EMil EPla NPro SPoG WBod
§ - 'Variegata' (f/v) More than 30 suppliers
- Windsor form (f) EPla EQua MBri
omeiensis BWJ 8048 WCru

Aurinia (*Brassicaceae*)

§ **corymbosa** LTwo
§ **saxatilis** ♀H4 ECho EPfP LAst MBar SPlb WFar WTel
- 'Argentea' ECho
§ - 'Citrina' ♀H4 ECGP ECha ECho ECtt SRms
- 'Compacta' CTri ECho ECtt ENot
- 'Dudley Nevill' ECho LRHS SIng
- 'Dudley Nevill Variegated' (v) ECha ECho ECtt EWes GMaP LIMB MHer NBir NGby SBla SIng WFar
- 'Flore Pleno' (d) ECho
- Gold Ball see *A. saxatilis* 'Goldkugel'
- 'Gold Dust' ECho ECtt SRms
- 'Golden Queen' ECtt MHer
§ - 'Goldkugel' ECho LRHS SPoG SRms
- 'Silver Queen' WEas
- 'Variegata' (v) EWin NPri SPoG
§ **sinuata** **new** STre
- 'Pebbles' LRav

Austrocedrus (*Cupressaceae*)

§ **chilensis** CKen CTho LRHS
- 'Thornhayes Ghost' **new** CTho

Austromyrtus (*Myrtaceae*)

§ **dulcis** ECou
tenuifolia CPLG

Avena (*Poaceae*)

candida see *Helictotrichon sempervirens*
sativa 'French Black' CSpe

Avenula see *Helictotrichon*

Ayapana see *Eupatorium*

Azalea see *Rhododendron*

Azara ✿ (*Flacourtiaceae*)

alpina CPLG ISea
dentata CBcs CHll CMac EBee LAst WFar
- 'Variegata' see *A. integrifolia* 'Variegata'
* **integerrima** GQui
integrifolia CCCN
- 'Uarie' CCCN
§ - 'Variegata' (v) ERea SDnm
lanceolata CDul CMCN CPLG CTri ECrN IDee ISea LEdu NSti SLon SPer WFar WGer WPic
microphylla ♀H3 CBcs CChe CDul CLnd CMCN CMHG CPLG CPSs CSBt CTri EBee

	EPfP EPla ISea LAst MAsh NSti SArc SBra SDnm SDry SPer SSpi WBod WFar WPGP WSHC WSpi WTel
- 'Gold Edge' (v)	IClo LBuc WFar
- 'Variegata' (v)	CBcs CDoC CMac CPLG CPMA CWib EBee EMil EPfP GQui IMGH ISea LAst LBMP LRHS MLan NHol NSti SDnm SLon SPoG SSpi SSta STre WFar WGer WPat WPic WSHC
N ***paraguayensis***	CDoC GGar SDnm WFar
petiolaris	EPfP WGer WPic
- G&P 5026	WPGP
serrata ♀H3	CBcs CDul CEnd CMCN CPLG CSBt CWib EBee EPfP EPla GGar IDee ISea NCGa SAga SDix SGar SPer SPoG SRms SSta WBor WCru WFar WGer WHar WSHC WSpi WTel
uruguayensis	CCCN CPLG EBee GBin

Azorella (*Apiaceae*)

filamentosa	ECou
glebaria A. Gray	see *Bolax gummifer*
glebaria misapplied	see *A. trifurcata*
gummifer	see *Bolax gummifer*
§ ***trifurcata***	CPar CSpe CTri ECho ECtt GAbr GEdr NLAp NWCA SBla SPlb WPer
- 'Nana'	ECho GGar MWat WPat

Azorina (*Campanulaceae*)

§ ***vidalii***	CSpe EShb SAPC SArc SGar
- 'Rosea'	CKob

B

Babiana (*Iridaceae*)

ambigua	CStu
angustifolia	CGrW CPLG
'Blue Gem'	EBrs ECho
disticha	see *B. plicata*
ecklonii	WCot
framesii	CStu
- var. ***kamiesbergensis***	CPLG
nana	CGrW CPBP CStu
odorata	CPLG
§ ***plicata***	CGrW
ringens	CPLG WCot
rubrocyanea	NWCA WCot
sambucina	CStu WCot
sinuata	CGrW WCot
stricta ♀H1-2	CPLG CStu EBrs ECho SBch WCot WRos
- var. ***erectifolia***	WPrP
- 'Purple Star'	CPLG EBrs ECho
- 'Tubergen's Blue'	EBrs ECho
truncata	CStu WCot
vanzyliae	CStu WCot
villosa	WCot
'Zwanenburg's Glory'	EBrs ECho

Baccharis (*Asteraceae*)

genistelloides	SMad
halimifolia	CBcs CTrC GQui LRav SEND SLon
- 'Twin Peaks'	SDry XPep
patagonica	CTrC GGar SAPC SArc SKHP WPat
salicifolia	WCot
'Sea Foam'	EMan LSou SMad

Bacopa (*Scrophulariaceae*)

caroliniana	EOHP
'Cinderella Strawberry' **new**	NPri
monnieri	EOHP EUnu
'Snowflake'	see *Sutera cordata* 'Snowflake'

Baeckea (*Myrtaceae*)

densifolia	ECou
gunniana	CPLG
linifolia **new**	SPlb
virgata	CBcs CTrC ECou SPlb

Baillonia (*Verbenaceae*)

juncea	WSHC

Balbisia (*Geraniaceae*)

peduncularis	CCCN WCot

Baldellia (*Alismataceae*)

ranunculoides	EMFW WMAq
- f. ***repens***	EMan

Ballota ✿ (*Lamiaceae*)

acetabulosa ♀H3-4	EBee ECha EGoo EMan EWes EWin MWgw SBch SDix WCot WKif XPep
'All Hallow's Green'	see *Marrubium bourgaei* var. *bourgaei* 'All Hallow's Green'
hirsuta	XPep
nigra	CArn EBee GPoy GWCH MHer MNHC MSal NMir SECG WMoo XPep
§ - 'Archer's Variegated' (v)	CBow EMan EWes LDai
- 'Variegata'	see *B. nigra* 'Archer's Variegated'
- 'Zanzibar' (v)	EMon
pseudodictamnus ♀H3-4	More than 30 suppliers
- from Crete	ECha

Balsamita see *Tanacetum*

Balsamorhiza (*Asteraceae*)

deltoidea **new**	SPhx
sagittata	ECho

banana see *Musa*

Bambusa ✿ (*Poaceae*)

glaucescens	see *B. multiplex*
gracilis	see *Drepanostachyum falcatum*
§ ***multiplex***	EFul XBlo
- 'Alphonso-Karrii'	CGHE EPla LEdu LPal SDry SRkn WPGP
- 'Elegans'	see *B. multiplex* 'Floribunda'
- 'Fernleaf'	see *B. multiplex* 'Floribunda'
§ - 'Floribunda'	CHEx EBee EFul EShb SDry XBlo
- 'Tiny Fern'	WPGP
- 'Wang Tsai'	see *B. multiplex* 'Floribunda'
pubescens	see *Dendrocalamus strictus*
ventricosa	SDry XBlo
vulgaris	XBlo
- 'Vittata'	XBlo

Banisteriopsis (*Malpighiaceae*)

caapi	MGol

Banksia (*Proteaceae*)

aemula	SOWG
burdettii	SOWG
canei	SPlb
coccinea	SOWG
ericifolia **new**	LRHS
- var. ***ericifolia***	CBcs CCCN CTrC SOWG SSta
grandis	CCCN LRHS SOWG
integrifolia	CBcs CCCN ECou SOWG SSta
marginata	CTrC ECou SOWG SPlb
- mauve-flowered	SOWG
media	SPlb
oblongifolia	CTrC SPlb

occidentalis SOWG
paludosa CTrC SPlb
robur CAbb CCCN CTrC SPlb
serrata SOWG SPlb
speciosa SPlb
spinulosa CTrC
- var. ***collina*** CTrC SOWG SPlb
- pink-flowered SOWG
- var. ***spinulosa*** CBcs CCCN
violacea SPlb

Baptisia (*Papilionaceae*)
§ ***alba*** NLar
§ - var. ***macrophylla*** CMdw CPle EBee EWes NBir NDov NLar SDix WCot
australis ♀H4 More than 30 suppliers
- 'Caspian Blue' CWCL LHop MLan MMHG MWrn SPla WHil WSHC
- 'Exaltata' ELan GBuc LHop
- var. ***minor*** NLar WCot
§ ***bracteata*** var. ***leucophaea*** EBee LSou
lactea see *B. alba* var. *macrophylla*
leucantha see *B. alba* var. *macrophylla*
leucophaea see *B. bracteata* var. *leucophaea*
pendula see *B. alba*
'Purple Smoke' EBee MDKP
tinctoria CArn

Barbarea (*Brassicaceae*)
praecox see *B. verna*
§ ***verna*** CArn GPoy MHer NGHP
vulgaris 'Variegata' (v) CArn CHal EBee ELan EMan LDai MDun MLan NBro NCob SPav WCot WMoo
- 'Variegated Winter Cream' (v) GAbr LSou

Barleria (*Acanthaceae*)
micans CCCN
obtusa variegated (v) new EShb
suberecta see *Dicliptera suberecta*

Barosma see *Agathosma*

Bartlettina see *Eupatorium*

Basella (*Basellaceae*)
rubra EUnu

Bashania (*Poaceae*)
faberi Og 94053 EPla
§ ***fargesii*** CDoC ENBC EPla ERod MRav MWht SEND
I ***qingchengshanensis*** CGHE EBee EPla WPGP

basil see *Ocimum basilicum*

Bauera (*Cunoniaceae*)
rubioides var. ***alba*** ECou
- 'Candy Stripe' SOWG
- pink-flowered ECou SOWG
- 'Ruby Glow' SOWG
sessiliflora SOWG

Bauhinia (*Caesalpiniaceae*)
alba hort. see *B. variegata*
corymbosa SOWG
galpinii EShb SOWG SPlb
monandra SOWG
natalensis EShb SPlb
tomentosa CCCN EShb
§ ***variegata*** MJnS
yunnanensis EShb SOWG WSHC

Baumea see *Machaerina*

bay see *Laurus nobilis*

Beaucarnea (*Dracaenaceae*)
recurvata ♀H1 CTrC LPal MBri NScw WFar

Beaufortia (*Myrtaceae*)
sparsa CTrC SOWG
squarrosa SPlb

Beaumontia (*Apocynaceae*)
grandiflora SOWG

Beauverdia see *Leucocoryne*

Beccariophoenix (*Arecaceae*)
madagascariensis LPal

Beckmannia (*Poaceae*)
eruciformis WRos
syzigachne CPLG

Beesia (*Ranunculaceae*)
calthifolia CLAP EBee EHrv EWld LTwo WCru WPGP
- DJHC 98447 CDes

Begonia ✿ (*Begoniaceae*)
B&SWJ 6881 from Taiwan WCru
B&SWJ 6606 from Thailand WCru
Chen Yi 5 WCot
DJHC 580 WCot
from China NShi
- BWJ 7840 WCru
from Ruwenzori, Uganda NShi
from Sikkim, India WCot
- B&SWJ 2692 EMan
from Vietnam ERhR NShi
'Abel Carrière' CHal ERhR NShi WDib
acerifolia see *B. vitifolia* Schott
acetosa NShi
acida ERhR NShi
aconitifolia ERhR EShb NShi
acutifolia ERhR NShi
'Aladdin' ERhR NShi
'Alamo III' ERhR NShi
albopicta hort. Bull. (C) CHal EBak ERhR NShi SAdn
- 'Rosea' CHal EShb NShi WDib
'Albuquerque Midnight Sky' (R) new NShi
alice-clarkiae ERhR NShi
'Alleryi' (C) ERhR NShi
alnifolia ERhR
'Alto Scharff' ♀H1 ERhR NShi
'Alzasco' (C) ERhR NShi
'Amazon Delta' (R) PBR new LRHS
'Amigo Pink' (C) ERhR NShi
ampla NShi
angularis see *B. stipulacea*
'Anita Roseanna' (C) ERhR NShi
'Ann Anderson' (C) ERhR NShi
'Anna Christine' (C) ERhR NShi
§ ***annulata*** ERhR NShi
'Aquarius' ERhR NShi
'Arabian Sunset' (C) ERhR NShi
'Arctic Breeze' PBR (R) new LRHS
'Argentea' (R) EBak MBri NShi
x ***argenteoguttata*** (C) CHal ERhR EShb NShi
'Aries' ERhR NShi
'Art Monday' (C) NShi
'Arthur Mallet' ERhR NShi
'Aruba' ERhR
'Atlanta Jazz' (R) new NShi

	'Autumn Glow' (T)	ERhR NShi
	'Avalanche' (T)	ERhR NShi
	'Axel Lange' (R)	NShi
	'Aya' (C)	NShi WDib
	'Baby Perfection'	NShi WDib
	'Bahamas'	ERhR NShi
	'Bantam Delight'	ERhR NShi
	'Barbara Ann' (C)	ERhR
	'Barbara Hamilton' (C)	ERhR
	'Barbara Parker' (C)	ERhR
	'Barclay Griffiths'	ERhR NShi
	'Beatrice Haddrell'	CHal ERhR NShi WDib
*	***benichoma***	WDib
	'Benitochiba' (R)	EBee ERhR NShi WCot
	'Bess'	ERhR NShi
	'Bessie Buxton'	ERhR NShi
	'Bethlehem Star'	ERhR NShi WDib
§	'Bettina Rothschild' (R)	CHal ERhR GGar LRHS NShi WDib
	'Beverly Jean'	ERhR NShi
	'Big Mac'	ERhR NShi
	'Bill's Beauty'	ERhR NShi
	'Bishop's Irish Eyes' (C)	NShi
	'Black Jack' (C)	ERhR NShi
	'Black Knight' (R)	CHal NShi
	'Black Raspberry'	ERhR NShi
	'Black Velvet'	NShi
	'Blanc de Neige'	ERhR NShi
	'Blue Vein'	ERhR NShi
	'Blue Wave'	NShi
	'Bokit'	ERhR NShi WDib
	'Bokit' x ***imperialis***	NShi WDib
	boliviensis	CDes CDoC NShi WCot WCru
	'Bonaire'	CHal
	'Bonfire' **new**	LBuc LRHS
	'Boomer' (C)	ERhR NShi
	'Botato'	NShi
	bowerae	CHal ERhR LRHS NShi
§	- var. ***nigramarga***	ERhR NShi
	'Boy Friend'	ERhR NShi
	bracteosa	ERhR
	bradei	ERhR
	brevirimosa	ERhR NShi
	'Bronze King' (R) **new**	NShi
	'Brown Lace'	NShi
	'Brown Twist'	NShi WDib
	'Bunchii'	ERhR NShi
	'Burgundy Velvet'	ERhR NShi WDib
	'Burle Marx' 𝕐H1	CHal ERhR EShb NShi SDix WDib
	'Bush Baby'	CHal NShi
	'Butter Cup'	NShi
	'Calico Kew'	ERhR
	'Calla Queen' (S)	ERhR NShi
	'Can-can' (R)	see *B.* 'Herzog von Sagan'
	'Can-can' (T)	NShi
	'Candy Floss'	NShi WCru
	'Captain Nemo' (R)	ERhR NShi
	cardiocarpa	ERhR NShi
	'Carol Mac'	ERhR NShi
	'Carolina Moon' (R) 𝕐H1	ERhR NShi
	carolineifolia	CHal NShi WDib
	carrieae	ERhR NShi
	x ***carrierei***	see *B.* Semperflorens Cultorum Group
	'Cathedral'	ERhR GGar NShi WDib
	'Champagne'	SPer
	'Chantilly Lace'	CHal ERhR NShi
	chapaensis	NShi
	- HWJ 642	WCru
	'Charles Chevalier'	ERhR NShi
	'Charles Jaros'	ERhR NShi
	'Charm' (S)	CHal ERhR NShi WDib
	x ***cheimantha*** 'Gloire de Lorraine'	NShi
	'Cherry Feast'	CHal
	'Cherry Jubilee' (C)	NShi
	'Cherry Sundae'	ERhR
	'Chesson'	ERhR NShi
	'China Curl' (R)	ERhR LRHS NShi
	'China Doll'	NShi
	'China Swirl' 𝕐H1	NShi
	chitoensis B&SWJ 1954 **new**	WCru
	chloroneura	ERhR WDib
	'Chocolate Box'	ERhR
	'Chocolate Chip'	ERhR NShi
	'Christine'	NShi
	'Christmas Candy'	ERhR WDib
	'Christy White'	NShi
	'Chuck Jaros' **new**	NShi
	'Chumash'	ERhR NShi
	'Cistine'	ERhR NShi
	'Clara' (R)	MBri NShi
	'Cleopatra' 𝕐H1	CHal ERhR MRav NShi WDib
	'Clifton'	ERhR NShi
	coccinea (C)	ERhR NShi WDib
	'Coconut Ice'	CDoC LAst SVil
	compta	see *B. stipulacea*
	'Comte de Lesseps' (C)	NShi WDib
	conchifolia var. ***rubrimacula***	ERhR NShi
	'Concord'	ERhR NShi
	'Connee Boswell'	ERhR NShi WDib
	convolvulacea	ERhR NShi
	cooperi	ERhR NShi
	'Cora Anne'	ERhR
	'Cora Miller' (R)	ERhR NShi
	x ***corallina***	EBak
§	- 'Lucerna' (C)	CHal EBak ERhR LRav
	- 'Lucerna Amazon' (C)	CHal ERhR NShi
	'Corbeille de Feu'	CHal ERhR NShi
	'Cosie' (C)	NShi
	'Cowardly Lion' (R)	ERhR NShi
	'Cracklin' Rosie' (C)	ERhR NShi
	crassicaulis	ERhR NShi
	'Crestabruchii'	ERhR NShi
	'Crystal Brook'	ERhR NShi
	cubensis	ERhR NShi
	cucullata	CHal ERhR NShi
	'Curly Fireflush' (R)	ERhR NShi
	'Curly Locks' (S)	CHal
	'Curly Merry Christmas' (R)	NShi
	'Dales' Delight' (C)	ERhR NShi
	'Dancin' Fred'	ERhR NShi
	'Dancing Girl'	ERhR NShi
	'Dannebo'	MBri
	'D'Artagnan'	ERhR NShi
	'David Blais' (R) 𝕐H1	NShi WDib
	'Dawnal Meyer' (C)	ERhR NShi WDib
I	'de Elegans'	ERhR NShi WDib
	'Decker's Select'	ERhR NShi
	'Deco Diamond Dust'	ERhR
	decora	ERhR NShi
	deliciosa	ERhR NShi
	'Delray Silver'	NShi
	'Dewdrop' (R) 𝕐H1	ERhR NShi WDib
	diadema	ERhR NShi
	'Di-anna' (C)	ERhR NShi
	dichotoma	ERhR NShi
	dichroa (C)	ERhR NShi
	'Dielytra'	ERhR NShi
	'Di-erna'	ERhR NShi
	dietrichiana Irmsch.	ERhR NShi
	'Digswelliana'	ERhR NShi
	dipetala	ERhR
	discolor	see *B. grandis* subsp. *evansiana*
	domingensis	ERhR NShi
	'Don Miller'	ERhR NShi WDib
	'Doublet Pink'	ERhR
	'Doublet Red'	ERhR
	'Doublet White'	ERhR

	'Douglas Nisbet' (C)	ERhR
	dregei (T) ♀H1	ERhR NShi
	- 'Bonsai'	NShi STre
	- 'Glasgow'	ERhR NShi
	- var. ***macbethii***	NShi
	'Druryi'	ERhR NShi
	'Dwarf Houghtonii'	ERhR NShi
	'Earl of Pearl'	ERhR NShi
*	'Ebony' (C)	CHal ERhR NShi
	echinosepala	ERhR NShi
	echinosepala x ***sanguinea***	NShi
I	'Edinburgh Brevirimosa'	ERhR NShi
	edmundoi	ERhR
	egregia	ERhR
	'Elaine'	ERhR NShi
	'Elaine Ayres' (C)	ERhR NShi
§	'Elaine Wilkerson'	ERhR NShi
	'Elaine's Baby'	see *B.* 'Elaine Wilkerson'
	'Elda'	ERhR NShi
	'Elda Haring' (R)	ERhR NShi
	'Elizabeth Hayden'	ERhR NShi
	'Elsie M. Frey'	ERhR NShi
	emeiensis	CKob
	'Emerald Beauty' (R) ♀H1 **new**	ERhR NShi
	'Emerald Giant' (R)	ERhR NShi WDib
	'Emerald Isle'	NShi
	'Emerald Princess'	NShi
	'Emma Watson'	CHal ERhR NShi
	'Enchantment'	ERhR NShi
	'Enech'	ERhR NShi
	'English Knight'	ERhR NShi
	'English Lace'	ERhR NShi
	epipsila	ERhR NShi
	x ***erythrophylla***	EShb NShi
	- 'Bunchii'	ERhR NShi
§	- 'Helix'	CHal ERhR NShi
	'Escargot' (R) ♀	GGar LRHS NShi WDib
	'Essie Hunt'	ERhR
	'Esther Albertine' (C) ♀H1	CHal ERhR NShi
	'Evening Star'	ERhR NShi
	'Exotica'	ERhR
	'Fairy'	ERhR NShi
	feastii 'Helix'	see *B.* x *erythrophylla* 'Helix'
	fernando-costae	ERhR NShi
§	'Feuerkönigin' (S)	ERhR NShi
	'Fever' (R)	NShi
	'Filigree'	ERhR NShi
	fimbriata Liebm.	EBrs
	'Fire Flush'	see *B.* 'Bettina Rothschild'
	'Fireworks' (R) ♀	ERhR LRHS NShi WDib
	'Five and Dime'	ERhR NShi
	'Flamboyant' (T)	ERhR MBri NShi
	Flaming Queen	see *B.* 'Feuerkönigin'
	'Flamingo'	ERhR NShi
	'Flamingo Queen'	ERhR NShi
	'Flo'Belle Moseley' (C)	CHal ERhR NShi WDib
	'Florence Carrell'	ERhR NShi
	'Florence Rita' (C)	ERhR NShi
	'Flying High'	ERhR NShi
	foliosa	CHal ERhR NShi WDib
	- var. ***amplifolia***	CHal ERhR NShi
	- var. ***miniata*** 'Rosea'	see *B. fuchsioides* 'Rosea'
	formosana	NShi
	- B&SWJ 7041	WCru
	'Frances Lyons'	ERhR NShi
	'Frau Hoffman' (R)	NShi
	'Freckles' (R)	ERhR NShi
	'Fred Bedson'	ERhR NShi
	'Fred Martin' (R)	NShi
	friburgensis	ERhR
	'Friendship'	ERhR NShi
	'Frosty' (T)	NShi WDib
	'Frosty Fairyland'	ERhR

	'Frosty Knight'	ERhR NShi
	'Fuchsifoliosa'	ERhR NShi
	fuchsioides ♀H1	CDTJ CDoC EBak ERhR EShb EWin LPio MArl NShi SDix WDib
	- pink-flowered	CCCN GGar LAst NShi SPoG
	- red-flowered	CCCN WFar
§	- 'Rosea'	CDoC CHal NShi
	fusca	ERhR NShi
	'Fuscomaculata'	ERhR NShi
	'Gaystar'	NShi
	gehrtii	ERhR NShi
	geranioides	ERhR
	glabra	ERhR
	glandulosa	ERhR
	glaucophylla	see *B. radicans* Vell.
	'Glen Daniels'	NShi
	'Gloire de Lorraine'	NShi
	'Gloire de Sceaux'	ERhR NShi
	goegoensis	ERhR NShi
	'Good 'n' Plenty'	ERhR NShi
	gracilis var. ***martiana***	NShi
	'Granada'	ERhR NShi
	grandis	NShi
§	- subsp. ***evansiana*** ♀H3-4	CHEx CKob CSam CStu ELan EMan EMar EMon ERhR EShb LEdu LPio MLLN MSte MTho NCiC NMRc NShi SBch SDix SMad WBrk WCot WCru WFar
	- - var. ***alba*** hort.	CAby CHal CMdw EMon ERhR EShb MSte MTho SMad SSpi WCot WPGP
	- - 'Claret Jug'	EBee EMan EMon LPio NShi WCot WPGP
	- - hybrid	ERos NShi
	- - 'Pink Parasol'	NShi WCru
	- - 'Simsii'	NShi WFar
	- 'Maria'	EBee WCot
	- 'Sapporo'	EBee EMar EPPr LPio MSte NShi SMrm WCru
*	'Great Beverly'	ERhR NShi
	'Green Acres' **new**	ERhR
	'Green Gold' (R)	NShi WDib
	'Green Lace'	ERhR NShi
	'Grey Feather'	ERhR NShi
	griffithii	see *B. annulata*
	'Gustav Lind' (S)	CHal ERhR EShb NShi
	'Guy Savard' (C)	NShi WDib
	'Gypsy Maiden' (T)	NShi
	haageana hort. ex W. Watson	see *B. scharffii*
	handelii	ERhR NShi
*	'Happy Heart'	ERhR NShi
	'Harbison Canyon'	NShi
*	'Harry's Beard'	ERhR NShi
	'Hastor'	ERhR NShi
	hatacoa	ERhR NShi
	- silver-leaved	CHal ERhR NShi
	- spotted-leaved	ERhR NShi
	'Hazel's Front Porch' (C)	ERhR NShi
	'Helen Lewis' ♀H1	ERhR NShi
	'Helen Teupel' (R)	ERhR NShi WDib
	'Helene Jaros'	ERhR NShi
	hemsleyana	NShi
	'Her Majesty' (R)	ERhR NShi
	heracleifolia var. ***longipila***	ERhR NShi
	- var. ***nigricans***	CHal NShi
	- 'Wisley'	NShi
§	'Herzog von Sagan' (R)	ERhR NShi
	x ***hiemalis*** 'Elatior'	LRHS
	'Hilo Holiday' (R) **new**	NShi
	hispida var. ***cucullifera***	ERhR NShi
	'Holmes Chapel'	ERhR NShi
	homonyma (T)	ERhR
	'Honeysuckle' (C)	ERhR NShi

'Hot Tamale'	ERhR NShi
'Hottentot'	NShi
'Houston Fiesta'	NShi
hydrocotylifolia	ERhR NShi
hypolipara	ERhR NShi
(Illumination Series) 'Illumination Apricot'	SCoo
- 'Illumination Rose'	SCoo
- 'Illumination Salmon Pink' ♀H2-3	SCoo
- 'Illumination White'	SCoo
imperialis	ERhR NShi
'Inca Fire'PBR (R) **new**	LRHS
incarnata (C)	ERhR NShi
- 'Metallica'	see *B. metallica*
'Indian Summer'PBR (R) **new**	LRHS
'Ingramii'	ERhR NShi
'Interlaken' (C)	ERhR NShi
'Irene Nuss' (C) ♀H1	ERhR NShi
'Ironstone' (R) ♀H1	NShi
'Ivy Ever'	ERhR NShi
'Jade'	NShi
'Jelly Roll Morton'	ERhR
'Joe Hayden'	CHal ERhR NShi
'John Tonkin' (C)	ERhR NShi
johnstonii	ERhR NShi
'Joy Porter' (C)	NShi
'Jubilee Mine'	ERhR
juliana	ERhR NShi
'Jumbo Jeans'	ERhR NShi
'Jumbo Jet' (C)	ERhR NShi
'Kagaribi' (C)	ERhR NShi
kellermanii (C)	ERhR NShi
'Ken Lau Ren' (C)	NShi
'Kentwood' (C)	ERhR NShi
kenworthyae	ERhR NShi
kingiana	NShi WDib
'Kit Jeans'	ERhR NShi
'Kit Jeans Mounger'	ERhR NShi
'Knutsford'	NShi
'Kyoto'	NShi
'La Paloma' (C)	NShi WDib
'Lacewing'	ERhR NShi
'Lady Carol'	CHal
'Lady Clare'	ERhR NShi
* 'Lady France'	ERhR MBri
'Lady Snow'	CHal
'Lana' (C)	ERhR NShi
'Langeana'	NShi
'Laurie's Love' (C)	ERhR
'Lawrence H. Fewkes'	ERhR NShi
'Lazy River' **new**	NShi
leathermaniae (C)	ERhR NShi
'Legia'	ERhR
'Lenore Olivier' (C)	ERhR NShi
'Leopard'	ERhR MBri NShi
'Lexington'	ERhR
'Libor' (C)	ERhR
'Lillian' (R)	NShi
'Lime Swirl'	ERhR NShi
limmingheana	see *B. radicans* Vell.
'Linda Dawn' (C)	ERhR NShi
'Linda Harley'	ERhR
'Linda Myatt'	ERhR NShi
lindeniana	ERhR NShi
listada ♀H1	CHal ERhR MBri NShi WDib
'Lithuania'	ERhR
'Little Brother Montgomery' ♀H1	ERhR GGar NShi SDix WDib
'Little Darling'	ERhR NShi
'Little Iodine'	NShi
'Lois Burks' (C)	CHal ERhR NShi WDib
'Loma Alta'	ERhR NShi
'Looking Glass' (C)	ERhR NShi WDib

'Lospe-tu'	ERhR NShi
'Lubbergei' (C)	ERhR NShi
'Lucerna'	see *B.* x *corallina* 'Lucerna'
'Lucy Closson' (R) **new**	NShi
'Lulu Bower' (C)	ERhR NShi
luxurians ♀H1	CHll CKob CSpe ERhR NShi WCot
- 'Ziesenhenne'	ERhR NShi
lyman-smithii	ERhR NShi
'Mabel Corwin'	ERhR NShi
'Mac MacIntyre'	NShi
macdougallii var. ***purpurea***	CHal NShi WDib
macduffieana	NShi
'Mac's Gold'	ERhR NShi
maculata ♀H1	ERhR NShi
- 'Wightii' (C)	CHal CSpe ERhR NShi WDib
'Mad Hatter'	ERhR NShi
'Madame Butterfly' (C)	ERhR NShi
'Magic Carpet'	ERhR NShi
'Magic Lace'	ERhR NShi
'Manacris'	ERhR NShi
'Mandarin Orange' (C)	NShi
manicata	ERhR NShi WDib
'Maori Haze' (R) **new**	LRHS
'Maphil'	MBri NShi
'Mardi Gras' (R) **new**	NShi
'Margaritae'	ERhR NShi
* 'Marginata Crispa White'	SPer
'Marmaduke' ♀H1	CHal NShi WDib
'Marmorata' (T)	LRHS
'Martha Floro' (C)	ERhR
'Martin Johnson' (R) ♀H1	ERhR NShi WDib
'Martin's Mystery'	ERhR NShi
masoniana ♀H1	ERea ERhR NShi WDib
- light-leaved	NShi
'Maui Mist'PBR (R) **new**	NShi
'Maurice Amey'	ERhR NShi
'Maverick'	ERhR NShi
mazae	ERhR NShi
'Medora' (C)	ERhR NShi
'Melissa' (T)	NShi
'Merry Christmas' (R) ♀H1	ERhR NShi WDib
metachroa	ERhR NShi
§ ***metallica*** ♀H1	CHal ERhR EShb NShi
'Meteor' (R) **new**	NShi
'Miami Storm' (R) **new**	NShi
'Michaele'	ERhR
'Midnight Magic' (R) ♀H1 **new**	NShi
'Midnight Sun'	ERhR NShi
'Midnight Twister'	ERhR NShi
'Mikado' (R) ♀H1	ERhR NShi
minor	ERhR
'Mirage' ♀H1	ERhR NShi
'Miss Priss' (C)	NShi
mollicaulis	ERhR
'Moon Maid'	ERhR
'Mr Kartuz' (T)	NShi
'Mrs Hashimoto' (C)	ERhR NShi
'Mrs Hatcher' (R)	ERhR NShi
'Mrs Schinkle' (C)	NShi
multinervia	ERhR
'Munchkin' ♀H1	CHal ERhR NShi WDib
'My Best Friend' **new**	NShi
* 'Mystic'	ERhR NShi
'Mystique'	ERhR NShi
'Namur' (R) ♀H1 **new**	NShi
'Nancy Cummings'	ERhR
natalensis (T)	ERhR NShi
'Nelly Bly'	ERhR
nelumbiifolia	ERhR NShi
nigramarga	see *B. bowerae* var. *nigramarga*
nigritarum	ERhR NShi
* ***nitida alba***	ERhR
'Nokomis' (C)	ERhR NShi

'Norah Bedson'	ERhR NShi
'Northern Lights' (S)	ERhR NShi
obliqua	ERhR
obscura	ERhR NShi
'Obsession'	ERhR
odorata	ERhR NShi
'Odorata Alba'	ERhR NShi
odorata hort. var. ***rosea***	NShi
olbia	ERhR
'Old Gold' (T)	ERhR
'Oliver Twist'	ERhR
'Orange Dainty'	ERhR
'Orange Pinafore (C)'	ERhR
'Orange Rubra' (C) 🏆H1	CHal ERhR NShi
'Orococo'	NShi
'Orpha C. Fox' (C)	ERhR NShi
'Orrell' (C)	ERhR NShi
'Othello'	ERhR NShi
'Otto Forster'	NShi
oxyphylla	ERhR
'Pachea' (R)	NShi
paleata	ERhR NShi
palmata	CAby CDes EBee EBla EMan LSou MHar NShi SKHP WCot WPGP
- B&SWJ 2692 from Sikkim	WCru
- from China	EBla NShi
- var. ***palmata***	CKob NShi
- - B&SWJ 7175	WCru
'Palomar Prince'	ERhR NShi
'Panasoffkee'	ERhR NShi
'Pantaloon'	NShi
'Panther'	ERhR NShi
'Papillon' (T)	ERhR NShi
paranaensis	ERhR NShi
* 'Parilis'	ERhR NShi
partita	ERhR EShb NShi
'Passing Storm'	ERhR NShi
'Patricia Ogdon'	ERhR NShi
'Paul Harley'	ERhR NShi
'Paul Henry'	NShi
'Paul-bee'	ERhR NShi
paulensis	ERhR NShi
pavonina **new**	NShi
'Peace' (R)	NShi
'Peach Parfait' (C)	ERhR NShi
pearcei	ERhR NShi
'Pearl Ripple'	ERhR NShi
'Pearls' (C)	ERhR NShi
'Peggy Stevens' (C)	ERhR
peltata	ERhR NShi
* 'Penelope Jane'	ERhR
'Persian Brocade'	ERhR NShi
'Petite Marie' (C)	ERhR
'Phil Corwin' (R)	NShi
'Piccolo'	ERhR NShi
'Pickobeth' (C)	ERhR NShi
'Picotee' (T)	CSut
'Pinafore' (C) 🏆H1	ERhR NShi
'Pink Basket'	NShi
'Pink Champagne' (R) 🏆H1	NShi WDib
'Pink Frosted'	NShi
'Pink Jade' (C)	NShi
'Pink Lady' (R)	NShi WCru
'Pink Nacre'	CHal ERhR NShi
'Pink Parade' (C)	ERhR NShi
'Pink Parfan'	NShi
'Pink Shasta' (C)	NShi
'Pink Slate' (C)	NShi
'Pink Spot Lucerne' (C)	ERhR NShi
'Pink Taffeta'	ERhR NShi
plagioneura	ERhR
platanifolia var. ***acuminatissima***	ERhR
'Plum Rose'	ERhR NShi
plumieri	ERhR

polyantha	ERhR NShi
polygonoides	ERhR
popenoei	ERhR
'Posy Wahl' (C)	NShi
'Potpourri'	ERhR
'Président Carnot' (C)	ERhR NShi
'Pretty Rose'	ERhR
'Preussen'	ERhR NShi
'Princess of Hanover' (R) 🏆H1	ERhR LRHS NShi WDib
'Princessa Rio de Plata'	ERhR NShi
prismatocarpa	ERhR NShi
procumbens	see *B. radicans* Vell.
'Purple Snow' (R) **new**	LRHS NShi
pustulata 'Argentea'	ERhR NShi
putii	NShi
- B&SWJ 7245	WCru
'Queen Mother' (R)	ERhR NShi
'Queen Olympus'	ERhR GGar NShi WDib
'Quinebaug'	ERhR NShi
§ ***radicans*** Vell. 🏆H1	CHal ERhR LRHS MBri NShi
rajah **new**	NShi
'Raquel Wood'	ERhR NShi
'Raspberry Swirl' (R) 🏆H1	CHal ERhR NShi WDib
ravenii	CKob EBee NShi WCot
- B&SWJ 1954	LSou WCru
'Raymond George Nelson' 🏆H1	CHal ERhR NShi
'Razzmatazz' (R)	NShi WDib
'Red Berry' (R)	ERhR NShi
'Red Planet'	ERhR NShi WDib
'Red Reign'	ERhR NShi
'Red Robin' (R)	NShi WDib
'Red Spider'	ERhR NShi
'Red Undies' (C)	NShi WCru
'Red Wing' (R)	NShi
'Regal Minuet' (R)	LRHS NShi WDib
'Reine des Neiges' (R)	NShi
rex	LRHS MBri MRav NShi
- 'Orient'	ERhR NShi
'Richmondensis'	ERhR EShb NShi
'Ricinifolia'	ERhR NShi
'Ricky Minter' 🏆H1	ERea ERhR NShi
'Rip van Winkle'	ERhR NShi
'Robert Blais' (R)	NShi
'Robin' (R)	ERhR NShi
'Robin's Red' (C)	ERhR NShi
'Rocheart' 🏆H1	NShi WDib
'Roi de Roses' (R) 🏆H1	ERhR NShi
roxburghii	ERhR NShi
'Royal Lustre'	ERhR NShi
'Rubacon'	ERhR NShi
rubro-setulosa	ERhR
'Sabre Dance' (R)	ERhR NShi
'Sachsen'	ERhR NShi
'Saint Albans Grey'	NShi
'Salamander' (R) **new**	NShi
'Sal's Comet' 🏆	NShi WDib
'Sal's Moondust'	NShi WDib
'San Diego Sunset' (R) **new**	NShi
sanguinea	ERhR NShi
'Savannah Pink Parfait' (R) **new**	NShi
'Scarlett O'Hara' (T)	ERhR
scharffiana	NShi
§ ***scharffii***	CHal EBak ERhR NShi SDix
'Scherzo'	CHal ERhR NShi WDib
'Scottish Star'	NShi
'Sea Captain'	NShi
'Sea Serpent' 🏆H1	NShi
'Secpuoc'	ERhR
semperflorens hort.	see *B.* Semperflorens Cultorum Group
§ Semperflorens Cultorum Group	MBri NShi

	'Serlis'	ERhR NShi
	serratipetala	CHal EBak ERhR MBri NShi WDib
	'Shamus'	ERhR NShi
	'Shaun Henthorn' (R) **new**	NShi
*	***sheperdii***	NShi WDib
	'Shiloh' (R)	ERhR NShi
*	'Shinihart'	ERhR NShi
	'Shoppy'	NShi
	'Sierra Mist' (C)	ERhR NShi
	'Silbreen'	NShi
	'Silver Cloud' (R) ♀H1	ERhR NShi WDib
*	'Silver Dawn'	ERhR NShi
	'Silver Dollar'	NShi
	'Silver Dots'	NShi
	'Silver Giant' (R)	ERhR NShi
	'Silver Jewell'	NShi WDib
	'Silver King' (R) ♀H1	NShi
	'Silver Lace'	NShi WDib
	'Silver Mist' (C)	ERhR NShi
	'Silver Points'	ERhR NShi
	'Silver Queen' (R) ♀H1	NShi
	'Silver Sweet' (R)	ERhR NShi
	'Silver Wings'	ERhR NShi
	'Sinbad' (C)	ERhR NShi
	sinensis	EMan NShi WCot
	- BWJ 8011	WCru
	aff. ***sinensis***	NShi
	-BWJ 8133	WCru
*	'Sir Charles'	ERhR
	'Sir John Falstaff'	ERhR NShi
	Skeezar Group	ERhR NShi
	- 'Brown Lake'	ERhR NShi
	'Snow Storm'	NShi
*	'Snowcap' (C) ♀H1	ERhR EShb NShi WDib
	socotrana	ERhR
	solananthera ♀H1	CHal ERhR EShb GGar LRHS NShi WDib
	soli-mutata	NShi WDib
	'Sophie Cecile' (C) ♀H1	CHal ERhR NShi
	'Sophie's Jenny'	NShi
	'Speckled Roundabout'	NShi
	'Speculata' (R)	ERhR NShi
	'Spellbound'	ERhR NShi WDib
	'Spindrift'	ERhR NShi
	'Spotches'	ERhR NShi
	'Stained Glass' (R)	NShi WDib
	'Starburst'	SPer
	'Stichael Maeae'	ERhR
§	***stipulacea***	CHal ERhR NShi
	subvillosa (S)	ERhR
	'Sugar Plum'	ERhR NShi
	'Summer Maid' **new**	NShi
	'Sun God'	NShi
	'Sun Set' **new**	NShi
	Superba Group (C)	NShi
	'Superba Azella' (C)	NShi
	sutherlandii ♀H1	CAvo CCCN CHal EABi EBak EOHP ERhR ERos GGar ITer LPio NBir NBlu NPer NShi SAdn SBch SDix WCot WDib WEas WFar WHer
	- 'Papaya'	CSpe LRHS
	'Swan Song'	ERhR
	'Sweet Magic'	CHal ERhR NShi
	'Swirly Top' (C)	ERhR NShi
	'Sylvan Triumph' (C)	ERhR NShi
	taiwaniana	NShi
	'Tapestry' (R)	ERhR NShi
	'Tar Baby' (T)	ERhR NShi
*	***taya***	WDib
	'Tea Rose'	ERhR NShi
	'Tequesta'	NShi
	teuscheri (C)	ERhR NShi
	'Texastar'	ERhR NShi WDib
	'The Wiz'	ERhR NShi
	thelmae	ERhR NShi
	'Think Pink'	NShi
	'Thrush' (R)	NShi
	'Thumotec'	ERhR
	'Thunderclap'	CHal ERhR NShi
	'Thurstonii' ♀H1	ERhR EShb NShi
	'Tickled Pink' **new**	LRHS
	'Tiger Paws' ♀H1	CHal ERhR MBri NShi
	'Tim Anderson' **new**	NShi
	'Tingley Mallet' (C)	ERhR NShi
	'Tiny Bright' (R)	ERhR NShi
	'Tiny Gem'	ERhR NShi
	'Tom Ment' (C)	ERhR NShi
	'Tom Ment II' (C)	ERhR NShi
	'Tomoshiba'	ERhR NShi
	'Tondelayo' (R)	ERhR NShi
	'Tornado' (R)	NShi
	'Tribute'	ERhR NShi
	'Trinidad'	ERhR NShi
	tripartita (T)	ERhR NShi WDib
	'Trout' (C)	NShi
	'Tucson Bonfire' (R) **new**	NShi
	'Twilight'	ERhR NShi
	'Two Face'	ERhR NShi WDib
	ulmifolia	ERhR NShi
	undulata (C)	CHal ERhR NShi
	'Universe'	ERhR NShi
	'Valentine'	NShi
	'Venetian Red' (R)	ERhR NShi
	venosa	CHal ERhR NShi
	'Venus'	CHal ERhR NShi
	'Vera Wyatt'	NShi
	x ***verschaffeltii***	ERhR NShi
	versicolor	ERhR
	'Vesuvius' (R)	NShi WDib
	'Viaudii'	ERhR NShi
	'Viau-Scharff'	ERhR
	'Vista' (R) **new**	NShi
§	***vitifolia*** Schott	ERhR NShi
	'Wally's World'	NShi
	'Wanda' **new**	NShi
	'Weltoniensis'	ERhR NShi
	'Weltoniensis Alba' (T)	ERhR
	'Westland Beauty'	NShi
	'White Cascade'	ERhR
	'Wild Swan'	NShi WCru
	williamsii	NShi
	'Witch Craft' (R)	ERhR NShi
	'Withlacoochee'	ERhR NShi WDib
	wollnyi	ERhR
	'Wood Nymph' (R)	ERhR NShi
	'Zuensis'	ERhR

Belamcanda (*Iridaceae*)

chinensis	CArn CHll CMea CPen EBee ELau EMan ERos EShb GKev GPoy LRHS MHer MLLN MSal SDnm SIng SPad SPav SPlb SRms WBrE WCru WGwG WPer
- B&SWJ 8692B	WCru
- 'Freckle Face'	EBee EKen GBri NBPC SPoG
- 'Hello Yellow'	EShb GBuc

Bellevalia (*Hyacinthaceae*)

atroviolacea **new**	EBrs ECho
brevipedicellata	EBrs ECho
ciliata	ERos
dubia	EBee WCot
forniculata	ERos
hackelii	EBrs ERos
hyacinthoides	CStu WCot
kurdistanica	ERos
maura	EBrs ECho
nivalis	EBrs

§ ***paradoxa***	CBgR CMea CPom CTca EBee EBrs ECho EHrv ERCP ERos ITim LBMP LRHS LTwo MAvo WCot
– white-flowered	EBrs ECho ERos
pycnantha misapplied	see *B. paradoxa*
romana	CFwr CPom CStu CTca EBee EBrs ECho ERCP ERos GBin MTho SPhx WCot WHil
sarmatica	ERos WCot
spicata	WCot
tabriziana	ERos
webbiana	ERos

Bellis (*Asteraceae*)

§ ***caerulescens***	GAbr NBir NBro SIng WOut
perennis	CArn EUnu NMir NSco
– 'Alba Plena' (d)	ECho
– 'Alice'	WCot
– 'Dawn Raider'	EMon
– 'Dresden China'	ECho EWes GAbr MTho WOut
– 'Galaxy White' (Galaxy Series) **new**	EPfP
– Hen and Chickens	see *B. perennis* 'Prolifera'
– 'Miss Mason'	GAbr WOut
– 'Parkinson's Great White'	GAbr
§ – 'Prolifera' (d)	WHer
– 'Red Buttons'	NBlu
– 'Rob Roy' (d)	WCot
– 'Robert'	GAbr
– 'Rusher Rose'	EPfP
– 'Single Blue'	see *B. caerulescens*
– 'The Pearl' **new**	WCot
rotundifolia 'Caerulescens'	see *B. caerulescens*
sylvestris	CArn

Bellium (*Asteraceae*)

* ***crassifolium canescens***	WPer
minutum	MTho

Beloperone see *Justicia*

guttata	see *Justicia brandegeeana*

Bensoniella (*Saxifragaceae*)

oregona	EMon

Benthamiella (*Solanaceae*)

patagonica WAL 9845 **new**	WAbe

Berberidopsis (*Flacourtiaceae*)

beckleri	WPGP
corallina	More than 30 suppliers

Berberis ✿ (*Berberidaceae*)

CC 4041	CPLG
CC 4730	CPLG
CC 4732	CPLG MGol
SDR 3055	GKev
SDR 3256	GKev
aggregata	EMac NBir SRms
amurensis var. ***latifolia*** B&SWJ 4353	WCru
aquifolium	see *Mahonia aquifolium*
– 'Fascicularis'	see *Mahonia* x *wagneri* 'Pinnacle'
N ***aristata*** ambig.	CAgr CArn CMCN
aristata Parker	see *B. glaucocarpa*
asiatica	CAgr CPLG GPoy
bealei	see *Mahonia japonica* Bealei Group
'Blenheim'	WFar
x ***bristolensis***	EPla SLon SPla SRms
buxifolia	LEdu WCFE
– 'Nana' missaplied	see *B. buxifolia* 'Pygmaea'
N – 'Pygmaea'	CAbP CBcs CSBt EBee LAst MBNS MBar MGos MRav NEgg NHol SPer WFar
calliantha	WFar
candidula C.K. Schneid.	EBee ECrN EPfP MBar MGan MSwo NHol NLar SLon SPer
– 'Jytte'	see *B.* 'Jytte'
x ***carminea*** 'Buccaneer'	EPfP
– 'Pirate King'	CSBt MRav SPer SWvt WFar WPat
chingii	CPle
chrysosphaera	WFar
coxii	GBin GGar
darwinii ♀H4	More than 30 suppliers
I – 'Compacta'	NLar SPoG
diaphana **new**	CMCN
dictyophylla ♀H4	CPMA EPfP MGos NLar SLon SPer SPoG SSpi WPat WSHC WSpi
dulcis 'Nana'	see *B. buxifolia* 'Pygmaea'
empetrifolia	WSpi
x ***frikartii*** 'Amstelveen' ♀H4	CDoC CSBt CSam EBee ELan ENot EPfP LAst MBNS MRav NHol NLar WFar
– 'Telstar'	ECrN LAst LBuc MGos MRav NLar NPro
gagnepainii misapplied	see *B. gagnepainii* C.K. Schneid. var. *lanceifolia*
gagnepainii C.K. Schneid.	CMac EBee EMac LRav MGan MRav NHol SLPl WTel
§ – var. ***lanceifolia***	CBcs CTri ECrN EPla MBar MDun MGos NEgg NHol NWea SLim WFar
– – 'Fernspray'	EPfP EPla MRav SBod SRms WBod
– 'Purpurea'	see *B.* x *interposita* 'Wallich's Purple'
'Georgei' ♀H4	CMHG CWib EPfP GQui SSpi
§ ***glaucocarpa***	EPfP EPla NHol
'Goldilocks'	CAbP CDul CPMA CPSs EPfP LAst MBlu
goudotii B&SWJ 10769 **new**	WCru
x ***hybridogagnepainii*** 'Chenaultii'	CBcs ELan NHol SPer
hypokerina	CMac
insignis	WFar
– subsp. ***insignis*** var. ***insignis***	WFar
– – B&SWJ 2432	WCru
§ x ***interposita*** 'Wallich's Purple'	CCVT ECrN EPfP MBar MDun MRav MSwo NHol SPer
julianae ♀H4	More than 30 suppliers
§ 'Jytte'	EBee
kawakamii	SLPl
koreana	CMCN EPfP NLar
– 'Rubin' **new**	CAgr
lempergiana	CMCN
lepidifolia	GBin
linearifolia	CMac
– 'Orange King'	CBcs CDoC CMac CTri ELan EPfP LRHS MAsh MGan MGos NLar SCoo SHBN SPer SPoG WFar WHar WPat
'Little Favourite'	see *B. thunbergii* f. *atropurpurea* 'Atropurpurea Nana'
x ***lologensis***	MGos
– 'Apricot Queen' ♀H4	CBcs CMac EBee EPfP LRHS MAsh MGos MRav NBlu NLar SCoo SHBN SPer SPoG WPat
– 'Mystery Fire'	CDoC LRHS MAsh MBlu MBri MGos NBlu NEgg NLar SCoo SPoG SWvt WFar WHar
– 'Stapehill'	CSam ELan EPfP LRHS MAsh MBri NHol SPoG
macrosepala var. ***macrosepala*** B&SWJ 2124	WCru
x ***media*** Park Jewel	see *B.* x *media* 'Parkjuweel'

§	- 'Parkjuweel'	CBcs EBee ECrN IArd MRav NLar SCoo WFar
	- 'Red Jewel' ♀H4	CDoC CMac CSBt EBee EPfP LRHS MGos MRav MWat NLar SCoo SPer SPoG WCFE WFar WMoo
	mitifolia	NLar
	montana	WPGP WPat
	x ***ottawensis*** f. ***purpurea***	CWib EBee MGos SBod WFar WHar
§	- - 'Superba' ♀H4	More than 30 suppliers
§	- 'Silver Miles' (v)	EQua MRav NLar WFar WPat
§	***panlanensis***	MBar SLon
	poiretii	CPLG NBhm NLar WHrl
	pruinosa	CDul
	'Red Tears'	CPMA CSam LRHS MBlu MBri MGos MLan MRav NLar SPer WHCG WMoo
	replicata	CPle
	sanguinea misapplied	see *B. panlanensis*
	sargentiana	SLPl
	sherriffii	WCwm
	sieboldii	LTwo MRav WPat WSpi
	soulieana	MGan
	x ***stenophylla*** Lindl. ♀H4	CBcs CDoC CSBt CTri EBee ECrN ENot EPfP GGar ISea LBuc LRHS MBar MBri MLan MRav NEgg NHol NWea SMer SPer SPoG WBod WCFE WFar WHar WMoo WTel
	- 'Claret Cascade'	EBee EQua LRHS MBri MGos MRav NHol NLar SPer WFar
	- 'Corallina'	SPer
	- 'Corallina Compacta' ♀H4	CFee CLyd ECho ELan EPfP EPot LHop LRHS MAsh NRya SPer SPoG SRms WAbe WPat
	- 'Crawley Gem'	GBin MBar MGos NHol NLar WFar
	- 'Etna'	ELan LRHS MAsh SPoG
	- 'Irwinii'	CMac LAst MBar MGos MSwo SPer WFar WMoo WTel
	- 'Nana'	SRms WAbe
	- 'Pink Pearl' (v)	CMHG MGos
	temolaica ♀H4	CGHE CPMA EPfP LRHS MDun MGos MRav NEgg NLar NPen NSti SDnm SPoG SSpi SSta WPGP WPat WSpi
	thunbergii ♀H4	CBcs CDoC CDul CSBt EMac ENot EPfP GBin LBuc MRav NEgg NWea SCoo SMer SPer SPlb SPoG WFar
	- f. ***atropurpurea***	CBcs CCVT CDul CSBt CTri EBee EMac ENot EPfP EWTr LAst LBuc MAsh MBar MGan MGos MNHC MSwo NBlu NEgg NWea SCoo SMer SPer SPoG WBVN WFar WMoo
	- - 'Admiration'	CAbP EPfP MAsh MBri MGos SPer SPoG
§	- - 'Atropurpurea Nana' ♀H4	More than 30 suppliers
	- - 'Bagatelle' ♀H4	CDoC EBee ELan EMil ENot EPfP EPot IArd LAst LHop LRHS LSRN MAsh MBar MBri MGos MLHP MRav NEgg SLim SPer SPoG SWvt WAbe WCFE WFar WPat WWeb
	- - 'Carmen'	MGos
	- - 'Dart's Purple'	WFar
	- - 'Dart's Red Lady'	CPLG CPMA CSBt CWib EBee ECrN ELan ENot EPfP LRHS MAsh MBri MRav NLar NPro SCoo SLim SPer SPoG SWvt WFar WPat
	- - 'Golden Ring' ♀H4	CBcs CDoC CDul EBee EMil EPfP LAst LRHS LSRN MAsh MBNS MBar MDun MGos MRav NHol NPri SEND SLim SPer SPla SPoG SWvt WBrE WFar WHar WMoo WPat
	- - 'Harlequin' (v)	CBcs CDoC CSBt EBee ELan EMil ENot EPfP LCro LRHS LSRN MAsh MBri MGos MRav NEgg SLim SPer SPla SPoG WBVN WBod WFar WHar WPat WWeb
	- - 'Helmond Pillar'	CDul CSBt CTri CWib EBee ELan EMil ENot EPfP LAst LCro LRHS MAsh MBar MBlu MBri MGos MRav NBlu NEgg SLim SMad SPer SPoG SWvt WBod WCFE WFar WPat
	- - 'Red Chief' ♀H4	CBcs CMHG EBee ECrN ELan EPfP LRHS MAsh MGos MRav NEgg SLim SLon SPer SPla SPoG SWvt WFar WHCG WHar WMoo WPat WTel WWeb
	- - 'Red King'	MRav
	- - 'Red Pillar'	CChe CDoC EBee ELan LAst LRHS MAsh MBar MGos MRav MWat NHol SHBN SPla WFar WPat
	- - 'Red Rocket'	EMil MBri MCCP NLar
	- - 'Rose Glow' (v) ♀H4	More than 30 suppliers
	- 'Atropurpurea Superba'	see *B.* x *ottawensis* f. *purpurea* 'Superba'
	- 'Aurea'	More than 30 suppliers
	- Bonanza Gold = 'Bogozam'[PBR]	CAbP CDoC EBee ELan EPfP LRHS MAsh MRav NLar SLim SPer SPoG WFar WPat
	- 'Carpetbagger'	WHar
	- 'Coronita'	MBri
	- 'Crimson Pygmy'	see *B. thunbergii* f. *atropurpurea* 'Atropurpurea Nana'
	- 'Erecta'	CMac EPfP MBar MGos MRav SPer WBod WCFE
	- 'Golden Carpet' **new**	LRHS SPoG
	- 'Golden Pillar' **new**	LRHS
	- 'Golden Rocket' **new**	LBuc MAsh SPer SPoG
	- 'Golden Torch'	CSBt EBee LSRN MBri MRav SPoG SWvt WWeb
	- 'Green Carpet'	EBee LHop MBar NLar SPoG WFar
	- 'Green Mantle'	see *B. thunbergii* 'Kelleriis'
	- 'Green Marble'	see *B. thunbergii* 'Kelleriis'
	- 'Green Ornament'	NHol
	- 'Green Ring'	EQua
§	- 'J.N. Variegated' (v)	SPer
§	- 'Kelleriis' (v)	CDoC EPfP LHop MBar MGos MRav NHol NLar NPro SLon SPoG WFar WRHF
	- 'Kobold'	EBee ENot EPfP LHop LRHS MAsh MBar MGos NHol NLar SLim SPer SPla SPoG WFar
	- 'Pink Queen' (v)	CDul EBee ELan ENot EPfP MAsh SPur WFar WHar WPat
	- 'Pow-wow'	CBcs EBee MGos NLar SCoo SPoG
	- 'Silver Beauty' (v)	CMHG EBee ELan MGos
	- 'Silver Mile'	see *B.* x *ottawensis* 'Silver Miles'
	- 'Somerset'	CMac
	- 'Starburst' (v)	CBcs EPfP MAsh MBri MGos SPoG
	- Stardust	see *B. thunbergii* 'J.N. Variegated'
	- 'Tiny Gold' **new**	SPoG
*	- 'Tricolor' (v)	CMac MRav WFar WPat
	valdiviana	CDul CGHE CPLG CPMA EBee EPfP EPla SKHP SMad SSpi WPGP WPat
	verruculosa ♀H4	CBcs CChe EBee EPfP LAst LHop MBar MGan MGos NHol NLar NWea SCoo SPer SRms WCFE WFar
	- 'Hard's Rob'	NLar
	aff. ***verticillata*** B&SWJ 10672 **new**	WCru
	virescens B&SWJ 2646D	WCru
	vulgaris	CArn CNat EMac EPfP GPoy
	- 'Wiltshire Wonder' (v)	CNat
	wilsoniae	CBcs CDul CTri EBee EMac EPfP EPla LHop MBar NEgg NHol NWea SCoo SHBN SPer WCFE WFar
	- L 650	CGHE WPGP

- blue	LRHS WFar WGer WPat
- var. ***guhtzunica***	EPla EWes

Berchemia (*Rhamnaceae*)

racemosa	CMen NLar SBra WSHC

bergamot see *Citrus bergamia*

Bergenia ✿ (*Saxifragaceae*)

'Abendglocken'	CMac EBee ECGP ECha ECtt EGle EPfP LHop LRHS MNFA MWat NGdn NSti SPla SWat WEas WFar
§ 'Abendglut'	More than 30 suppliers
'Admiral'	CBct ECha MLHP
* ***agavifolia***	CBct
'Apple Court White'	CBct
'Autumn Magic'	CBct COlW EBee GAbr LAst LHop LSou MSte NPri SPoG WHlf WSpi
'Baby Doll'	More than 30 suppliers
§ 'Ballawley' clonal ♀^{H4}	CFir CMac ECha IBlr IGor MLHP MRav NEgg SWat WCAu WCot WFar WMnd
'Ballawley Guardsman'	CBct EBee EHrv ERou
§ Ballawley hybrids	EBee SDix SWat WSpi
'Ballawley Red' **new**	GBin
'Ballawley' seed-raised	see *B.* Ballawley hybrids
beesiana	see *B. purpurascens*
'Beethoven'	CBct CDes CLAP EBee ECha EGle EPla IGor MRav NBir NBre SWat WCot WPGP WSHC
Bell Tower	see *B.* 'Glockenturm'
'Biedermeir' **new**	ECha
'Bizet'	CBct
'Borodin'	CBct
'Brahms'	CBct GBuc
'Bressingham Bountiful'	CBct
'Bressingham Ruby'^{PBR}	CBcs CBct CLAP CRez EBee EBrs ECha ECtt EPPr MRav NBir NCGa NEgg SHBN SWat WCAu WCot WPGP WSpi
'Bressingham Salmon'	CBct CHar EBee ECha ELan ELon EPfP ERou GMaP GSki MBri MRav SHBN WCot WMnd
'Bressingham White' ♀^{H4}	More than 30 suppliers
ciliata	CDes CFee CHEx CLAP EBee EBla EShb LEdu MLHP MRav MSte NBir NHol NLar SDix WCot WKif WLin WPGP WSHC WTin
- f. ***ciliata***	CBct WCot
- f. ***ligulata***	see *B. pacumbis*
- 'Patricia Furness'	CLAP GCrs NBir
- 'Wilton'	CLAP WCot
ciliata x ***crassifolia***	see *B.* x *schmidtii*
cordifolia	More than 30 suppliers
- 'Flore Pleno'	CBct
- 'Jelle'	GBin
- 'Purpurea' ♀^{H4}	CBcs CDoC CSBt EBee ECha ELan EMFW ENot EPfP GSki LBuc LCro LRHS MLHP MNFA MRav NBir SHBN SPer SPla SRms SWat WCAu WFar WPnP
- 'Rosa Schwester'	EBee
- 'Rosa Zeiten'	GBin
- 'Tubby Andrews' (v)	CBct CBow EBla ECtt EGle EMon EPPr ITer LEdu MBrN MBri MCCP MDKP MLLN NEgg NLar NPro
- 'Winterglut'	CHFP EBee ELan GMaP GQue IBal IFoB ITim MWgw NBre NGdn SWvt WBor WHil WPnP WRHF
crassifolia	EBee NBre NSum SRms
- 'Autumn Red'	CBct ECha
- 'Orbicularis'	see *B.* x *schmidtii*
* ***cyanea***	CLAP WCot
'David'	EMon EWes
delavayi	see *B. purpurascens* var. *delavayi*
'Delbees'	see *B.* 'Ballawley' clonal
'Doppelgänger'	EBee
'Eden's Dark Margin'	CBct CBgR EBee ERou NPro
'Eden's Magic Carpet'	CFir
'Eden's Magic Giant'	CBct EBee ERou GBin MAvo
emeiensis	CDes CLAP WCot WPGP
- hybrid	CBct MWat
'Eric Smith'	CBct ECha EPla GBin IGor MBri WCot WMnd
'Eroica'	CBct EBee ECha ELan EMon GBin LAst LHop MRav NBre NRnb NSti SHar SWat WCAu WMnd WPtf
'Evening Glow'	see *B.* 'Abendglut'
'Frau Holle'	MBri
§ 'Glockenturm'	CBct NEgg
'Hellen Dillon'	see *B. purpurascens* 'Irish Crimson'
'Herbstblute'	EBee EMon
'Jo Watanabe'	CBct MRav
'Lambrook'	see *B.* 'Margery Fish'
§ 'Margery Fish'	CBct SPer
milesii	see *B. stracheyi*
§ 'Morgenröte' ♀^{H4}	CBcs CBct CPrp EBee ECha EMil EPfP GMaP LAst MBNS MGos MRav MSte NHol NSti SHBN SPer SRms SWat SWvt WCot
'Morning Light'	LAst NPro NSti
Morning Red	see *B.* 'Morgenröte'
'Mrs Crawford'	CBct ECha
'Oeschberg'	CBct GBin WCAu
'Opal'	CBct
'Overture'	CBct EBee ECtt EGle EHrv GAbr GEdr LAst LDai LHop MBri MNFA MWat MWgw NCGa NCob NEgg NGby NGdn WCAu WCot WFar WWFP
§ ***pacumbis***	CBct CHEx CLAP EBee GBin GEdr MWgw NBid NBir NBre NSti SDix WCot
- B&SWJ 2693	WCru
- CC 1793	SBch
- CC 3616	ITim WCot
'Perfect'	CBct EBee WMnd
'Pink Dragonfly'	CWGN EBee GBin LHop NBPN NBhm NEgg SBra SMac SPoG
'Pinneberg'	EBee GBin
'Profusion'	SPer WCAu
'Pugsley's Pink'	CBct GCra SHBN
§ ***purpurascens*** ♀^{H4}	EBee GBuc GCrs GMaP GSki IFoB IGor MWgw SDix SPer WCot WTin
- ACE 2175	WCot
- SDR 1629	GKev
§ - var. ***delavayi*** ♀^{H4}	MBri NBre SRms WPnP
- - CLD 1366	WPer
§ - 'Irish Crimson'	CBct CGHE SBla WCot
aff. ***purpurascens***	SMad
- ACE 2175	WCot
'Red Beauty'	MGos NEgg NPen
'Reitheim'	CBct EBee
'Rosi Klose'	More than 30 suppliers
'Rosi Ruffles' **new**	EBee
'Rotblum'	CBct CBrm EBee ECGP ECtt EPfP GMaP GSki GWCH MAvo NBir NCob NGdn NOrc NRnb NVic WFar WPer WWeb
§ x ***schmidtii*** ♀^{H4}	CBct EBee IGor NBir NBre SDix WCot
'Schneekissen'	CBct CMac EBee ECGP EGle LAst MNFA MRav SWat WCAu
§ 'Schneekönigin'	CBct ECha GBin MRav
§ 'Silberlicht' ♀^{H4}	More than 30 suppliers
Silverlight	see *B.* 'Silberlicht'
'Simply Sweet'	WCot
Snow Queen	see *B.* 'Schneekönigin'

§ ***stracheyi***	CBct CPLG ECha EGle EGoo EMon IGor MLHP MRav NBid NLar SApp SDix WCot WEas
- CC 4609	GKev
- Alba Group	CBct CDes EBee ECha MSte WPGP
'Sunningdale'	CBcs CBct CMac EBee ECha ELan EMFW EPfP GCra GMaP GSki LHop LRHS MLLN MRav NBir NGdn SPer SWat SWvt WCAu WMnd
tianquanensis	EBee
'Walter Kienli' new	GBin
Winter Fairy Tales	see *B.* 'Wintermärchen'
§ 'Wintermärchen'	CBct CRez EBee ECha ELan EPfP GCra GSki LRHS MGos MRav MSte NCGa NMyG NOrc NPro NSti SPoG SWat WCot WMnd

Bergeranthus (*Aizoaceae*)

sp.	WThu
glenensis	EDAr
multiceps	SChr

Berkheya (*Asteraceae*)

draco new	EWld
macrocephala	WCot
multijuga	SBHP WCot
purpurea	More than 30 suppliers
- 'Silver Spike'	EDAr LSRN MBri WSel
- 'Zulu Warrior'	CBcs CEnt EKen ENor IPot SBHP SRkn

Berlandiera (*Asteraceae*)

lyrata	CBrm EBee EMan
- 'Chocolate Drop'	SPet

Berneuxia (*Diapensiaceae*)

thibetica	IBlr

Berula (*Apiaceae*)

erecta	EHon EMFW NPer

Berzelia (*Bruniaceae*)

galpinii	SPlb
lanuginosa	CTrC GGar IDee

Beschorneria (*Agavaceae*)

sp.	WPGP
septentrionalis	CAbP CFir CGHE CSpe CTrC EAmu EBee GAbr MBNS MSte WCot WLeb WPGP WPat
septentrionalis × ***yuccoides***	WPGP
tubiflora	CHEx EBee LEdu WPGP
wrightii	EBee WPGP
yuccoides ΨH3	CAbb CBcs CHEx CTrC EAmu EBee EShb IBlr IDee ISea LEdu MSte SAPC SArc SChr SDnm SLim SLon WKif WPGP XPep
- 'Quicksilver'	CBcs CBod CCCN CDoC CEnd CKno CTrC EBee EMan LRHS MBri MGos MSte NVic SDnm SPoG SSpi WCot WGer WLeb WPGP

Bessera (*Alliaceae*)

elegans	CAvo CFir CHHB EBee EBrs ECho EPot LRHS

Beta (*Chenopodiaceae*)

trigyna	WCot
vulgaris	EWin WHer
- 'Bull's Blood'	CArn CSpe EMan EWin MSte WCot WJek
- subsp. ***cicla*** var. ***flavescens*** 'Bright Lights' ΨH3	CArn
- - - 'Rhubarb Chard' ΨH3	WJek
- subsp. ***maritima***	CAgr

Betonica see *Stachys*

Betula ✿ (*Betulaceae*)

alba L.	see *B. pendula*, *B. pubescens*
albosinensis misapplied	see *B. utilis*
albosinensis Burkill ΨH4	CDul CLnd CMCN CTri EBee EPfP ISea NLar NWea SBLw SPer WFar WNor WOrn
- W 4106	CSto
- 'Bowling Green'	CPMA WPGP
- 'China Ruby'	CDul CLnd CPMA MBri SIFN SSpi
- 'Chinese Garden'	CPMA MBlu
- clone F	see *B. albosinensis* 'Ness'
- 'K.Ashburner'	CPMA CTho
- 'Kansu'	CLnd CPMA SCoo SIFN SSpi WHCr
§ - 'Ness'	CPMA CTho SLim
- 'Sable'	SLau SPer
- var. ***septentrionalis*** ΨH4	More than 30 suppliers
- - 'Purdom'	CPMA SIFN
§ ***alleghaniensis***	CCVT CDul CMCN CSto EBee ECrN EPfP IDee NLar NPen NWea
alnoides	WNor
apoiensis	WNor
- 'Mount Apoi'	CPMA SIFN
austrosinensis	WNor
borealis	see *B. pumila*
§ × ***caerulea***	CPMA CTho NLar WSpi
caerulea-grandis	see *B.* × *caerulea*
chichibuensis	WHer
chinensis	CMCN WNor
'Conyngham'	CTho MBlu SLau
cordifolia	see *B. papyrifera* var. *cordifolia*
costata misapplied	see *B. ermanii* 'Grayswood Hill'
costata Trautv.	CLnd CTho EBee ELan EPfP MSwo SBLw WOrn
* - 'Fincham Cream'	CPMA SIFN WHCr
cylindrostachya new	CExc EBee
dahurica Pall.	CDul CMCN IArd WNor
- B&SWJ 4247	WHCr
- 'Maurice Foster'	CPMA CTho
- 'Stone Farm'	CPMA
delavayi	SIFN
ermanii	CBcs CCVT CDoC CDul CLnd CMCN CMHG CSBt CSam CTho CTri EBee ECrN ELan EPfP GQui LPan LRHS MAsh MBlu MGos MRav NBea NEgg NWea SBLw WFar WMoo WNor
- from Hokkaido, Japan	CSto
- 'Blush'	CLnd CPMA EWTr SCoo SHBN WHCr
- var. ***ermanii*** MSF 865	EBee SKHP WPGP
§ - 'Grayswood Hill' ΨH4	CDul CEnd CLnd CMHG CPMA CTho EBee GQui LCro LRHS MAsh MBri MGos NWea SCoo SHBN SIFN SLim SMad SPer SSpi WHCr WOrn WPGP
- 'Hakkoda Orange'	CPMA CTho MBlu MBri SCoo
- 'Mount Zao' new	CTho
* - 'Pendula'	CPMA SCoo SIFN
- 'Polar Bear'	CPMA CWSG LRHS MBri SCoo SIFN SMad WHCr WHar
'Fetisowii'	CEnd CLnd CMCN CTho ECrN IMGH LRHS MBlu MBri SCoo SIFN SLim SSta
fruticosa	see *B. humilis*
glandulifera	see *B. pumila*
globispica	EWTr WNor
grossa	CMCN IDee
'Hergest'	EBee EPfP LRHS MAsh MBri MGos SCoo SLau SLim WHCr WPGP

§	***humilis***	CMCN GQui
	- B&SWJ 8801	WCru
	insignis	CExc
	'Inverleith'	see *B. utilis* var. *jacquemontii* 'Inverleith'
	jacquemontii	see *B. utilis* var. *jacquemontii*
	kamtschatica	see *B. humilis*
§	***kenaica***	CTho
	lenta	CLnd CMCN CSto EPfP IArd NLar NWea
	litvinovii	SIFN
	luminifera	CPMA ECrN IDee NLar SIFN
	lutea	see *B. alleghaniensis*
	mandshurica	GQui WHCr
§	- var. ***japonica***	CLnd ECrN NEgg NLar NPal NPen NWea WNor
	- - 'Whitespire'	CWSG
	- - 'Whitespire Senior'	CDul
	maximowicziana	CDoC CDul CLnd CMCN CTho CWib EPfP EWTr IArd LHop NEgg NLar NWea WNor
§	***medwedewii***	CDul CLnd CMCN CSto EBee ECrN EMil EPfP EPla GEdr GQui NEgg NHol NWea SCoo
	- from Winkworth	CTho
	- 'Gold Bark'	CDoC MBlu
	megrelica	see *B. medwedewii*
§	***michauxii***	EPot
	nana	CDul EBee MBar MRav NHol SIng SRms SSta STre
	- 'Glengarry'	EPot NLar
	- var. ***michauxii***	see *B. michauxii*
§	***neoalaskana***	WNor
	nigra	CBcs CCVT CDoC CDul CEnd CLnd CMCN CSBt CTho CTri ECrN EMil LPan MAsh MBri NEgg SBLw SHBN SSta WGer WMou WNor WOrn
	- Heritage = 'Cully' 𝕐H4	CDoC CDul CEnd CLnd CMCN CPMA EBee ECrN EMil ENot LPan LRHS MBlu MGos SCoo SIFN SLim SSta WFar WHCr WMoo WOrn
	- 'Little King'	CPMA MBri
	- 'Summer Cascade' **new**	MBri
	- Wakehurst form	EPfP LRHS SPer SPoG
	papyrifera	CBcs CCVT CDul CLnd CMCN CSBt CSto CTri EBee ECrN ELan EMac EPfP LBuc LRHS MAsh MBlu MGos MRav MSwo NBee NWea SHBN SPer WFar WNor WOrn
§	- var. ***cordifolia***	CSto
	- subsp. ***humilis***	see *B. neoalaskana*
	- var. ***kenaica***	see *B. kenaica*
	- 'Saint George'	CPMA CTho
	- 'Vancouver'	CPMA CTho
§	***pendula*** 𝕐H4	More than 30 suppliers
	- 'Bangor'	CLnd CPMA SIFN
*	- 'Boeugh's Variety'	CEnd GBin
	- f. ***crispa***	see *B. pendula* 'Laciniata'
	- 'Dalecarlica' misapplied	see *B. pendula* 'Laciniata'
	- 'Dalecarlica' ambig.	CBcs CCVT CSBt ECrN ENot MDun MRav SCrf SLim WFar
	- 'Dark Prince'	CPMA
	- 'Fastigiata'	CDoC CDul CLnd CSBt CTho EBee ECrN ELan LPan MGos NWea SBLw SCoo SLim SPer WFar WMoo WOrn
*	- 'Golden Beauty'	CDoC CTri ECrN LPan LRHS MAsh MGos NLar SCoo SLim SPer SPoG SSpi WFar WHCr WOrn
§	- 'Laciniata' 𝕐H4	CDoC CDul CMCN CTho CWSG CWib EBee ECrN ELan EPfP LAst LPan MAsh MGos MSwo NBea NBee NLar NWea SBLw SCoo SPer
	- 'Long Trunk'	CDul EBee ECrN EMil LPan

	- 'Obilisk' **new**	SIFN
	- 'Purpurea'	CBrm CCVT CDul CLnd CMCN CSBt CWib EBee ECrN ELan EPfP LAst LPan LRHS LSRN MGos MSwo NBea NBlu NEgg NWea SBLw SCoo SIFN SPer WFar WOrn
	- 'Silver Cascade'	MGos
	- 'Silver Grace'	EBee ECrN ENot MGos
	- 'Tristis' 𝕐H4	More than 30 suppliers
	- 'Youngii'	More than 30 suppliers
	platyphylla misapplied	see *B. mandshurica* var. *japonica*
	platyphylla Sukaczev	CMCN NWea
	- var. ***japonica***	see *B. mandshurica* var. *japonica*
	- var. ***kamtschatica***	see *B. mandshurica* var. *japonica*
	- subsp. ***platyphylla***	CMCN
	populifolia	CMCN CSto
§	***pubescens***	CCVT CDul CLnd CSto CTri ECrN EMil NBee NWea SBLw SLPl WFar WMou
§	***pumila***	GGar WCwm
	raddeana	WNor
	resinifera Britton	see *B. neoalaskana*
	'Royal Frost'	CPMA IClo
	schmidtii	EWTr IClo WCwm
	szechuanica	CLnd GQui WPGP
	- 'Liuba White'	CPMA CTho
	tianschanica	MDun WNor
§	***utilis***	CDul CMCN CMHG CSBt CSto EBee ECrN EMil ENot ERas ISea MAsh MBar MRav NBee NWea SSta WFar WNor WPGP
	- BL&M 100	CTho
	- F 19505	CTho
	- McB 1257	CTho
	- RSC 1 from Langtang, Nepal	CSto
	- Sch 2168	MBri
	- from Eastern Nepal	CSto
	- 'Buckland' **new**	ECrN
	- 'Darkness' **new**	SLon
	- 'Fascination'	CCVT CDul CPMA EMil IArd LPan LRHS MBri MGos NWea SCoo SIFN SLim SMad SSpi WHCr
*	- 'Fastigiata'	CLnd CPMA SIFN
	- 'Forrest's Blush'	CDul CLnd CPMA EBee MBri SIFN
	- 'Himalayan Pink' **new**	WSpi
N	- var. ***jacquemontii***	More than 30 suppliers
	- - Polunin	WPGP
	- - SF 00004	ISea
	- - 'Doorenbos' 𝕐H4	CCVT CDul CEnd CLnd CMCN CPMA CSBt CTho CWSG EBee EMui EPfP LPan LRHS LSRN MAsh MBlu MBri MGos NEgg NWea SCoo SIFN SLau SLim SSta WHCr WOrn
	- - 'Grayswood Ghost' 𝕐H4	CDul CEnd CLnd CMCN CMHG CPMA CTho ECrN ENot EPfP EWes LCro LPan LRHS MDun SHBN SIFN SLau SLim SMad SPer SSpi
§	- - 'Inverleith'	CDul CEnd CPMA EBee MAsh MBri MWya SCoo SIFN SLau SLim WFar WOrn WPGP
	- - 'Jermyns' 𝕐H4	CDul CEnd CLnd CMCN CPMA CTho CTri ECot EPfP LPan LRHS MBlu MBri SCoo SIFN SLau SMad SPer SSpi WHCr WOrn
	- - 'Macbeth' **new**	SLau
I	- - 'Pendula' **new**	SPoG
	- - 'Silver Shadow' 𝕐H4	CDul CLnd CMCN CPMA CTho CTri EBee EPfP LRHS MAsh MBlu NWea SCoo SIFN SLau SLim SMad SPer SPoG SSpi SSta WOrn WSpi
	- - 'Trinity College'	CLnd CPMA EBee MBri SIFN SSpi WHCr

	- 'Knightshayes'	CTho
	- 'Moonbeam'	CDul CLnd CPMA MBri SCoo SIFN WGer WHCr
	- var. ***occidentalis*** 'Kyelang'	CPMA CTho
	- var. ***prattii***	CEnd CTho
	- 'Ramdana River'	CTho MBlu
	- 'Wakehurst Place Chocolate'	CDul CPMA CWSG LRHS MAsh MBri SCoo SIFN SMad WHCr
	cf. ***utilis*** GWJ 9259	WCru
	- HWJK 2345	WCru
	verrucosa	see *B. pendula*

Biarum (*Araceae*)

	S&L 604	WCot
	SBLBL 597	WCot
	bovei	EBrs ECho WCot
	carratracense	WCot
	davisii	CStu EBrs ECho SKHP WCot
	dispar	WCot
	ditschianum	WCot
	galianii PB 435 new	WCot
	ochridense	EBrs WCot
	spruneri S&L 229	SKHP
	tenuifolium	EBrs ECho ERos SKHP WCot
	- subsp. ***abbreviatum*** MS 974	WCot
	- - from Greece	ECho
	- subsp. ***zelebori*** LB 300	WCot

Bidens (*Asteraceae*)

	B&SWJ 10276 from Mexico new	WCru
	atrosanguinea	see *Cosmos atrosanguineus*
§	***aurea***	EBee EBla ECtt EMon EPPr EWes LAst LRHS MDKP MNrw NCGa NPer SGar SPet SPhx STes WBor WFar WOld
	- B&SWJ 9049 from Guatemala	WCru
*	- B&SWJ 10366 new	WCru
	- 'All Gold'	EBee
	- 'Blacksmith's Flame' new	EBla
	- cream-flowered	MNrw MSte
	- 'Golden Drop'	EWes
	- 'Hannay's Lemon Drop'	CFwr CKno CPen CSev EBee EBla ECtt ELon EPPr GBri LHop MBnl MDKP MNrw MSte NCGa SPoG STes WHrl WMoo WPGP
	- 'Rising Sun'	EBee EWes
	- 'Super Nova'	EWes
	ferulifolia ♀H1+3	ECtt NPer
	- Peter's Gold Carpet = 'Peters Goldteppich'PBR	SVil
	- Peter's Gold Rush = 'Topteppich'PBR	LSou NPri
	- Solaire = 'Bidtis 1'	WGor
	- Solaire Yellow = 'Bidcomtis'PBR	NBlu
	'Golden Star'	LAst
	heterophylla misapplied	CKno CPLG ECha ECtt MCot MRav SCoo WFar WHal WHrl WMoo WPrP WTMC WWlt
	heterophylla Ortega	see *B. aurea*
	humilis	see *B. triplinervia* var. *macrantha*
	integrifolia	SMad
	pilosa	EBee
	triplinervia B&SWJ 10413 new	WCru
	- B&SWJ 10696	WCru
§	- var. ***macrantha***	EBee ELon LHop

Bignonia (*Bignoniaceae*)

	capreolata	CCCN WCot WSHC XPep
§	- 'Atrosanguinea'	LRHS
	- 'Dragon Lady'	WCot
	lindleyana	see *Clytostoma calystegioides*
	tweedieana	see *Macfadyena unguis-cati*
	unguis-cati	see *Macfadyena unguis-cati*

Bilderdykia see *Fallopia*

Billardiera (*Pittosporaceae*)

	cymosa	SOWG
	longiflora ♀H3	More than 30 suppliers
	- 'Cherry Berry'	CBcs EBee ELan ERea IArd IDee LRHS MAsh MCCP NLar SBra SLim SPer SPoG SRms SWvt
	- ***fructu-albo***	CBcs CPLG EBee ELan EWes GGar IDee ITer SLim SPer SPoG
	- red-berried	GGar
	- white-berried	LRHS

Billbergia (*Bromeliaceae*)

	nutans	CHEx CHal CPen EBak EOHP EShb IBlr IDee LEdu MBri NPal SChr SRms WGwG XPep
	- var. ***schimperiana***	EShb
*	- 'Variegata' (v)	CHll CSpe EShb NPal SChr WCot WGwG
	pyramidalis ♀H1	XBlo
I	- 'Variegata' (v)	IBlr
	x ***windii*** hort. Jacob-Makoy ex E. Morren ♀H1	CHEx CHal EBak SRms

Bismarckia (*Arecaceae*)

	nobilis	EAmu LPal

Bistorta see *Persicaria*

blackberry see *Rubus fruticosus*

blackcurrant see *Ribes nigrum*

Blechnum (*Blechnaceae*)

	from Chile new	SKHP
	alpinum	see *B. penna-marina* subsp. *alpinum*
	auriculatum	WRic
	brasiliense ♀H1	WRic
	chambersii new	EFer
N	***chilense*** ♀H3	CAby CDes CGHE CHEx CLAP CWil EBee ECha EPfP GCra GGar IBlr NVic SAPC SArc SDix SKHP WAbe WMoo WPGP WRic
	discolor	CBcs CLAP CTrC IDee LPal WRic
	fluviatile	CBcs CLAP CTrC IDee SKHP WRic
	gibbum	MBri
	- 'Silver Lady' new	MPes WRic
	magellanicum misapplied	see *B. chilense*
	magellanicum (Desv.) Mett. new	SKHP WRic
	minus	MGos WRic
	novae-zelandiae	CBcs CDTJ CTrC WRic
	nudum	EPfP EQua NMoo WRic
	penna-marina ♀H4	CCCN CElw CLAP CPLG CWil EFer EMon EPot GAbr GGar GMaP LEdu MBri NRya NVic NWCA SDix SRms SRot WAbe WEas WFib WMoo WRic
§	- subsp. ***alpinum***	CLAP ECha GGar SKHP WAbe WMoo
	- 'Cristatum'	CLAP GAbr GGar SRms WAbe
	punctulatum	WRic
	spicant ♀H4	More than 30 suppliers
	tabulare misapplied	see *B. chilense*
N	***tabulare*** (Thunb.) Kuhn ♀H1	CBcs EPfP WPGP WRic
	vulcanicum	CLAP
	wattsii	EAmu

Blepharocalyx (*Myrtaceae*)

cruckshanksii CPLG LRHS
- 'Heaven Scent' LAst LRHS MCCP NLar WBor

Blephilia (*Lamiaceae*)

ciliata EBee MSal

Bletilla ✿ (*Orchidaceae*)

hyacinthina see *B. striata*
ochracea EBee LEdu NLAp
Penway Sunset gx WCot
sinensis new EBrs
§ ***striata*** CBct CDes CFwr CPom CTri EBee EBrs ECho ERea ERos GSki IHer LAma LEdu MSal NCGa NHol NLAp NMen SChr SHdy SMeo SPer WFar WPGP
- ***alba*** see *B. striata* var. *japonica* f. *gebina*
- 'Albostriata' CBct CDes CHHB EBee EBla EBrs ECho ELan EMan LAma NCGa NLAp NWCA WCot
- var. ***japonica*** EPot
§ - - f. ***gebina*** CAby CDes CHHB CMdw CMea CTri EBee EBrs ECho EPot GSki LAma LEdu LRHS NLar SChr WCot WFar WPGP
- - - variegated (v) LEdu NMen WCot
- variegated (v) CBow
- yellow-flowered CHHB EBrs
Yokohama gx EBla

Bloomeria (*Alliaceae*)

crocea ECho
- var. ***aurea*** CBgR EBee EBrs ECho ERos GKev LRHS
- var. ***montana*** ECho

blueberry see *Vaccinium corymbosum*

Blumenbachia (*Loasaceae*)

insignias EUnu

Bocconia (*Papaveraceae*)

cordata see *Macleaya cordata* (Willd.) R. Br.
microcarpa see *Macleaya microcarpa*

Boehmeria (*Urticaceae*)

nivea MSal
sylvatica NLar

Boenninghausenia (*Rutaceae*)

albiflora CSpe GKev MGol
- B&SWJ 1479 WCru
- BWJ 8141 from China new WCru
- pink-flowered B&SWJ 3112 WCru
japonica B&SWJ 4876 WCru

Boesenbergia (*Zingiberaceae*)

longiflora CKob

Bolandra (*Saxifragaceae*)

aff. ***californica*** EBee

Bolax (*Apiaceae*)

glebaria see *B. gummifer*
§ ***gummifer*** ECho EPot WAbe

Bolboschoenus (*Cyperaceae*)

§ ***maritimus*** CRWN GFor WFar

Boltonia (*Asteraceae*)

asteroides CFee CSam ECtt EHrv EMon GQue GSki LEdu NGdn NSti SPer STes SWat WBVN WCAu WDyG WRHF
- var. ***latisquama*** EBee EPPr GMaP LSou MAvo MRav MSte MWat NLar SSvw WBor WFar WHal WHil WWFP
- - 'Nana' EGoo MLLN MRav MWgw NBre STes WPer
- - 'Snowbank' EBee EBla ELan EWsh
- 'Pink Beauty' EBla EMon LEdu SPhx
- var. ***recognita*** EMon LRHS
decurrens EBee NBre
incisa see *Kalimeris incisa*
* ***richardsonii*** EBee

Bomarea (*Alstroemeriaceae*)

aff. ***acuminata*** B&SWJ 10617 new WCru
acutifolia B&SWJ 9094 WCru
boliviensis EBee WCru
- RCB/Arg P-18 WCot
caldasii ♀H1 CBcs CCCN CFir CHEx CRHN EBee LSou SOWG WBGC WBor WFoF WPGP WSHC
x ***cantabrigiensis*** new EBee
costaricensis B&SWJ 10467 new WCru
§ ***edulis*** CGHE CHEx CRHN EBee ERea EShb WCot WHil WPGP WSPU
- B&SWJ 9017 WCru
- F&M 104 WPGP
hirtella see *B. edulis*
isopetala SKHP
multiflora CFir EBee EShb SKHP
ovata ERea
patacocensis CPle SKHP
salsilla CCCN CRHN SBla SKHP WCot WCru WPGP WSHC

Bongardia (*Berberidaceae*)

chrysogonum CAvo EBee EBrs ECho EPot GCrs LRHS WHal

Bonia (*Poaceae*)

§ ***solida*** CBig CHEx ERod LPal MMoz MWht NPal SDry

borage see *Borago officinalis*

Borago (*Boraginaceae*)

alba MNHC
laxiflora see *B. pygmaea*
officinalis CArn CBod CSev CWan ELau EPfP GPoy LRHS MHer MNHC NGHP NVic SBch WCot WHer WSel
- 'Alba' CBre CSev ELau ILis NGHP SBch SDnm SIde WHer WJek
- 'Bill Archer' (v) CNat
§ ***pygmaea*** CArn CHid CPLG CSev ELan EMar EOHP LHop MHar MHer MTho NGHP NMRc NSti STes SWat WGwG WMoo

Borinda (*Poaceae*)

albocerea EPla ERod MWht SDry
- Yunnan 1 new WPGP
- Yunnan 2 new MMoz WPGP
- Yunnan 3a new WPGP
boliana EPla
edulis EPla
frigida EPla SDry WPGP
grossa (Yi) new EPla SDry
lushuiensis new EPla

macclureana **new**	EPla SDry
- KR 5177	WPGP
papyrifera	EPla MWht SDry
scabrida	CGHE EPla MMoz MWht SDry WPGP
- 'Asian Wonder' **new**	NLar

Boronia (*Rutaceae*)

citriodora	SOWG
denticulata	ECou
heterophylla	CBcs CCCN CPLG CSWP ECou IDee SOWG WGer
- white-flowered	ECou
megastigma	ECou
- 'Brown Meg'	CBcs
mollis	SOWG
pinnata	ECou SOWG
serrulata	ECou

Bothriochloa (*Poaceae*)

§ ***bladhii***	EPPr MAvo
caucasica	see *B. bladhii*
§ ***ischaemum***	CBig EPPr

Botryostege see *Tripetaleia*

Bougainvillea (*Nyctaginaceae*)

'Alexandra'	MBri
'Apple Blossom'	see *B.* 'Elizabeth Doxey'
'Audrey Grey'	see *B.* 'Elizabeth Doxey'
'Aussie Gold'	see *B.* 'Carson's Gold'
'Bridal Bouquet'	see *B.* 'Cherry Blossom'
'Brilliance'	ERea
'Brilliant' misapplied	see *B.* x *buttiana* 'Raspberry Ice'
x ***buttiana*** 'Ametyst'	MBri
- 'Asia'	ERea
- 'Audrey Grey'	see *B.* 'Elizabeth Doxey'
- 'Barbara Karst'	LPan SOWG
- 'Coconut Ice' (v)	SOWG
§ - 'Lady Mary Baring'	ERea SOWG
§ - 'Mahara' (d)	ERea SOWG
- 'Mahara Double Red'	see *B.* x *buttiana* 'Mahara'
- 'Mahara Off-white'	see *B.* 'Cherry Blossom'
- 'Mahara Pink'	see *B.* 'Los Banos Beauty'
§ - 'Mardi Gras' (v)	ERea
§ - 'Miss Manila'	ERea SOWG
§ - 'Mrs Butt' ♀H1	ERea
§ - 'Poultonii'	ERea
§ - 'Poulton's Special' ♀H1	ERea
§ - 'Raspberry Ice' (v)	ERea EShb SOWG
- 'Ratana Red' (v)	ERea
§ - 'Roseville's Delight' (d)	SOWG
§ - Texas Dawn = 'Monas'	ERea
- 'Tiggy'	ERea
§ Camarillo Fiesta = 'Monle' (*spectabilis* hybrid)	SOWG
§ 'Carson's Gold' (d)	ERea
§ 'Cherry Blossom'	ERea
§ 'Chiang Mai Beauty'	ERea
§ 'Closeburn'	ERea SOWG
'Crimson Lake' misapplied	see *B.* x *buttiana* 'Mrs Butt'
'Dauphine'	see *B.* 'Los Banos Beauty'
'David Lemmer'	ERea
'Double Yellow'	see *B.* 'Carson's Gold'
§ 'Elizabeth Angus'	ERea
§ 'Elizabeth Doxey'	SOWG
'Elizabeth' (*spectabilis* hybrid)	ERea
'Enchantment'	see *B.* (Spectoperuviana Group) 'Mary Palmer's Enchantment'
'Flamingo Pink'	see *B.* 'Chiang Mai Beauty'
'Floribunda'	ERea
glabra ♀H1	CMen ERea MBri XPep
§ - 'Harrissii' (v)	ERea
§ - 'Magnifica'	SOWG
- 'Magnifica Traillii'	ERea
- 'P J Weeping Beauty'	ERea
- 'Peggy Redman' (v)	ERea
§ - 'Pride of Singapore'	ERea
§ - 'Sanderiana'	ERea LCro LPan
'Gloucester Royal'	SOWG
'Glowing Flame' (v)	ERea
'Golden Doubloon'	see *B.* x *buttiana* 'Roseville's Delight'
'Golden Tango'	ERea
'Harrissii'	see *B. glabra* 'Harrissii'
'Hawaiian Scarlet'	see *B.* 'San Diego Red'
'James Walker'	ERea
'Kauai Royal'	see *B.* 'Elizabeth Angus'
'Klong Fire'	see *B.* x *buttiana* 'Mahara'
'Lady Mary Baring'	see *B.* x *buttiana* 'Lady Mary Baring'
'Lavender Girl'	ERea
'Limberlost Beauty'	see *B.* 'Cherry Blossom'
'Little Caroline'	SOWG
'Lord Willingdon' misapplied	see *B.* 'Torch Glow'
§ 'Los Banos Beauty' (d)	ERea
'Magnifica'	see *B. glabra* 'Magnifica'
'Mahara Double Red'	see *B.* x *buttiana* 'Mahara'
'Mahara Off-white'	see *B.* 'Cherry Blossom'
'Mahara Orange'	see *B.* x *buttiana* 'Roseville's Delight'
'Mahara Pink'	see *B.* 'Los Banos Beauty'
'Mahara White'	see *B.* 'Cherry Blossom'
'Manila Magic Red'	see *B.* x *buttiana* 'Mahara'
'Mardi Gras'	see *B.* x *buttiana* 'Mardi Gras'
'Mary Palmer's Enchantment'	see *B.* (Spectoperuviana Group) 'Mary Palmer's Enchantment'
'Mini-Thai'	see *B.* 'Torch Glow'
'Mrs Butt'	see *B.* x *buttiana* 'Mrs Butt'
* 'Orange Flame'	SOWG
'Orange Glow'	see *B.* Camarillo Fiesta = 'Monle'
'Orange Stripe' (v)	ERea
'Pagoda Pink'	see *B.* 'Los Banos Beauty'
'Penelope'	see *B.* (Spectoperuviana Group) 'Mary Palmer's Enchantment'
'Pink Champagne'	see *B.* 'Los Banos Beauty'
'Pixie'	see *B.* 'Torch Glow'
'Poultonii'	see *B.* x *buttiana* 'Poultonii'
'Poultonii Special'	see *B.* x *buttiana* 'Poulton's Special'
'Pride of Singapore'	see *B. glabra* 'Pride of Singapore'
'Princess Mahara'	see *B.* x *buttiana* 'Mahara'
'Purple Robe'	ERea
'Raspberry Ice'	see *B.* x *buttiana* 'Raspberry Ice'
'Red Diamond'	ERea
'Red Fantasy' (v)	ERea
'Reggae Gold' (v)	MJnS
'Robyn's Glory'	see *B.* x *buttiana* Texas Dawn = 'Monas'
'Rubyana'	ERea SOWG
§ 'San Diego Red'	ERea SOWG
'Sanderiana'	see *B. glabra* 'Sanderiana'
Scarlett O'Hara	see *B.* 'San Diego Red'
'Smartipants'	see *B.* 'Torch Glow'
spectabilis 'Speciosa Floribunda'	ERea
Spectoperuviana Group (v)	ERea
§ - 'Mary Palmer's Enchantment'	ERea
- 'Mrs H.C. Buck'	ERea
'Tango'	see *B.* x *buttiana* 'Miss Manila'
'Temple Fire'	see *B.* 'Closeburn'
'Thai Gold'	see *B.* x *buttiana* 'Roseville's Delight'
§ 'Torch Glow'	EAmu
'Tropical Rainbow'	see *B.* x *buttiana* 'Raspberry Ice'
'Variegata'	see *B. glabra* 'Harrissii'
'Vera Blakeman'	ERea MJnS SOWG
'Wac Campbell' (d)	SOWG

Boussingaultia (*Basellaceae*)

	baselloides Hook.	see *Anredera cordifolia*

Bouteloua (*Poaceae*)

	curtipendula	CBig CRWN CSam EBee GFor LRav XIsg
§	***gracilis***	CAby CBig CHrt CSam EBee EQua EWsh GFor MBNS SWal WPGP WPer XIsg XPep
	hirsuta	XIsg

Bouvardia (*Rubiaceae*)

	x ***domestica***	EShb
	longiflora	ERea SOWG
	ternifolia	WCot

Bowiea (*Hyacinthaceae*)

	volubilis	CHal EBee EBrs EShb

Bowkeria (*Scrophulariaceae*)

	citrina	CPle
	cymosa	SPlb
	verticillata	CPLG

Boykinia (*Saxifragaceae*)

	aconitifolia	CAbP EBee EBla GBuc GGar MLLN MRav NLar NRya NSum SMad WCru WMoo WPnP WSHC
	elata	see *B. occidentalis*
	heucheriformis	see *B. jamesii*
§	***jamesii***	CGra CPLG GEdr GKev NWCA
	lycoctonifolia new	CPLG EBee
	major	CPLG EBee WBor
§	***occidentalis***	GGar WCru WMoo
	rotundifolia	EBee GBuc NBir WCru WMoo WPnP
	- JLS 86269LACA	EMon
	tellimoides	see *Peltoboykinia tellimoides*

boysenberry see *Rubus* 'Boysenberry'

Brachychilum see *Hedychium*

Brachychiton (*Sterculiaceae*)

	acerifolius	CHEx EShb
	discolor	EShb
§	***rupestris***	EShb

Brachyelytrum (*Poaceae*)

	japonicum	GFor LRav NLar

Brachyglottis ✿ (*Asteraceae*)

§	***bidwillii***	IDee SDry WGer
	- 'Basil Fox'	WAbe
§	***buchananii***	SDry WSHC
	- 'Silver Shadow'	GGar
§	***compacta***	ECou EPfP LRHS MAsh SDry SPer SPoG WEas
	compacta x ***monroi***	ECou LRHS
	'County Park'	ECou
	'Drysdale'	ELan EPfP GGar LRHS MAsh MBri MRav NPri SDry SPoG SRGP SWvt
§	(Dunedin Group) 'Moira Reid' (v)	CPLG EBee EGoo SDry
§	- 'Sunshine' ♀H4	More than 30 suppliers
	'Frosty'	ECou
	greyi misapplied	see *B.* (Dunedin Group) 'Sunshine'
§	***greyi*** (Hook. f.) B. Nord.	CTrG EBee EPfP MBar
	greyi x ***repanda***	CDoC CHEx EWin GGar SAPC SArc SKHP
	huntii x ***stewartii*** new	GGar
	laxifolia misapplied	see *B.* (Dunedin Group) 'Sunshine'
	'Leith's Gold'	CTrC
§	***monroi*** ♀H4	CBcs CSBt CWib EBee ECou EGoo ELan EPfP GGar LAst MLLN MRav SLon SPoG WEas XPep
	- 'Clarence'	ECou
	repanda	CBcs CHEx CTrG
§	***rotundifolia***	CBcs CCCN CDoC GGar IClo NLar WEas WGer
	'Silver Waves'	ECou
§	***spedenii***	GGar
I	'Sunshine Improved'	SWvt WSPU
	'Sunshine Variegated'	see *B.* (Dunedin Group) 'Moira Reid'
	Walberton's Silver Dormouse = 'Walbrach'	LBuc MAsh SPoG

Brachypodium (*Poaceae*)

	pinnatum	EBee
	retusum	XPep
	sylvaticum	CBig EHul GFor LBBr NNor XIsg

Brachyscome (*Asteraceae*)

	formosa	ECou
	'Lemon Drops'	SPet
	'Lemon Mist'	LAst
	'Mini Yellow'	NPri
	multifida	MBri NPri
	'Pink Mist'	LAst SPet
	rigidula	ECou
	'Strawberry Mousse'	CWsd LAst SPet
	'Tinkerbell'	LSou NPri SPoG SVil

Brachysema (*Papilionaceae*)

	celsianum	SOWG

Brachystachyum (*Poaceae*)

	densiflorum	EPla NLar SDry

Brachystelma (*Asclepiadaceae*)

	angustum new	LToo
	bracteolatum new	LToo
	caffrum new	LToo
	circinatum new	LToo
	dinteri new	LToo
	filifolium new	LToo
	foetidum new	LToo
	nanum new	LToo

Bracteantha see *Xerochrysum*

Brahea (*Arecaceae*)

	armata	CAbb CBrP EAmu EPfP EShb ETod LPal MGos MPRe NPal SAPC SAin SArc SChr SPer
	brandegeei	SAin
	dulcis new	EAmu
	edulis	CBrP EAmu LPal SAin

Brassaia see *Schefflera*

Brassica (*Brassicaceae*)

	japonica	see *B. juncea* var. *crispifolia*
§	***juncea*** var. ***crispifolia***	CArn MNHC
	nigra	CArn
	oleracea	WHer
*	***rapa*** var. ***japonica***	CArn WJek
*	- var. ***purpurea***	WJek

Bravoa (*Agavaceae*)

	geminiflora	see *Polianthes geminiflora*

Bretschneidera (*Bretschneideraceae*)

	sinensis new	CExc

Brillantaisia (*Acanthaceae*)

	subulugurica	CCCN EShb GFai

Brimeura (*Hyacinthaceae*)

§ ***amethystina*** ♀^{H4}	CAvo CBgR CPLG CPom EBrs ECho ERos GBin GCrs GKev MSte NWCA SMeo SPhx WCot WRHF
- 'Alba'	CAvo EBrs ECho EPfP ERos GKev MSte SMeo SPhx
§ ***fastigiata***	ERos

Briza (*Poaceae*)

maxima	CEnt CHrt CKno CTri EGoo EPla LEdu LHop MFOX MWgw NGdn NSti SBch WHal WHer WRos
media	More than 30 suppliers
- 'Limouzi'	CElw CFir CFwr CKno EAlp EBee EGle EGoo EHrv EMon EPPr LRHS MAvo MBri NSti SDys SMad SPoG WPrP
- 'Russells' **new**	CKno GBin LLWG NChi SHom
minor	WRos
subaristata	EBee EPPr LRHS MAvo NLar WHrl
triloba	EWes EWsh GBin LBBr MMHG WGwG WPrP WRos

Brodiaea (*Alliaceae*)

§ ***californica***	CBgR EBee EBrs ECho ERos NMen WCot
- NNS 00-108	WCot
capitata	see *Dichelostemma capitatum*
coronaria	CPBP WCot
'Corrina'	see *Triteleia* 'Corrina'
elegans	ERos WCot
ida-maia	see *Dichelostemma ida-maia*
jolonensis	ERos
laxa	see *Triteleia laxa*
§ ***minor***	WCot
pallida	WCot
peduncularis	see *Triteleia peduncularis*
purdyi	see *B. minor*
terrestris subsp. ***kernensis*** NNS 98-88	WCot

Bromus (*Poaceae*)

inermis 'Skinner's Gold' (v)	CHrt EAlp EBee EHul EMil EPPr EWes LLWG NLar NSti SPer SPoG WCot XIsg
lanatus B&SWJ 10698 **new**	WCru
secalinus **new**	XIsg

Broussonetia (*Moraceae*)

kazinoki	CArn CBcs EBee IDee NLar WPGP
papyrifera	CAbP CAgr CBcs CDoC CDul CMCN ELan IDee MBri SMad SPer WPGP
- 'Laciniata'	MBri NLar

Browallia (*Solanaceae*)

from Sikkim **new**	CSpe

Bruckenthalia see *Erica*

Brugmansia ✿ (*Solanaceae*)

'Apricot Goldilocks'	WVaB
'Apricot Queen'	MJnS
§ ***arborea***	CArn CDTJ CHEx SRms WVaB
§ - 'Knightii' (d) ♀^{H1}	CDTJ CHal ELan EPfP ERea LRHS MJnS SOWG WVaB
aurea	CCCN CHEx LRHS SAdn WVaB
'Baby Orange'	WVaB
'Butterfly'	WVaB
'Canary Bird'	MJnS
x ***candida***	CCCN CHEx ERea WVaB
- 'Angel's Flight' (d) **new**	WVaB
- 'Angel's Wings' (d) **new**	WVaB
- 'Culebra'	WVaB
- 'Flowerdream' (d) **new**	WVaB
§ - 'Grand Marnier' ♀^{H1}	CDTJ CHEx CHll ECot ELan EPfP ERea MJnS SOWG WVaB
- 'Maya'	MJnS WVaB
- 'Mon Amoure M' (d)	ERea MJnS WVaB
- 'Ocre'	WVaB
- 'Plena'	see *B. arborea* 'Knightii'
- 'Primrose'	ERea
- 'Salmon Perfektion' (d) **new**	WVaB
- 'Super Spot' **new**	WVaB
- 'Tiara' (d)	WVaB
§ - 'Variegata' (v)	CCCN CDTJ CKob CSam ERea MJnS WVaB
'Cerise Wonder' **new**	WVaB
'Charming'	WVaB
§ ***chlorantha***	CBcs
'Citronella'	WVaB
x ***cubensis*** 'Charles Grimaldi'	CSam WVaB
'Dark Rosetta'	MJnS WVaB
'Desirée' (d)	MJnS
'Double Apricot' (d) **new**	MJnS
'Flowerdream' (d) **new**	MJnS
'Frosty Pink'	WVaB
'Full Rosea Magic' (d)	MJnS WVaB
'Gilbert Reiss'	WVaB
'Golden Cornet'	MJnS
'Golden Lady' (d)	WVaB
'Golden Pausanne'	WVaB
'Goldrichter'	WVaB
'Herrenhäuser Gärten'	MJnS WVaB
'Herzenbrucke'	ERea MJnS
'Igea Pink'	CSam WVaB
§ x ***insignis***	CHll
- 90-95	WVaB
- 'Glockenfontäne'	WVaB
- 'Pink'	CTrG
- 'Pink Delight'	WVaB
§ - pink-flowered	CHEx EPfP
'Jacob'	WVaB
'Jean Pasko'	WVaB
'Kurfurst Ernst August'	WVaB
'Logee's Orange'	WVaB
'Loreley'	WVaB
'Madeira'	WVaB
'Marrakesch'	WVaB
meteloides	see *Datura inoxia*
'Mia'	WVaB
'Milk and Honey'	WVaB
'Mobishu'	EShb
'Morgensonne' **new**	MJnS WVaB
'Pink Lady'	MJnS
pink-flowered	WFar
'Pride of Hanover'	WVaB
'Rosabelle'	WVaB
'Rosalie'	WVaB
rosei	see *B. sanguinea* subsp. *sanguinea* var. *flava*
'Rosenrot'	WVaB
'Rosie'	WVaB
'Roter Vulkan'	WVaB
'Rothkirch'	WVaB
§ ***sanguinea***	CBcs CCCN CHEx CHll EShb IDee MSal SOWG
- 'Feuerwerk'	WVaB
- red-flowered	CHEx
- 'Rosea'	see *B.* x *insignis* pink-flowered
- 'Sangre'	WVaB
§ - subsp. ***sanguinea*** var. ***flava***	CHEx WVaB
- 'White Flame'	WVaB
'Shredded White Fantasy' (d)	WVaB

§ ***suaveolens*** ♀H1	CHEx CHll ELan ERea LCro SPlb WVaB
- pink-flowered	EShb WVaB
- ***rosea***	see *B.* x *insignis* pink-flowered
- 'Variegata' (v)	CKob EShb
- yellow-flowered	EShb
suaveolens x ***versicolor***	see *B.* x *insignis*
'Sunrise'	MJnS
'Variegata Sunset'	see *B.* x *candida* 'Variegata'
versicolor misapplied	see *B. arborea*
§ ***versicolor*** Lagerh.	CCCN ERea SOWG WVaB
- 'Ecuador Pink'	EPfP ERea MJnS WVaB
- 'Lachs'	WVaB
'White Marble'	WVaB
* 'Yellow Trumpet'	EPfP
yellow-flowered	WFar

Brunfelsia (*Solanaceae*)

americana	CCCN EShb SOWG
calycina	see *B. pauciflora*
jamaicensis	SOWG
lactea	CCCN
nitida	ERea
§ ***pauciflora*** ♀H1	ELan LRHS MBri
- 'Floribunda'	ERea SOWG
- 'Macrantha'	ERea SOWG

Brunia (*Bruniaceae*)

albiflora	SPlb

Brunnera (*Boraginaceae*)

§ ***macrophylla*** ♀H4	More than 30 suppliers
- 'Agnes Amez' **new**	CLAP
- 'Alba'	see *B. macrophylla* 'Betty Bowring'
§ - 'Betty Bowring'	More than 30 suppliers
- 'Blaukuppel'	CLAP EBee EBla EMar EMon EWes GBin LRHS NCob NDov WFar
§ - 'Dawson's White' (v)	More than 30 suppliers
- 'Gordano Gold' (v)	CBow WCot WHal
- 'Hadspen Cream' (v) ♀H4	More than 30 suppliers
- 'Jack Frost'PBR ♀H4	More than 30 suppliers
- 'Langford Hewitt' (v)	MNrw
- 'Langtrees'	More than 30 suppliers
- 'Looking Glass'	More than 30 suppliers
- 'Marley's Ghost' **new**	NCot
- 'Marley's White'	CElw CLAP CMea EBee EGle EHrv GKev NCob NDov WCot
- 'Silver Wings'	CElw EBee NLar
- 'Variegata'	see *B. macrophylla* 'Dawson's White'
sibirica	CDes CLAP EBee EMon EWes GBin

Brunsvigia (*Amaryllidaceae*)

pulchra **new**	WCot
radulosa	WCot
rosea 'Minor'	see *Amaryllis belladonna*

Bryonia (*Cucurbitaceae*)

dioica	GPoy MSal

Bryophyllum see *Kalanchoe*

Buchloe (*Poaceae*)

dactyloides	CBig CRWN XIsg

Buddleja ✿ (*Buddlejaceae*)

HCM 98.017 from Chile	WPGP
agathosma	SLon WEas WKif WLav WPGP WSHC XPep
albiflora	SLon WLav
alternifolia ♀H4	More than 30 suppliers
- 'Argentea'	CBcs CDoC CPMA CPle EBee ELan EPfP LRHS MAsh MBNS MRav NLar NSti SHBN SMad SPer SPla SPoG SRGP SSpi WCot WHCG WLav WPat WSHC XPep
asiatica ♀H2	CPLG ERea EShb SLon WLav
- B&SWJ 7214	WCru
auriculata	CBcs CBgR CMCN CPLG CPSs CTca CWib EBee EPfP ERea EShb LAst LRHS MRav NSti SAga SDix SLon SOWG SPoG WBor WCru WHCG WLav WPGP XPep
* 'Blue Trerice'	CPLG
* 'Butterfly Ball'	SLon
caryopteridifolia	EBee SLon
colvilei	CDoC CPle EPfP ERas IDee LAst MBri MRav SDnm SKHP WAbe WBor WSpi
- B&SWJ 2121	WCru
- GWJ 9399	WCru
- 'Kewensis'	CBcs CPLG CRHN CSam EBee EWes GCra LAst NEgg NLar NSti SKHP SLon WBod WCru WCwm WLav WPGP WSHC WSpi
cordata	SLon
coriacea	SLon
§ ***crispa***	CBcs CBgR CPSs CPle CSpe EBee ECha ELan EPfP EShb LRHS SAga SDnm SDry SHBN SLon SOWG SPer SRkn SSpi WEas WFar WHCG WKif WPGP WSHC WSpi XPep
- var. ***farreri***	CPLG CPle MSte SOWG
crotonoides amplexicaulis	SLon
curviflora f. ***venenifera***	SLon
- - B&SWJ 6036	WCru
davidii	CArn GWCH NWea SGar SHFr STre
- B&SWJ 8083	WCru
- Adonis Blue = 'Adokeep'PBR	ENot WWeb
- 'African Queen'	SLon SRGP
- var. ***alba***	CWib SHBN
- 'Beijing'	SLon WSFF
- 'Black Knight' ♀H4	More than 30 suppliers
- 'Blue Horizon'	CSam SEND SLon SRGP WCot WLav WMoo WRHF
- 'Border Beauty'	SLon
- Camberwell Beauty = 'Camkeep'	ENot
- 'Castle School'	CSam
§ - 'Charming'	CDul WMoo WSHC WWlt
- 'Croyde'	CSam
- 'Dartmoor' ♀H4	More than 30 suppliers
- 'Dart's Ornamental White'	MRav
- 'Dart's Papillon Blue'	SLPl
- 'Dubonnet'	SLon WLav
- 'Empire Blue' ♀H4	CBcs CDoC CDul CSBt EBee ECrN ECtt EPfP LAst LRHS MAsh MBri MGan MGos MNHC MRav NPer NWea SPer SPlb SRGP SRms WFar WTel WWeb WWlt
- 'Fascinating'	MGan MRav WLav
- 'Flaming Violet'	SLon WLav
- 'Florence'	NLar SBra WFar WMoo
- 'Glasnevin Hybrid'	NSti SAga SDix WLav
- 'Gonglepod'	SLon
- 'Harlequin' (v)	More than 30 suppliers
- 'Ile de France'	CBcs CWib MGos NWea SLon SRms WLav
- Marbled White = 'Markeep' **new**	ENot
- Masquerade = 'Notbud'PBR (v)	ENot MBri MGos MRav SLon WGor
§ - 'Nanho Blue' ♀H4	More than 30 suppliers
- 'Nanho Petite Indigo'	see *B. davidii* 'Nanho Blue'
- 'Nanho Petite Plum'	see *B. davidii* 'Nanho Purple'

- 'Nanho Petite Purple'	see *B. davidii* 'Nanho Purple'
§ - 'Nanho Purple' ♀H4	CDoC CMHG CTri CWib EBee ELan EPfP LRHS LSRN MAsh MBar MGos MRav NBlu NLar SLim SLon SPer SPla SPlb SPoG SRGP WHar
- Nanho White = 'Monite'	ELan EPfP MBar SPer SRms WFar WWeb
- var. ***nanhoensis***	CDul CHrt EBee SEND SIde WHCG WLav
- - blue-flowered	SLon SPer
- Operette = 'Courtabud'	NBlu
- 'Orchid Beauty'	WBod WLav
- 'Orpheus'	WLav
- 'Peace'	CChe CDoC CPLG CTri EBee EPfP MBri MRav SPoG WLav
- Peacock = 'Peakeep'PBR	ENot
- 'Petite Indigo'	see *B. davidii* 'Nanho Blue'
- 'Pink Beauty'	CEnt LAst SHBN SRGP WHCG
- 'Pink Charming'	see *B. davidii* 'Charming'
- 'Pink Pearl'	SEND SLon WLav
- 'Pink Spreader'	SLon
- 'Pixie Blue'	LAst LBMP MAsh NBlu NLar SRGP WWeb
- 'Pixie Red'	LBMP MAsh NLar NPri WWeb
- 'Pixie White'	MAsh MBNS NBlu NLar SRGP WLav
- Purple Emperor = 'Pyrkeep'	ENot
- 'Purple Friend'	WLav
- 'Red Admiral' **new**	LRHS SPoG
- 'Royal Purple'	SLim
- 'Royal Red' ♀H4	More than 30 suppliers
- 'Santana' (v)	CDul EWes LHop LRHS MGos MRav MWea NBlu NLar SAga SPoG WCot WMoo WPat WSpi
- 'Summer Beauty'	CWib MGos MRav SLon WLav
- 'Variegata' (v)	LRHS SMrm WLav WSFF
- var. ***veitchiana***	CPLG
- 'White Ball'	EPfP LRHS MBNS NEgg NLar SLon
- 'White Bouquet'	CCVT CEnt CSBt EBee EPfP EWTr LAst MAsh MHer MNHC MSwo NWea SEND SMer SPer SRGP SReu WBod WLav WTel
- 'White Butterfly'	SLon
- 'White Cloud'	CBgR ECrN GQui MGos SRms WGwG
- 'White Harlequin' (v)	WCFE WEas
- 'White Profusion' ♀H4	CBcs CDul CSam CTca EBee ECtt ELan EPfP LCro LRHS MBar MDun MGan MGos MLHP MRav NBlu NWea SHBN SLim SPla SWvt WBVN WBod WCFE WEas WFar WHCG WHar WMoo
- 'White Wings'	SLon WLav
§ ***delavayi***	CPLG NLar WCru
fallowiana misapplied	see *B.* 'West Hill'
fallowiana Balf. f.	ELan EWTr LRHS WLav
- ACE 2481	LRHS
- BWJ 7803	WCru
- var. ***alba*** ♀H3	CDoC EBee ECrN ELan EPfP LRHS MRav NLar NSti SLon SPer SPoG WAbe WEas WFar WPGP WSHC WWeb XPep
forrestii	CRHN WCru
globosa ♀H4	More than 30 suppliers
- RCB/Arg C-11	WCot
- 'Lemon Ball'	NPer WLav
glomerata	EBee EShb XPep
heliophila	see *B. delavayi*
indica	SLon WBor
japonica B&SWJ 8912	WCru
'Leela Kapila'	MAsh MGos
x ***lewisiana*** 'Margaret Pike'	SLon SOWG
limitanea	SLon
lindleyana	More than 30 suppliers
'Lochinch' ♀H3-4	More than 30 suppliers
loricata	CBgR CFis CPle CWib EBee EShb GQui IDee MSte SGar SKHP SLon SOWG SPlb SSpi WCFE WEas WLav WPGP XPep
macrostachya	WPGP
- HWJ 602	WCru
§ ***madagascariensis*** ♀H1	CRHN EShb SGar SOWG WCot XPep
marrubiifolia	XPep
megalocephala B&SWJ 9106	WCru
§ 'Morning Mist'	EMil LBuc MAsh NLar SLon SPoG
myriantha	XPep
* - f. ***fragrans***	EBee WCot
nappii	SLon
nicodemia	see *B. madagascariensis*
nivea	CMCN CPLG SOWG WLav XPep
- B&SWJ 2679	WCru
- pink-flowered	SLon
- var. ***yunnanensis***	MSte WCFE
- - B&SWJ 8146	WCru
officinalis ♀H2	CPLG CTca ERea XPep
paniculata	SLon
parvifolia MPF 148	WLav
'Pink Delight' ♀H4	More than 30 suppliers
'Pink Perfection'	WFar
saligna	CPle SLon XPep
'Salmon Spheres'	SKHP
salviifolia	CBcs CBgR CPLG CRHN CSWP CSam CTca CTrG EBee ELan EShb GGar GQui IDee LAst NSti SDnm SDry SWal WAbe WGwG WHer WLav XPep
- white-flowered	CRHN
Silver Anniversary	see *B.* 'Morning Mist'
stachyoides	SLon
stenostachya	CPLG
sterniana	see *B. crispa*
tibetica	see *B. crispa*
tubiflora	CPLG SLon SOWG WLav
venenifera B&SWJ 895	WCru
§ 'West Hill'	SLon SRGP WLav
x ***weyeriana***	CBgR CDul CRHN CSam EBee ECtt EPfP GQui IFoB MGos MNrw MSwo NBir SGar SPlb SWvt WBVN WBor WBrE WFar WHCG WLav WMoo WTel
- 'Golden Glow' (v)	CBow CSBt CTri ECrN EPfP LSRN SLon SPoG WLav WSFF
- 'Honeycomb' **new**	EShb
- 'Lady de Ramsey'	SEND WPer
- 'Moonlight'	CPLG SLon WCot WLav WSel
- 'Sungold' ♀H4	More than 30 suppliers
'Winter Sun'	SLon

Buglossoides (*Boraginaceae*)

§ ***purpurocaerulea***	CCge CHll CMHG CPom CSpe CWGN EBee ECha ELan EMan EMar LHop MLHP MSal MSte NBid WAul WCot WFar WSHC

Bukiniczia (*Plumbaginaceae*)

cabulica	CSpe WCot

Bulbine (*Asphodelaceae*)

annua misapplied	see *B. semibarbata*
bulbosa misapplied	see *B. semibarbata*
caulescens	see *B. frutescens*
§ ***frutescens***	CHll EWll WBrk WJek WPrP XPep
- 'Hallmark'	XPep
latifolia	EShb
§ ***semibarbata***	CCCN CPom

Bulbinella (*Asphodelaceae*)

angustifolia	ECho GCrs WCot

cauda-felis	WCot
eburnifolia	WCot
elata	WCot
floribunda	IBlr
gibbsii var. ***balanifera***	ECho GCrs
hookeri	CPom CWsd EBee ECou EUnu GCrs GEdr GGar GKev ITim NChi NDlv NLAp NWCA SRms WHal
nutans	CDes ECho
setosa var. ***latifolia***	CPne

Bulbinopsis see *Bulbine*

Bulbocodium (*Colchicaceae*)

vernum	CStu EBrs ECho EPot ERos GKev LAma MBri NHol NMin
- white-flowered	ECho

bullace see *Prunus insititia*

Bunias (*Brassicaceae*)

orientalis	CAgr EUnu MSal

Bunium (*Apiaceae*)

bulbocastanum	CAgr EUnu LEdu

Buphthalmum (*Asteraceae*)

salicifolium	CHrt CPLG CSam CSev EBee ELan EPfP LAst MBri MNFA MRav NBlu NBro NGdn SHGN SMer SPer SRms SWat WCAu WCot WFar WPer
- 'Alpengold'	ECha EShb GMaP NBre NLar
- 'Dora'	EMan WCot
- 'Sunwheel'	EWll LRHS NBre NPri SRms
speciosum	see *Telekia speciosa*

Bupleurum (*Apiaceae*)

angulosum	CDes CPom EBee NChi SBla SMrm WFar
- copper	see *B. longifolium*
benoistii	SBla
candollei GWJ 9405	WCru
falcatum	CArn CElw ECha EMan EPPr MFOX MLLN MSal NDov NLar SBri SPur WCot WFar
fruticosum	CBcs CPLG CPle CSpe EBee ECGP ECtt EPfP LHop LRHS SDix SDnm SMad SSpi SSta WCot WEas WPGP WPat WSHC WSpi XPep
gibraltaricum **new**	EBee EMan WCot
* ***griffithii***	MSal
- 'Decor'	CSpe
§ ***longifolium***	CElw CFee CPom CSpe EBee ECha EGle EWes GBin GBuc LRHS MDKP MFOX MNrw NCGa NChi NLar SBri SMrm WCot WHal WHoo
- short bronze	WCru
- subsp. ***aureum***	MAvo NChi NGby SPhx
- bronze-leaved	LSou MBNS
longiradiatum B&SWJ 729	WCru
ranunculoides	NLar
rotundifolium	MSal
- 'Copper'	MAvo NDov
spinosum	NLar SMad
stellatum	WBVN
tenue	CArn
- B&SWJ 2973	WCru

Bursaria (*Pittosporaceae*)

spinosa	CCCN ECou EShb NLar

butternut see *Juglans cinerea*

Butia (*Arecaceae*)

bonnetii	ETod
capitata	CAbb CBcs CBrP CCCN CHEx CPHo CTrC EAmu ETod LPJP LPal LPan MGos NPal SAPC SAin SArc SBLw SChr
eriospatha	EAmu ETod
yatay	EAmu ETod LPal

Butomus (*Butomaceae*)

umbellatus ♀H4	CBen CDWL CRWN CWat ECha ECtt EHon EMFW EPfP MCCP MRav NPer NSco SWat WFar WMAq WMoo WPnP WTin
- 'Rosenrot'	LLWG
- 'Schneeweisschen'	LLWG NLar WPnP

Buxus ✿ (*Buxaceae*)

aurea 'Marginata'	see *B. sempervirens* 'Marginata'
balearica ♀H4	EPla EQua IDee SDry SLan SLon WPGP WSPU XPep
bodinieri	EPla EQua SLan
- 'David's Gold'	WPen
colchica **new**	SLan
'Glencoe'	SLan
'Green Gem'	NGHP NHol SLan WSel
'Green Mound'	SLan
'Green Mountain'	SLan
'Green Velvet'	EPfP NHol SLan STop
harlandii hort.	EPla SLan SRiv
- 'Richard'	SLan STre
henryi	MBri
japonica 'Nana'	see *B. microphylla*
macowanii	SLan WSpi
§ ***microphylla***	CSWP MHer NHol NWea SIng SLan STre WSpi
- 'Asiatic Winter'	see *B. microphylla* var. *japonica* 'Winter Gem'
§ - 'Compacta'	NLAp SLan SRiv WCot WPat
- 'Curly Locks'	EPla MHer SLan
- 'Faulkner'	CCVT EBee ELan EPfP EQua LBuc LHop LPan LRHS MBNS MBlu MGos NHol SLan SPoG SRiv STop WSpi
- Golden Dream = 'Peergold'PBR **new**	SPoG
- 'Golden Triumph'PBR	SLan SPoG
- 'Grace Hendrick Phillips'	SLan
- 'Green Pillow'	SLan SRiv WSpi
- 'Helen Whiting'	SLan
- 'Henry Hohman'	SLan
- 'Herrenhausen'	LPan SLan
- var. ***insularis***	see *B. sinica* var. *insularis*
- var. ***japonica*** 'Belvédère' **new**	SLan
- - 'Gold Dust'	SLan
- - 'Green Beauty' **new**	SLan
- - 'Green Jade'	SLan
- - 'Jim Stauffer'	SLan
- - 'Morris Dwarf'	SLan
- - 'Morris Midget'	IArd NHol SLan
- - 'National'	MHer SLan WPGP
- - 'Sunnyside'	SLan
- - 'Trompenburg'	SLan
§ - - 'Winter Gem'	ENot MHer MRav NLar SLPl SLan
- - f. ***yakushima***	SLan
- 'John Baldwin'	SLan SRiv STop
- 'Kagushima'	SLan
- var. ***koreana***	see *B. sinica* var. *insularis*
- 'Quiet End'	SLan
- var. ***riparia***	see *B. riparia*
- var. ***sinica***	see *B. sinica*
- 'Winter Gem'	see *B. microphylla* var. *japonica* 'Winter Gem'

	'Newport Blue'	see *B. sempervirens* 'Newport Blue'
§	***riparia***	EPla SLan
	rugulosa	SLan
	sempervirens ♀H4	More than 30 suppliers
	- 'Abilene' **new**	SLan
	- 'Agram'	SLan
	- 'Anderson'	SLan
§	- 'Angustifolia'	EPla MGos MHer NHol SLan SMad
	- 'Arborescens'	EQua LPan
	- 'Argentea'	see *B. sempervirens* 'Argenteo-variegata'
§	- 'Argenteo-variegata' (v)	EPfP IFoB MRav NGHP SLan WFar
	- 'Aristocrat' **new**	SLan
	- 'Aurea'	see *B. sempervirens* 'Aureovariegata'
	- 'Aurea Maculata'	see *B. sempervirens* 'Aureovariegata'
	- 'Aurea Marginata'	see *B. sempervirens* 'Marginata'
	- 'Aurea Pendula' (v)	CPMA EPla SLan SLon
§	- 'Aureovariegata' (v)	CBcs CSBt ECrN EPfP ISea MAsh MBar MGan MGos MHer MNHC MRav NHol NSti SLan SMer SPer SRiv WFar WMoo WTel
	- 'Belleville'	SLan
	- 'Bentley Blue'	NHol
	- 'Berlin' **new**	SLan
	- 'Blauer Heinz'	ELan EMil LPan LRHS MHer SLPl SLan SRiv STop WSel WSpi
	- 'Blue Belle'	SLan
§	- 'Blue Cone'	CHar NHol
	- 'Blue Spire'	see *B. sempervirens* 'Blue Cone'
	- 'Bowles' Blue'	EQua SLan
	- 'Bullata' **new**	SLan
	- 'Claverton'	SLan
	- clipped ball	CWib EPfP LPan MGos MWgw NBlu NGHP NLar SLan SLim SRiv WFar
	- clipped cone	LPan
	- clipped pyramid	CWib EPfP LPan MGos MWgw NBlu NGHP NLar SLan SLim SRiv
	- clipped spiral	LPan NBlu SLan SLim SRiv
	- 'Crossley'	SLan
	- 'Dee Runk'	SLan
	- 'Denmark' **new**	SLan
	- 'Egremont'	SLan
	- 'Elegans'	SMer
§	- 'Elegantissima' (v) ♀H4	More than 30 suppliers
	- 'Emir'	SLan
	- 'Fiesta'	SLan
	- 'Fleur de Lys' **new**	SLan
	- 'Glauca'	SLan
	- 'Gold Tip'	see *B. sempervirens* 'Notata'
	- 'Golden Frimley' (v)	LHop
§	- 'Graham Blandy'	MHer NHol SLan SRiv STop WSpi
	- 'Grand Rapids' **new**	SLan
	- 'Green Balloon'	LBuc SLan
	- 'Greenpeace'	see *B. sempervirens* 'Graham Blandy'
	- 'Haller' **new**	SLan
	- 'Handsworthiensis'	CTca EBee ECrN LPan NHol SEND SLan SPer STop
	- 'Handsworthiensis' blue	SLan
	- 'Handsworthii'	CTri NWea SRms
	- 'Henry Shaw' **new**	SLan
	- 'Hermann von Schrenk'	SLan
	- 'Holland'	SLan
	- subsp. ***hyrcana***	SLan
	- 'Ickworth Giant'	SLan STop
	- 'Inglis'	SLan
	- 'Ingrid'	SLan
	- 'Inverewe'	SLan
	- 'Ipek'	SLan
	- 'Japonica Aurea'	see *B. sempervirens* 'Latifolia Maculata'
	- 'Kensington Gardens'	SLan WSpi
	- 'King Midas' **new**	SLan
	- 'Kingsville'	see *B. microphylla* 'Compacta'
	- 'Kingsville Dwarf'	see *B. microphylla* 'Compacta'
	- 'Krakow'	NLar
	- 'Lace'	NSti SLan
§	- 'Langley Beauty'	SLan
	- 'Langley Pendula'	see *B. sempervirens* 'Langley Beauty'
	- 'Latifolia Macrophylla'	SLan SLon SPoG WSel
§	- 'Latifolia Maculata' (v) ♀H4	CAbP CChe CDoC CWib EBee EPfP EPla LRHS MNHC NEgg NGHP NHol NPer SEND SLan SPoG SRiv STop STre WJek WSpi
*	- 'Latifolia Pendula'	NHol SLan
	- 'Linda' **new**	SLan
	- 'Longifolia'	see *B. sempervirens* 'Angustifolia'
§	- 'Marginata' (v)	CBrm ECtt EPla IFoB LHop MHer MRav MWgw SHBN SHFr SLan SLon SPer WBrE WHar WSel WSpi
	- 'Mary Gamble'	SLan
	- 'Memorial'	MHer NHol SLan SRiv STop WSpi
	- 'Molesworth'	SLan
	- 'Myosotidifolia'	CMHG EPla NPro SLan SRiv WPGP WSpi
	- 'Myrtifolia'	EPla MHer NHol SLan SLon WSpi
	- 'Natchez'	SLan
§	- 'Newport Blue'	SLan
	- 'Northern' **new**	SLan
§	- 'Notata' (v)	CSWP IFoB MAsh SPlb WRHF WSpi
	- 'Obelisk'	SLan
	- 'Ornament' **new**	SLan
	- 'Parasol'	MHer SLan
	- 'Pendula'	CMHG SLan SLon
	- 'Pinnacle' **new**	SLan
I	- 'Planifolia' **new**	SLan
	- 'Prostrata'	NHol NWea SLan WSpi
*	- 'Pygmaea'	SBla
	- 'Pylewell' **new**	WSpi
	- 'Pyramidalis'	EBee SLan WFar
	- 'Raket' **new**	SLan
	- 'Rosmarinifolia'	MRav SLan
	- 'Rotundifolia'	CLnd EBee ELan MGos SIde SLan STop WSpi
	- 'Roy Lancaster'	SLan
	- 'Saint Genevieve'	SLan
	- 'Salicifolia Elata'	SLan
	- 'Sentinelle' **new**	SLan
	- 'Silver Beauty' (v)	MGos
	- 'Silver Variegated'	see *B. sempervirens* 'Elegantissima'
	- 'Suffruticosa' ♀H4	More than 30 suppliers
I	- 'Suffruticosa Blue'	NHol
	- 'Suffruticosa Variegata' (v)	ECrN EOHP NEgg NWea SRms SWvt
	- 'Sultan' **new**	SLan
	- 'Sunningdale Silver' **new**	EQua
	- 'Twisty'	SLan WFar
	- 'Undulifolia' **new**	SLan
	- 'Vardar Valley'	NHol NPro SLan SLon SRiv STop WSpi
*	- 'Variegata' (v)	CTca ELan ENot LRHS SLan SLon
	- 'Varifolia' **new**	SLan
	- 'Waterfall'	SLan
	- 'Welleri'	SLan
	- 'William Borek' **new**	SLan
	- 'Wisley Blue'	SLan WSpi
§	***sinica***	SLan
§	- var. ***insularis***	MAsh NHol SLan
	- - 'Chegu'	SLan
	- - 'Filigree'	EPla NHol SLan WSel WSpi
	- - 'Justin Brouwers'	MHer SLan SRiv STop WSpi
	- - 'Pincushion'	SLan
	- - 'Tall Boy'	SLan
	- - 'Tide Hill'	SLan SRiv STop WFar WSel WSpi

- - 'Winter Beauty'	SLan
- - 'Wintergreen'	SLan
- var. ***intermedia***	SLan
wallichiana	CGHE EPla SLan WPGP

C

Cacalia (*Asteraceae*)

atriplicifolia	EBee LRHS
corymbosa HWJK 2214	WCru
delphiniifolia	EBee GEdr
- B&SWJ 5789	WCru
§ ***hastata***	EBee
muehlenbergii	EBee MSal
suaveolens	EBee

Caesalpinia (*Caesalpiniaceae*)

gilliesii	EBee NLar SOWG SPlb XPep
- RCB/Arg N-1	WCot
mexicana new	WPGP
pulcherrima	CCCN SOWG SPlb

Caladium (*Araceae*)

§ ***bicolor*** (v)	EBrs MBri
x ***hortulanum***	see *C. bicolor*
§ ***lindenii*** (v)	MJnS

Calamagrostis (*Poaceae*)

x ***acutiflora*** 'Avalanche' new	EPPr
N - 'Karl Foerster'	More than 30 suppliers
- 'Overdam' (v)	More than 30 suppliers
- 'Stricta'	EPPr EWsh SPhx
argentea	see *Stipa calamagrostis*
arundinacea	CElw COIW CPLG CSpe ECha ECou EPGN EPla LEdu MBNS MNrw NBid NHol NVic SDix SGar SPlb WFar WMoo WPGP WPer WPrP
'Avalanche' new	CKno
§ ***brachytricha***	More than 30 suppliers
emodensis	CBig CBod CBrm CFwr CKno CMil CPen EBee EPPr EPla LEdu MMoz NOak WLeb WPGP
epigejos	CBig EWsh GFor NBre NHol NNor WHrl WRos XIsg
splendens misapplied	see *Stipa calamagrostis*
varia	EPPr NDov WHrl

Calamintha (*Lamiaceae*)

alpina	see *Acinos alpinus*
§ ***ascendens***	CArn EAro EBee MLLN SGar SPhx WMoo WPtf
clinopodium	see *Clinopodium vulgare*
cretica	WPer
§ ***grandiflora***	CArn CSam CSev ECha ELan GGar GPoy LBMP LEdu MHer MRav MWgw NCGa NDov NPer SMad SPer SPet SPlb SSvw WBVN WCAu WCru WFar WMoo WTin WWeb
- 'Elfin Purple'	ENot EPfP LBMP LRav
- 'Variegata' (v)	CBrm CPrp CTca EAro EBee ELan ELon EMan EMil ERou EShb GGar GKev LAst LSou NPri STes WFar
§ ***menthifolia***	NBre NLar
- HH&K 163	GBri
§ ***nepeta***	CArn CWan EBee ECha GMaP LAst LBMP LCro LRHS MEHN MHer MNHC MSte MWgw NBir NBro NCGa NDov NPri NWCA SPhx SPlb SPoG SWat WCAu WFar WMoo WPer XPep
- subsp. ***glandulosa***	CEnt EAro EBee NEgg WLin WMoo WRHF
- - ACL 1050/90	LRHS WHoo
- - 'White Cloud'	CSpe EBee EHrv ELan ERou GBuc LLWP MBri MRav MSte NBir WCAu WMoo WOut XPep
- 'Gottfried Kuehn'	EBee MRav MSte WCAu
§ - subsp. ***nepeta***	CPrp ELan ELon EMon EPfP ERou LHop MHer MLHP MRav NDov NSti SPer WEas WFar WHal WTin
- - 'Blue Cloud'	CSam CSpe EAro EBee ECha EHrv EPfP GKev LCro MBri NBir NDov SAga SMeo SPhx SWat WCAu WFar WHil WMoo XPep
- 'Weisse Riese'	SPhx
nepetoides	see *C. nepeta* subsp. *nepeta*
officinalis misapplied	see *C. ascendens*
sylvatica	see *C. menthifolia*
I - 'Menthe'	EBee
vulgaris	see *Clinopodium vulgare*

Calandrinia (*Portulacaceae*)

caespitosa	CGra GKev
discolor	LRHS
grandiflora	MLLN
* ***ranunculina***	CGra
sibirica	see *Claytonia sibirica*
umbellata	EDAr LBMP NWCA WPer
- 'Ruby Tuesday'	NPri

Calanthe (*Orchidaceae*)

alismifolia	EFEx
arisanenesis	EFEx
aristulifera	EFEx GEdr
bicolor	see *C. striata*
caudatilabella	EFEx
discolor	EBee EBrs EFEx GEdr LAma NLAp SKHP WWst
- subsp. ***amamiana***	EFEx
- var. ***flava***	see *C. striata*
- subsp. ***tokunoshimensis***	EFEx
fargesii new	WCot
graciliflora	EFEx
Kozu gx	GEdr LEdu WWst
mannii	EFEx
nipponica	CBct EFEx GEdr LAma WWst
reflexa	EBee EBrs EFEx GEdr LAma NLAp
sieboldii	see *C. striata*
§ ***striata***	CBct EBee EBrs EFEx GEdr LAma SKHP WCot WWst
tricarinata	CBct EBrs EFEx GEdr LAma NLAp

Calathea (*Marantaceae*)

argyrophylla 'Exotica'	XBlo
crocata 🏆H1	LRHS MBri
'Greystar'	MBri
louisae 'Maui Queen'	MBri XBlo
§ ***majestica*** 🏆H1	XBlo
makoyana 🏆H1	MBri XBlo
metallica	MBri
oppenheimiana	see *Ctenanthe oppenheimiana*
ornata	see *C. majestica*
picturata 'Argentea' 🏆H1	MBri XBlo
roseopicta 🏆H1	LRHS MBri XBlo
rufibarba	XBlo
* ***stromata***	XBlo
veitchiana	MBri
warscewiczii	MBri
'Wavestar'	MBri
zebrina 🏆H1	MBri XBlo
'Zoizia'	XBlo

Calceolaria (*Scrophulariaceae*)

acutifolia	see *C. polyrhiza* Cav.
alba	CPLG EBee EMan GKev NLar

× ***banksii*** EBee
bicolor EBee WCot
§ ***biflora*** ECho EPfP GGar GKev LEdu NLAp NLar
- 'Goldcap' ECho
- 'Goldcrest Amber' ECho SPlb WPer
'Briga Elite' EBee EWin LSou
chelidonioides GGar MTho WLin
falklandica ECho GKev ITim NLAp SPav SRms WHer
fothergillii GKev NLAp
'Goldcrest' ECho EPfP LRHS SRms
'Hall's Spotted' NWCA
§ ***integrifolia*** 🏆H3 CDTJ CFis CHal CPLG CSpe EBee ELan SBHP SEND SGar SIng SPer SPoG SRms WAbe WWlt
- var. ***angustifolia*** SDry
- bronze SPer WAbe
'John Innes' ECho WWeb
'Kentish Hero' CHal MAJR WAbe
mexicana CPLG SHFr
perfoliata B&SWJ 10638 WCru
plantaginea see *C. biflora*
§ ***polyrhiza*** Cav. ECho NRya
rugosa see *C. integrifolia*
Sunset Series EPfP NBlu
tenella ECtt NWCA WAbe
uniflora ITim
- var. ***darwinii*** ECho GKev NLAp
'Walter Shrimpton' ECho EDAr EPot EWes SIng WAbe

Caldcluvia (*Cunoniaceae*)

paniculata ISea

Calea (*Asteraceae*)

zacatechichi MGol

Calendula (*Asteraceae*)

arvensis **new** CCCN
meuselii CFee
officinalis CArn ELau GPoy GWCH MHer MNHC MSal SIde SPav WJek WSel
- Fiesta Gitana Group 🏆H4 CPrp WJek
- 'Porcupine' **new** CTca
'Wintersun' LRav

Calibanus (*Dracaenaceae*)

hookeri EShb

Calibrachoa (*Solanaceae*)

(Callie Series) Callie Cream with Eye = 'Cal Cremey' **new** SVil
- Callie Deep Yellow = 'Cal Depyel' **new** SVil
- Callie Orange = 'Cal Oran' SVil
- Callie Purple = 'Cal Pur'PBR NBlu
- Callie Rose = 'Cal Rose'PBR NBlu SVil
- Callie Scarlet Red = 'Cal Scared'PBR NBlu
- Callie Sunrise = 'Cal Sunre'PBR NBlu SVil
- Callie White = 'Cal White'PBR NBlu
(Million Bells Series) LAst LSou SPoG
Million Bells Cherry = 'Sunbelchipi'PBR
- Million Bells Crackling Fire = 'Sunbelfire' **new** WGor
- Million Bells Lemon = 'Sunbelkic' LAst LSou SPoG WGor
- Million Bells Orange Glow **new** LSou
- Million Bells Red = 'Sunbelre'PBR LAst NBlu NPri
- Million Bells Terracotta = 'Sunbelkist' LAst NPri
- Million Bells Trailing Blue = 'Sunbelkubu'PBR NBlu WGor
- Million Bells Trailing Fuchsia = 'Sunbelrkup' 🏆H3 LAst NBlu WGor
- Million Bells Trailing Lavender Vein = 'Sunbelbura'PBR LAst WGor
- Million Bells Trailing Pink = 'Sunbelkupi'PBR 🏆H3 LAst
- Million Bells Trailing Soft Pink = 'Sunbelkuopi'PBR WGor
- Million Bells Trailing White = 'Sunbelkuho'PBR LAst
- Million Bells White = 'Sunbelho' LSou
(Superbells Series) LAst LSou NPri SPoG
Superbells Candy White = 'Uscali48'PBR
- Superbells Imperial Purple = 'Uscali100'PBR LAst LSou SVil
- Superbells Indigo = 'Uscali51'PBR LAst LSou
- Superbells Light Pink = 'Uscali67' **new** SVil
- Superbells Magenta = 'Uscali17'PBR LAst LSou NPri SVil
- Superbells Pink = 'Uscali11'PBR 🏆H3 LAst LSou SVil
- Superbells Red = 'Uscali28'PBR LAst LSou SPoG SVil
- Superbells Royal Blue = 'Uscali4'PBR LAst LSou SPoG
- Superbells Strawberry Pink = 'Uscali47'PBR LAst SVil

Calicotome (*Papilionaceae*)

spinosa XPep

Calla (*Araceae*)

aethiopica see *Zantedeschia aethiopica*
palustris CBen CWat EHon EMFW EPfP MCCP NPer SWat WFar WMAq WPnP

calamondin see × *Citrofortunella microcarpa*

Calliandra (*Mimosaceae*)

'Dixie Pink' **new** CCCN
emarginata 'Minima' LRHS SOWG
haematocephala SOWG
portoricensis **new** CCCN
surinamensis **new** CCCN
tweediei CCCN SOWG

Callianthemum (*Ranunculaceae*)

anemonoides GCrs SBla
coriandrifolium GEdr
kernerianum GCrs NMen

Callicarpa (*Verbenaceae*)

americana CPLG NLar
- var. ***lactea*** CMCN
bodinieri NBir WFar
- var. ***giraldii*** CEnt GBin MGan MRav NLar SMac WPic WWeb

- - 'Profusion' ♀H4	More than 30 suppliers
cathayana	CBcs CMCN MBri NLar
dichotoma	CPLG CTrG EBee ELan NLar WBod WFar
- 'Issai'	MBri MGos NLar
aff. ***formosana*** B&SWJ 7127	WCru
japonica	NLar
- B&SWJ 8587	WCru
- 'Koshima-no-homate'	MBri NLar
- 'Leucocarpa'	CBcs CMac CPLG ELan EPfP MRav NLar SPer WFar
- var. ***luxurians*** B&SWJ 8521	WCru
kwangtungensis	CBcs CMCN MBri NLar
mollis	NLar
I 'Selectie van der Broek'	NLar
shikokiana	NLar
x ***shirasawana***	NLar
yunnanensis **new**	NLar

Callirhoe (*Malvaceae*)

involucrata	CPBP EBee EMan GBri MGol NWCA SMad WHrl
* - var. ***alba*** **new**	LRav
triangulata	CPBP

Callisia (*Commelinaceae*)

elegans ♀H1	CHal
§ ***navicularis***	CHal
repens	CHal MBri

Callistemon ✿ (*Myrtaceae*)

acuminatus	XPep
'Awanga Dam'	ECou
brachyandrus	WGwG
'Burgundy'	SOWG
* 'Burning Bush'	MAsh SOWG
'Candy Pink'	SOWG
chisholmii	SOWG
citrinus	CHll CSBt CTri EBee ECot ECou EPfP ERom EShb GGar GSki LAst MCot SOWG SPad SPlb WBrE WHar
- 'Albus'	see *C. citrinus* 'White Anzac'
- 'Angela'	SOWG
- 'Canberra'	SOWG
- 'Firebrand'	CDoC LRHS SOWG
- 'Splendens' ♀H3	More than 30 suppliers
§ - 'White Anzac'	ELan EPfP LRHS SBra SOWG SPoG SSta
comboynensis	SOWG
'Coochy Coochy Station'	SOWG
'Dawson River Weeper'	SOWG
'Eureka' **new**	SOWG
'Flaming Fire' **new**	NLar SPoG
flavescens	SOWG
flavovirens	SOWG
formosus	SOWG
glaucus	see *C. speciosus*
'Hannah's Child'	SOWG
'Happy Valley'	SOWG
'Harkness'	SOWG
'Horse Paddock'	SOWG
'Injune'	SOWG
'Kings Park Special'	SOWG
laevis hort.	see *C. rugulosus*
linearis ♀H3	CBcs CMac CSBt CTrC CTri ECou ECrN ELan EPfP EPla LCro LRHS LRav LSRN MDun MHer MWgw SCoo SLim SLon SOWG SPlb SRms SSpi SWvt WNor WSHC
macropunctatus	SOWG SPlb
'Mauve Mist'	CDoC CHEx ELan ELon GBin LRHS MAsh SOWG
pachyphyllus	ECou SOWG
- var. ***viridis***	SOWG
pallidus	CBcs CHEx CMHG CMac CPLG CWib ECou ELan EPfP GGar LRHS MAsh MRav SOWG SPer SPlb SPoG SSta
- 'Candle Glow'	SOWG
- 'Father Christmas'	SOWG
paludosus	see *C. sieberi* DC.
pearsonii	SOWG
- prostrate	SOWG
- 'Rocky Rambler' **new**	SOWG
'Perth Pink'	CBcs CCCN CDoC ELan EMil SBra SOWG SPoG
'Phil May'	SOWG
phoeniceus	ECou SOWG
- 'Pink Ice'	SOWG
pinifolius	SOWG SPlb
- green-flowered	SOWG
- red-flowered	SOWG
- 'Sockeye'	SOWG
'Pink Champagne'	SOWG
§ ***pityoides***	CPLG ECou NHol SOWG WBod XPep
- from Brown's Swamp, Australia	ECou
polandii	SOWG
- dwarf	SOWG
'Purple Splendour'	SOWG
recurvus	SOWG
'Red Clusters'	CDoC CTrC CTrG ELan IArd LAst LRHS MAsh MDun NLar SBod SChF SMer SOWG SWvt
'Reeve's Pink'	SOWG
rigidus	CBcs CDoC CHEx CMHG CMac CPLG CSBt CTri CWib EBee ELan EMil EPfP GGar GSki IArd ISea LAst LRHS MBlu MGos MLan MRav MWat SBod SOWG WBod WWeb XPep
§ ***rugulosus***	NCob SOWG XPep
'Running River'	SOWG
salignus ♀H3	CBcs CCCN CDoC CHEx CPLG CSBt CTrC CTri ECrN EPfP GSki IDee ISea LRHS MHer SEND SHFr SLim SOWG SPer WBVN XPep
sieberi misapplied	see *C. pityoides*
§ ***sieberi*** DC.	CDoC CMHG CTrC ECou ELan EPfP EShb GGar GSki NBir NLar NPal SBod SBra SOWG SPlb SPoG WFar
- purple-flowered	SOWG
§ ***speciosus***	CDul NLar SOWG SPlb SPoG
subulatus	CDoC CHEx ECou MCCP NHol NLar SAPC SArc SOWG SPlb WMoo
- 'Crimson Tail'	CWCL GBin NEgg NLar
- 'Packers Selection'	ECou SOWG
'Taree Pink'	SOWG
teretifolius	SOWG
viminalis	CBcs CCCN CHEx SGar SOWG SPad SPlb
- 'Captain Cook'	ECou LRHS NLar SOWG SRms
- 'Endeavor'	CCCN
- 'Hannah Ray'	IArd SOWG
- 'Little John'	CBcs CWSG ECou GGar SOWG XPep
- 'Malawi Giant'	SOWG
- 'Wilderness White' **new**	SOWG
'Violaceus'	LRav XPep
viridiflorus	CTrC ECou GGar GQui MCCP SOWG SPlb SWal WGwG
- 'County Park Dwarf'	ECou
- 'Sunshine'	ECou
'White Anzac'	see *C. citrinus* 'White Anzac'

Callitriche (*Callitrichaceae*)

autumnalis	see *C. hermaphroditica*
§ ***hermaphroditica***	EPfP WMAq
§ ***palustris***	CDWL EHon EMFW
stagnalis	NSco
verna	see *C. palustris*

Callitris (*Cupressaceae*)

rhomboidea	CTrC GGar

Calluna ✿ (*Ericaceae*)

vulgaris	GWCH
- 'Aberdeen'	EHea
- 'Adrie'	EHea
- 'Ahrensdorf'	EHea
- 'Alba Argentea'	EHea
- 'Alba Aurea'	EHea MBar
- 'Alba Carlton'	EHea
- 'Alba Dumosa'	EHea
- 'Alba Elata'	CNCN EHea MBar
- 'Alba Elegans'	EHea
- 'Alba Elongata'	see *C. vulgaris* 'Mair's Variety'
- 'Alba Erecta'	EHea
- 'Alba Jae'	EHea MBar
- 'Alba Minor'	EHea
- 'Alba Multiflora'	EHea
- 'Alba Pilosa'	EHea
§ - 'Alba Plena' (d)	CSBt EHea MBar
- 'Alba Praecox'	EHea
- 'Alba Pumila'	EHea MBar
§ - 'Alba Rigida'	EHea LRHS MBar SRms
- 'Alec Martin' (d)	EHea
- 'Alex Warwick'	EHea
- 'Alexandra'PBR ♀H4	EHea LRHS SPoG SRms
- 'Alice Knight'	EHea
- 'Alicia'PBR ♀H4	CBcs EHea LRHS SPoG
- 'Alieke'	EHea
- 'Alina'	EHea
- 'Alison Yates'	EHea MBar
- 'Allegretto'	EHea
- 'Allegro' ♀H4	EHea EPfP MBar SRms
- 'Alportii'	EHea MBar
- 'Alportii Praecox'	CNCN EHea MBar
- 'Alys Sutcliffe'	EHea
- 'Amanda Wain'	EHea
- 'Amethyst'PBR	EHea MBar SPoG
- 'Amilto'	CNCN EHea LRHS SRms
- 'Andrew Proudley'	EHea MBar
- 'Anette'PBR ♀H4	EHea LRHS MBar
- 'Angela Wain'	EHea
- 'Anna'	EHea
- 'Annabel' (d)	EHea
- 'Anne Dobbin'	EHea
- 'Annegret'	see *C. vulgaris* 'Marlies'
- 'Anneke'	EHea
- 'Anneliese' **new**	EHea
- 'Annemarie' (d) ♀H4	CNCN CSBt EHea EPfP LRHS MBar NHol SCoo SPer SPlb SRms
- 'Anne's Zwerg'	EHea SRms
- 'Anthony Davis' ♀H4	CNCN EHea LRHS MBar NHol
- 'Anthony Wain'	EHea
- 'Anton'	EHea
- 'Antrujo Gold'	EHea
- 'Aphrodite'PBR	EHea
- 'Apollo'	EHea
- 'Applecross' (d)	CNCN EHea
- 'Arabella'PBR	EHea LRHS SRms
- 'Argentea'	EHea MBar
- 'Ariadne'	EHea
- 'Arina'	CNCN EHea LRHS MBri
- 'Arran Gold'	CNCN EHea MBar
- 'Ashgarth Amber'	EHea
- 'Ashgarth Amethyst'	EHea
- 'Ashgarth Shell Pink'	EHea
- 'Asterix'	EHea
- 'Atalanta'	EHea
- 'Atholl Gold'	EHea
- 'August Beauty'	CNCN EHea
- 'Aurea'	EHea
- 'Aurora'	EHea
- 'Autumn Glow'	EHea
- 'Babette'	EHea
- 'Baby Ben'	EHea
- 'Baby Wicklow'	EHea
- 'Barbara'	EHea
- 'Barbara Fleur'	EHea
- 'Barja'	EHea
- 'Barnett Anley'	CNCN EHea
- 'Battle of Arnhem'	CNCN EHea MBar
- 'Bayport'	EHea
- 'Beechwood Crimson'	CNCN EHea
- 'Bella Rosa'	EHea
- 'Ben Nevis'	EHea
- 'Bennachie Bronze'	EHea
- 'Bennachie Prostrate'	EHea
- 'Beoley Crimson'	EHea MBar
- 'Beoley Crimson Variegated' (v)	EHea
- 'Beoley Gold' ♀H4	CNCN CSBt CTri EHea EPfP LRHS MBar MBri MGos NHol SPer SRms
- 'Beoley Silver'	EHea MBar
- 'Bernadette'	EHea
- 'Betty Baum'	EHea
- 'Bispingen'	EHea
- 'Blazeaway'	CNCN CTri EHea EPfP LRHS MBar MBri NHol SRms
- 'Blueness'	EHea
- 'Bognie'	EHea
- 'Bonfire Brilliance'	CNCN CSBt EHea LRHS MBar NHol
- 'Bonita'PBR	EHea
- 'Bonne's Darkness'	EHea
- 'Bonsaï'	EHea
- 'Boreray'	CNCN EHea
- 'Boskoop'	CBrm EHea LRHS MBar NHol
- 'Bradford'	EHea
- 'Braemar'	CNCN EHea
- 'Braeriach'	EHea
- 'Branchy Anne'	EHea
- 'Bray Head'	EHea MBar
- 'Breivik'	EHea
- 'Brita Elisabeth' (d)	EHea
- 'Bronze Beauty'	EHea
- 'Bud Lyle'	EHea
- 'Bunsall'	EHea
- 'Buxton Snowdrift'	EHea
- 'C.W. Nix'	CSBt EHea MBar
- 'Caerketton White'	EHea
- 'Caleb Threlkeld'	EHea
- 'Calf of Man'	EHea
- 'Californian Midge'	EHea MBar NHol
- 'Camla Variety' **new**	EHea
- 'Carl Röders' (d)	EHea
- 'Carmen'	EHea
- 'Carngold'	EHea
- 'Carole Chapman'	EHea MBar
- 'Carolyn'	EHea
- 'Cassa'	EHea
- 'Catherine'	EHea
- 'Catherine Anne'	EHea
- 'Celtic Gold'	EHea
- 'Charles Chapman'	EHea
§ - 'Chernobyl' (d)	EHea NHol
- 'Chindit'	EHea
- 'Christina'	EHea
- 'Cilcennin Common'	EHea
- 'Clare Carpet'	EHea
- 'Coby'	EHea
- 'Coccinea'	EHea MBar

	- 'Colette'	EHea
	- 'Con Brio'	CBcs CNCN EHea LRHS SRms
	- 'Copper Glow'	EHea
	- 'Coral Island'	EHea MBar
	- 'Corbett's Red'	EHea
	- 'Corrie's White'	EHea
	- 'Cottswood Gold'	EHea NHol SRms
	- 'County Wicklow' (d) ♀H4	CNCN CTri EHea EPfP GGar LRHS MBar MBri NBlu NHol SRms
	- 'Craig Rossie'	EHea
	- 'Crail Orange'	EHea
	- 'Cramond' (d)	CNCN EHea MBar
	- 'Cream Steving'	EHea
	- 'Crimson Glory'	EHea LRHS MBar NBlu
	- 'Crimson Sunset'	CNCN EHea
	- 'Crinkly Tuft'	EHea
	- 'Crowborough Beacon'	EHea
	- 'Cuprea'	CNCN EHea EPfP LRHS MBar MBri NHol SPer
	- 'Dainty Bess'	EHea MBar MSwo
	- 'Dapiali' **new**	EHea
	- 'Dark Alicia'PBR **new**	EHea
	- 'Dark Beauty'PBR (d) ♀H4	CNCN EHea EPfP LRHS MBar NDlv NHol
	- 'Dark Star' (d) ♀H4	CBcs CNCN EHea EPfP LCro LRHS MBar MGos NHol SCoo SRms
	- 'Darkness' ♀H4	CNCN CSBt CTri EHea EPfP LRHS MBar MBri NHol SCoo SRms
	- 'Darleyensis'	EHea MBar
	- 'Dart's Amethyst'	EHea
	- 'Dart's Beauty'	EHea
	- 'Dart's Brilliant'	EHea
	- 'Dart's Flamboyant'	EHea
	- 'Dart's Gold'	EHea MBar
	- 'Dart's Hedgehog'	EHea
	- 'Dart's Parakeet'	EHea
	- 'Dart's Parrot'	EHea
	- 'Dart's Silver Rocket'	EHea
	- 'Dart's Squirrel'	EHea
	- 'David Eason'	CNCN EHea
	- 'David Hagenaars'	EHea
	- 'David Hutton'	EHea MBar
	- 'David Platt' (d)	EHea
	- 'Denkewitz'	EHea
	- 'Denny Pratt'	EHea
	- 'Desiree'	EHea
	- 'Devon' (d)	EHea
	- 'Diana'	EHea
	- 'Dickson's Blazes'	EHea
	- 'Dirry'	CNCN EHea
	- 'Doctor Murray's White'	see *C. vulgaris* 'Mullardoch'
	- 'Doris Rushworth'	EHea
	- 'Drum-ra'	EHea MBar SRms
	- 'Dunnet Lime'	EHea SPlb
	- 'Dunnydeer'	EHea
	- 'Dunwood'	EHea MBar
§	- 'Durford Wood'	EHea
	- 'Dwingeloo Delight'	EHea
	- 'E.F. Brown'	EHea
	- 'E. Hoare'	EHea MBar
	- 'Easter-bonfire'	CNCN EHea LRHS NHol
	- 'Eckart Miessner'	EHea
	- 'Edith Godbolt'	EHea
	- 'Elaine'	EHea
	- 'Elegant Pearl'	EHea MBar
	- 'Elegantissima'	CBcs EHea
	- 'Elegantissima Walter Ingwersen'	see *C. vulgaris* 'Walter Ingwersen'
	- 'Eleonore' (d) **new**	EHea
	- 'Elkstone White'	CNCN EHea MBar
	- 'Ellen'	EHea
	- 'Ellie Barbour'	EHea
	- 'Elly'	EHea
	- 'Else Frye' (d)	EHea

	- 'Elsie Purnell' (d) ♀H4	CNCN CSBt EHea EPfP LRHS MBar MGos NHol SPlb SRms
	- 'Emerald Jock'	EHea
	- 'Emma Louise Tuke'	EHea
	- 'Eric Easton'	EHea
	- 'Eskdale Gold'	EHea
	- 'Eurosa'PBR	EHea
	- 'Fairy'	EHea
	- 'Falling Star'	EHea
	- 'Feuerwerk'	EHea
§	- 'Finale'	EHea MBar
	- 'Findling'	EHea
	- 'Fire King'	EHea MBar
	- 'Fire Star'	EHea
	- 'Firebreak'	EHea MBar NHol
	- 'Firefly' ♀H4	CBcs CNCN CSBt EHea EPfP LRHS MBar MBri NHol SPer SRms
	- 'Flamingo'	CBcs CNCN CSBt EHea LRHS MBar MSwo NHol SRms
	- 'Flatling'	EHea
	- 'Flore Pleno' (d)	EHea MBar
	- 'Floriferous'	EHea
	- 'Florrie Spicer'	EHea
	- 'Fokko' (d)	EHea
	- 'Fort Bragg'	EHea
	- 'Fortyniner Gold'	EHea
	- 'Foxhollow Wanderer'	CNCN EHea MBar
	- 'Foxii'	EHea
	- 'Foxii Floribunda'	EHea MBar
	- 'Foxii Lett's Form'	see *C. vulgaris* 'Velvet Dome', 'Mousehole'
	- 'Foxii Nana'	CNCN EHea MBar NHol SRms
	- 'Foya'	EHea
	- 'Fred J. Chapple'	CNCN EHea LRHS MBar MBri NBlu
	- 'Fréjus'	EHea
	- 'French Grey'	CNCN EHea
	- 'Fritz Kircher'PBR	EHea
	- 'Gaia'	EHea
	- 'Gerda'	EHea
	- 'Ginkel's Glorie'	EHea
	- 'Glasa'	EHea
	- 'Glen Mashie'	EHea
	- 'Glencoe' (d)	EHea MBar MBri
	- 'Glendoick Silver'	EHea
	- 'Glenfiddich'	CSBt EHea LRHS MBar NHol
	- 'Glenlivet'	EHea MBar
	- 'Glenmorangie'	EHea MBar
	- 'Gloucester Boy'	EHea
	- 'Gnome'	EHea
	- 'Gold Charm'	EHea
	- 'Gold Finch'	EHea
	- 'Gold Flame'	EHea MBar
	- Gold Hamilton	see *C. vulgaris* 'Chernobyl'
	- 'Gold Haze' ♀H4	CBcs CNCN CTri EHea LRHS MBar MBri NHol SCoo SPer SRms
	- 'Gold Knight'	EHea EPfP MBar
	- 'Gold Kup'	EHea MBar
	- 'Gold Mist'	EHea
	- 'Gold Spronk'	EHea
	- 'Gold Star' (d)	EHea
	- 'Goldcarmen'	EHea
	- 'Golden Blazeaway'	EHea
	- 'Golden Carpet'	CNCN CSBt EHea MBar MBri MGos NDlv NHol SPer SRms
	- 'Golden Dew'	EHea
	- 'Golden Dream' (d)	EHea
	- 'Golden Feather'	CNCN CSBt EHea MBar
	- 'Golden Fleece'	CNCN EHea SRms
	- 'Golden Max'	EHea
	- 'Golden Rivulet'	EHea MBar MSwo
	- 'Golden Turret'	CNCN EHea LRHS NHol
	- 'Golden Wonder' (d)	EHea
	- 'Goldsworth Crimson'	CSBt EHea
	- 'Goldsworth Crimson Variegated' (v)	CNCN EHea MBar

	- 'Goscote Wine'	EHea
	- 'Grasmeriensis'	EHea MBar
	- 'Great Comp'	MBar
	- 'Green Cardinal'	EHea
	- 'Grey Carpet'	CNCN EHea LRHS MBar SRms
	- 'Grijsje'	EHea
	- 'Grizabella'	EHea
	- 'Grizzly'	EHea
	- 'Grönsinka'	EHea
	- 'Grouse'	EHea
	- 'Guinea Gold'	CNCN EHea LRHS MBar MBri
	- 'Gunilla Uggla' (d)	EHea
§	- 'H.E. Beale' (d)	CNCN CSBt CTri EHea EPfP LRHS MBar MBri MGos NHol
	- 'Hamlet Green'	CNCN EHea MBar
	- 'Hammondii'	CNCN EHea
	- 'Hammondii Aureifolia'	CNCN EHea MBar MBri SPlb
	- 'Hammondii Rubrifolia'	EHea MBar MBri SRms
	- 'Hannover'	EHea
	- 'Harlekin'	EHea
	- 'Harry Gibbon' (d)	EHea
	- 'Harten's Findling'	EHea
	- 'Hatje's Herbstfeuer' (d)	EHea
	- 'Hayesensis'	EHea
	- 'Heidberg'	EHea
	- 'Heidepracht'	EHea
	- 'Heidesinfonie'	EHea
	- 'Heideteppich'	EHea
	- 'Heidezwerg'	EHea
	- 'Heike' (d)	EHea
	- 'Herbert Mitchell'	EHea
	- 'Hester'	EHea
	- 'Hetty'	EHea
	- 'Hibernica'	EHea MBar
	- 'Hiemalis'	EHea MBar
	- 'Hiemalis Southcote'	see *C. vulgaris* 'Durford Wood'
	- Highland Cream	see *C. vulgaris* 'Punch's Dessert'
	- 'Highland Rose'	EHea SPlb SRms
	- 'Highland Spring'	EHea
	- 'Hilda Turberfield'	EHea
	- 'Hillbrook Limelight'	EHea
	- 'Hillbrook Orange'	EHea MBar
	- 'Hillbrook Sparkler'	EHea
	- 'Hinton White'	EHea
	- 'Hirsuta Albiflora'	EHea
	- 'Hirsuta Typica'	CNCN EHea
	- 'Hollandia'	EHea
	- 'Holstein'	EHea
	- 'Hookstone'	EHea MBar
	- 'Hoyerhagen'	EHea
§	- 'Hugh Nicholson'	CNCN EHea
	- 'Humpty Dumpty'	EHea LRHS MBar NHol
	- 'Hypnoides'	EHea
	- 'Ide's Double' (d)	EHea
	- 'Inchcolm'	EHea
	- 'Inchkeith'	EHea
	- 'Ineke'	CNCN EHea MBar
	- 'Inge'	EHea
	- 'Ingrid Bouter' (d)	EHea
	- 'Inshriach Bronze'	EHea MBar
	- 'Iris van Leyen'	CNCN EHea MBar
	- 'Islay Mist'	EHea
	- 'Isle of Hirta'	EHea MBar NHol
	- 'Isobel Frye'	EHea MBar
	- 'Isobel Hughes' (d)	EHea MBar
	- 'J.H. Hamilton' (d) ♀H4	CNCN CTri EHea LRHS MBar MBri NBlu NHol SRms
	- 'Jan'	EHea
	- 'Jan Dekker'	CNCN EHea LRHS MBar NHol
	- 'Janice Chapman'	EHea MBar
	- 'Japanese White'	EHea
	- 'Jenny'	EHea
	- 'Jill'	EHea
	- 'Jimmy Dyce' (d)	EHea
	- 'Joan Sparkes' (d)	CNCN EHea LRHS MBar

	- 'Jochen'	EHea
	- 'Johan Slegers'	EHea
	- John Denver	see *C. vulgaris* 'Marleen Select'
	- 'John F. Letts'	EHea MBar NHol SRms
	- 'Johnson's Variety'	CBcs CNCN EHea MBar
	- 'Jos' Lemon'	EHea
	- 'Jos' Whitie'	EHea
	- 'Josefine'	EHea
	- 'Joseph's Coat'	EHea
	- 'Joy Vanstone' ♀H4	CNCN CSBt EHea EPfP MBar MBri MGos NHol SRms
	- 'Julia'	EHea
	- 'Julie Ann Platt'	EHea
	- 'Juno'	EHea
	- 'Kaiser'	EHea
	- 'Karin Blum'	EHea
	- 'Kermit'	EHea
	- 'Kerstin' ♀H4	EHea LRHS MBar MSwo NHol SPlb SRms
	- 'Kinlochruel' (d) ♀H4	CNCN CSBt CTri EHea EPfP GGar LRHS MBar MBri MGos NHol SPlb SRms
	- 'Kir Royal'	EHea
	- 'Kirby White'	CNCN EHea LRHS MBar MBri NDlv NHol SPlb
	- 'Kirsty Anderson'	EHea
	- 'Kit Hill'	EHea MBar
	- 'Knaphill' **new**	EHea
	- 'Kontrast'	EHea
	- 'Kuphaldtii'	EHea MBar
	- 'Kuppendorf'	EHea
	- 'Kynance'	EHea MBar
	- 'Lady Maithe'	EHea
	- 'Lambstails'	EHea MBar
	- 'L'Ancresse'	EHea
	- 'Larissa'PBR	EHea
	- 'Lemon Gem'	EHea
	- 'Lemon Queen'	EHea
	- 'Leprechaun'	LRHS
	- 'Leslie Slinger'	EHea LRHS MBar NHol
	- 'Lewis Lilac'	EHea
	- 'Liebestraum'	EHea
	- 'Lilac Elegance'	EHea
	- 'Lime Glade'	CNCN EHea
	- 'Lime Gold'	EHea
	- 'Little John'	EHea
	- 'Llanbedrog Pride' (d)	EHea MBar
	- 'Loch Turret'	EHea MBar
	- 'Loch-na-Seil'	EHea MBar
	- 'Long White'	EHea MBar
	- 'Loni'	EHea
	- 'Lyle's Late White'	CNCN EHea
	- 'Lyle's Surprise'	EHea MBar
	- 'Lyndon Proudley'	EHea
	- 'Lüneberg Heath'	EHea
	- 'Macdonald of Glencoe'	EHea
§	- 'Mair's Variety' ♀H4	CBrm EHea MBar
	- 'Mallard'	EHea
	- 'Manitoba'	EHea
	- 'Manuel'	EHea
	- 'Marianne'	EHea
	- 'Marie'	EHea
	- 'Marion Blum'	EHea MBar
	- 'Marleen'	CNCN EHea LRHS MBar NHol
§	- 'Marleen Select'	EHea
§	- 'Marlies'	EHea
	- 'Martha Hermann'	EHea
	- 'Martine Langenberg'	EHea
	- 'Masquerade'	EHea MBar
	- 'Matita'	EHea
	- 'Mauvelyn'	EHea
	- 'Mazurka'	EHea
	- 'Melanie'	EHea LRHS MBar MSwo NHol
	- 'Mick Jamieson' (d)	EHea
	- 'Mies'	EHea

- 'Minima'	EHea MBar
- 'Minima Smith's Variety'	EHea MBar
- 'Miniöxabäck'	EHea
- 'Minty'	EHea
- 'Mirelle'	CNCN EHea
- 'Miss Muffet'	EHea NHol
- 'Molecule'	EHea MBar
- 'Monika' (d)	EHea
- 'Monja'	EHea
- 'Moon Glow'	EHea
- 'Mountain Snow'	EHea
§ - 'Mousehole'	CNCN EHea MBar NHol
- 'Mousehole Compact'	see *C. vulgaris* 'Mousehole'
- 'Mrs Alf'	EHea
- 'Mrs E. Wilson' (d)	EHea
- 'Mrs Pat'	CNCN EHea LRHS MBar NHol
- 'Mrs Pinxteren'	EHea
- 'Mrs Ronald Gray'	CNCN EHea MBar
- 'Mullach Mor'	EHea
§ - 'Mullardoch'	EHea MBar
- 'Mullion' ♀H4	EHea MBar
- 'Multicolor'	CNCN EHea LRHS MBar NHol SRms
- 'Murielle Dobson'	EHea MBar
§ - 'My Dream' (d) ♀H4	CNCN CSBt EHea EPfP LRHS MBar NHol SCoo
- 'Nana'	EHea
- 'Nana Compacta'	CNCN EHea MBar
- 'Natasja'	EHea
- 'Naturpark'	EHea MBar
- 'Nele' (d)	EHea
- 'Nico'	EHea
- 'Nofretete'	EHea
- Nordlicht	see *C. vulgaris* 'Skone'
- 'October White'	CNCN EHea
- 'Odette'	EHea
- 'Oiseval'	EHea
- 'Old Rose'	EHea
- 'Olive Turner'	EHea
- 'Olympic Gold'	EHea
- 'Orange and Gold'	EHea
- 'Orange Carpet'	EHea
- 'Orange Max'	EHea LRHS NHol
- 'Orange Queen'	CNCN CSBt EHea MBar
- 'Öxabäck'	EHea MBar
- 'Oxshott Common'	CNCN EHea GQui MBar
- 'Pallida'	EHea
- 'Parsons' Gold'	EHea
- 'Parsons' Grey Selected'	EHea
- 'Pastell' (d)	EHea
- 'Pat's Gold'	EHea
- 'Peace'	EHea
- 'Pearl Drop'	EHea MBar
- 'Peggy'	EHea
- 'Penhale'	EHea
- 'Penny Bun'	EHea
- 'Pennyacre Gold'	EHea
- 'Pennyacre Lemon'	EHea
- 'Pepper and Salt'	see *C. vulgaris* 'Hugh Nicholson'
- 'Perestrojka'	EHea
- 'Peter Sparkes' (d) ♀H4	CNCN CSBt EHea EPfP LRHS MBar MBri MGos NHol SRms
- 'Petra'	EHea
- 'Pewter Plate'	EHea MBar
- 'Pink Alicia' PBR	EHea
- 'Pink Beale'	see *C. vulgaris* 'H.E. Beale'
- 'Pink Dream' (d)	EHea
- 'Pink Gown'	EHea
- 'Pink Spreader'	EHea
- 'Pink Tips'	EHea
- 'Plantarium'	EHea
- 'Platt's Surprise' (d)	EHea
- 'Polly'	EHea
- 'Poolster'	EHea
- 'Porth Wen White'	EHea
- 'Prizewinner'	EHea
* - 'Procumbens'	EHea
- 'Prostrata Flagelliformis'	EHea
- 'Prostrate Orange'	CNCN EHea MBar
§ - 'Punch's Dessert'	EHea
- 'Purple Passion'	EPfP
- 'Pygmaea'	EHea MBar
- 'Pyramidalis'	EHea
- 'Pyrenaica'	EHea MBar
- 'Quail'	EHea
- 'R.A. McEwan'	EHea
- 'Radnor' (d) ♀H4	CBcs CNCN CSBt EHea LRHS MBar
- 'Radnor Gold' (d)	EHea MBar
- 'Raket'	EHea
- 'Ralph Purnell'	CNCN EHea MBar
- 'Ralph Purnell Select'	EHea
- 'Ralph's Pearl'	EHea
- 'Ralph's Red'	EHea
- 'Randall's Crimson'	EHea
- 'Rannoch'	EHea
- 'Rebecca's Red'	EHea SRms
- 'Red Carpet'	CNCN EHea LRHS MBar
- 'Red Favorit' (d)	CBcs EHea LRHS SRms
- 'Red Fred'	EHea NHol
- 'Red Haze'	CNCN EHea EPfP LRHS MBar NHol
- 'Red Max'	EHea
- 'Red Pimpernel'	CNCN EHea EPfP MBar NHol
- 'Red Rug'	EHea
- 'Red Star' (d)	CNCN EHea LRHS MBar NHol
- 'Red Wings'	EHea
- 'Redbud'	EHea
- 'Redgauntlet'	EHea
- 'Reini'	EHea NHol
- 'Rica'	EHea
- 'Richard Cooper'	EHea MBar
- 'Rieanne'	EHea
- 'Rigida Prostrata'	see *C. vulgaris* 'Alba Rigida'
- 'Rivington'	EHea
- 'Robber Knight'	EHea
- 'Robert Chapman' ♀H4	CNCN CSBt CTri EHea LRHS MBar MBri NHol SRms
- 'Rock Spray'	EHea
- 'Röding'	EHea
- 'Rokoko'	EHea
- 'Roland Haagen' ♀H4	EHea MBar
- 'Roma'	EHea MBar
- 'Romina'	CNCN EHea MSwo NHol
- 'Ronas Hill'	EHea
- 'Roodkapje'	EHea
- 'Rosalind' ambig.	CNCN CSBt EPfP MBar NHol
- 'Rosalind, Crastock Heath'	EHea
- 'Rosalind, Underwood's'	EHea EPfP LRHS
- 'Ross Hutton'	EHea
- 'Roswitha'	EHea
- 'Roter Oktober'	EHea
- 'Rotfuchs'	EHea
- 'Ruby Slinger'	CNCN EHea LRHS MBar NHol
- 'Rusty Triumph'	EHea
- 'Ruth Sparkes' (d)	CNCN EHea LRHS MBar NHol
- 'Sabrina' (d)	EHea
- 'Saima'	EHea
- 'Saint Nick'	EHea MBar
- 'Salland'	EHea
- 'Sally Anne Proudley'	CNCN EHea MBar
- 'Salmon Leap'	EHea LRHS MBar NHol
- 'Sam Hewitt'	EHea
- 'Sampford Sunset'	CSam EHea
- 'Sandhammaren'	EHea
- 'Sandwood Bay'	EHea
- 'Sandy' PBR	CBcs EHea LRHS NHol SPoG
- 'Sarah Platt' (d)	EHea
- 'Saskia'	EHea

	- 'Schneewolke'[PBR]	EHea
	- 'Scholje's Jimmy'	EHea
	- 'Scholje's Rubin' (d)	EHea
	- 'Scholje's Super Star' (d)	EHea
	- 'Schurig's Sensation' (d)	CNCN EHea LRHS MBar
	- 'Schurig's Wonder' (d)	EHea
	- 'Scotch Mist'	EHea
	- 'Sedloňov'	EHea
	- 'Sellingsloh'	EHea
	- 'September Pink'	EHea
	- 'Serlei'	EHea MBar
	- 'Serlei Aurea' ♀H4	CNCN CSBt EHea EPfP MBar NHol SRms
	- 'Serlei Grandiflora'	EHea MBar
	- 'Serlei Purpurea'	EHea
	- 'Serlei Rubra'	EHea
	- 'Sesam'	EHea
	- 'Sesse'	EHea
	- 'Shirley'	EHea MBar
	- 'Silberspargel'	EHea
	- 'Silver Cloud'	CNCN EHea MBar
	- 'Silver Fox'	EHea
	- 'Silver King'	CNCN EHea MBar
	- 'Silver Knight'	CBcs CNCN CSBt EHea EPfP GGar LCro LRHS MBar MBri MGos NHol SPlb SRms
	- 'Silver Pearl'	EHea
	- 'Silver Queen' ♀H4	CNCN EHea LRHS MBar MBri NHol SPer SRms
	- 'Silver Rose' ♀H4	CNCN EHea MBar
	- 'Silver Sandra'	EHea
	- 'Silver Spire'	CNCN EHea MBar
	- 'Silver Stream'	EHea MBar
	- 'Silver White'	EHea
	- 'Silvie'	EHea
	- 'Simone'	EHea
	- 'Sir Anthony Hopkins'	EHea
	- 'Sir John Charrington' ♀H4	CBcs CNCN CSBt EHea EPfP LRHS MBar MBri MGos NHol
	- 'Sirsson'	EHea MBar
	- 'Sister Anne' ♀H4	CNCN CSBt EHea EPfP LRHS MBri NHol SPer SRms
	- 'Skipper'	EHea MBar
§	- 'Skone' (v)	EHea
	- 'Snowball'	see *C. vulgaris* 'My Dream'
	- 'Snowflake'	EHea
	- 'Soay'	EHea MBar
	- 'Sonja' (d)	EHea
	- 'Sonning' (d)	EHea
	- 'Sonny Boy'	EHea
	- 'Sophia' (d)	EHea
	- 'Sparkling Stars'	EHea
	- 'Sphinx'	EHea
	- 'Spicata'	EHea
	- 'Spicata Aurea'	CNCN EHea MBar
	- 'Spicata Nana'	EHea
	- 'Spider'	EHea
	- 'Spitfire'	CNCN EHea LRHS MBar NHol
	- 'Spook'	EHea
	- 'Spring Cream' ♀H4	CNCN EHea GGar LRHS MBar MBri SPoG
	- 'Spring Glow'	CNCN EHea LRHS MBar MBri
	- 'Spring Torch'	CNCN CSBt EHea GGar LRHS MBar MBri SCoo SPoG SRms
	- 'Springbank'	EHea MBar
	- 'Stag's Horn'	EHea
I	- 'Startler'	EHea
	- 'Stefanie'	EHea NHol SRms
	- 'Stranger'	EHea
	- 'Strawberry Delight' (d)	EHea EPfP
	- 'Summer Elegance'	EHea
	- 'Summer Gold'	SRms
	- 'Summer Orange'	CNCN EHea LRHS MBar NHol
	- 'Summer White' (d)	EHea
	- 'Sunningdale'	see *C. vulgaris* 'Finale'
	- 'Sunrise'	CNCN CSBt EHea EPfP MBar MGos
	- 'Sunset' ♀H4	CNCN CSBt EHea LRHS MBar SRms
	- 'Sunset Glow'	EHea
	- 'Talisker'	EHea
	- 'Tenella'	EHea
	- 'Tenuis'	EHea MBar
	- 'Terrick's Orange'	EHea
	- 'The Pygmy'	EHea
	- 'Theresa'	EHea
	- 'Tib' (d) ♀H4	CSBt EHea LRHS MBar MBri NBlu SRms
	- 'Tijdens Copper'	EHea
	- 'Tino'	EHea
	- 'Tom Thumb'	EHea MBar
	- 'Torogay'	EHea
	- 'Torulosa'	EHea
	- 'Tremans'	EHea
	- 'Tricolorifolia'	CNCN EHea EPfP LRHS NHol
	- 'Underwoodii'	EHea MBar
	- 'Unity'	EHea
	- 'Valorian'	EHea
	- 'Van Beek'	EHea
§	- 'Velvet Dome'	EHea MBar
	- 'Velvet Fascination' ♀H4	CBcs CNCN EHea EPfP LCro LRHS MBar MGos NHol
	- 'Verena' **new**	EHea
	- 'Violet Bamford'	EHea
	- 'Visser's Fancy'	EHea
§	- 'Walter Ingwersen'	EHea
	- 'Waquoit Brightness'	EHea
	- 'Waquoit Gwen'	EHea
	- 'Westerlee Gold'	EHea
	- 'Westerlee Green'	EHea
	- 'Westphalia'	EHea
	- 'White Bouquet'	see *C. vulgaris* 'Alba Plena'
	- 'White Carpet'	EHea MBar
	- 'White Coral' (d)	EHea EPfP MGos
	- 'White Gold'	EHea
	- 'White Gown'	EHea
	- 'White Lawn' ♀H4	CNCN EHea LRHS MBar MSwo NDlv NHol SRms
	- 'White Mite'	EHea MBar
	- 'White Pearl' (d)	EHea
	- 'White Princess'	see *C. vulgaris* 'White Queen'
§	- 'White Queen'	EHea MBar
	- 'White Star' (d)	EHea
	- 'Whiteness'	CNCN EHea MBar
	- 'Wickwar Flame' ♀H4	CBcs CNCN CSBt EHea EPfP LCro LRHS MBar MBri MGos NHol SPlb SRms
	- 'Wilma'	EHea
	- 'Wingates Gem'	EHea
	- 'Wingates Gold'	EHea
	- 'Winter Chocolate'	CNCN CSBt EHea EPfP LRHS MBar MBri MSwo NDlv NHol
	- 'Winter Fire'	EHea
	- 'Winter Red'	EHea
	- 'Wollmer's Weisse' (d)	EHea
	- 'Wood Close'	EHea
	- 'Yellow Basket'	EHea
	- 'Yellow Beauty'[PBR]	EHea
	- 'Yellow Dome'	CNCN
	- 'Yellow Globe'	EHea
	- 'Yellow One'	EHea
	- 'Yvette's Gold'	EHea
	- 'Yvette's Silver'	EHea
	- 'Yvonne Clare'	EHea

Calocedrus (*Cupressaceae*)

§	***decurrens*** ♀H4	CBcs CDoC CDul CLnd CMac CTho CTri EHul EPfP LCon LLin LPan LRHS MBar MBlu MBri MGos MMuc NWea SBLw SLim SPer SPoG WEve WMou

	- 'Aureovariegata' (v)	CBcs CWib EHul LCon LPan LRHS MAsh MBar MBlu MBri MWya NLar SBLw SCoo SLim SPoG WEve WFar
	- 'Berrima Gold'	CDoC CKen EPfP LCon LRHS MGos NLar SLim SPoG WEve
§	- 'Depressa'	CKen
	- 'Intricata'	CKen NLar SLim
	- 'Maupin Glow' (v)	NLar SLim
	- 'Nana'	see *C. decurrens* 'Depressa'
	- 'Pillar'	CKen MAsh MBri NLar
	formosana	WPic
	macrolepis	EMon

Calocephalus (*Asteraceae*)

	brownii	see *Leucophyta brownii*
	'Silver Sand' **new**	LSou SVil

Calochortus (*Liliaceae*)

	albus	ECho
	- var. ***rubellus***	ECho WCot
	argillosus	CPBP
	'Cupido'[PBR]	EBrs ECho EPot
	luteus Douglas ex Lindl.	CPBP EPot LAma
	- 'Golden Orb'[PBR]	CBgR CGrW EBrs ECho LRHS
	splendens	LAma
	- 'Violet Queen'	ECho LEdu
	superbus	CBgR EBrs ECho EPot LRHS
	'Symphony' **new**	EBrs ECho EPot
	venustus	CGrW EBrs ECho EPot LAma LEdu LRHS

Calomeria (*Asteraceae*)

§	***amaranthoides***	WJek

Calonyction see *Ipomoea*

Calopsis (*Restionaceae*)

	levynsiae	CBig
	paniculata	CBig CCCN CCtw CHEx CTrC EAmu EBee IArd IDee WPGP

Caloscordum (*Alliaceae*)

§	***neriniflorum***	EBur WAbe WCot

Calothamnus (*Myrtaceae*)

	blepharospermus	SOWG
	gilesii	SOWG
	homolophyllus	SOWG
	quadrifidus	EShb SOWG
	- yellow-flowered	SOWG
	rupestris	SOWG
	sanguineus	SOWG
	validus	SOWG SPlb

Caltha ✿ (*Ranunculaceae*)

	'Auenwald'	CLAP CWsd LLWG
	'Honeydew'	CDes CLAP EBee GBuc WPGP
	howellii	see *C. leptosepala* subsp. *howellii*
	introloba	SWat
	laeta	see *C. palustris* var. *palustris*
	leptosepala	CLAP NLar
§	- subsp. ***howellii*** NNS 02-92	GKev
	palustris ♀H4	More than 30 suppliers
	- var. ***alba***	More than 30 suppliers
	- var. ***barthei***	CFir EBee GEdr SKHP WPnP
	- 'Flore Pleno' (d) ♀H4	More than 30 suppliers
	- var. ***himalensis***	MGol WCot
	- 'Marilyn'	CLAP GBuc LLWG
	- 'Multiplex' (d)	CFwr EBee GBuc WLin
§	- var. ***palustris***	CBre ECha EHon ELan EMFW EMon GGar SWat WCra WFar
	- - 'Plena' (d)	CWat ENot EPfP LRHS MCot SMac WFar
	- subsp. ***polypetala***	CDWL NPer SMad SWat WMAq
	- var. ***radicans***	GCrs
	- 'Semiplena' (d)	EMon
	- Trotter's form	GBuc
	- 'Yellow Giant'	CDWL
N	***polypetala*** misapplied	see *C. palustris* var. *palustris*
N	***polypetala*** Hochst. ex Lorent	CLAP CWat EWII GBuc WBor
	- from Turkey	GBuc
	scaposa	EBee

Calycanthus (*Calycanthaceae*)

	fertilis	see *C. floridus* var. *glaucus*
	- var. ***laevigatus***	see *C. floridus* var. *glaucus*
	- 'Purpureus'	see *C. floridus* var. *glaucus* 'Purpureus'
	floridus	CAgr CArn CBcs CMCN CPMA CTho CWib EBee ELan EPfP EWTr IDee LAst LEdu LRHS MBNS MBlu MBri SDnm SPer SPlb SPoG WBod WCot
	- 'Athens' **new**	CPMA
§	- var. ***glaucus***	EPfP MGos NBlu NLar WSHC
§	- - 'Purpureus'	CBcs CPMA MBlu MBri NLar
	- var. ***laevigatus***	see *C. floridus* var. *glaucus*
	- 'Michael Lindsay' **new**	CPMA
	occidentalis	CAgr CArn CBcs CMCN CWib ECrN EPfP IClo MBlu SGar SSpi
	- NNS 02-93	WCot

Calystegia (*Convolvulaceae*)

§	***hederacea*** 'Flore Pleno' (d)	EBee ELan EMon MCCP NCGa NLar NSti SMad WCot WFar
	japonica 'Flore Pleno'	see *C. hederacea* 'Flore Pleno'
	silvatica 'Incarnata'	EBee EMon
	soldanella	XPep
	- NNS 99-85	WCot

Calytrix (*Myrtaceae*)

	tetragona	SPlb
	- compact, pink-flowered	SOWG

Comarum see *Potentilla*

Camassia ✿ (*Hyacinthaceae*)

	biflora	EBee
	cusickii	More than 30 suppliers
	- white-flowered	IFoB
	- 'Zwanenburg'	CBgR CTca EBee EBrs GKev LRHS MSte
	esculenta Lindl.	see *C. quamash*
	fraseri	see *C. scilloides*
	howellii	EBee
	leichtlinii misapplied	see *C. leichtlinii* subsp. *suksdorfii*
	leichtlinii (Baker) S. Watson	ECho ISea
N	- 'Alba' hort.	see *C. leichtlinii* subsp. *leichtlinii*
*	- 'Alba Plena'	NBPC NBir
	- 'Blauwe Donau'	see *C. leichtlinii* subsp. *suksdorfii* 'Blauwe Donau'
	- Blue Danube	see *C. leichtlinii* subsp. *suksdorfii* 'Blauwe Donau'
§	- subsp. ***leichtlinii*** ♀H4	More than 30 suppliers
	- 'Magdalen'	CAvo CFFs
N	- 'Plena' (d)	ECha MSte
	- 'Semiplena' (d)	CAvo CFFs CFwr CMea CMil CTca EBee EBrs EMan EMon EPot GGar LRHS MSte NMen NSti SPhx WAul WCot WHoo
§	- subsp. ***suksdorfii***	CAvo CSam EBee ECho GBuc GCra LRHS MWat WAul
§	- - 'Blauwe Donau'	CTca EBee EBrs GKev MSte SMeo
	- - Caerulea Group	More than 30 suppliers
	- - 'Electra'	CAvo ECha
§	***quamash***	More than 30 suppliers

- 'Blue Melody' (v)	CBow CMea CTca EBee EBrs EMan EMon EPot GBuc GKev GMaP GMac GSki LRHS MCCP MWgw NMRc NMen SPhx WCra WLin
- var. ***breviflora*** new	CTca EBee EBrs
- 'Orion'	CMea CTca EBee EBrs EMon GBuc GMac NSti SMeo SPhx WAul WCot
§ ***scilloides***	WRos

Camellia ✿ (*Theaceae*)

'Annette Carol' new	CDoC
'Ariel's Song'	CDoC
'Auburn White'	see *C. japonica* 'Mrs Bertha A. Harms'
'Baby Bear'	CDoC
'Bacciochi'	NLar
'Barbara Clark' (*saluenensis* x *reticulata*)	CTrG LRHS MAsh MGos SCog SCoo
'Bertha Harms Blush'	see *C. japonica* 'Mrs Bertha A. Harms'
'Bett's Supreme'	CDoC
'Betty Ridley'	SImb
'Black Lace' (*reticulata* x *williamsii*) ♀H4	CCtw CTrh CTri EKen EPfP GLld LRHS MAsh MBri NPri SCam SCog SCoo SImb SPoG WCot WGob WMoo
'Blissful Dawn'	CTrh
'Bonnie Marie' (hybrid)	CBcs CDoC MGos SCam SCog SImb
brevistyla	CBcs
'Charles Cobb'	see *C. japonica* 'Mrs Charles Cobb'
* 'Chatsworth Belle'	CTrh SCam
'China Lady' (*reticulata* x *granthamiana*)	MBri
'Cinnamon Cindy' (hybrid)	CDoC SCam SCog
'Congratulations' new	SPer
'Contessa Lavinia Maggi'	see *C. japonica* 'Lavinia Maggi'
* 'Cornish Clay'	ISea
'Cornish Snow' (*cuspidata* x *saluenensis*) ♀H4	CDoC CSBt CSam CTri EPfP ISea MGos SCam SCog SHBN SImb SPer SPur SSpi WFar
'Cornish Spring' (*japonica* x *cuspidata*) ♀H4	CCCN CCtw CDoC CSBt CTrh ENot EPfP LHyd SCog SPoG
'Corsica'	SHBN
cuspidata	LHyd
'Czar'	see *C. japonica* 'The Czar'
'Dainty Dale' (hybrid)	CDoC LRHS SCam SSta
'Delia Williams'	see *C.* x *williamsii* 'Citation'
'Diana's Charm'	CDoC LSRN
'Doctor Clifford Parks' (*reticulata* x *japonica*) ♀H2	GLld LHyd SCam SCog
'Donckelaeri'	see *C. japonica* 'Masayoshi'
'Dorothy James' (hybrid)	SImb
'El Dorado' (*pitardii* x *japonica*)	CDoC CTrG
'Extravaganza' (*japonica* hybrid)	CBcs CTrh IArd MBri SCog SImb
'Felice Harris' (*sasanqua* x *reticulata*)	MBri SCam SCog
'Fire 'n' Ice'	SCam SCog
'Fragrant Pink' (*rusticana* x *lutchuensis*)	CTrh
'Francie L' (*saluenensis* x *reticulata*) ♀H3-4	CDoC CDul EPfP LHyd SCam SCog SSta
fraterna	CBcs
'Frau Minna Seidel'	see *C. japonica* 'Otome'
'Freedom Bell' (hybrid) ♀H4	CCtw CMHG CTrG CTrh ENot GGGa ISea LHyd LRHS MAsh SCam SCog SCoo SPoG
'Golden Anniversary'	see *C. japonica* 'Dahlohnega'
grijsii	CTrh LHyd
'Happy Anniversary' new	SPer
§ ***hiemalis*** 'Bonanza'	CTrh SCam SImb
- 'Chansonette'	CDoC SCam SCog SImb
- 'Christmas Candles' new	CSam
§ - 'Dazzler'	CBcs CSBt LHyd SCam SCog SImb
- 'Kanjirô'	CTrh LHyd SCam SCog
- 'Showa Supreme'	SCam SImb
- 'Shôwa-no-sakae'	SCog
§ - 'Sparkling Burgundy' ♀H3	CBcs CBrm CDoC ENot EPfP GLld LCro LHyd LRHS MGos SCam SCog SImb SPoG
'Hooker'	CDoC
'Howard Asper' (*reticulata* x *japonica*)	SCam
'Ice Follies'	SCam SCog
'Imbricata Rubra'	see *C. japonica* 'Imbricata'
'Innovation' (x *williamsii* x *reticulata*)	MAsh NBlu SCam SCoo SImb
'Inspiration' (*reticulata* x *saluenensis*) ♀H4	CBcs CDoC CMHG CMac CSBt CTrG CTrh CWSG ENot EPfP GGGa LHyd MAsh MBri MGos NBlu SBod SCam SCog SHBN SImb SPoG SSpi WBod WGob
japonica new	CBcs
- HTB 4	SCam
- HTB 10	SCam
- 'Aaron's Ruby'	CBcs CDoC LRHS SCam SCog SImb
- 'Ace of Hearts'	MBri
- 'Ada Pieper'	CTrh
- 'Adelina Patti' ♀H4	CBcs CCtw CMHG CSBt CTrh LHyd LRHS MAsh SCog SCoo SImb SPoG
- 'Adelina Patti' carmine sport	SImb
- 'Adolphe Audusson' ♀H4	More than 30 suppliers
§ - 'Akashigata' ♀H4	CDoC CMac CTrG ENot EPfP LRHS MAsh SCam SCog SCoo SImb SPer SPoG SSta WBod
- 'Alba Plena' ♀H4	CTrh CWSG LHyd MGos SCam SCog SImb WFar
- 'Alba Simplex'	CDoC CMac ELan EPfP LRHS SCam SCog SHBN SImb SPer SSpi SSta WGob
- 'Alexander Hunter' ♀H4	LHyd LRHS SCam SCog SImb
- 'Alexis Smith'	CBcs
- 'Alison Leigh Woodroof' new	CDoC
§ - 'Althaeiflora'	CBcs CDoC MGos SCam SCog SImb
- 'Ama-no-gawa'	LHyd
- 'Amazing Graces'	CDoC
- 'Anemoniflora'	CDoC CTrG ELan LRHS SCam SCog WBod WFar
- 'Angel'	CBcs SCam SCog SImb
- 'Angela Cocchi'	WBod
- 'Angello'	EKen
- 'Annie Wylam' ♀H4	CTrh LHyd SCog
- 'Apollo' Paul, 1911	CSam CTrG CTrh EPfP MGos MSwo NBlu SCam SCog SHBN SImb
- 'Apollo' ambig.	CBcs CDoC LRHS MAsh
§ - 'Apple Blossom' ♀H4	ELan SImb WBod
- 'Arajishi' misapplied	see *C. rusticana* 'Beni-arajishi'
* - 'Augustine Supreme'	CMac
- 'Augusto Leal de Gouveia Pinto'	WBod
- 'Australis' ♀H4	SCam
- 'Ave Maria' ♀H4	CDoC CTrh SImb
- 'Baby Pearl'	SCam
- 'Baby Sis'	SCam
- 'Ballet Dancer' ♀H4	CDoC MGos SCam SCog SImb
- 'Bambino'	CDoC
- 'Baron Gomer'	see *C. japonica* 'Comte de Gomer'
- 'Baronne Leguay'	SCam SImb
- 'Beau Harp'	SCam SImb
- 'Bella Romana'	SCam SImb

	- 'Benidaikagura'	SCam SImb
	- 'Benihassaku'	SImb
	- 'Benten' (v)	CTrG
	- 'Berenice Boddy' ♀H4	CBcs CTrh SCam SImb
	- 'Berenice Perfection'	CMHG LHyd SImb WFar
	- 'Betty Foy Sanders'	CTrh
	- 'Betty Robinson' **new**	SCam
	- 'Betty Sheffield'	CTrG MAsh MGos SCog SCoo SHBN SImb WFar
	- 'Betty Sheffield Pink'	CTrG LRHS SCam SImb
	- 'Betty Sheffield Supreme'	CBcs
	- 'Billie McCaskill'	SCam SImb
	- 'Black Tie'	CDoC LHyd LRHS MAsh MGos SCog SImb WGob
	- 'Blackburnia'	see *C. japonica* 'Althaeiflora'
	- 'Blaze of Glory'	CTrh NLar SCog
§	- 'Blood of China'	CBcs CCtw CDoC CSBt CWSG ENot LRHS MAsh MGos SCam SCog SCoo SImb SPer SPoG WBod WFar WMoo
	- 'Bob Hope' ♀H4	CBcs CDoC CTrh MGos NBlu SCam SImb
	- 'Bob's Tinsie' ♀H4	CDoC CMHG CSBt EPfP GBin ISea MAsh SCog
§	- 'Bokuhan' ♀H4	CCtw CDoC EPfP SCog
	- 'Bright Buoy'	CDoC
	- 'Brushfield's Yellow' ♀H4	CBcs CDoC CMHG CSBt ELan EPfP GLld IArd ISea LHyd LRHS MAsh MBri MDun MGos NBlu SCam SCog SCoo SImb SPer SSta WFar WGob
	- 'Bush Hill Beauty'	see *C. japonica* 'Lady de Saumarez'
§	- 'C.M. Hovey' ♀H4	CMHG CMac CTrh MAsh SCam SHBN SImb WBod
	- 'C.M. Wilson'	CDoC CMac SCog SImb WBod
	- 'Can Can'	CBcs CDoC CTrG SCam SCog
	- 'Canon Boscawen'	CTrG
	- 'Cara Mia'	CBcs CDoC SCam SImb
	- 'Carolina Beauty'	CDoC LRHS MAsh
	- 'Carter's Sunburst' ♀H4	CBcs CTrh ELan EPfP LRHS MAsh SCam SCog SImb WGob
	- 'Chandleri Elegans'	see *C. japonica* 'Elegans'
	- 'Charlotte de Rothschild'	CTrh CTri EPfP GLld SCam
	- 'Cheryll Lynn'	CTrh SImb
	- 'Christmas Beauty'	SCam WBod
	- 'Cinderella'	SCog SImb
	- 'Clarise Carleton'	CTrh GGGa LHyd MBri
	- 'Clarissa'	SCam SImb
	- 'Colonel Firey'	see *C. japonica* 'C.M. Hovey'
	- 'Commander Mulroy' ♀H4	CTrh MBri SCam SImb
	- 'Compton's Brow'	see *C. japonica* 'Gauntlettii'
§	- 'Comte de Gomer'	CDoC ELan EPfP LRHS SCam SCog
	- 'Conspicua'	CBcs
§	- 'Coquettii' ♀H4	CBcs CDul LRHS MAsh
	- 'Coral Beauty'	SImb WFar
	- 'Coral Pink Lotus'	CDoC SCam
	- 'Coral Queen'	SCam
§	- 'Dahlohnega'	CTrh SPer
	- 'Daikagura'	CBcs
	- 'Dainty'	CBcs
	- 'Daitairin'	see *C. japonica* 'Dewatairin'
	- 'Dark of the Moon'	CDoC
	- 'Dear Jenny'	CBcs CTrG
	- 'Debutante'	CBcs CDoC CMac CTrh LHyd MAsh SCam SCog SImb WBod
	- 'Deep Secret'	SCog
	- 'Desire' ♀H4	CBcs CDoC CMHG CTrh ENot GLld LRHS MDun SCam SCog SCoo SImb SPoG WGob
	- 'Devonia'	CBcs EPfP LHyd SCog
§	- 'Dewatairin' (Higo)	CDoC MGos SCam SCog SImb
	- 'Dixie Knight'	CBcs CDoC MGos SCam SCog SImb
	- 'Dobreei'	CMac
	- 'Doctor Burnside'	CBcs CDoC CMHG CTrh SCam SCog SImb
	- 'Doctor King' **new**	ENot
	- 'Doctor Olga Petersen'	SCog
	- 'Doctor Tinsley' ♀H4	CDoC GLld LRHS MAsh SCam SCoo SImb
	- 'Dolly Dyer'	CDoC
	- 'Dona Herzilia de Freitas Magalhaes'	CDoC SCam SCog SImb
	- 'Dona Jane Andresson'	SCam SImb
	- 'Donckelaeri'	see *C. japonica* 'Masayoshi'
	- 'Donnan's Dream'	CTrh
	- 'Doris Ellis'	CMHG
	- 'Double Rose' (d)	NBlu SCog
	- 'Drama Girl' ♀H2	CBcs CDoC SBod SCam SCog SImb
	- 'Duc de Bretagne'	ISea SCog
	- 'Duchesse Decazes'	CBcs MBri SImb
	- 'Duchesse Decazes Pink'	SImb
	- 'Duckyls Belle'	SImb
	- 'Edelweiss'	CDoC MGos SCam SCog SImb
	- 'Effendee'	see *C. sasanqua* 'Rosea Plena'
	- 'Eleanor Grant'	SImb
	- 'Eleanor Hagood'	CBcs
§	- 'Elegans' ♀H4	CBcs CDoC CMac CTrG ENot EPfP ISea LCro LRHS NBlu SBod SCam SCog SCoo SHBN SImb SPer SSta WFar
	- 'Elegans Champagne'	NPri
	- 'Elegans Splendor'	CDoC SImb
	- 'Elegans Supreme'	CDoC
	- 'Elegant Beauty'	see *C.* x *williamsii* 'Elegant Beauty'
	- 'Elisabeth'	WFar
	- 'Elizabeth Dowd'	CBcs SCog
	- 'Elizabeth Hawkins'	CTrh GLld LHyd LRHS MAsh
	- 'Elizabeth Rose Open' **new**	SImb
	- 'Ella Drayton'	SCog
	- 'Emily Wilson' **new**	CDoC
	- 'Emmett Barnes'	LHyd SCam SImb
	- 'Emmett Pfingstl'	SCam SImb
	- 'Emperor of Russia'	CBcs LHyd SImb WBod
	- 'Erin Farmer'	CBcs
	- 'Eugène Lizé'	SCam
	- 'Evelyn'	SCam SImb
	- 'Eximia'	LRHS NBlu SCam SCog
	- 'Extravaganza Pink'	SImb
	- 'Faith'	CBcs SImb
	- 'Fanny'	SCam SImb
	- 'Fashionata'	CDoC SCam SImb
§	- 'Fimbriata'	SCam SImb
	- 'Fimbriata Alba'	see *C. japonica* 'Fimbriata'
	- 'Finlandia Variegated'	CDoC SCam SCog
	- 'Fire Dance'	CTrh
	- 'Fire Falls' ♀H4	CMHG
	- 'Firebird'	CBcs
	- 'Flame'	CBcs WBod
	- 'Flashlight'	CDoC EPfP LRHS
§	- 'Fleur Dipater'	SCam SImb WBod
	- 'Flora'	WBod
	- 'Flowerwood'	SCam SCog SImb WFar
	- 'Forest Green'	ELan MAsh
	- 'Fortune Teller'	CBcs
	- 'Frans van Damme'	CBcs SImb
	- 'Fred Sander'	CBcs CDoC CWSG GLld MGos SCam SCog SCoo SImb SMer
	- 'Frosty Morn'	CBcs ELan
	- 'Furo-an'	MAsh SCam SImb
§	- 'Gauntlettii'	CBcs SImb
	- 'Geisha Girl'	SCam SCog SImb
§	- 'Gigantea'	NBlu SCam SImb
§	- 'Gigantea Red'	LRHS
	- 'Giuditta Rosani'	CDoC
	- 'Giuseppina Pieri'	LHyd
	- 'Gladys Wannamaker'	SCog
	- 'Glen 40'	see *C. japonica* 'Coquettii'

	– 'Gloire de Nantes' ♀H4	LRHS NBlu SCam SCog SImb WBod
	– 'Gold Tone'	MGos SCam SImb
	– 'Grace Bunton'	CBcs CDoC MGos SCam SCog
	– 'Granada'	SCog
	– 'Grand Prix' ♀H4	CDoC CTrh GLld LHyd LRHS MGos SBod SCam SCog SImb
	– 'Grand Slam' ♀H2	CBcs CDoC CDul CTrh EPfP SCam SCog SImb
	– 'Guest of Honor'	CBcs
	– 'Guilio Nuccio' ♀H4	CBcs CDoC CTrG CTri EPfP IArd LRHS MGos NPri SCam SCog SImb SMer SPer SPur WBod
	– 'Gus Menard'	SCam
	– 'Gwenneth Morey'	CBcs CDoC ELan EPfP SCam SImb
	– 'H.A. Downing'	SCam SImb
§	– 'Hagoromo' ♀H4	CDoC CTrh ELan EPfP LRHS MAsh SCog SHBN SImb SPer WBod WFar
§	– 'Hakurakuten' ♀H4	CMHG GLld IArd ISea SCog SImb
	– 'Hanafûki'	CDoC MGos SCam SCog SImb
	– 'Hanatachibana'	SCam
	– 'Hatsuzakura'	see *C. japonica* 'Dewatairin'
	– 'Hawaii'	CDoC CMac CSBt CTrh MGos SCam SCog SImb
	– 'Henry Turnbull'	SImb
	– 'Her Majesty Queen Elizabeth II'	CDoC
	– Herme	see *C. japonica* 'Hikarugenji'
	– 'High Hat'	CBcs LHyd SCog
	– 'High, Wide 'n' Handsome' new	CDoC
§	– 'Hikarugenji'	MGos SCog
	– 'Hime-otome'	SCam SImb
	– 'Hinomaru'	CMac
	– 'Holly Bright'	CTrh GLld
	– 'Ichisetsu' new	SCog
§	– 'Imbricata'	CBcs ENot ISea LRHS MAsh SCog SImb
	– 'Imbricata Alba'	SCam SImb
	– 'Italiana Vera'	LRHS MAsh
	– 'J.J. Whitfield'	CMac SImb
	– 'Jack Jones Scented'	CMHG
	– 'Janet Waterhouse'	CBcs SCoo WFar
	– 'Jean Clere'	CTrG GLld MGos MWea SCog SCoo SImb
	– 'Jingle Bells'	CBcs
	– 'Jitsugetsusei' new	CDoC
	– 'Joseph Pfingstl' ♀H4	CCtw CDoC CTri EPfP GLld LRHS MAsh NPri SCam SCog SImb
	– 'Joshua E. Youtz'	LHyd SCog SImb
	– 'Jovey Carlyon'	CDoC
	– 'Joy Sander'	see *C. japonica* 'Apple Blossom'
§	– 'Julia Drayton'	MAsh
	– 'Julia France'	SCog
	– 'June McCaskill' new	CDoC
	– 'Juno'	CBcs LRHS SCam
	– 'Jupiter' Paul, 1906 ♀H4	CBcs CDoC CMac CTrh CTri EPfP GKev ISea LHyd LRHS LSRN MAsh MGos SCog SCoo SHBN SImb
	– 'Justine Heurtin'	SCam SImb
§	– 'K. Sawada'	SCam SCog
	– 'Katherine Nuccio'	SImb
	– 'Katie'	MDun SCog
	– 'Kay Truesdale'	SImb
	– 'Kellingtoniana'	see *C. japonica* 'Gigantea'
	– 'Kenny'	CBcs
	– 'Kentucky'	LRHS SCam
	– 'Kewpie Doll'	CTrh
	– 'Kick-off'	CBcs CTrh SCog SCoo SImb
	– 'Kimberley'	CBcs CCtw CDoC EPfP SCog
	– 'King Size'	CDoC MGos SCam SImb
	– 'King's Ransom'	CDoC CMac LRHS
	– 'Kingyoba-shiro-wabisuke' new	CDoC
	– 'Kingyo-tsubaki'	WBod
	– 'Kinsekai'	see *C. rusticana* 'Kinsekai'
	– 'Kitty Berry'	CTrh SImb
	– 'Kokinran'	CDoC SCam SImb
§	– 'Konronkoku' ♀H4	CBcs CCtw CDoC LRHS MAsh SCog SImb WBod
	– 'Kouron-jura'	see *C. japonica* 'Konronkoku'
	– 'Kramer's Beauty'	SCoo SPoG
	– 'Kramer's Supreme'	CBcs CBrm CCCN CDoC CTrG CWSG ENot LRHS MAsh MGos NBlu NLar SBod SCam SCog SCoo SImb WFar
	– 'La Graciola'	see *C. japonica* 'Odoratissima'
	– 'La Pace Rubra'	SCam SImb
	– 'Lady Campbell'	CTri EBee ENot MAsh NBlu NPri SCam SImb
	– 'Lady Clare'	see *C. japonica* 'Akashigata'
§	– 'Lady de Saumarez'	CBcs CMac SImb
	– 'Lady Erma'	CBcs
	– 'Lady Loch'	CTrh LRHS MAsh MBri MGos SCam SImb
	– 'Lady McCulloch'	LRHS SCam
	– 'Lady Vansittart'	CBrm CDoC CSam CTrG ELan ENot EPfP GLld LHyd LRHS MAsh MGos NBlu SCog SCoo SImb SPer WBod WGob
§	– 'Lady Vansittart Pink'	CMac NBlu SCam SHBN
	– 'Lady Vansittart Red'	see *C. japonica* 'Lady Vansittart Pink'
	– 'Lady Vansittart Shell'	see *C. japonica* 'Yours Truly'
	– 'Latifolia'	GLld LRHS SCam
	– 'Laurie Bray'	SCog WFar
§	– 'Lavinia Maggi' ♀H4	CBcs CDoC CTrG CTrh CTri ELan ENot EPfP GLld LHyd LPan LRHS MAsh MGos NBlu NPri SCam SCog SCoo SHBN SImb SPer SPoG SReu SRms SSta WBVN WGob
	– 'L'Avvenire'	SCog
§	– 'Le Lys'	SCam
	– 'Lemon Drop'	CTrh SCam
	– 'Leonora Novick'	CDoC SCog
	– 'Lily Pons' ♀H4	CTrh GLld LHyd
	– 'Lipstick'	LHyd
	– 'Little Bit'	CBcs CDoC CMHG CTrh MGos SCam SCog SImb SPer
	– 'Little Slam'	CDoC
	– LOR 280	SCam
	– 'Lotus'	see *C. japonica* 'Gauntlettii'
	– 'Lovelight' ♀H4	CTrh
	– 'Ludgvan Red'	LRHS SCam
	– 'Lulu Belle'	SCog
	– 'Ma Belle'	CMHG
	– 'Mabel Blackwell'	SCam SImb
	– 'Madame de Strekaloff'	CMac SCam SImb
	– 'Madame Hahn' new	CDoC
	– 'Madame Lebois'	CDoC SCam SImb
	– 'Madame Martin Cachet'	SCog SCoo
	– 'Magic Moments'	SCam SCog
	– 'Magnoliiflora'	see *C. japonica* 'Hagoromo'
	– 'Magnoliiflora Alba'	see *C. japonica* 'Miyakodori'
	– 'Maiden's Blush'	CMac
	– 'Margaret Davis'	CCCN CDoC CSBt CTrG EBee ELan ENot EPfP GLld LHyd LSRN MAsh MGos MWea SCam SCoo SImb SPoG WGob
	– 'Margaret Davis Picotee' ♀H4	CBcs CMHG CTrh SCog SPer SSta
	– 'Margaret Rose'	SCam SImb
	– 'Margaret Short'	CDoC
	– 'Margherita Coleoni'	CBcs LHyd SHBN SImb
	– 'Marguérite Gouillon'	CBcs CDoC ISea LHyd SCam SImb
	– 'Marian Mitchell'	SCam SImb
	– 'Mariana'	CDoC SCog
	– 'Marie Bracey'	CBcs SCam SImb
	– 'Marjorie Magnificent'	LRHS MAsh
	– 'Mark Alan'	CDoC

	- 'Maroon and Gold'	CDoC SCog
	- 'Mars' Υ^{H4}	CBcs MGos SCam SCog WFar
	- 'Mary Alice Cox'	CDoC
	- 'Mary Costa'	CTrh WFar
§	- 'Masayoshi' Υ^{H4}	CSBt CTrG GLld LHyd SCog WBod
	- 'Masquerade'	SImb
	- 'Masterpiece'	SImb
	- 'Mathotiana'	WBod
	- 'Mathotiana Alba' Υ^{H4}	CBcs CDoC CMac CSBt CTri ELan EPfP LSRN MAsh MGos SCam SCog SImb SPer
	- 'Mathotiana Purple King'	see *C. japonica* 'Julia Drayton'
§	- 'Mathotiana Rosea' Υ^{H4}	CBcs CMac EBee SCam SHBN WBod
	- 'Mathotiana Supreme'	CDoC SCam SCog SImb WBod
	- 'Matterhorn'	CTrh MAsh
	- 'Mattie Cole'	LHyd SCam WGob
	- 'Mercury' Υ^{H4}	CBcs CMac CTrG CWSG GGGa SCog SHBN WBod
	- 'Mercury Variegated'	CMHG
	- 'Midnight'	CBcs CDoC CMHG LRHS MAsh SCam SImb WFar WGob
	- 'Midnight Magic'	CTrh CTri
	- 'Midnight Serenade'	CCtw CDoC SCam
§	- 'Mikenjaku'	CBcs CTrG ENot EPfP LRHS MAsh SCam SCog SCoo WGob
	- 'Minnie Maddern Fiske'	SCam SImb
	- 'Miriam Stevenson'	SCam
	- 'Miss Charleston'	CBcs LHyd SCog
	- 'Miss Lyla'	SCam SImb
	- 'Miss Universe'	CTrh
	- 'Mississippi Beauty'	CTrh
§	- 'Miyakodori'	EPfP
	- 'Mona Lisa'	SImb
	- 'Monsieur Faucillon'	CBcs
	- 'Monstruosa Rubra'	see *C. japonica* 'Gigantea Red'
	- 'Monte Carlo'	CDoC SBod SCam SCog
	- 'Moonlight Bay'	SCog
	- 'Moshe Dayan'	LRHS MAsh NPri SCam SCog SMer WGob
§	- 'Mrs Bertha A. Harms'	CDoC MGos SCam SCog
§	- 'Mrs Charles Cobb'	LPan
	- 'Mrs D.W. Davis'	CDoC EPfP SCam SImb
	- 'Mrs Derlocquer's Beauty' **new**	SImb
	- 'Mrs Lyman Clarke' **new**	CDoC
	- 'Mrs Sander'	see *C. japonica* 'Gauntlettii'
	- 'Mrs Tingley'	EBee SImb
	- 'Mrs William Thompson'	SCam
	- 'Myrtiflora' **new**	SImb
	- 'Nagasaki'	see *C. japonica* 'Mikenjaku'
	- 'Nigra'	see *C. japonica* 'Konronkoku'
	- 'Nina Avery' **new**	CDoC
	- 'Nobilissima'	CBcs CDoC CMac CTrG CTrh CTri ENot EPfP ISea LCro LRHS NBlu NLar NPri SCam SCog SCoo SHBN SImb SPer SPoG WFar
	- 'Nuccio's Cameo'	CDoC CTrh LRHS MAsh SCoo
	- 'Nuccio's Gem' Υ^{H4}	CDoC CMHG EBee ELan EPfP LHyd LRHS MGos SCam SCog SImb SSta
	- 'Nuccio's Jewel' Υ^{H4}	CBcs CCtw CDoC CTrh CWSG IMGH LHyd LRHS MAsh SCam SCog SImb SPer SPoG WGob WMoo
	- 'Nuccio's Pearl'	CBcs CCtw CDoC CTrh LRHS SCam SCog SMer WBVN WBod WGob WMoo
	- 'Nuccio's Pink Lace'	CBcs CDoC CTri
§	- 'Odoratissima'	CTrG
	- 'Olga Anderson'	MGos
	- 'Olive Honnor'	SCog
	- 'Onetia Holland'	CBrm CDoC LSRN MGos MWea SCam SCog SCoo
	- 'Optima'	CBcs CDoC LRHS SCog SCoo
	- 'Optima Rosea'	CTrG ENot
§	- 'Otome'	SImb WBod
	- 'Paulette Goddard'	SCam SImb
	- 'Paul's Apollo'	see *C. japonica* 'Apollo' Paul, 1911
	- 'Pax'	SImb
	- 'Peachblossom'	see *C. japonica* 'Fleur Dipater'
	- 'Pearl Harbor'	SCam SImb
	- 'Pensacola Red'	CDoC SCam
	- 'Pink Champagne'	NPri SBod
	- 'Pink Clouds'	CBcs
	- 'Pink Perfection'	see *C. japonica* 'Otome'
	- 'Pope Pius IX'	see *C. japonica* 'Prince Eugène Napoléon'
	- 'Preston Rose'	CBcs CDoC SImb
	- 'Pride of Descanso'	see *C. japonica* 'Yukibotan'
	- 'Primavera'	CTrh LHyd SCam SCog SImb
§	- 'Prince Eugène Napoléon'	GLld SCam SImb
	- 'Prince Murat' **new**	CDoC
	- 'Prince of Orange'	SImb
	- 'Princess Baciocchi'	CBcs SCam
	- 'Princess du Mahe'	CMac
	- 'Purple Emperor'	see *C. japonica* 'Julia Drayton'
	- 'R.L. Wheeler' Υ^{H4}	CBcs CDoC CSBt CTri LHyd LRHS LSRN MWea NPri SCog SCoo SImb
	- 'Rafia'	SCam
	- 'Ralph Peer Seedling' **new**	SImb
	- 'Red Cardinal'	SImb
	- 'Red Dandy'	CDoC MGos SCam SCog SImb
	- 'Red Elephant'	SCam
	- 'Red Red Rose'	CDoC
	- 'Reg Ragland'	CDoC CMHG MGos SCam SCog SImb
	- 'Reigyoku'	see *C. rusticana* 'Reigyoku'
	- 'Robert Strauss'	SCam SImb
	- 'Roger Hall'	CBcs CDoC ENot SCam SCog SCoo SPoG WGob
	- 'Rōgetsu'	SCam
	- 'Rosularis'	SCam SCog SPur
	- 'Rubescens Major' Υ^{H4}	LHyd SCam SImb
	- 'Ruby Creek' **new**	SImb
	- 'Ruddigore'	CTrh SCam
	- subsp. ***rusticana***	SImb
	rusticana 'Arajishi' **new**	SImb
	- 'Arajishi' misapplied	see *C. rusticana* 'Beni-arajishi'
§	- 'Beni-arajishi'	CBcs CDoC CDul LRHS SCam SCog SCoo WFar
§	- 'Kinsekai' (v)	SImb
§	- 'Reigyoku' (v)	CBcs GLld SImb
	- 'Sabiniana' **new**	LRHS MAsh
	- 'Saint André'	CMac
	- 'Sally Harrell'	SCam SImb
	- 'San Dimas' Υ^{H4}	CDoC CTrh SCam SCog SImb
	- 'Saturnia'	CCtw CDoC GLld LRHS MAsh
	- 'Sawada's Dream'	CDoC ISea SCog
	- 'Scented Red'	CDoC SCam SCog
	- 'Scentsation' Υ^{H4}	CDoC CMHG CTri SCog
	- 'Sea Foam'	LHyd LRHS SCam SSta
	- 'Sea Gull'	CTrh SCam SImb
	- 'Senator Duncan U. Fletcher' **new**	CDoC
	- 'Shiragiku'	CBcs CDoC SPer WBod
	- 'Shiro Chan'	CDoC MGos SCam SCog SImb
	- 'Shirobotan'	CDoC CTrG ENot GQui MGos SBod SCam SCog SPur
	- 'Shiro-daikagura'	WBod
	- 'Silver Anniversary'	CBcs CDoC CMHG CSBt CTrG CTrh CTri ELan ENot GLld GQui ISea LHyd LRHS LSRN MAsh MGos SCam SCog SCoo SImb SPer SPoG SReu SSta WGob
	- 'Silver Moon'	see *C. japonica* 'K. Sawada'
	- 'Silver Ruffles'	SCam SImb
	- 'Simeon'	SCam
	- 'Snow Chan'	CMHG

- 'Souvenir de Bahuaud-Litou' ♀H4	CBcs SCam SCog SImb WBod
- 'Spencer's Pink'	SCam SImb
- 'Splendens Carlyon'	LRHS MAsh SCoo
- 'Spring Fever'	SCam
- 'Spring Fling'	CTrh
- 'Spring Formal'	CTrh
- 'Spring Frill'	SCam SCog
- 'Stardust' **new**	SImb
- 'Strawberry Blonde'	SCog
- 'Strawberry Swirl'	SCog
- 'Sugar Babe'	CDoC CSBt MAsh SCam SCog WGob
- 'Sunset Glory'	CMHG SCam
- 'Sweetheart'	SCog
- 'Sylva' ♀H4	GGGa SImb SSpi WBod
- 'Sylvia'	CMac
- 'Tada Meibi'	CDoC
- 'Takanini'	CTrh
- 'Takayama'	SImb
- 'Tammia'	EPfP SCam
- 'Tear Drops' **new**	SImb
- 'Teresa Ragland'	CDoC SCam SImb
- 'Teringa'	CDoC
§ - 'The Czar'	CBcs SCog WBod
- 'The Mikado'	CDoC SCog
- 'Theo's Mini'	SCam
- 'Tickled Pink'	CDoC SCam
- 'Tiffany'	CBcs CDoC LHyd LRHS MGos SCam SCog SCoo SHBN
- 'Tiki'	MBri WFar
- 'Tinker Bell'	CDoC MBri SCog SImb
- 'Tom Thumb' ♀H4	CDoC CTrh LRHS MAsh SCam SImb SRms SSta WGob
- 'Tomorrow'	CDoC LRHS MAsh SCam SCog
- 'Tomorrow Park Hill'	CBcs SCog SImb
§ - 'Tomorrow Variegated'	MGos SCog
- 'Tomorrow's Dawn'	SCam
- 'Touchdown'	SCam SImb
- 'Tregye'	CBcs
- 'Trewithen White'	CDoC CSam
§ - 'Tricolor' ♀H4	CBcs CDoC CMHG CMac CSBt CTrh EPfP GLld LHyd LRHS MAsh MGos NBlu SCam SCog SCoo SHBN SImb WBod WBrE WFar
- 'Tricolor Red'	see *C. japonica* 'Lady de Saumarez'
- 'Trinkett'	CDoC
- 'Twilight'	SImb
- variegated (v)	SCog
- 'Victor de Bisschop'	see *C. japonica* 'Le Lys'
- 'Victor Emmanuel'	see *C. japonica* 'Blood of China'
- 'Ville de Nantes'	MGos
- 'Ville de Nantes Red'	SCog
- 'Virginia Carlyon'	CBcs CDoC
- 'Virginia Robinson'	SCam SImb
- 'Virgin's Blush'	SCam SImb
- 'Vittorio Emanuele II'	CTrh GLld LRHS MGos
- 'Vosper's Rose' **new**	CDoC
- 'Warrior'	SCam SCog
- 'White Nun'	CBcs SCog
- 'White Swan'	CSBt EBee GLld LRHS MAsh SCog SCoo
- 'Wilamina' ♀H4	CDoC CMHG CTrh
- 'Wildfire'	SCam SImb
- 'William Bartlett'	CTrh
- 'William Honey'	CTrh
- 'Winter Cheer'	SCog
- 'Wisley White'	see *C. japonica* 'Hakurakuten'
§ - 'Yours Truly'	CBcs CDoC CMac CTrh LHyd LRHS MAsh MDun SCam SCog
§ - 'Yukibotan'	CBcs
- 'Yukimi-guruma'	WBod
'Jury's Yellow'	see *C.* x *williamsii* 'Jury's Yellow'
'Lasca Beauty' (*reticulata* x *japonica*)	SCam
'Lavender Queen'	see *C. sasanqua* 'Lavender Queen'

'Leonard Messel' (*reticulata* x *williamsii*) ♀H4	CBcs CDoC CDul CMHG CTrG CTrh ENot EPfP GGGa LHyd LRHS MDun MGos NBlu SCam SCog SCoo SHBN SImb SMer SPer SReu WBod
'Liz Henslowe'	CDoC
lutchuensis	SCam
'Madame Victor de Bisschop'	see *C. japonica* 'Le Lys'
'Maud Messel' (x *williamsii* x *reticulata*)	SCam
'Milo Rowell'	SCam
'Mimosa Jury'	CDoC
'Monticello' **new**	CDoC
'Nicky Crisp' (*japonica* x *pitardii*)	GLld LHyd
'Nijinski' (*reticulata* hybrid)	CDoC
'Nonie Haydon' (*pitardii* hybrid)	CDoC
oleifera	CSam SCam SCog WFar
'Pink Spangles'	see *C. japonica* 'Mathotiana Rosea'
pitardii	SCog
- 'Snippet'	CDoC
'Polar Ice' (*oleifera* hybrid)	CDoC SCam SCog
'Polyanna'	CDoC SCog
'Quintessence' (*japonica* x *lutchuensis*)	GLld SCog SImb
reticulata 'Arch of Triumph'	CTrG
- 'Captain Rawes'	SCam
- 'Mary Williams'	ENot NBlu SCoo
rosiflora 'Cascade'	SImb
- 'Roseaflora Cascade'	CDoC
'Royalty' (*japonica* x *reticulata*) ♀H3	CTrG
saluenensis	SImb
- 'Exbury Trumpet'	CCtw
- 'Trewithen Red'	WBod
'Salutation' (*reticulata* x *saluenensis*)	SCam SImb WBod
sasanqua Thunb.	CDul CSBt CSam ISea LPan
- 'Baronesa de Soutelinho'	SCam SCog
- 'Ben'	SCog
- 'Bert Jones'	SImb
- 'Bettie Patricia'	SCog
- 'Bonanza'	see *C. hiemalis* 'Bonanza'
- Borde Hill form	SCam
- 'Cleopatra'	LPan MAsh
- 'Cotton Candy'	CDoC
- 'Crimson King' ♀H3	SCam SHBN SImb
- 'Dazzler'	see *C. hiemalis* 'Dazzler'
- 'Flamingo'	see *C. sasanqua* 'Fukuzutsumi'
- 'Fragrans'	SCog
- 'Fuji-no-mine'	CTrh SCog
§ - 'Fukuzutsumi'	CSBt CTrG SCam SImb
- 'Gay Sue'	CTrh LHyd SCam SImb
- 'Hiryû'	SCam SCog
- 'Hugh Evans' ♀H3	CAbP CBcs CDoC CTrh CTri LHyd LRHS MAsh SCam SCog SImb SSta WBod
- 'Jean May' ♀H3	CBcs CDoC ENot EPfP LHyd LRHS SCam SCog SCoo SImb SPer SSta WGob
- 'Kenkyô'	MGos SCam SCog SImb SSta
§ - 'Lavender Queen'	SCam SImb
- 'Little Pearl'	LHyd
- 'Lucinda'	SCog
- 'Maiden's Blush'	CSBt ISea SCam SCog SImb WFar WSpi
- 'Mignonne'	CTrh
- 'Narumigata'	CAbP CBcs CDoC CMac CTrh ENot EPfP LCro LHyd LRHS MAsh SCam SCog SCoo SPoG SSta WBod WGob WSHC

- 'New Dawn'	SCam SCog SImb
- 'Nyewoods'	CMac
- 'Papaver'	SCam SCog
- 'Paradise Baby Jane' **new**	SImb
- 'Paradise Belinda'^{PBR} **new**	SImb
- 'Paradise Blush'	CBcs GLld SCam SCog SImb
- Paradise Caroline = 'Parcaroline' **new**	SImb
- 'Paradise Glow'	GLld SCam SCog SImb
- 'Paradise Hilda'	CBcs SCog SImb
- Paradise Illumination = 'Parillumination' **new**	SImb
- Paradise Jennifer = 'Parjennifer' **new**	SImb
- 'Paradise Joan' **new**	SImb
- 'Paradise Little Liane'	CBcs SCam SCog SImb
- 'Paradise Pearl'	CBcs GLld SCam SCog
- 'Paradise Petite'^{PBR}	SCog SImb
- Paradise Sandra = 'Parsandra' **new**	SImb
- 'Paradise Sayaka' **new**	SImb
- 'Paradise Venessa'^{PBR}	CBcs SCog SImb
- 'Peach Blossom'	CBcs LHyd
- 'Plantation Pink'	CBrm CSBt CTrh EBee ENot GKev LRHS SCam SCog SImb SPer SPoG
- 'Rainbow'	CAbP CBcs CDoC CTrG CTrh GLld ISea LRHS SCam SCog SCoo SImb SSta WBod WFar WGob
- 'Rosea'	SCam
§ - 'Rosea Plena'	CBcs CMac
- 'Sasanqua Rubra'	CMac
- 'Sasanqua Variegata' (v)	SCam SCog SSta
- 'Setsugekka'	SCam SCog
- 'Shinonome' **new**	CBcs
- 'Shishigashira' Nihon Engei Kai Zasshi, 1894	CTrh SCam SImb
- 'Snowflake'	SCam SCog SSta
- 'Sparkling Burgundy'	see *C. hiemalis* 'Sparkling Burgundy'
- 'Tanya'	CDoC SImb
- 'Winter's Joy'	SCam
- 'Winter's Snowman'	CDoC SCam SCog
'Satan's Robe' (*reticulata* hybrid)	CDoC MGos NBlu SCam SCog WFar
'Scented Sun'	CTrh
'Show Girl' (*sasanqua* x *reticulata*)	LHyd SCam SCog
'Shôwa-wabisuke' (wabisuke)	CTrh
§ ***sinensis***	CCCN CTrG CTrh LPan LRHS SCam
'Snow Flurry' (*oleifera* hybrid)	SCam SCog
'Spring Festival' (*cuspidata* hybrid) $\mathbb{Y}^{H4}$	CDoC CMHG CTrh ENot LHyd LRHS SCam SCoo SImb WMoo
'Spring Mist' (*japonica* x *lutchuensis*)	CDoC CMHG CTrh LHyd SCam SImb
'Strawberry Parfait'	NPri
'Sugar Dream'	CDoC
'Swan Lake' (hybrid)	CTrG MAsh SCam SCog
'Tarōkaja' (wabisuke)	SCam
thea	see *C. sinensis*
'Tinsie'	see *C. japonica* 'Bokuhan'
'Tiny Princess' (*japonica* x *fraterna*)	CBcs
'Tom Knudsen' (*reticulata* x *japonica*) $\mathbb{Y}^{H3}$	CTrh SCam
'Tomorrow Supreme'	see *C. japonica* 'Tomorrow Variegated'
transnokoensis	CCtw ISea SCam
'Tricolor Sieboldii'	see *C. japonica* 'Tricolor'
'Tristrem Carlyon' (*reticulata* hybrid) $\mathbb{Y}^{H4}$	CBcs CDoC CTrG CTri NPri WGob
tsaii	CPLG
'Usu-ōtome'	see *C. japonica* 'Otome'
'Valley Knudsen' (*saluenensis* x *reticulata*)	SCog
x ***vernalis*** 'Hiryû'	SCog
- 'Star Above Star'	CMHG
- 'Yuletide'	SCam
'Volcano'	CDoC
x ***williamsii*** 'Angel Wings' **new**	SCam
- 'Anticipation' $\mathbb{Y}^{H4}$	More than 30 suppliers
- 'Anticipation Variegated'	CBcs GGGa
- 'Ballet Queen'	CDoC CSBt MGos SCam SImb SPoG WBod WFar
- 'Ballet Queen Variegated'	CDoC MGos SCog SImb
- 'Barbara Jane'	SImb
- 'Bartley Number Five'	CMac
- 'Beatrice Michael'	CMac SImb
- 'Bow Bells'	CDoC CDul LHyd LRHS NBlu SCam SSta
- 'Bowen Bryant' $\mathbb{Y}^{H4}$	GGGa GLld LRHS SCog
- 'Bridal Gown'	GGGa LHyd
- 'Brigadoon' $\mathbb{Y}^{H4}$	CBcs CDoC CMHG CTrG EPfP GGGa GLld LHyd MBri MDun MGos SCam
- 'Browncreek's Festivity' **new**	SImb
- 'Burncoose'	CBcs
- 'Burncoose Apple Blossom'	CBcs
- 'Buttons 'n' Bows'	CDoC SCog
- 'C.F. Coates'	CDoC SCog SImb SSta
- 'Caerhays'	CBcs SImb
- 'Carnation'	LRHS
- 'Carolyn Williams'	CBcs SCam
- 'Celebration'	CBcs SPer
- 'Charlean'	SCam SImb
- 'Charles Colbert'	CDoC
- 'Charles Michael'	CBcs
- 'Charles Puddle'	WBod
- 'China Clay' $\mathbb{Y}^{H4}$	CBcs CDoC CTrG EPfP LHyd SCog WBod
§ - 'Citation'	CBcs CMac SCog
- 'Clarrie Fawcett'	CDoC
- 'Contribution'	CTrh
- 'Crinkles'	CDul SCam SSta
- 'Daintiness' $\mathbb{Y}^{H4}$	LHyd SCog SImb
- 'Dark Nite'	CMHG
- 'Debbie' $\mathbb{Y}^{H4}$	More than 30 suppliers
- 'Debbie's Carnation'	CMHG
- 'Donation' $\mathbb{Y}^{H4}$	More than 30 suppliers
- 'Dream Boat'	CBcs CDoC LHyd
- 'E.G. Waterhouse'	CBcs CDoC CMHG CSBt CTrG CTrh CTri ENot EPfP LHyd LRHS MGos NBlu SCam SCog SCoo SImb SPoG SSta WBod WGob
- 'E.T.R. Carlyon' $\mathbb{Y}^{H4}$	CBcs CTrh CTri ENot EPfP GLld LHyd LRHS MAsh NLar SCam SCog SCoo SPoG WBVN
§ - 'Elegant Beauty' $\mathbb{Y}^{H4}$	CBcs CDoC CSBt CTrG CWSG GLld MDun SBod SCam SCog SImb SPer SPur WBVN
- 'Elizabeth Anderson'	CTrh
- 'Elizabeth de Rothschild'	SCam SImb
- 'Ellamine'	CBcs
- 'Elsie Jury' $\mathbb{Y}^{H3}$	CBcs CDoC CMac CSBt CTrG CTri CWSG GGar GLld GQui LHyd MGos NBlu SCam SCog SImb SPer WBod
- 'Exaltation'	CDoC SCog
- 'Francis Hanger'	CBcs CDoC CTrh LHyd MDun SCam SCog SImb
- 'Free Style'	SImb
- 'Galaxie' $\mathbb{Y}^{H4}$	CBcs CDoC SCog
- 'Garden Glory'	GGGa
- 'George Blandford' $\mathbb{Y}^{H4}$	CMac SCam
- 'Glenn's Orbit' $\mathbb{Y}^{H4}$	CBcs CDoC SCam SCog

- 'Golden Spangles' (v)	CBcs CDoC CSBt CTrG CTrh ELan ENot EPfP LHyd LRHS MGos SBod SCam SCog SImb SPer SPoG SSta WGob
- 'Grand Jury'	LRHS SCam
- 'Gwavas'	CBcs CCCN CDoC GLld LHyd LRHS MAsh SCam SCog SCoo
- 'Hiraethlyn'	LHyd SCam SImb WBod
- 'J.C. Williams' ♀H4	CBcs CMac CSam CTri CWSG EPfP ISea LCro LHyd SCog WBod
- 'Jamie'	CDoC
- 'Jean Claris'	CDoC SCog
- 'Jenefer Carlyon'	CDoC
- 'Jill Totty'	CTrh SCog
- 'Joan Trehane' ♀H4	LRHS MAsh
- 'Julia Hamiter' ♀H4	CBcs SCog SImb
§ - 'Jury's Yellow' ♀H4	CBcs CCCN CDoC CSBt CTrG CTrh CTri ELan ENot EPfP GGGa GLld GQui LHyd LRHS LSRN MAsh MGos NPri SCam SCog SCoo SHBN SImb SPer SPoG SSta WBVN WFar
- 'Lady's Maid' **new**	CBcs
- 'Laura Boscawen'	CDoC CTrG LHyd SCam SImb
- 'Les Jury' ♀H4	CDoC CGHE CMHG CSBt CTrh LSRN MWea SCog SPer
- 'Margaret Waterhouse'	CBcs CDoC SCam SCog
- 'Mary Christian' ♀H4	CBcs EPfP LHyd LRHS SCam SSta
- 'Mary Jobson'	CBcs CDoC SCam SImb
- 'Mary Phoebe Taylor' ♀H4	CBcs CDoC CTrG CWSG ENot ERas GLld MAsh NLar SCam SCog SCoo SHBN SPoG WBod
- 'Mildred Veitch'	CSBt
- 'Mirage'	CTrh
- 'Moira Reid'	CDoC
- 'Monica Dance'	CBcs LRHS
- 'Muskoka' ♀H4	CBcs CMHG SImb
- 'November Pink'	CBcs
- 'Phillippa Forward'	CBcs CMac WBod
- 'Red Dahlia'	CBcs
- 'Rendezvous'	CDoC SCog SImb
- 'Rose Bouquet' **new**	CDoC
- 'Rose Court'	WBod
- 'Rose Parade'	LHyd LRHS
- 'Rose Quartz'	LRHS
- 'Rosemary Williams'	CBcs SCam
- 'Ruby Bells'	CMHG
- 'Ruby Wedding'	CBcs CDoC CSBt CTrh ENot GLld GQui LHyd LRHS MAsh MWea NLar SCog SCoo SImb SPer SPoG WBVN
- 'Saint Ewe' ♀H4	CBcs CDoC CSBt CTrG CTrh CTri EPfP GKev GLld LHyd LRHS MBri MGos NPri SCam SCog SCoo SHBN SImb SPer SPoG WBod
- 'Saint Michael'	CDoC WBod
- 'Sayonara'	CBcs SCog
- 'Senorita' ♀H4	CDoC CTrh LHyd MAsh SBod SCam SCog SImb
- 'Simon Bolitho'	LHyd SCog
- 'Sun Song'	SCog
- 'Taylor's Perfection'	LRHS
- 'The Duchess of Cornwall'	CDoC
- 'Tiptoe'	CDoC CTrh LHyd MBri
- 'Tregrehan'	GLld
- 'Waltz Time'	CDoC SImb
- 'Water Lily' ♀H4	CBcs CDoC CTrh CTri EPfP MGos SCam SImb SPur WBod
- 'Wilber Foss' ♀H4	CBcs CDoC CMHG CTrh GLld LHyd MGos SCam SCog SImb
- 'William Carlyon'	CWSG
- 'Wynne Rayner'	LRHS SCam
- 'Yesterday'	LRHS NBlu
'Winter's Charm' (*oleifera* x *sasanqua*)	SCog
'Winter's Dream' (*hiemalis* x *oleifera*)	SCog
'Winter's Interlude' (*oleifera* x *sinensis*)	CDoC SCam SCog
'Winter's Joy'	SCog
'Winter's Toughie' (*sasanqua* hybrid)	SCam SCog
'Winton' (*cuspidata* x *saluenensis*)	CBcs CDoC SCam SImb
'Wirlinga Belle'	SCam SCog
'Yoimachi' (*fraterna* x *sasanqua*)	CTrh

Campanula ✿ (Campanulaceae)

from Iran	EBee NBre
abietina	see *C. patula* subsp. *abietina*
§ ***alliariifolia***	More than 30 suppliers
- 'Ivory Bells'	see *C. alliariifolia*
allionii	see *C. alpestris*
§ ***alpestris***	ECho GKev
alpina	MDKP
americana	SPav
argaea	NSfd WLin
armena	EBee ELan EWin NLar NSfd SWal
arvatica	CGra CLyd ECho GMaP LRHS MDKP NHar NMen NSfd WAbe WPat
- 'Alba'	CGra CLyd ECho GMaP NMen NSla WPat
aucheri	see *C. saxifraga* subsp. *aucheri*
autraniana	CGra ITim
'Azure Beauty' **new**	CSpe
§ 'Balchiniana' (v)	CBow
barbata	CGra EBee EDAr GKev GMaP ITim LHop MMHG NWCA WMoo WPer
- var. ***alba***	GAbr
bellidifolia	NBir NBre
besenginica **new**	CGra
§ ***betulifolia*** ♀H4	CGra CSam ITim WFar
- JCA 252.005	SBla
biebersteiniana	GKev
'Birch Hybrid' ♀H4	CMHG ECho ECtt EDAr ELan EPfP LBee LRHS NBlu NSfd SIng WFar WTel
bononiensis	LBBr LTwo NBre NSfd SRms
'Bumblebee'	CGra SBla WAbe
'Burghaltii' ♀H4	CDes CHar CMil CPom EBee ECha EHrv ELan EMon GMac LRHS MSte SBch SWat WCot WFar WMnd WPer
calaminthifolia	EBur
'Cantata'	CGra
§ ***carnica***	ECho MSte NSfd
carpatha	SBla
carpatica ♀H4	ECho EPfP GKev ITim MBar NBre NBro NGdn SBch SPlb SRms SWat
- f. ***alba***	GKev NBre NGdn SPlb SWat
- - 'Bressingham White'	SBla
§ - - 'Weisse Clips'	EBee ECho ECtt ELan ENot EPfP GGar GMaP LAst LCro LHop MDun MWgw NGdn SPer SPla SPoG SRms SWvt WFar WPat WPer WWeb
§ - 'Blaue Clips'	More than 30 suppliers
- blue-flowered	MRav
- Blue Clips	see *C. carpatica* 'Blaue Clips'
- 'Blue Moonlight'	EBur LRHS SMer
- 'Blue Uniform'	NSfd
- 'Chewton Joy'	CTri LRHS WLin
- 'Ditton Blue'	GMaP
- 'Karpatenkrone'	EBee
- 'Kathy'	GBuc
* - var. ***pelviformis***	SMHy
- 'Silberschale'	NBre
- 'Suzie'	SBla

- var. ***turbinata***	ECho SRms
- - 'Foerster'	GBin GBuc LRHS MTho SBla WHoo
- - 'Isabel'	CSpe LRHS
- - 'Jewel'	LRHS
- - 'Wheatley Violet'	SBla
- White Clips	see *C. carpatica* f. *alba* 'Weisse Clips'
- 'White Uniform'	NSfd
§ ***cashmeriana***	CGra EBur SBHP
- 'Blue Cloud'	CWib
cephallenica	see *C. garganica* subsp. *cephallenica*
cervicaria	EBee
§ ***chamissonis***	ECho GKev LTwo NSla WPat
- 'Major'	CPBP EDAr EWes LBee
- 'Oyobeni'	NLAp
§ - 'Superba' ♀^{H4}	EBur ECho ELan MTho NMen NSla
choruhensis	CGra CPBP GKev
§ ***cochlearifolia*** ♀^{H4}	CEnt CSpe CTri EBee ECho EDAr EPfP GAbr GMaP LRHS MDun MTho SBch SSvw STre WFar WHoo WPer WTel
- var. ***alba***	CSpe EDAr GMaP LRHS MHer MMuc NRya NSfd SBch SBla SRms WAbe WHoo WPer
- - 'Bavaria White'	CBrm ECho ITim LBMP WFar
- - double white-flowered (d)	WPat
- - 'White Baby' (Baby Series)	ECho ECtt EPfP GAbr GGar MWgw NHol NSfd SPoG
- 'Annie Hall'	ECho
- 'Bavaria Blue'	CBrm ECho ITim LBMP MWgw NHol NSfd NWCA
- 'Blue Baby' (Baby Series)	ECho EPfP GGar MHer NBlu NPro SPoG SRms
- 'Blue Tit'	GBuc
- 'Cambridge Blue'	NSfd WAbe WFar
- 'Elizabeth Oliver' (d)	CCge CGra CStu CTri ECho ECtt EDAr EPot EShb GBuc GGar GKev GMaP LAst LHop LRHS MAvo MHer MTho NLAp NWCA SBla SPlb SPoG SRms WAbe WFar WHoo
- 'Miss Willmott'	CLyd MTho NBir
- 'Oakington Blue'	SBla
- var. ***pallida*** 'Silver Chimes'	ECho ITim
- 'Tubby'	CLyd ECho GKev LRHS MHer MTho SRms
- 'Warleyensis'	see *C.* x *haylodgensis* W. Brockbank 'Warley White'
collina	CTri EBee GSki LTwo NBre NLar NSfd WCFE WPer
coriacea	CGra
- J&JA 0.253.800	NWCA
'Covadonga'	CMea ECho LHop LRHS LTwo
cretica	GKev NBre NSfd
'Crystal'	ECtt MAvo MNrw
dasyantha	see *C. chamissonis*
dolomitica	EBee GKev LTwo NLAp NMen
dzaaku new	CGra
'E.K. Toogood'	CElw CPBP EAlp ECho ECtt GKev MWat NBro NLAp NVic NWCA SBla SMac SRms WLin
'Elizabeth'	see *C. takesimana* 'Elizabeth'
eriocarpa	see *C. latifolia* 'Eriocarpa'
excisa	CPBP WAbe
'Faichem Lilac'	GCra GKev LSou LTwo NChi NLar NPro NRnb NSfd STes WOut
fenestrellata	MTho NBro NLAp NMen SRms WAbe WFar
finitima	see *C. betulifolia*
'Flashing Lights'	ERou
foliosa	ECtt WPer

formanekiana ♀$^{H2-3}$	EBur NSfd
fragilis	CGra EBur ECho
- 'Hirsuta'	ECho
garganica ♀^{H4}	ECho EPfP EWTr GAbr GGar GMaP GSki MDKP MRav NBlu NSfd SIng SWvt WFar WMoo WPer
- 'Aurea'	see *C. garganica* 'Dickson's Gold'
- 'Blue Diamond'	ECho LHop NBlu SBla WAbe WFar
§ - subsp. ***cephallenica***	CElw NBro
§ - 'Dickson's Gold'	More than 30 suppliers
- 'Erinus Major'	NSfd
- 'Hirsuta'	ECho
- 'Major'	EBee ECho LAst SPoG WFar
- 'Mrs Resholt' new	EWll
- 'W.H. Paine' ♀^{H4}	CLyd ECho ECtt ITim LRHS MDKP NMen NSla WAbe WFar WHoo
'Gaven'	IPot
'Glandore'	NPro
glomerata	CBgR CElw CEnt CPLG CRWN GCra LSRN MAvo MBNS NBro NLan NMir NSfd SPet SRms STes WBrk WEas WFar
- var. ***acaulis***	CChe CHFP CPrp CStu CWan EBee EPfP ERou GAbr LRHS MBNS NLar NSfd NWCA SPla WFar WPer WWeb
- var. ***alba***	CBcs CBgR EBee ELan EMFW EPfP ERou EShb GMaP GSki LBMP LRHS MNFA MRav MWat NBPC NBro NHol NRnb SPer SPla SPlb STes SWat WCAu WFar WGwG WMnd WPer WWeb
§ - - 'Alba Nana'	LAst
§ - - 'Schneekrone'	ECha EPfP ERou NBre SMrm WFar
- 'Caroline'	More than 30 suppliers
- Crown of Snow	see *C. glomerata* var. *alba* 'Schneekrone'
- var. ***dahurica***	CTri NBre NLar SPet WPer
- 'Joan Elliott'	CBgR ECha GBuc MRav MWat NGdn WAul WCra
- 'Nana Alba'	see *C. glomerata* var. *alba* 'Alba Nana'
- 'Purple Pixie'	LRHS
- 'Superba' ♀^{H4}	More than 30 suppliers
grossekii	EHrv ERCP EWll GMac LTwo MFOX NBre NEgg NRnb WHrl WOut
'Hallii'	LRHS NSfd NWCA
'Hannah'	LRHS
Hannay's form	CHar
x ***haylodgensis*** misapplied	see *C.* x *haylodgensis* 'Plena'
§ x ***haylodgensis*** W. Brockbank 'Marion Fisher' (d)	CCge CGra CMea CPBP EDAr NSfd SBla WAbe WCot WHoo
§ - 'Plena' (d)	EBee ECho EDAr ELan EPot LAst LBee LHop LRHS NBro NMen NSfd NWCA SBla SRms WAbe WCot WEas WFar WHoo WKif WPat
§ - 'Warley White' (d)	CStu EBur ECho ELan
- 'Yvonne'	EDAr GMaP LAst NEgg NSfd SPoG WFar
'Hemswell Starlight'	CLyd
hercegovina 'Nana'	CPBP LTwo WAbe
'Hilltop Snow'	CGra CPBP NMen NSfd
hoffmeisteri new	WHrl
hofmannii	CEnt CWan EBur ELan GKev NLar NSfd WFar WTMC
§ ***incurva***	CDMG CSpe EBee EBur EMan GAbr GKev MNrw MWea NOak NRya NSfd WLin
integrifolia 'Bells'	LSou
isophylla ♀^{H2}	ECho EPot
- 'Alba' ♀^{H2}	ECho
- 'Flore Pleno' (d)	EBur
- 'Mayi' misapplied	see *C.* 'Balchiniana'

	- 'Mayi' 🏆H2	CSpe
	- 'Variegata'	see *C.* 'Balchiniana'
	jaubertiana	CGra
	'Joe Elliott' 🏆H2-3	CStu ECho LRHS SBla WAbe
	kemulariae	EAlp LTwo NSfd SRms WPer
	- ***alba***	ITim
	'Kent Belle' 🏆H4	More than 30 suppliers
	khasiana	NSfd
	'Kifu' (v)	CBow EBee ENot EPPr LRHS
	kirpicznikovii **new**	CGra NSla
	lactiflora	CBrm CElw CMea CSev EBee ECha EPfP ERou EShb EWTr GAbr GCra GMaP IFoB LCro LRHS MLHP MNFA NChi NDov NVic SPer SSvw WBrE WFar WHoo WMoo WPer WTin
	- ***alba***	see *C. lactiflora* white-flowered
N	- 'Alba' 🏆H4	EBee EBla EGle ERou GAbr GMaP MAvo MDKP SMrm STes WMnd
	- 'Avalanche'	EBrs
	- 'Blue Avalanche'	EBee NSfd SMrm
	- 'Blue Cross'	EBee EBrs LRHS NBre NLar WTel
	- 'Blue Lady'	EBee NBre WFar
	- 'Dixter Presence'	IPot NDov SMHy
	- dwarf pink	SBHP SHar WCot
	- 'Favourite'	CFir CSpe EBee ERou MNrw NCGa NGdn NLar STes WFar
	- 'Loddon Anna' 🏆H4	More than 30 suppliers
	- 'Moorland Rose' **new**	WMoo
	- 'Pink Star'	SMrm
	- 'Pouffe'	CWCL EBee EBla ECtt ELan EPfP GGar GMaP LRHS MBri MDKP MRav NBro NCGa NGdn SPer SPet SPla SWat SWvt WFar
	- 'Prichard's Variety' 🏆H4	More than 30 suppliers
	- 'Senior'	MDKP
	- 'Superba' 🏆H4	EBee
	- 'Violet'	SWat WPer
	- 'White Pouffe'	EBee ECtt EGle ELan EPfP GKev GMaP GMac GSki LRHS MBri MDKP MRav NBPC NCGa NChi NLar SAga SMer SMrm SPer SPla SPoG STes SWat WFar WLin
§	- white-flowered	ECha LAst NBir SPer SWat WPer
	lasiocarpa	CGra GKev LRHS WFar
	latifolia	CArn EBee ECha GAbr LCro LRHS MWgw NBid NMir NOrc NSfd NSti NVic SMer SPer SRms WCAu WFar WMoo
	- var. ***alba***	ELan GAbr GCra MAvo MFOX MSte NGdn SPav SPer SRms WFar WHal WPer WSpi
	- - 'White Ladies'	NSfd
*	- 'Amethyst'	SDnm SPav
	- blue flowered **new**	WSpi
	- 'Brantwood'	EBee ECtt ERou GAbr GMac MRav NChi NOak NSfd SDnm SMer SPav SRms STes SWat WCot WMnd WSpi
	- 'Buckland'	SPav
§	- 'Eriocarpa'	NSfd
	- 'Gloaming'	CHFP EBee ECtt ERou MCot NSfd
	- var. ***macrantha***	EBee ELan EPfP ERou GMaP LHop LRHS MBri MHar MSte MWat NBPC NCGa NGdn NHol NRnb NSti SPav SWat SWvt WCAu WMoo WPer WWeb
	- - 'Alba'	CMMP ECha ECtt ERou EShb GMaP LHop LRHS MRav MSte NCGa NRnb NSfd SPhx WCAu WCot WMoo WPer
	- 'Misty Dawn'	WCot WFar
§	***latiloba***	CElw CMHG SBch WBrk WCot WFar
§	- 'Alba' 🏆H4	CBre CElw EBee EGle ELan EPPr EPfP GAbr GMaP MDKP NChi NGdn NSfd SBch SGar SSvw WBrk WEas WLin WOut WRHF
	- 'Hidcote Amethyst' 🏆H4	More than 30 suppliers
§	- 'Highcliffe Variety' 🏆H4	CSpe ELan EPfP GBuc GCra MFOX MNFA NCGa NSfd SPla WCAu WCot WEas WKif WMnd
*	- 'Highdown'	MLLN WFar
§	- 'Percy Piper' 🏆H4	CSam EBee ELan EWsh GBuc LRHS MAvo MFOX MRav NBre NBro NLar WFar WLin WOut WSpi
	- 'Splash'	CElw CFee EBee ECtt MAvo NSfd WHil
	linifolia	see *C. carnica*
	lourica **new**	CGra ITim
	makaschvilii	CEnt CSpe EBee ECtt GMac IGor LRHS MHer MWrn NCGa NLar NRnb NSfd SAga SBod STes WBrk WCot WHrl WPer WSHC WTMC
	'Marion Fisher'	see *C.* x *haylodgensis* W. Brockbank 'Marion Fisher'
	medium	LAst NRnb NSfd
	- 'Alba'	NSfd
§	- var. ***calycanthema*** hort.	ERou
	- 'Cup and Saucer'	see *C. medium* var. *calycanthema* hort.
	- 'Rosea'	NSfd
	'Milkshake'	EBee NBro
	mirabilis 'Mist Maiden'	CLyd LRHS WFar
	'Monic'	NBlu
	morettiana	GKev
	muralis	see *C. portenschlagiana*
	nitida	see *C. persicifolia* var. *planiflora*
	- var. ***planiflora***	see *C. persicifolia* var. *planiflora*
	'Norman Grove'	EPot
	ochroleuca	CMea CPom CSpe EBee LRHS NCGa SHGN SPoG STes SWat WCFE WCot WHrl WMoo
	- 'White Beauty'	CWib
	- 'White Bells'	NRnb WGwG
	odontosepala	CElw EMon EWTr
	'Oliver's Choice'	WHrl
	olympica misapplied	see *C. rotundifolia* 'Olympica'
§	***ossetica***	CElw CSpe EBee ECtt ELan EMan MLHP NCiC
	pallida subsp. ***tibetica***	see *C. cashmeriana*
	parviflora Lam.	see *C. sibirica*
	patula	EGoo NLar NSfd
§	- subsp. ***abietina***	NBre NLar SBla
	'Paul Furse'	EBee ECtt LRHS MDKP MLLN NBre NLar NPro NSfd NSti STes WCAu WCot WHal WLin WTin
	pelviformis	MNrw
§	***pendula***	CSpe CWan EPfP EWes GBuc NLar NSfd SHGN WFar WWeb
	persicifolia	CBcs CBrm CHrt CPrp CSBt CTri EBee EHon EPfP GAbr GKev GMaP LRHS MLHP MWgw NBid NBro NCob NHol NMir SDix SPer SPoG SSvw WCAu WCot WHoo WMoo WPer WTin
	- var. ***alba***	More than 30 suppliers
§	- 'Alba Coronata' (d)	CFir EMon GAbr LCro LRHS NBir WCAu WEas WFar
	- 'Alba Plena'	see *C. persicifolia* 'Alba Coronata'
	- Ashfield double ice blue (d)	NBre
	- 'Beau Belle'	EBee EMan ERou LSou MBNS NBPC NLar NMoo STes WHil
§	- 'Bennett's Blue' (d)	More than 30 suppliers
	- blue- and white-flowered	WHil
	- 'Blue Bell'	MWat
	- 'Blue Bloomers' (d)	CElw CHar CLAP CMil ECtt EGle EMon EWes GBri GMac LLWP MAvo MNFA MRav WBrk WCot WHal WWeb

- blue cup-in-cup (d)	EBla MBnl MDKP WFar WLin
- blue-flowered	IFoB LAst MRav NRnb SPlb WEas WFar
- 'Boule de Neige' (d)	CMMP CWCL EBee EBla ECtt LAst NOak NSfd WEas WSpi
- 'Caerulea Coronata'	see *C. persicifolia* 'Coronata'
* - 'Caerulea Plena' (d)	EWsh MBNS
§ - 'Chettle Charm'PBR ♀H4	More than 30 suppliers
- 'Cornish Mist' **new**	EBee EHrv SPoG
§ - 'Coronata' (d)	ECtt GCra NEgg
- 'Cristine'	MDKP
- cup and saucer blue (d)	GCra
§ - cup and saucer white (d)	EBla ELan GMaP WFar WPer
§ - double blue-flowered (d)	EGle NBir NBro NSfd WEas
- double white-flowered (d)	ELan NChi WMoo
- 'Eastgrove Blue'	NCob
- 'Fleur de Neige' (d) ♀H4	CSam ECtt LRHS MLLN NBre NCob NOak WAul WBrk WCot WHoo WLin
- 'Flore Pleno'	see *C. persicifolia* double blue
- 'Frances' (d)	CLAP EGoo EMon
- 'Frank Lawley' (d)	LRHS NSfd
- 'Gawen'	CWCL EBee GMaP GMac MAvo MNFA NBre NLar SAga WCot
- 'George Chiswell'PBR	see *C. persicifolia* 'Chettle Charm'
- 'Grandiflora'	NBre
- 'Grandiflora Alba'	GBuc LBMP NBre NSfd SMrm
- 'Grandiflora Caerulea'	NBlu NLar
§ - 'Hampstead White' (d)	ECtt EGle EHrv ERou GBuc LAst NBro NSti SBch SPla STes WCAu WEas WHer WHoo WLin WMnd WSpi
- 'Hetty'	see *C. persicifolia* 'Hampstead White'
- 'Kelly's Gold'	CFwr CHar EBee EBla ECtt ENot EPPr LAst LSou MBnl MCCP MFOX NBhm NBir NEgg NGdn NHol NLar NPri NPro NSfd NSti SPav SPoG SRGP WBor WCot WFar
- 'La Belle'	EMan EPyc ERou NLar NSfd STes
- 'La Bonne Amie'	EBee
- 'Moerheimii' (d)	EBee EPfP EShb MBnl MWea NBir STes WCAu WFar
- var. ***nitida***	see *C. persicifolia* var. *planiflora*
- 'Peach Bells'	MBNS
- 'Perry's Boy Blue'	NPer
§ - var. ***planiflora***	CPBP EBee GKev SBla
- - f. ***alba***	CMea
- 'Powder Puff' (d)	CHFP EBee LSou MBnl NCob WCot
- 'Pride of Exmouth' (d)	CCge CHar CMMP CSam EBee ECtt EHrv ELan EMan EShb GBuc LAst LCro LRHS MCCP MHer MNFA NOak NSfd WBrk WCFE WCot WCra WHoo WLin WSpi
- subsp. ***sessiliflora***	see *C. latiloba*
- - 'Alba'	see *C. latiloba* 'Alba'
- - 'Highcliffe'	see *C. latiloba* 'Highcliffe Variety'
- - 'Percy Piper'	see *C. latiloba* 'Percy Piper'
I - 'Snowball'	NSfd
- 'Snowdrift'	ELan SRms
- 'Telham Beauty' misapplied	CFwr CSBt CWCL EBee ECtt ELan ENot EPfP ERou EShb GAbr LCro LRHS MRav MSte MWgw NRnb SMer SMrm SPer SPla SRms SWvt WFar WMnd WPer WWeb
- 'Telham Beauty' ambig.	WSpi
- 'Telham Beauty' D. Thurston	LBMP NSfd
- 'Tinpenny Blue'	WTin
- 'White Bell'	MWat NEgg
- 'White Cup and Saucer'	see *C. persicifolia* cup and saucer white
- 'White Queen' (d)	WMnd
- 'Wortham Belle' misapplied	see *C. persicifolia* 'Bennett's Blue'
- 'Wortham Belle' ambig.	CSam CWGN EShb GBri WSpi
- 'Yellow Binstead' **new**	EBee
petrophila	CGra NSla SBla WAbe
'Pike's Supremo' (d)	NBir
pilosa	see *C. chamissonis*
- 'Superba'	see *C. chamissonis* 'Superba'
piperi 'Townsend Ridge'	CGra
- 'Townsend Violet'	CGra
planiflora	see *C. persicifolia* var. *planiflora*
'Polly Henderson'	CGra
§ ***portenschlagiana*** ♀H4	CBrm CElw CTri EBee ELan EPfP GGar GMaP LCro LHop MHer MRav NBro NDlv NPri NRya NVic SBla SDix SIng SPer SPet SPoG SRms SWvt WAbe WEas WFar WMoo XPep
- 'Lieselotte'	CElw GBuc GMaP LIMB NSfd WPat
- 'Major'	LAst WFar
- 'Resholdt's Variety'	CMea CSam EBee ECho EDAr EPfP GMaP LAst LBee LHop LRHS MRav NPri NSfd WPer
poscharskyana	More than 30 suppliers
- 'Blauranke'	EGoo EWes NSfd
- 'Blue Gown'	EGle GMaP GMac MNFA
- 'Blue Waterfall'	EBrs LRHS WFar
- 'E.H. Frost'	CBre CElw EBee ECho ECtt EDAr EGle EPPr EPfP EWTr GMaP LAst LCro LHop MBri NBro NRya NSfd SAga SPer SRGP SRms SWvt WBrk WFar WMoo WPer WTel
- 'Lilacina'	CElw EPPr
- 'Lisduggan Variety'	CElw EBee EBur ECtt EDAr EGle EPPr EWes GMaP LIMB MBri NBro NCGa NChi NSfd SBch SBla WBrk WCot WFar WMoo WPer
- 'Stella' ♀H4	EBee ECGP ECha ECho ECtt EGle LRHS MAvo MRav NBro NSfd SDix SPer SRGP SWvt WFar WMoo
- variegated (v)	IBlr
- white-flowered	ECho ELan LAst MDKP WFar
prenanthoides	see *Asyneuma prenanthoides*
primulifolia	CDMG CSsd EBee ELan EMan GAbr GKev MNrw MSte NCGa NSfd SBod SMad SRms WFar WLin WMoo WPer
- 'Blue Oasis'	CMHG LSRN NRnb WTMC WWeb
x ***pseudoraineri*** hort.	EBur EDAr EWes LRHS NMen
'Puff of Smoke'	WCot
pulla	CLyd CPBP CSpe EBur ECho ECtt EDAr ELan GMaP LAst LRHS MTho NRya NSfd NWCA SBla SPoG SRot WAbe WFar WPat WWFP
- ***alba***	EBur ECho ECtt EDAr SBla WAbe WPat
x ***pulloides*** hort.	EDAr
- 'G.F. Wilson' ♀H4	EBur ECho ECtt LTwo NSfd WFar
punctata	CMHG CMil CSpe EBee EHrv ERou GAbr LEdu LRHS NBPC NBro NEgg NSti NWCA SPer SPla SWat WAul WFar WGwG WMoo WPer
- f. ***albiflora***	CMMP EBee LHop LRHS MLLN MNrw NChi SHar WFar WHil
- - 'Alba'	CCVN GKev
- - 'Nana Alba'	SBch WFar
- 'Alina's Double' (d)	EBee GMac MNrw
- var. ***hondoensis***	GKev IGor MBrN MLHP MNrw NCGa SAga
- - 'Bossy Boots'	SMrm
- hose-in-hose (d)	CDes EBla NLar WFar WGwG
- 'Hot Lips'	More than 30 suppliers
* - var. ***howozana*** **new**	GKev
- var. ***microdonta***	NSfd WLin
- - B&SWJ 5553	WCru
- 'Millennium'	GMac MAvo WCot WFar
- 'Milly'	CStu EBee EMon EPPr WPGP

	- 'Mottled' (v)	NBre NRnb
*	- 'Nana'	CCVN
	- 'Pallida'	WBrE
	- 'Pantaloons' (d)	CSpe EBee EBla ECtt EKen ERou LHop LRHS MBnl MBri MDKP NChi NCob NLar NMRc SBch SHar WCAu WCot WCra
	- 'Pink Bells'	NSfd
	- 'Pink Chimes'PBR	CCge CPou EBee EPPr GKev LHop LSou MBri NBhm NEgg NPri NPro SRot STes
	- 'Pink Eclipse'	WFar
	- 'Reifrock'	GMac SMrm
	- 'Rosea'	SRms WFar
	- f. ***rubriflora***	More than 30 suppliers
	- - 'Beetroot'	EBee EBla ECtt EMon EPPr GBri LHop LSou MBNS MFOX MSte NLar NSfd WHrl WPGP
	- - 'Bowl of Cherries'PBR	CSpe EBee EBla EMan ENor EPPr ERou EShb GAbr LSou LTwo MBnl MBri MMHG NEgg NLar NMoo NPri NSti SHar SPav SRot STes
	- - 'Cherry Bells'	CElw CFir EBla ECtt EMan EPfP GSki IPot LAst LBMP LSRN MAvo MBri MCCP MNFA MNrw NBro NCob NLar NRnb NSfd SPav SPoG SSvw WCot
	- - 'Vienna Festival'	EBee ECtt LEdu LSou NBhm NLar NSfd NSti SSvw WCot
	- - 'Wine 'n' Rubies'	CElw ECtt EHrv EMan LSou MAvo MDKP MNrw NSfd SBch SHar SMrm SPav WCot
	- var. ***takesimana***	see *C. takesimana*
	- 'Twilight Bells'	NBre
	- 'Wedding Bells'	More than 30 suppliers
I	- 'White Bells'	EPPr MBNS MDKP NSfd NSti
	- white hose-in-hose (d)	EBee GMac MAvo MNFA MNrw NCob SAga WBrk WCot WFar
	'Purple Sensation'PBR	EBee EPfP SPoG WCot
	pusilla	see *C. cochlearifolia*
	pyramidalis	CSpe EBee ELan EPfP EShb GWCH MBNS MCCP NOrc NRnb NSfd SDnm SPav SPlb STes WPer
	- 'Alba'	CSpe CWib EBee ECtt ELan EPfP GWCH NBre NLar NRnb NSfd SDnm SPav SPlb WBrE WPer
	- lavender blue-flowered	CWib NRnb
	raddeana	CMdw ITim MAvo MDKP NEgg NLAp NLar WBrk WFar WLin
	raineri ♀H4	CGra LRHS NMen NSla NWCA SBla WAbe
*	- ***alba***	CGra SBla WAbe
§	***rapunculoides***	EBee EGoo GKev NBHF NBre NRnb SWat WFar WHer WMoo
§	- 'Afterglow'	MAvo WCot WDyG WFar
	- 'Alba'	EMon MAvo
	rapunculus	ILis MLLN NBHF
	recurva	see *C. incurva*
	lanceolatus L.	EBee GKev
	lanceolatus Gorter	see *C. rapunculoides*
	rotundifolia	CArn CHrt CRWN ECho EPfP GAbr GWCH LAst LBMP MHer NBid NBre NGBl NLan NMir NRya NSfd SIde SPlb SWat WAbe WBrk WPer WPtf
	- var. ***alba***	EBee WPer
	- 'Jotunheimen'	CPBP
§	- 'Olympica'	EBee EBur EPfP IGor MBNS NLar NPri WFar WHoo
	- 'Superba'	ECho
	- 'White Gem'	CHFP LBMP NBre NSfd SSvw WPtf
	'Royal Wave'	NBhm
	rupestris	EBur LTwo
	'Samantha'	CBow CHVG CSpe EBee EBla EMan ERou LAst LHop LSou MBri MWea NSfd SBch SHar SMrm SPoG SRGP SVil WCot WOVN
	'Sarastro'	More than 30 suppliers
	sarmatica	CGra EBee EMan EMon EPfP GAbr LBBr MSte NBid NOak NRnb NSfd NSti SMad SRms STes WBrk WPer
	- 'Hemelstraling' **new**	EBee
	sartorii	EBur
	saxifraga	EBur EDAr ITim NMen NWCA
§	- subsp. ***aucheri***	EBee EBur GKev NLAp WAbe
	scouleri	CPBP
	seraglio	CGra NSla
	shetleri	CGra
§	***sibirica***	NBHF NBre NSfd WPer
	- white-flowered	NLar
	siegizmundii	GMac NSfd
	'Sojourner'	CGra
	speciosa	EBee GKev NBHF NBre NSfd WPer
	'Stansfieldii'	CGra CPBP EBur NMen WPat
	stevenii	CGra
	'Summer Pearl'	CStu ERou GKev LAst MBNS NEgg SVil
§	'Swannables'	CPou EBee ECtt EGle EMan EWsh LTwo MNFA MRav NCGa NChi NSfd WOut
§	***takesimana***	More than 30 suppliers
	- B&SWJ 8499	WCru
I	- 'Alba'	EBee EBla EShb MDKP NBre NEgg SHar SSvw WMoo
	- 'Beautiful Trust'PBR	CLAP CSpe EBee EBla ECtt ENor ERou GMac LAst LHop MWea NBPC NBhm NLar NSfd NSti SHar SPoG SRGP WCru WOVN WPGP
§	- 'Elizabeth'	More than 30 suppliers
	- 'Elizabeth II' (d)	EPPr MAvo MTho WCot
	- 'White Giant' **new**	SHar
	teucrioides	GKev NWCA
	thyrsoides	EBee EWll MBNS NBre NRnb NSfd SDnm SPav WPer
	- SDR 3552	GKev
	- subsp. ***carniolica***	SGar
	'Timsbury Perfection'	NHar
	tommasiniana ♀H4	LRHS NSfd SBla WAbe
	trachelium	CEnt CMHG EBee EPfP GAbr LCro MBNS MNrw MRav NBPC NEgg NLan SAga SGar SPad STes WFar WHer WMoo WPer
	- var. ***alba***	CEnt CLAP EBee GAbr LRHS MNrw NLar STes WBrE WCot WFar WMoo WPer
	- 'Alba Flore Pleno' (d)	CBgR CDes CFir CHar CLAP CMil SBch STes WCot WFar
	- 'Bernice' (d)	More than 30 suppliers
	- lilac-blue-flowered	NRnb
	- 'Snowball'PBR	EBee ERou EShb LAst LSRN MWea
	tridentata	EBee
	troegerae	LRHS SBla
	'Tymonsii'	CPBP EBur ECho LRHS LTwo NBir NMen WFar
	'Van-Houttei'	CDes CElw CHar EBee EMon GMac SAga SBch WCot WFar WPer
	versicolor	NBre
	- G&K 3347	EMon
	vidalii	see *Azorina vidalii*
	waldsteiniana	CPBP LRHS LTwo WAbe WFar
	wanneri	EBur EMan EPfP LRHS NLar
	'Warley White'	see *C.* x *haylodgensis* W. Brockbank 'Warley White'
	'Warleyensis'	see *C.* x *haylodgensis* W. Brockbank 'Warley White'
	x ***wockei*** 'Puck'	EBur ECho ECtt LRHS LTwo NLar NSfd NWCA WAbe WPat
	zangezura	CWan EBee EBur EMan EPPr EShb GKev MLLN NGdn NSfd SGar SHGN SPad STes WCra

	zoysii	CGra LRHS SBla

Campanula x *Symphyandra* (*Campanulaceae*)

	C. punctata x ***S. ossetica***, 'Swannables'	see *Campanula* 'Swannables'

Campanumoea see *Codonopsis*

Camphorosma (*Chenopodiaceae*)

	monspeliaca	XPep

Campsis (*Bignoniaceae*)

	RCB/Arg L-8	WCot
	atrosanguinea	see *Bignonia capreolata* 'Atrosanguinea'
	grandiflora	CArn CBcs CSPN CWGN EBee ELan ENot EPfP GSki IMGH LRHS MAsh SPer SWvt WCFE XPep
	radicans	CArn CBcs CBrm CDul CMac CRHN CSBt CWib EBee ECrN ELan EPfP LAst LPan LRHS LSRN MSwo SHBN SLon SPer SPlb WBVN WBrE XPep
	- 'Atrosanguinea'	EPfP
	- 'Flamenco'	CDoC EBee ELan EShb GSki LAst LRHS MAsh SAdn SBod SBra SCoo SLim SPoG SWvt WCot WFar
§	- f. ***flava*** ♀H4	CBcs CDoC CHEx CTri EBee ELan ENot EPfP IMGH LHop LRHS MAsh MCCP MGos NBlu NPal NScw NSti SBra SLim SPer SPoG SSta SWvt WSHC XPep
	- 'Indian Summer'	CWGN ENot EPfP LRHS MBlu MBri MGos SCoo SHFr SLim SPoG WCot
	- 'Yellow Trumpet'	see *C. radicans* f. *flava*
	x ***tagliabuana*** Dancing Flame = 'Huidan'^{PBR}	EBee MGos NLar SPer
	- 'Madame Galen' ♀H4	More than 30 suppliers

Camptosema (*Papilionaceae*)

	praeandinum new	WPGP

Camptosorus see *Asplenium*

Camptotheca (*Cornaceae*)

	acuminata	WPGP

Campylandra see *Tupistra*

Campylotropis (*Papilionaceae*)

	macrocarpa	MBri NLar

Canarina (*Campanulaceae*)

	canariensis ♀H1	CCCN CStu WCot WPGP

Canavalia (*Papilionaceae*)

	gladiata	CPLG

Candollea see *Hibbertia*

Canna ✿ (*Cannaceae*)

	'Adam's Orange'	CDTJ CHEx
	'Aida' (Grand Opera Series)	MBri
	'Alberich'	CSam SHaC
	altensteinii	CDTJ WHil XBlo
	'Ambassador'	EBrs EShb LAma MBri
	'America'	EAmu LAma WCot
	'Angie Summers' new	CDWL
	'Annaeei' ♀H3	EAmu SChr SHaC
	'Anthony and Cleopatra' (v)	WCot
I	'Aphrodite' van Klaveren ♀H3	SHaC
	'Apricot Dream'	SHaC
	'Apricot Ice'	SHaC
	'Aranyálom'	LAma SHaC
	'Argentina'	SHaC
	'Aristote'	SHaC
	'Assaut'	SHaC
	'Atlantis'	XBlo
	'Australia'	CDTJ EAmu LAst LSou MJnS SHaC WCot WHil XBlo
	'Baby Pink' new	SHaC
	'Black Knight'	CDTJ CFir CSpe EAmu EBee EBrs ECGP ELan EWll IBal LAma LAst MJnS MSte SHaC SPad SPet WWlt XBlo
	'Bonfire'	CHEx
	'Bonnezeaux'	SHaC
	brasiliensis	CHll CPou CRHN WCot
	'Brillant'	CDWL ELan LAma SHaC WDyG
	'Caballero'	SHaC
	'Caliméro'	SHaC
	'Canary'	XBlo
	'Carnaval'	SHaC
	'Centenaire de Rozain-Boucharlat'	CHEx SHaC
	'Centurion'	LAma
	'Cerise Davenport'	CFir
	'Champigny'	SHaC
	'Champion'	SHaC
	'Cherry Red' Schmid	SHaC
	'Chinese Coral' Schmid	CHEx LAma
	'Chouchou'	SHaC
I	'Citrina'	XBlo
§	'City of Portland'	ELan LAma SChr SHaC
*	'Cleopatra'	CFir EAmu EBee EBrs LAma SHaC SPet WGwG WHil
*	'Cléopâtre'	SHaC WHil
§	'Colibri'	LAma WHil
	'Confetti'	see *C.* 'Colibri'
	'Corail'	SHaC
	'Corrida'	SHaC
	'Corsica' (Island Series) new	SHaC
	'Creamy White'	CDTJ CHEx SHaC XBlo
	'Crimson Beauty'	EBrs LAma LAst SHaC
	Crozy hybrids	LRav
	'Délibáb'	CSam LAma MBri NBPN SHaC SPet WDyG
	'Di Bartolo'	SHaC XBlo
	'Dollar'	SHaC
	'Dondo'	SHaC
	'Dondoblutrot'	SHaC
	'Durban' ambig.	IHer SHaC WGwG WPic
	'Durban' Hiley, orange-flowered	see *C.* 'Phasion'
	'E. Neubert'	SHaC
	edulis	CDTJ CHEx ETod
	- purple-leaved	ETod
§	x ***ehemanii*** ♀H3	CAvo CDTJ CKob CRHN CSev EBee MJnS SChr SDix SHaC WPGP
	'Emblème'	SHaC
	'En Avant'	CHEx LAma MBri SHaC SPlb
	'Endeavour'	CDWL CHEx LPJP SHaC
	'Erebus' ♀H3	CDWL SDix SHaC WHil
	'Ermine'	WCot
	'Espresso Festival' new	NBPN NGdn
	'Étoile du Feu'	SHaC XBlo
	'Evening Star'	LAma MBri SHaC
	'Extase'	SHaC
	'Fatamorgana'	LAma SHaC WHil
	'Felix Ragout'	LAma SHaC
*	'Felix Roux'	SHaC
	Firebird	see *C.* 'Oiseau de Feu'
	flaccida	CDWL SHaC
	'Flame'	XBlo
	'Flammèche'	SHaC
	'Florence Vaughan'	SHaC

	'Fournaise'	SHaC
	'General Eisenhower' ♀H3	ETod SHaC
	x ***generalis***	SHaC
	glauca	SDix SHaC
	'Gnom'	SHaC
*	'Gold Ader'	LAma
	'Gold Dream'	LAma
	'Golden Girl'	SHaC
	'Golden Lucifer'	CHEx EBrs ELan LAma
	'Gran Canaria'	EAmu SHaC
	'Grand Duc'	SHaC
	'Grande'	CFir ITer MJnS SHaC WPic
	'Heinrich Seidel'	CHEx
	'Hercule'	CHEx SHaC
	'Hiley' **new**	ETod
	'Horn'	SHaC
	hybrids	ELan
	'Ibis'	SHaC
	indica	CDTJ CHEx CPLG EFul EShb ETod MGol SAPC SArc SHaC SPlb WHil
	- 'Purpurea'	CDTJ CHEx LCro LEdu SChr SDix SHaC SPlb WCot WDyG WPGP
	- 'Red King Rupert'	CCCN
	- 'Russian Red' ♀H3	SHaC WHil
	'Ingeborg' ♀H3	LAma SHaC
	'Intrigue'	SHaC
	iridiflora misapplied	see *C.* x *ehemanii*
	iridiflora Ruiz & Pav.	CDTJ CDWL CHEx CSpe
	'Italia'	SHaC WHil
	'Jivago'	SHaC
	'Journey's End'	SHaC
	'Kansas City' (v)	WCot
	'King City Gold'	SHaC
I	'King Humbert' (blood-red)	CBcs CHEx EBrs EPfP LAma LAst MBri MGol MJnS MLan WCot XBlo
	King Humbert (orange-red)	see *C.* 'Roi Humbert'
	'King Midas'	see *C.* 'Richard Wallace'
	'Königin Charlotte'	SHaC SPad
	'La Bohème' (Grand Opera Series)	LAma
	'La Gloire'	SHaC
	'La Quintinie'	SHaC
	'La Traviata'	CDTJ
	'L'Aiglon'	SHaC
	'Lemon Zest' **new**	NScw
	'Lesotho Lil'	CHll
	'Libération'	SHaC
	'Liberté'	see *C.* 'Wyoming'
	'Lolita'	SHaC
	'Louis Cayeux' ♀H3	SDix SHaC
	'Louis Cottin'	CBcs CCCN CHEx EBee EBrs EPfP LAma NBPN SHaC SPad WHil
	'Lucifer'	CBcs CCCN CHEx CSpe EAmu EBrs EPfP LAma LAst LRHS MBri MLan NPer SHaC SPet SPlb WBrE WHil
	lutea	CHEx XBlo
	'Madame Angèle Martin'	EAmu EShb SHaC XBlo
	'Madame Paul Casaneuve'	SHaC
	'Madeira' (Island Series)	NScw
	'Maggie'	SHaC
	'Malawiensis Variegata'	see *C.* 'Striata'
	'Marabout'	CKob SHaC
	'Margaret Strange'	SHaC
	'Marvel'	LAma LAst
	'Meyerbeer'	SHaC
	'Monet'	ECho EPfP WHil
	'Montaigne'	SHaC
	'Mrs Oklahoma'	LAma SHaC
	'Musifolia' ♀H3	CDTJ CHEx CKob EAmu ETod EWes LPJP SChr SDix SHaC WDyG WPic XBlo
	'Mystique' ♀H3	EWes SDix SHaC
	'Ointment Pink'	XBlo
§	'Oiseau de Feu'	LAma SHaC
	'Oiseau d'Or'	SHaC
	'Orange Perfection'	CFir CHEx CSam LAma LAst MBri SHaC
	'Orange Punch'	SHaC WCot
	'Orchid'	see *C.* 'City of Portland'
	'Osric'	CSpe
	'Pacific Beauty'	LSou WCot
	'Pallag Szépe'	SHaC
	'Panache'	CDTJ CHEx CKob ITer SHaC WCot WDyG
	'Panama'	SHaC
	'Passionata'	SHaC
	'Pearlescent Pink'	XBlo
	'Perkeo'	LAma LAst MJnS SHaC SPet
	'Petit Poucet'	SHaC
§	'Pfitzer's Salmon Pink'	CHEx SHaC
§	'Phasion' (v) ♀H3	CHEx CHll CKob CSpe EBee EBrs ELan EPfP EWes LAst LCro LPJP LRHS MBri MJnS NGdn NPer NScw NVic SAga SDix SHBN SHaC SPoG WCot WHal XBlo
	'Picadore'	SHaC
	'Picasso' ♀H3	CBcs CCCN CDTJ CHEx CPLG EAmu EBrs EPfP EShb LAma LAst MGol MLan SHaC SPet XBlo
	'Pink Champagne'	XBlo
	'Pink Futurity' (Futurity Series)	SHaC
	'Pink Perfection'	SHaC
	'Pink Sunburst' (v)	CKob CSpe LAst NGdn SPlb
	'Pinky' **new**	WHil
	'Plantagenet'	SHaC
	'Plaster Pink'	XBlo
	'President'	CHEx CSut EBrs ECho EPfP LAma LAst SHaC SPet WBrE XBlo
	'President Carnot'	SHaC
	'Pretoria'	see *C.* 'Striata'
	'Primrose Yellow'	SHaC
	'Prince Charmant'	SHaC
	'Princess Di'	CMdw SHaC
	'Professor Lorentz'	see *C.* 'Wyoming'
	'Puck'	SHaC
	'Ra' ♀H3	CDWL SHaC WHil
	'Red Futurity' (Futurity Series)	MJnS
	'Red Wine'	SHaC
§	'Richard Wallace'	CPLG CSam CSut EBrs LAma LAst MJnS SHaC SPlb WCot XBlo
	'Robert Kemp'	EAmu SHaC
§	'Roi Humbert'	CSam MSte SHaC
	'Roi Soleil' ♀H3	CHEx LAma SHaC
	'Roitelet'	CHEx SHaC
	'Rosa'	SHaC
	'Rose Futurity' (Futurity Series)	SHaC
	'Rosemond Coles'	CDTJ CHEx CSam CSut EBrs LAma MJnS SHaC
	'Saladin'	SHaC
	'Salmon Pink'	see *C.* 'Pfitzer's Salmon Pink'
	'Salsa'	SHaC
	'Saumur'	SHaC
	Savennières = 'Turcasaw'	SHaC
	'Sémaphore'	EBee MBri NBPN SHaC XBlo
	'Shenandoah' ♀H3	SHaC
	'Singapore Girl'	SHaC
	'Snow-white'	XBlo
	speciosa	XBlo
	'Stadt Fellbach'	SHaC
	'Strasbourg'	CSam ETod LAma NPer SHaC
	'Strawberry Pink'	XBlo
	'Striata' misapplied	see *C.* 'Stuttgart'
§	'Striata' (v) ♀H3	CHEx CKob CSev CSpe EBee EBrs LAst LCro LPJP MPRe NGdn NMoo NScw NVic SAga SHBN SHaC SPet WCot WDyG WHal WHil WPic XBlo

'Striped Beauty' (v) CCCN CDWL EBrs SHaC
§ 'Stuttgart' (v) CDTJ CDWL CSpe EAmu EPfP EShb EWes IBal MJnS NMoo SHaC WCot WHil
'Summer Gold' XBlo
'Sundance' SHaC
'Sunset' WCot
'Südfunk' EAmu SHaC
'Tafraout' SHaC
'Talisman' SHaC XBlo
'Taney' CDWL SHaC
'Tango' SChr
'Taroudant' SHaC
'Tchad' SHaC
'Tirol' EBrs MBri NBPN
'Tricarinata' CHEx
'Triomphe' SHaC
'Tropical Red' **new** SGar
'Tropical Rose' CPLG LRHS SRms WCot
'Tropical White' **new** SGar
'Tropical Yellow' **new** SGar
Tropicanna see *C.* 'Phasion'
'Vainqueur' SHaC
'Valentine' WCot
'Vanilla Pink' XBlo
* 'Variegata' (v) LAma LRHS WCot
'Vera Cole' **new** WHil
'Verdi' ♀H3 CSpe LAma SChr SHaC
'Viva' SHaC
warscewiczii CDTJ CPLG WHil
'Whithelm Pride' ♀H3 SHaC
'Wine 'n' Roses' SHaC
'Woodbridge Pink' XBlo
§ 'Wyoming' ♀H3 CBcs CCCN CDTJ CHEx CSam EBrs ECGP ETod EWll LAma LAst MBri MCCP MJnS MSte NVic SEND SHaC WCot WHil XBlo
'Yara' EBrs
'Yellow Humbert' misapplied see *C.* 'Richard Wallace', *C.* 'Cleopatra', *C.* 'Florence Vaughan'
'Yellow Humbert' LAma LAst MBri MGol SHaC WHil

Cannomois (*Restionaceae*)

congesta CBig
virgata CBig

Cantleya (*Icacinaceae*)

* ***robusta*** NPal

Cantua (*Polemoniaceae*)

buxifolia ♀H2-3 CAbb CBcs CCCN CFee CPLG CPle ECre EShb SOWG WCot WPGP

Cape gooseberry see *Physalis peruviana*

Capnoides see *Corydalis*

Capparis (*Capparaceae*)

spinosa CCCN EBee XPep
- var. ***inermis*** XPep

Capsicum (*Solanaceae*)

annuum CCCN CSim MBri
- var. ***annuum*** (Longum Group) cayenne CCCN LRav
- - - jalapeno LRav
- - 'Oda' LRav
- - 'Prairie Fire' **new** CCCN
- - 'Purple Prince' LRav
- - 'Purple Tiger' LRav
- 'Apache' **new** CCCN
baccatum CSim
chinense CSim
- Habanero Group LRav
frutescens CSim
- Tabasco Group LRav
pubescens CSim EUnu
- 'Red Rocoto' **new** LRav
- 'Rocoto Orange' **new** LRav

Caragana (*Papilionaceae*)

CC 3945 CPLG
arborescens CAgr CArn EPfP MBar MGol NWea SBLw SEND SPer SPlb WBVN XPep
- 'Lorbergii' CEnd EPfP GBin IMGH MBlu SCoo SPer WFoF
- 'Pendula' CLnd CWib ELan ENot EPfP LAst MAsh MBar MBlu NBee NEgg NHol NPri SBLw SCoo SLim SPer SPoG
- 'Walker' CBcs CDul CEnd CWib EBee ELan ENot EPfP LPan LRHS MAsh MBar MBlu MBri MGos NEgg NHol SBLw SCoo SLim SPer WOrn WSpi
aurantiaca MBar
frutex 'Globosa' NBlu
jubata NLar
microphylla WNor
pygmaea **new** NLar

caraway see *Carum carvi*

cardamom see *Elettaria cardamomum*

Cardamine ✿ (*Brassicaceae*)

asarifolia misapplied see *Pachyphragma macrophyllum*
asarifolia L. CLAP
bulbifera CLAP CWsd EBee EPPr GBuc GEdr ITer LEdu NRya WCru WHal WSHC
californica EBee EMan EPPr NRya WCru WMoo
concatenata CLAP NLar SKHP SWat WCru WHal
diphylla CLAP EBee LEdu MLLN WCot WCru WFar
- 'Eco Cut Leaf' CDes EBee WCru WPGP
- 'Eco Moonlight' SKHP WCru
enneaphylla CLAP GBuc GMaP IBlr LEdu NDov NGby
glanduligera CDes CElw EBee EGle ELon LEdu NDov WCru WPGP WSHC
§ ***heptaphylla*** CAvo CLAP CWsd EBee ECha ELan ELon EWTr GBin GBuc IBlr MBri SWat WCru
- Guincho form CDes CLAP GBin IBlr WCot WPGP
- white-flowered CLAP GMaP
§ ***kitaibelii*** CLAP EBee ECha GBin GBuc IBlr LEdu NPol SIng WCru
latifolia Vahl see *C. raphanifolia*
lineariloba IBlr
macrophylla CAby CLAP EBee EWld LEdu NLar SWat WCot WFar
- 'Bright and Bronzy' GEdr WCru
maxima LEdu WCru
§ ***microphylla*** CLAP GCrs NDov WCru
pachystigma EBee
pentaphylla ♀H4 CPom CSpe EBee EBrs ECho EGle ELan ELon EMar EPPr ERos EWTr GBuc GCrs GEdr GGar IBlr MBri MDun MNFA NBir NDov WCot WCru WTin
- bright pink-flowered CLAP NPol WCot
pratensis CArn CHrt CRWN EBee EHon EMFW MHer NLan NMir NPri SIde SWat WFar WHer WMoo WPtf WSFF WShi

- var. ***angustifolia*** new — WCru
- 'Edith' (d) — CLAP EBee GBin GBuc MNrw NChi WPrP
- 'Flore Pleno' (d) — CBre CFee CSpe CWan EBee ECha ELan EMan ITer MFOX MHer MNrw MTho NBid NBir NBro NLar SBch SWat WFar WHoo WMoo WOut WSFF WSHC
- 'William' (d) — EBee EMan EPPr GBuc MNrw SHar WFar WMoo WPrP

quinquefolia — CDes CElw CLAP CMea CPom EBee ECha EGle EHrv ELon EMan EMar GBuc IBlr NDov SBch SBla SDys WBrk WCot WCru WFar WLin WPGP

§ ***raphanifolia*** — CBre CDes CLAP CPom EBee ECha EMan EPPr GAbr GBuc GGar IBlr LEdu LLWG MRav NBid NBro NChi SWat WBor WMoo WPGP WPtf WTin

trifolia — CSpe EBee ECha EGle EHrv EPPr EWTr GBuc GCrs GEdr GGar GMaP IBlr MBar NBir NBro NRya NVic SWat WCot WCru WFar WHer WMoo WTin

* - ***digitata*** — MTho

waldsteinii — CAby CDes CElw CLAP CPom CSpe CWsd EBee ECho EGle EHrv GBuc NCGa NDov SBch SBla SCnR SRot WCru WHoo WIvy

yezoensis — CDes IBlr
- B&SWJ 4659 — WCru

Cardiandra (*Hydrangeaceae*)

alternifolia — CLAP
- B&SWJ 5719 — WCru
- B&SWJ 5845 — WCru
- B&SWJ 6354 — WCru

amamiohshimensis new — WCru

formosana — CLAP
- B&SWJ 2005 — WCru
- B&SWJ 3618 — EWld
- B&SWJ 3632 — WCru
- 'Hsitou' — WCru

Cardiocrinum (*Liliaceae*)

cathayanum — CBct EBee MDun WCot WCra WPGP

cordatum — ECho
- B&SWJ 4841 — WCru
- var. ***glehnii*** — CCCN EBee EBrs ECho GBuc GEdr GGar WWst
- - B&SWJ 4758 — WCru
- red-veined — EBee EBrs GBuc GEdr

giganteum — CBcs CBct CCCN CHEx CHid CTca EBee EBrs ECho EPot GAbr GBuc GCra GEdr GGar GMaP LAma MBri MDun MNrw SMad WBVN WBod WCot WCru WFar WHer WPGP WPnP
- B&SWJ 2419 — WCru
- HWJK 2158 from Nepal — WCru
- var. ***yunnanense*** — CAbb CPom EBee EBrs ECho EPfP GAbr GBuc GEdr GGGa GGar GMaP ITim NBid WCru WPGP

cardoon see *Cynara cardunculus*

Carduus (*Asteraceae*)

benedictus — see *Cnicus benedictus*

nutans — WSFF

Carex (*Cyperaceae*)

from Uganda — MMoz SApp

acuta — CBig GFor LCro NBlu NBre XIsg

acutiformis — CBig CRWN GFor NBHF NBre NSco XIsg

alba — CBig EPPr GFor MAvo WDyG XIsg

albida — EHul LRHS

albula — CWsd MMoz

'Amazon Mist' new — GFor

appressa — CBig SApp

arenaria — CBig EPPr GFor NBHF NBre NNor XIsg

atrata — CGrW EBee EKen EPPr EPla LRHS WHrl

aurea — CBig EBee EPPr GFor IFoB NBre NHol XIsg

baccans — CBig CPLG LRav NOak

bebbii — EPPr

berggrenii — EBee ECou ECrN EHul ELan GFor GSki LEdu LRHS NBro NCob NWCA SPer SPlb SWat WMoo WPer WTin XIsg

binervis — CRWN

boottiana — EWes

brunnea — EWes
- 'Jenneke' — CKno EBee LLWG LRHS MBar MBri SLim SPoG SWvt
- 'Variegata' (v) — CBrm CEnt CPLG EAlp MMoz SApp WWFP

buchananii ♀H4 — More than 30 suppliers
- 'Viridis' — ELan GBin LRHS WHer

bushii — NCob

caryophyllea 'The Beatles' — EBee EGoo EPPr MMoz NBir NHol XIsg

chathamica — CBig CRez EBee MMoz

'China Blue' — CRez EPPr MMoz SApp WMoo

comans — COIW CWCL EBee EFul EMon EPPr EShb GQui GSki LRHS NBro NHol NPol XIsg
- bronze-leaved — More than 30 suppliers
- 'Bronze Perfection' — GBin SWal WFar
- 'Dancing Flame' — CPrp CWCL EBee EWsh SWal
- 'Frosted Curls' — More than 30 suppliers
- green-leaved new — GFor
- 'Kupferflamme' — EBee
- red-leaved — LAst MGos SRms
- 'Small Red' — see *C. comans* 'Taranaki'

§ - 'Taranaki' — EAlp EBee ELan EPPr EPfP MBNS MMoz NHol SWal WPtf

conica 'Hime-kan-suge' — see *C. conica* 'Snowline'
- 'Kiku-sakura' (v) — NHol

§ - 'Snowline' (v) — More than 30 suppliers

coriacea — CBig
- from Dunedin, New Zealand — EPPr

crinita — EPPr

cristatella — EBee EPPr

curta — CRWN

dallii — EBee ECou EKen EWes GBin MMoz NLar WWeb

davisii — EPPr

demissa — CRWN EBee

depauperata — CRWN EMon

digitata — CRWN

dioica — CRWN

dipsacea — More than 30 suppliers
- 'Dark Horse' — EBee NHol WPtf

dissita — CBig

divulsa subsp. ***divulsa*** — CRWN
- subsp. ***leersii*** — EPPr

dolichostachya 'Kaga-nishiki' (v) — CAby CMil CPen CRez EBee EMon EPPr EPla LAst LEdu LLWG LRHS MMoz SLim WPnP WPrP WPtf

duthiei — EBee
- KEKE 494 — MMoz WPGP

echinata — CRWN

§ ***elata*** — EPPr XIsg

§ - 'Aurea' (v) ♀H4 — More than 30 suppliers

	- 'Bowles' Golden'	see *C. elata* 'Aurea'
	- 'Knightshayes' ♀H4	CKno CPen EBee EPPr EWes GBin MMoz WCot
	'Evergold'	see *C. oshimensis* 'Evergold'
	fascicularis	CBig
	firma 'Variegata' (v)	MWat NMen NWCA SIng WAbe WThu
	flacca	CBig CRWN EPPr EWin GBin GFor NBre SWal WGwG XIsg
	- 'Bias' (v)	EMon EPPr EPla MMoz WDyG
§	- subsp. ***flacca***	EBee EWes MMoz NHol NSti WPGP
	flagellifera	More than 30 suppliers
	- 'Auburn Cascade'	EBee EPfP MAvo NHol NPro SApp SPad
	- 'Coca-Cola'	CKno CPen EBee
	- 'Rapunzel'	CWsd EBee EPPr MMoz WPGP
	flava	CBig CKno EPPr GFor XIsg
	fortunei	see *C. morrowii* Boott
	fraseri	see *Cymophyllus fraserianus*
	fraserianus	see *Cymophyllus fraserianus*
	geminata	CBig
	glauca Bosc. ex Boott	CBig CKno CWCL EBee EPla WPGP
	glauca Scopoli	see *C. flacca* subsp. *flacca*
	granularis	EPPr
I	'Grayassina' new	CKno EPPr
	grayi	CBgR CBig CKno EBee EMon EPla GBuc GFor LEdu MBlu MTho NCGa NLar NOak WCot WDyG WPer XIsg
§	***hachijoensis***	EMon EPot LAst WFar
	- 'Evergold'	see *C. oshimensis* 'Evergold'
	halleriana	XPep
	'Happy Wanderer'	SLPl
	hirta	CRWN NSco
	hispida	CBig GFor MCCP MMoz WMoo WPtf WRos
	hordeistichos	EBee
	hostiana	CRWN
	'Ice Dance' (v)	CKno CMea CWGN EAlp EBee EGle EPPr EPla GGar GQue MMoz NCGa NHol NLar NOak SBch STes SWvt WPGP WPrP XIsg
	(Japanese Trial) new	CKno
	kaloides	CSsd EAlp EBee EMan EMon EPPr LRHS MAvo
	'Kan-suge'	see *C. morrowii* Boott
	longebrachiata	CBig
	lucida	NNor
	lupulina	XIsg
	lurida	CBig CKno EBee EPfP GBin GFor MAvo MBNS NBre NLar XIsg
	macloviana	EPPr XIsg
	macrocephala	GFor NBre XIsg
	'Majken'	EBee GFor NBre XIsg
	maorica	CBig
	maritima	CRWN
	mertensii new	XIsg
	Milk Chocolate = 'Milchoc'PBR (v)	CAby CKno CPen CWGN EAlp EBee LBMP SApp
	montana	EBrs LRHS
	morrowii misapplied	see *C. hachijoensis*
§	***morrowii*** Boott	GKev WHil
	- 'Evergold'	see *C. oshimensis* 'Evergold'
	- 'Fisher's Form' (v)	CKno CTri EBee EPPr EPla EWsh LEdu LHop LRHS MMoz MRav NGdn NHol NMir SApp SMac SWvt WFar WPGP WPer
	- 'Gilt' (v)	EBee EMon EPPr LBMP MBNS NHol
	- 'Nana Variegata' (v)	CTri NBir WPGP
	- var. ***temnolepis*** 'Silk Tassel'	EPPr NHol XIsg
N	- 'Variegata' (v)	EHrv EHul ELan EMon EPPr EPfP EPla GKev GMaP LAst LRHS MBar MMoz MRav NBir NHol NSti SGar SHFr SLPl SMac SRms WCot WEas WFar WPnP XIsg
	muehlenbergii	EPPr
	muricata subsp. ***muricata***	EPPr
	muskingumensis	More than 30 suppliers
	- 'Ice Fountains' (v)	EBee EPPr ERou MAvo XIsg
	- 'Little Midge'	CBgR CKno CWsd EBee EPPr GBin LRHS XIsg
	- 'Oehme' (v)	CKno CWCL EBee EPPr EPla EPyc EShb GBin LEdu NBid WCot WDyG WPtf WTin
	- 'Silberstreif' (v)	CBrm CKno CPen CRez EBee EPPr GBin GGar LLWG NLar SApp XIsg
	nigra	CRWN EHon EPPr GSki NBHF NLar WPnP XIsg
§	- 'On-line' (v)	EHrv EPPr MMoz NBlu NHol SApp WBrk WMoo
	- 'Variegata'	see *C. nigra* 'On-line'
	No 1, Nanking (Greg's broad leaf)	MMoz
	No 4, Nanking (Greg's thin leaf)	EPPr MAvo SApp
	normalis	EPPr
*	***oblongatus*** new	SNin
	obnupta	EPPr XIsg
	obtrubae	CRWN
	ornithopoda 'Aurea'	see *C. ornithopoda* 'Variegata'
§	- 'Variegata' (v)	CBrm EBee ECtt EHul EPla EPot GFor MBrN MMoz NBro NGdn NHol SBch WFar WMoo WTin XIsg
§	***oshimensis*** 'Evergold' (v) ♀H4	More than 30 suppliers
	- 'Evergold Compact'	SMac
	- 'Variegata' (v)	NBir
	ovalis	CRWN SWal WRos
	pallescens 'Breckland Frost' (v)	EPPr XIsg
	- 'Wood's Edge' (v)	CNat
	panicea	CKno CRWN CWCL EBee EPPr EPla MMoz NBlu SApp WFar WMoo XIsg
	paniculata	CBig CRWN GFor NBre NSco XIsg
	pendula	More than 30 suppliers
	- 'Cool Jazz' (v)	EPPr MAvo XIsg
	- 'Moonraker' (v)	CWCL EBee EPPr EPla LEdu MAvo MBNS NHol SApp WCot WMoo WSpi XIsg
	petriei	CWCL ECha ETod EWes GBuc LLWP MAvo MBNS MMoz NVic SWal WCot WFar WPer WTin
	phyllocephala	EShb WCot WDyG WRos XIsg
	- 'Sparkler' (v)	More than 30 suppliers
	pilulifera 'Tinney's Princess' (v)	EPot LRHS NHol WHil
	plantaginea	CAby EBee EMon EPPr EPla GBin LEdu SApp WCot WDyG WFar WMoo WPGP XIsg
	praegracilis	CKno
	projecta	EPPr
	pseudocyperus	CRWN EHon EPPr EPla EWsh GBin GFor MMoz NBlu NNor NPer SRms SWal SWat WFar WMoo WPer WPnP XIsg
	pulicaris	CRWN
	reinii	WPrP
	remota	CBig CRWN EPPr LRHS NBre XIsg
	riparia	CBig CRWN EMFW LCro MMoz NHol NPer NSco SWal SWat WFar WRos WShi XIsg
	- 'Bowles' Golden'	see *C. elata* 'Aurea'
	- 'Variegata' (v)	CBen CBgR CDWL EBee EHon ELon EMFW EMon EPla EShb GMaP MAvo MMoz NBro NHol

	SAga SApp WAbb WCot WFar WHal WMoo WPnP
rostrata	CRWN
sabynensis	see *C. umbrosa* subsp. *sabynensis*
saxatilis 'Ski Run'	EBee
secta	CBig CKno EAlp ECou EPPr GFor GGar GMaP LRav MNrw NBre WDyG WMoo WPer XIsg
- from Dunedin, New Zealand	EPPr
- var. ***tenuiculmis***	see *C. tenuiculmis*
siderosticha	EShb SLPl WPGP WPer
- 'Banana Boat' (v) new	CKno EBee LSou MNrw NOrc SMad
- 'Elaine West' (v)	EBee
- 'Golden Fountains'	WCot
- 'Kisokaido' (v)	EBee WCot
- 'Old Barn'	EBee EPPr
- 'Shima-nishiki' (v)	CBcs CElw CHrt CPen CPrp EBee ECtt EPPr EPfP EPla EShb LAst LEdu LLWG NBPC NCGa NPro NScw SAga SMad WBor WLin
- 'Variegata' (v)	More than 30 suppliers
'Silver Sceptre' (v)	More than 30 suppliers
'Silver Sparkler'	NBir
solandri	CSam EWsh LEdu MAvo NLar SApp WMoo WPtf
spissa	CKno MAvo MNrw
sprengelii	EPPr
stricta Lamarck	EPla
stricta Gooden.	see *C. elata*
- 'Bowles' Golden'	see *C. elata* 'Aurea'
sylvatica	CBig CRWN EBee EPfP GFor
tasmanica	CBig
§ ***tenuiculmis***	CKno CWCL EAlp EBee EMon EPPr EShb EWsh GBin GWCH MAvo NHol NSti SBch SWal WTin XIsg
- 'Cappucino' new	CKno
tereticaulis	WCwm
testacea	More than 30 suppliers
- 'Old Gold'	CPrp EAlp EBee ELan EWes MBri MWgw NBPC NOak SMad SMer SPlb WBrE WFar WLeb
texensis	EPPr
trifida	CHEx CHrt CKno EBee EKen GFor GGar MMoz MNrw SMad WFar WMoo WPnP XIsg
- 'Chatham Blue'	CHid CKno EPPr GBin MAvo NBir SEND
umbrosa	CBig XIsg
- subsp. ***sabynensis*** 'Thinny Thin' (v)	EBee EMon EPPr
uncifolia	ECou
virgata	CBig
viridula subsp. ***viridula***	CRWN
vulpina	CBig EPPr NBre XIsg
vulpinoidea	EPPr
'Yellow Tassels'	ITer

Carica (*Caricaceae*)

goudotiana	CKob EUnu
x ***heilbornii*** (F)	CKob
quercifolia	CKob EUnu

Carissa (*Apocynaceae*)

grandiflora	see *C. macrocarpa*
§ ***macrocarpa*** (F)	ERea EShb

Carlina (*Asteraceae*)

acanthifolia	ECho WLin
- subsp. ***cyanara*** JJA 274.101	NWCA
acaulis	CArn CHrt ECho ELan EPfP GEdr GKev MNHC NEgg NPri NWCA SDnm SMer SPav SPlb SRms WFar WPer
- subsp. ***acaulis***	GPoy
- bronze	CAby EWll LDai MCCP WHil
- var. ***caulescens***	see *C. acaulis* subsp. *simplex*
§ - subsp. ***simplex***	ECha EMan GBuc GGar GMaP LRHS NPri WFar WJek WPer
- - bronze	CBow EBee GMaP MAvo NChi SMad SPhx
vulgaris	WPer

Carmichaelia (*Papilionaceae*)

'Abundance'	ECou
'Angie'	ECou
angustata 'Buller'	ECou
appressa	ECou GGar
- 'Ellesmere'	ECou
arborea	ECou
- 'Grand'	ECou
astonii	ECou
- 'Ben More'	ECou
- 'Chalk Ridge'	ECou
australis	EBee ECou WBod WSHC
- 'Bright Eyes'	ECou
- 'Cunningham'	ECou
- Flagelliformis Group	ECou
- 'Mahurangi'	ECou
- Ovata Group	ECou
- 'Solander'	ECou
'Charm'	ECou
'Clifford Bay'	ECou
corrugata	ECou
'Culverden'	ECou
curta	ECou
enysii	CCCN
exsul	ECou
fieldii 'Westhaven'	ECou
flagelliformis 'Roro'	ECou
glabrata	CHEx CPLG CPle
'Hay and Honey'	ECou
juncea Nigrans Group	ECou
kirkii	ECou
'Lilac Haze'	ECou
monroi	ECou
- 'Rangitata'	ECou
- 'Tekapo'	ECou
nana	ECou
- 'Desert Road'	ECou
- 'Pringle'	ECou
- 'Waitaki'	ECou
nigrans 'Wanaka'	ECou
odorata	CPLG ECou
- Angustata Group	ECou
- 'Green Dwarf'	ECou
- 'Lakeside'	ECou
- 'Riverside'	ECou
ovata 'Calf Creek'	ECou
'Parson's Tiny'	ECou
petriei	ECou SMad
- 'Aviemore'	ECou
- 'Lindis'	ECou
- 'Pukaki'	ECou
- Virgata Group	ECou
'Porter's Pass'	ECou
'Spangle'	ECou
'Tangle'	ECou
uniflora	ECou
- 'Bealey'	ECou
'Weka'	ECou
williamsii	ECou
'Yellow Eyes'	ECou

x Carmispartium (*Papilionaceae*)

astens	see x *C. hutchinsii*
§ ***hutchinsii***	ECou

- 'Butterfly' ECou
- 'County Park' ECou
- 'Delight' ECou
- 'Pink Beauty' ECou
- 'Wingletye' ECou

Carpenteria (*Hydrangeaceae*)

californica ♀H3 CPMA CSBt EBee ELan EPfP EWTr IMGH LCro LHop MBri MGos MLan MWat NPal SGar SHBN SPla SReu SSpi SSta WCot WHCG WPat WSHC WSpi
- 'Bodnant' CDul ELan ENot LRHS MBri MGos MWea SBra WBod WGer WPGP
- 'Elizabeth' CAbP CPMA CWGN EBee ELan ENot EPfP LRHS MAsh MBri SKHP SPer SPoG SSpi SSta WPGP WPat
- 'Ladhams' Variety' CBcs CPMA EBee EPfP LCro LRHS MGos MRav NEgg NLar SBra WKif WSPU WSpi

Carpinus ✿ (*Corylaceae*)

betulus ♀H4 More than 30 suppliers
* - 'A. Beeckman' SBLw
- 'Columnaris' CLnd CTho SBLw
* - 'Columnaris Nana' CMCN
§ - 'Fastigiata' ♀H4 CBcs CCVT CDoC CDul CEnd CLnd CMCN CSBt CTho CWib EBee ECrN ELan EPfP LBuc LPan MBar MGos NBee NWea SBLw SCoo SPoG WFar WOrn
- 'Frans Fontaine' CDoC CDul CLnd CMCN CTho EBee ENot IArd LAst LPan LRHS MBlu MBri MGos NBlu SBLw SCoo SIFN SLim SPer
- 'Horizontalis' CMCN
- 'Pendula' CDul CEnd CLnd CTho EBee LPan MBlu SBLw SIFN
- 'Purpurea' CBcs CDul CEnd MGos NBPN NLar SBLw SIFN
- 'Pyramidalis' see *C. betulus* 'Fastigiata'
- 'Quercifolia' CDul EBee SBLw

caroliniana CLnd CMCN NEgg WNor
caucasica SIFN
cordata CMCN SIFN WCwm
coreana CLnd CMCN WNor
fangiana CEnd CGHE CLnd CTho EBee EPla SIFN WPGP
fargesii see *C. viminea*
henryana CMen SIFN WHCr WNor
japonica ♀H4 CEnd CMCN CMen CTho EPfP IDee LPan MBlu SCoo SIFN
laxiflora CMen MPkF SIFN WFar WNor WPGP
- var. ***longispica*** B&SWJ 8772 WCru
- var. ***macrostachya*** see *C. viminea*

monbeigiana SEH 1208 new SIFN
orientalis CMCN WNor
polyneura CMCN WNor
pubescens SIFN WPGP
rankanensis ETOT 122 new SIFN
x ***schuschaensis*** SIFN
shensiensis CDul CMCN
tschonoskii CMCN
turczaninowii ♀H4 CBcs CDul CMCN CMHG CMen IDee NLar NPal NWea SIFN STre WNor
§ ***viminea*** CEnd CMCN WNor

Carpobrotus (*Aizoaceae*)

§ ***edulis*** CCCN CDTJ CDoC CHrt EShb EUnu EWin SAPC SArc SChr SEND WHer
- var. ***edulis*** CHEx
- var. ***rubescens*** CCCN CHEx

muirii CCCN EShb EWin
sauerae CCCN

Carpodetus (*Escalloniaceae*)

serratus CBcs CTrC

Carrierea (*Flacourtiaceae*)

calycina new WPGP

Carthamus (*Asteraceae*)

tinctorius CArn MNHC MSal SPav

Carum (*Apiaceae*)

carvi CArn CHrt CWan GPoy GWCH MHer MNHC NPri SIde WHer WJek WPer WSel
copticum EUnu MSal
petroselinum see *Petroselinum crispum*
roxburghianum EUnu

Carya ✿ (*Juglandaceae*)

aquatica CTho
cordiformis CMCN CTho EPfP
glabra CMCN WPGP
N ***illinoinensis*** (F) CAgr CBcs CMCN SSpi
- 'Carlson No 3' seedling CAgr
- 'Colby' seedling CAgr
- 'Cornfield' CAgr
- 'Lucas' CAgr

laciniosa (F) CTho EGFP EPfP SSpi WPGP
- 'Henry' (F) CAgr
- 'Keystone' seedling (F) CAgr

ovalis EGFP
ovata (F) CAgr CLnd CMCN CTho EPfP MBlu SSpi
- 'Grainger' seedling (F) CAgr
- 'Neilson' seedling (F) CAgr
- 'Weschke' seedling (F) CAgr
- 'Yoder no 1' seedling (F) CAgr

pallida EGFP
texana EGFP
tomentosa EPfP

Caryophyllus see *Syzygium*

Caryopteris ✿ (*Verbenaceae*)

'Autumn Pink'[PBR] new CWoW
x ***clandonensis*** EBee ECtt ENot MGan MLHP MWat NBir WBod WCFE WFar WHCG WHar WTel
- 'Arthur Simmonds' ♀H4 CSam CTri EBee ECha EPfP LHop SPer WGor
- 'Blaue Donau' EBee SPoG
- 'Dark Night' CHar EBee LBuc LRHS SPoG SPur
- 'Ferndown' CDoC CWib EBee ECrN EPfP EWTr LHop LRHS NLar SPer SPla SReu SRms WWeb
- 'First Choice' ♀H3-4 CAbP CSpe EBee ECrN ELan EPfP EShb LCro LHop LRHS LSRN MAsh MBri MGos NLar SPer SPoG SRkn SWvt WOVN WSpi
- Grand Bleu = 'Inoveris'[PBR] CSBt EBee ELan EMil ENot EQua EShb EWTr LSRN MAsh MBNS MGos MRav MSwo NCGa NLar SMad SPoG SPur WSpi
- 'Heavenly Baby' MAsh
- 'Heavenly Blue' More than 30 suppliers
- 'Kew Blue' More than 30 suppliers
- 'Longwood Blue' ELan EPfP LRHS
- 'Moody Blue' (v) EPfP SPoG
- 'Pershore' WSPU
- 'Summer Gold' MRav SPoG
- 'Summer Sorbet'[PBR] (v) CBcs CBow CDoC EBrs ELan EMil EPfP EWes LBuc LHop LRHS MAsh

	MGos MNHC MTPN NLar NPro SCoo SMad SMer SPoG WSpi
- 'Worcester Gold' ♀$^{H3-4}$	More than 30 suppliers
divaricata	EBee EMon WHil
- 'Electrum'	ECtt EMan EMon LSou MDKP WHil
- 'Jade Shades'	EBee ECtt EMon LSou
- variegated (v)	CBow
§ ***incana***	CMCN CWoW ECrN EPfP SPer WSHC XPep
- 'Autumn Pink'	CBgR ECrN EPfP
- 'Blue Cascade'	ENot
- 'Jason'^{PBR}	ENot EPfP
- weeping	EBee ELan GBuc MRav MSte NLar WLeb
mastacanthus	see *C. incana*
mongolica	XPep
odorata	EShb

Caryota (*Arecaceae*)

gigas new	EAmu
'Hymalaya'	LPal
mitis ♀^{H1}	EAmu LPal
- 'Himalaya' new	EAmu
obtusa	LPal
ochlandra	LPal
urens	LPal

Cassandra see *Chamaedaphne*

Cassia (*Caesalpiniaceae*)

corymbosa Lam.	see *Senna corymbosa*
marilandica	see *Senna marilandica*
obtusifolia	see *Senna obtusifolia*

Cassinia (*Asteraceae*)

aculeata	GGar
leptophylla	GGar SPer
- subsp. ***fulvida***	ECou GGar MBar SPer
- subsp. ***vauvilliersii***	CDoC CPLG GGar MCot SPer
- - BR 55	GGar
- - var. ***albida***	SKHP SPer
- - 'Silberschmelze'	SOWG
N ***retorta***	ECou
'Ward Silver'	CPLG CSpe ECou EWes GSki

Cassinia x *Helichrysum* (*Asteraceae*)

* hybrid	WKif

Cassiope ✿ (*Ericaceae*)

'Askival Arctic Fox'	GCrs
'Askival Snowbird'	GCrs ITim
'Askival Snow-wreath'	see *C.* Snow-wreath Group
'Askival Stormbird'	GCrs
'Badenoch'	ECho GCrs GEdr NDlv NLar
'Bearsden'	MBar NDlv
'Edinburgh' ♀^{H4}	ECho GCrs GEdr MBar NDlv NHar NLar WBod
fastigiata Askival strain x ***wardii***	GCrs
'Kathleen Dryden'	GCrs
lycopodioides 'Beatrice Lilley'	ECho GEdr LTwo NDlv NHar SRms WPat
= 'Jim Lever'	GCrs WAbe
'Medusa'	WPat WThu
mertensiana	ECho GCrs MBar NDlv SRms
- var. ***californica***	GCrs
- var. ***gracilis***	ITim
'Muirhead' ♀^{H4}	ECho GCrs GEdr MBar NDlv NRya SRms WAbe
'Randle Cooke' ♀^{H4}	ECho GCrs GEdr MBar NDlv SRms
selaginoides	NLar
- LS&E 13284	GCrs WAbe
§ Snow-wreath Group	GCrs ITim
tetragona	MBar SRms
wardii 'George Taylor'	GGGa

Castanea ✿ (*Fagaceae*)

'Bouche de Betizac' (F)	CAgr LPan
crenata	CAgr
dentata	EGFP
henryi	CBcs
'Layeroka' (F)	CAgr
'Maraval'	CAgr
'Maridonne' (F)	CAgr
'Marigoule' (F)	CAgr
'Marlhac' (F)	CAgr
'Marsol' (F)	CAgr
mollissima	CBcs CMCN ISea
'Précoce Migoule' (F)	CAgr
pumila	CAgr CMCN
'Rousse de Nay' (F)	CAgr
sativa ♀^{H4}	More than 30 suppliers
§ - 'Albomarginata' (v) ♀^{H4}	CDoC CDul CEnd CTho EBee EPfP IMGH MBlu MBri MDun MGos NBea SBLw WFar WOrn WPat
- 'Anny's Red'	MBlu
- 'Anny's Summer Red'	CDul LRHS MAsh SCoo SLon
- 'Argenteovariegata'	see *C. sativa* 'Albomarginata'
- 'Aspleniifolia'	CBcs CDul MBlu
- 'Aureomarginata'	see *C. sativa* 'Variegata'
- 'Belle Epine' (F)	CAgr
- 'Bournette' (F)	CAgr
* - 'Doré de Lyon'	CAgr
- 'Herria' (F)	CAgr
- 'Laguépie' (F)	CAgr
- 'Marron Comballe' (F)	CAgr
- 'Marron de Goujounac' (F)	CAgr
- 'Marron de Lyon' (F)	CAgr CDul CEnd CLnd CTho EMil EMui EPfP MBlu MCoo NWea SKee
- 'Marron de Redon' (F)	CAgr
- 'Numbo' (F)	CAgr
§ - 'Variegata' (v)	CBcs CLnd CMCN ECrN ELan EMil LPan MAsh MGos
- 'Verdale' (F)	CAgr
seguinii	CAgr
'Simpson'	CAgr
'Vignols' (F)	CAgr

Castanopsis (*Fagaceae*)

chinensis	CBcs
cuspidata	CBcs
platyacantha new	CExc

Castanospermum (*Papilionaceae*)

australe	CArn

Castilleja (*Scrophulariaceae*)

elegans new	WAbe
hispida	WAbe
miniata	GKev WAbe
sessiliflora new	GKev

Casuarina (*Casuarinaceae*)

cunninghamiana	CBcs ECou

Catalpa ✿ (*Bignoniaceae*)

bignonioides ♀^{H4}	More than 30 suppliers
- 'Aurea' ♀^{H4}	More than 30 suppliers
- 'Nana'	ECrN LRHS MBri SBLw
- 'Purpurea'	see *C.* x ***erubescens*** 'Purpurea'
- 'Variegata' (v)	CLnd CTho EBee EPfP LRHS MGos SSta WCot WPat
bungei	CLnd EGFP LPan MGos MJnS SAPC SArc SHGN WNor
- 'Purpurea'	ELan LAst
x ***erubescens***	SBLw
§ - 'Purpurea' ♀^{H4}	More than 30 suppliers
fargesii	CLnd
- f. ***duclouxii***	CDul CEnd CMCN EPfP MBlu NLar WPat

ovata CMCN EGFP WBVN
- ‘Slender Silhouette’ NLar

speciosa CBcs CDul CLnd CMCN EPfP SBLw SPer
- ‘Pulverulenta’ (v) CDoC CDul CEnd CMCN EMil MDun MGos NLar SPer WOrn

Catananche (*Asteraceae*)

caerulea More than 30 suppliers
- ‘Alba’ CMea EBee EBla ECha EPfP ERou GMac IFoB LRHS NBir NPri SGar SPer SPoG WCAu WMoo WPer
- ‘Amor White’ LRav
- ‘Bicolor’ CMMP EMan MHer MNrw SHGN STes WFar WHoo WMoo
- ‘Major’ ♀H4 ECrN LDai LRHS SRms WEas

caespitosa SBla

Catha (*Celastraceae*)

edulis CArn CKob GPoy MGol WJek

Catharanthus (*Apocynaceae*)

roseus ♀H1 GPoy MBri MSal
- Ocellatus Group MBri

Cathaya (*Pinaceae*)

argyrophylla WPGP

Caulophyllum (*Berberidaceae*)

thalictroides CArn CLAP EBee GBuc GEdr LEdu MGol MSal NLar WCru WFar WMoo WPnP WSHC
- subsp. ***robustum*** CLAP EBee WCru

Cautleya ✿ (*Zingiberaceae*)

cathcartii CLAP LEdu
- B&SWJ 2281 WCru
- B&SWJ 2314 CBct
- ‘Tenzing’s Gold’ CLAP WCru

§ ***gracilis*** CKob CLAP CPrp CWsd EBee ETod IBlr LEdu MJnS WPic
- B&SWJ 7186 WCru WDyG
- CC 1751 WCot

lutea see *C. gracilis*

spicata CBct CDTJ CDoC CHEx CKob EBee EBrs ECho EPPr IBlr ITer MJnS SBHP WCot
- B&SWJ 2103 WCru
- ‘Crûg Canary’ CLAP WCru
- * - var. ***lutea*** CBct CHEx CPne ETod MJnS
- ‘Robusta’ CAvo CGHE CHEx CLAP CMdw CPne CTca EAmu EMan EShb GCra IBlr LEdu MGol MNrw SMad WBor WCru WPGP WPic

Cayratia (*Vitaceae*)

§ ***thomsonii*** BWJ 8123 WCru

Ceanothus ✿ (*Rhamnaceae*)

‘A.T. Johnson’ CDul EBee LAst MWya SHBN SLim SPad SPer SRms

americanus CArn CPle MSal

arboreus SAPC SArc
- ‘Owlswood Blue’ LRHS
- ‘Trewithen Blue’ ♀H3 More than 30 suppliers

‘Autumnal Blue’ ♀H3 More than 30 suppliers

‘Basil Fox’ LRHS

‘Blue Buttons’ LRHS

* ‘Blue Carpet’ CWSG

‘Blue Cushion’ CBcs CDoC CPMA CWSG EBee LHop LRHS MGos MRav NHol NLar SLon SMer SWvt WFar WRHF

‘Blue Dreams’ WFar

‘Blue Jeans’ EBee ELan IArd LRHS SAga WLeb

* ‘Blue Moon’ LRHS

‘Blue Mound’ ♀H3 More than 30 suppliers

‘Blue Sapphire’PBR CBcs CDoC CFwr CMHG CRez CSBt CWGN CWSG EBee ELan EMil ENot EPfP LAst LHop LRHS MBlu MRav NLar SHBN SPer SPoG SWvt

‘Burkwoodii’ ♀H3 CBcs CDoC CDul CSBt CTri CWSG EPfP LAst LCro LRHS MAsh MDun MGan MGos MRav NHol SCoo SHBN SPer SPoG SWvt WFar WGwG

‘Cascade’ ♀H3 CBcs CTri CWSG EBee ENot LRHS MGos MWat NPri NSti SCoo SLon SPer SPlb WBod WHCG XPep

‘Centennial’ LBuc LCro LRHS MRav

‘Concha’ ♀H3 More than 30 suppliers

§ ***cuneatus*** var. ***rigidus*** LRHS NHol SDry SRms WSHC
- - ‘Snowball’ ELan EPfP LRHS

‘Cynthia Postan’ CMHG CSBt CWSG EBee EPfP ERas IArd ISea LRHS MAsh MBlu MWat NHol NLar SCoo SDix WWeb

‘Dark Star’ ♀H3 CBcs CBrm CChe CDoC CMHG CSPN CWSG EBee ELon EPfP LBMP LRHS MAsh MBlu MGos NHol NSti SCoo SEND SOWG SPla SPoG SSta SWvt

‘Delight’ CBcs EBee ELan EPfP EPla LRHS MGos NBlu WBod WFar WRHF

x ***delileanus*** ‘Gloire de Versailles’ ♀H4 CBrm CDoC CDul CMac CWSG CWib EBee ECrN ELan ENot EPfP ISea LAst LHop LRHS MGos MNHC MRav MSwo NEgg SHBN SPer SPla SPoG SWvt WFar WSHC
- ‘Henri Desfossé’ ELan ERas LRHS LSRN MRav NCGa NLar SOWG SPer WKif
- ‘Indigo’ WKif
- ‘Topaze’ ♀H4 CRez CWSG EBee ELan EMil EPfP ERas LRHS MRav NLar SLon SOWG WHar

dentatus misapplied see *C.* x ***lobbianus***

dentatus Torr. & A.Gray ENot GBin SPlb
- var. ***floribundus*** CSBt ELan LRHS SDix
- * - ‘Superbus’ EBee

‘Diamond Heights’ see *C. griseus* var. *horizontalis* ‘Diamond Heights’

divergens EBee

‘Edinburgh’ ♀H3 EBee EPfP GBin LRHS MWgw WFar

‘El Dorado’ (v) MGos SPoG

‘Eleanor Taylor’ EBee SLon

‘Fallen Skies’ LRHS

‘Frosty Blue’ LRHS

gloriosus EBee EWes SDry
- ‘Anchor Bay’ EBee ELan EPfP LRHS SLon SOWG WWeb
- ‘Emily Brown’ CBcs CDoC CSPN EBee ELan GGar LAst MBri MRav NHol NLar WFar
- ‘Hearts Desire’ LRHS

griseus var. ***horizontalis*** LCro
- § - - ‘Diamond Heights’ (v) MAsh MBri NPri SPer WFar
- - - ‘Hurricane Point’ WFar
- - - ‘Silver Surprise’PBR (v) CBcs CSPN CWGN EBee ELan EMil ENot EPfP LRHS MGos NLar NPri SHBN SLim SPer SPoG WOVN
- - - ‘Yankee Point’ CBcs CChe CDoC CSBt CWib EBee EMil ENot EPfP GGar ISea LRHS MGos MRav MSwo NHol NPri SCoo SHBN SLim SMer SPer SPlb SPoG SWvt WFar XPep

impressus CMHG CSBt CTri ECrN ELan EPfP LRHS MAsh MRav NPri SMer SPer SPla SWvt WCFE WFar WWeb XPep
- ‘Victoria’ ERas LBuc MGos NLar SRGP XPep

N	'Italian Skies' 🏆H3	CBcs CDoC CMac CSBt CWSG EBee ELan EMil EPfP LAst LCro LRHS MDun MGos MRav MSwo MWgw NPri SCoo SLim SLon SMer SPer SPlb SPoG SWvt WFar XPep
	'Joan Mirov'	LRHS
	'Julia Phelps'	CMHG EBee WEas WSPU
	'Ken Taylor'	LRHS
	'Kurt Zadnik'	LRHS
§	x ***lobbianus***	CBcs CTri NPri SPlb WFar
	- 'Russellianus'	MWya SHBN
	maritimus 'Frosty Dawn'	LRHS
	x ***pallidus*** 'Marie Simon'	CBcs CBrm CWib EBee ECrN ELan EMil EPfP LAst LBMP LHop LRHS MGos NPri SCoo SPer SPoG SRms SWvt WCFE WFar WKif WWeb
	- 'Perle Rose'	CBcs CMac CPle EBee EPfP LAst LRHS LTwo MGos SHBN SOWG SPer SPla SPoG WKif WSHC
	papillosus var. ***roweanus***	CPle ELan
§	'Pershore Zanzibar'PBR (v)	CBcs CChe CSBt CSPN CWSG EBee ELan ENot EPfP GGar LAst LBuc LRHS MGos MRav MSwo MWat MWgw MWya NPri SAdn SCoo SHBN SPer SPoG SRms SWvt WBrE WSPU WWeb
	'Pin Cushion'	CAbP CDoC CWSG CWib EPfP LRHS MAsh MWgw NHol WSPU
	'Point Millerton'	see *C. thyrsiflorus* 'Millerton Point'
	'Popcorn'	LRHS MGos SPoG
	prostratus	CPle MAsh SDry SHBN SMad WAbe
	'Puget Blue' 🏆H4	More than 30 suppliers
	purpureus	CPle LRHS WWeb
	'Ray Hartman'	NLar SMad XPep
	repens	see *C. thyrsiflorus* var. *repens*
	rigidus	see *C. cuneatus* var. *rigidus*
	'Snow Flurries'	see *C. thyrsiflorus* 'Snow Flurry'
	'Snow Showers'	WBod
	'Southmead' 🏆H3	CDoC CTri EBee ECrN ELan EMil EPfP ERas GBuc LRHS MAsh MGos MSwo MWat NEgg NHol WBrE WFar WHCG WMoo
	thyrsiflorus	CMac CTri CWSG CWib LBMP LRHS MAsh NHol SHBN SPer SRms SWvt WFar WHar WTel
§	- 'Millerton Point'	CWSG EBee EMil EPfP LAst LRHS MAsh MBlu MGos MWea NLar SCoo SLim SPoG WGwG XPep
§	- var. ***repens*** 🏆H3	More than 30 suppliers
	- 'Skylark' 🏆H3	CDoC CDul CWSG EBee ELan ENot EPau EPfP GGar LCro LHop LRHS MAsh MBri MGos MLHP NPri SDix SLim SSpi SSta WFar WPat WWeb
§	- 'Snow Flurry'	CBcs CWib EPfP MSwo WFar
	'Tilden Park'	LRHS SPoG
	x ***veitchianus***	CMac CSBt EBee ELan LRHS MAsh MBar MDun NHol SCoo SPer WGwG
	velutinus	MSal
	'White Cascade'	LRHS
	'Zanzibar'PBR	see *C.* 'Pershore Zanzibar'

Cedrela (*Meliaceae*)

	sinensis	see *Toona sinensis*

Cedronella (*Lamiaceae*)

§	***canariensis***	CArn CBod CHby CHrt CPrp CSev EShb EUnu GGar GPoy ILis MHer MNHC MSal NGHP NTHB SIde SOWG SWat WGwG WHer WPer WSel XPep
	mexicana	see *Agastache mexicana*
	triphylla	see *C. canariensis*

Cedrus (*Pinaceae*)

	atlantica	CDul CLnd CMen CSBt ECrN EHul EWTr LCon MBar NWea SEND WBVN WEve WMou
	- 'Aurea'	CDul CMac LCon LLin MBar MGan MGos NLar SSta WHar
	- 'Fastigiata'	CDoC CDul CMac EHul LCon MBar MBri MGos NLar SCoo SLim SPoG WEve
	- Glauca Group 🏆H4	More than 30 suppliers
	- - 'Glauca Fastigiata'	CKen CMen ECho WEve
	- - 'Glauca Pendula'	CDoC CDul CMen ECho ECrN EHul EOrn EPfP IMGH LCon LPan LRHS MBar MBlu MBri MGos NBlu NEgg SBLw SCoo SHBN SLim SMad SPoG SSta WEve WFar WOrn
	- - 'Saphir Nymphe'	ECho NLar
	- - 'Silberspitz'	CKen
	- 'Pendula'	CMac ECho GBin MAsh SHBN
	brevifolia	ECho LCon LLin LPan MBar MGos NLar STre WEve
	- 'Epstein'	ECho LCon MBar MGos NLar
	- 'Hillier Compact'	CKen MGos NLar
	- 'Kenwith'	CKen ECho LCon NLar
	deodara 🏆H4	More than 30 suppliers
	- 'Albospica' (v)	LLin SWvt
	- 'Argentea'	MBar MGos
	- 'Aurea' 🏆H4	CDoC CDul CKen CSBt CTho ECho ECrN EHul EOrn EPfP GBin IMGH LCon LLin LPan LRHS MBar MBri MGan MGos MWya NEgg SBLw SLim WEve WFar WOrn
I	- 'Aurea Pendula'	ECho
	- 'Blue Dwarf'	CKen ECho LLin NLar
*	- 'Blue Mountain Broom'	CKen
	- 'Blue Snake'	CKen NLar
	- 'Blue Triumph'	LPan
	- 'Bush's Electra' **new**	MBri NLar
	- 'Cream Puff'	CSli ECho LLin MBar MGos
	- 'Dawn Mist' (v)	ECho LLin
	- 'Devinely Blue'	CKen SLim
	- 'Feelin' Blue'	CDoC CDul CKen CRob CSli ECho EHul EPla IMGH LBee LCon LLin LRHS MAsh MBar MBlu MBri MGos MLan NHol SCoo SHBN SLim SPoG SWvt WEve WFar
	- 'Gold Cascade'	SLim
	- 'Gold Cone'	ECho MGos
	- 'Gold Gowa'	MGos NLar
	- 'Gold Mound'	CKen CSBt ECho MAsh WEve
	- 'Golden Horizon'	CDoC CKen CMen CSBt ECho ECrN EHul EOrn EPla IMGH LBee LCon LLin LPan LRHS MAsh MBar MBlu MBri MGos NBlu SCoo SHBN SLim SPoG SWvt WEve WFar
	- 'Karl Fuchs'	CDoC EWTr MAsh MBri NBlu NLar SCoo WGor
	- 'Kashmir'	CSli NLar
	- 'Kelly Gold'	LPan NLar
	- 'Mountain Beauty'	CKen
	- 'Nana'	CKen
	- 'Nivea'	CKen
	- 'Pendula'	CDoC CKen ECho EHul LCon LPan MBar MGos WEve WGor
	- 'Polar Winter'	SMad
	- 'Pygmy'	CKen
	- 'Raywood's Prostrate'	CKen
	- 'Robusta'	SBLw WEve
	- 'Roman Candle'	CSli ECho EOrn ISea SHBN WEve
	- 'Scott'	CKen
	- 'Silver Mist'	CKen MGos
	- 'Silver Spring'	MGos NLar
	libani 🏆H4	More than 30 suppliers
	- 'Comte de Dijon'	ECho EHul LCon LLin LRHS NLar

- 'Fontaine' NLar
- 'Gold Tip' new NLar
- 'Home Park' CKen NLar
- Nana Group CKen ECho
- 'Pampisford' ECho NLar
- 'Sargentii' CKen ECho EHul EOrn IMGH LCon LLin MBar MBlu MGos NLar SHBN WEve
- 'Taurus' MBar NLar

libanii 'Green Prince' new NLar
- 'Hedgehog' new NLar

Celastrus (*Celastraceae*)

orbiculatus CBcs CDoC CFwr CMac EBee ELan LRHS MBri MGol MRav NSti SLon SPer SReu SSta WBod WBor WFar WSHC
- 'Diana' (f) CMac NBea SSta
- 'Hercules' (m) CMac NBea NLar
- Hermaphrodite Group ♀H4 CBrm CSam GSki SBra SDix
- var. ***papillosus*** B&SWJ 591 WCru
- var. ***punctatus*** B&SWJ 1931 WCru

scandens CMac EBee GKev IMGH NScw SPlb

Celmisia ✿ (*Asteraceae*)

allanii IBlr
alpina IBlr
- large-leaved IBlr
angustifolia EPot GCrs IBlr
- silver-leaved IBlr
argentea ECho EPot GCrs IBlr WAbe
armstrongii ECho IBlr
asteliifolia IBlr
Ballyrogan hybrids IBlr
bellidioides ECho EPot EWes GCrs IBlr MDKP
bonplandii IBlr
brevifolia IBlr
coriacea misapplied see *C. semicordata*
coriacea Raoul see *C. mackaui*
coriacea (G. Forst.) Hook. f. EPot IBlr MDun
- 'Harry Bryce' see *C.* 'Harry Bryce'
costiniana IBlr
dallii IBlr
'David Shackleton' IBlr
densiflora EPot GCrs IBlr
- silver-leaved IBlr
discolor IBlr
glandulosa IBlr
gracilenta GCrs IBlr NSla
- CC 563 NWCA
graminifolia ECho IBlr
haastii IBlr
§ 'Harry Bryce' IBlr
hectorii GCrs IBlr WAbe
hectorii x ***ramulosa*** WAbe
holosericea IBlr
hookeri IBlr
incana GCrs IBlr
Inshriach hybrids IBlr NHar
insignis IBlr
latifolia IBlr
- large-leaved IBlr
longifolia GGar
- large-leaved IBlr
- small-leaved IBlr
§ ***mackaui*** GGar IBlr
markii IBlr
monroi IBlr
prorepens EPot IBlr
pugioniformis IBlr
ramulosa EPot GGar NLAp
- var. ***tuberculata*** GCrs IBlr NSla
saxifraga IBlr WAbe
§ ***semicordata*** GBuc GCra IBal IBlr NLAp NSla
- subsp. ***aurigans*** EPot IBlr
- subsp. ***stricta*** IBlr
sericophylla IBlr
- large-leaved IBlr
sessiliflora IBlr
- 'Mount Potts' IBlr
spectabilis ECho IBlr MDun WCot
- 'Eggleston Silver' NEgg
- subsp. ***magnifica*** IBlr
- subsp. ***spectabilis*** var. ***angustifolia*** IBlr
spedenii IBlr
tomentella IBlr
traversii IBlr WWeb
verbascifolia IBlr
viscosa IBlr
§ ***walkeri*** IBlr
webbiana see *C. walkeri*

Celosia (*Amaranthaceae*)

argentea var. ***cristata*** MBri
- - Plumosa Group MBri
- 'Venezuela' NBlu

Celsia see *Verbascum*

x *Celsioverbascum* see *Verbascum*

Celtica see *Stipa*

Celtis (*Ulmaceae*)

australis CAgr CBcs EGFP LEdu LPan MGos SBLw
bungeana CMCN IDee NLar
caucasica NLar
julianae IArd NLar WCwm WNor
occidentalis CDul ELan IArd IClo NBlu WBVN
- var. ***pumila*** WNor
sinensis CMen LEdu NLar WNor
tournefortii EGFP

Cenolophium (*Apiaceae*)

denudatum CDes CHrt EBee ECha NChi WPGP WTMC

Centaurea ✿ (*Asteraceae*)

HH&K 271 NBid
from Turkey WPGP
alba EBee LDai
alpestris CSam EBee ECho NBre NEgg NLar
atropurpurea LDai NDov NLar SPhx WHal WHil WHoo
bagadensis new EBee
bella CBgR CPrp CSam CSev EBee ECtt LAst LHop LRHS MHer MLHP MNFA MRav NBro NCGa NChi NEgg NMRc NSti SBla SMeo SPet SPhx SWat WFar WMnd WWFP XPep
benoistii CAby CDes CSpe EBee EGle ERou EWes GBin MBri MRav NBPC NDov NLar SMeo SPhx SPoG WHrl WPGP WSHC
cana hort. see *C. triumfettii* subsp. *cana*
candidissima misapplied see *C. cineraria*
'Caramia' EBee SMeo SSvw
cheiranthifolia CDes EBee ECha EMon EPPr NBir WFar WPGP
- var. ***purpurascens*** EMon MAvo
§ ***cineraria*** EBee EMan LDai SRms WEas

	- subsp. ***cineraria*** ♀H3	WCot
	cyanus	CArn GWCH LCro MHer MNHC NPri WFar WJek
	- 'Black Ball'	CSpe
	dealbata	CEnt COIW CPrp CWib EBee EPfP GAbr IFoB LAst LBMP LRHS NBlu NBro NMir NOrc SECG SMer WBor WCot WFar WMoo WPer WWeb
	- 'Steenbergii'	CAbP EBee EGle ELan ERou GGar LRHS MNFA NBid NGdn NPer NSti SBch SPer SPoG WAbb WCAu WCot WFar WHoo WMnd
	- 'Steenbergii' variegated (v) **new**	LDai
	debeauxii subsp. ***nemoralis***	LDai
	fischeri Willd.	CDes EBee EMon WPGP
	glastifolia	EBee EMon MLLN NBre WCot WPGP
	gymnocarpa	see *C. cineraria*
	hypoleuca	NBid
	jacea	CSam EShb GAbr NBid NLar WAul WCot WOut WPer
	'John Coutts'	More than 30 suppliers
	'Jordy'	EBee IPot LDai
	kotschyana	CDes EBee NBid NBre WPGP
	macrocephala	More than 30 suppliers
	maculosa **new**	LDai
	marschalliana	NBid
	mollis	NBid
	montana	More than 30 suppliers
	- 'Alba'	More than 30 suppliers
§	- 'Carnea'	CCVN CElw CPom CSam CTca EBee ECha EGle EMon ERou GMaP LLWP MAvo MNFA NChi NLar SAga SMeo SPhx STes WCAu WFar WMoo
	- 'Gold Bullion'	CDes CSpe EBee ECGP ECtt EGle ELan ELon EMon EPPr EWes GBuc GMaP LDai MBri MCCP MRav NBid NBir NLar NPro SMad SSvw WBor WCAu
	- 'Gold Strike'	EBee
	- 'Grandiflora'	EBee ERou MBri
	- 'Horwood Gold'	LHop
	- 'Joyce'	CDes CElw EBee EMon LDai NLar
	- 'Lady Flora Hastings'	CBre CDes CElw CKno CMdw CPom CSam CSpe CTca EBee GMac LDai MAvo NBid WPGP
	- lilac-flowered **new**	NBid
	- 'Ochroleuca'	EGoo EMon GBuc LDai MLLN NBid NBre
	- 'Parham'	CBcs CElw CMHG CPrp CSev EBee ELan EMan ERou LHop LLWP LRHS LSRN MNFA MRav MSte MWat NBid NEgg NSti SPer SPla SPlb SWat WMnd
	- 'Purple Heart' **new**	EBee IPot MAvo NBPC NBPN NPri
	- 'Purple Prose'	EMon
	- 'Purpurea'	CAby CDes CPom EBee
	- 'Rosea'	see *C. montana* 'Carnea'
*	- ***violacea***	NBid
	- 'Violetta'	MAvo NBir WFar WMoo
	montana x ***triumfettii*** **new**	CDes
	moschata	see *Amberboa moschata*
	nervosa	see *C. uniflora* subsp. *nervosa*
	nigra	CArn COld CRWN EBee LCro NBre NLan NMir NNor NPri NSco SECG WMoo WSFF
	- var. ***alba***	CArn CBre NBid
	- subsp. ***rivularis***	ECha LDai MNFA NBid NBre
	orientalis	CSam CSpe EBee ECha EWes MHar MMHG MNFA NBre NDov NLar SPhx WHal WPer
	pannonica subsp. ***pannonica***	NBid WSHC
	phrygia	COIW EBee GAbr NBid NBre NLar WPer WRos
	- subsp. ***pseudophrygia***	NBid
	pulcherrima	COIW EBee ECha EMan EMon MAvo MLLN NBre NChi NSti WPer XPep
	'Pulchra Major'	see *Stemmacantha centaureoides*
	rhapontica	see *Stemmacantha rhapontica*
	rhenana	WOut
	rigidifolia	EGle
	rothrockii	LDai
	rupestris	EBee NBre NDov NEgg SGar SMHy SPhx WPer WWeb
	ruthenica	EBee MNFA MSte NBre NDov NGdn NHol NLar SBch SPer SPlb WCot WLin
*	- 'Alba'	MSte
	scabiosa	CArn CRWN CWib EBee GWCH MHer NBid NBre NDov NLan NMir NPri NSco SECG SPoG WPer
	- f. ***albiflora***	CBgR EBee EMon LRHS MWgw NDov
	simplicicaulis	CDes CSam EBee ECrN EGle EMan GAbr GBri MTho SBla SRms WEas WHoo WPer WSHC
	thracica	EBee LDai SAga WCot
	triumfettii 'Blue Dreams'	EMon LDai MLLN
I	- subsp. ***cana*** 'Rosea'	CBrm WBrk
	- 'Hoar Frost'	CDes EMon
	- subsp. ***stricta***	CDes CPrp EBee EMon GAbr GBuc MSte NBre
	uniflora	EBee LDai
§	- subsp. ***nervosa***	NBid NBre NBro WPer
	woronowii **new**	LDai

Centaurium (*Gentianaceae*)

erythraea	CArn GPoy MHer MSal
scilloides	CStu MTho NLAp NMen NSla NWCA WAbe

Centella (*Apiaceae*)

§	***asiatica***	CArn EOHP GPoy ILis MSal WJek

Centradenia (*Melastomataceae*)

inaequilateralis **new**	CCCN
- 'Cascade'	CHal EMan EWin MBri SHFr SPet

Centranthus (*Valerianaceae*)

§	***lecoqii*** **new**	SPhx WCot
§	***ruber***	CArn COIW CRWN CSBt EBee ECtt ELau EPfP ERou GGar GPoy GWCH LAst LCro LHop MHer MLHP NBPC NPer NScw SECG SPer SRms SWvt WFar WHen WMoo WSFF XPep
*	- 'Alba Pura'	EWTr NBPC
§	- 'Albus'	More than 30 suppliers
	- 'Atrococcineus'	ECha EMan SPoG WPer
	- var. ***coccineus***	CBcs CHrt CKno EBee EDAr EGoo ELan ENot EPfP GAbr GMaP LAst LBMP LRHS MAvo MRav MWat MWgw NBlu NEgg NPri NVic SEND SMrm SPer SPhx SPla WCAu WCot WFar
	- mauve-flowered misapplied	see *C. lecoqii*
	- mauve-flowered	XPep
	- 'Roseus'	NEgg WMoo WOVN
	- 'Rosy Red'	EDAr
	- 'Snowcloud'	COIW CSev EBee ECtt WHil
	- 'Swanage'	CNat
	'White Cloud'	WJek

Centropogon (*Campanulaceae*)

costaricae B&SWJ 10455 **new**	WCru

Cephalanthera (*Orchidaceae*)

falcata	EFEx GEdr
longibracteata	EFEx GEdr

Cephalanthus (*Rubiaceae*)

occidentalis	CBcs CPle CWib EBee EMil IDee IMGH LRav MBNS MBlu MBri MGos NBlu NLar SPer SPoG SRms SSpi WBVN WFar

Cephalaria (*Dipsacaceae*)

HWJ 695	SPhx
§ ***alpina***	COlW EBee EBla ECho EHrv EMan EPfP LRHS MHer MNrw MRav NEgg NHol NLar NRnb SBch SPhx SRms SWat WCot WFar WPer
- 'Nana'	CMil EMon NMen NWCA
ambrosioides	MLLN
caucasica new	EMon
dipsacoides	CAby CEnt CFee CKno EBee EBla ECha GQue LDai LPio MFOX MGol MHer NBre NLar NRnb SMHy SPhx SPoG STes WHal WMoo
§ ***flava***	NBre
galpiniana	SPlb
- subsp. ***simplicior***	EBee
§ ***gigantea***	More than 30 suppliers
graeca	see *C. flava*
leucantha	COlW EMan GBuc MLLN NBre SPhx STes WMoo
litvinovii	CElw EMon SPhx
oblongifolia	NRnb
radiata	CSam EBee GBin NDov SPhx
tatarica hort.	see *C. gigantea*
tchihatchewii	EBee MLLN

Cephalotaxus (*Cephalotaxaceae*)

fortunei	SLon
- 'Prostrate Spreader'	EHul SLim
harringtonii	ECho LEdu MRav
- B&SWJ 5416	WPGP
- var. ***drupacea***	CDoC LCon NWea
- 'Fastigiata'	CBcs CDoC CDul EHul EOrn IArd IDee LCon LLin LRHS MAsh MBar MBri NPal SBLw SCoo SLim SPoG WFar WGer
- 'Gimborn's Pillow'	IClo IDee MBar
- 'Korean Gold'	CKen LCon NLar SLim
- 'Prostrata'	MBar
sinensis new	CMCN

Cephalotus (*Cephalotaceae*)

follicularis	SHmp

Cerastium (*Caryophyllaceae*)

alpinum	ECho SRms
- var. ***lanatum***	ECho EWes NLar
arvense	NDlv
candidissimum	EWes NLar XPep
tomentosum	CBrm CHal EAlp ECho EPfP GAbr GWCH NBlu NDlv NPri SPer SPet SPlb SPoG WFar WPer XPep
- var. ***columnae***	ECha ECho EPfP EWes SIng WCot
- 'Yo Yo'	SBch

Ceratoides (*Chenopodiaceae*)

lanata	see *Krascheninnikovia lanata*

Ceratonia (*Caesalpiniaceae*)

siliqua	ELau MSal XPep

Ceratophyllum (*Ceratophyllaceae*)

demersum	CBen CDWL EHon EMFW EPfP NSco SWat WMAq

Ceratostigma ✿ (*Plumbaginaceae*)

abyssinicum	ELan
'Autumn Blue'	EPfP LRHS
griffithii	CBcs CChe CDoC CDul CHll CSBt CWSG EBee ECtt ELan EPfP LAst LRHS MCCP MRav MSwo SPer SPla SPoG SWal WBrE WFar WKif WSHC XPep
- SF 149/150	ISea
§ ***plumbaginoides*** $\mathbb{Y}^{H3-4}$	More than 30 suppliers
willmottianum $\mathbb{Y}^{H3-4}$	More than 30 suppliers
- BWJ 8140	WCru
- Desert Skies = 'Palmgold'^{PBR}	CBcs CSBt EBee ELan EPfP ERas GBuc LAst LCro LHop LRHS MBri MGos MWgw NLar SCoo SHBN SMad SPer SPoG SSta SWvt WWeb
- Forest Blue = 'Lice'^{PBR}	CAbP CDoC CSBt CSpe CWSG EBee ELan ENot EPfP LAst LCro LHop LRHS LSRN MAsh MBri MRav NPri NSti SCoo SHBN SMer SPer SPla SPoG SReu WPat WWeb

Cercidiphyllum ✿ (*Cercidiphyllaceae*)

japonicum $\mathbb{Y}^{H4}$	More than 30 suppliers
- 'Boyd's Dwarf'	MBri
- 'Herkenrode Dwarf'	MBri
- 'Heronswood Globe'	CMCN CPMA EPfP MBlu NLar SSta
- 'Morioka Weeping' new	SSta
§ - f. ***pendulum*** $\mathbb{Y}^{H4}$	CBcs CDul CEnd CLnd CMCN CPMA CWSG EBee EMil EPfP LRHS MAsh MBlu MGos NEgg NLar SCoo SHBN SLim SPer SPoG SSpi WOrn
- - 'Amazing Grace'	CTho MBlu SSta
- 'Raspberry' new	MBri
- Red Fox	see *C. japonicum* 'Rotfuchs'
§ - 'Rotfuchs'	CBcs CEnd CMCN CPMA CTho EBee EPfP LRHS MAsh MBlu MBri MGos MLan NEgg NLar NPal SCoo SIFN SLim SMad SPoG SSpi SSta WPGP
- 'Ruby'	CPMA MBlu MBri NLar
- 'Strawberry'	CBcs MBlu MBri NLar
- 'Tidal Wave'	MBri NLar
magnificum	CBcs CDul CEnd CMCN EPfP MBri NLar WCru WPGP
- f. ***pendulum***	see *C. japonicum* f. *pendulum*

Cercis (*Caesalpiniaceae*)

canadensis	CAgr CBcs CDul CHEx CLnd CMCN EPfP EWTr MGos NHol NLar SCoo SLim SPer WNor WPat
- f. ***alba*** 'Royal White'	EPfP IArd MBlu
- 'Appalachian Red'	MBlu MBri NBhm NLar
- 'Covey'	MBri NLar
- 'Flame'	MBri NBhm
- 'Forest Pansy' $\mathbb{Y}^{H4}$	More than 30 suppliers
- 'Lavender Twist'	NLar
§ - var. ***occidentalis***	CAgr NLar SOWG
- 'Pauline Lily'	MBri NLar
- 'Rubye Atkinson'	MBri NLar
chinensis	CBcs NLar SPer SSta
- 'Avondale'	CAbP CBcs CDoC CEnd CPMA CWib EBee EMil ENot EPfP ERas EWes IArd LRHS LSRN MBlu MBri MGos NEgg NLar SCoo SLim SSpi SWvt WPGP
- 'Don Egolf' new	MPkF
gigantea	NLar
griffithii	EGFP LTwo NLar
occidentalis	see *C. canadensis* var. *occidentalis*
racemosa	IDee NLar WPGP
reniformis 'Oklahoma'	CPMA EBee MBlu MBri NLar
- 'Texas White'	CBcs CPMA IArd NLar SLim WSpi

siliquastrum ♀H4	More than 30 suppliers
- f. ***albida***	CLnd ECrN EPfP LPan LRHS LTwo SSpi WSpi
- 'Bodnant'	EBee EMil EPfP EWes LAst MBlu MBri NLar
yunnanensis	EBee NLar

Cerinthe (*Boraginaceae*)

glabra	NBre SPlb
major	LEdu WEas
- 'Kiwi Blue'	CHll LEdu MBri MDKP
- 'Purpurascens'	CChe CHrt CMea CSpe EBee EGoo EHrv ELan EPfP IFoB LBMP LCro MWat MWgw NLar SGar SMad SMrm SPer SPoG
- 'Yellow Gem'	NLar
retorta	LDai

Ceropegia (*Asclepiadaceae*)

barklyi	CHal LToo
conrathii new	LToo
fusca	EShb
§ ***linearis*** subsp. ***woodii*** ♀H1	CHal EShb MBri SRms
multiflora new	LToo
pubescens GWJ 9441	WCru
woodii	see *C. linearis* subsp. *woodii*

Ceroxylon (*Arecaceae*)

alpinum	CPHo LPJP LPal
ventricosum	LPal

Cestrum (*Solanaceae*)

aurantiacum	ERea EShb
auriculatum	SOWG
x ***cultum***	CHll
- 'Cretan Purple'	CHll CPle EBee ELon EPfP ERea LHop LRHS SPoG WCFE WSHC
diurnum x ***nocturnum*** new	EShb
§ ***elegans***	CHEx CHal CHll CPLG CSev LRHS MJnS SLon SOWG WCot WWlt
fasciculatum	CBcs EShb GBin SMad SOWG
'Newellii' ♀H2	CBcs CHEx CMHG CPLG CSev CWib EBak ELan ELon EPfP ERea EShb LRHS SDnm SEND SGar SOWG WBor WPic WSHC
nocturnum	CBcs CDoC CHal CHll CPle EBak ERea EShb MJnS SHBN SOWG WCFE XPep
parqui ♀H3	CAbb CBcs CHEx CHll CMHG CPLG CPle CWib EBee ELan EPfP ERea EShb IDee LRHS SDix SDnm SGar SLon SMad SMrm SOWG WCot WKif WSHC WWlt XPep
- 'Orange Essence'	WCot
psittacinum	CPLG
purpureum misapplied	see *Iochroma cyaneum* 'Trebah'
purpureum (Lindl.) Standl.	see *C. elegans*
roseum	CPLG CSev
- 'Ilnacullin'	CFee CPLG ERea
* ***splendens***	SOWG
violaceum misapplied	see *Iochroma cyaneum* 'Trebah'

Ceterach (*Aspleniaceae*)

officinarum	see *Asplenium ceterach*

Chaenomeles (*Rosaceae*)

x ***californica***	CTho
cathayensis	LEdu NLar
§ ***japonica***	ECrN ENot MBar SMer WFar XPep
- 'Cido'	CAgr LBuc NEgg
- 'Orange Beauty'	NEgg WFar
- 'Sargentii'	CMac NEgg
'John Pilger'	NHol
lagenaria	see *C. speciosa*
'Madame Butterfly'	CDoC CEnd EBee LSRN MAsh MBri MRav NLar SBra SMad SPer SPoG WLeb
maulei	see *C. japonica*
'Orange Star' new	EBee
sinensis	see *Pseudocydonia sinensis*
§ ***speciosa***	CMen CSam ISea MBar MGan NWea WNor
- 'Apple Blossom'	see *C. speciosa* 'Moerloosei'
- 'Aurora'	LRHS
- 'Brilliant'	EPfP
- 'Contorta'	CDoC SPoG
- 'Falconnet Charlet' (d)	MRav
- 'Geisha Girl' ♀H4	More than 30 suppliers
- 'Grayshott Salmon'	NCiC NHol NPro WFar
§ - 'Moerloosei' ♀H4	CDoC CEnd CPMA CSBt CSam CTri ELan EPfP IMGH LAst LCro LRHS MBri MGos MRav MSwo MWat NEgg NScw NSti SAga SHBN SLim SPer SPla SPoG SSta WPat WTin
- 'Nivalis'	More than 30 suppliers
- 'Port Eliot'	WWeb
- 'Rosea Plena' (d)	SPoG
- 'Rubra Grandiflora'	WBVN
- 'Simonii' (d)	CBcs EBee EPfP LRHS MGos MRav NEgg NHol NWea SPer WFar
- 'Snow'	CSBt MRav MSwo NHol NPro
- 'Umbilicata'	SPer SRms XPep
- 'Winter Snow'	ENot
- 'Yukigoten'	CWib EBee LRHS
x ***superba***	STre
- 'Boule de Feu'	CTri CWib ECtt MCoo
- 'Cameo' (d)	CAbP CChe CEnd EBee ECrN EPfP LHop LRHS MBri MRav NLar SLPl SPoG WWeb
- 'Clementine'	CWib
- 'Crimson and Gold' ♀H4	More than 30 suppliers
- 'Elly Mossel'	CMac CSBt CWib NBlu SMer WFar
- 'Ernst Finken'	EBee
- 'Fascination'	NLar
- 'Fire Dance'	CDul CMac CWib EBee ECrN ECtt MSwo NHol NLar SPer SPoG
- 'Hollandia'	MGos
- 'Issai White'	EBee LRHS MRav
- 'Jet Trail'	CBcs CSBt EBee ELan ENot EPfP LAst LRHS MAsh MGos MRav MSwo NBlu NPro SLPl SMac SPoG SSta WFar
- 'Knap Hill Scarlet' ♀H4	CDoC CDul EBee ECot EPfP LHop LRHS MAsh MGos MRav NEgg NHol SEND SLim SPer SPoG SRms WFar
- 'Lemon and Lime'	ELan ENot EPfP MGos MRav NSti SLon SPer
- 'Nicoline' ♀H4	CBcs CDoC CDul EBee EPfP LRHS MBri MRav NPri SBra SPoG WFar
- 'Pink Lady' ♀H4	More than 30 suppliers
- 'Red Joy'	NLar SPoG
- 'Red Trail'	MRav
- 'Rowallane' ♀H4	EBee ECrN ELan EPfP ERas IMGH MNHC MRav SHBN WRHF
- 'Salmon Horizon'	MGos NLar
- 'Tortuosa'	EBee LHop MBNS SPoG
- 'Vermilion'	MAsh MBNS
'Toyo-nishiki' new	EBee

Chaenorhinum (*Scrophulariaceae*)

§ ***origanifolium***	ECho EShb GKev MBrN NBlu NEgg NWCA SBch SPlb XPep
- 'Blue Dream'	CEnt CSpe EBee ECho ECtt EMan NLAp NVic SPet SPoG SWvt WFar WMoo WPer WWeb
- 'Summer Skies'	NPri

Chaerophyllum (*Apiaceae*)

	hirsutum 'Roseum'	More than 30 suppliers

Chamaebatiaria (*Rosaceae*)

	millefolium	NLar

Chamaecyparis ✿ (*Cupressaceae*)

	formosensis	CKen
	funebris	see *Cupressus funebris*
	lawsoniana	CDul CSBt EHul EMac LCon MBar NWea WBVN WMou
	- 'Albospica' (v)	ECho EHul MBar WFar
	- 'Albospica Nana'	see *C. lawsoniana* 'Nana Albospica'
	- 'Albovariegata' (v)	ECho EHul LLin MBar
	- 'Allumii Aurea'	see *C. lawsoniana* 'Alumigold'
	- 'Allumii Magnificent'	CDul ECho MAsh NLar
§	- 'Alumigold'	CDoC CSBt CWib ECho LCon LLin MAsh MBar MGos SCoo SMer SPoG
	- 'Alumii'	CMac CTri ECho EHul LLin MAsh MBar MGos NWea SPoG
	- 'Annesleyana'	NEgg
	- 'Argentea'	see *C. lawsoniana* 'Argenteovariegata'
§	- 'Argenteovariegata' (v)	CDoC CMac ECho LLin SPoG
	- 'Aurea'	CDul LLin
I	- 'Aurea Compacta'	ECho
	- 'Aurea Densa' ♀H4	CFee CKen CMac CRob CSBt CTri ECho EHul EOrn EPfP MAsh MBar MGos NEgg SCoo STre WEve WGor
	- 'Aureovariegata' (v)	MBar
§	- 'Barabits' Globe'	MBar
	- 'Barry's Gold'	EOrn
§	- 'Bleu Nantais'	CKen CMac CRob CSBt ECho EHul LBee LCon LRHS MAsh MBar MGos MWat SCoo SHBN SLim SPoG WCFE WEve WFar
	- 'Blom'	CKen EHul MBri
§	- 'Blue Gown'	ECho EHul LLin MBar MGos SRms
§	- 'Blue Jacket'	NWea
	- Blue Nantais	see *C. lawsoniana* 'Bleu Nantais'
	- 'Blue Surprise'	CKen EHul MBar WFar
	- 'Brégéon'	CKen NLar
	- 'Broomhill Gold'	CDoC CMac CRob CSBt ECho EHul LCon LLin MAsh MBar MBri MGos MWat NHol SCoo SLim SPer SPla SPoG WCFE WEve
	- 'Buckland Gold'	CDoC
*	- 'Burkwood's Blue'	MBar
	- 'Caudata'	CKen MBar NLar
	- 'Chantry Gold'	ECho EHul SCoo
§	- 'Chilworth Silver' ♀H4	CRob CSBt ECho EHul EOrn LBee LLin LRHS MAsh MBar NBlu SCoo SHBN SLim SPer SPoG SRms WBVN WFar
	- 'Chingii'	ECho EHul
	- 'Columnaris'	CBcs CDoC CMac ECho EPfP LBee LRHS MBar MBri MGos NBlu NEgg NWea SCoo SHBN SPoG WFar
	- 'Columnaris Aurea'	see *C. lawsoniana* 'Golden Spire'
N	- 'Columnaris Glauca'	CSBt CWib ECho EHul EOrn LCon LLin MAsh MGos NEgg SBod SCoo SPer WFar WTel
	- 'Crawford's Compact'	CMac
	- 'Cream Crackers'	ECho EHul
	- 'Cream Glow'	CDoC CKen CRob ECho LRHS MGos NLar SCoo SLim SPoG WFar WGor
	- 'Croftway'	EHul
	- 'Dik's Weeping'	CDoC LCon NWea WEve
	- 'Dorset Gold'	CMac
	- 'Drinkstone Gold'	ECho
	- 'Duncanii'	ECho EHul
	- 'Dutch Gold'	EHul MAsh
	- 'Dwarf Blue'	see *C. lawsoniana* 'Pick's Dwarf Blue'
	- 'Eclipse'	CKen
	- 'Elegantissima' ambig.	CKen CMac ECho MGos
	- 'Ellwoodii' ♀H4	CDul CMac CSBt CTri CWib ECho EHul EPfP LAst LCon MAsh MBar MGos NBlu NEgg NWea SCoo SLim SMer SPer SPoG WFar WMoo WTel
I	- 'Ellwoodii Glauca'	SPlb
	- 'Ellwood's Empire'	EHul WEve
	- 'Ellwood's Gold' ♀H4	CBcs CDoC CMac CSBt CWib ECho EHul EPfP LBee LCon LLin LRHS MAsh MBar MBri MGos MWat NBlu NHol NWea SMer SPer SPla SPlb SPoG STre WBVN WFar WMoo
	- 'Ellwood's Gold Pillar'	CRob CSBt ECho EHul EOrn LBee LCon MAsh MGos NEgg NHol SCoo SLim SPla SPoG WFar
§	- 'Ellwood's Nymph'	CKen CRob ECho EOrn LLin MAsh MBar SCoo SHBN SLim SPoG WFar WGor
	- Ellwood's Pillar = 'Flolar'	CDoC CMac CRob CSBt ECho EHul EOrn EPfP LAst LBee LCon LLin LRHS MAsh MBar MBri MGos MWat NEgg NHol SCoo SLim SPla SPoG WCFE WFar
	- 'Ellwood's Pygmy'	CMac ECho MBar
	- 'Ellwood's Silver'	ECho MAsh WFar
	- 'Ellwood's Silver Threads'	CMac ECho
*	- 'Ellwood's Treasure'	ECho
	- 'Ellwood's Variegata'	see *C. lawsoniana* 'Ellwood's White'
§	- 'Ellwood's White' (v)	CKen CMac CSBt ECho EHul EPfP MBar NBlu SHBN WFar
I	- 'Emerald'	CKen MBar
	- 'Emerald Spire'	CMac MAsh NHol
	- 'Empire'	WFar
	- 'Erecta Aurea'	ECho EHul LLin MGos SCoo
	- 'Erecta Filiformis'	MBar
	- 'Erecta Viridis'	CMac CTrG LLin MBar NEgg WFar
	- 'Ericoides'	EHul NEgg
	- 'Erika'	ECho MBar
	- 'Filiformis Compacta'	ECho EHul
	- 'Fleckellwood'	CRob CWib ECho EHul MAsh MBar SMer SPoG
	- 'Fletcheri' ♀H4	CMac CWib EHul LCon MAsh MBar NWea SBod SHBN SMer WFar
	- 'Fletcheri Aurea'	see *C. lawsoniana* 'Yellow Transparent'
	- 'Fletcher's White'	ECho EHul MBar
	- 'Forsteckensis'	CKen ECho EHul EOrn LLin MBar NLar NWea SCoo SPoG SRms WEve WFar WGor
	- 'Fraseri'	CMac LLin MBar NWea
	- 'Gimbornii' ♀H4	CMac ECho EHul LBee LCon MAsh MBar SCoo SLim SPoG SRms WCFE WFar
	- 'Glauca Spek'	see *C. lawsoniana* 'Spek'
	- 'Globosa'	MGos
	- 'Globus'	see *C. lawsoniana* 'Barabits' Globe'
	- 'Gnome'	CDoC CMac CRob ECho EHul EOrn GEdr LLin MBar MGos SCoo SLim SPoG
	- 'Gold Flake'	MBar MGos
	- 'Gold Splash'	MBar
	- 'Golden King'	ECho MBar NWea
§	- 'Golden Pot'	CDoC CRob CSBt CWib ECho EHul EOrn LBee LCon LRHS MBar MGos MWat NBlu NHol SCoo SPoG WFar

§ - 'Golden Queen' ECho EHul
- 'Golden Showers' ECho EHul
§ - 'Golden Spire' ECho LLin MBar NEgg NLar WFar
- 'Golden Triumph' EHul
- 'Golden Wonder' ECho EHul LBee LCon LLin MBar MGos NEgg NLar NWea SCoo SRms WFar
- 'Goldfinger' CDoC
- 'Grant's Gold' EHul
- 'Grayswood Feather' CDoC CRob CSBt ECho EHul LBee LLin LRHS MAsh MBar MGos NBlu SCoo SLim WEve
- 'Grayswood Gold' ECho EHul EOrn LBee LLin MBar WEve
- 'Grayswood Pillar' ♀H4 CMac ECho EHul EOrn LRHS MBar MGos
* - 'Grayswood Spire' CMac
- 'Green Globe' CDoC CKen CRob CSBt ECho EHul EOrn LBee LCon LLin LRHS MAsh MBar MGos SAga SCoo SLim SPoG WEve
§ - 'Green Hedger' ♀H4 CMac CSBt EHul LBuc LLin MBar NBlu NEgg SCoo SRms WFar
§ - 'Green Pillar' CRob CSBt CWib ECho LBee LCon LLin LRHS MBar NEgg SCoo SHBN
- 'Green Pinnacle' **new** CRob
- 'Green Spire' see *C. lawsoniana* 'Green Pillar'
- 'Hillieri' MBar
- 'Hogger's Blue Gown' see *C. lawsoniana* 'Blue Gown'
- 'Howarth's Gold' MBri
- 'Imbricata Pendula' CKen LCon NLar SLim
- 'Intertexta' ♀H4 EHul WEve
- 'Ivonne' ECho EHul MGos NBlu NEgg WEve WOrn
- 'Jackman's Green Hedger' see *C. lawsoniana* 'Green Hedger'
- 'Jackman's Variety' see *C. lawsoniana* 'Green Pillar'
- 'Kelleriis Gold' EHul MBar NEgg
- 'Kilmacurragh' ♀H4 MBar MGos NWea WCFE
- 'Kilworth Column' CDoC CRob ECho LLin MGos NLar NWea SCoo SPoG
- 'Kingswood' WEve
- 'Knowefieldensis' CMac ECho EHul LLin
- 'Lane' hort. see *C. lawsoniana* 'Lanei Aurea'
- 'Lanei' hort. see *C. lawsoniana* 'Lanei Aurea'
- 'Lanei' CSBt CWib ECho LCon LLin MGos NEgg SCoo
§ - 'Lanei Aurea' ♀H4 CMac ECho EHul MBar MGos NWea WFar
- 'Lemon Pillar' WEve
- 'Lemon Queen' CSBt ECho EHul LBee LRHS
- 'Limelight' EHul MGos
- 'Little Spire' ♀H4 CDoC ECho EOrn LBee LCon LLin LRHS MBar MBri MGos NHol SCoo SLim SPoG WEve WGor
- 'Lombartsii' ECho EHul LCon WFar
- 'Lutea' ♀H4 CMac ECho EHul MGos NWea
§ - 'Lutea Nana' ♀H4 CMac ECho EHul MAsh MBar MGos NLar SCoo
§ - 'Lutea Smithii' MBar NWea
- 'Luteocompacta' LBee SHBN
- 'Lycopodioides' ECho EHul MBar SPoG
* - 'MacPenny's Gold' CMac
- 'Magnifica Aurea' ECho
- 'Miki' WEve
- 'Milford Blue Jacket' see *C. lawsoniana* 'Blue Jacket'
§ - 'Minima' ECho MBar NEgg SRms WCFE
- 'Minima Argentea' see *C. lawsoniana* 'Nana Argentea'
- 'Minima Aurea' ♀H4 CDoC CDul CKen CMac CSBt CWib ECho EHul EOrn EPfP LBee LCon LLin LRHS MAsh MBar MBri MGos NBlu NEgg NHol NWea SHBN SLim SPer SPla SPoG WCFE WEve WFar
- 'Minima Densa' see *C. lawsoniana* 'Minima'
- 'Minima Glauca' ♀H4 CDul CMac CSBt ECho EHul EPfP LCon MAsh MBar MGos NEgg NHol NWea SCoo SHBN SLim SPer SPla SPoG WEve WFar
- 'Moonlight' MBar MGos
- 'Moonshine' ECho SPoG
* - 'Moonsprite' ECho LCon LLin LRHS SCoo SLim WEve
- 'Nana' ECho MBar
§ - 'Nana Albospica' (v) CBrm CRob ECho EHul EOrn LBee LCon LRHS MBar SCoo SPoG WFar WGor
§ - 'Nana Argentea' CKen CMac ECho EHul EOrn EPfP SCoo WFar WGor
- 'Nana Lutea' see *C. lawsoniana* 'Lutea Nana'
- 'New Silver' MGos SPoG
- 'Nicole' CDHC ECho MAsh SCoo SLim SPoG WGor
- 'Nidiformis' ECho EHul LBee MBar NWea SCoo SRms
- 'Nyewoods' see *C. lawsoniana* 'Chilworth Silver'
- 'Nymph' see *C. lawsoniana* 'Ellwood's Nymph'
- 'Parsons' CDoC
§ - 'Pelt's Blue' ♀H4 CBcs CDoC CDul CKen CSBt ECho EHul LBee LCon LLin LRHS MBar MBri MGos NEgg NLar SCoo SHBN SLim SPoG WFar WOrn
- 'Pembury Blue' ♀H4 CDoC CDul CMac CSBt CWib ECho EHul EPfP LBee LCon LLin LRHS MAsh MBar MGos MWat NWea SBod SCoo SHBN SLim SPer SPoG WFar
- 'Pendula' CDoC MBar
§ - 'Pick's Dwarf Blue' ECho EHul MBar MGos NHol SCoo WGor
- Pot of Gold see *C. lawsoniana* 'Golden Pot'
- 'Pottenii' CMac CSBt ECho EHul LBee LCon LLin LRHS MAsh MBar MGos NWea SCoo SHBN SPoG WEve WFar
- 'Pygmaea Argentea' (v) ♀H4 CKen CMac CWib ECho EHul EOrn EPfP LBee LCon LLin LRHS MAsh MBar MBri MGos NBlu NEgg NHol SLim SPoG SRms WCFE WFar
- 'Pygmy' ECho EHul LCon MBar NHol NLar SCoo SLim
- 'Rijnhof' EHul LLin SLim
- 'Rogersii' ECho MBar SRms WFar
- 'Romana' MBri NBlu
- 'Royal Gold' ECho EHul NBlu
- 'Silver Queen' (v) CKen MBar
- 'Silver Threads' (v) CMac CRob ECho EHul LBee LRHS MAsh MBar NBlu SPoG WFar
- 'Silver Tip' (v) ECho EHul SCoo SLim
- 'Slocock' SHBN
- 'Smithii' see *C. lawsoniana* 'Lutea Smithii'
- 'Snow Flurry' (v) CKen ECho EHul WFar
- 'Snow White' PBR (v) CDoC CRob ECho EHul LBee LCon LRHS MAsh MBar MBri MGos NHol SCoo SLim SPla SPoG WFar WGor
- 'Somerset' CMac MBar MGos
§ - 'Spek' MBar
- 'Springtime' PBR CDoC CRob ECho EHul EOrn LBee LCon SCoo SLim SPoG WGor
- 'Stardust' ♀H4 CBcs CDoC CDul CMac CRob CSBt CTri CWib ECho EHul LCon LLin LPan MAsh MBar MBri NBlu NEgg SBod SCoo SHBN SLim SPer SPoG
- 'Stewartii' CDul CTri LLin MBar NEgg NWea SBod SCoo SHBN SMer
- 'Stilton Cheese' MBar SCoo

*	- 'Summer Cream'	EHul
	- 'Summer Snow' (v)	CDoC CDul CMac CRob ECho EHul EPfP LBee LLin LRHS MAsh MBar MGos NBlu NEgg NHol SCoo SLim SPla SRms WEve WFar
	- 'Sunkist'	ECho SCoo SLim WFar
	- 'Tamariscifolia'	CDoC ECho EHul MBar SPoG WCFE WFar
	- 'Tharandtensis Caesia'	EOrn MBar WFar
	- 'Tilford'	EHul
	- 'Treasure' (v)	CRob CSli ECho EHul EPfP LBee LCon LRHS MAsh MBar NHol SCoo SLim SPoG WFar
	- 'Triomf van Boskoop'	MBar
	- 'Van Pelt'	see *C. lawsoniana* 'Pelt's Blue'
	- 'Van Pelt's Blue'	see *C. lawsoniana* 'Pelt's Blue'
	- 'Versicolor' (v)	MBar
	- 'Waterfall'	SMad
	- 'Westermannii' (v)	CMac EHul LCon LLin SCoo SLim
	- 'White Edge'	WFar
	- 'White Spot' (v)	ECho EHul LBee LLin LRHS MBar MBri NBlu NEgg SCoo SLim SPoG WBVN WFar
	- 'White Wonder'	MGos
	- 'Winston Churchill'	CSBt ECho MBar MGos NWea SBod
	- 'Wisselii' ♀^{H4}	CDoC CKen CMac CRob CTrG ECho EHul LBee LLin MBar NLar NWea SCoo SRms WFar WMoo
	- 'Wisselii Nana'	CKen ECho EHul
	- 'Wissel's Saguaro'	CDoC CKen LCon NLar SLim
	- 'Witzeliana'	CSBt ECho EOrn MBar MGos NLar WOrn
	- 'Wyevale Silver'	MBar
	- 'Yellow Cascade'	ECho
	- 'Yellow Queen'	see *C. lawsoniana* 'Golden Queen'
	- 'Yellow Success'	see *C. lawsoniana* 'Golden Queen'
§	- 'Yellow Transparent'	ECho LLin MBar SCoo SHBN SPoG WEve
	- 'Yvonne'	CRob ECho LLin LRHS MAsh MBar MGos NHol SCoo SLim SPoG WEve
	leylandii	see x *Cupressocyparis leylandii*
	nootkatensis	ECho MBar
	- 'Aurea'	ECho WEve
	- 'Aureovariegata' (v)	EHul SLim
	- 'Compacta'	CTri MBar
	- 'Glauca'	CTho LCon MBar NWea
	- 'Gracilis'	EHul
	- 'Green Arrow'	CKen ECho LCon SCoo SLim
	- 'Jubilee'	LCon SCoo SLim
	- 'Kanada' **new**	NLar
	- 'Lutea'	CTri MBar NWea SLim
	- 'Nana' **new**	CRob
	- 'Nidifera'	MBar
	- 'Nordkroken'	NLar
	- 'Pendula' ♀^{H4}	CDoC CDul CKen ECho ELan EOrn EPfP LCon LLin LPan LRHS MAsh MBar MBri MGos NBlu NWea SCoo WCFE WEve WFar WMou WOrn
	- 'Strict Weeper'	CKen NLar SLim
	- 'Variegata' (v)	LRHS MBar
	obtusa 'Albospica' (v)	ECho EHul
	- 'Albovariegata' (v)	CKen ECho
	- 'Arneson's Compact'	CKen
	- 'Aurea'	CDoC SCoo
	- 'Aureovariegata'	see *C. obtusa* 'Opaal'
	- 'Aurora'	CKen CRob ECho EMil EOrn LCon MGos SPoG WEve
*	- 'Autumn Gold'	MBar
	- 'Bambi'	CKen EOrn LCon LLin MGos NLar WEve
	- 'Barkenny'	CKen
	- 'Bartley'	CKen

	- 'Bassett'	CKen
	- 'Bess'	CKen
	- 'Brigitt'	CKen
	- 'Buttonball'	CKen
	- 'Caespitosa'	CKen
	- 'Chabo-yadori'	CDoC ECho EHul EOrn LBee LCon LLin LRHS MBar MGos SCoo SLim SPoG WFar
	- 'Chilworth'	CKen LCon MBar MGos NLar
	- 'Chima-anihiba'	CKen
	- 'Chirimen'	CKen MGos NLar SBla
	- 'Clarke's Seedling'	CDoC NLar
	- 'Confucius'	CDoC CRob EHul MGos NHol
	- 'Contorta'	EOrn MBar NLar
§	- 'Coralliformis'	CMac ECho EOrn LLin MBar
§	- 'Crippsii' ♀^{H4}	CBcs CDoC CDul ECho EHul EOrn LCon LLin LRHS MBar MGos NHol SCoo SLim
	- 'Crippsii Aurea'	see *C. obtusa* 'Crippsii'
	- 'Dainty Doll'	CKen EOrn LCon NLar
	- 'Densa'	see *C. obtusa* 'Nana Densa'
	- 'Draht'	CDoC MBar NLar SCoo WEve
	- 'Draht Hexe'	CKen
	- 'Elf'	CKen
	- 'Ellie B'	CKen EOrn
	- 'Ericoides'	CKen ECho EOrn
	- 'Erika'	ECho EOrn
	- 'Fernspray Gold'	CDoC CKen CMac CRob CTri ECho EHul EOrn LCon LLin MAsh MBar NEgg SBod SCoo SLim SPer SPla WFar
	- 'Flabelliformis'	CKen LCon
	- 'Gnome'	CKen CMen
	- 'Gold Fern'	CKen WFar
	- 'Gold Tip'	ECho EOrn
	- 'Golden Fairy'	CKen EOrn LCon WAbe WEve
	- 'Golden Filament' (v)	CKen
	- 'Golden Nymph'	CKen EOrn MGos NLar
	- 'Golden Sprite'	CDoC CKen MGos NLar WEve
	- 'Goldilocks'	ECho EHul
	- 'Gracilis Aurea'	CKen ECho
	- 'Graciosa'	see *C. obtusa* 'Loenik'
	- 'Green Diamond'	CKen
	- 'Hage'	CKen EOrn LCon
	- 'Hypnoides Nana'	CKen EOrn
	- 'Intermedia'	CDoC CKen EOrn MGos WAbe
	- 'Ivan's Column'	CKen
	- 'Junior'	CKen
	- 'Juniperoides'	CKen ECho EOrn WThu
	- 'Juniperoides Compacta'	CKen
	- 'Kamarachiba'	CDoC CKen ECho LBee LCon LLin LRHS NLar SCoo SLim SPoG WEve WFar
	- 'Kanaamihiba'	MBar NLar
	- 'Kerdalo'	NLar SLim
	- 'Konijn'	ECho EHul EOrn
	- 'Kosteri'	CDoC CKen CMac CRob ECho EHul ELan EOrn LBee LLin MAsh MBar NEgg NHol SCoo SHBN SLim WEve
	- 'Kyoto Creeper' **new**	CKen
	- 'Laxa'	LCon
	- 'Leprechaun'	NLar
	- 'Limerick' **new**	CKen
	- 'Little Markey'	CKen EOrn
§	- 'Loenik'	ECho EOrn MBar SCoo
	- 'Lycopodioides'	ECho EOrn MGos
	- 'Lycopodioides Aurea'	SCoo
	- 'Marian'	CKen MGos NLar
§	- 'Mariesii' (v)	CKen EHul EOrn LBee SCoo SHBN
	- 'Melody' **new**	CKen NLar
	- 'Minima'	CKen MGos NEgg
	- 'Nana' ♀^{H4}	CDoC CKen CMac CRob ECho LBee LCon MBar MGos WEve
	- 'Nana Albospica'	ECho

	– 'Nana Aurea' ♀H4	CDoC CRob ECho EHul EOrn EPfP MAsh MBar MGos NHol SHBN SMer SPla WBrE WFar
	– 'Nana Compacta'	EOrn
I	– 'Nana Confucius'	MGos
§	– 'Nana Densa'	CDoC CKen CMac NLar WBVN WEve
	– 'Nana Gracilis' ♀H4	CDoC CDul CKen CMen CSBt CSli ECho EHul ELan EOrn EPfP IMGH LCon LLin MAsh MBar MBri MGos NBlu NHol NWea SCoo SHBN SLim SMer SPla SPoG STre WEve WFar
I	– 'Nana Gracilis Aurea'	EHul WEve
I	– 'Nana Lutea'	CDoC CKen CRob CSBt ECho EHul EOrn EPfP LBee LCon LLin LRHS MAsh MBar MGos NDlv NHol NWea SCoo SLim SPla SPoG WGer
	– 'Nana Pyramidalis'	ECho LBee
	– 'Nana Rigida'	see *C. obtusa* 'Rigid Dwarf'
	– 'Nana Variegata'	see *C. obtusa* 'Mariesii'
§	– 'Opaal' (v)	ECho MBar
	– 'Pygmaea'	CSBt ECho EHul EOrn LCon LLin MBar MGos SCoo SLim SPoG WEve
	– 'Pygmaea Aurescens'	MBar NEgg
	– 'Reis Dwarf'	ECho LLin
	– 'Repens'	ECho
§	– 'Rigid Dwarf'	CDoC CKen ECho EHul EOrn IMGH LBee LCon LRHS MBar NLar SCoo SPoG WEve
	– 'Saffron Spray'	CKen SLim
	– 'Snowflake' (v)	CDoC CKen CRob ECho EOrn WEve WFar WGor
	– 'Snowkist' (v)	CKen
	– 'Spiralis'	CKen MBar
	– 'Stoneham'	CKen LCon MBar
	– 'Suirova-hiba'	SLim
	– 'Tempelhof'	CKen CSBt ECho EHul EOrn LCon LLin LRHS MAsh MBar MGos NEgg NLar SCoo SLim SMer WEve
	– 'Tetragona Aurea'	CBcs CBrm CMac ECho EHul EOrn IMGH LCon LLin MBar MGos SCoo SLim WEve
	– 'Tonia' (v)	CDoC CKen ECho EHul EOrn LCon NHol NLar SCoo SLim SPoG WEve WGor
	– 'Topsie'	CKen NLar
	– 'Torulosa'	see *C. obtusa* 'Coralliformis'
	– 'Tsatsumi' **new**	SCoo
	– 'Tsatsumi Gold'	CDoC CKen ECho NLar SCoo SLim
	– 'Verdon'	CKen
	– 'Winter Gold'	WEve
	– 'Wissel'	CKen EOrn
	– 'Wyckoff'	CKen
	– 'Yellowtip' (v)	CKen ECho EHul MBar MGos NLar WEve
	pisifera 'Aurea Nana' misapplied	see *C. pisifera* 'Strathmore'
	– 'Avenue'	ECho EHul
	– 'Baby Blue'	CKen ECho EPfP LCon LLin SCoo SLim WEve
	– 'Blue Globe'	CKen EOrn
	– 'Boulevard' ♀H4	CBcs CDoC CSBt CTri CWib ECho EHul EPfP LBee LCon LLin LRHS MAsh MBar MGos MWat NBlu NEgg NWea SLim SMer SPer SPoG SRms STre WBVN WEve WFar WMoo
	– 'Compacta'	ECho EOrn
	– 'Compacta Variegata' (v)	ECho EHul EOrn MBar NDlv
	– 'Curly Tops'	CRob ECho LCon LLin MGos SCoo SLim SPoG WEve
	– 'Devon Cream'	CRob ECho LBee LCon LRHS MAsh MBar NEgg SCoo WFar
	– 'Filifera'	CMac CSBt ECho MBar SCoo SLim SPoG WFar
	– 'Filifera Aurea' ♀H4	CKen CMac CSBt CWib ECho EHul EOrn LBee LCon LLin LRHS MAsh MBar MGos NEgg NHol NWea SCoo SPoG SRms WCFE WEve WFar
	– 'Filifera Aureovariegata' (v)	CMac ECho EHul LLin MBar SCoo SPoG
	– 'Filifera Nana'	ECho EHul ELan EOrn MBar SLim SPoG STre WFar
	– 'Filifera Nana Aurea'	see *C. pisifera* 'Golden Mop'
	– 'Filifera Sungold'	see *C. pisifera* 'Sungold'
	– 'Fuiri-tsukomo'	CKen
*	– 'Gold Cascade'	MGos
	– 'Gold Cushion'	CKen
	– 'Gold Dust'	see *C. pisifera* 'Plumosa Aurea'
	– 'Gold Spangle'	CKen ECho EHul MBar NEgg WFar
§	– 'Golden Mop' ♀H4	CKen ECho EHul MAsh
	– 'Green Pincushion'	CKen
	– 'Hime-himuro'	CKen ECho
	– 'Hime-sawara'	CKen CMen EOrn
	– 'Margaret'	CKen
	– 'Nana'	CKen CMen ECho EHul EPfP LLin MAsh MBar MGos NBlu NDlv NHol SMer WFar
I	– 'Nana Albovariegata' (v)	CDoC ECho EOrn LLin MAsh MBar SPoG WFar
	– 'Nana Aureovariegata' (v)	CDoC CMac CRob CSBt ECho EHul IMGH LBee LCon LLin LRHS MAsh MBar NDlv NEgg NHol SCoo SLim SPer WEve WFar
I	– 'Nana Compacta'	CMac ECho SRms
	– 'Nana Variegata' (v)	ECho LBee LRHS MBar SCoo SLim WFar
I	– 'Parslorii'	CKen
	– 'Pici'	CKen
	– 'Plumosa Albopicta' (v)	ECho MBar
§	– 'Plumosa Aurea'	CKen EHul MBar WFar
	– 'Plumosa Aurea Compacta'	CKen CMac ECho NDlv
I	– 'Plumosa Aurea Compacta Variegata' (v)	CMac NEgg
	– 'Plumosa Aurea Nana'	CRob ECho MBar MGos NBlu NDlv NHol WFar
I	– 'Plumosa Aurea Nana Compacta'	CMac
	– 'Plumosa Aurescens'	CDoC CMac
§	– 'Plumosa Compressa'	CDoC CFee CKen CRob ECho EHul EOrn GEdr LBee LCon MAsh MBar NEgg SCoo SLim WFar WGor
	– 'Plumosa Densa'	see *C. pisifera* 'Plumosa Compressa'
	– 'Plumosa Flavescens'	ECho EHul MBar SCoo
I	– 'Plumosa Juniperoides'	CKen ECho EHul EOrn LLin MBar NBlu NDlv SCoo SLim WFar WGor
	– 'Plumosa Purple Dome'	see *C. pisifera* 'Purple Dome'
I	– 'Plumosa Pygmaea'	ECho MGos NDlv WGor
§	– 'Plumosa Rogersii'	CRob ECho EHul EOrn MBar NHol WGor
	– 'Pompom'	CRob
§	– 'Purple Dome'	CRob ECho EHul EOrn MBar
I	– 'Pygmaea Tsukumo'	MGos
	– 'Rogersii'	see *C. pisifera* 'Plumosa Rogersii'
	– 'Silver and Gold' (v)	ECho EHul MBar
	– 'Silver Lode' (v)	CKen EOrn
	– 'Snow' (v)	CKen CMac EOrn MBar
	– 'Snowflake'	CKen ECho EHul
	– 'Spaan's Cannon Ball'	CKen
§	– 'Squarrosa'	MBar WFar
	– 'Squarrosa Dumosa'	CKen EHul MBar
	– 'Squarrosa Intermedia'	EHul MBar
I	– 'Squarrosa Lombarts'	CMac CSBt ECho EHul EOrn MBar SCoo
	– 'Squarrosa Lutea'	CKen MBar

	- 'Squarrosa Sulphurea'	CSBt ECho EHul EOrn EPfP LBee LCon LRHS MAsh MBar NEgg SLim SPer SPla STre WBVN WFar
	- 'Squarrosa Veitchii'	see *C. pisifera* 'Squarrosa'
§	- 'Strathmore'	CKen EHul LLin MBar NHol
§	- 'Sungold'	CDoC CKen CRob CSBt ECho EHul LCon LLin LRHS MAsh MBar NBlu NEgg SCoo SLim SPer SPla SPoG WEve
	- 'Tama-himuro'	CKen ECho
	- 'Teddy Bear'	ECho MBri NLar NScw
	- 'True Blue'	ECho
	- 'White Beauty' (v)	LCon SLim
*	- 'White Brocade'	CMac
	- 'White Pygmy'	EOrn
	thyoides 'Andelyensis'	CMac CRob CSBt ECho EHul EOrn LLin MBar SCoo WFar
	- 'Andelyensis Nana'	CKen
	- 'Aurea'	EHul MBar
	- 'Conica'	CKen
	- 'Ericoides' ♀H4	CKen CMac CRob CTri ECho EHul EOrn LBee LLin MBar MWat SPlb SPoG WFar
§	- 'Glauca'	EOrn
	- 'Kewensis'	see *C. thyoides* 'Glauca'
	- 'Little Jamie'	CKen
	- 'Red Star'	see *C. thyoides* 'Rubicon'
§	- 'Rubicon'	CKen CMac CRob CSBt ECho EHul EOrn EPfP LBee LCon LLin LRHS MAsh MBar MGos NBlu NEgg SLim SPla SPoG WFar WGer
	- 'Top Point'	CDoC CRob ECho EOrn LBee LCon MAsh MGos SCoo SLim SPoG
	- 'Variegata' (v)	ECho EHul MBar
	- 'Winter Wonder'	EHul

Chamaecytisus (*Papilionaceae*)

§	***albus***	GQui
§	***hirsutus***	MBri WLin WPGP WWeb
	prolifer	CPLG NLar
§	***purpureus***	CBgR CSBt EBee ELan EPfP LRHS MAsh MRav MSwo NLar NWea SBod SHBN SPer WBVN WCFE WFar WPat
	- f. ***albus***	CBcs EPfP SHBN SPer
§	- 'Atropurpureus' ♀H4	CBcs SPer WTel
	- 'Incarnatus'	see *C. purpureus* 'Atropurpureus'
§	***supinus***	CPLG SRms

Chamaedaphne (*Ericaceae*)

	calyculata	CBcs LRHS SPer WSHC
	- 'Nana'	CMHG MBar

Chamaedorea (*Arecaceae*)

	elegans ♀H1	LPal MBri
	erumpens	see *C. seifrizii*
	linearis	LPal
	metallica misapplied	see *C. microspadix*
	metallica O.F. Cook ex H.E. Moore ♀H1	LPal
§	***microspadix***	CPHo CTrC EAmu LPJP LPal SChr
	radicalis	CBrP CPHo EAmu LPJP LPal
§	***seifrizii*** ♀H1	LPal

Chamaelirium (*Melanthiaceae*)

	luteum	CArn

Chamaemelum (*Asteraceae*)

§	***nobile***	CArn CHby CHrt CPrp CSev CTri CWan ECho ELau EPfP GMac GPoy MBri MHer MNHC NGdn SPlb SRms WJek WPer WSel
	- 'Flore Pleno' (d)	More than 30 suppliers
	- 'Treneague'	More than 30 suppliers

Chamaenerion see *Chamerion*

Chamaepericlymenum see *Cornus*

Chamaerops (*Arecaceae*)

	excelsa misapplied	see *Trachycarpus fortunei*
	excelsa Thunb.	see *Rhapis excelsa*
	humilis ♀H3	More than 30 suppliers
§	- var. ***argentea***	CBrP CPHo EAmu ETod LPJP LPal MGos NPal SAin SChr
	- var. ***cerifera***	see *C. humilis* var. *argentea*
	- 'Vulcano'	EAmu LCro MBri MGos SAin SKHP

Chamaespartium see *Genista*

Chamaesphacos (*Lamiaceae*)

	ilicifolius misapplied	see *Siphocranion macranthum*

Chambeyronia (*Arecaceae*)

	macrocarpa	LPal

Chamelaucium (*Myrtaceae*)

	axillare	SOWG
	uncinatum	EShb SOWG

Chamerion (*Onagraceae*)

§	***angustifolium***	ECho GWCH NSco SWat WSFF
§	- 'Album'	More than 30 suppliers
	- 'Isobel'	CSpe MLLN MRav WAbb WCot
	- 'Stahl Rose'	CHid CMea CPom CWsd EBee EWes MSte SMrm SPhx SSvw WPGP WSHC
§	***dodonaei***	ELan EMan LHop MTho NEgg SPhx WEas WFar

Chasmanthe (*Iridaceae*)

	aethiopica	CPou EBee ERea GGar
	bicolor	CPLG CPou CStu EBee IDee
	floribunda	CHEx CHHB CPrp CSam CTca EBee EBrs ERea
	- var. ***duckittii***	CHHB CPrp EBee EBrs ECho EPfP WPGP
	- - 'Golden Wave' **new**	CTca EBrs
	- 'Saturnes' **new**	EBee
	- 'Venus' **new**	EBrs

Chasmanthium (*Poaceae*)

§	***latifolium***	More than 30 suppliers

Cheilanthes (*Adiantaceae*)

	acrostica	WAbe
	argentea	CLAP WAbe WRic
	distans	SRms WRic
	eatonii	WAbe
	lanosa	CCCN CLAP EBee EShb EWes MPes NMyG SRms WBor
	lindheimeri	WAbe WCot
	myriophylla	WAbe
	nivea	WAbe
	sieberi	WAbe
	sinuata	CLAP
	tomentosa	CCCN CLAP SRms WAbe WRic

Cheiranthus see *Erysimum*

Cheiridopsis (*Aizoaceae*)

	derenbergiana	EMan

Chelidonium (*Papaveraceae*)

	japonicum	see *Hylomecon japonica*
	majus	CArn CRWN GPoy GQui MHer MNHC MSal WHer WSFF
	- 'Chedglow' (v)	CNat
	- 'Flore Pleno' (d)	CBre MGol NBid NBro WHer

- var. ***laciniatum*** EMon WCot

Chelone (*Scrophulariaceae*)

barbata see *Penstemon barbatus*
§ ***glabra*** More than 30 suppliers
lyonii EBee LAst LEdu MDKP NBre NGdn NLar NRnb SHFr SPad WMoo WPer WPnP WShi
obliqua More than 30 suppliers
- var. ***alba*** see *C. glabra*
- 'Forncett Foremost' GQui
- 'Forncett Poppet' CBgR NBre
- 'Ieniemienie' EMon
- 'Pink Sensation' EBee MBri NBre WFar
* - ***rosea*** CHar EBee MLLN MMHG NBPC WGwG

Chelonopsis (*Lamiaceae*)

moschata CDes CLAP CPom ECha EMan LEdu MHar SMad WMoo WPGP WPrP
yagiharana EBee ELon GGar LBBr MBri MCCP MDKP MMHG MWea NBhm NBid NSti SPoG WHil WMoo WTMC

Chenopodium (*Chenopodiaceae*)

ambrosioides EUnu
bonus-henricus CAgr CArn CBod CHby CPrp CWan EUnu GPoy GWCH ILis MHer MNHC NTHB SIde WHer WSel
botrys MSal
giganteum ILis MNHC WJek
nuttaliae EUnu

cherimoya see *Annona cherimola*

cherry, Duke see *Prunus* x *gondouinii*

cherry, sour or morello see *Prunus cerasus*

cherry, sweet see *Prunus avium*

chervil see *Anthriscus cerefolium*

chestnut, sweet see *Castanea sativa*

Chiastophyllum (*Crassulaceae*)

§ ***oppositifolium*** ♀H4 More than 30 suppliers
- 'Frosted Jade' see *C. oppositifolium* 'Jim's Pride'
- 'Jane's Reverse' new WCot
§ - 'Jim's Pride' (v) EBee ECho EDAr EMon EPfP EWes GAbr GEdr GKev GMaP LAst LBee LRHS MDun MHer MRav NMen NPer NPri NSla SPet SPlb SPoG SRms SRot WAbe WFar WMoo WPat
simplicifolium see *C. oppositifolium*

Chiliotrichum (*Asteraceae*)

diffusum CWib GAbr GGar GSki
- 'Siska' CBcs GBin IArd SMad

Chimonanthus (*Calycanthaceae*)

fragrans see *C. praecox*
nitens NLar
§ ***praecox*** More than 30 suppliers
- 'Brockhill Goldleaf' SBra
- 'Grandiflorus' ♀H4 CEnd CPMA EPfP LRHS MAsh MBri SPoG SSpi SSta WPGP WPat
- 'Luteus' ♀H4 CEnd CPMA ELan ENot EPfP LRHS MBri MGos MRav NLar SPer SSpi SSta WPGP WPat
- 'Trenython' CEnd
yunnanensis NLar

Chimonobambusa (*Poaceae*)

falcata see *Drepanostachyum falcatum*
hejiangensis EPla
hookeriana misapplied see *Himalayacalamus falconeri* 'Damarapa'
macrophylla f. ***intermedia*** EPla SDry
§ ***marmorea*** CAbb CMCo EAmu EPla ERod LPal MMoz MWht NPal SDry WDyG WPGP
- 'Variegata' (v) CDTJ EFul EPla ERod MMoz SDry SLPl WPGP
§ ***quadrangularis*** CBcs CDTJ CDoC CGHE CHEx CTrG EBee EFul EPfP EPla ERod LEdu MMoz MWht NPal SDry WPGP
- 'Nagaminei' (v) EPla
- 'Suow' (v) CDTJ CGHE EBee EPla SDry WPGP
- 'Tatejima' EPla
tumidissinoda CAbb CDTJ CGHE CMCo EPla ERod MMoz NPal SDry WDyG WPGP

Chiogenes see *Gaultheria*

Chionanthus (*Oleaceae*)

foveolatus EShb
retusus CBcs CMCN EPfP IDee LRHS MPkF NLar SLon SSpi
virginicus CBcs CDoC CDul CEnd CMCN CPMA EBee ELan EPfP ERas EWTr IArd IDee IMGH LRHS MBlu MBri MMuc MRav SSpi SSta WHCG WOrn WPGP WSpi

Chionochloa (*Poaceae*)

conspicua CAby CBig CGHE CKno EBee EKen GKev GQue GSki LBMP MAvo MGol NBir NLar WPGP XIsg
- subsp. ***conspicua*** GGar
- subsp. ***cunninghamii*** CPLG
- 'Rubra' see *C. rubra*
flavescens EGoo GBin GSki ITer
flavicans CBcs CHrt CKno EWsh SGar
pallens CBig
§ ***rubra*** CBrm CElw CGHE CKno CPLG CSpe EAlp EBee ELan EPla EWes EWsh GFor GMaP GSki LBMP LEdu LHop MAvo MMoz MRav NChi SApp SHBN SMad WMoo WPGP WTin WWeb XIsg
- subsp. ***cuprea*** EBee GBin GGar

Chionodoxa ✿ (*Hyacinthaceae*)

cretica see *C. nana*
§ ***forbesii*** CTca EBrs ECho ENot EPfP EPot GAbr LRHS NBir SPer SRms WFar WShi
- 'Alba' ECho LAma
- 'Blue Giant' EBrs ECho EPot LRHS
- 'Rosea' EBrs ECho LAma
gigantea see *C. luciliae* Gigantea Group
lochiae new EBrs
luciliae misapplied see *C. forbesii*
luciliae ambig. IHer
luciliae Boiss. ♀H4 CAvo EPfP EPot LAma MBri NBlu SPer
- 'Alba' CBgR CFwr CRez EBrs ECho GGar LRHS SPer SPhx WLin
§ - Gigantea Group CHar EBrs ECho ELan EPot GKev LAma SPhx
- - 'Alba' EPot GKev
§ ***nana*** ECho
'Pink Giant' CAvo EBrs ECho ELan ENot EPfP EPot GGar GKev LAma LHop LRHS MAvo MMHG WCot WHil

sardensis ♀H4	CBgR CTca EBrs ECGP ECho EPot LAma LHop LRHS MMHG SGar WLin WRHF WShi

Chionographis (*Melanthiaceae*)

japonica	EBee EFEx WCru

Chionohebe (*Scrophulariaceae*)

§ ***densifolia***	GAbr GCrs NLAp
pulvinaris	GCrs WAbe

x *Chionoscilla* (*Hyacinthaceae*)

§ ***allenii***	CAvo EBrs ECho EPot

Chirita (*Gesneriaceae*)

'Aiko'	LRHS WDib
'Chastity'	CSpe LRHS WDib
'Diane Marie'	LRHS WDib
dielsii	CFir
heterotricha	LRHS WDib
'Keiko'	CSpe LRHS WDib
* ***latifolia* x *linearifolia***	WDib
linearifolia	LRHS WDib
linearifolia* x *sinensis	LRHS WDib
longgangensis	LRHS WDib
'New York'	CSpe LRHS WDib
sinensis ♀H1	CHal LRHS WDib
- 'Hisako'	CSpe LRHS WDib
speciosa HWJ 1056 **new**	WCru
'Stardust'	LRHS WDib
tamiana	CSpe LRHS WDib

Chironia (*Gentianaceae*)

baccifera	SPlb

x *Chitalpa* (*Bignoniaceae*)

tashkentensis	CBcs CEnd CMCN CTho EBee EPfP IDee IMGH MBlu MBri MWya NLar WPGP XPep
- 'Pink Dawn'	IArd MBri NLar
- 'Summer Bells'	CDoC EBee LRHS SCoo WCot

chives see *Allium schoenoprasum*

chives, Chinese see *Allium tuberosum*

Chlidanthus (*Amaryllidaceae*)

fragrans	CMdw CStu EBrs ECho EShb

Chloranthus (*Chloranthaceae*)

fortunei	CDes CLAP LEdu WPGP
henryi	EBee
japonicus	CLAP EBee WCru
oldhamii	CLAP LEdu
- B&SWJ 2019	WCru WPrP
serratus	CLAP EBee LEdu WCru

Chloris (*Poaceae*)

distichophylla	see *Eustachys distichophylla*

Chlorophytum (*Anthericaceae*)

comosum	EShb SEND
- 'Mandanum' (v)	CHal
- 'Variegatum' (v) ♀H1+3	CDTJ CHal LRHS MBri SRms
- 'Vittatum' (v) ♀H1+3	CHEx EShb NBlu SRms SWal
krookianum	CFir WCot
macrophyllum	EShb
majus	WCot
nepalense	WCot
- B&SWJ 2393	WCru
orchidastrum	EShb

Choisya (*Rutaceae*)

'Aztec Pearl' ♀H4	More than 30 suppliers
dumosa	LHop
- var. ***arizonica***	SDry
Goldfingers = 'Limo'PBR	More than 30 suppliers
ternata ♀H4	More than 30 suppliers
- 'Brica'PBR	see *C. ternata* Sundance
§ - Moonshine = 'Walcho'PBR	EBee GBin LRHS NLar SLon
- MoonsleeperPBR	see *C. ternata* Sundance
§ - Sundance = 'Lich'PBR ♀H3	More than 30 suppliers

Chondropetalum (*Restionaceae*)

* ***elephantinum***	CBig
hookerianum	CBig
mucronatum	CBcs CBig CTrC EAmu EBee LCro WPGP
tectorum	More than 30 suppliers
- dwarf	WPGP

Chondrosum (*Poaceae*)

gracile	see *Bouteloua gracilis*

Chordospartium (*Papilionaceae*)

muritai	ECou
- 'Huia Gilpen'	ECou
- 'Ron Feron'	ECou
- 'Wayne Nichols'	ECou
stevensonii	ECou EPfP NLar WBVN WSHC
- 'Duncan'	ECou
- 'Kiwi'	ECou
- 'Miller'	ECou

Chordospartium x *Corallospartium* (*Papilionaceae*)

Chordospartium stevensonii* x *Corallospartium sp.	ECou
- x ***Corallospartium crassicaule***, 'Coral Spears'	ECou

Chorisia (*Bombacaceae*)

speciosa	CCCN EAmu

Chorizema (*Papilionaceae*)

cordatum ♀H1	ECou
ilicifolium	CAbb CBcs CCCN CSPN EMil ERea SKHP

Chronanthus see *Cytisus*

Chrysalidocarpus see *Dypsis*

lutescens	see *Dypsis lutescens*

Chrysanthemopsis see *Rhodanthemum*

hosmariense	see *Rhodanthemum hosmariense*

Chrysanthemum ✿ (*Asteraceae*)

'Agnes Ann' (29K)	MNrw
'Albert's Yellow' (29Rub)	WOFF
'Alec Bedser' (25a)	NHal
'Alehmer Rote' (29Rub)	WOFF
'Alexandra'	NHal
'Aline' (29K)	CNCS
'Allison '88' (29Rub) **new**	MNrw
'Allouise' (25b) ♀H3	NHal
alpinum	see *Leucanthemopsis alpina*
'Amber Gigantic' (1)	NHal
'Anastasia' (28b)	CHid ECtt EMon EPPr GMac MNrw MRav NSti SRms WCot WFar WIvy WOFF WPer
N 'Anastasia Variegated' (28/v)	EMon
'Anastasia White' (28)	SSvw WCot WIvy
'Angela Blundell' **new**	WCot
'Anne Ratsey' (29Rub) **new**	CSam

	'Anne, Lady Brocket'	EMon EWsh MNrw NCGa WOFF
	'Apollo' (29K)	EMon EWll SPhx SSvw WCot
	'Apricot' (29Rub)	CPrp EBee EPPr EWTr MRav SSvw
	'Apricot Chessington' (25a)	NHal
	'Apricot Courtier' (24a)	NHal
	'Apricot Enbee Wedding'	see *C.* 'Bronze Enbee Wedding'
	arcticum L.	see *Arctanthemum arcticum*
	argenteum	see *Tanacetum argenteum*
	'Astro'	NHal
	'Aunt Millicent' (29K)	CNCS MNrw WOFF
	'Balcombe Perfection' (5a)	NHal
	balsamita	see *Tanacetum balsamita*
	Barbara = 'Yobarbara'PBR (22)	EPfP NHal
	'Beacon' (5a) ♀H2	NHal
	'Beppie Purple' (29)	NHal
	'Beppie Red' (29)	NHal
	'Bernadette Wade' (23a)	NHal
	'Bethanie Joy' (25b)	NHal
	'Betty' (29K)	MNrw
	'Big Wheel'PBR (22)	LAst
	'Bill Wade' (25a)	NHal
	'Billy Bell' (25a)	NHal
	'Blanche Poitevene' (5b) **new**	WOFF
	'Blenda'	CHrt
	'Bo-peep' (28)	EMon WOFF
	Bravo = 'Yobra' (22c) ♀H3	EPfP MNrw NHal
*	'Breitner's Supreme'	MNrw WCAu
	'Brennpunkt'	WHil
	'Brietner' (24b) ♀H3	NHal
	'Bright Eye' (28)	MNrw WMnd WOFF WPer
	'Brightness' (29K)	CNCS
	'Bronze Beauty' (25b)	WFar
	'Bronze Cassandra' (5b) ♀H2	NHal
	'Bronze Dee Gem' (29c)	NHal
§	'Bronze Elegance' (28b)	CSam EBee EBrs EMon MLLN NBir NGdn NSti SPla SRms WEas WIvy WMnd
§	'Bronze Enbee Wedding' (29d) ♀H3	NHal
	'Bronze Fairie' (28b) ♀H3	WOFF
	'Bronze Margaret' (29c) ♀H3	NHal
	'Bronze Matlock' (24b)	NHal
	'Bronze Max Riley' (23b) ♀H3	NHal
	'Bronze Mayford Perfection (5a) ♀H2	NHal
	'Bronze Mei-kyo'	see *C.* 'Bronze Elegance'
	'Bruera' (24b)	NHal
	'Bullfinch' (12a)	CNCS
	'Carmine Blush' (29Rub)	EBee WBrk WCot WHoo
	'Cassandra' (5b) ♀H2	NHal
	'Cherry Chessington' (25a)	NHal
	'Chesapeake' **new**	CNCS
	'Christopher Lawson' (24b)	NHal
	'Cinderella'	WMnd
	cinerariifolium	see *Tanacetum cinerariifolium*
	'Clapham Delight' (23a)	NHal
	'Clara Curtis' (29Rub)	More than 30 suppliers
	coccineum	see *Tanacetum coccineum*
	'Conjora' (22c)	LAst
	'Copper Margaret' (29c)	CHrt
	'Coral Reef' **new**	CNCS
	'Cornetto' (25b)	NHal
	corymbosum	see *Tanacetum corymbosum*
	'Cottage Apricot'	LHop MBNS MNrw WEas
	'Cottage Bronze' **new**	MNrw
	'Cottage Lemon' **new**	MNrw
	'Cottage Pink'	see *C.* 'Emperor of China'
	'Cottage Yellow'	MSte WCot WHoo
	'Courtier' (24a)	NHal
	'Cream Patricia Millar' (14b)	NHal
	Dana = 'Yodana' (25b) ♀H3	NHal
	'Daniel Cooper' (29Rub)	MNrw WOFF
	'Daphne Davis' (29d) ♀H3 **new**	CNCS
	'Darren Pugh' (3b)	NHal
	Debonair = 'Yodebo'PBR (22c) ♀H3	EPfP
	'Dee Gem' (29c) ♀H3	NHal
	'Denise' (28b) ♀H3	WOFF
§	'Doctor Tom Parr' (28b)	CPLG EBee ELan EMon IGor LHop MNrw SPhx WOFF WPtf
	'Doreen Statham' (4b)	NHal
	'Dorothy Stone' (25b)	NHal
	'Dorridge Crystal' (24a)	NHal
	'Duchess of Edinburgh' (29Rub)	CAby CPrp CSam EBee EBrs ECtt ELan EMon EShb LRHS MRav NCGa SSvw WCAu WMnd WOFF
	'Duke of Kent' (1)	NHal
	'Edelweiss' (29K)	CAby EMon WCot
	'Egret' (23b)	NHal
	'Elaine Johnson' (3b)	NHal
	'Elizabeth Lawson' (5b)	NHal
	'Elizabeth Shoesmith' (1)	NHal
	'Ellen' (29c)	CHrt NHal
	'Elsie Austin' (5) **new**	WOFF
*	'Emma Jane' (25a)	NHal
§	'Emperor of China' (29Rub)	CAby CElw CSam ECha ECtt EMon ENot EPPr IGor LRHS MNrw MRav MSte NCGa SPhx SSvw WBor WCot WFar WMnd WOFF
	'Enbee Wedding' (29d) ♀H3	NHal
	'Ermine' (23a)	WOFF
	'Esther' (29Rub)	EMon MNrw
	'Fairie' (28a) ♀H3	MNrw
*	'Fairy Rose' (29K)	MNrw WOFF
	'Flyaway' (10a) **new**	CNCS
	foeniculaceum misapplied	see *Argyranthemum foeniculaceum* misapplied
	foeniculaceum (Willd.) Desf.	see *Argyranthemum foeniculaceum* (Willd.) Webb & Sch.Bip.
	'Foxtrot'PBR ♀H3	LAst
	'Fred Raynor'	MNrw WOFF
	frutescens	see *Argyranthemum frutescens*
	'Gala'PBR (22) ♀H3	LAst
	'Gambit' (24a)	NHal
	'Geof Brady' (5a)	NHal
	'Geoff Sylvester' (25a)	NHal
	'George Griffiths' (24b) ♀H3	NHal
	'Georgia Girl' (10a) **new**	CNCS
	'Gigantic' (1)	NHal
I	'Gladys' (12a) **new**	CNCS
	'Gladys' (24b)	ELan
	'Gladys Emerson' (3b)	NHal
	'Gloria' (29K)	MNrw
§	'Gold Margaret' (29c) ♀H3	NHal
	'Golden Cassandra' (5b) ♀H2	NHal
	'Golden Chalice' (12a) **new**	CNCS
	'Golden Courtier' (24a)	NHal
	'Golden Gigantic' (1)	NHal
	'Golden Margaret'	see *C.* 'Gold Margaret'
	'Golden Mayford Perfection' (5a) ♀H2	NHal
	'Golden Plover' (22)	NHal
	'Golden Rain' (10a) ♀H2 **new**	CNCS
	'Golden Seal' (7b)	EMon
	'Goldengreenheart' (29Rub)	MNrw
	'Goldmarianne' (29K)	GBin

'Gompie Bronze'	NHal
'Gompie Red'	NHal
I 'Gompie Rose'	NHal
'Goshu Penta' **new**	CNCS
'Grace Wade' (25b)	NHal
'Grandchild' (29c)	CNCS MNrw WOFF
§ x ***grandiflorum***	SRms
'Hanenburg'	NHal
haradjanii	see *Tanacetum haradjanii*
'Harold Lawson' (5a)	NHal
'Harry Gee' (1)	NHal
'Hazy Days' (25b)	NHal
'Heather James' (3b)	NHal
'Heide' (29c) 🏆H3	NHal
'Hesketh Knight' (5b)	NHal
'Hilfred' **new**	CNCS
Holly = 'Yoholly' (22b) 🏆H3	NHal
'Honey Enbee Wedding' (29d)	NHal
'Horningsea Pink' (19d)	WBor
hosmariense	see *Rhodanthemum hosmariense*
'Imp' (28)	WOFF
'Innocence' (29Rub)	CAby CSam ELan EMon GMac IGor MNrw MRav NCGa NGdn NSti SAga SPla WHoo
'Janice'PBR (7a)	LAst
'Jante Wells' (28)	EMon WEas WOFF WTel
'Jessie Cooper'	see *C.* 'Mrs Jessie Cooper'
'Jinx' (7b) **new**	WOFF
'John Harrison' (25b)	NHal
'John Riley' (14a)	NHal
'John Wingfield' (14b)	NHal
'Joyce Frieda' (23b)	NHal
'Julia' (28)	GMac
'Julie Lagravère' (28)	WPtf
'Juweeltja' **new**	NHal
'Kay Woolman' (13b)	NHal
'Kimberley Marie' (15b)	NHal
'Kiyominomeisui' **new**	CNCS
x ***koreanum***	see *C.* x *grandiflorum*
'Lakelanders' (3b)	NHal
'Le Bonheur Red'	NHal
'Lemon Margaret' (29c) 🏆H3	NHal
'Leo' (28)	EMon
leucanthemum	see *Leucanthemum vulgare*
'Lilac Chessington' (25a)	NHal
Linda = 'Lindayo'PBR (22c)	NHal
'Lindie' (28)	WHil
'L'Innocence' (29K)	WOFF
'Long Island Beauty' (6b) 🏆H2	WTel
'Lorna Wood' (13b)	NHal
'Lucy' (29a) 🏆H2	NHal
'Lucy Simpson' (29K)	MNrw WOFF
'Lundy' (2)	NHal
'Luv Purple'	NHal
'Lynn Johnson' (15a)	NHal
Lynn = 'Yolynn'PBR (22c) 🏆H3	NHal
macrophyllum	see *Tanacetum macrophyllum* (Waldst. & Kit.) Sch.Bip.
'Malcolm Perkins' (25a)	NHal
'Mancetta Comet' (29a)	NHal
'Mandarin' (5b)	NCGa
maresii	see *Rhodanthemum hosmariense*
'Margaret' (29c) 🏆H3	NHal
'Marion' (25a)	WCot
'Mark Woolman' (1)	NHal
'Mary' (29K)	CNCS MNrw WOFF
'Mary Stoker' (29Rub)	More than 30 suppliers
'Mason's Bronze' (7b)	WOFF
'Matador' (14a)	NHal
'Matlock' (24b)	NHal
'Mavis' (28a) 🏆H3	WOFF
mawii	see *Rhodanthemum gayanum*
'Max Riley' (23b) 🏆H3	NHal
maximum misapplied	see *Leucanthemum* x *superbum*
maximum Ramond	see *Leucanthemum maximum* (Ramond) DC.
- 'Aglaia'	see *Leucanthemum* x *superbum* 'Aglaia'
- 'T.E. Killin'	see *Leucanthemum* x *superbum* 'T.E. Killin'
- 'Wirral Supreme'	see *Leucanthemum* x *superbum* 'Wirral Supreme'
'Maxine Johnson' (25b)	NHal
'May Shoesmith' (5a) 🏆H2	NHal
'Mayford Perfection' (5a) 🏆H2	NHal WOFF
'Mei-kyo' (28b)	CMea EBee EMon IGor MLLN MRav MWgw SPla SRms WBor WFar WHil WOFF
'Membury' (24b)	NHal
'Mermaid Yellow' 🏆H2	LAst
'Michelle Preston' (13b)	NHal
'Millennium' (25b)	NHal
'Moonlight' (29d/K)	MRav
'Mottram Minstrel' (29d)	WOFF
'Mottram Pink Lady' (29d) **new**	WOFF
'Mottram Sentinel' (29d)	WOFF
'Mottram Twotone' (29d)	WOFF
§ 'Mrs Jessie Cooper' (29Rub)	CAby ELan EWsh GMac GQue MNrw MSte NBir NLar SSvw WCot WHil WHoo WHrl WOFF WPtf
'Mrs Jessie Cooper No 1'	SSvw WTin
'Mrs Jessie Cooper No 2'	MNrw WTin
'Music' (23b)	NHal
naktongense	see *C. zawadskii* var. *latilobum*
'Nancy Perry' (29Rub)	CSam ELan EMon MNrw MRav SSvw WOFF
§ ***nankingense***	WFar
'Nantyderry Sunshine' (28b) 🏆H4	CSam EBee LRHS MNrw MWgw SPla WCot WEas WMnd WPer
'Nell Gwyn' (29Rub)	MNrw WOFF
'Netherhall Moonlight'	EMon SPhx
Nicole = 'Yonicole' (22c) 🏆H3	NHal
nipponicum	see *Nipponanthemum nipponicum*
'Orange Allouise' (25b)	NHal
'Orange Enbee Wedding' (29d)	NHal
'Oury'	EMon
pacificum	see *Ajania pacifica*
'Parkfield Tigger' (29c)	NHal
parthenium	see *Tanacetum parthenium*
'Patricia Millar' (14b)	NHal
'Paul Boissier' (30Rub)	CAby EMon NSti SPhx WCot WMnd WOFF
'Payton Dale' (29c) 🏆H3	NHal
'Payton Glow' (29c)	NBir
'Payton Linda' 🏆H3 **new**	CNCS
'Payton Prince' (29c) 🏆H3	NHal
'Payton Toffee' (29c)	NHal
'Peach Courtier' (24a)	NHal
'Peach Enbee Wedding' (29d) 🏆H3	NHal
'Peach John Wingfield' (14b)	NHal
'Pennine Bullion'	NHal
'Pennine Gift' (29c)	NHal
'Pennine Marie' (29a) 🏆H3	NHal
'Pennine Oriel' (29a) 🏆H3	NHal
'Pennine Polo' (29d) 🏆H3	NHal
'Pennine Ranger' (29d)	NHal
'Pennine Swan' (29c)	NHal
'Pennine Toy' (19d)	NHal
'Perry's Peach'	CNCS MNrw NPer

'Peter Rowe' (23b)	NHal
'Peterkin'	ECtt EMon MNrw MWgw
'Pink Champagne' (4b)	CNCS
'Pink Duke' (1)	NHal
'Pink John Wingfield' (14b)	NHal
'Pink Progression'	GMac MWgw NBir
'Pink Splendour' (10a) ♀H2 **new**	CNCS
'Polar Gem' (3a)	NHal
'Polaris' (9c)	EWll
'Primrose Allouise' (24b) ♀H3	NHal
'Primrose Courtier'	see *C.* 'Yellow Courtier'
'Primrose Dorothy Stone' (25b)	NHal
'Primrose Enbee Wedding' (29d) ♀H3	NHal
'Primrose John Hughes' (3b)	NHal
'Primrose Mayford Perfection' (5a) ♀H2	NHal
'Primrose West Bromwich' (14a)	NHal
'Promise' (25a)	NHal
ptarmiciflorum	see *Tanacetum ptarmiciflorum*
'Purleigh White' (28b)	CPrp GMac MNrw NSti SPla WOFF
'Purple Chempak Rose' (14b)	NHal
'Purple Fairie' (28b)	MNrw
'Purple Margaret' (29c)	NHal
'Ralph Lambert' (1)	NHal
'Raquel' (29K)	EPfP MNrw
'Rayonnante' (11)	WOFF
'Red Balcombe Perfection' (5a)	NHal
'Red Bella' (29c)	NBir
'Red Pennine Gift' (29c)	NHal
'Red Shirley Model' (3a)	NHal
'Red Wendy' (29c) ♀H3	CHrt
'Redbreast' **new**	CNCS
'Regal Mist' (25b)	NHal
'Ringdove' (12a) **new**	CNCS
'Rita McMahon' (29d) ♀H3	NHal
Robin = 'Yorobi'PBR (22c)	NHal
'Roen Sarah'	NHal
'Romany' (2)	CElw WEas
'Rose Enbee Wedding' (29d)	NHal
'Rose Mayford Perfection' (5a) ♀H2	NHal
'Rose Patricia Millar' (14b)	NHal
Rose Pink Debonair = 'Rosepink Yodebo'PBR (22c) ♀H2	LAst
roseum	see *Tanacetum coccineum*
'Royal Command' (29Rub)	EMon MNrw
rubellum	see *C. zawadskii*
'Ruby Enbee Wedding' (29d) ♀H3	NHal
'Ruby Mound' (29c/K) ♀H3	CNCS MNrw WEas WOFF
'Ruby Raynor' (29Rub)	CNCS MNrw WOFF
'Rumpelstilzchen'	CMea ECtt MNrw WPer
'Salhouse Joy' (10a) **new**	CNCS
'Salmon Allouise' (25b)	NHal
'Salmon Enbee Wedding' (29d) ♀H3	NHal
'Sam Vinter' (5a)	NHal
'Sarah Louise' (25b)	NHal
'Sarah's Yellow'	CAby CSam
'Sea Urchin' (29c/K) ♀H3	CNCS MNrw
'Seashell' (28b)	WOFF
'Senkyo-karyu' **new**	CNCS
'Shining Light' (29f/K)	MNrw
'Shirley Primrose' (1)	NHal
sinense	see *C.* × *grandiflorum*
'Skylark' (22a)	NPri
'Smokey' (29)	NHal
'Sonnenschein'	EWTr LHop WHen
'Sophie Elizabeth' (24a)	NHal
'Southway Shiraz' (29d)	NHal
'Southway Snoopy' (29d)	NHal
'Southway Strontium' (29d)	NHal
'Spencer's Cottage' (13b)	WOFF
'Stan's Choice' (29K)	WOFF
'Starlet' (29f/K)	MNrw
'Stockton' (3b) ♀H2	NHal
'Sunbeam' (28)	EBee
Sundoro = 'Yosun' (22d)	NHal
'Syllabub'	ECtt LAst
'Tapestry Rose' (29K)	CMea EMon IGor MCot MNrw NCGa SSvw WBor
'Thoroughbred' (24a)	NHal
'Tom Parr'	see *C.* 'Doctor Tom Parr'
'Tom Snowball' (3b)	NHal
'Tommy Trout' (28/K)	MNrw WOFF
'Tracy Waller' (24b)	NHal
Triumph = 'Yotri' (22)	NHal
uliginosum	see *Leucanthemella serotina*
'Uri'	SAga SPhx
'Vagabond Prince'	CSam MSte WHoo
'Valerie' (9f/10)	CNCS
'Venice' (24b)	NHal
'Wedding Day' (29K)	EBee EMon EWin MNrw WCAu WTin
'Wedding Sunshine' (29K)	LRHS MNrw
'Wembley' (24b)	NHal
'Wessex Eclipse' (29c)	NHal
'West Bromwich' (14a)	NHal
weyrichii	CBgR EBee ECho ECtt EShb GKev MTho NRya NWCA SAga SBla SPet SPoG SRms
'White Allouise' (25b) ♀H3	NHal
'White Cassandra' (5b)	NHal
'White Enbee Wedding' (29d)	NHal
'White Gloss' (29K)	LRHS
'White Margaret' (29c) ♀H3	NHal
'White Rayonnante' (11)	WOFF
'White Skylark' (22)	NHal
'White Tower'	MNrw
'Wilder Charms'	WHil
'Winning's Red' (29Rub)	EMon EWTr LHop MNrw SMad SPhx WOFF
'Wizard'PBR	LAst
'Woolman's Star' (3a)	NHal
'Woolman's Venture' (4b)	NHal
'Yellow Billy Bell' (15a)	NHal
§ 'Yellow Courtier' (24a)	NHal
'Yellow Egret' (23b)	NHal
'Yellow Ellen' (29c)	NHal
'Yellow Enbee Wedding' (29d)	NHal
'Yellow Hammer' (12a)	CNCS
'Yellow Hazy Days' (25b)	NHal
'Yellow Heide' (29c) ♀H3	NHal
'Yellow John Hughes' (3b) ♀H2	NHal
'Yellow John Wingfield' (14b)	NHal
'Yellow May Shoesmith' (5a)	NHal
'Yellow Mayford Perfection' (5a) ♀H2	NHal
'Yellow Pennine Oriel' (29a) ♀H3	NHal
'Yellow Ralph Lambert' (1)	NHal
'Yellow Rayonnante' (10a) **new**	WOFF

'Yellow Rylands Gem' (24b) NHal
'Yellow Starlet' (29f/K) MNrw
yezoense ♀H4 CSam CStu ELan WEas
- 'Roseum' CSam NSti WBor
§ ***zawadskii*** MLHP WFar
§ - var. ***latilobum*** LEdu

Chrysocoma (*Asteraceae*)

ciliata JJH 9401633 NWCA
coma-aurea EMan

Chrysogonum (*Asteraceae*)

australe EBee
virginianum CHal CMea CPrp EBee ECha EMan EMar EShb EWes LRHS MRav SBch WFar WMoo

Chrysopogon (*Poaceae*)

gryllus CBig EBee SApp WPGP XIsg

Chrysopsis (*Asteraceae*)

§ ***mariana*** EMon WOld
villosa see *Heterotheca villosa*

Chrysosplenium (*Saxifragaceae*)

alternifolium EMFW
davidianum CBre CPLG CSam EBee ECha EPot GEdr GKev ITer MNFA NBir NSla WBor WCot WCru WGer WMoo WPrP WPtf
flagelliferum B&SWJ 8902 **new** WCru
lanuginosum var. ***formosanum*** B&SWJ 6979 WCru
macrophyllum CExc EWld WCot WCru
macrostemon var. ***shiobarense*** EPot
- - B&SWJ 6173 WCru
oppositifolium EBee WHer WShi

Chrysothemis (*Gesneriaceae*)

pulchella ♀H1 CHal

Chusquea ✿ (*Poaceae*)

breviglumis misapplied see *C. culeou* 'Tenuis'
breviglumis Phil. NMoo
culeou ♀H4 More than 30 suppliers
- 'Breviglumis' see *C. culeou* 'Tenuis'
- 'Purple Splendour' EPla WPGP
§ - 'Tenuis' EPla ERod SDry WNor
gigantea CDTJ EPla LEdu MMoz MWht WPGP
- 'Bracken Hill' **new** MMoz
macrostachya EBee EPla WPGP
montana EPla
quila EPla MMoz SDry WPGP
ramosissima SDry
valdiviensis EPla WPGP

Cicerbita (*Asteraceae*)

sp. ECtt
B&SWJ 5162 WCru
B&SWJ 6588 WCru
BWJ 7891 from China WCru
§ ***alpina*** NBid NLar SGar SPlb
macrorhiza B&SWJ 2970 WCru
plumieri EMan EWes WCot WFar WPtf WRos

Cichorium (*Asteraceae*)

intybus CArn CHby CHrt CPrp EBee EBla ECrN ELan ELau GAbr GPoy ITer LHop MNHC NGHP NMir NPri SECG SIde SPer SPlb SPoG WFar WJek WMoo WSHC
- f. ***album*** CBod CPrp EBee EBla ECha EMan EPfP GMac LHop LRHS MAvo MRav NCGa NCob NGdn NSti SBch SPoG SWat WCAu
- var. ***foliosum*** EBee
- 'Roseum' CBod CPrp CSpe EBee EBla ECha ECot ELan EPfP GMac LHop LRHS MAvo MRav NCGa NCob NGdn SBch SPoG SWat WCAu

Cimicifuga see *Actaea*

acerina see *Actaea japonica*
americana see *Actaea podocarpa*
cordifolia Pursh see *Actaea podocarpa*
cordifolia (DC.) Torrey & A.Gray see *Actaea cordifolia*
foetida see *Actaea cimicifuga*
- var. ***cordifolia*** see *Actaea cordifolia*
- 'Purpurea' see *Actaea simplex* Atropurpurea Group
ramosa see *Actaea simplex* 'Prichard's Giant'
rubifolia see *Actaea cordifolia*
simplex 'Elstead Variety' see *Actaea matsumurae* 'Elstead Variety'
- var. ***matsumurae*** 'Elstead'Variety' see *Actaea matsumurae* 'Elstead

Cineraria (*Asteraceae*)

maritima see *Senecio cineraria*
saxifraga EShb

Cinnamomum (*Lauraceae*)

camphora CBcs CHEx CPLG CTrG
japonicum WPGP
micranthum WPGP

Cionura (*Asclepiadaceae*)

oreophila CFir EBee WPGP WSHC

Circaea (*Onagraceae*)

alpina **new** EBee
lutetiana MSal NSco WHer
- 'Caveat Emptor' (v) CBow CHid EBee NBid WCot WHer WHil

Cirsium (*Asteraceae*)

acaule NBre NLar
arvense WSFF
* ***atroroseum*** SWat
ciliatum EBee
diacantha see *Ptilostemon diacantha*
eriophoroides WCot
eriophorum LDai NLar
helenioides see *C. heterophyllum*
§ ***heterophyllum*** CDes CPom EBee EMan EMon GBri LBBr LDai LEdu NBre NEgg NLar SHar SPhx WCot WPGP WTin
japonicum 'Early Pink Beauty' LDai NBre
- 'Early Rose Beauty' NBre
- 'Pink Beauty' LHop NEgg NHol
- 'Rose Beauty' LRHS NBlu SPur
'Mount Etna' CSam EBee EBla ECGP EMar GBri LHop LRHS MWgw NCob NGdn
oleraceum LEdu NBid NBre NLar
purpuratum EMan MNrw WCot WPGP
rivulare CSam
- 'Atropurpureum' More than 30 suppliers
subcoriaceum pink-flowered B&SWJ 10245 **new** WCru
- yellow-flowered B&SWJ 10471 **new** WCru
tuberosum NDov SPhx

	vulgare	WSFF

Cissus (*Vitaceae*)

	antarctica ♀H1	CCCN MBri
	discolor	CHal
	pedata B&SWJ 2371	WCru
	rhombifolia ♀H1	MBri SEND
	- 'Ellen Danica' ♀H1	CHal
§	***striata***	CBcs CDoC CHEx CPLG CTrC CWCL EBee EMil EShb IMGH LRHS MRav SBra SLim SWvt WSHC WWeb

Cistus ✿ (*Cistaceae*)

	acutifolius misapplied	see *C. inflatus*, *C.* x *pulverulentus*
	x ***aguilarii***	CBcs CChe CPLG CSBt CTri EPfP EWTr LAst MRav SKHP WOut WSHC XPep
	- 'Maculatus' ♀H3	CDoC CHar CPLG CSam EBee ELan EPfP GGar LCro LRHS LSRN NCGa SCoo SDry SLPl SPer SPla SPoG SWvt WAbe WBod WCFE WGer WHCG WKif WWeb XPep
	albanicus	see *C. sintenisii*
	albidus	CArn EGoo LRav SDry WKif XPep
	- f. ***albus***	XPep
	algarvensis	see *Halimium ocymoides*
	'Ann Baker'	SLPl XPep
	'Anne Palmer'	see *C.* x *fernandesiae* 'Anne Palmer'
	x ***argenteus*** 'Blushing Peggy Sammons'	CDoC CSBt EBee MWgw WSPU XPep
	- Golden Treasure = 'Nepond' (v)	CBow EBee EPfP EQua SWvt
	- 'Paper Moon'	EBee LSRN XPep
§	- 'Peggy Sammons' ♀H3	CBgR CDoC EBee ECha ELan ENot EPfP EWTr IMGH LAst LBMP LHop LRHS LSRN MAsh MGos MRav SCoo SLim SMer SPer SPoG SWvt WBrE WFar WHar WSHC XPep
	- 'Silver Ghost'	CDoC XPep
	- 'Silver Pink' ambig.	More than 30 suppliers
	- 'Stripey'	XPep
	atriplicifolius	see *Halimium atriplicifolium*
	'Blanche'	see *C. ladanifer* 'Blanche'
	x ***bornetianus*** 'Jester'	CSBt EBee MAsh SPla WAbe XPep
	'Candy Stripe' (v)	MBNS
	x ***canescens***	XPep
	- f. ***albus***	CWib EBee EQua WEas WHCG WKif XPep
	'Chelsea Pink'	see *C.* 'Grayswood Pink'
	chinamadensis	XPep
	x ***chnoodophyllus***	XPep
	x ***clausonis***	XPep
§	***clusii***	CBgR NLar SPla XPep
	- subsp. ***multiflorus***	XPep
	x ***corbariensis***	see *C.* x *hybridus*
	creticus	CDoC CPLG EQua LAst MAsh MBri MGos MLHP MWgw SGar SLon SPoG WBVN WPGP
	- subsp. ***corsicus***	XPep
§	- subsp. ***creticus***	EBee ELan EPfP LRHS MRav MSte SCoo SPer WAbe WGer XPep
	- - f. ***albus***	XPep
*	- - 'Ano Moulia'	XPep
*	- - 'Bali'	XPep
	- - 'Lasithi'	WAbe
	- subsp. ***eriocephalus***	XPep
*	- - 'Michel Valantin'	XPep
§	- subsp. ***incanus***	WHCG
	- var. ***tauricus***	XPep
	x ***crispatus***	XPep
§	- 'Warley Rose'	GMaP SHBN WKif WWeb XPep
	crispus misapplied	see *C.* x *pulverulentus*
§	***crispus*** L.	EBee EGoo MRav WEas XPep
	- 'Prostratus'	see *C. crispus* L.
	- 'Sunset'	see *C.* x *pulverulentus* 'Sunset'
§	x ***cyprius*** ♀H4	CArn CDul ECtt ELan EPfP GGar LHop MGos MNHC MRav MWat MWgw SDix SEND SHBN SPer SRms WBrE WFar WWeb XPep
	- f. ***albiflorus***	MSte XPep
	- var. ***ellipticus*** f. ***bicolor***	WAbe XPep
§	- - 'Elma' ♀H3	EBee ELan EPfP ERas LHop LRHS MAsh MWgw SDry SPer SPla WBod WEas WGer WHCG WPGP XPep
§	x ***dansereaui***	CHar CMHG CSBt CSam CWib EBee ENot MGos MRav MSte WFar WSpi XPep
	- 'Albiflorus'	see *C.* x *dansereaui* 'Portmeirion'
	- 'Decumbens' ♀H4	CBcs CBrm CChe CMHG CTri ELan ENot EPfP LBMP MAsh MBNS MDun MRav MSwo MWgw NCGa SArc SCoo SHBN SMer SPer SPla SPoG SWvt WGer WHCG XPep
	- 'Jenkyn Place'	CDoC EBee GMaP MBNS MBri MGos SLPl SPoG WKif XPep
	- 'Little Gem'	XPep
§	- 'Portmeirion'	WFar XPep
	x ***dubius***	XPep
	'Elma'	see *C.* x *cyprius* var. *ellipticus* 'Elma'
	x ***escartianus***	XPep
	x ***fernandesiae***	XPep
§	- 'Anne Palmer'	CBgR CDoC EBee EPfP LSRN LTwo MAsh SPoG WBod WFar
	x ***florentinus*** misapplied	see x *Halimiocistus* 'Ingwersenii'
§	x ***florentinus*** Lam.	CAbP GGar XPep
*	- 'Béziers'	XPep
	- 'Fontfroide'	EBee WSPU WWeb
*	- 'Tramontane'	XPep
	formosus	see *Halimium. lasianthum* subsp. *formosum*
	x ***gardianus***	XPep
	'Gordon Cooper'	EBee SCoo WSPU XPep
§	'Grayswood Pink' ♀H4	More than 30 suppliers
	halimifolius	see *Halimium halimifolium* Willk.
	x ***heterocalyx*** 'Chelsea Bonnet'	EBee GMaP MSte SCoo SLim SPoG WPGP WPen WSPU WWeb XPep
	heterophyllus	XPep
	hirsutus Lam. 1786	see *C. inflatus*
	- var. ***psilosepalus***	see *C. inflatus*
§	x ***hybridus***	More than 30 suppliers
*	- 'Donadieu'	XPep
	- Gold Prize = 'Wyecis' (v)	ELan MBri MGos NLar SPoG SWvt WLeb
	incanus	see *C. creticus* subsp. *incanus*
§	***inflatus***	CPLG SDry WHar WHer XPep
	ingwerseniana	see x *Halimiocistus* 'Ingwersenii'
	'Jessamy Beauty'	SLPl WAbe XPep
	'Jessamy Bride'	SLPl XPep
	'Jessamy Charm'	SPhx XPep
	ladanifer misapplied	see *C.* x *cyprius*
	ladanifer L. ♀H3	CDoC CSBt CTri ECha ECrN ELan EPfP EWTr GCra IMGH LRHS MRav MSal MSwo NEgg SGar SPer WEas WFar WHar WSHC XPep
	- var. ***albiflorus***	EQua SKHP XPep
*	- - 'Bashful'	XPep
§	- 'Blanche'	CBgR EBee WKif XPep
§	- 'Paladin'	XPep
	- Palhinhae Group	see *C. ladanifer* var. *sulcatus*
	- 'Pat'	EBee ELan EPfP LRHS LSRN MAsh NBir SPoG
	- var. ***petiolatus***	XPep
	- - f. ***immaculatus***	XPep
§	- var. ***sulcatus***	CDoC CHar CPle EBee ELan EPfP LHop MSte SDry WAbe WFar
	- - f. ***bicolor***	EBee XPep
	- - f. ***latifolius***	XPep

	- var. ***tangerinus***	XPep
	lasianthus	see *Halimium lasianthum*
	laurifolius ♀H4	CDoC CHar EBee ENot EPfP LRav MGos MNrw MRav NBir NEgg NLar NSti SKHP SLPl SLon SPoG WHar XPep
	- subsp. ***atlanticus***	XPep
	x ***laxus*** **new**	WAbe
	- 'Snow White'	CAbP CDoC EPfP LAst LHop LRHS MDun MGos MSte MWgw NPer NPro SLPl SLim SLon SPoG SRms WKif WLeb XPep
	x ***ledon***	SLPl WWeb XPep
	libanotis	XPep
	x ***longifolius***	see *C.* x *nigricans*
	x ***loretii*** misapplied	see *C.* x *dansereaui*
	x ***loretii*** Rouy & Foucaud	see *C.* x *stenophyllus*
	x ***lucasii***	XPep
	x ***lusitanicus*** Maund	see *C.* x *dansereaui*
	'May Snow'	MBNS MWgw SPoG
	'Merrist Wood Cream'	see x *Halimiocistus wintonensis* 'Merrist Wood Cream'
	x ***mesoensis***	XPep
	monspeliensis	CAbP EBee EPfP EQua GGar LRHS SPer SPoG WFar XPep
	- CMBS 62	WPGP
	- Densifolius Group	XPep
	- 'Vicar's Mead'	CAbP CBgR CCCN CDoC EBee ELan MAsh MBNS SPla SPoG SRms XPep
	munbyi	XPep
§	x ***nigricans***	CPLG EBee ELan EWin XPep
	x ***oblongifolius***	XPep
	x ***obtusifolius*** misapplied	see *C.* x *nigricans*
	x ***obtusifolius*** ambig.	EAlp
	x ***obtusifolius*** Sweet	CAbP EPfP EWes SLPl WEas XPep
§	- 'Thrive'	MBri SCoo
	ochreatus	see *C. symphytifolius* subsp. *leucophyllus*
	ocymoides	see *Halimium ocymoides*
	osbeckiifolius	XPep
	'Paladin'	see *C. ladanifer* 'Paladin'
	palhinhae	see *C. ladanifer* var. *sulcatus*
	parviflorus misapplied	see *C.* 'Grayswood Pink'
	parviflorus Lam.	WCFE WSHC XPep
	x ***pauranthus***	XPep
*	- 'Natacha'	XPep
	'Peggy Sammons'	see *C.* x *argenteus* 'Peggy Sammons'
	x ***penarcleusensis***	XPep
	x ***picardianus***	XPep
	x ***platysepalus***	SLPl SPhx XPep
	populifolius	CMHG ECha LRHS LTwo SKHP SPer WAbe WBod WHer WPGP
	- var. ***lasiocalyx***	see *C. populifolius* subsp. *major*
§	- subsp. ***major*** ♀H3	CBgR CPle EBee EPfP LSRN WPGP XPep
	- subsp. ***populifolius***	XPep
	pouzolzii	XPep
	psilosepalus	see *C. inflatus*
§	x ***pulverulentus***	CPLG CTri ECha EPfP MMHG MWgw WAbe WSHC
*	- Delilei Group	XPep
	- - 'Fiona'	XPep
§	- 'Sunset' ♀H3	More than 30 suppliers
	- 'Warley Rose'	see *C.* x *crispatus* 'Warley Rose'
§	x ***purpureus*** ♀H3	More than 30 suppliers
	- 'Alan Fradd'	CBcs EBee ENot EPfP ERas EWTr LAst LBMP LCro LHop LRHS LSRN MAsh MDun MGos MSwo MWgw SCoo SEND SLim SMer SMrm SPla SPoG SWal SWvt WBor WFar WGer XPep
	- var. ***argenteus*** f. ***stictus***	EBee LSRN WAbe WSPU XPep
	- 'Betty Taudevin'	see *C.* x *purpureus*

	- var. ***holorhodos***	XPep
	x ***ralletii***	EBee XPep
	- f. ***subcreticus***	XPep
	x ***rodiaei*** 'Jessabel'	CBgR MAsh SCoo SPoG WAbe WLeb
	- 'Jessica'	CDoC EBee LAst NLar WAbe WSPU XPep
	rosmarinifolius	see *C. clusii*
	'Ruby Cluster'	CCCN CDoC SRms WLeb XPep
	sahucii	see x *Halimiocistus sahucii*
	salviifolius	CAbP CArn CCCN ERas LRHS WCFE WFar WHCG WWeb XPep
	- 'Avalanche'	EBee MRav WAbe
	- 'Gold Star'	EBee SPoG XPep
*	- 'Ivoire'	XPep
	- 'Prostratus'	ELan LRHS SPhx SPoG WHCG WPGP
*	- 'Sirocco'	XPep
*	- 'Villeveyrac'	XPep
	salviifolius x ***monspeliensis***	see *C.* x *florentinus* Lam.
	x ***sammonsii*** 'Ida'	XPep
	'Silver Pink' misapplied	see *C.* 'Grayswood Pink'
§	***sintenisii***	XPep
	x ***skanbergii*** ♀H3	More than 30 suppliers
*	- 'Akamas'	XPep
	'Snow Fire' ♀H4	CAbP CBgR CCCN CDoC CSBt EBee ENot EPfP LRHS LSRN MAsh MBri MGos NPro SCoo SLPl SPla SPoG SSpi WGer WLeb WSPU XPep
§	x ***stenophyllus***	CWib EBee SPer XPep
	- f. ***albiflorus***	XPep
*	- - 'Mistral'	XPep
*	- 'Elise'	XPep
	symphytifolius	WPGP XPep
§	- subsp. ***leucophyllus***	XPep
	- - MSF 98.019	WPGP
	x ***tephreus***	XPep
	'Thornfield White'	EBee
	'Thrive'	see *C.* x *obtusifolius* 'Thrive'
	tomentosus	see *Helianthemum nummularium* subsp. *tomentosum*
	x ***verguinii***	EBee EWin LHop SDix XPep
	- f. ***albiflorus***	XPep
	- f. ***albiflorus*** misapplied	see *C.* x *dansereaui* 'Portmeirion'
*	- 'Salabert'	XPep
	villosus	see *C. creticus* subsp. *creticus*
	wintonensis	see x *Halimiocistus wintonensis*

Citharexylum (*Verbenaceae*)

	spicatum	CPLG

x *Citrofortunella* (*Rutaceae*)

	sp.	CCCN
	floridana 'Lakeland' (F)	ERea
§	***microcarpa*** (F) ♀H1	CCCN CDoC EMui EPfP ERea MBri NLar SPoG WBVN
§	- 'Tiger' (v/F) ♀H1	EPfP ERea
	- 'Variegata'	see x *C. microcarpa* 'Tiger'
	mitis	see x *C. microcarpa*
	swinglei 'Tavares' (F)	ERea

citron see *Citrus medica*

x *Citroncirus* (*Rutaceae*)

	webberi 'Carrizo'	ERea

Citrullus (*Cucurbitaceae*)

	colocynthis	CArn

Citrus ✿ (*Rutaceae*)

	amblycarpa djeruk lime (F)	ERea

I ***aurantiata*** 'Chinese Citron' (F) **new**	ERea
aurantifolia 'Paduk' (f) **new**	ERea
aurantiifolia (F)	CCCN
- 'Breegold' (F) **new**	SPoG
- Indian lime (F)	ERea
- key lime (F)	CDoC ERea
aurantium 'Bouquet de Fleurs'	CCCN CKob ERea
- var. ***myrtifolia*** 'Chinotto' (F)	ERea
- 'Seville' (F)	ERea
bergamia bergamot	CKob ERea
calamondin	see x *Citrofortunella microcarpa*
'Fukushu'	CCCN EMui
hystrix	CCCN CKob EMui ERea
japonica	see *Fortunella japonica*
'Kulci'	CCCN
kumquat	see *Fortunella margarita*
'La Valette' (F)	CKob EPfP ERea LCro
latifolia (F/S)	CCCN EMui EPfP ERea
limetta	CCCN
- 'Romnya' (f) **new**	ERea
limettoides (F)	CArn ERea
limon (F)	CHEx EPfP ETod LPan MPRe SPoG STrG
- 'Amalfitanum' (f) **new**	ERea
- 'Four Seasons'	CCCN NLar
§ - 'Garey's Eureka' (F)	CDoC CKob EPfP ERea
- 'Genoa' **new**	ERea
- 'Imperial' (F)	ERea
- 'Lemonade' (F)	ERea
- 'Lisbon' (F)	ERea
- 'Mosquito' (v)	CHll
- 'Quatre Saisons'	see *C. limon* 'Garey's Eureka'
- 'Toscana'	EPfP ERea
- 'Variegata' (F/v) ♀H1	CCCN EMui ERea
- 'Villa Franca' (F)	ERea
- 'Yen Ben' (F)	ERea
x ***limonia*** 'Rangpur' (F)	ERea
'Lipo'	CCCN NLar
madurensis	see *Fortunella japonica*
maxima (F)	ERea
medica 'Cidro Digitado'	see *C. medica* var. *digitata*
§ - var. ***digitata*** (F)	CKob EMui ERea
- 'Ethrog' (F)	ERea
- var. ***sarcodactylis***	see *C. medica* var. *digitata*
x ***meyeri***	CHEx ETod
- 'Improved Meyer' (F) **new**	EMui
- 'Meyer' (F) ♀H1	CBcs CCCN CHll CKob EPfP ERea LCro LRHS MJnS NLar SPer
microcarpa Philippine lime	see x *Citrofortunella microcarpa*
mitis	see x *Citrofortunella microcarpa*
x ***nobilis*** Ortanique Group (F)	EPfP
- 'Silver Hill Owari' (F)	ERea
- Tangor Group (F)	ERea
x ***paradisi*** (F)	CCCN MPRe SPoG
- 'Foster' (F)	ERea
- 'Golden Special' (F)	ERea
- 'Marsh' (F)	ERea
- 'Star Ruby' (F/S)	EMui ERea
'Ponderosa' (F)	ERea
'Pursta'	CCCN ERea
reticulata (F)	CCCN MPRe
- Mandarin Group (F)	CDoC
- - 'Clementine' (F)	CDoC ERea
- - 'Encore' (F)	ERea
- Satsuma Group	see *C. unshiu*
sinensis (F)	CCCN ERea LPan SLon SPoG
- 'Egg' (F)	ERea
- 'Jaffa'	see *C. sinensis* 'Shamouti'
- 'Lane Late' (F)	ERea
- 'Malta Blood' (F)	ERea
- 'Moro Blood' (F)	ERea
- 'Navelina' (F/S)	CDoC ERea
- 'Prata' (F)	ERea
- 'Ruby' (F)	ERea
- 'Saint Michael' (F)	ERea
- 'Sanguinelli' (F)	ERea
§ - 'Shamouti' (F)	ERea
- 'Tarocco' (F)	ERea
- 'Thomson' (F)	ERea
- 'Trovita' (F) **new**	ERea
- 'Valencia' (F)	ECot EMui
- 'Valencia Late' (F)	ERea
- 'Washington' (F/S)	EPfP ERea
x ***tangelo*** 'Seminole' (F)	ERea
- 'Ugli' (F)	ERea
§ ***unshiu*** (F)	ERea
- 'Miyagawa'	CCCN ERea
wintersii	see *Microcitrus papuana*

Cladium (*Cyperaceae*)

mariscus	NLar XIsg

Cladothamnus see *Elliottia*

Cladrastis (*Papilionaceae*)

§ ***kentukea***	CArn CBcs CDul CLnd CMCN ELan EPfP IMGH MBlu MBri NLar SHBN SSpi WBVN WNor
§ - 'Perkins Pink'	MBlu MBri SSpi
- 'Rosea'	see *C. kentukea* 'Perkins Pink'
lutea	see *C. kentukea*
sinensis	CBcs CGHE EBee EPfP IDee MBlu SKHP SSpi WPGP WSHC

Clarkia (*Onagraceae*)

* ***repens***	CSpe

Clavinodum (*Poaceae*)

§ ***oedogonatum***	EPla SDry

Claytonia (*Portulacaceae*)

alsinoides	see *C. sibirica*
australasica	see *Neopaxia australasica*
caroliniana	EBee NLar
§ ***perfoliata***	CArn CPLG GPoy ILis WHer
§ ***sibirica***	CAgr CArn CElw EMan LSou WHen
- 'Alba'	CElw WCot WMoo
virginica	EHrv LAma WFar WMoo

Clematis ✿ (*Ranunculaceae*)

B&SWJ 599	WCru
CC 711	CPLG
CC 4427	CPLG MGol
CC 4478	MGol
CC 4513	CPLG MGol
CC 4710	CPLG MGol
BWJ 7630 from China	WCru
BWJ 8169 from China	WCru
WJS 8910 from Japan	WCru
'Abundance' (Vt) ♀H4	CBgR CDoC CElw CRHN CSPN CWCL EPfP ERob ESCh ETho LCro LRHS MBri MRav NBea NHol SBra SDix SHBN SPer SPet SPoG
acuminata var. ***sikkimensis*** B&SWJ 7202	WCru
addisonii	CBcs CSPN CWGN CWoW EBee ERob ESCh NHaw WSHC
aethusifolia	CSPN ERob
afoliata	CBcs CSPN CStu EBee ECou ERob ETho
afoliata x ***forsteri***	ECou
'Aino' (Vt)	ERob
'Ai-Nor' (EL) **new**	ETho

	'Akaishi' (EL)	CWGN EBee ERob ESCh ETho
	akebioides	CPLG LRHS SHBN WCru
	'Akemi' (EL)	ERob
	Alabast = 'Poulala'PBR (EL) ♀H4	CSPN CWoW EBee ERob ESCh ETho MWgw NBea NHaw SBra SCoo SMDP SPoG WBGC
	'Alba Luxurians' (Vt) ♀H4	More than 30 suppliers
	'Albatross'	ENot ERob ESCh
	'Albiflora' (A)	CSPN ECtt ESCh NSti
	'Albina Plena' (A/d)	ESCh ETho SMDP
	'Aleksandrit' (EL)	CWGN ERob NHaw
	'Alice Fisk' (EL)	CSPN ERob ESCh ETho LSRN MSwo NBea NHaw SBra SHBN SPoG WBGC WGor
	'Alionushka' (I) ♀H4	CBgR CElw CRHN CSam EBee ELan ENot EPfP ERob ESCh ETho LRHS LSRN MAsh MBri MGos MWgw NBea NHol SBra SLim SPer SPet SPla SPoG SWCr WBGC WCra
	'Allanah' (LL)	CRHN EPfP ERob ETho LSRN MGos MSwo NHaw SBra SCoo SLim SPoG WBGC WFar
	alpina ♀H4	ECtt EPfP ESCh GKev GSki LCro MBar MDun MRav NHaw NPer SHBN SPlb WBVN WFar
	- 'Albiflora'	see *C. sibirica*
	- 'Columbine White'	see *C.* 'White Columbine'
	- 'Jan Lindmark'	see *C.* 'Jan Lindmark'
I	- 'Odorata'	CSPN ERob LBuc MGos NBea NHaw
I	- 'Pamela Jackman' ♀H4	CDoC CSPN CWSG EBee ELan ESCh LAst LRHS MAsh MDun MGos NBea NCGa NEgg NHol NSti SBod SBra SCoo SDix SLim SPer SPoG SWvt WBGC WFar
	- pink-flowered	GKev
	- subsp. ***sibirica***	see *C. sibirica*
	- 'Stolwijk Gold' **new**	ESCh
	'Alpinist' (LL)	ERob
	alternata	CWGN ESCh ETho
	'Amelia Joan' (Ta)	ERob MWat
	'Ameshisuto' (EL)	ETho
	'Amethyst Beauty' (A)	ERob
	'Anders' (A/d)	ESCh
	'André Devillers'	see *C.* 'Directeur André Devillers'
	'Andromeda' (EL)	CSPN EBee ERob ESCh ETho NHaw WFar
	angustifolia	ETho
	'Anita' (Ta)	ERob ESCh ETho NHaw SBra SLim SPoG
	'Ann Thomson'	EBee
	'Anna' (EL)	ERob ESCh
	'Anna Carolina'	ESCh
	'Anna Herman' (EL)	ERob
	Anna Louise = 'Evithree'PBR (EL) ♀H4	CSPN CWoW EBee ERob ESCh ETho IBal LRHS MBri SBra SCoo SLim SPoG SWCr WBGC
	'Annabel' (EL)	CSPN ERob
	'Annemieke' (Ta)	ERob ESCh MGos SBra
	'Annie Treasure'	ERob
	Anniversary = 'Pynot'PBR (EL)	ENot ERob ESCh LSRN SCoo
	anshunensis	see *C. clarkeana* H.Lev. & Variot
	'Anti' (LL)	ESCh
	'Aotearoa' (LL)	ERob ESCh NHaw
	'Aphrodite'	CRHN ERob ESCh NHaw WBGC
	apiifolia	ERob
	- B&SWJ 4838	WCru
	'Apple Blossom' (Ar) ♀H4	More than 30 suppliers
	'Apulejus' (A)	ESCh
	'Arabella' (I) ♀H4	More than 30 suppliers
	Arctic Queen = 'Evitwo'PBR (EL) ♀H4	CSPN EBee ENot ESCh ETho IBal LCro LRHS LSRN MAsh MBNS NPri SCoo SLim SPer SPoG SWCr WBGC WFar
	armandii	More than 30 suppliers
	- 'Enham Star'	LBuc LRHS MBri MGos
§	- 'Little White Charm'	CSPN ERob MBlu NLar SHBN SPoG
	- 'Meyeniana'	see *C. armandii* 'Little White Charm'
§	- 'Snowdrift'	CBcs CSBt CSPN CSam CWSG ELan EPfP ERob ESCh ETho LCro LRHS MGos MLan NSti SHBN SPer SPoG SRms WBGC WSpi
	x ***aromatica***	CBcs CPrp CSPN CWGN EBee ELan EPfP ERob ESCh ETho LAst LCro LFol LPio LRHS MBNS MRav MWgw NBea NSti SBla SBra SCoo SPoG SWCr WBGC WSpi
§	'Asagasumi' (EL)	ERob ESCh ETho
	'Asao' (EL)	CElw CFir CRHN EBee ELan EPfP ERob ESCh ETho LAst LCro LRHS MGos MRav NBea SCoo SLim SPer SPet SPoG SWCr WBGC WOrn
	'Ascotiensis' (LL)	CBcs CRHN CSPN EBee EPfP ESCh ETho LRHS NBea NHaw NPri SCoo SDix SPer SPoG SWCr WBGC WFar
	'Ashva'	CWGN ESCh ETho
	'Aureolin' (Ta)	CSPN CWSG EPfP ERob ESCh ETho LRHS MBar NHol NPri SBra SCoo SLim SPoG WPGP
	australis	ERob
	Avant-garde = 'Evipo033' **new**	ETho
§	'Bagatelle' (EL)	CRHN CSPN ERob ESCh NHaw SMDP SWCr WBGC WFar WGwG
	'Bal Maiden' (Vt)	CRHN
§	'Ballerina in Blue' (A/d)	ERob ESCh NHaw
	'Ballet Skirt' (A/d) ♀H4	ERob ESCh LRHS MGos NHaw SLim SWCr
	'Bałtyk' (EL)	CSPN ERob ESCh
	'Barbara' (LL)	ESCh ETho MRav NHaw
	'Barbara Dibley' (EL)	CTri CWSG ERob ESCh LRHS MBNS MSwo NBea SBra SCoo SDix SPoG WBGC
	'Barbara Harrington'PBR (LL)	ENot ESCh NHaw WBGC
	'Barbara Jackman' (EL)	CSam EBee ECtt ENot ERob ETho LCro LRHS LSRN MBar MGos MRav MSwo NBea NEgg SBra SCoo SLim SPer SPoG SWCr WBGC WFar WFoF
	'Barbara Wheeler'	ERob
	barbellata	ERob
	'Basil Bartlett' (Fo)	ECou ERob
	'Beata' (LL)	CWGN ESCh NBea
	'Beauty of Richmond' (EL)	CWSG ERob ESCh
	'Beauty of Worcester' (EL)	CFir CSPN CWSG ELan EPfP ESCh ETho LAst LRHS LSRN MBar MSwo MWgw NBea NHaw SBra SCoo SDix SPer SPoG WBGC WFar WWeb
	'Bees' Jubilee' (EL)	More than 30 suppliers
	'Bella' (EL)	EBee ERob ESCh ETho NHaw SMDP
	'Belle Nantaise' (EL)	ERob ESCh LRHS SCoo SPet
	'Belle of Woking' (EL)	CRHN CSPN CWSG EBee ECtt ELan ENot EPfP ERob ESCh ETho LCro LRHS MBar MRav NBea NEgg SBra SCoo SDix SHBN SLim SPet SPoG SWCr WBGC WOrn
	'Benedictus' (EL)	ESCh
	'Bessie Watkinson'	ERob
§	'Beth Currie' (EL)	CSPN ERob ESCh SPoG
	'Betina'	see *C.* 'Red Beetroot Beauty'
	'Betty Corning' (Vt) ♀H4	CRHN CSPN CWGN EBee ELan EPfP ERob ESCh ETho LCro LFol LRHS MBri MGos NBea SBra SCoo SLim SLon SWCr

'Betty Risdon' (EL)	ERob ESCh ETho LRHS
'Big Bird' (A/d)	ERob ESCh
'Bill MacKenzie' (Ta) ♀H4	More than 30 suppliers
Black Madonna	see *C.* 'Czarna Madonna'
'Black Prince' (Vt)	CRHN CWGN ELan ERob ESCh ETho LRHS NHaw NLar SBra WBGC
'Black Tea' (LL)	ERob ESCh NBPN NHaw
§ 'Błękitny Anioł' (LL) ♀H4	CElw CRHN CSPN CWoW ERob ESCh ETho GMac LRHS MGos MWgw NBea NLar NPri SBra SCoo SPer SPet SPoG SWCr WBGC WFar
Blue Angel	see *C.* Błękitny Anioł'
'Blue Belle' (Vt)	CPou CRHN ELan LCro LRHS NBea NSti SBra SMDP SPet SPoG SWCr WBGC WFar
'Blue Bird' (A/d)	CBcs CWCL CWSG EBee ECtt ESCh LCro MWgw NBea NCGa SLim SPer SPoG
'Blue Boy' (I)	see *C.* x *diversifolia* 'Blue Boy' (I)
'Blue Boy' (L/P)	see *C.* 'Elsa Späth'
'Blue Dancer' (A)	CElw EPfP ERob ESCh EShb ETho IBal MGos NBea SPet SWCr WBGC
'Blue Eclipse' (A)	CSPN CWGN ERob ESCh LRHS MBri NHaw SMDP WBGC
'Blue Eyes' (EL)	CSPN EBee ERob ESCh NHaw
'Blue Gem' (EL)	ERob SPoG
'Blue Light'^{PBR} (EL/d)	CSPN ELan ERob ESCh ETho MGos NLar SBra WFar
Blue Moon = 'Evirin'^{PBR} (EL)	ENot ESCh ETho LAst LRHS LSRN MBNS MWgw NBea NLar NPri SBra SCoo SWCr WFar
Blue Pirouette = 'Zobluepi'^{PBR} (I)	CWGN EBrs ESCh ETho NLar SBra SMDP SWCr WBGC
Blue Rain	see *C.* 'Sinii Dozhd'
'Blue Ravine' (EL)	EBee EPfP ERob ESCh MGos NLar SCoo WBGC
'Blue Sensation' (I) **new**	ESCh
'Blue Stream' (A)	ESCh
'Blue Tapers' (A)	ERob ESCh NHaw
§ 'Blushing Ballerina' (A/d)	ERob ESCh
§ x ***bonstedtii*** 'Campanile' (H)	ERob ESCh NBir
- 'Crépuscule' (H)	CMdw ERob ESCh SMDP SRms WCot
'Boskoop Beauty' (EL)	ERob ESCh NHaw
'Bowl of Beauty' (Ar)	ERob MGos
'Bracebridge Star' (EL)	ECtt ERob ESCh NBea
brachyura	ERob
'Bravo' (Ta)	ERob
'Brocade' (Vt)	CRHN CSPN ERob ESCh ETho SMDP
'Broughton Bride'	CSPN CWGN ERob ESCh ETho
'Broughton Star' (M/d) ♀H4	More than 30 suppliers
'Brunette' (A)	CSPN EBee ELan EPfP ERob ESCh ETho MAsh MGos NBPN NHaw SHBN SMDP SPoG SWCr
buchananiana Finet & Gagnep.	see *C. rehderiana*
buchananiana DC.	CPLG EBee ERob
- B&SWJ 8333a	WCru
'Buckland Beauty' (V)	ESCh ETho
'Buckland Longshanks' (H)	SMDP
'Burford Bell' (V)	ERob
'Burford Princess' (Vt)	ERob NHaw
I 'Burford Variety' (Ta)	ERob ESCh
'Burford White' (A)	CSPN EBee EPfP ERob NLar
'Burma Star' (EL)	CElw CWGN EPfP ERob ESCh ETho NBea NHaw SMDP
'C.W. Dowman' (EL)	ERob ETho
'Caerulea Luxurians' (Vt)	CRHN CWGN ERob ESCh NHaw WSHC
calycina	see *C. cirrhosa* var. *balearica*

§ ***campaniflora***	CMea CRHN CSPN ERob EShb ETho NBea NWCA SDix SMDP SPoG WPGP
- 'Lisboa' (Vt)	ERob
'Campanile'	see *C.* x *bonstedtii* 'Campanile'
'Candida' (EL)	ESCh
'Candleglow' (A)	CElw CSPN EBee MBri SMDP
'Candy Stripe'	EBee ERob ESCh SCoo SLim WBGC
'Capitaine Thuilleaux'	see *C.* 'Souvenir du Capitaine Thuilleaux'.
'Cardinal Wyszynski'	see *C.* Kardynał Wyszyński'
'Carmencita' (Vt)	CRHN CSPN EBee ERob ESCh ETho NBea NHaw SBra SCoo SPet WBGC WFar
'Carnaby' (EL)	CSPN CWSG EBee ELan EPfP ERob ESCh ETho LAst LRHS MBar MBri MGos NBea SBra SCoo SLim SPoG SWCr WBGC WPGP
'Carnival Queen'	CSPN CWSG ERob ESCh
'Caroline' (LL)	CSPN CWGN EBee ERob ESCh ETho NBea NHaw SMDP
'Caroline Lloyd' (Vt)	ERob
x ***cartmanii*** hort. 'Avalanche'^{PBR} (Fo/m) ♀H3	CSPN ELan ERob ESCh ETho GBin LBuc LRHS MGos NLar NPri SBla SCoo SHBN SLim SPer SPoG WCot
- 'Joe' (Fo/m)	More than 30 suppliers
- 'Joe' x ***marmoraria*** (Fo)	ECho MGos
- 'Snow Valley'^{PBR} (Fo)	SBla
- 'White Abundance'^{PBR} (Fo/f)	ESCh ETho NLar SBla SLim SPoG
x ***cartmanii*** hort. x ***petriei*** (Fo)	ECho
Cezanne = 'Evipo023'^{PBR}	ETho LBuc
'Chacewater' (Vt)	CRHN
'Chalcedony' (EL)	CSPN CWGN ERob ESCh ETho MGos SBra
'Charissima' (EL)	CBcs CSPN CSam CWGN EPfP ERob ETho MGos SCoo SPet WBGC WFar
'Charlie Brown'	ERob
chiisanensis	CSPN ERob NEgg WBGC
- B&SWJ 4560	WCru
- B&SWJ 8706	WCru
- 'Lemon Bells' (A)	ELan LRHS MAsh SCoo SPoG SWCr
- 'Love Child' (A)	CElw CSPN EBee ELan ERob ESCh ETho MBlu SLim SMDP SPer WCot
chinensis misapplied	see *C. terniflora*
chinensis Osbeck	ERob
- RWJ 10042	WCru
Chinook = 'Evipo013'^{PBR}	ESCh LRHS MAsh WBGC
'Christian Steven' (LL)	CSPN ERob ESCh
'Christine'	LCro
chrysantha	see *C. tangutica*
- var. ***paucidentata***	see *C. hilariae*
chrysocoma misapplied	see *C. spooneri*
N ***chrysocoma*** Franch.	EPfP ERob MBar NHol SMDP WCru WSpi
- ACE 1093	CPou
- B&L 12237	NBea
'Cicciolina' (Vt)	ERob ETho NHaw
cirrhosa	CTri ELan LRHS MAsh MCot MGos SArc SWCr
§ - var. ***balearica***	More than 30 suppliers
- 'Ourika Valley'	EBee ERob ESCh ETho MAsh NLar SMDP SWCr WFar
- var. ***purpurascens*** 'Freckles' ♀H3	More than 30 suppliers
- - 'Jingle Bells'	CRHN EBee EPfP ERob ESCh ETho LCro LRHS MAsh NHol SBra SCoo SLim SPoG SWCr WFar WSpi
- - 'Lansdowne Gem'	CBgR CSPN CWGN CWib SMDP WSpi
- subsp. ***semitriloba***	ERob
- 'Wisley Cream' ♀H3	More than 30 suppliers

	'Citra'	see *C.* 'Claudius'
	'Claire de Lune'	EBee ENot WBGC
	clarkeana misapplied	see *C. urophylla* 'Winter Beauty'
§	***clarkeana*** H. Lév. & Vaniot	ETho
§	'Claudius' (A)	EBee ERob ESCh SMDP WSHC
	'Clochette Pride' (A/d)	ERob ESCh
	coactilis	ERob
	'Colette Deville' (EL)	ERob
	columbiana	ERob
§	- var. ***tenuiloba***	SBla
	- - 'Ylva' (A)	WAbe
	'Columbine' (A)	CWSG EBee ETho MBar MSwo NBea NHol SBra SDix SLim SPer SPoG WBGC
	'Columella' (A)	ERob ESCh ETho NHaw NLar
	'Comtesse de Bouchaud' (LL) ΨH4	More than 30 suppliers
	confusa HWJK 2200	WCru
	connata	ERob ESCh GQui SMDP
	- GWJ 9386	WCru
	- HWJCM 132	WCru
	aff. ***connata*** GWJ 9431 from West Bengal	WCru
	- HWJK 2176 from Nepal	WCru
	'Constance' (A) ΨH4	CElw CRHN CSPN CWoW EBee EPfP ERob ESCh ETho LCro LRHS NBea NHaw NSti SBra SCoo SPer SPet SRms SWCr WBGC WBor WPGP
	'Continuity' (M)	CWGN EBee ERob MAsh SDix SLim SPla
	'Corona' (EL)	CSPN ELan EPfP ERob ETho LAst LRHS MAsh MBar NBea NHaw SBra SCoo SPoG SWCr WBGC WFar
	'Corry' (Ta)	ERob ESCh NLar
	'Côte d'Azur' (H)	EBrs ERob MCCP SPer WPtf
	'Cotton Candy'	ERob
	'Countess of Lovelace' (EL)	CBcs CSPN CWSG EBee ELan EPfP ERob ESCh ETho LRHS MAsh MBar MBri MGos MRav NBea NEgg SBra SCoo SDix SLim SPer SPet SPoG SWCr WBGC WFar
	County Park hybrids (Fo)	ECou
	'Cragside' (A)	ETho SGar
	crassifolia B&SWJ 6700	WCru
§	'Crimson King' (LL)	ERob ESCh ETho NHaw WGor
	'Crinkle' (M) **new**	ESCh SMDP
§	***crispa***	CElw CPou CSPN CWoW ERob ESCh NBea WSHC
*	- 'Cylindrica'	ERob
§	Crystal Fountain = 'Evipo038'^{PBR} (EL)	ESCh ETho LCro LRHS NPri SCoo SPoG SWCr WBGC
	x ***cylindrica***	CSPN EBee ESCh
§	'Czarna Madonna' (EL)	ERob
	'Danae' (Vt)	CRHN ERob
	'Daniel Deronda' (EL) ΨH4	CDoC CSPN CWSG ECtt ELan ENot ERob ESCh ETho LCro LRHS LSRN MGos MRav MWgw NBea SBra SCoo SDix SHBN SLim SPet SPoG SWCr WBGC WFar WWeb
	'Darius' (EL) **new**	ESCh
	'Dark Secret' (A)	CSPN EBee EPfP ERob MAsh MBri
	'Dawn' (EL)	CCCN CSPN ERob ESCh ETho LRHS MAsh NBea SBra SCoo SLim SPoG SWCr WBGC
	'Débutante' (EL)	ESCh NHaw
	'Denny's Double' (EL/d)	CSPN CWGN CWSG ERob ESCh ETho MAsh
	'Diana' (LL)	ERob ESCh ETho
	dioica F&M 100 **new**	WPGP
	dioscoreifolia	see *C. terniflora*
§	'Directeur André Devillers' (EL)	ERob
§	x ***diversifolia***	CElw CRHN EBee ESCh LRHS MBNS MGos MSte NHaw NHol SBra SDix SGar SHBN SPer SPet WSpi
	- 'Amy' (I)	ERob
§	- 'Blue Boy' (I)	CBgR CElw CRHN CSPN CSam EBee EPfP ERob ESCh MGos NHaw SBra SPet
	- 'Floris V' (I)	ERob ESCh LPio NLar SHar
	- 'Heather Herschell' (I)	CBgR CElw CRHN CSPN EBee ERob ESCh NHaw NLar SBra SMDP SPet WBGC
§	- 'Hendersonii' (I)	CPrp CSam EBee ELan EPfP ERob ESCh ETho GSki LAst LHop LPio LRHS MRav MSwo MWgw NBea NBir NHol NSti SDix SLim SPer SPoG SWat WBGC WCra WSpi
	- 'Lauren' (I)	ERob
§	- 'Olgae' (I)	CPLG CSPN ESCh ETho NBea SBra SMDP
	'Docteur Le Bêle' (LL)	ERob
	'Doctor Penelope' (M)	ESCh
	'Doctor Ruppel' (EL)	More than 30 suppliers
	'Doggy' (Vt)	ERob
	'Dominika' (LL)	CSPN CWGN ERob ESCh ETho NHaw
	'Dorath'	ERob ESCh
	'Dorota' (EL)	ERob
	'Dorothy Tolver' (EL)	ERob ESCh ETho
	'Dorothy Walton'	see *C.* 'Bagatelle'
	'Double Cross' **new**	ECou
	'Dubysa'	ESCh
	'Duchess of Albany' (T)	CSPN CTri CWSG CWib EBee ELan EPfP ESCh ETho IBal LAst LCro LRHS LSRN MBar NBea NHol NSti SBra SGar SHBN SLim SPer SPet SWCr WBGC WFar
	'Duchess of Edinburgh' (EL)	More than 30 suppliers
	'Duchess of Sutherland' (EL)	ERob ESCh LRHS MGos NHaw SDix SPet WBGC
	'Dulcie'	NHaw
	x ***durandii*** ΨH4	CBcs CRHN CSPN EBee ELan ENot EPfP ESCh ETho LRHS LSRN MBar MBri MRav NBea NHol NSti SBra SCoo SDix SLim SPer SPla SPoG SWCr WBGC WFar WSpi
	'Dusky Star' (M)	CWGN EKen ESCh
	'Early Sensation' (Fo/f)	More than 30 suppliers
	'East Malling' (M)	ERob ESCh NHaw
	'Edith' (EL) ΨH4	ECtt EPfP ERob ESCh ETho NBea NHaw WGor
	'Edomurasaki' (EL)	ERob ESCh ETho
	'Edouard Desfossé' (EL)	ERob ESCh
	'Edward Prichard'	CSPN EBee EPfP ERob ESCh ETho MAvo MWea NBea NHaw SBra SMDP
	'Eetika' (LL)	ERob ESCh ETho
	'Ekstra' (LL)	EBee ERob ESCh ETho
	'Eleanor' (Fo/f)	ECou
	Eleanor of Guildford = 'Notpy'^{PBR} (EL)	ENot ERob ESCh
	'Elfin' (Fo/v)	ECou
	'Elizabeth' (M) ΨH4	More than 30 suppliers
§	'Elsa Späth' (EL)	More than 30 suppliers
	'Elten' (M)	CSPN CWGN ERob ESCh
	'Elvan' (Vt)	CRHN ERob ESCh NHaw NLar SPet
	'Emajõgi' (LL)	ESCh
	'Emerald Stars'	ESCh
	'Emilia Plater' (Vt)	CRHN CSPN ERob ESCh ETho NBea NHaw
	Empress = 'Evipo011' **new**	LRHS
	'Empress of India' (EL)	ERob ESCh
	'Entel' (Vt)	CWGN ERob ETho NHaw

	'Erik' (A)	ESCh
	x ***eriostemon***	see *C.* x *diversifolia*
	'Ernest Markham' (LL) ♀H4	More than 30 suppliers
	'Esperanto' (LL)	EBee ESCh SMDP
	'Essex Star'	ECou
	'Etoile de Malicorne' (EL)	ERob ESCh WGor
	'Etoile de Paris' (EL)	ERob ESCh
	Etoile Nacrée	see *C.* 'Sakurahime'
	'Etoile Rose' (Vt)	CRHN CSPN CTri CWoW ELan EPfP ERob ESCh ETho LAst LRHS LSRN MAsh MRav MWgw NBea NHol SBra SCoo SDix SLim SPer SPoG SWCr WBGC WFar WPGP WSHC
	'Etoile Violette' (Vt) ♀H4	More than 30 suppliers
	'Europa' (EL)	ERob
	'Eva' (LL)	ERob ESCh
	Evening Star = 'Evista'PBR	EPfP ERob SPoG WFar
	'Eximia'	see *C.* 'Ballerina in Blue'
	'Fair Rosamond' (EL)	EBee EPfP ERob ESCh LRHS NBea NHaw SDix SPoG WBGC
	'Fairy' (Fo/f)	ECou
	Fairy BluePBR	see *C.* Crystal Fountain
	'Fairy Queen' (EL)	ERob ESCh ETho
	fargesii var. ***souliei***	see *C. potaninii* var. *potaninii*
	x ***fargesioides***	see *C.* 'Paul Farges'
	fasciculiflora	CMHG CRHN CSPN ERob IClo IDee LRHS SMDP SSpi
	- L 657	WCru WPGP
	'Fascination'PBR (I)	CWGN EBrs EPfP ESCh ETho LRHS NHaw SBra SMDP
	fauriei	ERob WSHC
	finetiana misapplied	see *C. paniculata* J.G. Gmel.
	'Firefly' (EL)	ERob ESCh MGos
	'Fireworks' (EL)	CSPN CWGN CWoW EBee ECtt ENot EPfP ESCh ETho LAst LCro LRHS LSRN MAsh MBri MGos MRav NBea NPri SBra SPoG SWCr WBGC WFoF WGor
	'Flamingo' (EL)	CWSG ERob
	flammula	More than 30 suppliers
	- var. ***flavescens***	ERob
	- 'Ithaca' (F/v)	ERob
	- 'Rubra Marginata'	see *C.* x *triternata* 'Rubromarginata'
§	'Floral Feast' (A/d)	CSPN ESCh NBea
	'Floralia'	see *C.* 'Floral Feast'
	florida	CSPN CWGN ERob ESCh
	- 'Bicolor'	see *C. florida* var. *sieboldiana*
	- var. ***flore-pleno*** (d)	CFir CSPN EBee ELan EPfP ESCh ETho LAst LCro LRHS MAsh NBea NEgg NHol SBra SHBN SPla SPoG SWCr WCot WFar
	- Pistachio = 'Evirida'PBR (LL)	CSPN CWGN EBee EMil EPfP ESCh ETho IBal LBuc LCro MAsh MBNS NLar SBra SLim SMDP SPer SRkn SWCr WFar
§	- var. ***sieboldiana*** (d)	More than 30 suppliers
	- 'Thorncroft' new	ETho
	foetida	CBcs CSPN
	foetida x 'Lunar Lass' (Fo)	ECho ECou
	foetida x ***petriei***	ECho ECou
	'Fond Memories' (EL)	ETho
	forrestii	see *C. napaulensis*
§	***forsteri***	CBcs CSPN ERob ESCh ETho IClo IDee LFol SBra WPGP
	'Foxtrot' (Vt)	CRHN ERob ESCh
	'Foxy' (A) ♀H4	CBcs ERob NBea NHaw SLon WGob
	'Fragrant Joy' (Fo/m)	ECou ESCh
	'Fragrant Spring' (M)	CSPN CWGN ECtt ERob ETho MGos NHaw NLar SBod SBra SMDP WFar
	'Frances Rivis' (A) ♀H4	More than 30 suppliers
	'Francesca' (A)	ESCh MGos
	'Frankie' (A) ♀H4	CSPN ELan ENot ERob ESCh ETho LCro LRHS SCoo SLim SWCr WBGC
	Franziska Marie = 'Evipo008' (EL)	ESCh LRHS MAsh NPri WBGC
	'Frau Mikiko' (EL)	ERob ESCh ETho
	'Frau Susanne' (EL)	ETho
	'Freda' (M) ♀H4	More than 30 suppliers
	'Fryderyk Chopin' (EL)	CSPN ERob ESCh ETho NHaw NLar
	'Fuji-musume' (EL) ♀H4	CSPN CWGN ERob ESCh ETho NBea NHaw NLar SBra SLim SPet SWCr WBGC WFar
	'Fujinami' (EL)	ERob
	'Fukuzono' (I) new	ETho EVal WBGC
	fusca misapplied	see *C. japonica*
	fusca Turcz.	CWoW ERob WIvy WSHC
	- dwarf	CWGN
§	- var. ***fusca***	ESCh ETho
	- var. ***kamtschatica***	see *C. fusca* Turcz. var. *fusca*
	fusijamana	ERob
	'Fuyu-no-tabi' (EL)	ESCh ETho
	'G. Steffner' (A)	ERob ESCh
	'Gabrielle' (EL)	CSPN ERob ESCh NHaw
	Gazelle = 'Evipo014'PBR	ESCh LRHS MAsh WBGC
	'Gekkyuuden'	ERob
	'Gemini'	ERob ESCh
	'Generał Sikorski' (EL)	CBcs CMac CRHN CSPN CWSG ECtt ELan EPfP ESCh ETho LAst LCro LRHS LSRN MBri MGos NBea SBra SCoo SDix SHBN SLim SPer SPet SPoG SWCr WBGC
	gentianoides	ERob ETho WAbe WCot
	'Georg' (A/d)	ERob ESCh MGos NHaw
	'Georg Ots' (LL)	ERob ESCh
	Giant Star = 'Gistar'PBR (M)	CWGN ESCh LRHS MAsh MGos NCGa NLar NPer SMDP
	'Gillian Blades' (EL) ♀H4	CRHN CSPN CWoW EBee ELan ENot EPfP ERob ESCh ETho LAst LCro LRHS MAsh NBea NHaw NPri SBra SCoo SLim SPer SPet SPoG SWCr WBGC
§	'Gipsy Queen' (LL) ♀H4	CBcs CSPN CWSG EBee ECtt ELan ENot EPfP ERob ESCh ETho LCro LRHS LSRN MAsh MBar MRav MSwo NBea SBra SDix SHBN SLim SPet SPoG SWCr WBGC WFar
	'Girenas' new	ESCh
	'Gladys Picard' (EL)	ERob ESCh NHaw WFar
	glauca Turcz.	see *C. intricata*
	'Glynderek' (EL)	ERob ESCh
	'Golden Harvest' (Ta)	ERob ESCh NHol NLar WFar
	Golden Tiara = 'Kugotia'PBR (Ta) ♀H4	CSPN CWGN ERob ESCh ETho LRHS MBri MGos MWgw NBea NLar NPri SBra SPer WCot
	'Gornoe Ozero' (EL)	ERob
	'Gothenburg' (M)	EBee ERob ESCh NBea NHaw WFar
	gouriana	ERob
	- subsp. ***lishanensis*** B&SWJ 292	WCru
	'Grace' (Ta)	CRHN CSPN EBee ERob ESCh ETho NHaw NLar SMDP
	gracilifolia	ERob ESCh
	- var. ***dissectifolia***	ERob
I	'Grandiflora' (F)	LCro WFar
	'Grandiflora Sanguinea' Johnson	see *C.* 'Södertälje'
	'Grandiflora Sanguinea' (Vt)	ERob
	grata misapplied	see *C.* x *jouiniana*
	grata Wall.	CElw CPLG CWoW ERob
	- B&SWJ 6774	WCru
	'Gravetye Beauty' (T)	More than 30 suppliers
§	'Grażyna'	ESCh

'Green Velvet' (Fo/m)	ECou
grewiiflora	SMDP
- B&SWJ 2956	WCru
'Guernsey Cream' (EL)	CFir CSPN CSam CWSG EBee EMil ENot ESCh ETho LAst LCro LRHS MAsh MBri MWgw NBea NEgg SBra SCoo SDix SHBN SLim SPoG SWCr WBGC WFar WWeb
'Guiding Star' (EL)	ERob ETho NHaw
'H.F. Young' (EL)	CSPN CWSG EBee ELan EPfP ERob ESCh ETho LRHS MBar MBri MGan MGos MWgw NBea SBra SCoo SDix SHBN SLim SPer SPet WBGC
'Hagley Hybrid' (LL)	More than 30 suppliers
'Hainton Ruby' (EL)	ERob
'Haku-ōkan' (EL)	CSPN CWoW EBee EPfP ERob ESCh ETho LRHS MAsh NBea NLar SBra SCoo SLim SPoG WBGC
'Hakuree' (I)	ESCh ETho SMDP
'Hanaguruma' (EL)	CSPN ERob ESCh ETho NBea NHaw SBra WFar
'Hanajima' (I)	ERob ESCh ETho SBla
'Hania'	CWGN ESCh ETho
'Happy Anniversary' (EL) **new**	ETho
Harlow Carr = 'Evipo004'PBR	CWGN ESCh ETho LRHS MBri SBra SCoo SLim SWCr WBGC
'Harmony' (EL/d)	ERob ESCh
'Haru Ichiban' (EL)	ETho
'Haruyama' (EL)	ESCh
Havering hybrids (Fo)	ECou
'Helen Cropper' (EL)	ERob ESCh ETho MAsh
'Helios' (Ta)	CSPN EPfP ERob ESCh ETho LRHS MGos NBea NSti SBra SCoo SPoG WGwG
'Helsingborg' (A) ♀H4	CBcs CSPN EBee ECtt ELan EPfP ERob ESCh ETho LAst LCro LRHS MAsh NBea NEgg NHol NPri NSti SBra SCoo SPla SPoG SWCr WBGC
hendersonii Henderson	see *C.* x *diversifolia* 'Hendersonii'
hendersonii Koch	see *C.* x *diversifolia* 'Hendersonii'
hendersonii Stand.	see *C.* x *diversifolia*
I 'Hendersonii' (I)	CSam ERob ETho LRHS LSRN MSte NHol SPla SWCr WBGC
'Hendersonii Rubra' (Ar)	CSPN NLar
'Hendryetta'PBR (I)	CWGN EBrs EPfP ESCh ETho SBra SMDP SPoG SWCr WBGC
henryi	CDul ENot LSRN
- B&SWJ 3402	WCru
'Henryi' (EL) ♀H4	More than 30 suppliers
henryi var. ***morii*** B&SWJ 1668	WCru
heracleifolia	CBcs CBgR CFir CPou CWCL ECtt ESCh GAbr GSki MAsh NHol NLar SWCr WMoo WPer
- Alan BloomPBR	see *C. tubulosa* Alan Bloom
I - 'Alba' (H)	LPio
- 'Blue Dwarf'	ESCh ETho MGos SMDP
- 'Campanile'	see *C.* x *bonstedtii* 'Campanile'
- 'Cassandra'	EMar EPfP ESCh ETho MAvo NHol NLar NOrc SBla SMDP
- 'China Purple'	CBgR CPen CSpe EBee ERob ESCh IBal LPio MBNS MHer MNrw NLar WHoo WPtf
- var. ***davidiana***	see *C. tubulosa*
- 'Pink Dwarf'	CWGN ESCh ETho NLar SMDP
- 'Purple Princess' **new**	ESCh MAvo SPoG
- 'Roundway Blue Bird'	ESCh LHop LRHS NHaw
'Herbert Johnson' (EL)	ESCh
hexapetala misapplied	see *C. recta* subsp. *recta* var. *lasiosepala*
hexapetala Forster	see *C. forsteri*
hexasepala	see *C. forsteri*
'Hikarugenji' (EL)	CSPN ERob ESCh NHaw
§ ***hilariae***	ERob
hirsutissima	WIvy
- var. ***scottii***	EBee ERob WIvy
'Honora' (LL)	CSPN CWGN ERob ESCh SBra SCoo
'Horn of Plenty' (EL)	ERob ESCh LRHS NBea NHaw SBra SPoG
'Huldine' (LL) ♀H4	CBcs CElw CRHN CSPN CSam EBee ELan EPfP ESCh ETho LAst LCro LRHS MBar MRav NBea NEgg NSti SBra SDix SLim SPer SPet SPoG SWCr WAbe WBGC WWlt
'Huvi' (LL)	CWGN ERob ESCh ETho NHaw
'Hybrida Sieboldii' (EL)	CRHN EBee ERob ESCh SCoo WCot
Hyde Hall = 'Evipo009'PBR	CWGN ESCh ETho IBal LRHS MAsh MBri SBra SLim SWCr WBGC
'Hythe Egret' (Fo)	ECho ESCh LTwo
'Hythe Honeybells' (Fo) **new**	LTwo
I am a Little Beauty = 'Zolibe' (Vt) **new**	ESCh NHaw
I am Red Robin = 'Zorero' **new**	ETho
ianthina	ERob ESCh WPGP WSHC
- var. ***ianthina***	ETho
- var. ***kuripoensis***	ERob
- - B&SWJ 700	WCru
Ice Blue = 'Evipo003' (Prairie Series) **new**	ETho MAsh NPri WBGC
'Ice Queen'	ESCh LRHS MAsh
'Ideal' (EL)	ERob
'Ilka' (EL)	ERob ESCh
'Imperial' (EL)	ERob ESCh ETho NHaw
indivisa	see *C. paniculata* J.G. Gmel.
'Inglewood' (EL)	ERob
Inspiration = 'Zoin'PBR (I)	CSPN EBrs ELan ERob ESCh ETho MGos NLar SBra SCoo SMDP
integrifolia	More than 30 suppliers
I - 'Alba'	CBcs CElw CSPN CWoW EBee ECtt ESCh ETho GBuc LAst LHop LPio LRHS LSRN MBNS MDKP MSte NBea NBir NHaw NSti SBra SCoo SLim SPer SPet SPoG WCra
- 'Budapest'	ERob ESCh NHaw
- 'Cora' **new**	CWGN
- 'Hendersonii' Koch	see *C.* x *diversifolia* 'Hendersonii'
- var. ***latifolia***	ERob ESCh
- 'Olgae'	see *C.* x *diversifolia* 'Olgae'
- 'Ozawa's Blue'	CPrp EBee ESCh ETho LPio MBNS MSte NSti
- white	see *C. integrifolia* 'Alba'
§ ***intricata***	CBcs CPLG CSPN EBee EPfP ERob MGos
- 'Harry Smith' (Ta)	ERob ESCh
'Iola Fair' (EL)	CSPN ERob ESCh ETho NHaw
'Ishobel' (EL)	ERob
ispahanica	CWoW
'Iubileinyi-70' (LL)	EBee ERob ESCh
'Ivan Olsson' (EL)	CSPN ERob ESCh ETho
'Jackmanii' (LL) ♀H4	CBcs CMac CRHN CTri EBee ENot EPfP ERob ESCh ETho LCro LRHS LSRN MAsh MGos NBea NEgg NWea SBra SCoo SLim SPer SPet SPoG SWCr WBGC WBor WFar
'Jackmanii Alba' (EL)	ELan EPfP ERob ESCh ETho LAst LRHS LSRN MBar NBea SCoo SLim SPet SPoG SWCr WBGC
'Jackmanii Rubra' (EL)	ERob ESCh ETho NBea SBra
'Jackmanii Superba' misapplied	see *C.* 'Gipsy Queen'
'Jackmanii Superba' ambig. (LL)	More than 30 suppliers
'Jacqueline du Pré' (A) ♀H4	CBcs CSPN EBee ELan EPfP ERob ESCh ETho MGos NBea NHaw SBra SMDP SPet

	'Jacqui' (M/d)	ERob ESCh ETho LRHS MGos NHaw NLar SBra SPoG
	'James Mason' (EL)	CSPN ESCh ETho NBea NHaw
	'Jan Fopma' (I)PBR	CWGN ESCh ETho NBPN SMDP
§	'Jan Lindmark' (A/d)	CBcs EBee ERob ESCh ETho LCro LRHS MGos NBea NHol NLar NSti SCoo SMDP SWCr WBGC WFar
§	'Jan Paweł II' (EL)	CWSG CWoW EBee ECtt ELan EPfP ESCh ETho LRHS NBea SBod SBra SCoo SPer SPet SPoG WFar
	'Janina' **new**	CWGN
	'Jānis Ruplēns Number 1'	ERob
§	***japonica***	CSPN ERob ESCh ETho NHaw SMDP
§	– var. ***obvallata*** B&SWJ 8900	WCru
	'Jasper'	ERob ESCh
	'Jefferies' (Ar)	ESCh NLar
	'Jenny Caddick' (Vt)	CSPN ERob ESCh ETho NHaw SMDP
	'Jenny Keay' (M/d)	CWGN EBee ERob ESCh ETho MGos NHaw NLar SMDP SPoG
	'Jerzy Popiełuszko' **new**	ETho
	'Jim Hollis' (EL)	ERob
	'Joan Baker' (Vt)	ERob
	'Joan Gray' (EL)	ERob ESCh
	'Joan Picton' (EL)	CWSG ESCh MAsh NBea SBra
	'John Gould Veitch' (EL)	ERob
	'John Gudmundsson' (EL)	ERob ESCh
	'John Huxtable' (LL) ♀H4	CDoC CRHN EPfP ERob ESCh ETho LRHS NBea NHaw NPri SBra SLim SPoG SWCr WBGC WGor
	John Paul II	see *C.* 'Jan Paweł II'
	'John Treasure' (Vt)	CBgR CRHN ETho NHaw WBGC
	'John Warren' (EL)	CWSG EBee ERob ESCh ETho LRHS MAsh NHaw SBra SCoo SPer WBGC WFar
	'Jorma' (LL)	ERob
	Josephine = 'Evijohill'PBR (EL) ♀H4	CSPN EBee ENot EPfP ESCh ETho IBal LAst LCro LRHS LSRN MAsh MBNS NLar NPri SBra SCoo SPer SPoG SRkn SWCr WBGC WFar
§	x ***jouiniana***	CBgR CPLG EBee ERob MBlu MRav MWya NHol WGwG WSHC
	– 'Chance' (H)	ESCh NHaw
	'Julka' (EL)	ESCh ETho NHaw
	'June Pyne'	ESCh ETho LRHS NPri
	'Justa' (Vt)	CWGN ESCh
	'Juuli' (I)	ERob ESCh
	'Kaaru' (LL)	CRHN CSPN ERob ESCh ETho WBGC
	'Kacper' (EL)	CSPN ESCh ETho MGos NHaw
	'Kaiu' (V)	ERob ESCh WBGC
§	'Kakio' (EL)	CElw EBee ENot ERob ESCh ETho LAst LCro LSRN MGos NBea SBra SPer SPet SWCr WBGC WFar
	'Kalina' (EL)	ERob ESCh ETho NHaw
	'Kamilla' (EL)	CWGN ERob ESCh
§	'Kardynał Wyszyński' (EL)	EBee ERob ESCh ETho MGos NBea SBra SCoo SMDP
	'Karin' **new**	ESCh
§	'Kasmu' (Vt)	ERob ESCh
	'Kasugayama' (EL)	ERob
	'Katharina' (EL)	ERob ESCh
	'Kathleen Dunford' (EL)	ERob ESCh LAst LRHS LSRN NBea NHaw SCoo SMDP WBGC
	'Kathleen Wheeler' (EL)	ERob SDix
	'Kathryn Chapman' (Vt)	CRHN ESCh
	'Keith Richardson' (EL)	ERob ESCh
	'Ken Donson' (EL) ♀H4	CWoW EBee EPfP ERob ESCh MGos SCoo
	'Kermesina' (Vt) ♀H4	More than 30 suppliers
	'Ketu' (LL)	ERob
	'Kiev' (Vt)	ERob ESCh NHaw
	'Killifreth' (Vt)	CRHN
	'King Edward VII' (EL)	EBee EPfP ERob ESCh LRHS NBea SWCr WGor
	'King George V' (LL)	ERob ESCh
	'Kinokawa' (EL)	ERob
	'Kiri Te Kanawa' (EL)	CSPN EBee ERob ESCh ETho LAst LSRN NBea NHaw SBra SMDP
	kirilovii	ERob ESCh
	'Kirimäe' (LL)	ERob ESCh
	'Kjell' (EL)	ERob ESCh
	'Klaara' (EL)	ERob
	'Kommerei' (LL)	ERob ESCh ETho NHaw
	'Königskind' (EL)	CSPN ERob ESCh ETho NBea
	koreana	CElw ERob NHol SMDP WCru WSHC
	– 'Berry Red' **new**	CWGN
	– var. ***lutea***	EBee GGar SMDP WCru
	– 'Yellow Jester' **new**	CWGN
	'Kosmicheskaia Melodiia' (LL)	CSPN ERob ESCh
	'Kotkas' (LL)	ERob
	'Kuba' (LL)	ERob ESCh
	'Kunpuh' **new**	ESCh
	kweichowensis	ETho
	'Küllus' (LL)	CWGN ERob ESCh ETho
	ladakhiana	CSPN CWoW ESCh ETho GQui NBea NBir NHaw SMDP WPtf
	'Lady Betty Balfour' (LL)	CElw CSPN CWSG ERob ESCh ETho EVal LRHS MBNS SBra SCoo SDix SGar SPet SPoG WBGC WFar
	'Lady Bird Johnson' (T)	CWoW EBee ERob ESCh NPri SCoo SLim SPoG SWCr WBGC
	'Lady Caroline Nevill' (EL)	ERob ESCh NBea SLim SWCr
	'Lady Catherine' (EL/d)	ERob
	'Lady Londesborough' (EL)	EBee EPfP ERob ESCh LRHS NBea NHaw SBod SCoo SDix WBGC
	'Lady Northcliffe' (EL)	CSPN CTri CWSG EPfP ERob ESCh ETho LRHS NBea SBra SDix SPoG SWCr WBGC
	'Lambton Park' (Ta) ♀H4	CFir CRHN CWoW EBee EPfP ERob ETho LRHS NBea NHaw SBra SMDP WBGC
	lasiandra	ERob NHaw SMDP
	– B&SWJ 6775	WCru
	– white-flowered	ERob
	lasiantha B&SWJ 6252	WCru
	'Last Dance' (Ta)	CRHN ERob
	Lasting Love	see *C.* 'Grażyna'
	'Lasurstern' (EL) ♀H4	CBcs CRHN CSPN CTri EBee ECtt ELan EPfP ERob ESCh ETho LAst LCro LRHS MAsh MBar MBri MLan MRav MWgw NBea NEgg SBra SDix SLim SPer SPoG SWCr WBGC WFar
	'Laura' (LL)	ERob ESCh NHaw
	'Laura Denny' (EL)	ESCh ETho SMDP
	'Lavender Lace'	ERob ESCh
	'Lawsoniana' (EL)	CElw CRHN CWSG ETho LAst MBar WBGC
	'Lech Wałęsa' **new**	ETho
	'Leione'	ESCh
	'Lemon Chiffon' (EL)	CSPN EBee EMil ERob ESCh ETho NHaw SLim SWCr
	Liberation = 'Evifive'PBR (EL)	ERob ESCh LAst LRHS MAsh SCoo SPoG SWCr
§	***ligusticifolia***	ERob GSki NHaw
	'Liisu' (LL)	ESCh
	'Lilacina Floribunda' (EL)	CBcs CWoW EBee LRHS MBNS MBar NHaw
	'Lilactime' (EL)	ERob ESCh NHaw
	'Lincoln Star' (EL)	CRHN CWoW EPfP ERob ESCh LAst LRHS MBar MGos NBea NEgg NPri SBra SDix SLim SPer SPet SPoG WBGC
	'Little Bas' (Vt)	CRHN CSPN ERob ESCh NHaw NLar

'Little Butterfly' (Vt)	CRHN ERob ESCh NHaw
'Little Nell' (Vt)	CCCN CElw CRHN CSPN CWoW ELan ERob ESCh ETho LRHS MRav MWgw NBea NHol SBra SCoo SDix SPer SPet SPoG WFar WSpi
'Lord Herschell'	ERob ETho SMDP
'Lord Nevill' (EL)	CRHN CWSG EPfP ERob ESCh ETho LRHS NBea SBra SDix WBGC WFar
'Louise Rowe' (EL)	CElw EBee ELan ERob ESCh ETho LRHS MGos NBea NHaw SBra SLim SPoG WBGC
loureiroana HWJ 663	WCru
'Love Jewelry'	CWGN ESCh ETho NHaw
'Lucey' (LL)	ESCh
'Lucie' (EL)	NBea
'Lunar Lass' (Fo/f)	CRez CStu ECho EPfP ESCh ETho ITim NLAp NSla WAbe WPGP
I 'Lunar Lass Variegata' (Fo/v)	ECho LTwo SIng
'Luther Burbank' (LL)	ERob ESCh
§ 'M. Johnson' (A)	ERob ESCh
§ 'M. Koster' (Vt)	CDoC CRHN CSam CWoW EBee EPfP ESCh ETho LRHS MSwo NBea NHaw SBra SLim SPer SPet WBGC
'Macrantha' (F)	ERob
macropetala (d)	CBcs CSBt EBee ELan ENot EPfP ERob ESCh ETho LAst LCro LRHS MBar MGan MGos MRav NBea SDix SGar SLim SPer SPet SWCr WBGC WBrE WFar WOrn
- 'Alborosea'	see *C.* 'Blushing Ballerina'
- 'Blue Lagoon'	see *C. macropetala* 'Lagoon' Jackman 1959
§ - 'Chili' (A/d)	ERob
- 'Harry Smith'	see *C. macropetala* 'Chili'
- 'Lagoon' ambig.	LCro SPet
- 'Lagoon' Jackman 1956	see *C. macropetala* 'Maidwell Hall' Jackman
§ - 'Lagoon' Jackman 1959 (A/d) $\mathbb{Y}^{H4}$	CBgR CSPN EBee ERob ETho LRHS LSRN MSwo NBea NHol NSti SBra SCoo SLim SPoG SWCr WBGC
§ - 'Maidwell Hall' Jackman (A/d)	CSPN CTri CWSG EBee ECtt EPfP ERob ESCh ETho LRHS LSRN MAsh MGos NBea NHol SBra SHBN SPet SWCr WBGC WPGP WSHC
- 'Maidwell Hall' O.E.P. Wyatt (A)	MRav SCoo
- 'Wesselton' (A/d) $\mathbb{Y}^{H4}$	CSPN EPfP ERob ESCh ETho LCro MAsh MBri MGos NHaw NHol WFar
- 'White Moth'	see *C.* 'White Moth'
'Madame Baron-Veillard' (LL)	ECtt ESCh LAst LRHS MBar MWgw SBra SCoo SDix SWCr WBGC WFar
'Madame Edouard André' (LL)	CRHN CSPN EPfP ERob ESCh LRHS MAsh NBea SBra SCoo SDix SLim SPet SPoG SWCr WBGC WFar
'Madame Grangé' (LL) $\mathbb{Y}^{H4}$	CSPN EPfP ESCh LCro LRHS NBea NHaw SBra SCoo SPoG SWCr WBGC
'Madame Julia Correvon' (Vt) $\mathbb{Y}^{H4}$	More than 30 suppliers
'Madame le Coultre'	see *C.* 'Mevrouw Le Coultre'
'Madame van Houtte' (EL)	ERob ESCh
'Madeleine' (A)	ESCh
'Magnus Johnson'	see *C.* 'M. Johnson'
'Majojo' (Fo)	ESCh LTwo
'Mammut' (EL)	ERob
§ ***mandschurica***	CPLG ERob ETho SBra
- B&SWJ 1060	WCru
'Marcel Moser' (EL)	ERob
'Margaret Hunt' (LL)	CSPN ELan ERob ESCh ETho LRHS NBea NHaw SBra SPla
'Margaret Jones' (M/d)	EBee ERob ESCh NHaw
'Margaret Wood' (EL)	ERob
'Margot Koster'	see *C.* 'M. Koster'
'Maria Louise Jensen' (EL)	SBra
'Marie Boisselot' (EL) $\mathbb{Y}^{H4}$	More than 30 suppliers
'Marinka' (H)	ESCh MAvo SMDP
'Märjamaa' (LL)	ESCh
'Marjorie' (M/d)	More than 30 suppliers
'Markham's Pink' (A/d) $\mathbb{Y}^{H4}$	More than 30 suppliers
marmoraria $\mathbb{Y}^{H2-3}$	CStu ECho EPot ESCh GCrs LHop LRHS SBla SIng WAbe WFar
- hybrid (Fo)	EPot ITim WThu
marmoraria* x *petriei	ECho
'Marmori' (LL)	CWGN ERob ESCh ETho NHaw
'Mary Whistler' (A)	ESCh
'Mary-Claire' (EL/d)	ERob ESCh
§ 'Maskarad' (Vt)	CSPN ERob ESCh SWCr
Masquerade (Vt)	see *C.* 'Maskarad'
I 'Masquerade' (EL)	ETho LRHS MBri
'Matilda' (EL)	ESCh
'Matka Siedliska' (EL)	CSPN ERob
§ 'Matka Teresa' (EL)	ERob
'Matka Urszula Ledóchowska' (EL)	ERob
'Maureen' (LL)	CSPN CWGN CWSG ETho MAsh
mauritiana	ERob
maximowicziana	see *C. terniflora*
'Mayleen' (M) $\mathbb{Y}^{H4}$	CElw CPou CSBt CWSG EBee ECtt EPfP ERob ESCh ETho LCro LRHS MBri MGos MRav NBea NPri SAga SBod SBra SCoo SHBN SLim SPer SPet SPoG SWCr WBGC WFar
Medley = 'Evipo012'[PBR]	ESCh LRHS MAsh WBGC
'Meeli' (LL)	EBee ESCh
'Meloodia' (LL)	NBea
'Memm' (A/d)	ERob
§ 'Mevrouw Le Coultre' (EL)	MGan NBlu
'Mia' (EL/d)	ERob
'Michelle' (I)	ERob
microphylla	ECou
'Mikelite' (Vt)	ERob ESCh ETho NHaw
'Mikla' (LL)	ERob
'Miniseelik' (LL)	ERob ESCh ETho SMDP
'Minister' (EL)	ESCh ETho
'Minuet' (Vt) $\mathbb{Y}^{H4}$	CRHN CSPN EPfP ERob ESCh ETho LRHS MSwo NBea NHol SBra SCoo SDix SLim SPer SPla SPoG SWCr WBGC WSpi
'Miriam Markham' (EL)	ERob ESCh NBea NHaw
'Miss Bateman' (EL) $\mathbb{Y}^{H4}$	CDoC CElw CMac CRHN CSPN CTri CWSG EBee ECtt ELan EPfP ERob ESCh ETho LAst LCro LRHS MAsh MBar MBri NBea SBra SDix SLim SPer SPet SPla SPoG SWCr WBGC
'Miss Christine' (M)	ESCh ETho WFar
'Miss Crawshay' (EL)	ERob NHaw
'Moniuszko' (EL)	ESCh
N ***montana***	CBcs CPLG CSBt EBee ECtt MBar MGos NBea NHol SBod SBra SDix SHBN SLim SPet SPoG SSta WFar
- B&SWJ 6930	WCru
- BWJ 8189b from China	WCru
- HWJK 2156 from Nepal	WCru
- B&SWJ 6724 from Taiwan	WCru
- ***alba***	see *C. montana*
- 'Alexander'	CPou CWSG ERob LRHS MBNS MGos SWCr
- var. ***grandiflora*** $\mathbb{Y}^{H4}$	More than 30 suppliers
I - 'Lilacina'	ESCh MAsh
- 'Peveril'	CSPN ERob ESCh ETho
- 'Prosperity' **new**	ESCh
- var. ***rubens*** E.H. Wilson	More than 30 suppliers
- - 'Brookfield Clove'	ERob

I	- - 'Odorata'	EBee EPfP ERob ESCh ETho GSki LFol MGos MRav MWgw SBod SCoo SLim SPoG WGor
	- - 'Pink Perfection'	CDoC CElw CWSG EBee ECtt ELan EPfP ERob ESCh LAst LBMP LCro LRHS LSRN NBea NBlu NHol SBra SCoo SLim SPer SPet SPoG SWCr WBGC WFar
I	- 'Rubens Superba'	CMHG CTri CWSG EBee ECtt ESCh LBuc MGan NCGa SHBN SLim WBVN WFar
	- var. ***rubens*** 'Tetrarose' ♀H4	More than 30 suppliers
	- var. ***sericea***	see *C. spooneri*
	- 'Spooneri'	see *C. spooneri*
I	- 'Veitch's Form'	ESCh
§	- var. ***wilsonii***	More than 30 suppliers
	'Monte Cassino' (EL)	CRHN CSPN CWGN EBee ERob ESCh ETho NBea SMDP SPet
	'Moonbeam' (Fo)	CPrp EBee ECou ELan EPot ESCh GEdr GKev ITim LAst MGos MRav MSte MWgw NOrc SLon WAbe WCot
§	'Moonlight' (EL)	CElw CSPN ERob ESCh LAst LRHS
	'Moonman' (Fo)	LTwo
	Morning Cloud	see *C.* 'Yukikomachi'
	'Morning Yellow' (M) **new**	SMDP
	Mother Theresa	see *C.* 'Matka Teresa'
	'Mrs Bush' (LL)	ERob LRHS
	'Mrs Cholmondeley' (EL) ♀H4	More than 30 suppliers
	'Mrs George Jackman' (EL) ♀H4	CSPN ERob ESCh ETho MGos NBea SBra SCoo SPla
	'Mrs Hope' (EL)	ERob ESCh
	'Mrs James Mason' (EL)	ERob ESCh ETho NBea NHaw SBra SLim SMDP WBGC
	'Mrs N. Thompson' (EL)	CMac CSPN CTri EBee ELan ERob ESCh ETho LAst LCro LRHS LSRN MAsh MBar MBri MGos NBea NEgg NPer SBra SDix SHBN SLim SPer SPet SPoG WBGC
	'Mrs P.B. Truax' (EL)	ERob ESCh LRHS NBea SBra SDix SMDP WBGC
	'Mrs. P.T. James' (EL)	ERob ESCh
	'Mrs Robert Brydon' (H)	CBgR CChe CPLG EPfP ERob IPot MBNS NBPC NEgg NHol NSti SLim SRGP STes WCot WFar
	'Mrs Spencer Castle' (EL)	CSPN ERob ESCh ETho NBea
	'Mrs T. Lundell' (Vt)	CRHN CSPN EBee ERob ESCh ETho
	'Multi Blue' (EL)	More than 30 suppliers
	'Muran Rouge'	ESCh
	'My Angel'PBR (Ta)	CSPN ELan ESCh MGos NBPN NHaw NLar SMDP SPer WSpi
	'Myōjō' (EL)	CSPN EBee ERob ESCh LRHS SBra SPoG
	'Nadezhda' (LL)	ERob ESCh SMDP
§	***napaulensis***	CBcs CSPN CTri ERob ESCh ETho LFol LRHS WCru WFar WGwG WSpi
I	'Natacha' (EL)	CElw EBee ERob ESCh NBea NHaw SBra SCoo SLim SPet
	'Natascha' (EL)	ETho SPoG
	'Neapolitan' **new**	ESCh
	'Negritianka' (LL)	CSPN ERob ESCh NBPN NHaw
	'Negus' (LL)	ERob ESCh
	'Nelly Moser' (EL) ♀H4	More than 30 suppliers
	'New Dawn' (M)	CSPN ERob ESCh LCro NEgg NHaw
	'New Love'PBR (H)	CSPN CWGN EGle ERob ESCh ETho LBuc LHop MBlu MGos NHaw NLar NSti SLim
	New Zealand hybrids (Fo)	ECou
	'Night Veil' (Vt)	ETho
	'Nikolai Rubtsov' (LL)	CSPN ERob ESCh ETho SMDP

	'Niobe' (EL) ♀H4	More than 30 suppliers
	'Norfolk Queen' (EL)	ESCh
	'North Star'	see *C.* 'Põhjanael'
	'Nuit de Chine' (EL)	CWGN ERob ESCh
	'Nunn's Gift' (Fo)	ETho
	nutans var. ***thyrsoidea***	see *C. rehderiana*, *C. veitchiana*
	obscura	ERob
	obvallata	see *C. japonica* var. *obvallata*
§	***occidentalis***	NEgg
	'Ocean Pearl' (A)	ETho
	ochotensis	CSPN ERob SDys
	- 'Carmen Rose' (A)	ERob
	'Odoriba' (V)	CWGN ESCh ETho NLar
	'Ola Howells' (A/d)	ERob ESCh
	'Olga' (M)	ERob ESCh
	'Olimpiada-80' (EL)	ERob ESCh
	'Omoshiro' (EL)	CWGN ESCh ETho MGos NHaw
	'Oonagare'	ESCh
	Opaline	see *C.* 'Asagasumi'
	orientalis misapplied	see *C. tibetana* subsp. *vernayi*
	orientalis L.	CElw CPLG EBee GCra GSki LRHS NHol SCoo WFar
	- 'Orange Peel'	see *C. tibetana* subsp. *vernayi* var. *vernayi* 'Orange Peel' LS&E 13342
	- var. ***orientalis***	ERob
	- 'Sherriffii'	see *C.* 'Sherriffii'
	- var. ***tenuifolia***	ERob
	- var. ***tenuiloba***	see *C. columbiana* var. *tenuiloba*
	'Otto Fröbel' (EL)	CSPN ERob ESCh
	'Paala' (EL)	ERob
	'Paddington' (EL)	ERob
	'Pagoda' (Vt) ♀H4	CDoC CRHN EBee EPfP ESCh ETho LAst LRHS MBri MRav NBea NHol NSti SBra SCoo SPla SPoG SRms SWCr WBGC
	'Päkapikk' (LL)	ERob
	'Pamela' (F)	CSPN ERob ESCh ETho LBuc NHaw
	'Pamela Jackman'	see *C. alpina* 'Pamela Jackman'
	'Pamiat Serdtsa' (I)	ERob ESCh ETho
	'Pamina' (EL)	ETho
	'Pangbourne Pink' (I) ♀H4	CElw CSPN CWoW EBee EPfP ERob ESCh ETho GBuc LRHS MAsh NBea NHaw SBra SCoo SPoG SWCr WBGC
	paniculata Thunb.	see *C. terniflora*
§	***paniculata*** J.G. Gmel.	CSPN GGar LRHS WPGP
	- (f)	ETho
	- var. ***lobata***	LCro NLar
	'Paola' (EL/d)	ESCh
	'Paradise Queen' (EL)	ESCh LBuc NLar WFar
	'Parasol' (EL)	CSPN ERob ESCh
	Parisienne = 'Evipo019'PBR **new**	LBuc
	parviflora DC.	see *C. campaniflora*
	parviflora ambig.	ERob
	parviloba var. ***bartlettii***	WSHC
	- - B&SWJ 6788	WCru
	'Pastel Blue' (I)	ERob ESCh ETho NBea SMDP
	'Pastel Pink' (I)	ERob ESCh ETho SMDP
	'Pastel Princess' (EL)	ERob NHaw
	'Pat Coleman' (EL)	ETho
	patens from China	ERob
	- from Japan	ERob
	- 'Korean Moon' (EL)	WCru
§	- 'Manshuu Ki' (EL)	CDoC CElw CRHN CSPN CSam CWSG EBee ECtt EPfP ERob ESCh ETho LCro MRav MSwo MWgw NBea NEgg NPri SBra SGar SHBN SPer SPla WBGC WWeb
	- 'Nagoya' (EL)	ESCh
	- 'Sanda' (EL)	ESCh
	- 'Yukiokoshi' (EL)	ERob ESCh ETho
	Patricia Ann Fretwell = 'Pafar' (EL)	CSPN ERob LRHS

	Name	Suppliers
§	'Paul Farges' (Vt) 🏆H4	CBcs CSPN CStu CWGN CWoW EBee ERob ETho EVal MBlu NHol NSti SBra SMDP WBGC WWeb
	'Pauline' (A/d) 🏆H4	CBcs CWSG EBee ERob ESCh ETho LRHS NBea SCoo SWCr WBGC
	'Pearl Rose' (A/d)	CWSG ERob
	'Pendragon' (Vt)	CRHN CWGN ERob ESCh NHaw
	'Pennell's Purity' (LL)	ERob NHaw
	'Perle d'Azur' (LL)	More than 30 suppliers
	'Perrin's Pride' (Vt)	ERob ESCh LRHS MGos SBra SCoo SWCr WBGC
	'Peter Pan' (EL)	ERob
	peterae	ERob
	- var. ***trichocarpa***	ERob
	Petit Faucon = 'Evisix'PBR (I) 🏆H4	EBee ECtt ENot EPfP ERob ETho IBal LAst LRHS LSRN MAsh MBNS MBri MWgw NBea NSti SBra SCoo SLim SPer SPoG SRkn SWCr WBGC WPGP
	petriei	ECou
	- 'Princess' (Fo/f)	ECou
	- 'Steepdown' (Fo/f)	ECou
	'Peveril Peach'	ESCh
	'Peveril Pearl' (EL)	ERob ESCh ETho
	'Phoenix' (EL)	ESCh
	Picardy = 'Evipo024'PBR	ETho LBuc LRHS NPri
I	'Picton's Variety' (M)	CTri EBee ERob ESCh NHaw NHol SHBN WFar
	pierotii	ERob
	- B&SWJ 6281	WCru
	'Piilu' (EL)	CSPN CWGN ELan ERob ESCh ETho LBuc LRHS MAsh MBNS MBri MWea NHaw NPri SBra SCoo SLim SMDP SPoG SWCr WBGC
	'Pink Celebration'	ESCh ETho
	'Pink Champagne'	see *C.* 'Kakio'
	'Pink Fantasy' (LL)	CRHN CSPN CTri CWSG ERob ESCh ETho LCro LRHS MBar NBea SBra SCoo SLim SPoG SRkn SWCr WBGC
	'Pink Flamingo' (A) 🏆H4	CBcs CSPN EBee ECtt ELan ENot EPfP ERob ESCh ETho LCro LRHS NEgg NPri NSti SCoo SLim SPet SPoG SRkn SWCr WBGC WBrE
	'Pink Ice' (I)	ESCh
	'Pink Pearl' (EL)	ESCh
	'Pink Starlight' (M)	ESCh SMDP SWCr
	'Pirko' (Vt)	ERob ESCh
§	***pitcheri***	CPLG ERob ESCh
	'Pixie' (Fo/m)	CSPN ECou ELan ENot EPfP ESCh ETho GGar ITim LRHS MGos MWgw NHaw NHol NLar SCoo SPer SPoG
I	'Pleniflora' (M/d)	ESCh MGos NHaw
§	'Plum Beauty' (A)	CSPN ERob ESCh NHaw
§	'Põhjanael' (LL)	CSPN CWSG ERob ESCh ETho MGos NBea
	'Pointy' (A)	ESCh
	'Polish Spirit' (LL) 🏆H4	More than 30 suppliers
	'Polonez' (Vt) **new**	ETho
	potaninii	CCge CSPN CWoW ECtt EPPr GCra ITer NEgg SBod WPtf WSHC
§	- var. ***potaninii***	ERob SDix
	- var. ***souliei***	see *C. potaninii* var. *potaninii*
	- 'Summer Snow'	see *C.* 'Paul Farges'
	'Praecox' (H) 🏆H4	CPrp CRHN EBee ECtt ELan EPfP ERob ESCh ETho GSki LAst LHop LRHS MAvo MBar MBri MWgw NBea NBir NHol NSti SBra SDix SPet SPoG SWCr WCot
*	'Prairie'	LRHS
	Prairie Chinook	see *C.* Chinook
	Prairie Gazelle	see *C.* Gazelle
	Prairie Medley	see *C.* Medley
	'Prairie River' (A)	ERob ETho
	Pretty in Blue = 'Zopre'PBR (F)	ESCh ETho SBra SHBN SMDP
	'Pribaltika' (LL)	ERob ESCh
	'Primrose Star'PBR	see *C.* 'Star'
	'Prince Charles' (LL) 🏆H4	CElw CPou CRHN CSPN CTri EBee ELan EPfP ESCh ETho LCro LRHS LSRN NBea NBir SBra SCoo SDix SLim SPer SPet SPoG SWCr WBGC WSHC
	'Prince Philip' (EL)	ERob ESCh WFar
§	'Princess Diana' (T) 🏆H4	More than 30 suppliers
§	'Princess of Wales' (EL)	CSam EPfP ERob ESCh LRHS LSRN MBNS NLar NPri NSti WFar WSHC
	'Prins Hendrik' (EL)	ERob WGor
	'Prinsesse Alexandra'PBR	EBee ESCh ETho SPad
	'Propertius' (A)	CWGN EBee ERob ESCh ETho NHaw SMDP SWCr
	'Proteus' (EL)	CSPN ELan EPfP ESCh ETho LAst LCro LRHS MAsh MBNS NBea SBra SCoo SDix SLim SPer SPet SPoG WBGC
	'Pruinina'	see *C.* 'Plum Beauty'
	psilandra	SMDP
	'Pulmapäev' (LL)	ERob
	'Purple Haze' (Vt)	CRHN
	'Purple Spider' (A/d)	CBcs CSPN EBee ERob ESCh ETho MBlu MWgw NHaw NHol SBra SCoo SLim SMDP SPer SPet SPoG
	'Purpurea Plena Elegans' (Vt/d) 🏆H4	More than 30 suppliers
	quadribracteolata	ECou
	- 'Nancy's Lookout'	ECou
	'Queen Alexandra' (EL)	ERob ESCh
	'Radar Love' (Ta)	GMaP LTwo NLar WBrE
	'Radost' (EL)	ERob ESCh
	'Ragamuffin' (EL/d)	ENot ERob ESCh
	'Rahvarinne' (LL)	ERob ESCh ETho
	'Ramona' (LL)	ETho MAsh
	recta	CSPN CWoW ECtt EPfP ERob ETho GSki LPio LRHS MLLN MNrw NBea NEgg NLar SPer WPer WTin
§	- 'Lime Close' (F)	LPio MSte SMrm
I	- 'Peveril' (F)	CPrp ERob ESCh LAst MSte SMDP
	- 'Purpurea' (F)	More than 30 suppliers
§	- subsp. ***recta*** var. ***lasiosepala***	CSPN ERob
	- Serious Black	see *C. recta* 'Lime Close'
	- 'Velvet Night' (F)	CPrp CWGN EMan ERob ESCh GAbr LAst LHop MDun NEgg NHol SMDP WAul
	'Red Ballon' (Ta)	ERob ESCh SMDP
§	'Red Beetroot Beauty' (A)	CSPN ERob ESCh
	'Red Cooler'	see *C.* 'Crimson King'
	'Red Pearl' (EL)	ERob ESCh ETho MGos
§	***rehderiana*** 🏆H4	More than 30 suppliers
	- BWJ 7700	WCru
	- CC 3601	CPLG
	'Reiman' (LL)	ERob
	repens	see *C. montana* var. *wilsonii*
	- DJHC795	SMDP
	reticulata	ERob
	'Rhapsody' ambig.	ENot EPfP ETho LRHS MGos SCoo SPoG SWCr WFar
I	'Rhapsody' B. Fretwell (EL)	CSPN ERob LSRN NBea NHaw WBGC
	'Richard Pennell' (EL) 🏆H4	EBee ERob ESCh ETho LRHS MAsh NBea NPri SBra SDix SWCr WBGC
	'Ristimägi' (LL)	ERob
	'Rodomax' (A)	ERob ESCh
	'Roko' (LL)	ERob

	Name	Suppliers
	'Roko-Kolla' (LL)	CSPN EBee ERob ESCh ETho NBea SBra
	'Romantika' (LL)	CSPN EBee ELan ERob ESCh ETho NBPN NBea NHaw SBra SCoo SLim SPer SPoG
	'Roogoja' (LL)	ERob ESCh
	'Rooguchi' (I)	EBee ERob ESCh ETho LRHS SMDP SPoG SWCr
	'Rooran' (EL)	ETho
	'Rosa Königskind' (EL)	ERob ESCh ETho
	'Rose Supreme' (EL)	ESCh ETho
I	'Rosea' (I) ♀[H4]	CBcs CBgR CPrp CSPN EBee EPfP ERob ESCh EShb ETho LAst LHop LSRN MCot MSte MSwo MTho NBea NChi NSti SLim SPoG WCra
	'Rosea' (Vt)	ERob
	Rosebud = 'Robud'[PBR] (M/d)	EBee ESCh NCGa NLar NPer SMDP
	Rosemoor = 'Evipo002'[PBR]	CWGN ETho IBal LRHS MAsh MBri SBra SCoo SWCr WBGC
	'Rosy O'Grady' (A) ♀[H4]	EBee ELan ETho MBar MBri MGos NBea NHol NLar NSti SLim SPer
	'Rosy Pagoda' (A)	EBee ELan EPfP ERob ESCh LCro LRHS MBri NBea NBir NHaw WBGC
	'Rouge Cardinal' (LL)	More than 30 suppliers
	'Royal Velours' (Vt) ♀[H4]	CDoC CElw CRHN CSPN CTri EBee ELan EPfP ERob ESCh ETho LCro LRHS LSRN MWgw NBea NEgg NHol NSti SBra SCoo SDix SHBN SLim SPer SPet SWCr WBGC WFar
	Royal Velvet = 'Evifour'[PBR] (EL)	CSPN CWoW EPfP ESCh ETho IBal LAst LCro LSRN MBri MWgw SCoo SLim WBGC
	'Royalty' (EL) ♀[H4]	CElw CSPN ELan EPfP ERob ESCh IBal LRHS LSRN MAsh NBir NPri SBra SCoo SDix SLim SPer SPet SPoG SWCr WBGC
	'Rozalia' (EL)	ESCh
	'Rubens Superba'	see *C. montana* 'Rubens Superba'
	'Ruby' (A)	CMHG CSPN CWSG EBee EPfP ESCh ETho LRHS MAsh MGos MWgw NBea NEgg NHol NSti SBra SCoo SDix SHBN SLim SPer SPet SPoG WBGC
	'Ruby Glow' (EL)	EPfP ERob ESCh SCoo WBGC
	'Rüütel' (EL)	ERob ESCh ETho NBea NHaw SBra SCoo SLim SMDP SPoG
	'Saalomon' (LL)	ERob ESCh ETho
	'Sakala' (EL)	ERob ESCh
§	'Sakurahime' (EL)	EBee ERob ESCh
	'Sally Cadge' (EL)	ERob ESCh
	'Salmon Blush' (A/d)	ESCh
	'Samantha Denny' (EL)	CSPN ERob ESCh ETho MAsh NBea NHaw
	'Sander' (H)	CSPN ERob ESCh ETho
	'Sandra Denny' (EL)	ETho
	'Sano-no-murasaki' (EL)	ESCh
	'Satsukibare' (EL)	ERob ESCh MGos
I	'Saturn' (LL)	ERob ESCh NBea SPla
	'Saturn' (EL)	ESCh
	'Scartho Gem' (EL)	EPfP ERob ESCh NBea NPri SCoo WBGC
	'Sealand Gem' (EL)	ERob ESCh ETho LAst NBea NHaw SBra SLim WBGC
	'Semu' (LL)	CSPN CWGN ERob ESCh ETho NHaw
	'Serenata' (EL)	ERob ESCh
	serratifolia	CElw CWoW ERob ESCh ETho MDKP MLLN SDix SMDP SWal WBVN WFar
	- B&SWJ 8458 from Korea	WCru
	'Sheila Thacker' (EL)	ETho
I	'Sherriffii' (Ta)	ERob
	'Shin-shigyoku'	CWGN ESCh
	'Shirayukihime' (LL)	CSPN ESCh
§	'Shiva' (A)	ERob MBri
	'Shorty' (Ta)	ERob
	'Sho-un' (EL)	EBee ERob ESCh
	'Shropshire Blue'	ERob
	'Sialia' (A/d)	ERob ESCh
§	***sibirica***	EBee ERob SPla
	- var. ***tianschanica*** 'Riga' (A)	ERob
	'Signe' (Vt)	see *C.* 'Kasmu'
	'Siirus' (EL)	ERob
	'Silmakivi' (EL)	ERob ESCh
	'Silver Lady'	SPoG
	'Silver Moon' (EL)	CSPN ERob ESCh ETho LCro NBea SCoo
	'Simplicity' (A)	CBgR CSPN EBee ERob MAsh MBri SPet
	simsii Small	see *C. pitcheri*
	simsii Sweet	see *C. crispa*
	'Sinee Plamia' (LL)	ERob ESCh NHaw
§	'Sinii Dozhd' (I)	CSPN ERob ESCh SMDP
	'Sir Eric Savill' (M)	ESCh
	'Sir Garnet Wolseley' (EL)	ERob ESCh MAsh SDix
	'Sir Trevor Lawrence' (T)	CSPN CWoW EBee ERob ESCh ETho LAst LRHS NBea NHaw NHol NSti SBra SCoo SDix SLim SPer SPoG SWCr
	'Sizaia Ptitsa' (I)	ERob ESCh ETho
	'Snow Queen' (EL)	CSPN EBee EPfP ESCh ETho LRHS MAsh MBri MGos MSwo NBea SBra SPet WBGC
	'Snowbird' (A/d)	CSPN ERob ESCh MAsh NHaw NHol SBra
	'Snowdrift'	see *C. armandii* 'Snowdrift'
§	'Södertälje' (Vt)	CRHN ERob ESCh ETho NBea SBra SCoo SPoG WFar
	'Solidarność' (EL) **new**	ETho
	'Solweig' (EL)	ERob
	songarica	CWoW ERob ESCh NHol
	'Souvenir de J.L. Delbard' (EL)	ERob ESCh
§	'Souvenir du Capitaine Thuilleaux' (EL)	CWoW ESCh LAst MAsh MGos NBea SPoG WBGC
	'Special Occasion' (EL)	CSPN CWGN EBee ENot ERob ESCh ETho LBuc MBNS NBea NHaw NLar NPri SBra SCoo SLim WBGC WFar
§	***spooneri***	CElw CTri CWSG ECtt EPfP ERob ESCh GQui MAsh MGan MWgw SCoo SLim SRms WFoF
	'Spooneri Rosea' (M)	ERob
	'Sputnik' (I)	CSPN CWGN ERob ESCh NHaw
	stans	CPLG CPou EPfP ERob ESCh GSki ITer LRHS NLar SIng SMDP WBGC
	- B&SWJ 4567	WCru
	- B&SWJ 6345	WCru
	- 'Rusalka' (H)	ERob
§	'Star'[PBR] (M/d)	CBgR CDoC CFir CSPN CWGN EBee EPfP ERob ESCh LAst LRHS MAsh MBlu MGos MRav MSwo MWgw NHol NLar NPri SBra SPoG WBGC WFar
	'Star of India' (LL)	CElw CRHN EBee EPfP ERob ESCh ETho LCro LRHS MAsh MGos MRav NBea SBra SCoo SDix SLim SPer SPoG SWCr WBGC WFar
	'Starfish' (EL)	ERob ESCh NHaw
	'Stasik' (LL)	ERob ESCh NHaw
	'Stephanie'	ESCh
	'Strawberry Roan' (EL)	ESCh
	Sugar Candy = 'Evione'[PBR] (EL)	ERob ESCh IBal LAst MBri NPri SBra SCoo SLim
	Summer Snow	see *C.* 'Paul Farges'
	'Sundance'	CSPN EBee ERob ESCh

	'Sunrise'^{PBR} (M/d)	CSPN CWGN EBee ESCh ETho LBuc MSwo NHaw NLar SBra SPoG WFar
	'Sunset' (EL) Υ^{H4}	CWoW ERob ESCh LCro LRHS MBri NBea NEgg SBra SCoo SWCr WBGC
	'Sunstar'	SWal
	'Suruga' (EL)	ESCh
	'Susan Allsop' (EL)	ERob ESCh
	'Swedish Bells' (I)	ETho
	'Sylvia Denny' (EL)	CWSG CWoW EBee ELan EPfP ERob ESCh ETho LAst LRHS MBar MRav NBea SLim SPer SPet SPoG WBGC
	'Sympatia' (LL)	ERob ESCh NHaw
	'Syrena' (LL)	ESCh NBea NHaw
	szuyuanensis B&SWJ 6791	WCru
	'Tage Lundell' (A)	CBgR CSPN EBee EPfP ERob MGos NBea SMDP
	'Tamula' **new**	ESCh
	'Tango' (Vt)	CElw CRHN EBee ERob ESCh SMDP SPet
§	***tangutica***	More than 30 suppliers
	- subsp. ***obtusiuscula*** 'Gravetye Variety' (Ta)	ERob
	'Tapestry' (I)	ERob SMDP
	'Tartu' (EL)	CSPN ERob ESCh
	tashiroi	ERob ESCh ITer
	- B&SWJ 7005 purple-flowered	WCru
	- 'Yellow Peril'	WCru
	'Teksa' (LL)	ERob
	'Tentel' (LL)	ERob ESCh ETho
	tenuiloba	see *C. columbiana* var. *tenuiloba*
§	***terniflora***	CBcs CWoW EBee EPfP ESCh ETho LFol LRHS NHaw NSti SAga SBra SLim SPer
	- B&SWJ 5751	WCru
	- var. ***mandshurica***	see *C. mandschurica*
	- var. ***robusta***	see *C. terniflora* var. *terniflora*
§	- var. ***terniflora***	ERob LFol
	'Teruko'	ERob
	'Teshio' (EL)	CSPN EBee ERob ESCh ETho NHaw SBra SLim SPoG
	texensis	CBcs CElw
	- 'The Princess of Wales'	see *C.* 'Princess Diana'
	'The Bride' (EL)	CSPN CWGN ERob ESCh ETho NBea NHaw SBra WBGC
	'The Comet' (EL)	ERob
	'The First Lady' (EL)	CSPN ERob ESCh ETho LBuc
	'The President' (EL) Υ^{H4}	More than 30 suppliers
	'The Princess of Wales'	see *C.* 'Princess of Wales' (EL)
	'The Princess of Wales' (T)	see *C.* 'Princess Diana' (T)
	'The Vagabond' (EL)	CSPN CWSG ELan ERob ESCh ETho MAsh MGos NBea NHaw SBra SCoo SPet WBGC
	'The Velvet' (EL)	ERob
	'Theydon Belle' (EL)	ESCh
	thunbergii misapplied	see *C. terniflora*
	thunbergii Steud.	see *C. triloba*
	'Thyrislund' (EL)	CSPN EBee ESCh ETho
	'Tibetan Mix' (Ta)	CSPN ERob ESCh SMDP
	tibetana	MBar MNrw NEgg NHaw SLim SPer
	- CC 4167	MGol
	- SDR 1936	GKev
	- 'Black Tibet' **new**	ESCh
§	- subsp. ***vernayi***	CMHG ERob MSte NSti SBra SWCr
	- - var. ***laciniifolia***	ERob ESCh NHol
	- - LS&E 13342	see *C. tibetana* subsp. *vernayi* var. *vernayi* 'Orange Peel' LS&E 13342
§	- - var. ***vernayi*** 'Orange Peel' LS&E 13342	CBcs CDoC EPfP ERob ESCh ETho LRHS MRav NHol SBra SGar SLim SPer WFar WSpi
	Timpany NZ hybrids (Fo)	ITim
	'Tinkerbell'	see *C.* 'Shiva'
	'Titania' (EL)	ERob ESCh
	'Toki' (EL)	CWGN ESCh
	tongluensis GWJ 9358	WCru
	- HWJCM 076	WCru
	- HWJK 2368	WCru
	'Treasure Trove' (Ta)	CSPN NHol SMDP
	'Trianon' (EL)	ERob ESCh
	'Triibu' (LL)	ESCh
	'Triinu' (Vt)	ERob
	'Trikatrei' (LL)	ESCh
§	***triloba***	ETho
§	x ***triternata*** 'Rubromarginata' Υ^{H4}	More than 30 suppliers
	'Tsuzuki' (EL)	CSPN ERob ESCh ETho NBea
§	***tubulosa***	CPle CSPN EBee ESCh ETho MGos NHol SBch SMDP SRms
§	- Alan Bloom = 'Alblo'^{PBR} (H)	EBrs LRHS
I	- 'Alba' (H)	ERob
	- 'Wyevale' (H) Υ^{H4}	CPrp CSPN ELan ENot EPfP ERob ETho LHop LRHS MBlu MRav NHol SBra SCoo SDix SMad SPer SPla WCot WEas WHil
	'Tuchka' (EL)	ERob ESCh
	'Twilight' (EL)	CSPN ESCh ETho LCro SLim SPoG WBGC WFar
	'Ulrique' (EL)	ERob
	uncinata	ERob SDix
	- B&SWJ 1893	WCru
	- var. ***ovatifolia***	ERob
	urophylla	ERob
§	- 'Winter Beauty'	CBgR ESCh ETho MGos MRav SHBN SPoG
	urticifolia	ESCh WSHC
	- B&SWJ 8640	WCru
	- B&SWJ 8651	WCru
	'Valge Daam' (LL)	CWGN ERob ESCh ETho NHaw SLim
	'Vanessa' (LL)	CRHN ERob ESCh
	'Vanilla Cream' (Fo)	ECou
	x ***vedrariensis*** 'Hidcote' (M)	ERob ESCh NHaw
	- 'Highdown' (M)	ERob
	- 'Rosea'	see *C.* 'Spooneri Rosea'
	veitchiana	ERob
	'Velutina Purpurea' (LL)	ERob
	'Venosa Violacea' (Vt) Υ^{H4}	CBgR CElw CRHN CSPN CSam EBee ELan EPfP ERob ESCh EShb ETho LAst LCro LRHS LSRN MAsh MRav NBea NHol NSti SBra SCoo SDix SPer SPet SPla SWCr WBGC WFar
	'Vera' (M)	CElw CSPN EBee ECtt ERob ESCh ETho LRHS SBra SCoo SPet SPla SPoG
	vernayi	see *C. tibetana* subsp. *vernayi*
	'Veronica's Choice' (EL)	CRHN CSPN ELan ERob ESCh LRHS MGos MRav NBea NHaw SBra SPet WBGC
	Versailles = 'Evipo025' **new**	ETho
	versicolor	ERob ESCh
	verticillaris	see *C. occidentalis*
	'Vetka' (LL)	ERob
	Victor Hugo = 'Evipo007'^{PBR}	ENot ESCh ETho EVal IBal NLar SCoo SWCr
N	'Victoria' Cripps, 1867 (LL) Υ^{H4}	CRHN CSPN ERob ESCh ETho LAst LRHS MRav NBea NHaw SBra SCoo SDix SLim SPoG SWCr WBGC
	'Vilhelmine' **new**	ESCh
	'Ville de Lyon' (LL)	More than 30 suppliers
	'Vince Denny' (Ta)	ESCh ETho

	Vino = 'Poulvo'PBR (EL)	ERob IBal LRHS NHaw SCoo SPoG WBGC
I	'Viola' (LL)	CSPN EBee ERob ESCh ETho MBri NBea NHaw WFar
	'Violet Charm' (EL)	CWSG ERob ESCh
	'Violet Elizabeth' (EL)	ESCh MRav
	'Violet Purple' (A)	ERob ESCh MGos NHaw
	'Violetta' (EL)	ERob ESCh
	viorna	CElw CWoW ERob ESCh WSHC
	virginiana misapplied	see *C. vitalba*
	virginiana Hook.	see *C. ligusticifolia*
	virginiana L.	CElw ELau GKev
§	***vitalba***	CArn CRWN ERob ESCh ETho MBar MHer NHaw SECG WGwG WHer
	viticella ♀H4	CElw CRHN CWib ERob ESCh ETho MBri NBea NHaw SBra SDix WSHC
	- 'Chatsworth' **new**	LRHS
§	- 'Flore Pleno'	CRHN ERob ESCh ETho LAst NHaw SBra SWCr
	- 'Hågelby Pink'	CWGN ESCh
	- 'Hågelby White'	ERob ETho NHaw
	- 'Hanna' (Vt)	ERob ESCh ETho LRHS MAsh SWCr
	- 'Mary Rose'	see *C. viticella* 'Flore Pleno'
	'Vivienne'	see *C.* 'Beth Currie'
	'Vivienne Lawson' (LL)	ERob ESCh
	'Voluceau' (Vt)	CPou CRHN ELan ERob ESCh LAst MAsh MGos MRav NBea SBra SLim SPer WBGC
	'Vostok' (LL)	ERob ESCh
	'Vyvyan Pennell' (EL)	More than 30 suppliers
	'W.E. Gladstone' (EL)	CRHN ERob ESCh ETho LRHS NBea SBra SDix
	'W.S. Callick' (EL)	ERob
	'Wada's Primrose'	see *C. patens* 'Manshuu Ki'
	'Walenburg' (Vt)	CRHN CWGN ERob ESCh NHaw
	'Walter Pennell' (EL)	CBcs CWSG EBee ESCh ETho IBal NBea SCoo SLim WGor
	'Warszawska Nike' (EL) ♀H4	CRHN EBee ELan ENot EPfP ERob ESCh ETho LAst MAsh MBri MGos MWgw NBea SBra SCoo SHBN SPer SPet SPoG WBGC
	'Warszawska Olga' **new**	ETho
	'Warwickshire Rose' (M)	CRHN CSPN CWGN CWSG ECtt ERob ESCh ETho LSRN MAsh MGos NBea NHaw NHol SBra SPoG WBGC WCot WFar WPGP WSHC WWeb
	'Waterperry Star' (Ta)	ERob MWat
	'Wedding Day' (EL)	ETho
	'Wee Willie Winkie' (M)	CWGN ESCh SBra SCoo SMDP
	'Western Virgin' (Vb)	ERob
	'Westerplatte' (EL)	CRHN CSPN CWGN EPfP ERob ESCh ETho LAst LBuc LRHS MAsh MGos NBea NHaw SBra SMDP SPoG WBGC WFar
	'Whirlygig'	CSPN
§	'White Columbine' (A) ♀H4	CBgR EBee EPfP ERob ESCh ETho LAst NBea NSti SPet
	'White Lady' (A/d)	EPfP ERob ESCh NHaw
	'White Magic' (Vt) **new**	ESCh ETho MGos
§	'White Moth' (A/d)	CSPN CWSG EBee ELan ESCh ETho LRHS MAsh MGos MRav NEgg NHaw NHol SBra SLim SPer SPet SPla SPoG SRms
	'White Swan' (A/d)	CSPN EPfP ERob ESCh LRHS MBri MGos NBea NHol NSti SCoo SDix SLim SPla SPoG WFoF
	'White Tokyo' (A/d)	MGos
	'White Wings' (A/d)	CBcs EBee ERob ESCh LAst MWgw SPet SWCr
	'Wilhelmina Tull' (EL)	CSPN ERob ESCh
	'Will Goodwin' (EL) ♀H4	CBcs CWoW EBee ELan EPfP ERob ESCh ETho LAst LRHS MBri NBea NPri SBra SWCr WBGC
	'William Kennett' (EL)	CSam CWSG CWoW EBee ELan EPfP ESCh ETho LAst LRHS MBNS MBar MBri MGan MGos SDix SPet SPoG SWCr WBGC
	williamsii	ESCh
	'Willy' (A)	More than 30 suppliers
	Wisley = 'Evipo001'PBR	CBcs ESCh IBal LRHS MAsh MBri NLar SBra SPer SPoG SWCr WBGC
	'Xerxes' misapplied	see *C.* 'Elsa Späth'
	'Yaichi' (EL)	ESCh
	Yalta Study = 'Ialtinskii Etiud' (LL) **new**	ESCh
	'Yatsuhashi'	ERob
	'Yellow Queen' Holland	see *C. patens* 'Manshuu Ki'
	'Yellow Queen' Lundell/ Treasures	see *C.* 'Moonlight'
	'Yorkshire Pride' (EL)	ERob ESCh
§	'Yukikomachi' (EL)	CSPN ERob ESCh ETho NHaw SPoG
	'Yuki-no-yoso'oi' (EL)	ERob
	yunnanensis	ERob
	'Yvette Houry' (EL)	ERob ESCh NHaw NLar
	'Zingaro' (Vt)	ERob
	'Zolotoi Iubilei' (LL)	ERob

Clematopsis see *Clematis*

Clementsia see *Rhodiola*

Clerodendrum (*Verbenaceae*)

	bungei	More than 30 suppliers
	- 'Herfstleu'	MGos
	- 'Pink Diamond'PBR (v)	CDul CWib EBee EMil ENot EPfP EWes LBuc LRHS MAsh MGos MPkF NLar NSti SMad SPer SPoG WCot WFar
§	***chinense*** var. ***chinense*** (d) ♀H1	CCCN ERea
	- 'Pleniflorum'	see *C. chinense* var. *chinense*
	fragrans var. ***pleniflorum***	see *C. chinense* var. *chinense*
*	***mutabile*** B&SWJ 6651	WCru
	myricoides 'Ugandense' ♀H1	CCCN CHII CKob CMdw CRHN CSpe ELan ERea EShb MJnS SOWG
	philippinum	see *C. chinense* var. *chinense*
	quadriloculare	CCCN
	x ***speciosum***	ERea LRHS SOWG
	splendens ♀H1	SOWG
	thomsoniae ♀H1	ELan LRHS MBri MJnS SOWG
	trichotomum	CBcs CDul CMCN CPLG CSBt CSam CSpe CWib EBee EMil EPfP EPla ERom IArd LPan LRHS MAsh MRav NBlu SLPl SLim SLon SPer SReu SSpi SSta WBor WSHC WSpi
	- B&SWJ 4896A	WCru
	- 'Carnival' (v)	CAbP CBcs CDul CPMA EBee ELan EPfP EWes IArd LRHS MAsh MBlu MBri NLar SLim SMad SPer SPoG SSta WPat
	- var. ***fargesii*** ♀H4	More than 30 suppliers
	- 'Purple Haze'	MBri
	- white calyx B&SWJ 4896	WCru
	wallichii	CSpe EShb LRHS SOWG

Clethra ✿ (*Clethraceae*)

	acuminata	EPfP
	alnifolia	CBcs CBrm CDul CEnd CMCN CMHG CPLG CSBt CTrG ECrN EPfP IDee MBar SPer SRms WBor WCFE WFar
	- 'Anne Bidwell'	MBri NLar
	- 'Fern Valley Pink'	MBri NLar
	- 'Hokie Pink'	MBri NLar
	- 'Hummingbird'	CDoC CEnd CPLG EBee ELan EMil EPfP LRHS MAsh MBlu MBri

	MWgw NLar SSpi SWvt WBVN WFar WGer
- 'Paniculata' ♀H4	CDoC CPLG EPfP LRHS SAga SPoG SPur WFar
- 'Pink Spire'	CBcs CDoC CDul EBee ECrN EPfP IDee MRav NBlu NEgg NPal SCoo WFar WOrn
- 'Rosea'	CTri GQui IMGH MBar MBlu MGos SHBN SPer WFar
- 'Ruby Spice'	CBcs CBrm CEnd EBee ELan EMil EPfP IMGH LAst LRHS MAsh MBlu MBri NEgg SPer SPoG SSpi SSta SWvt WBVN WBod WGob
- 'September Beauty'	NLar
- 'Sixteen Candles'	NLar
arborea	CBcs CHEx CMHG CPLG CTrC NLar SSpi
barbinervis ♀H4	CBcs CMCN CPLG EBee EPfP IDee LRHS MBlu NLar SPer WBod WFar WSHC
- B&SWJ 5416	WPGP
- B&SWJ 8915	WCru
delavayi Franch.	CBcs CCCN CDoC CPLG EPfP EWes GGGa GQui NLar
- C&H 7067	GGGa
fargesii	EPfP IMGH MBri MGos NLar WBVN
monostachya	NLar
pringlei	NLar
tomentosa	MBri
- 'Cottondale'	MBri NLar

Cleyera (*Theaceae*)

fortunei	see *C. japonica* 'Fortunei'
- 'Variegata'	see *C. japonica* 'Fortunei'
§ ***japonica*** 'Fortunei' (v)	CCCN CMac CWib EBee SSta WFar
- var. ***japonica***	CGHE WPGP
- 'Tricolor' (v)	EBee
- var. ***wallichii***	WPGP

Clianthus (*Papilionaceae*)

maximus	ECou
§ ***puniceus*** ♀H2	CAbb CHEx CHll CPLG CPne CSBt CSpe CWib EBee ECou EMil EPfP ERea GGar LHop LRHS MLan SAga SGar SOWG SPer SPlb SPoG SSpi WCru WKif WPGP WPic WSHC
§ - 'Albus' ♀H2	CBcs CHEx CHll CPLG CWib EBee EMil EPfP ERea LRHS SBra SDry SGar SOWG SPoG WPGP
- 'Flamingo'	see *C. puniceus* 'Roseus'
- 'Kaka King'	CBcs
- 'Red Admiral'	see *C. puniceus*
- 'Red Cardinal'	see *C. puniceus*
§ - 'Roseus'	CBcs CPLG EMil ERea LRHS SBra SPoG WPGP
- 'White Heron'	see *C. puniceus* 'Albus'

Clinopodium (*Lamiaceae*)

acinos	see *Acinos arvensis*
ascendens	see *Calamintha ascendens*
calamintha	see *Calamintha nepeta*
georgianum	SKHP
grandiflorum	see *Calamintha grandiflora*
§ ***vulgare***	CArn CRWN EBee EMan EUnu MHer NGHP NMir NSco SECG SGar SIde WDyG WLin WMoo WOut WPtf

Clintonia (*Convallariaceae*)

HWJK 2339 from Nepal	WCru
andrewsiana	CLAP EBee ECho EHrv EWes GBuc GCrs GEdr GGGa GMaP WCru
borealis	SCnR WCru
udensis	WCru WWst
umbellulata	CLAP WCru
uniflora	CLAP EBee EBrs ECho EHrv EWes GBuc GEdr GGar WCru

Clivia ✿ (*Amaryllidaceae*)

caulescens	ERea
x ***cyrtanthiflora***	ERea
gardenii	ERea WCot
gardenii x ***miniata***	WCot
miniata ♀H1	CBcs CBgR CHal CSpe CTca ECho EShb LRHS MLan SChr SRms WCot
- 'Aurea' ♀H1	CSpe
- var. ***citrina*** ♀H1	CFwr ECho LAma
- - 'New Dawn'	ERea
- hybrids	ERea MBri NPal SEND
- 'Striata' (v)	CFwr ERea
nobilis ♀H1	ERea WCot

Clusia (*Clusiaceae*)

rosea new	CCCN

Clypeola (*Brassicaceae*)

jonthlaspi	WCot

Clytostoma (*Bignoniaceae*)

§ ***calystegioides***	CHll CRHN ERea EShb

Cneorum (*Cneoraceae*)

tricoccon	CKob SKHP XPep

Cnicus (*Asteraceae*)

§ ***benedictus***	CArn GPoy MHer MSal SIde SPav

Cobaea (*Cobaeaceae*)

lutea B&SWJ 9142A new	WCru
pringlei	ERea WPGP WSHC
scandens ♀H3	CCCN CDTJ CSpe EBee ELan EShb EWin IFoB LRav MAvo SGar SPer WPen
- f. ***alba*** ♀H3	CSpe MAvo SPer WPen

cobnut see *Corylus avellana*

Coccothrinax (*Arecaceae*)

argentea (Lodd. ex Schult.f.) Sarg. ex Becc.	EAmu
crinita	LPal

Cocculus (*Menispermaceae*)

§ ***orbiculatus***	CPLG
- B&SWJ 535	WCru
trilobus	see *C. orbiculatus*

Cochlearia (*Brassicaceae*)

armoracia	see *Armoracia rusticana*
glastifolia	MSal
officinalis	MHer MSal SECG WHer

Cocos (*Arecaceae*)

plumosa	see *Syagrus romanzoffiana*
weddelliana	see *Lytocaryum weddellianum*

Codiaeum ✿ (*Euphorbiaceae*)

variegatum var. ***pictum*** 'Excellent' (v)	LRHS
- - 'Petra' (v)	LRHS MBri

Codonanthe (*Gesneriaceae*)

gracilis	WDib
'Paula'	WDib

x *Codonatanthus* (*Gesneriaceae*)

'Golden Tambourine'	WDib
'Sunset'	WDib
'Tambourine'	WDib

Codonopsis ✿ (*Campanulaceae*)

	CC 4471	CPLG
	SDR 3019	GKev
	affinis HWJCM 70	WCru
	- HWJK 2151	WCru
	benthamii	EBee GKev WCot
	- GWJ 9352	WCru
	bhutanica	MGol WCot
	bulleyana	EBee MLul NLar
	cardiophylla	EBee EWld GKev WLin
	celebica HWJ 665	WCru
	clematidea	CHar CSpe EBee ECha ECho ECtt EPfP GKev LHop MCCP MTho NBid NChi SAga SMad SPlb SRms SWvt WBVN WCru WFar WKif WLin WSpi
	- 'Lilac Eyes'	MBri MCCP NBre NSti
	convolvulacea misapplied	see *C. grey-wilsonii*
	convolvulacea Kurz	CPne GBuc IGor MTho NSla WPGP
	- CC 4471	MGol
	- J&JA 4.220.705	NWCA
	- 'Alba'	see *C. grey-wilsonii* 'Himal Snow'
	- Forrest's form	see *C. forrestii* Diels
	- var. ***hirsuta*** B&SWJ 7812	WCru
	'Dangshen'	see *C. pilosula*
	dicentrifolia	EMan
	- HWJCM 267	WCru
	forrestii misapplied	see *C. grey-wilsonii*
§	***forrestii*** Diels	EBee GKev NHar WCot
	- BWJ 7776	WCru
§	***grey-wilsonii*** 🏆H4	CAby CHFP CHHB CLAP EBee EBrs ECho GCrs GEdr MAvo MGol SBla WCot WIvy
	- B&SWJ 7532	WCru
§	- 'Himal Snow'	CAby CLAP EBee GCrs GEdr MDKP SBla SPhx WCot WIvy
	handeliana	see *C. tubulosa*
	javanica B&SWJ 380	WCru
	- B&SWJ 8145	WCru
	kawakamii	EBee
	- B&SWJ 1592	WCru
§	***lanceolata***	CAby CPne NSti
	- B&SWJ 5099	WCru
	- B&SWJ 562	WCru
	lancifolia B&SWJ 3835	WCru
	macrocalyx	NChi
	mollis	ECho GSki NBre NGby NLar WFar
	nepalensis Grey-Wilson	see *C. grey-wilsonii*
	obtusa	EBee EWld GKev NChi WCot
	ovata	CFir CLyd EBee GBuc GKev MTho NBro NChi SBla SRms
§	***pilosula***	EBee GKev GPoy MGol MNrw MSal MTho NLar
	- BWJ 7910	WCru
§	***rotundifolia*** var. ***angustifolia***	EBee GKev MDKP
	- var. ***grandiflora***	GKev
	silvestris	see *C. pilosula*
	subscaposa SDR 1867 new	GKev
	tangshen misapplied	see *C. rotundifolia* var. *angustifolia*
	tangshen Oliv.	CAby CArn EBee GKev MNrw MSal MTho SHFr
	thalictrifolia MECC 93	WCru
§	***tubulosa***	EBee LRHS
	ussuriensis	see *C. lanceolata*
	vinciflora	CPne GEdr IGor SBla WBVN WCot WIvy WSHC
	viridiflora	WCru
	viridis HWJK 2435	WCru

Coffea (*Rubiaceae*)

	arabica	CCCN

coffee see *Coffea*

Coix (*Poaceae*)

	lacryma-jobi	MSal SWal

Colchicum ✿ (*Colchicaceae*)

	agrippinum 🏆H4	CAvo CFee CTca EBrs ECha ECho EPot GGar GKev ITim MRav NBir NMen NRya WHoo WTin
	'Antares'	ECha NBir
	atropurpureum	EBrs ECho EPot GEdr LAma
	- Drake's form	ECho
	'Attlee'	LAma
	'Autumn Herald'	CHHB EBrs ECho LAma
N	'Autumn Queen'	CHHB CTca EBrs ECho LAma
§	***autumnale***	CArn CAvo CFee EBrs ECho EPot GKev GPoy ITim LAma LRHS NMen NRya WFar WShi
*	- 'Albopilosum'	NBir
	- 'Alboplenum'	CHFP CHHB EBrs ECho EPot LAma WTin
	- 'Album'	CAvo CBgR CTca EBrs ECho EPot ERCP GAbr GEdr GGar LAma LRHS NBir SPer WFar WGwG WHoo WShi WTin
	- 'Atropurpureum'	ECho
	- var. ***major*** hort.	see *C. byzantinum* Ker Gawl.
	- var. ***minor*** hort.	see *C. autumnale*
§	- 'Nancy Lindsay' 🏆H4	EBrs ECho EPot SRot
	- 'Pannonicum'	see *C. autumnale* 'Nancy Lindsay'
§	- 'Pleniflorum' (d)	CBgR CStu EBrs ECho EPot GEdr LAma MMHG WFar
	- 'Roseum Plenum'	see *C. autumnale* 'Pleniflorum'
	baytopiorum	GEdr GKev
	'Beaconsfield'	GEdr
§	***bivonae***	CWsd EBrs ECha LAma
	- 'Apollo' new	EBrs
	Blom's hybrid	WTin
§	***boissieri***	CWsd EBrs ERos
	- MFF 2192	WCot
	bornmuelleri misapplied	see *C. speciosum* var. *bornmuelleri* hort.
	bornmuelleri Freyn	EPot GEdr LAma
	bowlesianum	see *C. bivonae*
§	***byzantinum*** Ker Gawl. 🏆H4	CTca EBrs ECho EPot LAma LRHS NBir WTin
	- ***album***	see *C. byzantinum* 'Innocence'
§	- 'Innocence'	EBrs EPot
	cilicicum	EPot LAma WHoo
	- 'Purpureum'	EBrs LAma LRHS WWst
	'Conquest'	see *C.* 'Glory of Heemstede'
	corsicum	EBrs ECho ERos NMen WThu
	crocifolium new	EBrs
	cupanii	CPBP EBrs EPot
	- var. ***pulverulentum***	EBrs
	'Daendels'	LAma
	davisii	GEdr
	'Dick Trotter'	CHHB EBrs EPot LAma MBri
	'Disraeli'	EBrs GEdr GKev
	doerfleri	see *C. hungaricum*
	'E.A. Bowles'	GEdr LAma
	falcifolium new	CHHB
§	***giganteum***	EBrs EPot GEdr LAma
§	'Glory of Heemstede'	EBrs GKev
	'Gracia' new	EBrs
	graecum new	EBrs
	'Harlekijn'	EBrs GEdr
§	***hungaricum***	EBrs
	- f. ***albiflorum***	EBrs EPot
	illyricum	see *C. giganteum*
	'Jochem Hof' new	EBrs
	'Jolanthe'	WWst
	kesselringii	WWst

	kotschyi	WWst
	laetum misapplied	see *C. parnassicum*
	'Lilac Bedder'	EBrs EPot
	'Lilac Wonder'	EBrs EPfP EPot GKev LAma LRHS MRav SPer WCot WFar
	lusitanum	LAma
	luteum	EBrs ECho WWst
	macrophyllum	EBrs ECho LAma
	parlatoris	EBrs
§	***parnassicum***	EBrs ECha
	peloponnesiacum	EBrs
	'Pink Goblet' ♀H4	LAma
	'Poseidon' **new**	EBrs
	procurrens	see *C. boissieri*
	pusillum	EBrs
	'Rosy Dawn' ♀H4	CAvo CTca EBrs ECha ECho GGar LAma SPhx
	sfikasianum	EBrs
	sibthorpii	see *C. bivonae*
	speciosum ♀H4	CAvo EBrs ECho EPot GEdr LAma LRHS NBir WCot
	- 'Album' ♀H4	CFee EBla EBrs ECha ECho EPot GEdr GKev LAma LRHS MBri NBir SPhx WCot
	- 'Atrorubens'	ECha LAma MBri
I	- var. ***bornmuelleri*** hort.	GEdr
	- var. ***illyricum*** hort.	see *C. giganteum*
	- 'Maximum'	LAma MBri
	- 'Ordu'	EBrs ECho LEdu
	szovitsii misapplied	see *C. falcifolium*
	szovitsii Fisch. & B. Mey.	EBrs WWst
	tenorei ♀H4	EBrs ECho EPot GKev LAma NBir WCot
	'The Giant'	CHHB EBrs EPot GKev LAma LRHS WCot
	triphyllum **new**	EBrs
	troodi ambig.	ERos
	variegatum	LAma
	'Violet Queen'	EBrs EPot LAma LRHS
	'Waterlily' (d) ♀H4	CAvo CHFP CHHB CLyd CTca EBrs ECho ELan EPfP EPot ERCP GAbr GGar GKev LAma LRHS NBir SPhx WCot WGwG WHoo
	'William Dykes'	EBrs GEdr LAma
	'Zephyr'	ECho LAma

Coleonema (*Rutaceae*)

	album	XPep
§	***pulchellum***	CCCN CHEx CSpe NSti XPep
	pulchrum misapplied	see *C. pulchellum*
	'Sunset Gold'	CPLG CSpe CTrC LHop LPio

Coleus see *Plectranthus, Solenostemon*

Colignonia (*Nyctaginaceae*)

	ovalifolia B&SWJ 10644 **new**	WCru

Colletia (*Rhamnaceae*)

	armata	see *C. hystrix*
	cruciata	see *C. paradoxa*
§	***hystrix***	CBcs CHEx CPLG CTrG CTri GBin GGar SAPC SArc SLon SMad SOWG WSHC
	- 'Rosea'	CTrC SKHP
§	***paradoxa***	CBcs CCCN CHEx CPle IClo IDee LPJP MBri NLar SAPC SArc

Collinsonia (*Lamiaceae*)

	canadensis	CArn ELan EMan MSal

Collomia ✿ (*Polemoniaceae*)

	debilis	NPol
	grandiflora	CSpe EMan NPol WCot
	mazama	NPol WLin

Colobanthus (*Caryophyllaceae*)

	canaliculatus	NMen
§	***quitensis***	ECho

Colocasia (*Araceae*)

	affinis var. ***jeningsii***	CKob EAmu
	antiquorum	see *C. esculenta*
§	***esculenta*** ♀H1	CDWL CHEx CKob EAmu EBrs MJnS SDix XBlo
	- 'Black Magic'	CDTJ CDWL CHEx EAmu LSou MJnS MNrw SAPC SArc WCot WGwG XBlo
	- 'Black Marble' **new**	CDTJ
	- 'Black Ruffles'	MJnS
	- 'Bun-long'	MJnS
	- burgundy-stemmed	CDTJ
	- 'Chicago Harlequin'	CDWL
	- 'Elepaio Keiki' (v)	MJnS
	- 'Fontanesii'	CDTJ CKob EAmu MJnS SKHP
	- 'Hilo Beauty'	XBlo
	- 'Illustris'	CDTJ CKob MJnS
	- 'Japanese Cranberry'	MJnS
	- 'Nancy's Revenge'	CDWL
	- 'Nigrescens'	EAmu
	- 'Palau Keiki'	MJnS
	- 'Ulaula Kumu-oha'	MJnS
	fallax	CDWL CKob EAmu SKHP WPrP
	formosana	CKob
	- B&SWJ 6909	WCru
	gigantea	CDTJ CDWL EAmu

Colquhounia (*Lamiaceae*)

	coccinea	CArn CHEx CHal CHll CTrC EShb GQui MRav NLar SGar SLon WBod WCru WPGP WSHC
	- Sch 2458	WPGP
	- var. ***vestita***	CBcs CPle CWib EBee EPfP GGar IMGH LHop LRHS MSte MWea SEND WBor
	- - B&SWJ 7222	WCru

Columnea (*Gesneriaceae*)

	'Aladdin's Lamp'	CHal WDib
	'Apollo'	WDib
	x ***banksii*** ♀H1	CHal WDib
	'Bold Venture'	WDib
§	'Broget Stavanger' (v)	WDib
	'Chanticleer' ♀H1	CHal MBri WDib
I	'Firedragon'	WDib
	'Gavin Brown'	WDib
	gloriosa	EBak
	hirta ♀H1	MBri WDib
	- 'Variegata'	see *C.* 'Light Prince'
	'Inferno'	WDib
	'Katsura'	MBri WDib
I	'Kewensis Variegata' (v) ♀H1	MBri
§	'Light Prince' (v)	WDib
	'Merkur'	WDib
	microphylla 'Variegata' (v)	MBri
I	'Midnight Lantern'	WDib
	'Rising Sun'	WDib
	'Robin'	WDib
	schiedeana	CHal EShb MBri WDib
	'Stavanger' ♀H1	CHal WDib
	'Stavanger Variegated'	see *C.* 'Broget Stavanger'
	Yellow Dragon Group	CHal

Colutea (*Papilionaceae*)

	arborescens	CArn CBcs CPLG CWib EBee ELan LHop LRHS MBlu MGos MSal SHBN SPer SPlb SPoG WHer XPep
§	***buhsei***	NLar SOWG
	x ***media***	LRav MBlu WOut

- 'Copper Beauty' — CBcs MBri MGos MRav NLar SPer WPat
orientalis — CCCN LHop XPep
persica misapplied — see *C. buhsei*

Combretum (*Combretaceae*)
erythrophyllum — MBri

Commelina (*Commelinaceae*)
coelestis — see *C. tuberosa* Coelestis Group
dianthifolia — CEnt EBee GKev LPio MTho NWCA SHGN SRms WPer
- 'Electric Blue' **new** — EAlp
- 'Sapphirino' — EMon
robusta — EBee LPio WCot
tuberosa — EBrs ELan EPfP LPio MSte WBrE
- B&SWJ 10353 — WCru
- 'Alba' — ELan LPio MSte WPer
- 'Axminster Lilac' — EMon WPer
§ - Coelestis Group — CBcs CEnt CWCL EBee ECha ELon EMan EWin GKev IGor MCot SGar SPet SRkn SRms WFar WPGP WPer WPtf WSHC
- - 'Hopleys Variegated' (v) — CBow EMan

Comptonia (*Myricaceae*)
peregrina — NLar WCru WRos

Conandron (*Gesneriaceae*)
ramondoides B&SWJ 8929 — WCru
- pink-flowered **new** — SBla
- white-flowered **new** — SBla

Conicosia (*Aizoaceae*)
pugioniformis — CTca CTrC

Coniogramme (*Adiantaceae*)
emeiensis **new** — WCot
intermedia — WRic

Conioselinum (*Apiaceae*)
morrisonense B&SWJ 173 — WCru
schugnanicum — WSHC

Conium (*Apiaceae*)
maculatum — CArn MSal

Conoclinium (*Asteraceae*)
greggii — SKHP WSFF

Conopodium (*Apiaceae*)
majus — CRWN WShi

Conradina (*Lamiaceae*)
verticillata — NLAp WPat

Conringia (*Brassicaceae*)
orientalis Tarishis **new** — CPLG

Consolida (*Ranunculaceae*)
§ **ajacis** — MNHC MSal
ambigua — see *C. ajacis*

Convallaria ✿ (*Convallariaceae*)
japonica — see *Ophiopogon jaburan*
keiskei — EBla
majalis ♀H4 — More than 30 suppliers
- 'Albostriata' (v) — CBct CBow CFwr CLAP EBee EBla EBrs ECha ECho EHrv ELan EMan EPPr EPfP MRav MTho MWrn NBir SAga SIng WCot WEas WHer WPGP WSHC
- 'Berlin Giant' — EBla NBre NRya
- 'Blush' — CAvo
- 'Dorien' — CBct CBre CFir MAvo
- 'Flore Pleno' (d) — EBla EHrv MAvo MTho
- 'Fortin's Giant' — CBct CLAP CMea EBla EMon EPla EPot GEdr MRav NBre NEgg NGby SMad WPGP WSel
- 'Gerard Debureaux' — see *C. majalis* 'Green Tapestry'
§ - 'Green Tapestry' (v) — CBct CBow CLAP EMon
- 'Haldon Grange' (v) — CLAP EMon SMad
- 'Hardwick Hall' (v) — CBct CBow CLAP CMdw EBee EBla ECha EHrv EPla EPot MAvo NBre WCot WTin
- 'Hofheim' (v) — WTMC
- 'Prolificans' — CAby CAvo CBct CFir CLAP CMdw EBrs ECho EMon ERos MRav SSvw WCot
- var. **rosea** — More than 30 suppliers
- 'Variegata' (v) — CAvo CHar CMea EBee EBla EPla ERou GCrs LHop NMen SBch SMad SSvw WHil WSel
- 'Vic Pawlowski's Gold' (v) — CLAP CPLG CStu CWsd EBee ELon MAvo
montana — LRHS NLar
transcaucasica — EBee WCot

Convolvulus (*Convolvulaceae*)
althaeoides — CHrt CMea ECGP ECho ELan EShb LRHS NBir SBch SBla SHFr SPer SPhx WAbb WEas WPGP WPtf
§ - subsp. **tenuissimus** — CSWP CSpe CWsd EBee ECtt EMan EWes WCFE WCot
- - 'Pink Fanfare' — WSpi
§ **boissieri** — CGra SBla WAbe WPat
cantabricus — CHll EMan MDKP NSla
chilensis — CCCN CSpe LSou
cneorum ♀H3 — More than 30 suppliers
- 'Snow Angel' — CSBt EBee GBin LBuc MAsh MRav SPoG SVil SWvt WSpi WWeb
elegantissimus — see *C. althaeoides* subsp. *tenuissimus*
humilis — ECho
lineatus — ECho EWes LRHS MTho NMen NWCA SBla SMrm WLin
mauritanicus — see *C. sabatius*
nitidus — see *C. boissieri*
oleifolius — XPep
§ **sabatius** ♀H3 — More than 30 suppliers
- dark-flowered — CCCN CSpe ECho ELan EMan MSte SMrm
- 'Moroccan Beauty' **new** — CSpe WSpi

x *Cooperanthes* see *Zephyranthes*

Cooperia see *Zephyranthes*

Copernicia (*Arecaceae*)
alba — LPal

Coprosma ✿ (*Rubiaceae*)
acerosa 'Hawera' — CBcs
- 'Live Wire' (f) — ECou
- 'Red Rocks' **new** — CBcs CTrC
areolata (m) — ECou
atropurpurea (f) — ECou NWCA
- (m) — ECou
'Autumn Orange' (f) — ECou
'Autumn Prince' (m) — ECou
baueri misapplied — see *C. repens*
'Beatson's Gold' (f/v) — CBcs CBrm CHal CHll CTrG EBee ELan EPfP ERea GGar ISea STre WHen WLeb WSHC
'Black Cloud' **new** — CBcs
'Blue Pearls' (f) — ECou
'Brunette' (f) — ECou
brunnea — CTrC ECho ECou IDee
- 'Blue Beauty' (f) — ECou

- 'Violet Fleck' (f)	ECou
'Bruno' (m)	ECou
'Cappuccino'PBR	CBcs EBee GBin
cheesemanii (f)	ECou
- (m)	ECou
- 'Hanmer Red' (f)	ECou
- 'Mack' (m)	ECou
- 'Red Mack' (f)	ECou
'Chocolate Soldier' (m)	ECou
'Clearwater Gold' **new**	CBcs CTrC
'Coppershine'	CPLG CTrC ERea
crassifolia x ***repens*** (m)	ECou
crenulata	WPic
x ***cunninghamii*** (f)	ECou
- ***macrocarpa*** (m)	ECou
'Cutie' (f)	ECou
depressa	ECou
- 'Orange Spread' (f)	ECou
'Evening Glow'PBR (f/v)	CBgR CCCN CDoC EBee ECou ELan EMil EPfP ERas LHop LRHS MAsh MGos SKHP SLim
'Fire Burst'PBR	CBcs CCCN CDoC ELan EMil EPfP ERas MRav SLim WCFE
'Green Girl' (f)	ECou
'Green Globe'	CHll
'Hinerua' (f)	ECou
'Indigo Lustre' (f)	ECou
'Jewel' (f)	ECou
'Karo Red'PBR (v)	CDoC CTrC EBee EMil EPfP LRHS MAsh MGos SPoG
x ***kirkii*** 'Gold Edge'	ECou
I - 'Kirkii' (f)	CHll ECou STre XPep
- 'Kirkii Variegata' (f/v)	CBcs CDoC CHal CStu CTrC EBee ECou NScw SOWG STre WBrE WSHC WWeb
'Kiwi' (m)	ECou
'Kiwi Red'	GGar
'Kiwi-gold' (m/v)	ECou EMil ERea
'Lemon Drops' (f)	ECou
linariifolia (m)	ECou
lucida (f)	ECou
- 'Mount White' (m)	ECou
- 'Wanaka' (f)	ECou
macrocarpa (f)	ECou
- (m)	CTrC ECou
'Middlemore'	CDoC
nitida (f)	ECou
parviflora (m)	ECou
- purple-fruited (f)	ECou
- red-fruited (f)	ECou
- white-fruited (f)	ECou
'Pearl Drops' (f)	ECou
'Pearl's Sister' (f)	ECou
'Pearly Queen' (f)	ECou
petriei	ECou WThu
- 'Don' (m)	ECou
- 'Lyn' (f)	ECou
'Pride'	CDoC CTrC CTrG
propinqua	SDry WSHC
- (f)	ECou
- (m)	ECou
- var. ***latiuscula*** (f)	ECou
- - (m)	ECou
'Prostrata' (m)	ECou
pseudocuneata (m)	ECou
pumila	EPot
quadrifida	ECou
'Rainbow Surprise'PBR (v)	CCCN CDoC EBee ELan ERas LRHS MAsh MGos MRav SLim SPoG WWeb
§ ***repens***	CPLG EShb XPep
- (f)	ECou
- (m)	ECou SEND
- 'Apricot Flush' (f)	ECou
- 'County Park Plum' (v)	ECou
- 'County Park Purple' (f)	ECou ERea
- 'County Park Red'	ECou
- 'Exotica' (f/v)	ECou
- 'Marble King' (m/v)	ECou
- 'Marble Queen' (m/v) ♀H1-2	CBcs CHll ECou EShb MGos WCot WFar
- 'Orangeade' (f)	ECou
- 'Pacific Night' **new**	ECou ENot SPoG
- 'Painter's Palette' (m)	CBcs EBee ECou
- 'Picturata' (m/v) ♀H1-2	EBee ECou EShb
- 'Pink Splendour' (m/v)	CBcs CDoC EBee ECou ERea EShb LHop MGos
- 'Rangatiri' (f)	ECou
- 'Silver Queen' (m/v)	ECou
- 'Variegata' (m/v)	ECou
rigida	ECou
- 'Ann' (f)	ECou
- 'Tan' (m)	ECou
robusta	CTrC ECou IClo SDry
- 'Cullen's Point' (f)	ECou
- 'Sally Blunt' (f)	ECou
- 'Steepdown' (f)	ECou
- 'Tim Blunt' (m)	ECou
- 'Variegata' (m/v)	ECou
- 'William' (m)	ECou
- 'Woodside' (f)	ECou
rotundifolia	ECou
'Roy's Red' (m)	CBgR CDoC EBee ECou GGar SLim
rugosa (f)	ECou
'Snowberry' (f)	ECou
'Taiko'	CTrC
tenuifolia (m)	ECou
'Translucent Gold' (f)	ECou
'Violet Drops' (f)	ECou
virescens (f)	ECou
'Walter Brockie'	CHll CTrC
'White Lady' (f)	ECou
'Winter Bronze' (f)	ECou
'Yvonne'	MGos SRGP

Coptis (*Ranunculaceae*)

japonica **new**	WCru
- var. ***dissecta***	EBee GEdr WCru
- var. ***major***	CDes WCru WSHC
quinquefolia	EBee GEdr
- B&SWJ 1677	WCru
ramosa **new**	WCru
- B&SWJ 6000	WCru

x *Coralia* (*Papilionaceae*)

'County Park'	ECou
'Essex'	ECou
'Havering'	ECou

Corallospartium (*Papilionaceae*)

crassicaule	ECou
- 'Jack Sprat'	ECou
- var. ***racemosum***	ECou

Cordyline (*Agavaceae*)

australis ♀H3	More than 30 suppliers
- 'Albertii' (v) ♀H3	CBcs CCCN CTrC LHop MBri NMoo SAPC SArc
- 'Atropurpurea'	CDoC IFoB WFar
- 'Black Night'	CCCN CTrC
- 'Black Tower'	CDoC CHll ELan MGos
- 'Coffee Cream'	CBcs EAmu EBee ELan EPfP NBlu SPer WFar
- 'Olive Fountain'	CCCN
- 'Peko'PBR	CCCN
- 'Pink Champagne'	CBcs CCCN EMil LBuc LRHS MGos SPoG
§ - 'Pink Stripe' (v)	CBcs CDTJ CDoC EBee ELan ENot EPfP ISea LRHS LSRN MAsh MBri

		MCCP NBlu NScw SLim SNew SPla SWvt WFar
	- 'Purple Heart'	CCCN CTrC
	- Purpurea Group	CBcs CChe CDTJ CDul CMHG CTrC CWSG EAlp EBee ELan EPfP ISea LAst LCro LRHS MGos NBlu SBLw SEND SGar SHBN SPer SPlb WFar WGer
	- 'Red Sensation'	CHEx CTrC ISea LRHS NBPN SWvt
	- 'Red Star'	CAbb CBcs CDoC CSBt CSam CTrC CWSG CWib EBee ELan ENot EPfP LAst LCro LRHS MCCP MLan MRav MSwo NBlu NPer NPri SNew SPoG SWvt WBrE WCot WFar WGwG WLin
	- 'Sparkler'	CBcs LBuc LRHS MGos
	- 'Sundance' ♀H3	More than 30 suppliers
	- 'Torbay Dazzler' (v) ♀H3	More than 30 suppliers
	- 'Torbay Red' ♀H3	CAbb CBcs CDoC CMHG CWSG EBee ELan EPfP ISea LHop LPan LRHS LSRN MAsh MBri MJnS NPri SPla SWvt WFar WWeb
	- 'Torbay Sunset'	CCCN CDoC CTrC ELan LRHS
	'Autumn'	WFar
	banksii	CTrC WPic
	'Dark Star'	CBcs CCCN CDTJ CDoC
	fruticosa 'Atom'	MBri
	- 'Baby Ti' (v)	MBri
	- 'Calypso Queen'	MBri
	- 'Kiwi'	MBri
	- 'New Guinea Black'	ELan
	- 'Orange Prince'	MBri
	- 'Red Edge' ♀H1	MBri XBlo
	- 'Yellow King'	MBri
	'Green Goddess'	CBcs CTrC GGar
§	***indivisa***	EAmu EBak GGar LPan LRHS MBri SPlb WPGP
	- 'Perkeo'	EBee MGos
	'Jurassic Jade'	CBcs CTrC
	kaspar	CHEx LEdu SAPC SArc
	obtecta	CCCN
	'Pacific Coral' **new**	LBuc
	'Pacific Sunset' **new**	LBuc
	'Pink Stripe'	see *C. australis* 'Pink Stripe'
	'Purple Sensation'	CCCN MAsh
	'Purple Tower' ♀H3	CDoC CHEx CTrC EAmu EMil ENot EPfP MGos NPri SLim SNew SPad SPoG WCot
	'Red Bush'	XBlo
	'Red Fountain'	WCot
§	***stricta***	CHEx MBri
	terminalis	see *C. fruticosa*

Coreopsis (Asteraceae)

	'Astolat'	EBee EMon LHop MNFA SPer SPet
	auriculata Cutting Gold	see *C.* 'Schnittgold'
	- 'Elfin Gold' **new**	EDAr
	- 'Nana'	EBee NBre WFar
	- 'Superba'	EBee
	- 'Zamphir'	EBee MNrw NBhm
	'Baby Gold'	see *C.lanceolata* 'Sonnenkind' (unblotched)
	Baby Sun	see *C.* 'Sonnenkind'
	basalis 'Sunshine' **new**	WPer
	'Calypso' (v)	EWes LRHS SCoo SMad WWeb
	'Cutting Edge' **new**	CEnt
	'Golden Gain'	see *C.* 'Schnittgold', *C. verticillata* 'Golden Gain'
	grandiflora	EBee NBlu SWat XPep
	- 'Badengold'	EBee EMil
	- 'Bernwode' (v)	EBee NLar SPoG
	- 'Domino'	EBee LHop NBre SHGN
	- 'Early Sunrise' ♀H4	CSBt EBee ECrN ECtt EPfP ERou EShb GMaP LBMP LDai LRHS MBri MHer MWat NBir NEgg NMir NPer SAga SGar SMer SPet SPoG STes SWal SWvt WFar WHen WPer WWFP
	- Flying Saucers = 'Walcoreop'PBR	GBri LRHS SCoo SPoG
	- 'Heliot'	EBee
	- 'Kelvin Harbutt'	ERou
	- 'Mayfield Giant'	CSBt EBee ERou EShb LHop LRHS MFOX MNrw NPri SPer SPoG SRms SWat SWvt
	- 'Rising Sun'	MBri NPri WPer
	- 'Sunburst'	EBee GSki LRHS MWgw NBre WPer
	- 'Sunray'	CBcs CDoC COIW CSBt CWib EBee ECtt EShb LAst LRHS LSRN MBri NGdn SPla SPlb SPoG SRms SWvt WFar WMoo WPer WWeb
	- 'Tetra Riesen'	NBre
	lanceolata	NBre NSti
	- 'Goldfink'	GSki MBrN MRav SRms
§	- 'Sonnenkind' (unblotched)	EBee EPfP MBNS NBlu NNor SWvt WFar WWeb
	- 'Walter'	EBee ENot LRHS MBri MCCP MMHG MWgw NBlu
	'Limerock Ruby'PBR	MNrw WFar
	maximiliani	see *Helianthus maximiliani*
	palmata	EPPr MDKP
	pubescens	EBee LSou
	- 'Sunshine Superman' **new**	CSam EDAr
	pulchra	EBee
	rosea	NLar WFar WPer
	- 'American Dream'	COIW CSBt EBee ELan EMil ENot EPfP EShb GAbr GSki LAst LBMP LRHS LSRN MCCP NCGa NEgg NGdn SGar SPer SPlb SPoG SRms SWal SWvt WBrE WFar WWeb
	- 'Heaven's Gate'	EBee EKen EPfP ERou GBri MAvo NBPC SPoG
	- 'Sweet Dreams'PBR	EBrs SPer WFar
§	'Schnittgold'	CWan EBee MWgw NBre WFar WPer WRHF
	'Sonnenkind' (unblotched)	see *C.lanceolata* 'Sonnenkind'
I	'Sonnenkind' (red-blotched)	EBee ECtt EMil LBMP MHer NBre WPer
	'Sterntaler'	CFir EBee EMil EPPr EPau ERou EShb GAbr LRHS MBri MWat NCGa NPri NVic SMad SPet SWvt WPer WWeb
	'Tequila Sunrise' (v)	EBee EMan MBNS NMoo
	tripteris	CAby CPou EMon GBin MDKP MSte MWea NBre SAga SHar SMad SPhx SSvw WMoo WPer
	- 'Mostenveld' **new**	EBee
	- 'Pierre Bennerup'	EMon
	verticillata	EBee ECha ECrN EHrv ENot EPfP LRHS MBrN MDun MHer MWat NPer SDix SRms SWat WFar WHal WTin
	- Crème Brûlée = 'Crembru' **new**	EBrs
I	- 'Golden Gain'	EBee ECtt EMan EPla GBri GSki LHop LRHS MArl MLLN NGdn WFar WMnd
	- 'Golden Shower'	see *C. verticillata* 'Grandiflora'
§	- 'Grandiflora' ♀H4	CBcs CPrp CTca EBee EBrs ELan EPfP ERou GMaP GSki MNFA MRav NCGa NGdn NHol NOak NVic SMad SPer SPla WCAu WCot WFar WMnd
	- 'Moonbeam' ♀H4	More than 30 suppliers
	- 'Old Timer' ♀H4	SDix
	- 'Zagreb' ♀H4	More than 30 suppliers

coriander see *Coriandrum sativum*

Coriandrum (*Apiaceae*)

sativum	CArn CSev GPoy ILis LRHS MHer MNHC NBlu NVic SIde WPer
- 'Leisure'	CSev NPri
- 'Santo'	ELau NGHP WJek

Coriaria ✿ (*Coriariaceae*)

arborea	WCru
intermedia B&SWJ 019	WCru
japonica	IDee NLar WCot WCru
- B&SWJ 2833	WCru
- subsp. ***intermedia*** B&SWJ 3877	WCru
kingiana	ECou WCru
§ ***microphylla***	WCru
- B&SWJ 8999	WCru
myrtifolia	CBcs EBee GSki NLar WCru WFar XPep
napalensis	EWld NLar WCru
- BWJ 7755	WCru
pteridoides	WCru
ruscifolia	WCru
- HCM 98178	WCru
sarmentosa	WCru
terminalis var. ***xanthocarpa***	CTrG EMan EPfP GBuc LSou NLar WCot WCru WPGP
- - GWJ 9204	WCru
- - HWJK 2112c	WCru
thymifolia	see *C. microphylla*

Coris (*Primulaceae*)

monspeliensis	XPep

Cornus ✿ (*Cornaceae*)

alba L.	CCVT CDoC CDul CLnd CTrG ECrN EMac EWTr ISea MDun MHer MRav NWea SRms WMou
* - 'Albovariegata' (v)	ECho IFoB
- 'Alleman's Compact'	CPMA
- 'Argenteovariegata'	see *C. alba* 'Variegata'
- 'Aurea' ♀H4	More than 30 suppliers
- Chief Bloodgood = 'Chblzam'	CPMA
- 'Cream Cracker'PBR (v)	MAsh NHol WPat
- 'Elegantissima' (v) ♀H4	More than 30 suppliers
- 'Gouchaultii' (v)	CBcs CMac CPMA EBee ECrN EMac EPfP EWTr LPan LRHS MBar MRav NPri SLim SPer SRms WFar
- 'Hessei' misapplied	see *C. sanguinea* 'Compressa'
- 'Hessei'	MRav WPat
- Ivory Halo = 'Bailhalo'PBR	EBee EMil ENot EPfP LRHS MAsh MBNS MBri MGos MRav NPri NWea SPer SPoG SRms WGer
- 'Kesselringii'	More than 30 suppliers
- 'Red Gnome'	CPMA LTwo WPat
- 'Ruby'	CPMA
- 'Siberian Pearls'	CBcs CPMA ELan MBlu MGos NEgg SSta
§ - 'Sibirica' ♀H4	More than 30 suppliers
- 'Sibirica Variegata' (v)	CBow CDoC CMac CPMA EBee ENot EPfP EPla EWTr GCra LCro LPan LRHS LSRN MAsh MBar MBlu MGos NCGa NEgg NPri SHBN SLim SPer SPoG SSpi SSta SWvt WFar
- 'Snow Pearls'	CPMA
- 'Spaethii' (v) ♀H4	More than 30 suppliers
§ - 'Variegata' (v)	CBcs ECho EQua LAst MGos
- 'Westonbirt'	see *C. alba* 'Sibirica'
alternifolia	CBcs CMCN CTho ELan MDun SSpi WPat
§ - 'Argentea' (v) ♀H4	More than 30 suppliers
- 'Silver Giant' (v)	CPMA WSpi
- 'Variegata'	see *C. alternifolia* 'Argentea'
amomum	CAbP CBcs NHol NLar WFar
- 'Blue Cloud'	CPMA
- subsp. ***obliqua***	WPGP
angustata	SPer
§ 'Ascona'	CBcs CEnd CPMA ELan EPfP EWTr IMGH LRHS MBlu MBri NEgg NLar SSpi SSta WPat
Aurora = 'Rutban' (Stellar Series)	CPMA MBlu MPkF NLar SKHP
canadensis ♀H4	More than 30 suppliers
candidissima Marshall	see *C. racemosa*
capitata	CAgr CBcs CBgR CDoC CDul CEnd CHEx CMac CPLG CPne CSBt CTho CTrG EPfP EShb GGar ITim LRHS MWya SEND SGar SSpi WBVN WCot WCru WCwm WFar WPGP WPat WSpi
- subsp. ***emeiensis***	SSpi
§ Celestial = 'Rutdan' (Stellar Series)	CPMA MPkF
'Centennial'	LRHS SSpi
chinensis	LMil SWvt
'Constellation' (Stellar Series)	CPMA SKHP
controversa	CBcs CDul CLnd CMCN CTri ECho ECrN ELan EMil EPfP EWTr LPan MBar MBlu MDun SHBN SLPl SReu SSpi SSta SWvt WFar WHCr WHar WOrn WPGP
§ - 'Frans Type' (v)	CBcs CEnd ELan ERom LSRN MBlu SHBN SReu SSta WHCG
I - 'Marginata Nord'	NPal WPGP
- 'Pagoda'	EPfP MBlu MBri NBhm NLar NPal SSpi
- 'Variegata' (v) ♀H4	More than 30 suppliers
- 'Variegata' Frans type	see *C. controversa* 'Frans Type'
- 'Winter Orange'	NLar
'Eddie's White Wonder' ♀H4	More than 30 suppliers
florida	CCVT CDul CLnd CMCN CTho EBee EPfP LAst LCro LRHS MBar NBlu NPen SPer WBVN WHCr WNor
- 'Alba Plena' (d)	CPMA NLar
- 'Andrea Hart'	CPMA
- 'Apple Blossom'	CMac CPMA ECho
- Cherokee Brave = 'Comco No 1'	CPMA CWib ECho LRHS MAsh MPkF NCGa NLar SSpi
- 'Cherokee Chief' ♀H4	CAbP CBcs CEnd CPMA CTri CWib ECho EPfP IMGH LRHS MGos MPkF NLar SBLw SHBN SPer SSta WBod WFar WGob WOrn WPat WSpi
- 'Cherokee Daybreak'	see *C. florida* 'Daybreak'
- 'Cherokee Princess'	CPMA ECho LRHS MPkF NCGa
- 'Cherokee Sunset'	see *C. florida* 'Sunset'
- 'Cloud Nine'	CBcs CDoC CPMA EBee ECho MGos MPkF NCGa NLar SPoG WOrn WSpi
* - 'Daniela'	NLar
§ - 'Daybreak' (v)	CBcs CEnd CPMA CWib ECho LSRN MBri MGos MPkF SPer SSta
- 'First Lady'	CMac CPMA ECho
- 'Fragrant Cloud'	ECho
- 'G.H. Ford' (v)	CPMA
- 'Gloria Burkett'	CAbP LMil LRHS SSpi
- 'Golden Nugget'	CPMA ECho
- 'Junior Miss'	CEnd CPMA EMil
- 'Junior Miss Variegated' (v)	CPMA
- 'Moonglow'	CPMA
- 'Pendula'	CBcs CPMA MPkF
- f. ***pluribracteata*** (d)	NLar
- 'Purple Glory'	CBcs CPMA ECho MBri NLar SSta
- 'Pygmaea'	NLar

	- 'Rainbow'	CAbP CBcs CPMA CWib EBee EPfP LRHS MAsh MBri MGos MPkF NEgg SBod SHBN SPer SPla SPoG
	- 'Red Giant'	CAbP CBcs CPMA ELan LMil LRHS MBri NLar SSpi
	- 'Royal Red'	CPMA MPkF
	- f. ***rubra***	CBcs CSBt CTri CWib ECho ELan EWTr LAst LRHS MBri MGos MWea SBLw SPer WFar WGer WNor WSpi
	- 'Spring Day'	ECho
	- 'Spring Song'	CMac CPMA ECho
	- 'Springtime'	CPMA ECho NLar
	- 'Stoke's Pink'	CEnd CPMA ECho WSpi
§	- 'Sunset' (v)	CBcs CEnd CPMA CWib ECho MAsh MGos MPkF NLar SBLw SHBN SPer SSta SWvt
	- 'Sweetwater'	CBcs CEnd CPMA EMil
	- 'Tricolor'	see *C. florida* 'Welchii'
	- 'Variegata'	SBLw
	- 'Weaver's White'	CBcs ECho MPkF
§	- 'Welchii' (v)	CEnd CPMA
	- 'White Cloud'	CPMA ELan MBri MPkF
	- 'Xanthocarpa'	MPkF
	hemsleyi	EPla
	hessei misapplied	see *C. sanguinea* 'Compressa'
	hongkongensis HWJ 1033	WCru
	'Kelsey Dwarf'	see *C. sericea* 'Kelseyi'
	'Kenwyn Clapp'	CPMA
	kousa	CDoC CDul CMCN CMac CPne CTho EBee ECho ECrN ELan EMac EPfP ERom ISea LRHS MBar MBri MDun MLan NBlu NEgg SHBN SPer SPlb WFar WHCG WHar
	- B&SWJ 5494	WCru
	- 'Aget'	CPMA
	- 'Akabana' **new**	CPMA
	- 'Akatsuki' **new**	CPMA
	- 'All Summer'	CPMA
	- 'Autumn Rose'	CPMA EPfP NLar
	- 'Beni-fuji'	CPMA NLar
	- 'Big Apple'	CPMA
	- 'Blue Shadow'	CPMA IDee MBri
	- 'Bonfire' (v)	CPMA
	- 'Bultinck's Beauty'	LRHS NLar
	- 'Bush's Pink'	CPMA
	- 'Cherokee' **new**	CPMA
	- 'China Dawn' (v)	CPMA
	- var. ***chinensis*** ♀H4	More than 30 suppliers
	- - 'Bodnant Form'	CEnd CPMA WPGP
	- - 'China Girl'	CAbP CBcs CDul CEnd CPMA CWib ELan EPfP EWTr LBuc LMil LRHS MAsh MBlu MBri MGos MSwo MWya SHBN SPer SPoG SSpi SSta WBod WOrn WPGP WPat
	- - 'Claudia' **new**	MBri
	- - 'Greta's Gold' (v)	CPMA
	- - 'Milky Way'	CMCN CPMA CWib ECho LBuc MBlu MBri MPkF NLar SHBN WSpi
	- - 'Snowflake'	CPMA
	- - Spinners form	CPMA
	- - 'Summer Stars'	CPMA
	- - 'White Dusted'	CPMA EPfP SPoG
	- - 'White Fountain'	MBlu MBri MPkF NLar
	- - 'Wieting's Select'	CPMA MBri MPkF
	- - 'Wisley Queen'	CAbP LRHS MAsh
	- 'Claudine'	CPMA
	- 'Doctor Bump'	CPMA
	- 'Doubloon'	CPMA ECho
	- 'Dwarf Pink'	CPMA NLar
	- 'Ed Mezitt'	CPMA
	- 'Elizabeth Lustgarten'	CPMA SSta
	- 'Fanfare'	CPMA
	- 'Galilean'	CPMA
	- 'Gay Head'	CPMA
I	- 'Girard's Nana'	CPMA
	- 'Gold Cup' (v)	CPMA MPkF
	- 'Gold Star' (v)	CAbP CBcs CEnd CMCN CMac CPMA CWib ECho ELan EMil EPfP LBuc LMil LRHS MAsh MBlu MBri MGos NEgg NLar SHBN SPla SPoG SSpi
	- 'Greensleeves'	CPMA
	- 'Heart Throb'	CPMA NLar
	- 'Highland'	CPMA
	- 'John Slocock'	SSpi
	- 'Kreus Dame'	CPMA MBri MPkF
	- 'Little Beauty'	CPMA
	- 'Lustgarten Weeping'	CPMA LRHS
	- 'Madame Butterfly'	CEnd CPMA LRHS MAsh MBri NLar WGob
	- 'Milky Way Select'	CBcs CPMA ECho LPan MGos
	- 'Minuma'	NLar
	- 'Miss Petty'	CPMA MPkF NLar
	- 'Moonbeam'	CPMA MBri MPkF
	- 'Mount Fuji'	CPMA NLar
	- 'National'	CPMA ECho LMil MBlu MGos MPkF NLar WPat
	- 'Nicole'	CDoC NLar WGob WPat
	- 'Peve Limbo' (v)	CPMA MPkF
	- 'Polywood'	CPMA
	- 'Radiant Rose'	CPMA MPkF NLar
	- 'Rasen'	CPMA MBri NLar
	- 'Rel Whirlwind'	CPMA
	- 'Rosea'	CPMA
	- Samaratin = 'Samzam' (v)	CEnd CPMA MBri MPkF
	- 'Satomi' ♀H4	More than 30 suppliers
	- 'Schmetterling'	CPMA MBri
	- 'Snowbird' **new**	CPMA
	- 'Snowboy' (v)	CBcs CEnd CPMA LRHS NLar
	- 'Southern Cross'	CPMA
	- 'Square Dance'	CPMA
	- 'Steeple'	CPMA
	- 'Summer Fun'	CPMA
	- 'Summer Majesty'	CPMA
	- 'Sunsplash' (v)	CPMA
	- 'Temple Jewel' (v)	CPMA LRHS
	- 'Teutonia'	CPMA MBri MPkF
	- 'Tinknor's Choice'	CPMA
	- 'Trinity Star'	CPMA
	- 'Triple Crown'	CPMA
	- 'Tsukubanomine'	CPMA NLar
	- 'U.S.A.'	MPkF
	- 'Vale Milky Way' (v)	NLar
	- 'Weaver's Weeping'	CPMA MPkF
	- 'Weiss Fontane' **new**	CPMA
	- 'Wisley Queen' **new**	CPMA
	- 'Wolf Eyes' (v)	CPMA MBlu MPkF SSta
	kousa* x *florida 'Aurea' **new**	MPkF
	macrophylla Wall.	CMCN EPfP WCwm WPGP
	mas	More than 30 suppliers
	- 'Aurea' (v)	CAbP CPMA EBee ELan EPfP LRHS MAsh MBri MGos MRav NEgg NLar SLim SPer SPoG SSpi SSta WPat
§	- 'Aureoelegantissima' (v)	CEnd CGHE CPMA CWib EBee MAsh MBri NLar SPer SSpi WFar WPGP WPat WSHC
	- 'Elegantissima'	see *C. mas* 'Aureoelegantissima'
I	- 'Flava'	CPMA NLar
	- 'Golden Glory' ♀H4	CBcs CPMA EPfP MBlu MBri NLar
	- 'Jolico'	CPMA MBlu MBri NLar
	- 'Pioneer'	CPMA
	- 'Redstone'	CPMA
	- 'Spring Glow'	CPMA NLar
	- 'Variegata' (v) ♀H4	CBcs CMCN CMac CPMA EBee EPfP LRHS MAsh MBlu MBri MGos NLar NPal SPer SPoG SSpi WFar WPat
N	'Norman Hadden' ♀H4	CAbP CBcs CDoC CDul CEnd CMCN CMac CPMA CSBt CTho

	CTri ECho EPfP IMGH LAst LRHS MBri MRav MWya SHFr SMad SSpi SSta WBor WFar WPGP WPat
nuttallii	CCVT CDul CTho CTri CWib ECrN ELan EPfP IMGH ISea LRHS MGos SHBN SPer SWvt WFar WNor
- B&SWJ 9651	WCru
- 'Ascona'	see *C.* 'Ascona'
- 'Barrick'	CPMA
- 'Colrigo Giant'	CPMA MPkF SSpi WPat
- 'Gold Spot' (v)	CMac CPMA ECho EPfP LRHS MGos WPat
- 'Monarch'	CPMA CTho NLar
- 'North Star'	CPMA MBri NLar
- 'Pink Blush'	MPkF NLar
- 'Portlemouth'	CEnd CPMA LRHS MAsh SSpi WGob WPat WSpi
- 'Zurico'	CPMA MPkF NLar
officinalis	CAgr CDul CMCN CTho EBee ECrN EMil EPfP LPan LRHS MAsh MBri MWea NLar WCwm
'Ormonde'	CPMA ECho LRHS NLar SKHP SSpi
'Pink Blush'	CPMA
'Porlock' Υ^{H4}	CDul CMCN CPMA EPfP IMGH LRHS MBri NLar SSpi
pumila	CPMA NLar
§ ***racemosa***	NLar WFar
rugosa	NLar WNor
x ***rutgersiensis*** Galaxy	see *C.* Celestial
- 'Ruth Ellen'	see *C.* Ruth Ellen
§ Ruth Ellen = 'Rutlan' (Stellar Series)	CPMA NLar
sanguinea	CBcs CCVT CDul CLnd CRWN CTri ECrN EMac EPfP LBuc MRav MSwo NWea SPer WHar WMou XPep
- 'Anny'	MAsh MBlu NHol
§ - 'Compressa'	EPfP NHol NLar WSPU
- 'Magic Flame'	MBri NHol
- 'Midwinter Fire'	More than 30 suppliers
- 'Winter Beauty'	CBgR CDoC CPMA CSBt CWib EBee EPfP ERas MBlu NEgg NLar SHBN SLon WFar WPat WSPU
§ ***sericea***	CArn EMac SRms WMoo
- 'Budd's Yellow'	LRHS MBri
- 'Cardinal'	EPfP LRHS MBri NLar
- 'Coral Red'	CPMA
- 'Flaviramea' Υ^{H4}	More than 30 suppliers
- 'Hedgerows Gold'	CPMA EMil LBuc LHop LRHS MAsh SPoG WPat
- 'Isanti'	CPMA
§ - 'Kelseyi'	CBgR CMac CPMA EBee EPla LRHS MBNS MBar MRav NPri NPro SBod SLPl SPer SPoG
- Kelsey's Gold = 'Rosco'	MAsh SLon WPat
- subsp. ***occidentalis*** 'Sunshine'	CPMA NLar NPro SAga
§ - 'White Gold' (v) Υ^{H4}	CBow CDoC CPMA EBee ECrN ENot EPla MBri MRav MSwo NPro SLon SPer SPoG WFar WMoo
- 'White Spot'	see *C. sericea* 'White Gold'
Stardust = 'Rutfan' (Stellar Series)	CPMA
Stellar Pink = 'Rutgan' (Stellar Series)	CPMA CWib MBri MPkF NLar SKHP
stolonifera	see *C. sericea*
- 'White Spot'	see *C. sericea* 'White Gold'
suecica	NHar
Venus = 'Kn30-8' new	MPkF
walteri	CMCN WCwm WFar
wilsoniana	CMCN

Corokia (*Escalloniaceae*)

buddlejoides	CBcs CDoC CMHG CTca CWib ECou GGar SOWG SPer WFar
'Coppershine'	CMHG
cotoneaster	CAbP CMac CSBt CTri EBee ECho ECou ELan EPfP EPot LRHS MGos SBod SDry SLon SMad SPer SPoG WBrE WCot WFar WPat
- 'Boundary Hill'	ECou
- 'Brown's Stream'	ECou
- 'Hodder River'	ECou
- 'Little Prince'	GGar
- 'Ohau Scarlet'	ECou
- 'Ohau Yellow'	ECou
- 'Swale Stream'	ECou
- 'Wanaka'	ECou
macrocarpa	CDoC ECou ISea SDix
x ***virgata***	CAbP CBcs CDoC CMHG CMac CPLG CTrC CTri ECou ELan EPfP ISea LRHS MBlu MCCP NScw SAPC SArc SPer SPlb SWvt WBVN WBod WHar WSHC
- 'Bronze King'	CBrm CDoC EBee SOWG SPer
- 'Bronze Lady'	ECou WGer
- 'Cheesemanii'	ECou GGar
- 'County Park Lemon'	ECou SOWG
- 'County Park Orange'	ECou
- 'County Park Purple'	ECou
- 'County Park Red'	ECou
- 'Envy'	ECou
- 'Everglades'	ECou
- 'Frosted Chocolate'	CBcs CDoC CTrC EBee ECou EPfP LHop LTwo MGos SKHP SOWG SSta WCot WFar
- 'Geenty's Green'	ECou
- 'Havering'	ECou
- 'Mangatangi'	MGos
- 'Pink Delight'	CDoC ECou EPfP MRav SSta
- 'Red Wonder'	CDoC CMHG CMac CPen CTrC EBee GGar LRHS MBri SDry SEND SOWG SPoG
- 'Sandrine'	ECou
- 'Silver Ghost'	ECou
- 'Sunsplash' (v)	CBcs CDoC CTrC ECou LBMP LHop LRHS LTwo MGos SAga SPoG
I - 'Virgata'	CChe ECou MGos
- 'Wingletye'	ECou
- 'Yellow Wonder'	CBcs CMHG CPen CTrC EBee ECot ECou GGar MGos NLar SBod SPoG WBod

Coronilla (*Papilionaceae*)

comosa	see *Hippocrepis comosa*
emerus	see *Hippocrepis emerus*
glauca	see *C. valentina* subsp. *glauca*
minima	SBla WAbe XPep
valentina	CDMG CDoC CMac CRHN CSPN EMil LHop SBra SDix XPep
§ - subsp. ***glauca*** Υ^{H3}	CBgR CDul CFee CMac CSBt CTca CWib EBee ELan EPfP ERea LAst LRHS SGar SPer SPoG SRms WAbe WBod WHCG WKif WPat XPep
- - 'Brockhill Blue'	CWGN SBra SKHP
- - 'Citrina' Υ^{H3}	More than 30 suppliers
* - - 'Pygmaea'	WCot WWFP
- - 'Variegata' (v)	CBcs CBgR CDoC CMac CSBt CSPN CTca CTri CWCL CWib EBee ELan EMil EPfP ERea LRHS MAsh SBod SBra SLim SLon SPer SPla SPoG WCot WEas WFar XPep
varia	CArn NLar NPri SRms XPep

Correa (*Rutaceae*)

alba	CCCN CDoC CPLG CTrC ECou EPfP WGwG XPep
- 'Pinkie' Υ^{H2}	CBcs CPLG ECou SAga SHGN SOWG WCot
backhouseana Υ^{H2}	CAbb CBcs CDoC CPLG CPle CTrG CTri EBee ECre EPfP GGar

		IDee LHop NLar SAga SBod SGar SLon SOWG SPoG WCot WGwG WSHC WSPU
	– 'Peaches and Cream'	SRkn
	baeuerlenii	CPLG ECou SOWG
	decumbens	CPLG CTrC ECou GSki SOWG
	'Dusky Bells' ♀H2	CBcs CCCN CDMG CDoC CHll CSWP CTrC CTri ECou EPfP LHop SAga SBra SOWG SRkn
	'Dusky Maid'	CCCN CPLG WAbe
	'Federation Belle'	CDoC ECou SOWG
	glabra	SOWG
	– red-flowered	ECou
	'Gwen'	CDoC ECou SOWG
	'Harrisii'	see *C.* 'Mannii'
	'Inglewood Gold'	ECou
	'Ivory Bells'	ECou
	lawrenceana	CDoC CPLG CTrC ECou SEND WAbe
§	'Mannii' ♀H2	CBcs CDoC CPLG CPom CSev EBee ECou EPfP SKHP SOWG SPoG WSHC
	'Marian's Marvel' ♀H2	CCCN CDoC CMHG CPLG ECou SGar SOWG SRkn WAbe
	'Peachy Cream'	CDoC EPfP SAga
	'Pink Mist'	ECou
	'Poorinda Mary'	ECou SOWG
	pulchella ♀H2	CDoC CPLG CTri SOWG
	– orange-flowered **new**	ECou
	reflexa ♀H2	CDoC CPLG ECou IDee SOWG WAbe
	– var. ***nummulariifolia***	ECou WAbe WCot
	– var. ***reflexa***	CPLG
	– var. ***scabridula*** 'Yanakie'	ECou SOWG
*	– ***virens***	CPLG WEas
	relexa 'Harbur' **new**	ECou
	schlechtendalii **new**	ECou

Cortaderia ✿ (*Poaceae*)

	RCB/Arg K2-2	WCot
	RCB/Arg Y-1	WCot
	argentea	see *C. selloana*
	'Candy Floss' **new**	CKno
	fulvida misapplied	see *C. richardii* (Endl.) Zotov
§	***fulvida*** (Buchanan) Zotov	CBcs CBig CHrt EBee EWes EWin EWsh GFor IDee MNrw SMad
	'Point du Raz' **new**	CKno
	richardii misapplied	see *C. fulvida* (Buchanan) Zotov
	richardii ambig.	EPau XIsg
§	***richardii*** (Endl.) Zotov ♀H3-4	CAby CBcs CBig CKno CMCo EPPr EPla EWes EWsh GAbr GGar GMaP IBlr LBMP NVic SAPC SArc SMad SWal WCot WCru WMnd
	– BR 26	GGar
§	***selloana***	CBcs CBig CDul CHEx CSBt CTrG CTri CWib EHul EPfP LBMP MAvo MBar MGos MRav NBir NBlu NHol SAPC SArc SPlb SWal WFar WMoo XIsg
§	– 'Albolineata' (v)	CBcs CBct CBrm EBee ELon EMil EWes MWht NOak SEND SLim SPer SPoG SSta SWvt WLeb WPat
§	– 'Aureolineata' (v) ♀H3	CBcs CBrm CDoC CMac CSam EBee ELan ENot EPfP LAst LRHS MAsh MGos MMoz SLim SPer SPoG WFar WLeb WPGP WPat
	– 'Cool Ice'	CKno CPen
	– 'Elegans'	CBig
	– 'Gold Band'	see *C. selloana* 'Aureolineata'
	– 'Icalma'	CPen CPrp EBee EPPr LBMP
	– 'Monstrosa'	SMad
	– 'Patagonia'	EPPr
	– 'Pink Feather'	EBee EPfP SAdn SApp WFar WWeb
	– 'Pumila' ♀H4	More than 30 suppliers
	– 'Rendatleri'	CBcs CBig CDoC ELan ENot EPfP EWsh LRHS MAsh SCoo SLim SMad SPer SPoG
	– 'Rosea'	CBig EAlp EBee EPfP LBMP LCro LRHS MBar MGos NBlu NGdn WFar
	– Silver Feather = 'Notcort' (v)	ENot EWsh
	– 'Silver Fountain' (v)	ELan EPfP LRHS MAsh
	– 'Silver Stripe'	see *C. selloana* 'Albolineata'
	– 'Splendid Star'PBR (v)	CBcs CDoC CKno GBin LBuc LHop MAsh MBri MGos NLar SAdn SBra SMad SPoG SWvt
	– 'Sunningdale Silver' ♀H3	CBcs CBig CDoC CMac COIW CPrp EBee ECha ECtt EHul ELan ENot EPfP GSki ISea LAst LCro LRHS MAsh MBri MGos SHBN SLim SMad SPer SPoG SWvt WFar
*	– 'White Feather'	CChe COIW EBee NGdn SApp SLim WFar WMoo WWeb
	Toe Toe	see *C. richardii* (Endl.) Zotov

Cortiella (*Apiaceae*)

aff. ***hookeri*** HWJK 2291	WCru

Cortusa (*Primulaceae*)

brotheri	ECho NEgg
matthioli	CPom EBee ECho EPfP GCrs NEgg NMen NWCA SRms WBVN WFar WRos
– 'Alba'	EBee ECho GBuc GEdr GKev NEgg NHol NMen NWCA SRms
– subsp. ***pekinensis***	CFir CLyd ECho GBuc GGar NHol NLar NMen SRms
– var. ***yezoensis***	EBee
turkestanica	ECho

Corydalis ✿ (*Papaveraceae*)

	CC 3862	WCot
	CLD 385	EMon
	from Sichuan, China	CPom MDKP NCot
	alexeenkoana subsp. ***vittae***	see *C. vittae*
	x ***allenii***	GCrs
	ambigua misapplied	see *C. fumariifolia*
	ambigua Cham. & Schldlt.	WWst
	angustifolia	NDlv
	– white-flowered	GCrs WWst
	anthriscifolia	CLAP WCot
	aquilegoides **new**	EBee
	aurea	WHil
	'Blackberry Wine'	CDes CHll CSpe EBee ECha GBri GBuc MAvo MDKP NCGa NPri SPur WFar
	'Blue Panda'	see *C. flexuosa* 'Blue Panda'
	bracteata white	WWst
	bulbosa misapplied	see *C. cava*
	bulbosa (L.) DC.	see *C. solida*
	buschii	CDes CHHB CLAP CPom EBee EBrs ECho ERos GCrs GEdr NHar NRya SBla SCnR WPGP WPrP WWst
	cashmeriana	CLAP CWCL GCrs GEdr NHar NLAp NMen SBla WAbe WHal
	– 'Kailash'	CLAP EMon GBuc MAvo NLar
	cashmeriana x ***flexuosa***	WAbe
	caucasica	ERos GBuc NMen
	– var. ***alba*** misapplied	see *C. malkensis*
§	***cava***	CLAP CPom CStu EBee EBrs ECho EPot LAma MWgw NMyG SHGN SPhx WAbe WFar WShi
	– 'Albiflora'	CLAP CSsd EBrs ECho EPot SBla SPhx WAbe
	– subsp. ***cava***	ECho
	chaerophylla	IBlr
	– B&SWJ 2951	WCru

	cheilanthifolia	CBcs CPLG CPrp CSpe EBee ECha EDAr EHrv EMar EPfP GEdr GSki LBMP LRHS NEgg SGar SIng SPhx SRms SWat WEas WPGP WPnn WTin
	'Craigton Blue' **new**	NHar
	curviflora	EBee
	- subsp. ***rosthornii***	EWes SSvw
	- - 'Blue Heron' **new**	SBla
	davidii	CExc EBee
I	***decipiens*** misapplied ♀H4	CPom EBrs ECho EPot MWgw WPrP
I	***decipiens*** misapplied, purple-flowered	EBee EBrs ECho WWst
	decipiens Schott, Nyman & Kotschy	see *C. solida* subsp. *incisa*
	degensis **new**	EBee
	densiflora	WWst
	'Early Bird'	EWes
	elata	More than 30 suppliers
	- 'Blue Summit'	CLAP EBee EBrs EPPr MSte SBla
	elata* x *flexuosa clone 1	CLAP CMdw CPom EGle GBin GCrs GEdr WPrP
	'Electric Blue' (V)	NBhm
	erdelii	EBrs ECho WWst
	flexuosa ♀H4	CFee CMil CPLG CSpe EBee ECho EDAr EGle EPfP EPot LAst MArl MLHP MNrw MTho NCob NRnb SGar WAbe WBor WFar WSHC
	- CD&R 528	MRav NRya
	- 'Balang Mist'	CLAP EGle SBla
	- 'Blue Dragon'	see *C. flexuosa* 'Purple Leaf'
§	- 'Blue Panda'	CElw EGle EWes GBuc GMaP MDun NHar NLar WFar
	- 'China Blue'	More than 30 suppliers
	- 'Copperhead'	ECho
	- 'Golden Panda' (v)PBR	CBct CBow EBee ECho LFur LHop LSou MBNS MCCP MMHG NLar SPoG WCot
	- 'Hale Cat'	EPPr
	- 'Hidden Purple' **new**	CHid
	- 'Nightshade'	EBee ECtt GBuc NBid NCob WCot WFar WPrP
I	- 'Norman's Seedling'	EBee ECtt EPPr WCot WPGP
	- 'Père David'	More than 30 suppliers
§	- 'Purple Leaf'	More than 30 suppliers
§	***fumariifolia***	EBrs ECho MTho
	glauca	see *C. sempervirens*
	glaucescens	ECho WWst
	- 'Early Beauty'	EBrs ECho
	- 'Pink Beauty'	WWst
	gracilis	WWst
	henrikii	WWst
	incisa	ECho
	- B&SWJ 4417	WCru
	- f. ***pallescens***	NRnb
	integra	WWst
	'Kingfisher'	CLAP EWes NHar NLar SBch SBla WAbe WFar
	kusnetzovii	WWst
	ledebouriana	EBrs ECho NMen
	leucanthema	CLAP CPom EBee
	- DJHC 752	CDes WPrP
	- 'Silver Spectre' (v)	CAby CBow CWsd LBMP NSti SKHP SPoG WLin WTMC
	linstowiana	CPom CWsd EMon EPPr NRnb SPhx
	- CD&R 605	CLAP
	luquanensis **new**	EBee
§	***lutea***	CBcs CRWN EBee EDAr EMar EPfP GBuc IBlr IFoB NCob NPer NVic SEND SHFr SPoG SRms WCot WMoo
	lydica	WWst
	magadanica	EWld LFur
§	***malkensis*** ♀H4	CMea EBee ERos GBin GBuc GCrs NBir NMen NRya SBla SCnR
	moorcroftiana **new**	CExc EBee
	muliensis **new**	CExc EBee
	nariniana	WWst
	nigro-apiculata **new**	EBee
	nobilis	CPom CSpe EBee EBrs ECho MLLN SPhx
	nudicaulis	EBrs ECho WWst
	ochotensis B&SWJ 917	WCru
§	***ochroleuca***	CDes CElw CSpe EBee EMar EPot GAbr GCrs LFur MTho NPol SBch WFar WHil WMoo
	ophiocarpa	CSpe CSsd EGoo ELan EMan EMar IBlr MBNS MRav NRnb SPoG WMoo
	oppositifolia	WWst
	- subsp. ***kurdica***	WWst
	ornata	WWst
	paczoskii	EBrs ECho ERos GBuc NDlv NMen
	- RS 12180	EBee
	pallida	MHar NRnb
	paschei	SBla WWst
	popovii	MTho SCnR
	pseudocristata	EBee
	pseudofumaria alba	see *C. ochroleuca*
	pseudomucronata **new**	EBee
	pumila	EPot WLin
	quantmeyeriana 'Chocolate Star' **new**	EBee
	'Rainier Blue' **new**	CWsd
	repens	EBee WWst
	rosea	IBlr
§	***saxicola***	EBee NPri
	scandens	see *Dicentra scandens*
	schanginii	WLin
	- subsp. ***ainii*** ♀H2	EBrs ECho WWst
	- subsp. ***schanginii***	EBrs ECho GCrs
	scouleri	NBir WCot
	seisumsiana	WWst
§	***sempervirens***	EMan WRos
	- 'Alba'	ECho MWgw WFoF
	shimienensis	EBee
	siamensis B&SWJ 7200	WCru
	smithiana	EBee GKev WFar
§	***solida***	CBgR CPLG CPom CStu EBee EBrs ECho ECtt ELan EPfP EPot GCrs IBlr ITim LAma MRav NMen NRya NWCA SIng WBVN WCot WFar WPnP WShi WTin
	- BM 8499	NHol
	- pink and red shades	CFwr
	- 'Bilbo' **new**	CHHB
	- 'Elrond' **new**	CHHB
	- 'Firecracker'	EBrs ECho GCrs LRHS
	- 'First Kiss'	CHHB WWst
	- 'Frodo' **new**	CHHB
	- 'Gandalf' **new**	CHHB
	- 'Gimli' **new**	CHHB
	- 'Gunite' **new**	CHHB
	- 'Harkov'	GCrs WWst
	- 'Highland Sunset'	GCrs
§	- subsp. ***incisa*** ♀H4	CBgR CRez EBee EBrs ECho GCrs GKev MNrw MTho WCot WPrP WShi
	- - 'Vermion Snow'	CHHB
	- 'King Arthur' **new**	CHHB
	- 'Lord of Moria' **new**	CHHB
	- 'Loth Lorien' **new**	CHHB
	- 'Margaret'	WWst
	- 'Merlin'	CHHB WWst
	- 'Mordorland' **new**	CHHB
	- Nettleton seedlings	EPot
	- 'Purple Beauty' **new**	EBrs WWst
	- 'Simaril' **new**	CHHB
	- 'Snowlark'	WWst

§ - subsp. ***solida***	CFwr CLAP CMil EBrs ECho EPot GCrs GGar LRHS NBir NDov NRya
- - from Penza, Russia	GBuc GCrs LRHS SBla
- - 'Alba'	NSla
- - 'Beth Evans'	CMea CRez EBee EBrs ECho EPot GBin GCrs GEdr GKev GMaP IPot LEdu LTwo NHar NMen SCnR SPhx WCot WLin
- - 'Blushing Girl'	CHHB
- - 'Dieter Schacht' ΨH4	EBee ECho GCrs LAma NLar NMen WAbe WCot
- - 'George Baker' ΨH4	CMea CPom CRez EBee EBrs ECho EPot GBuc GCrs GEdr GKev GSki IPot LAma LFur LRHS LTwo MTho NDov NMen NSla SPhx WAbe WCot WLin WWst
- - 'Highland Mist'	GCrs
- - 'Lahovice'	GCrs NMen WAbe WCot
- - 'Nettleton Pink'	EBrs
- - Prasil Group new	EBrs GKev
- - 'Snowstorm'	CHHB
- - 'White Knight'	GCrs
- 'Spring Bird'	CHHB
- subsp. ***subremota***	CHHB
- f. ***transsylvanica***	see *C. solida* subsp. *solida*
- 'White King'	WWst
- 'White Swallow' new	EBrs GCrs GKev WWst
- 'Yaroslavna'	CHHB
'Spinners'	CDes CElw CLAP EBee ECha EPPr SBch SMeo SPhx WPGP WSHC
stenantha new	EBee
taipishanica new	EBee
taliensis	EBee GKev MBNS
- ACE 2443	EPot
tauricola	GCrs WWst
temolana new	EBee
thalictrifolia Franch.	see *C. saxicola*
tomentella	GEdr SIng
'Tory MP'	CDes CElw CEnt CHid CLAP CPne CPom CSam EBee ECha GAbr GEdr GMac MDKP MNrw NBid NChi NHar WHoo WLin WMnd WPGP WPrP
transsylvanica	see *C. solida* subsp. *solida*
turtschaninovii	EBee WWst
- 'Vladivostok'	CHHB
* ***unguiculata*** new	EBee
§ ***vittae***	CHHB ECho WWst
vivipara	ECho EPot
wendelboi	EBrs ECho GCrs
- subsp. ***congesta***	WWst
- - 'Abant Wine'	CHHB
wilsonii	GEdr GKev IBlr NRnb SBla WEas
* ***woroshilovii***	WWst
zetterlundii	GBuc NDlv WWst

Corylopsis ✿ (*Hamamelidaceae*)

glabrescens	CPMA IMGH LRHS WNor
- var. ***gotoana***	EPfP LRHS MAsh MBri NLar SPoG SSpi SSta
- - 'Chollipo'	IClo LRHS MAsh MBri SSta
glandulifera	NLar
himalayana	CBcs NLar
pauciflora ΨH4	More than 30 suppliers
platypetala	see *C. sinensis* var. *calvescens*
- var. ***laevis***	see *C. sinensis* var. *calvescens*
sinensis	CLnd NEgg WPGP
§ - var. ***calvescens***	CBcs CPMA NLar WPGP
§ - - f. ***veitchiana*** ΨH4	CBcs CPMA ELan EPfP IDee MAsh SPoG
- - - purple-leaved	CPMA
- 'Golden Spring'	NLar
§ - var. ***sinensis*** ΨH4	CBgR CDoC CMHG CPMA EBee EPfP IMGH LAst MAsh SLon SReu WAbe WFar WSpi
- - 'Spring Purple'	CAbP CBcs CEnd CGHE CMac CPLG CPMA EBee EPfP IDee LRHS MBri NLar SPla SPoG SSpi SSta WFar WPGP
spicata	CBcs CPMA CSBt CSam EBee IDee LRHS MBlu MRav NBlu NEgg NLar SLim SSpi
- 'Red Eye'	MBri NLar
veitchiana	see *C. sinensis* var. *calvescens* f. *veitchiana*
willmottiae	see *C. sinensis* var. *sinensis*

Corylus ✿ (*Corylaceae*)

avellana (F)	CBcs CCVT CDoC CDul CLnd CRWN CTri ECrN EMac EPfP GAbr LAst LBuc LRHS MBar MBri MGos NWea SPer WHar WMou WOrn
- 'Anny's Compact Red'	MAsh NHol
- 'Anny's Red Dwarf'	WPat
- 'Aurea'	CBcs CDul CEnd CLnd CSBt CTho CTri EBee ECrN ELan EPfP EWTr LBuc LRHS MAsh MBlu MBri MGos MRav NEgg NHol NWea SIFN SLim SPer SPoG SSta SWvt WFar
- 'Bollwylle'	see *C. maxima* 'Halle'sche Riesennuss'
- 'Casina' (F)	CAgr CTho
- 'Contorta'	More than 30 suppliers
- 'Corabel' (F)	CAgr MCoo
- 'Cosford Cob' (F)	CAgr CDoC CDul CSBt CTho CTri ECrN EMui ERea GTwe LBuc LRHS MBlu MBri MGos SDea SKee SPer
- 'Fortin' (F)	ECrN
§ - 'Fuscorubra' (F)	CBgR ECrN LCro MRav MSwo SIFN
- 'Gustav's Zeller' (F)	CAgr MBri MCoo
§ - 'Heterophylla'	CEnd CTho EBee EPfP MBri NLar SIFN WMou
- 'Laciniata'	see *C. avellana* 'Heterophylla'
§ - 'Lang Tidlig Zeller'	CAgr MCoo
- 'Merveille de Bollwyller'	see *C. maxima* 'Halle'sche Riesennuss'
- 'Nottingham Prolific'	see *C. avellana* 'Pearson's Prolific'
- 'Pauetet' (F)	CAgr
§ - 'Pearson's Prolific' (F)	CAgr ECrN ENot GTwe LBuc SDea SKee
- 'Pendula'	LPan MBlu MBri SBLw SCoo SIFN SLim
- 'Purpurea'	see *C. avellana* 'Fuscorubra'
- 'Red Majestic' PBR	CDul CWib EBee EMil ENot ERas EWes GBin LAst LRHS MAsh MBri MPkF NBPN NLar NWea SCoo SHBN SPer SPoG WCot WGer WPat
- 'Tonda di Giffoni'	CAgr MBri MCoo
- 'Webb's Prize Cob' (F)	CAgr CDoC CDul ECrN ERea GTwe MBlu NLar SBLw SDea SKee WMou
chinensis	EGFP
colurna ΨH4	CAgr CCVT CDul CLnd CMCN CTho EBee ECrN EPfP EWTr IClo LPan LRHS MGos NBee NWea SBLw SCoo SPer WBVN WMou
x ***colurnoides*** 'Laroka' (F)	ECrN
Early Long Zeller	see *C. avellana* 'Lang Tidlig Zeller'
ferox GWJ 9293	WCru
maxima (F)	CLnd CTri ECrN EMac EMui GTwe MSwo NWea SDea
- 'Butler' (F)	CAgr CTho CTri ECrN ERea GTwe LRHS MBri SKee
- 'Ennis' (F)	CAgr ECrN ERea GTwe SDea SKee
- 'Fertile de Coutard'	see *C. maxima* 'White Filbert'
- 'Frizzled Filbert' (F)	ECrN ENot
- 'Frühe van Frauendorf'	see *C. maxima* 'Red Filbert'
- 'Garibaldi' (F)	MBlu
- 'Grote Lambertsnoot'	see *C. maxima* 'Kentish Cob'

- 'Gunslebert' (F)	CAgr CSBt CTho ECrN ERea GTwe LRHS MBri SDea SKee
- Halle Giant	see *C. maxima* 'Halle'sche Riesennuss'
§ - 'Halle'sche Riesennuss' (F)	CAgr ECrN ERea GTwe SEND SKee
§ - 'Kentish Cob' (F)	CAgr CBcs CDoC CDul CSBt CTho CWSG ECrN ENot EPfP ERea GTwe LBuc LRHS MBlu MBri MGan MGos MNHC SDea SFam SKee SPer SRms WHar WOrn
- 'Lambert's Filbert'	see *C. maxima* 'Kentish Cob'
- 'Longue d'Espagne'	see *C. maxima* 'Kentish Cob'
- 'Monsieur de Bouweller'	see *C. maxima* 'Halle'sche Riesennuss'
- 'Purple Filbert'	see *C. maxima* 'Purpurea'
§ - 'Purpurea' (F) ♀H4	More than 30 suppliers
§ - 'Red Filbert' (F)	CEnd CTho CWSG EMil ENot ERea GTwe LRHS MBlu MBri NLar SCoo SKee SLim WPat
- 'Red Zellernut'	see *C. maxima* 'Red Filbert'
- 'Spanish White'	see *C. maxima* 'White Filbert'
§ - 'White Filbert' (F)	CDoC ENot ERea GTwe MBri SKee WHar
- 'White Spanish Filbert'	see *C. maxima* 'White Filbert'
- 'Witpit Lambertsnoot'	see *C. maxima* 'White Filbert'
'Te Terra Red'	CMCN MBlu MBri SBLw SIFN SMad WMou

Corymbia see *Eucalyptus*

Corynabutilon see *Abutilon*

Corynephorus (*Poaceae*)

canescens	CBig CKno EAlp EBee GFor GQue MBar NBir SPad WHrl XIsg

Corynocarpus (*Corynocarpaceae*)

laevigatus	CHEx ECou MBri

Cosmos (*Asteraceae*)

§ ***atrosanguineus***	More than 30 suppliers
bipinnatus Bright Lights mixed (d) **new**	CSpe
- 'Purity'	CSpe LCro
- 'Sonata Carmine'	NPri
- 'Sonata Pink'	LCro NPri SPoG
- 'Sonata White'	CSpe LAst NPri SPoG
'Chocamocha' **new**	CBcs CCCN CSpe CWCL LAst LHop LSou SJoo SRot WOVN
§ ***peucedanifolius***	CAvo CSpe EBee
- 'Flamingo'	GBri NBPC NBhm
pucidanifolia	see *C. peucedanifolius*
sulphureus	MSal

costmary see *Tanacetum balsamita*

Costus (*Costaceae*)

barbatus	MJnS
speciosus	CKob

Cotinus (*Anacardiaceae*)

americanus	see *C. obovatus*
§ ***coggygria*** ♀H4	More than 30 suppliers
- 'Foliis Purpureis'	see *C. coggygria* Rubrifolius Group
- Golden Spirit = 'Ancot'[PBR]	More than 30 suppliers
- Green Fountain = 'Kolcot'[PBR]	LBuc
- 'Kanari'	EBee EMil NLar
- 'Nordine' **new**	NLar
- 'Notcutt's Variety'	ELan ENot EPfP MGos MRav NSti
- 'Pink Champagne'	CBcs CPMA EPfP MBri NLar WPat
- 'Red Beauty'	CBcs NLar WPat
- Red Spirit = 'Firstpur' **new**	NLar
- 'Royal Purple' ♀H4	More than 30 suppliers
§ - Rubrifolius Group	CBcs CMac EBee EPfP NHol SPer SWvt WFar
- Smokey Joe = 'Lisjo'	MAsh SPoG SSta
- 'Velvet Cloak'	CAbP CPMA EBee ELan EPfP LRHS MAsh MBri MGos MRav NLar SLon SPer SPla SWvt WHCG
- 'Young Lady'[PBR]	CBcs CDoC CWSG EBee EKen EMil ENot EPfP EWes GBin LAst MBlu MBri MPkF NCGa NLar SBra SCoo SJoo SPer WFar
'Flame' ♀H4	CAbP CBcs CDul CPMA EBee ELan EPfP LRHS MAsh MBlu MBri MGos MRav NEgg NLar SLim SPer SPla SPoG SSpi WHCG WPat
'Grace'	More than 30 suppliers
§ ***obovatus*** ♀H4	ELan EPfP IArd IDee MBlu MRav NLar SPer SSpi SSta

Cotoneaster ✿ (*Rosaceae*)

CC&McK 465	NWCA
acuminatus	EMac SRms
adpressus ♀H4	EPfP MGos MSwo MWgw WFar
§ - 'Little Gem'	ECho MGos NLar
- var. ***praecox***	see *C. nanshan*
- 'Tom Thumb'	see *C. adpressus* 'Little Gem'
affinis	SRms SSpi
albokermesinus	SRms
amoenus	SLPl SRms
- 'Fire Mountain'	NPro WFar
§ ***apiculatus***	MAsh SRms
§ ***ascendens***	SRms
assamensis	SRms
§ ***astrophoros***	CMac MBlu NEgg
atropurpureus	SRms
§ - 'Variegatus' (v) ♀H4	CBcs CDul CSBt CTri CWSG CWib EBee ELan ENot EPfP ISea LAst LBMP LRHS MAsh MBar MGos MRav NBlu NEgg NPer SLim SPer SPoG SRms SWvt WFar WMoo WWeb
boisianus	SRms
bradyi	SRms
§ ***bullatus*** ♀H4	CDul CLnd CTri EMac EPfP MGos NLar SPer SRms WCwm WOrn WTel
- 'Firebird'	see *C. ignescens*
- f. ***floribundus***	see *C. bullatus*
- var. ***macrophyllus***	see *C. rehderi*
- 'McLaren'	SRms
bumthangensis	SRms
buxifolius blue-leaved	see *C. lidjiangensis*
- 'Brno'	see *C. marginatus* 'Brno'
- f. ***vellaeus***	see *C. astrophoros*
camilli-schneideri	SRms
canescens	SRms
§ ***cashmiriensis*** ♀H4	MGos
cavei	SRms
cinerascens	SRms
cinnabarinus	SRms
§ ***cochleatus***	CPLG EBee EPot LAst MBar MGos NEgg NMen SRms WEas
§ ***congestus***	CSBt CWib EBee MBar MGos MRav MSwo NHol SPlb SRms WBod WHar
- 'Nanus'	CMea CTri ELan EOrn MGos NDlv NHol NLAp SCoo WBVN
conspicuus	CBcs EWTr SRms
- 'Decorus' ♀H4	CCVT CDoC CSBt CWSG EBee ECrN EPfP LRHS MBar MGan MGos MRav MSwo NEgg NHol NWea SLim SPer SPlb SPoG SWal WBVN WMoo WTel

	– 'Flameburst'	SHBN
	– 'Leicester Gem'	SRms
	cooperi	SRms
	cornifolius	SRms
N	***dammeri*** ♀^{H4}	More than 30 suppliers
§	– 'Major'	LAst LBuc NBlu WCFE
§	– 'Mooncreeper'	MBri SCoo
	– 'Oakwood'	see *C. radicans* 'Eichholz'
	– var. ***radicans*** misapplied	see *C. dammeri* 'Major'
	– var. ***radicans*** C.K.Schneid.	see *C. radicans*
	– 'Streib's Findling'	see *C.* 'Streib's Findling'
	dielsianus	EMac NWea SRms WHrl
	distichus var. ***tongolensis***	see *C. splendens*
	divaricatus	EMac EPfP NLar NWea SLon SRms WFar
	duthieanus 'Boer'	see *C. apiculatus*
	elatus	SRms
	elegans	SRms
	emeiensis	SRms
	'Erlinda'	see *C.* x *suecicus* 'Erlinda'
	falconeri	EBee MGol SRms
	fangianus	EMac
	fastigiatus	SRms
	flinckii	SRms
	floccosus	CSBt NWea
	floridus	SRms
	forrestii	SRms
	franchetii	CBcs CCVT CDul CSBt EBee ECrN ELan EMil ENot EPfP LBuc LHop LRHS MGos MRav MSwo MWat MWgw NEgg NWea SCoo SLim SPer SPoG SRms WCFE WFar WHar WTel
	– var. ***sternianus***	see *C. sternianus*
	frigidus	NWea SRms
N	– 'Cornubia' ♀^{H4}	CCVT CDoC CDul CSBt CTri EBee ECrN EPfP LAst LCro LHop LRHS MAsh MBar MBri MGos MRav MSwo NBlu NEgg NWea SHBN SLim SLon SPer SPla SPoG WJas WOrn
	– 'Notcutt's Variety'	ELan EPfP
§	– 'Pershore Coral'	WSPU
	– 'Saint Monica'	MBlu
	gamblei	SRms WCwm
	ganghobaensis	SRms
	glabratus	SLPl SRms
	glacialis	SRms
	glaucophyllus	IArd SEND SRms
§	***glomerulatus***	MBar SRms
	gracilis	SRms
	granatensis	SRms
	harrovianus	SLPl SRms
	hebephyllus	NLar
I	***hedegaardii*** 'Fructu Luteo'	SRms
	henryanus	CDoC SRms
	'Herbstfeuer'	see *C. salicifolius* 'Herbstfeuer'
	'Highlight'	see *C. pluriflorus*
§	***hjelmqvistii***	LBuc SRms WFar
	– 'Robustus'	see *C. hjelmqvistii*
	– 'Rotundifolius'	see *C. hjelmqvistii*
	hodjingensis	SRms
	horizontalis ♀^{H4}	More than 30 suppliers
	– 'Variegatus'	see *C. atropurpureus* 'Variegatus'
	– var. ***wilsonii***	see *C. ascendens*
	hualiensis	SRms
	humifusus	see *C. dammeri*
	hummelii	SRms
§	'Hybridus Pendulus'	More than 30 suppliers
§	***hylmoei***	SLPl SRms
	hypocarpus	SRms
	ignavus	SLPl SRms

§	***ignescens***	SRms
	ignotus	SRms
	induratus	SLPl SRms
	insculptus	SRms
	integerrimus	SRms
§	***integrifolius*** ♀^{H4}	EBee EPfP EPla MBar NMen SCoo SRms STre WMoo
	– 'Silver Shadow' **new**	NLar
	kangdingensis	SRms
	lacteus ♀^{H4}	CBcs CDul CTri EBee ECrN ELan EMac ENot EPfP EWTr LAst LBuc LRHS MBri MGos MRav NBlu NEgg NWea SCoo SEND SHBN SLon SPer SPla SPoG SRms WCFE WFar XPep
	– 'Variegatus' (v)	CEnd
	lancasteri	SRms
	langei	SRms
	laxiflorus	SRms
§	***lidjiangensis***	SRms WCot
§	***linearifolius***	CLyd GCra MWht
	lucidus	LBuc SRms
	ludlowii	SRms
	magnificus	SRms
§	***mairei***	SRms
	marginatus	MGol SRms
§	– 'Blazovice'	SRms
§	– 'Brno'	SRms
	marquandii	EPla SRms
	meuselii	SRms
	microphyllus misapplied	see *C. purpurascens*
	microphyllus Wall. ex Lindl.	CTri EBee ENot MBar MGos MRav NScw NWea SDix SHBN SPer SPoG STre WMoo WTel
	– var. ***cochleatus*** misapplied	see *C. cashmiriensis*
	– var. ***cochleatus*** (Franch.) Rehd. & Wils	see *C. cochleatus*
	– 'Donard Gem'	see *C. astrophoros*
	– 'Ruby'	SRms
	– 'Teulon Porter'	see *C. astrophoros*
	– var. ***thymifolius*** misapplied	see *C. linearifolius*
	– var. ***thymifolius*** (Lindl.) Koehne	see *C. integrifolius*
	milkedandai	SRms
	miniatus	SRms
	mirabilis	SRms
	monopyrenus	SRms
	'Mooncreeper'	see *C. dammeri* 'Mooncreeper'
	morrisonensis	SRms
	moupinensis	EBee SRms
	mucronatus	SRms
	multiflorus	SRms
§	***nanshan***	CAbP NLar NWea SRms WSPU
	– 'Boer'	see *C. apiculatus*
	newryensis	SRms
	nitens	SRms
	nitidifolius	see *C. glomerulatus*
	nohelii	SRms
	notabilis	SRms
	nummularioides	SRms
	nummularius	SRms
	obscurus	SRms
	obtusus	SRms
	pangiensis	SRms
	pannosus	SLPl SRms WFar
	– 'Speckles'	SRms
	paradoxus	SRms
	parkeri	SRms
	pekinensis	SRms
	permutatus	see *C. pluriflorus*
	perpusillus	SRms WFar
	'Pershore Coral'	see *C. frigidus* 'Pershore Coral'
§	***pluriflorus***	SRms
	poluninii	SRms

polycarpus	SRms
praecox 'Boer'	see *C. apiculatus*
procumbens	SLon SRms
- 'Queen of Carpets'	CDoC EBee EQua ERas LRHS LSRN MAsh MGos MRav NLar SCoo SLim SPoG SRms SWvt WMoo
- 'Streib's Findling'	see *C.* 'Streib's Findling'
prostratus	SRms
przewalskii	SRms
pseudo-obscurus	SRms
§ ***purpurascens***	MDun MGos SCoo WFar
pyrenaicus	see *C. congestus*
qungbixiensis	SRms
racemiflorus	SRms
§ ***radicans***	LRHS
§ - 'Eichholz'	MGos NHol NLar SPoG WWeb
§ ***rehderi***	CMHG NLar SRms
roseus	SRms
'Rothschildianus'	see *C. salicifolius* 'Rothschildianus'
rotundifolius	NLar SLon
'Royal Beauty'	see *C.* x *suecicus* 'Coral Beauty'
rugosus	SRms
salicifolius	MSwo SEND SPer SRms WFar
- Autumn Fire	see *C. salicifolius* 'Herbstfeuer'
§ - 'Avonbank'	CDoC CEnd NLar WSPU
- 'Bruno Orangeade'	SRms
- 'Elstead'	MRav
- 'Exburyensis'	CBcs CDoC EBee EPfP ERas LAst LRHS MAsh MBri MGos MRav NLar SCoo SHBN SPer SPla WFar WHCG
- 'Gnom'	CChe EBee ELan EPfP EQua LRHS MAsh MBar MBlu MGos MRav MWht NBir SPer SPoG SRms WFar WMoo
§ - 'Herbstfeuer'	LAst MGos MRav MSwo SRms WFar
- 'Merriott Weeper'	CDoC
- Park Carpet	see *C. salicifolius* 'Parkteppich'
§ - 'Parkteppich'	NWea
- 'Pendulus'	see *C.* 'Hybridus Pendulus'
- 'Repens'	CDoC CWib EPfP MGan NScw NWea SPer SPoG SRms WFar
§ - 'Rothschildianus' ♀H4	CCVT CDoC CDul CSBt CTri CWib EBee ECrN ECtt EMil ENot EPfP LAst LRHS MAsh MBar MGos MRav MSwo NBlu NEgg SLim SPer SPla SPoG SRms SWvt WFar WJas WMoo
- Franch. var. ***rugosus*** hort.	see *C. hylmoei*
salwinensis	SLPl SRms
sandakphuensis	SRms
scandinavicus	SRms
schantungensis	SRms
schlechtendalii 'Blazovice'	see *C. marginatus* 'Blazovice'
- 'Brno'	see *C. marginatus* 'Brno'
schubertii	SRms
serotinus	CAbP NLar SLPl SRms
shannanensis	SRms
shansiensis	SRms
sherriffii	SRms
sikangensis	GBin SLon SRms
simonsii ♀H4	CCVT CDoC CDul CLnd CTri EBee ELan EMac EPfP LAst LBuc LRHS MBar MGos NHol NScw NWea SCoo SPer SPoG SRms WFar WHar
§ ***splendens***	SRms WFar
- 'Sabrina'	see *C. splendens*
spongbergii	SRms
staintonii	SRms
§ ***sternianus*** ♀H4	EBee EPfP LRHS MBar SLPl SRms WHrl
- ACE 2200	EPot
§ 'Streib's Findling'	EBee MAsh NLar
suavis	SRms
subacutus	SRms
subadpressus	SRms
§ x ***suecicus*** 'Coral Beauty'	CCVT CDoC CTri CWSG CWib EBee ENot EPfP GGar LAst LBMP LBuc LRHS MAsh MBar MGos MSwo NBlu NEgg NHol SLim SMer SPer SPla SPoG SRms SWal WFar WMoo
§ - 'Erlinda' (v)	CEnd CWib EMil NLar SCoo SRms
- 'Ifor'	SLPl SRms
- 'Juliette' (v)	CWib ERas LAst LBMP LSRN MAsh MBar NBlu NLar NPro SCoo SPoG WFar WOrn
- 'Skogholm'	CBcs CSBt CWSG CWib EBee MBar MGos NWea SCoo SPer SRms WFar WHar
taoensis	SRms
tardiflorus	SRms
tauricus	SRms
teijiashanensis	SRms
tengyuehensis	SRms
thimphuensis	SRms
tomentellus	WCFE
tomentosus	SRms
turbinatus	SLPl SRms
'Valkenburg'	SRms
vandelaarii	SRms
veitchii	MBri NLar SRms
verruculosus	SRms
villosulus	SRms
vilmorinianus	SRms
wardii misapplied	see *C. mairei*
wardii W.W. Sm.	SRms
x ***watereri***	CCVT CSBt CWib EBee MSwo NEgg NWea WJas WTel
- 'Avonbank'	see *C. salicifolius* 'Avonbank'
- 'Corina'	SRms
- 'Cornubia'	see *C. frigidus* 'Cornubia'
- 'John Waterer' ♀H4	EPfP LRHS MGos SPer SPoG WFar
- 'Pendulus'	see *C.* 'Hybridus Pendulus'
- 'Pink Champagne'	CAbP EQua SPer
wilsonii	SRms
yallungensis	SRms
yinchangensis	SRms
zabelii	SRms

Cotula (*Asteraceae*)

C&H 452	NWCA
atrata	see *Leptinella atrata*
- var. ***dendyi***	see *Leptinella dendyi*
coronopifolia	CBen CWat EDAr EHon EMFW GGar NBlu NPer SWat
§ ***hispida***	CBrm CMea CTri EAlp EBee ECho EDAr EPot GAbr GMaP MAvo MBNS MBar MHer MTho MWat NHol NPer NRya NWCA SBla SPoG SRms WEas WFar WPat WPer WTin WWeb
lineariloba	ECha ECho EWes LBee LRHS
minor	see *Leptinella minor*
'Platt's Black'	see *Leptinella squalida* 'Platt's Black'
potentilloides	see *Leptinella potentillina*
pyrethrifolia	see *Leptinella pyrethrifolia*
rotundata	see *Leptinella rotundata*
sericea	see *Leptinella albida*
serrulata	see *Leptinella serrulata*
squalida	see *Leptinella squalida*

Cotyledon (*Crassulaceae*)

chrysantha	see *Rosularia chrysantha*
gibbiflora var. ***metallica***	see *Echeveria gibbiflora* var. *metallica*

oppositifolia	see *Chiastophyllum oppositifolium*
orbiculata	CHEx CStu CWsd SDix
- B&SWJ 723	WCru
- var. ***oblonga***	EBee EMan WCot WEas
simplicifolia	see *Chiastophyllum oppositifolium*
tomentosa subsp. ***ladismithensis***	EShb
undulata	WEas

Cowania see *Purshia*

Coxella (*Apiaceae*)

dieffenbachii	WCot

Crambe (*Brassicaceae*)

cordifolia 🏆H4	More than 30 suppliers
filiformis	WHal
maritima 🏆H4	CSev CSpe EBee ECGP ECha EPfP GMaP GMac GPoy LAst MLLN MRav MSal MWgw NSti SMad SPer SPhx SWat WBVN WCot WCru WFar WJek WMnd WPer WSpi
- 'Lilywhite'	CAgr ILis WCot
tatarica	NLar SHar WPer

cranberry see *Vaccinium macrocarpon, V. oxycoccos*

Craspedia (*Asteraceae*)

alpina from Tasmania	GGar

Crassula (*Crassulaceae*)

anomala	SChr
arborescens	see *C. atropurpurea* var. *arborescens*
argentea	see *C. ovata*
§ ***atropurpurea*** var. ***arborescens***	EShb SRms STre
brevifolia new	EPem
coccinea	CHEx EShb
columella	EPem
dejecta	EShb
elegans new	EPem
lactea	CHal STre
lycopodioides variegata	see *C. muscosa* 'Variegata'
milfordiae nana	see *C. setulosa* 'Milfordiae'
mollis new	EPem
multicava	CHEx
muscosa	EShb SChr SRot STre
§ - 'Variegata' (v)	EShb
obtusa	SRot
orbicularis	EPem
§ ***ovata*** 🏆H1	CHEx CHal EBak EOHP EPem EPfP MBri NBlu NPer NScw SWal
- 'Gollum'	EPem
- 'Hummel's Sunset' (v) 🏆H1	CHal EPem MAvo STre SWal
- 'Minima'	EPem
* - ***nana***	STre
- 'Variegata' (v)	CHal EBak WCot
pellucida subsp. ***marginalis***	CHal
- - f. ***rubra*** new	EPem
* - - 'Variegata' (v)	CHal
perfoliata var. ***falcata*** 🏆H1	EShb MBri SRot
perforata	CHal EPem
- 'Variegata' (v)	CHal EPem EWll SRot
portulacea	see *C. ovata*
rodgersii new	EPem
rupestris 🏆H1	EPem MBri
- subsp. ***marnieriana***	EPem
§ ***sarcocaulis***	CHEx CHal CStu CTri EAlp ECho ELan EWll GEdr GMaP ITim MTho NLAp NMen NVic NWCA SIng SPlb SPoG SRms SRot STre WAbe WEas WFar WPat WSHC
- ***alba***	CHal GEdr NLAp SHFr STre WPer
- 'Ken Aslet'	STre
schmidtii	CHal EDAr EPem MBri
sedifolia	see *C. setulosa* 'Milfordiae'
sediformis	see *C. setulosa* 'Milfordiae'
§ ***setulosa*** 'Milfordiae'	CTri ECho EDAr MBar NBir
socialis	CHal
tetragona	SEND
* ***tomentosa*** 'Variegata' (v)	EShb EWin
'Très Bon'	STre

+ *Crataegomespilus* (*Rosaceae*)

'Dardarii' new	MBri
'Jules d'Asnières'	MBri

x *Crataegosorbus* (*Rosaceae*)

§ ***miczurinii*** 'Ivan's Belle' new	CAgr

Crataegus ✿ (*Rosaceae*)

F&M 196 new	WPGP
arnoldiana	CAgr CDul CEnd CLnd CTri EBee ECrN EPfP IMGH LRHS MAsh MBri MCoo MLan MNHC NWea SCoo SEND SFam SLPl SPer WOrn
'Autumn Glory'	CEnd CLnd EBee ECrN WFar
azarolus	CAgr CLnd EPfP MBri
champlainensis	CLnd
chrysocarpa	EPfP
chungtienensis	WSpi
coccinea misapplied	see *C. intricata*
coccinea ambig.	NWea
§ ***coccinea*** L.	CAgr CLnd CTho EPfP MBri MCoo SCoo
coccinioides	EPfP
cordata	see *C. phaenopyrum*
crus-galli misapplied	see *C. persimilis* 'Prunifolia'
crus-galli L.	CCVT CDoC CDul CLnd CTho EBee ECrN EPfP LAst SPer WFar WJas
- thornless	MBlu
dahurica	EPfP
x ***dippeliana***	EPfP
douglasii	EPfP
dsungarica	EPfP
x ***durobrivensis***	CAgr CDul CLnd EPfP MBri MCoo NLar
ellwangeriana	CAgr CLnd ECrN EPfP
eriocarpa	CLnd
flabellata	CEnd
gemmosa	CEnd MAsh MBlu MBri MCoo NLar NWea SSpi
greggiana	EPfP
x ***grignonensis***	CBcs CCVT CDul CLnd ECrN EMil MAsh SBLw SEND SPer WJas
§ ***intricata***	EPfP
irrasa	EPfP
jonesiae	EPfP
laciniata Ucria	see *C. orientalis*
§ ***laevigata***	NWea
- 'Coccinea Plena'	see *C. laevigata* 'Paul's Scarlet'
- 'Crimson Cloud'	CDoC CDul CEnd CLnd CWSG CWib EBee ECrN ELan EMui ENot EPfP LBuc LRHS MAsh MBri MGos MSwo NWea SCoo SCrf SLim SLon SPer SPoG WHar WJas WOrn WPat
- 'Flore Pleno'	see *C. laevigata* 'Plena'
- 'Gireoudii'	CBcs CDul CEnd CPMA CWib LAst MBlu MGos NLar NSti WPat
- 'Mutabilis'	CLnd CTri SBLw
§ - 'Paul's Scarlet' (d) 🏆H4	More than 30 suppliers

- 'Pink Corkscrew'	EPfP MAsh MBlu MBri MGos SMad WPat
§ - 'Plena' (d)	CBcs CDoC CDul CLnd CSBt CTho CTri CWib EBee ECrN LAst LRHS MAsh MGos MSwo MWat NWea SBLw SCrf SHBN SLim SPer WHar WOrn
- 'Rosea Flore Pleno' (d) ♀H4	CCVT CDoC CDul CLnd CSBt CTho CTri CWSG EBee ECrN ELan ENot EPfP LAst LBuc LCro LRHS MAsh MBar MBri MGos MSwo NEgg NScw NWea SHBN SPer SPoG WJas WOrn
x ***lavalleei***	CCVT CDul CLnd CTri EBee ECrN EPfP MSwo NEgg NWea SCoo SFam SPer SPur
- 'Carrierei' ♀H4	CDoC CTho EPfP EWTr MAsh MBlu MBri NWea SBLw SCoo WOrn
lobulata	EPfP
mexicana	see *C. pubescens* f. *stipulacea*
mollis	CAgr CTho ECrN EPfP WSpi
monogyna	CBcs CCVT CDoC CDul CLnd CRWN CTri ELan EMac EPfP GWCH LAst LBuc LCro LRHS MBar MBri MGos NBlu NWea SPer WFar WMou
§ - 'Biflora'	CDul CEnd CLnd CTho CTri EBee ECrN MAsh MCoo MGos NWea SCoo SLim SPoG WSPU
- 'Compacta'	MBlu NLar
- 'Flexuosa'	MGos
- 'Praecox'	see *C. monogyna* 'Biflora'
- 'Stricta'	CCVT CDul CLnd CSBt EBee ECrN EPfP MBlu SBLw SPer
- 'Variegata' (v)	ECrN MRav
x ***mordenensis*** 'Toba' (d)	CDul CLnd EPfP SBLw
nigra	EPfP
§ ***orientalis***	CDul CEnd CLnd CMCN CTho CTri EBee ECrN EPfP IArd IDee LPan LRHS MAsh MBri MCoo MGos NBlu NWea SCoo SHBN SLPl SLim SMad SSpi WJas WMou WOrn WSpi
oxyacantha	see *C. laevigata*
pedicellata	see *C. coccinea* L.
pentagyna	EPfP
§ ***persimilis*** 'Prunifolia' ♀H4	More than 30 suppliers
- 'Prunifolia Splendens'	CCVT GBin IDee MBri MCoo SBLw SCoo WPat
§ ***phaenopyrum***	CDul CLnd CMCN CTho EPfP IArd MGos SLPl SMad
pinnatifida	EPfP
- var. ***major***	CEnd EBee EPfP MBri MCoo NWea SCoo
- - 'Big Golden Star'	CAgr CLnd CTho ECrN MAsh MCoo NLar SCoo
'Praecox'	see *C. monogyna* 'Biflora'
prunifolia	see *C. persimilis* 'Prunifolia'
pseudoheterophylla	EPfP
* ***pubescens*** f. ***major*** new	CAgr
§ - f. ***stipulacea***	CDul CLnd EPfP MBri
punctata	CTho SLPl
- f. ***aurea***	EPfP
sanguinea	EPfP
schraderiana	CAgr CDul CLnd CTho EBee EPfP MBri MCoo NWea SCoo
sorbifolia	EPfP
succulenta	EPfP
- var. ***macracantha***	EPfP SMad
suksdorfii	EPfP
tanacetifolia	CAgr CLnd CTho ECrN EPfP MBlu SPer
turkestanica	EPfP
viridis 'Winter King'	CDoC EPfP MAsh MBlu MCoo SLim
wattiana	EPfP

x *Crataemespilus* (*Rosaceae*)

grandiflora	CBcs CDul CEnd CTho WSpi

Crawfurdia (*Gentianaceae*)

speciosa B&SWJ 2138	WCru

Cremanthodium (*Asteraceae*)

sp.	WCot
angustifolium	EBee GKev
campanulatum	EBee
decaisnei new	EBee
aff. ***ellisii*** HWJK 2262	WCru
lineare	EBee
reniforme GWJ 9407	WCru
sagittifolium new	EBee

Cremastra (*Orchidaceae*)

variabilis	GEdr

x *Cremnosedum* (*Crassulaceae*)

§ 'Little Gem'	CStu EPem EPot NMen

Crenularia see *Aethionema*

Crepis (*Asteraceae*)

aurea	EBee
incana ♀H4	CFee CMea CPom ECho EGoo EMan GBri GSki LRHS MAvo MTho NBid NChi NSla NWCA SIng SPhx SRms WAbe WBVN WCot WPat
- 'Pink Mist'	GBin MBri NLar WWeb
rubra	LRHS

Crinitaria see *Aster*

Crinodendron (*Elaeocarpaceae*)

hookerianum ♀H3	More than 30 suppliers
- 'Ada Hoffmann'	CPLG EBee GBin LRHS MBlu MBri NDlv NLar SKHP SPer
patagua	CBcs CPLG CPle CSam CWib EBee GGar GQui IArd IClo MBri NLar SLon SPer WBVN WBod WFar WPic WSHC

Crinum (*Amaryllidaceae*)

americanum new	CDWL
amoenum	CHHB CTca EBee EBrs ECho
asiaticum new	WCot
- DJHC 970606	WCot
- var. ***sinicum***	CDes WCot
§ ***bulbispermum***	CFir EBee ELan WCot WPic
capense	see *C. bulbispermum*
'Carolina Beauty'	WCot
'Elizabeth Traub'	WCot
'Ellen Bosanquet'	CDes CFir CKno CTca EBee WCot
'Emma Jones' new	WCot
erubescens	WCot
'Hanibal's Dwarf'	CDes EBee WCot
'Heja Lodge' new	WCot
latifolium new	WCot
macowanii	WCot
moorei	CDes CFir CTca EBee EBrs ECho LEdu LPio SChr WCot WPGP
- f. ***album***	CAvo EBee LPio WCot
'Ollene' new	WCot
§ x ***powellii*** ♀H3	More than 30 suppliers
- 'Album' ♀H3	CAvo CDes CFFs CHEx CTca CTri EBee EBrs ECha ECho ELan EMan EShb EWes GCra LAma LEdu LHop LPio LRHS MBri MRav SSpi WCot WFar WPGP WPic

	– 'Harlemense'	SSpi
	– 'Longifolium'	see *C. bulbispermum*
	– 'Roseum'	see *C.* x *powellii*
	'Regina's Disco Lounge'	WCot
	variabile	EBee WCot
	yemense	WCot

Criogenes see *Cypripedium*

Crithmum (*Apiaceae*)

	maritimum	CArn CHrt CWan EMan GPoy MSal NLar NTHB SECG SPlb WJek XPep

Crocosmia ✿ (*Iridaceae*)

	'Alistair'	CTca ECtt EMar MPop
	'Anniversary'	CTca IBlr
	'Apricot Surprise'	MAvo
	aurea misapplied	see *C.* x *crocosmiiflora* 'George Davison' Davison
	aurea ambig.	CTca NBir
	aurea (Pappe ex Hook.f.) Planch.	CPne CPou ECtt IBlr NHol
	– subsp. ***aurea***	CTca IBlr
	– – 'Maculata'	IBlr
	– subsp. ***pauciflora***	IBlr
	'Auricorn'	IBlr NHol
	'Auriol'	IBlr
	'Aurora'	CHVG NGdn
	'Beth Chatto' new	CTca
	Bressingham Beacon = 'Blos'	EBee GGar IBlr LRHS WRHF
	'Bressingham Blaze'	CBre CMHG CTca EBee IBlr LRHS NBre NGdn NHol WCot WHil
	Bridgemere hybrid	NHol
	'Burnt Orange' new	WCra
	'Cadenza'	IBlr NCot
	'Carnival'	IBlr
	'Cascade'	IBlr NCot
	'Chinatown'	IBlr MAvo NCot NHol WHil
	'Citronella' misapplied	see *C.* x *crocosmiiflora* 'Honey Angels'
	'Comet'	CPrp GBuc IBlr NHol WHil
§	x ***crocosmiiflora***	CHEx COIW CTca CTri EBee EPla IBlr LAst NHol SIng SPlb SRms SWat WBrk WCot WFar WMoo WShi
	– 'A.E. Amos'	CTca
	– 'A.J. Hogan'	CPrp CTca GBin IBal IBlr NHol WHil
	– 'African Glow'	ENot
	– 'Amber Sun'	IBlr
	– 'Amberglow'	CElw CMea CPrp ECho IBal IBlr NBre NHol NPer WFar
	– 'Apricot Queen'	CTca IBlr NHol
	– 'Autumn Gold'	IBlr
	– 'Baby Barnaby'	CBre CDes CTca EBee IBlr NHol WPGP
	– 'Babylon'	More than 30 suppliers
	– 'Bicolor'	CPrp CTca IBal IBlr NHol WHil
	– 'Burford Bronze'	CPrp CTca IBal IBlr MAvo NHol WHil
	– 'Buttercup'	CTca GAbr GBri GKev IBlr MAvo MLLN MPop NBre NHol WBor WFar
	– 'Canary Bird'	CPne CPrp CSam CTca EBee ECho ECtt GAbr GMac IBal IBlr NBPC NGdn NHol WBrk WHil WRHF
	– 'Cardinale'	IBlr
	– 'Carmin Brillant' ♀H3-4	More than 30 suppliers
	– 'Carminea' new	CTca
	– 'Citrina' new	CTca
	– 'Citronella' J.E. Fitt	CPLG CPrp CSam CTca CTri EBee EBla ECha EMar EPfP GKev GMaP GQue ITim LAst LRHS MRav NGdn NHol SAga SPer WBVN WCot WCra
§	– 'Coleton Fishacre'	More than 30 suppliers
§	– 'Columbus'	CPar EBee EMan ENot GBin IBal IBlr LHop LRHS MWea NBPC NGdn NHol NRnb SGar SPer WBor WCot WFar WMnd
	– 'Colwall'	IBlr
	– 'Constance'	CBre CElw CSam CTca EBee ERou GGar GQue IBal IBlr LRHS MAvo MBNS MBri MNrw NBid NGdn NHol NRnb SRGP SRos WFar WHil WSel
	– 'Corona'	CPrp CTca EBee IBal IBlr MAvo NCot NHol WHil
	– 'Corten'	IBlr
§	– 'Croesus'	CTca GBri IBlr MAvo MRav NCot
	– 'Custard Cream'	CPrp CSpe CTca GBin IBlr LRHS NHol SRos WFar WHil WRHF
	– 'D.H. Houghton'	IBlr
	– 'Debutante'	CPrp CTca EBee ECtt IBal IBlr MAvo MHar NHol WCot WHoo WLin WSHC
§	– 'Diadème'	CSam MAvo NHol WHil
	– 'Dusky Maiden'	More than 30 suppliers
§	– 'E.A. Bowles'	CPou CPrp CTca IBlr
	– 'Eastern Promise'	CBre CMea CPrp CTca EBee IBal IBlr MAvo NCot SMrm
	– 'Eclatant'	IBlr
	– 'Elegans'	CBre CElw CTca ECtt IBlr
	– 'Emberglow'	More than 30 suppliers
§	– 'Emily McKenzie'	More than 30 suppliers
	– 'Etoile de Feu'	IBlr
	– 'Fantasie'	IBal
	– 'Festival Orange'	CTca IBlr MAvo
	– 'Firebrand'	IBlr NCot
	– 'Fireglow'	ECho ECtt IBlr WFar WPer
	– 'Flamethrower'	IBlr MAvo
	– 'George Davison' misapplied	see *C.* x *crocosmiiflora* 'Golden Glory', 'Sulphurea'
§	– 'George Davison' Davison	More than 30 suppliers
	– 'Gloria'	CTca IBlr WHil
	– 'Golden Glory' misapplied	see *C.* x *crocosmiiflora* 'Diadème'
§	– 'Golden Glory' ambig.	CPLG CSam CWCL ECho EHrv ELan IBal IBlr MAvo MSwo NBir NChi NEgg NHol SPlb SRos WBrE WCot WFar WHil
	– 'Goldfinch'	IBlr NCot NHol WHil
	– 'Hades'	CPrp IBal IBlr MAvo WHil
	– 'Harvest Sun'	IBlr
	– 'His Majesty'	CPne CPou CPrp CSam CSpe CTca IBal IBlr LRHS NHol SDys WFar WHil WLin WOut WPer
§	– 'Honey Angels'	More than 30 suppliers
	– 'Honey Bells'	CElw CTca WBrk
	– 'Irish Dawn'	CPrp CTca GBin GBri IBal IBlr NBre NCot NHol
§	– 'Jackanapes'	CPne CPrp CTca CWCL EBee ECtt EHrv ELan ELon EPfP GGar IBal IBlr LCro LRHS MBri MGos MLHP NHol SDys WFar WHil WWeb
	– 'James Coey' J.E. Fitt	CHar COIW CPrp EBee EBla ECha EHrv EPfP ERou GGar GSki IFoB LRHS MLHP NDov NGdn NHol SIng SRGP SWvt WCra WFar WMoo WWlt
	– 'Jesse van Dyke'	IBlr
§	– 'Jessie'	CElw CTca IBlr LPio WHil WPer
	– 'Kapoor'	IBlr
	– 'Kiautschou'	CAvo CTca EBee GMac IBlr MAvo NBre NHol SDys WHil
	– 'Lady Hamilton'	More than 30 suppliers
	– 'Lady McKenzie'	see *C.* x *crocosmiiflora* 'Emily McKenzie'
	– 'Lady Oxford'	CPrp CTca EMan IBlr LRHS NHol WHil
	– 'Lambrook Gold'	CAvo IBlr

– 'Lord Nelson'	CPrp CTca MAvo WHil
– 'Loweswater'	MAvo
– 'Lutea'	CTca EBee ECtt EMar IBlr NHol
– 'Marjorie'	WCot
– 'Mars'	CElw CPrp CTca EBla ECtt EWes EWll GAbr GBuc GGar GMac IBal IBlr IFoB LCro LPio LRHS NHol SPlb SRGP WBor WFar WPGP WPer WSel
– 'Mephistopheles'	CPrp CTca IBlr MAvo NCot WHil
– 'Merryman'	CTca ECtt GAbr GMac
– 'Météore'	CPrp CTca EBrs ECho GGar IBal MBNS MPop NBre NHol SBch WPrP WSel WWeb
– 'Morgenlicht'	CTca ECtt GBin IBal IBlr NHol WCot
– 'Mount Usher'	CFir CMdw CTca ECha ECtt GAbr IBlr MAvo NHol WFar
– 'Mrs David Howard'	SApp
§ – 'Mrs Geoffrey Howard'	CDes CMea CPrp CSam CTca ECtt IBal IBlr MAvo NCGa NHol WCru WPGP WPrP
– 'Mrs Morrison'	see *C.* x *crocosmiiflora* 'Mrs Geoffrey Howard'
– Newry seedling	see *C.* x *crocosmiiflora* 'Prometheus'
– 'Nigricans' **new**	CTca
– 'Nimbus'	CPrp CTca EBee IBal IBlr NHol WCot WHil
§ – 'Norwich Canary'	CMHG COlW CTca EBee ECha ECho EPPr EPfP ERou EShb GBuc GSki IBlr LCro LRHS MRav MWrn NBir NGdn NHol NPri NSti SMrm SWat WBrk WCot WCra WHil WMoo WSpi
– 'Olympic Fire'	IBlr
– 'Pepper'	IBlr
– 'Plaisir'	CTca IBlr WCra WFar WPrP
– 'Princess Alexandra'	CTca IBlr SMHy
– 'Prolificans'	IBlr
§ – 'Prometheus'	CPrp CTca IBal IBlr NHol WHil
§ – 'Queen Alexandra' J.E. Fitt	ECha IBlr LHop NCGa NHol SPer SWat WHal WMoo WPer
– 'Queen Charlotte'	CPrp CTca IBal IBlr
– 'Queen Mary II'	see *C.* x *crocosmiiflora* 'Columbus'
– 'Queen of Spain'	CPrp CTca IBal IBlr LRHS MBri MDKP MLLN NHol SWat WHil WLin
– 'Rayon d'Or'	IBlr
– 'Red King'	EBee EBla EBrs EPfP ERou IBal IBlr MPop WFar WHil WLin WSpi
– 'Red Knight'	CHVG CMMP GAbr IBlr MAvo NCot NHol WCot WHil
– 'Rheingold' misapplied	see *C.* x *crocosmiiflora* 'Diadème'
– 'Rose Queen'	IBlr NCot
– 'Saint Clements'	IBlr
– 'Saracen'	CHVG CSpe CTca EBee EGle EMan ERou GMac IBal IBlr IPot LAst MAvo MBNS NBre NCGa NCob NEgg NLar SMrm SPla SPoG WBrk WCot WFar WGwG WHil
– 'Sir Mathew Wilson'	CDes CTca EBee GBri IBal IBlr WCot WPGP
– 'Solfatare' Ψ^{H3}	More than 30 suppliers
– 'Solfatare Coleton Fishacre'	see *C.* x *crocosmiiflora* 'Coleton Fishacre'
– 'Star of the East' Ψ^{H3}	More than 30 suppliers
– 'Starbright'	IBlr
– 'Starfire'	ECtt
– 'Sultan'	CDes CElw CTca IBlr NCot WCot WFar WPGP
– 'Venus'	CBre CPen CPou CTca EBee ECtt EMar EShb EWll GBuc IBal IBlr LRHS NBre NHol NLar SRGP SRos STes WFar WLin WMoo WPrP WSel
– 'Vesuvius' W. Pfitzer	CElw IBlr WFar
– 'Vic's Yellow'	SGar SMrm
– 'Voyager'	CPrp CTca EBee EBrs ECho ENot EPot ERou IBlr LRHS MBNS MBri MPop NHol SIng SWal WPer WSel
– 'Zeal Tan'	CElw CPen CPrp CSam CTca EBee ECGP ECtt ELan ELon EMan EPPr GBin GMac GQue IBlr LAst MAvo MBNS MDKP NEgg SPla WBrk WCot WHil WWlt
§ x ***crocosmioides***	IBlr WHil
– 'Castle Ward Late'	CBgR CPou CTca ECha GAbr GBuc IBal IBlr LRHS MBNS MSte NBre NHol WHil WMoo WSHC
– 'Mount Stewart Late'	IBlr
– 'Vulcan' Leichtlin	IBlr WHil
'Darkleaf Apricot'	see *C.* x *crocosmiiflora* 'Coleton Fishacre'
'Doctor Marion Wood'	EBee NCot
'Eldorado'	see *C.* x *crocosmiiflora* 'E.A. Bowles'
'Elegance'	EBee IBlr
'Elizabeth'	NHol
'Ellenbank Canary'	CBgR GMac
'Ellenbank Firecrest'	CBgR GMac MAvo
'Ellenbank Skylark' **new**	GMac
'Fandango'	IBlr NCot
'Fernhill'	IBlr
* 'Feuerser'	ECtt
'Fire Jumper' **new**	CDes
'Fire King' misapplied	see *C.* x *crocosmiiflora* 'Jackanapes'
'Fire King' ambig.	WHil WSpi
'Fire Sprite'	IBlr
'Firefly'	IBlr NCot NHol
'Flaire'	IBlr
'Fleuve Jaune'	CPne ECtt
fucata	IBlr
– 'Jupiter'	see *C.* 'Jupiter'
fucata x ***paniculata***	CTca NHol
'Fugue'	IBlr
'Fusilade'	IBlr
'Gold Sprite'	IBlr NCot
'Golden Dew'	CTca EBee ECtt EGle GAbr GQue LSou MAvo MBNS MWgw NChi NCot WBrk WCot WGor WGwG WHil
Golden Fleece Lemoine	see *C.* x *crocosmiiflora* 'Coleton Fishacre'
'Harlequin'	CElw CTca
'Highlight'	IBlr MAvo NCot NHol WHil
'Irish Flame'	CTca NHol
'Irish Sunset'	NHol
'Jennine'	EBee NCot NHol WHil WLin
Jenny Bloom = 'Blacro'^{PBR}	CMMP EBrs GBin GBuc LRHS NBir NChi SMHy
'John Boots'	CPrp CTca EBee EBrs ECho EHrv GBuc IBlr LPio MBNS NCGa NHol NRnb SMrm SRGP WBor WFar WHil WLin WSel
§ 'Jupiter'	CBre CDes CPou CSam CWCL ECho GAbr GBuc GMac IBal IBlr MAvo MRav NChi NHol SApp WFar WHil
'Krakatoa' **new**	EBee SPoG
'Lady Wilson' misapplied	see *C.* x *crocosmiiflora* 'Norwich Canary'
'Lana de Savary'	CPrp CTca EBee EMan GBin IBal IBlr NCot NHol WCot WLin
'Late Cornish'	see *C.* x *crocosmiiflora* 'Queen Alexandra' J.E. Fitt
'Late Lucifer'	CHEx CTri IBlr LSRN SDix
x ***latifolia***	see *C.* x *crocosmioides*
'Limpopo' **new**	CKno CSpe CTca EBee ECtt EGle GAbr GMac GQue LSou MAvo

	MBNS NCot SMad SPer SPoG WCot WCra WHil
'Lucifer' ♀H4	More than 30 suppliers
'Mandarin'	IBlr
'Marcotijn'	CTca ECtt EMan EMar GGar IBlr IGor LPio NHol WHil WOut
masoniorum ♀H3	More than 30 suppliers
- 'African Dawn'	CPen EGle NCot
- 'Amber'	IBlr
- 'Dixter Flame'	ECtt IBlr IFoB LPio SDix
- 'Firebird'	EBrs GBuc IBlr IGor LRHS MBri NBre NHol SRos
- 'Flamenco'	IBlr
- 'Golden Swan'	ECtt
- 'Kiaora'	IBlr
- 'Moira Reid'	IBlr NHol
- red-flowered	IBlr
- 'Rowallane Apricot'	IBlr WHil
- 'Rowallane Orange'	CTca GAbr IBlr NHol
- 'Rowallane Yellow' ♀H3-4	CTca CWsd EBrs ECha ECtt GBri IBlr IGor LRHS MAvo MBri NCGa NHol SMHy SRos WCot WHil WOut
- 'Tropicana'	IBlr
mathewsiana	IBlr
'Mex' **new**	WCot
'Minotaur'	IBlr
'Mistral'	CMea CPrp CTca EBee EBrs EPfP GBuc IBlr MAvo MNrw MPop NBre NHol NRnb WBor WFar WHil WLin WMoo
'Mount Stewart'	see *C.* x *crocosmiiflora* 'Jessie'
'Mr Bedford'	see *C.* x *crocosmiiflora* 'Croesus'
'Ms Sinkins'	IFoB
'Mullard Pink' **new**	CTca MAvo
'Neptune'	ECtt
'Okavango' **new**	CPen CSpe CTca EBee ECtt EGle GAbr GBri GQue LSou MAvo MBNS MBnl NCot NLar WCot WCra WHil
Old Hat	see *C.* 'Walberton Red'
'Orange Devil'	CBre EBee ECtt IBlr MBri
'Orange Lucifer'	NBre NCot WPrP
'Orange Spirit'	WFar
'Orangeade'	CTca ECtt EMar GBin GBri IBal IBlr NCot NHol
'Out of the West'	WOut
'Pageant' **new**	NCot
§ ***paniculata***	CHEx COlW CPne CPou CTca EBla ECtt ERou GAbr GGar LRHS MNFA MNrw NBid NHol NOrc SAPC SPet WBrk WCot WMoo WPen WShi WTin
- brown/orange	IBlr
- 'Major'	CTri IBlr
- 'Natal'	CPrp CTca EBee ECtt NHol WFar
- red	CPLG CStu CTca IBlr SWvt
- triploid	IBlr
aff. ***paniculata***	ECtt IBlr
pearsei	IBlr
'Phillipa Browne'	CTca EBee EGle GAbr LSou MAvo MBNS NCot SPoG WCot WMoo
§ ***pottsii***	CFee CHVG CTca ECtt EPla GBin IBlr NHol WCot WFar
- CD&R 109	CPou
- 'Culzean Pink'	CBgR CDes CHVG CPom CPrp CTca EBee ECha ECtt ELon GAbr GBin GBuc GMac IBal IBlr MAvo MRav NBir NCob NCot NHol SMrm WCot WCra WHil WLin WOut WPGP
- deep pink-flowered	IBlr IGor
- 'Grandiflora'	IBlr
'Quantreau'	IBlr
'R.W. Wallace'	CPrp NHol
'Red Devils'	NHol
'Red Star'	CTca
'Roman Gold'	IBlr
rosea	see *Tritonia disticha* subsp. *rubrolucens*
'Rowden Bronze'	see *C.* x *crocosmiiflora* 'Coleton Fishacre'
'Rowden Chrome'	see *C.* x *crocosmiiflora* 'George Davison' Davison
'Ruby Velvet'	IBlr
'Rubygold'	IBlr
'Sabena'	MAvo WHil
'Saffron Queen'	IBlr
'Saturn'	see *C.* 'Jupiter'
'Scarlatti'	GAbr IBlr NCot NHol WHil
'Severn Sunrise' ♀H3-4	More than 30 suppliers
'Shocking'	IBlr NCot NHol
'Short Red'	CTca
'Son of Lucifer'	WFar
'Sonate'	CTca ECtt NHol SPlb WPer
'Spitfire'	More than 30 suppliers
§ 'Sulphurea'	CPou CPrp CSam CTca ECtt IBal IBlr NCot NHol SDix SIng WBrk WCot WEas WHal WHil WPer
'Sunset'	GSki
'Sunzest'	WFar
'Tangerine Queen'	ECtt EMar GAbr IBal IBlr NHol WCot
'Tiger'	CElw CTca EBee IBlr NCot
I 'Vulcan' A. Bloom	CMdw CPen CPrp CTca EBee EBrs ECtt GAbr GGar IBal IBlr LRHS MAvo NHol SAga WCot WFar
§ 'Walberton Red'	CDes CTca IBlr MAvo MBri SAga SApp SMad WCot WHil
Walberton Yellow = 'Walcroy'PBR	SApp SMHy WCot WHil
'Zambesi' **new**	CKno CTca EBee ECtt EGle EHrv GAbr GMac GQue LHop LSou MAvo MBNS MWgw NCot NLar SMad SPer WCot WCra WHil WWlt
'Zeal Giant'	CTca ECtt EMar IBlr NHol WHil
Zeal unnamed	CTca EBee IBlr NHol

Crocus ✿ (*Iridaceae*)

abantensis	ERos
adanensis	ERos
'Advance'	see *C. chrysanthus* 'Advance'
alatavicus	WWst
albiflorus	see *C. vernus* subsp. *albiflorus*
ancyrensis	EPot LAma
- 'Golden Bunch'	CHHB EBrs EPfP LRHS WLin WShi
§ ***angustifolius*** ♀H4	EPot ERos
- bronze-tinged **new**	NMin
- 'Minor'	EBrs
asturicus	see *C. serotinus* subsp. *salzmannii*
asumaniae	EBrs ECho ERos
aureus	see *C. flavus* subsp. *flavus*
banaticus ♀H4	EBrs ECho EPot ERos GCrs GEdr LTwo MSSP NHar NMen WWst
- ***albus***	ERos
baytopiorum	ERos
biflorus subsp. ***adamii***	EBrs ERos
- subsp. ***alexandri***	ERos
- subsp. ***biflorus***	CHHB EBrs ERos
§ - - 'Parkinsonii'	EPot ERos
- - 'Serevan'	EPot
- subsp. ***crewei***	ERos
- subsp. ***isauricus***	EBrs ERos
- subsp. ***melantherus***	EBrs ERos WWst
- 'Miss Vain'	CAvo CFFs CPBP EBrs EPot LAma MBri SPer
- var. ***parkinsonii***	see *C. biflorus* subsp. *biflorus* 'Parkinsonii'
- subsp. ***tauri***	LRHS WWst
- subsp. ***weldenii*** 'Albus'	EBrs EPot ERos LAma

- - 'Fairy'	EBrs EPot ERos LAma LRHS
boryi	EBrs ECho LTwo WCot
cambessedesii	EBrs ERos SBla SCnR
§ ***cancellatus*** subsp. ***cancellatus***	CHHB EBrs ECho ERos LAma
- var. ***cilicicus***	see *C. cancellatus* subsp. *cancellatus*
- subsp. ***lycius*** **new**	EBrs
- subsp. ***mazziaricus***	ERos
- subsp. ***pamphylicus***	ERos
candidus var. ***subflavus***	see *C. olivieri* subsp. *olivieri*
cartwrightianus 'Albus' misapplied	see *C. hadriaticus*
- 'Albus' Tubergen ♀H4	EBrs EPot ERos LRHS
§ ***chrysanthus*** 'Advance'	EBrs EGoo EPfP EPot LAma LRHS MBri SPer WLin
- 'Alionka'	WWst
- 'Ard Schenk'	EBrs EPot GKev LAma LRHS SGar WLin
- 'Aubade'	EBrs EPot
- 'Blue Bird'	EBrs EPot LAma LRHS MSte
- 'Blue Pearl' ♀H4	CAvo CFFs CMea EBrs EPfP EPot GKev LRHS MBri MSte NBir SBch SPer SPhx WShi
- 'Cream Beauty' ♀H4	CAvo CFFs CMea EBrs EPfP EPot GKev LAma LRHS MBri MSte NBir SPhx
- 'Dorothy'	EBrs LAma LRHS
- 'E.P. Bowles'	CAvo EBrs EPot LAma MBri
- 'Early Gold'	WWst
- 'Ego'	WWst
- 'Elegance'	EBrs LRHS
- var. ***fuscotinctus***	CPBP EBrs EPot LAma MBri WLin
- 'Gipsy Girl'	CAvo CFFs EBrs EPot LAma MBri
- 'Goldilocks'	EBrs LAma LRHS
- 'Goldmine'	WWst
- 'Herald'	CAvo EBrs EPot LAma MSte
- 'Jeannine'	EBrs EPot
- 'Ladykiller' ♀H4	CAvo CFFs EBrs EPot ERCP LAma LRHS MBri MSte SPer
- 'Little Amber'	WWst
- 'Milea' **new**	EBrs
- 'Moonlight'	LAma
- 'Nida'	WWst
- 'Prins Claus'	EBrs EPot LAma LRHS MBri SPer
- 'Romance'	CAvo CFFs EBrs EPot GKev LAma LRHS MBri SBch SPer WLin
- 'Saturnus'	EBrs EPot LAma
- 'Skyline'	EBrs EPot
- 'Snow Bunting' ♀H4	CAvo CFFs CTca EBrs EGoo EPfP EPot LAma LRHS NBir SPhx WShi
- 'Uschak Orange'	EBrs EPot
- 'White Triumphator'	LAma
- 'Zenith'	EPot
- 'Zwanenburg Bronze' ♀H4	EBrs EPfP EPot LAma LRHS MSte WLin
'Cloth of Gold'	see *C. angustifolius*
clusii	see *C. serotinus* subsp. *clusii*
corsicus ♀H4	EBrs EPot ERos LRHS
cvijicii	WWst
- white-flowered **new**	WWst
dalmaticus	EPot
- 'Petrovac'	WWst
danfordiae	ERos
'Dutch Yellow'	see *C.* x *luteus* 'Golden Yellow'
etruscus ♀H4	CHHB ERos
- 'Rosalind'	EBrs EPot
- 'Zwanenburg'	EBrs EPot LAma
flavus	WWst
§ - subsp. ***flavus*** ♀H4	EBrs EPot LAma LRHS WShi
fleischeri	CHHB EBrs EPot ERos LAma LRHS
gargaricus	ERos SCnR WWst
- subsp. ***gargaricus***	ERos
- subsp. ***herbertii***	ERos
'Golden Mammoth'	see *C.* x *luteus* 'Golden Yellow'
goulimyi ♀H4	EBrs ECho EPot ERos LAma LRHS NMen WCot
- 'Albus'	see *C. goulimyi* subsp. *goulimyi* 'Mani White'
§ - subsp. ***goulimyi*** 'Mani White' ♀H4	ERos SCnR
- subsp. ***leucanthus***	ERos
§ ***hadriaticus*** ♀H4	EBrs ECho ERos LAma LRHS
- var. ***chrysobelonicus***	see *C. hadriaticus*
imperati ♀H4	CHHB ERos
- subsp. ***imperati*** 'De Jager'	EPot ERCP LAma
- subsp. ***suaveolens***	EBrs ERos
'Janis Ruksans'	WWst
x ***jessoppiae***	EBrs EPot ERos LRHS WWst
karduchorum	EPot LAma
korolkowii	CGrW EBrs ERos LAma LRHS
- 'Agalik'	CHHB
- 'Dark Throat' **new**	CHHB
- 'Golden Nugget'	CHHB GCrs
- 'Kiss of Spring'	CBgR EBrs EPot
- 'Varzob'	CHHB
- 'Yellow Tiger'	WWst
kosaninii	CHHB EBrs EPot ERos
kotschyanus ♀H4	ECho LRHS NRya SPer
- 'Albus'	EBrs ECho
§ - subsp. ***kotschyanus***	CHHB EBrs EPot LAma
- var. ***leucopharynx***	EBrs LRHS
- 'Reliance' **new**	EBrs
kotschyanus x ***ochroleucus*** **new**	EBrs
laevigatus from Crete	EBrs
- 'Fontenayi'	EBrs EPot ERCP
- white-flowered **new**	EBrs
'Large Yellow'	see *C.* x *luteus* 'Golden Yellow'
ligusticus	EBrs
longiflorus ♀H4	EBrs ECho ERos GEdr
§ x ***luteus*** 'Golden Yellow' ♀H4	CAvo CFFs EBrs EPfP GKev LAma WShi
§ - 'Stellaris'	EBrs ERos
malyi ♀H2-4	CHHB EBrs ECho ERos
- 'Sveti Roc'	EPot
'Mammoth Yellow'	see *C.* x *luteus* 'Golden Yellow'
mathewii	EBrs EPot WCot
medius ♀H4	EPot ERos LAma
michelsonii	WWst
minimus	EBrs EPot ERCP ERos LAma
niveus	CAvo EBrs ECho EPot ERos LAma WCot
nudiflorus	CAvo EBrs ECho EPot ERos LAma NMen WCot
ochroleucus ♀H4	EBrs EPot ERos GKev LRHS MMHG SPhx
olivieri	ERos
- subsp. ***balansae***	EBrs ERos
- - 'Zwanenburg'	CMea EBrs EPot
§ - subsp. ***olivieri***	EBrs ECho EPot ERos
- - 'Little Tiger' **new**	EBrs
oreocreticus	EBrs
pallasii	EBrs ECho
- subsp. ***pallasii***	ERos
pestalozzae	EBrs ERos
- var. ***caeruleus***	EPot ERos SCnR
pulchellus ♀H4	CHFP CHHB EBrs ECho EPot ERCP ERos GCrs LAma LRHS NWCA SPhx
- ***albus***	EBrs ECho EPot
- 'Inspiration' **new**	EBrs
- 'Michael Hoog' **new**	EBrs
reticulatus	WWst
- subsp. ***reticulatus***	CHHB EPot
rujanensis	ERos
salzmannii	see *C. serotinus* subsp. *salzmannii*
sativus	CArn CAvo CBod CPrp CTca EBrs ECho ELan EPot ERCP GPoy IHer

	LAma LRHS MMHG MSal NBir NGHP SPer
- var. ***cashmirianus***	EBrs
scepusiensis	see *C. vernus* subsp. *vernus* var. *scepusiensis*
§ ***serotinus*** subsp. ***clusii***	EBrs EPot LAma LRHS
§ - subsp. ***salzmannii***	EBrs EPot ERos LAma
- - 'Erectophyllus'	EBrs
sibiricus	see *C. sieberi*
§ ***sieberi*** Y^{H4}	EPot ERos
§ - 'Albus' Y^{H4}	CAvo CBgR CFFs EBrs ECho EPot MBri MSte SPer
- subsp. ***atticus***	CBgR EBrs LAma LRHS
- 'Bowles' White'	see *C. sieberi* 'Albus'
- 'Firefly'	CPBP EBrs EPot LAma LRHS WLin
- 'Hubert Edelsten' Y^{H4}	CHHB EBrs EPot ERos LAma
- 'Ronald Ginns' **new**	EPot
- subsp. ***sublimis*** 'Tricolor' Y^{H4}	CAvo CBgR CFFs CHHB CMea CTca EBrs ECho EPfP EPot ERos GCrs GKev LAma LRHS MBri NBir NMen SBch SPer
- 'Violet Queen'	CAvo CFFs EBrs EPot LAma MBri MSte SPer
speciosus Y^{H4}	CAvo CTca EBrs EPot LAma LRHS NBir SPer WCot WHoo WShi
- 'Aino' **new**	EBrs
- 'Aitchisonii'	CPBP EBrs EPot LAma LRHS SPhx
- 'Albus' Y^{H4}	EBrs ECha EPot LRHS SPhx
- 'Artabir'	EBrs EPot LRHS
- 'Blue Webb'	WWst
- 'Cassiope'	EBrs EPot LAma LRHS
- 'Conqueror'	EBrs EPot LAma LRHS WBor
- 'Lakeside Beauty'	WWst
- 'Lithuanian Autumn'	WWst
- 'Oxonian'	EBrs EPot LAma LRHS NWCA SPhx
- subsp. ***speciosus*** **new**	EBrs
x ***stellaris***	see *C.* x *luteus* 'Stellaris'
- 'Golden Yellow'	see *C.* x *luteus* 'Golden Yellow'
susianus	see *C. angustifolius*
suterianus	see *C. olivieri* subsp. *olivieri*
tommasinianus Y^{H4}	CAvo CFFs CMea CTca EBrs ECho EPot LAma LLWP LRHS MBri MRav NBir SRms WShi
- f. ***albus***	CHHB EBrs EPot LAma LRHS NMin
- 'Barr's Purple'	EBrs EGoo EPot LAma LRHS SPer SPhx
- 'Eric Smith'	CAvo
- 'Lilac Beauty'	EBrs EPot LAma SPer
- var. ***pictus***	CAvo CFFs EBrs EPot ERos LAma NMen
- var. ***roseus***	CAvo CHHB CMea EBrs EPot ERos LAma LRHS NMen NMin WCot
- 'Ruby Giant'	CAvo CFFs EBrs EPfP EPot GKev LAma LRHS MBri NBir SGar SPer SPhx WLin WShi
- 'Whitewell Purple'	CAvo CFFs EBrs ECho EPot LAma MBri NBir SPhx WShi
tournefortii Y^{H2-4}	CHHB EBrs ECho ERos WCot
§ 'Vanguard' Y^{H4}	EBrs EPot ERCP LAma LRHS SBch SPer
veluchensis	EBrs EPot WWst
veneris	EBrs ECho
§ ***vernus*** subsp. ***albiflorus***	CHHB EBrs ECho EPot ERos
- 'Fantasy'	EBrs
- 'Flower Record'	EBrs EPfP GKev LRHS MBri NBir
- 'Glory of Sassenheim'	EPot
- 'Graecus'	CHHB EBrs ECho EPot ERos WWst
- 'Grand Maître'	CAvo CFFs EBrs LAma MBri
- 'Haarlem Gem'	EBrs EPot LRHS
- 'Jeanne d'Arc'	CAvo CFFs EBrs EPfP EPot LAma LRHS MBri NBir WLin WShi
- 'King of the Striped'	EBrs SPer WLin
- 'Michael's Purple' **new**	EBrs ECho
- 'Negro Boy'	EBrs EPot
- 'Pickwick'	CAvo CFFs CMea EBrs EPfP EPot LAma LRHS MBri NBir WShi
- 'Queen of the Blues'	CAvo CFFs EBrs EPot WLin
- 'Remembrance'	EBrs EPfP EPot LAma NBir SPhx WShi
- 'Vanguard'	see *C.* 'Vanguard'
- subsp. ***vernus*** **new**	NMin
- - Heuffelianus Group	EBrs EPot GCrs WWst
- - - 'Brian Duncan'	WWst
- - - 'Dark Eyes'	WWst
- - - 'National Park'	WWst
- - - 'Wildlife'	WWst
- - var. ***neapolitanus***	ERos
- - 'Oradea'	WWst
§ - - var. ***scepusiensis***	EBrs ERos
* ***versicolor***	ERos
- 'Picturatus'	EBrs EPot ERCP ERos LAma LRHS
vitellinus	EBrs WWst
'Yellow Mammoth'	see *C.* x *luteus* 'Golden Yellow'
'Zephyr' Y^{H4}	ECho EPot ERos LAma LRHS
zonatus	see *C. kotschyanus* subsp. *kotschyanus*

Croomia (*Stemonaceae*)

heterosepala	EBee WCru

Crotalaria (*Papilionaceae*)

laburnifolia **new**	CCCN

Crowea (*Rutaceae*)

exalata x ***saligna***	CPLG

Crucianella (*Rubiaceae*)

maritima	XPep
stylosa	see *Phuopsis stylosa*

Cruciata (*Rubiaceae*)

§ ***laevipes***	CNat NMir

Cryptanthus (*Bromeliaceae*)

bivittatus Y^{H1}	CHal
- 'Roseus Pictus'	CHal
bromelioides	MBri

Cryptogramma (*Adiantaceae*)

crispa	SRms WCot WHer WRic

Cryptomeria (*Cupressaceae*)

fortunei	see *C. japonica* var. *sinensis*
japonica Y^{H4}	CDul CMen ECho ISea LCon STre WEve WNor
- Araucarioides Group	CDoC EHul LCon NLar
- 'Atawai' **new**	NLar
- 'Aurea' **new**	NHol
- 'Bandai'	LBuc
- 'Bandai-sugi' Y^{H4}	CKen CMac CMen ECho EHul EOrn EPfP LCon LLin LRHS MBar MGos SCoo SLim SPla STre WEve WGor WRHF
- 'Barabits Gold'	MBar MGos WEve
- 'Compressa'	CDoC CKen CSli ECho EHul EPfP LBee LCon LLin MAsh MBar MGos SCoo SLim WGor
§ - 'Cristata'	CBcs CDoC CMac ECho ELan EOrn LAst LCon MBar MGos NEgg NPal SCoo SLim SPoG
* - 'Cristata Compacta'	ECho EOrn
- 'Dacrydioides'	IClo LCon SLim
- Elegans Group	CBcs CBrm CDul CMac CSBt CTri ECho EHul ELan EOrn EPfP LAst LCon LLin LRHS MBar MBri MGos MWat NEgg NWea SCoo SHBN SLim SPer SPoG WFar WOrn

	- 'Elegans Aurea'	CBcs CDoC CTri ECho EHul LCon LLin MAsh MBar MBri SPoG STre WEve
	- 'Elegans Compacta' 🏆H4	CDoC CRob CSBt CWib ECho EHul EOrn GBin IMGH LBee LCon LRHS MAsh MBar MBri SCoo SLim SPoG WBVN WEve
	- 'Elegans Nana'	ECho LBee LRHS SRms
	- 'Elegans Viridis'	ELan LBuc LRHS MBar SCoo SLim SPoG
	- 'Globosa'	ECho EOrn
	- 'Globosa Nana' 🏆H4	CDoC ECho EHul ERom LAst LBee LCon LLin LPan LRHS MAsh MBar MBri MGos NEgg NLar SCoo SHBN SLim SPoG WFar WGor
	- 'Golden Promise'	CDoC CRob EOrn LBee LLin MAsh NHol SCoo SLim SPoG WEve WGor
	- Gracilis Group	LCon
	- 'Jindai-sugi'	CMac ECho MBar NLar
	- 'Kilmacurragh'	CDoC CKen ECho EHul MBar NWea SLim
	- 'Knaptonensis' (v)	CDoC
	- 'Kohui-yatsubusa'	CKen ECho
*	- 'Konijn-yatsubusa'	CKen
	- 'Koshiji-yatsubusa'	EOrn MBar
	- 'Koshyi'	CKen NLar
	- 'Little Champion'	CDoC CKen LCon NLar SCoo SLim
	- 'Little Diamond'	CKen
	- 'Littleworth Dwarf'	see *C. japonica* 'Littleworth Gnom'
§	- 'Littleworth Gnom'	LLin NLar
	- 'Lobbii Nana' hort.	see *C. japonica* 'Nana'
§	- 'Mankichi-sugi'	ECho NHol NLar
	- 'Monstrosa'	MBar MBri
	- 'Monstrosa Nana'	see *C. japonica* 'Mankichi-sugi'
	- 'Mushroom'	LCon MGos WFar
§	- 'Nana'	CDoC CMac CTri ECho EHul EOrn EPfP LCon LLin SLim SPoG WFar
	- 'Osaka-tama' **new**	CKen
	- 'Pipo'	CKen NLar
	- 'Pygmaea'	ECho LLin MBar MGos SCoo SRms
	- 'Rasen-sugi'	ECho IDee LBuc LCon LLin MBar NEgg NLar NPal SCoo SLim SMad SPoG
	- 'Sekkan-sugi'	CBcs CCVN CDul CSli ECho EHul EOrn GBin IDee LBee LCon LLin LRHS MAsh MBar MGos NEgg NLar SAga SCoo SLim SPoG WEve WFar
	- 'Sekka-sugi'	see *C. japonica* 'Cristata'
§	- var. ***sinensis***	CMCN LAst
*	- - 'Vilmoriniana Compacta'	ECho EOrn
§	- 'Spiralis'	CDoC CKen CMac CRob ECho EHul EOrn EPfP LBee LCon LLin LRHS MAsh MBar MGos NHol NPal SCoo SLim SPer SPla SPoG WEve WFar
§	- 'Spiraliter Falcata'	CDoC LBuc MBar NLar
§	- 'Tansu'	CKen ECho EHul EOrn LCon LLin MBar MGos SPoG
	- 'Tenzan-sugi'	CDoC CKen LLin MAsh MGos SLim WThu
	- 'Tilford Cream'	ECho LAst
	- 'Tilford Gold'	ECho EHul EOrn LLin MBar MGos NBlu NEgg NHol WEve WFar
	- 'Toda'	CKen
	- 'Vilmorin Gold'	CKen EOrn WEve WFar
	- 'Vilmoriniana' 🏆H4	CDoC CKen CMen CRob CSli CTri ECho EHul EOrn EPfP IMGH LBee LCon LLin LRHS MBar MGos NBlu NHol SCoo SHBN SIng SLim SPer SPoG WEve WFar
	- 'Viminalis'	ECho NHol
	- 'Winter Bronze'	CKen
	- 'Yatsubusa'	see *C. japonica* 'Tansu'
	- 'Yore-sugi'	see *C. japonica* 'Spiralis', 'Spiraliter Falcata'
	- 'Yoshino'	CKen SLim
	sinensis	see *C. japonica* var. *sinensis*

Cryptostegia (*Asclepiadaceae*)

	grandiflora	CCCN

Cryptotaenia (*Apiaceae*)

	canadensis	MRav
	japonica	CAgr CPou EUnu MHer MNHC MSal NRnb WHer WJek
	- f. ***atropurpurea***	CArn CHar CSpe EBee ECha EMan GGar ITer LEdu NVic SPhx WFar

Ctenanthe (*Marantaceae*)

§	***amabilis*** 🏆H1	CHal
	lubbersiana 🏆H1	CHal XBlo
§	***oppenheimiana***	LRHS XBlo

Ctenium (*Poaceae*)

	concinnum	CBig

Cucubalus (*Caryophyllaceae*)

	baccifer	CArn NLar WPer WPrP

Cudrania see *Maclura*

cumin see *Cuminum cyminum*

Cuminum (*Apiaceae*)

	cyminum	CArn EUnu SIde

Cunninghamia (*Cupressaceae*)

§	***lanceolata***	CBcs CDoC CDul CGHE CMCN CTho EPla IArd LCon LLin LRHS MBlu SCoo SLim SMad SPoG SSta STre WEve WNor WPGP WSpi
§	- 'Bánó'	CMac EOrn
	- 'Compacta'	see *C. lanceolata* 'Bánó'
	- 'Glauca'	CTho WPGP
	- 'Little Leo'	CKen
	sinensis	see *C. lanceolata*
	unicaniculata	see *C. lanceolata*

Cunonia (*Cunoniaceae*)

	capensis	CPLG CTrC EShb

Cuphea (*Lythraceae*)

	blepharophylla	LRav
	caeciliae	CHal
*	***compacta***	LAst
	cyanea	CMHG CPLG SDix SOWG
	'Harlequin'	NPri
	hirtella	LHop SOWG
	aff. ***hookeriana*** B&SWJ 9039	WCru
	hyssopifolia 🏆H1	CHal CHll SOWG SRms SWvt
	- 'Alba'	CCCN SOWG SWvt
	- pink-flowered **new**	CCCN
	- red-flowered **new**	CCCN
	- 'Riverdene Gold'	EMan
	- 'Rosea'	SWvt
§	***ignea*** 🏆H1	CDMG CHal CWib MBri MLLN SOWG SRms WWlt
	- 'Variegata' (v)	CHal SOWG
§	***llavea*** 'Georgia Scarlet'	CCCN EWin LSou NPri SPoG WWlt
	- 'Tiny Mice'	see *C. llavea* 'Georgia Scarlet'
	macrophylla hort.	CHll
	platycentra	see *C. ignea*

x *Cupressocyparis* ✿ (*Cupressaceae*)

§	***leylandii*** 🏆H4	CBcs CCVT CChe CDoC CDul CMac CTri EHul ENot EPfP LBuc

		LCon LLin LPan LRHS MAsh MBar MBri MGos NBlu NEgg NWea SLim SPer SWvt WEve WHar WMou
§	- 'Castlewellan'	CBcs CCVT CChe CDoC CDul CMac CTri EHul EPfP ERom LBuc LCon LLin LPan LRHS MAsh MBar MBri MGos NBlu NEgg NWea SLim SPer SWvt WEve WFar WHar WMou
	- 'Douglas Gold'	CRob
	- 'Galway Gold'	see x *C. leylandii* 'Castlewellan'
	- 'Gold Rider' ♀H4	CDoC EHul ENot EPfP LCon LLin LRHS MAsh MBar MGos NEgg NWea SCoo SLim SPer SWvt WEve WHar
§	- 'Harlequin' (v)	CBcs LCon MBar SEND SWvt
	- 'Herculea'	CDoC LPan MAsh
	- 'Naylor's Blue'	CMac SEND
	- 'Olive's Green'	EHul LCon SWvt
	- 'Robinson's Gold' ♀H4	CMac EHul GQui LCon LRHS MBar NWea SLim WEve WFar WHar
	- 'Silver Dust' (v)	SRms WFar
	- 'Variegata'	see x *C. leylandii* 'Harlequin'
	- 'Winter Sun'	WCFE
	notabilis	WCwm
	ovensii	EHul

Cupressus (*Cupressaceae*)

	arizonica var. ***arizonica***	MGos
	- 'Conica Glauca'	ECho MBar
§	- var. ***glabra***	ECho WPGP
	- - 'Aurea'	ECho EHul LCon LLin LRHS MBar MGos SLim WFar
	- - 'Blue Ice' ♀H3	CBcs CDoC CDul CRob CTho ECho EHul EOrn LCon LLin LRHS MAsh MBar MGos SCoo SLim SPer SPoG SWvt WEve WFar WGer
	- - 'Compacta'	CKen
	- - 'Conica'	CKen
I	- - 'Fastigiata'	CCVT CDoC ECho ECrN EHul LCon LPan MBar SCoo WEve
	- - 'Glauca'	ECho EPfP MBlu NBlu
*	- - 'Lutea'	ECho EOrn SPoG WEve
	- 'Pyramidalis' ♀H3	CMac ECho EPfP WEve
I	- 'Sulfurea'	CDoC MAsh NLar
	cashmeriana ♀H2	CBcs CDTJ CTho CWsd ECho ELan EPla ERea LCon LLin LPan LRHS SLim WFar WNor
	duclouxiana	WCwm
§	***funebris***	CMCN
	gigantea	CDoC
	glabra	see *C. arizonica* var. *glabra*
	goveniana	MBar
	guadalupensis	CMHG
	lusitanica 'Brice's Weeping'	CKen SLim
	- 'Brookhall'	IDee
	- 'Glauca Pendula'	CKen EPfP LCon WEve
	- var. ***lusitanica***	CMCN
	- 'Pygmy'	CKen
	macrocarpa	CBcs CCVT CDoC CDul CSBt CTho ECho EHul SEND
	- 'Barnham Gold'	SRms
	- 'Compacta'	CKen
	- 'Donard Gold'	CBcs CMac CSBt ECho EOrn MBar
	- 'Gold Spread'	CDoC CRob ECho EHul EOrn LLin SCoo SLim SPoG WFar
	- 'Goldcrest' ♀H3	More than 30 suppliers
	- 'Golden Cone'	CKen CSBt ECho WEve
	- 'Golden Pillar' ♀H3	CDoC CRob ECho EHul EOrn LBee MAsh MBar NEgg SLim SPoG SWvt WFar WGer
	- 'Golden Spire'	WFar
	- 'Greenstead Magnificent'	ECho LCon MAsh SCoo SLim
	- 'Horizontalis Aurea'	EHul MBar
	- 'Lohbrunner'	CKen
	- 'Lutea'	CDoC CTrC ECho WFar
I	- 'Pendula'	ECho
	- 'Pygmaea'	CKen ECho
	- 'Sulphur Cushion'	CKen
	- 'Wilma'	ECho EHul LBee LCon LLin LRHS MAsh MGos NEgg SCoo SLim SPoG SWvt
	- 'Woking'	CKen
	sargentii	ECho
	sempervirens	CDul CMCN CPMA ECrN EHul ELan ERom ETod ISea LLin LPan NLar STop WEve WFar
	- 'Garda'	CDoC
	- 'Green Pencil'	CKen ECho EPfP
	- 'Pyramidalis'	see *C. sempervirens* Stricta Group
	- var. ***sempervirens***	see *C. sempervirens* Stricta Group
§	- Stricta Group ♀H3	CArn CBcs CCVT CKen CMCN CSWP ECho EHul EPfP LCon LLin LPan MAsh NBlu NLar SAPC SArc SBLw SCoo WEve WOrn
	- 'Swane's Gold'	CBcs CDoC CKen ECho EHul EOrn EPfP LCon LLin LRHS MAsh NPal SCoo SLim SPoG WEve WFar
	- 'Totem Pole'	CDoC CKen CSBt CTho CTri ECho EHul EOrn EPfP LBee LCon LLin LPan LRHS MGos NEgg NScw SCoo SEND SLim SPoG WEve WGor
	torulosa	EGFP IDee

x *Cuprocyparis* see x *Cupressocyparis*

Curculigo (*Hypoxidaceae*)

capitulata	CKob XBlo
crassifolia B&SWJ 2318	WCru

Curcuma (*Zingiberaceae*)

alismatifolia	ECho LRHS
amada	CKob
angustifolia	CKob
aromatica	CKob
'Blue Top'	CKob
'Cobra'	CKob
elata	CKob
longa	CKob MSal
ornata	CKob
petiolata 'Emperor' (v)	CKob
'Red Fire'	CKob
roscoeana	LAma
'Ruby'	CKob
'Siam Silver' **new**	LRHS
'Siam Suzy' **new**	LRHS
zedoaria	CKob EShb LAma LRHS

Curtonus see *Crocosmia*

Cuscuta (*Convolvulaceae*)

chinensis	MSal

Cussonia (*Araliaceae*)

gamtoosensis	CKob
paniculata	CDTJ CKob EShb WCot
- subsp. ***sinuata***	CKob
spicata	CKob EShb
transvaalensis	CKob EShb

custard apple see *Annona cherimola*

Cyananthus (*Campanulaceae*)

integer misapplied	see *C. microphyllus*
integer Wall. 'Sherriff's Variety'	WLin
lobatus ♀H4	ECho EMan GBuc GMaP NMen NSla SBla
- CC 4634	ITim

- 'Albus'	EPot EWes SBla WAbe WIvy
- dark	WAbe
- 'Dark Beauty'	ECho
- giant	EPot GEdr SBla
lobatus* x *microphyllus	NWCA WAbe WLin
macrocalyx	SBla WIvy
§ ***microphyllus*** ♕H4	ECho EPot GEdr GMaP NLAp NSla SBla WAbe WLin
sherriffii	EPot NMen WAbe WFar WLin

Cyanella (*Tecophilaeaceae*)

lutea	ECho

Cyanotis (*Commelinaceae*)

somaliensis ♕H1	CHal EPem

Cyathea (*Cyatheaceae*)

australis	CDTJ EAmu ETod LPal MGos WFib WPGP WRic
brownii	WRic
cooperi	CDTJ WFib WRic
* - 'Brentwood'	WRic
cunninghamii	CDTJ
dealbata	CAbb CBcs CDTJ CTrC EAmu LPal MGos WRic
dregei	SPlb WRic
incisoserrata	WRic
lepifera	LPal
medullaris	CAbb CBcs CDTJ CTrC EAmu ETod MGos WRic
milnei	LPal WRic
robusta	WRic
smithii	CBcs CDTJ CTrC EAmu WRic
tomentosissima	EAmu WRic

Cyathodes (*Epacridaceae*)

colensoi	see *Leucopogon colensoi*
fasciculata	see *Leucopogon fasciculatus*
fraseri	see *Leucopogon fraseri*
juniperina	see *Leptecophylla juniperina*
parviflora	see *Leucopogon parviflorus*
parvifolia	see *Leptecophylla juniperina* subsp. *parvifolia*

Cycas (*Cycadaceae*)

circinalis	LPal
media	LPal
panzihihuaensis	CBrP CKob LPal SPlb
revoluta ♕H1	CAbb CBrP CCCN CDoC CHEx CKob CTrC EAmu EPfP LPal LRHS MBri MPRe NLar NPal SAPC SArc SChr SEND WNor
revoluta* x *taitungensis	CBrP
§ ***rumphii***	CBrP CKob EAmu LPal LRHS
siamensis	LPal
taitungensis	CBrP
thouarsii	see *C. rumphii*

Cyclamen ✿ (*Primulaceae*)

africanum	CWCL EBrs ECho EJWh ITim LAma LRHS MAsh NWCA STil WCot
africanum* x *hederifolium	CWCL ECho MAsh
§ ***alpinum***	CWCL EBrs ECho EJWh LAma LRHS MAsh STil
balearicum	EBee EBrs ECho EJWh EPot ITim LAma LRHS MAsh NMen STil
cilicium ♕H2-4	CBgR CLAP CStu CWCL EBla EBrs ECho EJWh ERos ITim LAma LRHS MHer MSSP MTho NMen STil WAbe WFar WIvy WNor WPat
- f. ***album***	CWCL CWoo EBee EBrs ECho EJWh ERos ITim LAma LRHS MAsh NMen STil
- patterned-leaved	NBir
colchicum	ECho STil
§ ***coum*** ♕H4	More than 30 suppliers
- from Turkey	ERos
- var. ***abchasicum***	see *C. coum* subsp. *caucasicum*
§ - subsp. ***caucasicum***	ERos GBuc MAsh STil
- subsp. ***coum***	ECho MAsh
- - f. ***albissimum*** 'Golan Heights'	MAsh STil WIvy
- - f. ***coum*** Nymans Group	CWCL MAsh SBla
- - - Pewter Group ♕H2-4	CBel CPMA CWCL EBrs ECGP ECho ERos MAsh MTho SBla WIvy
- - - - bicoloured	EJWh
- - - - 'Blush'	GBuc STil
- - - - 'Maurice Dryden'	CAvo CBel CLAP CPBP CPMA CStu CWCL EBrs ECGP ECho EHrv GBuc GCrs LAma LRHS MAsh STil
- - - - red	LAma WPat
- - - - 'Tilebarn Elizabeth'	CBel CSsd CWCL EHrv MAsh NBir STil WHoo
- - - - white	GBuc MAsh
- - - plain-leaved red	STil
- - - 'Roseum'	CWCL EBrs GBuc STil
- - - Silver Group	CPMA CWoo EBee ECho EHrv GCrs GEdr LRHS NHol NSla WHoo WPGP
- - - - red	CAvo EPot MTho STil WHoo
- - - - 'Sterling Silver'	CBel
- - magenta	CWCL WHoo
- - f. ***pallidum*** 'Album'	CAvo CBel EBrs EPot ERos ITim LAma MAsh SIng STil WAbe WCot WHoo WNor WPat WSpi
- - - 'Marbled Moon'	MAsh STil
- dark pink	CAvo CLAP ECho ITim WHoo
- subsp. ***elegans***	see *C. elegans*
- marble-leaved	CBel CWCL ECho LHop WHoo
- plain-leaved	CBel CLAP EBla EPot WAbe
- red	CLAP CStu ECho SPhx
I - 'Rubrum' **new**	EBrs
creticum	CWCL ECho EJWh MAsh STil
cyprium	CWCL EBrs ECho EJWh ITim LRHS MAsh STil WIvy
- 'E.S.'	MAsh STil WAbe
x ***drydeniae*** **new**	CPMA
§ ***elegans***	EJWh MAsh STil
europaeum	see *C. purpurascens*
fatrense	see *C. purpurascens* subsp. *purpurascens* from Fatra, Slovakia
graecum	CStu CWCL CWoo EBla EBrs ECho EJWh LRHS MAsh NMen SBla SRot STil WAbe WCot WIvy
- f. ***album***	CWCL EBrs EJWh LRHS MAsh STil
- subsp. ***anatolicum***	STil
- subsp. ***candicum***	MAsh STil
- subsp. ***graecum*** f. ***graecum*** 'Glyfada'	STil
§ ***hederifolium*** ♕H4	More than 30 suppliers
- arrow-head	CLAP
- var. ***confusum***	MAsh STil WCot
- var. ***hederifolium*** f. ***albiflorum***	CAvo CBel CSWP CSam CStu CTri CWCL EHrv EPot ERos GBuc GKev LAma MBar MBri MPes NHol NMen NMyG SBla SIng SPhx STil WAbe WCot WHoo WPat WPnP
- - - 'Album'	EBrs MWgw
- - - Bowles' Apollo Group	GBuc
§ - - - - 'Artemis'	MAsh STil
- - - - 'White Bowles' Apollo'	see *C. hederifolium* var. *hederifolium* f. *albiflorum* (Bowles' Apollo Group) 'Artemis'
- - - 'Linnett Stargazer'	WCot
- - - 'Nettleton Silver'	see *C. hederifolium* var. *hederifolium* f. *albiflorum* 'White Cloud'
- - - 'Perlenteppich'	CWCL GBuc GMaP

- - - 'Tilebarn Helena' STil
§ - - - 'White Cloud' CBel CLAP EBee EBla EPot MAsh NEgg NSla STil WIvy
- - f. ***hederifolium*** Bowles' Apollo Group CLAP CWCL ECGP GBuc MAsh SBla STil
- - - 'Fairy Rings' MAsh
- - - red NEgg
- - - 'Rosenteppich' CWCL GBuc GMaP
- - - 'Ruby Glow' CBel CWCL GBuc MAsh NBir WCot WPat
- - - 'Silver Cloud' CBel CLAP EHrv GBuc MAsh NBir STil WCot WHoo WIvy WPGP WPat
- - - 'Stargazer' MAsh
- - 'Tilebarn Silver Arrow' CPMA STil
- long-leaved CPMA
- 'San Marino Silver' GEdr
- scented NHol STil
- silver-leaved CAby CAvo CPMA CWoo EBla EBrs ECGP ECho EPot GCrs LHop LRHS MAsh SBla SPhx SRot STil
x ***hildebrandii*** WIvy
ibericum see *C. coum* subsp. *caucasicum*
intaminatum CPBP CWCL CWoo EBee EBrs ECho EJWh EPot ERos LAma LRHS MAsh NMen SChr STil
- patterned-leaved CBel CWCL EJWh MAsh STil
- pink CWCL MAsh NMen STil
- plain-leaved MAsh STil WThu
latifolium see *C. persicum*
libanoticum CBel CWCL EBrs ECho EJWh ITim LAma LRHS MAsh NMen SBla STil WFar
mirabile ♀H2-3 CBel CWCL CWoo EBee EBla EBrs ECho EJWh LAma LRHS MAsh NMen STil WAbe WIvy WThu
- 'Tilebarn Anne' STil
- 'Tilebarn Jan' CPMA STil
- 'Tilebarn Nicholas' CBel CWoo EBla MAsh STil
neapolitanum see *C. hederifolium*
orbiculatum see *C. coum*
parviflorum EJWh MAsh STil
§ ***peloponnesiacum*** ♀H2-3 EJWh ERos MAsh
* - subsp. ***peloponnesiacum*** CWCL CWoo STil
* - subsp. ***rhodense*** MAsh STil
* - subsp. ***vividum*** STil
- white-flowered STil
§ ***persicum*** CStu CWCL EBrs ECho EJWh LRHS MAsh NMen SChr STil
- CSE 90560 STil
- var. ***persicum*** f. ***puniceum*** from Lebanon STil
- - - 'Tilebarn Karpathos' CWCL STil
- white-flowered new MAsh
pseudibericum ♀H2-3 CBel CWCL CWoo EBee EBrs ECho EJWh EPot LAma LRHS MAsh SBla STil
- 'Roseum' MAsh NMen STil
§ ***purpurascens*** ♀H4 CWCL EJWh EPot GBuc LRHS MAsh MSSP NMen SBla STil WHoo WIvy WPat
- f. ***album*** SBla
- var. ***fatrense*** see *C. purpurascens* subsp. *purpurascens* from Fatra, Slovakia
- 'Lake Garda' MAsh WPGP
§ - subsp. ***purpurascens*** from Fatra, Slovakia MAsh STil
- silver-leaved STil
- - from Limone, Italy SBla
repandum CAvo EBrs ECho EHrv EJWh ERos LAma LRHS MAsh MSSP NMen SBla SCnR STil WCot WHer
- subsp. ***peloponnesiacum*** see *C. peloponnesiacum*
- 'Pelops' misapplied see *C. peloponnesiacum* subsp. *peloponnesiacum*
- subsp. ***repandum*** f. ***album*** CLAP EJWh MAsh SBla STil
rohlfsianum CWCL EJWh LRHS MAsh STil
x ***saundersii*** EJWh MAsh STil
trochopteranthum see *C. alpinum*
x ***wellensiekii*** MAsh STil

Cyclosorus (*Thelypteridaceae*)

pennigerus WRic

Cydonia ✿ (*Rosaceae*)

japonica see *Chaenomeles speciosa*
oblonga (F) ECrN
- 'Agvambari' (F) SKee
- 'Aromatnaya' (F) ERea
- 'Champion' (F) CAgr CBcs ECrN ERea SGFT SKee WJas
- 'Early Prolific' (F) ECrN LAst
- 'Ekmek' (F) SKee
- 'Isfahan' (F) SKee
- 'Krymsk' (F) CAgr
- 'Leskovac' (F) ERea NLar
§ - 'Lusitanica' (F) CAgr CDoC CDul ERea GTwe MCoo SKee WJas
- 'Meech's Prolific' (F) CAgr CLnd CTho CTri ECrN EMil EMui ERea GTwe LRHS MBlu MGos MWat NLar SDea SFam SGFT SKee SPer
- pear-shaped (F) CDul ECrN ENot MCoo
- Portugal see *C. oblonga* 'Lusitanica'
- 'Shams' (F) SKee
- 'Sobu' (F) SKee
- 'Vranja' (F) ♀H4 More than 30 suppliers

Cymbalaria (*Scrophulariaceae*)

aequitriloba SIng
- 'Alba' GGar
§ ***hepaticifolia*** LRHS WPer
§ ***muralis*** EAlp ECho ECtt GGar MHer NPri SECG WGor XPep
- 'Albiflora' see *C. muralis* 'Pallidior'
§ - 'Globosa Alba' CHal EDAr
- 'Kenilworth White' WMoo
- 'Nana Alba' NPri SEND WPer
§ - 'Pallidior' ECho EWin
- 'Rosea' WFar
§ ***pallida*** CEnt CMea CPBP LRHS NSla SBch SBla SPlb WFar WMoo WPer
§ ***pilosa*** ECtt EMan NLar

Cymbopogon (*Poaceae*)

citratus CArn CBod CCCN CHby CHrt COld CSev CWan EUnu GPoy LRav MNHC MSal NGHP NPri NTHB SHDw SIde WJek
flexuosus CBig GWCH MHer
martini CArn GPoy MSal
nardus CArn GPoy MSal

Cymophyllus (*Cyperaceae*)

§ ***fraserianus*** CHEx EShb GBin

Cynanchum (*Asclepiadaceae*)

CC 4502 CPLG

Cynara (*Asteraceae*)

§ ***baetica*** subsp. ***maroccana*** LDai
cardunculus ♀H3-4 More than 30 suppliers
- ACL 380/78 SWat
I - 'Cardy' EBee EMan EShb EWin LCro NBre NCGa SMrm SPoG SWat WBrE
- dwarf WCot
I - 'Florist Cardy' IGor MFOX MWat NLar WCot
- 'Gobbo di Nizza' EBee ELau WHer

§ - Scolymus Group	More than 30 suppliers
- - 'Carciofo Violetto Precoce'	EBee WHer
- - 'Gigante di Romagna'	WHer
- - 'Gros Camus de Bretagne'	MAvo WCot
- - 'Gros Vert de Lâon'	CBcs ECha ELan NBhm WCot WPGP
- - 'Large Green'	EWin NLar NScw
- - 'Purple Globe'	CArn CPrp CSBt ELau
- - 'Romanesco'	EBee ELau EWin
- - 'Vert Globe'	CBod CHar CPrp CSBt CSev EBee ELau IFoB MWat NPer NVic
- - 'Violetto di Chioggia'	CSev EBee ELau WHer
- white-flowered	WCot
hystrix misapplied	see *C. baetica* subsp. *maroccana*
scolymus	see *C. cardunculus* Scolymus Group
'Violet de Provence' new	WHil

Cynodon (*Poaceae*)

aethiopicus	CBig CMHG GBin SPhx SWal
dactylon 'Santana'	XPep

Cynoglossum (*Boraginaceae*)

amabile ♀H4	GKev NCGa WTMC
- f. ***roseum*** 'Mystery Rose'	WPGP
- - 'Pink Shower' new	EDif
dioscoridis	NLar WPer
nervosum	CBcs EBee ECtt ELan EMil EPPr EPfP GMac LAst LHop LRHS MLHP MRav MWgw NChi NEgg NGdn NWCA SPer SPoG SWat WCAu WCot WFar WPnn WTMC
officinale	CArn MHer MSal NSti WHer

Cynosurus (*Poaceae*)

cristatus viviparous	CNat

Cypella (*Iridaceae*)

§ ***coelestis***	EDif EMan
herbertii	CPom EDif
peruviana	EMan
plumbea	see *C. coelestis*

Cyperus (*Cyperaceae*)

§ ***albostriatus***	CCCN CHEx CHal MBri
alternifolius misapplied	see *C. involucratus*
alternifolius L.	EAmu EBee WMAq
- 'Compactus'	see *C. involucratus* 'Nanus'
'Chira'	EKen MBNS WGwG
§ ***cyperoides***	MBri
diffusus misapplied	see *C. albostriatus*
§ ***eragrostis***	CArn CHal CMil CPLG EWsh GFor MCCP MFOX SDix SPlb SWal SWat WAbb WMAq WMoo
esculentus	CArn CBig GFor LRav SWal
fuscus	EKen MDKP WFar WHal WMoo
§ ***giganteus***	CDWL
glaber	EAlp EBee EPGN GFor LDai MBNS MBar MNHC NBre XIsg
haspan misapplied	see *C. papyrus* 'Nanus'
haspan L.	CDWL EShb
§ ***involucratus*** ♀H1	CBen CDTJ CHEx CHal CWCL EBak EHon EShb MBri SArc SWal SWat WFar WMoo
- 'Gracilis'	EBak MBri
§ - 'Nanus'	SWal
- 'Variegatus' (v)	ERea MJnS
longus	CBen CHrt CWat EHon EMFW EMon EPGN EPPr MBar MLHP NNor NPer SMad SWal SWat WFar WHal WMAq WPnP WPrP
papyrus ♀H1	CHEx CKno CMCo EAmu ERea EShb LPan LRHS MBri MJnS SAPC SArc SMad WHal XBlo
- 'Mexico'	see *C. giganteus*
§ - 'Nanus' ♀H1	CDWL CHEx LPal XBlo
prolifer new	LLWG
rotundus	MCCP NLar SBch SWal
sumula hort.	see *C. cyperoides*
ustulatus	CKno CTrC MDKP
vegetus	see *C. eragrostis*

Cyphomandra (*Solanaceae*)

abutiloides new	EUnu
betacea (F)	CCCN CHEx CPLG
- 'Goldmine' (F)	ERea
- 'Oratia Red' (F)	ERea
corymbiflora	CKob EUnu SKHP
fragrans new	EUnu

Cypripedium (*Orchidaceae*)

acaule	SHdy
Aki gx	GEdr NLAp WWst XFro
- 'Light'	EBee
- 'Pastel' new	XFro
arietinum new	SHdy
Axel gx new	GCrs
x ***barbeyi***	see *C.* x *ventricosum*
calceolus	CFir EHrv EPot GCrs NLAp SHdy WCot WWst
calcicolum	NLAp SHdy
californicum	GCrs NLAp SHdy
candidum	SHdy
cordigerum	SHdy
corrugatum	see *C. tibeticum*
debile	EFEx GEdr SHdy WWst
Emil gx	GEdr NLAp WWst XFro
fargesii new	SHdy
farreri	EFEx SHdy
fasciolatum	EFEx GCrs SHdy
flavum	CFir GKev NCGa NLAp SHdy WCot
- white-flowered	CFir GKev SHdy WCot
§ ***formosanum***	EBee EFEx LAma SBla SHdy SKHP
forrestii new	NLAp
franchetii	SHdy
Gisela gx	GCrs GEdr LAma NLAp WWst XFro
- 'Pastel'	GEdr NLAp WWst XFro
- 'Yellow'	LAma
guttatum	SHdy WWst
- var. ***yatabeanum***	see *C. yatabeanum*
Hank Small gx	NLAp WWst XFro
henryi	EBee EFEx LAma NLAp SHdy
himalaicum	EFEx
Inge gx	WWst XFro
Ingrid gx	GEdr NLAp WWst XFro
japonicum	EFEx GEdr WWst
- var. ***formosanum***	see *C. formosanum*
kentuckiense	CCCN CFir EPot GCrs GEdr NLAp SHdy SKHP WCot
lichiangense	SHdy WWst
macranthos	EFEx EHrv NLAp SHdy WWst
- f. ***albiflorum***	NLAp SHdy
- green-flowered	EFEx
- var. ***hotei-atsumorianum***	EFEx
- 'Kamanashi' new	GCrs
- var. ***rebunense***	EFEx
- var. ***speciosum***	EFEx
margaritaceum	EFEx SHdy
Memoria Gerd Kohls gx new	GCrs
Michael gx	NLAp XFro
montanum	EFEx SHdy
palangshanense new	SHdy
parviflorum 'Butterball'	GCrs
- var. ***makasin***	NLAp
§ - var. ***pubescens***	EPot GCrs LAma NLAp SHdy

	Philipp gx	XFro
	Pixi gx	GCrs
	plectrochilum new	SHdy
	Princess gx new	GKev
	pubescens	see *C. parviflorum* var. *pubescens*
	reginae	CCCN CFir EBee EHrv EPot EWes GCrs GEdr GKev LAma MDun NCGa NLAp NSum SHdy SKHP SSpi WBor WCot
	- f. ***albolabium*** new	SHdy
	reginae x ***tibeticum***	WWst
	Sabine gx	NLAp WWst XFro
	segawae	EFEx LAma SHdy
§	***tibeticum***	EFEx GCrs NLAp SHdy
	Ulla Silkens gx	EBee GCrs GEdr LAma NLAp WWst XFro
§	x ***ventricosum***	SHdy WWst
	wardii	EFEx SHdy
§	***yatabeanum***	EFEx
	yunnanense	SHdy

Cyrilla (*Cyrillaceae*)

parvifolia	SKHP
racemiflora	MBri

Cyrtanthus (*Amaryllidaceae*)

	from high altitude	WCot
	'Alaska'PBR	EBrs LRHS
§	***brachyscyphus***	CDes CSpe EBee EBrs ECho ERos EShb GGar SHFr WPrP WSPU
	breviflorus	CDes EBee ECho SKHP WPGP
	contractus	CDes
	'Edwina'	ECho EShb SPer
§	***elatus*** ♀H1	CHHB CHal CSev CSpe CStu CTca EBee EBrs ERea EShb LAma LEdu LRHS MCCP NCiC SIng WCot WGwG WHer WHil
	- 'Cream Beauty'	EBrs ECho WCot
	- 'Pink Diamond'	EBrs LRHS WCot
	'Elizabeth'	ECho SPer
	falcatus ♀H1	CHHB EBee EBrs
	flanaganii	CDes
	mackenii	CDes CPne EBee ECho WGwG WPGP
	- var. ***cooperi***	WCot
	- 'Himalayan Pink' new	EBee
	- pink-flowered new	WPrP
	- red-flowered	EBee
	- white-flowered	EBee EBrs
	- yellow-flowered new	WPrP
	montanus	EBee EBrs ECho WCot
	obliquus	EBee WCot
	parviflorus	see *C. brachyscyphus*
	purpureus	see *C. elatus*
	sanguineus	EBee ECho WCot WPGP
	smithiae	WCot
	speciosus	see *C. elatus*

Cyrtomium (*Dryopteridaceae*)

§	***caryotideum***	CLAP GQui WRic
§	***falcatum*** ♀H3	CFwr CHEx CHal CLAP CMHG CTrC EBee ELan EPfP GMaP IBal LRHS MPes NBlu NHol NMoo NMyG NOrc NSti SEND SPla SPoG SRms SRot WFar WPnP WRic
*	- 'Muricatum'	ELan
	- 'Rochfordianum'	CBcs CCCN WFib
§	***fortunei*** ♀H4	More than 30 suppliers
	- var. ***clivicola***	CFwr CPrp CTrC CWCL EBee EPfP EShb MAsh MBnl MGos MPes MRav MWgw NDlv NHol NLar NMoo SRot WRic
	lonchitoides	CLAP
	macrophyllum	CLAP

Cystopteris ✿ (*Woodsiaceae*)

bulbifera	CLAP GQui
dickieana	CLAP EBee EMon GBin GGar MPes NHol NVic SRms WCot WFib WRic
fragilis	ECha EFer GQui SRms WFib
- 'Cristata'	CLAP
moupinensis B&SWJ 6767	WCru
tennesseensis	WRic

Cytisus (*Papilionaceae*)

	albus misapplied	see *C. multiflorus*
	albus Hacq.	see *Chamaecytisus albus*
	'Amber Elf'	LRHS MBri SRms WBod
	'Andreanus'	see *C. scoparius* f. *andreanus*
	'Apricot Gem'	LRHS MBar MGos NLar SPoG WFar
	ardoinoi ♀H4	ECho
	battandieri ♀H4	More than 30 suppliers
	- 'Yellow Tail' ♀H4	CEnd LRHS MBri WPGP WSPU
	x ***beanii*** ♀H4	CPLG EBee ELan EPfP LRHS MBar SLon SRms WFar
	'Boskoop Ruby' ♀H4	CBgR CDoC CSBt EPfP GGar LAst LRHS NBlu SPer SPoG SWvt WFar
	'Burkwoodii' ♀H4	CBcs CDoC CDul CSBt CWSG EBee ELan ENot EPfP LAst LRHS LSRN MRav MSwo NHol SPoG WBod WFar
	canariensis	see *Genista canariensis*
	'Compact Crimson'	CDoC SPoG
	'Cottage'	EPot MAsh WAbe
	'Crimson King' new	WBod
	'Daisy Hill'	CSBt
	'Darley Dale Red'	EWTr
§	***decumbens***	CLyd MAsh NLar WLin
	'Donard Gem'	CDoC LRHS WWeb
	'Dorothy Walpole'	WFar
	'Dukaat'	SHBN
	'Firefly'	CBcs CSBt NBlu NBro NLar
	'Fulgens'	CSBt EPfP LRHS MBar SPer WWeb
	'Golden Cascade'	CBcs CDoC EBee ELan LAst LRHS
	'Golden Sunlight'	CSBt EPfP SHBN
	'Goldfinch'	CDoC CHar CSBt CWSG EBee ELan ENot MAsh MBri MNHC MSwo NPri SWal WBod WRHF
	hirsutus	see *Chamaecytisus hirsutus*
	'Hollandia' ♀H4	CBcs CBrm CDoC CSBt CWSG EBee EPfP MBar MGos MRav NBro NEgg NHol NPri SHBN SPer WFar
	x ***kewensis*** ♀H4	CBcs CSBt CWSG EBee ELan EPfP LRHS MAsh MBar MGos MRav NEgg SHBN SPer SPoG SRms WSpi
	- 'Niki'	EBee EPfP LRHS MAsh MGos NHol SPer SPoG SSta WGer
	'Killiney Red'	ECrN ELan MBri NEgg WBod WRHF
	'Killiney Salmon'	GGar LSRN MRav WFar
	'La Coquette'	CDoC EBee MAsh MBar NBlu SPlb SPoG
	'Lena' ♀H4	CDoC CHar CSBt EBee ENot EPfP GGar LAst LRHS MBar MBri MGos MRav MWat NBlu NEgg NHol NPri SRGP WBod WFar WWeb
	leucanthus	see *Chamaecytisus albus*
	'Luna'	EBee LRHS NBlu WFar
	maderensis	see *Genista maderensis*
	'Maria Burkwood'	EPfP MGos NEgg SHBN
	'Minstead'	CDoC EBee ELan EPfP GGar SPoG
	monspessulanus	see *Genista monspessulana*
	'Moonlight'	NBro
	'Moyclare Pink'	CMHG
§	***multiflorus*** ♀H4	LRav SRms
	nigrescens	see *C. nigricans*
§	***nigricans***	ECrN NEgg WPGP
	- 'Cyni'	ELan IArd LAst LRHS MAsh SPer SPoG SSpi

'Palette'	LAst LRHS MBar MGan
'Porlock'	see *Genista* 'Porlock'
x ***praecox***	CBrm CPSs CSBt EWTr LAst LRHS MAsh MGan NBlu NEgg NHol SPlb WBVN WBod WFar WWeb
- 'Albus'	CDoC CDul EBee ECrN ELan ENot EPfP GGar LAst LRHS MAsh MBar MGos MRav NBlu NEgg NHol SHBN SPer WBod WFar WWeb
- 'Allgold' 🏆^{H4}	More than 30 suppliers
- 'Canary Bird'	see *C.* x *praecox* 'Goldspeer'
- 'Frisia'	MBar MRav NBro WFar
§ - 'Goldspeer'	CSBt
- 'Lilac Lady'	LRHS
- 'Warminster' 🏆^{H4}	EBee ENot EPfP LRHS MBar MBri MRav NWea SPer SRms
purpureus	see *Chamaecytisus purpureus*
- 'Atropurpureus'	see *Chamaecytisus purpureus* 'Atropurpureus'
racemosus	see *Genista* x *spachiana*
Red Favourite	see *C.* 'Roter Favorit'
'Red Wings'	NEgg NHol SPer WBod
§ 'Roter Favorit'	EPfP MBar MGos MNHC NScw WGor
scoparius	CArn CDul CRWN EBee ECrN GWCH MCoo NWea SRms
§ - f. ***andreanus*** 🏆^{H4}	CDoC ENot EPfP MGos NWea SPer SPoG WFar
- - 'Splendens'	CBgR
- 'Cornish Cream'	CDoC ECot EPfP SPer WWeb
- 'Jessica'	NBlu SRGP
§ - subsp. ***maritimus***	GSki SLPl
- var. ***prostratus***	see *C. scoparius* subsp. *maritimus*
x ***spachianus***	see *Genista* x *spachiana*
supinus	see *Chamaecytisus supinus*
'Windlesham Ruby'	CDoC CPLG EBee ELan ENot EPfP LAst LRHS MBar MGan NLar SPer WBVN WBod WFar
'Zeelandia' 🏆^{H4}	CBcs EBee ENot EPfP LAst LRHS MBar MRav MWat NBlu NPri SPer SPoG WBod WFar WWeb

D

Daboecia ✿ (*Ericaceae*)

§ ***cantabrica*** f. ***alba***	CPLG CSBt EHea MBar MBri NHol SPer SRms
- - 'Alba Globosa'	CCCN EHea MBar MSwo
- - 'Creeping White'	EHea
- - 'David Moss' 🏆^{H4}	EHea MBar
- - 'Early Bride'	EHea
- - 'Snowdrift'	EHea MBar
- - 'White Carpet'	EHea
- 'Arielle' 🏆^{H4}	EHea
- 'Atropurpurea'	CCCN CNCN CSBt EHea SPer
- 'Barbara Phillips' 🏆^{H4}	EHea MBar
- 'Bellita'	EHea
- 'Bicolor' 🏆^{H4}	CNCN EHea
- 'Blueless'	EHea
- f. ***blumii*** 'Pink Blum'	EHea
- - 'Purple Blum' new	EHea
- - 'White Blum'	EHea
- 'Bubbles'	EHea
- 'Celtic Star'	EHea
- 'Chaldon'	EHea
- 'Charles Nelson' (d)	EHea MBar
- 'Cherub'	EHea
- 'Cinderella'	CNCN EHea MBar
- 'Cleggan'	EHea
- 'Clifden'	EHea
- 'Covadonga'	EHea MBar
- 'Cupido'	CNCN EHea
§ - 'Donard Pink'	EHea MBar
- 'Eskdale Baron'	EHea
- 'Eskdale Blea'	EHea
- 'Eskdale Blonde'	EHea
- 'Glamour'	EHea
- 'Globosa Pink'	EHea
- 'Harlequin'	EHea
- 'Heather Yates'	EHea
- 'Heraut'	EHea
- 'Hookstone Purple'	CCCN EHea MBar
- 'Irish Shine'	EHea
- 'Johnny Boy'	EHea
- 'Lilac Osmond'	EHea MBar
- 'Pink'	see *D. cantabrica* 'Donard Pink'
- 'Pink Lady'	EHea MBar
- 'Polifolia'	EHea SRms
- 'Porter's Variety'	EHea MBar
- 'Praegerae'	CCCN CNCN CTri EHea MBar
- 'Purpurea'	EHea MBar
- 'Rainbow' (v)	CNCN EHea MBar
- 'Rodeo' 🏆^{H4}	EHea
- 'Rosea'	EHea MBar
- 'Rubra'	EHea
- subsp. ***scotica*** 'Bearsden'	EHea MBar
- - 'Ben'	EHea
- - 'Cora'	EHea MBar
- - 'Golden Imp'	EHea
- - 'Goscote'	EHea MGos
- - 'Jack Drake' 🏆^{H4}	CNCN EHea MBar MBri
- - 'Katherine's Choice'	CBcs EHea
- - 'Red Imp'	EHea
- - 'Robin'	EHea
- - 'Silverwells' 🏆^{H4}	CBcs CNCN EHea MBar MBri
- - 'Tabramhill'	EHea MBar
- - 'William Buchanan' 🏆^{H4}	CNCN EHea GGar MBar MBri
- - 'William Buchanan Gold' (v)	CCCN CNCN EHea MBar MBri
- 'Tom Pearce'	CCCN
- 'Waley's Red' 🏆^{H4}	EHea GQui MBar
- 'Wijnie'	EHea

Dacrycarpus (*Podocarpaceae*)

§ ***dacrydioides***	ECou LEdu
- 'Dark Delight'	ECou

Dacrydium (*Podocarpaceae*)

bidwillii	see *Halocarpus bidwillii*
cupressinum	CAbb CBcs CDoC CTrC
franklinii	see *Lagarostrobos franklinii*
laxifolium	see *Lepidothamnus laxifolius*

Dactylis (*Poaceae*)

glomerata	WSFF
- 'Variegata' (v)	CPen EBee EMon EPPr MBlu MCCP NBid NBro NHol WFar XIsg

Dactylorhiza (*Orchidaceae*)

alpestris	CFir EBee GEdr MAvo NLAp WCot
aristata	EFEx GEdr WWst
Atlanta gx	GEdr SBla
x ***braunii***	ECha
- dark	ECha
§ ***elata*** 🏆^{H4}	CLAP EMon GAbr GCrs GMaP GQui IBlr LAma MBri NLAp NSum SPhx WCot
- 'Lydia'	GCra GCrs SPhx
Eskimo Nell gx	SBla
§ ***foliosa*** 🏆^{H4}	CCCN CDes CFir CWsd EPot ERas ERos GCra IBlr MAvo MDun MNrw MTho NLAp NSum WCot WFar WOld
§ ***fuchsii***	CCCN CMil EBee EPot ERos GAbr GBuc GCrs GKev MAvo MGos MNrw NLAp NMen NRya NSla

		NSum SCnR SHdy WCot WHer WTin
	- 'Bressingham Bonus'	GCrs
	- pink-flowered **new**	CFir
	- white-flowered	CFir NLAp SHdy
	x ***grandis***	CWsd EMon IBlr SCnR SMHy
	'Harold Esslemont' **new**	SBla
	hybrids	NLAp
	incarnata	CFir NLAp WSpi
	- subsp. ***cruenta***	NLAp
	insularis	NLAp
§	***maculata***	CFir CHid EBee EHrv ELan ENot EPfP LAma MDun NCGa NLAp NSum SHdy WBor WCot WFar WHer WHlf
	- subsp. ***ericetorum***	NLAp
	maderensis	see *D. foliosa*
§	***majalis***	CFir CLAP LAma NLAp SHdy WFar
	- subsp. ***praetermissa***	see *D. praetermissa*
§	- subsp. ***sphagnicola***	EBee MAvo NLAp WCot
	mascula	see *Orchis mascula*
§	***praetermissa***	CCCN CFir CFwr CLAP EBee EPot GEdr GKev MAvo MDun NCGa NLAp SHdy WCot WFar
	- 'Copenhaven' **new**	NLAp
	purpurella	CFir CLAP EBee MAvo NLAp NRya SHdy WCot WFar
	- 'Palmengarten' **new**	NLAp
	sphagnicola	see *D. majalis subsp. sphagnicola*

Dahlia ✿ (*Asteraceae*)

	'A la Mode' (LD)	CWGr
	'Abba' (SD)	CWGr
	'Abingdon Ace' (SD)	CWGr
	'Abridge Alex' (SD)	CWGr
	'Abridge Ben' (MinD)	CWGr
	'Abridge Florist' (SWL)	CWGr
	'Abridge Fox' (MinD)	CWGr
	'Abridge Natalie' (SWL)	CWGr
	'Abridge Primrose' (SWL)	CWGr
	'Abridge Taffy' (MinD)	CWGr
	'Adelaide Fontane' (LD)	CWGr
	'Admiral Rawlings' (SD)	CWGr MAJR WHal WWlt
	'Aimie' (MinD)	CWGr
	'Aitara Cloud' (MinC) **new**	NHal
	'Aitara Diadem' **new**	CWGr
	'Aitara Majesty' (GS-c) **new**	CWGr
	'Akita' (Misc)	CWGr MBri SPer
	'Albert Schweitzer' (MS-c)	CWGr
	'Alden Regal' (MinC)	CWGr
	'Alfred C' (GS-c)	CWGr
	'Alfred Grille' (MS-c)	CWGr EPfP LRHS SPer
	'Alice Ireland' (MinD)	CWGr
	'Aljo' (MS-c)	CWGr
	'All Triumph' (MinS-c)	CWGr
	'Allan Snowfire' (MS-c)	LAyl NHal
	'Allan Sparkes' (SWL) 🏆H3	CWGr LAyl
I	'Allegro' (LS-c) **new**	CWGr
	'Alloway Cottage' (MD)	CWGr NHal
	'Alltami Apollo' (GS-c)	CWGr
	'Alltami Cherry' (SBa)	CWGr
	'Alltami Classic' (MD)	CWGr
	'Alltami Corsair' (MS-c)	CWGr
	'Alltami Cosmic' (LD)	CWGr
	'Alltami Dandy' (SD) **new**	CWGr
	'Alltami Joy' (MD) **new**	CWGr
	'Alltami Ruby' (MS-c)	CWGr
*	'Allyson' (MinBa)	CWGr
	'Almand's Climax' (GD) 🏆H3	CWGr
	'Alpen Beauty' (Col)	CWGr
	'Alpen Fern' (Fim)	CWGr
	'Alpen Flame' (MinC)	CWGr
	'Alpen Mildred' (SS-c)	CWGr
	'Alpen Sun' (MinS-c)	CWGr
	'Alstergruss' (Col)	CWGr
	'Alva's Doris' (SS-c) 🏆H3	CWGr LAyl
	'Alva's Lilac' (SD)	CWGr
	'Alva's Supreme' (GD) 🏆H3	CWGr NHal
	'Amanda Jarvis' (SC)	CWGr
	'Amanjanca' (MinS-c)	CWGr
	'Amaran Candyfloss' (SD)	CWGr
	'Amaran Pentire' (SS-c)	CWGr
	'Amaran Pico' (MD)	CWGr
	'Amaran Relish' (LD)	CWGr
	'Amaran Return' (GD)	CWGr
	'Amaran Royale' (MinD)	CWGr
	'Amaran Troy' (SWL)	CWGr
I	'Amazone' (DwB)	LAst
	'Amber Banker' (MC)	CWGr
	'Amber Festival' (SD)	CWGr NHal
	'Amber Vale' (MinD)	CWGr
	'Amberglow' (MinBa)	CWGr LAyl
	'Amberley Jean' (SD)	CWGr
	'Amberley Joan' (SD)	CWGr
	'Amberley Nicola' (SD)	CWGr
	'Amberley Victoria' (MD)	CWGr
	'Ambition' (SS-c)	CWGr
	'Amelia's Surprise' (LD)	CWGr
	'American Copper' (GD)	CWGr
	'Amgard Coronet' (MinD)	CWGr
	'Amgard Delicate' (LD)	CWGr
	'Amgard Rosie' (SD)	CWGr
	'Amira' (SBa)	CWGr NHal
	'Amorangi Joy' (SC)	CWGr
	'Ananta Patel' (SD)	CWGr
*	'Anatol' (LD)	CWGr
	'Anchorite' (SD)	CWGr
	'Andrea Clark' (MD)	CWGr NHal
	'Andrew Lockwood' (Pom)	CWGr
	'Andrew Magson' (SS-c) 🏆H3	CWGr
	'Andrew Mitchell' (MS-c)	CWGr NHal
	'Andries' Amber' (MinS-c)	CWGr LBut
	'Andries' Orange' (MinS-c)	CWGr LBut
	'Angora' (SD/Fim)	CWGr
	'Ann Breckenfelder' (Col) 🏆H3 **new**	EHrv NHal WCot
	'Anniversary Ball' (MinBa)	CWGr LAyl
	'Apache' (MS-c/Fim)	CWGr SPer
	apiculata **new**	CWGr
	'Appetizer' (SS-c)	CWGr
I	'Appleblossom' (Col)	CWGr
	'Apricot Beauty' (MS-c)	CWGr LAyl
	'Apricot Honeymoon Dress' (SD)	CWGr
	'Apricot Jewel' (SD)	CWGr
	'Apricot Parfait' (SS-c)	CWGr
	'April Dawn' (MD)	CWGr
	'April Heather' (Col)	NHal
	'Arab Queen' (GS-c)	CWGr
	'Arabian Night' (SD)	More than 30 suppliers
	'Arc de Triomphe' (MD)	CWGr
	'Arlequin' (LD)	CWGr
	'Arnhem' (SD)	CWGr
	'Arthur Godfrey' (GD)	CWGr
	'Arthur Hankin' (SD)	CWGr
	'Arthur Hills' (SC)	CWGr
	'Arthur's Delight' (GD)	CWGr
	'Asahi Chohje' (Anem) 🏆H3	CWGr
	'Askwith George' (MinD)	CWGr
	'Aspen' (Dwf)	CWGr
	'Athalie' (SC)	CWGr
	'Athelston John' (SC)	CWGr
	'Atilla' (SD)	CWGr
	'Audacity' (MD)	CWGr LAyl
	'Audrey Grace' (SD)	CWGr
	'Audrey R' (SWL)	CWGr
	'Aurora's Kiss' (MinBa)	CWGr LBut NHal

	'Aurwen's Violet' (Pom)	CWGr LAyl NHal
	australis	EBee WPGP
	- B&SWJ 10358	WCru
	'Autumn Choice' (MD)	LAyl
	'Autumn Lustre' (SWL) ♀H3	CWGr
	'Avoca Salmon' (MD)	NHal
	'Awaikoe' (Col)	CWGr
	'B.J. Beauty' (MD)	CWGr LAyl NHal
	'Babette' (S-c)	LBut
	'Baby Fonteneau' (SS-c)	CWGr
	'Babylon' (GD)	EPfP
	'Babylon Purple' (SD) **new**	WBor
	'Bacchus' (MS-c)	CWGr
	'Bach' (MC)	CWGr LRHS
	'Bahama Red' (SD)	CBgR
	'Balcombe' (SD)	CWGr
	'Ballego's Glory' (MD)	CWGr
	'Bambino' (Lil)	CWGr
	'Banker' (MC)	CWGr
	'Bantling' (MinBa)	CWGr ECtt
	'Barb' (LC)	CWGr
	'Barbara' (MinBa)	CWGr
	'Barbara Schell' (GD)	CWGr
	'Barbara's Pastelle' (MS-c)	CWGr
	'Barbarossa' (LD)	CWGr
	'Barbarry Ball' (SBa)	CWGr
	'Barbarry Banker' (MinD)	CWGr LAyl
	'Barbarry Bluebird' (MinD)	NHal
	'Barbarry Cadet' (MinD)	CWGr
	'Barbarry Carousel' (SBa)	CWGr
	'Barbarry Cascade' (SD)	CWGr
	'Barbarry Challenger' (MinD)	CWGr
	'Barbarry Chevron' (MD)	CWGr
	'Barbarry Clover' (SB)	CWGr
	'Barbarry Cosmos' (SD)	CWGr
	'Barbarry Dominion' (MinD)	CWGr
	'Barbarry Drifter' (SD) **new**	CWGr
	'Barbarry Flag' (MinD)	CWGr
	'Barbarry Gem' (MinBa)	CWGr
	'Barbarry Ideal' (MinD)	CWGr
	'Barbarry Monitor' (MinBa)	CWGr
	'Barbarry Noble' (MinD)	CWGr
	'Barbarry Olympic' (SBa)	CWGr
	'Barbarry Oracle' (SD)	CWGr
	'Barbarry Pimpernel' (SD)	CWGr
	'Barbarry Pinky' (SD)	CWGr
	'Barbarry Pointer' (SD) **new**	NHal
	'Barbarry Polo' (MinD)	CWGr
	'Barbarry Quest' (MinD) **new**	CWGr
	'Barbarry Red' (MinD)	CWGr
	'Barbarry Riviera' (MinD)	CWGr
	'Barbarry Stockton' (SD) **new**	CWGr
	'Barbarry Triumph' (MinD)	CWGr
	'Barbetta' (MinD)	CWGr
	'Barbette' (MinD)	CWGr
	'Bareham's Beauty' (SD) **new**	CWGr
	'Baret Joy' (LS-c)	CWGr NHal
	'Bargaly Blush' (MD)	NHal
	'Baron Ray' (SD)	CWGr
	'Barry Williams' (MD)	CWGr
	'Bart' (SD)	CWGr
	'Barton Memory' (S-c)	NHal
	'Baseball' (MinBa)	CWGr
	'Bassingbourne Beauty' (SD)	CWGr
	'Bayswater Red' (Pom)	CWGr
	'Baywatch' (Anem) **new**	CWGr
	'Beach Boy' (SD)	CWGr
	'Beacon Light' (SD)	CWGr
I	'Beatrice' (MinBa)	CWGr
	'Beatrice' (MinD)	CWGr
	'Bedford Sally' (MD)	CWGr
	'Bednall Beauty' (Misc/DwB) ♀H3	CBgR CHll CSpe CWCL CWGr EBee ECtt EHrv ELan EMan EMil ERou EShb EWes EWin LHop MBri MRav NPri SDnm SDys SPav WCot WDyG WSpi
	'Bell Boy' (MinBa)	CWGr
	'Bella S' (GD)	CWGr
	'Belle Epoque' (MC)	CWGr
	'Belle Moore' (SD)	CWGr
	'Bell's Delight' (MSC)	CWGr
	'Beretta' (MD)	CWGr
	'Berger's Rekord' (S-c)	CSut CWGr EPfP LRHS
	'Berliner Kleene' (MinD/DwB)	CWGr LRHS
	'Bernice Sunset' (SS-c)	CWGr
	'Berolina' (MinD)	CWGr
	'Berwick Banker' (SBa)	CWGr
	'Berwick Wood' (MD)	CWGr NHal
	'Bess Painter' (SD)	CWGr
	'Betty Ann' (Pom)	CWGr
	'Betty Bowen' (SD)	CWGr
	'Biddenham Fairy' (MinD)	CWGr
	'Biddenham Strawberry' (SD)	CWGr
	'Biddenham Sunset' (MS-c)	CWGr
	'Big Red' (MD)	CWGr
	'Bill Homberg' (GD)	CWGr
	'Bill Sanderson' (Sin/DwB) **new**	CWGr
	'Bingley' (SD)	CWGr
	'Bingo' (MinD)	CWGr
	'Bishop of Auckland' (Misc)	EBee LRHS SPoG
	'Bishop of Canterbury' (Misc)	CBgR CWGr EBee ECtt LRHS MWea NBPN NGdn NHal SPoG
	'Bishop of Lancaster' (Misc)	CWGr LRHS SPoG
	'Bishop of Leicester' **new**	CBgR CSpe MWea NBPN
	'Bishop of Llandaff' (Misc) ♀H3	More than 30 suppliers
	'Bishop of Oxford' (Misc)	CBgR CSpe EBee MWea NBPC NGdn WHoo
	'Bishop of York' (Misc)	CBgR CSpe CWGr EBee MWea NBPC NBPN NGdn
	'Bishop Peter Price' (Sin) **new**	CHar
	'Bishop's Children' **new**	CTca
	'Bitsa' (MinBa)	CWGr
	'Bitter Lemon' (SD)	CWGr
	'Black Fire' (SD)	CWGr LAyl
*	'Black Knight' (MD)	CWGr
	'Black Monarch' (GD)	CWGr NHal
	'Black Narcissus' (MC)	CWGr WWlt
	'Black Spider' (SS-c)	CWGr
	'Black Tucker' (Pom)	CWGr
	'Blaisdon Red' (SD)	CWGr
	'Blaze' (MD)	CWGr
	'Blewbury First' (SWL)	CWGr
	'Bliss' (SWL)	CWGr
	'Blithe Spirit' (LD)	CWGr
	'Bloemfontein' (SD)	LRHS
	'Bloodstone' (SD)	CWGr
	'Bloom's Amy' (MinD)	CWGr
	'Bloom's Graham' (SS-c)	CWGr
	'Bloom's Kenn' (MD)	CWGr
I	'Blossom' (Pom)	CWGr
	'Blue Beard' (SS-c)	CWGr
	'Blue Diamond' (MC)	CWGr
	'Bluesette' (SD)	CWGr
	'Blushing Princess' (SS-c)	CWGr
	'Bob Fitzjohn' (GS-c)	CWGr
	'Bokay' (SWL)	CWGr
	'Bonaventure' (GD)	NHal

	'Bonesta' (SWL)	CWGr
	'Bonne Espérance' (Sin/Lil)	CWGr
	'Bonny Blue' (SBa)	CWGr
	'Bonny Brenda' (MinD)	CWGr
	'Boogie Woogie' (Anem)	CSut CWGr
	'Bora Bora' (SS-c)	CWGr
	'Border Princess' (SC/DwB)	CWGr
	'Border Triumph' (DwB)	CWGr
	'Boy Scout' (MinBa) **new**	CWGr
	'Brackenhill Flame' (SD)	CWGr
	'Brackenridge Ballerina' (SWL)	CSam CWGr LAyl NHal
	'Brandaris' (MS-c)	CWGr
	'Brandysnap' (SD)	CWGr
	'Brian R' (MD)	CWGr
	'Brian's Dream' (MinD)	NHal
	'Bride's Bouquet' (Col)	CWGr
	'Bridge View Aloha' (MS-c) ♀H3	CWGr EPfP
	'Bridgette' (SD)	CWGr
	'Bright Star' (SC)	CWGr
	'Brilliant Eye' (MinBa)	CWGr
	'Bristol Petite' (MinD)	CWGr
	'Brookfield Delight' (Sin/Lil) ♀H3	CWGr
	'Brookfield Dierdre' (MinBa)	CWGr
	'Brookfield Judith' (MinD)	NHal
	'Brookfield Rachel' (MinBa)	CWGr
	'Brookfield Rene' (Dwf MinD)	CWGr
	'Brookfield Snowball' (SBa)	CWGr
	'Brookfield Sweetie' (DwB/Lil)	CWGr
	'Brookside Cheri' (SC)	CWGr
	'Brookside Snowball' (SB)	CWGr
	'Brunello' (Misc) **new**	CWGr
	'Bryce B. Morrison' (SD)	CWGr
	'Bryn Terfel' (GD) **new**	NHal
	'Bud Flanagan' (MD)	CWGr
	'Butterball' (MinD/DwB)	CWGr
*	'Buttercup' (Pom)	CWGr
	'Buttermere' (SD)	CWGr
	'By George' (GD)	CWGr
	'Cabo Bell' (MSC)	CWGr
	'Café au Lait' (GD)	CBgR CWGr SEND SPer WSpi
	'Calgary' (SD)	CWGr
	'Camano Ariel' (MC)	CWGr
	'Camano Choice' (SD)	CWGr
	'Camano Passion' (MS-c)	CWGr
	'Camano Poppet' (SBa)	CWGr
	'Camano Regal' (MS-c)	CWGr
	'Cameo' (WL)	CSam CWGr LBut NHal
	'Campos Billy M' (LS-c)	CWGr
	'Campos Hush' (SS-c)	CWGr
	'Campos Philip M' (GD)	CWGr
*	'Canary Fubuki' (MD)	CWGr
I	'Candlelight' (GD)	CWGr NHal
I	'Candy' (SD)	CWGr
	'Candy Cane' (MinBa)	CWGr
	'Candy Cupid' (MinBa) ♀H3	CWGr LBut
	'Candy Hamilton Lilian' (SD)	CWGr
	'Candy Keene' (LS-c)	CWGr NHal
	'Caproz Jerry Garcia' (MD)	CWGr
	'Capulet' (SBa)	CWGr
	'Cara Tina' (Misc/DwO)	CWGr
	'Careless' (SD)	CWGr
	'Caribbean Fantasy'	CSut SPer
	'Carole Melville' (MinBa) **new**	CWGr
I	'Carolina' (Dwf)	CWGr
	'Carolina Moon' (SD)	CSam CWGr LAyl NHal
	'Carstone Cobblers' (SBa)	CWGr
	'Carstone Ruby' (SD)	CWGr NHal
	'Carstone Sunbeam' (SD)	CWGr
	'Carstone Suntan' (MinC)	CWGr NHal
	'Castle Drive' (MD)	CWGr
	'Catherine Bateson' (MinWL) ♀H3 **new**	CWGr
	'Catherine Deneuve' (Misc) **new**	CWGr
	'Catherine Ireland' (MinD)	CWGr
	'Cerise Prefect' (MS-c)	CWGr
	'Cha Cha' (SS-c)	CWGr
	'Chanson d'Amour' (SD)	CWGr
	'Chantal' (MinBa)	CWGr
	'Charles de Coster' (MD)	CWGr
	'Charlie Briggs' (SBa)	NHal
	'Charlie Dimmock' (SWL)	CWGr NHal
	'Charlie Kenwood' (MinD)	CWGr
	'Charlie Two' (MD)	CWGr NHal
	'Charlotte Bateson' (MinBa)	CWGr
	'Chat Noir' (MS-c)	CWGr ERCP LCro
	'Chee' (SWL)	CWGr
	'Cheerio' (SS-c)	CWGr
	'Cheerleader' (GS-c)	CWGr
	'Cherokee Beauty' (GD)	CWGr
	'Cherry Wine' (SD)	CWGr
	'Cherrywood Millfield' (MS-c)	CWGr
	'Cherrywood Stoddard' (MD)	CWGr
	'Cherrywood Turnpike' (SD)	CWGr
	'Cherrywood Wilderness' (MD)	CWGr
	'Cherubino' (Col)	CWGr
	'Cherwell Goldcrest' (SS-c)	CWGr NHal
	'Cherwell Siskin' (MD)	CWGr
	'Cherwell Skylark' (SS-c) ♀H3	CWGr NHal
	'Chessy' (Sin/Lil) ♀H3	CWGr EPfP LAyl LRHS NHal
	'Chic' (MinBa)	EBee ECtt NBPN WWeb
	'Chic en Rouge' **new**	NBPC NBPN
	'Chilson's Pride' (SD)	CWGr
	'Chiltern Amber' (SD)	CWGr
	'Chiltern Fantastic' (SC)	CWGr
	'Chiltern Herald' (MS-c)	CWGr
	'Chiltern Sylvia' (MinS-c)	CWGr
	'Chimacum Topaz' (MS-c)	CWGr
	'Chimborazo' (Col)	CWGr LAyl SDix
	'Chislehurst Charisma' (SD)	CWGr
	'Chocolate Orange' (Sin)	WCot
	'Chorus Girl' (MinD)	CWGr
	'Christine' (SD)	SPer
I	'Christine' (SWL)	CWGr
	'Christmas Carol' (Col)	CWGr
	'Christmas Star' (Col)	CWGr
	'Christopher Nickerson' (MS-c)	CWGr
	'Christopher Taylor' (SWL)	CWGr NHal
	'Clair de Lune' (Col) ♀H3	CBgR CHFP CWGr EBee EWin LAst NHal SPav WCot WGwG WSpi
	'Claire Diane' (SD)	CWGr
	'Claire Louise Kitchener' (MWL)	CWGr
	'Clara May' (MS-c/Fim)	CWGr
	'Clarence' (S-c)	CWGr
	'Clarion' (MS-c)	LRHS MAsh WCot
	'Classic A.1' (MC)	CWGr
	'Classic Elise' (Misc)	CWGr
	'Classic Masquerade'PBR (Misc)	CBgR EBee
	'Classic Poème'PBR (Misc)	CBgR EBee
	'Classic Rosamunde'PBR (Misc)	CBgR EBee NBPN NGdn

'Classic Summertime' (Misc)	CBgR CWGr EBee WWeb
'Classic Swanlake'PBR (Misc)	CBgR CWGr EBee
'Clearview Arla' (MinS-c) new	CWGr
'Clearview Irene' new	CWGr
'Clyde's Choice' (GD) new	CWGr
coccinea (B)	CBgR CHFP CHll CPLG CSpe CWGr EBee EBrs EHrv EMan EWin IHer LAst MSte MWgw NCob SDix SMHy SMad SPav WCot WDyG WHrl WPGP
- B&SWJ 9126	WCru
- var. ***palmeri***	CBgR CSpe MCCP MHar
coccinea x ***merckii*** (B)	EBla EMan EWes
coccinea x ***sherffii***	EBla
'Cocktail' (S-c)	CWGr
'Colac' (LD)	CWGr
'Color Spectacle' (LS-c)	CWGr
'Colour Magic' (LS-c) new	CWGr
'Coltness Gem' (Sin/DwB)	CWGr
'Comet' (Anem)	CWGr
'Como Polly' (LD)	CWGr
I 'Concordia' (SD)	CWGr
'Connie Bartlam' (MD)	CWGr
'Connoisseur's Choice' (MinBa)	CWGr
'Constance Bateson' (SD)	CWGr
'Constantine' (MD)	CWGr
'Contessa' (SWL) new	CWGr
'Conway' (SS-c)	CWGr
'Coral Puff' (DwAnem)	CWGr LRHS
'Coral Relation' (SC)	CWGr
'Coral Strand' (SD)	CWGr
'Coralle' (MD)	CWGr
'Cornel' (SBa)	CWGr LAyl LBut NHal
'Corona' (SS-c/DwB)	CWGr
'Coronella' (MD)	CWGr
'Corrie Vigor' (SS-c)	NHal
'Cortez Silver' (MD)	CWGr
'Cortez Sovereign' (SS-c)	CWGr
'Corton Bess' (SD)	CWGr
'Corton Olympic' (GD)	CWGr
'Corydon' (SD)	CWGr
'Cottesmore' (MD)	CWGr
'Cottonrail' (Col)	CWGr
'Country Boy' (MS-c)	CWGr
'Crazy Legs' (MinD)	CWGr
'Cream Alva's' (GD) ♀H3	CWGr
'Cream Delight' (SS-c)	CWGr
'Cream Klankstad' (SC)	CWGr
'Cream Linda' (SD)	CWGr
'Cream Moonlight' (MS-c)	CWGr
'Cream Reliance' (SD)	CWGr
'Crève Coeur' (GD)	CWGr
'Crichton Cherry' (MinD)	CWGr
'Crichton Honey' (SBa)	CWGr
'Croesus' (GS-c)	CWGr
'Crossfield Allegro' (SS-c)	CWGr
'Crossfield Anne' (MinD)	CWGr
'Crossfield Ebony' (Pom)	CWGr
'Crossfield Festival' (LD)	CWGr
'Croydon Jumbo' (GD)	CWGr
'Croydon Snotop' (GD)	CWGr
'Croydon Superior' (GD)	CWGr
'Crushed Velvet' (MinD)	CWGr
'Cryfield Harmony' (MinBa) new	CWGr
'Cryfield Jane' (MinBa)	CWGr
'Cryfield Keene' (LS-c)	CWGr
'Cryfield Max' (SC)	CWGr
'Cryfield Rosie' (SBa)	CWGr
'Crystal Ann' (MS-c)	CWGr
'Curate' (Misc)	CWGr
'Curiosity' (Col)	CWGr
'Currant Cream' (SBa)	CWGr
'Cyclone' (MD)	CWGr
'Cycloop' (SS-c)	CWGr
'Cynthia Chalwin' (MinBa)	CWGr
'Cynthia Louise' (GD)	CWGr
'D. Day' (MS-c)	CWGr
'Daddy's Choice' (SS-c)	CWGr
'Dad's Delight' (MinD)	CWGr
'Daleko Adonis' (GS-c)	CWGr
'Daleko Gold' (MD)	CWGr
'Daleko Jupiter' (GS-c)	CWGr NHal
'Daleko National' (MD)	CWGr
'Daleko Tangerine' (MD)	CWGr
'Dana' (SS-c)	CWGr
'Dana Champ' (MinS-c)	CWGr
'Dana Dream' (MinS-c)	CWGr
'Dana Iris' (SS-c)	CWGr
'Dana Sunset' (SC)	CWGr
'Dancing Queen' (S-c)	CWGr
'Danjo Doc' (SD)	CWGr
'Danum Belle' (SD)	CWGr
'Danum Cherry' (SD)	CWGr
'Danum Chippy' (SD)	CWGr
'Danum Cream' (MS-c)	CWGr
'Danum Fancy' (SD)	CWGr
'Danum Gail' (LD)	CWGr
'Danum Hero' (LD)	CWGr
'Danum Julie' (SBa)	CWGr
'Danum Meteor' (GS-c)	CWGr
'Danum Rebel' (LS-c)	CWGr
'Danum Rhoda' (GD)	CWGr
'Danum Salmon' (MS-c)	CWGr
'Danum Torch' (Col)	CWGr
'Dark Desire'PBR (Sin/DwB)	CAvo CBct CFFs CFir CHar CSpe CWCL EBee EWll GMaP LAst LCro LHop MBri SCoo SDnm SVil WHlf WOVN
'Dark Splendour' (MC)	CWGr
'Dark Stranger' (MC) ♀H3	CWGr
'Darlington Diamond' (MS-c)	CWGr
'Darlington Jubilation' (SS-c)	CWGr
'Davar Donna' (MS-c) ♀H3	CWGr
'Davar Hayley' (SC)	CWGr
'Davar Jim' (SS-c) new	CWGr
'Davenport Anita' (MinD)	CWGr
'Davenport Honey' (MinD)	CWGr
'Davenport Lesley' (MinD)	CWGr
'Davenport Sunlight' (MS-c)	CWGr
'Dave's Snip' (MinD)	CWGr
'David Digweed' (SD)	CWGr NHal
'David Howard' (MinD) ♀H3	More than 30 suppliers
'David Shaw' (MD)	CWGr
'David's Choice' (MinD)	CWGr
'Dawn Chorus' (MinD)	CWGr
'Dawn Sky' (SD)	LAyl
'Daytona' (SD)	CWGr
'Dazzler' (MinD/DwB)	CWGr
'Deborah's Kiwi' (SC)	CWGr NHal
'Debra Anne Craven' (GS-c)	CWGr NHal
'Decorette' (DwB/SD)	CWGr
'Decorette Bronze' (MinD/DwB)	CWGr
'Decorette Rose' (MinD/DwB)	CWGr
'Deepest Yellow' (MinBa)	CWGr
'Dentelle de Venise' (MC)	CWGr
'Deuil du Roi Albert' (MD)	CWGr
'Deutschland' (MD)	CWGr
I 'Devon Elegans' new	CWGr
'Devon Joy' (MinD)	CWGr

	'Diamond Rose' (Anem/DwB)	CWGr
	'Dick Westfall' (GS-c) **new**	CWGr
	'Dinah Shore' (LS-c)	CWGr
	'Director' (SD)	CWGr
	dissecta	WPGP
	'Doc van Horn' (LS-c)	CWGr
	'Doctor Anne Dyson' (SC)	CWGr
	'Doctor Arnett' (GS-c)	CWGr
	'Doctor Caroline Rabbitt' (SD)	CWGr
	'Doctor John Grainger' (MinD)	CWGr
	'Don Hill' (Col) ♀H3	NHal
	'Don's Delight' (Pom)	CWGr
	'Doris Bacon' (SBa)	CWGr
	'Doris Day' (SC)	CWGr LBut NHal
	'Doris Knight' (SC)	LBut
	'Doris Rollins' (SC)	CWGr
	'Dottie D.' (SBa)	CWGr
	'Downham Royal' (MinBa)	CWGr
	'Drummer Boy' (LD)	CWGr
	'Duet' (MD)	CWGr EPfP LRHS
	'Dusky Harmony' (SWL)	CWGr LBut
	'Dutch Baby' (Pom)	CWGr
	'Dutch Boy' (SD)	CWGr
	'Dutch Triumph' (LD)	CWGr
	'Earl Haig' (LD)	CWGr
	'Earl Marc' (SC)	CWGr LBut
	'Early Bird' (SD)	CWGr
	'Easter Sunday' (Col)	CWGr
	'Eastwood Moonlight' (MS-c)	CWGr NHal
	'Eastwood Star' (MS-c)	CWGr
	'Ebbw Vale Festival' (MinD)	CWGr
	'Edge of Gold' (GD)	CWGr
	'Edgeway Joyce' (MinBa)	CWGr
	'Edinburgh' (SD)	CWGr ERCP SWal
	'Edith Holmes' (SC)	CWGr
	'Edith Mueller' (Pom)	CWGr
	'Edna C' (MD)	CWGr
	'Eileen Denny' (MS-c)	CWGr
	'Eisprinzessin' (MS-c)	CWGr
	'El Cid' (SD)	CWGr
	'El Paso' (SD)	CSut CWGr MBri
	'Eldon Wilson' (DblO)	CWGr
	'Eleanor Fiesta' (MinS-c)	CWGr
	'Elgico Leanne' (MC)	CWGr
	'Elise' (MinD) **new**	SPer
	'Elizabeth Hammett' (MinD)	CWGr
	'Elizabeth Snowden' (Col)	CWGr
	'Ella Britton' (MinD)	LRHS MWgw
	'Ellen Huston' (Misc/DwB) ♀H3	CBgR CEnt CWGr EBee EBrs ECtt ERCP LPio LRHS MBri NHal SWal WCot WWeb
	'Elma E' (LD)	CWGr NHal
	'Elmbrook Chieftain' (GD)	CWGr
	'Elmbrook Rebel' (GS-c)	CWGr
	'Embrace' (SC)	NHal
	'Emma's Coronet' (MinD)	CWGr
	'Emmie Lou' (MD)	CWGr
	'Emory Paul' (LD)	CWGr
	'Emperor' (MD)	CWGr
	'Enfield Salmon' (LD)	CWGr
	'Engadin' (MD)	CWGr
	'Engelhardt's Matador' (MD)	CBgR EBee LAst LSou MBnl WCot WGwG WHrl
	'Enid Adams' (SD)	CWGr
	'Epping Forest' (GD) **new**	CWGr
	'Eric's Choice' (SD)	CWGr
	'Ernie Pitt' (SD)	CWGr
	'Esau' (GD)	CWGr
	'Eunice Arrigo' (LS-c)	CWGr
	'Eveline' (SD)	CBgR CWGr EBrs EPfP LRHS MBri
	'Evelyn Foster' (MD)	CWGr
	'Evelyn Rumbold' (GD)	CWGr
	'Evening Lady' (MinD)	CWGr
	excelsa (B)	CHll
	- B&SWJ 10233	WCru
	'Excentrique' (Misc) **new**	CWGr MWgw
	'Exotic Dwarf' (Sin/Lil)	CBgR CFir CWGr EBee LSou NHal WCot
	'Explosion' (SS-c)	CWGr
	'Extase' (MD)	CWGr LRHS
	'Eye Candy' **new**	LRHS
	'Fabula' (Col)	CWGr
	'Fairfield Frost' (Col)	NHal
	'Fairway Pilot' (GD)	CWGr
	'Fairway Spur' (GD)	LAyl NHal
	'Fairy Queen' (MinC)	CWGr
	'Falcon's Future' (MS-c)	CWGr
	'Fascination' (SWL/DwB) ♀H3	CBgR CHar COlW CSam EBee EBrs ECtt EWll LAyl LPio LSou MAJR MWea NBPN NEgg NPri SMeo WHoo WSpi WWeb
I	'Fascination' (Misc)	CWGr ECtt
	'Fascination Aus' (Col)	CWGr
	'Fashion Monger' (Col)	CWGr EBee EHrv NHal WCot
	'Fata Morgana' (Anem)	CWGr
	'Federwolke' (LD) **new**	CWGr
	'Fermain' (MinD)	CWGr
	'Fern Irene' (MWL)	CWGr
	'Ferncliffe Fuego' (MC)	CWGr
	'Ferncliffe Illusion' (LD)	CWGr
	'Fernhill Champion' (MD)	CWGr
*	'Fernhill Suprise' (SD)	CWGr LBut
	'Festivo' (Col)	CWGr
	'Feu Céleste' (Col)	CWGr
	'Fidalgo Blacky' (MinD)	CWGr
	'Fidalgo Bounce' (SD)	CWGr
	'Fidalgo Climax' (LS-c/Fim)	CWGr
	'Fidalgo Magic' (MD)	CWGr
	'Fidalgo Snowman' (GS-c)	CWGr
	'Fidalgo Splash' (MD)	CWGr
	'Fidalgo Supreme' (MD)	CWGr LAyl
	'Fiesta Dance' (SC)	CWGr
	'Figurine' (SWL) ♀H3	CWGr
	'Fille du Diable' (LS-c)	CWGr
	'Finchcocks' (SWL) ♀H3	CWGr LAyl
	'Fiona Stewart' (SBa)	CWGr
	'Fire Magic' (SS-c)	CWGr
	'Fire Mountain' (SD/MinD)	NHal
	'Firebird' (Sin)	CWGr LRHS
	'Firebird' (MS-c)	see *D.* 'Vuurvogel'
	'First Lady' (MD)	CWGr
	'Fleur' (MinD)	SPer
	'Fleur Mountjoy' (Col)	CWGr
	'Flevohof' (MS-c)	CWGr
	'Floorinoor' (Anem)	CWGr SPer
	'Flutterby' (SWL)	CWGr
	'Foreman's Jubilee' (GS-c)	CWGr
	'Formby Supreme' (MD)	CWGr
	'Forrestal' (MS-c)	CWGr
	'Frank Holmes' (Pom)	CWGr
	'Frank Hornsey' (SD)	CWGr
	'Frank Lovell' (GS-c)	CWGr
	'Franz Kafka' (Pom)	CWGr
	'Frau Louise Mayer' (SS-c)	CWGr
	'Fred Wallace' (SC)	CWGr
	'Freelancer' (LC)	CWGr
	'Freestyle' (SC)	CWGr
§	'Freya's Paso Doble' (Anem) ♀H3	CWGr LAyl
	'Freya's Thalia' (Sin/Lil) ♀H3	LAyl
	'Friendship' (LC)	CWGr
	'Frigoulet'	CWGr
	'Fringed Star' (MS-c)	LRHS
	'Frits' (MinBa)	CWGr

'Frivolous Glow' (Misc)PBR **new**	CBgR
'Funfair' (MD)	CWGr
'Funny Face' (Misc)	CWGr
'Fusion' (MD) ♀H3	CWGr
'Fuzzy Wuzzy' (MD)	CSut CWGr
'G.F. Hemerik' (Sin)	CWGr
'Gala Parade' (SD)	CWGr
'Gale Lane' (Pom)	CWGr
'Gallery Art Deco'PBR (SD) ♀H3	CWGr NHal
'Gallery Art Fair'PBR (MinD)	NHal
'Gallery Art Nouveau'PBR (MinD) ♀H3	CWGr MBri NHal WCot
'Gallery Cézanne'PBR (MinD)	CWGr
'Gallery Leonardo'PBR (SD) ♀H3	CWGr
'Gallery Matisse' (SD)	EPfP SPer
'Gallery Monet'PBR (SD) ♀H3	CWGr
'Gallery Rembrandt'PBR (MinD) ♀H3	CWGr
'Gallery Renoir'PBR (SD) ♀H3	CWGr NHal
'Gallery Singer'PBR (MinD)	CWGr
'Gallery Vermeer'PBR (MinD)	CWGr
'Gallery Vincent'PBR (MinD) ♀H3	CWGr
'Gamelan' (DwAnem)	CWGr
'Garden Festival' (SWL)	CWGr
'Garden Party' (MC/DwB) ♀H3	CWGr LAyl
'Garden Princess' (SC/DwB)	CWGr
'Garden Wonder' (SD)	EPfP LRHS
'Gargantuan' (GS-c)	CWGr
'Gateshead Angel' (MD) **new**	CWGr
Gateshead Festival	see *D.* 'Peach Melba' (SD)
'Gaudy' (GD)	CWGr
'Gay Mini' (MinD)	CWGr
'Gay Princess' (SWL)	CWGr LAyl
'Gay Triumph' (GS-c)	CWGr
'Geerlings' Cupido' (SWL)	CWGr
'Geerlings' Indian Summer' (MS-c) ♀H3	NHal
'Geerlings' Jewel' (MD)	CWGr
'Geerlings' Moonlight' (MD) **new**	CWGr
'Geerlings' Sorbet' (MS-c) **new**	CWGr
'Geerlings' Star' (SS-c)	CWGr
'Geerlings' Yellow' (SS-c)	CWGr
'Gelber Vulkan' (LS-c) **new**	CWGr
'Gemma Darling' (GD)	CWGr
'Gemma's Place' (Pom)	CWGr
'Genève' (MD)	CWGr
'Gentle Giant' (GD)	CWGr
'Geoffrey Kent' (MinD) ♀H3	NHal
'Gerald Grace' (LS-c)	CWGr
'Gerlos' (MD)	CWGr
'Gerrie Hoek' (SWL)	CSam CWGr LBut LRHS WSpi
'Gill's Pastelle' (MS-c)	CWGr
'Gilt Edge' (MD)	CWGr
'Gilwood Pip' (SD) **new**	CWGr
'Gilwood Terry G' (SC) **new**	CWGr
'Gina Lombaert' (MS-c)	CWGr LRHS SEND
'Ginger Willo' (Pom)	CWGr
'Giraffe' (Misc)	CWGr
'Giselle'	EBee SPer
'Gitts Perfection' (GD)	CWGr
'Gitty' (SBa)	CWGr
'Glad Huston' (DwSS-c)	CWGr
'Glenafton' (Pom)	CWGr
'Glenbank Honeycomb' (Pom)	CWGr
'Glenbank Paleface' (Pom)	CWGr
'Glenbank Twinkle' (MinC)	CWGr
'Glengarry' (SC)	CWGr
'Globular' (MinBa)	CWGr
'Gloria Romaine' (SD)	CWGr
'Glorie van Heemstede' (SWL) ♀H3	CHrt CSam CWGr LAyl LBut LPio LRHS NHal SEND WHrl
'Glorie van Naardwijk' (SD)	CHrt SWal
'Glorie van Noordwijk' (Min S-c)	CWGr
'Glory' (LD)	CWGr
'Glow Orange' (MinBa)	CWGr
'Go American' (GD)	CWGr NHal
'Gold Ball' (MinBa)	CWGr
'Gold Crown' (LS-c)	CWGr EPfP
'Gold Mine' (SS-c) **new**	CWGr
'Gold Standard' (LD)	CWGr
'Goldean' (GD)	CWGr
'Golden Emblem' (MD)	CWGr ECtt
'Golden Explosion' (MC)	CWGr
'Golden Fizz' (MinBa)	CWGr
'Golden Glitter' (MS-c)	CWGr
'Golden Heart' (MS-c)	CWGr
'Golden Horn' (MS-c)	CWGr
'Golden Impact' (MS-c)	CWGr
'Golden Jubilee' (D)	EPfP SPer
'Golden Leader' (SD)	CWGr
'Golden Scepter' (MinD)	CWGr EPfP
'Golden Symbol' (MS-c)	CWGr
'Golden Turban' (MD)	CWGr
'Golden Willo' (Pom)	CWGr
'Goldilocks' (S-c)	CWGr
'Goldorange' (SS-c)	CWGr
'Good Earth' (MC)	CWGr
'Good Hope' (MinD)	CWGr
'Good Intent' (MinBa)	CWGr
'Goshen Beauty' (SWL)	CWGr
'Goya's Venus' (SS-c)	CWGr
'Grace Nash' (SD)	CWGr
'Grace Rushton' (SWL)	CWGr
'Gracie S' (MinC)	NHal
'Grand Duc' (Col)	CWGr
'Grand Prix' (GD)	CWGr
'Grenadier' (Misc)	CWGr ECtt
'Grenadier' (SWL) ♀H3	CBgR EBee ECtt EMan ERou EWin LSou SDix SDys SPav WCot
'Grenidor Pastelle' (MS-c)	CWGr NHal
'Gretchen Heine' (SD)	CWGr
'Grock' (Pom)	CWGr
'Gunyuu' (GD)	CWGr
'Gurtla Twilight' (Pom)	CWGr NHal
'Gute Laune' (Min S-c) **new**	CWGr
'Gwyneth' (SWL) **new**	CWGr
'Gypsy Boy' (LD)	CWGr LAyl
'Hallmark' (Pom) **new**	CWGr
'Hallwood Asset' (MinD)	CWGr
'Hallwood Coppernob' (MD)	CWGr
'Hallwood Satin' (MD)	CWGr
'Hallwood Tiptop' (MinD)	CWGr
'Hamari Accord' (LS-c) ♀H3	CWGr LAyl
'Hamari Bride' (MS-c) ♀H3	CWGr LAyl
'Hamari Girl' (GD)	CWGr NHal
'Hamari Gold' (GD) ♀H3	CWGr NHal
'Hamari Katrina' (LS-c)	CWGr LRHS
'Hamari Rosé' (MinBa) ♀H3	CWGr LAyl NHal
'Hamari Sunshine' (LD) ♀H3	CWGr NHal

	'Hamilton Amanda' (SD)	CWGr
	'Hamilton Lillian' (SD) 🏆H3	CWGr
	'Hans Ricken' (SD)	CWGr
	'Happy Caroline' (MinD)	CWGr LRHS
	(Happy Single Series) Happy Single Juliet = 'HS Juliet' (Sin) **new**	NBPN
	- Happy Single Kiss = 'HS Kiss' **new**	NOrc
	'Haresbrook' (Sin)	EMan ERou EShb EWin LAst MSte NGdn SPav WSpi
	'Harvest' (LS-c/Fim)	CWGr
	'Harvest Amanda' (Sin/Lil) 🏆H3	CWGr
	'Harvest Brownie' (Sin/Lil)	CWGr
	'Harvest Dandy' (Sin/Lil)	CWGr
§	'Harvest Imp' (Sin/Lil)	CWGr LAyl
§	'Harvest Inflammation' (Sin/Lil) 🏆H3	CWGr NHal
§	'Harvest Samantha' (Sin/Lil) 🏆H3	CWGr LAyl NHal
§	'Harvest Tiny Tot' (Misc/Lil) 🏆H3	CWGr
	'Haseley Bridal Wish' (MC)	CWGr
	'Haseley Goldicote' (SD)	CWGr
	'Haseley Miranda' (SD)	CWGr
	'Haseley Triumph' (SD)	CWGr
	'Haseley Yellow Angora' (SD)	CWGr
	'Hayley Jayne' (SC)	CWGr SPer
	'Heather Huston' (MD)	CWGr
	'Heidi' (SSC)	CWGr
	'Helga' (MS-c)	CWGr
	'Helma Rost' (SS-c)	CWGr
	'Henri Lweii' (SC)	CWGr
	'Henriette' (MC)	CWGr
	'Herbert Smith' (D)	CWGr SEND
	'Hexton Copper' (SBa)	CWGr
	'Hi Ace' (LC)	CWGr
	'Higherfield Champion' (SS-c)	CWGr
	'Highgate Bobby' (SBa)	CWGr
	'Highness' (MinS-c)	CWGr
	'Hilda Clare' (Col)	CWGr
	'Hildepuppe' (Pom)	CWGr
	'Hillcrest Albino' (SS-c)	CWGr
	'Hillcrest Amour' (SD)	CWGr
	'Hillcrest Blaze' (SS-c)	CWGr
	'Hillcrest Bobbin' (SBa)	CWGr
	'Hillcrest Camelot' (GS-c)	CWGr
	'Hillcrest Carmen' (SD)	CWGr
	'Hillcrest Contessa' (MinBa)	CWGr
	'Hillcrest Delight' (MD)	NHal
	'Hillcrest Desire' (SC) 🏆H3	CWGr LAyl
	'Hillcrest Fiesta' (MS-c)	CWGr
	'Hillcrest Hannah' (MinD)	NHal
	'Hillcrest Heights' (LS-c)	CWGr
	'Hillcrest Hillton' (LS-c)	CWGr
	'Hillcrest Kismet' (MD)	LAyl NHal
	'Hillcrest Pearl' (MD)	CWGr
	'Hillcrest Regal' (Col) 🏆H3	CWGr
	'Hillcrest Royal' (MC) 🏆H3	CWGr NHal SDix
	'Hillcrest Suffusion' (SD)	CWGr
	'Hillcrest Ultra' (SD)	CWGr
	'Hill's Delight' (MS-c)	CWGr
	'Hindu Star' (MinBa)	CWGr
	'Hit Parade' (MS-c)	CWGr
	'Hockley Maroon' (SD)	CWGr
	'Hockley Nymph' (SWL)	CWGr
	'Holland Festival' (GD)	CWGr
	'Homer T' (LS-c)	CWGr
	'Honest John' (LD)	CWGr
	'Honey' (Anem/DwB)	CWGr LRHS
	'Honka' (SinO) 🏆H3	CBgR CWGr LAyl
	'Hot Chocolate' (MinD)	CBgR CWGr EPfP WCot
	'Hugh Mather' (MWL)	CWGr
	'Hulin's Carnival' (MinD)	CWGr
	'Huston Legacy' (GS-c) **new**	CWGr
	'Hy Clown' (SD)	CWGr
	'Hy Fire' (MinBa)	CWGr
	'Ice Queen' (SWL)	CWGr
	'Ida Gayer' (LD)	CWGr
	'I-lyke-it' (SS-c)	CWGr
	'Imp'	see *D.* 'Harvest Imp'
	imperialis (B)	CDTJ CHEx CHII CWGr EMon EShb EWes LRHS MJnS WBVN WDyG WHal
	- B&SWJ 8997	WCru
	aff. ***imperialis*** B&SWJ 10238 **new**	WCru
	'Impression Famosa'	MBri
	'Impression Fantastico'	MBri
	'Impression Festivo'	MBri
	'Impression Flamenco' (Col/DwB)	CWGr LRHS
	'Impression Fortuna' (Col/DwB)	CWGr
	'Inca Concord' (MD)	CWGr
	'Inca Dambuster' (GS-c)	CWGr NHal
	'Inca Matchless' (MD)	CWGr
	'Inca Metropolitan' (LD)	CWGr
	'Inca Panorama' (MD)	CWGr
	'Inca Royale' (LD)	CWGr
	'Inca Spectrum' (GS-c) **new**	CWGr
	'Inca Streamline' (S-c) **new**	CWGr
	'Inca Vanguard' (GD)	CWGr
	'Inca Vulcan' (GS-c)	CWGr
	'Indian Summer' (SC)	CWGr
	'Inflammation'	see *D.* 'Harvest Inflammation'
	'Inglebrook Jill' (Col)	CWGr LAyl
	'Inland Dynasty' (GS-c)	CWGr
	'Inn's Gerrie Hoek' (MD)	CWGr
	'Inskip' (SC)	CWGr
	'Invader' (SC)	CWGr
	'Iola' (LD)	CWGr
	'Irene Ellen' (SD)	CWGr
	'Irene van der Zwet' (Sin)	CWGr
	'Iris' (Pom)	CWGr
	'Irisel' (MS-c)	CWGr
	'Islander' (LD)	CWGr
	'Ivanetti' (MinBa)	CWGr NHal
	'Jack Hood' (SD)	CWGr
	'Jack O'Lantern' (Col)	CWGr
	'Jackie Magson' (SS-c)	CWGr
	'Jacqueline Tivey' (SD)	CWGr
	'Jake's Coronet' (MinD)	CWGr
	'Jaldec Jerry' (GS-c)	CWGr
	'Jaldec Joker' (SC)	CWGr
	'Jaldec Jolly' (SC)	CWGr
	'Jamaica' (MinWL)	CWGr
	'Jamie' (SS-c)	CWGr
	'Jan Carden'	CWGr
I	'Jan van Schaffelaar' (Pom)	CWGr
	'Janal Amy' (GS-c)	NHal
	'Jane Cowl' (LD)	CWGr
	'Jane Horton' (Col)	CWGr
	'Janet Beckett' (LC)	CWGr
	'Janet Clarke' (Pom)	CWGr
	'Janet Howell' (Col)	CWGr
	'Janet Jean' (SWL)	CWGr
	'Japanese Waterlily' (SWL)	CWGr
	'Jazzy' (Col)	CWGr
	'Je Maintiendrai' (GD)	CWGr
	'Jean Fairs' (MinWL) 🏆H3	CWGr LBut
	'Jean Marie'PBR (MD)	CWGr LRHS
	'Jean Melville' (MinD)	CWGr
	'Jeanette Carter' (MinD) 🏆H3	CWGr

'Jeanne d'Arc' (GC) CSut CWGr EPfP
'Jeannie Leroux' (SS-c/Fim) CWGr
'Jean's Carol' (Pom) CWGr
'Jennie' (MS-c/Fim) CWGr
'Jenny Smith' (Col) **new** CWGr
'Jersey Beauty' (MD) CWGr WOFF
'Jescot Buttercup' (SD) CWGr
'Jescot India' (MinD) CWGr
'Jescot Jess' (MinD) CWGr LBut
'Jescot Jim' (SD) CWGr
'Jescot Julie' (DblO) CWGr LAyl SMeo
'Jescot Lingold' (MinD) CWGr
'Jescot Nubia' (SS-c) CWGr
'Jescot Redun' (MinD) CWGr
'Jessica' (S-c) CWGr
'Jessie G' (SBa) CWGr
'Jessie Ross' (MinD/DwB) CWGr
'Jet' (SS-c) CWGr
'Jill Day' (SC) CWGr LBut
'Jill Doc' (MD) CWGr
'Jill's Blush' (MS-c) CWGr
'Jill's Delight' (MD) CWGr
'Jim Branigan' (LS-c) CWGr NHal
'Jive' (Anem) CWGr
'Jo Anne' (MS-c) CWGr
'Joan Beecham' (SWL) CWGr
'Jocondo' (GD) CWGr NHal
'Johann' (Pom) CWGr NHal
'Johanna Preinstorfer' (LC) **new** CWGr
'John Prior' (SD) CWGr
'John Street' (SWL) ♀H3 CWGr WSpi
'John's Champion' (MD) CWGr
'Joicie' (MinD) NHal
'Jomanda' (MinBa) ♀H3 CWGr LBut NHal
'Jorja' (MS-c) CWGr
'Jo's Choice' (MinD) CWGr LBut
'Joy Donaldson' (MC) CWGr
'Joyce Green' (GS-c) CWGr
'Joyce Margaret Cunliffe' (SD) CWGr
'Juanita' (MS-c) CWGr
'Judy Tregidden' (MWL) CSam
'Jules Dyson' (Misc) **new** SDys
'Julie One' (DblO) CWGr
'Julio' (MinBa) CWGr
'Jura' (SS-c) CWGr EPfP
'Just Jill' (MinD) CWGr
'Juul's Allstar' (SinO) ♀H3 CWGr
'Kaftan' (MD) CWGr
'Kaiser Wilhelm' (SBa) CWGr WOFF
'Kaiserwalzer' (Col) CWGr
'Karenglen' (MinD) ♀H3 CWGr LBut NHal
'Kari Blue' (SWL) CWGr
'Kari Quill' (SC) CWGr
'Karma Amanda' (SD) CWGr
'Karma Corona'PBR (SC) CWGr
'Karma Lagoon'PBR CWGr
'Karma Maarten Zwaan'PBR (SWL) CWGr
'Karma Sangria'PBR CWGr
'Karma Thalia'PBR CWGr
'Karma Yin Yang' (SD) CWGr
'Karras 150' (SS-c) CWGr
'Kasasagi' (Pom) CWGr
'Kate Mountjoy' (Col) CWGr
'Kathleen's Alliance' (SC) ♀H3 NHal
'Kathryn's Cupid' (MinBa) ♀H3 CWGr SWal
'Kathy' (SC) CWGr
'Katie Dahl' (MinD) CWGr NHal
'Katisha' (MinD) CWGr
'Kay Helen' (Pom) CWGr
'Kayleigh Spiller' (Col) CWGr
'Keith's Choice' (MD) CWGr NHal
'Kelsea Carla' (SS-c) ♀H3 CWGr NHal
'Kelvin Floodlight' (GD) CWGr EPfP
'Kenn Emerland' (MS-c) CSut EPfP
'Kenora Canada' (MS-c) CWGr
'Kenora Challenger' (LS-c) CWGr NHal
'Kenora Christmas' (SBa) CWGr
'Kenora Clyde' (GS-c) CWGr
'Kenora Jubilee' (LS-c) NHal
'Kenora Lisa' (MD) CWGr
'Kenora Macop-B' (MC/Fim) CSut
'Kenora Ontario' (LS-c) CWGr
'Kenora Peace' (MinBa) CWGr
'Kenora Sunburst' (LS-c) CWGr
'Kenora Sunset' (MS-c) ♀H3 CWGr LAyl LBut NHal
'Kenora Superb' (LS-c) CWGr NHal
'Kenora Valentine' (LD) ♀H3 CWGr LAyl NHal
'Ken's Choice' (SBa) NHal
'Ken's Coral' (SWL) CWGr
'Ken's Flame' (SWL) CWGr
'Kidd's Climax' (GD) ♀H3 CWGr
'Kilmorie' (SS-c) CWGr NHal
'Kim Willo' (Pom) CWGr
'Kimberley B' (MinD) CWGr
'Kingston' (MinD) CWGr
'Kismet' (SBa) CWGr
'Kiss' (MinD) CWGr EBee NBPN
'Kit Kat' (LC) CWGr
'Kiwi Brother' (SS-c) CWGr
'Kiwi Cousin' (SC) CWGr
'Kiwi Gloria' (SC) NHal
'Klankstad Kerkrade' (SC) CWGr
'Klondike' (MS-c) CWGr
* 'Kogano Fubuki' (MD) CWGr
'Korgill Meadow' (MD) CWGr
'Kotare Jackpot' (SS-c) CWGr
'Kung Fu' (SD) CWGr
I 'Kyoto' (SWL) CWGr
'L.A.T.E.' (MinBa) CWGr NHal
'L'Ancresse' (MinBa) CWGr LAyl NHal
'La Cierva' (Col) CWGr
'La Corbière' (MinBa) CWGr
'La Gioconda' (Col) CWGr
'Lady Day' (S-c) **new** CWGr
'Lady Jane' (SWL) CWGr
'Lady Kerkrade' (SC) CWGr
'Lady Linda' (SD) CWGr LBut NHal
'Lady Orpah' (SD) CWGr
'Lady Sunshine' (SS-c) CWGr
'Larkford' (SD) CWGr
'Last Dance' (MD) CWGr
'Laura Marie' (MinBa) CWGr
'Laura's Choice' (SD) CWGr
'Laurence Fisher' (MS-c) CWGr
'Lauren's Moonlight' see *D.* 'Pim's Moonlight'
'Lavendale' (MinD) CWGr
'Lavender Athalie' (SC) CWGr
'Lavender Chiffon' (MS-c) CWGr
'Lavender Freestyle' (SC) CWGr
'Lavender Leycett' (GD) CWGr
'Lavender Line' (SC) CWGr NHal
'Lavender Nunton Harvest' (SD) CWGr
'Lavender Perfection' (GD) CSut CWGr EPfP
'Lavender Prince' (MD) CWGr
'Lavengro' (GD) CWGr
'Le Batts Premier' (SD) CWGr
'Le Castel' (D) CWGr
'Le Patineur' (MD) CWGr
'Le Vonne Splinter' (GS-c) CWGr
'Leander' (GS-c) CWGr
'Lecta' (MS-c) CWGr

'Lemon' (Anem)	CWGr
'Lemon Cane' (Misc)	CWGr
'Lemon Elegans' (SS-c) ♀H3	CWGr LBut NHal
'Lemon Meringue' (SD)	CWGr
* 'Lemon Puff' (Anem)	CWGr
'Lemon Symbol' (MS-c)	CWGr
'Lemon Zing' (MinBa)	NHal
* 'Lenny' (MinD)	CWGr
'Lexington' (Pom)	CWGr
'Leycett' (GD)	CWGr
'Libretto' (Col)	CWGr
'Life Force' (GD)	CWGr
'Life Size' (LD)	CWGr
'Light Music' (MS-c)	CWGr
'Lilac Athalie' (SC)	CWGr
'Lilac Shadow' (S-c)	CWGr
§ 'Lilac Taratahi' (SC) ♀H3	CSam CWGr LAyl
'Lilac Time' (MD)	CWGr EPfP LRHS SPer
'Lilac Willo' (Pom)	CWGr
'Lilian Alice' (Col) **new**	NHal
'Lillianne Ballego' (MinD)	CWGr
'Linda's Chester' (SC)	CWGr LBut
'Linda's Diane' (SD)	CWGr
'Lisa'PBR	CWGr
'Lismore Canary' (SWL)	CSam
'Lismore Carol' (Pom)	CWGr NHal
'Lismore Moonlight' (Pom)	LAyl NHal
'Lismore Peggy' (Pom)	CWGr
'Lismore Robin' (MinD)	NHal
'Lismore Sunset' (Pom)	CWGr
'Lismore Willie' (SWL) ♀H3	CWGr LBut
'Little Beeswing' (MC) **new**	WOFF
'Little Dorrit' (Sin/Lil) ♀H3	CWGr
'Little Glenfern' (MinC)	CWGr
'Little Jack' (MinS-c)	CWGr
'Little John' (Sin/Lil)	CWGr
'Little Lamb' (MS-c)	CWGr
'Little Laura' (MinBa)	CWGr
'Little Matthew' (Pom)	CWGr
'Little Reggie' (SS-c)	CWGr
'Little Robert' (MinD)	CWGr
'Little Sally' (Pom)	CWGr
'Little Scottie' (Pom)	CWGr
'Little Shona' (MinD)	CWGr
'Little Snowdrop' (Pom)	CWGr
'Little Tiger' (MinD)	CWGr MBri
'Little Treasure'	CWGr EPfP
'Littledown Tango' (DwB) **new**	CWGr
'Liz' (LS-c)	CWGr
'Lois Walcher' (MD)	CWGr
'Lollypop' (SBa)	CWGr
'Lombada' (Misc)	CWGr
'Long Island Lil' (SD)	CWGr
'Longwood Dainty' (DwB)	CWGr
'Loretta' (SBa)	CWGr
'Loud Applause' (SC)	CWGr
'Louis V' (LS-c/Fim)	CWGr
'Louise Bailey' (MinD)	CWGr
'Lucky Devil' (MD)	CWGr
'Lucky Number' (MD)	CWGr
'Ludwig Helfert' (S-c)	CWGr LRHS SEND
'Lupin Dixie' (SC)	CWGr
'Luther' (GS-c) **new**	CWGr
'Lyn Mayo' (SD)	CWGr
'Lyndsey Murray' (MinD)	CWGr
'Mabel Ann' (GD)	CWGr LAyl NHal
'Madame de Rosa' (LS-c)	NHal
'Madame Elisabeth Sawyer' (SS-c)	CWGr
'Madame J. Snapper'	EShb WSpi
'Madame Simone Stappers' (WL)	CWGr LPio MMHG
'Madame Vera' (SD)	CWGr LBut
'Madelaine Ann' (GD)	CWGr
'Maelstrom' (SD)	CWGr
'Mafolie' (GS-c)	CWGr
'Magenta Magic' (Sin/DwB)	NHal
'Magic Moment' (MS-c)	CWGr
'Magnificat' (MinD)	CWGr
'Maisie' (SD)	CWGr
'Maisie Mooney' (GD)	CWGr
'Majestic Athalie' (SC)	CWGr
'Majestic Kerkrade' (SC)	CWGr
'Majjas Symbol' (MS-c)	CWGr
'Malham Honey' (SD)	CWGr
'Malham Portia' (SWL)	CWGr
'Maltby Fanfare' (Col)	CWGr
'Maltby Whisper' (SC)	CWGr LAyl
'Mandy' (MinD)	CWGr
'Marble Ball' (SBa)	CWGr
'March Magic' (MinD)	CWGr
'Margaret Ann' (MinD)	CWGr LAyl
'Margaret Brookes' (LD)	CWGr
'Margaret Haggo' (SWL)	CSam CWGr NHal
'Marie' (SD)	CWGr
'Marie Schnugg' (SinO) ♀H3	CWGr LAyl
'Mariposa' (Col)	CWGr
'Mark Damp' (LS-c)	CWGr
'Mark Lockwood' (Pom)	CWGr
'Market Joy' (SS-c)	CWGr
'Marla Lu' (MC)	CWGr
'Marlene Joy' (MS-c/Fim)	CWGr
'Maroen'PBR (Misc)	CWGr
'Mars' (Col)	CWGr
'Marshmello Sky' (Col)	CWGr
'Marston Lilac' (MinD) ♀H3	CWGr NHal
'Marta' (GD)	CWGr
'Martin's Red' (Pom)	CWGr
'Martin's Yellow' (Pom)	NHal
'Mary Eveline' (Col)	NHal LAyl
'Mary Hammett' (MinD)	WSpi
'Mary Jennie' (MinS-c)	CWGr
'Mary Layton' (Col)	CWGr
'Mary Lunns' (Pom)	CWGr
'Mary Magson' (SS-c)	CWGr
'Mary O' (SS-c) **new**	NHal
'Mary Partridge' (SWL)	CWGr
'Mary Pitt' (MinD)	CWGr
'Mary Richards' (SD)	CWGr
'Mary's Jomanda' (SBa) ♀H3	CWGr NHal
'Master David' (MinBa)	CWGr
'Master Michael' (Pom)	CWGr
'Match' (SS-c)	CWGr
'Matilda Huston' (SS-c)	CWGr NHal
'Matt Armour' (Sin)	CWGr
'Maureen Hardwick' (GD)	CWGr
'Maureen Kitchener' (SWL)	CWGr
'Maxine Bailey' (SD)	CWGr
'Maya' (SD)	CWGr
'Megan Dean' (MInBa) **new**	NHal
'Meiro' (SD)	CWGr
'Melanie Jane' (MS-c)	CWGr
'Melody Dixie'PBR (MinD)	CWGr
'Melody Dora'PBR (SD)	CWGr
'Melody Gipsy'PBR (SS-c)	CWGr WWeb
'Melody Latin'PBR **new**	CWGr
'Melody Lisa' **new**	CWGr
'Melody Swing'PBR	CWGr
'Melton' (MinD)	CWGr
merckii (B)	CBgR CGHE CMdw CPLG CSpe CWGr EGoo EWes LAyl LCro LFur LPio LRHS MNrw MSte SAga SMad WDyG WPGP WSHC
– F&M 222	WPGP
– ***alba*** (B)	CSpe LPio MSte WCru

	- compact (B)	EMan WPGP
	'Meredith's Marion Smith' (SD)	CWGr
	'Mermaid of Zennor' (Sin)	CFir CWGr EBee EMan MCot
	'Merriwell Topic' (MD)	CWGr
	'Mi Wong' (Pom)	CWGr
	'Miami' (SD)	CWGr
	'Michael J' (MinD)	CWGr
	'Michigan' (MinD)	CWGr
	'Mick' (SC)	CWGr
	'Mick's Peppermint' (MS-c)	CWGr
	'Midas' (SS-c)	CWGr
	'Midnight' (Pom)	CWGr
	'Mies' (Sin)	CWGr
	'Mignon Roxy' (Sin/DwB) **new**	NBPN
	'Mignon Silver' (DwSin)	CWGr
	'Minder' (GD)	CWGr
	'Mingus Alex' (MS-c/Fim)	CWGr
	'Mingus Gregory' (LS-c)	CWGr
	'Mingus Kyle D' (SD)	CWGr
	'Mingus Nichole' (LD)	CWGr
	'Mingus Tony' (Pom) **new**	WHlf
	'Mingus Tracy Lynn' (SS-c)	CWGr
	'Mingus Whitney' (GS-c)	CWGr
	'Mini' (Sin/Lil)	CWGr
	'Mini Red' (MinS-c)	CWGr
	'Minley Carol' (Pom) 🏆H3	CWGr LAyl NHal
	'Minley Linda' (Pom)	CWGr
	'Miramar' (SD)	CWGr
	'Miss Blanc' (SD)	CWGr
	'Miss Ellen' (SinO) 🏆H3	CWGr
	'Miss Rose Fletcher' (SS-c)	CWGr
	'Miss Swiss' (SD)	CWGr
	'Misterton' (MD)	CWGr
	'Mistill Beauty' (SC)	CWGr
	'Mistill Delight' (MinD)	CWGr
	'Mistral' (MS-c/Fim)	CWGr
	'Molly Trotter' (Sin) **new**	CHar
	'Mom's Special' (LD)	CWGr
I	'Mon Trésor' (Min SC)	CWGr
	'Monk Marc' (SC)	CWGr
	'Monkstown Diane' (SC)	CWGr
	'Monrovia' (MinBa)	CWGr
	'Moonfire' (Misc/DwB) 🏆H3	More than 30 suppliers
	'Moonglow' (LS-c)	CWGr
	'Moor Place' (Pom)	NHal
	'Moray Susan' (SWL)	CWGr
	'Moret' (SS-c)	CWGr
	'Morley Lady' (SD)	CWGr
	'Morley Lass' (SS-c)	CWGr
	'Morning Dew' (SC)	CWGr
	'Motto' (LD)	CWGr
	'Mount Noddy' (Sin)	CWGr
	'Mrs A. Woods' (MD)	CWGr
	'Mrs Black' (Pom)	CWGr
	'Mrs Clement Andries' (MS-c)	CWGr
	'Mrs George Le Boutillier' (LD)	CWGr
	'Mrs H. Brown' (Col)	CWGr
	'Mrs McDonald Quill' (LD)	CWGr
	'Mrs Silverston' (SD)	CWGr
	'Mummy's Favourite' (SD)	CWGr
	'Murdoch'	CBgR EBee ECtt EMan EPfP ERou EWin SDys SPav WCot WHrl WSpi
	'Muriel Gladwell' (SS-c)	CWGr
	'Murillo'	CWGr MBri WCot
	'Murray May' (LD)	CWGr
	'Musette' (MinD)	CWGr
	'My Beverley' (MS-c/Fim)	CWGr LAyl NHal
	'My Joy' (Pom)	CWGr
	'My Love' (SS-c)	CSut CWGr EPfP LRHS SEND SPer
	'My Valentine' (SD)	CWGr
	'Mystery Day' (MD)	CBgR CWGr EPfP MBri
	'München' (MinD)	CWGr NGdn
	'Nagano' (MD)	CWGr
	'Nancy H' (MinBa)	CWGr
	'Nankyoku' (GD)	CWGr
	'Nargold' (MS-c/Fim)	CWGr LAyl
	'Natal' (MinBa)	CAby EPfP SPer
	'National Vulcan' (MinD)	CWGr
	'Nationwide' (SD)	CWGr
	'Neal Gillson' (MD)	CWGr
	'Nellie Birch' (MinBa)	CWGr
	'Nellie Broomhead' (Pom) **new**	WOFF
	'Nellie Geerlings' (Sin)	CWGr
	'Nenekazi' (MS-c/Fim)	CWGr
	'Nepos' (SWL)	CWGr LBut
	'Nescio' (Pom)	CWGr EPfP
	'Nettie' (MinBa)	CWGr
	'New Baby' (MinBa)	CWGr LRHS
	'New Dimension' (SS-c)	CWGr EPfP SPer
	'New Look' (LS-c)	CWGr
	'Newby' (MinD) **new**	CWGr
	'Newchurch' (MinD)	CWGr
	'Newsham Wonder' (SD)	CWGr
	'Nichola Higgo' (MC/Fim)	CWGr
	'Nicola' (SS-c)	CWGr
	'Nicolette' (MWL)	CWGr
	'Night Editor' (GD)	CWGr
	'Night Life' (SC)	CWGr
I	'Night Queen' (Pom)	EPfP
	'Nijinsky' (SBa)	CWGr
	'Nina Chester' (SD)	CWGr
	'Nippon' **new**	CBgR MWea
	'Nonette' (SWL)	CBgR CHFP CWGr EBee ECtt LAst WCot WGwG
	'Norbeck Dusky' (SS-c)	CWGr
	'Noreen' (Pom)	CWGr NHal
	'Norman Lockwood' (Pom)	CWGr
	'North Sea' (MD)	CWGr
	'Northland Primrose' (SC)	CWGr
	'Northwest Cosmos' (Sin) **new**	CWGr
*	'Nuit d'Eté' (MS-c)	CWGr EBee ERCP LPio LRHS SEND
	Nunton form (SD)	CWGr
	'Nunton Harvest' (SD)	CWGr
	'Nutley Sunrise' (MC)	CWGr
	'Nymphenburg' (SD)	CWGr
	'Oakwood Diamond' (SBa)	CWGr LBut
	'Oakwood Goldcrest' (SS-c) **new**	CWGr
	'Old Boy' (SBa)	CWGr
	'Old Gold' (SD)	CWGr
	'Omo' (Sin/Lil) 🏆H3	CWGr LAyl
	'Onesta' (SD)	CSam CWGr
	'Only Love' (MS-c)	CWGr
	'Onslow Michelle' (SD)	CWGr
	'Onslow Renown' (LS-c)	CWGr
	'Oosterbeek Remembered' (Misc) **new**	CWGr
	'Opal' (SBa)	CWGr
	'Optic Illusion' (SD)	CWGr
	'Opus' (SD)	CWGr
	'Orange Berger's Record' (MS-c)	CWGr
	'Orange Cushion' (MinD)	CWGr
	'Orange Fire' (MS-c)	CWGr
	'Orange Jewel' (SD)	CWGr
	'Orange Keith's Choice' (MD)	CWGr
	'Orange Mullett' (MinD/DwB)	CWGr
	'Orange Nugget' (MinBa)	CWGr LRHS
I	'Orange Queen' (MC)	CWGr
	'Orange Sun' (LD)	CWGr

	'Oranjestad' (SWL)	CWGr
	'Orchid Lace' (MC)	CWGr
	'Orel' (Col)	CWGr
	'Oreti Classic' (MD)	NHal
	'Oreti Jewel' (MinS-c) ♀H3 **new**	CWGr
	'Oreti Snowflake' (Dw Anem) **new**	NHal
	'Orfeo' (MC)	CWGr
I	'Orion' (MD)	CWGr
	'Ornamental Rays' (SC)	CWGr
	'Osaka' (SD) **new**	CWGr
	'Oterilla' **new**	CWGr
	'Othello' (MS-c)	CWGr
	'Otto's Thrill' (LD)	EPfP
	'Pacific Argyle' (SD)	NHal
	'Paint Box' (MS-c)	CWGr
	'Palomino' (MinD)	CWGr
	'Pam Houdin' **new**	CWGr
	'Pamela' (SD)	CWGr
	'Papageno' **new**	CWGr
	'Pari Taha Sunrise' (MS-c)	CWGr
	'Park Princess' (SC/DwB)	CSut CWGr LRHS NGdn
	'Paroa Gillian' (SC)	CWGr
	'Party' **new**	NBPN
	'Party Girl' (MS-c/Fim)	NHal
	'Paso Doble' misapplied (Anem)	see *D.* 'Freya's Paso Doble'
	'Passion' (MinD) **new**	CWGr
	'Pat Knight' (Col) **new**	CWGr
	'Pat Mark' (LS-c)	CWGr NHal
	'Pat 'n' Dee' (SD)	CWGr
	'Pat Seed' (MD)	CWGr
	'Patricia' (Col)	NHal
	'Paul Chester' (SC)	CWGr
	'Paul Critchley' (SC)	CWGr
	'Paul Smith' (SBa)	CWGr
	'Peace Pact' (SWL)	CWGr
	'Peach Athalie' (SC)	CWGr
	'Peach Cupid' (MinBa) ♀H3	CWGr LBut
§	'Peach Melba' (SD)	NHal
	'Peaches and Cream' PBR	CWGr
	'Peachette' (Misc/Lil) ♀H3	CWGr
	'Pearl Hornsey' (SD)	CWGr
	'Pearl of Heemstede' (SD) ♀H3	CWGr LAyl NHal
	'Pearl Sharowean' (MS-c)	CWGr
	'Pearson's Benn' (SS-c)	CWGr
	'Pearson's Mellanie' (SC)	CWGr
	'Pearson's Patrick' (S-c) **new**	CWGr
	'Pembroke Pattie' (Pom)	CWGr
	'Pennsclout' (GD)	CWGr
	'Pennsgift' (GD)	CWGr
	'Pensford Marion' (Pom)	CWGr
	'Perfectos' (MC)	CWGr
	'Periton' (MinBa)	CWGr
	'Peter' (MinD)	CWGr
I	'Peter' (LD)	LRHS
I	'Peter' (SS-c)	EPfP
	'Peter Nelson' (SBa)	CWGr
	'Petit Bôt' (SS-c)	CWGr
	'Petit Byoux' (DwCol)	CWGr
	'Philis Farmer' (SWL)	CWGr
	'Phill's Pink' (SD) ♀H3 **new**	CWGr
I	'Phoenix' (MD)	CWGr
	'Pianella' (SS-c)	CWGr
§	'Pim's Moonlight' (MS-c)	CWGr
	'Pineholt Princess' (LD)	CWGr
	'Pinelands' Morgenster' (MS-c/Fim)	CWGr
	'Pinelands Pam' (MS-c)	CWGr
	'Pink Attraction' (MinD)	CWGr
	'Pink Breckland Joy' (MD)	CWGr
	'Pink Carol' (Pom)	CWGr
	'Pink Giraffe' (DblO)	CWGr EBla ERCP
	'Pink Honeymoon Dress' (SD)	CWGr
	'Pink Jewel' (Dw) **new**	CWGr
	'Pink Jupiter' (GS-c)	CWGr NHal
	'Pink Katisha' (MinD)	CWGr
	'Pink Kerkrade' (SC)	CWGr
	'Pink Leycett' (GD)	CWGr
	'Pink Loveliness' (SWL)	CWGr
	'Pink Newby' (MinD)	CWGr
	'Pink Pastelle' (MS-c) ♀H3	CWGr NHal
	'Pink Preference' (SS-c)	CWGr
	'Pink Robin Hood' (SBa)	CWGr
	'Pink Shirley Alliance' (SC)	CWGr LAyl
	'Pink Sylvia' (MinD)	CWGr
	'Pink Worton Ann' (MinD)	CWGr
	pinnata B&SWJ 10240	WCru
	'Piperoo' (MC)	CWGr
	'Piper's Pink' (SS-c/DwB)	CWGr LAyl
	'Playa Blanca'	CWGr LRHS
	'Playboy' (GD)	CWGr
	'Plum Surprise' (Pom)	CWGr
	'Poème'	SPer
	'Polar Sight' (GC)	CWGr
	'Polly Bergen' (MD)	CWGr
	'Polly Peachum' (SD)	CWGr
	'Polventon Supreme' (SBa)	CWGr
	'Pontiac' (SC)	CWGr
	'Pooh' (Col)	CWGr NHal
	'Pop Willo' (Pom)	CWGr
I	'Poppet' (Pom)	CWGr
	'Popular Guest' (MS-c/Fim)	CWGr
	'Porcelain' (SWL) ♀H3	LBut WSpi
	'Pot Black' (MinBa) **new**	CWGr
	'Potgieter' (MinBa)	CWGr
	'Pot-Pourri' (MinD)	CWGr
	'Prefect' (MS-c)	CWGr
	'Prefere' (Sin)	CWGr LRHS
	'Preference' (SS-c)	CWGr SWal
	'Preston Park' (Sin/DwB) ♀H3	CSam CWGr LAyl NHal
	Pride of Berlin	see *D.* 'Stolz von Berlin'
	'Prime Minister' (GD)	CWGr
	'Primeur' (MS-c)	CWGr
	'Primrose Accord' (LS-c)	CWGr
	'Primrose Pastelle' (MS-c)	CWGr NHal
	'Primrose Rustig' (MD)	CWGr
	'Prince Valiant' (SD)	CWGr
	'Princess Beatrix' (LD)	CWGr
	'Princess Marie José' (Sin)	CWGr
	'Pristine' (Pom)	CWGr
	'Procyon' (SD)	CBgR CSut CWGr EPfP LRHS
	'Prom' (Pom)	CWGr
	'Promise' (MS-c/Fim)	CWGr
	'Punky' (Pom)	CWGr
	'Purbeck Lydia' (LS-c)	CWGr
	'Purbeck Princess' (MinD)	CWGr
I	'Purity' (SS-c)	CWGr
	'Purper R'O'Sehen' (SD)	CWGr
	'Purpinca' (Anem)	CWGr
	'Purple Cottesmore' (MWL)	CWGr
	'Purple Gem' (SS-c)	CSut CWGr EPfP LRHS SPer
	'Purple Joy' (MD)	CWGr
	'Purple Sensation' (SS-c)	CWGr
	'Purple Tai Hei Jo' (GD)	CWGr
	aff. ***purpusii*** B&SWJ 10321 **new**	WCru
	'Pussycat' (SD)	CWGr
	'Quel Diable' (LS-c)	CWGr
	'Quick Step' (Anem)	CWGr
	'Rachel's Place' (Pom)	CWGr
	'Radfo' (SS-c)	CWGr

	'Radiance' (MC)	CWGr
	'Raffles' (SD)	CWGr LAyl
	'Ragged Robin'PBR (Misc)	CAvo CFFs CSpe EBee LCro MBri WOVN
	'Raiser's Pride' (MC)	CWGr NHal
	'Raspberry Ripple' (SS-c)	CWGr
	'Rebecca Lynn' (MinD)	CWGr
	'Red Admiral' (MinBa)	CWGr
	'Red Alert' (LBa)	CWGr
	'Red and White' (SD)	CWGr
	'Red Arrows' (SD)	CWGr
	'Red Balloon' (SBa)	CWGr
	'Red Beauty' (SD)	CWGr
	'Red Cap' (MinD)	CWGr
	'Red Carol' (Pom)	CWGr
	'Red Diamond' (MD)	CWGr NHal
	'Red Highlight' (LS-c)	CWGr
	'Red Kaiser Wilhelm' (SBa)	CWGr
	'Red Majorette' (SS-c)	CWGr
	'Red Pimpernel' (SD)	CWGr
	'Red Pygmy' (SS-c)	CWGr MBri
	'Red Riding Hood' (MinBa)	CWGr
	'Red Schweitzer' (MinD)	CWGr
	'Red Sensation' (MD)	CWGr
	'Red Sunset' (MS-c)	CWGr
	'Red Triumph' (SD)	CWGr
	'Red Velvet' (SWL)	CWGr
	'Red Warrior' (Pom)	CWGr
	'Reddy' (DwLil)	CWGr
	'Reedly' (SD)	CWGr LBut
	'Reese's Dream' (GD)	CWGr
	'Regal Boy' (SBa)	CWGr
	'Reginald Keene' (LS-c)	NHal
	'Reliance' (SBa)	CWGr
	'Rembrandt USA' (DwSin)	CWGr MBri
	'Renato Tozio' (SD)	CWGr
	'Reputation' (LC)	CWGr
	'Requiem' (SD)	CSut CWGr
	'Reverend P. Holian' (GS-c)	CWGr
	'Reverend Roy Gardiner' (LS-c) **new**	CWGr
	'Rhonda' (Pom)	CWGr NHal
	'Richard Howells' (MinD)	CWGr
	'Richard Marc' (SC)	CWGr
	'Richard S' (LS-c)	NHal
	'Riisa' (MinBa)	CWGr
	'Rip City' (MS-c)	CWGr LCro MCot
	'Risca Miner' (SBa)	CWGr
	'Rita Easterbrook' (LD)	CWGr
	'Rita Hill' (Col)	CWGr
	'Roan' (MinD)	CWGr
	'Robann Royal' (MinBa)	CWGr
	'Robbie Huston' (LS-c)	CWGr
	'Robert Catterini' (Dw) **new**	CWGr
	'Robert Too' (MinD)	CWGr
	'Robin Hood' (SBa)	CWGr
	'Rockcliffe Gold' (MS-c)	CWGr
	'Rokesly Mini' (MinC)	CWGr
	'Rokesly Radiant' (MinD)	CWGr
	'Rokewood Candy' (MS-c)	CWGr
	'Rokewood Opal' (SC)	CWGr
	'Romeo' **new**	NBPN
	'Roodkapje' (Sin)	CWGr
	'Rosalinde' (S-c)	CWGr
	'Rose Cupid' (MinBa)	CWGr
	'Rose Jupiter' (GS-c)	CWGr LRHS NHal
	'Rose Tendre' (MS-c)	CWGr
	'Rosella' (MD)	CSut CWGr EPfP LRHS
	'Rosemary Webb' (SD)	CWGr
	'Rossendale Luke' (SD)	CWGr
	'Rossendale Natasha' (MinBa) **new**	NHal
	'Rossendale Ryan' (SD) **new**	CWGr
	'Rosy Cloud' (MD)	CWGr
	'Rothesay Castle' (MinD/DwB)	CWGr
	'Rothesay Herald' (SD/DwB)	CWGr
	'Rothesay Reveller' (MD)	CWGr
	'Rothesay Robin' (SD)	CWGr
	'Rothesay Rose' (SWL)	CWGr
	'Rothesay Snowflake' (SWL)	CWGr
	'Rotonde' (SC)	CWGr
	'Rotterdam' (MS-c)	CWGr
I	'Roxy' (Sin/DwB)	CBgR CMMP CWGr EBee ECtt EHrv ELan EMan EMil EPfP ERou LAst LAyl LCro LRHS MAvo MBri MWgw NGdn NVic SPav SPla WCot WSpi WWeb
	'Royal Blood'PBR (Misc)	CAvo CSpe EBee MBri
	'Royal Visit' (SD)	CWGr
	'Royal Wedding' (LS-c)	CWGr
	'Ruby Red' (MinBa)	CWGr
	'Ruby Wedding' (MinD)	CWGr
	'Ruskin Andrea' (SS-c)	NHal
	'Ruskin Belle' (MS-c)	CWGr
	'Ruskin Buttercup' (MinD)	CWGr
	'Ruskin Charlotte' (MS-c)	CWGr LAyl NHal
	'Ruskin Delight' (SS-c)	CWGr
	'Ruskin Diana' (SD)	CWGr LBut NHal
	'Ruskin Dynasty' (SD)	CWGr
	'Ruskin Emil' (SS-c)	CWGr
	'Ruskin Gypsy' (SBa)	CWGr
	'Ruskin Marigold' (SS-c)	CWGr LAyl LBut NHal
	'Ruskin Myra' (SS-c)	LAyl NHal
	'Ruskin Orient' (SS-c)	CWGr
	'Ruskin Petite' (MinBa)	CWGr
	'Ruskin Sunshine' (MS-c) **new**	NHal
*	'Ruskin Tangerine' (SBa)	CWGr NHal
	'Russell Turner' (SS-c)	CWGr
	'Rustig' (MD)	CWGr
	'Rusty Hope' (MinD)	CWGr
	'Rutland Gem' (MinD)	CWGr
	'Rutland Water' (SD)	CWGr
	'Ryecroft Crystal' **new**	CWGr
	'Ryecroft Dream' (S-c) **new**	CWGr
	'Ryecroft Jan' (MinBa)	NHal
	'Ryedale King' (LD)	CWGr
	'Ryedale Pinky' (SD)	CWGr
	'Ryedale Rebecca' (GS-c)	CWGr
	'Ryedale Sunshine' (SD)	CWGr
	'Safe Shot' (MD)	CWGr
	'Sailor' (MS-c)	CWGr
	'Saint Croix' (GS-c)	CWGr
	'Saint Moritz' (SS-c)	CWGr
	'Saint-Saëns'	SEND
	'Saladin' (Misc)	CWGr
	'Salmon Carpet' (MinD)	CWGr
	'Salmon Hornsey' (SD)	CWGr
	'Sam Hopkins' (MWL/SWL)	CSam NHal SMeo
	'Sam Huston' (GD)	CWGr LAyl
	'Samantha'	see *D.* 'Harvest Samantha'
	'Sans Souci' (GC)	CWGr
	'Santa Claus' (MD)	CWGr
	'Sarabande' (MS-c)	CWGr
	'Sarah G' (LS-c)	CWGr
	'Sarah Louise' (SWL)	CWGr
	'Sarum Aurora' (SD)	CWGr
	'Sarum Queen' (SD)	CWGr
	'Sascha' (SWL) ♀H3	CWGr LAyl NHal
	'Sassy' (MinD)	CWGr
	'Satellite' (MS-c)	CWGr
	'Saynomore' (SWL)	CWGr
	'Scarborough Ace' (MD)	CWGr
	'Scarborough Fair' (MS-c) **new**	NHal

'Scarlet Comet' (Anem) CWGr
'Scarlet Kokarde' (MinD) CWGr
'Scarlet Rotterdam' (MS-c) CWGr
'Scaur Princess' (SD) CWGr
'Scaur Snowball' (MinD) NHal
'Scaur Swinton' (MD) CWGr LAyl NHal
'Schloss Reinbek' (Sin) CWGr
'Schweitzer's Kokarde' (MinD) CWGr
'Scottish Impact' (MinS-c) CWGr
'Scott's Delight' (SD) CWGr
'Scura' (DwSin) CBgR CWGr
'Seattle' (SD) CWGr LRHS
'Senior Ball' (SBa) CWGr
'Senzoe Brigitte' (MinD) CWGr
'Senzoe Ursula' (SD) CWGr
'Severin's Triumph' (LD) CWGr
'Shandy' (SS-c) CWGr LAyl NHal
'Shannon' (SD) CWGr SPer
'Sharon Ann' (LS-c) CWGr
'Sheila Mooney' (LD) CWGr
sherffii CPLG CWGr EBla MCCP MCot MNrw MWea SIng
'Sherwood Monarch' (GS-c) CWGr
'Sherwood Standard' (MD) CWGr
'Sherwood Sunrise' (SD) CWGr
'Sherwood Titan' (GD) CWGr
'Sherwood's Peach' (LD) CWGr
'Shining Star' (SC) CWGr
'Shirley' (LD) CWGr WHlf
'Shirley Alliance' (SC) CWGr
'Shooting Star' (LS-c) CWGr SPer
* 'Show and Tell' CWGr
'Shy Princess' (MC) CWGr
'Siedlerstolz' (LD) CWGr
'Siemen Doorenbos' (Anem) CWGr
'Silver City' (LD) CWGr NHal
'Silver Slipper' (SS-c) CWGr
'Silver Years' (MD) CWGr
'Sir Alf Ramsey' (GD) CWGr LAyl NHal
'Sisa' (SD) CWGr
'Skipley Spot' (SD) CWGr
'Skipper Rock' (GD) CWGr
'Sky High' (SD) CWGr
'Small World' (Pom) ΥH3 LAyl NHal
'Smart Boy' (LS-c) **new** CWGr
'Smokey' CWGr EPfP LRHS SEND SPer SWal
'Smoky O' (MS-c) CWGr
'Smoots' (SC/Fim) CWGr
'Sneezy' (Sin) CWGr ELan LRHS
'Snip' (MinS-c) CWGr
'Snoho Barbara' (MS-c) CWGr
'Snoho Christmas' CWGr
'Snoho Peggy' (SBa) CWGr
'Snoho Tammie' (MinBa) CWGr
'Snow Cap' (SS-c) CWGr
'Snow Fairy' (MinC) CWGr
'Snow White' (DwSin) CWGr
'Snowflake' (SWL) CWGr
'Snowstorm' (MD) CSut CWGr
'Snowy' (MinBa) CWGr
'So Dainty' (MinS-c) ΥH3 CWGr LAyl
'Sondervig' (SD) CWGr
'Song of Olympia' (SWL) CWGr
'Sonia' CWGr
'Sonia Henie' (SBa) CWGr
'Sorbet' (MS-c) **new** NHal
'Sorbet' (DwB) **new** NHal
sorensenii **new** CWGr
'Soulman' (Anem) CWGr
'Sourire de Crozon' (SD) CWGr
'Souvenir d'Eté' (Pom) CWGr
'Sparkler' CWGr
'Spartacus' (LD) CWGr NHal
'Spassmacher' (MS-c) CWGr
'Spectacular' (SD) CWGr
'Spencer' (SD) CWGr
'Spennythorn King' (SD) CWGr
'Spikey Symbol' (MS-c) CWGr
'Sprinter' CWGr
'Staleen Condesa' (MS-c) NHal
'Star Child' (SinO) CWGr
'Star Elite' (MC) CWGr LRHS
'Star Spectacle' (MS-c) CWGr
'Star Surprise' (SC) CWGr
'Starry Night' (MinS-c) CWGr
'Star's Favourite' (MC) CWGr
'Star's Lady' (SC) CWGr
'Stefan Bergerhoff' (Dwf D) CWGr
'Stella J' (SWL) CWGr
'Stella's Delight' (SD) CWGr
'Stellyvonne' (LS-c/Fim) CWGr
'Stephanie' (SS-c) CWGr
'Sterling Silver' (MD) CWGr
'Stevie D' (SD) ΥH3 CWGr
§ 'Stolz von Berlin' (MinBa) CWGr EPfP
'Stoneleigh Cherry' (Pom) CWGr LAyl
'Stoneleigh Joyce' (Pom) CWGr
'Storm Warning' (GD) CWGr
'Streets Ahead' (MinD) NHal
'Stylemaster' (MC) CWGr
'Sue Mountjoy' (Col) CWGr
'Sue Willo' (Pom) CWGr
'Suffolk Fantasy' (SD) CWGr
'Suffolk Punch' (MD) CBgR CWGr LAyl LBut SPer
'Sugartime Sunrise' (MinD) NHal
'Suitzus Julie' (Lil) CWGr
'Summer Festival' (SD) CWGr
I 'Summer Night' (SC) CAby CWGr ECGP LAyl LCro NHal SPer
'Summer's End' CWGr
'Summertime' SPer
'Sungold' (MinBa) CWGr
'Sunlight' (SBa) CWGr
'Sunlight Pastelle' (MS-c) CWGr
'Sunny Boy' (MinD) CWGr LRHS
'Sunray Glint' (MS-c) CWGr
'Sunray Silk' (MS-c) CWGr
I 'Sunshine' (Sin) ECtt LAyl WWeb
'Sunstruck' (MS-c) CWGr
'Super Rays' (MC) CWGr
'Super Trouper' (SD) CWGr
'Superfine' (SC) CWGr
'Supermarket' (MS-c) **new** CWGr
'Sure Thing' (MC) CWGr
'Susan Willo' (Pom) CWGr
'Susannah York' (SWL) CWGr
'Susan's Pride' (GD) **new** CWGr
'Suzette' (SD/DwB) CWGr
'Swallow Falls' (SD) CWGr
'Swan Lake' (SD) EShb SPer
'Swanvale' (SD) CWGr
'Sweet Content' (SD) CWGr
'Sweetheart' (SD) CBgR EBrs LRHS
'Swiss Miss' (MinBa/O) CWGr
I 'Sylvia' (SBa) CWGr EPfP
'Sylvia's Desire' (SC) CWGr
'Symbol' (MS-c) CWGr
'Syston Harlequin' (SD) CWGr
'Syston Sophia' (LBa) CWGr
'Tahiti Sunrise' (MS-c) CWGr
'Tally Ho' (Misc) ΥH3 CBgR CMMP CSam CWGr EBee EBla ECtt EHrv EMan ERou LCro LRHS MAvo MBri MRav NCob SDys SMad SPav SPla WCot
'Tam Tam' SWal
'Taratahi Lilac' see *D.* 'Lilac Taratahi'
'Taratahi Ruby' (SWL) ΥH3 CSam CWGr LAyl LBut NHal

'Taratahi Sunrise' (MS-c) **new**	CWGr
'Tartan' (MD)	CWGr
'Teesbrooke Audrey' (Col)	CWGr LAyl NHal
'Teesbrooke Red Eye' (Col) ♀H3	CWGr NHal
'Tempo' (MD) **new**	CWGr
'Temptress' (SS-c)	CWGr
'Tender Moon' (SD)	CWGr
tenuicaulis	CDTJ CWGr EBee
aff. ***tenuicaulis*** F&M 99 **new**	WPGP
'Thais' (Col)	CWGr
'Thames Valley' (MD)	CWGr
'That's It!' (SD)	CWGr
'The Baron' (SD)	CWGr
'Thelma Clements' (LD)	CWGr
'Theo Sprengers' (MD)	CWGr
'Thomas A. Edison' (MD)	CSut CWGr EPfP SWal
'Thoresby Jewel' (SD)	CWGr
I 'Tiara' (SD)	CWGr
'Tiffany Lynn' (SinO)	CWGr
'Tiger Eye' (MD)	CWGr
'Tiger Tiv' (MD)	CWGr
'Tinker's White' (SD)	CWGr
'Tiny Tot' (Lil)	see *D.* 'Harvest Tiny Tot'
'Tioga Spice' (MS-c/Fim)	CWGr NHal
'Tiptoe' (MinD) **new**	NHal
'Toga' (SWL)	CWGr
'Tohsuikyoh' (DblO)	CWGr
'Tommy Doc' (SS-c)	CWGr
'Tommy Keith' (MinBa)	CWGr WOFF
'Tomo' (SD)	LAyl NHal
'Top Affair' (MS-c)	CWGr
'Top Totty' (MinD)	NHal
* 'Topaz Puff'	LRHS
'Torra'	SPer
* 'Toto' (DwB)	CWGr NHal
'Tout-à-Toi' (SD)	CWGr
'Towneley Class' (SD)	CWGr
'Tramar' (SC)	CWGr
'Trampolene' (SS-c)	CWGr
'Trelawny' (GD)	CWGr
'Trelyn Kiwi' (SC)	CWGr
'Trengrove Autumn' (MD)	CWGr
'Trengrove d'Or' (MD)	CWGr
'Trengrove Jill' (MD)	CWGr LAyl
'Trengrove Millennium' (MD)	CWGr NHal
'Trengrove Summer' (MD)	CWGr
'Trengrove Tauranga' (MD)	CWGr
'Trengrove Terror' (GD)	CWGr
'Trevelyn Kiwi' (S-c)	NHal
'Trevor' (Col)	CWGr
'Trinidad' (GS-c)	CWGr
'Tropical Sunset' (SD)	CWGr SPer
'Troy Dyson' (Misc) **new**	SDys
'Tsuki-yorine-shisha' (MC)	CWGr
'Tu Jays Nicola' (Misc) ♀H3	CWGr
'Tu Tu' (MS-c)	CWGr
'Tudor 1' (DwB) **new**	NHal
'Tui Avis' (MinC)	CWGr
'Tui Orange' (SS-c)	CWGr
'Tui Ruth' (SS-c)	CWGr
'Tujays Lemondrop' (SD)	NHal
'Tula Rosa' (Pom)	CWGr
'Tutankhamun' (Pom)	CWGr
'Twiggy' (SWL)	CWGr LRHS
'Twilight Time' (MD)	CWGr EPfP LRHS
'Twyning's After Eight' (Sin) ♀H3	CWGr WCot
'Twyning's Aniseed' (Sin) **new**	CWGr
'Twyning's Candy' (Sin) ♀H3	CWGr
'Twyning's Chocolate' (Sin) ♀H3	CWGr
'Twyning's Cookie' (Sin) **new**	CWGr
'Twyning's Peppermint' (Sin)	CWGr
'Twyning's Pink Fish' (Col) ♀H3	CWGr
'Twyning's Smartie' (Sin) ♀H3	CWGr
'Twyning's White Chocolate' (Sin) **new**	CWGr
'Uchuu' (GD)	CWGr
'Union Jack' (Sin)	CWGr EMon WOFF
'United' (SD)	CWGr
'Utrecht' (GD)	CWGr
'Vader Abraham' (MinD)	CWGr
'Vaguely Noble' (SBa)	CWGr
'Valentine Lil' (SWL)	CWGr
'Valley Pop' (MinD)	CWGr
'Vancouver' (Misc)	CBgR CWGr
'Vanquisher' (GS-c)	CWGr
'Velda Inez' (MinD)	CWGr
'Vera's Elma' (LD)	CWGr
'Vesuvius' (MD)	CWGr
'Vicky Baum' (SBa)	CWGr
'Vicky Crutchfield' (SWL)	LBut
'Vicky Jackson' (SWL)	CWGr
'Victory Day' (LC)	CWGr
'Vidal Rhapsody' (MS-c)	CWGr
'Vigor' (SWL)	CWGr
'Vinovium' (MinBa)	CWGr
'Violet Davies' (MS-c)	CWGr
'Vivex' (Pom)	CWGr
'Volkskanzler' (Sin)	CWGr
'Vrouwe Jacoba' (SS-c)	CWGr
'Vulcan' (LS-c)	CWGr
§ 'Vuurvogel' (MS-c)	CWGr
'Walter Hardisty' (GD)	CWGr
'Walter James' (SD)	CWGr
'Wanborough Gem' (SBa)	CWGr
'Wanda's Aurora' (GD)	NHal
'Wanda's Capella' (GD)	CWGr
'Wanda's Moonlight' (GD)	CWGr
'Wandy' (Pom) ♀H3	CWGr
'War of the Roses'	WHer
'Warkton Willo' (Pom)	CWGr
'Warmunda' (MinBa)	LRHS
I 'Washington'	CWGr
'Waveney Pearl' (SD)	CWGr
'Welcome Guest' (MS-c)	CWGr
'Welsh Beauty' (SBa)	CWGr
'Wendy Spencer' (MinD)	CWGr
'Wendy's Place' (Pom)	CWGr
'Weston Aramac' (SS-c)	CWGr
'Weston Dove' (MinS-c) **new**	CWGr
'Weston Flamingo' (MinC) **new**	CWGr
'Weston Forge' (SC)	CWGr
'Weston Miss' (MinS-c)	CWGr NHal
'Weston Nugget' (MinC)	CWGr
'Weston Pandora' (S-c) **new**	CWGr
'Weston Perky' (MinC) **new**	CWGr
'Weston Pirate' (MinC) ♀H3	CWGr NHal
'Weston Princekin' (MinS-c)	CWGr
'Weston Spanish Dancer' (MinC) ♀H3	CWGr LAyl LBut NHal
'Weston Sunup' (MinC)	CWGr
'Weston Teatime' (DwfC) **new**	CWGr
'Wheel' (Col)	CWGr
'Whiston Sunrise' (MS-c)	CWGr
'White Alva's' (GD) ♀H3	CWGr LAyl NHal

	'White Aster' (Pom)	EPfP
	'White Ballerina' (SWL)	CSam LAyl NHal
	'White Ballet' (SD) ♀H3	CWGr LAyl LBut NHal
	'White Cameo' **new**	CWGr
	'White Charlie Two' (MD)	NHal
	'White Hunter' (SD)	CWGr
	'White Knight' (MinD)	NHal
	'White Linda' (SD)	CWGr NHal
	'White Mathilda' (Dw)	CWGr
	'White Merriwell' (SD)	CWGr
	'White Moonlight' (MS-c)	LAyl LBut NHal
	'White Nettie' (MinBa)	CWGr
	'White Orchid' **new**	NHal
	'White Pastelle' (MS-c)	CWGr
	'White Perfection' (LD)	CHrt CSut CWGr EPfP WSpi
	'White Polventon' (SBa)	CWGr
	'White Rustig' (MD)	CWGr
	'White Star' (MS-c)	CWGr LRHS
	'White Swallow' (SS-c)	NHal
	'Wicky Woo' (SD)	CWGr
	'Wildwood Marie' (SWL)	CWGr
	'Willemse Glory' (Misc Orch)	CWGr
	'William B' (GD)	CWGr
	'William Gregory' (Pom) **new**	CWGr
	'Williamsburg' (SS-c)	CWGr
	'Willo's Borealis' (Pom)	CWGr NHal
	'Willo's Night' (Pom)	CWGr
	'Willo's Surprise' (Pom)	CWGr NHal
	'Willo's Violet' (Pom)	CWGr NHal
	'Willowfield Jackie' (MinD) **new**	CWGr
	'Willowfield Matthew' (MinD)	NHal
	'Willowfield Mick' (LD)	CWGr LAyl
	'Winholme Diane' (SD)	CWGr NHal
	'Winkie Colonel' (GD)	CWGr
	'Winnie' (Pom)	CWGr
	'Winsome' (SWL)	CWGr
	'Winston Churchill' (MinD)	CWGr LBut WSpi
	'Winter Dawn' (SWL)	CWGr
	'Wise Guy' (GD)	CWGr
	'Wisk' (Pom)	CWGr
	'Wittem' (MD)	CWGr
	'Wittemans Superba' (SS-c) ♀H3	CWGr NHal SDix
	'Wootton Cupid' (MinBa) ♀H3	CWGr LBut NHal
	'Wootton Impact' (MS-c) ♀H3	NHal
	'Wootton Phebe' (SD)	CWGr
	'Wootton Tempest' (MS-c)	CWGr
	'Wootton Windmill' (Col) **new**	CWGr
	'Worton Blue Streak' (SS-c)	CWGr
	'Worton Revival' (MD)	CWGr
	'Worton Superb' (SD)	CWGr
	'Wundal Horizon' (LS-c)	CWGr
	'Yellow Abundance' (SD)	CWGr
	'Yellow Baby' (Pom)	CWGr
I	'Yellow Bird' (Col)	CWGr
	'Yellow Galator' (MC)	CWGr
	'Yellow Hammer' (Sin/DwB) ♀H3	CWGr LAyl NHal
	'Yellow Linda's Chester' (SC)	CWGr
	'Yellow Pages' (SD)	CWGr
	'Yellow Pet' (SD)	CWGr
	'Yellow Spiky' (MS-c)	CWGr
	'Yellow Star' (MS-c)	CSut CWGr
	'Yellow Symbol' (MS-c)	CWGr LBut
	'Yelno Enchantment' (SWL)	CWGr LAyl
	'Yelno Firelight' (SWL)	CWGr
	'Yelno Harmony' (SD) ♀H3	CWGr LBut
	'Yelno Petite Glory' (MinD)	CWGr
	'York and Lancaster' (MD)	CBgR CTca CWGr EMon IGor
	'Yorkie' (MS-c)	CWGr
	'Young Bees' (MD)	CWGr
	'Yukino' (Col)	CWGr
	'Zagato' (MinD)	CWGr
*	'Zakuro-fubuki' (MD)	CWGr
	'Zakuro-hime' (SD)	CWGr
I	'Zelda' (LD)	CWGr
	'Zest' (MinD)	CWGr
	'Zing' (LS-c)	CWGr
	'Zorro' (GD) ♀H3	CWGr NHal
	'Zurich' (SS-c)	CWGr

Dais (*Thymelaeaceae*)

	cotinifolia	CPLG EShb

Daiswa see *Paris*

Dalea (*Papilionaceae*)

	candida	NDov

Dalechampia (*Euphorbiaceae*)

	dioscoreifolia	CCCN
	spathulata **new**	CCCN

damson see *Prunus insititia*

Danae (*Ruscaceae*)

§	***racemosa***	CBcs CTri EBee ELan EMon ENot EPfP EPla IDee LBBr LCro LRHS MGos MRav SAPC SArc SDry SPer SRms SSpi WCot WPGP WPat WSpi

Danthonia (*Poaceae*)

	californica	CBig

Daphne ✿ (*Thymelaeaceae*)

	DJHC 98164 from China **new**	WCru
	SDR 2 **new**	GKev
	acutiloba	CPMA ECho EPot GAbr GKev SAga WPGP WSHC
	- 'Fragrant Cloud'	CPMA EWes SBla SChF
	albowiana	CPMA CPle EWes LRHS SAga SBla SChF SCoo
	alpina	CPMA SAga SBla WThu
	altaica	CPMA SBla
	arbuscula ♀H4	CPMA ECho EPot NMen SBla WAbe WThu
	- subsp. ***arbuscula*** f. ***albiflora***	SBla
	- 'Diva' **new**	SBla
	- f. ***grandiflora*** **new**	SBla
	- 'Muran Pride' **new**	CPMA SBla
	- f. ***platyclada*** **new**	SBla
	- f. ***radicans***	CPMA
	arbuscula x ***cneorum*** var. ***verlotii***	CPMA
	arbuscula x 'Leila Haines'	see *D.* x *schlyteri*
	bholua	CAbP CHll CPMA LHop LRHS MGos MWya SReu SSpi SSta WAbe WBod WCru WSpi
I	- 'Alba'	CBcs CEnd CLAP CPMA ECho ELan ENot EPfP GAbr GEdr LRHS MAsh MGos SCoo SPer SPoG SSpi SSta WBVN WCru WPGP
	- 'Darjeeling'	CBcs CLAP CPLG CPMA ENot EPfP GKev LRHS MAsh SCoo SKHP SSpi SSta WPGP
	- var. ***glacialis***	WCru
	- - 'Gurkha'	CBct CGHE CPMA EBee ELan ENot EPfP SBla SKHP SSpi WPGP WSpi
	- 'Glendoick'	EPfP GGGa
	- 'Jacqueline Postill' ♀H3	More than 30 suppliers

	- 'Peter Smithers'	CBcs CBct CLAP ENot LRHS MWea SBla SChF SCoo SPer SReu SSpi SSta WPGP
	- 'Rupina La'	SBla
	- 'Winter Bliss' **new**	MWya
	blagayana	CPMA ECho EPot GAbr MGos MWya NEgg SBla SPoG SRms SSpi WCFE WFar WPGP
	- 'Brenda Anderson'	ITim SBla
	blagayana x ***sericea*** Collina Group	CPMA
	'Bramdean'	see *D.* x *napolitana* 'Bramdean'
	x ***burkwoodii*** 🏆H4	CPLG EPot MWya SAga SHBN WBod
	- 'Albert Burkwood'	CPMA LRHS SBla
	- 'Astrid' (v)	CBcs CBow CPMA EBee LAst LRHS MGos SCoo SIng SMrm SPoG SSta
	- 'Briggs Moonlight' (v)	SBla
§	- 'Carol Mackie' (v)	CPMA GAbr LHop MGos SBla
	- 'G.K. Argles' (v) 🏆H4	CPMA LAst MAsh MGos MWya SBla WFar
I	- 'Gold Sport'	SBla
	- 'Gold Strike' (v)	CPMA
	- 'Golden Treasure'	LRHS SBla SChF
	- 'Lavenirei'	CPMA
	- 'Somerset'	CBcs CPMA EBee ELan ENot EPfP LAst MGos MSwo NBlu NScw NWea SAga SBla SCoo SHBN SLim SPer SPla WOrn
§	- 'Somerset Gold Edge' (v)	CPMA
§	- 'Somerset Variegated' (v)	LAst WPat
I	- 'Variegata' (v)	MGos WPat
	- 'Variegata' broad cream edge	see *D.* x *burkwoodii* 'Somerset Variegated'
	- 'Variegata' broad gold edge	see *D.* x *burkwoodii* 'Somerset Gold Edge'
	- 'Variegata' narrow gold edge	see *D.* x *burkwoodii* 'Carol Mackie'
	calcicola 'Gang-ho-ba' **new**	SBla
	- 'Sichuan Gold' **new**	SBla
	caucasica	CPMA EPot SBla
	circassica	SBla
	cneorum	CBcs CPMA ELan ENot EPfP MGos NMen
	- f. ***alba***	CPMA SBla SChF
	- 'Benaco' **new**	CPMA SBla
	- 'Blackthorn Triumph'	CPMA SBla
	- 'Ewesley' **new**	SBla
	- 'Eximia' 🏆H4	CBcs CPMA ECho EPot GAbr LHop MDun MGos SBla SHBN SIng SRms WAbe
	- 'Grandiflora'	see *D.* x *napolitana* 'Maxima'
	- 'Lac des Gloriettes'	SBla
	- 'Peggy Fell' **new**	SBla
	- 'Puszta'	CPMA SAga WAbe
	- var. ***pygmaea***	CPMA EPot SBla
	- - 'Alba'	CPMA SBla
	- 'Rose Glow'	CPMA ECho
	- 'Ruby Glow'	CPMA ECho MWya
	- 'Snow Carpet' **new**	SBla
	- 'Variegata' (v)	CPMA ECho EPot MGos SIng SPer WAbe
	- 'Velký Kosir'	CPMA SBla SChF WAbe
	collina	see *D. sericea* Collina Group
	x ***eschmannii*** 'Jacob Eschmann' **new**	SBla
	'Forarch' **new**	SBla
	genkwa	LRHS SBla
	giraldii	CPMA GKev SBla
	aff. ***giraldii***	NMen
	glomerata **new**	SBla
	gnidioides **new**	SBla
	x ***hendersonii***	CEnd CPMA
	- 'Appleblossom'	CPMA ECho LHop SBla
	- 'Aymon Correvon'	CPMA SBla
	- 'Blackthorn Rose'	CPMA SBla
	- 'Ernst Hauser'	CPMA ECho GAbr GEdr LHop LTwo MGos SBla WAbe
	- 'Fritz Kummert'	CPMA SBla WAbe
	- 'Jeanette Brickell'	SBla
	- 'Kath Dryden'	CPMA SBla
	- 'Marion White'	CPMA SBla
	- 'Rosebud'	CPMA SBla
	- 'Solferino' **new**	SBla
	'Hinton'	CPMA SBla
	x ***houtteana***	CPMA ECho LTwo MGos MWya NBir
	x ***hybrida***	CEnd CPMA SBla
	japonica 'Striata'	see *D. odora* 'Aureomarginata'
	jasminea	CPMA ECho NMen SBla WAbe
	jezoensis	CPMA LRHS SBla SSta WCru
	x ***jintyae*** 'Pink Cascade' **new**	SBla
	juliae	CPMA SBla
	'Kilmeston Beauty' **new**	SBla
	kosaninii	CPMA
	x ***latymeri*** 'Spring Sonnet' **new**	SBla
	laureola	CPMA CSWP EPfP GKev LRHS MGos MMHG MSte NBir NPer WCFE WPGP
	- 'Kingsley Green' **new**	SBla
	- 'Margaret Mathew'	CPMA EPot MGos SBla
	- subsp. ***philippi***	CBcs CBgR CPMA CPle CWSG ELan EPfP IDee LRHS MAsh MBri MGos NDlv NMen SPer SSta WCru WFar WSpi
	'Leila Haines'	CPMA SBla
	longilobata	CPle NSla
	- 'Peter Moore'	SBla
	longituba **new**	SBla
	x ***manteniana***	MGos
	- 'Audrey Vockins'	SBla
	- 'Manten'	CPMA ECho GEdr LHop MWya
	x ***mauerbachii*** 'Perfume of Spring'	CPMA ECho LHop SBla
	'Meon'	see *D.* x *napolitana* 'Meon'
	mezereum	More than 30 suppliers
	- f. ***alba***	CPMA CPle CWib ECho ERas GAbr LHop LRHS MBar MGos NChi NEgg SBla SPer SPoG SRms SWvt WBod WCFE WSpi
	- - 'Bowles' Variety'	CPMA EPot GAbr NBid
	- 'Kingsley Purple' **new**	SBla
	- 'Rosea'	ECho SRms
	- var. ***rubra***	CBcs CPMA CWSG CWib ECho ELan ENot EPfP LRHS MGan MGos MSwo NBlu SPer SPoG WAbe WFar WGwG WOrn
	x ***napolitana*** 🏆H4	CBcs CPMA ECho EPfP EPot GAbr GKev MGos SHBN SKHP SPer SRkn WBod WBrE WGob
§	- 'Bramdean'	CPMA ECho GEdr LHop MWya SBla
§	- 'Maxima'	MGos
§	- 'Meon'	CEnd CPMA ECho GEdr LHop LTwo MWya SBla WAbe WGob WPat
	odora	CBcs CPMA CPle EBee EPot LRHS MGos MSwo NMen SLim SSta WBod WSpi
§	- f. ***alba***	CBcs CCCN CPMA ECho GAbr GEdr GKev MGos MWea NDlv NLar SPer
	- - 'Sakiwaka'	CCCN CPMA ECho GEdr LTwo SBla SKHP WGob
I	- 'Aureamarginata Alba' (v)	CPMA
§	- 'Aureomarginata' (v) 🏆H3-4	More than 30 suppliers
	- 'Clotted Cream' (v)	CPMA

	- 'Geisha Girl' (v)	ELan ENot MAsh MGos SBla
	- var. ***leucantha***	see *D. odora* f. *alba*
	- 'Limelight'	SBla
	- 'Mae-jima'	LRHS SBla
	- 'Marginata'	see *D. odora* 'Aureomarginata'
	- var. ***rubra***	CBcs CCCN CFir ECho GEdr GKev LTwo MLan NDlv NLar SKHP SPer WBod WGob
	- 'Walberton' (v)	LRHS MGos SPoG
	oleoides	CPMA SBla
	petraea	SBla WAbe
	- 'Alba'	see *D. petraea* 'Tremalzo'
	- 'Cima Tombea' **new**	SBla
	- 'Corna Blacca' **new**	SBla
	- 'Flamingo' **new**	SBla
	- 'Flore Pleno' (d) **new**	SBla
	- 'Garnet' **new**	SBla
	- 'Grandiflora'	CPMA EPot GCrs SBla SChF WAbe
	- 'Idro' **new**	SBla
	- 'Lydora' **new**	SBla
	- 'Michele' **new**	CPMA SBla
	- 'Persebee'	CPMA SBla
	- 'Punchinello'	CPMA SBla
§	- 'Tremalzo'	SBla SKHP
	- 'Tuflungo'	CPMA
	petraea x ***sericea*** Collina Group	SSta
	'Pink Star' **new**	SBla
	pontica 🏆^{H4}	CBcs CGHE CPMA CPle ECho EPfP LRHS MAsh MBri NLar NMen SDix SKHP SPer SPoG SSpi WPGP
*	- 'Variegata' (v) **new**	SBla
	pseudomezereum	WCru
	retusa	see *D. tangutica* Retusa Group
	'Richard's Choice'	CPMA
	rodriguezii x ***sericea***	CPMA
	x ***rollsdorfii*** 'Arnold Cihlarz'	CPMA EPot LRHS WAbe
	- 'Wilhelm Schacht'	CPMA ECho EPot LHop SBla SChF
	'Rossetii'	CPMA
	'Rosy Wave'	CPMA SBla SChF
§	x ***schlyteri***	CPMA SBla
	- 'Lovisa Maria'	CPMA SBla
	sericea	CPMA SBla
§	- Collina Group	CPMA EPfP SBla SRms WThu
	'Spring Herald' **new**	SBla
	'Stasek' (v)	CPMA SBla WThu
	striata 'Wolfgang Reich'	SBla
	x ***suendermannii***	SBla
	'Blackthorn Gem' **new**	
	- 'Chris Brickell' **new**	SBla
	- 'Franz Suendermann' **new**	SBla
	sureil GWJ 9200	WCru
	x ***susannae*** 'Anton Fahndrich' x ***sericea*** Collina Group	CPMA
	x ***susannae*** 'Cheriton'	CPMA ECho EPfP EPot GEdr LHop SBla SChF SSta
	- 'Tichborne'	CPMA NMen SBla SChF WAbe WThu
	tangutica 🏆^{H4}	More than 30 suppliers
§	- Retusa Group 🏆^{H4}	CPMA ECho EPot GAbr GCrs GMaP LHop MAsh MBri NEgg NLAp NMen NRya SHBN SRms WCru WSHC WSpi
	- - SDR 3024	GKev
	x ***thauma***	NMen SBla
	x ***transatlantica*** 'Beulah Cross' (v)	CPMA ELan LRHS MAsh SBla SPer SPoG SSpi
	- Eternal Fragrance = 'Blafra'	CAbP ELan ENot LRHS MAsh MGos SBla SPer SPoG SSpi
	- 'Jim's Pride'	SBla
	'Valerie Hillier'	SBla
	velenovskyi	CPMA SBla
	x ***whiteorum*** 'Beauworth'	CPMA ECho LRHS LTwo SBla WAbe
	- 'Kilmeston'	CPMA NMen SBla
	- 'Warnford'	CPMA

Daphniphyllum (*Daphniphyllaceae*)

	calycinum B&SWJ 8225	WCru
	glaucescens B&SWJ 4058	WCru
	- subsp. ***oldhamii*** var. ***kengii*** B&SWJ 6872	WCru
	- - var. ***oldhamii*** B&SWJ 7056	WCru
§	***himalaense*** subsp. ***macropodum***	CBcs CCCN CGHE CHEx CWib EBee EPfP MBri NLar SAPC SArc SDix SLPl SMad SPer SSpi WCru WFar WPGP WSpi
	- - B&SWJ 581	WCru
	- - B&SWJ 2898	WCru
	- subsp. ***macropodum*** B&SWJ 6809 from Taiwan	WCru
	- - B&SWJ 8763 from Cheju-Do	WCru
	- - dwarf	WCru
	humile	see *D. himalaense* subsp. *macropodum*
	teijsmannii B&SWJ 3805	WCru

Darlingtonia (*Sarraceniaceae*)

	californica 🏆^{H1}	CHew CSWC EFEx MCCP SHmp WSSs
	- 'Siskiyou Dragon' **new**	SKHP

Darmera (*Saxifragaceae*)

§	***peltata*** 🏆^{H4}	More than 30 suppliers
	- 'Nana'	CHEx EBee ECha GBuc MBri NBid NLar SWat WCot WFar WMoo WPnP

Darwinia (*Myrtaceae*)

fascicularis	SOWG
taxifolia	SOWG

Dasylirion (*Dracaenaceae*)

	sp.	SBLw
§	***acrotrichum***	LPan SAPC SArc SChr XPep
	glaucophyllum	EAmu MPRe
	gracile Planchon	see *D. acrotrichum*
	leiophyllum	XPep
	longissimum	CAbb CBrP CTrC EAmu EShb SChr XPep
	serratifolium	EAmu
	texanum	CTrC LEdu XPep
	wheeleri 🏆^{H1}	CBrP CTrC EAmu SChr XPep

Dasyphyllum (*Asteraceae*)

diacanthoides	WPGP

date see *Phoenix dactylifera*

Datisca (*Datiscaceae*)

cannabina	CArn CDTJ CDes CFwr CHid EBee ECha EMan MGol NChi NLar SMHy SMrm WCot WHil WMoo WPGP

Datura (*Solanaceae*)

	arborea	see *Brugmansia arborea*
	chlorantha	see *Brugmansia chlorantha*
	cornigera	see *Brugmansia arborea*
§	***inoxia*** 🏆^{H3}	CHrt MGol MSal
	metel	MGol
	- 'Belle Blanche'	MGol
	meteloides	see *D. inoxia*
	rosea	see *Brugmansia* x *insignis* pink-flowered
	rosei	see *Brugmansia sanguinea*

sanguinea	see *Brugmansia sanguinea*
stramonium	CArn MGol MSal WHer
- var. ***chalybaea***	MSal
- var. ***inermis***	MSal
suaveolens	see *Brugmansia suaveolens*
versicolor	see *Brugmansia versicolor* Lagerh.
- 'Grand Marnier'	see *Brugmansia* x *candida* 'Grand Marnier'

Daucus (*Apiaceae*)

carota	CArn CHrt CRWN NMir NSco SECG WHer
- 'Ballydowling Lace'	CNat
- 'Jane's Lace'	CNat

Davallia (*Davalliaceae*)

mariesii ♀H3	CMen WAbe WCot
- var. ***stenolepis***	CMen WRic
tasmanii	WRic
trichomanoides	CMen
- f. ***barbata***	CMen

Davidia (*Cornaceae*)

involucrata ♀H4	More than 30 suppliers
- 'Sonoma'	MBlu
- var. ***vilmoriniana*** ♀H4	CBcs CDoC EBee ELan EPfP EWTr IMGH LRHS MAsh MCCP MGan MGos NBlu NEgg NPal SHBN SPer WOrn

Daviesia (*Papilionaceae*)

brevifolia	SPlb

Decaisnea (*Lardizabalaceae*)

fargesii	More than 30 suppliers
- B&SWJ 8070	WCru
insignis	WNor WPGP

Decodon (*Lythraceae*)

verticillatus	EMon

Decumaria (*Hydrangeaceae*)

barbara	CMac EBee EMil LRHS MBri NLar NSti SBra SHBN SLim SLon SSta WCru WFar WSHC
- 'Vicki'	NLar
sinensis	EBee EPfP LRHS MAsh SPoG SSpi WCru WSHC

Deinanthe (*Hydrangeaceae*)

bifida	CDes CLAP CPLG EBee EWes GEdr LEdu WCru WPGP
- B&SWJ 5012	WCru
- B&SWJ 5436	GEdr
- B&SWJ 5655	WCru
- 'Pink-Shi' **new**	WCru
bifida x ***caerulea***	CLAP CWsd
caerulea	CLAP CMil EBee GEdr IGor LEdu MHar NLar SBla WCru WPGP
- 'Blue Wonder' **new**	EBee WCot
- pale-flowered	GEdr

Delonix (*Caesalpiniaceae*)

regia	SOWG SPlb

Delosperma (*Aizoaceae*)

LEG 037	CStu
§ ***aberdeenense*** ♀H1	CHEx
* ***album***	EDAr
ashtonii	CCCN CStu EDAr GEdr WPer
basuticum **new**	NSla
'Basutoland'	see *D. nubigenum*
congestum	CStu EAlp ECho EDAr EShb EWll GEdr
- 'Gold Nugget' **new**	LRHS
cooperi	CCCN CStu EAlp ECho ECtt EDAr EWll GEdr ITim LRHS NLAp SIng SPlb WDyG WFar WPat WPer XPep
ecklonis	EDAr EWin
esterhuyseniae	EDAr
harazianum **new**	CPBP
* ***jamesonii*** **new**	EDAr
lineare	NBir XPep
lydenburgense	CHEx SChr
§ ***nubigenum***	CHEx CHal EAlp ECho ECtt EDAr ELan EPfP EPot EWin GEdr GGar GKev ITim LRHS NBlu SBHP SPoG WAbe WFar WPer
sutherlandii	EAlp ECho EDAr EShb EWin EWll GGar
- 'Peach Star'	EAlp EDAr EWin

Delphinium ✿ (*Ranunculaceae*)

HWJK 2179 from Nepal	WCru
HWJK 2263 from Nepal	WCru
'After Midnight'	CNMi
'Agnes Brookes'	ERou
'Ailsa'	CNMi
'Alice Artindale' (d)	CDes EMon EWes IFoB SAga SBla SMrm WCot WPGP
'Alie Duyvensteyn'	EBee ERou
'Amadeus' **new**	LCro
ambiguum	see *Consolida ajacis*
'Angela Harbutt'	CNMi
'Ann Woodfield'	CNMi
'Anne Kenrick'	CNMi
'Anne Page'	ERou
'Apollo'	NRnb
'Ariel' ambig.	LRHS WSpi
Astolat Group	CBcs CSBt CTri CWib EBee ELan EPfP EShb GMaP LBMP LRHS MBri MWat NBPC NBir NCob NEgg NLar NPri SMer SPer SPoG WCAu WFar WHil WHoo WWeb
'Atholl' ♀H4	ELar NRnb
Belladonna Group	EShb IFoB
- 'Atlantis' ♀H4	EBee ECha ERou LRHS NGby NLar SBla SMeo SMrm SWat WCot
- 'Balaton'	ELar
- 'Ballkleid'	ERou
- 'Capri'	EBee
- 'Casa Blanca'	EBee EShb GMaP NCGa NLar SMrm SWat WPer
- 'Cliveden Beauty'	EBee GBri LHop MRav MSte NCGa NChi NLar SPoG SWat WPer WSpi
- 'Delft Blue'PBR	EBee EPfP MLLN NMoo
- 'Janny Arrow'PBR **new**	LRHS
- 'Moerheimii'	CBod ERou MRav NGby SMrm WSpi
- 'Piccolo'	ECha ERou NLar SMrm SWat
- 'Pink Sensation'	see *D.* x *ruysii* 'Pink Sensation'
- 'Völkerfrieden' ♀H4	CBod ELar ERou MRav NCGa NGby NPro WSpi
x ***bellamosum***	NCGa NLar SWat WPer
'Berghimmel'	EBee NGby
'Beryl Burton'	CNMi ERou
Black Knight Group	More than 30 suppliers
'Blackberry Ice'	CNMi
'Blauwal'	CFir SWat WSpi
'Blue Arrow' ambig.	LCro
'Blue Arrow'	see *D.* 'Blue Max Arrow', *D.* (Belladonna Group) 'Janny Arrow'
Blue Bird Group	CBcs CSBt CTri EBee ELan EPfP GMaP LBMP LRHS MNHC MRav MWat MWgw NEgg NLar NMir NPri SMer SPer SPla SPoG WCAu WFar WHoo WWeb
'Blue Butterfly'	see *D. grandiflorum* 'Blue Butterfly'

	'Blue Dawn' 🏆^{H4}	CNMi ELar ERou
	Blue Fountains Group	CSBt ENot EPfP LRHS LSRN SPer SPet SPoG SRms
	'Blue Hex'	WCot
	Blue Jade Group	ERou
	'Blue Jay'	CBcs CTri EBee ECtt EPfP LCro LRHS LSRN MWat MWgw NBir NChi NLar NPri SPer SPoG WRHF
	'Blue Lagoon'	CNMi ELar
§	'Blue Max Arrow' **new**	LRHS
	'Blue Mirror'	SRms
	'Blue Nile' 🏆^{H4}	CNMi ELar ERou
	'Blue Oasis'	CNMi
	'Blue Skies'	ECtt NLar NRnb
	Blue Springs Group	NGdn NLar
	'Blue Tit'	CNMi ERou LCro
	'Bruce' 🏆^{H4}	CNMi ELar ERou WCFE
	'Butterball'	CNMi NRnb
	Cameliard Group	CBcs CSBt EBee ECtt ELan LBMP LRHS MNHC MWat MWgw NLar NPri SPer SPoG WHoo
	'Can-Can' 🏆^{H4}	CNMi ELar ERou
	cardinale	EHrv
	'Carl Topping'	ERou
	cashmerianum	ECho GEdr GKev
	'Cassius' 🏆^{H4}	CNMi ERou LCro
	'Celebration' 🏆^{H4}	ELar
	'Centurion Sky Blue' (Centurion Series)	NBHF
	ceratophorum var. ***ceratophorum*** BWJ 7799	WCru
	'Chelsea Star'	CNMi ERou
	'Cher'	CNMi
	'Cherry Blossom'	EPfP GAbr NLar
	'Cherub' 🏆^{H4}	ELar ERou LCro
	chinense	see *D. grandiflorum*
	'Christel'	ERou LRHS NGby
	'Circe'	ERou
	'Clack's Choice'	CNMi ERou
	'Claire' 🏆^{H4}	CNMi ELar
	Clear Springs Series	SGar
	'Clifford Lass'	NRnb
	'Clifford Sky' 🏆^{H4}	ELar
	Connecticut Yankees Group	SRms
	'Conspicuous' 🏆^{H4}	CNMi ELar ERou
	'Constance Rivett' 🏆^{H4}	ERou
	'Coral Sunset'^{PBR} (d)	ERou NMoo WCot
	'Corinth'	CNMi
	'Cressida'	ERou
	'Cristella'	ERou
	'Crown Jewel'	ELar ERou WCFE
	'Cupid'	CNMi ELar ERou
	'Darling Sue'	CNMi LCro
	'Darwin's Blue Indulgence'^{PBR}	EBee EPfP ERou MLLN SMrm
	'Darwin's Pink Indulgence'^{PBR}	ERou MLLN SMrm SPoG
	delavayi	EBee GKev WCot WRos
	- B&SWJ 7796	WCru
	'Demavand'	CNMi
	'Diamant'^{PBR} **new**	LRHS
	'Dolly Bird'	ERou
	'Dora Larkan'	ELar
	'Dreaming Spires'	SRms
	drepanocentrum HWJK 2263	WCru
	'Duchess of Portland'	NRnb
	'Dunsden Green'	CNMi
	'Dusky Maiden'	IFoB
	dwarf dark blue	LRHS
	dwarf lavender	LRHS
	dwarf pink	LRHS
	dwarf sky blue	LRHS
	'Eelkje'	ERou
	elatum	CArn EBee GKev NGdn SRms
	'Elisabeth Sahin'	CNMi ELar
	'Elizabeth Cook' 🏆^{H4}	CNMi
	'Elmfreude'	WSpi
	'Emily Hawkins' 🏆^{H4}	CNMi ERou NRnb
	'Eva Gower'	ERou
	'Fanfare'	CNMi ELar ERou NRnb
	'Father Thames'	ERou
	'Faust' 🏆^{H4}	CNMi ERou LCro MRav NRnb
	'Fenella' 🏆^{H4}	CNMi ELar LCro WCFE
	'Filique Arrow'	CFir
	'Finsteraarhorn'	ERou IPot LRHS NGby WCot WSpi
	'Florestan'	CNMi
	'Foxhill Nina'	CNMi ELar
	'Franjo Sahin'	CNMi ELar
	Galahad Group	More than 30 suppliers
	'Galileo' 🏆^{H4}	CNMi
	'Gemma'	CNMi
	'Gillian Dallas' 🏆^{H4}	CNMi ELar ERou LCro NRnb
	'Giotto' 🏆^{H4}	CNMi
	glaciale HWJK 2299	WCru
	'Gordon Forsyth'	CNMi ELar ERou
	'Gossamer'	CNMi NRnb
§	***grandiflorum***	GKev
§	- 'Blauer Zwerg'	EPfP GKev SHGN SPoG
§	- 'Blue Butterfly'	CSpe EBrs EBur LEdu LRHS SCoo SPlb SPoG WPer WSHC WWeb
	- Blue Dwarf	see *D. grandiflorum* 'Blauer Zwerg'
	'Guardian Lavender' **new**	NPri
	Guinevere Group	CBcs CSBt CWib EBee ECtt EPfP EWTr LBMP LCro LRHS MBri MNHC NBir NLar NPri SPer SPla SPoG WCAu WFar
	'Guy Langdon'	CNMi ERou
	'Harlekijn'	ERou NLar
	'Harmony'	ERou
	'Heavenly Blue'	NLar
	'Holly Cookland Wilkins'	CNMi
	'Hordon Blue'	NBHF
I	'Independence' **new**	LRHS
	Ivory Towers Group	ECtt
	'Jenny Agutter'	CNMi
	'Jill Curley'	CNMi LCro
	'Joan Edwards'	CNMi
	'Joyce Roffey'	ERou
	'Kathleen Cooke'	CNMi
	'Kennington Calypso'	CNMi
	'Kennington Classic'	CNMi
	'Kestrel'	CNMi ERou
	King Arthur Group	CBcs CSBt EBee ECtt ELan EPfP LBMP LSRN MNHC MRav MWat MWgw NBPC NEgg NLar NPri SMer SPer SPoG WBVN WCAu WFar WHoo
	'La Bohème'	CWCL ERou WCot
	'Lady Guinevere'	ERou
	'Langdon's Orpheus' **new**	LCro
§	'Langdon's Royal Flush' 🏆^{H4}	CNMi ELar
	'Lanzenträger'	LRHS SMeo WSpi
	laxiflorum	CEnt
	'Leonora'	CNMi ERou
	'Lilian Bassett' 🏆^{H4}	ELar
	'Lillian Basset'	CNMi
	'Little Flamingo' **new**	ERou
	'Loch Leven' 🏆^{H4}	CNMi ERou
	'Loch Lomond'	NRnb
	'Loch Nevis'	CNMi
	'Lord Butler' 🏆^{H4}	CNMi ELar LRHS NRnb
	'Lorna'	ERou
	'Lucia Sahin' 🏆^{H4}	CNMi ELar
	Magic Fountains Series	CSam CWCL GAbr GMaP IFoB MRav NBlu NPri SPlb SPoG WFar WGor WHil WRHF

- 'Magic Fountains Cherry Blossom'	CBrm EShb SPoG WFar
- 'Magic Fountains Dark Blue'	CBrm ENot EPfP GAbr GMaP LSRN NLar SPoG WFar
- 'Magic Fountains Deep Blue'	NLar
- 'Magic Fountains Lavender'	CBrm EPfP WWeb
- 'Magic Fountains Lilac Pink'	ENot SPoG
- 'Magic Fountains Lilac Rose'	NLar NVic WFar WWeb
- 'Magic Fountains Pure White'	ENot EPfP EShb NBHF NLar WFar WWeb
- 'Magic Fountains Sky Blue'	CBrm EPfP EShb LRHS NVic SPoG WFar
'Margaret Farrand'	ERou
menziesii	ERos
'Merlin' ambig.	LRHS WSpi
'Michael Ayres' ΨH4	CNMi ELar ERou NRnb
micropetalum CNDS 031	WCru
'Mighty Atom'	CNMi ERou LCro NRnb
'Min' ΨH4	CNMi ERou NRnb
'Molly Buchanan'	CNMi ERou
'Moonbeam'	ELar
'Mother Teresa'	ERou
'Mrs Newton Lees'	ERou MRav
'Mrs T. Carlile'	ERou
'Mulberry Rose'	NBHF
'Mystique'	ERou
'Ned Rose'	ERou
'Ned Wit'	ERou
New Century hybrids	CBcs
'Nicolas Woodfield'	CNMi
'Nimrod'	ERou
'Nobility'	ELar ERou LCro
nudicaule	CBod ECho EPfP LAst NWCA SPoG
- 'Fox'	LSou
- 'Laurin'	ECho NRnb SGar WFar
'Olive Poppleton' ΨH4	CNMi LCro SAga
'Oliver' ΨH4	CNMi NRnb
'Our Deb' ΨH4	CNMi ELar
Pacific hybrids	CWCL ENot EPfP LRHS LSRN MHer MLHP NBlu NLar SGar SPet SRms SWal SWvt WBor WFar
'Pagan Purples' (d)	ELar IFoB
'Pandora'	CNMi ELar LCro
'Parade'	ERou
'Patricia Johnson'	ELar ERou
Percival Group	LRHS NLar
'Pericles'	LCro NRnb
'Perlmutterbaum'	SMeo SPhx
'Pink Petticoat' (d)	EMon
'Pink Ruffles'	CNMi ELar
'Polar Sun'	NRnb
Princess Caroline = 'Odabar'[PBR]	CBcs
'Purity'	ERou NRnb
'Purple Ruffles'	EPfP ERou NLar
'Purple Triumph'	ERou
'Purple Velvet'	CNMi ELar LCro
'Pyramus'	ERou
'Rainbow Select'	NRnb
'Rakker'	ERou
'Red Caroline'	CBcs ENot SPoG
requienii	CBre CSpe NBir SBHP SBch WCot WEas
'Rona'	CNMi
'Rose Butterfly' (d) **new**	GKev
'Rosemary Brock' ΨH4	ELar ERou NRnb
Round Table Mixture	CTri
'Royal Flush'	see *D.* 'Langdon's Royal Flush'
'Royal Velvet'	NRnb
§ x ***ruysii*** 'Pink Sensation'	CFir ERou GBri NGby NLar NPro SMrm WFar WPGP WSpi
'Samantha'	ERou
'Sandpiper' ΨH4	CNMi
'Sarita'[PBR]	EBee ERou
'Secret'[PBR] **new**	LRHS
'Sentinel'	CNMi
'Shimmer'	ERou
siamense B&SWJ 7278	WCru
'Silver Jubilee'	CNMi ELar ERou
'Silver Moon'	ERou
'Sir Harry Secombe'	CNMi
'Skyline'	CNMi ERou
'Snow Queen Arrow' **new**	LRHS
'Snowdon'	CNMi
'Solomon'	ERou
'South Seas'	CNMi
* 'Space Fantasy'	SBla
'Spindrift' ΨH4	CNMi NRnb
stapeliosmum B&SWJ 2954	WCru
staphisagria	CArn ECGP EOHP MSal MSte
'Starmaker'	EPfP ERou
'Strawberry Fair'	CNMi ERou NLar WSpi
'Summer Haze'	ERou
Summer Skies Group	CBcs CSBt CTri EBee ECtt ELan EPfP LBMP LHop LRHS MBri MNHC MWat MWgw NBir NEgg NLar NPri SMer SPer SPoG WBrE WCAu WFar WWeb
'Summer Wine' **new**	ELar
'Summerfield Miranda' ΨH4	CNMi
'Summerfield Oberon'	CNMi ELar WCot
'Sungleam' ΨH4	ELar ERou LCro NLar
'Sunkissed' ΨH4	CNMi LCro
'Sunny Skies' (New Millennium Series) **new**	ELar
'Susan Edmunds' (d)	EMil SPoG
sutchuenense	WCot
- BWJ 7867	WCru
tatsienense	EBee GKev SRms WCru
- 'Album'	EWes
tenii B&SWJ 7693	WCru
- BWJ 7906	WCru
'Tessa'	ERou
'Thundercloud'	ERou
'Tiddles' ΨH4	LCro
'Tiger Eye'	CNMi ELar
'Tiny Tim'	CNMi
'Titania'	LCro
tricorne	CLAP ELon
'Turkish Delight'	ELar ERou LCro
'Vanessa Mae'	CNMi
'Vespers'	ELar
vestitum	ECtt NBir SBch
viscosum HWJK 2268	WCru
'Walton Beauty'	CNMi
'Walton Benjamin'	CNMi
'Walton Gemstone' ΨH4	CNMi ELar
'Watkin Samuel'	ERou
'White Arrow' **new**	LCro
'White Ruffles'	CNMi ELar
'Wishful Thinking'[PBR]	ERou SMrm
Woodfield strain	WHrl
'Yvonne'	ERou NLar

Dendranthema (*Asteraceae*)

cultivars	see *Chrysanthemum* cultivars
nankingense	see *Chrysanthemum nankingense*
pacificum	see *Ajania pacifica*

Dendriopoterium see *Sanguisorba*

Dendrobenthamia see *Cornus*

Dendrocalamus *(Poaceae)*

asper	XBlo
calostachys	SPlb
giganteus	XBlo
§ ***strictus***	XBlo

Dendromecon *(Papaveraceae)*

rigida	CBcs CPle EPfP LRHS MBri MWea NLar SAga SKHP SMad SSpi WPGP WSHC

Dennstaedtia *(Dennstaedtiaceae)*

punctilobula	CLAP WCot WRic

Dentaria see *Cardamine*

microphylla	see *Cardamine microphylla*
pinnata	see *Cardamine heptaphylla*
polyphylla	see *Cardamine kitaibelii*

Deparia *(Woodsiaceae)*

pycnosora	WRic

Dermatobotrys *(Scrophulariaceae)*

saundersii	ECre

Derwentia see *Parahebe*

Deschampsia *(Poaceae)*

cespitosa	CBig CEnt CHrt CKno CNat CRWN CWib EPPr EPfP EWTr GFor LBuc LCro MBar MWat NNor SPlb WCFE WCot WGwG WMnd WMoo WPer WPnP WTin XIsg
- subsp. ***alpina***	LEdu
- Bronze Veil	see *D. cespitosa* 'Bronzeschleier'
§ - 'Bronzeschleier'	CEnt CKno CMea CSam CWCL EBee ELan ELon EPla EWsh GBri GMaP LEdu MAvo MBnl MSte NGdn SApp SPer SPhx SPla WMoo WPtf WTin
- brown	SApp
- 'Fairy's Joke'	see *D. cespitosa* var. *vivipara*
- 'Fose'	SApp
- Gold Dust	see *D. cespitosa* 'Goldstaub'
- Golden Dew	see *D. cespitosa* 'Goldtau'
- Golden Pendant	see *D. cespitosa* 'Goldgehänge'
- Golden Shower	see *D. cespitosa* 'Goldgehänge'
- Golden Veil	see *D. cespitosa* 'Goldschleier'
§ - 'Goldgehänge'	CSam EBee EHul EPPr EPfP EPla MMHG NBir NLar NPro SLPl
§ - 'Goldschleier'	CBig CBrm CEnt CPrp EBee ECGP ECha EMon EPPr EPla EWsh GGar GMaP GQue LEdu NGdn SApp SPhx SWal WMoo WPGP XIsg
§ - 'Goldstaub'	EPPr
§ - 'Goldtau'	More than 30 suppliers
- 'Morning Dew'	WFar
- 'Northern Lights' (v)	CBrm CWCL EAlp EBee ELan ENot LEdu LHop LLWG MAvo MBnl MWgw SApp SLim SPer SPla SPoG SRms WCot WMoo WPGP WPnP
- 'Schottland'	EBee GBin
- 'Tardiflora' **new**	EBee
- 'Tauträger'	MSte
§ - var. ***vivipara***	CBig EBee EMon EPPr EPla MWgw NBid NBro NHol NLar SWal WRos
- 'Waldschatt' **new**	EBee XIsg
- 'Willow Green'	MRav SCoo
elongata	CBig
flexuosa	CBig CBrm EWsh GFor MWat NBir WPer XIsg
- 'Tatra Gold'	More than 30 suppliers
holciformis	CBig

Desfontainia *(Loganiaceae)*

§ ***spinosa*** ♀H3	More than 30 suppliers
- 'Harold Comber'	CMac MDun WBod WCru
- f. ***hookeri***	see *D. spinosa*

Desmanthus *(Mimosaceae)*

illinoensis	EMan MGol MSal

Desmodium *(Papilionaceae)*

callianthum	CMac EBee EPfP LRHS WSHC
canadense	CPom EBee EMan MGol NLar
§ ***elegans*** ♀H4	CBcs CHEx EBee ELan EPfP MBri MGol NLar WBod WCru WHer WPGP WSHC
- white-flowered **new**	MGol
praestans	see *D. yunnanense*
tiliifolium	see *D. elegans*
§ ***yunnanense***	CHEx CPle EPfP LRHS WSHC

Desmoschoenus *(Cyperaceae)*

spiralis	CTrC

Deutzia ✿ *(Hydrangeaceae)*

CC 4548	CPLG MGol
CC 4550	CPLG
calycosa	GQui WPat
- B&SWJ 7742	WCru
- 'Dali'	CExc SDys WPGP
chunii	see *D. ningpoensis*
compacta	SLon WBod WFar WPGP
- 'Lavender Time'	CMac CPLG EBee GSki LRHS MAsh WCFE
cordatula B&SWJ 6917	WCru
coreana BWJ 8588	WCru
corymbosa	CDoC
crenata 'Flore Pleno'	see *D. scabra* 'Plena'
- var. ***heterotricha*** BWJ 8896	WCru
- var. ***nakaiana***	SIng WPat
- - 'Nikko'	see *D. gracilis* 'Nikko'
§ - 'Pride of Rochester' (d)	CBcs CMCN CWib CWoW EBee EWTr MBar MGos MRav NLar SLim SLon SPoG WHar
aff. ***crenata*** BWJ 8879	WCru
discolor 'Major'	CPLG
x ***elegantissima***	MRav SRms
- 'Fasciculata'	EPfP SPer WLeb
- 'Rosealind' ♀H4	CBcs CMac CPLG CTri EBee ECrN ENot EPfP EWTr LHop LRHS MBri MGos MRav NEgg NSti SPer SPoG SRGP SRms SSpi WBod WKif WLeb WSHC WSpi
glabrata B&SWJ 617	GQui WCru
glomeruliflora B&SWJ 7748	WCru
gracilis	CDoC CHar CSBt CWoW EBee ELan EPfP EWTr GQui LBMP MBar MGos MRav MSwo SDix SPer SPoG WBod WFar WGwG WRHF WSpi
- B&SWJ 5805	WCru
- 'Aurea'	CBcs
- 'Carminea'	see *D.* x *rosea* 'Carminea'
§ - 'Marmorata' (v)	CBow CPMA NLar SLon WHCG
§ - 'Nikko'	CAbP CBcs CMCN CPBP CPLG CStu CTri EBee ECho EMil EWTr EWes MBar MGos MHer NBlu NLar NPro SPlb WHCG WKif WRHF WSHC
- 'Rosea'	see *D.* x *rosea*
- 'Variegata'	see *D. gracilis* 'Marmorata'
hookeriana	EBee LRHS WFar
- KW 6393	WPGP
x ***hybrida*** 'Contraste'	CMac CPLG SPer
- 'Joconde'	CPLG MBri WFar WKif

- 'Magicien'	CBrm CDoC CDul CMHG CPLG CSBt CSam CWib EBee ECrN EPfP GQui LHop MAsh MBri MRav MSwo SHBN SLon SPer SWvt WFar WHCG WHar WPat
- 'Mont Rose' ♀H4	More than 30 suppliers
§ - 'Strawberry Fields' ♀H4	CBcs CGHE CHar CPLG CTri EBee ELan EPla EWTr LAst LBMP LBuc LRHS LSRN MAsh MBar MBlu MBri MDun MGos NPro SBod SLon WBVN WBod WKif WPGP
'Iris Alford'	SLon
x ***kalmiiflora***	CMac CPLG CPMA CSBt CTri EBee GQui LRHS MBar MBri MRav NEgg SLPl SPer SPoG SRms WBod
longifolia 'Veitchii' ♀H4	CPle CSBt ERas GQui MRav WCFE
- 'Vilmoriniae'	MRav
x ***magnifica***	CBcs EBee ELan EPfP GQui MBri SRms WHCG WHar WSpi
- 'Rubra'	see *D.* x *hybrida* 'Strawberry Fields'
monbeigii	CPLG WKif
- BWJ 7728	WCru
§ ***ningpoensis*** ♀H4	CAbP CBcs CPLG EBee GBin GQui LRHS SLPl SPer WBod WPGP
parviflora var. ***barbinervis*** B&SWJ 8427	WCru
'Pink Pompon'	see *D.* 'Rosea Plena'
pulchra	CAbP CDoC CHar CMCN CPom ECha EPfP IDee MRav NPro SKHP SLon SPer SSpi WFar WHCG WPGP WSpi
- B&SWJ 3870	WCru
- B&SWJ 6908	WCru
aff. ***purpurascens*** BWJ 8007	WCru
rehderiana BWJ 7859 new	WCru
§ x ***rosea***	CDul CWib EBee ECrN ENot EPfP LAst LRHS MBar SHBN SMer SPoG SRms WBod WFar WKif
- 'Campanulata'	CPLG ENot EPfP NEgg
§ - 'Carminea'	MSwo NCGa SPlb SRms WFar WMoo WPat
§ 'Rosea Plena' (d)	CBcs CDoC CPLG CSBt CWib EBee EPfP MAsh MGos NBlu NEgg NLar SLim SMac SPoG SSta WBod WFar WGwG WPat WRHF
scabra	CDul CTri
- B&SWJ 8924	WCru
§ - 'Candidissima' (d)	CMac ECrN GQui MRav NLar SMer SPer WBod
- 'Codsall Pink'	MRav
§ - 'Plena' (d)	CPLG EBee ECtt ELan EPfP IMGH LRHS MRav NEgg SHBN SPer SPur WBod
- 'Pride of Rochester'	see *D. crenata* 'Pride of Rochester'
- 'Punctata' (v)	SRms WFar
- 'Variegata' (v)	CDul CMac
setchuenensis	CMac EPfP GQui SSpi WHCG WPat WSHC
- var. ***corymbiflora*** ♀H4	CBcs CDoC CDul CGHE CSam CTri EBee EPfP IClo IDee LRHS MBri NEgg SPoG WFar WKif WPGP
taiwanensis	EBee EMil NLar
- B&SWJ 6858	WCru
'Tourbillon Rouge'	CDoC EBee EQua WSpi
x ***wellsii***	see *D. scabra* 'Candidissima'
x ***wilsonii***	SRms

Dianella ✿ (*Phormiaceae*)

caerulea	CWsd ECou ELan GBuc IFoB IGor NBir SOWG
- Breeze = 'Dcnco'	ECou ELan EPPr
- 'Cassa Blue'	CCtw CPrp EBee ELan EMan EPPr EWes GGar LHop
- 'Kulnura'	ECou
- Little Jess = 'Dcmp01'	CPrp EBee EPPr GGar LRHS
- var. ***petasmatodes***	EMan WCot
- 'Variegata'	see *D. tasmanica* 'Variegata'
intermedia	CTrC IBlr WCot WPic
- 'Variegata' (v)	EBee IBlr
nigra	CBcs CFir CPen CPou CTrC CWil ECou LEdu NCGa WFar WHer
- 'Margaret Pringle' (v)	CPen CTrC EMil
- 'Taupo'	ECou
revoluta	CFir CWil ECou IBlr
- 'Baby Bliss' new	LLWG
- 'Baby Blue'	ECou
- 'Hartz Mountain'	ECou
- Little Rev = 'Dr5000'	CCtw CPrp EBee ECou ELan EPPr EPfP GGar LHop MMHG
tasmanica	More than 30 suppliers
- 'Emerald Arch' new	ELan
- 'Prosser'	ECou
- 'Tas Red'	CCtw EBee ELan EPPr EPfP LRHS MCot MMHG WAul
§ - 'Variegata' (v)	CBct CDTJ CFir CPen CSpe CStu EBee ECou ELan EMan IBlr LHop MSte WCot

Dianthus ✿ (*Caryophyllaceae*)

ACW 2116	LBee
'A.A. Sanders' (b)	SAll
'Activa' (pf)	SBai
'Adam James' (b)	SAll
'Admiral Crompton' (pf)	CNMi
'Admiral Lord Anson' (b)	WKin
'Alan Titchmarsh' (p)	CCge EBee ENot EPfP EWll MMHG NEgg SBai SPoG SWvt
'Aldridge Yellow' (b)	SAll
'Alfred Galbally' (b)	SAll
'Alice' (p)	EPfP SAll WKin
'Alice Forbes' (b)	SAll
'Alice Lever' (p)	WAbe
'Alloway Star' (p)	WKin
'Allspice' (p)	MRav SBch SSvw WEas WHoo WKin WOFF
'Allspice Sport' (p)	WKin
Allwoodii Alpinus Group (p)	CBrm SRms WFar
'Allwood's Crimson' (pf)	SAll
alpinus ♀H4	CLyd ECho GKev ITim LRHS NBlu NEgg NMen SRms WFar WPer
- 'Albus'	ECho LRHS WLin
§ - 'Joan's Blood' ♀H4	GBuc LHop NHar SBla WAbe WFar
- 'Millstream Salmon'	CLyd EAlp
'Alyson' (p)	SAll
amurensis	ECho LCro LRHS NDov SSvw WGwG WPer
- 'Andrey'	SHar
- 'Siberian Blue'	GBin
anatolicus	CTri ECho LBee LRHS MHer NDlv NGdn NWCA SSvw WOut WPer XPep
'Andrew Morton' (b)	SAll
'Angelo' (b)	SAll
'Annabelle' (p)	EBee ECho LRHS
'Anne Jones' (b)	EPfP
'Annette' (pf)	CEnt EBee ECho EWin GKev LRHS SWvt
'Annie Claybourne' (pf)	CNMi
'Apricot Sue' (pf)	CNMi
'Arctic Star' (p)	CMea CTri ECho GMaP LAst MBnl NCGa NEgg NLar NPri SPet SPoG SRot SWvt WFar
arenarius	GKev NEgg SPlb SSvw WPer
'Argus'	IGor WKin WOFF
* 'Arlene' (b)	SAll

	armeria	EDAr SECG WHer WOut WPer
	'Arthur' (p)	WKin
	'Arthur Leslie' (b)	SAll
§	x ***arvernensis*** (p) ♀H4	EAlp ECha ECho EPot
	- 'Albus'	ECho
	'Atletico'	SBai
	'Audrey's Frilly' (p)	WKin
	'Autumn Tints' (b)	SAll
	'Auvergne'	see *D.* x *arvernensis*
	'Avenarius' (p)	SAll
	'Baby Treasure' (p)	ECho SRot
	'Badenia' (p)	LRHS
	'Bailey's Anniversary' (p)	CBcs SBai SEND
	'Bailey's Celebration' (p)	CBgR EBee ENot EPfP SBai SRGP
§	'Bailey's Daily Mail' (p) ♀H4	CBcs EBee SBai
	'Bailey's Festival' (p)	SBai
	barbatus	CHrt GWCH SECG
	- 'Black Adder' new	CSpe
	- 'Bodestolz'	LSou
	- 'Donnet's Variety' (p,a)	WEas
	- Nigrescens Group (p,a) ♀H4	CBre CHrt CMea CSpe EMon SAga
I	- 'Sooty' (p,a)	EBee ELan GBri LSou NDlv NGdn WCFE
	- 'Tuxedo Black'	MWea
	- 'Woodfall'	WBor
	'Bath's Pink' (p)	LRHS
§	'Bat's Double Red' (p)	IGor SAll SSvw WKin WOFF
	'Beauty of Cambridge' (b)	SAll
	'Beauty of Healey' (p)	WKin
	'Becky Robinson' (p) ♀H4	SAll
	'Bella' (p)	CPBP
	'Berlin Snow'	CLyd CPBP EAlp ECho EPot GKev
	'Betty Morton' (p) ♀H4	CEnt ECtt IFoB MWea SBla SSvw WFar WKif WKin WThu
	'Binsey Red' (p)	SSvw WKin
	Black and White Minstrels Group	CLyd
	Blakeney seedling (p)	WKin
*	'Blue Carpet'	WPer
	'Blue Hills' (p)	CLyd ECho GCrs GKev MWea SIng
	'Blue Ice' (b)	SAll
	'Blush'	see *D.* 'Souvenir de la Malmaison'
	'Bobby' (p)	SAll
	'Bob's Highlight' (pf)	CNMi
	'Bookham Heroine' (b)	SAll
	'Bookham Lad' (b)	SAll
	'Bookham Sprite' (b)	SAll
	'Border Special' (b)	SAll
	'Bourboule'	see *D.* 'La Bourboule'
	'Bovey Belle' (p) ♀H4	CBcs LRHS SBai
	'Bressingham Pink' (p)	ECho ECtt
	'Brian Tumbler' (b) ♀H4	SAll
	'Bridal Veil' (p)	GAbr SAll SSvw WKin
	'Brigadier' (p)	ECho
	'Brilliance' (p)	ECho
	'Brilliant'	see *D. deltoides* 'Brilliant'
	'Brilliant Star' (p) ♀H4	CBgR ECho LBee SPet SWvt WWFP
	'Brymos' (p)	CWsd
	'Brympton Red' (p)	ECha MRav SBch SSvw WEas WKin
	'Bryony Lisa' (b) ♀H4	SAll
§	'Caesar's Mantle' (p)	WKin
	caesius	see *D. gratianopolitanus*
	callizonus	GEdr NMen
	'Calypso Star' (p) ♀H4	CPBP EBee ECho ECtt EWin GBuc GMaP NCGa NEgg SPet SPoG STes
	'Camelford' (p)	WKin
	'Camilla' (b)	SSvw WKin
	'Can-can' (pf)	ECho ECtt
	'Candy Clove' (b)	SAll
	Candy Floss = 'Devon Flavia' (p)	CBgR EWll LBMP
	'Candy Spice'PBR (p)	MRav
	Cano = 'Loncano'PBR (pf) new	SBai
	'Carmine Letitia Wyatt'PBR (p) ♀H4	EBee SPoG
	carthusianorum	CArn CBrm CKno EWTr IGor LCro LDai MNFA MSte NDlv NDov SAga SGar SMeo SPhx SSvw STes SWat WEas WKin WOut WPGP WPer XPep
	caryophyllus	CArn GWCH MNHC WHer
	- Giorgia = 'Longiorgia'PBR (pf) new	SBai
	'Casser's Pink' (p)	GBuc
§	'Cedric's Oldest' (p)	WKin
	'Charles' (p)	SAll
	'Charles Allwood' (pf) new	EMal
	'Charles Edward' (p)	SAll
	'Charles Musgrave'	see *D.* 'Musgrave's Pink'
	'Chastity' (p)	SBla WHoo WKin
	Cheddar pink	see *D. gratianopolitanus*
	'Cherry Clove' (b)	SAll
	'Cherry Moon'	LRHS
	'Cherry Pie' (p)	EBee ENot EPfP NEgg WMnd
	'Cheryl'	see *D.* 'Houndspool Cheryl'
	'Chetwyn Doris' (p) ♀H4	SBai
	'Chianti' (pf)	NGdn
	'China Doll' (p)	SBai
	chinensis (p,a)	CArn WHer WKin
	- 'Black and White' new	CSpe
	'Chomley Farran' (b)	ITer
	'Chris Crew' (b) ♀H4	SAll
	'Christine Hough' (b)	SAll
	'Christopher' (p)	LRHS SAll
	'Clara' (pf)	CNMi
	'Clara's Lass' (pf)	CNMi
	'Clare' (p)	SAll
	'Claret Joy' (p) ♀H4	CBcs CFir EBee EPfP LAst NPri SAll WRHF
I	'Clifford Pink' (p)	WKin
	'Clunie' (b)	SAll
§	'Cockenzie Pink' (p)	IGor NChi SAll SSvw WEas WKin
	'Coconut Sundae' (p) new	CBgR EWll
	'Constance' (p)	SAll
	'Constance Finnis'	see *D.* 'Fair Folly'
	'Consul' (b)	SAll
	'Conwy Silver'	WAbe
	'Conwy Star'	CPBP WAbe
	'Cornish Snow' (p)	NChi
	'Corona Cherry Magic'	LRHS
	'Coronation Ruby' (p) ♀H4	CBcs SAll SBai
	corsicus	XPep
	'Coste Budde' (p)	IGor WEas WKin WSHC
	'Cottage Pink' (b) new	WKin
	'Cranborne Seedling' (p)	WKin
	'Cranmere Pool' (p) ♀H4	CCge CEnt CMea EBee ECtt ELan EPfP LAst LBMP LRHS NPri SBai SPoG SWvt WFar WMnd
	cretaceus	NWCA
	'Crimson Chance' (p)	NSla
	'Crimson Joy' (p) ♀H4	SPoG
	crinitus	SHFr
	'Crompton Classic' (pf)	CNMi
	cruentus	MSte NDov SPhx SSvw STes WPer
	'Dad's Choice' (p)	SBai
	'Dad's Favourite' (p)	CCge CEnt IGor SAll SRms SSvw WEas WHer WKin
	'Daily Mail' (p)	see *D.* 'Bailey's Daily Mail'
	'Dainty Dame' (p) ♀H4	CPBP CSpe CTri EBee ECho GBuc LRHS MNHC MSte MWea SBla SPoG SRot WFar
	'Damask Superb' (p)	IGor WKin
	'Daphne' (p)	SAll
	'Dark Star' (p)	ECho
	'Dartington Double' (p)	ECho
	'Dartington Laced' (p)	WKin

	'David' (p)	SAll
	'David Russell' (b) ♀H4	SAll
	'Dawlish Charm' (p)	SBai
	'Dawlish Joy' (p)	EBee SRGP
	'Dawn' (b)	SAll
	'Dawn' (pf)	ECho
	'Dedham Beauty' **new**	WCot
	deltoides ♀H4	CArn CEnt CSev ECha ECho ELau EPfP GWCH NSco SECG SHGN SPlb SRms WFar WJek WRHF
	- 'Albus'	ECha EPfP MNHC NBlu NEgg NPri SSvw SWat WMoo WRos
	- 'Arctic Fire'	CWib ECho NGdn WMoo
	- 'Bright Eyes'	CCge ECho
§	- 'Brilliant'	CTri ECho EPau MDun MFOX MNHC NPri NVic SAll SRms SWat WGor
	- 'Canta Libra'	SWal
	- 'Dark Eyes'	EWes
	- 'Erectus'	EPfP
	- Flashing Light	see *D. deltoides* 'Leuchtfunk'
§	- 'Leuchtfunk'	CHrt ECho ECtt EPfP GGar IBal LAst LRHS NEgg NMir NNor SPoG SWal WFar WHen WMoo WRHF WRos
	- 'Microchip'	WFar
	- 'Nelli' (p)	ECho SSvw
	- red	NBlu
	'Denis' (p)	SAll
	'Desert Song' (b)	SAll
	'Devon Charm' (p)	LRHS
	'Devon Cream' PBR (p)	CSBt EBee ENot LBMP LRHS NEgg NPri WMnd WRHF
	'Devon Dove' PBR (p) ♀H4	CBgR CMea EBee EPfP LAst LBMP NDov NEgg NPri WWFP
	'Devon General' PBR (p)	CTri EBee ECtt SPoG
	'Devon Glow' PBR (p) ♀H4	EBee EPfP LBMP LRHS NEgg SPoG
	'Devon Joy' (p)	LRHS
	'Devon Magic' PBR (p)	SPoG WFar
	'Devon Maid' (p) ♀H4	EPfP
	'Devon Pearl' PBR (p)	EBee LHop
	'Devon Wizard' PBR (p) ♀H4	CBgR CHar EPfP LRHS NPri SPoG WCAu WFar
	'Devon Yvette' PBR	CCge EBee MBNS NEgg
	'Dewdrop' (p)	CMea CTri EBee ECho ECtt EPot EWin LRHS MHer NBir NGdn NPro SAll WAbe WFar WKin WPer
	'Diana'	see *D.* Dona = 'Brecas'
	'Diane' (p) ♀H4	EBee ELan EPfP NEgg SAll SPla SWvt WMnd
	'Diplomat' (b)	SAll
§	Dona = 'Brecas' (pf)	LRHS SRGP
	'Dora' (p)	LRHS
	'Doris' (p) ♀H4	CBcs CHar CMea CTri EBee EGoo ENot EPfP ERou LAst LBMP LCro LHop LRHS MRav NEgg SAll SBai SPer SPla SPlb SPoG SRGP SRms SSvw SWvt WCAu WKif WMnd WTel
	'Doris Allwood' (pf)	CNMi CSBt EMal SAll
	'Doris Elite' (p)	SAll
	'Doris Galbally' (b)	SAll
	'Doris Majestic' (p)	SAll
	'Doris Ruby'	see *D.* 'Houndspool Ruby'
	'Doris Supreme' (p)	SAll
	'Double North'	NWCA
	'Dover' (pf)	SBai
§	'Dubarry' (p)	CTri CWan ECho ECtt WGor WPer WRHF
	'Duchess of Westminster' (M)	EMal SAll
	'Duke of Norfolk' (pf)	EMal
	'Dusky' (p)	WKin
	'Earl of Essex' (p)	SAll SSvw WKin
	'Ebor II' (b)	SAll
	'Edenside Scarlet' (b)	SAll
	'Edenside White' (b)	SAll
	'Edna' (p)	SAll
	'Edward Allwood' (pf)	SAll
	'Eileen' (p)	SAll
	'Eileen Lever' (p)	CPBP ITim SBla WAbe WFar
	'Eileen Neal' (b) ♀H4 **new**	SAll
	'Eleanor's Old Irish' (p)	WCot WHoo WKin WTin
	'Elfin Star' (p)	ECho MSte SPet
	'Elizabeth' (p)	CEnt WEas
	'Elizabethan' (p)	CFee CFis CStu GMac WKin WOFF
*	'Elizabethan Pink' (p)	CCge SAll
	'Emile Paré' (p)	WKin
	'Emjay' (b)	SAll
	'Emma James' (b)	SAll
	'Emperor'	see *D.* 'Bat's Double Red'
	'Enid Anderson' (p)	WKin
	'Enid Burgoyne' (p)	WKin
	erinaceus	EAlp ECho GKev LRHS NWCA SRot WAbe
	- var. ***alpinus***	EPot ITim
	'Erycina' (b)	SAll
	'Ethel Hurford' (p)	WHoo WKin
	'Eva Humphries' (b)	SAll
	'Evening Star' (p) ♀H4	CBgR ECho EWin LBee MWgw SPet SPoG SWvt
	'Excelsior' (p)	SSvw
	'Exquisite' (b)	SAll
§	'Fair Folly' (p)	SAll SSvw WKin
	'Fanal' (p)	NBir
	'Farnham Rose' (p)	SSvw
	'Fenbow Nutmeg Clove' (b)	CWan MBrN WKin WMnd
	ferrugineus	MSte
	'Fettes Mount' (p)	EWin GAbr SSvw WCot WKin WSPU
	'Feuerhexe' (p)	LRHS NPro
	'Fiery Cross' (b)	SAll
	'Fimbriatus' (p)	WHoo WKin
	'Fiona' (p)	SAll
	'Fireglow' (b)	SAll
	'Firestar' (p)	LBee SPet SWvt
	'First Lady' (b)	ECho SAll
	'Flanders' (b) ♀H4	SAll
	'Fleur' (p)	SAll
	'Forest Glow' (b)	SAll
	'Forest Sprite' (b)	SAll
	'Forest Treasure' (b)	SAll
	'Forest Violet' (b)	SAll
I	'Formosa' (pf) **new**	SBai
	'Fortuna' (p)	SAll
	'Fountain's Abbey' (p)	IGor NChi WKin
	'Fragrant Ann' (pf) ♀H1	CNMi
*	***fragrantissimus***	LRHS
	'Frances Isabel' (p)	SAll
	'Frank's Frilly' (p)	WKin
	'Freda' (p)	SAll
	freynii	CLyd ECho EPot EWes GKev NDlv NLAp SBla WAbe
*	- var. ***nana*** **new**	GKev
N	fringed pink	see *D. superbus*
	'Fusilier' (p)	CElw CEnt CMea CTri ECho EDAr EPfP GMaP LAst LHop LRHS MBar MSte MWgw NCGa NEgg NPri NWCA SAll SRot STes SWvt WAbe WBVN WFar WPat
	'Gail Graham' (b)	SAll
	'Garland' (p)	CTri LRHS WGor
	'Gaydena' (b)	SAll
	'George Allwood' (pf)	SAll
	giganteus	CSpe MSte MWea WGwG WKin WSHC
	'Gingham Gown' (p)	EPot NBir SBla SPoG
	glacialis	GKev ITim SSvw
*	- ***elegans***	GKev
	'Gloriosa' (p)	WKin

	'Gold Fleck'	EPot SIng
	'Grana' (pf)	SBai
	'Grandma Calvert' (p)	SAll
	graniticus	EPot
	'Gran's Favourite' (p) ♀H4	CBcs CCge CEnt CMea CSBt CTri EBee ECtt ENot EPfP LAst LRHS NPri SAll SBai SPlb SPoG SRGP SRms SWvt WEas WFar WKin
§	***gratianopolitanus*** ♀H4	CArn CBod CTri EPfP EPot GKev LRHS MHer MNHC MNrw MRav NBid NChi NWCA SRms WGwG WKin
	- 'Albus'	EPot
	- 'Compactus Eydangeri' (p)	GBin
	- 'Flore Pleno' (d)	SHGN SSvw
	- 'Grandiflorus' **new**	SHGN
§	- 'Tiny Rubies' (p)	ECho WAbe WKin
	'Gravetye Gem' (b)	SRms
	'Gravetye Gem' (p)	WKin
	'Green Lane' (p)	CHll
	'Grenadier' (p)	ECho ELan
	'Grey Dove' (b) ♀H4	SAll
	'Gypsy Star' (p)	EBee ECho EWin GMaP NCGa NEgg SPet SPoG
	haematocalyx	NMen NWCA SSvw WAbe WFar WPer WThu
	- 'Alpinus'	see *D. haematocalyx* subsp. *pindicola*
§	- subsp. ***pindicola***	CGra GKev LTwo NLAp NMen
	'Hannah Louise' (b) ♀H4	SAll
	'Harkell Special' (b)	SAll
	'Harlequin' (p)	WPer
	'Harmony' (b)	SAll
	'Harry Oaks' (p)	WKin
	'Haytor'	see *D.* 'Haytor White'
	'Haytor Rock' (p) ♀H4	EBee EPfP SPoG
§	'Haytor White' (p) ♀H4	CWib EBee EPfP LAst LRHS MRav SAll SBai SRms WCot WEas
	'Hazel Ruth' (b) ♀H4	SAll
	'Heath' (b)	WKin
	'Heidi' (p)	EPfP SHGN
	'Helen' (p)	SAll
	'Helena Hitchcock' (p)	SAll
	'Herbert's Pink' (p)	WKin
	'Hereford Butter Market' (p)	EBee WKin
	'Hidcote' (p)	CLyd CTri EBee ELan LRHS NMen SBla WFar WKin
	'Hidcote Red'	ECho LBee LRHS
	'Highland Fraser' (p)	SRms WEas WKif WKin
	'Highland Queen' (p)	WKin
	'Hoo House' (p)	WKin
	'Hope' (p)	SSvw WKin
	'Horsa' (b)	SAll
§	'Houndspool Cheryl' (p) ♀H4	CTri EBee ENot EPfP LRHS SAll SRGP SRms WFar
§	'Houndspool Ruby' (p) ♀H4	CBgR EBee EPfP SAll SBai WCAu WEas
	'Ian' (p)	SAll SBai
	'Iceberg' (p)	ECho
	'Icomb' (p)	CLyd SRms WHoo WKin WPer
	'Ina' (p)	EGoo SRms
	'Inchmery' (p)	SAll SHGN SSvw WEas WHoo WKin WTin
	'India Star'^{PBR} (p) ♀H4	CBgR CCge CTri ECho LAst NEgg SPet STes
	'Inglestone' (p)	CTri NHol SBla WLin WPer
	'Inshriach Dazzler' (p) ♀H4	CMea CPBP EAlp ECho ECtt EWin GAbr GGar GMaP LBee LHop MHer MWea NDlv NHar NHol NRya SBla SIng SPoG SRot WAbe WLin
	'Inshriach Startler' (p)	CLyd CMea
	'Ipswich Pink' (p)	LRHS MNHC SRms

	'Irene Della-Torré' (b) ♀H4	SAll
	'Irene Hobbah' (b)	SAll
	'Jacqueline Ann' (pf) ♀H1	CNMi
	'James Portman' (p)	CBgR WMnd
	'Jane Austen' (p)	WKin WPer
	'Jane Barker' (b)	SAll
	'Janelle Welch' (pf)	CNMi
	'Janet Walker' (p)	GMaP
	'Jess Hewins' (pf)	CNMi SAll
*	'Jewel'	ECho
	'Joan Schofield' (p)	ECho SBch SPoG
	'Joan Siminson' (p)	WKin
	'Joanne's Highlight' (pf)	CNMi
	'Joan's Blood'	see *D. alpinus* 'Joan's Blood'
	'Joe Vernon' (pf)	CNMi
	'John Ball' (p)	SSvw WKin WOFF
	'John Grey' (p)	WKin
	'Joy' (p) ♀H4	ECho ECtt EPfP LAst LRHS SAll SPoG
	'Julian' (p)	SAll
	'Julie Ann Davis' (b)	SAll
	'Kessock Charm' **new**	MNrw
	'Kesteven Chamonix' (p)	WPer
	'Kesteven Kirkstead' (p) ♀H4	CSWP MNrw
	'Kingstone Red Velvet' (p) **new**	WKin
	'Kiro' (pf)	SBai
	kitaibelii	see *D. petraeus* subsp. *petraeus*
	'Kiwi Far North'	SHGN
	knappii	EPfP LDai LHop NDov NLar NVic SEND SMeo SRms SSvw WKin WMoo WPer XPep
	- 'Yellow Harmony' (p,a)	LRHS MBNS SGar
	'Komachi' (pf) ♀H1	SBai
§	'La Bourboule' (p) ♀H4	CMea CTri EAlp ECho EDAr EPot GAbr LRHS MBar NHol NMen NPri SBla SRms WKin WLin WPat
	'La Bourboule Alba' (p)	CTri ECho EDAr EPot GCrs ITim SBla WFar WGor
	'Laced Hero' (p)	IGor NWCA WKin
	'Laced Joy' (p)	SAll
	'Laced Monarch' (p)	CBcs CEnt EBee ECtt GCra LRHS NLar SAll SBai SPlb SPoG WKin
	'Laced Mrs Sinkins' (p)	MLHP SAll SHGN SPer
	'Laced Prudence'	see *D.* 'Prudence'
	'Laced Romeo' (p)	SAll WKin
	'Laced Treasure' (p)	SAll
	'Lady Bacon' (p) **new**	WKin
	'Lady Emma Tennant' (b) **new**	WKin
	'Lady Granville' (p)	IGor SAll SBch SHGN SSvw WKin
	Lady in Red = 'WP04 Xanthe' (p) **new**	CBgR LBMP
	'Lady Madonna' (p)	CBgR CMea LBMP
	'Lady Salisbury' (p)	WKin
	'Lady Spring' (pf)^{PBR} **new**	SBai
§	'Lady Wharncliffe' (p)	IGor SBch WKin
	'Lady Windermere' (M) **new**	EMal
	langeanus NS 255	NWCA
	'Laura' (p)	SAll
	'Lavastrom' (p)	SBla
	'Lawley's Red' (p)	WKin
	'Lemsii' (p) ♀H4	ECho ECtt NMen WPer
	'Leslie Rennison' (b)	SAll
	'Letitia Wyatt' (p) ♀H4	CMea EBee ENot EPfP SPoG SRGP
	'Leuchtkugel'	ECho LTwo NHar NMen
	leucophaeus var. ***leucophaeus***	EPot
I	'Lily the Pink' (p)	CBgR ENot
	'Linfield Annie's Fancy' (pf)	CNMi
	'Linfield Dorothy Perry' (p) ♀H4	SAll
	'Linfield Isobel Croft' (p)	SAll
	'Lionheart' (p)	LRHS

	'Little Ben' (p)	SAll
	'Little Gem' (p)	WKin
	'Little Jock' (p)	CCge CPBP ECho EDAr EPot GGar LRHS MBar MHer MNHC MRav SAll SBla SIng SPlb SPoG SRms WEas WFar WKin WLin
	'Little Miss Muffet' (p)	CHll
	'Liz Rigby' (b)	SAll
	'London Brocade' (p)	SHGN SSvw WKin
	'London Delight' (p)	WKin
	'London Glow' (p)	SAll WKin
	'London Lovely' (p)	SAll SHGN SSvw WKin
	'London Poppet' (p)	NDlv SAll SSvw WKin
	'Loveliness' (p,a)	CBre
	lumnitzeri	ECho LTwo WPer XPep
	'Lustre' (b)	SAll
	'Mab' (p)	WKin
	'Madame Dubarry'	see *D.* 'Dubarry'
	'Maisie Neal' (b) ♀H4	SAll
	'Mandy' (p)	SAll
	'Manningtree Pink'	see *D.* 'Cedric's Oldest'
	'Marjery Breeze'	SAll
	'Marmion' (M)	EMal SAll
	'Mars' (p)	ECho ECtt ELan NDlv WAbe
	'Marshwood Melody' (p)	SBai
	'Marshwood Mystery' (p)	WKin
I	'Mary's Gilliflower' (p)	WKin
	'Matthew' (p)	WHoo WKin
	'Maudie Hinds' (b)	SAll
	'Maybole' (b)	SAll
	'Maythorne' (p)	SRms
	'Melocoton'	SBai
	'Mendip Hills' (b)	SAll
	Mendlesham Minx = 'Russmin'^{PBR} (p)	EBee ECho EDAr GBuc GGar LBee SAll SPet SWvt
	'Merlin'	CPen
	'Messines Pink' (p)	SAll SSvw
	'Michael Saunders' (b) ♀H4	SAll
	microlepis	CGra ECho GCrs ITim NGdn SBla WAbe WLin
	- f. ***albus***	CGra
	- 'Leuchtkugel'	ECho WAbe
	- var. ***musalae***	CLyd ECho EPot ITim LTwo NHar NMen WAbe
	'Mike Briggs' (b)	SAll
	'Miss Sinkins' (p)	SPet SPla
	'Monica Wyatt' (p) ♀H4	EPfP LRHS NEgg SBai SPoG SRGP
	monspessulanus	GKev NDlv SSvw WMoo WPer
	- subsp. ***sternbergii***	SBla
	'Montrose Pink'	see *D.* 'Cockenzie Pink'
	'Moortown Plume' (p)	WKin
	Morning Star = 'Devon Winnie'^{PBR}	LBee MWgw SPet
	'Moulin Rouge' (p) ♀H4	CBgR CEnt EBee ERou SHGN SPoG WWFP
	'Mrs Clark'	see *D.* 'Nellie Clark'
	'Mrs Gumbly' (p)	WKin
	'Mrs Macbride' (p)	SAll WKin
	'Mrs N. Clark'	see *D.* 'Nellie Clark'
	'Mrs Perkins' (b)	SAll
	'Mrs Roxburgh' (p)	CSam WKin
	'Mrs Sinkins' (p)	More than 30 suppliers
	'Murray Douglas' (p)	SSvw
	'Murray's Laced Pink' (p)	WKin WSPU
N	'Musgrave's Pink' (p)	ECha MRav SAga SAll SBch SBla SSvw WEas WKin
	'Musgrave's White'	see *D.* 'Musgrave's Pink'
	myrtinervius	CLyd CPBP ECho GBin GEdr NLar NWCA SRms
	- subsp. ***caespitosus***	NHar
	'Mystic Star' **new**	CMea
	'Nan Bailey' (p)	SBai
	'Napoleon III' (p)	SSvw
	nardiformis	SSvw WPer
	'Natalie Saunders' (b) ♀H4	SAll
	'Nautilus' (b)	SAll
	neglectus	see *D. pavonius*
§	'Nellie Clark' (p)	CLyd ECho
	'Neon Star'^{PBR} (p) ♀H4	ECho EDAr GKev SPoG WFar
	'New Picasso' (pf)^{PBR} **new**	SBai
	'Night Star' (p) ♀H4	CBgR ECho EWin GKev GMaP LSou MNrw NCGa NEgg SPet SRot WBVN WFar
	nitidus	CLyd GKev NBir SSvw WPer
	noeanus	see *D. petraeus* subsp. *noeanus*
	'Nonsuch' (p)	WKin
	'Northland' (pf)	CNMi EMal SAll
	'Nyewoods Cream' (p)	CMea CTri CWan EAlp ECho EPot GAbr LBee LRHS MBar MHer MRav NHol NMen NPri SIng WPat WPer WTin
§	'Oakington' (p)	CTri LRHS MRav NPri WKin WTel
	'Oakington Rose'	see *D.* 'Oakington'
	'Oakwood Gillian Garforth' (p) ♀H4	SBai
	'Oasis'^{PBR} **new**	SBai
	'Old Blush'	see *D.* 'Souvenir de la Malmaison'
	'Old Dutch Pink' (p)	IGor SSvw WKin WOFF
	'Old French Red' (pf)	EMal
	'Old Fringed Pink' (p)	WKin
	'Old Irish' (p)	IGor WKin WOFF
	'Old Mother Hubbard' (p)	CFee CHll
	'Old Red Clove' (p)	WCot WEas
§	'Old Square Eyes' (p)	MNrw SAll SSvw WEas WFar WKin
	'Old Velvet' (p)	MNrw SAll WKin
	'Oliver' (p)	SAll
	'Orange Maid' (b)	SAll
	'Oscar' (b)	SAll
	'Paddington' (p)	WKin WOFF
	'Painted Beauty' (p)	NBir
	'Painted Lady' (p)	IGor SAll WKin
	'Paisley Gem' (p)	SSvw WKin WOFF
§	***pavonius*** ♀H4	CLyd CPBP EWes GKev NGdn NLar NWCA SBla WPer
	- 'Nancy Lindsay' (p)	SSvw
	- ***roysii***	see *D.* 'Roysii'
§	***petraeus***	EWes
§	- subsp. ***noeanus***	EPot LTwo WHal WPer
	- - ***albus***	GCrs
§	- subsp. ***petraeus***	WPer
	'Petticoat Lace' (p)	SAll
	'Pheasant's Eye' (p)	SAll SSvw WHer WKin
*	'Picton's Propeller' (p)	GBuc
	'Pike's Pink' (p) ♀H4	CCge CSpe CTri EBee ECho EDAr ELan EPfP GGar LHop LRHS MHer MRav NMen SAll SBla SIng SPet SPoG SRms SSvw WBVN WEas WKin WLin WTel
	pindicola	see *D. haematocalyx* subsp. *pindicola*
	pinifolius	ITim NLar
	'Pink Devon Pearl'^{PBR}	CBgR CMea SAll SPoG
	'Pink Dover' (pf)	SBai
	'Pink Fantasy' (b)	SAll
	'Pink Jewel' (p)	CLyd CMea EAlp ECho EPot LRHS MHer NMen SAll SIng WEas
	'Pink Mrs Sinkins' (p)	ECha MHer MLHP SAll WKin
	'Pixie' (b)	EPot
	'Pixie Star'^{PBR} (p) ♀H4	ECho EPfP GMaP SPoG SRot
	plumarius	SAll SRms SSvw WHer WMoo WPer
	- 'Albiflorus'	WPer
	pontederae	NDlv WPer
	'Popstar' **new**	EWll
	'Pretty' (p)	LRHS
	'Pretty Lady' (p)	ECho
	'Prince Charming' (p)	ECho EPot NEgg NPri SIng SRms WPer
	'Princess of Wales' (M)	EMal SAll
	'Priory Pink' (p)	SAll

§	'Prudence' (p)	SAll WKin WOFF
	'Pudsey Prize' (p)	CLyd CPBP WAbe
	'Pummelchen' (p)	EPot ITim SBla
	'Purple Jenny' (p)	SAll
	pygmaeus	NBro
*	- 'Pink Frills'	NEgg
	pyrenaicus 'Cap Béar'	XPep
	'Queen of Hearts' (p)	CTri ECho LRHS NWCA WPer
§	'Queen of Henri' (p)	ECho ECtt GEdr LBee LRHS MHer SBla SHGN SHar WBVN WFar WKin
	'Queen of Sheba' (p)	SHGN SSvw WKif WKin
	'Rachel' (p)	ECtt WPat
	'Rainbow Loveliness' (p,a)	SAll SRms WHil
	'Ralph Gould' (p)	ECho
	'Raspberry Sundae' (p)	CBgR LBMP SPoG
	'Rebecca' (b)	SAll
	'Red and White' (p)	WKin
	'Red Lips' (pf) **new**	SBai
	'Red Star'PBR ♀H4	GGar MMHG MSte SPet SPoG SRot
	'Red Velvet'	CLyd LRHS
	'Reine de Henri'	see *D.* 'Queen of Henri'
	'Revell's Lady Wharncliffe'	see *D.* 'Lady Wharncliffe'
	'Rififi' (pf)	SBai
	'Rivendell' (p)	CLyd CPBP ECho NMen WAbe
	'Robert Allwood' (pf)	SAll
	'Robin Ritchie' (p)	WHoo WKin
	'Robina's Daughter'	GAbr
	'Roodkapje' (p)	SSvw WKin
	Rosalba = 'Lonrosalb' (pf) **new**	SBai
	'Rose de Mai' (p)	CSam CSev SAll SBch SHGN SSvw WHoo WKin
	'Rose Devon Pearl'PBR	EBee EPfP NEgg SRGP WMnd
	'Rose Joy' (p) ♀H4	EBee EPfP NLar
§	'Roysii' (p)	NDlv WPer
	rubicunda var. ***rubicunda*** **new**	GKev
	'Rubin' (p)	WEas
	'Ruby'	see *D.* 'Houndspool Ruby'
	'Ruby Doris'	see *D.* 'Houndspool Ruby'
	'Rudheath Ruby' (b)	SAll
	rupicola	CSpe
	'Saint Edith' (p)	WKin
	'Saint Nicholas' (p)	SSvw WKin
	'Saint Winifred' (p)	WKin
	'Sam Barlow' (p)	EGoo SAll SSvw WKin
	sanguineus	NDov SMHy
	'Santa Claus' (b)	SAll
	Scarlet Beauty = 'Hilbeau'	NBlu
	'Schubert' (pf)	SBai
	scopulorum perplexans	ITim
	seguieri	SSvw WPer
	serotinus	EPot SSvw WCot
	shinanensis **new**	GKev
	Shiplake seedling (p)	WKin
	'Shot Silk' (pf)	SAll
	'Show Aristocrat' (p)	SAll
	'Show Beauty' (p)	SAll
	'Show Glory' (p)	SAll
	'Show Harlequin' (p)	SAll
	'Show Satin' (p)	SAll
	'Shrimp' (b)	CWib
	'Sir Cedric Morris'	see *D.* 'Cedric's Oldest'
	'Sir David Scott' (p)	WKin
*	'Six Hills'	NHol WPat
	'Snowflake' (p)	ECho
	'Snowshill Manor' (p)	WPer
	Solar Oro = 'Lonsolaro'PBR (pf) **new**	SBai
	'Solomon' (p)	SSvw WKin
	'Solomon's Hat' (p)	WKin
	'Sops-in-wine' (p)	CSam ECha GBuc NChi SAll WKin
	'Southmead' (p)	ECho
§	'Souvenir de la Malmaison' (M)	EMal SAll
	'Spangle' (b)	SAll
	'Spencer Bickham' (p)	MNrw SHGN WKin
	spiculifolius	EAlp EPot NWCA
	'Spooky' **new**	MWea
	'Spring Beauty' (p)	NBir WHer
	'Spring Star' (p)	ECtt EWin NPri SRot
	'Square Eyes'	see *D.* 'Old Square Eyes'
	squarrosus	ECho EPot NWCA
*	- ***alpinus***	ECho
	- 'Nanus'	ECho ELan EWes LBee LRHS
I	'Star' (pf)	SBai
	Starlight = 'Hilstar' **new**	CMea
	'Starry Eyes' (p) ♀H4	CMea EAlp GKev GMaP MWea NCGa SRot STes SWvt WFar
	'Storm' (pf)	EMal SAll
	'Strawberries and Cream' (p)	CHar CSBt EBee ECtt LAst LRHS NEgg NOrc SPla SPoG WMnd
	'Strawberry Kiss'	LRHS WWeb
*	***strictus*** subsp. ***pulchellus***	CPBP GCrs
	subacaulis	GAbr NGdn NLar
	- subsp. ***brachyanthus***	NMen WAbe
	- - 'Murray Lyon'	NHar WThu
	suendermannii	see *D. petraeus*
	'Summerfield Adam' (p)	SAll
	'Summerfield Amy Francesca' (p)	SAll
	'Summerfield Blaze' (p)	SAll
	'Summerfield Debbie' (p)	SAll
	'Summerfield Emma Louise' (p)	SAll
	'Summerfield Rebecca' (p)	SAll
	(Sunflor Series) 'Sunflor Althea'	NBlu
	- 'Sunflor Campari'	NBlu
	- 'Sunflor Original'	NBlu
	- 'Sunflor Pink Campari'	NBlu
	- 'Sunflor Surprise'PBR	NBlu
	'Sunray' (b)	SAll
	'Sunstar' (b)	SAll
§	***superbus***	EGoo MNFA MSal NDov WHal WHer WKin WMoo WPer WRHF
	- 'Crimsonia'	MBrN WOut WPtf
	- var. ***longicalycinus***	MNrw MSte WHer
I	- 'Primadonna'	WPer WPtf
*	- 'Rose'	WPer
	- 'Snowdonia'	WPer
	- subsp. ***speciosus***	GKev
	'Susan' (p)	SAll
	'Susannah' (p)	SAll
*	'Susan's Seedling' (p)	SAll
	'Swanlake' (p)	SAll
	'Sway Belle' (p)	SBai
	'Sway Delight' (p)	SBai
	'Sway Sorbet' (p)	SBai
	'Sweet Sophie' (pf)	CNMi
	'Sweet Sue' (b)	SAll
	'Sweetheart Abbey' (p)	GBuc IGor SSvw WKin
	sylvestris	SSvw
	'Syston Beauty' (p)	WKin
	'Tamsin' (p) ♀H4	WKin
	'Tamsin Fifield' (b) ♀H4	SAll
	'Tatra Fragrance' (p)	CMdw
	'Tayside Red' (M)	EMal SAll
	the Bloodie pink	see *D.* 'Caesar's Mantle'
	'Thomas' (p)	CFis
	'Thora' (M)	EMal SAll
	Tickled Pink = 'PP11'	CBgR EAlp EWll LAst LRHS SPoG WWeb
	'Tiny Rubies'	see *D. gratianopolitanus* 'Tiny Rubies'
	'Toledo' (p)	WKin
	'Tony's Choice' (pf)	CNMi
	'Treasure' (p)	ECho
	'Trevor' (p)	SAll

turkestanicus	MWea NBir WGwG
'Tweedale Seedling'	GBuc
Tyrolean trailing carnations	SAll
'Unique' (p)	MNrw SAll SSvw WHoo WKin WOFF
'Ursula Le Grove' (p)	IGor SSvw WKin WOFF
'Valda Wyatt' (p) 🏆H4	CBcs EBee ELan EPfP LAst LRHS NEgg SAll SBai SPla SPoG SRGP SWvt WMnd
'Viv Masters' **new**	SPhx
'W.A. Musgrave'	see *D.* 'Musgrave's Pink'
'W.H. Brooks' (b)	SAll
'Waithman Beauty' (p)	CTri ECGP ECtt GAbr MBar SAll SBla WHoo WKin WPer WTin
'Waithman's Jubilee' (p)	SAll SRms WSHC
'Warden Hybrid' (p)	CMea CTri ECho ECtt EPfP EWin GMaP LAst LRHS MWea SHGN SPoG SWvt WAbe WFar WLin
'Wedding Bells' (pf)	SAll
'Weetwood Double' (p)	CFee WSPU
weyrichii	CLyd ECho
'Whatfield Anona' (p)	SAll
'Whatfield Beauty' (p)	CPBP ECho ECtt ELan LRHS
'Whatfield Brilliant' (p)	ECho
'Whatfield Cancan' (p) 🏆H4	CMea ECho ECtt EWin LHop LRHS MWgw NCGa NEgg NPri SAll SBch SPoG SWvt WWFP
'Whatfield Cream Lace'	NWCA
'Whatfield Cyclops' (p)	CLyd ECho LRHS SAll WKin
'Whatfield Dawn' (p)	CLyd ECho
'Whatfield Dorothy Mann' (p)	ECho SAll
'Whatfield Fuchsia Floss' (p)	CLyd SAll
'Whatfield Gem' (p)	CHVG CLyd CPBP ECho ECtt ELan EWin LAst LRHS MSte MWgw NPri SAll SWvt WBVN WFar WKin WPer
'Whatfield Joy' (p)	CLyd ECho ECtt ELan EPfP EPot EWin LBee LRHS MHer NMen NPri SAll WFar WPat
'Whatfield Magenta' (p) 🏆H4	CLyd ECho ELan EPfP EPot LBee LEdu LRHS NMen NWCA SAll SPoG WAbe WEas
'Whatfield Mini' (p)	SAll SRms WPer
'Whatfield Miss' (p)	SAll
'Whatfield Misty Morn' (p)	ECho SAll
'Whatfield Peach' (p)	SAll
'Whatfield Pretty Lady' (p)	ECho SAll
'Whatfield Rose' (p)	ECho EPot
'Whatfield Ruby' (p)	CEnt ECho ELan LAst LRHS NWCA SAll WFar WPer
'Whatfield Supergem' (p)	CLyd ECho ECtt EPot
'Whatfield White' (p)	ECho ECtt EWTr LRHS SAll SRms
'Whatfield White Moon' (p)	ECho
'Whatfield Wisp' (p)	CPBP CTri EAlp ECho EPot EWin GAbr GEdr MRav NBir NMen NWCA
'White and Crimson' (p)	SAll
'White Joy'PBR (p) 🏆H4	MRav SPoG
'White Ladies' (p)	ELan MRav SAll WKin
'Whitecliff' (b)	SAll
'Whitehill' (p) 🏆H4	ECho EPot MHer NMen NWCA SIng
'Whitesmith' (b) 🏆H4	SAll
'Whitford Belle' (p)	SBai
'Widecombe Fair' (p) 🏆H4	CCge CTri EBee ECtt ELan LRHS MLHP SAll SPoG SRms
'Wild Velvet' (p)	WKin
'William Brownhill' (p)	SSvw WKin
'Winnie Lesurf' (b)	SAll
'Zebra' (b)	SAll
zederbaueri	SIng

Diarrhena (*Poaceae*)

americana	EPPr GFor XIsg
japonica	EPPr GFor LBBr LRav XIsg
* ***mandschurica***	EPPr
obovata	EPPr LBBr

Diascia ✿ (*Scrophulariaceae*)

'Appleby Appleblossom'	LSou
'Appleby Apricot'	NDov
'Apricot'	see *D. barberae* 'Hopleys Apricot'
barberae	ELan
- 'Belmore Beauty' (v)	CCge ECtt EMan EWes EWin LIMB LSou MHer
- 'Blackthorn Apricot' 🏆H3-4	EAlp ECha ECtt EDAr ELan EPfP EShb GBuc LAst LRHS MHer MRav MSte SBla SMrm SPav SPer SPlb SPoG SWvt WFar WPer WSHC
- 'Crûg Variegated' (v)	EMan
§ - 'Fisher's Flora' 🏆H3-4	EPyc NDov WFar
- 'Fisher's Flora' x 'Lilac Belle'	ECtt SHFr
§ - 'Hopleys Apricot'	EPfP
§ - 'Ruby Field' 🏆H3-4	CMea ECha ECtt EDAr ELan EPfP LAst LRHS MDun MHer MRav NBlu NGdn SBla SPer SPla SPoG SRms SWvt WCFE WFar
Blue Bonnet = 'Hecbon'	ECtt EMan LSou SWvt WFar
'Blush'	see *D. integerrima* 'Blush'
'Coldham'	CMdw EMan
Coral Belle = 'Hecbel'PBR 🏆H3-4	CHar ECtt EMan EPfP EWes EWin LAst LHop LRHS LSou MDun MSte NEgg SIng SPav WFar WPer
cordata misapplied	see *D. barberae* 'Fisher's Flora'
cordifolia	see *D. barberae* 'Fisher's Flora'
'Dark Eyes' 🏆H3-4	MSte
Eclat = 'Heclat'PBR	ECtt WFar
elegans misapplied	see *D. fetcaniensis*, *D. vigilis*
'Elizabeth' 🏆H3-4	WSPU
'Emma'	SWvt
felthamii	see *D. fetcaniensis*
§ ***fetcaniensis***	CMHG CMea EPfP EShb EWin NEgg SPer WBrk WCFE WHal WKif WSPU WWlt
- 'Daydream'	LBuc LRHS WHil WSPU WWeb
flanaganii misapplied	see *D. vigilis*
flanaganii Hiern	see *D. stachyoides*
(Flying Colours Series)	SPoG
Flying Colours Appleblossom = 'Diastara'PBR **new**	
- Flying Colours Apricot = 'Diastina'PBR **new**	SPoG
- Flying Colours Coral = 'Diastis'PBR **new**	SPoG
- Flying Colours Red = 'Diastonia'PBR **new**	SPoG
'Frilly' 🏆H3-4	ECtt MSte
'Hector Harrison'	see *D.* 'Salmon Supreme'
'Hector's Hardy' 🏆H3-4	MSte
Ice Cracker = 'Hecrack'	CMea ECtt ELan EMan EWin LAst LHop LRHS SHGN SPav
Ice Cream = 'Icepol'	CHar CSpe LAst LSou NLar SCoo SMrm
Iceberg = 'Hecice'PBR	CHar CSpe SWvt
§ ***integerrima*** 🏆H3-4	ECha ELan ELon EMan LLWP SBla SGar SPla WCot
- 'Alba'	see *D. integerrima* 'Blush'
§ - 'Blush'	CAby CSpe EGoo EMan MSte NEgg SGar SHGN SMrm
- 'Ivory Angel'	see *D. integerrima* 'Blush'
integrifolia	see *D. integerrima*
'Jack Elliott'	see *D. vigilis* 'Jack Elliott'
'Jacqueline's Joy'	CMea EMan MSte NGdn NPer SBch WBrk WFar
'Joyce's Choice' 🏆H3-4	EWes EWin LRHS MSte SBri WFar
'Kate'	LRHS
'Katherine Sharman' (v)	ECtt EMan EWes EWin LSou NGdn SAga

'Lady Valerie' ♀H3-4	EWes EWin MSte WPer
'Lilac Belle' ♀H3-4	CCge CMea ECtt EDAr ELan EPfP LAst LRHS MHar NEgg NGdn SBch SMrm SPla SPlb SPoG WFar WPer
'Lilac Mist' ♀H3-4	NPer
lilacina* x *rigescens	CCge
Little Dancer = 'Pendan'PBR	LAst LSou SCoo SIng SMrm WGor
Little Dreamer = 'Pender'	SVil
'Louise'	GBuc
'Miro'	NLar
patens	CHll
personata	LHop
Pink Delight = 'Codiink'	WFar
Pink Panther = 'Penther'PBR	ECtt LHop NEgg NLar SCoo SPav SPoG SWvt WGor
'Pink Queen'	ECtt SRms
'Pink Spires'	CElw
Prince of Orange = 'Hopor'PBR	LAst LHop LSou NLar SMrm
Red Ace = 'Hecrace'PBR	CHVG EPfP EWin LAst LHop NEgg NPer SMrm SPav SPoG SWvt
Redstart = 'Hecstart'	ECtt EPfP EWin LAst LHop NGdn SPet SWvt WFar
rigescens ♀H3	CHEx COlW CPrp CSpe CWCL ECha ECtt ELan EPfP EShb ISea LHop MHer MLLN MRav MWrn NPer SAga SPlb SWvt WAbe WCFE WFar WPGP WSHC WSpi
§ - 'Anne Rennie'	EBee ECtt EMan SPoG
- pale	see *D. rigescens* 'Anne Rennie'
'Ruby Field'	see *D. barberae* 'Ruby Field'
'Rupert Lambert' ♀H3-4	EMon GBuc LLWP NDov SBri WLin WPer
§ 'Salmon Supreme'	ECtt ELan EPfP EWin LRHS NGdn NPer SPet SPhx SPoG SRms WFar WMoo WPer
'Selina's Choice'	GBuc
§ ***stachyoides***	SBch
(Sun Chimes Series) Sun Chimes Apricot Delight = 'Codicot'	NPri WFar
- Sun Chimes Blush = 'Codiblim'	NPri
- Sun Chimes Blush Delight = 'Codiush'	WFar
- Sun Chimes Peach = 'Codipeim'	LAst
- Sun Chimes Denim **new**	NPri
Susan = 'Winsue'PBR	WFar
tugelensis	WFar
'Twinkle' ♀H3-4	ECtt EPfP LAst LRHS NBir NGdn NPer SPet WFar
* 'Twins Gully'	SMrm
§ ***vigilis*** ♀H3	CFee CMHG CMea CPLG ECha EDAr EPfP EWin GMaP LAst LRHS MCot NBro NEgg SGar WHal
§ - 'Jack Elliott'	EWin SPla WCFE
(Whisper Series) Whisper Apricot Improved = 'Balwhisaptim'	SCoo
- Whisper Cranberry Red = 'Balwhiscran'PBR	NPri SCoo
- Whisper Lavender Pink = 'Balwhislapi'PBR	NPri
- Whisper Tangerine = 'Balwhistang' **new**	LSou NPri SGar
- Whisper White = 'Balwhiswhit'PBR **new**	NPri SGar
'White Cloud'	WHil WSPU
(Wink Series) Wink Garnet Red **new**	WHlf
- Wink Lavender Pink = 'Balwinlapi'PBR	NBlu WHlf
- Wink Orange = 'Balwinorg' **new**	NPri WHlf
- Wink Strawberry Improved = 'Balwinimstr'	NPri WHlf
- Wink White = 'Balwinwite' **new**	NPri WHlf

Dicentra ✿ (*Papaveraceae*)

CC 4452	CPLG
'Adrian Bloom'	EBee EBrs ECho ECtt EHrv EPfP EPla GSki MBNS NBid NCob NPri NSti SCoo SPer SWvt WBrE WFar WMnd WMoo
'Angel Heart'	MBNS NGdn
'Bacchanal' ♀H4	More than 30 suppliers
'Boothman's Variety'	see *D.* 'Stuart Boothman'
'Bountiful'	EBee GMaP GSki LRHS MLLN MNFA MRav NCob NGdn NSti SPer SPla SWvt
'Brownie'	GBuc
canadensis	CLAP EPot GBuc GSki MAvo MTho NLar NSti WCru WHal
'Candy Hearts'	EBee ELan ENot EPfP IPot LFur MBNS NBPC NBro NCob NGdn NLar NSti
'Coldham'	WCru WSHC WTin
cucullaria	CElw CLAP CStu CWCL EBee EBrs ECho EPot ERos GBuc GCrs GEdr GGar GSki LRHS MRav MTho NDov NMen NWCA SBla SPhx WAbe WBVN WCru WLin
- 'Carl Gehenio' **new**	SBla
- 'Pittsburg'	EBee EPPr GBuc SCnR WCot
* 'Dark Stuart Boothman'	ECho
'Dragon Heart'	MBNS
eximia misapplied	see *D. formosa*
eximia (Ker Gawl.) Torr.	CSpe NEgg SWat
- 'Alba'	see *D. eximia* 'Snowdrift'
§ - 'Snowdrift'	CLAP EBee ECho ECtt EHrv ELan EPfP MBri MDun MTho NGdn NRnb SPoG SRms WFar WMnd WMoo WPnP WPrP
§ ***formosa***	CBcs CTri EBee ECha EHrv ELan EPfP GGar GSki LAma LAst LBMP LRHS MLHP NBro NCob NGdn NMen NOrc NPri NSti SIng SPla SPlb SPoG SRms WBrE WEas WFar WMoo
- ***alba***	CPLG CTri ECha GAbr GMaP MLHP MWrn NBir SPla SRms STes WCAu WCru WFar
- 'Aurora'	EBee EBrs ECho ELon GBin GSki LAst LCro LRHS MRav NBPC NCGa NGdn NRnb NSti SPer SPet SPoG SWvt WFar WMnd WPnP
- 'Cox's Dark Red'	CLAP EBee EWes GBuc NMen
- dark	WMoo
- subsp. ***oregana***	CLAP EBee EPPr GAbr GBuc GCrs GGar NBre NChi NMen WAbb WCru WHal
- - 'Rosea'	EPPr
- 'Spring Gold'	ECha WMoo
'Ivory Hearts'PBR	CLAP EBee ELan ENot EPPr EPfP GBri LRHS MBNS NBro NCGa NCob NLar NSti SPer
'King of Hearts'	More than 30 suppliers
'Langtrees' ♀H4	More than 30 suppliers
lichiangensis	WCru
- GWJ 9376	WCru
'Luxuriant' ♀H4	CBcs EBee EBrs ECho ECtt ELan EPfP GAbr GSki MBri MLLN MRav NCob NPri SMer SPer SPoG SRms STes SWat SWvt WBVN WBor WCAu WCot WCra WFar WLin WMoo WPnP

macrantha	CAby CDes CLAP EBee ECha EPfP GBuc GCra LAma MTho SMad WCru WPGP WSHC
macrocapnos	CBcs CFir EBee EMil EPfP GBuc GQui IDee MDKP MTho MWgw NSti WCru
'Paramount'	GBin
'Pearl Drops'	CElw EHrv ELan GBuc GGar GMaP MRav NBid NEgg NGdn NMen SPla SRms WAbb WEas WMoo WTin
§ ***scandens***	CMHG CRHN CSpe CStu EBee ECho EPfP ITim LAst MCCP MTho MWgw NCob NLar SHGN WCru WSHC WSPU
- GWJ 9438	WCru
- SDR 3804	GKev
- 'Shirley Clemo'	CPLG
'Silver Beads'	ECho
Snowflakes = 'Fusd'	EWes MCCP MRav NBre NDov
spectabilis ♀H4	More than 30 suppliers
- 'Alba' ♀H4	More than 30 suppliers
- 'Gold Heart'PBR	CBow EBrs EMan ENot EPfP GBri MRav NLar NSti SPoG WFar
'Spring Morning'	CElw CMHG CMil CSam EBee EHrv EPPr EPfP MHar NBre NSti WEas WRHF
§ 'Stuart Boothman' ♀H4	More than 30 suppliers
thalictrifolia	see *D. scandens*
torulosa B&SWJ 7814	WCru

Dichelostemma (*Alliaceae*)

§ ***capitatum*** NNS 95-213	WCot
congestum	CAvo CFFs EBee EBrs ECho EPot ERos LEdu WCot
§ ***ida-maia***	CAvo CFFs CTca EBee EBrs ECho EPot GAbr GCrs ILad LEdu LRHS WCot
- 'Pink Diamond'	EBee EBrs ECho GCrs LEdu
multiflorum	WCot
pulchellum	see *D. capitatum*
volubile	WCot
- NNS 95-220	WCot

Dichondra (*Convolvulaceae*)

argentea 'Silver Falls'	CSpe EShb LAst LSou NPri SCoo SPoG WPtf
§ ***micrantha***	EShb XPep
repens misapplied	see *D. micrantha*

Dichopogon (*Anthericaceae*)

strictus	ECou

Dichorisandra (*Commelinaceae*)

* ***pendula***	MJnS
thyrsiflora	MJnS

Dichroa (*Hydrangeaceae*)

Guiz 48 new	CKob
febrifuga	CAbb CBcs CDoC CHEx CHll CKob CMil CPLG CWib EBee ELan EWes LRHS SOWG WCot WCru WOVN WPGP
- B&SWJ 2367	WCru
- HWJK 2430	WCru
- pink-flowered	CHEx
hirsuta B&SWJ 8207 from Vietnam new	WCru
aff. ***hirsuta*** B&SWJ 8371 from Lao	WCru
- from Thailand	CKob
versicolor	CKob
- B&SWJ 6565	WCru
aff. ***versicolor***	WPGP
- Guiz 48	WPGP

Dichromena see *Rhynchospora*

Dicksonia ✿ (*Dicksoniaceae*)

antarctica ♀H3	More than 30 suppliers
berteriana	WRic
fibrosa ♀H3	CAbb CBcs CDTJ CTrC EAmu ETod IDee SChr SPoG WRic
sellowiana	LPal WRic
squarrosa ♀H2	CAbb CBcs CCCN CDTJ CTrC ETod LPan NBlu NMoo SAPC SArc SPoG WRic

Dicliptera (*Acanthaceae*)

§ ***suberecta***	CDes CHal CHll CMdw EBee EMan ERea EShb LHop LSou MWea SHFr SOWG SRkn WCot WDyG WPGP WSHC XPep

Dicoma (*Asteraceae*)

anomala new	SPlb

Dicranostigma (*Papaveraceae*)

lactucoides CC 3756	WRos
leptopodum	CSpe

Dictamnus ✿ (*Rutaceae*)

albus	More than 30 suppliers
§ - var. ***purpureus*** ♀H4	More than 30 suppliers
* - var. ***roseus*** new	WCot
caucasicus	SMHy
fraxinella	see *D. albus* var. *purpureus*
tadshikorum	EBee

Dictyosperma (*Arecaceae*)

album	LPal

Didymochlaena (*Dryopteridaceae*)

lunulata	see *D. truncatula*
§ ***truncatula***	CHal MBri XBlo

Dieffenbachia (*Araceae*)

'Camille' (v) ♀H1	LRHS
'Compacta' (v)	LRHS

Dierama ✿ (*Iridaceae*)

ambiguum	CStu EWld SHFr
argyreum	CBgR CCCN CElw IBlr ITer LFur NFir SAga WCot WKif
'Ariel'	IBlr
'Ballerina'	CFir
'Black Knight'	CPrp IBlr
'Blush'	IBlr
'Candy Stripe'	GBri GSki STes
'Castlewellan'	WCra
'Cherry Chimes'	CPen EBee ENot IBal LBuc MGos
cooperi	CElw CPrp GBri IBlr LFur WCot
'Coral Bells'	CDes WPGP
dissimile new	NFir
'Donard Legacy'	GBri IBlr SKHP
§ ***dracomontanum***	More than 30 suppliers
- JCA 3.141.100	WPGP
- dwarf, pale pink-flowered	WWeb
- Wisley Princess Group	LCro MBri
dracomontanum x ***pulcherrimum***	SMad
dubium	IBlr
ensifolium	see *D. pendulum*
erectum	CBgR CCCN CHid CLAP IBlr NLar WCot WLin
'Fairy Bells'	CPen EBee IPot MBNS NCob
floriferum	IBlr
formosum	CGHE WPGP
galpinii	CGHE CLAP GSki MWrn NFir NLar STes WLin WPGP

grandiflorum	ECho IBlr WCru
'Guinevere'	More than 30 suppliers
igneum	More than 30 suppliers
- CD&R 278	CPou WBVN
insigne	EBee
'Iris'	IBlr
jucundum	CPne EBee GBri GBuc MLLN
'Knee-high Lavender'	CDes CSpe EPla SAga WPGP
'Lancelot'	More than 30 suppliers
latifolium	CGHE CHid EBee GSki IBlr NFir SMad
luteoalbidum	CDes CLAP CStu EBee WPGP
'Mandarin'	CDes IBlr WPGP
medium	CGHE CPen CWsd EBee GSki SMrm SWat WCot WPGP
'Milkmaid'	CPrp IBlr
'Miranda'	CHFP CPen EBee ERou GKev LFur MBNS NCob NCot NFir NSti SDnm WCot WSpi WTMC
mossii	CCCN EBee GAbr IBlr MWrn NBre NLar SPlb SPoG WLin WPGP
nixonianum	IBlr
'Oberon'	EBee MRav
'Pamina'	CPrp IBlr
'Papagena'	IBlr
'Papageno'	IBlr
pauciflorum	CBgR CFir CGHE CHid CPLG CPrp CStu CWCL CWib EBee EDAr ERos GSki MHer MWrn NBir NEgg NFir NLAp NLar SWat WCot WHoo WPGP WSHC
- CD&R 197	CPBP MDKP
§ ***pendulum***	More than 30 suppliers
- var. ***pumilum***	EShb
'Petite Fairy' **new**	CPen
pictum	IBlr
Plant World hybrids	MWrn
'Pretty Flamingo'	CPrp IBlr
'Puck'	CDes CPen EBee IBlr IGor MLLN MRav WPGP
pulcherrimum	More than 30 suppliers
- var. ***album***	CCCN CGHE CHar CLAP CWCL ECha ECho EDAr ELan GBuc GKev GSki IBlr IPot LPio LRHS MNrw MWgw NCGa NCob NFir STes WAul WLin WPGP WSpi
- 'Blackbird'	CBgR CCCN CDes CLAP CPLG CSam CWGN EBee ECho EDAr ELan EPfP EPla GAbr GKev IBlr ITim LPio LSRN MHer NCGa NLar SGar SPoG SSwd STes WCot WLin WPGP
- dwarf	GSki IPot
- 'Falcon'	IBlr
- 'Flamingo'	IBlr
- 'Flaring Tips'	IPot
- lilac-flowered	GAbr
- 'Merlin'	More than 30 suppliers
- 'Pearly Queen'	EBee
- 'Peregrine'	WPGP
- 'Red Orr'	ITim
- 'Redwing'	IBlr
- Slieve Donard hybrids	CLAP CWCL EBee ECho ECtt EMan GBri GGar IPot ITim LAst LHop LRHS MFOX MHer MWrn SPet WCra WHrl WMnd WSpi
pumilum misapplied	see *D. dracomontanum*
'Purple Passion' **new**	CPen CWGN ENot LBuc
'Queen of the Night'	IBlr
reynoldsii	CAbb CDes CGHE CHid CPrp EBee EMan GBuc GSki IBlr LFur LRHS MLLN MWrn NFir SGar SMad SPlb SPoG STes WAul WBVN WHoo WKif WLin WPGP
'Rich Pink'	CPen
robustum	CGHE CLAP CPou GBri GSki IBlr NFir WBVN WPGP
'Sarastro'	CPrp IBlr
'September Charm'	IBlr
sertum	EBee
'Snowgoose'	WCra
'Tamino'	IBlr
'Tiny Bells'	CDes EDAr WPGP
'Titania'	CPen IBlr
trichorhizum	CBgR CCCN CGHE CLAP CPBP CWCL EBee ECho EDAr EKen GAbr GBri GSki IBlr LFur MNrw MWrn NFir NLar SAga SPoG STes
'Tubular Bells'	IBlr
'Violet Ice'	IBlr
'Westminster Chimes'	CDes EBee IBlr WPGP
Wilside hybrids **new**	CWsd
'Zulu Bells'	ELon

Diervilla ✿ (*Caprifoliaceae*)

lonicera	CHar SLon SMac WFar WHil
middendorffiana	see ***Weigela middendorffiana***
§ ***sessilifolia***	CBcs CHar CMac CWoW EBee ECrN IDee IMGH LAst MAsh MRav SGar SLon WBVN WBod WCot WFar WMoo WPat
- 'Butterfly'	CMac
x ***splendens***	CAbP CCge CMHG CPLG CWib EBee ELan EPfP LAst LHop LRHS MBNS MBar MGos MRav MSwo NHol SGar SLPl SMac SPer SPla SPoG

Dietes (*Iridaceae*)

bicolor	CAbb CDes CHEx CPen CPne CTrC EMan ERea EShb LEdu LPio LSou SDnm
* ***compacta***	CPen
grandiflora	CAbb CArn CDes CFee CFwr CMdw CPen CPne ECho EDif EMan ERea EShb LEdu LPio NEgg SBch WCot WThu
§ ***iridioides***	CDes CPen CPne CSWP EBee EBrs ECho EShb LPio MSte WPGP

Digitalis ✿ (*Scrophulariaceae*)

ambigua	see *D. grandiflora*
apricot hybrids	see *D. purpurea* 'Sutton's Apricot'
cariensis	EShb SPav
ciliata	CFir CPLG EBee ELan MLLN SPav
davisiana	GBuc MWea MWgw NRnb SPav SPhx STes WHrl WMoo WPer
dubia	EPfP ERCP NBir SDnm SPav WAbe
'Elsie Kelsey'	CEnt CSam MBNS MBri NRnb SDnm SPav SPoG WHil
eriostachya	see *D. lutea*
ferruginea ♀H4	More than 30 suppliers
- 'Gelber Herold'	EBee ERou EWin GMaP LRHS MDKP MSte NBre NLar NRnb SPhx SPoG
- 'Gigantea'	EBee EMan ERou GQue LRHS MBNS MBri NBPC NEgg NPri NRnb NSti SPhx SWat WCot WSel
- var. ***schischkinii***	CPLG EShb MAvo NRnb SDnm SPav WBor
'Flashing Spires'	see *D. lutea* 'Flashing Spires'
* ***floribunda***	EBee SPav
fontanesii	CEnt EPPr GBuc
x ***fulva***	MLLN NBir
'Glory of Roundway'	CDes EBla MEHN MFOX MHer WCot WFar
§ ***grandiflora*** ♀H4	More than 30 suppliers
- 'Carillon'	CSam CWan EBee EPau EShb IFoB LDai MBNS MSte NBir NGHP NLar NPri SPhx WGor WGwG WHil WPer WPtf

- 'Dwarf Carillon' — ECtt
- 'Temple Bells' — SWat WPer
heywoodii — see *D. purpurea* subsp. *heywoodii*
'John Innes Tetra' — CSam EBee EShb LRHS SWat WPGP
kishinskyi — see *D. parviflora*
laevigata — CEnt CHar CHrt CSam EBee EBla EBrs ERou MSte NBro NCGa NGHP NRnb SDnm SPav SPhx WMnd WMoo WPer
- white-flowered — NRnb SPhx
lamarckii misapplied — see *D. lanata*
lamarckii Ivanina — EBee
§ ***lanata*** — More than 30 suppliers
- 'Café Crème' — LSou MBri MNHC NBPC WRHF
§ ***lutea*** — More than 30 suppliers
§ - subsp. ***australis*** — EBla LDai SDnm SHFr SPav
§ - 'Flashing Spires' (v) — CBow EKen EMan GBri NBHF NEgg NRnb
- 'Yellow Medley' — WCot
x ***mertonensis*** 🏆[H4] — More than 30 suppliers
- 'Summer King' — CBcs ECtt LSRN NBre NGHP WGor WSel WTMC
micrantha — see *D. lutea* subsp. *australis*
nervosa — SPav
obscura — EBee ECho EHrv ERCP ERou EShb NBir NCob NGHP NPri SBla SDnm SIde SPav WGor WMnd
* - 'Dusky Maid' — NBHF
orientalis — see *D. grandiflora*
§ ***parviflora*** — More than 30 suppliers
- 'Milk Chocolate' — CBcs CMHG CRez CWCL ECtt EPfP GQue LFur LSRN MBri MHer MNHC NBre NEgg NRnb SBHP SIde SPet SSvw WPnP WRHF WSel
purpurea — CArn EBee ECtt EDAr ELau ENot EUnu GPoy MHer MLHP MNHC NBlu NCGa NCob NLan NMir NPri SECG SIde SPlb SPoG SWal WMoo WPer WWFP
- 'Alba' — see *D. purpurea* f. *albiflora*
§ - f. ***albiflora*** — More than 30 suppliers
- - 'Anne Redetzky'[PBR] — EBee ENot GAbr LSou MAvo NBir NSti SPoG WMnd
- - unspotted — CWan EMar
- Camelot Series — NGHP
- - 'Camelot Cream' — EBee NPri
- - 'Camelot Lavender' — EBee NPri
- - 'Camelot Rose' — EBee EWll
- dwarf red-flowered — MBNS
- Excelsior Group — CBcs CHrt CSBt CSam CTri EBee ENot EPfP ERou GKev GMaP LCro MAvo MBri MNHC MWat NMir NVic SMer SPer SPoG SRms SWvt WFar WGor WWeb
- - primrose-flowered — ERou
- - (Suttons; Unwins) 🏆[H4] — ECtt MRav
- - white-flowered — ERou
- Foxy Group — CWib ECtt EHrv MBNS SPet SPoG SRms WFar WHen WWeb
- - 'Foxy Apricot' — CBcs CWCL NSti SPla SWvt WOVN
- - 'Foxy Pink' — NSti SPla
- - 'Foxy Primrose' — NPri
- Giant Spotted Group — ECtt EHrv EPfP LCro LHop LRHS SCoo
- Glittering Prizes Group — SWat
- Gloxinioides Group — ELan ENot EPfP NCob SHFr
- - 'The Shirley' 🏆[H4] — ECtt SGar WGor
§ - subsp. ***heywoodii*** — CHrt EBee ELan GBuc SDnm SPav SPer WMoo
- - 'Silver Fox' — LSRN SPoG WRHF
- 'Jellito's Apricot' — CSam
- 'Pam's Choice' — CHVG CPLG CSpe EBee EMar EWin IPot LAst LHop LRHS LSRN MAvo MNFA MWea NBPC NChi SPer SRGP SWal WBor WHrl WMnd WPnP WRHF
- 'Primrose Carousel' — EBee ECtt EWin MBri MWat NEgg SPhx
- 'Snow Thimble' — EBee EWin GAbr MBri MNFA NCGa NLar NVic STes WCot WWeb
§ - 'Sutton's Apricot' 🏆[H4] — More than 30 suppliers
* - 'Sutton's Giant Primrose' — EMan EWll MAvo
purpurea x ***thapsi*** — WGwG
'Red Skin' **new** — MBNS
sibirica — EBee GBuc NEgg NRnb SPhx WPer WTMC
* ***spaniflora*** — NEgg NLar NRnb SPhx
'Spice Island' — EBee ENot LBuc SHar SPoG
* ***stewartii*** — CDMG CHar CWan ECtt ELan EShb EWes GCra LDai LFur MAvo MBNS MFOX MHar NBPC NChi NRnb SBod SPav WKif WLin WMoo
thapsi — CArn CEnt CWan ECtt ERCP GKev MBNS MLLN NBPC NPri NWCA SBla SBod SDnm SIde SPav WMoo WPer WTMC WWFP
- JCA 410.000 — EBee
- 'Spanish Peaks' — SPoG
trojana — ECtt GBuc SGar
viridiflora — EBee ECtt EDAr EShb MBNS MDKP NBro NChi SGar SPav SPhx SWat WFar WPer
- 'Moss Green' — NBHF
white-flowered, perennial **new** — CDes

dill see *Anethum graveolens*

Dionaea (*Droseraceae*)

muscipula — CSWC LRHS MCCP SHmp WSSs
- 'Akai Ryu' — WSSs
- 'Royal Red' — CSWC
- shark-toothed — CSWC
- 'Spider' — CSWC

Dionysia (*Primulaceae*)

'Annielle' — WAbe
aretioides 🏆[H2] — WAbe
- 'Bevere' — WAbe
- 'Gravetye' — ECho
- 'Phyllis Carter' — ECho
'Charlson Moonglow' — WAbe
'Charlson Terri' — WAbe
'Monika' — WAbe
tapetodes — WAbe
- farinose — ECho

Dioon (*Zamiaceae*)

califanoi — CBrP
caputoi — CBrP
edule 🏆[H1] — CBrP LPal
- var. ***angustifolium*** — CBrP
mejiae — CBrP LPal
merolae — CBrP
rzedowskii — CBrP LPal
spinulosum — CBrP LPal

Dioscorea (*Dioscoreaceae*)

CC 4500 — MGol
CC 4701 — MGol
araucana — LSou
batatas — ELau LEdu MGol MSal
deltoidea — CPLG
elephantipes 🏆[H1] — EShb
japonica — CAgr EShb ITer WBVN
nipponica — EWld MSal
villosa — CArn ELau MSal

Diosma (*Rutaceae*)

ericoides	SWvt
- 'Pink Fountain'	EBee LBuc SPoG
- 'Sunset Gold'	EBee LBuc SCoo SPoG
hirsuta 'Silver Flame'	LBuc

Diosphaera (*Campanulaceae*)

asperuloides	see *Trachelium asperuloides*

Diospyros (*Ebenaceae*)

austroafricana	SPlb
* ***hyrcanum*** **new**	NLar
kaki (F)	CAgr CBcs CMCN CTho EPfP ERom LPan MPRe NLar
- 'Fuyu' **new**	CAgr
- 'Kostata'	CAgr
- 'Mazelii' **new**	CAgr
lotus	CAgr CBcs CLnd CMCN CTho LEdu MBri NLar SPlb WFar WPGP
- (f)	CAgr
- (m)	CAgr
lycioides	EShb SPlb
rhombifolia	WPGP
virginiana (F)	CAgr CBcs CMCN CTho EPfP NLar SSpi

Dipcadi (*Hyacinthaceae*)

serotinum subsp. ***lividum***	WPGP

Dipelta (*Caprifoliaceae*)

floribunda ♀H4	CBcs CBrm CDul CMCN CPMA EBee ELan EMil EPfP LHop LRHS MBlu NLar SPer SSpi SSta WPGP WPat
ventricosa	CAbP CBcs CGHE CPMA CPle EPfP LRHS MAsh MBlu MBri NLar SPoG SSpi WFar WPGP WPat
yunnanensis	CBcs CPLG CPMA CTri EBee ELan EMil EPfP LBuc LRHS MWea NLar SSpi SSta WPGP WPat

Diphylleia (*Berberidaceae*)

cymosa	CLAP ECha GEdr MRav MSal SPhx WCot WCru WTin
grayi	CLAP GEdr WCru
sinensis	CLAP EBee GEdr WCru

Dipidax see *Onixotis*

Diplacus see *Mimulus*

Dipladenia see *Mandevilla*

Diplarrhena (*Iridaceae*)

§ ***latifolia***	EPot GGar GMac IBlr WAbe
- Helen Dillon's form	IBlr
moraea	CAbP CDes CMea CStu CWCL CWsd EBee ECho EGle GMac GSki IBlr IFoB ITim LRHS MDun NCGa NLAp SAga WAbe WBrE WCot WPGP WSHC
- ***minor***	IBlr
- 'Slieve Donard'	IBlr
- West Coast form	see *D. latifolia*

Diplazium (*Woodsiaceae*)

wichurae	EPPr

Diplolaena (*Rutaceae*)

dampieri	SOWG

Diplostephium (*Asteraceae*)

alveolatum B&SWJ 10686 **new**	WCru

Diplotaxis (*Brassicaceae*)

muralis	CArn ELau WJek
tenuifolia	NGHP

Dipsacus (*Dipsacaceae*)

§ ***fullonum***	CArn CPrp CWan EDAr EPfP MBri MHer MNHC NBid NDov NMir NPri NVic SBch SIde WHer WJek WSFF
inermis	CPom CSam EBee ECha EMon NBid NDov NLar SPhx WFar WHer
japonicus	MSal
- HWJ 695	WCru
pilosus	CPom NDov
sativus	NLar
strigosus	SPhx
sylvestris	see *D. fullonum*

Dipteracanthus see *Ruellia*

Dipteronia (*Aceraceae*)

sinensis	CBcs CGHE CMCN EBee LRHS MBri NLar WNor WPGP

Disanthus (*Hamamelidaceae*)

cercidifolius ♀H4	CAbP CBcs CMCN EPfP IClo IDee IMGH LRHS NEgg NLar SSpi WPGP
- 'Ena-nishiki' (v)	NLar
- 'Liku'	NLar

Discaria (*Rhamnaceae*)

chacaye	LEdu WPGP

Diselma (*Cupressaceae*)

archeri	CDoC CKen MBar NLar SCoo
- 'Read Dwarf'	CKen

Disphyma (*Aizoaceae*)

crassifolium	SChr

Disporopsis (*Convallariaceae*)

aspersa	CDes CLAP CWsd EBee EPPr EWld LEdu WCru WPGP
- tall	WCru
fuscopicta	CBct CExc CLAP EBee EHrv EPPr MAvo WCru WTin
longifolia	CLAP
- B&SWJ 5284	WCru
* ***luzoniensis*** B&SWJ 3891	WCru
'Min Shan'	CBct ELon
* ***nova*** **new**	EBee
§ ***pernyi***	More than 30 suppliers
- B&SWJ 1490	WFar
- B&SWJ 1864	EPPr WCru
- 'Bill Baker'	EBee MAvo
taiwanensis	CAvo
- B&SWJ 3388	WCru
undulata	WCru

Disporum (*Convallariaceae*)

austrosinense B&SWJ 9777 **new**	WCru
bodinieri	CDes EBee LEdu
aff. ***bodinieri*** **new**	WPGP
cantoniense	CDes CFir CLAP CPom EBee GEdr LEdu WCot WCru WFar WPGP WWst
- B&L 12512	CLAP
- B&SWJ 1424	WCru
- DJHC 98485	CDes
I - 'Aureovariegata'	CDes EBee WCot
- var. ***cantoniense*** f. ***brunneum*** B&SWJ 5290	WCru

- 'Green Giant'	CDes
- var. ***kawakamii*** B&SWJ 350	WCru
- 'Night Heron'	SKHP WCot
flavens	CBct CDes CGHE CLAP CPom CStu EBee ECho EMan EPfP LBBr LEdu NBid SBch SMHy WFar WPGP WSHC WTin
- B&SWJ 872	WCru
* ***flavum***	ECho LRHS
hookeri	CLAP CPom EBee EBrs ECho EPot GGar MAvo NMen WCot WCru
- var. ***oreganum***	EBee GCrs IBlr WCru
lanuginosum	CBct GCrs GEdr MAvo WCot WCru
leschenaultianum B&SWJ 9484 **new**	WCru
leucanthum B&SWJ 2389	WCru
longistylum L 151 **new**	WCru
lutescens	WCru
maculatum	CBct CLAP SMac WCru
megalanthum	CLAP EHrv WCot WCru
- CD&R 2412B	EPPr LBBr
nantouense	CDes CStu LEdu WCot WPGP
- B&SWJ 359	CBct EBee WCru
sessile	EBee ECho GGar GMaP LEdu WCru
- AGSJ 146	NMen
- B&SWJ 2824	WCru
I - 'Aureovariegatum' (v)	ECho WCru
- 'Cricket'	EBee GEdr
I - 'Robustum Variegatum'	EBee MAvo
- 'Variegatum' (v)	CFwr CHEx EBee EBrs ECha ECho ELan EPPr EPfP EPla EPot GEdr GMaP LBBr LEdu LRHS MRav NBid SMac WAul WCot WCru WFar WHil WPGP WPnP
- 'White Lightning' (v)	WCot
shimadae B&SWJ 399	WCru
smilacinum	NLar WCru WFar
- B&SWJ 713	WCru
* - 'Aureovariegatum' (v)	MAvo WCot WCru
- double-flowered (d)	GCrs GEdr WCru
- pink	WCru
smithii	CBct CPom CStu EBee EBrs ECho EPfP EPot ERos GBuc GCrs GEdr GGar ITim LEdu NBir NMen WCot WCru WPGP
- 'Riele'	SBla
taiwanense B&SWJ 1513	WCru
- B&SWJ 2018	WCru
trabeculatum 'Nakafu'	WCru
uniflorum	CWsd LEdu WCru
- B&SWJ 651	WCot WCru
viridescens	CBct LEdu SKHP WCru
- B&SWJ 4598	WCru

Distictis (*Bignoniaceae*)

buccinatoria	SOWG
'Mrs Rivers'	SOWG

Distylium (*Hamamelidaceae*)

myricoides	CMCN NLar WFar
racemosum	CBcs CMac EPfP LRHS MBlu MBri NLar SHBN SLPl SLon SReu SSta WBVN WFar WSHC

Diuranthera see *Chlorophytum*

Dizygotheca see *Schefflera*

elegantissima	see *Schefflera elegantissima*

Dobinea (*Podoaceae*)

vulgaris B&SWJ 2532	WCru

Dodecatheon (*Primulaceae*)

alpinum	EBee GEdr GKev NHar SRms WAbe
- subsp. ***alpinum*** NNS 04-128 **new**	GKev
amethystinum	see *D. pulchellum*
'Aphrodite'^{PBR}	EBee EMan MBri NLar WAul WTMC
austrofrigidum	NHar
clevelandii	EBee MDKP
- subsp. ***insulare***	CWsd EBee LRHS NWCA
- subsp. ***patulum***	EBee GBuc LRHS NLAp
conjugens	CPom
cusickii	see *D. pulchellum* subsp. *cusickii*
dentatum $\mathbb{Y}^{H4}$	CElw CPBP EBee GBuc GEdr GKev MDKP MTho NHar NSla WAbe WFar
- subsp. ***ellisiae***	GCrs
frigidum	WAbe
§ ***hendersonii*** $\mathbb{Y}^{H4}$	GBuc NMen SRms
integrifolium	see *D. hendersonii*
§ ***jeffreyi***	EBee EBrs EPPr GSki LRHS MBri NBPC NBid NCGa NLAp NLar NMen NMyG SBla WAbe WBor WFar WLin
- 'Rotlicht'	SRms WPer
* x ***lemoinei***	WAbe
§ ***meadia*** $\mathbb{Y}^{H4}$	More than 30 suppliers
- from Cedar County	WAbe
- f. ***album*** $\mathbb{Y}^{H4}$	CBcs CFwr CSWP CStu CTri EBee EBrs ECho EGle ELan EPfP EPot GEdr GGar GSki LAma LHop LRHS MNFA MTho NHol NMen NMyG SBla SPoG SRms SWvt WPnP WSpi
- 'Aphrodite'	NBPC
* - 'Goliath'	GSki NLar WMoo
- membranaceous	WAbe
- 'Purple Rose'	NEgg
- 'Queen Victoria'	EBee EBrs ECho GSki MAvo SMeo SRGP WFar WPnP
pauciflorum misapplied	see *D. pulchellum*
pauciflorum (Dur.) E. Greene	see *D. meadia*
poeticum	SBla
§ ***pulchellum*** $\mathbb{Y}^{H4}$	CStu GCrs GEdr GKev GSki LHop LRHS MNrw NLAp NMen SIng WPer
- ***album***	SIng
§ - subsp. ***cusickii***	NWCA SRms
- subsp. ***pulchellum*** 'Red Wings'	CFwr CMea EBee EBrs ECho EPot ERou GEdr MDKP NMen NSla NWCA SMeo WHoo WLin WPnP
- ***radicatum***	see *D. pulchellum*
- 'Sooke's Variety'	CStu WAbe
radicatum	see *D. pulchellum*
redolens	EBee GKev NHar
tetrandrum	see *D. jeffreyi*

Dodonaea (*Sapindaceae*)

viscosa	CTrC ECou SPlb XPep
- (f)	ECou
- (m)	ECou
- 'Picton' (f)	ECou
- 'Purpurea' (m)	ECou
- 'Purpurea'	CAbb CBcs CDoC CPLG CPne CTrC EBee ECou EMan EShb IClo ISea LRav LSou MAsh WGer XPep
- 'Purpurea' (f)	ECou
- 'Red Wings' (f)	ECou

Doellingeria (*Asteraceae*)

scabra	see *Aster scaber*

Dolichos (*Papilionaceae*)

purpureus	see *Lablab purpureus*

Dombeya (*Sterculiaceae*)

burgessiae	IDee SOWG

calantha new	CCCN
x ***cayeuxii*** new	CCCN

Dondia see *Hacquetia*

Doodia (*Blechnaceae*)

aspera	WPrP WRic
§ ***caudata***	WRic
media	GBin LTwo MAvo MGos WRic
squarrosa	see *D. caudata*

Doronicum (*Asteraceae*)

austriacum	NBid NBre
carpetanum	CSam
cataractarum	NBre
caucasicum	see *D. orientale*
§ ***columnae***	CBcs EBee GKev
cordatum	see *D. columnae*
§ x ***excelsum*** 'Harpur Crewe'	CPSs CPrp EBee ERou LEdu MNFA MRav NBre NPer NVic WCAu WEas
'Finesse'	EBee EDAr EPfP EWin NBre SPoG SRms WLin WMoo
'Little Leo'	COlW EBee ELan EMan ENot GMaP LHop LRav MAvo MHer MLHP NCGa NEgg NLar NVic SAga SPet SPoG SRGP STes WBVN WBrE WWeb
§ ***orientale***	CWan EBee EPfP LRHS NBid NBlu NEgg SPer SPoG SWat
- 'Goldcut'	NBre NGdn SWal
- 'Leonardo' new	LAst
- 'Magnificum'	CHrt CSBt CSam EBee ECGP EDAr EPfP GAbr GMaP LAst LRHS MBri MHer NMir SPoG SRms WFar
pardalianches	CMea ECha NBre NSco WCot WRHF
- 'Goldstrauss'	EBee
plantagineum new	CPLG
- 'Excelsum'	see *D.* x *excelsum* 'Harpur Crewe'
'Riedels Goldkranz'	WCot

Doryanthes (*Doryanthaceae*)

excelsa	CHEx
palmeri	CHEx

Dorycnium see *Lotus*

Doryopteris (*Adiantaceae*)

pedata	MBri

Douglasia see *Androsace*

vitaliana	see *Vitaliana primuliflora*

Dovea (*Restionaceae*)

macrocarpa	CBig CCCN

Dovyalis (*Flacourtiaceae*)

caffra (F)	CPle XBlo

Doxantha see *Macfadyena*

Draba (*Brassicaceae*)

aizoides	ECho LRHS MWat NBlu SIng SPlb SPoG SRms
aizoon	see *D. lasiocarpa*
alticola	EPot
bruniifolia	EBur ECho EWes LRHS
- subsp. ***heterocoma*** var. ***nana***	WLin
bryoides	see *D. rigida* var. *bryoides*
compacta	see *D. lasiocarpa* Compacta Group
crassifolia	ECho
cretica	ECho NMen
cuspidata	EPot
dedeana	ECho EWes
densifolia	WLin
§ ***lasiocarpa***	SGar
§ - Compacta Group	ECho NWCA
longisiliqua 🏆H2	SIng
- EMR 2551	EPot
mollissima	EPot NWCA WAbe
oligosperma subsp. ***subsessilis***	NWCA WLin
ossetica	GKev
paysonii var. ***treleasei***	WAbe
polytricha	WAbe
§ ***rigida*** var. ***bryoides***	ECho ITim WThu
- var. ***imbricata*** f. ***compacta***	EPot
scardica	see *D. lasiocarpa*
sphaeroides	GKev
ventosa	WAbe
yunnanensis	WLin

Dracaena ✿ (*Dracaenaceae*)

congesta	see *Cordyline stricta*
draco 🏆H1	CArn CTrC EShb IDee
fragrans	MBri
- (Compacta Group) 'Compacta Purpurea'	MBri
- - 'Compacta Variegata' (v)	MBri
- (Deremensis Group) 'Lemon Lime' (v) 🏆H1	LRHS MBri
- - 'Warneckei' (v) 🏆H1	MBri
- - 'Yellow Stripe' (v) 🏆H1	MBri
* - ***glauca***	MBri
- 'Janet Craig'	MBri
- 'Massangeana' (v) 🏆H1	MBri
indivisa	see *Cordyline indivisa*
'Lemon Lime Tips'	XBlo
marginata (v) 🏆H1	LRHS MBri XBlo
- 'Colorama' (v)	MBri
- 'Tricolor' (v) 🏆H1	XBlo
sanderiana (v) 🏆H1	LRHS MBri
* ***schrijveriana***	MBri
steudneri	MBri
stricta	see *Cordyline stricta*

Dracocephalum (*Lamiaceae*)

altaiense	see *D. imberbe*
argunense	CWCL GEdr GKev LRHS NLAp SBch SBla SGar SPhx SRms WPat WPer
* - 'Album'	NEgg
- 'Blue Carpet'	CBgR
- 'Fuji Blue'	CEnt CHFP EBee LSRN NEgg NLar SPad
- 'Fuji White'	CEnt EBee EMan GEdr LSRN NEgg SBla SHGN SPhx WPer WWeb
austriacum	WPer
botryoides	EMan NWCA SHGN WMoo WPer
foetidum	GKev
forrestii	EPot
grandiflorum	CBod CEnt CHar CMHG EBee LTwo MMHG NEgg SAga SPhx WFar WMoo WPer WWeb
hemsleyanum	LTwo WPat
§ ***imberbe***	MLLN
isabellae	EBrs
mairei	see *D. renatii*
moldavica	EUnu SIde
nutans	NLar
peregrinum	CHar
- 'Blue Dragon'	NChi
prattii	see *Nepeta prattii*
§ ***renatii***	CEnt GEdr SPhx WPer
rupestre	EBee GBri MBri NLAp

	ruyschiana	CBcs EBee ELan EMan GEdr LRHS MLLN MRav NLar NWCA SPhx
	sibiricum	see *Nepeta sibirica*
	tanguticum	WWeb
*	***tataricum***	EBee
	virginicum	see *Physostegia virginiana*
	wendelboi	MLLN NBir NWCA

Dracunculus (*Araceae*)

	canariensis	CStu ITer WCot
	muscivorus	see *Helicodiceros muscivorus*
§	***vulgaris***	CArn CFwr CHid CMea CPom CSpe CStu EBee EBrs ECho EHrv EMon EPot GGar LEdu LRHS MCCP MRav NWCA SDix SEND WCot WFar WHil WPnP
	- var. ***creticus***	WCot
	- white-flowered	WCot WPnP

Dregea (*Asclepiadaceae*)

	sinensis -	CBcs CCCN CHEx CHll CRHN CSam EBee ELan EPfP ERea EShb EWes LRHS MAsh SBra SOWG SPer SPoG WCot WFar WPGP WSHC
	- 'Variegata' (v)	EWes WCot

Drepanocladus (*Amblystegiaceae*)

	revolvens	EMFW

Drepanostachyum (*Poaceae*)

§	***falcatum***	CAbb
	falconeri J.J.N. Campbell. ex D. McClintock	see *Himalayacalamus falconeri*
	hookerianum	see *Himalayacalamus hookerianus*
§	***khasianum***	CGHE EPla WPGP
§	***microphyllum***	EPla SDry

Drimiopsis (*Hyacinthaceae*)

	maculata	CStu LToo WCot

Drimys (*Winteraceae*)

	aromatica	see *D. lanceolata*
	colorata	see *Pseudowintera colorata*
	granatensis	CGHE WPGP
§	***lanceolata***	More than 30 suppliers
	- (f)	CTrC ECou GGar NCGa SPer
	- (m)	CDoC CTrC ECou GGar SPer
	- 'Mount Wellington'	GBin
	- 'Suzette' (v)	MBlu MGos
*	***latifolia***	CBcs CHEx
	winteri ♀H4	CBcs CDoC CDul CGHE CHEx CMac CPle CPne CSBt CSam CTrG EBee ELan EPfP IArd LHop LRHS NBea SAPC SArc SHBN SLim SPer SPoG WBrE WCwm WFar WGer WPic WSHC
	- var. ***andina***	CPLG EPfP EPla SKHP WPGP
§	- var. ***chilensis***	CDul CPLG EPfP GGar ISea LRHS SKHP SPoG SSpi WCru WPGP
	- Latifolia Group	see *D. winteri* var. *chilensis*

Drosanthemum (*Aizoaceae*)

	hispidum	CStu EAlp ECho ELan EPfP EPot GMaP ITim LRHS MTho NMen NWCA SBHP SIng SPlb SPoG XPep
	speciosum	ECho
*	***sutherlandii***	ECho

Drosera (*Droseraceae*)

	admirabilis	CHew
	aliciae	CSWC SHmp
	andersoniana	EFEx
	anglica	CHew
	ascendens	CHew
	binata	SHmp
§	- subsp. ***dichotoma***	CSWC
	- 'Multifida'	CHew MCCP
	browniana	EFEx
	bulbigena	EFEx
	bulbosa subsp. ***bulbosa***	EFEx
	- subsp. ***major***	EFEx
	callistos	CHew
	capensis	CSWC LRHS MCCP SHmp
	- 'Albino'	MCCP
	- red	CSWC
	citrina	CHew
	dichotoma	see *D. binata* subsp. *dichotoma*
	dichrosepala	CHew
	erythrorhiza	EFEx
	- subsp. ***collina***	EFEx
	- subsp. ***erythrorhiza***	CHew EFEx
	- subsp. ***magna***	EFEx
	- subsp. ***squamosa***	EFEx
	filiformis var. ***filiformis***	CSWC
	gigantea	EFEx
	graniticola	EFEx
	heterophylla	EFEx
	lasiantha new	CHew
	loureiroi	EFEx
	macrantha	EFEx
	- subsp. ***macrantha***	EFEx
	macrophylla subsp. ***macrophylla***	EFEx
	mannii	CHew
	marchantii subsp. ***prophylla***	EFEx
	menziesii subsp. ***basifolia***	EFEx
	- subsp. ***menziesii***	EFEx
	- subsp. ***thysanosepala***	EFEx
	modesta	EFEx
	nidiformis	CHew
	orbiculata	EFEx
	peltata	CSWC EFEx
	platypoda	EFEx
	ramellosa	EFEx
	rosulata	EFEx
	rotundifolia	EBla SHmp WHer
	salina	EFEx
	scorpioides	CSWC SHmp
	slackii	CHew
	spatulata	SHmp
	stelliflora	CHew
	stolonifera subsp. ***compacta***	EFEx
	- subsp. ***humilis***	EFEx
	- subsp. ***porrecta***	EFEx
	- subsp. ***rupicola***	EFEx
	- subsp. ***stolonifera***	EFEx
	tubaestylus	EFEx
	zonaria	EFEx

Drosophyllum (*Droseraceae*)

	lusitanicum	CHew

Dryandra (*Proteaceae*)

	formosa	EShb SPlb

Dryas (*Rosaceae*)

	drummondii	ECho SBla WAbe WFar
§	***integrifolia***	NMen
	- 'Greenland Green'	WAbe
	octopetala ♀H4	CMea CSam ECho EPfP GMaP ITim LHop LRHS MWat NChi NLAp NVic SBla SIng SPoG SRms WFar
	- 'Minor' ♀H4	ECho LBee NMen WAbe
	x ***suendermannii*** ♀H4	EPfP EPot GMaP LRHS NMen WAbe WBVN
	tenella Pursh	see *D. integrifolia*

Dryopteris ✿ (*Dryopteridaceae*)

	from Emei Shan, China	WPGP
	aemula	SRms WRic
§	***affinis*** ♀H4	CBrm CFwr CLAP EBee ECha EMFW EMon EPfP ERod GMaP LBuc MAsh MGos MMoz MPes MRav NBlu NHol NMoo SPer SRms WFib WRic WShi
§	- subsp. ***borreri***	SRms STre
	- subsp. ***cambrensis***	EFer
	- - 'Crispa Barnes'	WPGP
	- - 'Insubrica'	EFer
	- 'Congesta'	CLAP
	- 'Congesta Cristata'	CLAP CWCL EBee EFer EPfP GMaP MAsh NHol NSti SPla SRot
	- Crispa Group	CLAP ENot EWsh GBin LAst LRHS MMoz MPes
§	- 'Crispa Gracilis' ♀H4	CFwr CLAP CPrp EFer ELan EPPr ERod GBin MCCP MPes NBir WRic
*	- 'Crispa Gracilis Congesta'	NHol WBor WFib WPat
§	- 'Cristata' ♀H4	More than 30 suppliers
	- 'Cristata Angustata' ♀H4	CChe CFwr CLAP CPrp EFer ELan EMon ETod GBin MAsh MMoz MPes MWgw NBid NDlv NHol SRms WFib WMoo WPGP WPrP WRic WSpi
	- 'Cristata The King'	see *D. affinis* 'Cristata'
	- 'Grandiceps Askew'	EFer SRms WFib
	- 'Pinderi'	CLAP EBee EFer ELan GBin MPes NHol SEND SRms WRic
	- Polydactyla Group	CLAP GQui MDun SPer WFar
	- 'Polydactyla Dadds'	CFwr CLAP EQua MPes SMac WBor
	- 'Polydactyla Mapplebeck' ♀H4	CLAP GBin NBid NHol SRms WFib WRic
	- 'Revolvens'	CLAP EFer EWsh SRms
	atrata	CWCL LRHS MAsh NMoo
	atrata misapplied	see *D. cycadina*
	x ***australis***	CLAP CRez WRic
	austriaca	see *D. dilatata*
	bissetiana	WRic
	blanfordii	WPGP WRic
	borreri	see *D. affinis* subsp. *borreri*
	buschiana	CLAP EBee MBri MPes MRav NBlu NLar
	carthusiana	CLAP EBee EFer GBin MPes NLar SRms WPtf WRic
	celsa	WRic
	championii	CCCN CLAP WRic
	clintoniana	CFwr CLAP EFer GBin MAsh MPes WPGP WRic
	x ***complexa*** 'Stablerae'	CFwr CLAP GBin WFib WPGP WRic
	- 'Stablerae' crisped	WFib
	coreanomontana	MAsh
	crassirhizoma	CCCN CLAP GBin WRic
	cristata	CFwr CLAP CWCL EBee EMon EPfP MLan MPes WMoo WRic
§	***cycadina*** ♀H4	More than 30 suppliers
	dickinsii	EBee EMon
§	***dilatata*** ♀H4	CBgR CRWN ECha EFer ELan EMon EPfP ERod MAsh MPes MRav MSte MWgw NHol SRms WFib WHal WRic WShi
	- 'Crispa Whiteside' ♀H4	CBgR CFwr CLAP CPrp CWCL EBee EFer EMon EPfP ERod MAsh MBnl MBri MPes MRav NHol NLar NMyG SMac SPlb SRms WFib WPGP WRic
	- 'Grandiceps'	CLAP EFer EMon NHol WFib
	- 'Jimmy Dyce'	CLAP
	- 'Lepidota Crispa Cristata'	CLAP EWsh LRHS MPes WPat
	- 'Lepidota Cristata' ♀H4	CChe CFwr CLAP CMHG CWCL ELan EMon ERod GBin IMGH MAsh NHol NVic SMac SRms WFib WMoo WPrP WRic
	- 'Lepidota Grandiceps'	CFwr CLAP
*	- 'Recurvata'	CLAP CRez WRic
	erythrosora ♀H4	More than 30 suppliers
	- 'Brilliance'	CCCN CLAP CRez
	- 'Prolifera'	see *D. erythrosora* var. *prolifica*
§	- var. ***prolifica*** ♀H4	CChe CLAP MAsh MBnl MGos MMoz MPes MSte NBir NDlv NHol NMyG NSti SPla WCot WFib WPat WRic
	expansa	EMon
	filix-mas ♀H4	CChe CSBt CTri CWCL EBee ECha EHon EMFW ENot EPfP ERod GMaP LCro LEdu LRHS MAsh MMoz MPes MRav MWat NHol NMoo SGar SPer SRms STre WBrk WFar WFib WShi
	- 'Barnesii'	CFwr CLAP CWCL EFer ERod ETod EWsh GBin MAsh MPes MSte NDlv NLar NMoo SPlb SPoG WRic
	- 'Crispa'	CLAP EHon MPes NHol SRms WFib
	- 'Crispa Congesta'	see *D. affinis* 'Crispa Gracilis'
	- 'Crispa Cristata'	CBgR CChe CFwr CLAP CPrp CWCL EFer ELan EMon EPfP ERod GMaP LCro MAsh MBnl MBri MDun MPes MWgw NBid NBir NHol NSti SPoG SRms SWat WBor WFib WGor WRic
	- 'Cristata' ♀H4	CFwr CLAP EFer ELan MMoz MPes NOak NOrc SRms SWat WBVN WMoo
	- Cristata Group	EFer WRic
	- - 'Fred Jackson'	CLAP NHol WFib
*	- 'Cristata Grandiceps'	EFer
	- 'Cristata Jackson'	CLAP SPlb
	- 'Cristata Martindale'	CFwr CLAP NBid NHol SRms WFib
	- 'Depauperata'	CLAP WPGP
	- 'Euxinensis'	CLAP
*	- 'Furcans'	CLAP WRic
	- 'Grandiceps Wills' ♀H4	EMon NBid NHol WFib
	- 'Linearis'	CMHG EFer EHon ELan EMon EWsh MGos NEgg NHol SRms WFib
	- 'Linearis Congesta'	WPGP
	- 'Linearis Cristata'	WRic
	- 'Linearis Polydactyla'	CBgR CBrm CFwr CLAP CWCL EBee EFer EPfP GBin IMGH LRHS MAsh MMoz MPes MWgw NBlu NHol NMoo NMyG SPoG WAbe WFar WIvy WMoo WPtf
	- 'Parsley'	CLAP
*	- Polydactyla Group	MGos MRav
	- 'Rich Beauty'	WBor
I	***filix-mas*** 'Revolvens' **new**	WFib
	goldieana	CFwr CLAP CMHG EBee EFer GBin GMaP LRHS MAsh MPes NBir NCob NEgg NLar NMyG SPoG WCru WFar WFib WMoo WPat WPnP WRic WSpi
	hirtipes	see *D. cycadina*
	hondoensis	WRic
	'Imperial Wizard'	CFir
	intermedia **new**	WRic
	lacera	WRic
	ludoviciana **new**	WRic
	marginalis	CFwr CLAP EBee EKen GBin LRHS MMoz MPes NHol NLar WMoo WRic
	oreades	SRms WAbe
	pacifica	CLAP
	paleacea	CLAP
	pseudofilix-mas	CRez WRic
	pseudomas	see *D. affinis*

pycnopteroides	WRic
x ***remota***	SRms WRic
sieboldii	CFwr CHEx CLAP CWCL EBee ELan EMon ERod EShb GAbr GEdr IMGH LRHS MAsh MAvo MPes MSte NDlv NHol SMac SMad SRms WAbe WCot WCru WFib WMoo WPGP WRic
stewartii	CLAP GBin WRic
tokyoensis	CFwr CLAP CRez EBee GBin MPes MSte NEgg NHol NLar WRic WSpi
uniformis	CLAP ELan EMon
wallichiana ♀H4	More than 30 suppliers

Duchesnea (*Rosaceae*)

chrysantha	see *D. indica*
§ ***indica***	CBgR CPLG CSWP ELon EUnu GAbr IGor LEdu MRav NHol WMoo WOut WRHF
§ - 'Harlequin' (v)	CPLG MCCP MTho
* - 'Snowflake' (v)	WMoo
- 'Variegata'	see *D. indica* 'Harlequin'

Dudleya (*Crassulaceae*)

abramsii subsp. ***affinis*** NNS 01-156	WCot
cymosa subsp. ***paniculata*** NNS 98-221	WCot
- subsp. ***pumila***	WCot
edulis	WCot
farinosa	CHEx
lanceolata	WCot
saxosa subsp. ***aloides*** NNS 99-141	WCot
verityi NNS 01-159	WCot

Dugaldia (*Asteraceae*)

hoopesii	see *Hymenoxys hoopesii*

Dulichium (*Cyperaceae*)

arundinaceum	LAst LLWG

Dunalia (*Solanaceae*)

australis	see *Iochroma australe*
- blue	see *Iochroma australe* 'Bill Evans'
- white	see *Iochroma australe* 'Andean Snow'

Duranta (*Verbenaceae*)

§ ***erecta***	EShb LRHS MJnS
- 'Geisha Girl'	CCCN EShb
plumieri	see *D. erecta*
repens	see *D. erecta*
serratifolia new	EShb

Duvernoia see *Justicia*

aconitiflora	CPLG

Dyckia (*Bromeliaceae*)

frigida	WCot
marnier-lapostollei	WCot
'Morris Hobbs'	EMan WCot
remotiflora	SChr
velascana	CHEx

Dymondia (*Asteraceae*)

margaretae	CFee WAbe
* ***repens***	XPep

Dypsis (*Arecaceae*)

§ ***decaryi***	CCCN EAmu LPal
decipiens	CBrP
§ ***lutescens*** ♀H1	LPal LRHS MBri

Dysosma see *Podophyllum*

E

Ebenus (*Papilionaceae*)

cretica	LEdu XPep

Ecballium (*Cucurbitaceae*)

elaterium	CArn CDTJ LEdu MSal SGar SIde WHer WPGP

Eccremocarpus (*Bignoniaceae*)

scaber	CBcs CEnt CHrt CRHN CTrG EBee ELan ENot EPfP LBMP MBri MEHN MNrw MWgw NPer SGar SLim SRms WBrE
- apricot-flowered	EMar
- 'Aureus'	EPfP GKev MAsh SPoG
- 'Carmineus'	EPfP EWin EWld GGar MAsh SGar SPoG
- cream-flowered new	LRHS
- orange-flowered	MAsh
I - 'Roseus'	EWld NLar SPoG
- 'Tresco Cream'	CSpe EWin

Echeandia (*Liliaceae*)

formosa B&SWJ 9147 new	WCru

Echeveria ✿ (*Crassulaceae*)

B&SWJ 10396 from Guatemala new	WCru
B&SWJ 10277 from Mexico new	WCru
affinis	EBrs MBri
agavoides ♀H1	MRav
* - 'Metallica'	MBri
* 'Black Prince'	CAbb CBow CDoC CTca EBee EMan GBin NPer SPlb SRot WCot WDyG WFar
* ***cana***	CBct EWll SRot
'Crûg Ice'	WCru
x ***derosa***	EPfP
- 'Worfield Wonder' ♀H1	WEas
'Duchess of Nuremberg'	CDoC EBee SRot WFar
elegans ♀H1	CHEx CHal EBee EPfP EWin GAbr MBri SAPC WBrE WDyG WGwG
§ ***gibbiflora*** var. ***cristata***	GAbr
§ - var. ***metallica*** ♀H1	EPfP WEas
* x ***gilva*** 'Red' ♀H1 new	WEas
glauca Baker	see *E. secunda* var. *glauca*
- cristata	see *E. gibbiflora* var. *cristata*
harmsii ♀H1	CHal CSWP WGwG
'Hens and Chicks'	CHEx
'Mahogany'	MAvo
'Meridian'	CHEx
nodulosa	WCot
'Paul Bunyon'	CHal MAvo
peacockii	EBee EWin SPet SPoG SWal WRos
'Perle d'Azur'	CHEx WCot
pulidonis ♀H1	EPfP WCot
pulvinata ♀H1	CHal
rosea	WCot
runyonii 'Topsy Turvy'	CDoC CHEx EBee EPfP SRot
secunda	CAbb STre SWal
§ - var. ***glauca*** ♀H1	CDTJ CHEx CStu EAmu EBee ELan EPfP EShb ETod EWin LPJP MAvo NBir NBlu SArc STrG STre WCot WGwG
* - - 'Gigantea'	NPer
setosa ♀H1	EPfP
- var. ***ciliata***	EShb
shaviana	CBow EBee EWll SRot

Echinacea ✿ (*Asteraceae*)

angustifolia	CArn CBod CCge CWCL EBee EBla EMan EPfP GPoy LPio LRHS MHer MLLN MNHC MSal MWgw NGHP NSti SPhx STes WCAu WCot WSel
'Art's Pride'[PBR]	More than 30 suppliers
'Evan Saul' (Big Sky Series) **new**	WCot
'Fatal Attraction' **new**	EHrv ERou LPio MWea
'Green with Envy' **new**	WCot
Harvest Moon	see *E.* 'Matthew Saul'
Mango Meadowbrite = 'CBG Cone3' **new**	CSpe EBee MAvo NPri WCot
'Matthew Saul' (Big Sky Series) **new**	CHFP CMea EBee EGle LFur LHop LSou MBnl MDKP NCob NDov WCot WCra WGwG
pallida	More than 30 suppliers
paradoxa	More than 30 suppliers
- 'Yellow Mellow'	EKen EPfP IBal LCro NLar SPer
Pixie Meadowbrite = 'CBG Cone 2' **new**	EBee ECtt LFur NDov WCot WCra
§ ***purpurea***	More than 30 suppliers
- 'Alba'	CCge EBla EShb LBMP MNHC NVic
- 'Augustkönigin'	CKno EBee EHrv GSki MSte NBir NCob NEgg NRnb WWlt
- Bressingham hybrids	EBee EBla ELan LRHS MRav MWgw SPer WFar
- dark-stemmed	SAga SPhx
- Doppelganger	see *E. purpurea* 'Doubledecker'
§ - 'Doubledecker'	CBrm CHll CWCL EBee EDAr GWWP ILad ITim LBMP LTwo MCCP MDKP NChi NGHP SMad SPhx STes WHil WPer WSel
- 'Elton Knight' ΨH3 **new**	MBri SRkn
- 'Fancy Frills'	CHar MDKP NBhm NGHP SPoG WCot
- 'Fatal Attraction' **new**	MBri WCot
- 'Fragrant Angel'	EBee ERou IPot MDKP NGHP SPoG WCot
- 'Green Edge'	LCro
- 'Green Eyes'	NBhm NGHP
- 'Hope' **new**	MMHG
- 'Indiaca'	CHFP EBee EMan MBNS NGHP WSpi
- 'Jade'	CSpe EBee EGle EHrv EPfP IBal LCro LPio MBNS MBri NDov NLar NPri
- 'Kim's Knee High'[PBR]	More than 30 suppliers
- 'Kim's Mop Head'	More than 30 suppliers
§ - 'Leuchtstern'	CBrm CKno EBee NBir NBre NDov NGdn NLar NRnb SMad SWat WHal WPer
- 'Little Giant'	EBee NBhm
- 'Magnus' ΨH4	More than 30 suppliers
- 'Maxima'	EBee EHrv LPio LRHS MBnl MLLN NCob NDov WCot WGwG
- 'Pica Bella' **new**	EBee
- 'Prairie Frost' (v)	NGHP
- 'Primadonna Deep Rose'	CEnt MWea NBre NGBl WHrl
- 'Razzmatazz'[PBR] (d)	CKno CWCL EBee ECtt EGle EHrv EPfP ERou EWes IBal IPot LHop LSou MDKP MNrw MWea NCob NGHP NGdn NMoo NPri NSti SPer SPoG WCot WCra WWlt
- 'Robert Bloom'	EBee EBla ECtt EGle EHrv GQue LHop MLLN MNFA NCob NRnb SWat WCAu WCot
- 'Rubinglow'	CBgR CElw CWCL EBee EBla ECha ECtt EHrv IBal LAst LHop MBNS MBnl MBri MSte NBir NCGa NCob NDov NGHP NLar NRnb SPhx SPoG SWvt WCAu
- 'Rubinstern' ΨH4	More than 30 suppliers
- 'Ruby Giant' ΨH4	More than 30 suppliers
- 'Sparkler' (v)	WCot
- 'Sunrise' **new**	MBri
- 'The King'	EBee ECtt IBal LRHS NRnb SRGP WWeb
- 'Verbesserter Leuchtstern'	EBee NBre NGHP NLar
- 'White Lustre'	CHFP EBee ECha EPfP GSki LPio MBNS NBre NDov NGHP NMoo SPav WFar
- 'White Swan'	More than 30 suppliers
'Ruby Glow'	EGle IBal IPot LAst MDKP
'Starlight'	see *E. purpurea* 'Leuchtstern'
'Sunrise' (Big Sky Series) **new**	More than 30 suppliers
'Sunset' (Big Sky Series) **new**	CKno CMil CWCL CWGN EBee EGle EHrv ENot EPfP ERou EWes IBal IPot LDai LFur LPio LRHS LTwo MAvo MBNS MBnl NDov NGHP SPoG WCot WCra WTMC
tennesseensis	CArn CBrm CDes EBee EShb GPoy MNFA
- 'Rocky Top'	More than 30 suppliers
'Twilight' (Big Sky Series) **new**	WCot
'Vintage Wine'[PBR]	CHFP CKno CSpe CWCL CWGN EBee ECtt EGle EHrv ELan ERou GBri GQue IBal IPot LCro LRHS MBNS MLLN NBPC NCob NDov NGHP NSti SPoG WCot WCra

Echinops (*Asteraceae*)

RCB/TQ H-2	WCot
albus	see *E.* 'Nivalis'
araneosus **new**	EBee
§ ***bannaticus***	CBcs EBee GSki NBid WFar WTel
* - 'Albus'	EPfP EWll LAst LRHS NBre NGdn SPoG
- 'Blue Globe'	CMHG COIW CWan EBee EMan EPfP ERou EShb GMaP GSki IBal LAst LBMP LCro LRHS LSRN MBri NCGa NChi NGdn SCoo STes WBrE WCAu WFar WMnd WPer WWeb
- 'Blue Pearl'	CMMP EBee
- 'Taplow Blue' ΨH4	More than 30 suppliers
commutatus	see *E. exaltatus*
§ ***exaltatus***	NBir NBre
maracandicus	EBee WCot
§ 'Nivalis'	CBre EBee ERou LBMP SEND
ritro misapplied	see *E. bannaticus*
§ ***ritro*** L. ΨH4	More than 30 suppliers
- subsp. ***ruthenicus*** ΨH4	ECGP ELan EWTr GBuc IGor MHar MRav NBre WPGP
- - 'Platinum Blue'	CWCL EBee NBPC NLar SPet WMnd WPer
- 'Veitch's Blue' misapplied	see *E. ritro* L.
- 'Veitch's Blue'	More than 30 suppliers
sphaerocephalus	EMan GQue NBid NBre SPlb WPer
- 'Arctic Glow'	More than 30 suppliers
strigosus	EBee NBre
tjanschanicus	EBee EUnu LDai MHar NLar NMoo
tournefortii	GBin

Echinospartum see *Genista*

Echium (*Boraginaceae*)

aculeatum	XPde
- 'Bicolor' **new**	XPde
- 'Rosea' **new**	XPde
amoenum	CFir NWCA
boissieri	CCCN CPLG ELan WOut XPde
brevirame	XPde
§ ***candicans*** ΨH2-3	CAbb CBcs CCCN CCtw CFir CHEx COIW CPLG CTrC EAmu ECre EShb IDee LRHS MGos MPRe SAPC SArc SChr WFar WSpi XPde

	fastuosum	see *E. candicans*
	– 'Ciel' **new**	XPde
	– 'Marine' **new**	XPde
	– 'Rouge' **new**	XPde
	gentianoides	XPde
	– 'Maryvonne'	XPde
	– 'Pablina'	XPde
	giganteum	CHII XPde
	handiense	XPde
	italicum	CCCN CDTJ CPLG EBee NLar SIde XPde
	lusitanicum	CCCN
	– subsp. ***polycaulon***	NEgg WHil WOut XPde
	nervosum	CPLG
	onosmifolium	CHII XPde
§	***pininana*** 𝕐H2-3	More than 30 suppliers
	– 'Pink Fountain'	CCCN CDTJ ECre ELan LSou NLar NRnb XPde
	– 'Snow Tower'	CCCN CDTJ CEnd CPLG ECre ELan EUnu NRnb WSel XPde
	pinnifolium	see *E. pininana*
	plantagineum	CCCN XPde
	rossicum	SPlb
	rosulatum	CCCN XPde
	russicum	CCCN CPLG EBee EShb EWll MNFA NBPC NCGa NChi NLar SDnm SGar SIde SPav SPhx WAul WCot WWeb XPde
	simplex	CCCN CDTJ WSpi XPde
	strictum	CCCN XPde
	sventenii	XPde
	tuberculatum	CCCN CDTJ CFir EWld NLar SBod SPhx WHil WMoo WOut XPde
	vulgare	CArn CCCN EGoo ELan EOHP MHer MNHC MSal NLar NMir NPri NSco SBch SECG SIde WBrE WHer WJek WPnn WSel
	– Drake's form	CCge SGar
	wildpretii 𝕐H2-3	CBow CCCN CDTJ EWll ITer SMad XPde
	– subsp. ***wildpretii***	SPav

Eclipta (*Asteraceae*)

	alba	see *E. prostrata*
§	***prostrata***	MSal

Edgeworthia (*Thymelaeaceae*)

§	***chrysantha***	CBcs CPMA CTri CWib EPfP IClo LBuc LPan MBri MGos NPal SChF SKHP SPer WBod WSHC WSpi
	– B&SWJ 1048	WCru
I	– 'Grandiflora'	CPMA MGos NLar
§	– 'Red Dragon'	CPMA
	– f. ***rubra*** hort.	see *E. chrysantha* 'Red Dragon'
	gardneri	NLar WCot
	papyrifera	see *E. chrysantha*

Edraianthus (*Campanulaceae*)

	croaticus	see *E. graminifolius*
	dalmaticus	GKev SBla
	dinaricus	NMen NSla
§	***graminifolius***	ECho GKev NLAp NMen WFar
	owerinianus **new**	CPBP GKev
§	***pumilio*** 𝕐H4	CGra CLyd ECho GKev GMaP ITim LRHS NLAp NMen SBla SRms WAbe WLin
§	***serpyllifolius***	ECho NMen SBla
	– 'Major'	NMen SBla WAbe
	tenuifolius 'Albus'	GKev

Ehretia (*Boraginaceae*)

	dicksonii	CHEx CPLG MBri WPGP

Ehrharta (*Poaceae*)

	thunbergii	EPPr

Eichhornia (*Pontederiaceae*)

	crassipes	CBen CWat EMFW SCoo
	– 'Major'	CDWL NPer

Elaeagnus ✿ (*Elaeagnaceae*)

	angustifolia	CAgr CBcs CDul EBee ECrN EMac EPfP EWTr MBar MBlu MCoo MGos MRav NLar NWea SHBN SPer SRms WBVN WFar XPep
	– Caspica Group	see *E.* 'Quicksilver'
	argentea	see *E. commutata*
§	***commutata***	CAgr CBcs CMCN CMac EBee ECrN EPfP EWTr IMGH LEdu LHop MBlu MWgw NLar SPer WPen WSpi
	– 'Zempin'	ECrN
§	x ***ebbingei***	More than 30 suppliers
	– 'Coastal Gold' (v)	CAbP CBcs CDoC CDul EBee EQua LRHS LSRN MAsh MGos SLim SRms WBod
	– 'Gilt Edge' (v) 𝕐H4	More than 30 suppliers
	– Gold Splash = 'Lannou' (v)	CDoC CDul CWSG EBee EPfP EQua ERas LRHS MAsh MBri SArc SPoG SWvt
	– 'Lemon Ice' (v) **new**	NLar
	– 'Limelight' (v)	More than 30 suppliers
	– 'Salcombe Seedling'	CCCN NLar
	glabra	EPfP
	– 'Reflexa'	see *E.* x ***reflexa***
	macrophylla	CMac EPfP SDry WMoo
	multiflora	CDul IDee MBri MCoo SPer WPGP
	parvifolia	CCCN EPfP
	pungens	ERom NBir
	– 'Argenteovariegata'	see *E. pungens* 'Variegata'
	– 'Aureovariegata'	see *E. pungens* 'Maculata'
	– 'Dicksonii' (v)	CBcs CBow CWib EBee LRHS NLar SLon SPer SRms WFar
	– 'Forest Gold' (v)	CAbP ELan EPfP LRHS MAsh
	– 'Frederici' (v)	CBcs CBrm CDoC CMHG CMac EBee ELan EPfP EPla ERas LHop LRHS MAsh MRav SHBN SLim SPer SPla SPoG WBor WHCG WPat WWeb
	– 'Goldrim' (v) 𝕐H4	CMac EPfP MGos SHBN SLim
	– 'Hosuba-fukurin' (v)	LTwo MAsh SPoG
§	– 'Maculata' (v)	More than 30 suppliers
§	– 'Variegata' (v)	CBcs CMac CPLG EPla EQua NBir SHBN SPer WGer WHCG
§	'Quicksilver' 𝕐H4	More than 30 suppliers
§	x ***reflexa***	CBcs WHCG WPGP
	x ***submacrophylla***	see *E.* x *ebbingei*
	umbellata	CAgr CBcs CBrm CPLG CPle EBee ECrN EMac EPfP EWTr MBlu MBri NLar SPer WHCG WRHF WSHC XPep
	– var. ***borealis*** 'Polar Lights'	MBri

Elatostema (*Urticaceae*)

	repens var. ***pulchrum*** 𝕐H1	CHal MBri
	– var. ***repens***	CHal
	rugosum	CHEx

elderberry see *Sambucus nigra*

Elegia (*Restionaceae*)

	capensis	CAbb CBct CBig CBrm CCCN CCtw CDoC CFir CHEx CPLG CPen CTrC EAmu EBee EShb GGar IDee SPlb WDyG WNor WPGP WPnP
	cuspidata	CBig EShb
	equisetacea	CBig WNor
	filacea	CBig

	fistulosa	CBig
	grandis	CBig
	grandispicata	CBig
	persistens	CBig
	racemosa	CCtw
	spathacea	CBig CFir CPLG
	thyrsoidea	CBig

Eleocharis (*Cyperaceae*)

	acicularis	CWat EMFW EPfP WPnP
	palustris	CRWN EMFW

Elettaria (*Zingiberaceae*)

	cardamomum	CArn EOHP EShb GPoy LEdu MBri MSal SHDw WJek

Eleutherococcus (*Araliaceae*)

	hypoleucus B&SWJ 5532	WCru
	nikaianus B&SWJ 5027	WCru
	pictus	see *Kalopanax septemlobus*
	sciadophylloides B&SWJ 4728	WCru
	senticosus	GPoy
	- B&SWJ 4528	WCru
	septemlobus	see *Kalopanax septemlobus*
	sessiliflorus B&SWJ 8457	WCru
	sieboldianus	CBcs MGos MRav WFar
	- 'Variegatus' (v)	CBcs CSpe EBee ECrN ELan EPfP EQua IDee LAst MBlu MGos MRav NEgg NLar WHer WSHC
	trifoliatus RWJ 10108	WCru

Elingamita (*Myrsinaceae*)

	johnsonii	ECou

Elisena (*Amaryllidaceae*)

	longipetala	see *Hymenocallis longipetala*

Elliottia (*Ericaceae*)

	bracteata	see *Tripetaleia bracteata*
*	***paniculata latifolia***	NLar
	pyroliflora	CStu

Ellisiophyllum (*Scrophulariaceae*)

	pinnatum	CFee WBor WMoo
	- B&SWJ 197	WCru WDyG WPrP

Elmera (*Saxifragaceae*)

	racemosa	MGol WPtf

Elodea (*Hydrocharitaceae*)

	canadensis	EHon EMFW WMAq
	crispa	see *Lagarosiphon major*

Elsholtzia (*Lamiaceae*)

	ciliata	CArn MSal
	fruticosa	CArn CPle
	stauntonii	CArn CBcs CPLG CPle EBee ECha EPPr GPoy LRHS MFOX MHer SPer WAul WBor XPep
	- 'Alba'	CArn CBcs LRav

Elymus (*Poaceae*)

	arenarius	see *Leymus arenarius*
	californicus	CBig
	canadensis	CBig CRWN EPPr GFor SWal XIsg
	- f. ***glaucifolius***	CFir
	cinereus from Washington State, USA	CDes
	elongatus	SApp
	giganteus	see *Leymus racemosus*
	glaucus misapplied	see *E. hispidus*
§	***hispidus***	CBod EAlp EBee EGoo EPPr EPau EWsh GFor LRHS MBlu MBri MMoz MPRe MWrn NDov NSti SPer SPla WCFE WCot WPrP WRos XIsg
N	***magellanicus***	More than 30 suppliers
	- 'Blue Sword'	NBPC WPtf
	repens subsp. ***repens*** 'Julie Ann' (v)	WCot
	riparius	EPPr
§	***scabrus***	SMrm
	sibiricus	EPPr SWal
	solandri	EBee EWes GBin GFor GGar LRav NNor
	- JCA 5.345.500	WPGP
	villosus	EPPr
	- var. ***arkansanus***	EPPr MAvo
	virginicus	EBee EPPr

Embothrium ✿ (*Proteaceae*)

	coccineum	CGHE CPLG CTrG CTri EBee EPfP MGos MPRe NPen SDry SPlb SReu WBrE WNor WPGP WPat
	- Lanceolatum Group	CDoC CDul CEnd CPLG CSBt ELan EPfP GGar ISea LRHS MAsh MBlu MDun NPal SAPC SArc SHBN SPer SPoG SSpi SSta WFar WPic
	- - 'Inca Flame'	CBcs CCCN CDoC CPLG CPMA CSBt ELan EPfP ISea MDun NLar SSta SWvt WPat
	- - 'Ñorquinco' ♀H3	CBcs CDoC GGar WBod
	- Longifolium Group	CCCN IArd IBlr ISea

Eminium (*Araceae*)

	albertii	EBrs ECho
	spiculatum	WCot

Emmenopterys (*Rubiaceae*)

	henryi	CBcs CCCN CGHE CMCN EBee EPfP IArd IDee MBri NLar SMad SPoG WPGP

Empetrum (*Empetraceae*)

	luteum	MBar
	nigrum	GPoy MBar NLar WThu
	rubrum 'Tomentosum'	WThu

Empodium (*Hypoxidaceae*)

	plicatum new	EBrs ECho

Encelia (*Asteraceae*)

	farinosa	XPep

Encephalartos ✿ (*Zamiaceae*)

	altensteinii	CBrP
	caffer	CBrP
	cycadifolius	CBrP LPal
	friderici-guilielmi	CBrP
	ghellinckii	LPal
	horridus	CBrP
	kisambo	LPal
	lanatus	CBrP
	lebomboensis	CBrP
	lehmannii	CBrP LPal
	natalensis	CBrP LPal
	senticosus	LPal
	umbeluziensis	CBrP
	villosus	CBrP LPal

Endymion see *Hyacinthoides*

Enkianthus ✿ (*Ericaceae*)

	campanulatus ♀H4	More than 30 suppliers
	- var. ***campanulatus*** f. ***albiflorus***	CBcs LRHS MAsh
I	- 'Hollandia'	CPMA MBri
	- var. ***palibinii***	EPfP GGGa LRHS MAsh MGos NLar SSpi SSta WBrE WNor

- 'Red Bells' — CBcs CDoC EPfP GBin LRHS MBri MGos NEgg NLar SPoG SSpi SSta SWvt WFar
- 'Red Velvet' — NLar
- 'Ruby Glow' — MBri NLar
- var. ***sikokianus*** — CAbP EPfP GGGa MAsh
- 'Tokyo Masquerade' — CPMA
* - 'Variegatus' (v) — LRHS MAsh SPoG
- 'Venus' — CBcs NLar
- 'Victoria' <u>new</u> — NLar
- 'Wallaby' — MBri NLar

cernuus f. ***rubens*** ♀H4 — CBcs CMac EPfP GGGa LRHS MBri NBea NEgg SSpi WNor WPic
chinensis — EPfP GGGa IMGH LRHS MAsh WNor
deflexus — CDul CMCN LRHS SSpi WPGP
- GWJ 9225 — WCru

perulatus ♀H4 — CBcs EPfP NEgg WFar

Ensete (*Musaceae*)

glaucum — CDTJ CKob EAmu MJnS
- from China — CKob
- from Thailand — CKob

superbum — CKob MJnS
- from Thailand — CKob

§ ***ventricosum*** ♀H1+3 — CCCN CDTJ CDoC CHrt CKob EAmu LPal MJnS SAPC SArc XBlo
§ - 'Maurelii' — CBrP CCCN CDTJ CHEx CKob CSpe EAmu EShb ETod LRHS MJnS MPRe NScw SAPC SArc SDix WCot WPGP
- 'Montbeliardii' — CKob
- 'Rubrum' — see *E. ventricosum* 'Maurelii'

Entelea (*Tiliaceae*)

arborescens — CHEx ECou EShb

Eomecon (*Papaveraceae*)

chionantha — CDes CHEx CHid CMCo CPLG CSam CSpe EBee ECho EHrv EMar EPot ERos GAbr GCra GEdr GSki LEdu LRHS MLHP MRav NBid SMad WFar WHer WMoo WPnP WSHC WTMC

Epacris (*Epacridaceae*)

longiflora — SOWG
paludosa — ECou GCrs GGGa
petrophila — GCrs GGGa
serpyllifolia — ECou

Ephedra (*Ephedraceae*)

sp. — SAPC SArc
americana var. ***andina*** — EMil
chilensis 'Mellow Yellow' — EBee WCot
- 'Quite White' — EBee WCot

distachya — GPoy MSal
equisetina — MSal
fragilis — SDry
gerardiana — GEdr
- var. ***sikkimensis*** — CStu EPla NLar SDry WBod WOld WPer

intermedia RCB/TQ K-1 — WCot
§ ***major*** — SDry WHer
minima — GEdr NWCA WThu
minuta <u>new</u> — CKen
nebrodensis — see *E. major*
nevadensis — GPoy MSal
sinica — MGol MSal
viridis — CArn MSal

Epigaea (*Ericaceae*)

gaultherioides — GGGa

Epilobium (*Onagraceae*)

angustifolium — see *Chamerion angustifolium*
- f. ***leucanthum*** — see *Chamerion angustifolium* 'Album'
- 'Starl Rose' — MWat SWat

californicum misapplied — see *Zauschneria californica*
canum — see *Zauschneria californica* subsp. *cana*
crassum — GBuc MBNS
dodonaei — see *Chamerion dodonaei*
garrettii — see *Zauschneria californica* subsp. *garrettii*
N ***glabellum*** misapplied — CSpe EMan GMaP LRHS NBir WEas WWlt
hirsutum — SECG SWat
- 'Album' — SPoG
- 'Pistils at Dawn' — CNat
- 'Well Creek' (v) — MLLN WCot WHrl

microphyllum — see *Zauschneria californica* subsp. *cana*
obcordatum — CStu NEgg
rosmarinifolium — see *Chamerion dodonaei*
septentrionale — see *Zauschneria septentrionalis*
villosum — see *Zauschneria californica* subsp. *mexicana*

Epimedium ✿ (*Berberidaceae*)

from Yunnan, China — CDes CPom
acuminatum — CDes CElw CHHB CLAP CWsd EBee EFEx MDun MLul MNFA SMac WAbe WPGP WSHC
- L 575 — EHrv MSte SBla
- 'Galaxy' — CLAP CPMA CWsd EBee

'Akebono' — CDes CLAP CPMA EBee NLar
alpinum — CFis CMac EBee EPPr GBuc NHol WMoo WSHC
'Amanogawa' — CDes CLAP CPMA CWsd SBla WPrP
Asiatic hybrids — CElw CLAP CPMA WHal WPnP
'Beni-chidori' — EBee
'Beni-kujaku' — CLAP CPMA EBee GBuc
brachyrrhizum — CDes CMil CPMA CPom CWsd EBee LTwo WPGP
brevicornu — CLAP CPMA CPom EBee
- f. ***rotundatum*** — CDes CLAP CPMA EBee WPGP

'Buckland Spider' — CDes CLAP CWsd EBee WPGP
campanulatum — CPMA
x ***cantabrigiense*** — CMac CPom ECtt EPla EWTr GGar LRHS MRav NBre NHol SMac WCot
chlorandrum — CDes CLAP EBee WPGP
cremeum — see *E. grandiflorum* subsp. *koreanum*
davidii — CDes CPMA CWsd EBee ECha GBri GCrs GEdr MDun MNFA MSte NLar SMac WAbe WFar WHal WHoo WPGP WSHC
- CPC 960079 — SBla
- EMR 4125 — CElw CLAP EHrv
- dwarf <u>new</u> — SBla

diphyllum — CPom CPrp CWsd EHrv ELan SAga WBVN WHal
dolichostemon — CElw CLAP CPMA EGle MSte
ecalcaratum — CDes CLAP CPMA CPom CWsd EBee WPGP
elongatum — CHHB CLAP EBee GEdr
'Enchantress' — CLAP CPMA CPom CWsd EGle EHrv GBuc MSte SAga WAbe WHal WHoo
epsteinii — CDes CLAP CPMA CPom CWsd EBee EPPr LTwo WPGP
fargesii — CDes CHHB CMil CWsd EBee EHrv GEdr WCot WPGP
- 'Pink Constellation' — CLAP CPMA CPom CWsd SBch SBla

flavum — CDes CLAP CPMA CWsd EHrv WPGP
franchetii — CHHB CPom

	- 'Brimstone Butterfly'	CDes CLAP CPMA CWsd EBee SBla WAbe WHoo WPGP
	'Golden Eagle'	CBow CPMA EWes WPrP
§	***grandiflorum*** ♀H4	CBcs CElw CFis CMac CTri EBee EHrv ELan EPfP EWTr GAbr GEdr LBMP MNFA NBir NLAp NLar NMen SAga SBla SPer WAbe WBor WCAu WFar WPnP
	- 'Album'	CLAP CWsd EBee
	- 'Crimson Beauty'	CLAP CPMA EBee GBuc MRav SMac WHal WHoo WSHC
	- 'Crimson Queen'	CBow CDes WPGP
	- 'Elfenkönigin'	WAbe
	- 'Koji'	EGle MSte NLar WSHC
§	- subsp. ***koreanum***	CHHB CLAP CWsd EBee ECha EFEx WAbe
	- - 'La Rocaille'	CDes CLAP
	- lilac	CLAP WFar WHal
	- 'Lilacinum'	CDes SBla
	- 'Lilafee'	More than 30 suppliers
	- 'Mount Kitadake'	CLAP WAbe
	- 'Nanum' ♀H4	CDes CLyd CPMA CPom CWsd EBee ECho EHrv NMen NWCA SAga WAbe WPGP
	- 'Pallidum'	EBee
	- pink	EHrv
	- 'Queen Esta'	CDes CLAP CWsd SBla WPGP
	- 'Red Beauty'	CLAP GAbr MSte NLar
	- 'Rose Queen' ♀H4	CMMP CPrp EBee ECha EHrv ELan EPfP GBuc GGar GMaP LAst LRHS MAvo MBri MRav NSti SBla SPoG SWvt WBVN WCAu WMoo
	- 'Roseum'	CHid CLAP CWsd EBee GBri NMen WSHC
	- 'Rubinkrone'	EBee GMaP NHol WOVN
	- 'Saturn'	CDes CPMA SBla
	- 'Shikinomai'	CLAP CPMA EGle WAbe
	- 'Sirius'	CDes CLAP CPMA EBee
	- f. ***violaceum***	CFir CLAP CPMA CPrp CWsd SAga SBch SMac WAbe WSHC
	- 'White Beauty'	EGle WSHC
	- 'White Queen' ♀H4	CFir CPMA CPrp EBee EHrv MRav NOak SBla WAbe WHal
	- 'Yellow Princess'	CDes CLAP CPMA SBla WCot
	higoense	WCot WHal
	ilicifolium	CDes WPGP
	- Og 93020	SBla
	'Kaguyahime'	CBow CDes CLAP CWsd EHrv MSte WAbe WHil
	latisepalum	CBow CDes CLAP CMil CPMA CPom EBee EHrv GEdr WCot WPGP
	leptorrhizum	CDes CLAP CPMA CWsd EBee EGle EHrv EMon GBuc GCrs MNFA SWat WAbe WHal WSHC
	- 'Mariko'	CLAP CWsd SBla
	lishihchenii	CDes WPGP
	- Og 96.024	SBla
	'Little Shrimp'	CLyd CPMA CTri EGle GBuc LTwo MNFA NLar WPat
	macranthum	see *E. grandiflorum*
	membranaceum	CDes CLAP CPMA CPom EBee LTwo WHal WPGP
	myrianthum	CBow CDes CPMA WPGP
	ogisui	CDes CLAP CPMA CPom EBee EGle EHrv MSte WHil WPGP
	- Og 91.001	WAbe
§	x ***omeiense*** 'Akame'	CBow CDes CLAP CMil CPMA EBee WPGP
	- 'Emei Shan'	see *E.* x *omeiense* 'Akame'
	- 'Pale Fire Sibling'	CPom
	- 'Stormcloud'	CDes CLAP CPMA CPom CWsd EBee SMac WPGP
	pauciflorum	CLAP CPMA CPom WHil
	x ***perralchicum*** ♀H4	CMac CPMA CTri EBee GBuc GKev MLHP MNFA NLar SGar SLPl WBVN WPnP
	- 'Frohnleiten'	More than 30 suppliers
	- 'Lichtenberg'	CDes
	- 'Nachfolger'	EBee
	- 'Wisley'	CElw CPMA CSam EHrv EWes SBla
	perralderianum	CHEx CSam EBee EGle ELan GMaP MDun SRms WAbe WHal WHen WPnP
	'Pink Elf'	SPla
	pinnatum	EBrs ECho GMaP MDun WHal
§	- subsp. ***colchicum*** ♀H4	CLAP CMac CPMA CPom EBee ELan EPfP EWsh GAbr GEdr LRHS MRav MSte NGdn NHol NRya SAga SDix SMac SPer SPla SPoG WAbe WCAu WCot WFar WPnP WTin
	- - 'Black Sea'	CLAP CPMA EBee EHrv NLar SAga
	- ***elegans***	see *E. pinnatum* subsp. *colchicum*
	platypetalum	CBow CDes CHHB CLAP CPMA CWsd EBee NLAp WCot
	- Og 93.085	EGle
	- ***album***	CHHB EBee
	pubescens	CPMA EBee EHrv SAga
	pubigerum	CHid CPMA EBee ECha EGle EHrv GAbr GBuc GEdr MLan MNFA NEgg NHol NMyG NPri WCAu WHal WPtf WSpi
	reticulatum new	EBee WHil
	rhizomatosum	CDes CHHB CLAP CPom EBee LTwo WCot WPGP
	- Og 92.114	CPMA
	x ***rubrum*** ♀H4	More than 30 suppliers
	sagittatum	CLAP EFEx
	'Sasaki'	CLAP EBee GBuc WPnP
	sempervirens	CLAP CPMA EBee WHal
	- var. ***sempervirens***	CLAP
	x ***setosum***	CPMA CWsd EBee ECha EHrv MSte NLar SMac WAbe WHal WSPU
	'Shiho'	EBee
	'Sohayaki'	EBee
	stellulatum new	EBee
	- 'Wudang Star'	CDes CLAP CPom CWsd EBee EHrv EWes GEdr SMac WPGP WSPU WSpi
	'Tama-no-genpei'	CPMA CPom
	x ***versicolor***	CBow CPLG CPrp LAst WMoo
	- 'Cupreum'	CPom SMHy SMac
	- 'Neosulphureum'	CDes CLAP CMMP EBee EMon SBla SLPl WThu
	- 'Sulphureum' ♀H4	More than 30 suppliers
I	- 'Versicolor'	CLAP CPom CWsd ECha EHrv SAga SBla
	x ***warleyense***	CElw CPMA CPom CPrp EBee EBrs ECha ELan EPfP EWTr LAst LCro LRHS MBri MRav MWgw NEgg NHol NWCA SBla SMac SPet WCra WFar WHal WLin WPGP WPnP WSpi
	- 'Orangekönigin'	CPom CWCL EBee EGle GBuc MBri MNFA MRav NBro NLar NMyG NSti SPla WAbe WBor WCAu WHal WMoo WPnP
	wushanense	CLAP CPMA CWsd
	- 'Caramel'	CBow CDes CFee CLAP CPMA CPom CWsd EBee EHrv LEdu SBla WPGP
	x ***youngianum***	CBcs CMac EGle MNFA
	- 'Merlin'	CFir CLAP CPMA CWsd ECha EHrv EPfP NLar NMyG NSti WAbe WCAu WHal WSHC
	- 'Niveum' ♀H4	More than 30 suppliers
	- 'Roseum'	More than 30 suppliers
	- 'Tamabotan'	CBow CDes CLAP CWsd EBee GBuc

- 'Typicum'	CLAP EGle WAbe WSHC
- white	NMen WLin
- 'Yenomoto'	CLAP CPMA
zhushanense	CHHB EBee GEdr

Epipactis (*Orchidaceae*)

gigantea	CAvo CDes CFir CStu EBee EBla ECha ELan EPot ERos GCrs GEdr GKev GMaP IBlr LRHS MAvo MRav MTho NLAp NMen NMyG NSum NWCA SHdy WAbe WFar WHil WPGP
helleborine	WHer
Lowland Legacy gx 'Irène'	WWst
palustris	EBee EBla GEdr IPot NLAp NLar NMyG SHdy SSvw WHer
- 'Popcorn' **new**	WWst
- 'Purple Fog' **new**	WWst
'Renate'	GCrs WWst
royleana	SBla
Sabine gx	SHdy WWst
* - 'Frankfurt'	NMen SBla
thunbergii	EFEx GEdr WWst
veratrifolia	SHdy WWst

Epipremnum (*Araceae*)

§ ***aureum*** ♀H1	MBri
§ ***pinnatum***	LRHS MBri
- 'Aureum'	see *E. aureum*
- 'Marble Queen' (v)	CHal LRHS

Episcia (*Gesneriaceae*)

'Country Kitten'	CHal
cupreata	CHal
dianthiflora	CHal SRms WDib
'Pink Panther'	CHal
'San Miguel'	CHal WDib

Equisetum ✿ (*Equisetaceae*)

arvense	CArn MSal
'Bandit' (v)	CBgR CBow CNat EMon SMad
x ***bowmanii***	CNat
* ***camtschatcense***	CBgR CDes CMCo CNat EBee IDee ITer SMad
x ***dycei***	CNat
fluviatile	CNat NLar
giganteum	CTrC
hyemale	CDWL CHEx CKno CMil CNat CTrC EBla EPfP EPla LCro NPer NSti SPlb WDyG WFar WMoo WPrP
§ - var. ***affine***	CBgR CNat EBee ELan EMan EMon EPla LEdu LSou MBlu SMad SPur WMAq
- var. ***robustum***	see *E. hyemale* var. *affine*
palustre	GWCH
ramosissimum	CNat
- var. ***japonicum***	EMFW MCCP NScw SWat WPnP
scirpoides	CDWL CNat CPen CTrC EBee EFer EMFW EMon EPfP EPla MCCP NBlu NHol NPer SPlb SWat WMAq WMoo WPrP
sylvaticum	CNat
telmateia	CNat
variegatum	NVic

Eragrostis (*Poaceae*)

sp.	EBee
RCB/Arg S-7	WCot
abyssinica	see *E. tef*
airoides	CHar CHrt CKno CSam EBee EKen EWsh GQui ILad LAst MWat NPro SMad SPoG WHrl WMnd WMoo WRos
chloromelas	EPPr MSte SPhx WPGP
curvula	More than 30 suppliers
- S&SH 10	MSte WPGP
- 'Totnes Burgundy'	CAby CBig CDes CKno CPen CWCL EBee ECha EPPr LCro LEdu MAvo MMoz MNrw NOak SPhx WHal WHrl WPGP WPrP
elliottii	CKno EBee EPPr GFor MSte WOut
gummiflua	CBig
'Silver Needles'	see *Agrostis canina* 'Silver Needles'
spectabilis	CAby CBig CFir CHrt CKno EBee EPPr GFor ILad LDai MAvo MDKP NBHF NChi NLar SMad SPhx SSvw XIsg
§ ***tef***	SMad
trichodes	CAby CBig CBrm CFir CKno EGoo EWTr LDai LEdu NBre SMad SPhx WPer XIsg

Eranthemum (*Acanthaceae*)

pulchellum ♀H1	ECre

Eranthis (*Ranunculaceae*)

cilicica	see *E. hyemalis* Cilicica Group
§ ***hyemalis*** ♀H4	CMea CTca CTri EBrs ECho EHrv ELan EMon EPfP EPot GKev IHer LAma LRHS MBri MRav SPer SPhx WBVN WCot WFar WGwG WRHF WShi
§ - Cilicica Group	CPLG EBrs ECho EHrv ELan EMon EPot GKev GMaP LAma LHop LRHS
§ - Tubergenii Group	EPot WAbe
- - 'Guinea Gold' ♀H4	EBrs ECho GCrs
pinnatifida	EBrs EFEx GCrs
x ***tubergenii***	see *E. hyemalis* Tubergenii Group

Ercilla (*Phytolaccaceae*)

volubilis	CBrm CFee CPLG CRHN EBee EMil EWes NSti NVic WCot WCru WSHC

Eremophila (*Myoporaceae*)

bignoniiflora	SOWG
§ ***debilis***	ECou
glabra 'Burgundy'	SOWG
- orange-flowered **new**	ECou
'Kilbara Carpet'	ECou SOWG
maculata	ECou
- var. ***brevifolia***	SOWG
- pale pink-flowered	SOWG
- 'Peaches and Cream'	SOWG
* 'Summer Blue'	SOWG
'Yellow Trumpet'	ECou

Eremurus (*Asphodelaceae*)

aitchisonii 'Albus'	WCot
altaicus JCA 0.443.809	WCot
'Brutus'	EBee EBrs ERou LAma LRHS MSte
bungei	see *E. stenophyllus* subsp. *stenophyllus*
'Emmy Ro'	EBee EBrs ERou LAma LRHS MSte SPur
fuscus **new**	WCot
'Helena'	EBee LAma SPur
himalaicus	CAvo CTca EBee EBrs ECho EHrv ELan EPot ERou EWTr LAma LRHS MHer MSte SMad SPer SPhx WBVN WCra WHil WWst
'Image'	EBee EBrs ERou LRHS MBNS
x ***isabellinus*** 'Cleopatra'	More than 30 suppliers
- 'Obelisk'	CMea EBee EBrs ELan ERCP ERou LAma LRHS SPhx WCot
- 'Pinokkio'	CAvo CTca EBee EBrs EGoo EPot ERou LAma LRHS MAvo MHer

	- Ruiter hybrids	CMea CSWP EBee EBrs ECot ELan EMon ENot EPfP ERou LAma LAst LRHS MLLN MNFA SPer SPet WAul WBVN WFar
	- Shelford hybrids	CAvo CBcs CBct CFFs EBee EBrs ELan EMon LAma LBMP LRHS MLLN MNrw WBVN WFar
	'Jeanne-Claire'	EBee LAma NLar SPur
	'Joanna'	EBee LAma NLar
	'Line Dance'	LAma
	'Luca Ro' new	EBee
	'Moneymaker'	EBee EBrs EPot ERou LAma LRHS NLar
	'Oase'	CAvo CHFP CMea CTca EBee EBrs EHrv ELan ERou LAma LRHS MSte NLar SPer WCot WHil
	'Rexona'	EBee EBrs ERou LAma LRHS
	robustus ♀H4	CAvo CBcs CMea CTca EBee EBrs EHrv ELan EMon EPot ERou EWTr LAma LCro LRHS MAvo MHer MSte NLar SPer SPhx SPlb SWat WAul WBVN WCot WCra WFar WWFP
	'Roford'	EBee EBrs ERou LAma NMoo
	'Romance'	CAvo CHFP CMea CTca EBee EBrs EMon EPot ERCP ERou LAma LRHS MSte WHil
	'Rumba'	LAma
	'Samba'	LAma
	sogdianus	EBee EBrs
	- JCA 0.444/090	WCot
	stenophyllus ♀H4	CBgR CFFs CTca CTri CWib EBrs EPot ERou LBMP LCro LHop LRHS MAvo MNFA SMrm SPhx SPoG WCot WFar
§	- subsp. ***stenophyllus***	CAvo CBcs CMea EBee EHrv EMon EPfP ERou EShb GMaP LAma LAst MHer MLLN MNrw MRav NBPC NPer NPri SPer WBVN WCra WFar WLin
	'Tap Dance'	LAma
	tauricus new	EBee EBrs
	'Yellow Giant'	EBee EBrs ERou WCot WHil
	zenaidae new	WCot

Erianthus see *Saccharum*

	strictus ambig.	XIsg

Erica ✿ (*Ericaceae*)

	'African Fanfare'	EHea
	x ***afroeuropaea***	EHea
	alopecurus	SPlb
	arborea	CNCN CTrG SPlb
§	- 'Albert's Gold' ♀H4	CBcs CNCN CSBt CTri EHea ELan EPfP LRHS MAsh MBar MBri MGos MSwo NHol SPer SPla SPoG SRms WBod
	- var. ***alpina*** ♀H4	CDoC CNCN CTri EHea EPfP LRHS MBar NHol SPer SPoG SRms
	- 'Arbora Gold'	see *E. arborea* 'Albert's Gold'
	- 'Arnold's Gold'	see *E. arborea* 'Albert's Gold'
	- 'Estrella Gold' ♀H4	CDoC CNCN CSBt CTri EHea ELan EPfP LRHS MAsh MBar MGos NHol SPer SPla SPoG SRms
	- 'Picos Pygmy'	EHea
	- 'Spanish Lime'	EHea
	- 'Spring Smile'	EHea
	australis ♀H4	CBcs MBar
	- 'Castellar Blush'	CNCN EHea
	- 'Holehird'	EHea
	- 'Mr Robert' ♀H3	EHea EPfP MBar
	- 'Riverslea' ♀H4	CTri EHea MBar WBod
	caffra	CTrC IDee SPlb
	canaliculata ♀H3	CBcs EHea
	carnea	ELan
	- 'Accent'	EHea
	- 'Adrienne Duncan' ♀H4	CNCN EHea MBar MBri NDlv NHol WTel
	- 'Alan Coates'	CNCN EHea MBar
	- 'Alba'	EHea
	- 'Altadena'	CNCN EHea MBar
	- 'Amy Doncaster'	see *E. carnea* 'Treasure Trove'
	- 'Ann Sparkes' ♀H4	CNCN CSBt CTri EHea EPfP LRHS MBar MBri MSwo NHol SPla SRms
	- 'Atrorubra'	CNCN EHea MBar
	- 'Aurea'	CNCN CSBt EHea MBar NHol SRms
	- 'Barry Sellers'	EHea
§	- 'Bell's Extra Special'	EHea EPfP
	- 'Beoley Pink'	CNCN EHea
I	- 'Carnea'	CNCN EHea MBar
	- 'Catherine Kolster'	EHea
	- 'Cecilia M. Beale'	CNCN EHea MBar
	- 'Challenger' ♀H4	CNCN EHea EPfP MBar MGos NHol SCoo SPer SPla SRms
	- 'Christine Fletcher'	EHea
	- 'Clare Wilkinson'	CNCN EHea
	- 'David's Seedling'	EHea
	- 'December Red'	CBcs CNCN CSBt EHea EPfP LRHS MBar MBri MSwo NHol SPer SPla SRms
	- 'Dømmesmoen'	EHea
	- 'Dwingeloo Pride'	EHea
	- 'Early Red'	EHea
	- 'Eileen Porter'	CNCN EHea MBar
	- 'Eva'	EHea
	- 'Foxhollow' ♀H4	CNCN CSBt CTri EHea EPfP IArd LRHS MBar MBri MGos MSwo MWat NHol SPla SRms WTel
	- 'Foxhollow Fairy'	CBcs EHea MBar SRms
	- 'Gelber Findling'	EHea
	- 'Gelderingen Gold'	EHea
	- 'Golden Starlet' ♀H4	CNCN CTri EHea EPfP LRHS MBar MGos NBlu NHol SPer SPla SRms
	- 'Gracilis'	EHea MBar
	- 'Hamburg'	EHea
	- 'Heathwood'	CNCN EHea MBar NHol SCoo SPla SRms
	- 'Hilletje'	CNCN EHea SRms
	- 'Ice Princess' ♀H4	CBrm CNCN EHea EPfP LRHS NHol SCoo SPer SPla SRms
	- 'Isabell' ♀H4	CNCN EHea EPfP LRHS SCoo SPla SRms
	- 'Jack Stitt'	EHea MBar
	- 'James Backhouse'	CTri EHea
	- 'January Sun'	EHea
	- 'Jason Attwater'	EHea
	- 'Jean'	EHea NHol
	- 'Jennifer Anne'	CNCN EHea MBar
	- 'John Kampa'	CNCN EHea MBar NHol
	- 'John Pook'	EHea
	- 'King George'	CNCN CSBt CTri EHea LRHS MBar NHol
§	- 'Kramer's Rubin'	EHea
	- 'Kramer's Weisse'	EHea
	- 'Lake Garda'	EHea
	- 'Late Pink'	EHea
	- 'Lena' new	EHea
	- 'Lesley Sparkes'	CSBt EHea MBar
	- 'Little Peter'	EHea
	- 'Lohse's Rubin'	EHea LRHS
	- 'Lohse's Rubinfeuer'	EHea
	- 'Lohse's Rubinschimmer'	EHea
	- 'Loughrigg' ♀H4	CNCN CSBt CTri EHea MBar NHol SPla SRms WTel
	- Madame Seedling	see *E. carnea* 'Weisse March Seedling'
	- 'March Seedling'	CNCN EHea EPfP MBar MBri NHol SRms
	- 'Margery Frearson'	EHea

	- 'Martin'	EHea
	- 'Moonlight'	EHea
	- 'Mrs Sam Doncaster'	CNCN EHea MBar
	- 'Myretoun Ruby' ℽH4	CBcs CNCN CSBt CTri EBrs EHea EPfP LCro LRHS MBar MBri MGos MWat NBlu NDlv NHol SPer SPla SRms
	- 'Nathalie' ℽH4	CNCN EHea LRHS MSwo NHol SCoo SRms
	- 'Netherfield Orange'	EHea
	- 'Oriënt'	EHea SRms
	- 'Pallida'	EHea
	- 'Pink Beauty'	see *E. carnea* 'Pink Pearl'
	- 'Pink Cloud'	CNCN EHea
	- 'Pink Mist'	EHea LRHS SPer SRms
§	- 'Pink Pearl'	CNCN EHea MBar
	- 'Pink Spangles' ℽH4	CBcs CNCN CSBt CTri EHea MBar MBri MGos MSwo NHol SRms WTel
	- 'Pirbright Rose'	EHea SRms
	- 'Polden Pride'	EHea
	- 'Porter's Red'	EHea MBar
	- 'Praecox Rubra' ℽH4	CBcs CNCN EHea EPfP MBar NHol
	- 'Prince of Wales'	CNCN CSBt EHea
	- 'Queen Mary'	CNCN EHea
	- 'Queen of Spain'	EHea
	- 'R.B. Cooke' ℽH4	CBrm CNCN EHea EPfP MBar SCoo SPla SRms
	- 'Red Rover'	EHea
	- 'Robert Jan'	EHea
	- 'Romance'	EHea
	- 'Rosalie' ℽH4	CBcs CNCN EHea EPfP IArd LCro LRHS MSwo SCoo SPer SPla SRms
	- 'Rosalinde Schorn'	EHea
	- 'Rosantha'	EHea SRms
	- 'Rosea'	SPlb
	- 'Rosy Gem'	CNCN EHea MBar
	- 'Rosy Morn'	EHea
	- 'Rotes Juwel'	EHea
	- 'Rubinteppich'	EHea SRms
	- 'Ruby Glow'	CNCN EHea LRHS MBar MSwo NHol SPla WTel
	- 'Scatterley'	EHea
	- 'Schatzalp'	EHea
	- 'Schneekuppe'	EHea
	- 'Schneesturm'	EHea SRms
§	- 'Sherwood Creeping'	EHea MBar
	- 'Sherwoodii'	see *E. carnea* 'Sherwood Creeping'
	- 'Smart's Heath'	CNCN EHea
	- 'Sneznik'	EHea
	- 'Snow Prince'	EHea
	- 'Snow Queen'	CNCN EHea MBar
	- 'Snow White'	EHea
	- 'Spring Cottage Crimson'	EHea MBar
	- 'Spring Day'	EHea MSwo
	- 'Springwood Pink'	CBcs CNCN CSBt CTri EHea LRHS MBar MBri NHol SRms
	- 'Springwood White' ℽH4	CBcs CNCN CSBt CTri EBrs EHea EPfP LRHS MBar MBri MGos MSwo MWat NHol SPer SPla SRms WTel
I	- 'Startler'	EHea LRHS MBar NHol
	- 'Sunshine Rambler' ℽH4	CNCN EHea MBar NHol
	- 'Thomas Kingscote'	CNCN EHea MBar
§	- 'Treasure Trove'	EHea
	- 'Tybesta Gold'	CNCN EHea
	- 'Urville'	see *E. carnea* 'Vivellii'
	- 'Viking'	CNCN EHea NHol
§	- 'Vivellii' ℽH4	CNCN CSBt CTri EHea LRHS MBar MBri MWat NDlv NHol SRms
	- 'Vivellii Aurea'	EHea
	- 'Walter Reisert'	EHea
	- 'Wanda'	EHea MBar
§	- 'Weisse March Seedling'	EHea
	- 'Wentwood Red'	EHea
	- 'Westwood Yellow' ℽH4	CNCN CSBt EHea LRHS MBar MBri MGos NHol SPer SPla SRms
	- Whisky	see *E. carnea* 'Bell's Extra Special'
	- 'Whitehall'	EHea LCro LRHS NHol SRms
	- 'Winter Beauty'	CNCN EHea MGos NDlv NHol
	- 'Winter Gold'	EHea
	- 'Winter Melody'	EHea
	- Winter Rubin	see *E. carnea* 'Kramer's Rubin'
	- 'Winter Snow'	EHea SCoo SRms
	- 'Winter Sport'	EHea
	- 'Winterfreude'	EHea
	- 'Wintersonne'	CBcs EHea EPfP SRms
	ciliaris 'Aurea'	CNCN EHea MBar SRms
	- 'Bretagne'	EHea
	- 'Camla'	EHea MBar
	- 'Corfe Castle'	CNCN EHea MBar
	- 'David McClintock'	EHea MBar
	- 'Fada das Serras' **new**	EHea
	- 'Globosa'	EHea
	- 'Mawiana'	EHea
	- 'Mrs C.H. Gill' ℽH4	EHea
	- 'Ram'	EHea
	- 'Rotundiflora'	EHea
	- 'Stapehill'	EHea
	- 'Stoborough' ℽH4	CNCN EHea MBar
	- 'White Wings'	EHea
	- 'Wych'	EHea
	cinerea f. ***alba*** 'Alba Major'	CNCN CSBt EHea MBar
	- f. ***alba*** 'Alba Minor' ℽH4	CNCN EHea MBar MBri NHol
	- - 'Celebration'	EHea MBar
	- - 'Doctor Small's Seedling'	EHea
	- - 'Domino'	CNCN EHea MBar
	- - 'Godrevy'	EHea
	- - 'Hookstone White' ℽH4	CNCN EHea MBar NDlv
	- - 'Jos' Honeymoon'	EHea
	- - 'Marina'	EHea
	- - 'Nell'	EHea MBar
	- - 'Snow Cream'	EHea MBar
	- - 'White Dale'	EHea MBar
	- 'Alette'	EHea
	- 'Alfred Bowerman'	EHea
	- 'Alice Ann Davies'	EHea
	- 'Angarrack'	EHea
	- 'Anja Bakker'	EHea
	- 'Anja Blum'	EHea
	- 'Anja Slegers'	EHea
	- 'Ann Berry'	EHea MBar
	- 'Apple Blossom'	EHea
	- 'Apricot Charm'	CSBt EHea MBar MSwo
	- 'Aquarel'	EHea
	- 'Ashdown Forest'	EHea
	- 'Ashgarth Garnet'	EHea MBar
	- 'Atropurpurea'	CNCN EHea MBar
	- 'Atrorubens'	EHea MBar SRms
	- 'Atrorubens, Daisy Hill'	EHea
	- 'Atrosanguinea'	CNCN MBar
	- 'Atrosanguinea Reuthe's Variety'	EHea
	- 'Atrosanguinea, Smith's Variety'	EHea
	- 'Baylay's Variety'	EHea MBar
	- 'Bemmel'	EHea
	- 'Blossom Time'	EHea MBar
	- 'Bucklebury Red'	EHea
	- 'C.D. Eason' ℽH4	CBcs CNCN CSBt CTri EHea EPfP MBar MBri NHol SRms
§	- 'C.G. Best' ℽH4	CNCN ECho EHea MBar
	- 'Cairn Valley'	EHea
	- 'Caldy Island'	EHea MBar
	- 'Carnea'	EHea
	- 'Cevennes'	CNCN EHea MBar
	- 'Champs Hill' ℽH4	EHea
	- 'Cindy' ℽH4	CNCN EHea MBar NHol

	– 'Coccinea'	EHea
	– 'Colligan Bridge'	EHea MBar
	– 'Constance'	EHea MBar
	– 'Contrast'	EHea MBar
	– 'Crimson Glow'	EHea
	– 'Daphne Maginess'	CNCN
	– 'Discovery'	EHea
	– 'Duncan Fraser'	CNCN EHea MBar
	– 'Eden Valley' ♀H4	CNCN EHea MBar NHol SRms
	– 'Eline'	EHea
	– 'England'	EHea
	– 'Felthorpe'	EHea
	– 'Fiddler's Gold' ♀H4	CNCN EHea MBar NHol
	– 'Flamingo'	EHea
	– 'Foxhollow Mahogany'	EHea MBar
	– 'Frances'	EHea
	– 'Frankrijk'	EHea
	– 'Fred Corston'	EHea
	– 'G. Osmond'	EHea MBar
	– 'Geke'	EHea
	– 'Glasnevin Red'	EHea MBar
	– 'Glencairn'	EHea MBar NHol
	– 'Golden Charm'	CNCN EHea NHol
	– 'Golden Drop'	CNCN CSBt EHea MBar MBri MSwo NHol
	– 'Golden Hue' ♀H4	CNCN EHea MBar NHol
	– 'Golden Sport'	EHea
	– 'Golden Striker' **new**	EHea
	– 'Golden Tee'	EHea
	– 'Goldilocks'	EHea
	– 'Graham Thomas'	see *E. cinerea* 'C.G. Best'
	– 'Grandiflora'	EHea MBar
	– 'Guernsey Lime'	EHea MBar
	– 'Guernsey Pink'	EHea
	– 'Guernsey Plum'	EHea
	– 'Guernsey Purple'	EHea
	– 'Hardwick's Rose'	EHea MBar
	– 'Harry Fulcher'	EHea
	– 'Heatherbank'	EHea
	– 'Heathfield'	EHea
	– 'Heidebrand'	EHea MBar
	– 'Hermann Dijkhuizen'	EHea
	– 'Honeymoon'	EHea MBar
	– 'Hookstone Lavender'	EHea
	– 'Hutton's Seedling'	EHea
	– 'Iberian Beauty'	EHea
	– 'Jack London'	EHea
	– 'Janet'	EHea MBar
	– 'Jersey Wonder'	EHea
	– 'Jiri'	EHea
	– 'John Ardron'	EHea
	– 'John Eason'	EHea
	– 'Jos' Golden'	EHea
	– 'Joseph Murphy'	EHea MBar
	– 'Josephine Ross'	EHea MBar
	– 'Joyce Burfitt'	CNCN EHea
	– 'Katinka'	CNCN EHea MBar MSwo NHol
	– 'Kerry Cherry'	EHea
	– 'Knap Hill Pink' ♀H4	CNCN EHea MBar
	– 'Lady Skelton'	EHea MBar
	– 'Lavender Lady'	EHea
	– 'Lilac Time'	EHea MBar
	– 'Lilacina'	EHea MBar
	– 'Lime Soda' ♀H4	CNCN EHea
	– 'Lorna Anne Hutton'	EHea
	– 'Maginess Pink'	CNCN
	– 'Michael Hugo'	CNCN EHea
	– 'Miss Waters'	EHea MBar
	– 'Mrs Dill'	EHea MBar
	– 'Mrs E.A. Mitchell'	EHea NHol SPlb
	– 'Mrs Ford'	EHea MBar
	– 'My Love'	CNCN EHea MBar
	– 'Neptune' **new**	EHea
	– 'Newick Lilac'	EHea MBar
	– 'Next Best'	EHea MBar

	– 'Novar'	EHea
	– 'Old Rose'	EHea
	– 'P.S. Patrick' ♀H4	CNCN EHea MBar
	– 'Pallas'	EHea
	– 'Pallida'	EHea
	– 'Patricia Maginess'	CNCN
	– 'Paul's Purple'	EHea
	– 'Peñaz'	EHea
	– 'Pentreath' ♀H4	EHea MBar
	– 'Pink Foam'	EHea MBar
	– 'Pink Ice' ♀H4	CNCN CTri EHea EPfP MBar MBri MSwo NHol
	– 'Plummer's Seedling'	EHea MBar
	– 'Promenade'	EHea
	– 'Prostrate Lavender'	EHea
	– 'Providence'	EHea
	– 'Purple Beauty'	CNCN EHea MBar
	– 'Purple Robe'	EHea
	– 'Purple Spreader'	EHea
	– 'Purpurea'	EHea
	– 'Pygmaea'	EHea MBar
	– 'Red Pentreath'	EHea
	– 'Robert Michael'	EHea
	– 'Rock Pool'	EHea MBar NHol
	– 'Rock Ruth'	EHea
	– 'Romiley'	EHea MBar
	– 'Rose Queen'	EHea
	– 'Rosea'	EHea
I	– 'Rosea Splendens'	EHea
	– 'Rosy Chimes'	EHea MBar
	– 'Rozanne Waterer'	EHea
	– 'Ruby'	CNCN EHea MBar
	– 'Sandpit Hill'	EHea MBar
	– 'Schizopetala'	EHea MBar
	– 'Screel'	EHea
	– 'Sea Foam'	EHea MBar
	– 'Sherry'	CNCN EHea MBar
	– 'Smith's Lawn'	EHea
	– 'Spicata'	EHea
	– 'Splendens'	EHea
	– 'Startler'	EHea MBri
	– 'Stephen Davis' ♀H4	CNCN EHea MBar MBri NHol
	– 'Strawberry Bells'	EHea
	– 'Sue Lloyd'	EHea
	– 'Summer Gold'	CNCN EHea LRHS NDlv
	– 'Summer Wonder'	EHea
	– 'Tilford'	EHea
	– 'Tom Waterer'	EHea MBar
	– 'Underwood Pink'	EHea
	– 'Uschie Ziehmann'	EHea
	– 'Velvet Night' ♀H4	CNCN CSBt EHea MBar MBri NHol SRms
	– 'Victoria'	EHea MBar
	– 'Violacea'	EHea
	– 'Violetta'	EHea
	– 'Vivienne Patricia'	EHea MBar
	– 'W.G. Notley'	EHea
	– 'West End'	EHea
	– 'Windlebrooke' ♀H4	EHea MBar NHol
	– 'Wine'	EHea
	– 'Yvonne'	EHea
	curviflora	EHea SPlb
	x ***darleyensis*** 'Ada S. Collings'	CNCN EHea MBar
	– 'Alba'	see *E.* x *darleyensis* 'Silberschmelze'
	– 'Archie Graham'	EHea
	– 'Arthur Johnson' ♀H4	CBcs CNCN CSBt CTri EHea LRHS MBar NHol SRms
	– 'Aurélie Brégeon'	CBcs EHea SRms
	– 'Cherry Stevens'	see *E.* x *darleyensis* 'Furzey'
§	– 'Darley Dale'	CBcs CNCN CSBt EHea EPfP LRHS MBar MBri NBlu NHol SCoo SPer SRms
	– 'Dunreggan'	EHea

- 'Dunwood Splendour'	MBar
- 'Epe'	EHea
- 'Erecta'	EHea
- 'Eva'	see *E.* x *darleyensis* 'Eva Gold'
- 'Eva Gold' PBR	EHea LRHS SRms
§ - 'Furzey' ♀H4	CNCN CSBt EHea EPfP LCro LRHS MBar MBri MGos NHol SCoo SPer SRms WTel
- 'George Rendall'	CNCN CSBt CTri EHea EPfP LRHS NHol SCoo SPla
- 'Ghost Hills' ♀H4	CBcs CNCN CSBt EHea EPfP LRHS MBar MSwo NHol SCoo SPer SRms
- 'J.W. Porter' ♀H4	CBcs CNCN EHea EPfP LCro MBar NDlv SCoo SEND SPla SRms WTel
- 'Jack H. Brummage'	CNCN CSBt CTri EHea IArd LRHS MBar MBri MGos MSwo NHol SPla SRms
- 'James Smith'	EHea MBar
- 'Jenny Porter' ♀H4	CNCN CSBt EHea EPfP LRHS MBar MBri
- 'Kramer's Rote' ♀H4	CBcs CNCN CSBt CTri EBrs EHea EPfP LRHS MBar MBri MGos NBlu NDlv NHol SPer SPla SRms
- 'Margaret Porter'	CBcs CNCN CSBt EHea EPfP SPer SPla
- 'Mary Helen'	CBcs CBrm CNCN CSBt EHea EPfP LCro LRHS NBlu NHol SCoo SPer SPla SRms
- Molten Silver	see *E.* x *darleyensis* 'Silberschmelze'
- 'Moonshine' **new**	LRHS
- 'Mrs Parris' Red'	EHea
- 'N.R. Webster'	CNCN EHea
- 'Pink Perfection'	see *E.* x *darleyensis* 'Darley Dale'
§ - 'Silberschmelze'	CBcs CNCN CSBt CTri EHea EPfP LRHS MBar MBri MGos MSwo NBlu NDlv NHol SPer SRms WTel
- 'Spring Surprise' PBR	EHea EPfP LRHS
- 'Tweety' **new**	EHea
- 'W.G. Pine'	EHea
- 'White Fairy'	EHea
- 'White Glow'	CNCN CSBt CTri EHea NHol SPla
- 'White Perfection' ♀H4	CBcs CNCN CSBt EHea EPfP IArd LRHS MBar NHol SCoo SPla SRms
discolor	EHea
erigena 'Alba'	EHea MBar
- 'Brian Proudley'	CNCN EHea MBar
- 'Brightness'	CBcs CNCN CSBt EHea EPfP MBar MBri MSwo MWat NHol SCoo WTel
- 'Coccinea'	EHea
- 'Ewan Jones'	EHea MBar
- 'Glauca'	EHea
- 'Golden Lady' ♀H4	CNCN CSBt EHea LRHS MBar MBri MSwo NHol SCoo
- 'Hibernica'	EHea
- 'Hibernica Alba'	EHea MBar
- 'Irish Dusk' ♀H4	CNCN CSBt CTri EHea EPfP MBar MGos NHol SCoo SPla SRms
- 'Irish Salmon'	CNCN CSBt EHea MBar
- 'Irish Silver'	EHea MBar
- 'Ivory'	EHea
- 'Maxima'	EHea
- 'Mrs Parris' Lavender'	EHea
- 'Mrs Parris' White'	EHea
- 'Nana'	EHea
- 'Nana Alba'	CNCN EHea MBar
- 'Nana Compacta'	EHea
- 'Rosea'	EHea MBar
- 'Rosslare'	EHea
- 'Rubra'	EHea
- 'Superba'	CNCN EHea MBar MGos SRms
- 'Thing Nee'	EHea
- 'W.T. Rackliff' ♀H4	CBcs CNCN CSBt EHea EPfP MBar MGos MSwo NBlu NHol SCoo SPer SPla SRms
- 'W.T. Rackliff Variegated' (v)	EHea
x ***garforthensis*** 'Tracy Wilson'	EHea
glauca var. ***glauca***	SPlb
gracilis	SPoG
x ***griffithsii*** 'Ashlea Gold'	EHea
- 'Elegant Spike'	EHea
§ - 'Heaven Scent'	CNCN EHea LRHS
- 'Jaqueline'	EHea SPla SRms
- 'Valerie Griffiths'	EHea LRHS MBar NHol SCoo SRms
'Heaven Scent'	see *E.* x *griffithsii* 'Heaven Scent'
'Hélène'	EHea
x ***hiemalis*** hort.	SPoG
- 'Ghislaine'	EHea
x ***krameri*** 'Otto'	EHea
- 'Rudi'	EHea
lusitanica ♀H3	CBcs CNCN CTrG EHea MBar SPer
- 'George Hunt'	CNCN EHea ELan EPfP LRHS NHol SPer SPla SPoG
- 'Sheffield Park'	EHea ELan LRHS SPer SPoG
mackayana subsp. ***andevalensis***	EHea
- subsp. ***andevalensis*** f. ***albiflora***	EHea
- 'Ann D. Frearson' (d)	EHea
- 'Doctor Ronald Gray'	EHea MBar
- 'Donegal'	EHea
- 'Errigal Dusk'	EHea
- 'Galicia'	CNCN EHea
- 'Lawsoniana'	EHea
- 'Maura' (d)	EHea
- 'Plena' (d)	CNCN EHea MBar
- 'Shining Light'	EHea SDys
- 'William M'Calla'	EHea
mammosa	SPlb
manipuliflora	MBar
- 'Aldeburgh'	CNCN EHea
§ - 'Cascades'	EHea
- 'Corfu'	EHea
- 'Don Richards'	EHea
- 'Ian Cooper'	EHea
- 'Korçula'	EHea
- 'Toothill Mustard' **new**	EHea
- 'Waterfall'	see *E. manipuliflora* 'Cascades'
mediterranea	see *E. erigena*
multiflora	XPep
- 'Formentor'	EHea
x ***oldenburgensis*** 'Ammerland'	EHea
- 'Oldenburg'	EHea
patersonia	see *E. patersonii*
§ ***patersonii***	SPlb
x ***praegeri***	see *E.* x *stuartii*
racemosa	EHea
scoparia subsp. ***azorica***	EHea
- subsp. ***maderincola*** 'Madeira Gold'	EHea
- subsp. ***platycodon***	EHea
§ - subsp. ***scoparia*** 'Minima'	EHea MBar
- - 'Pumila'	see *E. scoparia* subsp. *scoparia* 'Minima'
spiculifolia	MBar WThu
- f. ***albiflora***	EHea
- 'Balkan Rose'	CStu EHea
straussiana	SPlb
§ x ***stuartii***	MBar
- 'Charles Stuart'	EHea
- 'Connemara'	EHea
- 'Irish Lemon' ♀H4	CNCN CSBt EHea EPfP LCro LRHS MBar MSwo NHol
- 'Irish Orange'	CBcs CNCN CSBt EHea LRHS MBar NBlu NHol
- 'Irish Rose'	EHea

	- 'Nacung'	EHea
	- 'Pat Turpin'	EHea
	subdivaricata	CTrC EHea
§	***terminalis*** ♀H4	CNCN EHea MBar SRms
	- 'Golden Oriole'	EHea
	- ***stricta***	see *E. terminalis*
	- 'Thelma Woolner'	CNCN EHea MBar
	tetralix	SRms
	- 'Alba'	EHea
	- 'Alba Mollis' ♀H4	CNCN CSBt EHea MBar MBri NHol
	- 'Alba Praecox'	EHea
	- 'Allendale Pink'	EHea
	- 'Ardy'	EHea
	- 'Bala'	EHea
	- 'Bartinney'	EHea MBar
	- 'Con Underwood' ♀H4	CNCN CSBt EHea LRHS MBar MSwo NHol SRms
	- 'Curled Roundstone'	EHea
	- 'Dänemark'	EHea
	- 'Daphne Underwood'	EHea
	- 'Darleyensis'	EHea
	- 'Dee'	EHea
	- 'Delta'	EHea MBar
	- 'Derry Gold'	EHea
	- 'Foxhome'	EHea MBar
	- 'George Fraser'	EHea
	- 'Gratis'	EHea
	- 'Hailstones'	EHea MBar
	- 'Helma'	EHea
	- 'Helma Variegated' (v)	EHea
	- 'Hookstone Pink'	CNCN EHea MSwo
	- 'Humoresque'	EHea
	- 'Jos' Creeping'	EHea
	- 'Ken Underwood'	EHea MBar
	- 'L.E. Underwood'	EHea MBar NHol
	- 'Mary Grace'	EHea
	- 'Melbury White'	CNCN EHea MBar
	- 'Morning Glow'	see *E.* x *watsonii* 'F. White'
	- 'Pink Glow'	EHea
	- 'Pink Pepper'	EHea
	- 'Pink Star' ♀H4	CNCN EHea MBar NHol SRms
	- 'Renate'	EHea
	- 'Riko'	EHea SRms
	- 'Rosea'	EHea
	- 'Rubra'	EHea
§	- 'Ruby's Variety'	EHea MBar
	- 'Ruby's Velvet'	see *E. tetralix* 'Ruby's Variety'
	- 'Ruth's Gold'	EHea MBar NHol
	- 'Salmon Seedling'	EHea
	- 'Samtpfötchen'	EHea
	- 'Silver Bells'	CSBt EHea MBar
	- 'Stikker'	EHea
	- 'Swedish Yellow'	EHea
	- 'Terschelling'	EHea
	- 'Tina'	CNCN EHea
	- 'Trixie'	EHea
	- 'White House'	EHea
	umbellata	EHea MBar
	- 'Anne Small'	EHea
	- 'David Small'	EHea
	vagans 'Alba Nana'	see *E. vagans* 'Nana'
	- f. ***anandra***	EHea
	- 'Bianca'	EHea
	- 'Birch Glow' ♀H4	CNCN EHea EPfP
	- 'Carnea'	EHea
	- 'Charm'	EHea
	- 'Chittendenii'	EHea
	- 'Cornish Cream' ♀H4	CBcs CNCN EHea EPfP MBar NHol
	- 'Cream'	CNCN EHea
	- 'Diana Hornibrook'	CNCN EHea MBar
	- 'Diana's Gold'	EHea
	- 'Fiddlestone'	CNCN EHea MBar
	- 'French White'	CNCN EHea MBar
	- 'George Underwood'	EHea MBar
	- 'Golden Triumph'	EHea MBar

	- 'Grandiflora'	CNCN EHea MBar
	- 'Holden Pink'	CNCN EHea
	- 'Hookstone Rosea'	EHea MBar
	- 'Ida M. Britten'	EHea MBar
	- 'J.C. Fletcher'	EHea
	- 'Kevernensis Alba' ♀H4	EHea MBar
	- 'Leucantha'	EHea
	- 'Lilacina'	CNCN EHea MBar
	- 'Lyonesse' ♀H4	CNCN CTri EHea LCro MBar MBri MGos MSwo NHol SRms
	- 'Miss Waterer'	EHea MBar
	- 'Mrs D.F. Maxwell' ♀H4	CBcs CNCN CSBt CTri EHea MBar MBri MGos MSwo NHol SPer SRms
	- 'Mrs Donaldson'	EHea
§	- 'Nana'	EHea MBar
	- 'Pallida'	EHea
	- 'Peach Blossom'	EHea MBar
	- 'Pyrenees Pink'	CNCN EHea MBar
	- 'Rosea'	EHea
	- 'Rubra'	CNCN EHea MBar
	- 'Saint Keverne'	CNCN CSBt CTri EHea IArd MBar NHol
	- 'Summertime'	CNCN EHea MBar
	- 'Valerie Proudley' ♀H4	CNCN CSBt EHea MBar MBri MGos MWat NHol SPer SRms
	- 'Valerie Smith'	EHea
	- 'Viridiflora'	EHea MBar
	- 'White Lady'	EHea MBar
	- 'White Rocket'	MBar
	- 'White Spire'	EHea
	- 'Yellow John'	CBcs CNCN EHea MBar
	x ***veitchii*** 'Brockhill'	EHea
	- 'Exeter' ♀H3	CNCN CSBt EHea ELan EPfP LRHS MBar NHol SPer SPoG WFar
	- 'Gold Tips' ♀H4	CNCN CSBt EHea EPfP MBar MBri NHol
	- 'Pink Joy'	CNCN EHea MBri
	ventricosa	SPoG
	versicolor	SPlb
	verticillata	CTrC EHea
	viridescens	EHea
	x ***watsonii*** 'Cherry Turpin'	EHea
	- 'Dawn' ♀H4	CNCN EHea MBar
	- 'Dorothy Metheny'	EHea
	- 'Dorset Beauty'	EHea
§	- 'F. White'	EHea MBar
	- 'Gwen'	CNCN EHea MBar
	- 'H. Maxwell'	CNCN EHea
	- 'Mary'	EHea
	- 'Pink Pacific'	EHea
	- 'Rachel'	EHea
	- 'Truro'	EHea
	x ***williamsii*** 'Cow-y-Jack'	EHea
	- 'Croft Pascoe'	EHea
	- 'David Coombe'	EHea
	- 'Gew Graze'	EHea
	- 'Gold Button'	EHea MBar
	- 'Gwavas'	CNCN EHea MBar
	- 'Jean Julian'	EHea
	- 'Ken Wilson'	EHea
	- 'Lizard Downs'	EHea
	- 'Marion Hughes'	EHea
	- 'P.D. Williams' ♀H4	CNCN EHea MBar
I	'Winter Fire' (*oatesii* hybrid)	EHea

Erigeron (Asteraceae)

	from Bald Mountains	NWCA
	from Big Horn	NMen
	'Adria'	EBee EBla ECtt GBuc LTwo MBNS NEgg NGdn SPer SPla WFar
§	***alpinus***	LRHS NLAp SPoG
	'Amity'	GMac
	annuus new	NDov
	aurantiacus	EBee EDAr EPfP MBNS MHer NBre NBro NNor NPri

§	***aureus***	NSla
	- NNS 96-87	NWCA
	- 'Canary Bird' ♀H4	CPBP EPfP EPot NBir NMen NSla WAbe WFar WLin
	'Azure Beauty'	EBee EPfP
	Azure Fairy	see *E.* 'Azurfee'
§	'Azurfee'	CSBt EBee ELan EPfP GMaP LCro MBNS MWat NBir NEgg NLar NPri SGar SPer SPhx SPla SPoG SWvt WMoo WPer
	Black Sea	see *E.* 'Schwarzes Meer'
	'Blue Beauty'	LRHS SRms
	'Charity'	LRHS MRav WBrE
	chrysopsidis new	GKev
	- 'Grand Ridge'	EPfP EPot LHop LRHS LTwo SBla WAbe
	compositus	CPBP CTri SRms WPer
§	- var. ***discoideus***	EBur NBre NLar NMen SPlb WPer
	- 'Rocky'	EBee ECho GQue SPoG SRot
	Darkest of All	see *E.* 'Dunkelste Aller'
	deep pink-flowered	CHEx
	'Dignity'	EBee EBla EGle EKen ELan LHop LTwo MWat NBro WCot WFar
	'Dimity'	CMea ECha EDAr NBre SAga WBrk WFar WHal WSFF
	'Dominator' new	GBin
§	'Dunkelste Aller' ♀H3	CPrp CSam EBee EBla ECtt ELan ENot EPfP ERou GMaP LBMP LHop LRHS MBri MRav NGdn SBch SMer SPer SPoG SRms SWvt WBrE WCAu WEas WFar WHlf
	elegantulus	CMea
*	***ereganus***	NBre
*	***eriocalyx*** new	GKev
	'Felicity'	EBee ERou
	flettii	NLAp WPat
	'Foersters Liebling' ♀H4	EBee EBla EPfP GBin NGdn WAul WCAu
	foliosus var. ***hartwegii*** NNS 00-288	EPPr
	formosissimus	GBin
	'Four Winds'	EBee ECtt ELan EWes LHop MRav NGdn NMen WPer
	frigidus new	NMen
	'Gaiety'	EBee NBre
	glaucus	CHrt CSBt EBee EWll GAbr GGar MRav MWgw NBre NGdn NVic SIng SMad WBrk WCot WFar WHoo WWeb
	- 'Albus'	EBee EShb EWll LHop LRHS SMad WPer
	- 'Elstead Pink'	COlW CTri EBee ELan NEgg SAga SPla WFar WSHC
	- pink-flowered	SPla
	- 'Roger Raiche'	MRav SMrm
	- 'Roseus'	CBcs CHal ERou
	- 'Sea Breeze'	COlW CPrp GGar GMaP LHop MBNS MBri NBre NEgg NLar NPri SPoG WCot
	howellii	EBee NBre WCot
§	***karvinskianus*** ♀H3	More than 30 suppliers
	- 'Stallone'	NPri
	leiomerus	LBee LTwo
	'Lilofee'	NGby
	linearis	LTwo NBre NMen
	'Mrs F.H. Beale'	EBee EBla LRHS SRGP WSpi
	mucronatus	see *E. karvinskianus*
	multiradiatus	WFar
	'Nachthimmel'	EBee EBla ECtt EMan LAst MWgw NBre NGdn
	nanus	NWCA WPer
	'Offenham Excellence' new	WCot
	philadelphicus	CElw IGor NBir NBro
	- 'Lilac Sky' new	SKHP
	'Pink Beauty'	ECtt
	Pink Jewel	see *E.* 'Rosa Juwel'
	pinnatisectus	GKev NWCA WFar WPer
	'Profusion'	see *E. karvinskianus*
	pyrenaicus misapplied	see *E. alpinus*
	pyrenaicus Rouy	see *Aster pyrenaeus*
	'Quakeress'	CPrp CSam EBee EBla ECtt EMan EPfP GMaP GMac LAst LBMP LEdu MBri MRav NBro NGdn SMrm SPoG WAul WCot WEas WFar WOut WTel
§	'Rosa Juwel'	CSBt CTri EBee ECtt ELan ENot EPfP GMaP LAst MBNS MRav NBir NEgg NOak NPri SPer SPla SPoG SRms SWvt WHen WMnd WMoo WPer WWeb
	'Rosenballett'	WCot
	'Rotes Meer'	CPrp EBee EBla ECtt ELan ERou MRav WBrk WCot WFar
	rotundifolius 'Caerulescens'	see *Bellis caerulescens*
	salsuginosus misapplied	see *Aster sibiricus*
§	'Schneewittchen'	CMMP EBee EBla ECtt ELan EMan EPfP LHop MRav MWat MWgw NCGa NVic SPet SPla SPoG SSvw SWvt WCAu
§	'Schwarzes Meer'	EBee ERou NGdn SPer WCot WFar
	scopulinus	CPBP WPat
	simplex	CPBP LRHS
	'Sincerity'	WFar
	'Snow Queen'	WFar
	Snow White	see *E.* 'Schneewittchen'
	'Sommerabend'	EBee GBin
	'Sommerneuschnee'	ECha GBin LCro WMnd
	speciosus	SMer
	- 'Grandiflora'	NBre
	'Strahlenmeer'	CPrp EBee MWgw NBre NGdn WFar
	trifidus	see *E. compositus* var. *discoideus*
	uniflorus	LTwo SRms
	vagus	CPBP GKev LTwo
	'Wayne Roderick'	EBee
	'White Quakeress'	CMea EGle ERou GBuc MRav MWrn WCot WRHF
	'Wuppertal'	EBee MRav NBro NEgg NGdn

Erinacea (*Papilionaceae*)

§	***anthyllis*** ♀H4	SIng XPep
	pungens	see *E. anthyllis*

Erinus (*Scrophulariaceae*)

	alpinus ♀H4	CTri ECho ECtt EPfP GKev GMaP MLHP MWat NHol NLAp NPri NWCA SBch SIng SPet SPoG SRms WEas WFar WPer
	- var. ***albus***	ECho NHol NLAp NLar NMen SRms WHoo WPer
	- 'Doktor Hähnle'	ECho EDAr LRHS NLar NMen SRms WHoo WPer WSpi
	- 'Mrs Charles Boyle'	NMen

Eriobotrya (*Rosaceae*)

	deflexa	CHEx IDee
	- 'Coppertone'	SBLw SCoo
	japonica (F) ♀H3	CAbb CBcs CDul CHEx CKob CMCN EAmu EPfP ERom EShb GQui LCro LEdu LPan LRHS MPRe SArc SBLw SCoo SDry SPer WHer WNor WSHC

Eriocapitella see *Anemone*

Eriocephalus (*Asteraceae*)

	africanus	SPlb WJek

Eriogonum (*Polygonaceae*)

	KM 0135	CDes

	cespitosum	CGra NLAp SBla
	corymbosum	EBee
	flavum	WPer
	- var. ***piperi*** new	CGra
	jamesii	NLAp WPat
	kennedyi	CGra
	latifolium new	EBee GFor
	ovalifolium var. ***nivale***	NWCA SBla WLin
	thymoides	CGra
	umbellatum	ECho EPot EShb LRHS NLAp
	- var. ***haussknechtii***	see *E. umbellatum* var. *polyanthum*
	- var. ***humistratum***	SBla WLin WPat
§	- var. ***polyanthum***	WLin
	- var. ***torreyanum***	CMea GEdr NLAp WLin WPat
	- var. ***umbellatum***	LBee

Eriophorum (*Cyperaceae*)

	angustifolium	CBen CRWN CWat EGle EHon EMFW EPla MCCP SPlb SWat WHer WMAq WMoo WPer WPnP WSFF XIsg
	latifolium	XIsg
	vaginatum	GFor LLWG NSco WSFF XIsg

Eriophyllum (*Asteraceae*)

	lanatum	CFis EBee ECha EPfP EShb MDKP MEHN NBid NBre SAga SPhx WPen WWeb

Eritrichium (*Boraginaceae*)

	rupestre var. ***pectinatum***	NSla
*	***sibiricum***	EDif

Erodium ✿ (*Geraniaceae*)

	absinthoides	LRHS
	- var. ***amanum***	see *E. amanum*
§	***acaule***	NCiC NLar WFar
§	***amanum***	EBee EPot EWes LRHS WAbe
	balearicum	see *E.* x *variabile* 'Album'
	'Bidderi'	NChi NLAp WAbe
	'Carmel'	NLAp
	'Caroline'	LPio
	carvifolium	CElw EBee EWsh GKev LRHS NLAp NWCA SBch WFar
§	***castellanum***	EBee GKev LTwo NBre NBro NLAp NMen NSti SBch SBla SHGN SRms WFar
	- 'Dujardin'	SPhx
	celtibericum	EPot NLAp
	chamaedryoides	see *E. reichardii*
	- 'Roseum'	see *E.* x *variabile* 'Roseum'
	cheilanthifolium 'David Crocker'	NMen
	chrysanthum	More than 30 suppliers
	- pink	CSpe ECha NMen SBla SMrm SPhx SRot
	corsicum	EBur ECho MTho NMen NWCA XPep
	- 'Album'	ECho LAst LTwo NLar NMen
	'County Park'	CMea EBee ECha ECou MLHP NLAp SBla SHar SRms
	daucoides misapplied	see *E. castellanum*
	daucoides Boiss.	EBee
	'Eileen Emmett'	EPot
	'Florida' new	MAga
	foetidum	EAlp EGle NMen XPep
	- 'Pallidum'	see *E.* 'Pallidum'
	'Fran's Choice'	see *E.* 'Fran's Delight'
§	'Fran's Delight'	CMea CSpe GMaP MLHP NLAp NMen SBla WHoo
	'Géant de Saint Cyr'	ECtt EMan
N	***glandulosum*** ♀H4	EBee ECho EPfP LHop MHer MWea SBla SRms SRot WFar WKif WPat
	gruinum	EDAr SPhx
	guttatum misapplied	see *E.* 'Katherine Joy'
N	***guttatum*** (Desf.) Willd.	ECho EPot GMaP MWat NMen SRms
	x ***hybridum*** Sünderm.	WAbe
	hymenodes L'Hér.	see *E. trifolium*
	'Julie Ritchie'	CMea WHoo
§	'Katherine Joy'	CElw CLyd EBee EPot EWes MHer NChi NDlv NLAp NRya SRot WAbe
	x ***kolbianum***	NDlv NLAp SMHy SMrm WAbe WFar WHoo WKif
	- 'Natasha'	CMHG EAlp EBee EPot EWes GGar GMaP LBee LRHS MHer NChi NLAp NMen SPoG SWat WAbe WFar WKif
	x ***lindavicum***	NChi
	- 'Charter House'	LPio
	macradenum	see *E. glandulosum*
	manescavii	More than 30 suppliers
	'Merstham Pink'	CMHG GMaP NChi NDlv NLAp NLar SBla SRms
	moschatum	ECho
	'Nunwood Pink'	NWCA
§	'Pallidum'	CSam
	pelargoniiflorum	CPom CSpe EBee EDAr EPfP EWTr GSki LPio MTho NBro NChi NDov NLar NRnb SBod SEND SPhx SRms STes WEas WFar WHil WKif WPer WPnP WWFP
	'Peter Vernon'	NWCA
	petraeum subsp. ***glandulosum***	see *E. glandulosum*
	- subsp. ***petraeum***	EPot MHer SBla
	'Pickering Pink'	EBee LIMB NDlv NLAp NMen SRot SWat
	'Pippa Mills'	CElw
	'Princesse Marion'	LPio MLHP NChi
*	'Purple Haze'	CSpe EBee NEgg SPoG SRms SRot WFar
§	***reichardii***	CTri ECho ECtt GSki ITim LRHS MHer MTho NLAp NWCA SPet SPoG SRms SWat WCFE WFar WTel
	- 'Album'	CEnt EAlp ECho NEgg NMen SPet SPoG WFar WHoo
	- 'Bianca'	EBee
	- 'Pipsqueak'	SRot
*	- 'Rubrum'	CElw ECho
	'Robertino'	MLHP
	'Robespierre'	SPhx
	'Robin'	NLAp
	rodiei	EBee EWes
	romanum	see *E. acaule*
§	***rupestre***	EBee ECho ECtt GMaP MWea NDlv NWCA SRms SRot
	sebaceum 'Polly'	NWCA
	'Spanish Eyes'	NChi NLAp SMrm SRot WAbe WCot WFar
	'Stephanie'	CElw CFis CLyd CMHG ECho EWes GMaP LBee LRHS MHer NChi NDlv NLAp SMHy SRot SWal
	supracanum	see *E. rupestre*
	'Tiny Kyni'	NLAp WFar
	tordylioides	EBee
	trichomanifolium L'Hér.	EWes LBee LRHS MHer
§	***trifolium***	CBgR CHrt CMea EBee ECho ELan EPfP EPot MHer NCiC NSla SBri SGar SIng SPhx WCru WTMC XPep
	x ***variabile***	CBrm ECtt NLAp
§	- 'Album'	EBee ECho EDAr EPot EWin GBuc MBar MHer MTho NEgg NPri NWCA SBla SHFr SRms SRot WAbe WBrk WFar WPat WPer WTel
I	- 'Bishop's Form'	More than 30 suppliers
	x ***variabile*** 'Candy'	EAlp EDAr SRot
	x ***variabile*** 'Derek'	ECho

	- 'Flore Pleno' (d)	CStu EBee ECho EDAr ELan EWes NLAp NMen SHFr SIng SRms SRot WBrk WFar WPer
	- 'Red Rock'	EBee EWes SIng
§	- 'Roseum' ♀H4	EAlp ECho ECtt EDAr ELan EPfP GGar GSki LBee LRHS NLAp NWCA SPlb SRms WBrk WFar WPer
I	'Westacre Seedling'	EWes
	'Whitwell Superb'	CDes CElw NWCA
	x ***willkommianum***	NWCA

Erpetion see *Viola*

Eruca (*Brassicaceae*)

	vesicaria	CWan MNHC
	- subsp. ***sativa***	CArn CSpe ELau GPoy MHer MNHC MSal NGHP SIde WJek WSel

Eryngium ✿ (*Apiaceae*)

	CD&R	EWes
	F&M 224	WPGP
	PC&H 268	EKen MLHP NLar
	RB 94054	ITer
§	***agavifolium***	More than 30 suppliers
	alpinum ♀H4	More than 30 suppliers
	- 'Amethyst'	GBuc IPot LRHS MBri MRav MSte NBro SPhx SWat
	- 'Blue Jacket'	NSti WBrE
	- 'Blue Star'	CHar CSpe EBee EBla EDAr EHrv ELan EPfP ERou GAbr GMac MNFA MRav MSte MWat NCGa NChi NDov NEgg SMad SPhx SPla SRkn WHoo WPer WSpi WTin WWeb
	- 'Holden Blue'	MAvo
	- 'Slieve Donard'	see *E.* x *zabelii* 'Donard Variety'
	- 'Superbum'	CSpe ECtt EHrv ERou GAbr GBri GBuc GSki MBri MNrw NCob NEgg NLar SPla SPoG SRms SWat WCot WGwG
	amethystinum	CMdw EBee EGoo EHrv EMan GSki LPio MAvo MNrw NChi SPla WBVN WPer WSHC
	biebersteinianum	see *E. caeruleum*
	'Blue Jackpot'	CWCL EBee EHrv EWes GMac IBal MAvo MBNS MBri MLLN NBhm NCob NMoo NOrc NPri SMrm SPoG SWat
	'Blue Steel'	MAvo NChi
	bourgatii	More than 30 suppliers
	- Graham Stuart Thomas's selection	More than 30 suppliers
	- 'Oxford Blue' ♀H4	CEnt CSpe EBee EHrv GMaP GMac GSki LAst MHer NLar SAga SGar SPer SWvt WEas WHoo WOld
	- 'Picos Amethyst'	CBcs CWGN EBee EGle EKen ENot GBri LCro LHop LSRN NLar NSti SPhx SPoG SVil WOVN
	- 'Picos Blue' PBR	CBod CKno CMHG CSpe CWCL CWGN EBee EBla EGle EHrv IPot LFur LHop LSRN MAvo NCob NDov NLar NSti SMrm SPer SPhx SPoG SVil SWat SWvt WHoo WPGP
	bromeliifolium misapplied	see *E. agavifolium*, *E. eburneum*
§	***caeruleum***	GBuc GMac MGol MNrw NChi NEgg WOut
	campestre	EWll MDKP MHer NChi NGby NLar WFar WPer
	carlinae	NDov
	caucasicum	see *E. caeruleum*
	'Cobalt Star' new	GMac
	creticum	NBir NBro NChi
	decaisneanum misapplied	see *E. pandanifolium*
	Delaroux	see *E. proteiflorum*
	dichotomum	NChi
	ebracteatum	CSpe EBla LPio MCot MWrn SPhx WCot
	- var. ***poterioides***	SMad SPhx
§	***eburneum***	CBcs CGHE CKno EBee ECha EPfP EWes GBuc GMaP LPio LRHS MWgw MWrn NBro NChi NEgg NSti SMad SPhx WCot WCru WFar WPic WSpi
	aff. ***eburneum***	WPGP
	elegans var. ***elegans*** CDPR 3076 new	WPGP
	foetidum	CArn
§	***giganteum*** ♀H4	More than 30 suppliers
	- 'Silver Ghost' ♀H4	More than 30 suppliers
	glaciale	CPLG
	- JJA 461.000	NWCA
	guatemalense B&SWJ 8989 new	WCru
	horridum misapplied	see *E. eburneum*
	horridum ambig.	EBee EWes LEdu LPio LRHS MEHN MNrw NChi SAPC SArc SPoG WCAu WFar WMnd WPGP
	maritimum	CArn CPou CWCL EBee EGoo GPoy MHer MWgw NLar SECG SPhx SPlb WCot WFar WSel
	Miss Willmott's ghost	see *E. giganteum*
	monocephalum	EBee WPGP
	x ***oliverianum*** ♀H4	More than 30 suppliers
	palmatum	NChi
§	***pandanifolium*** ♀H4	CHEx CHrt CMHG CTrG EBee EPfP EWes GWWP ITer LPio NDov SAPC SArc SGar SMad SPav SPlb SPoG SWvt WCot WPGP
	- 'Physic Purple'	CAby SMHy SPhx WCot
	paniculatum	EBee WPGP
	pectinatum B&SWJ 9109	WCru
	petiolatum	MNrw
	planum	More than 30 suppliers
	- 'Bethlehem' ♀H4	EBee LRHS MBNS MBri NBro NLar SWat WSpi
§	- 'Blauer Zwerg'	CKno EBee LCro LHop SPla SWat WFar WHlf WSpi
	- 'Blaukappe'	CFir CHar CMea COIW CWCL EBee EDAr ERou GBri GMac LCro LDai LRHS NChi NLar SMrm SPhx WAul WBrE WFar WGwG WHil WSHC
*	- 'Blue Candle'	NLar WFar
	- Blue Dwarf	see *E. planum* 'Blauer Zwerg'
	- 'Blue Ribbon'	EBee EBla LAst LRHS LSou MBNS MRav MWgw NEgg NGdn SWat
	- 'Blue Thimbles'	GMac
	- 'Flüela'	EBee EBla ECtt ERou EWes GMaP LRHS LSRN NBro SBch SPla SWat WFar WHrl WTin
	- 'Hellas'	CSpe EBee ERou MBNS NBPC NLar
	- 'Paradise Jackpot' new	NBPC SPer
	- 'Seven Seas'	CFir CKno EBee EBla LRHS MBri NBro NGdn SPla SWat WPer
	- 'Silver Stone'	EBee EBla GMaP LDai LRHS MBri MDKP NBre NBro NOrc NPri NSti SPoG SSvw WCAu
*	- 'Tetra Petra'	CBcs EBee GBri MAvo NBPC NEgg SRkn WHil WPer
§	***proteiflorum***	COIW EBee EDAr GSki ITer LPio LRHS MDKP MWrn NCGa NDov SMad SPlb WAul WCot WGwG
	serbicum	MAvo
	serra	CAby EBee EDAr EWes GBuc LDai LRHS WBor
	- RB 90454	MDKP
	spinalba	GSki SPhx

	strotheri B&SWJ 9109 new	WCru
	tricuspidatum	ECtt GSki LRHS WPer WSpi
	x ***tripartitum*** ♀H4	More than 30 suppliers
*	***umbelliferum***	CBcs EDAr GKev MDKP NChi
	variifolium	More than 30 suppliers
	venustum	CDes LPio MAvo SPhx
	yuccifolium	CArn CBct CHEx EBee EBla EPfP ERou EWes LBMP LEdu LPio NHol NVic SDix SDnm SPav SPhx SPlb SWvt WBrE WFar WHoo WTin
	x ***zabelii***	ECha GMac LPio MAvo NBir NChi NDov SMeo SMrm SPhx WPGP
§	- 'Donard Variety'	CSpe GMac IPot ITim LRHS MDKP MNFA NLar SWat
	- 'Forncett Ultra'	CDes EMon GMac MAvo WPGP
	- 'Jewel'	CDes MAvo SApp SMHy SWat
	- 'Jos Eijking'	EBrs EMan ENot GMac LRHS MRav NLar SPer WBor
	- 'Spring Hill Seedling'	MAvo
	- 'Violetta'	ECha ELan GBuc GMac IGor MAvo MBri MSte NGby SWat WFar WHoo WPen

Erysimum (*Brassicaceae*)

	from Madeira	CPLG
	amoenum	CPBP
	'Apricot Delight'	see *E.* 'Apricot Twist'
§	'Apricot Twist'	More than 30 suppliers
	arkansanum	see *E. helveticum*
	'Bowles' Mauve' ♀H3	More than 30 suppliers
	'Bowles' Purple'	LAst NCob SRms SWvt WBVN
	'Bowles' Yellow'	GBuc SMer
	'Bredon' ♀H3	CBgR EBee EPfP EWin LRHS LSou MAsh NBlu NPer SBch WKif WSpi
	brevistylum new	GKev
	'Butterscotch'	CFee CSam ECtt EGoo MMHG NCob SAga WEas WHoo WTin
	'Butterscotch Variegated' (v)	GBri NCob WCot
	candicum	XPep
	cheiri	CArn GWCH MHer NSco WCot
	- 'Blood Red' new	CSpe
	- 'Bloody Warrior' (d)	CElw ECtt GBuc WEas
	- 'Fire King'	LCro
§	- 'Harpur Crewe' (d)	CBgR CEnt CFee CSsd CTri EBee ELan ELon EPfP ERou EShb GMaP LRHS MTho NPer SRms WPnn
	- 'Jane's Derision'	CNat
	'Chelsea Jacket'	EBee ECtt EPfP ERou EWin GBri LHop SAga WEas
	concinnum	see *E. suffrutescens*
	'Constant Cheer'	More than 30 suppliers
	'Cotswold Gem' (v)	CElw EBee ECtt ELan EMil EPPr EPfP EShb GBri LAst LBMP LDai MAsh MHer NBPC NCob NEgg NPer NSti SAga SBri SHBN SLim SMrm SPoG STes SWvt WCot WGwG WWlt
	'Cream Delight'	EBee EWin
	'Dawn Breaker'	CElw CWGN EBee ENor EWes GBin GBri LSou MAsh MBNS NCob SPoG WCot WLin
	'Devon Gold'	see *E.* 'Plant World Gold'
	'Devon Sunset'	GBri MRav SAga
	'Dorothy Elmhirst'	see *E.* 'Mrs L.K. Elmhirst'
	dwarf lemon	WHoo
	'Ellen Willmott'	CEnt GBin
*	***gelidum*** var. ***kotschyi***	SBla
	'Golden Gem'	EWin NBlu NDlv SPoG WFar WPer
	'Golden Jubilee'	EAlp ECho ERou GGar LBMP LIMB WFar
	'Hector's Gate Post' new	ENor LSRN SRkn
	'Hector's Gatepost' new	EBee SPoG
§	***helveticum***	CEnt CMdw ECho ILad SRms
	'Jacob's Jacket'	CStu ECtt EPyc MBNS NPer WEas
	'Jaunty Joyce'	GBri
	'Joan Adams' new	LHop SAga
	'John Codrington'	CSam EBee GBri GBuc LHop NPer SAga WKif WSpi WWFP
	'Joseph's Coat'	LIMB
	'Julian Orchard'	CHII CSpe NCiC SSth
	kotschyanum	CLyd CPBP ECho ECtt LBee NLAp NMen SRms
	'Lady Roborough'	CFee GBuc
	linifolium	EBur SRms WFar WGor XPep
§	- 'Variegatum' (v)	CArn CBrm CCCN CSBt EBee ECtt ELan EPfP EPot ERou LAst LRHS NPer NPri SPer SPoG SRot STes WHoo WPGP
	'Mayflower'	NCob
	menziesii subsp. ***yadonii***	WLin
	'Miss Hopton'	WEas
	'Moonlight'	CSam ECtt EPot GBuc GMaP LCro MHer MTho NCGa NDov SBla SRms WBVN
§	'Mrs L.K. Elmhirst'	MDKP MMHG NDov NPer WCot WWFP
	mutabile	CBgR CTri EGoo MAsh MRav NBir SIde WHal
	- 'Variegatum' (v)	WEas
	'Orange Flame'	CMea EAlp ECho ECtt EPot ERou EWin GGar LAst LBee LHop LSou MHer NHol NPer NWCA SAga SPoG WFar WPer
	'Orange Queen'	WWeb
	'Parish's'	CBgR CMdw CSpe ECtt EWTr MRav SAga
	'Pastel Patchwork'	CSpe EBee WHlf
	perofskianum	WEas
	Perry's hybrid	NPer
	'Perry's Peculiar'	NPer
	'Plant World Antique'	MAvo
§	'Plant World Gold'	CElw
	'Plant World Lemon'	CPLG EBee ERou EWin GBri LSou MBnl MBri MEHN SDnm SRot
§	***pulchellum***	ECha SRot
	- 'Variegatum' (v)	GGar WBrE WSFF
	pumilum DC.	see *E. helveticum*
	'Rosemoor'	ECha
	rupestre	see *E. pulchellum*
	'Ruston Royal'	EBee EWin
	'Sissinghurst Variegated'	see *E. linifolium* 'Variegatum'
	'Sprite'	CLyd CTri ECho ECtt EDAr EPot NPer
	'Stars and Stripes' new	CWGN EBee LBuc SPoG
§	***suffrutescens***	XPep
	'Sweet Sorbet'	CHrt EBee EPfP ERou EWin LAst MBri MSte NBPC NDov NPri SPav SPoG SRkn SWvt WHoo
*	'Tricolor'	WHil
	'Turkish Bazaar'	ECho
	Walberton's Fragrant Sunshine = 'Walfrasun'	LRHS MAsh SCoo SPoG
	'Wenlock Beauty'	GBin LDai SRms WHoo WMnd
	'Winter Joy'	CBow CHar EBee ERou LSou MBnl
	witmannii	SSth

Erythraea see *Centaurium*

Erythrina (*Papilionaceae*)

	x ***bidwillii***	CCCN
	crista-galli	CAbb CBcs CCCN CDTJ CHEx CPle CSpe CWCL ELan ERea GQui IDee LRHS MLan MPRe MWea SOWG SPlb WCot WPGP WPat WSHC
	- 'Compacta'	SMad
	flabelliformis	MGol
§	***humeana***	CDTJ

	indica	see *E. variegata*
	princeps	see *E. humeana*
§	***variegata*** (v)	CDTJ

Erythronium ✿ (*Liliaceae*)

	albidum	CHHB CLAP EBee ECho EPot GBuc GGar IBlr LAma NMen SGar
	americanum	CAby CArn CHHB CLAP CWoo EBee EBrs ECho EPot GBuc GCrs GEdr GGar IBlr LAma MLLN MSSP NLAp NMen WCru WWst
	'Apple Blossom' new	CWsd
	'Beechpark'	IBlr
	'Blush'	CWsd GBuc IBlr
	'Brimstone' new	CWsd
	'Californian Star'	IBlr
	californicum ♀H4	CAby CHHB CLAP CWoo CWsd EBee EBrs ECho GBuc GCrs ITim SCnR WAbe WCru
	- J&JA 1.350.209	CWoo
	- J&JA 13216	CLAP
	- JCA 1.350.200	WWst
*	- var. ***candidum*** MS 01/009 new	WWst
	- 'Harvington Snowgoose' new	CLAP EHrv
	- Plas Merdyn form	IBlr
§	- 'White Beauty' ♀H4	More than 30 suppliers
	californicum x ***hendersonii*** new	IBlr
	caucasicum	CLAP
	citrinum	CWoo CWsd GBuc NMen
	- J&JA 1.350.410	CWoo
	- J&JA 13462	CLAP CWoo
	- JCA 13462	WWst
	citrinum x ***hendersonii***	IBlr
	'Citronella'	CLAP EHrv GBuc GKev IBlr ITim MSSP NDlv NMen NMyG WAbe WCru WFar WTin
	cliftonii hort.	see *E. multiscapoideum* Cliftonii Group
	dens-canis ♀H4	More than 30 suppliers
	- JCA 470.001	CLAP
	- from Slovenia	CLAP
	- 'Charmer'	EBee GEdr WWst
	- 'Frans Hals'	CHHB CLAP CWsd EBee EBrs ECho EPot ERos GBuc GCrs GEdr GGar MNFA MTho WAbe WCru WHal WHil
	- 'Lilac Wonder'	CHHB CWsd EBee EBrs ECho EPot GEdr GMaP LAma LEdu LRHS MNrw MTho NHol WWst
*	- 'Moerheimii' (d)	CHHB GEdr IBlr WWst
	- var. ***niveum***	CHHB ERos IBlr
	- 'Old Aberdeen'	CLAP CWsd IBlr MNrw
	- 'Pink Perfection'	CHFP CHHB EBee EBrs ECho EPot ERos GEdr GGar LEdu LRHS NHol WCru WHil
	- 'Purple King'	CHFP CHHB CWsd EBee EBrs ECho EPot ERos GEdr GMaP LAma LRHS MNrw NLar WAbe WCru
	- 'Rose Queen'	CAby CPLG EBee EBrs ECho EPot ERos GAbr GBuc GGar GKev GMaP LAma MAvo MTho NLAp SPhx WHal WLin
*	- 'Semi-plenum' (d)	IBlr
	- 'Snowflake'	CAvo CLAP CMea CTca EBee EBrs ECha ECho EPot ERos GBuc GCrs GEdr GGar GKev LAma LRHS MNFA MNrw NBir NMen WAbe WCru WHil
	- 'White Splendour'	ECho ERos IBlr WWst
	elegans	CHHB EBee EBrs ECho EHrv SBla WWst
	'Flash'	IBlr
§	***grandiflorum***	CLAP EBee EBrs ECho EPot GBuc GCrs GEdr NMen
	- M&PS 007	CLAP
	- M&PS 96/024	NMen
	- subsp. ***chrysandrum***	see *E. grandiflorum*
	helenae	CLAP CWoo CWsd GEdr IBlr
	- J&JA 11678	WWst
	hendersonii	CLAP CWoo CWsd EHrv MSSP WAbe WWst
	- J&JA 1.351.301	CWoo
	- J&JA 12945	CLAP CWoo
	- JCA 11116	CLAP
	howellii	CLAP CWsd GCrs
	- J&JA 13428	WWst
	- J&JA 13441	CLAP
	'Janice' new	CWsd
	japonicum	CBcs CHHB EBee EBrs ECho EFEx EPot GBuc GCrs GEdr GGar LAma MNrw NHol NMen NMyG WCru WFar
	'Jeanette Brickell'	CLAP CWsd IBlr WWst
	'Jeannine'	CWsd GBuc GEdr IBlr WCru
	'Joan Wiley' new	CWsd
	'Joanna'	CWsd GBuc IBlr MNrw NMen WWst
	'Kondo'	CTri EBee EBrs ECho EPfP EPot ERos GBuc GEdr GGar GMaP IBal IBlr IPot ITim LAma LEdu LRHS MAvo MTho NBir NHol NMen SPer WAbe WCru WFar WHil
	'Margaret Mathew'	CLAP CWsd IBlr WWst
	'Minnehaha'	CWsd WWst
	montanum	EBee EHrv WWst
§	***multiscapoideum***	CLAP CWoo CWsd ECho SBla WCot
	- JCA 1.352.100	WWst
	- NNS 99-163	WWst
§	- Cliftonii Group	CHHB CLAP CWsd EBrs WAbe
	'Oregon Encore' new	IBlr
	oregonum	CLAP CWoo EBee EBrs ECho EHrv GBuc GCrs GGar IBlr MNrw MSSP SBla
	- subsp. ***leucandrum***	CLAP CWsd WWst
	- - J&JA 13494	CWoo
	- - JCA 4.352.400	WWst
I	- 'Sulpher Form' new	CLAP
	- yellow-flowered new	CWsd
	'Pagoda' ♀H4	More than 30 suppliers
	pluriflorum	EBrs
	purdyi	see *E. multiscapoideum*
	revolutum ♀H4	CAby CAvo CFir CLAP CWoo EBrs ECho EHrv EPot GBuc GCrs GGar GKev GMaP IBlr ITim MNrw MSSP NMen SBla SCnR SKHP SRot WAbe WCFE WCru
	- from God's Valley	WWst
	- early-flowering new	CWsd
	- 'Guincho Splendour'	IBlr
	- Johnsonii Group	CWoo WAbe WCru WWst
	- 'Knightshayes' new	CWsd
	- 'Knightshayes Pink'	CLAP EHrv GBuc IBlr
	- late-flowering new	CWsd
	- 'Pink Beauty'	WNor
	- Plas Merdyn form	IBlr
	- 'Rose Beauty'	CHHB EBrs NMen
	- 'White Beauty'	see *E. californicum* 'White Beauty'
	- 'Wild Salmon' new	CLAP
	'Rippling Waters'	IBlr
	'Rosalind'	CWsd IBlr SCnR
	sibiricum	EBee EBrs ECho GCrs GGar NMen NMyG SPer WWst
	- from Siberia	MPhe
	- 'Altai Snow'	CHHB
	- white-flowered	WWst
	'Sundisc'	CAby ECha ECho IBlr MSSP MTho NMen WAbe WWst

'Susannah' new	CWsd WWst
tuolumnense ♀H4	CLAP CMea CTca CWCL CWsd EBee EBrs ECho EHrv EPot ERos GBuc GCrs GEdr GGar GKev GMaP IBlr IHer LAma LEdu MCCP NMen WAbe WCot
- EBA clone 2	WAbe
- EBA clone 3	WAbe
- 'Spindlestone'	CWsd IBlr WWst
umbilicatum	GCrs IBlr WWst

Escallonia ✿ (*Escalloniaceae*)

'Alice'	SLPl SPer
'Apple Blossom' ♀H4	More than 30 suppliers
§ ***bifida*** ♀H3	CDoC CFee CPle EQua WFar WSHC
'Brians Gold' new	EPau
'C.F. Ball'	CBcs CSBt CTri EBee ELan GGar LBMP LBuc MGan MSwo NBlu NEgg NScw NWea SEND SRms WBVN WFar WMoo WTel
'Compacta Coccinea'	CBcs
'Dart's Rosy Red'	NHol SLPl
'Donard Beauty'	SRms WBod
'Donard Radiance' ♀H4	More than 30 suppliers
'Donard Seedling'	More than 30 suppliers
'Donard Star'	CSBt CWib ENot EPfP LAst NWea SLPl WCFE
'Edinensis'	CBcs ENot EPfP MBar NLar SBch SEND SLim WFar WGer WMoo WSpi
'Erecta'	EPfP SHGN
'Everest' new	LBuc LRHS
x ***exoniensis***	SRms
'Gwendolyn Anley'	SLPl SPer WFar
'Hopleys Gold'PBR	see *E. laevis* 'Gold Brian'
illinita	EBee NLar
'Iveyi' ♀H3	More than 30 suppliers
§ ***laevis***	SDry WFar
§ - 'Gold Brian'PBR	CDul CMHG CSBt EBee ELan ENot EPfP GGar LRHS LSRN MAsh MGos MWat SCoo SMer SPer SPoG SWal WBod WFar WHar
- 'Gold Ellen' (v)	CBcs CChe CTri CWSG EBee ELan EPfP LAst LRHS MAsh MGos MRav MSwo SAga SCoo SEND SLim SPer SPla SPoG SRms SWvt WBod WMoo WWeb
Lanarth No 1	CBcs
'Langleyensis' ♀H4	CBcs CPLG CSBt CTri CWib NWea WFar WHar
'Little Treasure'	ENot SPoG
mexicana	WFar
x ***mollis***	SPer
montevidensis	see *E. bifida*
'Newry'	SPer
organensis	see *E. laevis*
'Peach Blossom' ♀H4	CBcs CChe CDoC CDul CSam CWib EBee ECrN ELan EMil EPfP GGar LRHS MAsh MBNS MBri MLHP MSwo NBir NCGa NEgg SCoo SHBN SLPl SLim SPer SPoG SRms WFar
'Pink Elf'	MSwo NHol
'Pride of Donard' ♀H4	CBcs CDoC CPLG CSBt EBee EPfP GGar MAsh MGan NCGa NPri SRms WBrE
punctata	see *E. rubra*
'Red Dream'	CWSG EBee ERas LAst LRHS MAsh MBri MGos MSwo NBlu NHol NLar SAga SCoo SPoG SRms SWvt WFar WGer
'Red Elf'	EBee ECrN ELan EPfP GGar LAst LRHS MAsh MBar MBri MGos MRav MSwo MWat NEgg NHol SCoo SGar SLPl SPer SPlb SPoG SRms SWvt WBVN WFar WHen WWeb
'Red Hedger'	CDoC CSBt CTrG CWib ELan LRHS MRav SCoo SRms
'Red Robin'	CBcs MAsh SPoG
resinosa	CBcs CPLG CPle SAPC SArc WHCG WJek
revoluta	SDry
§ ***rubra***	MLHP
- 'Crimson Spire' ♀H4	More than 30 suppliers
- 'Ingramii'	CSBt CWib NWea SHBN
- var. ***macrantha***	CBcs CChe CDoC CDul CSBt CWSG CWib EBee ECrN EPfP GGar IArd LAst LRHS MHer NBir NBlu NEgg NWea SCoo SLim SMer SPer SPoG WAbe WFar WGer WMoo WWeb XPep
* - - ***aurea***	NScw
- 'Pygmaea'	see *E. rubra* 'Woodside'
- var. ***uniflora***	SDry
§ - 'Woodside'	ECho EPfP LTwo MLHP NHol SRms WHCG
'Saint Keverne'	CBcs
'Silver Anniversary'	MSwo
'Slieve Donard'	CBcs EBee ENot EPfP MRav NEgg NHol NWea SLPl SLim SLon SRms WFar

Eschscholzia (*Papaveraceae*)

caespitosa 'Sundew'	CSpe
californica ♀H4	XPep
- 'Ivory Castle'	LRav
- 'Jersey Cream'	CSpe
- var. ***maritima***	XPep
lobbii	CSpe

Eucalyptus ✿ (*Myrtaceae*)

acaciiformis	LRav
aggregata	CCVT LRav SAPC SArc WCel
albida new	LRav
alpina	SPlb
apiculata new	LRav WCel
approximans subsp. ***approximans***	LRav WCel
archeri	CCVT CDoC CTho EBee ECrN EPfP GQui LRHS MBNS WCel WOVN WPGP
baeuerlenii	LRav WCel
barberi	LRav
§ ***bridgesiana***	LRav MHer WCel
caesia	SPlb
camaldulensis	LRav SPad SPlb
camphora	CTho LRav WCel
cinerea	GQui LRav SPlb WCel
citriodora	CWib EOHP GQui ISea LRav MHer MNHC NGHP SPlb WCel WNor
coccifera	CBcs CCVT CDoC CDul CMHG CSBt CTho EBee ELan EPfP GGar LRHS MCCP MLan NBlu NPer NPri SPlb SPoG WCel WNor WPGP
cordata	CCVT LRav NEgg WCel
cosmophylla new	WCel
crenulata	CTrC GQui LRav WCel
crucis subsp. ***crucis***	SPlb
cypellocarpa	SPlb
dalrympleana ♀H3	CAbb CBcs CCVT CDoC CDul CMHG EBee ECrN ELan ENot EPfP EWes LRHS MGos MSwo NBea NEgg NPer SCoo SLim SPer SPoG SRms WBrE WCel WHar WPGP WWeb
deanei	WCel
debeuzevillei	see *E. pauciflora* subsp. *debeuzevillei*

	delegatensis	CMHG EBee LRav NPer WCel
	- subsp. ***tasmaniensis***	GGar WNor
	divaricata	see *E. gunnii* subsp. *divaricata*
	dives	LRav
	erythrocorys	SPlb
	eximia	SPlb
	ficifolia	CDTJ
	forrestiana	LRav
	fraxinoides	SPlb WCel
	gamophylla	SPlb
	glaucescens	CCVT CMHG CTho EPfP EWes GQui LRHS LRav NEgg NPri SAPC SArc SPer WCel WGer WPGP
	globulus	CHEx LRav MNHC MSal SBLw WCel WFar
	goniocalyx	EPfP WCel
§	***gregsoniana***	CCVT CDoC CTho LRav SPlb WCel WPGP
	gunnii 🏆^{H3}	More than 30 suppliers
§	- subsp. ***divaricata***	CCVT EPfP GQui LRHS LRav MBri WCel WGer
	- 'Silver Rain'	LRav
	johnstonii	CDul CMHG EBee ECrN LRav NLar SPer WCel
	kitsoniana	GGar LRav WCel
	kruseana	SPlb
	kybeanensis	CCVT GQui LRav MGos WCel
§	***lacrimans***	WCel WPGP
	lehmannii	SOWG
	leucoxylon	WCel
	- subsp. ***megalocarpa***	SPlb
	ligustrina	LRav WCel
	'Little Boy Blue'	CWib
	macarthurii	LRav WCel
	macrocarpa	SPlb
	macroryncha	SPlb
	mannifera subsp. ***elliptica***	LRav WCel
	- subsp. ***praecox***	LRav
	mitchelliana	LRav WCel
*	***moorei nana***	LRav MHer WNor
	neglecta	EPfP LRav WCel
	nicholii	CCVT CDul EBee EPfP ERas EWes GQui LHop LRHS MGos NLar SCoo SPoG WCel WGer WOVN WPGP
	niphophila	see *E. pauciflora* subsp. *niphophila*
	nitens	CCVT CDTJ CMHG EGFP LRav SAPC SArc SCoo SPlb WCel
§	***nitida***	GGar WCel WNor
	nova-anglica	CMHG LRav
	obliqua	GGar
	olsenii	WCel
	ovata	GGar
	paliformis new	WCel
	parviflora	WBVN
	parvifolia 🏆^{H4}	CBcs CCVT CDoC CDul CLnd CMHG EPfP EShb LRHS LRav NEgg SCoo SDry SEND WCel WPGP
	pauciflora	CCVT CDoC CSBt CTho ELan EPfP MGos NEgg NHol NLar SPer WBrE WCel WNor
	- subsp. ***acerina***	WCel
§	- subsp. ***debeuzevillei***	CCVT CDoC CDul CMHG CTho EBee EPfP EWes GQui LPan LRHS MGos SAPC SArc WCel WPGP WWeb
	- subsp. ***hedraia***	WCel
	- var. ***nana***	see *E. gregsoniana*
§	- subsp. ***niphophila*** 🏆^{H4}	More than 30 suppliers
	- - 'Pendula'	see *E. lacrimans*
	- subsp. ***pauciflora***	LRav
	perriniana	CBcs CCVT CDul CLnd CMHG CSBt EBee ECrN ELan EPfP LPan LRHS MBri MGos NEgg SCoo SDry SLim SPer SPlb SPoG WBVN WCel WFar WNor WOrn WPGP
	phoenicea	SOWG
	pulchella	LRav WCel
	pulverulenta	CDul CEnd LRHS LRav SPlb WGer
	- 'Baby Blue'	LRav MBri MGos WCel
	regnans	GGar
	risdonii	GGar LRav WNor
	rodwayi	GGar LRav
	rubida	CMHG LRav WCel
	scoparia	LRav
	sideroxylon	SPlb
	- 'Rosea'	SPlb
	simmondsii	see *E. nitida*
	stellulata	LRav NEgg WCel
	stricklandii	LRav
	stricta	LRav
	stuartiana	see *E. bridgesiana*
	sturgissiana	LRav
	subcrenulata	CCVT CMHG EPfP GGar GQui LHop LRav MBNS WCel
	tenuiramis	LRav
	tetraptera	LRav SPlb
	torquata	SPlb
	urnigera	CCVT CDoC EBee LHop LRHS MBNS SCoo WCel
	vernicosa	CCVT GGar WCel
	viminalis	CArn CHEx EBee LRav WCel
	youmanii	LRav

Eucharidium see *Clarkia*

Eucharis (*Amaryllidaceae*)

§	***amazonica*** 🏆^{H1}	CHHB EBrs ECho EShb LAma LRHS SPav
	grandiflora misapplied	see *E. amazonica*

Eucodonia (*Gesneriaceae*)

'Adele'	EABi WDib
andrieuxii 'Naomi'	WDib
verticillata	CSpe

Eucomis ✿ (*Hyacinthaceae*)

	autumnalis misapplied	see *E. zambesiaca*
§	***autumnalis*** (Mill.) Chitt. 🏆$^{H2-3}$	CAbb CAvo CDWL CFFs CHEx CPou CRHN CSWP CTca EBee EBrs ECho EPot ERCP GBin GSki IHer LAma LPio LRHS MAvo MCCP SDnm SPav SPer SPlb WBrE WHil WPGP WTin
	- subsp. ***amaryllidifolia***	CPen WPGP
	- subsp. ***autumnalis***	WPGP
	- - 'Peace Candles'	CPen
	- subsp. ***clavata***	CTca EBee WCot
	bicolor 🏆$^{H2-3}$	More than 30 suppliers
	- 'Alba'	CAvo CFFs CPLG CTca EAmu EBee EBrs ECho EPot GSki LPio LRHS SDnm
	- 'Stars and Stripes'	WCru
	'Cabernet Candles'	CPen
§	***comosa***	CAvo CBrm CDWL CFFs CHEx CHll CPrp CRHN CSam CTca EBee EBrs EShb GAbr LAma LEdu LPio LRHS SDnm SMad SPav WEas WHil WTin
	- 'Cornwood'	CAvo CFFs CTca
	- 'First Red'	CDes CPou EBee WPGP
	- purple-leaved	EShb SBla
	- 'Sparkling Burgundy'	More than 30 suppliers
	humilis new	CPen
	hybrid	SDix
	'John Treasure'	WHil
	'Joy's Purple'	CPen LBuc LRHS
	montana	CCtw CPen WPGP

pallidiflora ♀H4	CGHE CHEx CPen LEdu WPGP
pole-evansii	CDes CFir CHEx CPLG CPen CRHN CTca EBee EBrs ECGP EDAr EMar EShb LPio LRHS MLLN MMHG MPop MRav MWgw SMrm SPla WPGP WTin
- bronze	CPne
- 'Burgundy'	EBla
punctata	see *E. comosa*
regia	CPLG
* ***reichenbachii***	CDTJ CTca
'Swazi Pride'	CTca
undulata	see *E. autumnalis*
vandermerwei	CAvo CDes CPLG CPen CTca EBee LRHS WHil WPGP WTin
- 'Octopus'	CPen CTca MBri
§ ***zambesiaca***	CPen EBee GBin LPio SSvw
- 'White Dwarf'	CStu ECho EShb MLan SPer
'Zeal Bronze'	CAbb CBcs CDes CGHE CMHG CRHN CTca EBee ELan EPfP LPio NSti WPGP

Eucommia (*Eucommiaceae*)

ulmoides	CBcs CCCN CDul CMCN EPfP NLar SMad WPGP

Eucryphia ✿ (*Eucryphiaceae*)

citrinum	CAbP CBcs CGHE CMac CWib CWoW GGar ISea SSpi WBod
- Crarae hardy form	GGGa
§ ***citrinum*** x ***lucida***	CBcs CCCN ELan ISea NEgg NPen SPer SRot WPGP WPat
glutinosa ♀H4	CBcs CCCN CDul ELan EPfP IMGH LRHS MAsh MBar MBri MDun NBea NBir NEgg SPer SSpi SSta WBVN WFar WNor WOrn
x ***hillieri***	WSpi
- 'Winton'	CMHG GQui
x ***intermedia***	CPLG CTrC CTrG CWSG CWoW EBee ELan EPfP GGGa LRHS MAsh NPal NPri NVic SHBN SPer SRms SRot SSpi WFar WPat
- 'Rostrevor' ♀H3	CBcs CDul CMHG CMac CPMA CSBt CWib EBee ELan EPfP GAbr GQui IArd IMGH LHyd LRHS LSRN MAsh MDun MGos NCGa SReu SSta WBod WFar WPGP WPat WSHC WSpi
'Leatherwood Cream' new	WSpi
lucida	CCCN CDoC CTrC EBee ELan EPfP GGar GSki IArd IMGH MDun NLar WBod WFar WNor WSpi
- 'Ballerina'	CPMA GGar ISea LRHS MAsh MGos NVic SCoo SKHP SPoG SRot SSpi SSta WAbe WFar
- 'Dumpling'	CGHE SKHP WPGP
- 'Gilt Edge' (v)	CWGN ISea LRHS LTwo SHBN
- 'Leatherwood Cream' (v)	IArd ISea
- 'Pink Cloud'	More than 30 suppliers
- 'Pink Whisper'	see *E. milliganii* 'Pink Whisper'
- 'Spring Glow' (v)	CWGN EMil ISea LRHS LTwo MAsh SKHP SSta
milliganii	CAbP CDoC CDul CPMA CTrC EBee ELan EPfP GAbr GGar GQui LHop LRHS MBlu NPal SBod SHBN SPer SRms SSpi SSta WAbe WBod WPGP WSHC WSpi
§ - 'Pink Whisper'	ISea
moorei	CBcs CCCN CMac ELan GQui
x ***nymansensis***	CTrG CWib ENot MLan NEgg SAPC SArc SDnm SKHP SReu SRkn SRms SSpi WBVN WFar WHCG
- 'George Graham'	GGGa IArd IMGH WBod
- 'Mount Usher'	WBod
- 'Nymansay' ♀H3	More than 30 suppliers
'Penwith' misapplied	see *E. cordifolia* x *lucida*
'Penwith' ambig.	CDoC CPMA GQui NEgg SPer WBrE WFar WGer WMoo

Eugenia (*Myrtaceae*)

australis	CMen IDee
myrtifolia	ERom
uniflora new	CCCN

Eumorphia (*Asteraceae*)

prostrata	EBee

Eunomia see *Aethionema*

Euodia (*Rutaceae*)

daniellii	see *Tetradium daniellii*
hupehensis	see *Tetradium daniellii* Hupehense Group

Euonymus (*Celastraceae*)

B&L 12543	EPla EWes
B&SWJ 4457	WPGP
CC 4522	CPLG
alatus ♀H4	More than 30 suppliers
- B&SWJ 8794	WCru
- var. ***apterus***	EPfP
- Chicago Fire	see *E. alatus* 'Timber Creek'
- 'Ciliodentatus'	see *E. alatus* 'Compactus'
§ - 'Compactus' ♀H4	More than 30 suppliers
§ - 'Fire Ball'	EPfP MBri
- Little Moses = 'Odom'	MBlu
* - 'Macrophyllus'	CPMA EPfP MBri
- 'Rudy Haag'	CPMA EPfP MBri
- 'Select'	see *E. alatus* 'Fire Ball'
- 'Silver Cloud'	EPfP
§ - 'Timber Creek'	CPMA EPfP MBlu MBri NLar
americanus	EPfP MBlu MBri NLar
- 'Evergreen'	EPfP
- narrow-leaved	EPfP
atropurpureus	EPfP
'Benkomoki'	MWgw
bungeanus	CMCN EPfP EPla NLar
- 'Dart's Pride'	CPMA EPfP NLar
- 'Fireflame'	CPMA EPfP NLar
* - var. ***mongolicus***	EPfP
- 'Pendulus'	EPfP MBlu SCoo SIFN
- var. ***semipersistens***	CPMA EPla
carnosus	EPfP NLar
'Copper Wire'	EMil SPoG
cornutus var. ***quinquecornutus***	CPMA EPfP LPan MBlu NBhm NLar SIFN WPGP WPat
'Den Haag'	EPfP MBri
echinatus	EPfP EPla
- BL&M 306	SLon
europaeus	More than 30 suppliers
- f. ***albus***	CPMA CTho EPfP EQua LTwo NLar
- 'Atropurpureus'	CMCN CTho EPfP MBlu MBri NLar SIFN
- 'Atrorubens'	CPMA
- 'Aucubifolius' (v)	CMac EPfP
* - 'Aureus'	CNat
- 'Brilliant'	EPfP
* - f. ***bulgaricus***	EPfP
- 'Chrysophyllus'	EPfP MBlu NLar
- 'Howard'	EPfP
- var. ***intermedius***	EPfP MAsh MBlu NLar
- 'Miss Pinkie'	CEnd
- 'Red Cascade' ♀H4	More than 30 suppliers
- 'Scarlet Wonder'	CPMA EPfP MBri NLar
- 'Thornhayes'	CTho EPfP
I - 'Variegatus'	EPfP
europeaus 'Pumilis'	EPfP
farreri	see *E. nanus*
fimbriatus	CBcs CPMA EPfP
fortunei	LEdu

	- Blondy = 'Interbolwi'PBR (v)	More than 30 suppliers
	- 'Canadale Gold' (v)	CDoC EBee EPla EQua LRHS MAsh MGos NHol SPoG
	- 'Coloratus'	CMac EPfP MBar MSwo NHol SHBN SLon SPer
	- 'Dart's Blanket'	CDul ECrN ELan EPla MRav WFar
	- 'Emerald Gaiety' (v) ♀H4	More than 30 suppliers
*	- 'Emerald Green'	IFoB
	- 'Emerald 'n' Gold' (v) ♀H4	More than 30 suppliers
	- 'Emerald Surprise' (v) ♀H4	EBee ENot EPfP MBri SRGP
	- 'Gold Spot'	see *E. fortunei* 'Sunspot'
	- 'Gold Tip'	see *E. fortunei* Golden Prince
	- 'Golden Harlequin' (v) **new**	SPoG
§	- 'Golden Pillar' (v)	EPla WFar
§	- Golden Prince (v)	CMac EPfP EPla MBar MGos MRav MSwo SLim SRms WGor
	- Goldy = 'Waldbolwi' **new**	ENot
	- 'Harlequin' (v)	CBcs CSBt CWSG EBee ELan EPfP EPla LAst LBuc LRHS LSRN MAsh MBar MGos MLHP MNHC MRav NPro SAga SHBN SLim SPer SPla SRms SWvt WBod WFar
	- 'Kewensis'	CMac CWib EBee EPfP MBar MRav SAPC SArc SBod SLon SPoG WCru WFar
	- 'Minimus'	CDul CTri EPla MGos NHol NPro WFar
*	- 'Minimus Variegatus' (v)	ECho SPlb
§	- var. ***radicans***	EWld MGan
	- - 'Variegatus' (v)	MAsh
	- 'Sheridan Gold'	CMac CTri EPla MRav SHBN
	- 'Silver Gem'	see *E. fortunei* 'Variegatus'
	- 'Silver Pillar' (v)	CPLG EBee ECrN ENot WFar
	- 'Silver Queen' (v)	More than 30 suppliers
	- 'Silverstone' (v)PBR **new**	SPoG
	- 'Sunshine' (v)	CAbP ELan LRHS MAsh MGos NEgg
§	- 'Sunspot' (v)	CBcs CWSG ECrN ELan EPla IFoB LAst MBar MGos MSwo NHol SLim SRms WFar WHar WRHF WTel
	- 'Tustin' ♀H4	EPla SLPl
§	- 'Variegatus' (v)	MBar SPer SRms STre
	- var. ***vegetus***	EPla
	- 'Wolong Ghost'	SKHP
	frigidus	EPfP WPGP
	grandiflorus	CPMA CPle EPfP MBlu NLar SCoo SIFN SSpi WFar
	- 'Red Wine'	CPMA CTho EBee EPfP MBri WPGP WPat
	- f. ***salicifolius***	CPMA EPfP
	hamiltonianus	CMCN EPfP SSpi WFar
I	- 'Calocarpus'	CPMA MBlu SCoo SIFN
	- 'Coral Chief'	SLon
	- 'Fiesta'	EPfP MBri
I	- 'Harlequin'	CPMA
	- subsp. ***hians***	see *E. hamiltonianus* subsp. *sieboldianus*
	- 'Indian Summer'	CPMA EPfP LRHS MAsh MBlu MBri MWea NLar SCoo SIFN SKHP SPur SSpi SSta WPGP
	- 'Koi Boy'	CPMA LRHS MAsh MGos SIFN SPoG
	- 'Miss Pinkie'	CDul CPMA EPfP LRHS MAsh MGos NLar SCoo SIFN SSpi SSta WPat
	- 'Pink Delight'	CPMA EPfP MBri
	- 'Poort Bulten'	EPfP MBlu MBri
	- 'Popcorn'	CPMA EPfP MBlu MBri
	- 'Rainbow'	CPMA EPfP MBri NLar
	- 'Red Chief'	EPfP
	- 'Red Elf'	CPMA EPfP MBri
	- 'Rising Sun'	CPMA EPfP MBlu MBri NLar
§	- subsp. ***sieboldianus***	CDul CMCN CPLG CPMA CTho EPfP MBri MRav SLPl WFar
	- - 'Calocarpus'	EPfP MBri
	- - 'Coral Charm'	CPMA EPfP MBri NLar
	- - Semiexsertus Group	EPfP MBri
*	- - var. ***yedoensis*** f. ***koehneanus***	EPfP
	- 'Snow'	EPfP MBlu NLar WPat
	- 'Winter Glory'	CPMA EPfP LRHS MBlu MBri NLar WPat
	- var. ***yedoensis***	see *E. hamiltonianus* subsp. *sieboldianus*
	hibarimisake	see *E. japonicus* 'Hibarimisake'
	japonicus	CBcs CDoC CDul ECrN EPfP SAPC SArc SPer STop XPep
	- 'Albomarginatus'	CBcs CChe CTri MBar NBlu SEND SRms STop
	- 'Aureopictus'	see *E. japonicus* 'Aureus'
	- 'Aureovariegatus'	see *E. japonicus* 'Ovatus Aureus'
§	- 'Aureus' (v)	CBcs CChe CDoC CSBt CWib EBee ECrN ENot SCoo SHBN SLon SPer WHar WTel WWeb
	- 'Benkomasaki'	EPfP
	- 'Bravo'	CDoC CDul EBee ECrN EMil ERas LAst LPan LRHS MGos MWea NLar SCoo SLim SPer SPoG SWvt WFar
	- 'Chollipo' ♀H4	ELan EPfP EPla LRHS MAsh MGos
	- 'Compactus'	SAPC SArc SCoo
	- 'Duc d'Anjou' misapplied	see *E. japonicus* 'Viridivariegatus'
	- 'Duc d'Anjou' Carrière (v)	CBcs CHrt EBee ELan EPla EWes LPan MRav NHol SDry SEND SPoG
	- Exstase = 'Goldbolwi'PBR (v) **new**	ENot SPoG
	- 'Francien' (v)	SPoG
	- 'Golden Maiden'	ELan EPfP LRHS MAsh SLim SPoG SWvt
	- 'Golden Pillar'	see *E. fortunei* 'Golden Pillar'
	- 'Green Spider'	SPoG
	- 'Grey Beauty'	EBee NLar
§	- 'Hibarimisake'	EPfP SBla
	- 'Kathy'PBR	ERas MGos SPoG
§	- 'Latifolius Albomarginatus'	CDul ELan EPfP EPla MRav MSwo SPer SPoG WWeb
	- 'Luna'	see *E. japonicus* 'Aureus'
	- 'Macrophyllus Albus'	see *E. japonicus* 'Latifolius Albomarginatus'
	- 'Maiden's Gold'	CSBt
	- 'Marieke'	see *E. japonicus* 'Ovatus Aureus'
	- 'Microphyllus'	CDoC MRav STre WFar WGwG
§	- 'Microphyllus Albovariegatus' (v)	CBcs CChe CDoC CDul CMea CSBt CTri CWSG ELan EMil EPfP EPla LAst LRHS MBar MGos NHol SBla SHBN SLim SLon SPla SPoG SRms SWvt WFar WHCG WPat WWeb
§	- 'Microphyllus Aureovariegatus' (v)	CDoC CMea EMil EPfP MGos NLar WPat
	- 'Microphyllus Aureus'	see *E. japonicus* 'Microphyllus Pulchellus'
§	- 'Microphyllus Pulchellus' (v)	CBcs CDoC CSBt CWSG EBee ECrN ENot EPfP EPla LHop MBar MRav NHol SPoG SWvt WHCG WWeb
	- 'Microphyllus Variegatus'	see *E. japonicus* 'Microphyllus Albovariegatus'
§	- 'Ovatus Aureus' (v) ♀H4	CChe CDoC CDul CPLG CSBt CTri CWSG EBee ECrN ENot EPfP LAst LRHS MBar MGos MRav MSwo NBlu SLim SPer SPlb SPoG SRms STop SWvt WBod WFar WTel
	- 'Président Gauthier' (v)	CDoC EBee ECrN EQua MGos MWea SCoo SLim SWvt
	- 'Pulchellus Aureovariegatus'	see *E. japonicus* 'Microphyllus Aureovariegatus'

I	- 'Pyramidatus'	EPfP
	- 'Robustus'	EPfP EPla
	- 'Royal Gold'	SPoG
	- 'Silver Krista' (v)	SPoG
	- Silver Princess = 'Moness'	SHBN
	- 'Susan'	EPla EQua NHol SRGP
§	- 'Viridivariegatus' (v)	LRHS
	kiautschovicus	EPfP EPla
	- 'Berry Hill'	EPfP NLar
	- 'Manhattan'	EPfP NLar
	latifolius	CMCN CPMA EPfP
	macropterus	CPMA EPfP
	maximowiczianus	EPfP MBlu MBri NLar WPat
	morrisonensis	EPfP
	- B&SWJ 3700	WCru
	myrianthus	CPMA EPfP MBlu NLar SIFN
§	***nanus***	CWib EPfP EPla NHol NLar WSHC
	- var. ***turkestanicus***	EPfP EPla LHop MBri SLon SRms WFar
	obovatus	EPfP NLar
	occidentalis	EPfP
	oresbius	CPMA EPfP
	oxyphyllus	CMCN CPMA EPfP SCoo WCru
	- 'Angyo Elegant' (v)	EPfP
	- 'Waasland'	CPMA EPfP MBri NLar
	pauciflorus	EPfP MBri
	pendulus	CHEx CHll CPLG
	phellomanus Υ^{H4}	CEnd CTho CWSG EBee EPfP EWTr LHop LRHS MBar MBlu MBri MGos MRav NLar SCoo SHBN SIFN SPoG WFar WPGP WPat
	- 'Silver Surprise' (v)	CPMA EPfP MBri NLar WPat
	Pierrolino = 'Heespierrolino'^{PBR}	SCoo SPoG
§	***planipes*** Υ^{H4}	More than 30 suppliers
	- 'Dart's August Flame'	EPfP MBri NLar
	- 'Gold Ore'	EPfP NLar
	- 'Sancho'	CPMA EPfP MBri
	quelpaertensis	EPfP
	radicans	see *E. fortunei* var. *radicans*
	'Rokojô'	CLyd
	rongchuensis	EPfP MBri
	rosmarinifolius	see *E. nanus*
	sachalinensis misapplied	see *E. planipes*
	sacrosanctus	EPfP
	sanguineus	CPMA EPfP MBri NLar SSpi
	spraguei	EPfP
	tingens	EPfP NLar SIFN
	trapococcus	EPfP NLar
	vagans	EPfP
	- L 551	EPla SLon
	velutinus	EPfP MBri NLar
	verrucosus	CPMA EPfP EPla MBri NLar SIFN
	vidalii	EPfP MBri
	wilsonii **new**	NLar
	yedoensis	see *E. hamiltonianus* subsp. *sieboldianus*

Eupatorium (*Asteraceae*)

	B&SWJ 9052 from Guatemala	WCru
§	***album***	NBid SWat WPer
	- 'Braunlaub'	CPrp EBee EMan EMon LRHS NBre NGdn NSti SWat WCAu WHrl WMnd
	altissimum	MSal SRms
	aromaticum	EBee MLLN MRav NBre NBro SWat WPer WSFF
	atrorubens	CCCN CKob ERea MJnS
	cannabinum	CArn EBee EHon ELan EMFW GGar GPoy IFoB LEdu MBNS MHer MNHC MRav MSal NBir NGHP NMir NPer NRnb SECG SPav SWat WBVN WPer WSFF
	- 'Album'	EMon NDov SPhx
	- 'Flore Pleno' (d)	More than 30 suppliers
	- 'Spraypaint'	CNat EPPr
*	- 'Variegatum' (v)	CBow EBee EMan ERou EWTr MDKP MLHP WCot WSFF
	capillifolium	EShb LSou MCot MLLN SDix SMrm WCot WPGP
	- 'Elegant Feather'	CSpe EBee ECtt EMan EWes EWin LHop MAvo MDKP SAga SHar SMad SPhx WHil
	chinense	EBee
	coelestinum	EBee EMan EShb EWes LHop MDKP SMad WFar WSFF
*	***cyclophyllum***	EMan NBre
	fistulosum	MGol NGdn
*	- 'Atropurpureum'	CKno EShb IBal WPer WWeb
	fortunei	CArn SKHP
*	- 'Variegatum' (v)	CBow CKno EBee EMan LSou MAvo WCot WPGP
	glechonophyllum	MDKP
§	***ligustrinum*** Υ^{H3}	CBcs CDoC CMHG CPLG CRHN CTri CWib EBee ECha ELan EMan EPfP IDee ISea LRHS NCGa SAga SDix SLim SPer WFar WHCG WMnd WPat WSFF WSHC WSpi
	maculatum	see *E. purpureum* subsp. *maculatum*
	- 'Carin' **new**	WSFF
	madrense	WBor
	micranthum	see *E. ligustrinum*
	occidentale NNS 94-53	WCot
	perfoliatum	CArn GPoy MNrw MSal NBre NLar SPav WPer
	'Phantom' **new**	EBee
	purpureum	More than 30 suppliers
	- 'Album'	CTri EPPr MLLN SPhx
	- 'Bartered Bride'	CKno EBrs ECtt EWes
	- 'Joe White' **new**	WSFF
	- 'Little Red' **new**	WSFF
§	- subsp. ***maculatum***	CAby CPLG EBee EHrv EMon MDKP NGHP NGdn NLar SBri STes WFar WHil WHrl WOut WPer
	- - 'Album'	EBee ECha EMon GBin NBir NDov NSti SMad WSpi
	- - 'Atropurpureum' Υ^{H4}	More than 30 suppliers
	- - 'Gateway'	EBrs WTin
	- - 'Glutball'	CKno EBee EBrs MNrw NChi SMad
	- - 'Riesenschirm'	CKno CSam EBee ECGP EGle EPPr EWes IBal LRHS MSte SPhx SWat WCAu
	- 'Purple Bush'	CKno CSam EBee ECha EGle EMon EWTr MDKP NBre NDov NEgg SMad SPhx SSvw WSFF
	rugosum	CHid EBee EGle ELan EPfP MCot MGol NLar SPav SPhx SSvw WSpi WTin
	- ***album***	see *E. album*
	- 'Brunette'	EHrv
	- 'Chocolate' Υ^{H4}	More than 30 suppliers
*	'Snowball'	SMrm
	triplinerve	MSte
*	***variabile*** 'Variegatum' (v)	EMan EWes MDKP SMad WCot
	weinmannianum	see *E. ligustrinum*

Euphorbia ✿ (*Euphorbiaceae*)

	'Abbey Dore'	WCot WSHC
	altissima	MSte
	ambovombensis **new**	LToo
	amygdaloides	ECtt NBlu SWat
	- 'Bob's Choice'	EMon EWes
	- 'Brithembottom'	CSam
	- 'Craigieburn'	CDes CSam EBee EGle EMan EWes GBri GCra LRHS MAsh MBNS MRav NDov NSti WCra WPGP WWeb

- 'Mark's Red'	WCot
§ - 'Purpurea'	More than 30 suppliers
- 'Red Shank'	SBla
§ - var. ***robbiae*** ♀H4	More than 30 suppliers
- - dwarf	EPot EWes
- - 'Pom Pom'	CDes EBee EMan LSou WPGP
- - 'Redbud'	EBee EMan EPla EWes LSou SLPl
- 'Rubra'	see *E. amygdaloides* 'Purpurea'
- 'Signal'	EMon
- 'Variegata' (v)	GBuc SMad
- 'Winter Glow'	CSpe
- yellow-leaved	WCot
ankarensis new	LToo
aureoviridiflora	LToo
barrelieri	WCot
baselicis	CBow CPom CSpe EBee EDAr EMan EMon EWll GKev LFur LPio LSou MGol WHrl
biglandulosa Desf.	see *E. rigida*
Blackbird = 'Nothowlee'	CBcs CSpe EBee ELan ENot EPfP EWes GBin IPot LAst LBuc LCro LRHS LSRN LTwo MBri MGos NPri NSti SJoo SLim SPoG WCot
'Blue Haze'	SBla SMeo
'Blue Lagoon'	NBhm
bulbispina	LToo
canariensis	EPfP
capitulata	EPot EWes MTho
cashmeriana	EBee NWit
- CC&McK 607	EWes
- CC&McK 724	GBin
ceratocarpa	CFis CFwr EBee EMon EPPr EWes EWin GBuc GMaP MAvo MBri NWit SMad WCot WPGP WSHC
characias	CBcs CHEx COlW EBee ECtt EPfP LCro MDun MRav NChi NEgg NOak NPer NPri NVic SPer SRms WCot WFar WHen WMnd WPer XPep
- Ballyrogan hybrids	IBlr NBhm
- 'Black Pearl'	CBcs CHrt CWCL EBee EPfP ERou LAst LFur MBNS MCCP MSte NBPC NCGa NEgg NSti SDnm SMer SPav SPoG SWvt WFar WOVN
- 'Blue Wonder'	CRez CSpe EBee ECtt EHrv EPfP GMaP LCro LFur LHop LRHS MCCP MSte NEgg NLar NWit SAga SDnm SPav WCot WGer WGwG WWeb
- subsp. ***characias***	EBee EHrv GMaP MGos SMHy SPoG WCru
- - 'Blue Hills'	ECtt EGle GBin GBuc NWit SMrm
- - 'Burrow Silver' (v)	CFir CTca EBee LDai MBNS MRav NCGa NEgg SCoo SDnm SPav SPer SWvt WFar WHil
- - 'Green Mantle'	IBlr
- - 'H.E. Bates'	NBir
- - 'Humpty Dumpty'	More than 30 suppliers
- - 'Perry's Winter Blusher'	ECtt NWit
- dwarf	SMrm
- 'Forescate'	CSWP CWCL EBee EMil EPfP EWin LPio MSte NCGa NWit SDnm SPav WFar WMnd
- 'Giant Green Turtle'	CMil
- 'Goldbrook'	EBee EGle EMan LHop MBNS MNFA MRav MSte MWgw SAga SHBN
- 'Kestrel' (v) new	WCot
- 'Portuguese Velvet' ♀H4	CBct CDes CSam CSpe CWCL EBee ECha EGle EHrv ELan EWsh LHop LPio MNFA NCGa NDov SPav WCot WMnd WPen WSpi WWeb
- Silver Swan = 'Wilcott'PBR (v)	CBcs CMdw CSpe EBee ELan EMan ENot EPfP EWes LBuc LSRN MGos MRav NBPC NPri NSti SBra SJoo SPoG SWvt
- 'Sombre Melody'	IBlr
- 'Spring Splendour'	EWes NWit
- 'Starbright'	EBee NWit
- 'Whistleberry Jade'	NWit
- subsp. ***wulfenii*** ♀H3-4	More than 30 suppliers
- - 'Bosahan' (v)	CBcs GCra NWit
- - 'Emmer Green' (v)	CBow CDes CSpe EBee EHrv EWes GBri GMaP NWit SBla SHBN SPoG WCot WFoF
- - 'Jimmy Platt'	EGle ERCP MTho SBHP SRms WBrE WCot WGwG WPic
§ - - 'John Tomlinson' ♀H3-4	EBee EHrv EShb EWes GBin GMaP MRav NEgg WCot WSpi
- - Kew form	see *E. characias* subsp. *wulfenii* 'John Tomlinson'
- - 'Lambrook Gold' ♀H3-4	CSam ECtt EGle EPfP GCra LPio MRav MWat MWgw NLar NPer SMad WFar WGer WGwG WMnd WSpi
- - 'Lambrook Gold' seed-raised	see *E. characias* subsp. *wulfenii* Margery Fish Group
- - 'Lambrook Yellow'	EWsh GBuc WSPU
§ - - Margery Fish Group	EBee EGle NBir
- - 'Perry's Tangerine'	EWes NPer NWit
§ - - 'Purple and Gold'	CRez CSpe EBee EWes GMaP LFur NLar NWit SHBN SWvt WCot WSpi
- - 'Purpurea'	see *E. characias* subsp. *wulfenii* 'Purple and Gold'
- - 'Silver Shadow'	SBla
- - 'Thelma's Giant'	NWit
clavarioides var. ***truncata***	WCot
'Copton Ash'	CSpe EBee EWes MAvo NWit SKHP
corallioides	CSsd ECha EMan IBlr LRHS NDov NPer NSti SHFr SPav SRms WBrE WHer WPnP XPep
§ ***cornigera*** ♀H4	CElw CFwr EBee ECha EPfP GBin GMac IBlr LPio LRHS MAvo MNFA MRav NBid NCGa NDov NGdn NLar NSti NWit SWat WCot WCru WHoo WLin WPGP WPen
- 'Goldener Turm'	EMan ERou NSti WCot
croizatii	LToo
cylindrifolia var. ***tubifera***	LToo
cyparissias	CArn CBcs CHrt EBee ECha ELan GAbr LRHS MLHP MRav NBir NGdn NMen NSti SPav SRms WEas WFar WFoF WPer WTin XPep
- 'Baby'	WFar
- 'Betten'	see *E.* x *gayeri* 'Betten'
- 'Bushman Boy'	GBri IBlr
- 'Clarice Howard'	see *E. cyparissias* 'Fens Ruby'
- clone 2	WCot
§ - 'Fens Ruby'	More than 30 suppliers
- 'Orange Man'	CWan EBee EDAr EMon EPPr EPfP ERou EWes GBin IBlr LAst LRHS MWgw NBro NHol NSti SPla SWat SWvt WAul WFar
- 'Purpurea'	see *E. cyparissias* 'Fens Ruby'
- 'Red Devil'	CBre IBlr NWit
- 'Tall Boy'	EMon EWes IBlr XPep
deflexa	EBee GKev
denticulata	SBla
'Despina'PBR	NLar
§ ***donii***	CDes EGle EWes IBlr NDov NWit SDix SMHy WFar
- HWJK 2405	WCru
- 'Amjilassa'	SAga
dulcis	CBre CStu ECtt NBro NWit WEas WHen

- 'Chameleon'	More than 30 suppliers
'Efanthia'PBR	CCVN CEnd CMil CRez CSpe EBee ERou EWes LHop LSou MBri NLar NPri SMrm SPoG STes SVil
enopla	EPem EPfP
epithymoides	see *E. polychroma*
esula Baker's form	NWit
Excalibur = 'Froeup'PBR ♀H4	CSpe CWCL EBee ELan EMan GBin GBuc LFur LHop LRHS MBNS MBri MCCP MRav MSte MWgw NBir NCGa NSti SHBN SPoG WFar WPnP WSHC
fragifera	EBee NWit
'Garblesham Enchanter'	EPPr
§ x ***gayeri*** 'Betten'	EBee
glauca	CFir CPLG ECou NWit SKHP
'Golden Foam'	see *E. stricta*
gottlebei	LToo
griffithii	CHll MLHP NBro SPav SWat WFar WGer WMoo WTel
- 'Dixter' ♀H4	More than 30 suppliers
- 'Dixter Flame'	NWit
- 'Fern Cottage'	CElw CWCL EBee EHrv EWes GAbr SMrm WMnd
- 'Fireglow'	More than 30 suppliers
- 'King's Caple'	EBee GBin MBNS NWit SPoG WCru
- 'Wickstead'	EBee GAbr MLHP NLar
'Helena' **new**	LHop LTwo NLar NPri SJoo SPoG SVil WOVN
hirta	CLyd
hyberna	CFis GBri IBlr LTwo MLLN NMen NWit SWat
hypericifolia Diamond Frost = 'Inneuphe'	CCVN CSpe LHop LSou SVil WOVN
jacquemontii	ECha EMan LPio MLLN MNrw MRav NChi NDov NWit
'Jade Dragon'	CSpe SPoG
'Jessie'	EBee MAvo SPoG WCot
Kalipso = 'Innkalff'PBR	EBee ERou NLar SJoo SVil
lambii	EShb
'Lambrook Silver' **new**	SRkn
lathyris	CArn CBre EMar ILad MDun MHer MLHP NBid NLar NPer NRnb NWit SRms WEas
longifolia misapplied	see *E. cornigera*
longifolia D. Don	see *E. donii*
longifolia Lam.	see *E. mellifera*
margalidiana	EWes
x ***martini*** ♀H3	More than 30 suppliers
- 'Aperitif'	CBow EPfP IBal MBNS WCot
- 'Baby Charm'	CPen LBuc LRHS SJoo
- dwarf	CFir
- 'Helen Robinson' **new**	WCot
- 'Red Dwarf'	CMil WHrl
- 'Tiny Tim'	SPoG
§ ***mellifera*** ♀H3	More than 30 suppliers
milii ♀H1	CHal EBak SHFr
* - 'Variegata' (v)	CHal
- yellow-flowered	CHal
moratii **new**	LToo
myrsinites ♀H4	More than 30 suppliers
nereidum	EWes NWit
nicaeensis	CDes EBee EMan EMon NWit SMad SPhx WCot WPGP XPep
- subsp. ***glareosa***	NWit
oblongata	EBee EMan EWes GBuc IBlr NWit
'Orange Grove'	NBhm
pachypodioides	LToo
palustris ♀H4	More than 30 suppliers
- 'Walenburg's Glorie'	CMHG EBee ECha ELan EWTr GBin LRHS MBri MNrw MRav NCGa NSti NWit SMad SWat WRHF WSpi
- 'Zauberflöte'	CHrt SRms WFar
x ***paradoxa***	NWit

paralias	NWit WHer XPep
x ***pasteurii***	CBgR CFir CKob CPLG CPom EBee EWes LSou MAvo SMHy WPGP
- 'John Phillips'	SKHP WPGP
pekinensis	MSal NDov NWit SKHP
pilosa 'Major'	see *E. polychroma* 'Major'
piscatoria	WPGP
pithyusa	CBgR CPom CSam CSpe EBee ECha ECtt ELan EMan EMon EPfP LRHS MAvo MRav NGdn SHBN XPep
§ ***polychroma*** ♀H4	More than 30 suppliers
§ - 'Candy'	CHar CSam EBee EBrs ECha EHrv ELan EPfP MCCP MDun NCGa SEND SPla WCot WFar WLin WMnd
- compact **new**	LBuc
- 'Emerald Jade'	GBri IBlr NWit WPGP
§ - 'Lacy' (v)	CDoC EBee ECtt EHrv EMan ERou EWes LAst MCCP MRav NBir NCob NEgg NGdn NSti NWit SMad SPla SPoG WCot
§ - 'Major' ♀H4	CMHG CPLG SAga SPer SPhx WCot WEas
- 'Midas'	EGle GBin MNrw NWit SMrm
- 'Purpurea'	see *E. polychroma* 'Candy'
* - 'Senior'	MGos NWit
- 'Sonnengold'	EWes
- 'Variegata'	see *E. polychroma* 'Lacy'
portlandica	NWit WHer
§ x ***pseudovirgata***	CFis EMan IBlr NWit
'Purple Preference'	EPPr
Redwing = 'Charam'PBR ♀H4	CBcs EBee ELan EMan ENot EPfP LCro LRHS MBri MGos MRav NDov NLar NWit SBra SCoo SPer SPoG SWvt
reflexa	see *E. seguieriana* subsp. *niciciana*
§ ***rigida*** ♀H4	CDes CSpe EBee ECha EGle EHrv ELan EMan EPfP EPyc EWes GMaP LPio MAvo MLLN NDov NSti SBla SKHP SPhx WCot WFar WHoo WPGP WSHC WSpi
- 'Sardis'	NWit
robbiae	see *E. amygdaloides* var. *robbiae*
'Rosies Surprise'	LTwo MTho
rothiana GWJ 9479a	WCru
'Roundway Titan' **new**	SSpi
sarawschanica	EBee ECha EMan GBin NWit SPhx
schillingii ♀H4	CMHG CMea CPrp CWCL EBee ELan EPfP GAbr GCra GKev GMaP LPio LRHS MRav MWgw NDov NEgg SDix SPer SPoG STes SWal WCot WCru WFar WGwG WHoo WPGP WSpi WTin
seguieriana	ECha EMan NBir NLar WPer
§ - subsp. ***niciciana***	CBow EMan EMon EWsh GBin NBir SBla
serrata	XPep
serrulata Thuill.	see *E. stricta*
sikkimensis ♀H4	CBow CHrt CMHG CMea CPLG CPom CSam CSpe EBee ECha ELan GAbr LPio MAvo NBid NEgg NPer SMrm SPav SRms WCot WCru WEas WFar
- GWJ 9214	WCru
soongarica	MSte NWit
spinosa	NWit XPep
§ ***stricta***	EBee GBri IBlr MCCP WRos WTin
stygiana	CFir CHid CPLG CSam CSpe EMon EPla EWes LPio MAvo MSte NWit SAga SKHP SMeo WCot WCru WPGP WSHC
- 'Devil's Honey'	NWit WCot

	symmetrica new	LToo
	terracina	WCot
	tirucalli	EShb
	uralensis	see *E.* x *pseudovirgata*
	valdevillosocarpa	WCot
	verrucosa	NWit
	- Baker's form	EPPr
	viguieri ♀H1	LToo
	villosa Waldst. & Kit. ex Willd.	NWit
§	***virgata***	EWes NSti NWit SPav WCot
	x ***waldsteinii***	see *E. virgata*
	wallichii misapplied	see *E. donii*
	wallichii Kohli	see *E. cornigera*
	wallichii Hook. f.	CPLG CSam EBee EMan IBlr MBri NBid NOrc WPGP WSHC
	- 'Lemon and Lime'	CWib LSou WFar
	'Whistleberry Garnet' new	LCro WWlt

Euptelea (*Eupteleaceae*)

	franchetii	see *E. pleiosperma*
§	***pleiosperma***	EBee EPfP GGGa NLar SSpi
	polyandra	EPfP NLar WPGP

Eurya (*Theaceae*)

japonica	WPGP
- 'Moutiers' (v)	WPat
- 'Variegata' misapplied	see *Cleyera japonica* 'Fortunei'

Euryops (*Asteraceae*)

	abrotanifolius	CTrC
§	***acraeus*** ♀H4	CMea CPle CSBt ECho GKev LHop LRHS MDun MWat NMen NWCA SAga SIng WAbe WFar WLin
	candollei	WAbe
§	***chrysanthemoides***	CCCN CHEx CSam ERea EShb MSte
	- 'Sonnenschein'	CHal EBee EWin SPet
	decumbens	WLin
	evansii	see *E. acraeus*
	lateriflorus new	SPlb
	pectinatus ♀H2	CBcs CCCN CDTJ CDoC CHEx CPLG CSam CTrC CTrG CTri EBee ERea EShb GGar LRHS MAsh MNrw MRav SDry SGar SHBN SOWG WCFE WHer WPic XPep
	speciosissimus	LEdu
	tysonii	CStu EBee GEdr GGar SPlb WCot
	virgineus	CBcs CTrC CTrG EBee GGar IDee WGer

Euscaphis (*Staphyleaceae*)

japonica	NLar

Eustachys (*Poaceae*)

§	***distichophylla***	EBee EPPr MAvo WCot WPrP

Eustoma (*Gentianaceae*)

§	***grandiflorum***	LRHS MBri
	russellianum	see *E. grandiflorum*

Eustrephus (*Philesiaceae*)

latifolius	ECou

Eutaxia (*Papilionaceae*)

obovata	ECou

Euterpe (*Arecaceae*)

edulis	LPal

Euthamia (*Asteraceae*)

§	***gymnospermoides***	EWes

Evolvulus (*Convolvulaceae*)

§	***glomeratus*** 'Blue Daze'	ERea
	pilosus misapplied	see *E. glomeratus*

Ewartia (*Asteraceae*)

planchonii	WAbe

Exacum (*Gentianaceae*)

affine ♀H1+3	LRHS MBri
- 'Rococo'	MBri

Exochorda (*Rosaceae*)

giraldii	CPle WGwG
- var. ***wilsonii***	CSam EBee EPfP GBin IMGH LHop MAsh MBNS MBlu NLar NPen SLim SPoG SSta SWvt
x ***macrantha***	MNHC
- 'The Bride' ♀H4	More than 30 suppliers
racemosa	EPfP ISea MGos NBlu NLar SHBN SPer WHCG
serratifolia	EPfP
- 'Northern Pearls'	CPMA
- 'Snow White'	CPMA EBee EWes LBuc MBlu MBri NLar

F

Fabiana (*Solanaceae*)

imbricata	CAbP EMil EPfP GGar GQui LRHS SAga SBra SLon SPer
- 'Prostrata'	EBee EPfP LRHS SDry SSpi WAbe WBod
- f. ***violacea*** ♀H3	CBcs CFee CPLG CSBt CTri EBee EPfP GQui LRHS MBar SPer WAbe WKif XPep

Fagopyrum (*Polygonaceae*)

	cymosum	see *F. dibotrys*
§	***dibotrys***	EBee ECha ELan EPPr EWld LEdu MGol NSti WMoo
	- 'Variegatum' new	CBow

Fagus ✿ (*Fagaceae*)

§	***crenata***	CMCN CMen WNor
	engleriana	CMCN SIFN
	grandifolia	CMCN
	japonica	CMCN
	longipetiolata new	CBcs
	lucida	CMCN
	orientalis	CMCN ECrN
	sieboldii	see *F. crenata*
	sylvatica ♀H4	More than 30 suppliers
§	- 'Albomarginata' (v)	CLnd CMCN
	- 'Albovariegata'	see *F. sylvatica* 'Albomarginata'
	- 'Ansorgei'	CEnd CLnd CMCN MBlu
N	- Atropurpurea Group	More than 30 suppliers
	- 'Aurea Pendula'	CEnd CMCN ECrN MBlu SBLw
	- 'Bicolor Sartini'	MBlu
	- 'Birr Zebra'	CEnd
	- 'Black Swan'	CEnd CMCN ECrN ENot IArd LPan MBlu NLar SBLw SLon SMad WGor
	- 'Brathay Purple'	MBlu
	- 'Cochleata'	CMCN
	- 'Cockleshell'	CDul CMCN MBlu SHBN
	- 'Cristata'	CMCN MBlu
N	- Cuprea Group	NWea
§	- 'Dawyck' ♀H4	CBcs CDoC CDul CLnd CMCN CSBt CTho EBee ECho ECrN ELan EMil EPfP LAst LPan MBar MBri MGos NWea SBLw SLau SLim SPer WOrn
	- 'Dawyck Gold' ♀H4	CAbP CBcs CDoC CDul CEnd CLnd CMCN CTho CTri EBee ECrN ENot IMGH LPan LRHS

		MAsh MBar MBlu MBri MGos MSwo NBea NEgg NWea SBLw SLim SPer WFar WOrn
	- 'Dawyck Purple' Υ^{H4}	CAbP CBcs CDoC CDul CEnd CLnd CMCN CTho CTri CWib EBee ECrN ENot EPfP LAst LRHS MBar MBlu MBri MGos NBea NBee NEgg NWea SCrf SHBN SLim SPer WFar WOrn
	- 'Fastigiata' misapplied	see *F. sylvatica* 'Dawyck'
	- 'Felderbach'	MBlu SLon
	- 'Franken' (v)	MBlu
	- 'Frisio'	CDul CEnd CMCN
	- 'Grandidentata'	CMCN LPan SLon
	- 'Greenwood'	CDul CMCN MBlu
*	- 'Haaren'	CMCN
	- var. ***heterophylla***	CLnd CSBt CTho ECho NWea WOrn
	- - 'Aspleniifolia' Υ^{H4}	CBcs CDoC CDul CEnd CMCN ECrN ELan EMil EPfP IMGH LPan LRHS MAsh MBar MBri MGos NEgg SBLw SCoo SHBN SLau SLon SPer SPoG WMou WNor
	- - f. ***laciniata***	CMCN MBlu
	- 'Horizontalis'	CMCN SLon
	- f. ***latifolia***	SBLw
	- 'Luteovariegata' (v)	CEnd CMCN
	- 'Mercedes'	CDoC CMCN MBlu WPat
	- 'Miltonensis'	IArd LPan SMad
N	- 'Pendula' Υ^{H4}	CBcs CDoC CDul CEnd CLnd CMCN CSBt CTho EBee ECho ECrN ELan IMGH LPan MBar MGos MSwo NWea SBLw SCrf SHBN SLau SPer WHar WMou WOrn
	- 'Prince George of Crete'	CDul CEnd CMCN
	- 'Purple Fountain' Υ^{H4}	CDoC CDul CEnd CMCN EBee ELan EMil LAst LPan LRHS MAsh MBar MBlu MBri MGos NBPN NLar SBLw SIFN SLau SLim SPoG WOrn
	- Purple-leaved Group	see *F. sylvatica* Atropurpurea Group
	- 'Purpurea Nana'	CMCN
	- 'Purpurea Pendula'	More than 30 suppliers
§	- 'Purpurea Tricolor' (v)	CDoC CDul CEnd CMCN ECrN MBar MBri MGos MWya NBea NBlu NEgg NWea SCoo SCrf SHBN SPer WOrn
	- 'Quercifolia'	CMCN MBlu
I	- 'Quercina'	CMCN SLon
	- 'Red Obelisk'	see *F. sylvatica* 'Rohan Obelisk'
	- 'Riversii' Υ^{H4}	More than 30 suppliers
	- 'Rohan Gold'	CDul CEnd CLnd CMCN EBee MBlu
§	- 'Rohan Obelisk'	CDul CEnd CMCN EBee ELan IArd MBlu MGos WOrn
I	- 'Rohan Pyramidalis'	CDul CEnd CMCN
	- 'Rohan Trompenburg'	CMCN MBlu
	- 'Rohan Weeping'	MBlu
	- 'Rohanii'	CAbP CBcs CDoC CDul CEnd CLnd CMCN CTri EBee ECho ECrN ELan EMil EPfP IMGH LPan NBee NEgg SCoo SCrf SHBN WFar WHar WOrn
	- 'Roseomarginata'	see *F. sylvatica* 'Purpurea Tricolor'
	- 'Rotundifolia'	CDoC CDul LPan MBlu
	- 'Silver Wood'	CMCN
	- 'Spaethiana'	CMCN EWTr NBPN
	- 'Striata'	CMCN SIFN
	- 'Tortuosa Purpurea'	CMCN MBlu
	- 'Tricolor' (v)	CBcs CLnd CMac CSBt CWib EBee ELan LPan MAsh SBLw SHBN
	- 'Tricolor' misapplied	see *F. sylvatica* 'Purpurea Tricolor'
	- 'Tricolor' ambig.	SLau
	- 'Viridivariegata' (v)	CMCN
	- 'Zlatia'	CBcs CDoC CDul CLnd CMCN CSBt CWib ELan EPfP MBar MGan MGos MSwo NBee NEgg SBLw SCoo SHBN SLau SPer WOrn

Falkia (*Convolvulaceae*)

	repens	CFir

Fallopia (*Polygonaceae*)

	aubertii	see *F. baldschuanica*
§	***baldschuanica***	More than 30 suppliers
	- Summer Sunshine = 'Acofal'^{PBR}	MCCP
x	***bohemica*** 'Spectabilis' (v)	CBow EMon
§	***japonica*** var. ***compacta***	NBre NLar NPri WFar WMoo
	- var. ***compacta*** 'Fuji Snow'	see *F. japonica* var. *compacta* 'Milk Boy'
§	- - 'Milk Boy' (v)	CBow EShb EWes EWin ITer SMad
	- - f. ***rosea*** hort.	CSpe WSpi
	- - 'Variegata' misapplied	see *F. japonica* var. *compacta* 'Milk Boy'
	- 'Crimson Beauty'	SMHy
§	***multiflora***	CArn EOHP MSal
	- var. ***hypoleuca***	EBee MCCP NPri SCoo SPoG
	- - B&SWJ 120	WCru
	sachalinensis	EBee EWes NLar

Farfugium (*Asteraceae*)

§	***japonicum***	CHEx EPPr MTho
	- B&SWJ 884	WCru
	- 'Argenteum' (v)	CFir CHEx SMad WCot WFar
§	- 'Aureomaculatum' (v) Υ^{H1}	CAbb CFir CHEx CKob EBee EMan ENot EPfP LFur MBNS MCCP MTho SDnm SMad SPav SWat WFar WHer
	- 'Crispatum'	More than 30 suppliers
	- var. ***formosanum*** B&SWJ 7125	WCru
	- var. ***giganteum***	CHEx WCot
	- 'Kagami-jishi' (v)	WCot
	- 'Kinkan' (v)	WCot WHil
I	- 'Nanum'	CHEx
	- 'Ryuto'	EBee EPPr WCot
I	- 'Tsuwa-buki'	WCot
	tussilagineum	see *F. japonicum*
	- 'Aureomaculatum'	see *F. japonicum* 'Aureomaculatum'

Fargesia (*Poaceae*)

	from Jiuzhaigou, China	ETod MBri MMoz NLar
	adpressa new	EPla
	angustissima	EPla MWht SDry WPGP
	contracta	EPla
	denudata	CEnt ENBC EPla
	- L 1575	CGHE MMoz MWht WPGP
	- Xian 1 new	MMoz
	dracocephala	CAbb CDoC CEnt CGHE EBee EPfP EPla GBin LEdu MAvo MBrN MBri MMoz MWht NGdn SDry SLPl SPoG WMoo WNor WPGP
	ferax	EPla WPGP
	fungosa	EPla WPGP
§	***murielae*** Υ^{H4}	More than 30 suppliers
	- 'Amy'	NLar NMoo
	- 'Bimbo'	CHEx EBee EPfP EPla ETod EWsh GBin LAst MWht NPal WMoo WPGP XIsg
	- 'Gentle Giant' new	MBri
	- 'Grüne Hecke'	MWht
	- 'Harewood'	CWSG EBee GBin MMoz MWgw MWht NMoo SWvt WFar WPGP
	- 'Joy'	NLar WMoo WPnP
	- 'Jumbo'	More than 30 suppliers
	- 'Kranich'	NLar

- 'Lava'	MBri
- 'Leda' (v)	SDry
- 'Little John'	ENBC
- 'Mae'	CDTJ EBee MWht
- 'Novecento'	ELan
- 'Pinocchio'	MBri
- 'Simba' ♀H4	More than 30 suppliers
- 'Vampire'	MBri
- 'Willow'	EBee MBri
§ ***nitida***	More than 30 suppliers
* - from Jiuzhaigou, China	EMui EPla EWsh MAvo MWht WPGP
- 'Anceps'	EPla MWht
- 'Chennevières' **new**	EPla
- 'Eisenach'	CAbb EBee EPla MBri MMoz NGdn WFar WMoo
- Gansu 2	CGHE EPla
- 'Great Wall'	ENBC ETod MBri MWht
- 'Nymphenburg' ♀H4	CEnd CFwr CPMA ENBC EPla MBar MBri MMoz MWht NLar NMoo NPri WFar WMoo WPGP
- 'Wakehurst'	EPla MWht NLar
perlonga Yunnan 95/6 **new**	MMoz
robusta	CAbb CDTJ CEnd CEnt EBee EFul ENBC EPfP EPla ETod LPal MBrN MBri MMoz MWht NGdn NLar NMoo SDry SLPl WDyG WNor
- 'Ming Yunnan' **new**	LEdu
- 'Pingwu'	EBee ERas ETod MBri MWht NLar
- 'Red Sheath'	EPla ERod MMoz MWht NPal SEND WPGP
- 'White Sheath'	ENBC
- 'Wolong'	CDoC EPla MMoz MWht WPGP
rufa	CAbb CEnt CTca EBee ENBC ENot EPPr EPfP EPla EShb MAvo MBar MBrN MBri MCCP MMoz MWht NLar NPal WNor WPGP
spathacea misapplied	see *F. murielae*
utilis	EPla ERod EWsh LEdu MAvo MBri MMoz MWht NLar NPal SDry SEND WNor WPGP
yulongshanensis	EPla MWht SDry
aff. ***yulongshanensis***	EPla

Farsetia (*Brassicaceae*)

clypeata	see *Fibigia clypeata*

Fascicularia (*Bromeliaceae*)

andina	see *F. bicolor*
§ ***bicolor***	More than 30 suppliers
§ - subsp. ***canaliculata***	CHEx EPla IBlr LEdu LPio SChr WCot WPGP WPic
kirchhoffiana	see *F. bicolor* subsp. *canaliculata*
pitcairniifolia misapplied	see *F. bicolor*
pitcairniifolia (Verlot) Mez	see *Ochagavia* sp.

x *Fatshedera* (*Araliaceae*)

lizei ♀H3	CBcs CDoC CDul CHEx CTri EBee EPfP EPla EWTr GQui IDee LRHS MPRe MRav MWgw NPal SAPC SArc SBra SDix SDry SMac SPer SPla SPlb SPoG SWvt WCFE WFar
§ - 'Annemieke' (v) ♀H3	CBcs CBow CDoC CHEx EBee EPfP LHop MPRe MRav SBra SMac SMad SPer SPoG
§ - 'Aurea' (v)	ELan LRHS SBra SDry SEND
- 'Aureopicta'	see x *F. lizei* 'Aurea'
- 'Lemon and Lime'	see x *F. lizei* 'Annemieke'
- 'Maculata'	see x *F. lizei* 'Annemieke'
* - 'Silver Prusca'	EPla
- 'Variegata' (v) ♀H3	CAbb CBcs CHEx EBee ELan EPfP ERas LAst LRHS MGos MPRe MWgw NPal SBra SDry SEND SHGN SMac SMer SPer SPla SPoG SWvt WFar

Fatsia (*Araliaceae*)

§ ***japonica*** ♀H4	More than 30 suppliers
- 'Golden Handshake'	CBow
- 'Moseri'	CAbP CMdw CSam CTrC EBee ECtt EMan IBal LHop MSte MWgw NGdn NLar SWvt WCot WPat
- 'Murakumo-nishiki' (v)	NPal SPer
- 'Spider's Web' (v)	CBow LHop NBhm NGdn SPoG WCot WGwG
- 'Variegata' (v) ♀H3	CBcs EBee EPfP LRHS MBri MGos MRav NPal SArc SLim SPer
papyrifera	see *Tetrapanax papyrifer*
polycarpa	CHEx SKHP WPGP
- B&SWJ 7144	WCru
- RWJ 10133	WCru

Faucaria (*Aizoaceae*)

tigrina ♀H1	EPfP

Fauria see *Nephrophyllidium*

Feijoa see *Acca*

Felicia (*Asteraceae*)

aethiopica **new**	GFai
§ ***amelloides***	CHEx ERea EShb LAst LRHS MCot MLan SGar SPlb
- 'Read's Blue'	CSpe EWin SDnm XPep
- 'Read's White'	ERea EWin SDnm
- 'Santa Anita' ♀H3	CHal CTri ERea
§ - variegated (v)	CHal ECtt EWin LAst MBri MCot MSte NBlu NPer NPri SHFr SPet
- variegated, white-flowered (v)	EWin
§ ***amoena***	CTri SRms
- 'Variegata' (v)	CTri
capensis	see *F. amelloides*
- 'Variegata'	see *F. amelloides* variegated
coelestis	see *F. amelloides*
erigeroides	CHal GFai
filifolia	SPlb XPep
fruticosa	CHII
natalensis	see *F. rosulata*
pappei	see *F. amoena*
§ ***petiolata***	CTri EBee EWin NSti SGar WCot WEas WWFP
§ ***rosulata***	CPBP ECho EMon GCrs MBrN MHer MTho NBro SFgr SKHP SRms SRot
uliginosa	ECho EWes GEdr GGar LRHS MTho WFar

fennel see *Foeniculum vulgare*

fenugreek see *Trigonella foenum-graecum*

Ferraria (*Iridaceae*)

§ ***crispa***	ECho
undulata	see *F. crispa*

Ferula (*Apiaceae*)

assa-foetida	CArn LDai LEdu MSal NDov
chiliantha	see *F. communis* subsp. *glauca*
§ ***communis***	CArn CMea CSpe EBee ECGP ECha ELan EShb IDee LEdu LPio MEHN NBid NLar NSti SDix SDnm SMad SPav SPlb SPoG WCAu WCot WJek WPGP
- 'Gigantea'	see *F. communis*
§ - subsp. ***glauca***	EMan EWes SDix SGar SPhx WHal WPGP XPep

	'Giant Bronze'	see *Foeniculum vulgare* 'Giant Bronze'
	tingitana	EBee SMad
	- 'Cedric Morris'	ECha EMan SDix SPhx WSHC

Festuca (*Poaceae*)

	actae	CBig SGar WHrl
	amethystina	CBig CBrm CHrt CKno CWCL CWib EAlp EBee EMon GFor LEdu MBnl MNHC MNrw NBlu NCiC NGdn NHol NNor SPer WMoo WPer WRos WTin XIsg
	- 'Aprilgrün'	EPPr
	arundinacea	CRWN
	californica	CBig CKno EBee EPPr
	coxii	MAvo WCot
	curvula subsp. ***crassifolia***	EPla EShb NHol
	'Eisvogel'	EBee
	elegans	EPPr
	eskia	CKno CWan EAlp EBee EHul EPPr NHol SPer SPla WDyG
	filiformis	XIsg
	'Fromefield Blue'	EHul
§	***gautieri***	CBrm EAlp EBee EPPr GBin GFor MBar NBre NGdn XIsg
	- 'Pic Carlit'	EMon GBin
	gigantea	CBig GFor NBre XIsg
	glauca	More than 30 suppliers
I	- 'Auslese'	CPLG EPPr GBin GFor NGdn NPro XIsg
	- 'Azurit'	CBig CPrp EAlp EBee EPPr EWes EWsh LAst MBnl NHol SIng SPoG
§	- 'Blaufuchs' ♀H4	CBig CPMA CSam EBee ECot EHrv EPPr EPfP EWes GGar LBuc LRHS MAvo MBlu MBnl MGos MMoz MRav MSte NHol SHBN SLim SMer SPer SPla SPlb SWvt WBrE WCAu WFar
§	- 'Blauglut'	CBig EAlp EBee EHul EPPr EPfP EPla GSki LRHS MBri MRav MWgw NHol WCra
	- 'Blauspatz' **new**	XIsg
	- Blue Fox	see *F. glauca* 'Blaufuchs'
	- Blue Glow	see *F. glauca* 'Blauglut'
	- 'Elijah Blue'	More than 30 suppliers
	- 'Euchre' **new**	LSRN
	- 'Golden Toupee'	CBcs CBig CWSG EAlp EBee ECha ELan ENot EPfP EWes LAst LRHS MBar MBlu MGos MMoz MRav NBir NHol NSti SLim SPer SPlb SWvt WCot WFar XIsg
	- 'Harz'	CBrm EAlp EHul EPla LBuc MBar NCGa SApp
*	- ***minima***	CCCN EAlp SPoG
	- 'Pallens'	see *F. longifolia*
	- Sea Urchin	see *F. glauca* 'Seeigel'
§	- 'Seeigel'	CBig EAlp EBee EPPr MBnl MMoz NHol NPro
	- Select	see *F. glauca* 'Auslese'
	- 'Seven Seas'	see *F. valesiaca* 'Silbersee'
	- 'Silberreiher'	EBee EPPr XIsg
	- 'Uchte'	CWCL EBee WPtf XIsg
	idahoensis	CBig EShb
§	***longifolia***	EBee EPPr
	mairei	CKno EBee EPPr GFor GQue NBHF SWal WDyG XIsg
	novae-zelandiae	CWCL EBee NNor
	ovina	CWan NGdn WPer WSFF XIsg
	- var. ***duriuscula***	CRWN
I	- 'Kulturform'	NNor
	- 'Söhrewald'	EPPr WMoo
*	- 'Tetra Gold'	SWvt
	paniculata	CKno EPPr EPla EWsh WMoo
	- subsp. ***spadicea***	NHol
	pulchella	CBig
	punctoria	GFor WMoo XIsg
	rubra	CBig CRWN WSFF
	- var. ***nankotaizanensis*** B&SWJ 3190	WCru
	scoparia	see *F. gautieri*
	'Siskiyou Blue'	CKno
	tatrae	CBrm EBee WCot
	valesiaca	WFar
	- var. ***glaucantha***	CBig CWib EBee EPPr EWll GWCH NBre NGdn NLar XPep
§	- 'Silbersee'	CBig EBee ECha EPPr EPot EWsh LRHS MBar MBnl MSte NHol SRms WFar WSpi
	- Silver Sea	see *F. valesiaca* 'Silbersee'
	violacea	EPPr GFor MBNS NNor SIng SPer SWal WRos
	vivipara	CNat CPrp EGoo EMon LEdu NBid SBch WRos
*	'Willow Green'	SLim SPlb

Fibigia (*Brassicaceae*)

§	***clypeata***	LDai SGar
	- 'Select'	CSpe

Ficus ✿ (*Moraceae*)

	afghanistanica	ERea
	australis misapplied	see *F. rubiginosa* 'Australis'
	benghalensis	MBri
	benjamina ♀H1	CHal LRHS MBri SRms
	- 'Exotica'	CHal LRHS MBri
	- 'Golden King' (v)	LRHS MBri
	- 'Starlight' (v) ♀H1	LRHS MBri
	capitola 'Long'	ERea
	carica (F)	CCCN ETod LPan MBri MPRe SArc SLon
	- 'Abbey Slip' (F)	CHEx
*	- 'Acanthifolia'	XPep
	- 'Adam' (F)	ERea
	- 'Alma' (F)	ERea
	- 'Angélique' (F)	ERea
	- 'Archipel'(F)	ERea
	- 'Beall' (F)	ERea
	- 'Black Ischia' (F)	ERea
	- 'Black Mission' (F)	ERea
	- 'Bourjassotte Grise' (F)	ERea SDea
	- 'Brogiotto' (F) **new**	CCCN NLar
	- 'Brown Turkey' (F) ♀H3	More than 30 suppliers
	- 'Brunswick' (F)	CAgr CCCN CHll CWib EMui ENot ERea GTwe MCoo NGHP SLim WCot
	- 'Castle Kennedy' (F)	ERea GTwe
	- 'Colummaro Black Apulia' (F) **new**	CCCN
	- 'Colummaro White Apulia' (F) **new**	CCCN
	- 'Conandria' (F)	ERea
	- 'Dalmatie' (F)	ECrN ELan ERea LRHS
I	- 'Digitata' (F)	MBlu
	- 'Drap d'Or' (F)	ERea
	- 'Figue d'Or' (F)	ERea
	- 'Filacciano' (F) **new**	CCCN
	- 'Goutte d'Or' (F)	ERea SDea
	- 'Grise de Saint Jean' (F)	ERea
	- 'Kaape Bruin' (F)	ERea
	- 'Kadota' (F)	ERea NLar
*	- 'Laciniata' (F)	MBri SMad
	- 'Lisa' (F)	ERea
	- 'Little Yellow Wonder' (F)	ERea
	- 'Longue d'Août' (F)	ERea
	- 'LSU Purple' (F) **new**	ERea
	- 'Malcolm's Giant' (F)	ERea
	- 'Malta' (F)	ERea GTwe
	- 'Marseillaise' (F)	ERea GTwe SDea
	- 'Melanzana' **new**	CCCN

	- 'Negro Largo' (F)	ERea
	- 'Newlyn Coombe'	CHEx
	- 'Newlyn Harbour' (F)	CHEx
	- 'Noir de Provence'	see *F. carica* 'Reculver'
	- 'Noire de Carombe'	ERea
	- 'Osborn's Prolific' (F)	ECrN ERea SWvt
	- 'Panachée' (F)	ERea
	- 'Peter's Honey' (F)	ERea
	- 'Petite Grise' (F)	ERea
	- 'Petite Nigra' (F) **new**	ERea
	- 'Pied de Boeuf' (F)	ERea
	- 'Pittaluse' (F)	ERea
	- 'Porthminster' (F) **new**	CHEx
	- 'Précoce de Dalmatie' (F)	EMil ERea WPGP
	- 'Précoce Ronde de Bordeaux' (F)	ERea
§	- 'Reculver' (F)	ERea
	- 'Rouge de Bordeaux' (F)	CCCN ERea SDea
	- 'Saint Johns' (F)	ERea
	- 'San Pedro Miro' (F)	ERea
	- 'Snowden' (F)	ERea
	- 'Sollies Pont' (F)	ERea
	- 'Sugar 12' (F)	ERea
	- 'Sultane' (F)	ERea
	- 'Tena' (F)	ERea
	- 'Texas Everbearing' (F) **new**	ERea
	- 'Trojano' (F)	ERea
	- 'Verte d'Argenteuil' (F)	ERea
	- 'Violette Dauphine' (F)	ERea
	- 'Violette de Sollies' (F)	ERea
	- 'Violette Sepor' (F)	ERea
	- 'White Genoa'	see *F. carica* 'White Marseilles'
	- 'White Ischia' (F)	ERea
§	- 'White Marseilles' (F)	CCCN CWib ECrN EMui EPfP ERea MBri MCoo NGHP SDea
	cyathistipula	MBri
	deltoidea var. ***diversifolia***	MBri
	elastica	LRHS
	- 'Doescheri' (v) Ÿ^{H1}	NScw
	- 'Robusta'	MBri
	foveolata Wallich	see *F. sarmentosa*
	lyrata Ÿ^{H1}	MBri
	microcarpa	STre
	- 'Hawaii' (v)	CHal
	pubigera	CPLG
	pumila Ÿ^{H1}	CHEx CHal LRHS MBri XPep
	- 'Minima'	CFee
	- 'Sonny' (v)	MBri
	- 'Variegata' (v)	CHEx CHal MBri
	radicans 'Variegata'	see *F. sagittata* 'Variegata'
§	***rubiginosa*** 'Australis'	MBri
	- 'Variegata' (v) Ÿ^{H1}	CHal
§	***sagittata*** 'Variegata' (v)	MBri
§	***sarmentosa***	MBri

fig see *Ficus carica*

filbert see *Corylus maxima*

Filipendula ✿ (*Rosaceae*)

	alnifolia 'Variegata'	see *F. ulmaria* 'Variegata'
	camtschatica	CFir CMCo ECha ELan NBid NLar NMir NPol WFar WMoo WPGP
	- RBS 0224	ITer MGol
	- 'Rosea'	LHop MRav SMad
	digitata 'Nana'	see *F. multijuga*
	formosa B&SWJ 8707	WCru
	hexapetala	see *F. vulgaris*
	- 'Flore Pleno'	see *F. vulgaris* 'Multiplex'
	'Kahome'	CMCo CPrp EBee EBrs EPla EShb GBuc GGar GMaP GMac IFoB LAst LHop LRHS NBir NGdn NLar NMir NOrc SMer SPer SPla SVil SWat WBor WFar WHoo WMoo WPnP
	kiraishiensis B&SWJ 1571	EBee WCru
§	***multijuga***	EBee GGar IFoB NHol WBor WFar WMoo
	palmata	ECha GSki MBri MLHP NBre SWat WFar WMoo
	- 'Digitata Nana'	see *F. multijuga*
	- dwarf	CLAP GSki MLHP
	- 'Elegantissima'	see *F. purpurea* 'Elegans'
	- 'Nana'	see *F. multijuga*
	- ***purpurea***	see *F. purpurea*
	- 'Rosea'	ERou IBlr NBir
	- 'Rubra'	CTri GCra GSki MRav NGdn
	- ***rufinervis*** B&SWJ 941	WCru
	- - B&SWJ 8611	WCru
§	***purpurea*** Ÿ^{H4}	CKno CSBt ECha EPfP GGar GSki LRHS MBri MWrn WBVN WCru WFar WMoo WPnP
	- f. ***albiflora***	EBee MBri NPri WMoo WPnP
§	- 'Elegans'	EBee ECha EMil ERou EWsh GGar GMac LAst MLHP MSte NBPC NBid NHol NPri NSti SWat WFar WMoo WSpi
	- 'Nephele'	EBee GMac SMHy
	- 'Pink Dreamland'	EBee EPPr SAga SPhx
*	- 'Plena' (d)	NLar
	- 'White Dreamland'	EBee
	'Queen of the Prairies'	see *F. rubra*
§	***rubra***	GAbr LAst LSRN MCot NBid WBVN WCra WFar WSFF
§	- 'Venusta' Ÿ^{H4}	More than 30 suppliers
	- 'Venusta Magnifica'	see *F. rubra* 'Venusta'
§	***ulmaria***	CArn CBen CHby COld CRWN CWan EBee EHon ELau EMFW GMaP GPoy LRHS MHer MNHC NHol NLan NMir SECG SIde SWat WFar WMoo WPer WSFF WShi
	- 'Aurea'	More than 30 suppliers
	- 'Flore Pleno' (d)	CBre EBee GSki LAst LHop LRHS MRav NBid NBre NGdn SIde SPer SWat WCAu WCot WFar WPnP WTin
	- 'Rosea'	CDes IBlr WPGP
§	- 'Variegata' (v)	More than 30 suppliers
§	***vulgaris***	CArn CFee CRWN CTri CWan ECtt LAst MDun MLHP MNHC MSal MWgw NBlu NBro NMir NNor NPri SWat WPer
	- 'Alba'	EBee
	- 'Flore Pleno'	see *F. vulgaris* 'Multiplex'
	- 'Grandiflora'	EPPr WCot
§	- 'Multiplex' (d)	EBee ECha EGle ELan ERou EShb GMaP GSki LRHS MBri MHer MLLN MRav NBid NBir NPri NRya SMer SPer SRms WAul WEas WFar WLin WMoo WTin
	- 'Plena'	see *F. vulgaris* 'Multiplex'
	- 'Rosea'	EBee NBre

Firmiana (*Sterculiaceae*)

	simplex	CHEx EShb WPGP

Fittonia (*Acanthaceae*)

	albivenis Argyroneura Group Ÿ^{H1}	CHal LRHS
	- - 'Nana'	CHal
§	- Verschaffeltii Group Ÿ^{H1}	CHal
	verschaffeltii	see *F. albivenis* Verschaffeltii Group

Fitzroya (*Cupressaceae*)

	cupressoides	CBcs CDoC CMac CTho IArd IDee LCon LRHS MBar SCoo SLim

Fockea (*Asclepiadaceae*)

	edulis	EShb

Foeniculum (*Apiaceae*)

	vulgare	CArn CHEx CHby CPrp CWan ECha ELan ELau EPfP GMaP GPoy LHop MGos MHer MNHC MSal NGHP NPri SECG SIde SPer SPlb WMoo WPer WSel XPep
	- 'Bronze'	see *F. vulgare* 'Purpureum'
	- var. ***dulce***	CSev SIde
§	- 'Giant Bronze'	CChe EBee ELan LCro SMad SPhx WHen
§	- 'Purpureum'	More than 30 suppliers
	- 'Smokey'	ECha MRav

Fontanesia (*Oleaceae*)

	phillyreoides	CBcs CMCN

Fontinalis (*Sphagnaceae*)

	antipyretica	WFar

Forestiera (*Oleaceae*)

	neomexicana	see *F. pubescens*
§	***pubescens***	CBcs

Forsythia ✿ (*Oleaceae*)

	'Arnold Dwarf'	ECrN NLar SRms
	'Beatrix Farrand' ambig.	CTri CWSG EBee LRHS MGos MWat NEgg SPer SRms WBod
	'Beatrix Farrand' K. Sax	IMGH NLar
	'Fiesta' (v)	CWSG EBee ELon EPfP LAst LRHS MAsh MBar MGos MRav MSwo NBlu NEgg NWea SLim SPer SPoG WCot WFar WRHF
	giraldiana	EBee MSwo SLon SRms WBod WSpi
	Gold Tide PBR	see *F.* Marée d'Or = 'Courtasol'
	'Golden Bells'	CDul ENot
	'Golden Nugget'	ELan EPfP LRHS MAsh MBri SCoo SLon SMer SPoG WCFE
	'Golden Times' (v)	CBcs ERas EWes LBuc LSRN MAsh MGos NHol NLar SCoo SPoG SWvt WBod WFar
	x ***intermedia***	ECrN
	- 'Arnold Giant'	MBlu WBod
	- 'Densiflora'	NWea
	- 'Goldrausch'	MAsh MBri
	- 'Goldzauber'	NWea
	- 'Josefa' (v)	ELan LBuc MAsh
	- 'Lynwood Variety' ♀H4	More than 30 suppliers
	- 'Lynwood Variety' variegated	CWib
	- Minigold = 'Flojor'	EPfP LAst MGos MSwo MWat NBlu NEgg SRms WBVN WRHF
	- 'Spectabilis'	CDul EMac EPfP LBuc MAsh MBar MGan NWea SCoo SLim WBod WFar WTel
	- 'Spectabilis Variegated' (v)	CBow MBNS NPro
	- 'Spring Glory'	MHer WSpi
	- 'Variegata' (v)	NSti NWea WGwG
	- Week-End = 'Courtalyn' PBR ♀H4	CWSG ECrN ENot EPfP LBuc MAsh MBri MGos NLar NWea SEND SLPl SLim SLon SMer SPlb SPoG WFar
	koreana 'Ilgwang' (v)	CPMA
§	Marée d'Or = 'Courtasol' PBR ♀H4	CWSG EMil LRHS MBri MGos MRav NLar NWea SMer
	Mêlée d'Or = 'Courtaneur'	LRHS SCoo SPer
	Melissa = 'Courtadic'	NLar NWea
	ovata 'Tetragold'	CBcs EMil MBar NEgg
	'Paulina'	NLar
	suspensa	CArn CTri CWib ENot EOHP EPfP LRHS MBar MSal NWea SHBN SPer SPlb SRms WSpi WTel
	- f. ***atrocaulis***	CDul CPle NWea WSpi
	- 'Decipiens'	WBod
	- var. ***fortunei***	MBri NEgg
	- 'Nymans'	EPfP MBri MRav NSti
§	- 'Taff's Arnold' (v)	CPLG CPMA WSPU
	- 'Variegata'	see *F. suspensa* 'Taff's Arnold'
	'Tremonia'	ECrN NLar SLon WGwG
	'Verfors Minor Gold' **new**	MBri
	viridissima	NWea
	- 'Bronxensis'	ECho EPot GEdr MAsh NBir NLar
	- 'Weber's Bronx'	NLar

Fortunella (*Rutaceae*)

	'Fukushu' (F) ♀H1	ERea
§	***japonica*** (F)	EPfP SLon
§	***margarita*** (F)	CDoC MBri

Fothergilla (*Hamamelidaceae*)

	gardenii	CBcs CPMA EBee ELan EPfP EWTr MBlu MBri MGos MRav NEgg NLar SPer SPoG SSpi
	- Beaver Creek = 'Klmtwo' **new**	NLar
	- 'Blue Mist'	CAbP CDoC CEnd CPMA CWSG EBee ELan EPfP LRHS NLar SMad SPer SPla SReu SSta WBod WFar WPat
	- 'Harold Epstein' **new**	NLar
	- 'Suzanne'	MBri NLar
	- 'Zundert' **new**	NLar
	'Huntsman'	CCCN WFar
	major ♀H4	CBcs CDul CEnd CPMA CSam CWib CWoW EBee ELan ENot EPfP LCro LRHS MBri MGos MLan NBlu NEgg SHBN SPer SPoG SReu SSpi WBod WFar WNor WPat WSpi
	- 'Bulkyard'	MBri
	- Monticola Group	CDoC CEnd CPMA CSBt CWSG EBee ELan EPfP IMGH LCro LRHS MAsh MBar MDun MGos MMuc NHol NPal SHBN SLim SPer SSpi SSta SWvt WBrE WFar
	- 'Red Licorice' **new**	CPMA NLar
	- 'Seaspray' **new**	NLar
	'Mount Airy'	CMCN CPMA EPfP IMGH MBri NLar SPoG SSpi

Fragaria (*Rosaceae*)

	from Taiwan	WHer
	alpina	see *F. vesca* 'Semperflorens'
	- 'Alba'	see *F. vesca* 'Semperflorens Alba'
	x ***ananassa*** (F)	CPLG
	- 'Alice' PBR (F)	CAgr CSut EMui MCoo
	- 'Aromel' (F) ♀H4	CSBt CWSG EPfP GTwe LRHS SDea
	- 'Bogota' (F)	LRHS
	- 'Bolero' PBR (F)	EMui MBri
	- 'Calypso' PBR (F)	CSBt EMui LRHS SDea SKee
	- 'Cambridge Favourite' (F) ♀H4	CAgr CSBt CTri CWSG EMui EPfP GTwe LRHS MBri MCoo MGan SDea SKee
	- 'Cambridge Late Pine' (F)	CWSG EMui LRHS
	- 'Cambridge Rival' (F)	LRHS
	- 'Cambridge Vigour' (F)	CWSG GTwe LRHS SDea
	- 'Challenger' (F)	EMui
	- 'Chelsea Pensioner' **new**	EMui
	- 'Darselect' PBR (F)	EMui
	- 'Elsanta' PBR (F)	CSBt CTri CWSG EMui EPfP GTwe IArd LRHS MGan NPri SDea SPer
	- 'Elvira' (F)	EMui
*	- 'Emily' (F)	GTwe NPri
	- 'Eros' PBR (F)	EMui GTwe NPri SKee
	- 'Everest' PBR (F) **new**	LBuc
	- 'Evie' (F) **new**	SGFT
	- 'Flamenco' (F) PBR **new**	CSut EMui

- 'Florence'PBR (F)	CAgr CSBt CSut EMil EMui GTwe LRHS MBri SKee SPer
- fraise des bois	see *F. vesca*
- 'Gariguette' (F) new	EMui
- 'Hampshire Maid' (F)	LRHS
- 'Hapil' (F) ♕H4	CTri EMui EPfP GTwe LRHS NPri
- 'Honeoye' (F) ♕H4	CAgr CSBt EMui GTwe LRHS MBri SKee SPer
- 'Korona'PBR (F)	EMui
- 'Kouril' (F)	LRHS
- 'Loran' (F) new	WHlf
- 'Mae' (F)	CSut EMui
- 'Malling Opal' (F) new	EMil
- 'Malling Pearl' (F) new	EMil
- 'Maxim' (F)	EMui
- 'Pantagruella' (F)	LRHS
- 'Pegasus'PBR (F) ♕H4	CAgr CSBt EMil EMui GTwe LRHS
- Pink Panda = 'Frel'PBR (F)	CBcs EBee ELan EWsh LBuc MRav NEgg NHol NLar SIng SPer SPoG WCAu WEas WFar WWFP
- pink-flowered(F)	CFee EMui
- Red Ruby = 'Samba'PBR	EBee MNrw NEgg NGdn NLar SIng SPer SPoG WCAu
- 'Redgauntlet' (F)	EPfP GTwe LRHS
- 'Rhapsody'PBR (F) ♕H4	GTwe LRHS
- 'Rosie'PBR (F)	EMui SDea
- 'Royal Sovereign' (F)	GTwe LRHS MGan
- 'Sophie'PBR (F)	CAgr LRHS
- 'Symphony'PBR (F) ♕H4	CAgr EMil EMui EPfP MBri SKee
- 'Tamella' (F)	EMui LRHS
- 'Tenira' (F)	EMui
- 'Totem' (F)	GTwe
§ - 'Variegata' (v)	CArn CSev EBee EMon EPla LDai LHop MCCP MHar MRav NHol SIng SPer SPoG WMoo
- 'Victoria' (F) new	EMil
- 'Viva Rosa' (F)	EMui LBuc LRHS
'Bowles' Double'	see *F. vesca* 'Multiplex'
chiloensis (F)	CAgr EMon ILis LEdu SHar
- 'Chaval'	CHid ECha EGoo EHrv EMon EPPr MRav WMoo
- 'Variegata' misapplied	see *F.* x *ananassa* 'Variegata'
daltoniana	GCra
indica	see *Duchesnea indica*
'Lipstick'	EWsh NLar WRos WSel WSpi
moschata	CAgr
nubicola	GPoy
'Variegata'	see *F.* x *ananassa* 'Variegata'
§ ***vesca*** (F)	CAgr CArn CRWN CWan EPfP GPoy LRHS MHer MNHC NGHP NMir NPri SECG SIde SPlb WGwG WJek WPer WSFF WShi
- 'Alexandra' (F)	CArn CBod CPrp ELau EWin GAbr LRHS NVic SIde
- 'Flore Pleno'	see *F. vesca* 'Multiplex'
- 'Fructu Albo' (F)	CAgr CArn CBgR CBre EBee NLar WMoo WPer
- 'Golden Alexandra'	ELau EWes LRav LSou WHer
- 'Mara des Bois'PBR (F)	EMui GTwe MBri
- 'Monophylla' (F)	EMon IGor SIde WHer
§ - 'Multiplex' (d)	CBgR CDes CSev EMon ILis MRav NGHP NHol NLar SMac WHer WOut WRHF
§ - 'Muricata'	CBre CPou EOHP IGor ILis ITer LEdu WHer
- 'Pineapple Crush'	WHer
- 'Plymouth Strawberry'	see *F. vesca* 'Muricata'
- 'Rügen' (F)	IGor
§ - 'Semperflorens' (F)	ILis
§ - 'Semperflorens Alba' (F)	CAgr
- 'Variegata' misapplied	see *F.* x *ananassa* 'Variegata'
* - 'Variegata' ambig. (v)	EHrv NGHP SMac WFar WHrl WPer WSel
virginiana	CAgr
- subsp. ***glauca***	EPPr
viridis	CAgr

Francoa (*Saxifragaceae*)

appendiculata	CAbP CEnt EBla EMan GQui MDKP NBre SGar SWal WFar WHer WHrl WMoo WPnP
- red-flowered	CDes CKno EBee
Ballyrogan strain	IBlr
'Confetti'	CDes CKno CPLG ELan EMan ERou GBin GMaP MAvo MFOX MNrw MWgw NCob NEgg SWal WCot WCra WFar WPGP WTMC
'Purple Spike'	see *F. sonchifolia* Rogerson's
ramosa	CCVN CMCo CTri EHrv EMan GBuc IBlr MLan MNrw NBro NEgg SAga SDix SHGN SPav WFar WMoo
* - 'Alba'	CSpe
sonchifolia	More than 30 suppliers
- 'Alba'	CHFP MDKP NRnb SMrm WFar WHrl WMoo
- 'Culm View Lilac'	CCVN
- 'Doctor Tom Smith'	WCot
- 'Molly Anderson'	MAvo
§ - Rogerson's	More than 30 suppliers

Frangula (*Rhamnaceae*)

§ ***alnus***	CArn CCVT CLnd CRWN ECrN EMac LBuc MBlu NWea SLPl STre WFar WMou WSFF
- 'Aspleniifolia'	CTho EBee EMil EPfP LBuc MBlu MBri MMuc MRav NLar WFar
- 'Columnaris'	EMil SLPl
- 'Minaret' new	MBri

Frankenia (*Frankeniaceae*)

laevis	SRms XPep
thymifolia	CBrm CTri EAlp ECho GGar LRHS MBar MHer MWat SPlb WFar WPer WTel WTin XPep

Franklinia (*Theaceae*)

alatamaha	CBcs CMCN CPMA EPfP LHyd MBlu MBri WFar WNor

Fraxinus ✿ (*Oleaceae*)

americana	CDul CMCN EPfP SBLw
- 'Autumn Purple'	CDul CEnd CMCN CTho EBee ECrN EPfP LRHS MAsh MBlu SBLw SLon
- 'Rosehill'	CTho
angustifolia	CMCN EGFP
- 'Raywood' ♕H4	CBcs CCVT CDoC CDul CEnd CLnd CMCN CTho CTri CWib EBee ECrN ELan EPfP EWTr LCro MAsh MBlu MGos MSwo NEgg NPal NWea SBLw SMad SPer SPoG WFar WJas WOrn
* - 'Variegata' (v)	MGos
bungeana	EGFP
chinensis	CLnd CMCN EGFP
elonza	CLnd
excelsior	CBcs CCVT CDoC CDul CLnd CRWN CSBt CTri CWib EBee ECrN EMac ENot EPfP LAst LBuc LPan MBar MGos NBee NWea SBLw SHBN SHFr SLim STre WMou WOrn
- 'Allgold'	CEnd
- 'Aurea'	SBLw
- 'Aurea Pendula'	CDul CEnd CMCN CWib EBee ECrN EPfP LRHS MBlu MGos SBLw SPoG
- 'Crispa'	MBlu NEgg NLar SBLw
- f. ***diversifolia***	CDul CLnd
- 'Globosa'	SBLw

- 'Jaspidea' ♀H4	CBcs CCVT CDoC CDul CEnd CLnd CMCN CTho CWib EBee ECrN EPfP ERod EWTr LPan LRHS MAsh MBar MBlu MBri MGos MRav MSwo NEgg NWea SHBN SPer WFar WJas WOrn
- 'Nana'	EMon SBLw WPat
- 'Pendula' ♀H4	CCVT CDoC CDul CEnd CLnd CTho EBee ECrN ELan EPfP LAst LPan LRHS MBlu MBri NBee NEgg NPal NWea SBLw SHBN SLim SPer SPoG WJas WMou WOrn
- 'R.E. Davey'	CDul CNat
- variegated (v)	ECrN
- 'Westhof's Glorie' ♀H4	CCVT CDoC CLnd EBee ECrN NEgg SBLw WFar WJas WOrn
insularis var. ***henryana***	CDul CMCN WPGP
latifolia	CLnd
mandshurica new	MBri
mariesii	see *F. sieboldiana*
nigra	CMCN
- 'Fallgold'	CEnd
ornus ♀H4	CCVT CDul CLnd CMCN CTri EBee ECrN ELan EMac EPfP EWTr IMGH MBri MSwo NPal NPen NWea SBLw SPer WFar WMoo WOrn
- 'Arie Peters'	CDul LPan SBLw
- 'Mecsek'	MBlu
- 'Obelisk'	MBri SMad
- 'Rotterdam'	EBee SBLw
pennsylvanica	CDul CLnd CMCN
- 'Variegata' (v)	CLnd EBee MAsh MBri WPat
§ ***sieboldiana***	CDoC CDul CLnd CMCN CPMA EPfP MBlu MBri NLar SSpi WPGP WPat
velutina	CDul CLnd SLPl
xanthoxyloides var. ***dumosa***	MBri WPGP

Freesia (*Iridaceae*)

'Cinderella'	CAvo
hybrids	EBrs
laxa	see *Anomatheca laxa*
'Oberon'	CAvo
'Seagull'	CAvo
xanthospila	EBrs

Fremontodendron (*Sterculiaceae*)

'California Glory' ♀H3	More than 30 suppliers
californicum	CSBt CTri CWib EBee ELan EMil MBri NBlu SHBN SLim SOWG SPlb WBod WCFE WFar WNor WOrn
mexicanum	NLar XPep
'Pacific Sunset'	CPMA ENot EPfP LHop MGos MRav SAga SBra SPoG
'Tequila Sunrise'	CBcs CBrm CPMA EBee GBin ISea MGos MRav NLar SPoG SRkn

Freylinia (*Scrophulariaceae*)

cestroides	see *F. lanceolata*
densiflora	GFai
§ ***lanceolata***	CBcs CCCN CTrC CWib EShb
tropica	CHII GFai
visseri	GFai SOWG

Fritillaria ✿ (*Liliaceae*)

acmopetala ♀H4	CAvo CFFs CFwr CMea CPom CWCL EBee EBrs ECho EPot ERos GBuc GCrs GEdr ITim LAma LRHS MSSP MSte MTho NMen SPhx WCot WCra WLin
- 'Brunette'	EBrs ECho MSte WCot WWst
- subsp. ***wendelboi***	CHHB EBrs ECho EPot LAma SPhx WCot
affinis	CWCL ECho GBin GBuc GCrs GKev LAma MSSP NMen SBla WCot WWst
- 'Limelight'	ECho
- 'Sunray'	EBrs GCrs GEdr SKHP WWst
§ - var. ***tristulis***	ERos NMen
- 'Vancouver Island'	EBrs ECho EPot WWst
alfredae subsp. ***glaucoviridis***	WCot WWst
arabica	see *F. persica*
armena	CHHB EBrs ECho
assyriaca	EPot
aurea	ECho MSSP NMen WCot WWst
- 'Golden Flag'	CHHB EBrs ECho EPfP EPot GKev LTwo
biflora	ECho GCrs GEdr
- 'Martha Roderick'	EBrs ECho ERCP GMaP LAma MSSP NMen SBla WWst
§ ***bithynica***	CHHB CStu EBrs ECho GCrs GEdr ITim LAma MSSP
bucharica	CHHB EBee ECho GKev
camschatcensis	CHHB CPom CWCL EBrs ECha ECho EFEx EPfP EPot ERCP GCrs GEdr GMaP LAma LRHS MSSP MTho NBir NDov NHar NMen SPer SPhx WAbe WCru WLin
- from Alaska	GCrs
I - ***alpina aurea***	GCrs GEdr
- 'Aurea'	GBuc NHar NMen WWst
- black-flowered	ECho GBuc
- double-flowered (d)	CFir CHHB EBrs ECho NMen
- f. ***flavescens***	EBrs ECho EFEx GEdr LAma
- green-flowered	MSSP NMen
- 'Lutea' new	CHHB
- 'Tomari' new	CHHB
carduchorum	see *F. minuta*
carica	CHHB EBrs ECho GEdr LRHS MSSP NMen
- brown-flowered	ECho
caucasica	EBrs ECho NMen
cirrhosa	EBrs ECho GCrs GEdr WWst
- brown-flowered	EBrs GEdr NMen WWst
- green-flowered	GEdr NMen WWst
citrina	see *F. bithynica*
§ ***collina***	ENot GCrs NMen
conica	CHHB GCrs NMen WCot WWst
crassicaulis	WCot
crassifolia	ECho LAma MSSP
- subsp. ***crassifolia***	CGra
§ - subsp. ***kurdica***	EBrs EPot GCrs NMen WCot WWst
davidii	ECho
davisii	EBrs ECho EPot GBuc GCrs GEdr LAma LRHS NMen WCot
davisii x ***graeca*** new	WCot
delavayi	CExc
delphinensis	see *F. tubiformis*
drenovskii	WWst
eduardii	EBrs ECho GCrs GKev WCot WWst
ehrhartii	SBla
elwesii	CHHB EBee EBrs ECho EPot GEdr NMen WCot
ferganensis	see *F. walujewii*
fleischeriana	CHHB
frankiorum	WCot
gentneri	SKHP
glauca	LAma MSSP WCot
* - 'Golden Flag'	ECho
- 'Goldilocks'	EBrs ECho EPot NMen
graeca	CBgR EBrs ECho EPot GBuc GCrs LRHS MTho NMen
- subsp. ***ionica***	see *F. thessala*
gussichiae	CHHB EBrs GCrs MSSP NMen WWst
hermonis subsp. ***amana***	CTca EBrs ECho EPot GCrs GEdr GKev ITim LAma LPio LRHS LTwo NMen NWCA WCot WLin

	- - 'Cambridge' ♀H4	WCot WWst
	- - yellow-flowered	EPot
	- subsp. ***hermonis*** new	WCot
	hispanica	see *F. lusitanica*
	imperialis	ECGP IHer MBri WBVN WCra WTin
	- 'Argenteovariegata' (v)	CHHB
	- 'Aureomarginata' (v)	CHHB EBrs LAma
	- 'Aurora'	CSam EBee EBrs EPot GKev LAma LRHS NGHP NLar NPer SPer SPhx WFar
	- 'Garland Star'	EBee EBrs LAma
	- 'Indora Purpurea' new	CTca
	- var. ***inodora***	EBee EBrs
	- 'Lutea'	CAby CAvo CHHB CMea CSam CTca EBrs ELan ENot EPfP GKev LRHS MSte NBPC SMeo SPad SPhx WFar
	- 'Lutea Maxima'	see *F. imperialis* 'Maxima Lutea'
	- 'Maxima'	see *F. imperialis* 'Rubra Maxima'
§	- 'Maxima Lutea' ♀H4	EBee ELan EMon EPfP EPot LAma NLar SPer
	- 'Orange Brilliant'	CHHB EBee EBrs LRHS MSte
	- 'Prolifera'	CHHB CTca EBee EBrs ECho LAma MNFA NLar WCot WHer
	- 'Rubra'	CTca EBee EBrs ECho ENot ERCP GKev LAma LRHS NBir NLar SMeo SPer WFar
§	- 'Rubra Maxima'	CAby CHHB EBee EBrs ELan EPfP EPot LAma LRHS MSte
	- 'Slagzwaard'	EBee EBrs
	- 'Sulpherino'	CHHB EBee EBrs EMon LAma
	- 'The Premier'	EBee EBrs ECho LAma SMeo WCot
	- 'William Rex'	CAvo CFFs EBee EBrs EPot ERou LAma
	- yellow-flowered	CFFs
	involucrata	EBrs ECho WCot WWst
	ionica	see *F. thessala*
	japonica var. ***koidzumiana***	EBrs EFEx GEdr WWst
	karadaghensis	see *F. crassifolia* subsp. *kurdica*
	kotschyana	EBrs ECho EPot GCrs GEdr NMen WCot
	lanceolata	see *F. affinis* var. *tristulis*
	latakiensis	EBrs ECho EPot GEdr WCot
§	***latifolia***	GEdr WCot
	- var. ***nobilis***	see *F. latifolia*
§	***lusitanica***	MSSP NMen SBla SKHP WWst
	lutea Bieb.	see *F. collina*
	maximowiczii	ECho
	meleagris	More than 30 suppliers
	- var. ***unicolor*** subvar. ***alba*** ♀H4	CAvo CMea EBrs ECGP ECho GBri GBuc LAma LEdu LRHS MBri MSSP MWat NHol NLAp SPer WAul WCot WShi
	- - - 'Aphrodite'	EPot GBuc NBir
	meleagroides	EBrs WCot WWst
§	***messanensis***	GCrs MSSP SBla WCot
	- subsp. ***gracilis***	GCrs MSSP
	michailovskyi ♀H2	CAvo CFFs CFwr CTca CTri EBrs ECho EHon EPfP EPot GBuc GEdr GGar GKev LAma LRHS MNrw MTho NLAp NMen NWCA SRms WFar WHil WLin
§	***minuta***	CStu EBrs ECho EPot GCrs NMen
	montana	EBrs ECho NMen WCot
	nigra Mill.	see *F. pyrenaica*
	obliqua	WCot
	olivieri	GCrs WWst
§	***orientalis***	ECho WCot WWst
	pallidiflora ♀H4	CAvo CLAP CTca CWCL EBee EBrs ECho EMon EPot ERos GBuc GEdr LAma LPio MNFA MSSP MSte MTho NBid NBir NMen NSla SMeo SPhx WCru WLin WPnP

§	***persica***	CTca EBrs ECha ECho ECtt EHrv EPfP EPot ERCP LAma LHop LRHS MAvo MBri NBPC NMen SGar SMeo SPer SPhx WFar WHil
	- 'Adiyaman' ♀H4	CAvo CFFs CTca EBrs ELan EMon SMeo SPhx
	- 'Ivory Bells'	EBrs ECho EPot ERCP LAma LPio MSte SPhx
	pinardii	ECho EPot GCrs NMen
	pontica ♀H4	CAvo CBgR CLAP EBrs ECho EPot ERos GBuc GCrs GEdr GKev ITim LAma LPio LRHS MLLN MSSP MTho NMen NSla SBla SMeo SPer SPhx WAbe WCot WCru WLin WPnP
	- subsp. ***substipilata***	WCot
	pudica	CHHB EBrs ECho GBuc GCrs GEdr GKev ITim LAma MSSP MTho NMen WAbe WLin
*	- 'Fragrant'	NMen
	- 'Giant'	EBrs ECho EPot GCrs WWst
	- 'Richard Britten'	GCrs NMen
	puqiensis	CExc
	purdyi	EBrs ECho MSSP
§	***pyrenaica*** ♀H4	CLAP EBrs ECho ERos GCra GCrs GEdr LPio MSSP NMen NSla SBla SPhx WCot WCru WTin WWst
	- 'Cedric Morris'	MSSP WCot
	- 'Lutea'	NSla
	raddeana	CHFP CHHB EBee EBrs ECho EPot ERCP LAma SPhx
	recurva	EBrs SKHP
	rhodocanakis	EBrs ECho NMen WWst
	- subsp. ***argolica***	ECho NMen
	rubra major	see *F. imperialis* 'Rubra Maxima'
	ruthenica	EBrs ECho ERos GCrs MSSP NMen SBla
	sewerzowii	EBrs EPot GCrs WCot WWst
	sibthorpiana	WCot
	sphaciotica	see *F. messanensis*
	stenanthera	CHHB EBrs ECho EPot GCrs LAma NMen WWst
	stribrnyi	EBrs WWst
	tachengensis	see *F. yuminensis*
	tenella	see *F. orientalis*
§	***thessala***	CHHB EBrs GBuc MSSP MTho NMen SPhx WCot
	thunbergii	CHHB EBee EBrs ECho GCrs GEdr NMen WAbe WCot
	tortifolia	NMen
§	***tubiformis***	EBrs GEdr MSSP WWst
	tuntasia	WCot
	unibracteata var. ***unibracteata*** new	CExc
	uva-vulpis	CMea CSam CTca EBrs ECrN ECtt EHon EPot GBuc GEdr GKev LAma LHop LPio LRHS MNrw MTho NBir NMen SMeo SPer SPhx WCot WCru WFar
	verticillata	CBgR CMea EBee EBrs ECha ECho EHrv EPot GEdr LAma MTho NMen SPhx WCru
§	***walujewii***	EPot GEdr MSSP WCot
	whittallii	EBrs ECho EPot GCrs MSSP NMen WCot
	- 'Green Light' new	EBrs WWst
§	***yuminensis***	ECho WCot
	- var. ***roseiflora***	GEdr

Fuchsia ✿ (*Onagraceae*)

'A.M. Larwick'	EBak EKMF SRiF
'A.W. Taylor'	EBak
'Aalt Groothuis'	SRiF WPBF
'Aan de Linge' (d) new	WPBF
'Aat van Wijk' (d)	WPBF

'Abbé Farges' (d)	CDoC CLoc CWVF EBak EKMF EPts MWhe SLBF SPet SRiF WFFs WRou
'Abbigayle Reine' (v)	SRiF
'Abigail'	CWVF EKMF WPBF WRou
'Acclamation' (d)	WPBF
'Achievement' ♀^{H4}	CDoC CLoc EKMF LCla MJac SPet WFFs WPBF
'Adagio' (d)	CLoc
'Adelaide Hoodless'	WRou
'Adinda'	CDoC EKMF EPts LCla MWar SLBF SRiF
'Admiration'	EKMF
'Aiguillette'	WPBF
'Ailsa Garnett'	EBak
'Aintree'	CWVF
'Airedale'	CWVF WFFs
'Aisen'	WRou
'Ajax' (d)	SRiF
'Aladna's Sanders'	CWVF SRiF WPBF
'Alan Ayckbourn'	CWVF
'Alan Dyos' **new**	SRiF
'Alan Titchmarsh' (d)	CDoC EKMF EPts LCla MWar SLBF
'Alaska' (d)	CLoc EBak EKMF WPBF
'Albertina'	SRiF WRou
'Albertus Schwab'	LCla
'Alde'	CWVF
'Alderford'	SLBF WPBF
'Alf Thornley' (d)	CWVF MWhe WPBF
'Alfred Rambaud' (d)	CDoC SRiF
'Ali' (d)	EKMF
'Alice Ashton' (d)	EBak EKMF
'Alice Blue Gown' (d)	CWVF
'Alice Doran'	CDoC EKMF LCla SRiF
'Alice Hoffman' (d) ♀$^{H3-4}$	More than 30 suppliers
'Alice Mary' (d)	EBak EMan
'Alice Sweetapple'	CWVF SRiF
'Alice Travis' (d)	EBak
'Alipat'	EBak EKMF
'Alisha Jade'	SRiF WPBF
'Alison Ewart'	CLoc CWVF EBak EKMF MJac MWhe SPet WPBF WRou
'Alison Patricia' ♀^{H3}	CWVF EBak EKMF EMan LAst MJac MWar SLBF SRGP WFFs WPBF WRou
'Alison Reynolds' (d)	CWVF
'Alison Ruth Griffin' (d)	MJac
'Alison Ryle' (d)	EBak
'Alison Sweetman' ♀$^{H1+3}$	CWVF EKMF MJac MWhe
'Allure' (d)	CWVF
'Alma Hulscher' (d)	CWVF
Aloha = 'Sanicomf'^{PBR} (Sunangels Series)	SLBF SRiF
§ ***alpestris***	CDoC EBak LCla SRiF
- Berry 64-87	EKMF
'Alton Water' (d/v)	MWar
'Alwin' (d)	CWVF MWhe SRiF
'Alyce Larson' (d)	CWVF EBak MJac SRiF
'Amanda Bridgland' (d)	EKMF
'Amanda Jones'	EKMF MWhe
'Amazing Maisie' (d)	MWar
'Ambassador'	EBak SPet SRiF
'Amelie Aubin'	CLoc CWVF EBak EKMF
'America'	CWVF
'American Flaming Glory' (d)	WPBF
'Amethyst Fire' (d)	SRiF
'Amigo'	EBak SRiF
§ ***ampliata***	CDoC EKMF LCla
'Amy'	MJac
'Amy Lye'	CLoc EBak EKMF
'Amy Ruth'	CWVF
§ 'Andenken an Heinrich Henkel'	CDoC CLoc CWVF EBak EKMF MWhe WRou
'Andre Eyletten' **new**	WPBF
'André Le Nostre' (d)	CWVF EBak SRiF
'Andreas Schwab'	LCla
andrei	CDoC LCla
- Berry 4637	EKMF
'Andrew'	CDoC EBak EKMF
'Andrew Carnegie' (d)	CLoc
'Andrew George'	MJac
'Andrew Hadfield'	CWVF EKMF MWar WRou
'Andrew Simmons'	WPBF
'Andromeda' ambig.	WPBF
'Angela Leslie' (d)	CLoc CWVF EBak EKMF SRiF
'Angela Rippon'	CWVF MJac
'Angelika Fuhrmann' (d) **new**	WPBF
'Angel's Flight' (d)	EBak
'Anita' (d)	CCCN CLoc CWVF EKMF EPts LAst MJac MWar MWhe SLBF WFFs WGor WRou
'Anja van Ossel' (d) **new**	WPBF
'Anjo' (v)	CWVF SLBF SRiF
'Ann Howard Tripp'	CDoC CLoc CWVF MBri MJac MWhe SRiF WPBF WRou
'Ann Lee' (d)	EBak
'Anna'	WPBF
'Anna Douling'	WPBF
'Anna Louise'	EKMF SLBF
'Anna of Longleat' (d)	CCCN CWVF EBak EMan MJac SPet
'Anna Silvena' **new**	CCCN
'Annabel' (d) ♀^{H3}	CCCN CDoC CLoc CTri CWVF EBak EKMF EMan EPts LAst LCla MBri MJac MWar MWhe SLBF SPet SRGP WBVN WFFs WRou
'Annabelle Stubbs' (d)	LAst SRGP
'Anneke de Keijzer'	LCla
'Annie Den Otter'	WPBF
'Annie Earle'	EKMF
'Annie MG Schmidt'	WPBF
'Anthea Day' (d)	CLoc
'Anthony Heavens'	SRiF WFFs
'Antigone'	SLBF SRiF WPBF
apetala	EKMF
- DG 1044	EKMF
'Aphrodite' (d)	CLoc CWVF EBak SRiF
'Applause' (d)	CLoc CWVF EBak EKMF EPts LVER SPet
'Apple Blossom'	EKMF
aprica misapplied	see *F.* x *bacillaris*
aprica Lundell	see *F. microphylla* subsp. *aprica*
'Aquarius'	MWhe SRiF
'Arabella'	CWVF MWhe
'Arabella Improved'	CWVF EKMF
arborea	see *F. arborescens*
§ ***arborescens***	CBcs CDoC CHEx CLoc CWVF EBak EKMF EShb LCla LRHS SRiF SWal WRou WWlt
'Arcadia Gold' (d)	CWVF MWhe
'Arcady'	CLoc CWVF
'Arethusa' **new**	WPBF
'Ariel'	CDoC SRiF WRou
'Arjan Spek' **new**	WPBF
'Arlendon'	CWVF
'Army Nurse' (d) ♀^{H4}	CDoC CLoc CWVF EKMF EPts MAsh MGos MWhe NBir NDlv SLBF SPet SWal WFFs
'Art Deco' (d)	WPBF
'Arthur Baxter'	EBak SRiF
'Arthur Bland' (d) **new**	WPBF
'Ashley'	CDoC LCla
'Ashley and Isobel'	CWVF WPBF
'Ashtede'	SLBF
'Athela'	EBak SRiF
'Atlantic Star'	CWVF EKMF MJac
'Atlantis' (d)	CWVF MJac
'Atlas' **new**	SRiF
'Atomic Glow' (d)	EBak

	'Aubergine'	see *F.* 'Gerharda's Aubergine'
	'Aubrey Harris' **new**	SRiF
	'Audrey Booth' (d)	SRiF
	'Audrey Dahms' **new**	SRiF
	'Audrey Hepburn'	CWVF EKMF
	'Audrey Lamotte'	WPBF
	'Augustin Thierry' (d)	EKMF MWhe
	'Aunt Juliana' (d)	EBak
	'Auntie Jinks'	CCCN CDoC CWVF EBak EKMF LAst LCla MJac MWhe SPet WRou
	'Auntie Kit' **new**	SRiF
	'Aurora Superba'	CLoc CWVF EBak EKMF SRiF WRou
	'Australia Fair' (d)	CWVF EBak SRiF
§	***austromontana***	EBak SRiF
	'Autumnale' 🏆H1+3	CCCN CDoC CHEx CLoc CWVF EBak EKMF EMan EPts LAst LCla LVER MWhe NVic SLBF SMrm SPet SPoG WPBF WRou
	'Avalanche' ambig. (d)	CDoC CLoc EBak EKMF SLBF
	'Avocet'	CLoc EBak SRiF
	'Avon Celebration' (d)	CLoc
	'Avon Gem'	CLoc SRiF
	'Avon Glow'	CLoc
	'Avon Gold'	CLoc
	ayavacensis	CDoC LCla
	- Berry 3601	EKMF
	'Aylisa Rowan' **new**	EKMF
	'Azure Sky' (d)	EKMF MJac WPBF
	'Babette' (d)	EKMF SRiF
	'Baby Blue Eyes' 🏆H3-4	CDoC CWVF EKMF MPop WFFs
	'Baby Bright'	CDoC CWVF EPts MWar SLBF SRiF WFFs WPBF WRou
	'Baby Chang'	LCla SRiF WPBF
	'Baby Pink' (d)	CWVF
	'Baby Thumb' (d)	EPts
§	x ***bacillaris***	CChe CDoC CDul CEnt EBak EWes EWin ITim MBlu SLBF SPoG SRms WPBF
§	- 'Cottinghamii'	CDoC EKMF IDee WSHC
	- 'Oosje'	see *F.* 'Oosje'
§	- 'Reflexa'	CAbP CCCN CTrC GQui LAst LSou WFFs
	'Baden Powell' **new**	SRiF
	'Bagworthy Water'	CLoc
	'Baker's Tri'	EBak
	'Balcon Queen'	MWhe
	'Balkon'	CWVF
	'Balkonkönigin'	CLoc EBak SRiF
	'Ballerina'	CDoC
	'Ballerina Blue'	LAst
	'Ballet Girl' (d) 🏆H1+3	CHrt CLoc CWVF EBak EKMF SLBF SPet SRiF
	'Balmoral' **new**	SRiF
	'Bambini'	CWVF SRiF
	'Banks Peninsula'	GBin GQui
	'Barbara'	CLoc CWVF EBak EKMF EPts MJac MWar MWhe SPet SRiF WEas WPBF WRou
	'Barbara Evans'	MWar SLBF SRiF WRou
	'Barbara Norton' **new**	CCCN
	'Barbara Pountain' (d)	CWVF
	'Barbara Windsor'	CWVF LAst MJac MWar SRiF
	'Barbara's Gem' (d)	SRiF
	'Baron de Ketteler' (d)	EKMF SRiF
	'Baroness van Dedem'	SRiF
	'Barry M. Cox'	WPBF
	'Barry's Queen'	EBak SPet
	'Bartje'	WPBF
	'Barts Janneke' **new**	WPBF
	'Bashful' (d)	CDoC EPts LCla LRHS SPet WFFs
	'Beacon'	CDoC CLoc CWVF EBak EKMF EMan EPts LAst MBri MJac MWhe NDlv SPet SPoG SRGP WFFs WPBF WRou
	'Beacon Rosa'	CCCN CDoC CLoc CWVF EKMF EMan EPts MBri MJac MWhe NDlv SLBF SPet SPoG WPBF WRou
	'Bealings' (d)	CDoC CLoc CWVF EMan MBri SRiF
	'Beansweyr' (d) **new**	WPBF
	'Beau Nash'	CLoc
	'Beautiful Bobbie' (d)	WPBF
	'Beauty of Bath' (d)	CLoc EBak
	'Beauty of Bexley' **new**	SRiF
	'Beauty of Cliff Hall' Monk	EKMF
	'Beauty of Clyffe Hall' Lye	EBak
	'Beauty of Exeter' (d)	CWVF EBak EKMF
	'Beauty of Prussia' (d)	CDoC CLoc CWVF
	'Beauty of Swanley'	EBak
	'Beauty of Trowbridge'	CWVF LCla
	'Becky'	SRiF WPBF
	'Becky Reynolds' **new**	SRiF
	'Bella Forbes' (d) 🏆H1+3	CLoc EBak EKMF
	'Bella Harris' **new**	SRiF
	'Bella Rosella' (d)	CCCN CWVF EKMF EPts LAst MJac SCoo SLBF
	'Bellbottoms' **new**	SRiF
	'Belsay Beauty' (d)	CWVF MJac SRiF
	'Belvoir Beauty' (d)	CLoc
	'Ben de Jong'	CDoC LCla MJac SRiF WRou
	'Ben Jammin'	CBgR CDoC CLoc CWVF EPts LAst LCla LSou MJac MWar SPoG SRiF WFFs WGor WRou
	'Ben Turner' (d) **new**	SRiF
	'Béranger' Lemoine, 1897 (d)	EBak EKMF
	'Berba's Delight' **new**	WPBF
	'Berba's Happiness' (d)	CWVF
	'Bergnimf'	SRiF WRou
	'Berliner Kind' (d)	CWVF EBak
	'Bermuda' (d)	CWVF SRiF
	'Bernadette' (d)	CWVF
	'Bernie's Big-un' (d)	MJac
	'Bernisser Hardy' 🏆H3-4	CDoC EKMF EPts LCla WFFs
	'Bert de Jong'	WPBF
	'Bertha Gadsby'	EKMF
	'Beryl Shaffery'	WPBF
	'Beryl's Choice' (d)	SRiF
	'Berys'	EKMF MWar
	'Bessie Kimberley'	CDoC EKMF LCla MWar WPBF
	'Beth Robley' (d)	CWVF
	'Betsy Ross' (d)	EBak
	'Bette Sibley' (d)	SRiF
	'Betty Jean' (d)	MWar WPBF
	Betty = 'Shabetty'^{PBR} (Shadowdancer Series)	LAst NEgg
	'Beverley'	CWVF EBak EKMF EPts SPet SRiF WFFs WPBF
	'Bewitched' (d)	EBak
	'Bianca' (d)	CWVF WPBF
	'Bicentennial' (d)	CCCN CDoC CLoc CWVF EBak EKMF EPts LAst LSou LVER MJac MWar MWhe SPet
	'Big Slim'	SRiF WPBF
	'Bilberry Sorbet'	WPBF
	'Bill Gilbert'	SRiF
	'Billy'^{PBR}	CDoC SRGP
	'Billy Green' 🏆H1+3	CDoC CLoc CWVF EBak EKMF EPts LCla MJac MWar MWhe SLBF SPet SRiF WPBF WRou
	'Bishop's Bells' (d)	CWVF
	'Bits' (d)	SRiF
	'Black Beauty' (d)	CWVF
	'Black Prince'	CDoC CWVF MWar SRiF
	'Blackmore Vale' (d)	CWVF
	'Blacky'	CCCN EBak LAst SPet WFFs
I	'Blanche Regina' (d)	CWVF MJac MWhe
	'Bland's New Striped'	CDoC EBak EKMF EPts SLBF SRiF
	'Blauer Engel'	WPBF
	'Blaze Away' (d)	MBri

	'Bliss'	WPBF
	'Blood Donor' (d)	EKMF MJac
	'Blowick'	CDoC CWVF EMan MBri MJac MWhe SPet
	'Blue Beauty' (d)	EBak EKMF
	'Blue Bush'	CWVF EKMF EPts MJac
	'Blue Butterfly' (d)	CWVF EBak SRiF
	'Blue Eyes' (d)	CDoC SPet
	'Blue Gown' (d)	CDoC CLoc CWVF EBak EKMF LRHS LVER MGos MWhe SPet WFFs WRou
	'Blue Ice'	MWhe
	'Blue Lagoon' ambig. (d)	CWVF
	'Blue Lake' (d)	CWVF LVER
	'Blue Mink'	EBak SRiF
	'Blue Mirage' (d)	CLoc CWVF EKMF MJac SRiF
	'Blue Mist' (d)	EBak
	'Blue Pearl' (d)	CWVF EBak SRiF
	'Blue Pinwheel'	CWVF EBak
	'Blue Sails'	SRiF
	'Blue Satin' (d)	MWhe
	'Blue Tit'	LCla
	'Blue Veil' (d)	CCCN CLoc CWVF EKMF LVER MJac MWar SCoo SRiF
	'Blue Waves' (d)	CLoc CSBt CWVF EBak MJac MWar MWhe SPet SRiF
	'Blush o' Dawn' (d)	CLoc CWVF EBak EKMF EPts LVER SPet SRiF
	'Blythe' (d)	SRiF
	'Bob Bartrum' new	EKMF
	'Bob Pacey'	CWVF
	'Bobby Boy' (d)	EBak
	'Bobby Dazzler' (d)	CWVF EKMF SRiF
	'Bobby Shaftoe' (d)	EBak MWhe SRiF WPBF
	'Bobby Wingrove'	EBak
	'Bobby's Girl'	EPts
	'Bobolink' (d)	EBak
	'Bob's Best' (d)	CWVF EPts MJac SRiF
	'Boerhaave'	EBak SRiF
	boliviana Britton	see *F. sanctae-rosae*
§	***boliviana*** Carrière	CDoC CHEx CLoc CWVF EBak EKMF LCla SHFr SRiF WRou
§	- var. ***alba*** ♀H1+3	CDoC CLoc EBak EKMF EPts LCla SChr SRiF WRou
	- var. ***boliviana***	CRHN
	- f. ***puberulenta*** Munz	see *F. boliviana* Carrière
	- var. ***luxurians*** 'Alba'	see *F. boliviana* Carrière var. *alba*
	'Bon Accorde'	CLoc CWVF EBak EKMF EPts SLBF SRiF WRou
	'Bon Bon' (d)	CWVF EBak
	'Bonita' (d)	CWVF MJac
	'Bonnie Bambini' new	SRiF
	'Bonnie Lass' (d)	EBak
	'Bonny' (d)	CLoc
	'Bora Bora' (d)	CWVF EBak EKMF
	'Borde Hill' (d)	EPts SLBF
	'Border Princess'	EBak SRiF WPBF
	'Border Queen' ♀H3-4	CDoC CLoc CWVF EBak EKMF EMan EPts LCla MJac MWar SPet SRiF WFFs WRou
	'Border Raider'	MWar SLBF WPBF
	'Border Reiver'	CWVF EBak WPBF
	'Börnemann's Beste'	see *F.* 'Georg Börnemann'
	'Boson's Norah' new	SRiF
	'Bouffant'	CLoc
I	'Bountiful' Munkner (d)	CLoc CWVF EKMF MWhe SPet
	'Bouquet' (d)	CDoC EKMF SRiF
	'Bow Bells'	CDoC CLoc CWVF MJac MWhe SPet
	'Boy Marc'	LCla SRiF WPBF
	'Braamt's Glorie'	WPBF
	bracelinae	CDoC EKMF WPBF
	'Brancaster'	SRiF
	'Brandt's Five Hundred Club'	CLoc EBak SPet
	'Brann's Blossom' new	SRiF
	'Breakaway' new	SRiF
	'Brechtje'	WPBF
	'Breckland'	EBak
	'Brecklands' new	SRiF
	'Breeders' Delight'	CWVF MBri SRiF WFFs
	'Breeder's Dream' (d)	EBak WPBF
	'Breevis Dia' new	WPBF
	'Breevis Evelien'	WPBF
	'Breevis Hageni' new	WPBF
	'Breevis Homerus'	WPBF
	'Breevis Iris'	WPBF
I	'Breevis Jordani'	WPBF
	'Breevis Karna'	WPBF
I	'Breevis Lowi'	WPBF
	'Breevis Luna'	WPBF
	'Breevis Minimus' new	SLBF WPBF
	'Breevis Natalica'	WPBF
I	'Breevis Paradoxa'	WPBF
	'Breevis Scylla' (d) new	WPBF
	'Breevis Selene'	WPBF
	'Breevis Sylvata' (d) new	WPBF
	'Brenda' (d)	CLoc CWVF EBak WFFs
	'Brenda White'	CDoC CLoc CWVF EBak WRou
	'Brentwood' (d)	EBak
	brevilobis Berry 4445	EKMF
	'Brian C. Morrison'	EKMF LCla SRiF
	'Brian G. Soanes'	EBak SRiF
	'Brian Hilton'	MWar
	'Brian Kimberley'	EKMF LCla MWar
	'Bridal Veil' (d)	EBak
	'Bridesmaid' (d)	CWVF EBak SPet SRiF
	'Brigadoon' (d)	CLoc EBak
	'Bright Lights'	EKMF WPBF
	'Brighton Belle'	CDoC CWVF SRiF
	'Brilliant' ambig.	CWVF NDlv
	'Brilliant' Bull, 1865	CDoC CLoc EBak EKMF LCla MWhe
	'Briony Caunt'	EKMF
	'British Jubilee' (d)	CWVF EKMF
	'British Sterling' (d)	SRiF
	'Brixham Orpheus'	CWVF
	'Brodsworth'	EKMF
	'Bronze Banks Peninsula'	EKMF
	'Brookwood Belle' (d)	CWVF LCla MJac SLBF WFFs
	'Brookwood Dale'	MWhe
	'Brookwood Joy' (d)	CWVF MJac SLBF
	'Brookwood Lady'	MWhe
	'Brutus' ♀H4	CDoC CLoc CWVF EBak EKMF EMan EPts LAst LRHS MHar MPop MWat MWhe SPet SPoG WBod WFFs
	'Bryan Breary'	LCla SRiF
	'Bubba Jack'	SLBF
	'Bubble Hanger'	SRiF
	'Buddha' (d)	EBak
	'Bugle Boy'	EPts LCla MWar
	'Bunny' (d)	CWVF EBak SRiF
	'Burton Brew'	MJac
	'Buster' (d)	EKMF LCla SLBF
	'Buttercup'	CLoc CWVF EBak
	'C.J. Howlett'	EBak EKMF SRiF
	'Caballero' (d)	EBak
	'Caesar' (d)	CWVF EBak
	'Caitlin'	WPBF
	'Caitlin Isabelle'	WPBF
	'Caledonia'	EBak EKMF
	'California'	WRou
	'Callaly Pink'	CWVF
	'Cambridge Louie'	CWVF EBak MBri MWar MWhe SPet SRiF
	'Camcon' new	MWar
	'Camelot'	SRiF
	'Cameron Ryle'	WPBF
	'Camillius Maria' (d) new	WPBF

campii	EKMF
campos-portoi	CDoC LCla WPBF
- Berry 4435	EKMF
'Candlelight' (d)	CLoc EBak
'Candy Stripe'	CLoc
canescens Benth.	EKMF
canescens misapplied	see *F. ampliata*
'Cannel's Gem' **new**	SRiF
'Cannenburch Floriant'	WPBF
'Canny Bob'	MJac
'Canopy' (d)	CWVF
'Capri' (d)	CWVF EBak
'Cara Mia' (d)	CLoc CWVF SPet
'Caradela' (d)	CLoc EKMF MJac MWar
'Caramel Blue' **new**	CCCN
'Cardinal'	CLoc EKMF WPBF
'Cardinal Farges' (d)	CLoc CWVF EKMF SLBF SPet SRiF
'Careless Whisper'	LCla SLBF WPBF
'Carillon van Amsterdam'	MWhe
'Carioca'	EBak
'Carisbrooke Castle' (d)	EKMF SRiF
'Carl Wallace' (d)	EKMF SRiF
'Carla Johnston' Υ^{H1+3}	CDoC CLoc CWVF EKMF EPts LVER MBri MJac MWar MWhe WRou
'Carleton George'	MWar
'Carmel Blue'	CDoC CLoc LAst LCla LSou MWar MWhe NBlu SPet WGor WPBF WRou
'Carmen' Lemoine (d)	CDoC EKMF
'Carmine Bell'	EKMF
'Carnea'	CWib
'Carnival' (d)	WPBF
'Carnoustie' (d)	EBak
'Carol Grace' (d)	CLoc
'Carol Lynn Whittemore' (d)	SRiF WPBF
'Carol Nash' (d)	CLoc
'Carol Roe'	EKMF
'Caroline'	CLoc CWVF EBak EKMF EPts MWhe WPBF WRou
'Caroline's Joy'	CCCN MJac MWar MWhe SCoo SPet
'Cascade'	CCCN CDoC CLoc CWVF EKMF EMan EPts MBri MJac MWhe SPet WPBF
'Caspar Hauser' (d)	CWVF SLBF SRiF
'Catharina'	SRiF
'Catherine Bartlett'	CWVF EKMF
'Cathie MacDougall' (d)	EBak
'Cecil Glass'	EKMF SRiF
'Cecile' (d)	CCCN CDoC CWVF EKMF EPts LAst LCla MJac MWhe SLBF SRGP WPBF WRou
'Celadore' (d)	CWVF LVER SRiF
'Celebration' (d)	CLoc CWVF
'Celia Smedley' Υ^{H3}	CCCN CDoC CLoc CWVF EBak EKMF EPts LAst LCla LVER MBri MJac MWar MWhe SLBF SPet WFFs WPBF WRou
'Celine'	MWar
'Centerpiece' (d)	EBak
'Ceri'	CLoc
'Chameleon'	SPet
'Champagne Celebration'	CLoc
'Champagne Gold' **new**	SRiF
'Champion' **new**	SRiF
'Chancellor'	CWVF
'Chandleri'	CWVF EKMF SLBF
'Chang' Υ^{H1+3}	CLoc CWVF EBak EKMF LCla MWar MWhe SLBF WPBF
'Chantry Park'	LCla SRiF
'Charles Edward'	EKMF SRiF
'Charles Lester' **new**	SRiF
'Charles Welch'	EPts
Charlie Dimmock = 'Foncha'^{PBR}	CLoc LAst MWhe WPBF
'Charlie Gardiner'	CWVF EBak MWhe
'Charlie Girl' (d)	EBak
'Charlie Pridmore' (d) **new**	SRiF
'Charlotte Clyne'	SRiF
'Charm of Chelmsford'	LCla
'Charming'	CDoC CLoc CWVF EBak EKMF MJac MWar SPet WRou
'Chartwell' **new**	WPBF
'Chase Delight' (v)	CDoC
'Chatt's Delight'	EKMF
'Checkerboard' Υ^{H3}	CCCN CLoc CWVF EBak EKMF EPts LCla LVER MJac MWar MWhe SLBF SPet WFFs WPBF
'Cheeky Chantelle' (d)	SLBF
'Cheerio' (d) **new**	SRiF
'Cheers' (d)	CWVF EKMF MWhe
'Chelsea Louise'	EPts
'Chenois Godelieve'	WPBF
'Cherry' Götz ^{PBR}	LAst WPBF
'Cherry Pie'	SRiF
'Chessboard'	CLoc
'Chillerton Beauty' Υ^{H3}	CLoc CTri CWVF EKMF EPts LCla LRHS MJac MWhe SLBF SPer SPet WBod WMnd WPBF WRou
'China Doll' (d)	CWVF EBak MWhe
'China Lantern'	CLoc CWVF EBak EKMF SRiF
'Chomal' (d) **new**	SRiF
'Chor Echo'	WPBF
'Chris'	WPBF
'Chris Nicholls'	EKMF WPBF
'Christ Driessen'	WPBF
'Christina Becker'	SRiF
'Christine Bamford'	CDoC CWVF WFFs WPBF
'Christine Shaffery' (d)	WPBF
'Churchtown'	CWVF SRiF
cinerea	LCla
- Berry 004-86	EKMF
'Cinnabarina'	CLoc SLBF SRiF
* 'Cinnamon'	WPBF
'Cinque Port Liberty' (d)	SLBF SRiF
'Cinvenu'	LCla
'Cinvulca'	LCla
'Circe' (d)	CWVF EBak EKMF
'Circus'	EBak
'Circus Spangles' (d)	CLoc EKMF LAst
'Citation'	CDoC CLoc CWVF EBak
'City of Adelaide' (d)	CLoc MWhe
'City of Leicester'	CWVF SPet
'City of Liverpool'	WPBF
'Claire'	WRou
'Claire de Lune'	CDoC CWVF EBak WRou
'Claire Evans' (d)	CWVF
'Claire Oram'	CLoc
'Clare Dawson'	WPBF
'Clare Frisby'	EKMF
'Claudia' (d)	LAst LCla MJac MWar WRou
'Cliantha' (d)	CCCN MJac MWhe WRou
'Clifford Gadsby' (d)	EBak SRiF
'Cliff's Hardy'	EKMF LCla SPet WFFs
'Cliff's Unique' (d)	CWVF EPts
'Clifton Beauty' (d)	CWVF MJac
'Clifton Belle'	CWVF
'Clifton Charm'	EKMF LCla MJac
'Clipper'	CWVF
'Cloth of Gold'	CLoc CWVF EBak MJac MWhe SPet SRiF
'Cloverdale Jewel' (d)	CDoC CWVF EBak MWhe SPet
'Cloverdale Joy'	EBak
'Cloverdale Pearl'	CWVF EBak EKMF EMan ENot EPfP MWhe SPet SPoG WFFs
'Coachman' Υ^{H4}	CLoc CWVF EBak EKMF EMan EPts LCla MWar MWhe SLBF SPet WBVN WRou

	coccinea	CDoC EKMF LCla
	'Cochilla' (d) **new**	SRiF
	x ***colensoi***	CDoC ECou EKMF LCla SHFr
	'Colibri' **new**	SRiF
	'Collingwood' (d)	CLoc CWVF EBak
	'Colne Fantasy' (v)	EKMF SRiF
	'Come Dancing' (d)	CDoC CWVF SPet
I	'Comet' Tiret (d)	CLoc EBak SPet
	'Comet' Banks	CWVF
	'Comperen Libel'	WPBF
	'Comperen Stepera' **new**	WPBF
	'Conchilla'	EBak
	'Congreve Road'	SRiF
	'Connie' (d)	EBak EKMF SRiF WPBF
	'Conspicua' ♀H3-4	CWVF EBak EKMF
	'Constable Country' (d)	CWVF SRiF
	'Constance' (d)	CDoC CLoc CWVF EKMF LCla MJac MWar MWhe NDlv SLBF SPet WFFs WPBF WRou
	'Constance Comer'	MJac
	'Constellation' ambig.	CWVF
	'Constellation' Schnabel, 1957 (d)	CLoc EBak
	'Contramine'	WPBF
	'Coombe Park'	MJac
	'Coq au Vin' (d)	WPBF
	'Coquet Bell'	CWVF EBak WPBF
	'Coquet Dale' (d)	CWVF EBak SRiF WPBF
	'Coquet Gold' (d/v)	SRiF
	'Coral Baby'	LCla
	'Coral Cluster'	MWhe
	'Coral Seas'	EBak
§	'Coralle'	CCCN CDoC CLoc CWVF EBak EKMF EMan EPts LCla MJac MWar MWhe SLBF SRiF WPBF WRou
	'Corallina' ♀H3-4	CDoC CLoc EBak EKMF MWhe SPet WFar
I	'Corallina Variegata' (v)	WPBF
*	***cordata*** B&SWJ 9095	WCru
	cordifolia misapplied	see *F. splendens*
	cordifolia Benth.	CBcs EBak EKMF WRou
	'Core'ngrato' (d)	CLoc CWVF EBak
	coriacifolia	EKMF
	'Cornelia Smith'	LCla
	'Cornwall Calls' (d)	EBak
	'Corrie Palm'	WPBF
	'Corsage' (d)	CWVF
	'Corsair' (d)	EBak
	corymbiflora misapplied	see *F. boliviana* Carrière
	corymbiflora Ruíz & Pav.	CDoC EBak EKMF
	- Berry 4688	EKMF
	- alba	see *F. boliviana* Carrière var. *alba*
	'Cosmopolitan' (d)	EBak
	'Costa Brava'	CLoc EBak
	'Cotta 2000'	EKMF LCla SRiF
	'Cotta Bright Star'	CWVF EKMF LCla WFFs
	'Cotta Carousel'	EKMF LCla
	'Cotta Christmas Tree'	CDoC EKMF LCla SLBF SRiF
	'Cotta Fairy'	CWVF EKMF
	'Cotta Vino'	EKMF SRiF
	'Cottinghamii'	see *F.* x *bacillaris* 'Cottinghamii'
	'Cotton Candy' (d)	CLoc CWVF LCla MWhe
	'Countdown Carol' (d)	EPts WPBF
	'Countess of Aberdeen'	CLoc CWVF EBak EKMF SLBF SRiF
	'Countess of Maritza' (d)	CLoc CWVF
	'County Park'	ECou EWes
	'Court Jester' (d)	CLoc EBak
	'Cover Girl' (d)	EBak EPts LAst MWhe SPet
	'Coxeen'	EBak
	'Crackerjack'	CLoc EBak
	crassistipula	LCla
	- Berry 3553	EKMF
	'Crescendo' (d)	CLoc CWVF
	'Crinkley Bottom' (d)	EPts LVER MJac SLBF SRiF WRou
	'Crinoline' (d)	EBak
	'Crosby Serendipity'	CLoc
	'Crosby Soroptimist'	CWVF MJac MWar MWhe SRiF WFFs WRou
	'Cross Check'	CWVF EMan MBri MJac SRiF
	'Crusader' (d)	CWVF
	'Crystal Blue'	EBak
	'Cupid'	EBak
	'Curly Q'	EBak SPet
	'Curtain Call' (d)	CLoc CWVF EBak
	'Cutie Karen' (d)	SRiF
	x ***cuzco***	EKMF
	cylindracea misapplied	see *F.* x *bacillaris*
	cylindracea Lindl.	LCla SRiF
	- (m) BRE 43908	EKMF
	'Cymon' (d)	CWVF MWhe SRiF
	'Cyndy Robyn'	SRiF
	cyrtandroides Berry 4628	EKMF
	'Dainty'	EBak
	'Dainty Lady' (d)	EBak
	'Daisy Bell'	CDoC CLoc CWVF EBak EKMF LCla MJac SPet WPBF WRou
	'Dalton'	EBak
	'Dana Samantha'	EPts
	'Dancing Bloom'	EPts
	'Dancing Elves'	WPBF
	'Dancing Flame' (d) ♀H1+3	CCCN CHrt CLoc CWVF EBak EKMF EMan EPts LAst LCla LVER MBri MJac MWar MWhe SLBF SPet WFFs
	'Daniel Lambert'	WPBF
	'Danielle'	LAst WPBF WRou
	'Danielle Frijstein'	WPBF
	'Danielle's Dream' (d)	WPBF
	'Danish Pastry'	CWVF SPet
	'Danny Boy' (d)	CLoc CWVF EBak EKMF MWhe WPBF
	'Danny Kaye' (d)	WPBF
	'Danson Belle' (d) **new**	SRiF
	'Daphne Arlene'	WPBF
	'Dark Eyes' (d) ♀H4	CCCN CLoc CWVF EBak EKMF EMan LAst MBri MJac MWhe NBlu SLBF SPet SSea
	'Dark Lady'	MWhe
	'Dark Mystery' (d)	WPBF
	'Dark Secret' (d)	EBak
	'Dark Treasure' (d)	CDoC EKMF
	'Darreen Dawn' (d)	WPBF
	'Daryn John Woods'	CDoC LCla SRiF
	'Dave's Delight'	EKMF WPBF
	'David' ♀H3-4	CDoC CLoc CWVF EKMF EOHP EPts LAst LCla LSou MWhe SLBF SRiF WFFs WGor WRou WSPU WWeb
	'David Alston' (d)	CLoc CWVF EBak
	'David Lockyer' (d)	CLoc CWVF
	'David Savage' (d)	LCla
	'David Ward' (d)	WPBF
	'Dawn'	EBak
	'Dawn Carless' (d)	WPBF
	'Dawn Fantasia' (v)	CLoc EKMF EPts MWar WPBF
	'Dawn Redfern'	CWVF
	'Dawn Sky' (d)	EBak
	'Dawn Star' (d)	CCCN CWVF LAst MJac MWhe
	'Day Star'	EBak SRiF
	'De Groot's Beauty' (d)	WPBF
	'De Groot's Black Beauty' **new**	WPBF
	'De Groot's Dikbuil'	WPBF
	'De Groot's Moonlight'	WPBF
	'De Groot's Night'	WPBF
	'De Groot's Parade'	WPBF
	'De Groot's Pipes'	WPBF
	'De Groot's Regenboog'	WPBF
	'De Groot's Tricolore'	WPBF

	'De Groot's Vulkaan'	WPBF
	'Deal Marine' (d) **new**	SRiF
	'Debby' (d)	EBak
	'Deben Petite'	LCla
	'Deben Rose'	SRiF
	'Deborah Street'	CLoc
§	***decussata*** Ruíz & Pav.	CDoC EBak
	- Berry 3049	EKMF
	'Dee Copley' (d)	EBak
	'Deep Purple' (d)	CCCN CDoC CLoc CWVF EKMF LAst MJac SCoo SLBF SPoG WPBF
	'Delilah' (d)	CWVF
	'Delta's Angelique'	WPBF
	'Delta's Bride'	SLBF
	'Delta's Dream'	CWVF WPBF
	'Delta's Drop'	SLBF SRiF WPBF
	'Delta's Groom'	LCla WRou
	'Delta's Matador'	CCCN LAst
	'Delta's Night'	WPBF
	'Delta's Paljas'	WPBF
	'Delta's Parade' (d)	EPts WPBF
	'Delta's Pim'	WPBF
	'Delta's Pride'	WPBF
	'Delta's Robijn'	WPBF
	'Delta's Sara' (d)	MPop WPBF
	'Delta's Song'	WPBF WRou
	'Delta's Symphonie' (d)	CWVF
	'Delta's Wonder'	WPBF
	'Demi van Roovert'	WPBF
§	***denticulata***	CDoC CLoc CWVF EBak EKMF EPts LCla SLBF SRiF WRou
	dependens	CDoC EKMF
	'Derby Imp'	CWVF SRiF WFFs
	'Desire'	WPBF
	'Desperate Daniel'	EPts
	'Devonshire Dumpling' (d)	CCCN CDoC CLoc CWVF EBak EKMF EMan EPts LAst LCla LVER MBri MJac MWar SLBF SPet
	'Diablo' (d)	EBak
	'Diamond Celebration' (d)	EKMF MWar SLBF
	'Diamond Wedding'	SRiF
	'Diana' (d)	EBak
	'Diana Wills' (d)	CWVF MWhe
	'Diana Wright'	EKMF WSPU
	'Diane Brown'	CWVF EKMF MWhe
	'Diane Marie'	EKMF WPBF
	'Dick Swinbank' (d)	SRiF
§	'Die Schöne Wilhelmine'	WPBF
	'Dijmph Werker van Groenland' **new**	WPBF
	'Dilly-Dilly' (d)	CWVF
	'Dimples' (d)	MBri SRiF
	'Dipton Dainty' (d)	CLoc EBak SRiF
	'Dirk van Delen'	MWhe
	'Display' ♀H4	CCCN CDoC CLoc CWVF EBak EKMF EMan EPts LAst LCla LVER MBri MJac MWhe NPer SLBF SPet SPoG SSea WFFs WFar WRou
	'Doc'	CDoC EPts SPet
	'Doctor'	see *F.* 'The Doctor'
	'Doctor Foster' ♀H4	CDoC CLoc CTri EBak EKMF ENot EPfP WEas
	'Doctor Mason'	CWVF
	'Doctor Olson' (d)	CLoc EBak SRiF
	'Doctor Robert'	CWVF EPts MBri MJac MWhe SRiF
	'Doctor Topinard'	CLoc EBak EKMF
	'Dodo'	WPBF
	'Dollar Princess'	see *F.* 'Dollar Prinzessin'
§	'Dollar Prinzessin' ♀H4	CCCN CDoC CLoc CWVF EBak EKMF EMan EPfP EPts LAst LCla MAsh MBri MJac MWar MWhe NBlu NDlv NPer SLBF SPet SPlb WBVN WFFs WFar
	'Dolly Daydream' (d)	EKMF
	'Dominique' (d)	EKMF
	'Dominyana'	EBak EKMF LCla
	'Don Peralta'	EBak
	'Donicetto'	SLBF
	'Donkse Parel' (d) **new**	WPBF
	'Dopy' (d)	CDoC EPts SPet WPBF
	'Doreen Redfern'	CLoc CWVF MJac SPet WRou
	'Doreen Stroud'	CWVF
	'Dorian Brogdale' **new**	SRiF
	'Doris Coleman' (d)	EMan
	'Doris Hobbs'	WPBF
	'Doris Joan'	SLBF WPBF
	'Dorking Blue' (d) **new**	SRiF
	'Dorking Delight'	SRiF
	'Dorothea Flower'	CLoc CWVF EBak EKMF WPBF
	'Dorothy'	EKMF LCla SLBF SPet WFFs
	'Dorothy Ann'	LCla SLBF
	'Dorothy Cheal'	CWVF
	'Dorothy Day' (d)	CLoc
	'Dorothy Hanley' (d)	CBgR CCCN CLoc EKMF EPts LAst LSRN LSou MAsh MBri MJac MWhe SLBF SPet SPoG SRiF WFFs WGor WPBF WRou WWeb
	'Dorothy Oosting' (d) **new**	WPBF
	'Dorothy Shields' (d)	CWVF MJac WPBF
	'Dorrian Brogdale'	LCla
	'Dorset Abigail' **new**	CWVF
	'Dorset Delight' (d)	CWVF
	'Dot Woodage'	SRiF
	'Dove House'	EKMF
	'Drake 400' (d)	CLoc
	'Drama Girl'	CWVF
	'Drame' (d)	CDoC CWVF EBak EKMF LCla SPet SRiF WRou
	'Drum Major' (d)	EBak
	'Du Barry' (d)	EBak
	'Duchess of Albany'	CLoc EBak
	'Duchess of Cornwall' (d)	EPts SRiF
	'Duet' (d)	SRiF
	'Duke of Wellington' Haag, 1956 (d)	CLoc
	'Dulcie Elizabeth' (d)	CWVF EBak MJac SPet
	'Dusky Beauty'	CWVF WRou
	'Dusky Rose' (d)	CLoc CWVF EBak MJac MWhe
	'Dusted Pink' (d)	CWVF
	'Dutch Kingsize'	WPBF
	'Dutch Mill'	CLoc CWVF EBak SRiF
	'Duyfken'	CWVF SRiF
	'Dying Embers'	CLoc
	'Dymph Werker van Groenland'	LCla MWar
	'Earre Barré'	SRiF
	'East Anglian'	CLoc EBak SRiF
	'Easter Bonnet' (d)	CLoc CWVF
	'Ebanflo'	EBak MWar
	'Ebbtide' (d)	CLoc EBak
	'Echo'	CLoc CWVF
	'Ector's Isle Cora'	WPBF
	'Ectors Nursery'	WPBF
	'Ed Largarde' (d)	EBak EKMF
	'Eden Lady'	CDoC CLoc SPet SRiF WPBF WRou
	'Eden Princess'	CWVF MJac
	'Eden Rock' (d)	SRGP
	'Eden's Delight'	WPBF
	'Edie Lester' **new**	SRiF
	'Edit van Kessel'	WPBF
	'Edith' ambig.	EPts NDlv WRou
	'Edith' Brown (d)	EKMF LCla SLBF
	'Edith' Banks **new**	SRiF
	'Edith Emery' (d)	SPet SRiF
	'Edna May'	CWVF
	'Edna W. Smith'	CWVF
	'Edwin J. Goulding'	WPBF
	'Edwin J. Jones'	SLBF
	'Eileen Drew'	SLBF
	'Eileen Raffill'	EBak

	'Eileen Saunders'	EBak
	'Eileen Storey'	EKMF WPBF
	'Eisleban' **new**	SRiF
	'Eisvogel'	WPBF
	'El Camino' (d)	CWVF
	'El Cid'	CLoc EBak EKMF SRiF
	'Elaine Ann'	EPts MJac
	'Elaine Taylor' (d)	MJac
	'Eleanor Clark'	WPBF
	'Eleanor Leytham'	CWVF EBak EKMF LCla SRiF WRou
	'Eleanor Rawlins'	EBak EKMF SRiF
	'Elfin Glade'	CLoc CWVF EBak EKMF SRiF WMnd
	'Elfrida' (d)	EKMF WPBF
	'Elfriede Ott'	CLoc EBak LCla MWhe SRiF
	'Elizabeth' Tiret, 1970 (d)	WPBF
	'Elizabeth' Whiteman, 1941	EBak EKMF
	'Elizabeth Broughton'	EKMF
	'Elizabeth Haverkamp'	LCla
	'Elizabeth Tompkins' (d)	MJac
	'Elizabeth Travis' (d)	EBak
	'Ellen Morgan' (d)	CWVF EBak
	'Elma'	CDoC LCla
	'Elsa' (d)	CWVF LRHS SPet
	'Elsie Maude' (d)	CWVF SRiF
	'Elsie Mitchell' (d)	CWVF MWhe SPet SRiF WRou
	'Elsstar'	SRiF WPBF
	'Elysée'	EKMF
§	'Emile de Wildeman' (d)	CWVF EBak EKMF LVER SPet WPBF
	'Emily'	WPBF
	'Emily Austen'	CWVF EKMF
	'Emma Alice' (d)	CWVF
	'Emma Louise' (d)	CWVF
	'Emma Margaret'	SLBF
	'Emma Massey'	SRiF
	'Empress of Prussia' 🏆^{H4}	CDoC CLoc CWVF EBak EKMF EMan EPts ERas LAst LRHS SLBF SPet WMnd WPBF WRou
	'Enchanted' (d)	CWVF EBak MWar
	'Enchanting Emma' (d)	SLBF
	encliandra subsp. ***encliandra***	CDoC EKMF WBor WRou
	- subsp. ***microphylloides*** Berry & Brako 7592	EKMF
§	- subsp. ***tetradactyla***	EKMF
§	'Enfant Prodigue' (d)	CDoC CLoc EKMF SDix SLBF SMrm WMnd WPBF
	'English Rose' (d)	CWVF SRiF
	'Enstone'	see *F. magellanica* var. *molinae* 'Enstone'
	'Erecta'	NPri
	'Erica Julie' (d)	MWhe
	'Eric's Everest' (d)	EKMF WPBF
	'Eric's Majestic' (d)	EKMF MJac SRiF
	'Erik' **new**	SLBF
	'Erika Borz' (d)	WPBF
	'Erika Köth'	LCla SRiF
	'Ernie'^{PBR}	SRGP
	'Ernie Bromley'	CWVF SLBF SRiF
	'Ernie Wise' (d)	MJac SCoo
	'Errol' (d)	CLoc
	'Eruption' **new**	WPBF
	'Esmerelda'	MJac WPBF
	'Estafette' (d) **new**	SRiF
	'Estelle Marie'	CLoc CWVF EBak MBri MWar MWhe SLBF SPet WPBF WRou
	'Eternal Flame' (d)	CWVF EBak EPts MBri MWhe
	'Ethel May'	MJac
	'Eureka Red' (d)	CWVF LAst
	'Eurydice' (d)	CLoc
	'Eusebia' (d)	MJac SRiF
	'Eva Boerg'	CCCN CLoc CTri CWVF EBak EKMF EMan LAst LCla MBri MWar SPet WFFs WKif WPBF

	'Evelyn Stanley' (d)	CWVF
§	'Evelyn Steele Little'	EBak
	'Evening Sky' (d)	EBak SRiF
	'Evensong'	CLoc CWVF EBak MWhe
	excorticata	CBcs CDoC CPLG EKMF IDee SPlb
	'Expo '86' **new**	SRiF
	'Eynsford' (d) **new**	SRiF
	'Fabian Franck'	CDoC LCla SRiF
	'Fairy Falls'	WRou
	'Falklands' (d)	SLBF SRiF
	'Falling Stars'	CLoc CWVF EBak MWhe
	'Fan Dancer' (d)	EBak
	'Fancy Free' (d)	MBri
	'Fancy Pants' (d)	CLoc CWVF EBak
	'Fanfare'	CDoC EBak EKMF LCla WRou
	'Farningham' **new**	SRiF
	'Fascination'	see *F.* 'Emile de Wildeman'
	'Fashion' (d)	EBak
	'Favourite'	EBak
	'Felicity Kendal' (d)	MJac SCoo
	'Feltham's Pride'	CWVF
	'Femke Comperen'	WPBF
	'Fenman'	CWVF SRiF
	'Fergie' (d)	SRiF
	'Festival' (d)	MWhe
	'Festival Lights'	SLBF
	'Festoon'	EBak
	'Fey' (d)	CWVF EKMF SRiF
	'Ffion'	EPts
	'Fiery Spider'	EBak
	'Finn'	CWVF EPts
	'Fiona'	CLoc CWVF EBak SPet SRiF
	'Fiona Pitt'	SRiF
	'Fiorelli Flowers' (d) **new**	WPBF
	'Fire Mountain' (d)	CLoc
	'Firecracker'^{PBR}	see *F.* 'John Ridding'
	'Firelite' (d)	EBak
	'Firenza' (d)	CWVF SRiF WRou
	'First Kiss'	CWVF
	'First Lady' (d)	CWVF
	'First Lord'	CWVF
	'First of the Day' **new**	SRiF
	'First Success'	CDoC CWVF EKMF LCla SRiF WRou
	'Flair' (d)	CLoc CWVF
	'Flame'	EBak
	'Flamenco Dancer' (d)	CLoc CWVF LAst WPBF
	'Flash' 🏆$^{H3-4}$	CLoc CTri CWVF EBak EKMF EPfP EPts LCla MJac MWhe SLBF SPet SRiF WFFs WRou
	'Flashlight'	CDoC CWVF EPfP LAst LSou MJac WFFs WPBF
	'Flat Jack o' Lancashire' (d)	EKMF SLBF
	'Flavia' (d)	EBak
	'Fleur de Picardie'	SLBF WPBF
	'Flirtation Waltz' (d)	CLoc CWVF EBak EKMF EMan EPts LVER MJac MWhe SPet SRiF
	'Flocon de Neige'	EBak EPts
I	'Flora' Tolley (d) **new**	WPBF
	'Floral City' (d)	CLoc EBak
	'Florama' **new**	WPBF
	'Florence Mary Abbott'	EMan
	'Florence Taylor'	CWVF
	'Florence Turner'	EBak EKMF MWhe SRiF
	'Florentina' (d)	CLoc CWVF EBak EKMF
	'Florrie Bambridge' **new**	WPBF
	'Florrie Lester' (d) **new**	SRiF
	'Florrie's Gem' (d)	SLBF
	'Flowerdream'	CWVF
	'Flyaway' (d)	EBak
	'Fly-by-night' (d)	CWVF
	'Flying Cloud' (d)	CLoc CWVF EBak EKMF MBri
	'Flying Scotsman' (d)	CCCN CDoC CLoc CWVF EBak EKMF EPts MJac SCoo WRou
	'Fohnhimmel' (d)	WPBF

	Name	Suppliers
	'Fokkos Katrientje'	WPBF
	'Folies Bergères' (d)	EBak
	'Foolke'	EBak SRiF
	'Forfar's Pride' (d)	MWar SRiF
	'Forget-me-not'	CLoc CWVF EBak EKMF WFFs WPBF
	'Fort Bragg' (d)	CWVF EBak SRiF
	'Fort Royal'	WRou
	'Forward Look'	CDoC MWhe SRiF
	'Fountains Abbey' (d)	CWVF EMan
	'Four Farthings' (d)	EKMF WPBF
	'Foxgrove Wood' ♀H3-4	CWVF EBak EKMF SLBF WFFs
	'Foxtrot'	CWVF
	'Foxy Lady' (d)	CWVF EKMF WPBF
	'Frances Haskins'	MWhe SRiF WRou
	'Frank Saunders'	CWVF LCla WPBF
	'Frank Unsworth' (d)	CWVF EKMF EPts MJac SPet WPBF
	'Frankie's Magnificent Seven' (d)	EPts
	'Frau Hilde Rademacher' (d)	CDoC CWVF EBak EKMF EMan EPts SLBF SRiF
	'Fred Hansford'	CWVF SLBF
	'Fred Shepherd' **new**	SRiF
	'Frederick Woodward' **new**	WPBF
	'Fred's First' (d)	CDoC EKMF SRiF WPBF
	'Freefall'	EBak
	'Friendly Fire' (d)	CLoc
	'Frosted Flame'	CCCN CDoC CLoc CWVF EBak EKMF LCla MJac MWar MWhe SPet SSea
	'Frozen Tears'	WPBF
	'Frühling' (d)	EBak EKMF
	'Fuchsiade'	WRou
	'Fuchsiade '88'	CLoc CWVF EBak EKMF MWhe
	'Fuchsiarama '91'	CWVF WRou
	'Fuji-San'	CDoC ELon EPts SRiF WPBF
	'Fuksie Foetsie'	CDoC SRiF
	fulgens ♀H1+3	CDoC EKMF LCla MWhe WFFs WRou
	- var. ***goselli***	WPBF
*	- var. ***minuata***	EKMF
*	- 'Variegata' (v)	CDoC CLoc EKMF EPts LCla SRiF WRou
	'Fulpila'	LCla SRiF
	furfuracea	EKMF
	'Für Elise' (d)	EBak
	'Gala' (d)	EBak
	'Galadriel'	WPBF
	'Ganzenhof'	LCla
	'Garden News' (d) ♀H3-4	CCCN CDoC CLoc CWVF EKMF EPts LAst LCla LRHS LVER MJac MWar MWhe NPer SLBF SPet SWal WFFs WFar WPBF WRou
	'Garden Week' (d)	CWVF MWhe
	'Gartenmeister Bonstedt' ♀H1+3	CCCN CDoC CLoc CWVF EBak EKMF LCla NBlu SPet SRiF SSea
	'Gary Rhodes' (d)	EBak MJac SCoo
	'Gay Fandango' (d)	CLoc CWVF EBak SPet
	'Gay Future'	EKMF
	'Gay Parasol' (d)	CCCN CLoc LAst MJac WRou
	'Gay Paree' (d)	EBak WPBF
	'Gay Senorita'	EBak
	'Gay Spinner' (d)	CLoc
	'Geesche' **new**	WPBF
	'Geeskie Guskie' **new**	SRiF
	gehrigeri	EBak EKMF
	gehrigeri x ***nigricans***	EKMF
	'Gelre'	WPBF
	'Gemma Fisher' (d)	EPts
	Gene = 'Goetzgene'PBR (Shadowdancer Series)	LAst LSou SCoo
	'Général Charles de Gaulle'	SRiF WPBF
	'Général Monk' (d)	CDoC CWVF EBak EKMF EMan EPts LAst MBri SRGP SRiF WPBF
	'General Wavell' (d)	SRiF
	'Genii' ♀H4	More than 30 suppliers
	'Geoffrey Smith' (d)	EKMF EPts
§	'Georg Börnemann'	CLoc CWVF EBak SRiF WFFs
	'Georgana' (d)	MWhe WPBF
	'George Allen White' **new**	CDoC CWVF
	'George Barr'	EKMF LRHS SRiF WPBF
	'George Johnson'	CDoC SPet
	'George Travis' (d)	EBak SRiF
	'Georges Remy'	WPBF
§	'Gerharda's Aubergine'	CDoC CLoc CWVF EKMF SRiF
	'Gerharda's Kiekeboe'	WPBF
	'Gerharda's Sofie'	WPBF
	'Gerrie Spek-Hofmeijer' **new**	WPBF
	'Gerrit Hasselerharm' **new**	WPBF
	'Gerrit van Lagen' **new**	WPBF
	'Gesneriana'	CDoC CLoc EBak SRiF WWlt
	'Giant Pink Enchanted' (d)	CLoc EBak
	'Gilda'	CWVF MJac
	'Gillian Althea' (d)	CDoC CWVF SRGP SRiF
	'Gilt Edge' (v)	CLoc
	'Gimlie' **new**	WPBF
I	'Gina'	WPBF
	'Gina Bowman'	LCla SLBF
	'Gina's Gold' (d)	WPBF
	'Ginger' **new**	WPBF
	Ginger = 'Goetzginger'PBR (Shadowdancer Series)	LAst LSou NEgg SCoo SVil
	'Gingham Girl' (d)	SRiF
	'Giovanna and Wesley' (d)	SRiF
	'Gipsy Princess' (d)	CLoc
	'Girls' Brigade'	CWVF EKMF
	'Gitana'	WPBF
	'Gladiator' (d)	EBak EKMF LCla
	'Gladys Godfrey'	EBak
	'Gladys Lorimer'	CWVF EPts
	'Gladys Miller'	CLoc
	glazioviana	CDoC CWVF EKMF LCla SLBF SRiF SWal WRou
	'Glenby' (d)	CWVF SRiF
	'Glendale'	CWVF
	'Glitters'	CWVF EBak
§	'Globosa'	CAgr EBak EKMF SRiF
	'Gloria Johnson'	EKMF
	'Glow'	EBak EKMF
	'Glowing Embers'	EBak
	Glowing Lilac (d)	EMan EPts
	'Glyn Jones' (d)	EKMF
	'Godelieve' (d)	WPBF
	'Godelieve Elli' (d) **new**	WPBF
	'Gold Brocade'	MBri SPet SPoG
	'Gold Crest'	EBak
	'Gold Leaf'	CWVF
	'Golden Amethyst' (d) **new**	SRiF
	'Golden Anniversary' (d)	CLoc CWVF EBak EKMF EMan LVER MJac WPBF
	'Golden Arrow'	CDoC LCla SRiF
	'Golden Border Queen'	CLoc
	'Golden Dawn'	CLoc CWVF EBak SPet SRiF
	'Golden Eden Lady' (v)	MWhe
	'Golden Girl'	SLBF
	'Golden Herald'	SLBF
	'Golden Jessimae' (v)	WPBF
	'Golden La Campanella' (d/v)	CLoc MBri
	'Golden Lena' (d/v)	CWVF EMan
	'Golden Marinka' (v) ♀H3	CCCN CLoc EBak EKMF LAst LRHS LSou MBri SPet
	'Golden Melody' (d)	SRiF
	'Golden Monique'	WPBF
	'Golden Peppermint Stick' (d) **new**	SRiF
	'Golden Runner' (v)	WPBF
	'Golden Swingtime' (d)	MBri MJac SPet SSea
	'Golden Treasure' (v)	CLoc CWVF EKMF MBri MWar

	'Golden Vergeer' (v)	SLBF
	'Golden Wedding'	EKMF
	'Goldsworth Beauty'	LCla SRiF
	'Golondrina'	CWVF EBak
	'Goody Goody'	EBak SRiF
	'Gooseberry Hill'	SRiF WPBF
	'Goosebery Belle' **new**	SRiF WRou
	'Gordon Thorley'	EKMF MWhe
	'Gordon's China Rose'	LCla
	'Gorgeous Gemma' (d)	WPBF
	'Gota' **new**	WPBF
	'Gottingen'	EBak EKMF SRiF WPBF
	'Governor Pat Brown' (d)	EBak
	'Grace Darling'	CWVF EBak MWhe
	gracilis	see *F. magellanica* var. *gracilis*
	'Graf Witte'	CDoC CWVF EKMF SPet SRiF
	'Granada' **new**	SRiF
	'Grand Duchess'	WPBF
	'Grand Duke' (d)	CWVF
	'Grandad Hobbs' (d)	LCla
	'Grandma Hobbs'	LCla
	'Grandma Sinton' (d)	CLoc CWVF EMan MBri MWhe
	'Grandpa George' (d)	LCla SRiF
	'Grandpa Jack' (d)	SLBF
	'Grasmere'	SRiF
	'Grayrigg'	CDoC EKMF EPts LCla SRiF WPBF
	'Great Ouse' (d)	EPts
	'Great Scott' (d)	CLoc
	'Green 'n' Gold'	EBak WPBF
	'Greenpeace'	EKMF WPBF
	'Greta'	MWar SRiF WRou
	'Gretna Chase'	MBri MWhe SRiF
	'Grey Lady' (d)	SRiF
	'Grietje'	WPBF
	'Gris' **new**	SRiF
	'Grobo '60' (d)	WPBF
	'Groene Boelvaar' (d)	WPBF
	'Grumpy'	CDoC CWVF EPts LRHS MWhe SPet WPBF
	'Gruss aus dem Bodethal'	CLoc CWVF EBak EKMF EPts SRiF WPBF
	'Guinevere'	CWVF EBak
	'Gustave Doré' (d)	EBak EKMF
	'Guurtje' **new**	WPBF
	'Guy Dauphine' (d)	EBak
	'Gwen Burralls' (d)	EKMF
	'Gwen Dodge'	LCla SRiF WPBF
	'Gwendaling' **new**	SRiF
	'Gypsy Girl' (d)	CWVF
	'H.G. Brown'	EBak EKMF MWhe SRiF
	'Halsall Beauty' (d)	MBri
	'Halsall Belle' (d)	MBri SRiF
	'Halsall Pride' (d)	MBri
	'Hampshire Blue'	CDoC CWVF
	'Hampshire Prince' (d)	LVER
	'Hanau'	WPBF
	'Hanna' (d)	SRGP
	'Hanna Improved' **new**	SRiF
	'Hannah Gwen' (d)	EKMF
	'Hannah Louise' (d)	EPts
	'Hannah Rogers'	MWar
	'Hans Callaars'	SLBF
	'Happy'	CDoC CWVF EPts LCla SPet WPBF
	'Happy Anniversary'	CLoc WFFs WPBF
I	'Happy Anniversary' (d/v)	EKMF
	'Happy Fellow'	CDoC CLoc EBak NDlv SRiF
	'Happy Wedding Day' (d)	CDoC CLoc CWVF EKMF EPts LAst MJac MWhe SCoo SPet SRGP
	'Hapsburgh'	EBak SRiF
	'Harbour Lites'	MWar SLBF WPBF WRou
	'Harlow Car'	CDoC CWVF EKMF EPts SRiF
	'Harlow Perfection'	EKMF
	'Harmony' Niederholzer, 1946	EBak
	'Harnser's Flight'	SRiF

	'Harold Smith' **new**	SRiF
	'Harry Dunnett'	EBak
	'Harry Gray' (d)	CCCN CLoc CWVF EBak EMan EPts LAst MBri MJac MWhe SPet SRGP
	'Harry Pullen'	EBak
	'Harry Taylor' (d)	EPts
	'Harry's Sunshine'	SLBF
	'Hartis Phönix'	WPBF
	hartwegii	CDoC EKMF LCla
	'Harvey's Reward'	SLBF
	'Hathersage' (d)	EBak
	'Hathor'	WPBF
	hatschbachii	CDoC LCla SRiF
	- Berry 4464	EKMF
	- Berry 4465	EKMF
	'Haute Cuisine' (d)	CLoc EMan MWhe
	'Hawaiian Sunset' (d)	CLoc CWVF EPts LCla SLBF SRiF WPBF
	'Hawkshead' ♀$^{H3-4}$	More than 30 suppliers
	'Hazel' (d)	CCCN CWVF MWhe WPBF
	'Heart Throb' (d)	EBak
	'Heavenly Hayley' (d)	SLBF SRiF WPBF
	'Hebe'	EBak MWhe
I	'Hedens Montana'	WPBF
	'Heidi Ann' (d) ♀^{H3}	CCCN CDoC CHrt CLoc CWVF EBak EKMF EMan EPts LAst MBri MWhe SLBF SPet WFFs WPBF
	'Heidi Blue' (d)	SLBF
§	'Heidi Weiss' (d)	CDoC CLoc CWVF MBri SPet
	'Heinrich Henkel'	see *F.* 'Andenken an Heinrich Henkel'
	'Heinzelmännchen'	WPBF
	'Heirloom' (d)	EKMF
	'Helen Clare' (d)	CLoc CWVF EBak
	'Helen Elizabeth' (d)	EKMF
	'Helen Gair' (d)	CWVF
	'Helen Nicholls' (d)	EKMF WPBF
	'Helen Spence' (d)	EKMF
	'Helena Rose'	EKMF
	'Hella'	WPBF
	'Hellen Devine'	CWVF
	'Hello Moideer' **new**	SRiF
	'Hemsleyana'	see *F. microphylla* subsp. *hemsleyana*
	'Henkelly's Apmist'	WPBF
	'Henkelly's Athena' **new**	WPBF
	'Henkelly's Benjamin'	WPBF
	'Henkelly's Dikbuik'	WPBF
	'Henkelly's Elegantie'	WPBF
	'Henkelly's Elisabeth' **new**	WPBF
	'Henkelly's Leerbroek' **new**	WPBF
	'Henkelly's Meuleke' (d)	WPBF
	'Henkelly's Sam'	WPBF
	'Henkelly's Stippelke'	WPBF
	'Hennie Bouman' (d)	WPBF
	'Henning Becker' ♀^{H3}	CWVF WPBF
	'Henri Poincaré'	EBak EKMF
	'Herald' ♀^{H4}	CDoC CWVF EBak EKMF MHar SLBF SRiF WPBF
	'Herbé de Jacques'	see *F.* 'Mr West'
	'Heritage' (d)	CLoc EBak EKMF SRiF WPBF
	'Herman de Graaff' (d)	EKMF
	'Hermiena'	CLoc CWVF EPts MWar MWhe SLBF WFFs
	'Hermienne'	WRou
	'Heron'	EBak EKMF SRiF
	'Herps Bazuin' **new**	WPBF
	'Herps Bonang'	WPBF
	'Herps Buikorgel'	WPBF
	'Herps Kwikstep' **new**	WPBF
	'Herps Pierement'	SLBF
	'Hertogin van Brabant' (d)	WPBF
	'Hessett Festival' (d)	CWVF EBak
	'Heston Blue' (d)	CWVF EKMF

'Het Halens Helmpje'	WPBF
'Het Wijnmenneke' (d) **new**	WPBF
'Hettenheuvel'	WPBF
'Hetty Blok' (d)	WPBF
'Heydon'	CWVF
'Hi Jinks' (d)	EBak
hidalgensis	see *F. microphylla* subsp. *hidalgensis*
'Hidcote Beauty'	CDoC CLoc CWVF EBak LCla MWhe SLBF SPet WFFs
'Hidden Treasure'	MWar WFFs WPBF
'Highland Pipes'	EKMF LCla
'Hilda Fitzsimmons'	WPBF
'Hilda May Salmon'	CWVF WPBF
'Hilke'	WPBF
'Hindu Belle'	EBak SRiF
'Hinnerike'	CWVF LCla WRou
'Hiroshige'	LCla WPBF
'His Excellency' (d)	EBak
'Hobo' (d)	SRiF
'Hobson's Choice' (d)	CWVF SLBF
'Hokusai'	WPBF
'Holly's Beauty' (d)	CDoC CLoc EKMF EPts LAst MWar SRGP WPBF
'Hollywood Park' (d)	EBak
'Hot Coals'	CLoc CWVF EKMF EPts MCot MJac MWar MWhe SRiF WPBF WRou
'Howerd Hebden'	CDoC EKMF
'Howlett's Hardy' ♀H3-4	CDoC CLoc CWVF EBak EKMF LRHS NLar SRiF WMnd WPBF WRou
'Huckeswagen' **new**	SLBF
'Hugh Morgan' (D) **new**	SRiF
'Hula Girl' (d)	CDoC CWVF EBak EKMF MJac MWar MWhe SPet SRiF WPBF
'Humboldt Holiday' (d)	EKMF
'Hummeltje'	WPBF
'Huntsman' (d)	CCCN CDoC LAst MJac MWhe
'I Love You' **new**	WPBF
'Ian Brazewell' (d)	CLoc
'Ian Leedham' (d)	EBak EKMF
'Ian Storey'	EKMF
'Ice Cream Soda' (d)	EBak
'Ice Maiden' ambig. (d)	WPBF
'Iceberg'	CWVF EBak
'Icecap'	CWVF EKMF MBri
'Iced Champagne'	CLoc CWVF EBak MJac
'Ichiban' (d)	CLoc SRiF
'Icicle' (d)	WPBF
'Ida' (d)	EBak
'Igloo Maid' (d)	CLoc CWVF EBak EKMF MWhe SPet
'Illusion'	WPBF
'Impala' (d)	CWVF
'Imperial Fantasy' (d)	CWVF
'Impudence'	CLoc CWVF EBak SPet
'Impulse' (d)	CLoc
'Ina Jo Marker'	SRiF
'Indian Maid' (d)	CWVF EBak LVER WPBF
inflata	EKMF WPBF
'Ingleore'	WPBF
'Ingrid van der Sande'	WPBF
'Insulinde'	CDoC CFee CWVF EPts LCla MJac MWar SLBF
'Interlude' (d)	EBak
'Iolanthe'	CWVF
'Irene L. Peartree' (d)	CWVF LCla SRiF
'Irene Sinton' (d)	CCCN MJac
'Iris Amer' (d)	CDoC CLoc CWVF EBak
'Irish Dawn'	MWar
'Irving Alexander' (d)	WPBF
'Isabel Erkamp'	WPBF
'Isis' ambig.	WPBF
'Isle of Mull'	CDoC SPet WPBF
'Isle of Purbeck'	SRiF
'Italiano' (d)	CWVF MJac
'Ivana van Amsterdam'	SLBF
'Jaap Brummel' (d)	WPBF
'Jack Acland'	CWVF
'Jack Coast' **new**	SRiF
'Jack King' **new**	SRiF
'Jack Shahan' ♀H3	CCCN CDoC CHrt CLoc CWVF EBak EKMF EMan LAst LCla MBri MJac MWar MWhe NBlu SPet SRGP WFFs WPBF
'Jack Stanway' (v)	CWVF EKMF MWar SRiF
'Jackie Bull' (d)	CWVF EBak
'Jackpot' (d)	EBak
'Jackqueline'	CWVF
'Jadas Mam'	WPBF
'Jam Roll' (d)	LVER
'Jamboree' (d)	EBak
'James Eve' (d) **new**	SRiF
'James Hammond' **new**	SRiF
'James Lye' (d)	CWVF EBak EKMF SRiF
'James Shaffery'	WPBF
'James Travis' (d)	CDoC EBak EKMF LCla SRiF
'Jan Murray'	SLBF
'Jan van Erp'	WPBF
'Jandel'	CWVF
'Jane Amanda' (d) **new**	SRiF
'Jane Humber' (d)	CWVF EKMF
'Jane Lye'	EBak
'Janice Ann'	EKMF LCla MWar WFFs
'Janice Perry's Gold' (v)	CCCN CLoc MJac SRiF
'Janie' (d)	MAsh
'Janjopiet Driessen'	WPBF
'Janneke Brinkman-Salentijn'	SRiF
'Jap Vantveer'	LCla WPBF
'Jasper's Vlammetje'	WPBF
'Jaunty Jack'	SLBF
'Javelin'	WPBF
'Jayess Helen' (d) **new**	SRiF
'Jean Campbell'	EBak
'Jean Clark'	WPBF
'Jean Frisby'	CLoc
'Jean Temple'	WPBF
'Jeane'	EKMF NEgg
'Jeangil'	WPBF
'Jef van der Kuylen' (d) **new**	WPBF
'Jennie Rachael' (d)	SRiF
'Jennifer'	EBak
'Jennifer Lister' (d)	EKMF
'Jenny Brinson' (d)	WPBF
'Jenny May'	CLoc EPts WPBF
'Jenny Sorensen'	CWVF EKMF SRiF WRou
'Jess'	LCla SLBF
'Jessica Reynolds'	SRiF
'Jessie Pearson'	CWVF
'Jessimae'	CWVF SPet SRiF
'Jester' Holmes (d)	CLoc
'Jet Fire' (d)	EBak
'Jezebel'	SRiF WPBF
'Jiddles'	EKMF LCla SRiF WRou
'Jill Harris'	WPBF
'Jill Whitworth'	CDoC
'Jim Coleman'	CWVF MWhe SRiF
'Jim Dodge' (d)	EPts WPBF
'Jim Hawkins'	EBak SRiF
'Jim Muncaster'	CWVF EKMF
'Jim Todd' **new**	SRiF
'Jim Watts'	CDoC EKMF WPBF
jimenezii	CDoC EKMF LCla
– hybrid	EKMF
'Jimmy Carr' (d)	EKMF
'Jimmy Cricket'	CDoC
'Jingle Bells'	MWhe

	'Jinlye'	EKMF
	'Jo Tamerus' (d)	WPBF
	'Joan Barnes' (d)	CDoC CWVF SRiF
	'Joan Cooper'	CLoc CWVF EBak EKMF SLBF SRiF
	'Joan Gilbert' (d)	SRiF
	'Joan Goy'	CWVF EKMF MJac MWhe
	'Joan Knight'	CLoc
	'Joan Margaret' (d)	MJac
	'Joan Morris'	SLBF
	'Joan Pacey'	CDoC CWVF EBak EKMF SRiF
	'Joan Paxton' (d)	LCla
	'Joan Smith'	EBak SRiF
	'Joan Waters' (d)	CWVF
	'Joanne'	WPBF
	'Jo-Anne Fisher' (d)	EPts
	'Joan's Delight'	WPBF
	'Joe Kusber' (d)	CWVF EBak
	'Joe Nicholls' (d)	EKMF
	'Joel'	CLoc WPBF
	'Joergen Hahn' **new**	WPBF
	'Johannes Novinski' **new**	SRiF
	'John Bartlett'	CLoc
	'John E. Caunt' Υ^{H3-4}	EKMF
	'John Green'	EKMF SLBF WPBF
	'John Grooms' (d)	CLoc WRou
	'John Lockyer'	CLoc CWVF EBak SRiF
	'John Maynard Scales'	CDoC CWVF LCla MJac MWhe WPBF WRou
§	'John Ridding'^{PBR} (v)	CHEx CLoc LAst SPoG SVil
	'John Stephens'	EPts
	'John Suckley' (d)	EBak
	'John Wright'	EKMF LCla
	'Joke's Othello' (d)	WPBF
	'Jomam' Υ^{H3}	CLoc CWVF MWar WPBF
	'Jon Oram'	CLoc CWVF
	'Jonne Comperen'	WPBF
	'Jopie' (d)	WPBF
	'Jorma van Eijk' (d)	WPBF
	'Jose Tamerus' (d) **new**	WPBF
	'Joseph Holmes'	WPBF
	'Jose's Joan' (d)	CWVF
	'Joy Bielby'	EKMF
	'Joy Patmore'	CLoc CWVF EBak EKMF MBri MWar MWhe SLBF SPet WPBF
	'Joyce'	WPBF
	'Joyce Adey' (d)	CWVF SRiF
	'Joyce Sinton'	CWVF EMan MBri
	'Joyce Wilson' (d)	EPts LCla
	'Jubie-Lin' (d)	WPBF
	'Jubilee Quest'	EKMF MWar WPBF
	'Judith Coupland'	CWVF
	'Juella'	WPBF
	'Jules Daloges' (d)	EBak EKMF SRiF
	'Julia' (d)	EKMF WPBF
	'Julie Ann'	MWar
	'Julie Horton' (d)	WPBF
	'Julie Marie' (d)	CWVF MJac
	'June Gardner'	CWVF EKMF
	'Jungle'	LCla WPBF
I	'Juno' Kennett	EBak
	juntasensis	EKMF
	'Jupiter Seventy'	EBak SRiF
	'Just William' **new**	SRiF
	'Justin's Pride'	CDoC EKMF SRiF
	'Jülchen'	CWVF WPBF
	'Kaboutertje'	EKMF
	'Kaleidoscope' (d)	EBak
	'Kallinga'	WPBF
	'Kara Faye' **new**	EKMF
	'Karen Isles'	CDoC LCla WRou
	'Karen Louise' (d)	CLoc
	'Kate Taylor' (d)	SLBF
	'Kate Wylie'	MWar
	'Kath Kirk'	EKMF
	'Kath van Hanegem'	SLBF SRiF WPBF WRou
	'Kathleen Galea' **new**	SRiF
	'Kathleen Muncaster' (d)	EKMF
	'Kathleen Smith' (d)	EKMF
	'Kathleen van Hanegan'	CLoc MWar
	'Kathryn Maidment'	WPBF
	'Kathy Louise' (d)	EMan
	'Kathy's Pipes'	EKMF
	'Kathy's Prince'	EKMF
	'Kathy's Sparkler' (d)	EKMF
	'Katie Elizabeth Ann' (d)	MWar
	'Katie Reynolds' (d) **new**	SRiF
	'Katie Rogers'	EPts
	'Katie Susan'	LCla SLBF
	'Katinka'	CDoC CWVF LCla SRiF
	'Katjan'	EKMF LCla SLBF
	'Katrien Michiels'	WPBF
	'Katrina' (d)	CLoc EBak
	'Katrina Thompsen'	CLoc CWVF EKMF EPts MWar SRiF
	'Katy James'	EKMF MWar
	'Katy M'	WPBF
	'Keepsake' (d)	CLoc EBak
	'Keesje'	WPBF
	'Kegworth Carnival' (d)	CWVF SRiF
	'Kelly's Dream' (d)	WPBF
	'Kelsey's Kisses'	WPBF
	'Ken Goldsmith'	CWVF
	'Ken Jennings'	CWVF
	'Ken Shelton'	SRiF
	'Kenny Dalglish' (d)	EKMF
	'Kenny Holmes'	CWVF
	'Kenny Walkling'	SLBF
	'Kernan Robson' (d)	CLoc CWVF EBak SRiF
	'Keteltje'	WPBF
	'Kevin R. Peake' (d)	MWar
	'Keystone'	EBak SRiF
	'Kim Nicholls'	CDoC EKMF WPBF
	'Kim Wright' (d)	MWhe
	'Kimberley Hadfield' **new**	MWar
	'Kimberly' (d)	EBak
	'King of Bath' (d)	EBak
	'King of Hearts' (d)	EBak
	'King's Ransom' (d)	CLoc CWVF EBak LRHS MWhe SPet
	'Kiss 'n' Tell'	CWVF MJac MWhe SRiF
	'Kit Oxtoby' (d)	CCCN CDoC CHrt CWVF EKMF EMan LCla LVER MJac SVil WPBF
	'Kiwi' (d)	EBak
	'Knockout' (d)	CWVF EKMF
	'Kolding Perle'	CWVF EKMF SPet SRiF
	'Königin der Nacht'	WPBF
	'Kon-Tiki' (d)	CLoc SPet
	'Koralle'	see *F.* 'Coralle'
	'Krimar'	WPBF
	'Krommenie'	WPBF
	'Kwintet'	CWVF EBak MJac SPet SRiF
	'Kyoto'	CWVF
	'La Bianca'	EBak
	'La Campanella' (d) Υ^{H3}	CCCN CDoC CHrt CLoc CWVF EBak EKMF EMan EPts LAst LCla LSou MBri MJac MWar MWhe NBlu NVic SPet WFFs WPBF
	'La Fiesta' (d)	EBak
	'La France' (d)	EBak EKMF
	'La Neige' ambig.	CWVF
	'La Neige' Lemoine (d)	EBak EKMF
	'La Porte' (d)	CLoc CWVF
	'La Rosita' (d)	EBak SLBF SRiF
	'La Traviata' ambig.	WPBF
I	'La Traviata' Blackwell (d)	EBak SRiF
	'La Violetta' (d)	MWhe
	'Lace Petticoats' (d)	EBak EKMF
	'Lady Bacon'	EWes SDys SLBF
	'Lady Bartle Frere' (d) **new**	SRiF

	'Lady Boothby'	CDoC CHEx CPLG CPle CWVF EBak EKMF EShb LRHS SLBF SMrm SPet SPoG WPBF
	'Lady Framlingham' (d)	EPts
	'Lady Heytesbury'	EKMF
	'Lady in Grey' (d)	CCCN EKMF LAst MJac SRiF WPBF
	'Lady Isobel Barnett'	CDoC CLoc CWVF EBak EKMF MBri MJac MWar MWhe SPet WPBF
	'Lady Kathleen Spence'	CWVF EBak MWhe SPet WRou
	'Lady Lupus'	EPts
	'Lady Patricia Mountbatten'	CWVF EKMF EMan MJac WRou
	'Lady Ramsey'	EBak SRiF
	'Lady Rebecca' (d)	CLoc
	'Lady Thumb' (d) ♀H3	More than 30 suppliers
	'Lady's Smock'	EKMF
	'Laing's Hybrid'	CWVF EBak
	'Lakeland Princess'	EBak
	'Lakeside'	EBak
	'Laleham Lass'	EKMF
	'Lambada'	LAst MWar MWhe SRiF WRou
	'Lancashire Lad' (d)	LAst MWar
	'Lancashire Lass'	CWVF MBri
	'Lancelot'	EBak SRiF
	'Land van Beveren'	MWar SLBF WPBF
	'Langsford' **new**	SRiF
	'Lapshead White' **new**	CPLG
	'Lark'	CWVF WPBF
	'Lassie' (d)	CDoC CLoc CWVF EBak
	'Last Chance' **new**	SLBF
	'Laura' ambig.	CWVF WRou
I	'Laura' (Dutch)	CLoc EPts LCla MWar SLBF SRiF
I	'Laura' Martin (d)	EKMF MWhe WPBF
	'Lavaglut'	WPBF
	'Lavender Beauty' (d) **new**	SRiF
	'Lavender Kate' (d)	CLoc CWVF EBak
	'Lavender Lace'	MWhe
	'Lazy Lady' (d)	CWVF EBak
	'Le Postier'	WPBF
	'Lea de Smedt'	WPBF
	'Lea's Aubergine'	WPBF
	'Lechlade Apache'	CDoC LCla
	'Lechlade Chinaman'	CDoC EKMF SRiF WFFs
	'Lechlade Debutante'	CDoC LCla SRiF
	'Lechlade Fire-eater'	CDoC LCla SRiF
	'Lechlade Gorgon'	CDoC CWVF EKMF LCla SLBF WFFs
	'Lechlade Magician'	CDoC EKMF EPts LCla SPet SRiF WFFs
	'Lechlade Maiden'	CWVF LCla SRiF
	'Lechlade Martianess'	LCla SRiF WPBF
	'Lechlade Potentate'	LCla
	'Lechlade Rocket'	WPBF
	'Lechlade Tinkerbell'	LCla SRiF
	'Lechlade Violet'	CDoC EKMF LCla SRiF
	lehmanii	LCla
	'Leicestershire Silver' (d)	WPBF
	'Leila' (d)	WPBF
	'Lemmeke'	WPBF
	'Len Bielby'	CDoC CWVF LCla
	'Lena' (d) ♀H3	CDoC CLoc CTri CWVF EBak EKMF EPts LAst MBri MJac MWhe NDlv SPer SPet SRGP SSea WEas WPBF
	'Lena Dalton' (d)	CLoc CWVF EBak MWhe SRiF
	'Leonhart von Fuchs'	WPBF
	'Leonie Boffe' (d) **new**	WPBF
	'Leonora'	CDoC CLoc CWVF EBak EKMF MBri MWhe SLBF SPet SRiF WRou
	'Lesley'	CWVF LCla
	'Lett's Delight' (d)	CWVF EPts
	'Letty Lye'	EBak SRiF
	'Leverhulme'	see *F.* 'Leverkusen'
§	'Leverkusen'	CDoC CLoc EBak LCla MJac MWhe WRou

	'Li Kai Lin'	SRiF
	'Liebesträume' ambig.	WPBF
I	'Liebesträume' Blackwell (d)	EBak
	'Liebriez' (d) ♀H3-4	EBak EKMF SPet SRiF
	'Liemers Lantaern'	CWVF
	'Lieze Brantze'	WPBF
	'Likalin'	CWVF
	'Lilac'	EBak
	'Lilac Lustre' (d)	CLoc CWVF EBak SPet
	'Lilac Queen' (d)	EBak
	'Lilian'	EKMF WPBF
	'Lillian Annetts' (d)	CCCN CDoC CWVF EKMF LAst LCla MJac MWar SLBF SRiF WPBF WRou
	'Lillibet' (d)	CLoc CWVF EBak
	'Lillydale' (d)	SRiF
	'Lilo Vogt'	SRiF
	'Lime Lite' (d)	MJac
	'Linda Goulding'	CWVF EBak MWhe WRou
	'Linda Grace'	EKMF MJac MWar
	'Linda Mary Nutt'	MWar
	'Linda Rosling' (d)	CDoC EKMF
	'Lindisfarne' (d)	CLoc CWVF EBak EKMF MJac SPet WPBF
	'L'Ingénue'	WPBF
	'Linlithgow Lass'	MWar
	'Lionel'	SRiF
	'Lisa' (d)	CDoC EPts SPet
	'Lisa Ashton'	SRiF
	'Lisa Jane'	MWhe
	'Lisa Rowe' (d)	WPBF
	'Lisi'	WPBF
	'Little Annie Gee'	MWar
	'Little Baby'	EKMF SRiF
	'Little Beauty'	CDoC CWVF EKMF MWhe WPBF
	'Little Boy Blue'	EPts
	'Little Brook Gem'	SLBF
	'Little Catbells'	SLBF
	'Little Chris'	WPBF
	'Little Cupido' (d) **new**	WPBF
	'Little Gene'	EBak
	'Little Jewel'	SPet SRiF
	'Little Nan'	SLBF WPBF
	'Little Orphan Annie'	LCla
	'Little Ouse' (d)	CWVF MWhe
	'Little Ronnie' (d)	SRiF
	'Little Snow Queen'	WPBF
	'Little Witch'	EKMF SLBF SRiF
	'Liz' (d)	EBak EKMF
	Liza = 'Goetzliza'^{PBR} (Shadowdancer Series)	CDoC LAst LSou
	'Liza Todman' (d) **new**	SRiF
	'Lochinver' (d)	CWVF
	'Loeke's Marie-Lou'	WPBF
	'Loeky'	CLoc CWVF EBak SPet SRiF WPBF
	'Logan Garden'	see *F. magellanica* 'Logan Woods'
	'Lolita' (d)	CWVF EBak
	'London 2000'	LCla MJac MWar SLBF SRiF WPBF
	'London Eye' **new**	SLBF
	'London in Bloom'	SLBF WPBF
	'Lonely Ballerina' (d)	CLoc CWVF
	'Long Distance'	LCla WPBF
	'Long Wings'	EKMF LCla
	'Lonneke'	WPBF
	'Lord Byron'	CLoc EBak EKMF SRiF
	'Lord Jim'	CDoC LCla
	'Lord Lloyd Webber' (d)	MJac
	'Lord Lonsdale'	CWVF EBak EPts LCla MWhe WRou
	'Lord Roberts'	CLoc CWVF SLBF
	'Lorelei'	WPBF
	'Lorna Fairclough'	MJac
	'Lorna Florence' **new**	SLBF
	'Lorna Swinbank'	CLoc CWVF SRiF

	'Lottie Hobby' ♀H1+3	CDoC CLoc CWVF EKMF EPfP EPts EShb ISea LCla MHar MLHP MWhe SIng SPet WFFs WRou
	'Lou Rinzema'	WPBF
	'Louise Emershaw' (d)	CWVF EBak MJac
	'Louise Nicholls'	EKMF MJac SLBF SRiF
	'Lovable' (d)	EBak
	'Loveliness'	CLoc CWVF EBak EKMF MWhe SRiF
	'Lovely Chipi'	WPBF
	'Lovely Jenny' (d) **new**	WPBF
	'Lovely Les' (d)	SRiF
	'Lovely Linda'	SLBF
	'Lovely Zhara' **new**	WPBF
	'Love's Reward' ♀H1+3	CLoc CWVF EKMF MJac MWar MWhe SLBF WFFs WPBF WRou
	'Lower Raydon'	EBak
I	'Loxensis'	CDoC CWVF EBak EKMF
	- Berry 3233	EKMF
	- DG 1001	EKMF
	loxensis misapplied	see *F.* 'Speciosa', *F.* 'Loxensis'
	'Loxhore Calypso'	EKMF
	'Loxhore Lullaby'	LCla
	'Loxhore Mazurka'	SRiF WPBF WRou
	'Loxhore Minuet'	LCla WRou
	'Loxhore Posthorn'	LCla
	'Lucinda'	CWVF
	'Lucky Strike' (d)	CLoc EBak
	Lucy = 'Goetzlucy' (Shadowdancer Series)	EBak WPBF
	'Lucy Locket'	MJac
	'Lukas'	WPBF
	'Lunter's Glorie' **new**	WPBF
	'Lunter's Klokje'	WPBF
	'Lunter's Trots' (d)	WPBF
	'Luscious Lisa'	WPBF
	'Lustre'	CWVF EBak
	'Lut' (d) **new**	WPBF
	'Lutz Bogemann'	WPBF
	lycioides misapplied	see *F.* 'Lycioides'
§	***lycioides*** Andrews	EBak EKMF
I	'Lycioides'	LCla
	'Lye's Elegance'	EKMF SRiF
	'Lye's Excelsior'	EBak SRiF
	'Lye's Own'	EBak SPet
	'Lye's Perfection'	EKMF
	'Lye's Unique' ♀H1+3	CCCN CDoC CHrt CLoc CWVF EBak EKMF EPts LCla MJac MWar MWhe SLBF SPet SRiF WRou
	'Lynda' (d)	WPBF
	'Lynette' (d)	CLoc
	'Lynn Ellen' (d)	CDoC CWVF EBak
	'Lyric'	WPBF
	'Maartje'	SRiF WPBF
	'Mabel Greaves' (d)	CWVF
	'Mac Wagg'	WRou
	'Machu Picchu'	CLoc CWVF EKMF EPts LCla WPBF WRou
	macrophylla	CDoC WMoo
	- BEA 922539	EKMF
	- Berry 80-539	EKMF
	- Berry 80-541	EKMF
	- Berry 3080	EKMF
	macrostigma	EKMF
	'Madame Aubin'	EKMF
	'Madame Butterfly' (d)	CLoc
	'Madame Cornélissen' (d) ♀H3	More than 30 suppliers
	'Madame Eva Boye'	EBak
	'Madeleine Sweeney' (d)	MBri
	'Madleina' (d)	WPBF
	'Maes-y-Groes'	EKMF
	'Maetsuycker' **new**	WPBF
	'Magda van Bets' (d) **new**	WPBF
	magdalenae	EKMF

	magellanica	CAby CDoC COld CTrG CWib EKMF GGar NChi NPer NWea SPer WFar WPnn
	- Dahl, S.	EKMF
	- 'Alba'	see *F. magellanica* var. *molinae*
I	- 'Alba Aureovariegata' (v)	CBgR CDoC EPfP LAst MBri SPer WFar WOut
	- 'Alba Variegata' (v)	ENot NPol
	- 'Americana Elegans'	CDoC
	- var. ***conica***	CDoC EKMF
	- var. ***discolor***	MAsh
	- 'Duchy of Cornwall' **new**	CDoC
§	- var. ***gracilis*** ♀H3	CAgr CDoC CHEx CLoc CTri CWVF EKMF LRHS MLHP MWhe SCoo WPnn WSpi
	- - 'Aurea' ♀H3-4	CBcs CDoC CWVF EKMF ELan ENot EPfP GAbr GQui ISea LAst LCla LRHS MRav MWhe SAga SCoo SDix SLBF SPer SPet SPla SPoG WFar WHen WRou WSpi
§	- - 'Tricolor' (v) ♀H3	CBgR CDoC EKMF EPts EWes EWin GAbr LCla LRHS SLBF SRms WCFE WFFs WPBF WPnn WRou
	- - 'Variegata' (v) ♀H3	CBgR CDoC EBak EBee EKMF EPfP GGar LCla LRHS LSou MGos MRav SAga SDix SIng SPet SRiF WFFs WPnn WSpi
	- 'Guiding Star' **new**	CDoC
	- 'Lady Bacon'	CDoC EKMF MSte
§	- 'Logan Woods'	CDoC EKMF ISea SLBF
	- 'Longipedunculata'	CDoC EKMF SLPl
	- 'Lyonesse Lady' **new**	CDoC
	- var. ***macrostema***	EKMF
§	- var. ***molinae***	More than 30 suppliers
§	- - 'Enstone' (v)	CSBt EKMF EMil EPts SRiF
	- - 'Enstone Gold'	EKMF
	- - 'Golden Sharpitor' (v)	CBgR CCCN LAst LSou MDKP MHar WAbe WHen
§	- - 'Sharpitor' (v)	More than 30 suppliers
	- var. ***myrtifolia***	CDoC EKMF
	- var. ***pumila***	CBgR CDoC CEnt EShb EWes ITim LAst MLHP SBla SHGN SIng SMHy SRot WAbe WBor
	- 'Seahorse' **new**	CDoC
	- 'Sea King' **new**	CDoC
	- 'Sea Spray' **new**	CDoC
§	- 'Thompsonii' ♀H3-4	CDoC ECGP EKMF SBch SMHy
§	- 'Versicolor' (v)	More than 30 suppliers
	'Magenta Flush'	CDoC CWVF
	'Maggie Rose' **new**	SLBF
	'Magic Flute'	CLoc CWVF MJac
	'Maharaja' (d)	EBak SRiF
	'Maharini' (d)	WPBF
	'Majebo' (d)	SRiF
	'Major Heaphy'	CDoC CWVF EBak EKMF MWhe SRiF
	'Malibu Mist' (d)	CWVF LVER SRiF
	'Mama Bleuss' (d)	EBak SRiF
	'Mancunian' (d)	CWVF
I	'Mandarin' Schnabel	EBak
	'Mandi'	LCla
	'Mandy Oxtoby' **new**	SRiF
	'Mantilla'	CDoC CLoc CWVF EBak EKMF LCla MJac MWhe
	'Maori Maid'	SRiF WPBF
	'Maori Pipes'	WPBF
	'Marcel Michiels' (d) **new**	WPBF
	'Marcia' PBR (Shadowdancer Series)	LAst LSou
	'Marcus Graham' (d)	CCCN CLoc CWVF EBak EKMF MWar MWhe SCoo SRiF WPBF WRou
	'Marcus Hanton' (d)	CWVF EKMF LCla SRiF
	'Mardi Gras' (d)	EBak SRiF

	'Margaret' (d) ♀H4	CDoC CLoc CTri CWVF EBak EKMF ENot EPts ISea LCla LVER MWar MWhe NDlv SLBF SPet
	'Margaret Bird'	LCla
	'Margaret Brown' ♀H4	CDoC CLoc CTri CWVF EBak EKMF LCla MHar MWhe SLBF SPet SRGP SRiF WPBF WRou
	'Margaret Davidson' (d)	CLoc
	'Margaret Ellen'	WPBF
	'Margaret Hazelwood'	EKMF SRiF
	'Margaret Lowis' **new**	MWar
	'Margaret Pilkington'	CWVF MWar SRiF
	'Margaret Roe'	CDoC CWVF EBak EKMF MJac SPet SRiF WPBF
	'Margaret Susan'	EBak
	'Margaret Tebbit'	CCCN LAst MJac WGor
	'Margery Blake'	CDoC EBak SRiF
	'Margharita' (d) **new**	SRiF
	'Margrit Willimann'	WPBF
	'Maria Landy'	CWVF EKMF EMan LCla MJac MWar WRou
	'Maria Mathilde' (d) **new**	SLBF WPBF
	'Maria Merrills' (d)	EMan SRiF
	'Maria Paulus' **new**	WPBF
	'Marie Helene Meus'	WPBF
	'Marie-Louise Luyckx' (d) **new**	WPBF
	'Mariken'	WPBF
	'Marilyn Olsen'	CWVF
	'Marin Belle'	EBak SRiF
	'Marin Glow' ♀H3	CLoc CWVF EBak MWhe SLBF SPet WPBF
	'Marina Kelly'	WRou
	'Marinka' ♀H3	CCCN CHrt CLoc CWVF EBak EKMF EMan EPts LAst LCla LVER MBri MJac MWar MWhe SLBF SPet WPBF
	'Marion Hilton'	MWar
	'Mark Kirby' (d)	CWVF EBak EKMF WPBF
	'Marlea's Oui Oui' **new**	WPBF
	'Marlea's Schouwpijpke'	WPBF
	'Marlies de Keijzer'	LCla SLBF
	'Martin Beije'	WPBF
	'Martina'	SLBF
	'Martin's Anouska' **new**	WPBF
	'Martin's Brigitte' **new**	WPBF
	'Martin's Delight' (d) **new**	WPBF
	'Martin's Inspiration'	LCla MWar
	'Martin's Jennifer' **new**	WPBF
	'Martin's Midnight' (d)	WPBF
	'Martin's Umbrella'	WPBF
	'Martin's Yellow Surprise'	LCla SLBF
	'Martinus' (d)	WPBF
	'Marton Smith'	MWhe
	'Marty' (d)	EBak
	'Mary' ♀H1+3	CDoC CLoc CWVF EKMF EPts LCla LRHS MWar MWhe SLBF
	'Mary Jones' (d)	EKMF
	'Mary Lockyer' (d)	CLoc EBak SRiF
	'Mary Poppins'	CWVF
	'Mary Reynolds' (d)	CWVF
	'Mary Shead' (d)	MWar
	'Mary Sturman' **new**	SRiF
	'Mary Thorne'	EBak EKMF SRiF
	'Mary's Millennium'	CWVF
	'Masquerade' (d)	EBak EMan
	mathewsii	EKMF
	'Maureen Ward'	EKMF
	'Mauve Beauty' (d)	CWVF EKMF SLBF
	'Mauve Lace' (d)	SRiF
	'Max Jaffa'	CWVF SRiF
I	'Maxima'	EKMF LCla WPBF
	'Maxima's Baby' **new**	WPBF
	'Maybe Baby'	LAst WPBF WRou
	'Mayblossom' (d)	CWVF SPet
	'Mayfayre' (d)	CLoc
	'Mayfield'	CWVF MWhe
	'Mazda'	CWVF SRiF
	'Meadowlark' (d)	CWVF EBak SRiF
	'Mechtildis de Lechy'	WPBF
	'Meditation' (d)	CLoc
	'Melanie'	CDoC
	'Melissa Heavens'	CWVF
	'Melody'	EBak MWhe SPet SRiF
	'Melody Ann' (d)	EBak
	'Melpomene' **new**	WPBF
	'Melting Moments' (d)	EKMF SCoo
	'Mendocino Mini'	WPBF
	'Menna'	WPBF
	'Mephisto'	CWVF
	'Merlin'	CDoC EKMF LCla SRiF
	'Merry England' (d)	WPBF
	'Merry Mary' (d)	CWVF EBak EKMF WPBF
I	'Mexicali Rose' Machado	CLoc
	'Michael' (d)	CWVF EPts
	'Michael Wallis'	EKMF LCla SLBF SRiF
	michoacanensis misapplied	see *F. microphylla* subsp. *aprica*
	michoacanensis Sessé & Moç. B&SWJ 8982	WCru
	'Micky Goult' ♀H1+3	CLoc CWVF EKMF EPts LCla MJac MWhe SPet SRiF WPBF WRou
	'Microchip'	LCla
	microphylla	CBcs CBgR CBrd CDoC CElw CLoc CPLG CWVF EBak GGar LRHS MLan MWhe STre WBor WCru WEas
	- B&SWJ 9101	WCru
§	- subsp. ***aprica***	CDoC LCla
	- - BRE 69862	EKMF
§	- subsp. ***hemsleyana***	CDoC CPLG EKMF LCla MWhe SRiF WOut
§	- subsp. ***hidalgensis***	CDoC EKMF LCla WPBF
	- subsp. ***microphylla***	EKMF
	- subsp. ***quercetorum***	CDoC EKMF LCla
	- 'Variegata' (v)	EWes MCCP
	'Midas'	CWVF MBri
	'Midnight Sun' (d)	CWVF EBak
	'Midwinter'	CWVF LAst SRiF WPBF
	'Mieke Alferink'	SRiF
	'Mieke Meursing' ♀H1+3	CLoc CWVF EBak EKMF MJac MWhe SPet SRiF
	'Mien Kuypers'	WPBF
	'Miep Aalhuizen'	CDoC LCla SRiF WPBF WRou
	'Mike Foxon'	EKMF
	'Mike Foxton'	WPBF
	'Mike Oxtoby'	CWVF EKMF
	'Mikey's Reward'	WPBF
	'Mildred Wagg'	MWar
	'Millennium'	CLoc EBak EPts MJac SCoo WFFs
	'Millie' **new**	SRiF
	'Millie Butler'	CWVF
	'Ming'	CLoc SRiF
	'Mini Skirt'	SRiF
	'Miniature Jewels'	SLBF
	minimiflora misapplied	see *F.* x *bacillaris*
	'Minirose'	CCCN CDoC CWVF EPts MJac MWar MWhe WRou
	'Minnesota' (d)	EBak
	'Mipan'	SLBF
	'Miss California' (d)	CDoC CLoc CWVF EBak MBri MWhe
	'Miss Great Britain'	CWVF
	'Miss Lye'	EKMF SRiF
	'Miss Marilyn'	SRiF
	'Miss Muffett' (d)	EPts
	'Miss Vallejo' (d)	EBak
	'Mission Bells'	CDoC CLoc CWVF EBak EKMF EPts SPet
	'Mistoque'	SRiF

	'Misty Haze' (d)	CWVF
	'Molesworth' (d)	CWVF EBak MJac MWhe SPet
	'Mollie Beaulah' (d)	EKMF SRiF
	'Money Spinner'	CLoc EBak
	'Monica Dare'	WPBF
	'Monique Comperen'	WPBF
	'Monsieur Thibaut' ♀H4	EKMF ENot SPet
	'Monte Rosa' (d)	CLoc CWVF SRiF
	'Monterey'	MWhe
	'Montevideo' (d)	CWVF
	'Monument' (d)	SRiF
	'Mood Indigo' (d)	CWVF WRou
	'Moon Glow'	LAst MJac
	'Moonbeam' (d)	CLoc
	'Moonlight' **new**	CCCN
	'Moonlight Sonata'	CLoc CWVF EBak SPet
	'Moonraker' (d)	CWVF SRiF
	'More Applause' (d)	CLoc EKMF MWhe
	'Morning Cloud' (d)	SRiF
	'Morning Light' (d)	CLoc EBak SPet
	'Morning Mist'	EBak
	'Morning Star'	MBri
	'Morrells' (d)	EBak
	'Morton Martianette'	EKMF
	'Morton Splendide' **new**	EKMF
	'Moth Blue' (d)	CWVF EBak SPet SRiF
	'Mountain Mist' (d)	CWVF EKMF
	'Moyra' (d)	CWVF
	'Mr A. Huggett'	CLoc CWVF EKMF EPts MWhe SLBF SPet SRiF
	'Mr P.D. Lee'	MWhe
	'Mr W. Rundle'	EBak
§	'Mr West' (v)	EKMF SPet WRou
	'Mrs Churchill'	CLoc
	'Mrs Lawrence Lyon' (d)	EBak
	'Mrs Lovell Swisher' ♀H4	CWVF EBak EKMF LCla MWhe SPet SRiF WPBF
	'Mrs Marshall'	CWVF EBak SLBF SPet
	'Mrs Popple' ♀H3	More than 30 suppliers
	'Mrs Susan Brookfield' (d)	SRiF
	'Mrs W.P. Wood' ♀H3	CBgR CDoC CLoc CWVF EKMF MBri WPBF WRou
	'Mrs W. Rundle'	CLoc CWVF EBak EKMF LRHS MWhe SLBF SPet
	'Multa'	LAst MJac WRou
	'Muriel' (d)	CLoc CWVF EBak EKMF
	'Murru's Pierre Marie' (d) **new**	SLBF
	'My Delight'	CWVF
	'My Fair Lady' (d)	CLoc CWVF EBak SPet SRiF
	'My Mum'	LCla SLBF
	'My Pat' **new**	EKMF
	'My Reward' (d)	CWVF
	'Nananice' **new**	SRiF
	'Nancy Lou' (d)	CDoC CLoc CWVF LAst LVER MJac MWhe SLBF SPet SRGP WRou
	'Nanny Ed' (d)	CWVF MBri
	'Natal Bronze' **new**	SRiF
	'Natalie Jones'	SRiF
	'Natasha Sinton' (d)	CCCN CLoc CWVF EKMF EMan LAst LVER MBri MJac MWhe NBlu SLBF SPet WRou
	'Native Dancer' (d)	CWVF EBak
	'Naughty Nicole' (d)	SLBF WPBF
	'Nautilus' (d)	EBak
	'Neapolitan' (d)	CDoC MWhe SLBF WFFs
	'Neil Clyne'	MWhe
	'Nell Gwyn'	CLoc CWVF EBak
	'Nellie Nuttall' ♀H3	CLoc CWVF EBak EKMF EPts MWar MWhe SLBF SPet SRiF
	'Neopolitan'	CLoc WPBF
	'Nettala'	CDoC SRiF WPBF
	'Neue Welt'	CWVF EBak EKMF
	'New Fascination' (d)	EBak
	'New Millennium'	LVER
	'Nice 'n' Easy' (d)	MBri MJac NBlu SRiF
	'Nicki's Findling'	CDoC CWVF EKMF EPts LCla MJac WPBF WRou
	'Nicky Veerman'	WPBF
	'Nicola'	EBak
	'Nicola Jane' (d)	CDoC CWVF EBak EKMF EPts LCla MBri MJac MWhe SHar SLBF SPet WPBF WRou
	'Nicola Storey'	EKMF
	'Nicolette'	CWVF MJac
	'Nielske Hakkens' **new**	WPBF
	'Nightingale' (d)	CLoc EBak WPBF
§	***nigricans***	CDoC EKMF
	'Nimue'	SRiF
	'Nina Wills'	EBak
	'Niobe' (d)	EBak
	'Niula'	CDoC EKMF LCla
	'No Name' (d)	EBak
	'Nonchalance'	LCla SLBF
	'Nora' (d)	WPBF
	'Norfolk Ivor' (d)	WPBF
	'Normandy Bell'	EBak SPet
	'North Cascades' (d)	WPBF
	'Northern Dancer' (d)	EKMF
	'Northumbrian Belle'	EBak SRiF
	'Northumbrian Pipes'	LCla
	'Northway'	CLoc CWVF MJac MWhe SPet
	'Norvell Gillespie' (d)	EBak
	'Novato'	EBak SRiF WPBF
	'Novella' (d)	CWVF EBak
	'Noyo Star' (d)	SRiF
	'Nuance'	LCla WPBF
	'Nunthorpe Gem' (d)	CDoC SRiF
	obconica	EKMF LCla
	'Obcylin'	CDoC EKMF LCla SRiF WRou
	'Obergärtner Koch'	CDoC EKMF LCla SLBF
	'Ocean Beach'	EPts SRiF
	'Oddfellow' (d)	CDoC SRiF WPBF
	'Oetnang' (d)	CTri SCoo
	'Old Dick'	SLBF
	'Old Somerset' (v)	CCCN LCla SRiF
	'Oldbury' **new**	SRiF
	'Oldbury Gem' **new**	SRiF
	'Oldbury Pearl' **new**	SRiF
	'Olive Moon' (d)	WPBF
	'Olive Smith'	CWVF EPts LCla MJac MWar MWhe SRiF WFFs WRou
	'Olympia'	EKMF MWhe
	'Olympic Lass' (d)	EBak
	'Omeomy' **new**	SRiF
	'Onward'	EKMF WFFs WPBF
§	'Oosje'	CDoC LCla SLBF SRiF WFFs WRou
	'Opalescent' (d)	CLoc CWVF
	'Orange Crush'	CCCN CLoc CWVF EBak MJac MWhe SPet
	'Orange Crystal'	CCCN CWVF EBak EKMF MJac MWhe SPet WPBF
	'Orange Drops'	CLoc CWVF EBak EKMF EPts MWhe SPet WPBF
	'Orange Flare'	CLoc CWVF EBak MWhe SLBF SRiF WRou
	'Orange King' (d)	CLoc CWVF EMan
	'Orange Mirage'	CLoc CWVF EBak LAst MWhe SPet WRou
	'Orangeblossom'	SLBF SRiF WPBF
	'Oranje Boven' **new**	WPBF
	'Oranje van Os'	CWVF MWhe
	'Orchid Flame'	WPBF
	'Orient Express'	CCCN CDoC CWVF LAst MJac MWhe WFFs WPBF WRou
	'Oriental Flame'	EKMF
	'Oriental Lace' **new**	SRiF
	'Oriental Sunrise'	CWVF MWhe
	'Ornamental Pearl'	CLoc CWVF EBak SRiF

'Orwell' (d)	CWVF WPBF
'Oso Sweet'	CWVF SRiF
'Other Fellow'	CWVF EBak EKMF EPts LCla MJac MWhe SLBF SPet SRiF WFFs WRou
'Oulton Empress'	SLBF
'Oulton Fairy'	SLBF WFFs
'Oulton Painted Lady' **new**	WRou
'Oulton Red Imp'	LCla SLBF
'Oulton Travellers Rest'	SLBF
'Our Boys' **new**	WPBF
'Our Darling'	CWVF MWhe SRiF
'Our Debbie'	MWar
'Our Nan' (d)	MJac
'Our Ted'	EBak EPts LCla SRiF WPBF
'Our William'	SLBF
'Overbecks'	see *F. magellanica* var. *molinae* 'Sharpitor'
'Overbecks Ruby'	GBuc
'Pabbe's Torreldöve'	WPBF
'Pacemaker'	MGos
'Pacific Grove' Greene	see *F.* 'Evelyn Steele Little'
'Pacific Grove' Niederholzer (d)	EBak
'Pacific Queen' (d)	CLoc EBak
'Pacquesa' (d)	CDoC CWVF EBak MWhe SPet SRiF
'Padre Pio' (d)	CWVF EBak MJac
pallescens	EKMF
'Paloma'^{PBR}	LAst WPBF
'Pam Plack'	EKMF LCla SLBF
'Pamela Knights' (d)	EBak
'Pam's People'	LCla
'Pan'	MWar SRiF
'Pan America' (d)	EBak
'Panache' (d)	LCla WPBF
'Pangea'	EKMF LCla
paniculata Υ^{H1+3}	CCCN CDoC CEnd CFee CRHN CWVF EBak EKMF EPts LCla SHFr SLBF SRiF WCru WPBF
'Panique'	CDoC LCla
'Pantaloons' (d)	EBak
'Pantomine Dame' (d)	CWVF
'Panylla Prince'	CDoC LCla SRiF WRou
'Papa Bleuss' (d)	CLoc CWVF EBak SRiF
'Papoose' (d)	CDoC EBak EKMF LCla SRiF WFFs
'Papua' (d)	SLBF WPBF
'Paramour'	SRiF
'Parasol'	WPBF
'Parkstone Centenary' (d)	CWVF
'Party Frock'	CDoC CLoc CWVF EBak LVER SPet
'Party Time' (d)	CWVF
parviflora misapplied	see *F.* x ***bacillaris***
parviflora Lindl.	see *F. lycioides* Andrews
'Pastel'	EBak
'Pat Meara'	CLoc EBak SRiF
'Patatin Pataton' (d)	WPBF
'Pathétique' (d)	CLoc
'Patience' (d)	CWVF EBak
'Patio King'	EBak EKMF
'Patio Princess' (d)	CCCN CWVF EPts LAst LSou MBri MWhe NBlu SSea WFFs WGor
'Patricia' Wood	EBak
'Patricia Bervoets' (d)	WPBF
'Patricia Hodge'	WRou
'Pat's Smile'	SLBF
'Patty Evans' (d)	CWVF EBak
'Patty Sue' (d)	CDoC MBri MWar SRiF WFFs WRou
'Paul Berry'	EKMF LCla WPBF
'Paul Cambon' (d)	EBak EKMF SRiF
'Paul Kennes'	EKMF WPBF
'Paul Pini' **new**	SRiF
'Paul Roe' (d)	MJac
'Paul Storey'	CDoC EKMF WPBF
'Paula Jane' (d)	CCCN CDoC CLoc CWVF LAst LCla MBri MJac MWar MWhe SLBF SRGP WGor WPBF WRou
'Pauline Rawlins' (d)	CLoc EBak
'Paulus'	WPBF
'Peace' (d)	EBak
'Peachy' (d)	CCCN CDoC CLoc EKMF LAst MJac SCoo WPBF
'Peachy Keen' (d)	EBak WPBF
'Peacock' (d)	CLoc
'Pee Wee Rose'	EBak EKMF
'Peggy Belle G'	EKMF LCla
'Peggy Burford'	LCla
Peggy = 'Goetzpeg'^{PBR} (Shadowdancer Series)	CDoC LAst LSou SCoo
'Peggy King'	CDoC EBak EKMF MWhe SPet
'Peloria' (d)	CLoc EBak
'Pennine'	MBri
'People's Princess'	MJac
'Peper Harow'	EBak SRiF
'Pepi' (d)	CLoc CWVF EBak SPet SRiF
'Peppermint Candy' (d)	CWVF EKMF LAst MJac
'Peppermint Stick' (d)	CDoC CLoc CWVF EBak EKMF EMan LRHS MBri MWhe SPet WRou
'Perky Pink' (d)	CWVF EBak EPts MWhe SPet SRiF
'Perry Park'	CWVF EBak MBri MJac SRiF
'Perry's Jumbo'	NBir NPer
perscandens	CPLG EKMF LCla MWhe
'Personality' (d)	EBak
'Peter Bellerby' (d)	EKMF
'Peter Bielby' (d)	CWVF EKMF MWar SRiF
'Peter Boor'	SLBF
'Peter Crookes'	CWVF SRiF
'Peter Grange'	EBak
'Peter Hornby' **new**	SRiF
'Peter James' (d)	EKMF SRiF
'Peter Pan'	CWVF
'Peter Peeters' (d) **new**	WPBF
'Peter Shaffery'	LCla
petiolaris	CDoC LCla WFFs
- Berry 3142	EKMF
'Petit Four'	CWVF SRiF WPBF
'Petite' (d)	EBak
'Petra van Britsom' **new**	SLBF
'Petronella' (d)	SRiF
'Pfaffenhutchen' (d) **new**	WPBF
'Phaidra'	CDoC LCla
'Pharaoh'	CLoc
'Phénoménal' (d)	CWVF EBak EKMF LRHS SRiF
'Philippe'	WPBF
'Phillip Taylor'	MJac
'Phryne' (d)	EBak EKMF SRiF
'Phyllis' (d) Υ^{H4}	CAgr CDoC CLoc CWVF EBak EKMF EPts LCla MHar MJac MWhe SHar SLBF SPet SRGP WFFs WFar WRou
'Piet G. Vergeer'	WRou
'Piet Heemskerk'	WPBF
'Piet van der Sande'	CDoC LCla MWar
'Pijekna Helena'	WPBF
pilaloensis	EKMF
x ***pilcopata***	LCla
'Pinch Me' (d)	CWVF EBak LVER SPet
'Pink Aurora'	CLoc
'Pink Ballet Girl' (d)	CLoc EBak
'Pink Bon Accorde'	CDoC CLoc CWVF WPBF
'Pink Cloud'	CLoc EBak SRiF
'Pink Cornet'	LCla SRiF
'Pink Darling'	CLoc EBak MWhe
'Pink Dessert'	EBak
'Pink Domino' (d)	EKMF
'Pink Fairy' (d)	EBak SPet
'Pink Fandango' (d)	CLoc
'Pink Fantasia'	CCCN CDoC CLoc CWVF EBak EKMF EPts LAst LCla MJac MWar MWhe SRiF WPBF

	'Pink Flamingo' (d)	CLoc EBak
	'Pink Galore' (d)	CCCN CLoc CWVF EBak EKMF EMan LAst LCla LVER MBri MJac MWhe SPet
	'Pink Goon' (d)	CDoC EKMF LCla LRHS SLBF SRiF WPBF
	'Pink Jade'	CWVF EBak
	'Pink la Campanella'	CWVF EBak EMan LAst MBri MWar MWhe WBVN WFFs WGor
	'Pink Lace' (d)	SPet
	'Pink Lady' Ryle-Atkinson	MWhe
	'Pink Marshmallow' (d) 𝕐H1+3	CCCN CDoC CLoc CWVF EBak EKMF EMan LAst LCla LVER MJac MWar SLBF SSea WPBF
	'Pink Panther' (d)	EKMF MJac WFFs
	'Pink Pearl' Bright (d)	EBak EKMF LVER
	'Pink Poppet'	EKMF
	'Pink Profusion'	EBak
	'Pink Quartet' (d)	CLoc CWVF EBak SPet SRiF
	'Pink Rain'	CWVF EKMF MJac WFFs WRou
	'Pink Slippers'	CLoc
	'Pink Spangles'	CCCN CWVF EMan MBri
	'Pink Temptation'	CLoc CWVF EBak
	'Pink Trumpet'	WPBF
	'Pinkmost' (d)	EKMF
	'Pinocchio'	WPBF
	'Pinto de Blue' (d)	EKMF MWar SRiF
	'Pinwheel' (d)	CLoc EBak SRiF
	'Piper' (d)	CDoC CWVF SRiF
	'Piper's Vale'	CCCN LAst MJac SLBF SRiF
	'Pippa Rolt'	EKMF EPts
	'Pirbright'	CWVF EKMF
	'Pixie'	CDoC CLoc CWVF EBak EKMF MJac SLBF SPet
	'Playford'	CWVF EBak SRiF
	'Plenty'	EBak
	'Plumb Bob' (d)	CWVF
	'Poermenneke'	LCla
	'Pol Jannie' (d)	WPBF
	'Pole Star'	SRiF
	'Polynesia' (d)	WPBF
	'Pop Whitlock' (v)	CWVF EKMF SPet WPBF
	'Popely Pride' (d)	WPBF
	'Poppet'	CWVF
	'Popsie Girl'	MWar SLBF WPBF WRou
	'Port Arthur' (d)	EBak SRiF
	'Postiljon'	CCCN CWVF EBak MJac SPet WFFs WPBF
	'Powder Puff' ambig.	CWVF MBri SPet
	'Powder Puff' Hodges (d)	CLoc LVER
	'Präsident Walter Morio'	WPBF
	'Prawn Cracker' **new**	MPop
I	'Prelude' Kennett (d)	EBak EKMF
	'Prelude' Blackwell	CLoc
	'President'	CDoC EBak EKMF
	'President B.W. Rawlins'	EBak SRiF
§	'President Elliot'	EKMF MWhe SRiF
	'President George Bartlett' (d)	CCCN CDoC CLoc EKMF EPts LAst LCla MJac MWar MWhe SLBF WFFs WPBF WRou
	'President Jim Muil'	SLBF WPBF
	'President Joan Morris' (d)	EKMF SLBF
	'President Leo Boullemier'	CDoC CWVF EBak EKMF LCla MJac SPet
	'President Margaret Slater'	CLoc CWVF EBak EMan LCla MWhe SPet
	'President Moir' (d)	SLBF WPBF
	'President Norman Hobbs'	CWVF EKMF
	'President Roosevelt' (d)	CDoC
	'President Stanley Wilson'	CWVF EBak EPts SPet
	'President Wilf Sharp' (d)	SRiF
	'Preston Guild' 𝕐H1+3	CDoC CLoc CWVF EBak EKMF LRHS MWar MWhe NPer SLBF SPet SRiF WFFs WPBF WRou
	'Pride of Ipswich'	SRiF WPBF
	'Pride of Roualeyn'	WRou
	'Pride of the West'	EBak EKMF
	'Prince of Orange'	CLoc CWVF EBak EKMF WPBF
	'Prince of Peace' (d)	SRiF
	'Prince Syray' **new**	SRiF
	'Princess Dollar'	see *F.* 'Dollar Prinzessin'
	'Princess of Bath' (d)	CLoc
	'Princess Pamela' (d)	SLBF
	'Princessita'	CWVF EBak EMan MWhe SPet
	procumbens	CBcs CCCN CDoC CHEx CLoc CPLG CStu CTrC CWVF EBak ECou EKMF EPts EShb GGar IDee ITim LCla MWhe NWCA SHFr SLBF SRiF SSea SWal WDyG WRou
	- 'Argentea'	see *F. procumbens* 'Wirral'
	- 'Variegata'	see *F. procumbens* 'Wirral'
§	- 'Wirral' (v)	CDoC CHEx CLoc CStu CTrC EKMF ELon EQua SRiF WBor WFFs WPrP
	'Prodigy'	see *F.* 'Enfant Prodigue'
	'Profusion' ambig.	MWhe
I	'Profusion' Wood **new**	SRiF
	'Prosperity' (d) 𝕐H3	CDoC CLoc CWVF EBak EKMF ENot EPfP EPts LCla LRHS LVER MJac MRav MWhe NDlv SPet WPBF WRou
	'Pumila'	CPLG CWib EKMF ELan EPfP EPts SLBF SPer SPet WRou
	'Purbeck Mist' (d)	CWVF EKMF
	'Purperklokje'	CWVF EBak WPBF
	'Purple Ann'	EKMF
	'Purple Emperor' (d)	CLoc
	'Purple Heart' (d)	CLoc EBak
	'Purple Lace'	SRiF
	'Purple Patch'	MBri WRou
	'Purple Pride'	MBri
	'Purple Rain'	CLoc EKMF EPts LCla WRou
	'Purple Showers'	SRiF
	'Purple Splendour' (d)	CDoC SRiF
	'Pussy Cat'	CLoc CWVF EBak SRiF
	'Putney Pride'	EPts
	'Put's Folly'	CWVF EBak MJac SLBF SPet WFFs
	putumayensis	EBak EKMF SRiF
	'Quasar' (d)	CCCN CDoC CLoc CWVF EKMF EPts LAst LCla LSou LVER MJac MWhe SLBF SPet WBVN WPBF WRou
	'Queen Elizabeth II'	EKMF LCla
	'Queen Mabs'	EBak
	'Queen Mary'	CLoc EBak EKMF WPBF
	'Queen of Bath' (d)	EBak
	'Queen of Derby' (d)	CWVF
	'Queen Victoria' Smith (d)	EKMF
	'Queen's Park' (d)	EBak
	'Query'	EBak SRiF
	'R.A.F.' (d)	CCCN CLoc CWVF EBak EKMF EPts LCla MWar SLBF SPet WFFs WPBF
	'Rachel Craig' (d)	MWar
	'Rachel Sinton' (d)	EMan LAst MBri SRGP WRou
	'Radcliffe Beauty'	MWhe
	'Radcliffe Bedder' (d)	EKMF
	'Radings Gerda'	LCla SLBF
	'Radings Inge'	LCla
	'Radings Juma'	WPBF
	'Radings Karin'	CDoC WPBF
	'Radings Mapri'	WPBF
	'Radings Michelle'	CWVF
	'Rahnee'	CWVF SRiF
	'Rainbow'	CWVF
	'Raintree Legend' (d)	SRiF
	'Ralph Oliver' (d)	WPBF
	'Ralph's Delight' (d)	CCCN CWVF EKMF LAst SRiF WPBF
	'Rambling Rose' (d)	CLoc CWVF EBak MJac

'Rams Royal' (d)	CDoC CWVF SRiF
'Raspberry' (d)	CLoc CWVF EBak MWhe
'Raspberry Sweet' (d)	CWVF
'Rasputin' (d) **new**	WPBF
'Ratae Beauty'	CWVF
'Ratatouille' (d)	EKMF SRiF
ravenii	LCla
'Ravenslaw'	EKMF
'Ray Redfern'	CWVF
'Razzle Dazzle' (d)	EBak
'Reading Show' (d)	CWVF EKMF EPts SRiF
'Rebecca Williamson' (d)	CWVF MJac MWhe
'Rebeka Sinton'	CLoc EBak MBri
'Red Ace' (d)	WPBF
'Red Jacket' (d)	CWVF EBak
'Red Petticoat'	CWVF
'Red Rain'	CWVF LCla SRiF WRou
'Red Ribbons' (d)	EBak
'Red Rover'	MWar SRiF
'Red Rum' (d)	SPet
'Red Shadows' (d)	CLoc CWVF EBak
'Red Spider'	CCCN CLoc CWVF EBak EKMF EMan LAst MWar MWhe SCoo SPet WGor WPBF
'Red Sunlight'	WPBF
'Red Wing'	CLoc
'Reflexa'	see *F.* x *bacillaris* 'Reflexa'
'Reg Gubler'	SLBF
'Regal'	CLoc
'Regal Robe' (d)	CDoC
regia var. ***alpestris***	see *F. alpestris*
- subsp. ***regia***	CDoC LCla SRiF WPBF
- - Berry 77-87	EKMF
- - Berry 87-87	EKMF
- - Berry 4450	EKMF
- subsp. ***reitzii***	CDoC LCla
- - Berry 04-87	EKMF
- - Berry 67A-87	EKMF
- subsp. ***serrae***	CDoC
- - Berry 11-87	EKMF
- - Berry 49-87	EKMF
- - Berry 4504	EKMF
'Remember Eric'	EKMF WPBF
'Remembrance' (d)	EKMF EPts LCla SLBF
'Remy Kind' (d)	SRiF WPBF
'Rene Schwab'	LCla
'Renee'	WPBF
'Renee-Madeleine'	WPBF
'Rensina'	WPBF
'Requiem'	CLoc
'Reverend Doctor Brown' (d)	EBak
'Reverend Elliott'	see *F.* 'President Elliot'
'Revival' **new**	SRiF
I 'Rhapsody' Blackwell (d)	CLoc
'Ria V.D. Leest'	WPBF
'Rianne Foks'	SRiF WPBF
'Riant' (d)	SRiF
'Riccartonii' ♀H3	More than 30 suppliers
'Richard John' (v)	SRiF
'Ridestar' (d)	CLoc CWVF EBak EMan MWhe SRiF
'Rijs 2001'	MWar SLBF WPBF
'Rina Felix'	WPBF
'Ringwood Market' (d)	CWVF EPts MJac SCoo SPet SRiF WPBF
'Rise and Shine'	WPBF
'Rita Mary' **new**	SRiF
'Riverside' (d) **new**	SRiF
rivularis	WPBF
'Robbie'	EKMF WPBF
'Robert Hall' **new**	WPBF
'Rocket'	WPBF
'Rocket Fire' (d)	CWVF LAst MJac WPBF
'Rodeo'	WPBF

'Roesse Algenib' (d)	WPBF
'Roesse Algieba' (d)	WPBF
'Roesse Alsuhail' (d) **new**	WPBF
'Roesse Betelgeuze' (d) **new**	WPBF
'Roesse Blacky'	CDoC EKMF WPBF
'Roesse Esli'	WPBF
'Roesse Femke'	WPBF
'Roesse Grafias' (d)	WPBF
'Roesse Himalia' (d)	WPBF
'Roesse Marie'	WPBF
'Roesse Mizar' (d) **new**	WPBF
'Roesse Nash' (d)	WPBF
'Roesse Peacock' (d)	WPBF
'Roesse Procyon'	WPBF
'Roesse Rhea' (d) **new**	WPBF
'Roesse Skat' (d)	WPBF
'Roesse Thurban' (d)	WPBF
'Roesse Titan' (d)	WPBF
'Roesse Tricolor'	WPBF
'Roesse Wega'	WPBF
'Roesse Zibai' (d)	WPBF
'Roger de Cooker'	CLoc MWar SLBF WPBF
'Rohees Alioth' (d)	WPBF
'Rohees Azha'	WPBF
'Rohees Canopus'	WPBF
'Rohees Diadem' (d) **new**	WPBF
'Rohees Emperor' (d)	WPBF WRou
'Rohees Grumiun' (d)	WPBF
'Rohees Heka'	WPBF
'Rohees Heza' **new**	WPBF
'Rohees Izar'	WPBF
'Rohees King'	WPBF
'Rohees Ksora' (d)	WPBF
'Rohees Lava' **new**	SLBF
'Rohees Leada' (d)	SLBF
'Rohees Maasym'	WPBF
'Rohees Metallah'	WPBF
'Rohees Minkar'	WPBF
'Rohees Mintaka' (d)	WPBF
'Rohees Mira'	WPBF
'Rohees Naos'	WPBF
'Rohees Nekkar'	WPBF
'Rohees New Millennium' (d)	SLBF SRiF WPBF
'Rohees Nunki'	WPBF
'Rohees Princess'	WPBF
'Rohees Prins' (d)	WPBF
'Rohees Queen'	WPBF
'Rohees Rana'	WPBF
'Rohees Reda' (d)	WPBF
'Rohees Rialto'	WPBF
'Rohees Rotanev'	WPBF
'Rohees Sadir'	WPBF
'Rohees Segin'	WPBF
'Rohees Tethys' (d) **new**	SLBF
'Rohees Vega'	WPBF
'Rohees Zaurak'	WPBF
'Roland von Bremen' **new**	WPBF
'Rolla' (d)	CWVF EBak EKMF WPBF
'Rolt's Bride' (d)	EKMF SRiF
'Rolt's Ruby' (d)	CWVF EKMF SRiF
'Roman City' (d)	CLoc SRiF
'Romance' (d)	CWVF
'Romany Rose'	CLoc
'Ron Chambers Love'	MWar
'Ron Ewart'	EKMF MWhe WRou
'Ron Holmes' **new**	SRiF
'Ronald L. Lockerbie' (d)	CLoc CWVF EKMF
'Rondo' **new**	MJac
'Ron's Ruby'	LCla MWhe WPBF
'Roos Breytenbach'	CCCN CDoC EKMF LAst LCla MJac SRiF WPBF WRou
'Rosamunda'	CLoc
'Rose Ample' **new**	WPBF

'Rose Aylett' (d)	EBak
'Rose Bower'	WPBF
'Rose Bradwardine' (d)	EBak
'Rose Churchill' (d)	MBri MJac
'Rose Fantasia'	CCCN CDoC CLoc CWVF EKMF EPts LAst LCla MJac MWar MWhe SLBF WPBF
'Rose Marie' (d)	CLoc
'Rose of Castile'	CDoC CLoc EBak EKMF LCla LRHS MJac MWhe WFFs WRou
'Rose of Castile Improved' ♀H4	CWVF EBak EKMF LCla MJac MWar SPet SRiF WPBF
'Rose of Denmark'	CCCN CLoc CWVF EBak LAst MBri MJac MWar MWhe NBlu SCoo SPet SWal WGor
'Rose Reverie' (d)	EBak
'Rose Winston' (d)	LAst SCoo
rosea Ruíz & Pav.	see *F. lycioides* Andrews
rosea misapplied	see *F.* 'Globosa'
'Rosebud' (d)	EBak
'Rosecroft Beauty' (d)	CWVF EBak MWhe SRiF
'Rosella' **new**	SLBF
Rosella = 'Goetzrose'PBR (Shadowdancer Series)	WPBF
'Rosemarie Higham'	CCCN MJac SCoo
'Rosemary Day'	CLoc
'Rosemoor' **new**	SRiF
'Roslyn Lowe' (d)	CDoC
'Roswitha'	SLBF WPBF
'Rosy Bows'	CWVF
'Rosy Frills' (d)	CWVF MJac MWhe
'Rosy Morn' (d)	CLoc EBak
'Rosy Ruffles' (d)	EKMF
'Rothbury Beauty' **new**	SRiF
'Rough Silk'	CLoc CWVF EBak
'Roy Castle' (d)	CWVF
'Roy Sinton'	LAst
'Roy Walker' (d)	CLoc CWVF LVER
'Royal Academy' **new**	EPts
'Royal and Ancient'	CWVF WPBF
'Royal Mosaic' (d)	CCCN CDoC CWVF LAst MJac SRiF
'Royal Orchid'	EBak
'Royal Parade' (d) **new**	SLBF WRou
'Royal Purple' (d)	EBak EKMF MBri
'Royal Ruby' **new**	SRiF
'Royal Serenade' (d)	CWVF
'Royal Touch' (d)	EBak
'Royal Velvet' (d) ♀H3	CCCN CLoc CWVF EBak EKMF EMan EPts LAst LCla LVER MJac MWar MWhe NBlu SLBF SPet WRou
'Royal Welsh'	WRou
'Rubra Grandiflora'	CWVF EBak EKMF LCla SLBF SRiF WRou
'Ruby Wedding' (d)	CWVF EKMF SLBF
'Ruddigore'	CWVF
'Ruffles' (d)	CWVF EBak
§ 'Rufus' ♀H3-4	CDoC CLoc CWVF EBak EKMF EPfP EPts LCla LRHS MHar MJac MWar MWhe NDlv SLBF SPet WFar WRou
'Rufus the Red'	see *F.* 'Rufus'
'Rummens Trots'	WPBF
'Ruth Brazewell' (d)	CLoc
'Ruth King' (d)	CWVF EBak
'Sabrina'	WRou
'Sailor'	EPts WFFs
'Salmon Cascade'	CWVF EBak EKMF EMan EPts LCla MJac MWhe SLBF WPBF WRou
'Salmon Glow'	CWVF MJac MWhe
'Salmon Perfection' **new**	WPBF
'Salmon Queen'	WPBF
'Sam' (d) **new**	WPBF
'Sam Sheppard' **new**	SLBF
'Samba'	LAst
'Sammy Girl' **new**	SRiF
'Samson' (d/v)	EBak
'San Diego' (d)	CWVF
'San Francisco'	EBak
'San Leandro' (d)	EBak
'San Mateo' (d)	EBak
§ ***sanctae-rosae***	CDoC EBak EKMF LCla SRiF
'Sandboy'	CWVF EBak
'Sanguinea'	EKMF
'Sanrina'	CDoC EKMF
'Santa Cruz' (d)	CWVF EBak EKMF MWhe SLBF SWal
'Santa Lucia' (d)	CLoc EBak
'Santa Monica' (d)	EBak
'Santorini Sunset'	WPBF
'Sapphire' (d)	EBak
'Sara Helen' (d)	CLoc EBak
'Sarah Eliza' (d)	CCCN SCoo
'Sarah Jane' (d)	EBak
'Sarah Louise'	CWVF
'Sarina' **new**	SRiF
'Sarong' (d)	EBak
'Saskia van der Heijden' (d)	WPBF
'Satellite'	CLoc CWVF EBak EKMF SPet WPBF
'Saturnus'	CWVF EBak SPet
scabriuscula	CDoC EKMF LCla
scandens	see *F. decussata* Ruíz & Pav.
'Scarcity'	CDoC CWVF EBak EKMF MWhe SPet SRiF SWal
'Scarlet Cascade'	EKMF
'Schiller' ambig.	EKMF WPBF
'Schimpens Glorie' (d)	WPBF
'Schlosz Bentheim'	WPBF
'Schneeball' (d)	CDoC EBak EKMF
'Schneewitcher'	CDoC EKMF EPts
'Schneewittchen' ambig.	WPBF
'Schneewittchen' Hoech	EKMF
'Schneewittchen' Klein	EBak
'Schönbrunner Schuljubiläum'	EBak
'Schone Hanaurin' **new**	SLBF
'Schöne Wilhelmine'	see *F.* 'Die Schöne Wilhelmine'
'Scotch Heather' (d)	CWVF
'Sea Shell' (d)	CWVF EBak
'Seaforth'	EBak EKMF SRiF
'Sealand Prince'	CDoC CWVF EKMF LCla SRiF
'Sebastopol' (d)	CLoc
'Senna Krekels' (d)	WPBF
'Seppe'	WPBF
serratifolia Hook.	see *F. austromontana*
serratifolia Ruíz & Pav.	see *F. denticulata*
sessilifolia	EKMF
'Seventh Heaven' (d)	CCCN CLoc CWVF LAst MJac SCoo
'Shady Blue'	CWVF
'Shangri-La' (d)	EBak
'Shanley'	CWVF
'Sharon Allsop' (d)	CWVF MWhe SRiF
'Sharon Caunt' (d)	EKMF
'Sharonelle'	EKMF
'Sharpitor'	see *F. magellanica* var. *molinae* 'Sharpitor'
'Shauna Lindsay'	LCla WPBF
'Shawna Ree'	EKMF
'Sheila Crooks' (d)	CWVF EBak EMan MJac
'Sheila Kirby'	CWVF MJac
'Sheila Mary' (d)	EKMF
'Sheila Steele' (d)	CWVF
'Sheila's Love'	MJac
'Shelford'	CDoC CLoc CWVF EBak EKMF EMan EPts MJac MWar MWhe SLBF WFFs WPBF WRou
'Shelley Lyn' (d)	SRiF
'Shirley Halladay' (d)	EKMF LCla WPBF

	'Shirley'[PBR] (Shadowdancer Series)	CDoC LAst LSou SCoo
	'Shooting Star' (d)	EBak
	'Showfire'	EBak
	'Showtime' (d)	CWVF
	'Shy Lady' (d)	SPet WPBF
	'Siberoet'	LCla SLBF WPBF
	'Sierra Blue' (d)	CLoc CWVF EBak
	'Silver Anniversary' (d)	EKMF
	'Silver Dawn' (d)	EKMF
	'Silver Dollar'	MWhe WPBF
	'Silver King'	WPBF
	'Silverdale'	CDoC EKMF EPts MWhe
	'Simmari'	WPBF
	'Simon J. Rowell'	EKMF LCla SRiF
	'Simone Delhommeau'	WPBF
	'Simple Simon'	SRiF
	simplicicaulis	CDoC EBak EKMF LCla
	'Sincerity' (d)	CLoc
	'Sint Bartholomeus' (d)	WPBF
	'Sinton's Standard'	MBri
	'Siobhan'	CWVF
	'Siobhan Evans' (d)	MWar SLBF
	'Sipke Arjen'	WRou
	'Sir Alfred Ramsey'	CWVF EBak MWhe
	'Sir Matt Busby' (d)	EKMF EPts LAst MJac WRou
	'Sir Steve Redgrave' (d)	MJac
	'Sir Thomas Allen'	SLBF
	'Siren' Baker (d)	EBak
	'Sissy Sue'	WPBF
	'Sister Ann Haley'	EKMF EPts
	'Sister Sister' (d)	SLBF WPBF
	'Six Squadron'	EKMF
	'Sjan Schilders' (d) **new**	WPBF
	skutchiana	CPLG SMrm
	'Sleepy'	EPts SPet WPBF
	'Sleigh Bells'	CDoC CLoc CWVF EBak EKMF MWhe SPet
	'Small Pipes'	CWVF EKMF LCla SRiF
	'Smokey Mountain' (d)	MJac MWar
	'Smouldering Fires'	WPBF
	'Sneezy'	EPts MWhe
	'Snow Burner' (d)	CCCN CDoC CLoc CWVF LAst WPBF
	'Snow White' (d)	SPet
	'Snowbird' (d)	SLBF WPBF
§	'Snowcap' (d) 🏆H3-4	CBgR CCCN CDoC CLoc CWVF EBak EKMF EPts LAst LCla LVER MAsh MBri MGos MJac MWar MWhe NBlu NPer SLBF SPet SPla WFFs WFar WRou
	'Snowdon' (d)	CWVF
	'Snowdonia'	WRou
	'Snowdrift' ambig.	WPBF
	'Snowdrift' Colville (d)	CLoc
	'Snowdrift' Kennett (d)	EBak
	'Snowfall'	CWVF
	'Snowfire' (d)	CLoc CWVF EKMF MWhe SCoo
	'Snowflake'	EKMF LCla SLBF WBor WRou
	'Snowstorm' (d)	SPet WPBF
	'So Big' (d)	EKMF SRiF
	'Son of Thumb' 🏆H4	CDoC CLoc CWVF EKMF EMan EPfP EPts LAst MAsh MBar MGos MJac MWhe NDlv SIng SLBF SLim SPet WFar WPBF WRou
	'Sonata' (d)	CLoc CWVF EBak
	'Sophie Louise'	CWVF EKMF EPts MWar WPBF WRou
	'Sophie's Silver Lining'	MJac
	'Sophie's Surprise'	WPBF
	'Sophisticated Lady' (d)	CLoc CWVF EBak EKMF EPts SPet
	'Soroptimist International'	WRou
	'South Gate' (d)	CLoc CWVF EBak EKMF EMan EPts LAst MBri MJac MWar MWhe NBlu SPet
	'South Seas' (d)	EBak
	'Southern Pride'	SLBF
	'Southlanders'	EBak
	'Southwell Minster'	EKMF
	'Space Shuttle'	CLoc EKMF LCla MWhe SLBF SRiF
	'Sparky'	CWVF EPts LCla MWar MWhe SRiF WPBF WRou
§	'Speciosa'	CDoC EBak EKMF LCla MWhe SRiF SWal WRou
	'Spion Kop' (d)	CCCN CWVF EBak EKMF LAst MWhe NBlu SPet WGor
§	***splendens*** 🏆H1+3	CCCN CDoC CLoc EBak EKMF IDee LCla NPer SLBF SRiF WRou
	– B&SWJ 10469	WCru
	– 'Karl Hartweg'	CDoC
	'Spring Bells' (d)	MWhe
	'Squadron Leader' (d)	CWVF EBak EPts
	'Square Peg' (d)	SRiF
	'Stad Genk' (d) **new**	WPBF
	'Stadt Telc' **new**	SLBF
	'Stan'	WPBF
	'Stanley Cash' (d)	CLoc CWVF EKMF LVER MWar SPet
	'Star Wars'	CLoc EPts MBri MJac MWar SRiF SVil WPBF WRou
	'Stardust'	CWVF EBak MJac MWhe
	'Starlite' (d)	WPBF
	'Steirerblut'	SRiF WPBF
	'Stella Ann'	CWVF EBak EPts LCla SRiF WPBF
	'Stella Didden' (d)	WPBF
	'Stella Marina' (d)	CLoc EBak
	'Stephanie' **new**	WPBF
	'Sterretje'	WPBF
	'Stewart Taylor'	MJac
	steyermarkii DG 1057	EKMF
	'Stolze von Berlin' (d) **new**	SRiF
	'Stoney Creek' (d)	SRiF
	'Storeytime'	EKMF
	'Straat Fiji'	LCla
	'Straat Futami' **new**	WPBF
	'Straat Kobi'	LCla
	'Straat Magelhaen'	LCla
	'Straat Moji'	WPBF
	'Straat Napier'	WPBF
	'Straat of Plenty'	LCla SLBF
	'Straat Susanna D Diykman'	LCla
	'Straat Van Diemen'	LCla
	'Strawberry Delight' (d)	CLoc CWVF EBak EKMF MJac MWhe SPet
	'Strawberry Fizz'	WPBF
	'Strawberry Sundae' (d)	CLoc CWVF EBak
	'Strawberry Supreme' (d)	EKMF
	'String of Pearls'	CLoc CWVF EKMF LCla MJac SLBF SPet
	'Stuart Joe'	CWVF EKMF
*	***subparamosis*** Green 1006	EKMF
	'Sue' SLBF	
	'Sugar Almond' (d)	CWVF
	'Sugar Blues' (d)	CDoC EBak
	'Summer Bells'	WPBF
	'Summerdaffodil'	WPBF
	'Summerwood' (d)	SRiF
	(Sunbeam Series) 'Sunbeam Ernie' **new**	WPBF
	– 'Sunbeam Hillary' **new**	WPBF
	'Sunkissed' (d)	EBak
	'Sunningdale'	CDoC CWVF LCla WPBF
	'Sunny'	SRiF
	'Sunny Smiles'	CWVF EKMF SPet SRiF
	'Sunray' (v)	CLoc CWVF EBak EKMF ENot GGar LRHS MAsh MWar MWat NBlu NEgg NMRc SCoo SLim SPla SPoG SWal
	'Sunset'	CLoc CWVF EBak MWhe SPer

	'Supernova'	WPBF
	'Supersport' (d)	WPBF
	'Superstar'	CWVF EPts WPBF
	'Susan' (d)	LAst
	'Susan Drew'	SLBF
	'Susan Ford' (d)	CWVF SPet SRiF
	'Susan Gasaway'	WPBF
	'Susan Green'	CWVF EBak EKMF EMan MJac MWar MWhe SPet
	'Susan McMaster'	CLoc
	'Susan Olcese' (d)	CWVF EBak
	'Susan Skeen'	MJac WPBF
	'Susan Travis'	CLoc CWVF EBak EKMF MAsh MWhe SPet SRiF WPBF
	'Susanna D. Dijkman' **new**	WPBF
	'Suzanna' **new**	WPBF
	'Swanley Gem' ♀H3	CLoc CWVF EBak EKMF MWhe SLBF SPet WRou
	'Swanley Pendula'	CLoc
	'Swanley Yellow'	CWVF EBak
	'Sweet Leilani' (d)	CLoc EBak
	'Sweet Sarah'	SLBF
	'Sweet Sixteen' (d)	CLoc
I	'Sweetheart' van Wieringen	EBak
	'Swingtime' (d) ♀H3	CCCN CLoc CWVF EBak EKMF EMan EPts LAst LCla LVER MGos MJac MWar MWhe NBlu SLBF SPet WPBF
	'S'Wonderful' (d)	CLoc EBak
	sylvatica misapplied	see *F. nigricans*
	'Sylvia' Veitch (d) **new**	SRiF
	'Sylvia Barker'	CWVF LCla MWar WFFs WRou
	'Sylvia Noad'	MWar
	'Sylvia Rose' (d)	CWVF SRiF
	'Sylvia's Choice'	EBak
	'Sylvy'	MWhe
	'Symphony'	CLoc CWVF EBak
	'T.S.J.'	LCla
	'Taatje'	WPBF
	'Taco'	CDoC LCla
	'Taddle'	CWVF EMan SLBF SPet
	'Taffeta Bow' (d)	CLoc EKMF LVER
	'Taffy'	EBak
	'Tahoe'	WPBF
	'Tamerus Dream' (d)	WPBF
	'Tamerus Hoatzin'	WPBF
	'Tamerus Hop' (d)	WPBF
	'Tamerus Nandoe' **new**	WPBF
	'Tamerus Toerako'	WPBF
	'Tamworth'	CLoc CWVF EBak MJac
	'Tangerine'	CLoc CWVF EBak MWhe WRou
	'Tanja's Snowball'	WPBF
	'Tantalising Tracy' (d)	WPBF
	'Tanya'	CLoc EKMF SPet
	'Tanya Bridger' (d)	EBak
	'Tarra Valley'	LCla MWhe SRiF
	'Task Force'	CWVF SRiF
	'Tasty Tracey'	SRiF
	'Taudens Heil' (d)	WPBF
	'Tausendschön' (d)	CLoc WPBF
	'Ted Heath' (d)	WPBF
	'Ted Perry' (d)	CWVF
	'Ted's Tribute'	EKMF WPBF
	'Temptation' ambig.	CWVF SPet
	'Temptation' Peterson	CLoc EBak
	'Tenderlight'	WPBF
	'Teneriffe Magic'	WPBF
	'Tennessee Waltz' (d) ♀H3	CDoC CLoc CWVF EBak EKMF EMan EPts LRHS LVER MJac MWar MWhe SLBF SPer SPet SWal WEas WFFs WRou
	tetradactyla misapplied	see *F.* x *bacillaris*
	tetradactyla Lindl.	see *F. encliandra* subsp. *tetradactyla*
	'Texas Longhorn' (d)	CLoc CWVF EBak EKMF

	'Texas Star'	WPBF
	'Thalia' ♀H1+3	CCCN CDoC CDul CHEx CHrt CLoc CWVF EBak EKMF EPfP EPts LAst LCla LRHS LVER MBri MJac MWar MWhe NPri SLBF SPer SPet SPla SPoG SRiF SWal WEas WPBF WRou
	'Thamar'	CDoC CLoc CWVF EPts MWhe WPBF WRou
	'That's It' (d)	EBak
	'The Aristocrat' (d)	CLoc EBak
	'The Boys'	WPBF
	'The Cannons' (d) **new**	SRiF
§	'The Doctor'	CLoc CWVF EBak MWhe
	'The Jester' (d)	EBak
	'The Madame' (d)	CWVF EBak
	'The Tarns'	CWVF EBak EKMF NCiC SRiF
	'Théroigne de Méricourt'	EBak EKMF SRiF
	'Thilco'	CDoC EKMF
	'This England' (d)	SRiF
	'Thistle Hill' (d)	EKMF
	'Thomas' (d)	EPts
	'Thomas Pips' **new**	WPBF
	'Thomas Ritchie'	LCla SLBF
	'Thompsonii'	see *F. magellanica* 'Thompsonii'
	'Thornley's Hardy'	EKMF EMan MRav SPet SRiF
	'Three Cheers'	CLoc EBak
	'Three Counties'	EBak
	'Thunderbird' (d)	CLoc CWVF EBak
	thymifolia	CWVF EAlp GCra GQui LHop LRHS MWgw SHFr SHGN WKif
	- subsp. ***minimiflora***	EKMF LCla
	- subsp. ***thymifolia***	CDoC EKMF LCla
	'Tiara' (d)	EBak
	'Tickled Pink'	MWar WRou
	'Tiffany' Reedstrom (d)	EBak
	'Tijl Uilenspiegel'	WPBF
	'Tilla Dohmen' (d)	WPBF
	tillettiana	EKMF
	'Tillingbourne' (d)	SLBF
	'Tillmouth Lass'	WPBF
	Tilly = 'Goetztil'PBR (Shadowdancer Series)	LAst
	'Timlin Brened'	CWVF EBak MWhe SRiF
	'Timothy Titus'	LCla MWar SLBF SRiF
	'Tina's Teardrops' (d)	WPBF
	'Ting-a-ling'	CDoC CLoc CWVF EBak MWhe SLBF SPet WPBF WRou
	'Tinker Bell' Hodges	EBak
I	'Tinker Bell' Tabraham	EKMF
	'Tintern Abbey'	CWVF
	'Tiny Whisper'	WPBF
	'Tjinegara'	CDoC LCla
	'Toby Bridger' (d)	CLoc EBak
	'Tolling Bell'	CWVF EBak EKMF MJac MWhe SPet WPBF WRou
	'Tom Goedeman'	LCla
	'Tom H. Oliver' (d)	EBak
	'Tom Knights'	CDoC EBak MWhe SPet
	'Tom Silcock'	WPBF
	'Tom Thorne'	EBak
	'Tom Thumb' ♀H3	More than 30 suppliers
	'Tom West' misapplied	see *F.* 'Mr West'
	'Tom West' Meillez (v)	CDoC CHEx CLoc CMHG CSBt CWVF CWib EBak EKMF EPts LCla LHop LVER MAsh MJac MWar MWhe NVic SAga SDix SLBF SRiF SSea SWal WFar WPBF
	'Tom Woods'	CWVF MWhe
	'Tommy Tucker' **new**	SRiF
	'Tony Galea'	SRiF
	'Tony's Treat' (d)	EPts
	'Topaz' (d)	CLoc EBak
	'Topper' (d)	CWVF EMan
	'Torch' (d)	CLoc CWVF EBak

	'Torchlight'	CWVF EPts LCla WRou
	'Torvill and Dean' (d)	CCCN CLoc CWVF EKMF EPts LAst LRHS LVER MJac MWhe SPet WGor WPBF WRou WWeb
	'Tosca'	CWVF
	'Toven' **new**	WPBF
	'Town Crier' **new**	SLBF
	'Trabant'	WPBF
	'Tracid' (d)	CLoc
	'Tracie Ann' (d)	EKMF
	'Trail Blazer' (d)	CLoc CWVF EBak MJac SPet
	'Trailing King'	WPBF
	'Trailing Queen'	EBak EKMF MJac
	'Trase' (d)	CDoC CWVF CWib EBak EKMF SRiF SWal
	'Traudchen Bonstedt'	CDoC CLoc CWVF EBak EKMF LCla MWhe SLBF SPet SRiF
	'Traviata'	see *F.* 'La Traviata' Blackwell
	'Treasure' (d)	EBak
	'Treslong'	WPBF
I	'Triantha'	WPBF
	'Tric Trac'	WPBF
	'Tricolor'	see *F. magellanica* var. *gracilis* 'Tricolor'
	'Tricolorii'	see *F. magellanica* var. *gracilis* 'Tricolor'
	'Trientje'	LCla SLBF
	'Trimley Bells'	EBak
	'Trio' (d)	CLoc
	triphylla	EBak EKMF LRHS
	- 'Dominica'	WPBF
	'Trisha'	WPBF
	'Trish's Triumph'	EPts
	'Tristesse' (d)	CLoc CWVF EBak SRiF
	'Trix Brouwer'	WPBF
	'Troika' (d)	EBak EKMF
	'Troon'	CWVF
	'Tropic Sunset' (d)	MBri MWhe
	'Tropicana' (d)	CLoc CWVF EBak WPBF
	'Troubador' Waltz (d)	CLoc
	'Trudi Davro'	CCCN LAst MJac SCoo
	'Trudy'	CWVF EBak EKMF SPet
	'True Love'	WPBF
	'Truly Treena' (d)	LCla SLBF
	'Trumpeter' ambig.	CDoC CWVF LAst
	'Trumpeter' Fry	SRiF
	'Trumpeter' Reiter	CLoc EBak EKMF EPts LAst LCla MJac MWhe
	'Tsjiep'	CDoC SRiF
	'Tubular Bells'	EKMF LCla SRiF WPBF
	'Tumbling Waters' (d)	LVER
	'Tuonela' (d)	CLoc CWVF EBak MWhe WPBF
	'Turandot'	WPBF
	'Turkish Delight'	LAst MWar WPBF WRou
	'Tutone' (d)	SRiF
	'Tutti-frutti' (d)	CLoc
	'Twinkling Stars'	CWVF MJac
	'Twinney'	CWVF
	'Twinny'	EKMF EPts LCla MWar
	'Twirling Square Dancer' (d)	WPBF
	'Twist of Fate' (d)	EKMF
	'Two Tiers' (d)	CWVF EKMF
	'Twydale' **new**	SRiF
	'U.B.' (d) **new**	SRiF
	'U.F.O.'	CWVF
	'Uillean Pipes'	WPBF
	'Ullswater' (d)	CWVF EBak WPBF
	'Ultramar' (d)	EBak
	'Uncle Charley' (d)	CDoC CLoc EBak EKMF
	'Uncle Jinks'	SPet
	'Uncle Steve' (d)	EBak
	'University of Liverpool'	CLoc MJac WPBF
	'Upright Bob'	WPBF
	'Upward Look'	EBak EKMF
	'Valda May' (d)	CWVF
	'Vale of Belvoir'	SRiF
	'Valentine' (d)	EBak
	'Valerie Ann' (d)	EBak SPet
	'Valerie Hobbs' (d)	LCla
	'Valerie Tooke' (d)	LCla
	'Valiant'	EBak
	'Van Parijs Emile' (d) **new**	WPBF
	'Vanessa' (d)	CLoc
	'Vanessa Jackson'	CLoc CWVF MJac MWhe
	'Vanity Fair' (d)	CLoc EBak
	vargasiana	CDoC
	'Variegated Brenda White' (v)	EKMF
	'Variegated la Campanella' (d/v)	MWhe
	'Variegated Lottie Hobby' (v)	EKMF SRiF WPBF
	'Variegated Pink Fascination'	WRou
	'Variegated Pixie'	EKMF
	'Variegated Procumbens'	see *F. procumbens* 'Wirral'
	'Variegated Snowcap' (d/v)	MWhe
	'Variegated Superstar' (v)	MBri
	'Variegated Swingtime' (v)	EBak LAst
	'Variegated Triphylla' (v) **new**	SRiF
	'Variegated Vivienne Thompson' (d/v)	MBri
	'Variegated Waveney Sunrise' (v)	MBri
	'Variegated White Joy' (v)	EKMF
	'Vechtweelde'	WPBF
	'Veenlust'	CCCN EBak LAst MJac SRiF WRou
	'Vendeta'	CDoC LCla
	'Venus Victrix'	EBak EKMF MWhe SLBF SRiF WPBF
	venusta	CDoC EBak EKMF LCla
	'Versicolor'	see *F. magellanica* 'Versicolor'
	'Vespa' **new**	SRiF
	'Vesuvio'	EKMF
	'Vicky'	EKMF
	'Victoria' ambig.	WPBF
	'Victory' Reiter (d)	EBak
	'Vielliebchen'	CDoC
	'Vignero Louis' (d) **new**	WPBF
	'Vincent van Gogh'	WPBF
	'Vintage Dovercourt'	LCla
	'Violet Bassett-Burr' (d)	CLoc EBak
	'Violet Gem' (d)	CLoc
	'Violet Rosette' (d)	CWVF EBak
	'Violetta' ambig. **new**	WPBF
	Violetta = 'Goetzviol'PBR (Shadowdancer Series)	CDoC LAst LSou SCoo SVil
	'Viva Ireland'	EBak
	'Vivien Colville'	CLoc EKMF
	'Vivienne Thompson' (d)	WFFs
	'Vobeglo'	CWVF WPBF
	'Vogue' (d)	EBak
	'Voltaire'	EBak EKMF SRiF
	'Voodoo' (d)	CCCN CDoC CLoc CWVF EBak EKMF EMan EPts LAst LSou SCoo SLBF SPet WRou
	'Vreni Schleeweiss' (d) **new**	WPBF
	vulcanica	CDoC EKMF LCla SRiF
*	- subsp. ***hitchcockii***	EKMF
	'Vyvian Miller'	CWVF MJac
	'W.F.C. Kampioen'	WPBF
	'W.P. Wood'	CDoC
§	'Wagtails White Pixie'	EBak
	'Waldfee'	CCVN CDoC EKMF LCla MWhe SRiF WBor WFFs WPBF
	'Waldis Geisha' (d)	SLBF
	'Waldis Lea'	WPBF
	'Waldis Ovambo'	SLBF

'Waldis Spezi'	CDoC LCla
'Wally Yendell' (v)	SRiF WPBF
'Walsingham' (d)	CWVF EBak WPBF
'Walton Jewel'	EBak SRiF
'Walz Banjo'	WPBF
'Walz Beiaard'	WPBF
'Walz Bella'	LCla WPBF
'Walz Blauwkous' (d)	CWVF
'Walz Bombardon'	WPBF
'Walz Brandaris' **new**	WPBF
'Walz Cello'	WPBF
'Walz Cimbaal' **new**	SRiF
'Walz Cocktail'	WPBF
'Walz Duimelot' **new**	SRiF
'Walz Epicurist'	WPBF
'Walz Fagot' **new**	SRiF
'Walz Fanclub'	LCla
'Walz Floreat'	WPBF
'Walz Fluit'	CCCN LAst MJac WPBF WRou
'Walz Fonola'	WPBF
'Walz Freule'	CWVF EKMF MJac
'Walz Gitaar'	WPBF
'Walz Gong'	WPBF
'Walz Gusla'	WPBF
'Walz Harp'	CDoC CWVF SRiF WPBF
'Walz Hoorn'	WPBF
'Walz Jubelteen'	CDoC CLoc CWVF EKMF EMan EPts LCla MJac MWar MWhe SLBF SSea WPBF WRou
'Walz Kattesnoor'	WPBF
'Walz Klarinet'	WPBF
'Walz Lucifer'	CWVF LCla MWar WPBF
'Walz Luit'	WPBF
'Walz Mandoline' (d)	CWVF WPBF
'Walz Nugget'	WPBF
'Walz Orgelpijp'	WPBF
'Walz Panfluit'	LCla WPBF
'Walz Parasol'	WPBF
'Walz Pauk' (d)	WPBF
'Walz Piano'	WPBF
'Walz Piston'	WPBF
'Walz Polka'	LCla
'Walz Sitar' **new**	WPBF
'Walz Spinet'	WPBF
'Walz Telescope'	WPBF
'Walz Toorts'	WPBF
'Walz Triangel' (d)	EKMF
'Walz Trombone'	WPBF
'Walz Trommel' (d)	WPBF
'Walz Tuba'	SRiF WPBF
'Walz Ukelele'	WPBF
'Walz Wipneus'	WPBF
'Wapenveld's Bloei'	CDoC LCla SLBF
'War Dance' (d)	MWhe
'War Paint' (d)	CLoc EBak
'Warton Crag'	CWVF
'Water Nymph'	CLoc SLBF WPBF
'Wave of Life'	CWVF EKMF MWhe
'Waveney Gem'	CDoC CWVF EBak EKMF EMan LCla MJac MWar SLBF SPet WFFs
'Waveney Queen'	CWVF
'Waveney Sunrise'	CWVF MJac MWar MWhe SPet
'Waveney Unique'	CWVF
'Waveney Valley'	CWVF EBak MJac
'Waveney Waltz'	CWVF EBak
'Waxen Beauty' **new**	WPBF
'Welsh Dragon' (d)	CLoc CWVF EBak SRiF WPBF
'Wendy' Catt	see *F.* 'Snowcap'
'Wendy Atkinson' (d)	EKMF
'Wendy Harris' (d)	MJac
'Wendy Leedham' (d)	EKMF
'Wendy van Wanten'	WPBF
'Wendy's Beauty' (d)	CCCN CLoc EBak EPts MJac SRiF WPBF WRou
'Wentworth'	CWVF

'Wessex Belle' (d/v)	CWVF
'Wessex Hardy'	EKMF
'Westgate'	WPBF
'Westham'	LCla
'Westminster Chimes' (d)	CLoc CWVF MWhe SPet
'Wharfedale' ♀H3	MJac SLBF SRiF
'Whickham Blue'	CWVF MWar
'Whirlaway' (d)	CLoc CWVF EBak
'White Ann'	see *F.* 'Heidi Weiss'
'White Bride' **new**	WPBF
'White Clove'	CDoC SRiF WPBF
'White Fairy'	WPBF
'White Galore' (d)	CWVF EBak EKMF EMan LVER SPet
'White Général Monk' (d)	CDoC
'White Gold' (v)	EBak WPBF
'White Heidi Ann' (d)	MWhe
'White Joy'	EBak
'White King' (d)	CLoc CWVF EBak EKMF EMan LVER MWhe SPet WPBF WRou
'White Lady Patricia Mountbatten'	EMan
'White Marshmallow' (d)	WPBF
'White Pixie' ♀H3-4	CDoC EKMF EPts LVER MJac SLBF SPer SPet
'White Pixie Wagtail'	see *F.* 'Wagtails White Pixie'
'White Princess' **new**	SRiF
'White Queen' ambig.	CWVF
'White Queen' Doyle	EBak MWhe
'White Spider'	CLoc CWVF EBak MWhe SPet WPBF
'White Veil' (d)	CWVF
'White Water'	WPBF
'Whiteknights Amethyst'	CDoC EKMF
'Whiteknights Blush'	CChe CDoC CMdw CPLG EPts EWes GGar GQui SMrm
'Whiteknights Cheeky'	CWVF EBak EPts LCla SRiF
'Whiteknights Green Glister'	CDoC EKMF EPfP
'Whiteknights Pearl' ♀H1+3	CDoC CWVF ECha EKMF EPfP EPts LCla SHGN SLBF SMHy SPet WFFs WPBF
'Whiteknights Ruby'	LCla SRiF WFFs
'Whitney' **new**	SRiF
'Whitton Starburst'	LCla
'Wicked Queen' (d)	CDoC SRiF WPBF
'Widow Twanky' (d)	CWVF
'Wiebke Becker'	EKMF
'Wigan Pier' (d)	LCla MWar SLBF WRou
'Wight Magic' (d)	MJac
'Wild and Beautiful' (d)	CWVF EKMF SPet SRiF
'Wilf Langton'	MWar WPBF
'Wilhelmina Schwab'	CDoC LCla
'Will van Brakel'	WPBF
'William Caunt'	EKMF
'Willie Tamerus'	WPBF
'Willy Winky'	SRiF
'Wilma van Druten'	CDoC LCla
'Wilma Versloot'	WPBF
'Wilson's Colours'	EPts
'Wilson's Joy'	LCla MJac
'Wilson's Pearls' (d)	CWVF SLBF SPet
'Wilson's Sugar Pink'	EPts LCla MJac MWhe
'Wim van der Palen' (d) **new**	WPBF
'Win Oxtoby' (d)	CWVF EKMF
'Windhapper' **new**	LCla
'Windmill'	CWVF
'Wine and Roses' (d)	EBak
'Wings of Song' (d)	CWVF EBak
'Winston Churchill' (d) ♀H3	CCCN CLoc CWVF EBak EKMF EMan LAst LCla LVER MBri MJac MWar MWhe NBlu NVic SCoo SPet SPlb SSea WWeb
'Winter's Touch'	EKMF WPBF
'Witchipoo'	SLBF

	'Woodnook' (d)	CWVF
	wurdackii	EKMF
	'Xmas Tree'	WPBF
	'Ymkje'	EBak
	'Yolanda Franck'	CDoC WRou
	'Yonder Blue' (d)	WPBF
	'Yours' **new**	SRiF
	'Youth'	EKMF
	'Yvonne Priest' **new**	SRiF
	'Yvonne Schwab'	CDoC LCla SRiF
	'Zara'	MWhe
	'Zeebrook' **new**	SRiF
	'Zellertal'	WPBF
	'Zets Alpha'	WPBF
	'Zets Bravo'	CDoC SRiF
	'Ziegfield Girl' (d)	EBak SRiF
	'Zifi'	SLBF
	'Zita' **new**	WPBF
	'Zulu King'	CDoC SRiF WFFs
	'Zwarte Dit'	WPBF
	'Zwarte Snor' (d)	CWVF

Fumana (*Cistaceae*)

	ericoides	XPep
	thymifolia	XPep

Fumaria (*Papaveraceae*)

	lutea	see *Corydalis lutea*
	officinalis	CArn MSal

Furcraea (*Agavaceae*)

	bedinghausii	CAby CBct CCCN CHll CTrC LEdu MAga WPGP
§	***foetida***	CCCN
	gigantea	see *F. foetida*
	longaeva	CAbb CCtw CDTJ CFir CHEx CPen CTrC EAmu EBee LEdu SAPC SArc SChr SDix WCot WPGP
	selloa	MAga
	- var. ***marginata*** (v)	CDoC MAga

G

Gagea (*Liliaceae*)

	lutea	CExc EPot
	pratensis	EPot

Gahnia (*Cyperaceae*)

	filum	GGar
	xanthocarpa	GGar

Gaillardia (*Asteraceae*)

	aristata 'Maxima Aurea'	EBee EBla LAst LRHS NBre SPhx WCAu WWeb
	'Arizona Sun'	ECtt ERou LRHS LSou MHer NPri
	'Bijou'	CBrm EBee MBri NBre NHol NVic SWvt
	'Dwarf Goblin'	LAst NWCA SPet
§	'Fackelschein'	NBre SRms XPep
	'Fanfare'^{PBR}	EBee LBuc LSou MBri SCoo SPer SPoG WCot
	Goblin	see *G.* x *grandiflora* 'Kobold'
	x ***grandiflora*** 'Amber Wheels' **new**	EDAr
	- 'Aurea'	LRHS
	- 'Bremen'	EBee MBri NNor NPri STes
	- 'Burgunder'	CSBt EBee EBla ECtt EHrv ELan EPfP ERou EShb GMaP LAst LHop LRHS LSRN MBri MLHP MWgw NMir NPri NVic SPer SPhx SPla SPoG SRms SWvt WCAu WCra WPer WWeb
	- 'Dazzler' ♀^{H4}	CSBt EBee EBla ECtt ELan EPfP ERou LAst LBMP LRHS MWgw NLar NPri NVic SECG SPer SPoG WCAu WGor WPer
§	- 'Kobold'	More than 30 suppliers
	- Monarch Group	WSpi
	- 'Tokajer'	EBee EPfP NBre NLar
	'Mandarin'	LRHS SRms
*	new giant hybrids	WFar
§	'Oranges and Lemons'^{PBR}	SHar
	Saint Clements^{PBR}	see *G.* 'Oranges and Lemons'
	'Torch Red Ember' **new**	SPoG
	Torchlight	see *G.* 'Fackelschein'

Galactites (*Asteraceae*)

	tomentosa	CHrt CSpe EBee EHrv ELan EMan EMar EPfP EPyc EWTr LDai LRHS NDov SBHP SDnm SGar SPav WEas WWeb
	- white	EGoo

Galanthus ✿ (*Amaryllidaceae*)

	x ***allenii***	MAsh WIvy
	alpinus	CLAP
	- var. ***alpinus***	LAma LFox MTho NMen
	- - late-flowering	LRHS
	- var. ***bortkewitschianus***	LFox
§	***angustifolius***	CHHB
	'Armine'	CAvo CSna LFox
	'Atkinsii' ♀^{H4}	CAvo CBel CBgR CElw CHHB CLAP ECha EHrv EMon EPot GCrs GEdr IHer LAma LFox LRHS MAsh MAvo MHom MRav NBir SChr WPGP WShi WTin
	'Barbara's Double' (d)	CLAP CWsd
	'Benhall Beauty'	CBel CSna LFox
	'Bertram Anderson'	LFox MAsh
	'Brenda Troyle'	CBel CLAP ECha EHrv EPot GCrs GEdr IGor LFox MAsh NPol WIvy
	byzantinus	see *G. plicatus* subsp. *byzantinus*
	caucasicus misapplied	see *G. elwesii* var. *monostictus*
	caucasicus ambig.	GCrs
	caucasicus (Bak.) Grossh.	see *G. alpinus* var. *alpinus*
	- 'Comet'	see *G. elwesii* 'Comet'
	- var. ***hiemalis*** Stern	see *G. elwesii* var. *monostictus* Hiemalis Group
	- 'Maidwell'	see *G. elwesii* var. *elwesii* 'Maidwell L'
	- 'Mrs McNamara'	see *G. elwesii* 'Mrs McNamara'
	cilicicus	EBrs WCot
	'Clare Blakeway-Phillips'	CLAP
	'Colesborne'	EHrv
	corcyrensis spring-flowering	see *G. reginae-olgae* subsp. *vernalis*
	- winter-flowering	see *G. reginae-olgae* subsp. *reginae-olgae* Winter-flowering Group
	'Cordelia' (d)	CLAP EMon LFox LRHS
	'Cowhouse Green'	EHrv
	'Desdemona' (d)	CLAP EPot GCrs LFox WCot WIvy
	'Dionysus' (d)	CBgR CLAP CPLG EHrv EPot ERos GCrs GEdr LFox MHom NBir
§	***elwesii*** ♀^{H4}	CTca CTri EBrs ECho ELan EMon ENot EPfP EPot ERas ERos ERou GCrs IGor IHer LAma LFox LRHS MAsh NBir NPol SGar SRms WBVN WCot WShi
	- 'Cedric's Prolific'	CBel ECha
§	- 'Comet'	CBel CElw EMon WWst
	- 'David Shackleton'	EHrv
	- Edward Whittall Group	CLAP
	- var. ***elwesii*** 'Fred's Giant'	GCrs
	- - 'Kite'	MAsh
	- - 'Magnus'	CLAP
	- - 'Maidwell L'	CAvo CBel CSna EHrv GCrs LFox MAsh

*	- 'Flore Pleno' (d)	EBrs ENot LFox
	- (Hiemalis Group) 'Barnes'	EHrv
	- - 'Earliest of All' **new**	WWst
	- 'J. Haydn'	CElw ECho IHer LAma WWst
§	- var. ***monostictus*** ♀^{H4}	CAvo EBrs ECho EHrv EMon MAsh WIvy WLin
	- - from Ukraine	MPhe
	- - 'G. Handel'	CElw IHer LAma WWst
*	- - 'Green Tips'	NPol
	- - 'H. Purcell'	CElw ECho IHer LAma WWst
§	- - Hiemalis Group	CBel ECha EHrv EMon EPot GCrs LRHS WCot
	- - 'Warwickshire Gemini'	MAvo
§	- 'Mrs McNamara'	CBel
	- 'Selborne Green Tips'	EMon
	- 'Zwanenburg'	EMon LRHS
	'Faringdon Double' (d)	EHrv
	fosteri	EBrs EHrv ERou GCrs SCnR
	'Galatea'	CBel CLAP CSna EHrv EMon LFox LRHS MAsh MHom WIvy
	'Ginns'	CLAP LFox
§	***gracilis***	CBgR CLAP CPLG ERos GCrs LFox MTho NPol
	- 'Highdown'	CAvo CElw CLAP MHom
	- 'Vic Horton'	GEdr WThu
	graecus misapplied	see *G. gracilis*
	graecus Orph. ex Boiss.	see *G. elwesii*
	Greatorex double (d)	CLAP
	'Greenfields'	CBel
	'Hill Poë' (d)	CBel CElw CLAP EPot GCrs IGor LFox MAsh
	'Hippolyta' (d)	CAvo CElw CLAP CWsd ECha EHrv EPot GCrs GEdr LFox MAsh WIvy
	x ***hybridus*** 'Merlin'	CAvo CBel CElw CWsd GCrs IGor LFox MAsh MAvo MHom WCot WIvy
	- 'Robin Hood'	CFee CLAP EHrv ERos GCrs LFox MAsh
§	***ikariae*** Bak.	CElw EPot ERos IGor ITim WFar
	- subsp. ***ikariae*** Butt's form	NPol
	- Latifolius Group	see *G. platyphyllus*
	- subsp. ***snogerupii***	see *G. ikariae* Bak.
	'Imbolc'	CAvo
	'Jacquenetta' (d)	CBel CDes CElw CLAP EHrv GCrs MAsh MHom WPGP
	'James Backhouse' **new**	CBel WHoo
	'John Gray'	CAvo CBel CSna EMon ITim LFox LRHS MAsh
	'Ketton'	CAvo CElw LFox MAsh NRya WIvy
	'Kingston Double' (d)	CBgR CLAP
	'Lady Beatrix Stanley' (d)	CAvo CElw CLAP ECha EHrv EMon EPot ERos GEdr LFox LLWP LRHS MAsh MTho
	lagodechianus	CHHB EBrs
	'Lapwing' **new**	CSna
	latifolius Rupr.	see *G. platyphyllus*
	'Lavinia' (d)	CAvo CElw CLAP
	'Lerinda'	EHrv
	'Limetree'	CBel CBgR CLAP EHrv LFox NPol
	'Little John'	EHrv
	lutescens	see *G. nivalis* Sandersii Group
	'Lyn'	EHrv
	'Magnet' ♀^{H4}	CAvo CBel CFee CHHB CLAP ECha EMon EPot GCrs GEdr IGor ITim LFox MAsh NPol WHoo WPGP WWst
	'Mighty Atom'	CBel CDes CFee CLAP EHrv GCrs LFox MAsh
	'Moccas'	CBgR CElw
	'Modern Art'	CSna
	'Mrs Backhouse No 12'	EHrv
	'Mrs Thompson'	CBel EHrv WIvy
	'Neill Fraser'	LFox
	nivalis ♀^{H4}	CPLG CTca CTri EBrs ECho ELan ENot EPfP EPot GAbr GKev IHer ITim LAma LFox LRHS MAsh MBri MNHC NRya SECG SHFr SPer SRms WBrk WCot WFar WGwG WShi WWFP
	- 'Anglesey Abbey'	CAvo CBel EMon
	- var. ***angustifolius***	see *G. angustifolius*
	- 'April Fool'	LFox MHom
	- 'Bitton'	CLAP LFox NPol
	- dwarf	GAbr LFox
	- 'Greenish'	CAvo CDes CSna
	- subsp. ***imperati***	CPLG WBrk
	- 'Lutescens'	see *G. nivalis* Sandersii Group
	- 'Melvillei'	EMon
	- f. ***pleniflorus*** (d)	CTca GKev MAsh
	- - 'Blewbury Tart' (d)	CAvo CLAP CSna
	- - 'Flore Pleno' (d) ♀^{H4}	CPLG CStu CTri EBrs EPfP EPla EPot GAbr LAma LFox LHop LRHS NRya SPer SRms WBrk WCot WFar WHen WHoo WShi
	- - 'Hambutt's Orchard' (d)	LFox
	- - 'Lady Elphinstone' (d)	CAvo CBgR CLAP CSna EHrv GCrs LFox MAsh MTho NRya WIvy
	- - 'Pusey Green Tip' (d)	CAvo CElw CLAP EPot GCrs GEdr LFox WPGP WTin
	- Poculiformis Group	CLAP EMon LRHS
§	- Sandersii Group	CAvo CDes
§	- Scharlockii Group	CAvo CBel CBgR CWsd EBrs EMon IGor LFox LRHS MAsh
	- 'Tiny'	GCrs MAvo MHom
	- 'Tiny Tim'	EBrs NRya
	- 'Virescens'	CLAP
	- 'Viridapice'	CAvo CBgR CPLG EBrs ECha ECho EMon EPot ERou GEdr LAma LFox LRHS MAsh NMen NPol WCot WFar WHoo WPGP WShi
	- 'Warei'	LFox
	'Ophelia' (d)	CAvo CBel EPot GCrs IGor LFox MAsh WHoo
	'Peg Sharples'	CSna
	peshmenii	EBrs ECho EPot SCnR WCot
§	***platyphyllus***	CPLG EBrs LFox
	plicatus ♀^{H4}	CAvo CBel CElw CFee ECho EHrv EMon EPot GEdr LFox LRHS NMen WShi WTin
	- from Ukraine	MPhe
	- 'Augustus'	CAvo CBel CDes CFee CSna EHrv ERos GCrs LFox MAsh MHom WIvy
	- 'Baxendale's Late'	CAvo CLAP
	- 'Bowles' Large'	ERos MHom
§	- subsp. ***byzantinus***	ERos LCro LFox
	- - 'Ron Ginns'	LFox
	- 'Colossus'	CBel
	- 'Edinburgh Ketton'	CSna EHrv
	- 'Florence Baker'	EHrv
	- large-flowered	NPol
	- 'Sally Passmore'	CAvo
	- 'Sophie North'	CLAP GCrs
	- 'The Pearl'	EHrv
	- 'Three Ships'	EHrv
	- 'Trym'	CLAP WFar
	- 'Warham'	CWsd EHrv EPot GEdr MAvo WPGP
	- 'Wendy's Gold'	CWsd EMon GCrs LRHS
	reginae-olgae	CAvo EBrs EHrv ERos GCrs MAsh
	- subsp. ***reginae-olgae*** 'Cambridge'	EBrs MAsh
§	- - Winter-flowering Group	LFox
§	- subsp. ***vernalis***	EBrs LRHS
	rizehensis	CAvo CLAP EHrv GEdr
	'S. Arnott' ♀^{H4}	More than 30 suppliers
	'Saint Anne's'	CDes CElw CSna WIvy
	'Sally Ann'	LFox

'Scharlockii'	see *G. nivalis* Scharlockii Group
'Silverwells'	CElw CSna EHrv GEdr MAvo
§ 'Straffan'	CAvo CBel EPot GCrs GEdr IGor LFox LRHS MHom NPol
'The Apothecary'	EHrv
'The Linns'	GCrs
'The O'Mahoney'	see *G.* 'Straffan'
'Titania' (d)	EHrv
'Trotter's Merlin'	CSna
'Tubby Merlin'	CLAP CSna LFox MAsh WIvy
'Washfield Warham'	CSna ECha EMon ITim
'White Wings'	CSna
'William Thomson'	CSna EMon LFox
'Winifrede Mathias'	CLAP LFox
'Wisley Magnet'	ECha
woronowii 𝕐H4	CElw CHHB CLAP CTca EBrs ECho EMon ENot GKev LAma LRHS MHom WCot WFar

Galax (*Diapensiaceae*)

aphylla	see *G. urceolata*
§ ***urceolata***	GCrs IBlr

Galega (*Papilionaceae*)

bicolor	MLLN NBir NBre SRms STes SWat WFar
'Duchess of Bedford'	CFir CFwr EBee SWat
x ***hartlandii***	CPLG IBlr
- 'Alba' 𝕐H4	CFwr EBee EGle EHrv ELon EWes GBri IBlr MArl MBri MRav SMHy SPhx SWat WCot WHoo WPrP WSHC
- 'Candida'	NBir
- 'Lady Wilson' 𝕐H4	CElw CPom EBee ECtt EGle ELon EWes MArl MBri MRav NSti WCot WCra WFoF WHoo WOut WPen
- 'Spring Light' (v)	ECtt EMan EWes LSou
'Her Majesty'	see *G.* 'His Majesty'
§ 'His Majesty'	CKno EBee ECtt EGle ELon EMan GBri MArl MBri MLHP MRav NBre NCob NGby SAga SWat WCot WFar WHoo WPGP WWlt
officinalis	More than 30 suppliers
- 'Alba' 𝕐H4	CBgR CPom CPrp EBee ECtt ELan ELau EMan EPfP MBrN MHer MNHC NCob SPer SPoG SWal WAul WFar WHer WHil WHrl WMoo WOut WSpi
- Coconut Ice = 'Kelgal'PBR (v)	NCob SPer WHer
- 'Lincoln Gold' **new**	MTPN
orientalis	CDes CFir EBee ECha ECtt EPPr EWes LCro MArl MLLN MRav SMac SPhx SWat WAbb WCot WMoo WOut WPGP WSHC

Galeobdolon see *Lamium*

Galium (*Rubiaceae*)

aristatum	ECha EMan MLLN
cruciata	see *Cruciata laevipes*
mollugo	CArn CRWN MSal NSco SECG SIde
§ ***odoratum***	More than 30 suppliers
verum	CArn CRWN GPoy GWCH MHer MNHC MSal NLan NMir NPri NSco SECG SIde WHer

Galtonia ✿ (*Hyacinthaceae*)

candicans 𝕐H4	More than 30 suppliers
- 'Moonbeam' (d) **new**	EBee
princeps	EBrs ECha ERos ERou GBuc WPGP WTin
regalis	CPLG ERos GEdr WPGP
viridiflora	CAvo CBct CFFs CFwr CHar CPLG CStu EBee EBrs ECha ECho ELan EPot ERCP ERos GEdr IHer LAst MNrw MSte NChi NWCA SDnm WFar

Galvezia (*Scrophulariaceae*)

speciosa	XPep

Garcinia (*Clusiaceae*)

mangostana **new**	CCCN

Gardenia (*Rubiaceae*)

augusta	see *G. jasminoides*
florida L.	see *G. jasminoides*
globosa	see *Rothmannia globosa*
grandiflora	see *G. jasminoides*
§ ***jasminoides*** 𝕐H1	CBcs EBak LRHS MBri
- 'Kleim's Hardy'	CHll EBee ELan EPfP EShb EWes LRHS MAsh NLar SAPC SArc SOWG SPoG SSta
- 'Star'	SOWG
- 'Veitchiana'	EShb
magnifica	SOWG
thunbergia	EShb SPlb

garlic see *Allium sativum*

garlic, elephant see *A. ampeloprasum* 'Elephant'

Garrya ✿ (*Garryaceae*)

F&M 215 **new**	WPGP
congdonii	NLar
elliptica	CBcs CDul EBee ECrN EMui ENot EPfP ISea LCro LPan LRHS LSRN MBri MGos MNHC NEgg NHol NWea SPet SPlb WFar WHar WPat
- (f)	LAst MSwo SWvt
- (m)	CCVT CDoC CSBt CTri GGar MAsh MGan NBlu SLim SPoG WBod WFar
- 'James Roof' (m) 𝕐H4	More than 30 suppliers
fremontii	NLar
x ***issaquahensis*** 'Glasnevin Wine'	CAbP CDoC CPMA EBee ELan EPfP IMGH LRHS MAsh MBlu MGos NEgg NHol NLar NPal NSti SCoo SLim SPoG SSta WFar WSpi
- 'Pat Ballard' (m)	CPMA EPfP NHol NLar
x ***thuretii***	MBri MGos NLar WFar

Gasteria ✿ (*Aloaceae*)

nitida var. ***nitida*** variegated (v) **new**	WCot
verrucosa	EShb

x *Gaulnettya* see *Gaultheria*

Gaultheria ✿ (*Ericaceae*)

adenothrix	NMen WAbe
antarctica	WThu
cardiosepala	GEdr
- CLD 1351	GEdr
cumingiana B&SWJ 1542	WCru
cuneata 𝕐H4	ECho GEdr GKev LRHS MAsh MBar SPoG
- 'Pinkie'	ECho LRHS
hispidula	ECho
hookeri	IBlr
itoana	ECho GEdr MBar
'Jingle Bells'	MGos SPoG
macrostigma	WThu
- BR 67	GGar
§ ***mucronata***	CBrm CDul EPfP MBar NWea WGwG
- (m)	CBcs CDoC CSBt CTri CWSG ENot EPfP LAst MAsh MBar MGos NBlu SPer SPoG SRms

- 'Alba' (f)	MBar MGos SLon
§ - 'Bell's Seedling' (f/m) 🏆H4	CBcs CDoC CDul CTri CWSG EPfP GGar LRHS MAsh NBir SPer SPoG SReu SSta
§ - 'Crimsonia' (f) 🏆H4	CBcs EPfP MAsh MBar SPer SPur SRms
- 'Indian Lake'	NHol
- lilac-berried (f)	NBlu
- 'Lilacina' (f)	CBcs
- 'Lilian' (f)	CSBt CWSG EBee ENot EPfP GSki LAst MAsh SMer SPer
- Mother of Pearl	see *G. mucronata* 'Parelmoer'
§ - 'Mulberry Wine' (f) 🏆H4	CSBt CTri EPfP LRHS MGos NHol SPoG
§ - 'Parelmoer' (f)	CSBt LAst SPer SPoG SPur
§ - 'Pink Pearl' (f) 🏆H4	SRms
- red-berried (f)	NBlu
- 'Rosea' (f)	MBar MGos
- 'Rosie' (f)	SBod
§ - 'Signaal' (f)	CBcs CBrm ENot EPfP GWCH LAst LRHS MAsh MGos SPer
- Signal	see *G. mucronata* 'Signaal'
§ - 'Sneeuwwitje' (f)	CBcs CWSG EBee ENot EPfP GSki LAst LRHS NBir SMer SPer SPoG SPur
- Snow White	see *G. mucronata* 'Sneeuwwitje'
- 'Thymifolia' (m)	EPfP
- white-berried (f)	NBlu
§ - 'Wintertime' (f) 🏆H4	CBrm MGos SRms
* ***mucronifolia*** dwarf	NWCA
§ ***myrsinoides***	GKev
nummularioides	GEdr GGGa NHol NLar
'Pearls'	GCrs NHol WThu
'Pink Champagne'	ITim
procumbens 🏆H4	More than 30 suppliers
prostrata	see *G. myrsinoides*
- ***purpurea***	see *G. myrsinoides*
pumila	GAbr GCrs LEdu MBar NHol
- 'E.K. Balls'	NHol
schultesii	WThu
shallon	CAgr CBcs CDoC CSBt EBee EPfP MBar MDun MGos SHBN SPer SRms SWvt WFar
- 'Snowqualmi Pass'	NLar
sinensis lilac-berried	WThu
tasmanica	ECou GAbr
thymifolia	GEdr
x ***wisleyensis***	LRHS SLon SRms SSta
- 'Pink Pixie'	ECho LRHS MAsh MBar NLar SPer SSta
- 'Wisley Pearl'	CBcs CDoC IBlr IDee MBar NLar SCoo SReu WFar
yunnanensis	SReu

Gaura (*Onagraceae*)

lindheimeri 🏆H4	More than 30 suppliers
- Cherry Brandy = 'Gauchebra'PBR	CEnt CSpe EBee ECtt EPfP ERou EWes EWin EWll LAst LBMP LHop MAvo NLar SWal SWat SWvt WCra WFar
- 'Corrie's Gold' (v)	CBcs CWSG EBee ECha ECtt ELan EPfP ERou LAst LBMP LRHS MHer NBlu SGar SPav SPer SPoG WMnd XPep
- 'Crimson Butterflies'PBR	EBee ENot EPfP EShb LRHS MCCP SPoG
§ - 'Heather's Delight'PBR	LCro SHar
- 'Heaven's Harmony'	EPPr ERou EWin
- In the PinkPBR	see *G. lindheimeri* 'Heather's Delight'
- 'Jo Adela' (v)	ELan EPfP
- Karalee Petite = 'Gauka'	CHVG CSpe CWCL EPPr EPfP LAst LHop NLar NPri SCoo SIng SPoG SVil
- Karalee Pink	MBri
- Karalee White = 'Nugauwhite'PBR	CSpe CWCL LAst LHop MBri NLar SCoo SIng SPoG
- 'Madonna' (v)	CBow
- 'My Melody'PBR (v)	CWCL EBee ERou EWin EWll LAst LSou NLar SPoG
- 'Passionate Blush' **new**	IBlr LAst SPoG
- 'Passionate Pink'PBR	CBcs
- 'Passionate Rainbow' (v) **new**	EPfP SPoG
- 'Pink Dwarf' **new**	EPfP
- short	LSou SGar
- 'Siskiyou Pink'	More than 30 suppliers
- 'Sunset Dreams' **new**	NBPN
- 'The Bride'	CEnt CTri EBee EPfP LRHS LSou MRav MWat MWgw NGdn SMrm SPav SPet SPla SRGP STes SWal SWvt WBVN WHil WMnd
- 'Val's Pink'	WHoo WSPU
- 'Whirling Butterflies'	CKno CSpe CWCL EBee ECtt ELan EMil EMon ENot EPfP GMaP LCro NBlu SBod SMad SMrm SPav SPer SPoG SWat SWvt WMnd XPep
- 'White Heron'	MNrw
I 'Variegata' (v)	CWCL

Gaussia (*Arecaceae*)

maya	LPal

Gaylussacia (*Ericaceae*)

baccata (F)	NLar
brachycera	GGGa

Gazania (*Asteraceae*)

'Aztec' 🏆H1+3	CCCN CHal EWin
'Bicton Cream'	CHal
'Bicton Orange'	CCCN LSou MAJR SCoo
'Blackberry Ripple'	CCCN GGar LAst MAJR NCiC SCoo
'Blackcurrant Ice' **new**	MCot
'Christopher'	CHal GGar MSte SCoo
'Christopher Lloyd'	CCCN COlW LAst MAJR
'Cookei' 🏆H1+3	CSpe MAJR MSte SAga WCot
'Cornish Pixie'	CCCN CHal
cream-flowered	CHal NCiC
'Cream Beauty'	MSte
'Cream Dream'	LAst
Daybreak Series	WFar
double bronze	CHal
'Garden Sun'	MLan
* ***grayi***	CHal
* 'Hazel'	MSte
(Kiss Series) 'Kiss Bronze Star'	SGar
- 'Kiss Rose'	SGar
- 'Kiss Yellow'	SGar
krebsiana	CCCN XPep
linearis 'Colorado Gold'	CFir
'Magic'	CCCN LAst MAJR NPri SCoo
'Northbourne' 🏆H1+3	GGar MSte
'Orange Beauty'	CHEx ELan
'Red Velvet'	CHEx MSte
rigens var. ***uniflora*** 🏆H1+3	MSte XPep
- 'Variegata' (v) 🏆H1+3	CBow CCCN COlW ELan LAst LSou MAvo
'Silverbrite'	CHal
Sunset Jane = 'Sugaja'PBR **new**	CCCN
'Talent'	SEND
'Tiger Eye' **new**	CCCN CHVG LAst LSou WHlf
'Torbay Silver'	CHEx

Geissorhiza (*Iridaceae*)

corrugata	CStu
imbricata	CStu

Gelasine (*Iridaceae*)

	azurea	see *G. coerulea*
§	***coerulea***	EBee EMan

Gelidocalamus (*Poaceae*)

	fangianus	see *Drepanostachyum microphyllum*

Gelsemium (*Loganiaceae*)

	rankinii	MBri NLar WSHC
	sempervirens ♀H1-2	CArn CHll CRHN CWoW EBee EShb IDee LSRN MSal NCGa SBra SOWG SPoG WBor

Genista (*Papilionaceae*)

	aetnensis ♀H4	CBcs CEnd CHEx CTri ECrN ELan EPfP LRHS MDun NLar SAPC SArc SDix SHBN SMad SPer SPoG SRms SSpi WBVN WPat WSpi XPep
§	***canariensis***	CPLG CSBt CWib ERea NBlu WBrE
	cinerea	WCFE
	decumbens	see *Cytisus decumbens*
	delphinensis	see *G. sagittalis* subsp. *delphinensis*
	'Emerald Spreader'	see *G. pilosa* 'Yellow Spreader'
	fragrans	see *G. canariensis*
	hispanica	CBcs CCVT CDul CSBt CTri EBee ECrN ELan EPfP GGar LRHS MBar MGos MNHC NWea SHBN SLim SPer SPoG SRms SWvt WCFE WFar WHar WTel XPep
	humifusa	see *G. pulchella*
	lydia ♀H4	More than 30 suppliers
§	***maderensis***	EWes WPic
	monosperma	see *Retama monosperma*
§	***monspessulana***	ECho XPep
	pilosa	CTri EPot ISea MBar NMen
	- 'Lemon Spreader'	see *G. pilosa* 'Yellow Spreader'
	- var. ***minor***	NLar NMen
	- 'Procumbens'	CMea MDKP WCFE WPat
	- 'Vancouver Gold'	CBcs CSBt ELan EPfP MGos MRav SMad SPer SPoG SRms WFar WGor
§	- 'Yellow Spreader'	CBcs CMHG CSBt GEdr MSwo
§	'Porlock' ♀H3	CBcs CDoC CDul CPLG CSBt CSPN CWSG EBee LRHS MAsh MBri MRav SEND SPoG WBod WWeb
§	***pulchella***	CTri EPot
	sagittalis	CTri NBir NLar NWCA SBla SPer WTin WWFP
§	- subsp. ***delphinensis*** ♀H4	NMen
	- ***minor***	see *G. sagittalis* subsp. *delphinensis*
§	x ***spachiana*** ♀H1	CTri ENot SPoG
	tenera 'Golden Shower'	CPLG SLPl
	tinctoria	CArn GPoy GWCH ILis MGol MHer MSal SIde WHer
§	- 'Flore Pleno' (d) ♀H4	ECho GEdr MGos NMen NPro SRot
	- 'Humifusa'	EPot GEdr NWCA
	- 'Plena'	see *G. tinctoria* 'Flore Pleno'
	- 'Royal Gold' ♀H4	CWSG CWib EPfP MAsh MGos MRav SHBN SPer SPlb SPoG WBod
	villarsii	see *G. pulchella*

Gentiana ✿ (*Gentianaceae*)

§	***acaulis*** ♀H4	CStu ECho ELan EPot GCrs GKev GMaP LHop LRHS MWat NCGa NEgg NGdn NHol NLAp NMen NRya NWCA SBla SIng SPlb SRms WAbe WBrE WCFE WEas WFar WPat
	- f. ***alba***	LTwo NLAp WThu
	- 'Belvedere'	EPot GCrs NMen WAbe
	- 'Coelestina'	EPot WThu
	- 'Dinarica'	see *G. dinarica*
	- 'Holzmannii'	NMen
	- 'Krumrey'	EPot GKev
	- 'Max Frei'	CStu GCrs
I	- 'Maxima Enzian'	EPot GCrs NHar
	- 'Rannoch'	EPot GEdr NMen
	- 'Stumpy'	EPot
	- 'Trotter's Variety'	EPot WAbe
	- 'Undulatifolia'	EPot
	affinis	GAbr NLAp
	'Alex Duguid'	GEdr
	'Amethyst'	EPot GCrs GEdr GMaP SIng WAbe
	angustifolia	GCrs WAbe WLin
	- 'Rannoch'	GKev
	'Ann's Special'	GEdr
	asclepiadea ♀H4	More than 30 suppliers
	- var. ***alba***	GBuc GGar GMaP IGor MDKP MTho NBid NChi NLAp SRms WAbe WCru WTin
	- 'Knightshayes'	EBee GKev
	- pale blue-flowered	WPGP
	- 'Phyllis'	CFir EBee GBuc GKev
	- 'Pink Swallow'	GBuc NSum WHoo
	- 'Rosea'	CDes GBuc GMaP MDKP MNrw WPGP
	atuntsiensis	GKev NLAp
	'Barbara Lyle'	WAbe
	bavarica var. ***subacaulis***	SPlb
	x ***bernardii***	see *G.* x *stevenagensis* 'Bernardii'
	'Berrybank Dome' **new**	NHar
	'Berrybank Sky' **new**	NHar
	'Berrybank Star' **new**	NHar
	bisetaea	SRms
	'Blauer Diamant'	GCrs
	'Blue Flame'	GCrs
	'Blue Silk'	EPot EWes GBin GBuc GCrs NHar NLAp SBla SIng WAbe
	'Blue Spot'	NLAp
	brachyphylla	WAbe
	- subsp. ***favratii***	WAbe
	'Cairngorm'	GAbr GBin GCrs GEdr NDlv
	'Cambrian White'	WAbe
	x ***caroli***	SBla WAbe
	'Christine Jean'	GCrs SIng
	clusii	EPot WAbe
	'Compact Gem'	EPot GBin GCrs GEdr NHar NHol NLAp SIng WAbe
	crassicaulis	GCrs
§	***cruciata***	GAbr MMHG MTho
§	***dahurica***	EBee ECho GAbr NGdn SBla
	'Dark Hedgehog'	GCrs GEdr
	dendrologi	WHil
	depressa	MTho WAbe
	'Devonhall'	GEdr WAbe
§	***dinarica***	CLyd ECho EPot MTho NLAp NMen NSum
	- 'Colonel Stitt'	GEdr WThu
	- 'Frocheneite'	WThu
	divisa	EPot
	'Dumpy'	CPBP EPot GEdr NLAp WAbe
	'Dusk'	GCrs
	'Eleanor'	GCrs
	'Elehn' **new**	NHar
	'Elizabeth'	GEdr
	'Ettrick'	GEdr
	'Eugen's Allerbester' (d)	GCrs GEdr LTwo NHar WAbe
	'Eugen's Bester'	NHar SIng
	'Excalibur' **new**	NHar
	'Excelsior'	NHar
	farreri	EWes GCrs NLAp NSla WAbe
	- 'Duguid'	GEdr WAbe
	- hybrids	WAbe
	'Fasta Highlands'	NBir

fetissowii	see *G. macrophylla* var. *fetissowii*
'Gellerhard' __new__	NHar
'Gewahn' __new__	NHar
Glamis strain	GEdr NHar
'Glen Isla'	EWes
'Glendevon'	WAbe
§ ***gracilipes***	ECho LRHS MWat SPlb SRms
- 'Yuatensis'	see *G. macrophylla* var. *fetissowii*
x ***hascombensis***	see *G. septemfida* var. *lagodechiana* 'Hascombensis'
'Henry'	WAbe
x ***hexafarreri***	GCrs
hexaphylla	WAbe
'Indigo'	WAbe
Inshriach hybrids	GCrs
'Inverleith' 🏆^{H4}	EWes GCrs GEdr GKev NHol NLAp SPlb
'Kirriemuir'	EWes NDlv
kochiana	see *G. acaulis*
kurroo	NLAp
- var. ***brevidens***	see *G. dahurica*
lagodechiana	see *G. septemfida* var. *lagodechiana*
ligustica	GCrs
lucerna	GEdr NDlv NHol NLAp
lutea	EBee ECho GAbr GKev GPoy MAvo NBid NChi NLAp SDix SMad SRms WAul WCAu WLin WPer
x ***macaulayi*** 🏆^{H4}	GCrs SIng SRms
- 'Elata'	GCrs NHol
- 'Kidbrooke Seedling'	CTri EWes GCrs GEdr GMaP NDlv NHol NLAp SPer WAbe
- 'Kingfisher'	CTri GAbr GEdr NBir SBla SIng WAbe
§ - 'Praecox'	GCrs GEdr NLAp
§ - 'Wells's Variety'	GCrs GEdr WAbe
§ ***macrophylla*** var. ***fetissowii***	GAbr GKev NLAp
makinoi 'Royal Blue'	CWCL GBin GBri IDee MAvo NChi
'Margaret'	WAbe
'Maryfield'	GEdr
'Melanie'	GEdr NHar NHol
'Merlin'	GCrs
'Nostradamus' __new__	NHar
occidentalis	EPot GCrs NLAp
Olga's pale	GCrs
oreodoxa	GCrs
paradoxa	CLyd EBee GKev NLAp WPat
- 'Blauer Herold'	NCGa
phlogifolia	see *G. cruciata*
pneumonanthe	SPlb
prolata	GKev NLAp
pumila subsp. ***delphinensis***	WAbe WPat
purdomii	see *G. gracilipes*
'Robyn Lyle'	WAbe
'Saphir Select'	EDAr GEdr NHol
saxosa	CPBP GCrs GEdr NBir NLAp WAbe
scabra	CStu GCrs NBlu
- 'Ishusuki'	SBla
- 'Zuikorindo'	EBee NLar
'Sensation'	GEdr NHar
septemfida 🏆^{H4}	CEnt EPot GCrs GEdr LBee LHop LRHS MBri MTho MWat NBir NBlu NLAp NWCA SBla SIng SPlb SRms WHoo
- 'Alba'	NBir
§ - var. ***lagodechiana*** 🏆^{H4}	NMen SRms WBVN WFar
§ - - 'Hascombensis'	ECho
- - 'Select'	NSum
'Serenity'	GEdr WAbe
'Shot Silk'	CPBP CSam CTri EWes GCrs GEdr GGar GMaP NBir NHol SPer WAbe
sikkimensis	GCrs
'Silken Giant'	GEdr WAbe

'Silken Night' __new__	WAbe
'Silken Seas'	GEdr NHol WAbe
'Silken Skies'	GBuc GEdr WAbe
sino-ornata 🏆^{H4}	CTri ECho GCrs GEdr GGar GKev LSRN MBri NBlu NLAp NMen SIng SPer SRms WAbe WBVN WFar
- CLD 476B	GEdr
- 'Alba'	WFar
- 'Angel's Wings'	GEdr NHol
- 'Bellatrix'	GEdr NHar NHol
- 'Brin Form'	SRms WAbe
- 'Downfield'	GCrs NHol
- 'Edith Sarah'	GCrs GEdr SRms
- 'Mary Lyle'	GEdr WAbe
- 'Praecox'	see *G.* x *macaulayi* 'Praecox'
- 'Purity' __new__	WAbe
- 'Starlight'	NHar
I - 'Trotter's Form'	EWes
- 'Weisser Traum'	GEdr NHar NHol
- 'White Wings'	EWes GCrs
'Sir Rupert' __new__	NHar
'Soutra'	GEdr
x ***stevenagensis*** 🏆^{H4}	CTri NLAp SIng
§ - 'Bernardii'	GCrs GEdr SIng WAbe
- dark	WAbe WFar
- 'Frank Barker'	WAbe
straminea	EBee GCrs GKev LTwo MDKP
'Strathmore' 🏆^{H4}	CTri EWes GAbr GBin GCrs GEdr GKev GMaP NHar NHol NLAp SIng SPlb WAbe
'Suendermannii'	LTwo
syringea	WAbe
ternifolia 'Cangshan'	GCrs GEdr WAbe
- 'Dali'	GCrs GEdr NBir NHar
tibetica	CArn EBee EDAr EUnu GEdr GPoy MFOX MWat NBid WAul WBVN WCAu WEas WPer WTin
aff. ***tibetica***	NLAp
- CC 3935	MGol
trichotoma	GCrs
triflora	GBuc WFar WPGP
- 'Alba'	GBuc
- var. ***japonica***	GBri GBuc WBor
- 'Royal Blue'	EBee
Tweeddale strain	GCrs
veitchiorum	GCrs GKev
verna	CPBP EBee ECho EPfP EPot EWes GCrs ITim LHop LRHS LSRN MTho NLAp NMen NSla SBla SIng SPoG WAbe WFar WHoo WPat
- 'Alba'	GCrs ITim NLAp WAbe WFar WPat
- subsp. ***balcanica***	CLyd ELan MTho NLAp SRms WPat
- subsp. ***oschtenica***	NSla WAbe
- slate blue	NLAp WPat
- subsp. ***tergestina***	EDAr GKev NLAp
'Violette'	GCrs GEdr NDlv NHol
waltonii	ECho EWes
wellsii	see *G.* x *macaulayi* 'Wells's Variety'
wutaiensis	see *G. macrophylla* var. *fetissowii*

Geranium (*Geraniaceae*)

from Pamirs, Tadzhikistan	WPnP
from Sikkim	NWCA
aconitifolium misapplied	see *G. palmatum*
aconitifolium L'Hér.	see *G. rivulare*
'Alan Mayes'	CCge CElw CPrp CSev EBee EBla EPPr MAvo MNFA MSte NGdn NSti SRGP WCra WWpP
albanum	CBgR CCge CElw EBee EMar EPPr EWsh GAbr GSki LLWP MNrw NSti SDix SRGP WMoo WPtf WTMC WWpP
albiflorum	CCge CMCo EPPr SRGP WMoo WPnP WWpP

	'Amanda's Blush'	SMrm
	anemonifolium	see *G. palmatum*
	'Ann Folkard' ♀H4	More than 30 suppliers
	'Ann Folkard' x ***psilostemon***	LSRN NChi
	'Anne Thomson' ♀H4	CElw CSam CSev CSpe EBee EBla ECho EPPr GMaP IFoB LAst LPio LRHS MNrw MSte NCGa NCot NGdn NLar NRnb NSti SAga SPla SRGP STes WBrk WCra WCru WPnP WWpP
	x ***antipodeum***	SRms SWat
	- 'Black Ice'	GBuc WCru
	- 'Chocolate Candy'PBR	EPfP WWeb
§	- Crûg strain	EHrv EMan LRHS MDKP MDun NGdn NWCA SHBN WCru
	- 'Elizabeth Wood'	CCge EMan LSou
	- 'Kahlua'	EBee EHrv EMan EPfP MBNS
	- 'Pink Spice'PBR	CCge EBla ECtt MGos
	- 'Sea Spray'	CMHG EBee ECtt EMar GBuc GCra GGar LRHS MNrw MSte NBro NGdn SWat WCru WMnd WTMC WWpP
	- 'Stanhoe'	CSpe EBee ECtt MAvo SRot WBrk WFar
	antrorsum	ECou
	aristatum	CDes CPou EBee EBla EPPr EWes GGar MNFA MNrw MRav NBir NCot SPav SRGP STes WCru WMoo WPnP WTMC WWpP
	- NS 649	NWCA
	armenum	see *G. psilostemon*
	asphodeloides	CBre CElw CHid CSsd EBee GAbr GSki LLWP MBNS MNFA MNrw NBid NCot NSti SPav SRGP STes SWat WBrk WFar WHCG WHen WMnd WMoo WTin WWpP
	- subsp. ***asphodeloides*** 'Prince Regent'	EMan EPPr MNFA SBch WPtf WWpP
	- - white-flowered	CCge EBla EMan EPPr SRGP WFar WHen WMoo WWpP
	- subsp. ***crenophilum***	EBee
	- 'Starlight'	NBid
	atlanticum Hook. f.	see *G. malviflorum*
	'Aussie Gem'	CFwr EBee WWpP
	'Aya'	LPio
	'Baby Blue'	see *G. himalayense* 'Baby Blue'
	'Bertie Crûg'	CCge CDes EBee EBla ECtt EHrv EPot GAbr LCro LTwo NBir NEgg NMoo SPoG SRms SRot SWat SWvt WCru WFar WPat WWpP
	biuncinatum	WPnP
	'Blue Boy'	MNFA
	'Blue Cloud' ♀H4	CDes CElw CMea EBee EBla EGle EMar EPPr EPfP GMaP LRHS MAvo MNFA MSte NBid NBir NCob NCot SMeo SPhx SRGP SSvw WCra WHoo WMoo WPnP WSpi WTMC WWpP
	'Blue Pearl'	EBee EPPr MAvo NBir NSti SRGP SVil WCra WMoo WPnP WWpP
§	Blue Sunrise = 'Blogold'PBR ♀H4	CBod CBow CCge CWGN EBee EBla ECtt ELan IBal IPot LAst LRHS MCCP MSte NBPC NCob NCot NEgg NLar NSti SAga SPla SPoG SRkn SRms WCot WCra WFar WTMC WWpP
	'Bob's Blunder'	CCge CElw CSpe EBee EBla ECtt EGle MBNS NCob NEgg SAga SPla SWvt WCot WFar WTMC WWpP
	bohemicum	CCge EBla GSki NCot SRGP WBrk WHen WHer WWpP
	- 'Orchid Blue'	EPfP SWvt WFar
	'Brookside' ♀H4	More than 30 suppliers
	brycei	MNrw

	'Buckland Beauty'	CWsd EBee EPPr SBch SBla
	'Buxton's Blue'	see *G. wallichianum* 'Buxton's Variety'
	caeruleatum	EBee EBla EMon EPPr SBch WWpP
	caffrum	CCge GBuc GSki NChi SRGP WCru WOut WWpP
	californicum	GBuc
	canariense	see *G. reuteri*
	candicans misapplied	see *G. lambertii*
§	x ***cantabrigiense***	CBrm CSBt ECtt EShb GAbr IBlr LAst LVER MHer MNrw NBid NBir NBro NPer NSti SGar SIng SRms WBrk WCru WFar WHCG WHil WLin WMoo
	- 'Berggarten'	CDes CElw CMCo EBee EPPr SBch SRGP WPtf WWpP
	- 'Biokovo'	More than 30 suppliers
	- 'Cambridge'	More than 30 suppliers
	- 'Karmina'	CElw CMCo EBee EBla EGle EPPr EPfP EPla EPot GSki NRnb SBch SPoG WHoo WMoo WPnP WTMC WWpP
	- 'Show Time'	CMCo EBla WWpP
	- 'St Ola'	More than 30 suppliers
	- 'Westray'PBR	CCge CHid EBee EPPr EShb GAbr GQue MCCP MDun MSte NBlu NEgg NGdn SPoG SRms STes SVil SWvt WCra WWeb
*	***cariense*** **new**	EBee
	cataractarum	CCge MLLN
	- subsp. ***pitardii***	SRGP
	'Chantilly'	CElw CMCo CSam EBee EBla EPPr GBuc MAvo MNFA MNrw NBir NPro SBch WCru WMoo WPnP WPtf WTMC WWpP
	christensenianum B&SWJ 8022	WCru
	cinereum	CCge CWCL EBla ECho
	- 'Album'	ECho NChi
	- 'Apple Blossom'	see *G.* x ***lindavicum*** 'Apple Blossom'
	- 'Ballerina'	see *G.* (Cinereum Group) 'Ballerina'
I	- 'Heather'	CCge EBla EGle LRHS MBNS NBro
	- 'Janette'	LAst LRHS
	- subsp. ***ponticum***	see *G. ponticum*
	- 'Purple Pillow'	More than 30 suppliers
	- Rothbury Gem = 'Gerfos'PBR	CCge EBla
	- 'Sateene' **new**	CElw EBee EBla WCra
	- 'Signal' **new**	EBla
	- 'Souvenir de René Macé'	LBuc MBri
	- subsp. ***subcaulescens*** var. ***ponticum***	see *G. ponticum*
	(Cinereum Group) 'Alice'PBR **new**	CElw EBee EBla MWea
§	- 'Ballerina' ♀H4	More than 30 suppliers
	- 'Carol'	CCge CDes CElw EBee EBla EPPr EWes LAst MBNS MBri MWhe NBro NLar NMRc SWvt WCra WFar
	- 'Giuseppii'	CCge CHFP EBee EBla ECtt EPPr EShb GSki LAst MBri MNFA MNrw MRav MWhe NBPC NBro NCot NPri SMer SPla SRGP SRot WBrE WCra WFar WPnP WRHF WWeb
	- 'Laurence Flatman'	More than 30 suppliers
	- 'Sugar Babe'PBR	CCge
	'Claridge Druce'	see *G.* x ***oxonianum*** 'Claridge Druce'
	clarkei 'Kashmir Blue'	see *G.* 'Kashmir Blue'
	- 'Kashmir Pink'	More than 30 suppliers
§	- 'Kashmir White' ♀H4	More than 30 suppliers
	- 'Mount Stewart'	WCru WHil WPGP
	- (Purple-flowered Group) 'Kashmir Purple'	More than 30 suppliers

'Coffee Time'	WWpP
collinum	EPPr GAbr GBuc MNrw NBir NCot SRGP WBrk WCru WPnP WTMC WWpP
aff. ***collinum***	CDes
'Coombland White'	More than 30 suppliers
Crûg strain	see *G.* x *antipodeum* Crûg strain
'Cyril's Fancy'	EBee EBla EPPr MAvo MNFA WPtf WWpP
dahuricum	EBee WCru
dalmaticum ♀H4	More than 30 suppliers
- 'Album'	CBod CSsd EBee EBla ECho ECtt ELan EPPr EPot LRHS MRav MTho MWhe NChi NRya SIng SMer SPer SRGP SRms SRot SWat WAbe WCra WCru WFar WHCG WWpP
- 'Bressingham Pink'	EPPr WPnP WWpP
- 'Bridal Bouquet'	EBee GBri NChi NMen NSla WAbe WHer WHil
dalmaticum x ***macrorrhizum***	see *G.* x *cantabrigiense*
delavayi misapplied	see *G. sinense*
delavayi Franch.	CDes EBee
'Dilys' ♀H4	CCge CElw EBee EBla EGle ELan EPPr LPio MAvo MLHP MNFA MNrw MSte NBir NChi NGdn NSti SRGP WCru WFar WHal WHen WMoo WPnP WTMC WWpP
dissectum	CHll MSal
'Distant Hills'	CMCo EBee EBla EPPr MAvo SRGP WPtf WWpP
'Diva'	CElw CSam EBee EBla ENot EPPr MAvo MBnl MNrw NSti SBch SRGP WCru WPnP WTMC WWpP
donianum HWJCM 311	WCru
'Dragon Heart' **new**	EBee NSti SPoG
'Dusky Crûg'	More than 30 suppliers
'Dusky Rose'	ELan ENot EPfP LAst LRHS MBNS MGos
'Elizabeth Ross'	MAvo MNrw SBch WCru WHoo WTMC WWpP
'Elke' **new**	EBee EPfP MWea NGdn SPer
'Ella' **new**	CWGN
'Elworthy Dusky'	CCge CElw
'Elworthy Eyecatcher'	CCge CElw SBch
'Elworthy Tiger' **new**	CElw
'Emily'	SRGP WWpP
endressii ♀H4	CBre CElw CSev EBee EBla ECha ECho EHrv EPPr EPfP GMaP GSki MBNS MHer NBro NCGa NEgg NPer SGar SPlb SRGP SRms WFar WMoo WWpP
- 'Album'	see *G.* 'Mary Mottram'
- 'Betty Catchpole'	EPPr
- 'Castle Drogo' ♀H4	EBee EBla ECtt EPPr MAvo SRGP WTMC WWpP
- 'Prestbury White'	see *G.* x *oxonianum* 'Prestbury Blush'
- 'Priestling's Red'	CMCo
- 'Rose'	WPer WWpP
- 'Wargrave Pink'	see *G.* x *oxonianum* 'Wargrave Pink'
- white-flowered	WPtf
erianthum	CCge GBuc GMaP GMac MLHP NBre NLar SRGP STes WCru WWpP
- 'Calm Sea'	CCge EBla GBuc WCru WMoo WTMC WWpP
- 'Neptune'	EPPr GMac NCot WCru WWpP
eriostemon Fischer	see *G. platyanthum*
'Eva'	WPnP
'Expression'PBR	see *G.* 'Tanya Rendall'
'Farncombe Cerise Star' **new**	NCot
§ ***farreri***	CCge EBla EGle GBri GBuc LHop NBir NChi SBla SIng WEas
'Flower Fairy Rose' **new**	LSou
fremontii	EWld
goldmannii	SKHP
gracile	CCge EBee EPla GBuc GMaP LSou MNrw NBir NBre SRGP WBrk WCru WMoo WPnP WTMC WWpP
- 'Blanche'	CElw EBee EPPr SBch WWpP
- 'Blush'	CElw CMCo CWsd EBee EPPr WWpP
grandiflorum	see *G. himalayense*
- var. ***alpinum***	see *G. himalayense* 'Gravetye'
guatemalense B&SWJ 10461 **new**	WCru
'Gwen Thompson'	WOut
gymnocaulon	CCge CMCo CMHG EBee EBla EPPr LRHS MAvo NSti SRGP WCru WWFP WWpP
gymnocaulon x ***platypetalum***	EBee WCra
'Harmony'	EPPr WWpP
harveyi	CBrm CMea CSpe EBee EBla EPPr EWes GSki SPhx SRGP WCru WKif WPGP WPat WSpi
§ ***hayatanum***	NCot WTMC
- B&SWJ 164	CBod WCru WMoo WWpP
§ ***himalayense***	More than 30 suppliers
- CC&McK 442	CMCo
- from Tibetan border	WWpP
- - CC 1957	EPPr
- ***alpinum***	see *G. himalayense* 'Gravetye'
§ - 'Baby Blue'	CCge CElw CSpe EBee EBla EGle EPPr GBuc GCra MAvo MBri MNFA MNrw NCot NGdn NSti SRGP WCru WHen WMoo WPnP WTMC WWpP
- 'Birch Double'	see *G. himalayense* 'Plenum'
- 'Derrick Cook'	CElw EBee EPPr MAvo NCot WCra WWpP
- 'Devil's Blue'	EPPr NCot SRGP WPtf WWpP
§ - 'Gravetye' ♀H4	More than 30 suppliers
- 'Irish Blue'	CElw CMCo EBee EBla ECtt EGle EPPr GBuc LBMP MBri MNFA MSte NCot NPol NSti SRGP WAbb WCra WCru WHal WHen WMoo WTMC WTin WWpP
- ***meeboldii***	see *G. himalayense*
§ - 'Plenum' (d)	More than 30 suppliers
- 'Spiti Valley'	EBee NCot
himalayense x ***pratense***	NEgg
hispidissimum	CFee
ibericum misapplied	see *G.* x *magnificum*
ibericum Cav.	CCge CSBt CTri EBla EPla NBre NLar SMac SPav SRGP STes WFar WPtf WWpP
- 'Blue Springs'	ECtt
- subsp. ***ibericum***	EBee EPPr WWpP
- subsp. ***jubatum***	CElw EBla EPPr MNFA MNrw NCot NSti SRms WCru WPnP WTMC WWpP
- - 'White Zigana'	CDes CFwr EBee NCot WPnP WWpP
- subsp. ***jubatum*** x ***renardii***	SWvt
- var. ***platypetalum*** misapplied	see *G.* x *magnificum*
- var. ***platypetalum*** Boissier	see *G. platypetalum* Fisch. & C.A. Mey.
ibericum x ***renardii***	NSti
incanum	CCge CHll CSev EBee EShb EWes MNrw NBir SGar SMrm SRGP SRot WWpP XPep
- var. ***multifidum***	EPPr WCru WFar
- white-flowered	SRGP
incanum x ***robustum***	CMea CSpe WCru
'Incognito'	MAvo

	'Ivan' 🏆H4	CCge CElw CEnt CMCo EBee EBla ECGP EPPr GBuc LPio LRHS MBNS MNFA NChi NCob NCot NGdn SAga SRGP WCra WCru WMoo WPnP WSHC WWpP
	'Jack of Kilbryde'	GBri
	'Jean Armour'	CDes EBee LRHS MAvo MSte NGdn SRGP WCra WCru WTMC WWpP
	'Jean's Lilac'	see *G.* x *oxonianum* 'Jean's Lilac'
	'Johnson's Blue' 🏆H4	More than 30 suppliers
	'Jolly Bee' PBR	More than 30 suppliers
	'Jolly Pink' **new**	WPnP
	'Joy'	More than 30 suppliers
§	'Kashmir Blue'	CCge CDes EBee EPPr ERou EWsh GMaP MAvo MBnl MNFA NCot NGdn SBch SWat WCAu WMoo WPnP
	'Kashmir Green'	EPPr GBin MAvo NCot SPhx WMoo WPnP
	'Kashmir Lilac'	WHen
§	'Kate'	EBla EPPr WCru WWpP
	'Kate Folkard'	see *G.* 'Kate'
§	'Khan'	CMCo EBee EBla EPPr IPot MAvo MNrw NPro SDys SMHy SRGP WCru WWpP
	kishtvariense	EBee EBla EPPr LRHS MNrw MRav NHol NSti WCru WPnP WPtf
	koraiense	CBod EBla NBre NSti WMoo WWpP
	- B&SWJ 797	WCru
	- B&SWJ 878	EBee WCru
	koreanum misapplied	see *G. bayatanum*
	- B&SWJ 602	WCru
	koreanum ambig.	CCge CDes CEnt EBla GBuc LRHS WFar WHil WMoo WTMC
§	***kotschyi*** var. ***charlesii***	EBee EBla EPPr
	krameri	EBla
	- B&SWJ 1142	EBla WCru
§	***lambertii***	CCge EBla EWes GBuc GCra MNrw NBir NChi WTMC
	- 'Swansdown'	EBla GBuc MNrw WCru WPtf WSHC
	'Lambrook Helen' **new**	CFis
I	***libani***	EBee ELon EPPr GBuc LLWP MTho MWhe NBid NChi NCot NSti WBrk WCot WCru WEas WPnP WTMC WTin WWpP
	libani x ***peloponnesiacum***	CCge CDes CWsd EBee
	'Libretto'	WCru
§	x ***lindavicum*** 'Apple Blossom'	CLyd EBla EBrs GBuc GSki LRHS MSte NChi NMen SBla WAbe WBrE WHCG WLin WSpi
	- 'Gypsy'	SBla
	- 'Lissadell'	SBla
	linearilobum subsp. ***transversale***	EPPr NCot SRot WCru
§	'Little David'	EPPr MAvo SRGP WWpP
	'Little Devil'	see *G.* 'Little David'
	'Little Gem'	CCge CDes CElw CMea EBee EBla EBrs LRHS MAvo NChi NDov NLar WCra WCru WFar WTMC WWpP
	lucidum	MSal NSti NVic
	'Luscious Linda' PBR	CCge EBee GAbr MAvo MBNS MWea NBPN NLar SPer WFar WPnP WWpP
	'Lydia'	SRGP WWpP
§	***macrorrhizum***	More than 30 suppliers
	- AL & JS 90179YU	CHid EPPr
	- 'Album' 🏆H4	More than 30 suppliers
	- 'Bevan's Variety'	More than 30 suppliers
	- 'Bulgaria'	CMCo EPPr WTMC WWpP
	- 'Camce'	EPPr
	- 'Czakor'	More than 30 suppliers
I	- 'De Bilt'	EBee EWes WWpP
	- 'Freundorf'	EPPr MNFA
	- 'Ingwersen's Variety' 🏆H4	More than 30 suppliers
	- 'Lohfelden'	CDes EBee EPPr EWes GBuc MNFA NChi SRGP WPGP WWpP
	- 'Mount Olympus'	see *G. macrorrhizum* 'White-Ness'
	- 'Mount Olympus White'	see *G. macrorrhizum* 'White-Ness'
	- 'Mytikas'	EBee NCot
	- 'Pindus'	CBgR CPrp EBla EPPr GAbr MNFA NBre NCot NSti SPoG SRGP WCru WFar WPnP WTMC WWpP
	- 'Ridsko'	CFee CMCo EPPr GBuc MNFA NBro SRGP WCru WTMC WWpP
	- ***roseum***	see *G. macrorrhizum*
	- 'Rotblut'	EPPr SRGP
	- 'Sandwijck'	CCge EBee EPPr MAvo WWpP
	- 'Snow Sprite'	CBod CCge CEnt CMea COlW EPPr EPyc GSki LSou MCCP MFOX NCot NPro SPoG STes WCra WHrl WWpP
	- 'Spessart'	CCge EBee EBla ELan EPPr EPfP GQue LAst LBMP MSte NCGa NPri WBVN WCra WCru WFar WOVN WPnP WRHF WTMC WWFP WWpP
	- 'Variegatum' (v)	EBee EBla ECha EHrv ELan GMaP LRHS MHer MNFA MTho NBPC NBir NSti SPer SRGP SRms WBrk WCot WEas WFar WHen WMnd WSHC WTMC WWFP WWpP
	- 'Velebit'	CCge EPPr MSte SRGP WCru WTMC WWpP
§	- 'White-Ness'	More than 30 suppliers
	macrostylum	CDes CPou EBrs WBVN WCot WCru WPer WPnP WWpP
	- MP 8103D	EBee WCot
§	- 'Leonidas'	EBee EBrs NCot SPhx WCot WPnP WWpP
	- 'Talish' **new**	LRHS NCot
	maculatum	CElw CMea CSev EBee ECha EPfP EWTr GPoy LLWP LRHS MAvo MRav MSal NSti SMac SWat WCra WCru WHal WHen WPnP WWpP
	- f. ***albiflorum***	CElw EBee EBla EGle EMan EMon EPPr LBBr MNFA MNrw NBid NChi NSti SRGP STes WBrk WCru WMoo WPnP WPtf WTMC WWpP
	- 'Beth Chatto'	More than 30 suppliers
	- 'Elizabeth Ann'	CElw CSam CWGN EBee ECtt EGle EHrv EPPr EPfP GGar LCro LSou MAvo MBNS MWea NBPN NCot NLar NSti WCot WCra WPnP WPtf WTMC
	- 'Espresso'	More than 30 suppliers
	- from Kath Dryden	EPPr WWpP
	- purple-flowered	EPPr WWpP
	- 'Shameface'	EBee EPPr MSte SBch SDys SGar
	- 'Spring Purple'	EBee NCot
	- 'Sweetwater' **new**	EPPr
	- 'Vickie Lynn'	EBee WWpP
	maderense 🏆H2	More than 30 suppliers
	- white-flowered	LDai WCot
§	x ***magnificum*** 🏆H4	More than 30 suppliers
	- 'Blue Blood'	CElw CWGN ECtt EGle EKen EPPr GBri IPot LSou MBri NCob NCot NSti SPoG SRGP WCot WPtf WWpP
	- 'Ernst Pagels' **new**	NCot
	- 'Hylander'	EBee EPPr WWpP
	- 'Peter Yeo'	EBee EPPr SRGP WWpP
	- 'Rosemoor'	CBgR CCge CElw CHid CWCL EBee EBla EHrv ELan EPPr EPfP LCro LHop MBri MNFA MSte NCot NPro NSti WMnd WPtf WTMC WWpP

- 'Vital' CWCL EBee MBri NCot
magniflorum EWes MRav NBid NEgg NGdn SMer WCru
§ ***malviflorum*** CDes CElw CMHG EBee ECha ELan EMar EPPr LLWP LRHS MNFA MNrw MTho SBch SMeo SPhx SRms WAul WCot WCra WCru WFar WHoo WPnP
- from Spain EPPr EWes WSHC
- pink-flowered CDes CMil EBee WCru WMoo WPnP
§ 'Mary Mottram' CElw CMCo EBee EPPr LPio NBir NCot NSti WEas WPnP WWpP
§ 'Mavis Simpson' 🏆^{H4} More than 30 suppliers
maximowiczii CElw CMCo EBee
'Maxwelton' NCot WTMC
'Memories' **new** CElw EBee MBNS NSti
'Menna Bach' WCru WPnP
'Meryl Anne' SRGP WPtf
microphyllum see *G. potentilloides*
x ***monacense*** CMCo EBee EBla ELan EMar EPla GGar GSki LEdu LRHS MWgw SBch SMac SWat WBrk WCru WHer WMoo WPnP WWpP
- var. ***anglicum*** CCge EBla ECtt EPPr GMaP MNFA MRav MWhe WMoo WPnP WWpP
- 'Anne Stevens' NCot
- 'Breckland Fever' EBee EPPr MAvo WWpP
- 'Claudine Dupont' CElw EBee EPPr MAvo NCot WCot WWpP
- dark-flowered CGrW WMoo WWpP
- var. ***monacense*** EBla WFar WHen
§ - - 'Muldoon' CSev EBla EPPr EPla GSki LFur NBir NEgg NOak STes WFar WHCG WHen WMoo WPer WPnP WTMC WWpP
moupinense EBee
'Mourning Widow' see *G. phaeum* var. *phaeum* black-flowered
multisectum WCru WTMC
napuligerum misapplied see *G. farreri*
'Natalie' CDes CElw EBee EBla EPPr NChi SBch WCra WWpP
nepalense CMCo EBee SRGP SRms WMoo WWpP
'Nicola' CCge CElw EBee EBla EPPr GMac MNFA NCob SAga SBch WCra WTMC WWpP
'Nicola Jane' MNFA
'Nimbus' 🏆^{H4} More than 30 suppliers
nodosum More than 30 suppliers
- dark-flowered see *G. nodosum* 'Swish Purple'
- 'Julie's Velvet' CDes LBBr MAvo MSte NCot WHoo WPGP WTin WWpP
- pale-flowered see *G. nodosum* 'Svelte Lilac'
- 'Pascal' WWpP
- 'Saucy Charlie' SBch
- 'Silverwood' CElw EPPr MAvo SBch
- 'Simon' **new** WWpP
§ - 'Svelte Lilac' CElw EBee EBla ECGP EGle EPPr EPfP LBBr MNFA MSte SRGP SWat WCAu WCot WCru WFar WMoo WPnP WWpP
§ - 'Swish Purple' CElw CMCo EBee EBla ELon EPPr LBBr MAvo MNFA MSte NCiC NLar SIng SRGP SWat WCru WFar WHen WMoo WPGP WPnP WWpP
- 'Whiteleaf' CCge CElw CMea EBee EBla EPPr MAvo NPro SBch SRGP SWat WCru WFar WHal WMoo WPnP WTMC WWpP
- 'Whiteleaf' seedling EBla EGle EMan
'Nora Bremner' EBee NChi SRGP WWpP
'Nova' **new** CSpe
'Nunnykirk Pink' EMan EWes MAvo
'Nunwood Purple' CMCo EPPr MAvo NCot WPtf WTMC WWpP
ocellatum CCge
oreganum CCge
§ ***orientalitibeticum*** More than 30 suppliers
'Orion' 🏆^{H4} More than 30 suppliers
'Orkney Blue' WCru
'Orkney Cherry' **new** LRHS
'Orkney Dawn' WCru WTMC
'Orkney Pink' CCge CDes EBee EBla ECtt EPPr EPfP GBuc LHop LSRN MDun MLHP MSte NChi NGdn NLAp NSti NWCA SAga SBla SPer SPoG SRGP SWat WCru WFar WHoo WWeb WWpP
ornithopodon NCot
'Out of the Blue' WOut
x ***oxonianum*** NCot NEgg WMoo
- 'A.T. Johnson' 🏆^{H4} More than 30 suppliers
- 'Anmore' EPPr SRGP
- 'Beholder's Eye' 🏆^{H4} CCge CHid CMCo EBee EBla ECGP EPPr GAbr MNFA MSte NBre SBch SRGP WPnP WPtf WTMC WWpP
- 'Breckland Sunset' EPPr NCot SBch SRGP WPnP WTMC WWpP
- 'Bregover Pearl' CBre CElw CMCo CWsd EBee EBla EPPr MNFA NCot SRGP WMoo WTMC WWpP
- 'Bressingham's Delight' CMCo EBla ECtt LRHS SRGP WCra WTMC WWpP
- 'Buttercup' EBee EMan EPPr NCot WWpP
I - 'Cally Seedling' EBee EBla EWes
§ - 'Claridge Druce' More than 30 suppliers
- 'Coronet' CCge EPPr MNFA SRGP WMoo WWpP
- 'David Rowlinson' **new** EPPr
- 'Dawn Time' WWpP
- 'Diane's Treasure' NCot
- 'Dirk Gunst' CElw
- 'Elsbeth Blush' EBla NCot WWpP
- 'Elworthy Misty' CCge CElw CMCo EBee EBla EPPr NCot SBch WWpP
- 'Frank Lawley' CElw CFis CMCo EBee EBla EPPr GBuc GMac LLWP NBid SBch SMrm SRGP WBrk WMoo WTMC WWpP
§ - 'Fran's Star' (d) EBee EBla EGoo WBrk WCru WRHF WTMC WWpP
- 'Frilly Gilly' **new** EBee
- 'Hexham Pink' CCge CMCo EBee EPPr NChi NPro SBch SRGP WTMC WWpP
- 'Hollywood' CCge CMCo EBee EBla ELan EPPr EPfP GBuc LRHS MBnl MBri MSte MTho NCot NLar NPer SRGP SRms WBor WBrk WCra WFar WMoo WPnP WPtf WTMC WWpP
- 'Jean's Lilac' NCot
- 'Julie Brennan' EBee EPPr GAbr GBin GMac NGdn NSti SRGP WWpP
- 'Julie Searle' SRos
- 'Kate Moss' EBee EBla EPPr GCai MBnl NSti SBch SRGP WCra WTMC WWpP
- 'Katherine Adele' CCge CHFP CSpe EBee EBla ECtt ENot EPPr EWes GGar IPot LSou MBnl MWea NBPN NBhm NCot NLar NSti SPoG SRGP
§ - 'Kingston' CElw CMCo EBee EPPr WWpP
- 'Klaus Schult' LPio
- 'Königshof' EBee EPPr EWes NCot NLar WWpP
- 'Kurt's Variegated'^{PBR} see *G.* x *oxonianum* 'Spring Fling'
- 'Lace Time' CBre CCge CElw CMCo CSev EBee EBla EPPr GBuc GMac LBMP MBnl MNFA MNrw MWhe NCGa NCot NEgg NGdn NHol NOak SBch

	SRms WCAu WMnd WMoo WPnP WTMC WWpP
- 'Lady Moore'	CCge CMCo EBee EBla EPPr EPla GBuc MNrw NBro NCot SRGP WCra WHen WMoo WPnP WTMC WWpP
- 'Lambrook Gillian'	CCge CFis CWsd EBee EPPr MNFA NCot SBch SRGP WBrk WPnP WPtf WTMC WWpP
- 'Lasting Impression'	EBee EPPr SRGP WWpP
- 'Little John' **new**	EWes
- 'Maid Marion' **new**	EWes
- 'Man of Mystery' **new**	EBee
- 'Miriam Rundle'	CElw EPPr MNrw NCot SRGP WCru WMoo WPnP WTMC WWpP
- 'Moorland Jenny'	CElw WMoo WWpP
- 'Moorland Star'	MAvo WMoo
- 'Old Rose'	EBee EGle ENot EPPr LRHS MNFA SBch SRGP WCra WCru WPnP WTMC WWpP
- 'Pat Smallacombe'	CElw EBla EPPr NCot SRGP WCru WMoo WTMC WWpP
- 'Patricia Josephine'	WCAu
- 'Pearl Boland'	EBee EPPr SRGP
- 'Phoebe Noble'	CBre CCge CElw CMCo EBee EBla EGle EPPr MNFA MNrw MWgw NCob NCot SAga SRGP WCra WMoo WPnP WPtf WTMC WWpP
- 'Phoebe's Blush'	EBee EBla EPPr GMac SBch WTMC WWpP
- 'Pink Lace'	CCge LSou SMad
§ - 'Prestbury Blush'	CBre CElw CMCo EPPr SRGP WCru WTMC WWpP
- 'Prestbury White'	see *G.* x *oxonianum* 'Prestbury Blush'
- 'Raspberry Ice'	EBee EBla EWes
- 'Rebecca Moss'	CSev EBee EBla EMar EPPr GBuc GMac LRHS MNFA MSte NCot NSti SAga SBch SHBN SRGP WCra WFar WPnP WPtf WTMC WWpP
- 'Rodbylund' **new**	EBee
- 'Rose Clair'	CCge CElw CHid CMCo CTca EBee EBla EGle LAst LRHS MNFA NBir SGar SMer SPet SRGP SRms WBrk WCru WEas WHen WMnd WMoo WPer WTMC WWpP
- 'Rosemary'	SBch WWpP
- 'Rosemary Verey'	SBch
- 'Rosenlicht'	CElw CSev EBee EBla EPPr LRHS MNFA MRav NLar SRGP WCAu WCra WCru WMnd WMoo WPnP WPtf WWpP
- 'Rosewood'	SRos
§ - 'Spring Fling'^{PBR} (v)	CCge CRez EBee EBla ECtt EHrv EPPr GQue GSki LFur MBNS NCot NGdn NSti SPla SPoG SRGP STes WCAu WCot WSpi WWeb
- 'Stillingfleet'	see *G.* x *oxonianum* 'Stillingfleet Keira'
§ - 'Stillingfleet Keira'	EBee NCot NSti SRGP WWpP
- 'Summer Surprise'	CElw CFwr EBee EPPr EWes NCob NLar SBch SRGP WCru WPnP WTMC WWpP
- 'Susan'	EBee EBla EPPr EWes
- 'Susie White'	CElw CMCo EPPr MAvo SRGP WCru WWpP
§ - f. ***thurstonianum***	More than 30 suppliers
- - 'Armitageae'	EBee EPPr MNFA NCot SRGP WTMC WWpP
- - 'Breckland Brownie'	CElw CMCo EBee EBla EPPr EWes MAvo NCot SRGP WWpP
- - 'Crûg Star'	CCge
- - 'David McClintock'	CCge CMCo EPPr MNFA SBch SRGP WFar WMoo WTMC WWpP
- - 'Peter Hale'	CMea SAga

- - 'Red Sputnik'	EBee EPPr MAvo SRGP WWpP
- - 'Sherwood'	CBod CCge EBee EBla ECtt EPPr GQue MBnl MTho MWgw NBro NCob NEgg NRnb NVic SApp SGar SRGP WCAu WCra WFar WLin WMoo WPnP WPtf WWpP
- - 'Southcombe Double' (d)	CElw CMCo CSev EBee EBla EGle EHrv EPPr EPfP MNFA NChi NCot NGdn SRGP SRms WBrk WCra WCru WFar WHen WMoo WTMC WWpP
§ - - 'Southcombe Star'	EBee EBla EPPr GAbr MBnl NBro NGdn SRGP WBrk WCru WFar WHen WMoo WPer WPnP WTMC WWpP
- - 'Sue Cox'	NCot NLar
- 'Trevor's White'	EBee EBla EGle EPPr MBnl MNFA MNrw SBch SRGP WCru WTMC WWpP
- 'Wageningen'	CBre CMCo EBee EGle EPPr GMac MSte NCot NGdn NPro SAga SRGP SRms WBrk WCra WCru WHen WHer WMoo WPtf WTMC WWpP
- 'Walter's Gift'	More than 30 suppliers
§ - 'Wargrave Pink' ♀H4	More than 30 suppliers
- 'Waystrode'	CMCo EBla EPPr SRGP WTMC WWpP
- 'Whitehaven'	EBee NCot WWpP
- 'Winscombe'	CElw CMCo EBee LLWP LRHS MRav MTho MWgw NCob WCAu WFar WHen WMnd WMoo WWpP
- 'Winston Churchill'	WWpP
'Pagoda'	CCge MNrw
x ***oxonianum*** x ***sessiliflorum*** subsp. ***novae-zelandiae*** 'Nigricans'	EHrv
§ ***palmatum*** ♀H3	More than 30 suppliers
palmatum x ***maderense*** **new**	WCru
palustre	CElw CMCo EBee EBla EPPr MNFA MNrw NBro NHol SRGP WFar WHen WMoo WPnP WTMC WTin WWpP
papuanum	SBla WCru
'Patricia' ♀H4	More than 30 suppliers
peloponnesiacum	EBee EPPr GGar WFar
- NS 660	CElw
'Perfect Storm' **new**	CWGN EBee SPoG
phaeum	More than 30 suppliers
- 'Album'	More than 30 suppliers
- 'Alec's Pink'	EBla EPPr LLWP SHar WOut WTMC WWpP
- 'All Saints'	EBee EMon LEdu WTMC WWpP
- 'Angelina' **new**	NCot
- 'Anne Claire' **new**	NCot
- 'Aureum'	see *G. phaeum* 'Golden Spring'
- black-flowered	see *G. phaeum* var. *phaeum* black-flowered
- 'Blauwvoet'	CFwr EBee MAvo NCot WTMC WWpP
- 'Blue Shadow'	CDes CElw CMCo EBee EBla EPPr MAvo NCot WTMC WWpP
- 'Calligrapher'	CElw EBla EPPr MAvo MNFA SBch SRGP WMoo WTMC WWpP
- 'Chocolate Chip'	CMCo EBla WTMC WWpP
- 'Conny Broe' (v)	EBee NCot
- dark-flowered	CElw SWat
- 'David Bromley'	EMon WCru WPrP WPtf WTMC
- 'Geele Samobor'	EBla WTMC
- 'George Stone'	EBee EBla EPPr WWpP
- 'Golden Samobor' **new**	CElw
§ - 'Golden Spring'	CCge CElw EBee EBla EPPr MAvo MNFA NChi NCot NPro SBch SRGP WTMC WWpP

	- 'Hannah Perry'	CElw EBla EPPr LLWP MBnl WPtf WTMC
	- var. ***hungaricum***	EBee EPPr SRGP WCru WTMC WWpP
	- 'James Haunch' **new**	WTMC
	- 'Klepper'	CFwr CMCo EBee GBin NCot WTMC WWpP
	- 'Lily Lovell'	More than 30 suppliers
	- 'Lisa' **new**	EBee NCot
	- 'Little Boy'	CMCo EBee EBla EMon EPPr NGdn SRGP WTMC WWpP
	- var. ***lividum***	CBgR CBre CElw CFee EMar EWTr GMaP LLWP MAvo MRav MWgw NCot NEgg NHol SRGP SRms WCAu WFar WHen WPer WPnP WTMC WWpP
	- - 'Joan Baker'	CBgR CBre CElw COlW CSam EBee EPPr GBuc LLWP MAvo MBnl MNFA MWhe NChi NCot NGdn NSti SBch SPhx SRGP SWal SWat WCra WCru WFar WMoo WPnP WTin WWpP
	- - 'Majus'	CCge CElw EBee ECtt EMon EPPr EPfP EPyc LLWP SBch SPhx SWat WFar WMoo WPnP WTMC WWpP
	- 'Maggie's Delight' (v)	NCot SRGP
	- 'Marchant's Ghost'	MAvo NGdn SMHy SPhx WTMC
	- 'Margaret Hunt' **new**	NLar
	- 'Margaret Wilson' (v)	CBow CDes CElw CFir EBla ECha ECtt EPPr EWes LEdu LPio MBNS NCot SRGP WCot WPnP WTMC WWpP
	- 'Mierhausen'	CElw CMCo EBee EPPr EShb MAvo NCot WPtf WTMC WWpP
	- 'Moorland Dylan'	MAvo WMoo WTMC WWpP
	- 'Mourning Widow'	see *G. phaeum* var. *phaeum* black-flowered
	- 'Mrs Charles Perrin'	CBgR CCge CElw EBee EBla EPPr MAvo STes WTMC WWpP
	- 'Night Time'	EBee EPPr MNFA WWpP
	- 'Our Pat'	NCot WWpP
	- var. ***phaeum***	LCro NBPN SBch WOut
§	- - black-flowered	EGle EPPr EShb MWhe NCob NCot NDov SGar SRGP SRms SWat WCru WHen WMoo WWpP
	- - 'Langthorns Blue'	CCge CElw CMCo CSev EBee ELan EPPr LEdu MAvo MNFA MNrw NBre SRGP WCra WHen WTMC WWpP
	- - 'Samobor'	More than 30 suppliers
I	- 'Ploeger de Bilt'	EPPr WTMC
	- purple-flowered	MDun
	- 'Rachel's Rhapsody'	CMCo EBee EBla EPPr MAvo NCot WWpP
	- 'Raven'	EBee WTMC WWpP
	- red-flowered	MRav WTMC
	- 'Rise Top Lilac'	CCge CMCo EBee NCot WTMC WWpP
	- 'Rose Air'	CMCo EBee EGoo EPPr MAvo MNFA SRGP WMoo WPnP WPtf WTMC WWpP
	- 'Rose Madder'	CBgR CCge CElw EBee EGle EPPr EPyc GBuc LHop LLWP LPio MNFA MNrw MSte NChi NCot NMRc SPhx SRGP WCru WMoo WWpP
	- 'Saturn'	WTMC WWpP
	- 'Séricourt'	WCot
	- 'Small Grey'	EBla EPPr WTMC
	- 'Springtime' PBR	CElw EBee EPPr EPfP MAvo MBnl NBPN NBhm NCot NSti SPoG
	- 'Stillingfleet Ghost'	CBow CElw EBee EBla EPPr LEdu NCot NPro NSti WTMC
	- 'Taff's Jester' (v)	CCge CElw EBee EWes NHol SApp SMrm SRGP WCot WTMC WWpP
§	- 'Variegatum' (v)	More than 30 suppliers
	- 'Walküre'	CMCo EBee EPPr EWes MAvo MSte WTMC WWpP
	- 'Zit Factory'	WTMC
	'Philippe Vapelle'	More than 30 suppliers
	'Pink Delight'	CElw EBee EBla LPio MAvo SPhx WWpP
	'Pink Ghost' **new**	CBow
	'Pink Splash'	LSou STes
§	***platyanthum***	CCge CWsd EBee EPPr GGar MNrw NBre SRGP WBrk WCru WHCG WHen WMoo WPer WWpP
	- giant	EPPr SGar
	- var. ***reinii***	WCru
	- - f. ***onoei***	WCru
	platypetalum misapplied	see *G.* x *magnificum*
	platypetalum Franch.	see *G. sinense*
§	***platypetalum*** Fisch. & C.A. Mey.	EPPr EWsh LRHS NBid NBir NBre NSti SRGP SRms SWat WCru WPtf WTMC WWpP
	- 'Georgia Blue'	MSte WCru WFar WPtf
§	***pogonanthum***	CDes CWsd EBee GBuc NBir NChi WCru WMoo WOut WPtf WWpP
	polyanthes	EBee GBuc NEgg WTMC WWpP
	- HWJCM 276	WCru
§	***ponticum***	CHar NSti
§	***potentilloides***	CCge EBee GSki NBir SRGP WWpP
	pratense	CArn CBre CHrt CMCo CRWN EBee EBla ECtt ELan EPPr GMaP LRHS NBPC NCot NLan NMir NPri SPer SPlb SRms SWat WBVN WCot WFar WHen WMoo WPer WPnP WSFF WWpP
	- Black Beauty = 'Nodbeauty' PBR	CBct CPen EBee ELan ENot EWes EWld LSou MGos NPri SCoo SDnm SPav SPer SPoG SRot WHlf
	- 'Bittersweet'	CBgR CHar CMCo EBee EBla EMon EPPr WWpP
	- 'Cluden Sapphire'	CAbP EBla NBre NCot NGdn NHol NPro WCru WFar WWpP
	- 'Feebers Double' (d) **new**	CFee
	- 'Flore Pleno'	see *G. pratense* 'Plenum Violaceum'
I	- 'Himalayanum'	NLar
	- 'Hocus Pocus'	EBee EGle EHrv EPfP ERou LPio MAvo MBNS NBPN NBhm NBid NBro NLar NMoo SHBN WCAu WPnP WPtf
	- 'Ilja' **new**	EBee
	- 'Janet's Special'	WHoo
	- 'Lilac Lullaby'	EBee WWpP
	- Midnight Reiter strain	More than 30 suppliers
	- 'Mrs Kendall Clark' ♀H4	More than 30 suppliers
	- 'New Dimension'	EBee ELan ENot EPPr EPfP GBin LRHS MGos MWea NBPN NBre NSti SSvw WCot WWpP
	- 'Okey Dokey'	EBee WWpP
	- pale-flowered	EBee WPnP WWpP
	- 'Picotee'	EBee NCot
	- 'Plenum Album'	EGle NCob NCot NGdn NLar SPer SPoG WCra WGwG WTMC
	- 'Plenum Caeruleum' (d)	CHar CMHG EBee EGle EPPr GBuc GMaP MBNS MDun MRav NBid NGdn NHol NSti SHBN SPer SPla SRGP STes SWat WCra WCru WFar WHCG WMoo WPnP WSHC WTel WWlt WWpP
	- 'Plenum Purpureum'	see *G. pratense* 'Plenum Violaceum'
§	- 'Plenum Violaceum' (d) ♀H4	More than 30 suppliers
	- var. ***pratense*** f. ***albiflorum***	CElw CSam EPPr GCra GMaP MNrw NBid NCot NEgg NOrc SPer WCru WHCG WHen WMnd WMoo WPnP WTMC WWpP

	- - - 'Galactic'	CBgR CCge EBee EPPr NBir NBre NGby SPhx WCru WHen WMoo WPnP WWpP
	- - - 'Plenum Album' (d)	CDes EBee EPPr NEgg NLar NSti WCot WPnP
	- - - 'Silver Queen'	CBre CCge CHar EBee EBla ECtt EPPr MNrw NBir NBre SRGP WFar WHen WMoo WPGP WPnP WTMC WWpP
	- 'Purple Heron'	CDes EBee EBla EPPr LAst LFur LSRN MBri MCCP MNrw MSte MTPN NEgg NGdn SPla STes WCra WFar WGor
*	- 'Purple-haze'	CCge CTca GBuc GSki LSou MCCP NCob NLar WHrl WWpP
	- 'Rectum Album'	see *G. clarkei* 'Kashmir White'
§	- 'Rose Queen'	CBgR EBee EBla EPPr MNrw MRav NBir NEgg NHol NLar SRGP WCra WCru WHen WPnP WTMC WWpP
	- 'Roseum'	see *G. pratense* 'Rose Queen'
	- 'Splish-splash'	see *G. pratense* 'Striatum'
	- 'Stanton Mill'	NBid
	- var. ***stewartianum***	EBee MRav
	- - 'Elizabeth Yeo'	CCge EBee EBla EPPr NCot NLar SGar WCru WTMC WWpP
	- - 'Purple Silk'	EPPr
§	- 'Striatum'	More than 30 suppliers
	- 'Striatum' dwarf	WCru
	- 'Striatum' pale-flowered	CBre
§	- Victor Reiter Junior strain	More than 30 suppliers
	- 'Wisley Blue'	CMCo EBee EBla EPPr MSte SBch SRGP WHal WWpP
	- 'Yorkshire Queen'	CBgR CMCo EBee EPPr NCob NGdn WCru WWpP
	'Prelude'	CBre CCge CDes CElw EBee EPPr NBir NCot NPro SRGP WCra WTMC WWpP
	'Priestley's Pink'	WWpP
	procurrens	CBre CElw COlW CPLG CSev EBee EMar EPPr EShb GAbr GGar LLWP MLLN NBid NGdn NSti WBrk WCru WFar WHen WMoo WPnP WPtf WRos WWpP
§	***psilostemon*** ♀H4	More than 30 suppliers
	- 'Bressingham Flair'	CMCo CPrp EBla ECtt EGle EPfP GAbr GCra GSki LHop LRHS MNFA MRav NBid NChi NGdn NHol NLar SMer SRms WCAu WCru WFar WMoo WSHC WTMC
	- 'Goliath'	EPPr EWes
	- hybrid	CElw
	- 'Madelon'	EBee NCot NLar
	pulchrum	CHid CSpe EBee EPPr MNrw SGar SRGP STes SWat WCot WPer WRos WWpP
	punctatum hort.	see *G.* x *monacense* var. *monacense* 'Muldoon'
	- 'Variegatum'	see *G. phaeum* 'Variegatum'
	pusillum	MSal
	pylzowianum	CCge CMCo EBee GGar MRav NBid NRya SBch WFar WHen WMoo WTel WWpP
	pyrenaicum	CCge CRWN CSev EBee EWsh GAbr NBre NEgg NSti SBch SWat WBrk WHen WTMC WWpP
	- f. ***albiflorum***	CCge CHrt EBee EBla GAbr LLWP MNFA MNrw NBir NEgg SAga SRGP WBrk WPer WPnP WWpP
	- 'Barney Brighteye'	CCge EBee SRGP
	- 'Bill Wallis'	More than 30 suppliers
	- 'Bright Eyes' **new**	NCot
	- Gordon's strain	NEgg
	- 'Isparta'	CElw EBee EGle EPPr NCot SBch SPhx SRGP WBrk
	- 'Summer Sky'	CCge EBrs GBin LFur NCot SPav SRGP WPtf WWpP
	- 'Summer Snow'	CCge EPyc LFur NCot NLar SBod SPoG WWpP
	'Rachel'	CBow
	'Rambling Robin'	EBee ECtt EMan EPPr EWes LSou WCru XPep
§	Rambling Robin Group	CBow ECre GSki LFur LSou MCCP SMad
	'Ray's Pink'	CCge NPro WWpP
	rectum	EPPr NBre WCru
	- 'Album'	see *G. clarkei* 'Kashmir White'
	'Red Admiral'	CMCo EBee NCot SRGP WCra
	'Red Dwarf'	CCge WMoo
	reflexum	CSev EBla EPPr WFar WTMC WWpP
	refractoides	CFwr EBee MLul
	refractum	EBee
	- from China	MLul
	regelii	CCge CElw CMCo CSam EBee EPPr LEdu MNFA NCot SBch WCra WCru WMoo WPnP WWpP
	renardii ♀H4	More than 30 suppliers
	- 'Beldo'	EBee
	- blue-flowered	see *G. renardii* 'Whiteknights'
	- 'Heidi Morris'	WWpP
	- 'Tcschelda'	CMCo EBee EBla ECha EMil EShb LPio NCGa SBod SPla SRms SWat WCra WFar WPnP WWpP
§	- 'Whiteknights'	CElw EBee EBla ECha GBuc MAvo NBir WCru
	- 'Zetterlund'	CElw CMCo EBee EBla ECGP EGle EHrv EPPr EWTr LLWP LPio MAvo MLLN MNFA MWat MWhe NPri SWat WBrk WCAu WCra WCru WFar WMnd WMoo WTMC WWpP
	repens B&SWJ 9089 **new**	WCru
§	***reuteri***	CCge CHEx IDee LDai SBod SChr SDnm SGar SPav SRGP WCru WPnP WSHC
	'Richard John'	CCge MNFA
	richardsonii	CCge EBee EBla EPPr MNrw NBir NCot SRGP SRms WCru WPnP WPtf WTMC WWpP
	x ***riversleaianum*** 'Mavis Simpson'	see *G.* 'Mavis Simpson'
	- 'Russell Prichard' ♀H4	More than 30 suppliers
§	***rivulare***	CCge EBla GMac GSki NBre NSti WHCG WMnd WPtf WWpP
	- 'Album'	EBla
	robertianum	CArn CCge EPPr GWCH MHer SECG SRms WHen WWpP
§	- 'Album'	CBgR CBod EBla EPPr SHar SRms
	- f. ***bernettii***	see *G. robertianum* 'Album'
	- 'Celtic White'	CBgR CBre CCge EMon EPPr GSki MHer NGHP SPav SRGP WHen WOut WPnP WWpP
	robustum	EGoo EPPr GSki MNrw NBro NChi SMad SPav SRGP STes WCot WCru WFar WHal WKif WPGP WSHC WWpP XPep
	- Hannays' form	CCge CSev CSpe EBee
	'Rosie Crûg'	CCge CHid SWvt WCru
	rosthornii	WCru
	Rozanne = 'Gerwat'PBR	More than 30 suppliers
	rubescens	see *G. yeoi*
	rubifolium	GGar MNFA NChi NHol WCru WTMC
§	'Ruprecht'	CWsd LFur WCra
	ruprechtii misapplied	see *G.* 'Ruprecht'
	ruprechtii (Grossh.) Woronow	CCge CElw EBee EPPr MAvo MNrw NBre SRGP WPer WWpP
	Sabani Blue = 'Bremigo'	CSpe EBee EWes GBin LCro LEdu LHop LRHS MSte MWea NLar NSti SPer SPoG SRkn

	'Salome'	More than 30 suppliers
	sanguineum	More than 30 suppliers
	- Alan Bloom = 'Bloger'^{PBR}	EBrs LRHS SIng WCra WTMC
	- 'Album' ♀H4	More than 30 suppliers
	- 'Alpenglow'	EPPr SBch SRGP
	- 'Ankum's Pride' ♀H4	CBgR CCge CMMP EBee EBla EGle EMon EPPr GMac IPot LPio LRHS NChi NCot NDov NGdn NSti SWat WCra WCru WFar WMoo WPnP WTMC WWpP
	- 'Apfelblüte'	CRez EBee NCot NLar SSvw WFar
	- 'Aviemore' ♀H4	EBee EPPr GBin NCot SBch WWpP
	- 'Barnsley'	CElw CPrp EBee EPPr NBro NPro WHrl WTMC WWpP
	- 'Belle of Herterton'	CMCo EBee EPPr MSte NBid NPro SBch WCru WTMC WWpP
	- 'Bloody Graham'	EBee EGle EPPr MWhe SBch WMoo WWpP
	- 'Canon Miles'	EBee EPPr GGar LRHS NCot
	- 'Catforth Carnival'	EPPr WWpP
	- 'Cedric Morris'	CElw EBla ECha EGle EPPr GCra LPio MAvo MTho NBid SAga SRGP WCru WHen WPnP WTMC WWpP
	- 'Compactum'	CFwr EBee WWpP
§	- 'Droplet'	SRGP WPnP WWpP
	- 'Elsbeth'	CBgR CCge CElw CMCo EBee EBla ECha ECtt EPPr EWes GBuc NCot NEgg NGdn NSti SPoG SRGP WCra WCru WFar WHal WMoo WPnP WTMC WWpP
	- 'Feu d'Automne'	EPPr WWpP
	- 'Fran's Star'	see *G.* x *oxonianum* 'Fran's Star'
	- 'Glenluce'	More than 30 suppliers
	- 'Hampshire Purple'	see *G. sanguineum* 'New Hampshire Purple'
	- 'Holden'	CElw EPPr SBch WWpP
	- 'Inverness'	CFwr EBee EPPr NCot WWpP
	- 'Joanna'	MAvo
	- 'John Elsley'	CCge CElw CMCo CPrp EBee EBla ECtt EPPr LLWP LRHS MWhe NBro NCot NGdn NLar SRGP SWat WBVN WCra WMnd WPer WPnP WTMC WWpP
	- 'John Innes'	CFwr EBee NCot WWpP
	- 'Jubilee Pink'	CElw EBla SBla WCru WTMC
	- var. ***lancastrense***	see *G. sanguineum* var. *striatum*
	- 'Leeds Variety'	see *G. sanguineum* 'Rod Leeds'
§	- 'Little Bead'	EBla ECho WCru WPnP WWpP
	- 'Max Frei'	More than 30 suppliers
	- 'Minutum'	see *G. sanguineum* 'Droplet'
	- 'Nanum'	see *G. sanguineum* 'Little Bead'
§	- 'New Hampshire Purple'	CBgR CCge CPrp EBee ECho EPPr GGar LSou NBro NGdn NLar NSti SSvw WCra WTMC WWpP
	- 'Nyewood'	EBee ECGP EMon EPPr MLLN SEND SRGP WCra WCru WWpP
I	- 'Plenum' (d)	EPPr WWpP
	- var. ***prostratum*** (Cav.) Pers.	see *G. sanguineum* var. *striatum*
	- 'Purple Flame'	see *G. sanguineum* 'New Hampshire Purple'
§	- 'Rod Leeds'	CBgR EBee LPio MSte MWea NPro NSti WPnP WTMC WWpP
	- 'Sandra'	WWpP
	- 'Sara'	WHen WPnP WWpP
	- 'Shepherd's Warning' ♀H4	CBgR CCge CMea CSev CTca CTri EBee EBla ECtt EPPr MLLN NBir NLar SEND SRGP SWat WCra WCru WHCG WHoo WSpi WTel WTin WWpP
	- 'Shooting Star'	EBee
	- 'South Nutfield'	MAvo
§	- var. ***striatum*** ♀H4	More than 30 suppliers
	- - deep pink-flowered	CSBt MSwo SWvt WWpP
	- - 'Reginald Farrer'	GBuc WCru WWpP
	- - 'Splendens' ♀H4	CCge CElw CEnt CSev CWib EBla ELan EPPr LBee LHop NBid NChi NCot WCru WEas WPnP WTin WWpP
	- 'Vision Violet'	CCge CFwr EBee EBla NCot NHol SGar SWvt WFar WPer WPnP WWpP
	- 'Vision Light Pink'	WPtf
	- 'Westacre Poppet'	EPPr EWes WWpP
	saxatile <u>**new**</u>	EBee EPPr
	schlechteri	EBee GKev
	'Sea Fire'	CCge MNrw
	'Sea Pink'	CElw MNrw
	'Sellindge Blue'	NCot WCra WWpP
	sessiliflorum	ECou
	- subsp. ***novae-zelandiae*** green-leaved	SWat
I	- - 'Nigricans'	CCge EBee EBla ECha ECho EHrv ELan EPfP GAbr GGar IPot LFur MHer NMoo NWCA SBch SRGP WBrE WEas WFar WHCG WPnP WTMC WWpP
§	- - 'Porter's Pass'	CBow CSpe CWib EBee ECho EWes GBuc LAst MCCP MNrw NBir SBch SPlb SWat WFar WHoo WPnP WTMC WWpP
	- - red-leaved	see *G. sessiliflorum* subsp. *novae-zelandiae* 'Porter's Pass'
*	- 'Rubrum'	GSki WBVN
	'Sheilah Hannay'	CSpe
	shikokianum	EShb LFur MCCP NLar SAga SGar SPer SRGP WCra WHrl WWpP
	- var. ***kaimontanum***	EBee EBla WCru
	- var. ***quelpaertense***	CDes EBee EBla WPtf
	- - B&SWJ 1234	WCru
	- var. ***yoshiianum***	CCge CElw GBuc NChi WMoo WTMC
	- - B&SWJ 6147	WCru
	'Shocking Blue'	EBee LCro MWea NSti
	'Shouting Star' <u>**new**</u>	CDes
	Silver Cloak Group	see *G.* Rambling Robin Group
*	'Silver Shadow'	LDai NSti SPhx WMnd
§	***sinense***	CFir CMHG EBee EBla EPPr LFur MBri MNrw NGdn NSti SPoG SRGP WCru WHer WMoo WPer WPnP WTMC WWpP
	- B&SWJ 7870	WCru
	'Sirak' ♀H4	More than 30 suppliers
	soboliferum	CBod CWsd EBee EBla ELan EPPr MAvo NBir NDlv NSti SPla SRGP WCru WMoo WPtf WWpP
	- Cally strain	MSte
	'Southcombe Star'	see *G.* x *oxonianum* f. *thurstonianum* 'Southcombe Star'
	'Southease Celestial'	SMHy SSth
	'Spinners'	More than 30 suppliers
	stapfianum var. ***roseum***	see *G. orientalitibeticum*
	'Stephanie'	CDes CElw CMCo EBee EPPr EWes GGar MAvo MWea NCot WWpP
	'Strawberry Frost'	EBla LTwo MBNS
	subcaulescens ♀H4	More than 30 suppliers
	- 'Signal'	EBee
	- 'Splendens' ♀H4	CSpe CTri EBee EBla ECtt EDAr EPPr EPfP LHop MBNS MDun MHer MWhe NDov NPri NSla NSti SHBN SPla SRms SWat WFar WPat WPnP WWpP
*	- 'Violaceum'	EPPr NEgg
	'Sue Crûg'	More than 30 suppliers
	'Sue's Sister' <u>**new**</u>	WCru
	'Summer Cloud'	EBee EBla EPPr NCot SRGP WCra WHrl
§	Summer Skies = 'Gernic'^{PBR} (d)	CCge CFir CWGN EBee EGle EPPr EPfP GBri GKev GMaP LRHS LSou MAvo MBNS MBnl NBro NCob NCot NLar NMoo SPer SPoG

	WCAu WCot WCra WFar WHil WPnP WSHC WTMC
(Sunstar Series) 'Sunstar Red' **new**	LSou
- 'Sunstar Salmon' **new**	LSou
suzukii	WPtf
- B&SWJ 016	WCru
swatense	MLLN SWat
sylvaticum	CBgR CMMP CRWN EBee EBla MSal NBid NGdn WBVN WBrk WHen WMoo WPer WShi WTMC WWpP
- f. ***albiflorum***	CBre CCge CElw EBee ELan EMar MWhe NSti WCru
- 'Album' ♀H4	More than 30 suppliers
- 'Amy Doncaster'	More than 30 suppliers
- 'Angulatum'	CElw EBee EPPr MNFA SBch WMoo WWpP
- 'Birch Lilac'	CElw EBee EBla EPPr EPfP GBuc MAvo MNFA WCra WFar WMoo WPnP WTMC WWpP
- 'Birgit Lion'	EBee NCot
- 'Caeruleum'	WLin
* - 'Heron'	CCge
- 'Ice Blue'	EBla EPPr GBin NCot WWpP
- 'Immaculée'	EBee EPPr MRav WCot WWpP
- 'Kanzlersgrund'	CElw EPPr
- 'Lilac Time'	EBla EPPr WWpP
- 'Mayflower' ♀H4	More than 30 suppliers
- 'Meran'	CCge EPPr
- 'Nikita'	EPPr WWpP
- f. ***roseum***	CCge EPPr GGar NBre NLar WOut
- - 'Baker's Pink'	CBgR CCge CElw EBee EBla EGle EPPr MNFA MRav NCot SBch SRGP WCra WCru WFar WHCG WMoo WPnP WTMC WWpP
- 'Silva'	CElw EBee ECtt EPPr MAvo MNFA MRav SWat WCru WWpP
- subsp. ***sylvaticum*** var. ***wanneri***	CCge EBee EPPr SBch WCru WTMC WWpP
§ 'Tanya Rendall'[PBR]	EBee GAbr GBin GQue MBNS MBri MWea NBPN NBhm NMoo NSti SMer SPer WBVN WCot WCra WFar WPnP WTMC WWFP WWpP
'Terre Franche'	EBee EPPr LHop MAvo NGby NLar SSvw WFar
'Thorn's Blue'	CCge
§ ***thunbergii***	CCge CEnt CHFP CHid CPLG EBee EBla EDAr EShb EWes GAbr GGar GSki LAst LLWP LSou MSte NBid NOak NSti SRGP SWat WHen WMoo WPer WPnP WTMC WWpP
- dark-flowered	EMar WSpi
- 'Jester's Jacket' (v)	CCge EKen EPPr GWWP ITer LFur MCCP NPro NSti SGar SRGP WCot WCru WHrl WOut WPnP WPtf WTMC WWpP
- pink-flowered	EPPr SRGP WCru WTMC
- white-flowered	EPPr SRGP WTMC
thurstonianum	see *G.* x *oxonianum* f. *thurstonianum*
'Tidmarsh'	EBee
'Tinpenny Mauve'	WHoo WTin
'Tiny Monster'	CCge CDes CFwr CHFP CMCo EBee EBla EPPr EWes LSou MAvo MBNS MBnl MBri NCot NGby NLar NSti SKHP WGer WWpP
transbaicalicum	CCge CFwr EBee EPPr GBin MNrw SRGP WCra WWpP
traversii	CAbb CCge CWib GGar LRHS WRos
- var. ***elegans***	CFee CSpe CWib ECtt GGar LRHS MNrw WCru WEas WHCG WKif
tuberosum	CElw CHid CHrt EBee EBla EBrs ECha ECho ELan EShb EWsh LRHS MNFA MTho MWhe NBir NBro NGdn NSti SGar SMeo SPhx WCra WFar WPnP WSpi
- var. ***charlesii***	see *G. kotschyi* var. *charlesii*
- 'Leonidas'	see *G. macrostylum* 'Leonidas'
- subsp. ***linearifolium***	WCru
- pink-flowered	WCru WHal
'Ushguli Grijs'	EBee EBla IPot NCot
'Vera May'	CElw
'Verguld Saffier'	see *G.* Blue Sunrise
versicolor	CElw CMea COIW CRWN EBee EBla EMar EPfP GAbr GGar GSki MHer MNrw MTho MWhe NVic SPet SRms WBrk WCru WFar WHCG WMoo WPnP WWpP
- 'Kingston'	see *G.* x *oxonianum* 'Kingston'
- 'Knighton'	WWpP
§ - 'Snow White'	CCge CElw CMCo ECtt EGoo EPPr MNFA MNrw MWhe NBre NCot SRGP WCra WCru WMoo WPnP WTMC WWpP
- 'The Bride'	CMea EMar
- 'White Lady'	see *G. versicolor* 'Snow White'
'Victor Reiter'	see *G. pratense* Victor Reiter Junior strain
violareum	see *Pelargonium* 'Splendide'
viscosissimum	EBla GSki SRGP WMnd
- var. ***incisum***	EWsh MCCP NBre WTMC WWpP
- rose pink-flowered	NBir
wallichianum	CBod CCge CHrt CMCo CPou EBee ECGP NBir NChi NSti WFar WHen WMoo WTMC
§ - 'Buxton's Variety' ♀H4	More than 30 suppliers
- 'Chadwell's Pink'	CCge EBee NEgg
- 'Chris'	EPPr SRGP
- pale blue-flowered	CElw
- 'Pink Buxton'	EBee EWes NLar
- pink-flowered	EBla GBuc NCot WCru WWpP
- 'Rosie'	SRGP
- 'Syabru'	CCge CElw CMea EBla EMar GBuc GSki MNrw NCot NLar SAga WFar WMoo
'Wednesday's Child'	WFar
'Welsh Guiness'	WCru WTMC
wilfordii misapplied	see *G. thunbergii*
wilfordii Maxim.	CCge
Wisley hybrid	see *G.* 'Khan'
'Wisley Jewel' **new**	EBee ENot
wlassovianum	More than 30 suppliers
- 'Blue Star'	CCge MRav NPro SRGP WFar WTMC WWpP
§ ***yeoi***	CSpe EPPr MNrw NBir NBro NDov NSti SRGP WCru WOut WTMC
yesoense	EBla EPPr GGar NBir NSti SRGP SWat WCru WFar WOut
- var. ***nipponicum***	WCru
yoshinoi misapplied	see *G. thunbergii*
yunnanense misapplied	see *G. pogonanthum*
yunnanense ambig.	CFir
yunnanense Franchet BWJ 7543	WCru

Gerrardanthus (*Cucurbitaceae*)

macrorhiza	ERea

Gesneria (*Gesneriaceae*)

cardinalis	see *Sinningia cardinalis*
x ***cardosa***	see *Sinningia* x *cardosa*
* ***macrantha*** 'Compacta'	EShb

Gethyum (*Alliaceae*)

atropurpureum	WCot
cuspidatum	WCot

Geum (*Rosaceae*)

'Abendsonne'	CElw MAvo

	aleppicum	CFee NBre SBri
	alpinum	see *G. montanum*
	andicola	NBre
	'Beech House Apricot'	More than 30 suppliers
	'Bell Bank'	CElw CFee CSam EBee EPPr GAbr GBri MAvo MFOX MHer MRav NBir NBre NChi NCot NDov NGby NPro WCot WMoo
	'Birkhead's Cream'	NBir
	'Birkhead's Creamy Lemon'	CElw MAvo SBri
	'Blazing Sunset' (d)	CElw EBee EBla ECtt ERou EUnu IPot LSou MAvo MBNS MDKP MHer MNHC MRav MWrn NBre NCob NDlv NPro SHGN SPad WFar WHil
N	'Borisii'	More than 30 suppliers
	'Borisii' x ***montanum***	LHop
	'Bremner's Nectarine' new	MAvo NChi
	bulgaricum	CElw EBee LRHS MAvo MRav NBir NLar NPro NRya WPnP WPrP WTMC WTin
	'Butterscotch' new	EBee
	'Caitlin'	EMon
	calthifolium	EBee EPPr EWTr MCCP MLLN MRav NBre NBro
	capense	LSou NBre NPro SHGN SPlb
	- JJ&JH 9401271	EBee EWes
§	***chiloense***	EBla LEdu
	- P&W 6513	GBri NWCA
	- 'Farncombe'	NCot
	- 'Red Dragon'	EBee LTwo
	'Chipchase'	MAvo NChi
	coccineum misapplied	see *G. chiloense*
	coccineum ambig.	EBla GKev MLHP
	coccineum Sibth. & Sm. MESE 374	EBee
	- 'Cooky'	CSam ERCP EWTr EWll GBri LRHS LSou NGBl NPri SPoG SWal WHil WRHF
	- 'Eos'	CDes EBee MAvo WCot
§	- 'Werner Arends'	CMHG CSev EBee EBla GAbr MAvo MBnl MNrw MRav NBro SBri WCot WFar WMoo
	'Coppertone'	CDes CElw COlW EBee EBla ECha ECtt EHrv ELan EMon MAvo MNrw MRav NBir NBro NChi NRya SBri SPav WAul WHoo WMoo WPrP WTMC WTin
	'Dingle Apricot'	CElw CFir ECtt EMan GBin MAvo MNrw MRav NBir
	'Dolly North'	EBee EMan EPyc GAbr GBri GGar LRHS MAvo MBNS MNrw MRav NBro NGdn WAul WCAu WHal WPrP WTMC WTin
	elatum	EBee EBla
	'Farmer John Cross'	CBre CDes CElw EBee EBla ECtt MAvo MHar MNrw NCob NCot NLar SBri WCra WHal WMoo
	fauriei x ***kamtschatica***	EBee EBla
	'Feuerball'	NBre NGdn
	'Feuermeer'	EBee EBla MSte NLar NPro SBri
	'Fire Opal' 🏆^{H4}	CDes EBee EWes MAvo MNrw NBir NBre WMoo WPGP
	'Fireball'	NBhm
	'Flames of Passion'^{PBR}	CHar EBee EBla ECtt EMan GBin GMac MAvo MBNS MBri MWea NBPC NLar SBri STes WAul WCAu WCot
	'Georgenburg'	CElw CPrp CSam EBee EBla ECtt EPfP GGar GMaP LRHS MAvo MHer MNrw MRav NBir NBre NCob NGdn SPer SPoG SRms SWvt WAul WFar WHoo WMoo WPrP WTMC
	glaciale album	NBre
	'Herterton Primrose'	CElw ECtt GBri LTwo MAvo SBri WHal WHoo
	'Hilltop Beacon' new	WPrP
*	***hybridum luteum***	NSti
	x ***intermedium***	CBre EBee EBla EGle EMon EPPr GBri MAvo MBnl MNrw NGdn NLar NPro SBri SHGN WFar WMoo WPtf WTMC
	- 'Diane'	MAvo NBre NChi WHil
I	***japonicum*** 'Variegatum' (v) new	EBee
	'Karlskaer'	CElw EBee EBla ECtt EPfP EWes GBin LRHS MAvo MBnl MBri MHar MNrw NCob NGdn SBri WCot WFar WLin WMoo WPnP
	'Kashmir'	MAvo SBri
	'Kath Inman'	MAvo
	'Lady Stratheden' 🏆^{H4}	More than 30 suppliers
	'Lemon Drops'	More than 30 suppliers
	'Lionel Cox'	More than 30 suppliers
	'Lisanne'	EBee NCot
	'Llyn Cream' new	WOut
	macrophyllum	EBee EMan
	magellanicum	EBee EBla EWes NBre NLar
	'Mandarin'	CFir EBla GAbr
	'Marmalade'	EBee EBla ECtt GAbr MAvo MBnl MHar MNrw NBre NLar NPro SAga SBri SDys SMHy SPhx WCra WHrl WKif WMoo
§	***montanum*** 🏆^{H4}	CEnt EBla ECho EDAr GCra LEdu NBir NBre NGdn NPri NRya SRms WMoo WPat
	- 'Diana'	EMon MNrw NCot NDov NLar SBri
	'Moorland Sorbet'	MAvo WFar WMoo
	'Mrs J. Bradshaw' 🏆^{H4}	More than 30 suppliers
	'Mrs W. Moore'	CBre CDes CElw EBee ECtt EShb GAbr GBri LBMP MAvo MBnl MHer MLLN MNrw NBir NChi NCot NLar NPro SRGP WMoo WPrP WTMC
	'Nordek'	EBee EMan GAbr GBuc IPot LAst MAvo MWgw NCob SBri WSpi
*	'Orangeman'	MAvo MNrw
	parviflorum	GGar LEdu MLLN NBre NBro
	'Paso Doble'	CElw SBri WRHF WRos
§	***pentapetalum***	GEdr WAbe WFar
	- 'Flore Pleno' (d)	WAbe
	'Pink Frills'	CElw EBee EBla ECha GAbr GBri LBMP LFur NCot NDov NLar SBri SMHy STes WPrP
	ponticum	WOut
	'Present'	CElw EBee EBla ECtt MAvo NBre NChi SBri
	'Primrose'	GAbr GQue NGdn NLar NPro WTMC
	'Prince of Orange'	CElw EBla GAbr IGor MNrw NBre WFar WMoo
	'Prinses Juliana'	CElw EBee EBla EMar EShb EWTr GBuc GCra GMac LAst LCro MAvo MBNS MBri MNFA MRav NBPC NBir NBro NCiC NDov SPla STes WCAu WCot WCra WFar WMnd WMoo WPnP
	pyrenaicum	EBee EBla NBre
	quellyon	see *G. chiloense*
I	'Rearsby Hybrid'	MAvo MRav NChi
	'Red Wings'	CMMP EBee EBla EMan MBNS MNrw MRav NBro SHar
	reptans	see *Sieversia reptans*
	x ***rhaeticum***	EBee MNrw WMoo
	rhodopeum	EBee NBre
	'Rijnstroom'	CElw EBee EBla ELan ERou LDai MWea NBPC NBro WPtf
	rivale	More than 30 suppliers

- 'Album'	More than 30 suppliers
- 'Barbra Lawton'	EBla MAvo MDKP
- 'Cream Drop'	EBla MSte NChi NGby NPro SBri
- cream-flowered, from Tien Shan, China	CFee
- 'Leonard's Double' (d)	CPrp MAvo SHar WFar WHil WMoo WTMC
- 'Leonard's Variety'	More than 30 suppliers
- 'Marika'	CBre CCVN CHid EBee EBla MNrw NBre WMoo WOut
- 'Marmalade'	EBla LFur MSte NBPC NChi
- 'Oxford Marmalade'	CElw SApp
- 'Snowflake'	NChi
roylei	NBre
'Rubin'	CElw EBee EBla ECtt EPPr EPyc GBuc MBNS MNrw NBre NBro NDov SBch SBri SMHy WAul WCAu WTMC
'Sigiswang'	CDes CElw EBee GAbr GMac MAvo MNrw MRav MSte NBre NPro SBri WMoo WPGP
I 'Starker's Magnificum'	WCot
'Susan Grayer' (v)	CNat
'Tangerine'	EBla GGar LSou MAvo MNrw MRav NPro SBri
'Tinpenny Orange'	CElw MAvo WTin
x ***tirolense***	EBee EBla NBre
triflorum	CFwr EBee EBla EHrv EPla MCCP MNrw NLar SPhx SRot WFar WLin WPnP WTin
- var. ***campanulatum***	GBri NChi NPro NRya
urbanum	CArn ELau GWCH NLan NPri NSco SECG SWat WHer WMoo
- from Patagonia	EBla MAvo MDKP
- 'Checkmate' (v)	EMon
'Werner Arends'	see *G. coccineum* 'Werner Arends'

Gevuina (*Proteaceae*)

avellana	CBcs CHEx CTrG WPGP

Gilia ✿ (*Polemoniaceae*)

aggregata	see *Ipomopsis aggregata*
'Red Dwarf'	NPol
tricolor	NPol

Gillenia (*Rosaceae*)

stipulata	EBee EGle EMon LEdu NDov NLar SPhx
trifoliata ♀H4	More than 30 suppliers
- 'Pixie'	EBee WPGP

Ginkgo ✿ (*Ginkgoaceae*)

biloba ♀H4	More than 30 suppliers
- B&SWJ 8753	WCru
- 'Anny's Dwarf'	SCoo SIFN
- 'Autumn Gold' (m)	CBcs CEnd CMCN EBee ECrN MBlu MGos MPkF SIFN SMad WPGP
I - 'Barabits Nana'	CMCN SIFN SMad
- 'Chase Manhattan' **new**	NBhm
- 'Chi-chi' **new**	SIFN
- 'Chotek'	SIFN
- 'Doctor Causton' (f)	CAgr
- 'Doctor Causton' (m)	CAgr
- 'Elsie'	SIFN
- 'Fairmount' (m)	CMCN MBlu SIFN
- 'Fastigiata' (m)	CLnd CMCN EPfP LPan MGos SBLw
- 'Golden Globe'	NLar
- 'Hekt Leiden'	CMCN
- 'Horizontalis'	CLnd CMCN CMen LCon MBlu SIFN
- 'Jade Butterflies'	CBcs MPkF NLar SLim
- 'King of Dongting' (f)	CMCN MBlu SIFN
- 'Mariken'	LCon MAsh MGos MPkF NLar NPal SIFN SLim
- 'Mayfield' (m)	SIFN
- Ohazuki Group (f)	CAgr SIFN
- Pendula Group	CEnd CMCN CTho EPfP IDee MPkF NPal SIFN SLim
- 'Pixie' **new**	SIFN
- 'Princeton Sentry' (m)	IDee MBlu SIFN SMad
I - 'Prostrata'	CPMA
- 'Saratoga' (m)	CBcs CDoC CEnd CLnd CMCN CPMA CTho MBri MGos MPkF SIFN SLim WPGP
- 'Tit'	CEnd CMCN CMen EPfP MGos NLar SIFN WPGP
- 'Tremonia'	CMCN EPfP IClo MBlu MPkF NLar SIFN SLim
- 'Troll'	SCoo SIFN
- 'Tubifolia'	CMCN CMen LLin MBlu NLar SIFN SLim SMad
- 'Umbrella'	CMCN SIFN
- Variegata Group (v)	CMCN CMen CPMA LLin MBlu MPkF NLar SIFN SLim

ginseng see *Panax ginseng*

Gladiolus (*Iridaceae*)

'About Face' (Min)	MSGs
acuminatus	WCot
alatus	EBee EBrs LPio
- white-flowered **new**	WCot
'Alba' (N)	CGrW
'Alexander S' (L)	MSGs
'Alexandra' (P)	WCot
'Allosius' (S)	CGrW
'Amanda P' **new**	MSGs
'Amsterdam' (G)	CGrW MSGs
'Andre Viette'	EBee EMan LFur WCot
'Angel' (P) **new**	MSGs
angustus	CGrW WCot
'Anna Leorah' (L)	MSGs
antakiensis	CPou
'Antica' (L)	CGrW
'Antique Lace' (L)	CGrW
'Antique Rose' (M)	CGrW
'Anyu S' (L)	MSGs
'Arctic Day' (M/E)	CGrW
'Atom' (S/P)	CGrW EBee EBrs WHil
atroviolaceus	WCot WPGP
'August Days' (L)	MSGs
aurantiacus	WCot
'Bangledesh' (M)	MSGs
Barnard hybrids	CGrW
'Beau Rivage' (G)	MSGs
'Beautiful Angel'	CGrW MSGs
'Beauty Bride' (L)	CGrW MSGs
'Beauty of Holland'PBR (L)	CGrW MSGs
'Bella Donna' **new**	MSGs
'Ben Venuto' (L)	CGrW
'Bizar'	EPfP
'Black Cherry' **new**	WCot
'Black Jack'	CSpe EMan EPfP LCro NBPN SPer
'Black Pearls' (S)	MSGs
'Blackbird' (S)	CGrW
blandus var. ***carneus***	see *G. carneus*
'Blue Bird' **new**	MSGs
'Blue Clouds' (L)	CGrW
'Blue Conqueror' (L)	LRHS
'Blue Tropic'	CSut
I 'Blushing Bride' (L) **new**	CGrW
bonaespei	WCot
'Bono's Memory'	LRHS
'Bradley W' (M)	MSGs
'Breathless'	MSGs
'Brittania' (L)	CGrW
'Burgundy Queen' (M)	WCot
byzantinus	see *G. communis* subsp. *byzantinus*

caeruleus	CGrW CPou WCot
callianthus	CFFs CSWP CStu EBla ECho EPfP LPio MSte NCGa SGar SPet WFar WHil
'Calliope' (L/E)	CGrW
'Candy' (L) **new**	CGrW
cardinalis	CAby CDes CMea CPne CPrp EBla EMan IBlr SAga SKHP WCot WCru WPGP
carinatus	CDes CGrW WCot WHil
carinatus x ***orchidiflorus***	EBee WCot
carmineus	CGrW CWsd WCot WPGP
§ ***carneus***	CGrW CHHB CPou EBee EBrs EMan LPio SMeo WPGP
'Carquirenne' (G)	CGrW MSGs
'Carved Ivory' (M)	MSGs
caryophyllaceus	CPou
'Century Mark' (G)	MSGs
'Charm' (N/Tub)	CAvo CFFs CPrp EBee EBla
'Charming Beauty' (Tub)	EBrs ECho
'Charming Lady' (Tub)	ECho
'Chartreuse Ruffles' (S) **new**	CGrW
'Chinon'^{PBR} (L)	CGrW
'Chloe' (M)	MSGs
'Christabel' (L)	ERos
'Cindy' (B)	ECho SPer
citrinus	see *G. tribonemifolius*
'Claudia' (N)	CGrW EBrs
'Clemence' (Min)	CGrW MSGs
x ***colvillii***	CPne IBlr
- 'Albus'	CHHB EBrs EPot LPio SPhx WHil
- 'The Bride' ♀H3	CAvo CElw CFFs CHFP CPrp EBee EBla ECho GGar GMac ITim LAma LDai LEdu LPio MWgw
'Comet' (N)	EBrs LPio WHil
§ ***communis*** subsp. ***byzantinus*** ♀H4	More than 30 suppliers
'Contessa Queen'	CGrW
'Coral Dream' (L)	CGrW
'Côte d'Azur' (G)	CGrW MSGs
crassifolius	CFir GBuc
'Cream of the Crop' (M)	MSGs
'Cream Perfection' (L)	CGrW MSGs
'Creamy Yellow' (S)	MSGs
'Cristabel' **new**	WCot
'Crusader' (L)	CGrW
§ ***dalenii***	CPou CPrp CSam EBee ERos IBlr LFur LPio SKHP WCot WPGP
- subsp. ***dalenii***	IBlr
- green-flowered	CDes IBlr
- hybrids	WCot
- orange-flowered	CDes
* - f. ***rubra***	IBlr WCot
- yellow-flowered	CDes EBee WPGP
'Darlin' Clementine' (L)	CGrW MSGs
'Daydreamer' (L)	CGrW
'Day's End' (S)	CGrW
'Deanna' (L) **new**	CGrW
'Deans List' (L) **new**	CGrW MSGs
'Desirée' (B)	MSGs
'Doris Darling' (L)	MSGs
'Drama' (L)	CGrW MSGs
ecklonii	WPGP
'Edie' (P) **new**	MSGs
'Elegance' (G)	CGrW MSGs
'Elvira' (N)	EBee EBla EBrs ECho WPGP
'Emerald Spring' (S)	CSpe WCot
'Emir' (S)	MSGs
'Esperanto' (M)	MSGs
'Esta Bonita' (G)	CGrW MSGs
'Fabienne'	SPer
'Felicta' (L)	MSGs
'Femme Fatale' (L)	CGrW
ferrugineus	LPio
'Final Touch' (G)	CGrW
'Fineline' (M)	CGrW
'Finishing Touch'^{PBR} (L)	CGrW MSGs
'Fireball II' (L)	MSGs
flanaganii	CPBP CSpe EBrs ECho GBin GCrs LPio SKHP WCot
- JCA 261.000	EBee
'Flevo Amico' (S)	CGrW WCot
'Flevo Bambino' (S)	CGrW
'Flevo Clown' (S)	WCot
'Flevo Cosmic' (Min)	CGrW LPio MSGs
'Flevo Eclips'^{PBR} (G)	CGrW MSGs
'Flevo Eyes'^{PBR} (L)	CGrW
'Flevo Fire'^{PBR} (M)	CGrW MSGs
'Flevo Jive' (S)	CGrW
'Flevo Junior' (S)	CGrW
'Flevo Party' (S)	CGrW
'Flevo Smile' (S)	CGrW MSGs
'Flevo Souvenir'^{PBR} (L)	CGrW
'Flevo Sunset'^{PBR} (L)	CGrW
'Flevo Touch' (S)	MSGs
'Flevo Vision' (L)	CGrW MSGs
floribundus	EBee
'French Silk' (L)	CGrW
'Friendship' (L)	LRHS
garnieri	CWsd
'Gladiris' (L)	MSGs
'Gold Struck' (L)	CGrW
'Golden Melody' (M)	MSGs
'Golden Sunset' (L)	MSGs
gracilis	WCot
grandis	see *G. liliaceus*
'Green Isle' (M/E)	CGrW
'Green Star' (L)	CGrW CSut MSGs
'Green with Envy' (L)	MSGs
'Green Woodpecker' (M)	EBee LAma LRHS
'Guernsey Glory' (N)	EBrs
'Gwendolyn'	MSGs
'Halley' (N)	ECho
'Helvetia' (L) **new**	CGrW
'Hi-Lite' (L)	CGrW
'Hint o' Mint' (S) **new**	CGrW
hirsutus	CGrW
'Honeydew'	MSGs
'Hotline'	MSGs
'Hunting Song' (L)	LAma
'Huron Dancer' (L) **new**	CGrW
'Huron Frost' (L)	CGrW MSGs
'Huron Heaven' (L)	CGrW
'Huron Jewel' (M)	MSGs
'Huron Kisses'	MSGs
'Huron Lady'	CGrW
'Huron Meadow' (M) **new**	CGrW
'Huron Pleasure' **new**	CGrW
'Huron Silk' (L)	CGrW MSGs
'Huron Touch' **new**	CGrW MSGs
'Huron White' (M)	CGrW
huttonii	CGrW WCot
huttonii x ***tristis***	CPou
huttonii x ***tristis*** var. ***concolor***	WCot
hyalinus	WCot
'Ice Cream'	SPer
'Ice Follies' (L)	MSGs
illyricus	CPen CSam GBuc GKev WBVN WPGP
imbricatus	CHHB EBee EBrs ECho ERos GBuc GCrs
'Impressive' (N)	EBrs EPot WHil
'Irish Blessing' (S)	CGrW
§ ***italicus***	CGrW CPen EBee EBrs ELan LEdu MSte SPhx WHil
'Ivory Priscilla'^{PBR} (L)	CGrW MSGs
'Ivory Queen'	MSGs

'Ivory Towers' (G)	MSGs
'Jayvee' (S)	CGrW
'Jean K' (M)	CGrW
'Jim S' (G)	CGrW MSGs
'Jo Ann' (L)	CGrW
'Jolly Joker'	SPer
'Jupiter' (B)	LRHS
'Karen P' **new**	MSGs
kotschyanus	EBee EBrs ECho GCrs
'Kristin' (L)	CGrW MSGs
'Lady Caroline' (P)	MSGs
'Lady Helen' (P) **new**	MSGs
'Lady in Red' (L)	MSGs
'Lady Lucille' (M)	CGrW MSGs
'Lady Millicent' (P) **new**	MSGs
'Laura Jay' (P) **new**	MSGs
'Lavender Flare' (S)	CGrW
'Lavender Maiden' (L)	CGrW
'Lavender Rose' (L)	MSGs
'Lemon Drop' (S)	MSGs
'Lemon Zest' (M)	CGrW
§ ***liliaceus***	CDes CGrW WCot
'Lime Green' (P)	LRHS
'Linne' (S)	MSGs
'Little Jude' (P)	MSGs
'Little Rainbow' (P)	WCot
'Loulou' (G)	CGrW
'Lowland Queen' (L)	CGrW MSGs
maculatus	WPGP
'Maggie' (S)	CGrW
'Maria K' (L) **new**	CGrW MSGs
'Marj S' (L)	CGrW MSGs
'Mary Housley' (L)	SPer
meliusculus	WCot
'Mexico' **new**	CSut
'Mileesh' (L)	CGrW MSGs
'Millennium' (L)	CGrW
miniatus	EBee
'Mirella' (N)	EBrs MRav
'Mon Amour'PBR	CSut
montanus **new**	CPen
monticola	EBee
'Moon Mirage' (G)	MSGs
'Moon Shadow' (M/E)	CGrW
mortonius	CMdw WPGP
'Mother Theresa' (M)	MSGs
'Mr Chris' (S)	MSGs
'Mrs Rowley' (P)	GBri
§ ***murielae*** ♀H3	CAvo CFFs CGrW CHHB CMea EBee EBrs EWll LAma SMeo SPer STes SWal WGwG WHal WHoo
'Murieliae'	see *G. murielae*
natalensis	see *G. dalenii*
'Nathalie' (N)	CGrW EBee EBrs LEdu WHil
'New Elegance'	MSGs
'Nicholas' (S)	MSGs
'Nikita' (P)	MSGs
'Nova Lux' (L)	LAma LRHS SPer
'Nymph' (N)	CAvo CElw CFFs CHFP CMea EBee EBla EBrs ECGP EPot ITim LAma LDai LEdu LPio SPur SWal WHil
'Oasis'PBR (G)	CGrW
'Obrigado' (L) **new**	CGrW
ochroleucus	EBee
'Of Singular Beauty' (G)	CGrW MSGs
§ ***oppositiflorus***	CDes CPou EBee WPGP
- subsp. ***salmoneus***	see *G. oppositiflorus*
orchidiflorus	CGrW CPou
'Orient Express'	MSGs
'Oscar' (G)	LRHS
palustris	ERos WCot
'Pansy Face' **new**	MSGs
papilio	More than 30 suppliers
- 'David Hills'	WCot WHal
§ - Purpureoauratus Group	CSam EBee EMan ERos IBlr SRms
- 'Ruby'	CAby CPen SMad
- yellow-flowered	SMHy SMad
pappei	CDes EBee WPGP
'Peach Cobbler'	CGrW
'Perky' (Min)	SPer
permeabilis	EBee WPGP
'Perth Ivory' (M)	MSGs
'Perth Pearl' (M)	CGrW MSGs
'Peter Pears' (L)	CSut LRHS
'Phyllis M' (L)	CGrW
Pilbeam hybrids	CGrW
'Pillow Talk'	MSGs
'Pink Elegance' (L)	CGrW
'Pink Elegance' **new**	MSGs
'Pink Elf' (S)	MSGs
'Pink Lady' (L)	CGrW MSGs
'Pink Light' **new**	MSGs
'Pink Phantom' (L)	CGrW
'Pinnacle' (L)	CGrW MSGs
'Plaisir' **new**	MSGs
'Plum Tart' (L)	LRHS SMeo
'Polar Sunset'	MSGs
'Polar Sunshine'	MSGs
'Pop Art'	LRHS
primulinus	see *G. dalenii*
'Princess Margaret Rose' (Min)	LAma
'Prins Claus' (N)	CGrW CMea EBee EBla EBrs LRHS WHil
'Priscilla' (L)	LAma
'Pulchritude' (M)	MSGs
punctulatus var. ***punctulatus***	ERos
'Purple Haze'	MSGs
'Purple Prince' (M)	CGrW WCot
'Purple Spray' **new**	WCot
purpureoauratus	see *G. papilio* Purpureoauratus Group
'Raspberry Swirl' (L/E)	CGrW
'Red Alert' (L)	MSGs
'Red Beauty'	LRHS
'Revelry' (S)	MSGs
'Robinetta' (*recurvus* hybrid) ♀H3	CElw EBee EBla EBrs ECho EPfP GGar LAma LDai SPur WHil
'Roma' (L)	MSGs
'Rose Elf' (S)	MSGs
'Rose Laguna'	MSGs
'Royal Spire'	CGrW
'Ruth Ann'	CGrW MSGs
'Sabu'	LRHS
'Sailor's Delight' (L)	MSGs
'Salmon Sorbet'	CGrW
'San Remo'PBR (L)	CGrW
'Santa Lucia' (L)	CGrW
'Sarajevo' **new**	MSGs
'Satin 'n' Lace' (L)	CGrW
saundersii	WCot WPGP
'Sceptre' (L)	CGrW
seedling 95-042-03 **new**	MSGs
seedling 98-053-03 **new**	MSGs
seedling S376-6 **new**	MSGs
seedling S378-2 **new**	MSGs
seedling T473-1 **new**	MSGs
segetum	see *G. italicus*
'Serafin' (Min)	LRHS
sericeovillosus	IBlr
'Sharkey' (G)	CGrW
'Show Chairman' (L)	MSGs
'Show Star' (L)	CGrW
'Show Stopper' (G)	CGrW
'Silvana' (S)	CGrW
'Silver Dream' **new**	MSGs
'Silver Green' (L) **new**	CGrW
'Sirael' (L/E)	CGrW MSGs WCot
'Sky High' (M)	CGrW

'Smoke Stack' (L) **new** CGrW
'Snow Cap' (L) CGrW MSGs
'Snow Queen' (L) **new** CGrW
'Solveiga' (L/E) CGrW
'Sophie'PBR CGrW
'Sparkle Plenty' MSGs
'Spic and Span' (L) CSut
splendens CDes CGrW WCot WPGP
'Spontaneous Combustion' MSGs
'Spring Thaw' (L/E) CGrW
'Starfish' (S) MSGs
'Stella' **new** SPer
'Stromboli' (L) MSGs
'Sue' (P) MSGs
'Sunset Fire' (G) CGrW MSGs
'Super High Brow' (G) CGrW MSGs
'Sylvia' MSGs
'Tante Ann' (M) CGrW
teretifolius WPGP
'Tesoro' (M) MSGs
'Think Pink' (L) MSGs
'Tiger Eyes' (S) CGrW
'Topaz' (L) CGrW MSGs
'Trader Horn' (G) LAma SPer
§ ***trichonemifolius*** WPGP
tristis CElw CGHE CGrW CMea CPne CPou EBee EBrs ECha EDif ELan EMan LPio LRHS NCGa SAga SDix WFar WHal WPGP WSHC
- var. ***concolor*** CGrW CPrp EBee EMan ERos LFur LPio WCot
undulatus ERos WCot WPGP
usyiae CPou
'Vanilla Swirl' (L) **new** MSGs
'Velvet Eyes' (M) SPer
venustus WPGP
'Vesuvio' MSGs
'Victoria' (M) LRHS
'Video' (L) CGrW
'Vienna' (L) CGrW
'Violetta' (M) CGrW ECho EMan MSGs SPer
virescens CPou LFur WCot
'Visual Arts' (M) CGrW
'Wandering Eyes' MSGs
watermeyeri WPGP
watsonioides CPou ERos SKHP
watsonius WPGP
'White City' (P/S) LRHS
'White Friendship' (L) LAma
'White Ice' MSGs
'White Out' (M) CGrW
'White Prosperity' (L) CSut LRHS
'Wine and Roses' (L) SPer

Glandularia see *Verbena*

Glaucidium (*Glaucidiaceae*)

palmatum ♀H4 EBee EFEx GCra GCrs GEdr GKev NSla SPoG WAbe WBVN WCru WHal
- 'Album' see *G. palmatum* var. *leucanthum*
§ - var. ***leucanthum*** EFEx GCrs NSla

Glaucium (*Papaveraceae*)

§ ***corniculatum*** CSpe EBee MLLN MWgw NLar SEND SPav SPhx SPoG WCot WEas
flavum CArn CHrt CSpe ECha EGoo ELan EWsh LRHS MHer NLar SMad SMeo SPav XPep
- ***aurantiacum*** see *G. flavum* f. *fulvum*
§ - f. ***fulvum*** ECha EMan EWTr SDix WCot WHil
- orange-flowered see *G. flavum* f. *fulvum*
- red-flowered see *G. corniculatum*
phoenicium see *G. corniculatum*

Glaux (*Primulaceae*)

maritima WPer

Glechoma (*Lamiaceae*)

hederacea CArn GPoy LAst MHer NMir NSco WHer XPep
- 'Barry Yinger Variegated' (v) EBee WCot
§ - 'Variegata' (v) EWin LRHS MBri NBlu SPet

Gleditsia (*Caesalpiniaceae*)

caspica CArn SMad
japonica EPfP
macrantha EGFP
sinensis NLar
triacanthos CAgr CDul CWib ECrN EMac LEdu LPan MGol SBLw SPlb WBVN WNor
- 'Bujotii' SBLw
- 'Calhoun' CAgr
- 'Elegantissima' (v) SPer
- 'Emerald Cascade' CBcs CDul CEnd EBee MBri WFar
- f. ***inermis*** CAgr SBLw WNor
- 'Millwood' CAgr
- 'Rubylace' CBcs CDul CEnd CMCN EBee ECrN ELan EPfP LBuc LCro LPan LRHS MAsh MBar MBlu MGos MRav MSwo SBod SHBN SLim SPer WCot WFar WOrn
- 'Shademaster' NLar SBLw
- 'Skyline' SBLw
- 'Sunburst' ♀H4 More than 30 suppliers

Globba (*Zingiberaceae*)

andersonii CKob
* ***cathcartii*** CKob
'Emerald Isle' LRHS
marantina CKob EBrs ECho LEdu
'Mount Everest' EBrs
winitii LRHS
I - 'Pink Dancing Girl' ECho
- 'Ruby Queen'PBR **new** MJnS

Globularia (*Globulariaceae*)

alypum XPep
bellidifolia see *G. meridionalis*
bisnagarica WLin
cordifolia ♀H4 EBee ECho EDAr EPot GEdr LRHS MTho NLAp NMen SBla SIng WFar
- NS 696 NWCA
incanescens LRHS
§ ***meridionalis*** CFee CPBP EBee ECho EPot EWes GMaP NLAp NMen SAga SBla WFar WHal WPat
- 'Blue Bonnets' GEdr NHar
- 'Hort's Variety' CPBP NMen WAbe
nana see *G. repens*
nudicaulis GEdr SBla SIng
- 'Alba' WIvy
punctata CSpe GKev GMaP LRHS NChi NWCA SRms
pygmaea see *G. meridionalis*
§ ***repens*** CLyd EPot MTho NMen SIng WAbe WPat
spinosa NWCA WLin
trichosantha CFee ECho EPot SPet SRms WFar WPer

Gloriosa (*Colchicaceae*)

lutea see *G. superba* 'Lutea'
rothschildiana see *G. superba* 'Rothschildiana'
superba ♀H1 CAby CHHB EShb MBri
- 'Carsonii' EBee
§ - 'Lutea' CHHB EBee EBrs LAma LRHS

§ - 'Rothschildiana' CBcs CDul CRHN CStu EBee EBrs ECho EPfP LAma LRHS SOWG SRms

Glottiphyllum (*Aizoaceae*)

nelii CStu

Gloxinia (*Gesneriaceae*)

nematanthodes 'Evita' new SKHP WCot
sylvatica CHal CSpe EShb WDib

Glumicalyx (*Scrophulariaceae*)

flanaganii GCrs GKev NLAp WAbe
- HWEL 0325 NWCA
montanus CFee EMan IDee MHar

Glyceria (*Poaceae*)

aquatica variegata see *G. maxima* var. *variegata*
maxima CRWN EMFW GFor NPer SPlb XIsg
§ - var. ***variegata*** (v) More than 30 suppliers
spectabilis 'Variegata' see *G. maxima* var. *variegata*

Glycyrrhiza (*Papilionaceae*)

echinata CAgr CArn MSal
§ ***glabra*** CAgr CArn CBod CCCN CHby CWan ELau EShb GPoy GWCH MHer MNHC MSal NLar NTHB SIde WJek XPep
glandulifera see *G. glabra*
uralensis CArn ELau GPoy MHer MSal

Glyptostrobus (*Cupressaceae*)

pensilis CGHE EGFP WPGP

Gmelina (*Verbenaceae*)

hystrix new CCCN

Gnaphalium (*Asteraceae*)

'Fairy Gold' see *Helichrysum thianschanicum* 'Goldkind'
mackayi new EDAr
trinerve see *Anaphalis trinervis*

Godetia see *Clarkia*

Gomphocarpus (*Asclepiadaceae*)

§ ***physocarpus*** CArn LFur MBri NLar WCot

Gomphostigma (*Buddlejaceae*)

virgatum CDes CPLG CPle CSpe CTrC EBee EMan EPPr EShb LFur MLLN MSte SPlb SSvw WCot WHrl WPGP WPic WSHC
- 'White Candy' SHGN

Gonatanthus (*Araceae*)

pumilus SKHP

Goniolimon (*Plumbaginaceae*)

§ ***incanum*** XPep
- 'Blue Diamond' EBee
§ ***tataricum*** CWoW NBre NLar
§ - var. ***angustifolium*** EBee NBlu SRms WPer
- 'Woodcreek' NLar

Goodia (*Papilionaceae*)

lotifolia CCCN

Goodyera (*Orchidaceae*)

biflora EFEx
pubescens EFEx LRHS
schlechtendaliana EFEx

Gordonia (*Theaceae*)

axillaris CCCN CHll

gooseberry see *Ribes uva-crispa*

gooseberry, Cape see *Physalis peruviana*

Gossypium (*Malvaceae*)

herbaceum CCCN MSal

granadilla, giant see *Passiflora quadrangularis*

granadilla, purple see *Passiflora edulis*

granadilla, sweet see *Passiflora ligularis*

granadilla, yellow see *Passiflora laurifolia*

grape see *Vitis*

grapefruit see *Citrus* x *paradisi*

Graptopetalum (*Crassulaceae*)

bellum Υ^{H1} CStu SChr
filiferum EWll SRot
§ ***paraguayense*** CHal SEND

Gratiola (*Scrophulariaceae*)

officinalis CArn CWan EHon EMFW EMan LLWG MHer MSal NBlu WSel

Greenovia (*Crassulaceae*)

§ ***aurea*** SIng

Grevillea ✿ (*Proteaceae*)

alpina CFee CPLG CPle SOWG
- 'Olympic Flame' CBcs CCCN CDoC CPLG CSBt CWib EBee LHop LRHS SCoo SOWG SPoG SRms
aquifolium SOWG
arenaria SOWG
- subsp. ***canescens*** SOWG
'Austraflora Copper Crest' see *G.* 'Copper Crest'
baileyana SOWG
banksii 'Canberra Hybrid' see *G.* 'Canberra Gem'
- var. ***forsteri*** hort. SOWG SPlb
banyabba SOWG
barklyana SOWG SSta
baueri SOWG
beadleana SOWG
bedggoodiana SOWG
bipinnatifida SOWG
'Bonnie Prince Charlie' CPLG SOWG
'Bronze Rambler' SOWG
§ 'Canberra Gem' Υ^{H3-4} More than 30 suppliers
'Clearview David' CCCN CPLG IDee LBuc SCoo SOWG
confertifolia SOWG
§ 'Copper Crest' SOWG
'Cranbrook Yellow' CDoC CPLG SOWG
crithmifolia SOWG SPlb
diffusa subsp. ***evansiana*** SOWG
drummondii subsp. ***pimeleoides*** SOWG
endlicheriana SOWG
'Evelyn's Coronet' SOWG
'Fanfare' SOWG
fulgens SOWG
x ***gaudichaudii*** SOWG
* 'Honey Eater Heaven' SOWG
'Honey Gem' SOWG
iaspicula ECou
involucrata SOWG
johnsonii CMac EShb SKHP SOWG
juniperina CBcs CCCN CMac CPLG EBee GGar MGos SLim WBod WCwm
- 'Molonglo' CPLG LBuc

	- f. ***sulphurea***	CCCN CDoC CHll CPLG CSBt CTrG EPfP SOWG SPer SPlb WPat WSHC
	lanigera	CPLG ECou
I	- 'Lutea'	SOWG
	- 'Mount Tamboritha'	CBcs CCCN CDoC CPLG CTrC IDee LBuc LHop SKHP WFar
	- prostrate	ECou NLAp SOWG WPat
	- yellow-flowered **new**	ECou
*	***laspicalla***	SOWG
	leucopteris **new**	SPlb
	levis	SOWG
	longistyla	SOWG
	'Majestic'	SOWG
	'Mason's Hybrid'	SOWG
	'Moonlight'	SOWG
	nudiflora	ECou SOWG
	obtusifolia 'Gingin Gem'	SOWG
	olivacea 'Apricot Glow'	SOWG
	'Orange Marmalade'	SOWG
	paniculata	SOWG SPlb
	'Pink Lady'	ECou SOWG
	'Pink Surprise'	SOWG
	'Poorinda Elegance'	SOWG
	'Poorinda Peter'	CPLG SOWG
	'Poorinda Rondeau'	CPLG
	pteridifolia	SOWG
	quercifolia	SOWG
	'Red Dragon' (v) **new**	LBuc
	repens	SOWG
	rhyolitica	SOWG
	robusta ♀H1+3	CHal SBLw SOWG SPlb SSta
	'Robyn Gordon'	SOWG
	'Rondeau'	CCCN CEnd EShb
	rosmarinifolia ♀H3	More than 30 suppliers
	- 'Desert Flame'	CPLG
	- 'Jenkinsii'	CDoC CPLG CSBt SLim
	'Sandra Gordon'	SOWG
	'Scarlet Sprite'	SOWG
§	x ***semperflorens***	CBcs CDoC CEnd CPLG CTrC CWib SCoo SOWG
	sericea	SOWG
	shiressii	SOWG
	'Sid Reynolds'	CPLG
	'Spider Man'	LBuc
	'Splendour'	SOWG
	thelemanniana	ECou
	- 'Silver'	CPLG
	- Spriggs' form	SOWG
	thyrsoides	CBcs SDry
	tolminsis	see *G.* x *semperflorens*
	venusta	SOWG
	victoriae	ECou SKHP SOWG WCot
*	- subsp. ***tenuinervis***	SOWG
	- subsp. ***victoriae***	CPLG
	williamsonii	ECou SOWG WPat

Greyia (*Greyiaceae*)

	sutherlandii	CKob CTrC SGar SOWG SPlb

Grindelia (*Asteraceae*)

§	***camporum***	CWCL EBee MSal NBre NLar SPlb WPer
	chiloensis	CAbb ECha LRav SDix SDry SKHP SMad WCot
	integrifolia	CSam EBee
	robusta	see *G. camporum*
	stricta	CArn

Griselinia (*Griseliniaceae*)

	littoralis ♀H3	More than 30 suppliers
	- 'Bantry Bay' (v)	CAbP CDoC CWSG EBee ELan LRHS MAsh MSwo NCGa SAga SEND SLim SPer SPoG SWvt WCru WFar
	- 'Brodick Gold'	CPLG EBee EQua GGar
	- 'Crinkles'	CPMA SDry SLon
	- 'Dixon's Cream' (v)	CBcs CDul CMac CSBt EBee EPfP GQui IArd IFoB MDun SAga SDry SLon SPoG WCru
	- 'Green Jewel' (v)	CBcs CEnd CPMA CTrC CWib NLar SDry SPla
	- 'Variegata' (v) ♀H3	More than 30 suppliers
	lucida 'Variegata' (v)	IFoB
	scandens	WSHC

guava, common see *Psidium guajava*

guava, pineapple see *Acca sellowiana*

guava, purple or strawberry see *Psidium littorale var. longipes*

Gueldenstaedtia (*Papilionaceae*)

	himalaica B&SWJ 2631	WCru

Gunnera (*Gunneraceae*)

	arenaria	GGar
	chilensis	see *G. tinctoria*
	dentata	WGwG
	flavida	EBee EShb GGar GSki NWCA WGwG
	hamiltonii	CStu EBee EBla ECha ECou GGar NBir NWCA WMoo
	magellanica	More than 30 suppliers
	- 'Muñoz Gamero'	WShi
	- 'Osorno'	WPGP
	manicata ♀H3-4	More than 30 suppliers
	monoica	GGar GSki
	perpensa	CCCN CDes
	prorepens	CEnt CFee CHEx CStu EBee EBla ECha ECou GEdr GSki NBir NWCA WMoo
	scabra	see *G. tinctoria*
§	***tinctoria***	CBct CCCN CDWL CHEx CMHG CPLG CTrG CWib EBee EBla ECha EHon ELan EPfP EPla GAbr GGar LBMP MDun NCot NVic SDix SWat SWvt WBVN WCot WFar WPGP

Guzmania (*Bromeliaceae*)

	'Gran Prix'	MBri
	'Surprise'	see x *Niduregelia* 'Surprise'
	'Vulkan'	MBri

Gymnadenia (*Orchidaceae*)

	conopsea	EFEx SHdy

Gymnocarpium (*Woodsiaceae*)

	dryopteris ♀H4	CLAP EBee EBrs EFer EMar EMon EPot GGar GKev GMaP MMoz NLar NWCA SRms WFib WNor WPnP WRic
	- 'Plumosum' ♀H4	CFwr CLAP CWCL CWsd EBee EPfP EPla ERod GBin GQui MAsh MPes MWgw NBid NHol NLar NVic SMac SMad SPoG WFib WHal WMoo
	fedtschenkoanum	WRic
	oyamense	CLAP EFer SKHP
	robertianum	CLAP EFer

Gymnocladus (*Caesalpiniaceae*)

	chinensis	CBcs WNor
	dioica	CBcs CDul CLnd CMCN EBee ELan EPfP LEdu LRHS MBlu MBri NEgg SPer SSpi WGer WNor WPGP

Gymnospermium (*Berberidaceae*)

§	***albertii***	EBrs GCrs

Gynandriris (*Iridaceae*)

sisyrinchium EBee EBrs ECho EMan LEdu
* - ***purpurea*** ECho

Gynerium (*Poaceae*)

argenteum see *Cortaderia selloana*

Gynostemma (*Cucurbitaceae*)

pentaphyllum CAgr
- B&SWJ 570 WCru

Gynura (*Asteraceae*)

§ ***aurantiaca*** 'Purple Passion' ♀H1 MBri
sarmentosa misapplied see *G. aurantiaca* 'Purple Passion'

Gypsophila (*Caryophyllaceae*)

acutifolia EBee ELan
aretioides ECho EPot LRHS NMen WRos
§ - 'Caucasica' EBur ECho EPot LTwo NDlv SIng
- 'Compacta' see *G. aretioides* 'Caucasica'
briquetiana WPat
cerastioides CSpe CTri ECho ECtt EDAr GAbr GGar LAst LHop LRHS MRav NDlv NLAp NMen NWCA SPlb SRms WHoo WPer WPnn
dubia see *G. repens* 'Dubia'
fastigiata EBee WPer
- 'Silverstar' LSou SPoG
(Festival Series) 'Festival'PBR SPoG
- 'Festival Pink' EBee ECtt GMac LRHS SHar WFar
- Happy Festival = 'Danghappy' LRHS
- 'White Festival'PBR (d) EBee WFar
gracilescens see *G. tenuifolia*
'Jolien' (v) CBow EBee ELan WWeb
muralis 'Garden Bride' SWvt
- 'Gypsy Pink' (d) SWvt
nana 'Compacta' CLyd CPBP
oldhamiana EShb MLLN
'Pacific Rose' **new** MRav
pacifica EBee EShb MWea NBre NBro NLar NPri WPer
paniculata EBee GWCH LAst MGos NBre NMir SECG SRms SWat
- 'Bristol Fairy' (d) ♀H4 CSBt CTri EBee ECha ECtt ELan EPfP ERou GMaP LCro LRHS NBlu NEgg NOrc NPri SPoG SWvt WCAu
- 'Compacta Plena' (d) EBee ECtt EGle ELan EPfP GMaP LHop MLHP MRav MWgw NDov NEgg NVic SPet SPla SRms WPer
- 'Flamingo' (d) CBcs ECha ECot ERou NLar SCoo SPer
- 'Perfekta' CBcs SPer
§ - 'Schneeflocke' (d) EBee EShb EWsh GMaP NBre NLar NPri SPhx SRms WPer
- Snowflake see *G. paniculata* 'Schneeflocke'
§ ***petraea*** EPot
repens ♀H4 CBrm CTca ECtt EMil LBee MWat SBch SHGN SPlb SWvt WFar WPer
- 'Dorothy Teacher' CLyd CMea ECho ECtt LBee SIng WEas WGor
§ - 'Dubia' CLyd EAlp ECha ECho ECtt EDAr EPot MHer SPoG SRms WLin WPer WSHC
- 'Fratensis' ECho ECtt ELan ITim NMen
- Pink Beauty see *G. repens* 'Rosa Schönheit'
§ - 'Rosa Schönheit' ECha EPot LRHS NLar
- 'Rose Fountain' WPat
- 'Rosea' CBrm CMea CPBP CTri CWib EBee ECho ECtt EDAr EPfP EShb GAbr GMaP LAst MWat NWCA SAga SBla SPet SPoG SRms SWvt WFar WHoo WTin
- 'Silver Carpet' (v) LAst
- white CWib EBee ECho ELan EPfP EWin LAst SPet SWvt WPer WRHF
§ 'Rosenschleier' (d) ♀H4 CMea CPrp EBee ECha ECtt ELan EPfP LAst MRav MWat NDov SAga SPer SRms SWvt WCAu WEas WHoo WLin WSHC WTin
'Rosy Veil' see *G.* 'Rosenschleier'
§ ***tenuifolia*** EAlp ECho EPot LBee NDlv NHol NMen SBla SIng
transylvanica see *G. petraea*
Veil of Roses see *G.* 'Rosenschleier'

H

Haberlea (*Gesneriaceae*)

ferdinandi-coburgii CLAP CStu ECho GBuc NMen NWCA
- 'Connie Davidson' GBuc GEdr NMen
rhodopensis ♀H4 CDes CElw CFee CStu CWsd EBee ECho GCrs GEdr GGar MSte MWat NLAp NMen NSla NWCA SBla SIng SRms WAbe WPGP WPat WTin
- 'Virginalis' CElw CLAP CStu NMen NSla SBla WThu

Habranthus ✿ (*Amaryllidaceae*)

andersonii see *H. tubispathus*
brachyandrus SRms
gracilifolius CStu ERos SIng WThu
martinezii CStu
§ ***robustus*** ♀H1 CDes CWsd EBee EBrs ECho EDif EPot EShb IHer LAma LHop LRHS WCot WHil WPGP
texanus CGHE ERos WAbe
§ ***tubispathus*** ♀H1 CStu EBee ECho EDif ERos NWCA SIng WCot WPrP

Hackelia (*Boraginaceae*)

floribunda EDif SBod

Hacquetia (*Apiaceae*)

epipactis ♀H4 More than 30 suppliers
§ - 'Thor' (v) CBow CDes EBee EMon EWes GBri GCrs GEdr LTwo NMen SBla WCot WPGP
- 'Variegata' see *H. epipactis* 'Thor'

Haemanthus (*Amaryllidaceae*)

sp. **new** CMdw
albiflos ♀H1 CHEx CHal CSpe CStu ITer LAma LToo SRms WCot
amarylloides subsp. ***polyanthes*** ECho
barkerae ECho
coccineus ♀H1 ECho
humilis ECho
- subsp. ***hirsutus*** WCot
katherinae see *Scadoxus multiflorus* subsp. *katherinae*
pauculifolius ECho WCot
pubescens subsp. ***leipoldtii*** ECho
sanguineus ERea

Hakea (*Proteaceae*)

§ ***drupacea*** CTrC EShb
epiglottis CTrC ECou
laurina SPlb
lissocarpha CTrC
§ ***lissosperma*** CDoC ECou EPfP EPla SPlb WPGP
microcarpa ECou SLon

	nodosa	CTrC
	platysperma	SPlb
§	***salicifolia***	CCCN EBee IMGH LRHS SPlb
	- 'Gold Medal' (v)	CTrC EBee
	saligna	see *H. salicifolia*
	scoparia	CTrC
	sericea misapplied	see *H. lissosperma*
	sericea Schrad. & J.C. Wendl.	ECou
	- pink-flowered	SPlb
	suaveolens	see *H. drupacea*
	teretifolia	CTrC

Hakonechloa (*Poaceae*)

	macra	CAby CEnt CGHE CKno CPrp CSam EBee EPla EShb LCro MAvo MMoz MRav MWgw SMad SPhx SPoG WCot WDyG WPGP WSHC XIsg
§	- 'Alboaurea' ♀H4	More than 30 suppliers
	- 'Albovariegata'	CKno CWan EBee LEdu LHop WDyG WSpi
	- 'All Gold' **new**	EBee EGle SMad
	- 'Aureola' ♀H4	More than 30 suppliers
*	- 'Mediopicta' (v)	SApp
*	- 'Mediovariegata' (v)	CGHE CWCL EPPr EPla WPGP
	- 'Variegata'	see *H. macra* 'Alboaurea'

Halenia (*Gentianaceae*)

	elliptica	EBee GKev

Halesia (*Styracaceae*)

§	***carolina***	More than 30 suppliers
	- 'Wedding Bells' **new**	CPMA
	diptera	CMCN MBlu
	- var. ***magniflora***	MBlu
	monticola	CBcs CLnd CMCN EBee ELan EPfP IClo LRHS NLar SPer SSpi WFar WNor
	- var. ***vestita*** ♀H4	CAbP CDoC CDul CPMA CTho EBee EPfP EWTr IMGH LRHS MBlu MBri MRav NLar NVic SHBN SSpi WFar WGob WHCG WPGP WPat
	- - f. ***rosea***	CBcs CPMA EPfP MBlu
	tetraptera	see *H. carolina*

x *Halimiocistus* (*Cistaceae*)

	sp. **new**	WBod
	algarvensis	see *Halimium ocymoides*
§	'Ingwersenii'	CBcs CDoC CTca ELan EWes LRHS SPer SPoG SRms WPer
	revolii misapplied	see x *H. sahucii*
	revolii (Coste & Soulié) Dansereau	XPep
§	***sahucii*** ♀H4	CBgR CDoC CSBt CTri EBee ECha ELan EPfP LAst LBMP LRHS MAsh MBNS MRav MSwo MWat SDys SGar SHBN SPer SPoG SRms SWvt WFar WWeb XPep
	- Ice Dancer = 'Ebhals'PBR (v)	CDoC EBee ENot EPfP LAst MAsh SPer SWvt
	'Susan'	see *Halimium* 'Susan'
§	***wintonensis*** ♀H3	CBcs CDoC CSBt EBee ELan EPfP LRHS MAsh MRav SHBN SPer SPla SRms WCFE WHar WWeb XPep
§	- 'Merrist Wood Cream' ♀H3	CBcs CBgR CDoC CSBt EBee ELan ENot EPfP LAst LHop LRHS MAsh MRav MSwo MWgw NBir SBod SPer SPla SPoG SSpi SWvt WAbe WFar WKif WPat XPep

Halimione (*Chenopodiaceae*)

§	***portulacoides***	XPep

Halimium ✿ (*Cistaceae*)

§	***atriplicifolium***	LRav XPep
§	***calycinum***	CAbP CChe CTca EBee ELan EPfP GKev LRHS MAsh MBri NBlu SCoo SLim SPer SPoG SWvt WAbe WBod WCFE WWeb XPep
	commutatum	see *H. calycinum*
	formosum	see *H. lasianthum* subsp. *formosum*
	halimifolium misapplied	see *H.* x *pauanum*, *H.* x *santae*
§	***halimifolium*** Willk.	XPep
§	***lasianthum*** ♀H3	CBcs CHar CPLG CSBt CWib EBee ELan EPfP LRHS MBri MRav SLim WBod WBrE WCFE WEas WKif
	- 'Concolor'	CDoC CWib EMil MSwo SDry SWvt
§	- subsp. ***formosum***	CHar SBod XPep
	- - 'Sandling'	EBee ELan EPfP LRHS SRms
	- 'Hannay Silver'	SPla
	libanotis	see *H. calycinum*
§	***ocymoides*** ♀H3	CBcs CChe CDoC CWib EBee ELan EPfP LRHS MAsh MMHG MSwo SLon WHar WKif WLin XPep
§	x ***pauanum***	EBee LRHS NPro XPep
	x ***santae***	XPep
	'Sarah'	EBee LRHS MAsh MBNS XPep
§	'Susan' ♀H3	CDoC EBee ELan EPfP LHop LRHS LSou MAsh MBNS MMHG SCoo SLim SPer SPoG WAbe
§	***umbellatum***	CFul EBee LRHS SPer WHCG WKif
	verticillatum	XPep
	wintonense	see x *Halimiocistus wintonensis*

Halimodendron (*Papilionaceae*)

	halodendron	CArn CBcs CDul EBee LRav MBlu NBlu SPer

Halleria (*Scrophulariaceae*)

	lucida	CCCN WBor

Halocarpus (*Podocarpaceae*)

§	***bidwillii***	CDoC ECou

Haloragis (*Haloragaceae*)

	erecta 'Rubra'	WCot WPer
	- 'Wellington Bronze'	CBow CEnt CPLG CSpe EBee ECtt EDAr EMan EPPr EUnu GGar GSki LEdu LRHS MBNS MCCP MLHP SBod SBri SDys SWal WEas WHer WMoo

Hamamelis ✿ (*Hamamelidaceae*)

	'Brevipetala'	CBcs NHol
	x ***intermedia*** 'Advent'	NLar
	- 'Angelly'	CPMA MBlu MBri MGos SPoG
	- 'Aphrodite'	EPfP LRHS MBlu MBri MGos MRav NBhm NLar SSpi
	- 'Arnold Promise' ♀H4	More than 30 suppliers
	- 'August Lamken'	NLar
	- 'Aurora'	MBlu NHol NLar
	- 'Barmstedt Gold' ♀H4	CWib EBee EMil EPfP LRHS MAsh MBlu MBri MGos MRav NHol NLar SReu SRms SSpi SSta
	- 'Carmine Red'	CMac MGos NLar WNor
	- 'Copper Beauty'	see *H.* x *intermedia* 'Jelena'
	- 'Diane' ♀H4	More than 30 suppliers
§	- 'Feuerzauber'	CMac EMil LBuc MSwo NBlu NLar NScw SPer SRms WBVN WOrn
*	- 'Fire Cracker'	CSBt WPat
	- 'Gingerbread'	LRHS
	- 'Girard's Orange'	EPfP
	- 'Glowing Embers'	LRHS
	- 'Harry'	LRHS MBri NLar SSpi
	- Hillier's clone	NHol
	- 'Hiltingbury'	LRHS
§	- 'Jelena' ♀H4	More than 30 suppliers
	- 'John' **new**	MAsh

	- 'Lansing'	NLar
	- 'Livia'	LRHS NLar SPoG SSpi
	- Magic Fire	see *H.* x *intermedia* 'Feuerzauber'
	- 'Moonlight'	CPMA NLar
	- 'Nina'	LRHS MAsh
	- 'Orange Beauty'	CBcs MGos NLar WGwG
	- 'Orange Peel'	EPfP LRHS MBri NLar
	- 'Pallida' ♀H4	More than 30 suppliers
	- 'Primavera'	CWSG LPan MLan NHol SPla
	- 'Ripe Corn'	EPfP LRHS MAsh
	- 'Rubin'	LRHS SSpi
	- 'Ruby Glow'	CBcs CWib EBee ECho MGos NLar NWea SPer SPoG
	- 'Strawberries and Cream'	MAsh
	- 'Sunburst'	EPfP MGos
	- 'Vesna'	CMac EMil EPfP LRHS MAsh MBlu SPoG SSpi
§	- 'Westerstede'	CWSG EBee LPan LRHS MGos MLan MRav NBlu NHol NLar NScw NWea SLim WHar
	japonica	WFar
	- 'Arborea'	WNor
	- 'Pendula'	NLar
	- 'Robin'	CDul
	mollis ♀H4	More than 30 suppliers
	- 'Boskoop'	NLar
	- 'Coombe Wood'	LRHS MAsh
	- 'Goldcrest'	CPMA
	- 'Jermyns Gold'	EPfP
	- 'Princeton Gold'	CWib
	- 'Select'	see *H.* x *intermedia* 'Westerstede'
	- 'Superba'	LRHS
	- 'Wisley Supreme'	ELan LRHS MAsh SPoG SSpi
	'Rochester'	NLar
	vernalis 'Amethyst' new	NLar
	- 'Lombart's Weeping'	CFwr NLar
	- purple	MBlu
	- 'Sandra' ♀H4	CMCN ELan EPfP LRHS MBri MGos MRav NLar SHBN SLon SPoG SReu SSta WCot
	virginiana	CAgr ECrN GBin GPoy IDee NWea WFar WHCr
	'Yamina'	NLar

Hamelia (*Rubiaceae*)

	patens new	CCCN

Hanabusaya (*Campanulaceae*)

§	***asiatica***	CHar CPom EBee NChi NSfd WFar

Haplocarpha (*Asteraceae*)

	rueppellii	CFee NBro SRms SRot WPer

Haplopappus (*Asteraceae*)

	brandegeei	see *Erigeron aureus*
	coronopifolius	see *H. glutinosus*
§	***glutinosus***	EBee ECha ECho ECtt EPot GEdr MTho NLar NWCA SEND SPlb SRms XPep
	lanceolatus	see *Pyrrocoma lanceolata*
	lyallii	see *Tonestus lyallii*
	prunelloides	GEdr NWCA
	- var. ***mustersii***	CPBP CStu
	rehderi	EBee WFar WMoo

Hardenbergia (*Papilionaceae*)

	comptoniana ♀H1	CHid CSpe EBee
	- 'Rosea'	ERea
	violacea ♀H1	CAbb CBcs CHII CRHN CSPN CSpe CTrC EBee ELan ERea GQui IDee LRHS SBod SLim SPer WCot
	- f. ***alba***	CBcs IDee
	- - 'White Crystal'	ERea WPGP
	- 'Happy Wanderer'	ERea LRHS MAsh SChF SOWG SPer SPoG WPGP
	- f. ***rosea***	CBcs EBee

Harpephyllum (*Anacardiaceae*)

	caffrum (F)	XBlo

Harrimanella see *Cassiope*

Hastingsia (*Hyacinthaceae*)

	alba	GBuc
	- NNS 98-310	WCot
	- NNS 98-311	WCot

Haworthia ✿ (*Aloaceae*)

	attenuata	SWal
	'Black Prince'	EPfP
	cymbiformis	EPfP
	fasciata	EPfP
	glabrata var. ***concolor***	EPfP
	heidelbergensis new	EPem
	maraisii var. ***maraisii*** new	EPem
	radula	EPfP
	reinwardtii ♀H1	CHal
	rigida new	EPem

hazelnut see *Corylus*

Hebe ✿ (*Scrophulariaceae*)

	albicans ♀H4	CChe CPLG ECou ELan EPfP GGar IFoB LAst LRHS MBar MBri MGos MRav MWgw NEgg SCoo SHBN SPer SPoG STre WFar WHCG WTel
	- 'Cobb'	ECou
	- 'Pink Elephant'	see *H.* 'Pink Elephant'
	- prostrate	see *H. albicans* 'Snow Cover'
	- 'Red Edge'	see *H.* 'Red Edge'
*	- 'Snow Carpet'	CCCN
§	- 'Snow Cover'	EWes
	- 'Snow Drift'	see *H. albicans* 'Snow Cover'
§	- 'Sussex Carpet'	STre
§	'Alicia Amherst'	SPer SRms
	allanii	see *H. amplexicaulis* f. *hirta*
	'Amanda Cook' (v)	MCCP NPer SDry
	amplexicaulis clone 4	STre
§	- f. ***hirta***	NDlv NHol
§	'Amy'	LRHS MBri NPer SHBN SPer SPoG
	x ***andersonii***	CDul
§	- 'Andersonii Aurea' (v)	SDry
§	- 'Andersonii Variegata' (v)	CWib SDry SPla SRms WCot WRHF
	- 'Argenteovariegata'	see *H.* x *andersonii* 'Andersonii Variegata'
	- 'Aureovariegata'	see *H.* x *andersonii* 'Andersonii Aurea'
	'Andressa Paula'	CCCN
	'Anita' new	SPoG
	anomala misapplied	see *H.* 'Imposter'
	anomala (Armstr.) Cockayne	CCCN LRHS
	'Aoira'	see *H. recurva* 'Aoira'
§	***armstrongii***	ECho GGar MBar MGos WPer
	'Arthur'	ECou
	astonii	ECho
	'Autumn Glory'	CPLG CSBt CWSG ECho ELan EPfP GGar LAst LRHS MBar MGos MLHP MSwo NBir NBlu NPri NWea SBod SGar SHBN SPer SPla SPlb SPoG SWal SWvt WBod WTel
	azurea	see *H. venustula*
	'Azurens'	see *H.* 'Maori Gem'
	'Baby Marie'	CAbP CChe CSBt ECho ECot ECou ELan EPfP LAst LRHS MGos MSwo NBlu NHol NMen NPer NPri SCoo SPla SPoG SRms SRot SWvt WCFE
	barkeri	ECou
	'Beatrice'	NDlv

	'Beverley Hills'PBR	LRHS
	'Bicolor Wand'	CCCN
	bishopiana	ECou ELan EPfP LRHS MGos SBod SCoo
	- 'Champagne'	see *H.* 'Champagne'
	'Black Beauty' **new**	ENot
	'Blue Clouds' ♀H3	ECou LAst LRHS MSwo NDlv SPer SWal WCFE
§	'Blue Gem'	LRHS
	'Blue Star'	LRHS MAsh SPoG
	bollonsii	GGar MSte
	'Boscawenii'	CTrG EWin MGos
	'Bouquet'PBR	SPoG
§	'Bowles' Hybrid'	CCCN CSBt ECou EWin LEdu MSwo NBlu SRms STre
	'Bowles' Variety'	see *H.* 'Bowles' Hybrid'
	brachysiphon	CTrC CTri EPfP EWin GWCH MGos MRav SHBN SPer WBVN WHCG
	brevifolia	ECou
	'Bronzy Baby' (v) **new**	SPoG
	buchananii	ECho GGar MBar MGos MHer MTho NDlv NHol NPer WPer
§	- 'Fenwickii'	ECho WHoo
	- 'Minima'	ECho
	- 'Minor'	ECho GBin GCrs MBar NBir NDlv NWCA SIng
*	- 'Nana'	MGos
	buxifolia misapplied	see *H. odora*
	buxifolia (Benth.) Ckn. & Allan	NHol NWea WHar
	- 'Champagne'	see *H.* 'Champagne'
N	'C.P. Raffill'	ECou
§	'Caledonia' ♀H3	CCCN CSBt ECou ENot EPfP LRHS MAsh MBri MGos MSte NPer SCoo SPoG WFar
	'Candy'	ECou
§	***canterburiensis***	ECou GGar
N	'Carl Teschner'	see *H.* 'Youngii'
	'Carnea Variegata' (v)	EShb MGos SBod SPer WOut
	carnosula	EWin GGar LRHS MGos NBir SPer WHar WPer
	catarractae	see *Parahebe catarractae*
	'Celine'	GGar MGos SPoG
I	'Chalk's Buchananii'	SBla
§	'Champagne'	CCCN LAst LCro LRHS NBPN NHol
	'Champion'	EKen MWea NBPN SPoG
*	'Charming White'	CChe EQua LRHS SCoo SPoG
	chathamica	ECou GGar SDry
	'Christabel'	EWin
	ciliolata x ***odora***	GGar
	'Clear Skies'PBR	CAbP ECou LRHS SPoG
	'Colwall'	ECho WHen
	'Conwy Knight' **new**	WAbe
	'County Park'	ECou EWes GMaP NHol NMen
	cupressoides	CBcs NDlv SEND
	- 'Boughton Dome'	CTri EAlp ECho EPfP ERas EWin GGar MAsh MGos MTho NLAp NMen WHoo WPer WSHC
	darwiniana	see *H. glaucophylla*
	'Dazzler' (v)	CAbP CSBt ELan LRHS
	decumbens	ECou EWes GGar MGos NHol
	'Diana'	ECou
	dieffenbachii	GGar
	diosmifolia	CAbP CDoC ELan WAbe
	- 'Marie'	ECou
	divaricata	ECou
*	- 'Marlborough'	ECou
	- 'Nelson'	ECou
	x ***divergens***	NDlv
	'Dorothy Peach'	see *H.* 'Watson's Pink'
	'E.A. Bowles'	ECou WBVN
	'E.B. Anderson'	see *H.* 'Caledonia'
	'Early Blue'	CSpe NBir

	'Edinensis'	WSHC WSPU
	'Edington'	CHal LRHS SPer WCFE
	elliptica	CDul ECou
	- 'Anatoki'	ECou
	- 'Charleston'	ECou
	- 'Kapiti'	ECou SWal
	- 'Variegata'	see *H.* 'Silver Queen'
	'Emerald Dome'	see *H.* 'Emerald Gem'
§	'Emerald Gem' ♀H3	CTri ECho ENot EPfP GGar MAsh MBar MBri MGos MHer MSwo MWat MWgw NDlv NHol NMen NWCA SCoo SPer SPlb WBod WFar WPat
	'Emerald Green'	see *H.* 'Emerald Gem'
	epacridea	ECho EWes NHol
§	'Eveline'	CSBt NBir SPer WCot WKif
	evenosa	GGar NDlv
	'Eversley Seedling'	see *H.* 'Bowles' Hybrid'
	'Fairfieldii'	CPLG WPat
	'First Light'PBR	CWSG NEgg SCoo SPoG
	'Fragrant Jewel'	CWib SEND SWal
	x ***franciscana***	ECou LAst SWal
	- 'Blue Gem' ambig.	ECho GGar LRHS MWea NBir NPer SPer SPlb SRms SWal WGer WHar XPep
	- 'Purple Tips' misapplied	see *H. speciosa* 'Variegata'
	- 'Variegata'	see *H.* 'Silver Queen'
I	- 'White Gem'	SRms
	- yellow-variegated (v)	SPer
	'Franjo'	ECou
	'Garden Beauty'	LRHS MGos
	'Gauntlettii'	see *H.* 'Eveline'
	'Gibby'	ECou
N	***glaucophylla***	SBod
	- 'Clarence'	ECou GGar
I	'Glaucophylla Variegata' (v)	CTri NBir SPer WCot WKif
	'Glengarriff'	NHol
	'Gnome'	LRHS
	'Gold Beauty'	LBuc LRHS
	'Goldrush'PBR (v)	MGos SPoG
	'Gran's Favourite'	CCCN
	'Great Orme' ♀H3	More than 30 suppliers
	'Green Globe'	see *H.* 'Emerald Gem'
	'Greensleeves'	ECou GGar
	'Grethe' **new**	SPoG
	'Gruninard's Seedling'	GGar
	haastii	EPfP GGar NLar
	'Hadspen Pink'	LRHS
	'Hagley Park'	CSBt EPfP GMaP SAga WHCG
§	'Hartii'	MRav
	'Heartbreaker'PBR (v)	ELan ENot LBuc LRHS MGos NPri SCoo SPoG
	'Hinderwell'	NPer
	'Hinerua'	GGar NNor
	'Holywell'	SBod SWal
	hookeriana	see *Parahebe hookeriana*
	hulkeana ♀H3	EMan EWin LSou MHer NBir SAga WEas WHCG WKif WPat WTin
	'Ian Young'	ITim
§	'Imposter'	CWib SRms
	insularis	ECho ECou
	'Jack's Surprise'	EWin
	'James Stirling'	see *H. ochracea* 'James Stirling'
	'Janet'	SGar
	'Jean Searle'	LAst
	'Joanna'	ECou
§	'Johny Day'	MBNS
	'Judy'	ECou
	'Just Judy'	LBuc LRHS
	'Karen's Pink' **new**	WAbe
	'Karna' **new**	SPoG
	'Karo Golden Esk'	NEgg
	'Katrina' (v) **new**	SPoG
	'Kirkii'	EMil EPfP EWin SCoo SPer
	'Knightshayes'	see *H.* 'Caledonia'

§	'La Séduisante'	CSBt ECou MLHP SCoo SEND SHBN WKif WOut
	'Lady Ann'PBR (v)	CWSG NLar NPri SPoG
	'Lady Ardilaun'	see *H.* 'Amy'
	laevis	see *H. venustula*
	latifolia	see *H.* 'Blue Gem'
	lavaudiana	WAbe
	'Lavender Spray'	see *H.* 'Hartii'
	'Linda' **new**	SPoG
	'Lindsayi'	ECou
	'Lisa' **new**	SPoG
§	'Loganioides'	GGar
	'Lopen' (v)	ECou EWes
	'Louise'	LIMB SGar
	lyallii	see *Parahebe lyallii*
	lycopodioides	EWes WThu
	- 'Aurea'	see *H. armstrongii*
	mackenii	see *H.* 'Emerald Gem'
	macrantha ♀H3	ECho EPfP GCrs GGar ITim LRHS SPer SRms WAbe
	macrocarpa	ECou EWin LRHS
	- var. ***latisepala***	ECou
§	'Maori Gem'	GGar
	'Margery Fish'	see *H.* 'Primley Gem'
	'Margret'PBR ♀H4	CSBt EMil ENot EPfP ERas LAst LRHS MAsh MGos NPri SCoo SHBN SPer SPoG
	'Maria' **new**	SPoG
	'Marjorie'	CDul CSBt ELan ENot EPfP LRHS MGos MRav MSwo NPer NWea SBod SPer SRms SWal WCFE WTel
	matthewsii	WPat
	'Mauvena'	SPer
	'McKean'	see *H.* 'Emerald Gem'
	'Megan'	ECou
§	'Mercury'	ECou
	'Midsummer Beauty' ♀H3	ECou EPfP GGar ISea LAst LRHS MGos MLHP MRav NBir SBod SHBN SPer SPlb STre SWvt WFar WOut WSFF
	'Milmont Emerald'	see *H.* 'Emerald Gem'
*	***minima*** 'Calvin'	ECho
	'Miss Fittall'	ECou
	'Misty'	CCCN
§	'Mohawk'PBR	MGos NLar SCoo
	'Monica'	NHol
*	'Moppets Hardy'	SPer
§	'Mrs Winder' ♀H4	More than 30 suppliers
	'Mystery'	ECou ELan SWal
	'Mystery Red'	MGos
	'Nantyderry'	CCCN CHal GBri LRHS SPla SWal WOut
§	'Neil's Choice' ♀H4	CCCN ECou MSte STre SWal
	'Netta Dick'	ECou
	'Nicola's Blush' ♀H4	CBrm CSBt CSam ECou ENot EPfP EShb GGar LAst LHop LRHS MGos MRav MWat NBir NCot NHol SBod SCoo SGar SHBN SIng SPer SPoG SRms STre SWvt WFar
	obtusata	ECou SCoo
	ochracea	MGos NBlu
§	- 'James Stirling' ♀H4	CSBt ECho ELan ENot EPfP GGar LRHS MAsh MBar MBri MGos MRav MSwo MTho NBir SLim SPer SPlb SPoG SRGP STre SWvt WCFE WFar
	'Oddity'	LRHS
§	***odora***	ECou EPfP GGar MGos MRav WCFE
I	- 'Nana'	EPfP EWin MAsh MBar
	- 'New Zealand Gold'	EWin LRHS MAsh MGos NDlv SCoo SLon
	- var. ***patens***	WHCG
	- 'Summer Frost'	CRez NHol NPri
	- 'Wintergreen'	MRav
	'Oratia Beauty' ♀H4	LRHS MRav NPri
	'Orphan Annie'PBR (v)	CWSG ENot LRHS MGos SCoo SPer SPoG
	parviflora misapplied	see *H.* 'Bowles' Hybrid'
§	***parviflora*** (Vahl) Cockayne & Allan	GGar
	- 'Holdsworth'	LRHS SDys
	- 'Palmerston'	ECou
	- var. ***angustifolia***	see *H. stenophylla*
	- var. ***arborea***	see *H. parviflora* (Vahl) Cockayne & Allan
	'Pascal' ♀H4	CCCN ECou ELan ENot EPfP LRHS MBNS MBri MRav SCoo SPer SPoG
	pauciramosa	SRms SWal
	'Pearl of Paradise'PBR	SPoG
	perfoliata	see *Parahebe perfoliata*
	'Perry's Rubyleaf'	NPer
	'Petra's Pink'	CCCN
	'Pewter Dome' ♀H4	CDoC CSBt ECou EPfP MGos MRav NDlv NEgg NHol SBod SDix SPer SPoG SRms STre WBrE WHen
	pimeleoides	ECou NHol
	- 'Glauca'	NPer
	- 'Glaucocaerulea'	ECou
	- 'Mercury'	see *H.* 'Mercury'
	- 'Quicksilver' ♀H4	CSBt CTri ECou ELan ENot EPfP GGar GMaP LAst LRHS MBar MGos MRav MSwo NBir NHol NPer SCoo SPer SPoG STre SWal WPat
	- 'Red Tip'	ECho
	- var. ***rupestris***	ECou
	pinguifolia	ECou SPlb WFar
	- 'Hutt'	ECou
	- 'Pagei' ♀H4	More than 30 suppliers
	- 'Sutherlandii'	CDoC ECho GGar LEdu MBar MGos MWgw NDlv SCoo WFar WRHF
§	'Pink Elephant' (v) ♀H3	CAbP CSBt ELan EPfP LAst LBuc LRHS MAsh SCoo SPer SPla SPoG
	'Pink Fantasy'	CChe LRHS MRav NHol
	'Pink Goddess'	LRHS
	'Pink Lady'PBR	SPoG
	'Pink Paradise'PBR	CAbP ELan ENot EPfP LRHS MGos NHol SBod SPoG
	'Pink Payne'	see *H.* 'Eveline'
	'Pink Pixie'	LSou MBri SCoo
	'Pinocchio' (v) **new**	SPoG
	'Porlock Purple'	see *Parahebe catarractae* 'Delight'
§	'Primley Gem'	CCCN EQua
	propinqua	MHer NMen
	- 'Minor'	NDlv
I	'Prostrata'	CSBt NDlv
	'Purple Emperor'	see *H.* 'Neil's Choice'
	'Purple Paradise'PBR	EPfP LBuc LRHS MBri SPoG
	'Purple Picture'	SDry
	'Purple Pixie'PBR	see *H.* 'Mohawk'
	'Purple Princess'	LRHS
§	'Purple Queen'	CSBt ELan EPfP EShb LIMB LRHS SHFr SPla SPoG WAbe
	Purple Shamrock = 'Neprock'PBR (v)	CSBt ENot EPfP LBuc LRHS MBri MGos NPri SCoo SPer SPoG SWal
	'Purple Tips' misapplied	see *H. speciosa* 'Variegata'
	'Rachel'	LRHS
	rakaiensis ♀H4	More than 30 suppliers
	ramosissima	NDlv
	raoulii	NMen NWCA WAbe WFar
	recurva	CSam CTri ECou EPfP GGar LAst LRHS MGos NHol SHFr SRms WBrE WCot
§	- 'Aoira'	ECou
	- 'Boughton Silver' ♀H3	ELan EPfP LRHS MBNS MWgw SDry
	- 'White Torrent'	ECou

§	'Red Edge' ♀H4	More than 30 suppliers
	'Red Rum' **new**	ELan
	'Red Ruth'	see *H.* 'Eveline'
	rigidula	LRHS MGos NHol
	'Ronda'	ECou
	'Rosie'PBR	CBcs EPfP MWea NMen SCoo SPer
	'Royal Purple'	see *H.* 'Alicia Amherst'
	salicifolia	CCCN CChe CTca ECou ELan EPfP GGar LAst LRHS MDun MRav NEgg NHol SHBN SPer SPlb SRms SWal WFar WHCG WTel
	- BR 30	GGar
	'Sandra Joy'	CCCN
	'Sapphire' ♀H4	CDoC ECou EPfP LRHS MBar MGos NBlu NPri SCoo SPer SPoG SWal WGer
	'Sarana'	CCCN ECou
	selaginoides hort.	see *H.* 'Loganioides'
	'Shiraz'	LRHS SCoo
	'Silver Dollar' (v)	CAbP CCCN CMMP CPLG CSBt ELan EPfP LAst LHop LRHS MAsh MGos NPri SPer SPoG WSpi
	'Silver Princess' **new**	ENot
§	'Silver Queen' (v) ♀H2	CDul CSBt ECou ELan ENot EPfP EShb MBar MGos MNHC MRav NBlu NPer NPri SPer SWal WBod WHar WOut
	'Simon Délaux'	CEnt CSBt ECou LRHS NCiC SPoG WOut
I	'Southlandii'	ECho
	speciosa	ECho
	- 'Johny Day'	see *H.* 'Johny Day'
	- 'Rangatira'	ECou
§	- 'Variegata' (v)	CHal NPer SDry WEas
	'Spender's Seedling' misapplied	see *H. stenophylla*
	'Spender's Seedling' hort.	ECou EPfP EWin LRHS MRav SEND SPoG SRms STre
	'Spring Glory'	LRHS
§	***stenophylla***	ECou EShb EWin SAPC SArc SDix SHFr
	stricta	ECou
	- var. ***egmontiana***	ECou
	- var. ***macroura***	ECou SDry
	subalpina	CSBt ECho ECou ERas NHol
	'Summer Blue'	EPfP EWin LRHS MRav
	'Sussex Carpet'	see *H. albicans* 'Sussex Carpet'
	'Sweet Kim' (v)	LBuc LRHS SPoG
	'Tina'	ECou NHol
	'Tiny Tot'	MTho
	'Tom Marshall'	see *H. canterburiensis*
	topiaria ♀H4	CAbP CChe CSBt CSam ECho ECou EMil EPfP GGar LAst LHop LRHS MAsh MBrN MSwo MWgw NHol NPri SCoo SHBN SPer SPla SPoG STre WAbe WFar
*	- 'Doctor Favier'	LRHS
	townsonii	ECou EWin LHop SAga SCoo
	traversii	ECou MSte NHol SRms
	- 'Mason River'	ECou
	- 'Woodside'	ECou
	'Tricolor'	see *H. speciosa* 'Variegata'
	'Trixie'	CCCN ECou
	'Twisty'	ELan LRHS LSou MBNS MGos
	urvilleana	ECou
	'Valentino'PBR	LRHS SPer
	'Veitchii'	see *H.* 'Alicia Amherst'
§	***venustula***	ECou GGar IArd
	- 'Patricia Davies'	ECou
	vernicosa ♀H3	CChe ECho ECou EPfP LAst LRHS MBar MGos MHer NDlv NHol SCoo SPer SPlb SPoG SRot STre SWvt WAbe WFar WHCG
	'Vogue'	EPfP LRHS
	'Waikiki'	see *H.* 'Mrs Winder'
	'Warley Pink'	LRHS
	'Warleyensis'	see *H.* 'Mrs Winder'
§	'Watson's Pink'	ECou GGar MWea SPer WKif
	'Whistleberry Sapphire'	SWal
	'White Gem' (*brachysiphon* hybrid) ♀H4	CCCN ECou MGos NBlu NDlv NPer SPer WFar
	'White Heather'	LRHS NBir
	'White Paradise' **new**	SPoG
	'White Spreader'	EWin
	'Willcoxii'	see *H. buchananii* 'Fenwickii'
	'Wingletye' ♀H3	CCCN ECho ECou EPot LRHS MWgw NDlv NEgg NNor WAbe WPer
	'Winter Glow'	CCCN EWin LSou MGos NHol SCoo
	'Wiri Blush'	SHBN SWvt
	'Wiri Charm'	CAbP CDoC CDul CSBt EPfP GGar LAst LBMP LRHS MGos MLan MRav MSwo SHBN WBVN WOut
	'Wiri Cloud' ♀H3	CAbP CBcs CSBt EPfP EWin GGar LRHS MSwo SWal
	'Wiri Dawn' ♀H3	CAbP CSBt ELan EPfP EWes EWin LRHS LSou MGos SCoo SHBN SWvt WHrl
	'Wiri Desire'	CCCN
	'Wiri Gem'	EWin LRHS MRav
	'Wiri Image'	CDoC CSBt EWin LRHS
	'Wiri Joy'	LRHS SEND
	'Wiri Mist'	CBcs CTrC EWin GGar LRHS MGos NBlu
	'Wiri Prince'	EWin LRHS
	'Wiri Splash'	CDoC CSBt CTrC EWin LRHS MGos SCoo SHBN
	'Wiri Vision'	CSBt LRHS
§	'Youngii' ♀H3-4	CSBt EAlp ELan ENot EPfP LAst LRHS MBar MGos MHer MRav MWat NBir NMen NPri NWCA SBod SPer SPlb SPoG SRms STre SWvt WCFE WHoo WTel

Hebenstretia (*Scrophulariaceae*)

	dura	CPBP GGar
*	***quinquinervis***	LSou

Hedeoma (*Lamiaceae*)

	hyssopifolia	SPhx

Hedera ✿ (*Araliaceae*)

	algeriensis	see *H. canariensis* hort.
	- 'Gloire de Marengo'	see *H. canariensis* hort. 'Gloire de Marengo'
§	***azorica***	EShb WFar WFib
	- 'Pico'	WFib
	- 'Variegata' (v)	WCot
§	***canariensis*** hort.	CDoC CDul SAPC SArc WFib WGwG
	- 'Algeriensis'	see *H. canariensis* hort.
	- var. ***azorica***	see *H. azorica*
	- 'Cantabrian'	see *H. maroccana* 'Spanish Canary'
§	- 'Gloire de Marengo' (v) ♀H3	More than 30 suppliers
	- 'Gloire de Marengo' arborescent (v)	SPer
	- 'Marginomaculata' ♀H3	CDoC EPfP EShb LRHS MAsh SMad SPoG WCot WFib WWeb
	- 'Montgomery'	LRHS MWht
	- 'Ravensholst' ♀H3	CMac WFib
	- 'Variegata'	see *H. canariensis* hort. 'Gloire de Marengo'
	chinensis	see *H. nepalensis* var. *sinensis*
	- typica	see *H. nepalensis* var. *sinensis*
§	***colchica*** ♀H4	EPfP LRHS SPer WCFE WFar WFib
	- 'Arborescens'	see *H. colchica* 'Dendroides'
	- 'Batumi'	MBNS

§	– 'Dendroides'	WCot
	– 'Dentata' ♀H4	EPla MRav WFib
	– 'Dentata Aurea'	see *H. colchica* 'Dentata Variegata'
§	– 'Dentata Variegata' (v) ♀H4	More than 30 suppliers
	– 'My Heart'	see *H. colchica*
	– 'Paddy's Pride'	see *H. colchica* 'Sulphur Heart'
§	– 'Sulphur Heart' (v) ♀H4	More than 30 suppliers
	– 'Variegata'	see *H. colchica* 'Dentata Variegata'
	cristata	see *H. helix* 'Parsley Crested'
§	***cypria***	WFib
	'Dixie'	NLar
	helix	CArn CCVT CRWN CTri MBar MGos NBlu NWea SHFr WFar WHer WSFF XPep
	– 'Adam' (v)	CWib LAst MBri MTho WFib
	– 'Amberwaves'	MBri WFib
§	– 'Angularis'	ECot
	– 'Angularis Aurea' ♀H4	EPfP MWht NBir NHol SHBN WFib
	– 'Anita'	CBgR GBin WFib WGwG
§	– 'Anna Marie' (v)	CMac LRHS MBri SRms WFib
	– 'Anne Borch'	see *H. helix* 'Anna Marie'
	– 'Arborescens'	CNat EBee MGos NPal WCot
	– 'Ardingly' (v)	WFib
	– 'Asterisk'	WFib
	– 'Atropurpurea'	CNat EPPr EPla GBin MBar WFib
	– 'Baby Face'	WFib
	– var. ***baltica***	WFib
	– 'Barabits' Silver' (v)	EGoo EPla
	– 'Bill Archer'	WFib
	– 'Bird's Foot'	see *H. helix* 'Pedata'
	– 'Blue Moon'	WFib
	– 'Bodil' (v)	SHFr
	– 'Boskoop'	WFib
	– 'Bowles Ox Heart'	WFib
	– 'Bredon'	MRav
§	– 'Brokamp'	MWht SLPl WFib
	– 'Bruder Ingobert' (v)	WHrl
	– 'Buttercup'	More than 30 suppliers
	– 'Buttercup' arborescent	MAsh SPoG
	– 'Caecilia' (v) ♀H4	EPfP EQua LRHS MSwo NLar NSti SLim SWvt WCot WFar WFib WWeb
N	– 'Caenwoodiana'	see *H. helix* 'Pedata'
	– 'Caenwoodiana Aurea'	WFib
	– 'Calico' (v)	WFib
	– 'California Gold' (v)	WFib
	– 'Calypso'	WFib
	– 'Carolina Crinkle'	CBgR GBin WFib
	– 'Cathedral Wall'	WFib
§	– 'Cavendishii' (v)	SRms WFib WRHF
	– 'Cavendishii Latina' **new**	WCot
§	– 'Ceridwen' (v) ♀H4	CRHN EBee MBri SPlb WFib WWeb
	– 'Chalice'	EBee WFib
	– 'Chedglow Fasciated'	CNat WFar
	– 'Cheeky'	WFib
	– 'Cheltenham Blizzard' (v)	CNat
	– 'Chester' (v)	LRHS MAsh WFar WFib
	– 'Chicago'	CWib WFib
	– 'Chicago Variegated' (v)	WFib
	– 'Chrysophylla'	EPla MSwo
	– 'Clotted Cream' (v)	CBrm EBee LBMP LHop LRHS MAsh MWat WBod WFar WFib
	– 'Cockle Shell'	WFib
	– 'Colin'	GBin
§	– 'Congesta' ♀H4	EPla GCra MTho MWgw NBir SRms STre WFib
	– 'Conglomerata'	CBcs ELan EPla MBar NBir NEgg SRms WFib WTel
	– 'Conglomerata Erecta'	CSWP NVic SRms WCFE WFib
	– 'Courage'	WFib WGwG
	– 'Crenata'	WFib
	– 'Crispa'	MRav
	– 'Cristata'	see *H. helix* 'Parsley Crested'
	– 'Cristata Melanie'	see *H. helix* 'Melanie'
	– 'Curleylocks'	see *H. helix* 'Manda's Crested'
	– 'Curley-Q'	see *H. helix* 'Dragon Claw'
	– 'Curvaceous' (v)	WCot WFib
	– 'Cyprus'	see *H. cypria*
	– 'Dainty Bess'	CWib
	– 'Dead Again'	WCot
§	– 'Dealbata' (v)	CMac WFib
	– 'Deltoidea'	see *H. hibernica* 'Deltoidea'
	– 'Discolor'	see *H. helix* 'Minor Marmorata', *H. helix* 'Dealbata'
§	– 'Donerailensis'	CBgR MBlu WFib
	– 'Don's Papillon'	CBgR CNat
	– 'Dovers'	WFib
§	– 'Dragon Claw'	EPla WFib
	– 'Duckfoot' ♀H4	CBgR CDoC CHal EDAr EShb GBin MTho WFar WFib WOut
	– 'Dunloe Gap'	see *H. hibernica* 'Dunloe Gap'
	– 'Egret'	WFib
	– 'Eileen' (v)	WFib
	– 'Elfenbein' (v)	WFib
	– 'Emerald Gem'	see *H. helix* 'Angularis'
	– 'Emerald Jewel'	WFib
	– 'Erecta' ♀H4	CBgR CTca EBee EPPr EPfP EPla LRHS MBar MGos MTho NBlu NGHP NHol SHGN SPer SPlb SPoG WCot WFar WFib XPep
	– 'Erin'	see *H. helix* 'Pin Oak'
	– 'Ester' (v)	EQua LAst SLim SRGP WFib
§	– 'Eva' (v)	MGos NBir WFib
	– 'Fanfare'	WFib
	– 'Fantasia' (v)	CBcs MBri MRav WFib
	– 'Feenfinger'	WFib WGwG
	– 'Ferney'	WFib
	– 'Filigran'	NLar SMad WFib WHer
	– 'Flashback' (v)	WFib
	– 'Flavescens'	WFib
	– 'Fluffy Ruffles'	WFib
I	– 'Francis Ivy'	WFib
	– 'Frizzle'	WFib
	– 'Frosty' (v)	WFib
	– 'Funny Girl' **new**	WFib
	– 'Gavotte'	EPPr MTho MWht WFib
	– 'Ghost'	WFib
	– 'Gilded Hawke'	WFib WGwG
	– 'Glache' (v)	SHFr WFib
	– 'Glacier' (v) ♀H4	More than 30 suppliers
	– 'Glymii'	EPla GBin WCFE WFar WFib WTin
	– 'Gold Harald'	see *H. helix* 'Goldchild'
	– 'Gold Ripple'	SEND
§	– 'Goldchild' (v) ♀H3-4	CBcs CDoC CSam EBee ENot EPfP EPla LAst LCro LRHS MAsh MBar MGos MRav MSwo NBir NBlu NHol SAga SHFr SLim SPer SPoG SWvt WFib WTel
	– 'Goldcraft' (v)	WFib
	– 'Golden Ann'	see *H. helix* 'Ceridwen'
*	– 'Golden Arrow'	ELan MAsh SPoG
	– 'Golden Curl' (v)	EPfP LRHS WWeb
	– 'Golden Ester'	see *H. helix* 'Ceridwen'
	– 'Golden Gate' (v)	LAst WFib
	– 'Golden Girl'	WFib
	– 'Golden Ingot' (v) ♀H4	ELan EPla EQua GBin LBMP MBar WFib WGwG
	– 'Golden Kolibri'	see *H. helix* 'Midas Touch'
	– 'Golden Mathilde' (v)	CHal GBin
	– 'Golden Pittsburgh' (v)	WFib
	– 'Golden Snow' (v)	WFib
	– 'Goldfinch'	MBri WFib
	– 'Goldfinger'	MBri WFib
	– 'Goldheart'	see *H. helix* 'Oro di Bogliasco'
	– 'Goldstern' (v)	CBgR MRav WFib
	– 'Gracilis'	see *H. hibernica* 'Gracilis'
§	– 'Green Feather'	EGoo
	– 'Green Finger'	see *H. helix* 'Très Coupé'

§	– 'Green Ripple'	CBcs CSBt CTri CWib EBee ECrN EShb EWTr LRHS MAsh MBar MGos MRav MSwo MWht NBro SEND SLim SPer SPlb SRms WBor WFar WFib WHen
	– 'Greenman'	WFib WGwG
	– 'Hahn's Green Ripple'	see *H. helix* 'Green Ripple'
	– 'Halebob'	MBri WFib WGwG
	– 'Hamilton'	see *H. hibernica* 'Hamilton'
	– 'Harald' (v)	CTri CWib EBee WFib
*	– 'Hazel' (v)	WFib
	– 'Hedge Hog'	WFib
	– 'Heise' (v)	WFib
	– 'Heise Denmark' (v)	WFib
	– 'Helvig'	see *H. helix* 'White Knight'
	– 'Henrietta'	WFib
	– 'Hester'	WFib
	– subsp. ***hibernica***	see *H. hibernica*
	– 'Hispanica'	see *H. maderensis* subsp. *iberica*
	– 'Hite's Miniature'	see *H. helix* 'Merion Beauty'
	– 'Holly'	see *H. helix* 'Parsley Crested'
	– 'Hullavington'	CNat
	– 'Humpty Dumpty'	CPLG MBar
	– 'Ice Cream'	MBlu
	– 'Imp'	see *H. helix* 'Brokamp'
	– 'Ingelise' (v)	WFib
	– 'Ingrid' (v)	WFib
	– 'Irish Lace'	WFar
	– 'Itsy Bitsy'	see *H. helix* 'Pin Oak'
	– 'Ivalace' ♀H4	CBcs CRHN EBee ECha ECrN EPfP EPla MGos MNrw MRav MSwo MWht NBid SRms WFib WTin
	– 'Jake'	MBri WFib
	– 'Jasper'	WFib
	– 'Jersey Doris' (v)	WFib
	– 'Jerusalem'	see *H. helix* 'Schäfer Three'
	– 'Jessica'	SLim
	– 'Jester's Gold'	ELan ENot EPfP EPla MBri MGos
	– 'Jubilee' (v)	WCFE WFar WFib
	– 'Kaleidoscope'	WFib
	– 'Kevin'	WFib
	– 'Knülch'	WFib
	– 'Kolibri' (v)	CDoC CRHN EBee EMil EPfP LAst MBar MBri MGos MWht NBlu WFib
§	– 'Königer's Auslese'	CRHN WFib
	– 'Lalla Rookh'	MRav WFib WGwG WHrl
	– 'Lemon Swirl' (v)	WFib
	– 'Leo Swicegood'	CBgR WFib
	– 'Light Fingers'	LRHS SPoG WFib WGwG WHrl
	– 'Limey'	WFib
	– 'Little Diamond' (v)	CDoC CTri ELan EPfP LHop LRHS MAsh MBar MBri MWht NHol SHBN SLon SWvt WFar WFib WHrl WTin
	– 'Little Silver'	LRHS
	– 'Little Witch'	EPla
	– 'Liz'	see *H. helix* 'Eva'
	– 'Lucille'	WFib
I	– 'Lutzii' (v)	WFib WGwG
	– 'Luzii' (v)	EBee MBar MGos SGar SHBN WFib
	– 'Maculata'	see *H. helix* 'Minor Marmorata'
§	– 'Manda's Crested' ♀H4	CSWP NLar WFib WGwG
	– 'Maple Leaf' ♀H4	GBin WFib
	– 'Maple Queen'	MBri
	– 'Marginata' (v)	SRms
	– 'Marginata Elegantissima'	see *H. helix* 'Tricolor'
	– 'Marginata Minor'	see *H. helix* 'Cavendishii'
I	– 'Marmorata' Fibrex	WFib
	– 'Masquerade' (v)	WGor
	– 'Mathilde' (v)	EBee LRHS MWht WFib
	– 'Maxi'	SLim
	– 'Meagheri'	see *H. helix* 'Green Feather'
§	– 'Melanie' ♀H4	ECha EPla WCot WFib WGwG
	– 'Meon'	WFib
§	– 'Merion Beauty'	WFib
§	– 'Midas Touch' (v) ♀H3-4	CWib EPfP MBri NLar WFib
	– 'Mini Ester' (v)	EPfP MBri
	– 'Mini Heron'	LAst MBri
	– 'Mini Pittsburgh'	LAst
	– 'Minikin' (v)	WCot WFib
	– 'Minima' misapplied	see *H. helix* 'Spetchley'
	– 'Minima' Hibberd	see *H. helix* 'Donerailensis'
	– 'Minima' M. Young	see *H. helix* 'Congesta'
§	– 'Minor Marmorata' (v) ♀H4	CHal WSHC
	– 'Mint Kolibri'	MBri
	– 'Minty' (v)	EPla LRHS MWht SLim WFib
	– 'Misty' (v)	WFib
	– 'New Ripples'	MWht
	– 'Niagara Falls'	LRHS
	– 'Nigra Aurea' (v)	WFib
	– 'Norfolk Lace'	EWes
	– 'Obovata'	MRav WFib
N	– 'Oro di Bogliasco' (v)	More than 30 suppliers
	– 'Ovata'	WFib
§	– 'Parsley Crested' ♀H4	CMac CSBt EBee EPfP EQua MBar MGos SGar SPer SRms WBVN WFar WFib WGwG
	– 'Patent Leather'	WFib
N	– 'Pedata'	EPfP MSwo WFib
	– 'Perkeo'	CHal EGoo WFib
	– 'Persian Carpet'	WFib
	– 'Peter' (v)	WFib
	– 'Peter Pan'	WFib WGwG
*	– 'Pin Oak'	SIng WFar
	– 'Pink 'n' Curly'	WFib
	– 'Pink 'n' Very Curly'	WCot
§	– 'Pittsburgh'	MGos WFib
	– 'Plume d'Or'	CHal WFib
§	– f. ***poetarum***	CNat EPla MBlu WFib
	– – 'Poetica Arborea'	ECha SDix
	– 'Poetica'	see *H. helix* f. *poetarum*
	– 'Raleigh Delight' (v)	WCot
	– 'Ray's Supreme'	see *H. helix* 'Pittsburgh'
	– subsp. ***rhizomatifera***	WFib
	– 'Richard John' **new**	WFib
	– 'Ritterkreuz'	WFib WGwG
	– 'Romanze' (v)	WFib WGwG
	– 'Russelliana'	WFib
	– 'Sagittifolia' misapplied	see *H. helix* 'Königer's Auslese'
	– 'Sagittifolia' ambig.	MAsh
	– 'Sagittifolia' Hibberd	see *H. hibernica* 'Sagittifolia'
	– 'Sagittifolia Variegata' (v)	EBee LRHS MBri NBea WFib WRHF
	– 'Saint Agnes'	LRHS
	– 'Sally' (v)	WFib
	– 'Salt and Pepper'	see *H. helix* 'Minor Marmorata'
§	– 'Schäfer Three' (v)	CWib MRav WFib
	– 'Shadow'	WFib
	– 'Shamrock'	EPfP MWht WFib
	– 'Silver Butterflies' (v)	WFib
	– 'Silver King' (v)	MRav MWht NBir WFib WGwG
	– 'Silver Queen'	see *H. helix* 'Tricolor'
	– 'Spectre' (v)	WHer
§	– 'Spetchley' ♀H4	CHal EPla MAsh MBar MRav NPer SMad WCFE WCot WFib WGwG WHrl WPat WPrP WPtf WTin
	– 'Spiriusa'	WFib
	– 'Stuttgart'	WFib
	– 'Sunrise'	MRav WFib
	– 'Suzanne'	see *H. nepalensis* var. *nepalensis* 'Suzanne'
	– 'Tamara'	SLim
	– 'Tanja'	WFib
	– 'Telecurl'	WFib
	– 'Tenerife'	WFib
	– 'Tiger Eyes'	CBcs WFib
	– 'Topazolite' (v)	WFib
§	– 'Très Coupé'	CBcs CBgR CDoC EBee EGoo LRHS MAsh SAPC SArc

§	- 'Tricolor' (v)	CBcs CTri EBee EPfP LRHS MGos MWht SBra SHBN WCFE WFib
	- 'Trinity' (v)	WFib
	- 'Tripod'	CBcs WFib WGwG
	- 'Triton'	MBar WFib
	- 'Troll'	EDAr WFib WPat
	- 'Tussie Mussie' (v)	WFib
	- 'Ursula' (v)	WFib
*	- 'Variegata' (v)	MGos
	- 'White Heart'	ENot MGos MRav
§	- 'White Knight' (v) ♀H4	WFib
	- 'White Mein Herz' (v)	GBin WFib
	- 'White Wonder'	SLim
	- 'William Kennedy' (v)	WFib
	- 'Williamsiana' (v)	CBcs WFib
	- 'Woeneri'	MWht WFib
	- 'Wonder'	WFib
	- 'Yellow Ripple'	MBri MRav SLim
	- 'Zebra' (v)	WFib
§	***hibernica*** ♀H4	CBcs CDul CNat CSBt LBuc MBar MRav MSwo NBlu NWea SPer SRms WFib
	- 'Anna Marie'	see *H. helix* 'Anna Marie'
	- 'Aracena'	EPla SLPl
	- 'Betty Allen'	WFib
§	- 'Deltoidea' ♀H4	EPla MWht WFib
I	- 'Digitata Crûg Gold'	WCru
§	- 'Dunloe Gap'	EPla
§	- 'Gracilis'	WFib
§	- 'Hamilton'	WFib
	- 'Harlequin' (v)	WFib
	- 'Lobata Major'	SRms
	- 'Maculata' (v)	EPla SLPl WSHC
	- 'Palmata'	WFib
	- 'Rona'	WFib WGwG
§	- 'Sagittifolia'	CTri EPfP GBin LBMP LRHS MBar SHFr SPer SRms WFar
	- 'Sulphurea' (v)	MGos WFib
	- 'Tess'	EPla
	- 'Variegata' (v)	MBar
	maderensis	WFib
§	- subsp. ***iberica***	WFib
	maroccana 'Morocco'	WFib
§	- 'Spanish Canary'	WFib
	nepalensis	WFib
§	- var. ***nepalensis*** 'Suzanne'	MBar WFib
§	- var. ***sinensis***	MWht WFib
	- - L 555	EPla
	pastuchovii	EShb WFib
	- from Troödos, Cyprus	see *H. cypria*
	- 'Ann Ala'	EBee WFib WGwG
§	***rhombea***	WCot WFib
	- 'Eastern Dawn'	WFib
	- 'Japonica'	see *H. rhombea*
I	- f. ***pedunculata*** 'Maculata'	CWib
	- var. ***rhombea*** 'Variegata' (v)	WFib

Hedychium ✿ (*Zingiberaceae*)

	B&SWJ 3110	WPGP
	B&SWJ 7155	WPGP
	from Tresco **new**	CKob
	'Anne Bishop'	CKob MJnS WPGP
	aurantiacum	CBct CHEx EAmu LAma LEdu MJnS NPal WPnP
	brevicaule B&SWJ 7171 **new**	CKob
	chrysoleucum	CAvo CCCN CHEx EShb LAma SHaC
	coccineum ♀H1	CBcs CDTJ CKob EAmu EBee EBrs ECho EShb ETod LRHS MJnS MNrw SSwd
	- B&SWJ 5238	CKob WCru
	- var. ***angustifolium***	CDes CGHE CRHN EPfP WPGP
	- 'Tara' ♀H3	CBct CDes CDoC CGHE CHEx CKob CPne CRHN CSam EAmu EPfP ERea IBlr IGor LEdu LPJP MJnS MNrw MSte SAPC SArc SChr SDix WCot WCru WPGP WPic
	coronarium	CBct CDTJ CDes CKob EAmu EBee EBrs EShb LEdu LFur LRHS MJnS MSte SHaC WCot WPGP
	- B&SWJ 8354	WCru
	- 'Andromeda'	CKob
	- var. ***flavescens***	see *H. flavescens*
	- 'Gold Spot'	CKob SChr SKHP SSwd
	- var. ***maximum***	ETod
	- 'Orange Spot'	EAmu
	coronarium x ***ellipticum***	CKob
	coronarium x ***gardnerianum***	MJnS SPer SSwd
	'Dave Case'	CKob MJnS
	densiflorum	CBct CBrd CDTJ CDes CHEx CHll CKob CPne EAmu ECha EShb ETod IBlr LEdu MLLN SDix SSpi WCru WPGP
	- EN 562	CKob
	- 'Assam Orange'	CAvo CBct CDoC CGHE CHEx CKob CPne CRHN CSam EAmu ERea EShb IBlr LEdu MJnS MNrw MSte SChr SDix SSwd WBVN WCru WPGP WSHC
	- 'Sorung'	CKob LEdu
	- 'Stephen'	CAvo CBct CDTJ CDes CGHE CHEx CKob CSam EAmu EBee EPfP LEdu MJnS MNrw MSte WPGP
	'Devon Cream' **new**	CKob EAmu
	'Doctor Moy' (v)	CDTJ CKob MJnS
	'Double Eagle'	CKob MJnS WPGP
	'Elizabeth'	CDes CKob EBee LEdu MJnS WPGP
	ellipticum	CHEx CKob EAmu EBee ERea ETod LAma LEdu MJnS MNrw
	- B&SWJ 7171	WCru
	- red bracts	CKob
	'Filigree'	CDes CFir CKob LEdu MJnS WPGP
§	***flavescens***	CBcs CBct CKob CPne EAmu EBrs EShb LAma LEdu LRHS MJnS MNrw SChr WCru WPGP WPnP
	flavum 'Royale' **new**	IBlr
	forrestii misapplied	CKob
	forrestii	CDes CHEx CKob CPLG EAmu EShb ETod IBlr ITer LPJP MJnS MNrw MPRe MSte SAPC SArc WKif WPGP
	gardnerianum ♀H1	More than 30 suppliers
	- B&SWJ 7155	WCru
	- var. ***pallidum***	CKob
	'Gold Flame'	CDes CFir CKob CMdw EBee LEdu MJnS MNrw WPGP
	gomezianum **new**	CKob
	gracile	CKob EAmu LEdu
	greenii	CBct CDoC CFir CHEx CKob CRHN CSam EBee EBrs ECho EShb LEdu LRHS MJnS MNrw MSte SArc SChr SDix SHaC SSwd WBor WCru WPGP WPic WPnP
	griffithianum	CSpe MJnS MNrw
	'Hardy Exotics 1'	CHEx
	hasseltii	CKob
	horsfieldii	CKob
	hybrid from Great Dixter	MJnS
I	x ***kewense***	CKob SSwd
	'Kinkaku'	CKob MJnS WDyG WPGP
	'Lemon Sherbet'	CFir CKob MJnS
	'Luna Moth'	CDes CKob MJnS WPGP
	maximum	CKob MJnS SSwd WDyG WPGP

	- B&SWJ 8261A	WCru
	- HWJ 604	WCru
	'Nikasha-cho'	CKob
	'Orange Brush'	CKob
	'Pink Flame'	CKob LEdu MJnS
	'Pink Sparks'	CKob
	'Pink V'	CKob WPGP
	pink-flowered	CDes CKob
	'Pradhan'	CFir CHEx CKob MJnS
	x ***raffillii***	CKob MJnS MNrw
	'Shamshiri'	CKob MJnS
	spicatum	CBcs CDes CFir CHEx CKob CMdw CPLG CPne CRHN EMan GPoy IBlr LEdu MNrw MSte SSwd WCFE
	- B&SWJ 2303	WPGP
	- BWJ 8116	WCru
	- CC 1705	CKob
	- CC 3249	WCot
	- PB 57188	WPGP
	- from Salween Valley, China	CKob
	- var. ***acuminatum***	WPGP
	- 'Singalila'	WCru
	stenopetalum	CKob
	'Telstar 4'	CKob
	thyrsiforme	CKob CPne EAmu EBee ERea EShb LEdu MJnS WCru
	villosum	EBee EBrs ECho WPic
	wardii	CHEx CKob WPGP
	yunnanense	CDes CHEx CKob EBee ERea IBlr LEdu MJnS MNrw WCot WPGP
	- B&SWJ 7900	CKob
	- BWJ 7900	WCru
	- L 633	CKob

Hedysarum (*Papilionaceae*)

	coronarium	CArn CSpe EBee EHrv ELan EPfP LFur MBrN MCot SGar WKif
	multijugum	CBcs EBee MBlu SPer

Heimia (*Lythraceae*)

	salicifolia	CArn CBrm EMan EUnu IDee LRav MBlu MGol MSal SGar
	- RCB/Arg P-7	WCot

Helenium ✿ (*Asteraceae*)

	'Autumn Lollipop'	EBee IBal LSou MBNS MCCP NLar NOrc NSti SPav
	autumnale	CSBt CSam CTri EBee EGoo EPPr LDai LSRN MBNS MLHP MNHC MSal NChi NEgg SPet SWvt WBVN WFar WMoo
	- 'All Gold'	SWvt
I	- 'Cupreum'	SBch
	- Helena Series, mixed	LBMP
	- - 'Helena Gold'	EBee EDAr NBre
	- - 'Helena Rote Töne'	EBee LBMP NBHF SPhx
	- 'Praecox'	MWrn
	'Baronin Linden'	CSam
	'Baudirektor Linne' ♀H4	CSam WSpi WWpP
	'Biedermeier'	CAby CPrp CSam CWCL EBee EBla ECtt EShb LAst LHop MAvo MLLN NCob NGdn SAga SPla
	bigelovii	CSam
	- 'Big Top' **new**	CSam
	'Blütentisch' ♀H4	CHVG COIW CPrp CSam EBee EMan GMaP GMac LCro MBnl MNFA MWgw NCGa NLar NVic SPoG SPur WHal WMnd WWpP
	'Bressingham Gold'	CSam MAvo MNrw WBrk WHrl WWpP
	'Bruno'	CAby CHar CWCL EBrs EGle ELan ERou GMac GSki MArl NGby NLar NRnb WSpi WWpP
	'Butterpat' ♀H4	ECtt EHrv EPfP ERou GCra GMaP GMac IBal LBMP MRav NBPC NCGa NPri NSti WWpP
	'Can Can'	CSam
	'Chelsey'	EBee EHrv ELan ENot EPfP ERou GMac IBal IPot LCro MBNS MBnl MBri MLLN MPop NBPC NBhm NChi NLar NMoo NPri NSti SPer SPoG WWlt WWpP
	'Chipperfield Orange'	CAby CBgR CElw CSam ECtt ERou GBri LHop MArl MHar MRav NBre NGdn NVic WOld WOut WWpP
	'Coppelia'	CTca EBrs LBMP NBir NGdn WOld WTel
	Copper Spray	see *H.* 'Kupfersprudel'
	'Crimson Beauty'	CMea EBee ECtt ELan EPfP LRHS MLLN MRav WSpi
	Dark Beauty	see *H.* 'Dunkelpracht'
	'Dauerbrenner'	CSam
	'Die Blonde'	CAby NBre NDov SMHy SPhx WWpP
	'Double Trouble' **new**	EGle EHrv ERou GBri IPot MAvo MBNS MBnl NPri WWlt
§	'Dunkelpracht'	More than 30 suppliers
	'Feuersiegel' ♀H4	CAby CSam NBre NDov WOld WWpP
	'Fiesta'	CSam
	'Flammendes Käthchen'	CAby CSam CWCL EBee EBrs IPot LRHS NBre NDov SAga SPhx WWpP
	'Flammenrad'	CSam EBee
	'Flammenspiel'	ECtt LRHS MCot MNFA MNrw MRav WSpi WWpP
	flexuosum	EBee EShb MWrn NBre WPer
	'Gartensonne' ♀H4	CSam NBre WWpP
	'Gay-go-round'	CSam
	'Gold Fox'	see *H.* 'Goldfuchs'
	'Gold Intoxication'	see *H.* 'Goldrausch'
	Golden Youth	see *H.* 'Goldene Jugend'
§	'Goldene Jugend'	CElw CMea CSam ECtt ELan MRav WCot WEas WHal WOld WWpP
§	'Goldfuchs'	CSam CWCL WCot WWpP
§	'Goldlackzwerg'	MBri NBre
§	'Goldrausch'	CHar CPrp CSam EBee EBla MDKP MHar MWat NBre NGdn WHlf WOld WSpi WWpP
	'Goldreif'	CSam
	'Hartmut Reiger' **new**	CSam
	'Helena'	MWea NEgg NLar NRnb WPer
	hoopesii	see *Hymenoxys hoopesii*
	'Indianersommer'	CElw CSam CWCL EBee EBla ECtt EGle EHrv EMan GMaP GMac IBal LCro LDai MBNS MBnl MLLN NBPC NCGa NLar NMRc NOrc SMHy SMer WFar WWpP
	'Jam Tarts' **new**	WCot
	'July Sun'	NBir
	'Kanaria'	CAby CBre CPrp EBee EMil ERou EWll LRHS NCob NLar SPoG SPur WLin WMnd WOld WSpi WWpP
	'Karneol' ♀H4	CSam LHop NBre WWpP
	'Kleiner Fuchs'	CSam EHrv NLar WWpP
	'Kokarde'	CSam
	'Königstiger'	CSam EBee EBrs GMac LRHS MNrw NBre WWpP
	'Kugelsonne'	LCro NBre WWpP
§	'Kupfersprudel'	CSam MRav
	'Kupferzwerg'	CAby CElw CSam CWCL EBee IPot NBre NDov WEas
	'Luc'	CSam
	'Mahagoni'	CSam
	'Mahogany'	see *H.* 'Goldlackzwerg'
	'Margot'	CSam CWCL NBre WWpP
	'Marion Nickig' **new**	CSam
	'Meranti'	CMea CSam

'Moerheim Beauty' ♀H4	More than 30 suppliers
'Orange Beauty'	WHlf
'Patsy' **new**	CSam
Pipsqueak = 'Blopip'	CWCL EBrs ECtt GBri LRHS NBre
'Potter's Wheel'	CSam IPot WWpP
puberulum	SPav WOut
'Pumilum Magnificum'	CBgR CDes CHar CPrp CSam CTca CWCL EBee EPfP GSki LEdu LHop LRHS MBnl MNFA MWat SPer WFar WPGP WTel
'Ragamuffin' **new**	CSam
'Rauchtopas'	CSam IBal IPot NDov
Red and Gold	see *H.* 'Rotgold'
'Red Army'	EBee EKen GMac IBal MNrw NCGa NGdn NRnb
'Red Glory'	EHrv
'Ring of Fire' ♀H4	CSam IPot
'Riverton Beauty'	CSam EBee ERou NChi WHoo
'Riverton Gem'	CSam ECtt EHrv NBre NChi WHoo
§ 'Rotgold'	CMea ECtt LSRN MWrn NBre NChi NEgg NOak NRnb SGar SRms STes WFar WMoo WPer WWeb
'Rotkäppchen'	CSam
'Rubinkuppel'	NDov SPhx
'Rubinzwerg' ♀H4	More than 30 suppliers
'Ruby Tuesday' **new**	CElw EHrv MBNS MBnl MPop SPoG
'Sahin's Early Flowerer' ♀H4	More than 30 suppliers
'Septemberfuchs'	GMac LEdu MCot NBre
'Septembergold'	WWpP
'Sonnenwunder'	ECha LEdu MLHP NBre WOld WWpP
'Sunshine'	MGol WBrk
'The Bishop'	More than 30 suppliers
'Tip Top' **new**	EBee EDAr
'Vivace'	CSam
'Waltraut' ♀H4	More than 30 suppliers
'Wesergold' ♀H4	CSam EBee LTwo SMHy SPoG
'Wonnadonga'	WWpP
'Wyndley'	More than 30 suppliers
'Zimbelstern'	CAby CElw CMdw EBee ECha ECtt ERou LHop LRHS MNFA MRav NDov SPhx WAul WFar WWpP

Heliamphora (*Sarraceniaceae*)

minor	SHmp
nutans	SHmp

Helianthella (*Asteraceae*)

§ ***quinquenervis***	CPLG EBee EMan GBin NLar WFar

Helianthemum ✿ (*Cistaceae*)

'Albert's Brick' **new**	CFul
'Albert's Gold' **new**	CFul
'Albert's Pink' **new**	CFul
'Alice Howarth'	CFul WHoo
alpestre serpyllifolium	see *H. nummularium* subsp. *glabrum*
'Amabile Plenum' (d)	CFul EPfP GAbr LIMB MBNS NLar
'Amber'	CFul
'Amy Baring' ♀H4	CFul CTri GAbr LIMB LRHS WPer
'Annabel'	CFul ECho EPfP GAbr IGor MWya SBla SMer WPer
apenninum	CFul SRms XPep
- var. ***roseum***	ECho
'Apricot'	CFul CTri SPer
'Apricot Blush'	CFul WAbe
I 'Aurantiacum' **new**	CFul
'Avalanche'	CFul
'Baby Buttercup'	CFul CLyd CMea GAbr LIMB
'Banwy Copper'	CFul
'Banwy Velvet' **new**	WBVN
'Beech Park Red'	CFul ECho ECtt LIMB MHer WAbe WFar WHoo WKif WRHF
'Ben Afflick'	CFul ECho LIMB LRHS MBNS SPer SRms WFar
'Ben Alder'	CFul ECho GAbr LIMB MHer
'Ben Attow'	CFul
'Ben Dearg'	CFul CMea ECho ECtt GAbr LIMB SRms
'Ben Fhada'	CBcs CFul CMea COlW CPBP CTca CTri EAlp ECho ECtt EPfP GAbr GEdr GKev GMaP LBee LIMB LRHS MHer NEgg NPri SBla SPer SPoG SRms WAbe WBVN WBrE WFar WPer
'Ben Heckla'	CFul CSam CTri ECho ECtt EPfP GAbr GEdr LIMB LRHS MSte SBla WPer
'Ben Hope'	CFul CTca ECho ECtt EPfP EWTr GAbr GEdr LIMB SPer SRGP
'Ben Lawers'	CFul
§ 'Ben Ledi'	CBcs CFul CPBP ECho ECtt EPfP GAbr GBuc GEdr GMaP LHop LIMB MBar MHer NChi NHol NPri NSla SPer SPoG SRms WAbe WFar WPer
'Ben Lomond'	CFul ECho GAbr LIMB
'Ben Lui' **new**	CFul
'Ben Macdhui'	CFul GAbr LIMB
'Ben More'	CBcs CFul COlW CTca ECho ECtt EPfP EWin GAbr GGar LHop LIMB LRHS MSwo MWat NBir NPri SPer SPoG SRGP SRms WFar
'Ben Nevis'	CFul CTri ECha ECho GAbr GEdr LIMB SBla SPer SRms WFar
'Ben Vane'	CFul COlW GAbr LIMB LRHS
'Bentley'	CFul
'Birch White'	CFul
'Bishopsthorpe'	CFul
'Blutströpfchen' **new**	CFul
'Boughton Double Primrose' (d)	CFul CPBP ECho ELan EWes GMaP LHop SBla SMer WEas WHoo WSHC WSel WTin
'Braungold' **new**	CFul
'Brilliant'	CFul NBir
'Broughty Beacon'	CFul GAbr LIMB WGor
'Broughty Orange'	WSel
'Broughty Sunset'	CFul CSam GAbr LIMB NBir WHoo WSel
'Brown Gold' (d)	ECho
'Bunbury'	CFul CMea COlW GAbr LIMB MBrN NBir SPer SPoG SRms
* 'Butter and Eggs'	CTca LIMB
'Butterball' (d)	CFul
canum	SBla
'Captivation'	CFul GAbr LIMB
caput-felis	XPep
I 'Carminium Plenum' **new**	CFul
'Cerise Queen' (d)	CFul CTri EAlp ECha ECho GAbr GKev LHop LIMB MSwo SDix SPer SRms WHoo
chamaecistus	see *H. nummularium*
'Cheviot'	CFul CMea ECha GAbr LIMB NBir SAga WEas WHoo WPer WSHC
'Chichester'	CFul
'Chocolate Blotch'	CFul CRez ECho GAbr GCra GEdr LHop LIMB LRHS NChi NHol SEND SPla SRms WPer
'Coppernob'	CFul
'Cornish Cream'	CFul CTca ECho GAbr LBee LIMB LRHS
croceum	LTwo
cupreum	CFul GAbr
'David'	CFul EGoo
'David Ritchie'	WHoo
'Devon Cream' **new**	CTca
'Diana'	CMea SAga
'Die Braut'	CFul

	'Dompfaff' **new**	CFul
	'Dora' **new**	CFul
	double apricot-flowered (d)	GAbr LIMB
	double cream-flowered (d)	ECha ECho SPer
	double pink-flowered (d)	ECha
	double primrose-flowered (d)	CHVG GAbr LIMB
	double red-flowered (d)	NChi
	'Eisbar' **new**	CFul
	'Elfenbeinglanz'	CFul
	'Elisabeth'	CFul EGoo
	'Ellen' (d)	CMea
	'Etna'	CFul LIMB STre
	'Everton Ruby'	see *H.* 'Ben Ledi'
	'Fairy'	CFul ECho LIMB LTwo
	'Feuerbraund' **new**	CFul
§	'Fire Dragon' 🏆^{H4}	CFul CMea ECha ECho EPfP GAbr GMaP GQue LIMB LRHS NBir NEgg NWCA SAga SBla SEND SPoG SRms WAbe XPep
	'Fireball'	see *H.* 'Mrs C.W. Earle'
	'Firegold'	CFul LIMB WAbe WFar
	'Flame'	CFul
	'Frau Bachtaler' **new**	CFul
	'Gelber Findling' (d) **new**	CFul
	'Georgeham'	CFul CTca ECho ECtt EPfP GAbr LBee LHop LIMB LRHS NBir SAga SBla SMer SPer SPoG SRms WEas WGor WHoo WPer
	georgicum	CPBP
	'Gloiriette'	CFul
§	'Golden Queen'	CFul ECho ECtt EPfP GAbr LIMB MBNS MSwo NLar SPer SPoG WFar WPer
	'Goldring' **new**	CFul
	'Hampstead Orange' **new**	CTri
	'Hartshorn' **new**	CFul
	'Henfield Brilliant' 🏆^{H4}	CBrm CFul CHVG CPBP CPLG CTca ECho EPfP GAbr LHop LIMB LRHS MRav NBir NHol SMad SMer SPer SPla SPoG SRms WEas WHoo WLin WPer WSHC WSel
	'Hidcote Apricot'	CFul NEgg SPer
	'Highdown'	CFul GAbr SRms
	'Highdown Apricot'	CTca EAlp LHop LIMB MWea SPoG WFar
	'Highdown Pink' **new**	CFul
	'Honeymoon'	CFul GAbr LIMB WSel
	'Ilna's Master' (d) **new**	CFul
	'John Lanyon'	CFul
	'Jubilee' (d) 🏆^{H4}	CBrm CFul COlW CTca CTri ECho ECtt ELan EPfP GAbr LAst LHop LIMB NBir NChi SBla SDix SPer SPoG SRms WEas WFar WKif WSel
I	'Jubilee Variegatum' (v)	CFul GAbr LIMB
	'Karen's Silver'	CFul WAbe
	'Kathleen Druce' (d)	CFul CTca ECho EWes GAbr LIMB MWat SAga WHoo
	'Kathleen Mary'	CMea
	'Lawrenson's Pink'	CFul ECho ECtt GAbr LIMB SRGP
	'Lemon Queen'	CFul NPri
	'Linton Rose'	NBir
	'Loxbeare Gold' **new**	CFul
	'Lucy Elizabeth'	CFul GAbr LIMB
	lunulatum	CFul CLyd CMea ECtt LRHS NLAp NMen WAbe WPat
I	'Lunulatum Mutabile' **new**	CFul
	'Magnificum'	CFul MWat
	'Marianne' **new**	CFul
	'Mette' **new**	CFul
§	'Mrs C.W. Earle' (d) 🏆^{H4}	CFul COlW CTca CTri ECGP ECho ECtt ELan GAbr GBuc LAst LIMB MWat MWya NPri SBla SDix SPer SRms WFar WSel
	'Mrs Clay'	see *H.* 'Fire Dragon'
	'Mrs Croft'	LIMB WPer
	'Mrs Hays'	CFul GAbr LIMB
	'Mrs Jenkinson'	CFul LIMB
	'Mrs Lake'	CFul GAbr LIMB
	'Mrs Moules'	CFul SRms
	mutabile	CEnt CFul SPhx SPlb
§	***nummularium***	GPoy MHer MNHC NMir NSco SHGN WPat WSFF XPep
§	- subsp. ***glabrum***	CFul GAbr MNHC NHol NLAp WPat
	- subsp. ***grandiflorum***	CFul
	- subsp. ***pyrenaicum***	CFul
§	- subsp. ***tomentosum***	CFul GAbr MWat
I	'Oblongatum' **new**	CFul
	oelandicum	NWCA SRms
	- subsp. ***alpestre***	CFul CLyd NLAp NMen WPer
	- subsp. ***piloselloides***	CLyd WAbe
	'Old Gold'	CFul EGoo GAbr LIMB SRms WAbe WPer WSel
	'Orange Phoenix' (d)	CFul CRez EPfP GAbr GKev LIMB LSou NEgg SRot WFar
	'Ovum Supreme'	CFul GAbr LIMB
	'Peach' **new**	CFul
	'Pershore Orange'	CFul
I	'Pilosum Rosea' **new**	CFul
	'Pink Angel' (d) **new**	CBow
	'Pink Glow'	CFul WPer
	'Praecox'	CFul CMea CTri ECho GAbr LBee LIMB SRms WHoo WPer
	'Prima Donna'	CFul ECGP NBir
	'Prostrate Orange'	CFul LIMB SRms
	'Raspberry Ripple'	CBow CBrm CFul CHar ECho ECtt ELan EPfP EPot LAst LHop LIMB LRHS MWrn NHol SPoG SRms WAbe WFar WHoo
	'Ravens Oranje' **new**	CFul
	'Razzle Dazzle' (v)	CBow CFul LAst LHop LIMB LTwo SRms SRot WFar
	'Red Dragon'	CFul LIMB WAbe
	'Red Orient'	see *H.* 'Supreme'
	'Regenbogen' (d)	CFul ECha GAbr LIMB SBla
§	'Rhodanthe Carneum' 🏆^{H4}	More than 30 suppliers
§	'Rosakönigin'	CFul CTca ECho ECtt GAbr LIMB MHer WAbe WLin
	'Rose of Leeswood' (d)	CBrm CFul CMea CPBP CTca CTri GMaP LBee LIMB NChi NEgg SAga SBla SPer SPoG SRms WEas WFar WHoo WKif WSHC WSel
	Rose Queen	see *H.* 'Rosakönigin'
	'Roxburgh Gold'	CFul SRms
	'Rushfield's White'	CFul
	'Ruth'	CFul
	'Saint John's College Yellow'	CFul CSam ECho GAbr LIMB LRHS
	'Salmon Beauty'	CFul
	'Salmon Bee'	CFul
	'Salmon Queen'	CFul ECho ECtt GAbr LBee LHop LIMB LRHS NPri SRms WPer WRHF WSel
*	***scardicum***	CFul CMea NLAp
	'Schnee' (d)	CFul ECha EGoo LIMB
	serpyllifolium	see *H. nummularium* subsp. *glabrum*
	'Shot Silk'	CFul CPBP CTca ECho EWes
	'Snow Queen'	see *H.* 'The Bride'
	'Southmead'	CFul ECho GAbr LIMB
	'Sterntaler'	CFul GAbr LIMB SRms
	'Sudbury Gem'	CFul CTri ECha ECho EWin GAbr LIMB LRHS SMer
	'Sulphur Moon' **new**	CFul
	'Sulphureum Plenum' (d)	CFul ECtt EPfP
	'Summertime'	CFul
	'Sunbeam'	CFul CSam ECho GAbr LIMB SRms
	'Sunburst'	CFul LIMB
§	'Supreme'	CFul ECho ELan EPfP EWes LBee LIMB SDix SRms WSel WWeb

'Tangerine' — CFul ECha GAbr LIMB
'Terracotta' — CRez
§ 'The Bride' ♀H4 — More than 30 suppliers
'Tigrinum Plenum' (d) — CFul CPBP ECho EWes LIMB SBla
'Tomato Red' — CFul ECha NSla
tomentosum — see *H. nummularium*
umbellatum — see *Halimium umbellatum*
'Venustum Plenum' (d) — CFul WEas
'Victor' (d) **new** — CFul
'Voltaire' — CFul ECho EPfP GAbr LIMB NHol
'Watergate Rose' — CFul ECho LIMB MWat NBir
'Watfield Mist' — CHar
'Welsh Flame' — CFul LIMB WAbe WFar
'Windmill Gold' — CFul LBee
'Wisley Pink' — see *H.* 'Rhodanthe Carneum'
'Wisley Primrose' ♀H4 — More than 30 suppliers
'Wisley White' — CFul CTri EAlp ECha ECho ECtt EGoo EPfP GAbr LIMB
'Wisley Yellow' — CBrm
'Yellow Queen' — see *H.* 'Golden Queen'
I 'Zonatus' **new** — CFul

Helianthus (*Asteraceae*)

RCB/Arg CC-3 — WCot
angustifolius — WFar WPer
atrorubens — EBee LRHS MRav NBro WFar
'Bronze Teppich' — CFul
'Capenoch Star' ♀H4 — CElw CPrp EBee ECha ECtt ERou GBuc GMaP LAst LEdu MArl MAvo MLLN MRav NBPC NBro NLar SDix SMrm SPoG WCAu WFar WMoo WOld
'Capenoch Supreme' — ECtt
decapetalus — CHar WHal WHil
- 'Maximus' — SRms
- Morning Sun — see *H.* 'Morgensonne'
divaricatus — NBre
x ***doronicoides*** — SRms
giganteus 'Sheila's Sunshine' — CBre CElw GBri MAvo MNFA MSte NDov WOld
gracilentus — NBre
'Gullick's Variety' ♀H4 — CBre EBee ECtt EPfP EShb IBlr LLWP MBnl NBro NChi NEgg NSti SPur STes WOld
'Hazel's Gold' — ECtt NBre
hirsutus — EBee NBre
x ***kellermanii*** — CAby EBee EMon MWgw NBre NDov SAga
§ x ***laetiflorus*** — EBee ELan GAbr MDKP NBre NLar NOrc
* - 'Superbus' — IBlr
§ 'Lemon Queen' ♀H4 — More than 30 suppliers
'Limelight' — see *H.* 'Lemon Queen'
'Loddon Gold' ♀H4 — CElw CHar EBee ECtt ELan EPfP ERou EShb IBlr MAvo MRav NEgg NPri NVic SAga SRGP WBrE WBrk WCot WFar
§ ***maximiliani*** — EBee EShb LDai LEdu LRav MDKP MSte SPav SWal XPep
microcephalus — EBee
'Miss Mellish' ♀H4 — NRnb WBrk WCot WHoo
mollis — EBee EShb NBre SPav WPer
'Monarch' ♀H4 — CFwr CMea EBee ERou GMac MDKP MRav MSte MWgw NBre NCGa SDix SMad SPhx WCot WOld
§ 'Morgensonne' — CPrp ECtt EHrv MAvo MWat NRnb WCot WFar
x ***multiflorus*** 'Anemoniflorus Flore Pleno' — MBri
- 'Meteor' — EBee ECtt MAvo NBre NChi
occidentalis — IBlr WPer
orgyalis — see *H. salicifolius*
quinquenervis — see *Helianthella quinquenervis*
rigidus misapplied — see *H.* x *laetiflorus*
§ ***salicifolius*** — CFwr EBee ELon EMan EMon EPPr EShb LEdu LRHS MBri MSte NCGa SDix SMad SMrm WBVN WCot WFar WHil WHlf WMnd WMoo WSpi WTin XPep
- 'Hot Chocolate' — WCot
- 'Low Down'^{PBR} — CSpe EBee GBri IPot MCCP MNrw NBro NLar NMoo
scaberrimus — see *H.* x *laetiflorus*
'Soleil d'Or' — EBee ECtt IPot WCAu WHal
strumosus — WCot
'Triomphe de Gand' — GBri MRav MWat WFar WOld
tuberosus — CArn EBee EBrs EUnu GPoy
- 'Dwarf Sunray' — LEdu
- 'Fuseau' — LEdu SWal
- 'Garnet' — LEdu
- 'Sugarball' — LEdu

Helichrysum (*Asteraceae*)

from Drakensberg Mountains, South Africa — NWCA
adenocarpum — SPlb
alveolatum — see *H. splendidum*
ambiguum — CFis
amorginum Ruby Cluster = 'Blorub'^{PBR} — WFar
angustifolium — see *H. italicum*
- from Crete — see *H. microphyllum* (Willd.) Cambess.
arenarium — ECho
§ ***arwae*** — EPot WAbe
basalticum — WAbe
bellum — NWCA
chionophilum — NWCA WAbe
'Coco' — see *Xerochrysum bracteatum* 'Coco'
conglobatum — XPep
coralloides — see *Ozothamnus coralloides*
'County Park Silver' — see *Ozothamnus* 'County Park Silver'
'Dargan Hill Monarch' — see *Xerochrysum bracteatum* 'Dargan Hill Monarch'
depressum — WAbe
doerfleri — XPep
'Elmstead' — see *H. stoechas* 'White Barn'
fontanesii — SPer WHer XPep
frigidum — CPBP ITim LRHS WAbe
heldreichii NS 127 — NWCA
hookeri — see *Ozothamnus hookeri*
§ ***hypoleucum*** — ECha GGar WCot WHer
§ ***italicum*** ♀H3 — CArn CEnt CWan ECha ELau GPoy MBar MHer MLHP MNHC MWgw NBlu NGHP SECG SPet SRms WGwG WHCG XPep
- from Crete — NWCA
- 'Dartington' — CBod EBee EOHP EWin NGHP SIde WJek WSel
I - 'Glaucum' — CWib
- 'Korma'^{PBR} — CAbP EBee ELan ENot EPfP EWTr EWin MAsh NGHP NPri SIde SLon SPoG STes WJek
- subsp. ***microphyllum*** — see *H. microphyllum* (Willd.) Cambess.
- 'Nanum' — see *H. microphyllum* (Willd.) Cambess.
§ - subsp. ***serotinum*** — CChe EBee EGoo EPfP GGar GPoy MRav NBlu SLim SMer SPer SPla SRms STre SWal SWvt WPer WRHF WSel WTel XPep
lanatum — see *H. thianschanicum*
ledifolium — see *Ozothamnus ledifolius*
marginatum misapplied — see *H. milfordiae*
microphyllum misapplied — see *Plecostachys serpyllifolia*
§ ***microphyllum*** (Willd.) Cambess. — EPot MHer MNHC NBlu SIde SPer WJek WSel XPep

§ ***milfordiae*** ♀H2-3	EChо EDAr GEdr NWCA SIng SRms WAbe
montanum	NWCA
orientale	EBee EPot SMer SPoG XPep
pagophilum	CPBP NLAp
§ ***petiolare*** ♀H2	EBak ECtt EWin NBlu SGar SPer
- 'Aureum'	see *H. petiolare* 'Limelight'
- 'Goring Silver' ♀H2-3	NPri SPet
§ - 'Limelight' ♀H2	CHal ECtt EWin NBlu NPri SPer SPet
- 'Roundabout' (v)	LSou
- 'Variegatum' (v) ♀H2	CHal ECtt NPri SPet SPoG
petiolatum	see *H. petiolare*
plumeum	ECou EPot
populifolium misapplied	see *H. hypoleucum*
rosmarinifolium	see *Ozothamnus rosmarinifolius*
rupestre	XPep
§ 'Schwefellicht'	EBee ECha EGle EPPr EPfP ERou EShb LRHS MLHP MNFA MWgw SMer SPer SWat WCAu WEas WKif WSHC
selago	see *Ozothamnus selago*
serotinum	see *H. italicum* subsp. *serotinum*
serpyllifolium	see *Plecostachys serpyllifolia*
sessile	see *H. sessilioides*
§ ***sessilioides***	EPot NSla WAbe
§ ***sibthorpii***	ECho LRHS NWCA
§ ***splendidum*** ♀H3	CStu EPfP NBro NWCA SKHP SLon WBrE WPer XPep
stoechas	CArn XPep
§ - 'White Barn'	CSpe EBee WCot
Sulphur Light	see *H.* 'Schwefellicht'
§ ***thianschanicum***	EShb SRms XPep
- Golden Baby	see *H. thianschanicum* 'Goldkind'
§ - 'Goldkind'	EPfP NBir NBlu NPri
thyrsoideum	see *Ozothamnus thyrsoideus*
trilineatum	see *H. splendidum*
tumidum	see *Ozothamnus selago* var. *tumidus*
virgineum	see *H. sibthorpii*
woodii	see *H. arwae*

Helicodiceros (*Araceae*)

§ ***muscivorus***	CDes CHid EBee WCot

Heliconia ✿ (*Heliconiaceae*)

angusta 'Holiday'	MJnS
- 'Yellow Christmas'	MJnS
bourgaeana	LPal
caribaea 'Purpurea'	XBlo
'Golden Torch'	MJnS XBlo
indica 'Spectabilis'	XBlo
latispatha 'Orange Gyro'	MJnS XBlo
- 'Red Gyro'	XBlo
lingulata 'Fan'	LPal
metallica	XBlo
psittacorum	CCCN
rostrata	EAmu LPal MJnS XBlo
stricta 'Dwarf Jamaican'	MJnS

Helictotrichon (*Poaceae*)

§ ***sempervirens*** ♀H4	More than 30 suppliers
- var. ***pendulum***	EBee EMon EPPr GBin MAvo MLLN XIsg
- 'Saphirsprudel'	CKno CMdw EBee EPPr GBin LRHS WCot WPGP

Heliophila (*Brassicaceae*)

carnosa	SPla
longifolia	CSpe

Heliopsis ✿ (*Asteraceae*)

Golden Plume	see *H. helianthoides* var. *scabra* 'Goldgefieder'
helianthoides	EMon LRHS MLHP NBre WHil
- 'Limelight'	see *Helianthus* 'Lemon Queen'
- Loraine Sunshine = 'Helhan'PBR (v)	LRHS
- var. ***scabra***	MDKP WHil WMnd
- - 'Asahi'	EBee ECtt ELan ERou MCCP NLar NSti WHoo WWlt
- - Ballerina	see *H. helianthoides* var. *scabra* 'Spitzentänzerin'
- - 'Benzinggold' ♀H4	MRav SMrm
- - Golden Plume	see *H. helianthoides* var. *scabra* 'Goldgefieder'
§ - - 'Goldgefieder' ♀H4	EBee EPfP LRHS MBnl MBri NBre NBro WFar
- - Goldgreenheart	see *H. helianthoides* var. *scabra* 'Goldgrünherz'
§ - - 'Goldgrünherz'	EBee ERou NBre
- - 'Hohlspiegel'	EBee NBre
- - 'Incomparabilis'	MRav MWgw WCAu
- - 'Karat'	EBee
- - 'Lohfelden' **new**	EBee
- - 'Mars'	EBee
- - 'Patula'	EBee NBro
§ - - 'Sommersonne'	CSBt EBee ECtt ERou LBMP MRav NBro NGBl NHol NPer SPer SRms STes WCAu WFar WMnd WPtf WWeb
- - 'Sonnenschild' **new**	EBee
§ - - 'Spitzentänzerin' ♀H4	EBee MBri NBre NGby
- - 'Summer Nights'	CSam ENot LBMP LDai MDKP MSte NDov NHol SPhx WHil
- - Summer Sun	see *H. helianthoides* var. *scabra* 'Sommersonne'
- - 'Venus'	EBee ECtt ENot ERou GBri LAst NBhm NLar NRnb NSti WCAu WFar

Heliotropium ✿ (*Boraginaceae*)

§ ***amplexicaule***	SDys
anchusifolium	see *H. amplexicaule*
§ ***arborescens***	CArn EPfP EShb MAJR MCot MHom
- 'Atlantis' **new**	CSpe WHrl
- 'Chatsworth' ♀H1	CAby CCCN CSev ECre ECtt EMan ERea EShb MAJR MHom MSte SDnm SMad WFar
- 'Chequerboard'	ERea MAJR
- 'Dame Alice de Hales'	CHal ERea MAJR MHom
- 'Florence Nightingale'	MAJR
- 'Fowa'	MAJR
- 'Gatton Park'	ERea MAJR MHom MRav SMrm
- 'Lord Roberts'	ERea MAJR MHom WWlt
- 'Marine'	ECtt EWin SGar SPav WGor WWlt
- 'Marino 2000' **new**	MAJR
- 'Mary Fox'	ERea MAJR MHom
- 'Mrs J.W. Lowther'	MAJR MHom
- 'Nagano'PBR	EWin
- 'Netherhall White'	ERea
- 'P.K. Lowther'	WEas
- 'President Garfield'	MAJR MHom SMrm WFar
- 'Princess Marina' ♀H1	CSev CSpe EMan ERea LAst LRHS LSou MAJR MSte NLar SDys SPav
- 'Reva' **new**	MAJR
- 'Seifel'	ERea MAJR
* - 'The Queen'	ECtt ERea MAJR
- 'The Speaker'	ERea MAJR MHom
- 'White Lady'	CCCN CHal CPLG CSev CSpe ECtt ERea EWin LSou MAJR MHom NLar
- 'White Queen'	ECtt MAJR MHom
- 'Woodcote'	MAJR MHom
peruvianum	see *H. arborescens*
'Purple Prince'	NBlu

Helipterum see *Rhodanthe*

Helleborus ✿ (*Ranunculaceae*)

	abschasicus	see *H. orientalis* Lam. subsp. *abchasicus* (A. Braun) B. Mathew
§	***argutifolius*** ♀^{H4}	More than 30 suppliers
	- from Italy	EHrv
	- 'Janet Starnes' (v)	MAsh
	- mottled-leaved	see *H. argutifolius* 'Pacific Frost'
§	- 'Pacific Frost' (v)	CBow CLAP EWes NEgg NPro WBVN
	- 'Silver Lace'^{PBR}	CBow CFir CHid CMil CPen CSpe CWCL EBee ELan EPfP LDai LFur LHop MCCP MGos MSte NBir NEgg NHol NLar NMyG NSti SPer SPoG WPtf
	atrorubens misapplied	see *H. orientalis* Lam. subsp. *abchasicus* Early Purple Group
	atrorubens Waldst. & Kit.	CDes NEgg WPGP
	- from Croatia	EBee EBrs
	- - WM 9805	MPhe
	- from Slovenia	CBel GBuc
	- - WM 9028	MPhe
	- - WM 9216	WCru
	- 'Spotted Fern'	MPhe
	x ***ballardiae***	CLAP MAsh WAbe WFar
	- double-flowered (d)	CLAP
	bocconei subsp. ***bocconei***	see *H. multifidus* subsp. *bocconei*
	colchicus	see *H. orientalis* Lam. subsp. *abchasicus*
	corsicus	see *H. argutifolius*
	croaticus	GBuc SSth WFar
	- WM 9313	MPhe
	- WM 9416	MPhe
	- WM 9810 from Croatia	MPhe
	cyclophyllus	EBrs EPfP GBin GBuc GEdr GMaP MAsh MHom MPhe SPer WFar
	dumetorum	CBel EBee EBrs GBuc GMaP MAsh NLar WCru WFar
	- WM 9209 from Hungary	MPhe
	- WM 9209 from Slovenia	MPhe
	- WM 9627 from Croatia	MPhe
§	x ***ericsmithii***	More than 30 suppliers
	- 'HGC Silvermoon'^{PBR} **new**	LCro
	foetidus ♀^{H4}	More than 30 suppliers
	- from Italy	WCot
	- 'Chedglow'	CNat
	- 'Curio' (v)	CNat
	- 'Gold Bullion'	CBow CSpe
	- 'Green Giant'	MTho WCru
	- 'Miss Jekyll's Scented'	ITer LFur
	- 'Pewter' **new**	CLAP
	- 'Ruth'	MAsh MPhe
	- scented	MHom
	- 'Sopron'	CLAP MAsh MBri WCru
	- Wester Flisk Group	CBel CWCL EBee EHrv ENot EPfP GBuc LAst MAsh MBri MDun MGos MNrw MRav MWgw NBid NCGa NDov NHol NPer SPer SPoG STes SWal WCAu WCot WFar WHoo WPGP WTin
N	x ***hybridus***	More than 30 suppliers
	- 'Agnes Brook'	WFib
	- 'Alys Collins'	WFib
	- anemone-centred	CLAP EHrv NRar WFar
	- 'Angela Tandy'	WFib
	- 'Antique Shades'	WFar
	- 'Apple Blossom'	EHrv WFar
	- apricot-flowered	CLAP EHrv GBuc SPla WFar WTin
	- Ashwood Garden hybrids	CPMA EBrs EHrv ENot EPPr EPfP GWWP LRHS MAsh MGos MRav SCoo SHBN WSpi
	- Ashwood Garden hybrids, anemone-centred	CPMA MAsh
	- Ashwood Garden hybrids, double-flowered (d)	MAsh
	- 'Baby Black'	ECot
	- Ballard's Group	CLAP EBee GEdr ITer MBnl MBri MNFA MNHC NCGa NRar WCot WCru WFar WMnd WSpi
	- 'Black Beauty'	GKev ITer SJoo WBVN
	- black-flowered	CBel CLAP EHrv EPPr GBuc SSth WCru WFar WHoo WTin
	- 'Blue Lady'	CHFP COIW CWCL EBee EBrs ENot EPfP GBin GEdr LAst MBNS MGos MNFA MSte MWea NCGa NMoo SMad SPer SPoG STes WBVN WSpi WWeb
	- 'Blue Metallic Lady'	CHFP CWCL EBee LAst MBNS SHBN WSpi
	- blue-grey-flowered	CBel EHrv
	- Blumen Group	MBri
	- Bradfield hybrids	EHrv
	- Bradfield hybrids, anemone-centred	EHrv
	- Bradfield Star Group	EHrv
	- Caborn hybrids	LLWP
	- 'Carlton Hall'	WFib
	- 'Cheerful'	NBir WCru
	- 'Cherry Davis'	WFib
	- 'Citron'	CLAP
	- 'Clare's Purple'	GBin WBor
	- cream-flowered	CBel CLAP CPMA MCCP WFar WTin
	- dark purple-flowered	SPoG
	- 'David's Star' (d)	CFir
	- deep red-flowered	CBel CLAP NHol WFar WTin
	- 'Double Vision' (d)	CBrm
	- double-flowered (d)	CBel CLAP GBuc LHop NRar SHBN WCot WFar WHoo
	- double, black-flowered (d)	NRar
	- double, red-flowered (d)	GBin SPoG WSpi
	- double, yellow-flowered (d)	GBin
	- double, white-flowered (d)	GBin
	- 'Dove Cottage Double Pink'	NDov
	- 'Dusk'	WCru
	- 'Elizabeth Coburn'	WFib
	- 'Fibrex Black'	WFib
	- 'Fred Whitsey'	WFib
	- 'Garnet'	WFar
	- 'Gertrude Raithby'	WFib
	- 'Gladys Burrow'	WFib
	- 'Good Little Green' **new**	NDov
	- 'Good Little Yellow' **new**	NDov
	- 'Green Ripple'	WFar
	- 'Greencups'	WCru
	- green-flowered	MBNS WCru WFar
	- 'Günther Jürgl' (d)	SSth
	- 'Hades' seedling	WCru
	- 'Harvington Apricots'	LCro NLar SPoG
	- 'Harvington Double Purple' (d) **new**	NLar
	- 'Harvington Double Red' (d) **new**	LCro NLar
	- 'Harvington Double White' (d) **new**	NLar
	- 'Harvington Double Yellow' (d) **new**	NLar
	- 'Harvington Picotee'	LCro MGos NLar SPoG
	- 'Harvington Pink'	LCro LRHS MGos MHer NLar SPoG
	- 'Harvington Pink Speckled'	LCro NLar SPoG
	- 'Harvington Red'	LCro LRHS MGos MHer NLar SPoG
	- 'Harvington Shades of the Night'	LCro MGos MHer NLar SPoG WSpi
	- 'Harvington Speckled'	LRHS MHer SPoG
	- 'Harvington Speckled White' **new**	LCro

- 'Harvington White'	LCro LRHS MHer NLar SPoG WSpi
- 'Harvington Yellow'	LCro LRHS MHer NLar SPoG
- 'Harvington Yellow Speckled'	MHer NLar SPoG WSpi
- 'Hazel Key'	WFib
- 'Helen Ballard'	GKev
- 'Helena Hall'	WFib
- 'Hidcote Double' (d)	NRar
- 'Ian Raithby'	WFib WSpi
- ivory-flowered	WFar
- 'John Raithby'	WFib
- Joy hybrids	EBee
- Kaye's garden hybrids	EPfP NBPC WMnd
- Kochii Group	CAvo WCru
- 'Lady Charlotte Bonham-Carter'	WFib
- 'Lady Macbeth'	EWes
- Lady Series	NSum SHBN
- large, pink-flowered	WTin
- 'Le Max Creme'	EBee
- 'Little Black'	ECho
- maroon-flowered	CBel NRar SPla WCru WFar
- 'Mary Petit'	WFib
- 'Maureen Key'	WFib
- 'Mrs Betty Ranicar' (d)	CHFP CPen ENot EPfP ERas EWes GBin LAst LBuc LRHS MBNS MMHG MNFA NBPC NLar NSum SHBN SPoG WBVN WCot WFar
- 'Mystery'	WCru
- nearly black-flowered	CBel
- 'Pamina'	EHrv
§ - Party Dress Group (d)	EHrv SBla WFar
- 'Pebworth White'	WFib
- 'Philip Ballard'	WCru
- Picotee Group	CBel SSth
- 'Picotee'	CLAP EHrv GBuc NDov NRar SPla SPoG WCot WCru WFar WHoo
- 'Pink Lady'	EBee EBrs ENot EPfP GBin GQue MWgw NCGa SHBN SPer WWeb
- pink-flowered	CLAP CPMA GBuc MBNS MCCP NEgg NRar SPla SSth WAbe WCru WFar WHoo WTin
- plum-flowered	CBel CLAP EHrv SSth WFar WTin
- primrose-flowered	CLAP GBuc MBNS NRar SPla SSth WAbe WFar WTin
- 'Purple Haze'	CBcs EWTr
- purple-flowered	CBel CLAP CPMA NHol NRar SSth WAbe WBor WCru WFar WHoo
* - 'Purpurascens'	MCCP
- 'Queen of the Night'	CLAP
- 'Ray Peters'	WFib
- 'Red Lady'	CBcs CHFP CWCL EBee ENot EPfP GBin GQue IBal MBNS MGos MSte MWea MWgw NMoo SHBN SPer SPoG WCot WWeb
- 'Red Mountain'	MBNS
- red-flowered	NCGa
- 'Rosina Cross'	WFib
- 'Shades of Night'	EHrv LRHS
- slaty blue-flowered	CBel CLAP EHrv GBuc SSth WCot WFar
- slaty purple-flowered	GBuc NRar WFar
- 'Smokey Blue'	LCro NEgg WPtf
- smokey purple-flowered	WFar WPtf
- 'Snow Queen'	EHrv
- 'Speckled Draco'	CPLG
- spotted	CAvo CLAP EPfP GAbr GBuc LAst MBnl MCCP NCGa NEgg SBla SPer WCot WCru WHoo WTin
- 'Spotted Lady'	ENot GBin SHBN
- spotted, cream	CBel CLAP NBir SSth WTin
- spotted, green	CLAP SSth WFar WTin
- spotted, ivory	CLAP
- spotted, pink	CLAP GBuc NBir NDov NHol NRar SEND SPla WFar WHoo WTin
- spotted, pink, double (d)	GBin SPoG
- spotted, primrose	CLAP GBuc WFar WTin
- spotted, white	GBuc NBir NDov NRar SPla SSth WAbe WCru WFar WTin
- spotted, white, double (d)	GBin
- 'Sunny'	WCru
I - 'Sunshine Selections' **new**	GKev IBal
- 'Ushba'	CLAP
- 'Ushba' seedlings	NBir
- 'Victoria Raithby'	WFib
- 'Violetta'	WCru
- Washfield double-flowered (d) **new**	CWCL MBnl SPoG
- white-flowered	CBel ITer NRar SSth WCFE WCru WFar WHoo WTin
- 'White Lady'	COlW EBee ENot GEdr GQue MGos MWea NCGa SHBN SPer SPoG WCot WWeb
- 'White Lady Spotted'	CWCL EBee EPfP GQue MSte NBPC NGHP SMad SPoG WWeb
- white-veined	WFar
- 'Yellow Lady'	EBee GQue MNFA MSte MWea MWgw SPer SPoG WCot WWeb
- yellow-flowered	CBel CBow NDov SSth WCru WFar WHoo WHrl WTin
- Zodiac Group	ENot GBuc LBuc
lividus ♀H2-3	CAby CHar CLAP ECho ENot EPfP EWes LHop LRHS MPhe NBir SBla SSth SWat WFar
- subsp. ***corsicus***	see *H. argutifolius*
Marion White Group	SBla
'Moonshine'PBR	EKen GCai WCot
multifidus	EBee EPfP NBir WFar
§ - subsp. ***bocconei***	CBel EHrv MAsh MHom WFar
- - WM 9719 from Italy	MPhe
- subsp. ***hercegovinus***	EHrv MDun SBla WFar
- - WM 0020	MPhe
- subsp. ***istriacus***	GBuc MAsh WFar
- - WM 9225	WCru
- - WM 9322	MPhe
- - WM 9324	MPhe
- subsp. ***multifidus***	CBel EHrv MHom SMHy
- - WM 9529	MPhe
- - WM 9748 from Croatia	MPhe
- - WM 9833	MPhe
niger ♀H4	More than 30 suppliers
- Ashwood strain	CLAP MAsh
- Blackthorn Group	CBow CLAP EHrv LRHS SBla
- 'Christmas Carol'	MAsh
I - 'Crûg Hybrid'	WCru
- Harvington hybrids	EHrv LRHS MHer SPoG
§ - subsp. ***macranthus***	EBee MNHC NCGa NGHP NMoo
- ***major***	see *H. niger* subsp. *macranthus*
- 'Maximus'	CLAP COlW EBee EWes NCGa
- 'Potter's Wheel'	CDes CLAP CPMA EBee ECho ECot ELan ENot GBuc LRHS MAvo MRav SHBN SPla WCru
- 'Praecox'	CWan EBee ENot EPfP EWes GBin SHBN SPur SVil WWeb
- 'Ras Buis'	NMoo
- Sunrise Group WM 9519	MPhe
- Sunset Group WM 9113	GBuc
- 'White Christmas'	LRHS
- 'White Magic'	CPMA GMaP MGos MNrw WCru
x ***nigercors*** ♀H4	CAby CDes CElw CHFP EBrs ECtt EHrv GBin GEdr GMaP LHop MAsh MAvo MBri WAbe WCot WPGP
- double-flowered (d)	CAvo EHrv ERou IBal LAst LSou MBNS NCGa SPoG WTMC
- 'HGC Green Corsican'PBR **new**	LCro
- 'Pink Beauty'	ENot LBuc SHBN
- 'Vulcan Beauty'	SHBN

	x ***nigristern***	see *H.* x *ericsmithii*
	odorus	CAvo CBel EHrv EWes GMaP MAsh MPhe SPer WFar WPGP
	- WM 0312 from Bosnia	MPhe
	- WM 9202	WCru
	- WM 9310	GBuc
	- WM 9415	MPhe
	- WM 9728 from Hungary	MPhe
N	***orientalis*** misapplied	see *H.* x *hybridus*
	orientalis Lam.	CBcs CBel CChe EWTr EWes LAst LCro MPhe MSwo NEgg SMer STre WWeb
§	- subsp. ***abchasicus***	EBee GEdr MAsh SRms
§	- - Early Purple Group	CAvo CBre CTri MRav WFar
	- subsp. ***guttatus***	EBee EWTr GGar NEgg NHol SPla SRkn WCru
	'Pink Beauty'PBR	CPen MBri
	purpurascens	CBel CSsd EBee EBrs EHrv GBuc GEdr IFoB MAsh MBNS MNFA MRav NBir SPer WAbe WBrE WFar WPnP
	- WM 9211 from Hungary	MPhe WCru
	- WM 9412	MPhe WCru
	- WM 9922	EPot
	- from Hungary	WCAu
	Snowdon strain	CSBt ENot GCai LBuc NEgg SHBN WSpi
	x ***sternii***	More than 30 suppliers
	- Ashwood strain	MAsh
	- 'Beatrice le Blanc'	MAsh
	- Blackthorn Group 🏆H3-4	CBcs CElw CPMA CSpe EHrv ENot EPfP GBuc ITer MBri MRav MSte SBla SPoG WBrk WCru WFar WHoo WPGP
	- Blackthorn dwarf strain	CLAP EBee GBuc SHBN
	- Boughton Group	GBin MAsh
	- 'Boughton Beauty'	CAvo CLAP EBee EHrv ELan GBuc LHop MTho NSum WSpi
	- Bulmer's blush strain	WSpi
	- dwarf	WFar
	- 'Joy's Purple'	CPen CPrp LAst LRHS SPer
	- pewter-flowered	CSpe EBrs EDAr
	thibetanus	CLAP EBrs EFEx EHrv EPot EWes GBuc GEdr GKev LAma MAsh MPhe WCru
	- red-flowered	GBin
	torquatus	CBel EBee EBrs EHrv MAsh MBri MPhe MTho SPer WFar WTin
	- WM 9745	EHrv
	- WM 9820 from Bosnia	MPhe
	- WM 9106 from Montenegro	GBuc MPhe WCru
	- Caborn hybrids	LLWP
	- 'Dido' (d)	WFar
	- double-flowered hybrids (d)	WFar
	- double-flowered, from Montenegro (d)	WFar
	- hybrids	ECGP EHrv SBla WFar
	- Party Dress Group	see *H.* x *hybridus* Party Dress Group
	- semi-double-flowered (d)	WFar
	- Wolverton hybrids	SBla WFar
	vesicarius	CDes EHrv EWes
	viridis	EBee ECha EHrv EPfP IFoB SRms WCru WFar WTin
	- WM 0444	MPhe
	- subsp. ***occidentalis***	CBel EHrv MAsh MHom
	- - WM 9401	MPhe
	- - WM 9502 from Germany	MPhe
	- subsp. ***viridis*** WM 9723 from Italy	MPhe
	'White Beauty'PBR	CPen ENot EPPr EPfP EWes LBuc MBri MRav SHBN

Helonias (*Melanthiaceae*)

	bullata	GEdr IBlr WCot

Heloniopsis (*Melanthiaceae*)

	acutifolia	GEdr
	- B&SWJ 218	WCru
	- B&SWJ 6817	WCru
	japonica	see *H. orientalis*
§	***kawanoi***	CDes CLAP CWsd GEdr NMen SKHP WCru
§	***orientalis***	CLAP CWsd EBee ECho GBri GBuc GCrs GEdr GGar LRHS NMen NSla WCot WCru
	- var. ***breviscapa***	CWsd WCru WPGP
	- from Japan B&SWJ 5873 **new**	WCru
	- - B&SWJ 6380	WCru
	- from Korea	GEdr SKHP
	- - B&SWJ 822	WCru
	- - B&SWJ 4173	WCru
	- variegated (v)	GEdr WCru
	- var. ***yakusimensis***	see *H. kawanoi*
	umbellata	CDes CLAP GEdr SKHP
	- B&SWJ 1839	WCru
	- B&SWJ 6836	WCru

Helwingia (*Helwingiaceae*)

chinensis	CPle CSam NLar SSpi WBor
himalaica	CGHE WPGP
japonica	EFEx NLar WFar

Helxine see *Soleirolia*

Hemerocallis ✿ (*Hemerocallidaceae*)

'Aabachee'	CCol SApp
'Absolute Zero'	SDay SRos
'Adah'	SDay
'Added Dimensions'	SApp
'Addie Branch Smith'	EGol SDay
'Admiral'	CHar WCAu
'Adoration'	SPer
'Age of Miracles'	SPol
'Ah Youth'	SApp
'Alan'	ECtt MNFA MRav WFar
'Alaqua'	CFir EGle EMar IBal LAst MBNS MFOX MNrw NRnb SApp SHBN SPer
'Albany'	CCol
'Alec Allen'	SRos
'Alien Encounter'	SPol
'All American Baby'	EBee MBNS SPol
'All American Plum'	CWCL EMar EPfP GBin IBal IPot MBNS WAul
'All American Tiger'	SRos
'All Fired Up'	CCol SPol
'Alpine Rhapsody' **new**	SPol
'Alpine Snow'	SRos
altissima	CHEx EMon EPla MNFA MNrw SMrm SPhx
'Always Afternoon'	CCol CKel EMar GBri GBuc MBNS NCGa SApp SRos WAul WCAu WHrl
'Amadeus'	SApp SDay
'Amazon Amethyst'	WCAu
'Ambassador'	CBgR
'Amber Classic'	SApp
'American Revolution'	More than 30 suppliers
'Amersham'	EGle GSki MNFA SApp
'Andrea Nicole'	CCol
'Andrew Christian'	SPol
'Angel Artistry'	SApp SDay
'Angel Curls'	EGol
'Angel Unawares'	SApp WTin
'Ann Kelley'	MSte SApp SDay

	'Annie Welch'	EPla MBNS NBre
	'Antarctica'	SApp
	'Antique Rose'	CKel EMar SDay
	'Anzac'	COlW ECha ECtt EHrv EMar EPla ERou GMac LRHS MNFA NBre NGdn NHol NPri SAga SApp SPav SRos SWvt WFar WLin WMoo WSel WTMC
	'Apache Uprising'	SDay SRos
	'Apollodorus'	EMar
	'Apple Court Chablis'	SApp
	'Apple Court Champagne'	SApp
	'Apple Court Damson'	SPol
	'Apple Court Ruby'	SApp SPol
	'Apple Crisp'	SApp
	'Après Moi'	EKen EMar MBNS MLLN NLar WBrE WCAu
	'Apricot Angel'	SApp
	'Apricot Beauty' (d)	ECho EMar WHlf WSpi
	'Apricotta'	WCot WPnP
	'Arctic Snow'	CBgR CCol EBee EBrs EGle EMar EPfP LAst MLan MNrw NBPC NLar SDnm SMer SPav SPoG SRos SWal WAul WSel
	'Ariadne'	CWsd
	'Arriba'	MNFA NBro
	'Arthur Moore'	SDay
	'Artistic Gold'	WTin
	'Asiatic Pheasant'	CCol SPol
	'Aten'	CCol MNFA WAul
	'Atlanta Bouquet'	SRos
	'Atlanta Fringe'	SApp
	'Atlanta Full House'	SDay
	'August Orange'	MNFA
	'Autumn Minaret'	CCol
	'Autumn Red'	CBcs CBgR EMar MBNS MNrw NBir NOak SPol WCot
	'Ava Michelle'	SApp SDay
	'Avant Garde'	SPol
	'Awakening Dream'	SRos
	'Awesome Blossom'	CPen GBin MBNS NMoo
	'Azor' **new**	CWsd
	'Aztec Furnace'	SDay
	'Baby Blues'	SPol
	'Baby Darling'	SDay
	'Baby Talk'	CFir GBuc LRHS
	'Bailey Hay'	see *H.* 'Bali Hai'
	'Baja'	MNFA WFar
	'Bald Eagle'	CMCo EGle
§	'Bali Hai'	CEnt EBee EMar ENot GBin MBNS NRnb WHrl WSpi
	'Ballerina Girl'	SRos
	'Ballet Dancer'	ERou
	'Bamboo Blackie'	SPol
	'Banbury Cinnamon'	MBNS
	'Bandolero' (d)	EBee
	'Bangkok Belle'	CWat
	'Barbara Mitchell'	CCol MBNS MNFA MNrw NCGa NMoo SApp SDay SRos WAul
	'Barbary Corsair'	SApp SDay
	'Barley Hay'	MSte
	'Baronet's Badge'	SPol
	'Baroni'	ECha GBin
	'Battle Hymn'	WCAu
	'Bayou Bride'	CCol
	'Bayou Ribbons'	MBNS
	'Beat the Barons'	SPol SRos
	'Beautiful Edgings'	SRos
	'Beauty Bright'	WCAu
	'Beauty to Behold'	SApp SDay SRos
	'Becky Lynn'	CCol ECtt MBNS
	'Bed of Roses'	MNFA
	'Bedarra Island'	SDay
	'Bejewelled'	EGol EPla NMoo SApp WTin
	'Bela Lugosi'	More than 30 suppliers

'Beloved Returns' ♀^{H4}	WCAu
'Benchmark'	EMar MNFA SApp SRos
'Berlin Lemon' ♀^{H4}	MNFA
'Berlin Maize'	SApp
'Berlin Oxblood'	MNFA WAul
'Berlin Red' ♀^{H4}	CPrp EBla ECha EGle EMar EPla LBMP MBNS MNFA SApp
'Berlin Red Velvet' ♀^{H4}	MNFA
'Berlin Tallboy'	SApp
'Berlin Watermelon'	MBNS
'Berliner Premiere'	MNFA
'Bernard Thompson'	EMar MNFA SApp SRos
'Bertie Ferris'	NLar SRos
'Bess Ross'	CMHG MNFA WCAu
'Bess Vestale'	GBuc MNFA MWat NHol
'Bette Davis Eyes'	EMar SApp SPol SRos
'Betty Benz'	SRos
'Betty Jenkins'	SRos
'Betty Lyn'	SApp
'Betty Warren Woods'	SDay SRos
'Betty Woods' (d)	SDay SRos
'Big Apple'	SApp SRos
'Big Bird'	CMCo CPar EBee MBNS NCGa SApp SHBN SHar WAul
'Big City Eye' **new**	MBNS
'Big Smile'	CWCL EBee EMar IPot MBNS MNrw NBPC NBro NMoo
'Big Snowbird'	EMar SRos
'Big Time Happy'	MBNS SPoG
'Big World'	MNFA
'Bill Norris'	SApp SDay SRos
'Bird Bath Pink'	SPol
'Bitsy'	EGle EGol MNFA MSte SPet WMnd
'Black Ambrosia'	SDay
'Black Emmanuella'	CDWL ECho EMar ERCP LDai MNrw SBch
'Black Eyed Stella'	CKel MBNS WSpi
'Black Knight'	NLar SRms
'Black Magic'	CHar CTri CWat EBla EGol ELan EMar EPla ERou GMaP GMac LRHS MNFA MRav MWgw NBir NGdn NHol SAga SPer SPoG WHer WMoo
'Black Plush'	CCol SPol SRos
'Black Prince'	CFir EBee EWll MBNS NBPN NBre NBro WAul
'Blackberry Candy'	GBri MBNS WAul WCAu
'Blaze of Fire'	WCAu
'Blessing'	SRos
'Blonde Is Beautiful'	SDay SRos
'Blue Moon'	SApp
'Blue Sheen'	CFir EBee ECtt EGle EGol EMar GMaP LAst MBNS MCCP MSte NGdn WCAu WFar WMoo WRHF WSpi WWeb
'Blueberry Candy'	MBNS WAul
'Blueberry Cream'	CWCL EPfP ERou MBNS MNrw MWea
'Blushing Belle'	CMil EBee EBla EMar LRHS MBNS MNFA NBro SApp
'Bold Courtier'	CBgR WCAu
'Bold One'	CMHG SPol SRos
'Bold Ruler'	CCol
'Bold Tiger'	SDay
'Bonanza'	More than 30 suppliers
'Boney Maroney'	SApp SRos
'Booger'	SRos
'Bookmark' **new**	EMar
'Boom Town' **new**	EMar
'Born Yesterday'	SApp
'Boulderbrook Serenity'	SDay
'Bourbon Kings'	EBee EGol EMar ERou MBNS NBre SPav WHrl
'Bowl of Roses'	SApp WCAu
'Brand New Lover'	SApp
'Brass Buckles'	see *H.* 'Puddin'

'Breed Apart' **new**	CCol
'Brenda Newbold'	SPol
'Bridget'	ELan
'Bright Banner'	WCAu
'Bright Spangles'	CCol SApp SDay SRos WEas
'Brilliant Circle'	SApp
'Broadway Valentine'	SApp
'Brocaded Gown'	CCol ELan SApp SDay SRos
'Brookwood Wow'	SApp
'Brunette'	MHar SAga SApp
'Bruno Müller'	MNFA SApp
'Brutus' **new**	EMar
'Bubbly'	SApp SDay SRos
'Bud Producer'	SPol
'Buffy's Doll'	EBee EMar MBNS MNFA SApp SDay SRos WGob
'Bumble Bee'	CWat EMar MBNS NBre NRnb SApp
'Buried Treasure'	MNFA
'Burlesque'	CWsd SPol
'Burning Daylight' ♀H4	CWsd EBee ECtt EHrv EMar EPfP EPla ERou GSki LBBr LRHS MNFA MNrw MPop MRav NBre NHol SPer SRms WCFE WCot WFar WSel WWHy
'Bus Stop'	SApp SPol
'Buttered Popcorn' **new**	LLWG
'Butterfly Ballet'	SDay SRos
'Butterscotch'	WFar
'Butterscotch Ruffles'	SDay
'Buzz Bomb'	CWat EGle EHrv EMFW EMar GMac GSki LRHS LSRN MHar MNFA MSte NCob NGdn SApp SPer SRos WCAu
'Cabbage Flower'	SDay
'Calico Spider'	SRos
'California Sunshine'	SRos
'Camden Glory'	SApp
'Camden Gold Dollar'	EGol SApp SRos
'Cameron Quantz'	SApp
'Cameroons'	CCol SDay
'Campfire Embers'	GBin
'Canadian Border Patrol'	CWCL EMar EPfP IBal IPot MBNS MNrw NLar SPer SPol SRos WHil
'Canary Feathers'	SApp
'Canary Glow'	CSBt CTri ERou SRos WFar
'Canary Wings'	CCol
'Candide'	SApp SDay
'Candor' **new**	SDay
'Cantique'	SApp
'Capernaum Cocktail'	SPol
'Captive Audience'	SRos
'Cara Mia'	CBgR EMar MBNS WFar
'Carmine Monarch' **new**	SRos
'Carolicolossal'	SPol
* 'Caroline'	WHrl
'Carolipiecrust'	SApp
'Cartwheels' ♀H4	EBee EBla ECha EHrv EMFW EMar EPfP EPla ERas ERou GBuc GMaP LRHS MBNS MNFA NBro NRnb SBch SPer SPla SRos WCAu WFar WMoo WTin
'Casino Gold'	SRos
'Castle Strawberry Delight'	SPol
'Catherine Neal'	SDay SRos
'Catherine Woodbery'	More than 30 suppliers
'Cathy's Sunset'	CKel CSam EBee EBla ECha ECtt EMar EPla EWTr MBNS MSte MWat MWgw NBre NBro NGdn NRnb SRGP
'Cat's Cradle'	CCol
'Cedar Waxwing'	EGol MSte
'Cee Tee'	SRos
'Cerulean Star'	SApp
'Challenger' **new**	EMar
'Champagne Memory'	SApp
'Chance Encounter'	MBNS SDay
'Chantilly Lace'	CMHG
'Charbonier'	MNFA
'Charles Johnston'	CBgR CKel CMMP EMar GBin LAst MBNS NRnb SApp SDay SRos WAul WTMC
'Charlie Pierce Memorial'	EMar SPol SRos
'Chartreuse Magic'	CMHG EGol EPla ERou SPer
'Cherry Cheeks'	CFir ECtt EGol ELan EPfP ERou LRHS MBNS MBri MHar MRav NBPC NHol NRnb SApp SPav SRos WAul WCAu WCot WFar WGob WWeb
'Cherry Eyed Pumpkin'	SRos
'Cherry Kiss'	SRos
'Cherry Ripe' **new**	EQua
'Cherry Smoke'	SApp
'Cherry Tiger'	MBNS
'Cherry Valentine'	MBNS
'Chesières Lunar Moth'	SApp SPol SRos
'Chester Cyclone'	SDay
'Chestnut Lane'	SApp SRos
'Chewonki'	EMar
'Chic Bonnet'	SPer
'Chicago Antique Tapestry' **new**	SDay
'Chicago Apache'	CDWL CFir EGle EMar EPfP GBuc LLWG MBNS MNFA MSte NBir NCGa NRnb SApp SDay SPer SPol SRos WAul WSpi
'Chicago Blackout'	CFir CSpe CWat EGol EPfP MBNS NBPN NHol NRnb SApp WCAu
'Chicago Cattleya'	CFir EGle EGol LAst MRav NRnb SApp WAul
'Chicago Cherry'	NRnb
'Chicago Fire'	EGol EPfP MBNS NBPC NBhm SHar
'Chicago Heirloom'	CFir EGle EGol MBNS NRnb WAul WCAu
'Chicago Jewel'	CFir EGle EGol NRnb NSti WAul
'Chicago Knobby'	EMar MBNS
'Chicago Knockout'	CFir EGle EGol ELan EPfP MBNS NRnb SPer WAul WCAu
'Chicago Peach'	IPot MBNS NBir WCAu
'Chicago Petticoats'	EGol NHol SApp SDay
'Chicago Picotee Lace'	EGle EGol EPfP NGdn SApp WCAu
'Chicago Picotee Memories'	EBee EGle MBNS WCAu
'Chicago Picotee Pride'	SDay
'Chicago Picotee Queen'	MNFA SApp
'Chicago Princess'	EGle EGol
'Chicago Queen'	WMnd
'Chicago Rainbow'	CBgR MBNS WAul
'Chicago Rosy'	EGol
'Chicago Royal'	ELon
'Chicago Royal Crown'	EBee EMar
'Chicago Royal Robe'	CWat EGol EPla ERou EWll LLWP MBNS MNFA MRav MSte NBid NCGa SPer SWat WCot WTin
'Chicago Ruby'	SApp WWHy
'Chicago Silver'	CFir COIW EGle EGol IPot MBNS WCAu
'Chicago Star'	SRos
'Chicago Sunrise'	CSBt EBee EBla EGol EMar ENot EPla GMaP IBlr LBBr LRHS MBNS MBri MNFA MRav NGdn NHol NMoo NOrc NRnb SApp SPet SRos SWvt WCot WPer WWeb
'Chicago Violet'	WCAu
'Chicago Weathermaster' **new**	EMar
'Chief Sarcoxie' ♀H4	SApp SRos WCAu
'Child of Fortune'	SApp
'Children's Festival'	COIW CSBt CWat EBee EGle EGol EMar EMil EWTr GMaP GSki LRHS

	MBNS MRav SApp SPoG SRos STes SWvt WFar WMoo WPer WPnP WTel WWeb
'China Bride'	SApp SRos
'China Lake'	EMar
'Chinese Autumn'	SApp SRos
'Chinese Cloisonne'	EMar
'Chorus Line'	SApp SRos
'Chosen Love'	SApp
'Christmas Carol'	SApp
'Christmas Is'	CBgR CCol EBee EBla EGol EMar MBNS MBri MNFA NMoo SApp SDay SDnm SPav SPhx SPol WAul WCAu WGob
'Christmas Island'	CDWL EMil NBre NCGa
'Churchill Downs'	MNFA
'Ciao'	EMar MHar SApp
'Cimarron Knight'	SPol
'Circle of Beauty' **new**	SPol
citrina	CBgR CHid CPLG CWsd ELan LCro LFur LRHS MNFA MSte NGdn WCot WTin XPep
'Civil Law'	SDay
'Civil Rights'	SRos
'Classic Simplicity'	WCAu
'Classic Spider'	SApp
'Claudine'	SApp
'Cleopatra'	CPar SRos
'Cloth of Gold'	WCot
'Clothed in Glory'	CWCL MBNS NMoo WCot
'Colonial Dame'	WTin
'Colour Me Yellow'	SApp
'Comanche Eyes'	SApp
'Comet Flash'	SPol
'Coming Up Roses'	SApp SRos
'Commandment' **new**	EMar
'Condilla' (d)	SApp SDay
'Cool It'	CKel EBee EGle EMar GBuc IPot LRHS MBNS NBre NCGa NMoo NRnb SApp WCAu
'Cool Jazz'	EMar SApp SDay SRos
'Copper Dawn'	NChi SApp
'Copperhead' **new**	SPol
'Coral Crab'	SApp
'Coral Mist'	CCol CSBt MBNS NBre NRnb
'Corky' Υ^{H4}	More than 30 suppliers
'Cornwall' **new**	EMar
'Corryton Pink'	SPol
'Corsican Bandit'	CMMP SDay
'Cosmic Hummingbird'	SApp
'Cosmopolitan' **new**	MBNS
'Country Club'	EGle EGol LAst MBNS NHol SApp WCAu
'Country Fair Winds'	CCol
'Country Melody'	SDay SRos
'Court Magician'	CCol EMar SApp SRos
'Court Troubadour' **new**	SPol
'Crackling Rosie' **new**	EMar
'Cranberry Baby'	CCol EGle EMar SDay SRos WHoo WTin
'Crawleycrow'	EMar
'Crazy Pierre'	CCol EMar SPol
'Cream Drop'	CPrp EBee EBla ECtt EGle EGol EMar GMaP LFur LRHS MHer MPop MRav NBro NGdn NSti SApp SDnm SPav SPer WAul WCAu WCot WMoo WTMC WTel WTin
'Creative Art'	SRos
'Creative Edge'	ERou MBNS SDnm SPav WAul
'Crimson Icon'	MSte SDay WTin
'Crimson Pirate'	CBgR CBre CCol EBee ELon EMar EMil EPPr ERou GKev LRHS LSRN MBNS MHer MNFA NBir NBlu NCGa NHol NMoo NOrc NPro SApp SPlb SPoG SWat WHrl WTin

'Crimson Wind'	SApp
'Croesus'	NHol SRms
'Crystalline Pink'	SRos
'Cupid's Bow'	EGol
'Cupid's Gold'	SDay SRos
'Curls'	SDay
'Curly Cinnamon Windmill'	SRos
'Curly Ripples'	SApp
'Curly Rosy Posy' **new**	SRos
'Custard Candy'	CWCL MBNS MBri NBir NMoo SApp SRos WAul WCAu
'Cynthia Mary'	EGle EMar EQua LRHS MBNS MNFA NBro SRGP WFar
'Dad's Best White'	EMar WTin
'Daily Dollar'	EBee EBla LRHS MBNS NGdn SApp
'Dainty Pink'	EGol
'Dallas Spider Time'	MNFA
'Dallas Star'	EMar SApp SPol
'Dan Mahony' **new**	MBNS
'Dan Tau'	CKel
'Dance Ballerina Dance'	SDay SRos
'Dancing Dwarf'	SApp SDay
'Dancing Shiva'	SApp SDay
'Dancing Summerbird'	SPol SRos
'Daring Deception'	CFir CKel EMar IPot LAst MBNS MLLN NCGa NMoo SApp WHrl
'Daring Dilemma'	CCol SPol
'Daring Reflection'	SDay
'Dark Avenger'	CSpe MBNS
'Dark Elf'	SApp SDay
'Darker Shade' **new**	SRos
'David Kirchhoff'	IPot MBNS SApp WAul WCAu
'Dazzle'	SApp
'Decatur Imp'	EGol
'Dee Dee Mac'	SApp
'Deep Fire' **new**	SRos
'Delicate Design'	SApp
'Delightsome'	SRos
'Demetrius'	MNFA MWea NCGa SApp
'Desdemona'	CMil
'Designer Gown'	SApp SDay
'Designer Jeans'	SPol SRos
'Destined to See'	More than 30 suppliers
'Devil's Footprint'	SDay SPol
'Devonshire'	SApp SDay SRos
'Dewberry Candy'	SRos
'Diamond Dust'	CKel EBee EGle EMar EPla LRHS MBNS MNFA MSte NLar SApp SPer SPhx WSpi WTin
'Dido'	CTri ERou GBuc
'Diva Assoluta'	SApp
'Divertissment'	CCol ELon EMar SApp
'Doll House'	SRos
'Dominic'	CPar EBee EMar MBNS SApp SRos WMoo
'Don Stevens' **new**	EMar
'Dorethe Louise'	SDay SPol SRos
'Dorothy McDade'	COlW
'Dottie's Rompers' **new**	EMar
'Double Action' (d)	SPol
'Double Coffee' (d)	SApp SPav SPol
'Double Confetti' (d)	SApp
'Double Corsage' (d)	SApp SPol
'Double Cutie' (d)	CMCo MBNS NBre NLar SDay WAul
'Double Daffodil' (d)	WCAu
'Double Dream' (d)	EMar GBuc
'Double Firecracker' (d)	CBcs CWat EMar IBal MBNS NBro NLar NMoo SPoG WCra WHrl
'Double Grapette' (d)	SApp
'Double Oh Seven' (d)	ELon SApp
'Double Pink Treasure' (d)	SApp
'Double Pompon' (d)	WCAu

'Double River Wye' (d)	CBgR CCol CDWL CFir COlW CWat EBee ECtt EGol EMar EMil IPot MBNS MNrw MSte NGdn NPri SApp SHBN SHar SPol SRos SWat WAul WCot WHoo WMnd WTin
§ 'Doubloon'	COlW ERou GBuc NHol
'Dragon Dreams'	SApp
'Dragon King'	SPol
'Dragon Mouth'	EGol
'Dragon's Eye'	CCol CWat SApp SDay
'Dragon's Orb'	CKel
'Dream Baby'	NBre
'Dreamy Cream'	SRos
'Dresden Doll'	SPer
'Driven Snow'	SApp
'Duke of Durham'	SApp SMeo
dumortieri	CAvo CSam ECha EGol EHrv ELan EMar EPla GGar LFur MNFA MNrw MRav NBid NBir NHol NSti NVic SPer WCot WTin
- B&SWJ 1283	WCru
'Dune Needlepoint'	SPol
'Dutch Beauty'	EMar EPla WFar WTMC
'Dutch Gold'	MNrw NBro
'Earlianna'	SPol
'Earth Angel'	SApp SPol
'Easy Ned'	SDay SRos WTin
'Ed Murray'	CSBt EBee MNFA NBPN SRos WAul WCAu
'Edelweiss'	SDay
'Edgar Brown'	MBNS
'Edge Ahead'	CCol MBNS MBri NRnb
'Edge of Darkness'	CKel CWGN EGle EPfP IPot MBNS MWea NBro NLar NSti SDnm SPav WAul WCAu WHil
'Edna Spalding'	SApp SRos
'Eenie Allegro'	CBgR EGol EMar ENot IBal MBNS SPer SPla WHil WMnd
'Eenie Fanfare'	EGle EGol LRHS MBNS MNFA NBir WAul
'Eenie Gold'	LRHS
'Eenie Weenie'	CBgR CFee EBla ECtt EGle EGol EPla ERos GKev IBal LRHS MBNS MHar MNFA NBro SAga SApp SHBN SPer SRms WPer WTMC
'Eenie Weenie Non-stop'	EPPr
'Eggplant Escapade'	EMar SPol SRos
'Egyptian Ibis'	MBNS WMnd
'Egyptian Queen' **new**	SRos
'El Desperado'	More than 30 suppliers
'El Padre'	SApp
'Elaine Strutt'	EGol MBNS MNFA MNrw NCGa NMoo SApp SDay SRos SWvt WSpi
'Eleanor Marcotte'	SDay
'Elegant Candy'	CCol CKel CPen EBee ENot MBNS NMoo NRnb SApp SRos WGob
'Elegant Greeting'	ERou MBNS NOak
'Elf's Cap' **new**	SDay
'Elizabeth Ann Hudson'	MNFA
'Elizabeth Salter'	CWCL EBee IPot MBNS NMoo SApp SRos WCAu
'Elizabeth Yancey'	EGol
'Embuscade' **new**	EMar
'Emerald Enchantment'	SApp
'Emerald Eye' **new**	CCol
'Emerald Lady'	SRos
'Emily Anne'	SApp
'Emily Jaye'	SApp
'Emperor Butterfly'	SApp
'Emperor's Dragon'	CCol
'Enchanter's Spell'	SDay
'English Toffee'	SApp
'Entransette'	SApp
'Entrapment' **new**	MBNS
'Erin Prairie'	SApp

esculenta	SMad
'Eternal Blessing'	SPol SRos
'Ethel Smith'	LLWG SApp
'Etruscan Tomb'	SPol
'Evelyn Lela Stout'	SApp
'Evening Bell'	SApp
'Evening Glow'	SApp SRos
'Ever So Ruffled'	SRos
'Exotic Love'	SDay
'Eye-yi-yi'	SPol
'Ezekiel' **new**	EMar
'Fabergé'	SApp
'Fabulous Prize'	SApp SRos
'Fairest Love'	EBee EMar LDai MBNS
'Fairy Charm'	SApp SDay
'Fairy Summerbird'	SRos
'Fairy Tale Pink'	CCol MNFA SApp SDay SPol SRos
'Fairy Wings'	SPer
'Faith Nabor'	EMar SRos
'Fall Guy'	SApp
'Fama'	SRos
'Fan Club'	EMar
'Fan Dancer'	EGol
'Fandango'	MNFA
'Farmer's Daughter'	SApp SRos
'Fashion Model'	SApp WPer
'Fazzle'	SApp
'Feather Down'	SDay
'Feelings'	SApp
'Femme Osage'	SRos
'Ferris Wheel'	SApp
'Festive Art'	MBNS SRos
'Final Touch'	CBgR IPot MBNS MLLN NBhm NBro WGob
'Finlandia'	MNFA
'Fire Dance'	SRos
'Fire from Heaven'	SApp
'Fire Tree'	SPol
'Firestorm'	SApp SPol
'First Formal'	SPer
'Flames of Fantasy'	SRos
'Flaming Sword'	EBee GBuc LRHS NBlu NHol WRHF
flava	see *H. lilioasphodelus*
'Fleeting Fancy'	SRos
'Flint Lace'	SApp
'Floyd Cove'	SDay
'Flutterbye'	SRos
'Fly Catcher'	EMar SRos
'Flyaway Home' **new**	SPol
'Fol de Rol'	SRos
'Fooled Me'	MBNS SRos
'Forgotten Dreams'	EBee MBNS MWea SPoG
forrestii	CExc EBee GKev
- 'Perry's Variety'	CCol EMon
'Forsyth Lemon Drop'	SDay
'Forsyth White Sentinal'	SRos
'Forty Second Street'	CFir EBee MBNS MLLN NCGa NMoo SPer WFar
'Fragrant Bouquet'	SRos
'Fragrant Pastel Cheers'	SDay SRos
'Frances Fay'	SPol SRos WAul
'Frandean'	MNFA
'Frank Gladney'	MNFA SApp SRos
'Frans Hals'	More than 30 suppliers
'French Doll'	SApp
'French Porcelain'	SDay
'Frosted Encore'	SApp
'Frozen Jade'	SRos
'Fuchsia Dream'	EMar
'Fuchsia Fashion'	CCol
'Full Reward'	WCAu
fulva	CTri ELan EMar IBlr LRHS MHar MWgw NBir NBre SHBN SPol SRms WBVN WBrk

N	- 'Flore Pleno' (d)	More than 30 suppliers
N	- 'Green Kwanso' (d)	CBgR CPLG CSWP ECGP ECha EMon EPla IBlr LBMP MMHG NVic SMad SPla WAul WFar WPnP WTin
*	- var. ***kwanso*** B&SWJ 6328 **new**	WCru
	- 'Kwanso' ambig. (d)	NOrc
	- var. ***littorea***	EPla
	- var. ***rosea***	EMon MNFA SMHy WCot
§	- 'Variegated Kwanso' (d/v)	CBow EGle ELan EMon EPPr GCra IBlr MRav MTho NBir SBod SPav WCot WFar WHer WHoo
	'Funky Fuchsia'	SPol
	'Gadsden Goliath'	CCol SPol
	'Gadsden Light'	CCol SDay
	'Gala Gown'	SApp
	'Garden Portrait'	CMil SRos
	'Gaucho'	MNFA
	'Gay Octopus'	CBgR SRos
	'Gay Rapture'	SPer
	'Gemini'	SRos
	'Gentle Country Breeze'	SApp SPol SRos
	'Gentle Shepherd'	More than 30 suppliers
	'George Cunningham'	ECtt EGol EHrv ELan ERou MNFA MRav NBir SPol SRos WCAu WFar
	'Georgette Belden'	EBee EBla MBri MPop NHol WTin
	'Georgia Cream' (d)	MBNS
	'German Ballerina'	SPol
	'Giant Moon'	CMHG ELan EMar EPla ERou LRHS MBNS NHol SRms WFar WHal
	'Gingerbread Man'	MBNS SApp
	'Girl Scout'	SApp SRos
	'Glacier Bay'	CBgR EBee LHop
	'Glazed Heather Plum'	SApp
	'Gleber's Top Cream'	SApp
	'Glomunda'	SApp
	'Glory's Legacy'	SRos
	'Glowing Gold'	WCAu
	'Gold Crest'	MNFA
	'Gold Dust'	SRos
	'Gold Imperial'	EWll NBre
	'Golden Bell'	NGdn NHol
	'Golden Chance'	WCAu
	'Golden Chimes' ♀H4	More than 30 suppliers
	'Golden Empress'	SApp
	'Golden Ginkgo'	LRHS MBri MNFA SApp WSPU
	'Golden Nugget'	MBNS
	'Golden Orchid'	see *H.* 'Doubloon'
	'Golden Peace'	SRos
	'Golden Prize'	CBgR EPla MNFA NGdn NPri SApp SDay SRos WCot WFar
	'Golden Scroll'	SApp SDay SRos
	Golden Zebra = 'Malja' PBR (v)	CWGN ENot EPfP LBuc MGos MRav NLar NSti SDnm SPoG WFar WSpi
	'Goldeneye'	SApp
	'Golliwog'	SDay
	'Good Looking'	EGol
	'Grace and Favour'	SDay SPol
	'Graceful Eye'	SApp SRos
	'Graceland'	EMar
	'Grain de Lumiere' **new**	EMar
	'Grand Masterpiece'	CMMP IPot NGdn NRnb SPet WAul
	'Grand Palais'	SApp SRos
	'Grape Magic'	EGol SRos WTin
	'Grape Velvet'	CHar CPar CSpe EGle EGol MBNS MCCP MFOX MHar MNFA NBre NMyG NRnb NSti SApp SRos WAul WCAu WMnd
	'Great Northern'	SApp
	'Green Dolphin Street'	SDay SRos
	'Green Dragon'	SDay
	'Green Drop'	SAga WFar
	'Green Eyed Giant'	MNFA
	'Green Eyed Lady'	SDay
	'Green Flutter' ♀H4	EBee EPfP LRHS LSRN MBNS MNFA NBir NBre NCGa NGdn NSti SApp SPhx SPol SRos WSpi WWlt
	'Green Glitter'	MNFA
	'Green Gold'	CMHG MNFA
	'Green Puff'	NBir
	'Green Spider'	SDay SRos
	'Green Valley'	MNFA
	'Grumbly'	ELan WPnP
	'Guardian Angel'	WCFE WTin
	'Gusto'	WCAu
	'Hail Mary'	SDay
	'Halo Light'	MNFA
	'Hamlet'	SDay
	'Happy Returns'	CBgR CHid CTri EBee EBla ECha EGol ELan EMar IBal LAst MBNS MBri MHar MNFA MSte NEgg NGdn SApp SDay SRGP SRos WCAu WCFE WTin
	'Harbor Blue'	CCol SDay
	'Hawaiian Punch'	EGol
	'Hawaiian Purple'	EGol
	'Hawk'	SApp SDay SPol
	'Hazel' **new**	SRos
	'Hazel Monette'	EGol
	'Heartthrob'	WCAu
	'Heather Green'	SApp
	'Heavenly Treasure'	SApp SRos
	'Heidi Eidelweiss'	CPLG
	'Heirloom Lace'	SDay WCAu WFar
	'Helen Boehm'	EMar
	'Helle Berlinerin' ♀H4	MNFA SApp SPol SRos
	'Her Majesty's Wizard'	MAvo MBNS MHer NBro SPoG SPol
	'Hercules'	NBre
	'Hey There'	SDay SRos
	'High Energy'	SApp
	'High Tor'	GQui MNFA SPol WTin
	'Highland Belle'	SApp
	'Highland Lord' (d)	MBNS SDay
	'Holiday Mood'	ELan ERou SApp
	'Holly Dancer'	SPol
	'Honey Jubilee'	SPol
	'Hope Diamond'	CCol SDay WCAu
	'Hornby Castle'	LRHS NHol WPer
	'Hot Ticket'	SApp SRos
	'Hot Town' **new**	ELan
	'Hot Wire'	SRos
	'Houdini'	EGle EGol WCAu WMnd
	'House of Orange'	SApp SPol
	'Howard Goodson'	MNFA
	'Humdinger'	SRos
	'Hush Little Baby' **new**	CCol
	'Hyperion'	CBgR CPrp CSev CTri CWat ECha ECtt EGol EPfP LAst LEdu MLan MNFA MRav NGdn NHol SApp SHBN SPer SPla SPoG SRos WCot WTMC
	'Ice Carnival'	CBgR CKel EGle ELon EPfP ERou LCro LDai LRHS MBNS MNFA NBhm NBre NGdn NOrc SPet SPoG WSpi
	'Ice Castles'	CTri SApp
	'Ice Cool'	SApp SRos
	'Ice Cream Dream' **new**	CCol
	'Icecap'	WAul WFar WMoo WPnP
	'Icy Lemon'	SRos
	'Ida Duke Miles'	SDay SRos
	'Ida Munson'	EGol
	'Ida's Magic'	EBee
	'Imperator'	EPla NHol
	'Imperial Lemon'	SApp
	'Impromptu'	SDay
	'In Depth' (d)	EPfP MBNS NBro NCGa NLar SWal WCot

	'Inchon'	EMar
	'Indian Giver'	CCol
	'Indian Paintbrush'	EGle LHop MBri NBir SPol WCAu
	'Indian Sky' **new**	SRos
	'Indigo Moon'	SApp
	'Indy Rhapsody' **new**	CCol
	'Indy Snowfall' **new**	CCol
	'Inner View'	ECtt MBNS NLar NRnb SApp WMnd
	'Inspired Edge'	MBNS
	'Inspired Word'	SRos
	'Invicta'	SRos
	'Iridescent Jewel'	SDay
	'Irish Elf'	ELon GBuc GMac SApp WTin
	'Isle of Capri'	SRos
	'Isle of Dreams'	SPol
	'Jake Russell'	CWsd LCro MBNS MNFA SAga
	'James Marsh'	CBgR CCol CPar EGle EPfP EWes MBNS MBri MNFA MNrw NCGa NRnb NSti SApp SRos WAul WCAu WCot WMnd
	'Janet Gordon'	SPol SRos
	'Janice Brown'	CCol CKel CWCL EMar MBNS MNFA NLar NMoo SApp SDay SRos
	'Jan's Twister'	CCol MNrw SApp SRos
	'Jason Salter'	NCGa SApp SDay WAul
	'Java Sea'	EBee
	'Jay Turman'	SApp
	'Jazz' **new**	EMar
	'Jazz Diva' **new**	EMar
	'Jean Swann'	CCol MBNS
	'Jedi Brenda Spann'	SApp
	'Jedi Dot Pierce'	SApp SRos
	'Jedi Irish Spring'	SApp
	'Jedi Rose Frost'	SApp
	'Jedi Rust Frost'	SApp
	'Jenny Wren'	EBee EBla EMar EPPr EPla ETod GSki LRHS MBNS MNFA MPop NBre NBro NEgg NHol SRGP WAul WCAu
	'Jersey Spider' **new**	EMar
	'Jerusalem'	SRos
	'Jesse James'	SApp SPol
	'Jo Jo'	WCAu
	'Joan Cook'	EGle
	'Joan Senior'	More than 30 suppliers
	'Jocelyn's Oddity'	SApp
	'Jock Randall'	MNFA
	'Jockey Club' (d)	EMar MBNS
	'John Bierman'	SRos
	'John Robert Biggs'	SApp
	'Jolyene Nichole'	SApp SRos
	'Journey's End'	SDay
	'Jovial'	SApp SDay SRos
	'Judah'	SApp SDay SRos
	'Judge Roy Bean' **new**	SPol SRos
	'Justin June'	CCol
	'Kate Carpenter'	SRos
	'Kathleen Salter'	SRos
	'Katie Elizabeth Miller'	SDay SRos
	'Kazuq'	SApp
	'Kecia'	MNFA
	'Kelly's Girl'	SRos
	'Kempion' **new**	EMar
	'Kent's Favorite Two'	SRos
	'Kimmswick'	SApp
	'Kindly Light'	CCol EMar MNFA SRos WCAu
	'King Haiglar'	CCol EGol SApp SPhx SRos
	'King's Gold' **new**	CCol
N	'Kwanso Flore Pleno'	see *H. fulva* 'Green Kwanso'
N	'Kwanso Flore Pleno Variegata'	see *H. fulva* 'Variegated Kwanso'
	'La Peche'	SDay
	'Lacy Marionette'	SApp SPol

	'Lady Cynthia'	CKel CSBt
	'Lady Fingers'	CBgR CCol MNFA
	'Lady Hillary'	SApp
	'Lady Inma'	SApp
	'Lady Limelight'	SDay
	'Lady Liz'	MNFA
	'Lady Mischief'	SApp
	'Lady Neva'	CCol SApp SDay SRos
	'Lady Scarlet' **new**	LLWG
	'Ladykin'	SApp SPol SRos
	'Lake Norman Spider'	CCol MNFA SApp
	'Lark Song'	EGol WFar
	'Lauren Leah'	SRos
	'Lavender Bonanza'	WCAu WCFE
	'Lavender Deal'	EMar MNrw
	'Lavender Flushing'	SApp
	'Lavender Illusion'	SApp
	'Lavender Memories'	SDay
	'Lavender Silver Cords'	SPol
	'Lavender Spider'	SApp
	'Leebea Orange Crush'	EMar
	'Lemon Bells' ♀H4	EBee EBla ECGP ECha EGle EMFW EMar EPPr EPfP GMaP GSki MBNS MNFA MWgw NBro NCGa NGdn SApp SDay SRos WCAu WSpi
	'Lemon Dessert'	SRos
	'Lemon Mint'	EGol SRos
	'Lemonora'	SDay
	'Lenox'	SDay SRos
	'Leonard Bernstein'	SApp SRos
	'Light the Way'	ECha
	'Light Years Away'	MAvo MBNS NBro
	'Lil Ledie'	SApp
	'Lilac Wine'	ECha
§	***lilioasphodelus*** ♀H4	More than 30 suppliers
	'Lillian Frye'	EGol
	'Lilting Belle'	CCol SRos
	'Lilting Lady'	SApp SDay
	'Lilting Lady Red'	SApp
	'Lilting Lavender'	SDay
	'Lime Frost'	SRos
	'Linda'	ERou EWll MRav NHol SRos
*	'Liners Moon'	EGol
	'Lines of Splendor'	CCol
	'Lipstick Print'	SRos
	'Little Angel'	SApp
	'Little Audrey'	EGle MHar SApp
	'Little Bee'	MBNS NBre
	'Little Beige Magic'	EGol
	'Little Big Man'	SDay
	'Little Bugger'	MBNS NEgg NGby NLar
	'Little Bumble Bee'	CFir COlW EGol EMar EMil MBNS MNFA SApp WCAu
	'Little Business'	MBNS MNFA SApp SDay WAul
	'Little Cadet'	MNFA
	'Little Cameo'	EGol
	'Little Carpet'	MBNS SPer
	'Little Carrot Top'	WCAu
	'Little Cranberry Cove'	EGol
	'Little Dandy'	EGol
	'Little Dart'	ECha
	'Little Deeke'	MHar MNFA SApp SDay SRos
	'Little Fantastic'	EGol
	'Little Fat Dazzler'	SApp SDay SPol SRos
	'Little Fellow'	MBNS
	'Little Fruit Cup'	SApp
	'Little Grapette'	CPrp EGle EGol EMil EPfP GCra GQue MBNS MNFA NLar NSti SApp SRos WAul WBrk WCAu WCot WTin
	'Little Greenie'	EMar SDay
	'Little Gypsy Vagabond'	CWat SDay SRos
	'Little Heavenly Angel'	SPol
	'Little Lassie'	MBNS
	'Little Lavender Princess'	EGol

'Little Maggie'	MHar MSte SApp SDay SPol
'Little Missy'	CBgR CHFP CWat EMar EMil LAst MBNS NBre SPet WGob WHoo
'Little Monica'	SApp SDay
'Little Orange Slices' **new**	CCol
'Little Pumpkin Face'	EGol
'Little Rainbow'	EGol
'Little Red Hen'	CSam EBla ECGP EMar GBuc LRHS MBNS MNFA NBro NEgg NGdn SDay
'Little Show Stopper'	EWTr MBNS NBro NMRc NMoo
'Little Sweet Sue'	MNFA
'Little Sweet Talk'	SRos
'Little Tawny'	WCAu
'Little Toddler'	SApp SDay
'Little Violet Lace'	GSki SApp SDay
'Little Wart'	EGol MNFA SDay
'Little Wine Cup'	More than 30 suppliers
'Little Wine Spider'	SApp
'Little Women'	SDay
'Little Zinger'	SDay
'Littlest Clown'	SDay
'Lochinvar'	GBuc MRav SRos
'Lonesome Dove' **new**	SPol
'Long John Silver'	SRos
'Long Stocking'	CCol SPol SRos
'Longfield Purple Edge'	EBee MBNS
'Longfield's Beauty'	EGle MBNS NCGa
'Longfield's Glory'	CCol MBNS NBre NCGa NMoo WGob
'Longfield's Pride'	CDWL ECho MBNS
'Longfield's Purple Eye'	MBNS NCGa NLar NMoo
'Longfield's Twins'	EBee EKen MBNS NMoo WCot
longituba B&SWJ 4576	WCru
'Look Away'	SApp
'Lotus Land'	SDay
'Love Glow'	CFir
'Loving Memories'	SApp
'Lowenstine'	SApp
'Lucretius'	MNFA
'Luke Senior Junior'	SApp
'Lullaby Baby'	CCol EGle EGol ELan MBNS SApp SDay SPol SRos
luna	NOak
'Lusty Lealand'	CDWL CPar EGle EGol EMar MBNS SRos
'Luverne' **new**	SRos
'Luxury Lace'	CPrp CSpe CWat EBla ECho ECtt EGle EGol ELan EMar EPfP EPla LRHS MNFA NBir NGdn NHol NPri SPer SPol SRos WAul WCAu WCFE WFar WMoo WPnP WTMC WTin
'Lydia Bechtold'	CCol SRos
'Lynn Hall'	EGol MBNS WSpi
'Lyric Opera'	SDay
'Mabel Fuller'	CBgR MRav SRos WHrl
'Macbeth' **new**	MBNS
'Mae Graham'	SApp
'Maggie Fynboe'	SPol
'Magic Carpet Ride'	SPol
'Magic Lace'	SRos
'Magnificent Eyes' **new**	EMar
'Mahogany Magic'	SRos
'Malayasian Masquerade'	SApp
'Malaysian Monarch'	SRos WMnd
'Mallard'	CWat ECGP ECtt EGol EHrv EMar EPla LLWP LRHS MBNS MRav SApp SRos SWat WPer WTMC
'Malmaison Plum' **new**	SDay
'Manchurian Apricot'	SRos
'Marble Faun'	SApp SRos
'Margaret Perry'	CFee GBin MNrw WAul
'Marion Caldwell'	SPol
'Marion Vaughn' ♀H4	CSev CWsd ECot EGle EGol EHrv ELan EPfP GMaP LBMP LHop LRHS MNFA NSti SBch SDix SPer SRGP SRos SSpi WCAu WFar
'Mariska'	SApp SDay SRos
'Mark My Word'	SApp
'Marse Connell'	CCol SRos
'Martha Adams'	CCol
'Mary Todd'	EGle EGol MBNS MNFA SApp WCAu WMnd
'Mary's Gold'	SDay SPol SRos
'Mask Ball'	SRos
'Matador Orange'	EWsh
'Matt'	SRos
'Mauna Loa'	CCol EBee EGle EMar GQue MBNS MNFA MNrw MSte MWea NBre NRnb SApp WAul WCAu WCot
'May Hall'	CMCo
'May May'	SApp SPol
'Meadow Mist'	EGle EGol
'Meadow Sprite'	SRos
'Medieval Guild'	SApp
'Mega Stella'	SApp
'Melody Lane'	CMCo EGol MNFA
'Meno'	EGol
'Merlot Rouge'	WAul
'Metaphor'	EMar SApp SDay SRos
'Michele Coe'	CMMP EBee EBla EGol EHrv EMar EQua LRHS MBNS MNFA NBre NBro NCGa NEgg NGdn SApp SPav SRGP SRos WCAu WMoo
middendorffii	CAvo EBee EMon GMaP MNFA NSti WCAu WFar WPnP WSpi
- 'Elfin'	EMon
- var. ***esculenta***	EMon
- 'Major'	CFee
'Midnight Dynamite' **new**	MBNS
'Midnight Magic'	EMar
'Mikado'	LRHS
'Milady Greensleeves'	CCol SDay SRos
'Milanese Mango'	SDay
'Mildred Mitchell'	MBNS NLar NMRc
'Millie Schlumpf'	EMar SApp SDay SRos
'Mimosa Umbrella'	SPol
'Ming Lo'	SDay
'Ming Porcelain'	CMil SApp SDay SRos
'Mini Pearl'	CBgR CMMP EGol EPfP LRHS MBri SApp SDay SRos WPer
'Mini Stella'	ECtt ENot IBal MBNS NBre NOrc WAul WFar
miniature hybrids	SRms WPer
minor	CWsd EGol EMon GBin NGdn SRms
- B&SWJ 8841	WCru
'Miressa Purple'	EBee
'Miss Amelia' **new**	SRos
'Miss Jessie' **new**	SRos
'Missenden' ♀H4	MNrw SApp SRos
'Mission Moonlight'	EGol MHar WCAu
'Missouri Beauty'	CCol CPar EBee ERou LRHS MBNS NPri SApp WWeb
'Missouri Memories'	SRos
'Mojave Mapeor'	SApp
'Mokan Butterfly'	SDay
'Mokan Cindy'	EMar
'Moment of Truth'	MBNS NBre
'Monica Marie'	SRos
'Moon Snow' **new**	SDay
'Moon Witch'	SDay SPol SRos
'Moonbeam'	SApp
'Moonlight Masquerade'	CDWL CWat EPfP SApp
'Moonlight Mist'	CCol SApp SRos
'Moonlit Caress'	EBee IPot MBNS NBro SRos WAul
'Moonlit Crystal'	CSpe SApp SPol
'Moonlit Masquerade'	CCol CPen CWGN EGle EMar ERou GBuc MBNS MBri MCCP

	MLLN NCGa NRnb SDnm SPav SPer SRos WAul WCAu WGob WHrl
'Mormon Spider'	SApp SPol
'Morning Dawn'	EGle
'Morning Sun'	EMar MBNS NBre WCot
'Morocco'	SPol
'Morocco Red'	CMdw CTri ELan EPla GSki NBre
'Morrie Otte'	SPol
'Mosel'	SDay
'Mount Joy'	SPer
'Mountain Laurel'	ECGP LDai LRHS LSRN MNFA MRav SApp SPol WFar
'Mrs B.F. Bonner'	WAul
'Mrs David Hall'	CMdw
'Mrs Hugh Johnson'	CSev ECot EWTr GCra LAst MSte NHol SHBN
'Mrs John J. Tigert'	ERou
* 'Mrs Lester'	SDay
multiflora	EMon MNFA NHol
'Mumbo Jumbo'	SApp
'My Belle'	SApp SRos
'My Darling Clementine'	SApp SDay SRos
'My Melinda'	SDay
'My Sweet Rose'	SRos
'Mynelle's Starfish'	SDay SPol SRos
'Mysterious Veil'	EGol
'Nacogdoches Lady'	CCol
'Nairobi Dawn'	SRos
nana	CFir EPot GKev
'Nanuq'	SApp SDay SRos
'Naomi Ruth'	EGle EGol LAst MBNS SApp WCAu WHoo WTin
'Nashville'	ELan ERou IBlr WHrl
'Nashville Lights'	SPol
'Natural Veil'	SPol
'Navajo Princess' **new**	EPfP ERou MBNS MNrw
'Neal Berrey'	SApp SRos
'Nefertiti'	CBgR CMCo ELon LHop NBir SAga SPer WAul WCAu WTin
'Neon Rose'	EBla SRos
'Netsuke'	SApp
'New Swirls'	SApp
'Neyron Rose' $\mathbb{Y}^{H4}$	CHar EGol EMar EPfP EPla ERou GSki LAst MBNS MNFA NBre NEgg NGdn SRos WCAu WMoo
'Night Beacon'	CBgR ECho ECtt EGol EMar EWes EWll IBal MBNS MBri MLLN MNFA MNrw NCGa NLar NMoo SApp SDay SRos WGob WHrl
'Night Hawk' **new**	CWsd
'Night Raider'	EMar SApp SDay SRos
'Nigrette'	NHol
'Nile Crane'	CBgR EBee ERou MBNS MNrw NCGa SApp SDay SPer WAul
'Nile Grave'	SApp
'Nile Plum'	SApp
'Nivia Guest'	SApp SDay
'Nob Hill'	CMdw EGol EPla GBin MNFA SApp SRos
'Nordic Night'	CCol EMar
'North Star'	SApp
'Norton Orange'	MNFA SAga WFar
'Nosferatu'	SDay
'Nova' $\mathbb{Y}^{H4}$	CPrp CWsd MNFA SApp SRos
'Nuka'	EMar
'Numinous Moments'	SDay
'Ocean Rain'	SApp SRos
'Octopus Hugs' **new**	SRos
'Oklahoma Kicking Bird' **new**	CCol
'Old Tangiers'	EMar SRos
'Olive Bailey Langdon'	EGol SApp SRos
'Olympic Showcase'	SRos
'Omomuki'	SApp SRos
'On and On' **new**	MBNS
'Oom Pah Pah'	ECha
'Open Hearth'	CCol SPol SRos
'Orange Crush' **new**	LLWG
'Orange Dream'	SDay
'Orange Prelude'	SApp
'Orange Velvet'	SApp SDay SRos
'Orangeman' hort.	EBla EPla GSki LRHS MBNS NGdn NHol
'Orchid Beauty'	ECha MLHP WMoo
'Orchid Candy'	MBNS NBir WAul WHil
'Orchid Corsage'	SApp SDay
'Oriental Ruby'	EGol MNFA SRos
'Outrageous'	SApp SRos
'Paige Parker'	EGol
'Paige's Pinata'	EBee MBNS NBPC
'Paint Your Wagon'	SApp
'Paintbrush'	CRez
'Painted Lady'	MNFA SApp
'Painted Pink' **new**	SDay
'Painted Trillium'	CMil
'Painter Poet'	EMar
'Painter's Touch'	SDay
'Palace Guard'	MNFA
'Pandora's Box'	More than 30 suppliers
'Pantaloons'	SApp
'Pantherette'	SApp SPol
'Paper Butterfly'	CCol EMar SPol SRos
'Paradise Prince'	EGol
'Pardon Me'	CMHG CMMP ECho EGle EGol ELan GMaP IBal MBNS MNFA NCGa NGdn NHol SApp SPol SRos SWal WAul WBor WCAu
'Parfait' **new**	EMar
'Pas de Deux'	SApp
'Pastel Ballerina'	SRos
'Pastel Classic'	SApp SRos
'Pastilline'	SPol
'Pat Mercer'	SApp
'Patchwork Puzzle'	SRos
'Patricia'	EPfP MBNS SPoG
'Patricia Fay'	SApp SRos
'Patsy Bickers'	CCol SApp
'Peach Petticoats'	SRos
'Peacock Maiden'	SApp
'Pear Ornament'	SRos
'Pearl Lewis'	SDay
'Pemaquid Light'	CMHG
'Penelope Vestey'	EBla EGle EMar GBuc LRHS MBNS MNFA NCGa SApp SPol SRGP SRos
'Penny's Worth'	EGol MBNS NOrc WAul WCot WFar WHoo
'Persian Princess'	CMCo
'Persian Ruby'	EMar SPol
'Petite Ballerina'	SDay
'Piano Man'	EMar MBNS MWea NLar NMoo WAul WGob
'Piccadilly Princess'	SRos
'Pink Attraction'	SApp
'Pink Ballerina'	EGol
'Pink Charm'	COIW EBee ECha EMar EWsh GMaP LRHS MHar MNFA MWgw NBro NGdn NHol SHBN SPla SRos WCAu
'Pink Cotton Candy'	SRos
'Pink Damask' $\mathbb{Y}^{H4}$	More than 30 suppliers
'Pink Dream'	EMar EQua LRHS MBNS MNFA NBir NBre NHol SPol WCAu
'Pink Flirt' **new**	SDay
'Pink Glow'	CMMP
'Pink Grace'	SPol
'Pink Heaven'	EGol
'Pink Lady'	ERou MNrw MRav SHBN SRms
'Pink Lavender Appeal'	EGol WCAu
'Pink Prelude'	EBee EMar LRHS MBNS MNFA MWat NBro

	'Pink Puff'	ERou MBNS NBir NBre NCGa NLar WGob
	'Pink Salute'	SRos
	'Pink Sundae'	ECha
	'Pink Super Spider'	MNFA SRos
	'Pinocchio'	MBNS NMoo
	'Pirate Treasure'	MBNS
	'Pirate's Patch'	SPol SRos
	'Pixie Parasol'	WMnd WSpi
	'Pixie Pipestone'	CCol SApp
	'Pocket Size'	SApp
	'Pojo'	SDay
	'Pompeian Purple'	EGol
	'Pony'	EGol SDay SRos
	'Ponytail Pink'	EGol
	'Pookie Bear'	SApp
	'Prague Spring'	EMar MNFA SRos WCAu
	'Prairie Belle'	CBcs CSWP MBNS NBre SApp SPol WCAu WFar
	'Prairie Blue Eyes'	CCol ECha ECho EGle EGol LFur LRHS MBNS MNFA NMoo NPri NRnb SApp SPlb SPol SRos WAul WCAu WCot WHrl WMnd WTMC
	'Prairie Charmer'	WHrl
	'Prairie Moonlight'	SRos
	'Prairie Sunset'	WCAu
	'Prelude to Love'	EMar
	'Pretty Mist'	EMar MBri
	'Pretty Peggy'	MNFA
	'Primrose Mascotte'	NBir
	'Prince of Purple' **new**	SRos
	'Prince Redbird'	SDay SRos
	'Princess Blue Eyes'	SPol
	'Princess Eden'	SApp
	'Princess Ellen'	SApp
	'Princeton Eye Glow'	SDay
	'Princeton Point Lace'	SApp
	'Princeton Silky'	SRos
	'Prize Picotee Deluxe'	SRos
	'Prize Picotee Elite'	EMar SPol SRos WTin
	'Protocol'	SDay
§	'Puddin'	CWat NHol SDay WAul
	'Pudgie'	SApp
	'Pumpkin Kid'	SApp SRos
	'Puppet Show'	SDay
	'Purbeck Silk'	CCol
	'Pure and Simple'	SDay SPol SRos
	'Purple Corsage'	SApp
	'Purple Pinwheel'	SPol
	'Purple Rain'	CWat MBNS MWea SApp SDay SPol SRos SWvt
	'Purple Rain Dance'	SPol
	'Purple Waters'	CCol EPfP EWll LRHS MBNS MWgw NBre NOrc NPri WAul WPnP
	'Pursuit of Excellence'	SRos
	'Pyewacket'	SApp
	'Pygmy Plum'	SDay
	'Queen of May'	SApp WCot
	'Queens Fancy'	SApp
	'Queen's Gift'	SApp
	'Queensland'	SApp
	'Quick Results'	SApp SRos
	'Quilt Patch' **new**	SRos
	'Quinn Buck'	EMar SDay
	'Ra Hansen'	SDay
	'Radiant'	CBcs
	'Radiant Greetings'	MNFA
	'Raging Tiger'	SDay
	'Rainbow Candy'	LTwo MBNS NMoo
	'Raindrop'	EGol
	'Rajah'	CBgR EMar MBNS NBro SPer WHrl WRHF WWeb
	'Raspberry Candy'	CEnt ECho EMar EWll GCra MBNS MLLN MNrw NBhm NBro NCGa NOrc SApp SRos WAul WCAu WGob WHrl
	'Raspberry Pixie'	EGol MNFA SPol
	'Raspberry Wine'	ECha MHar
	'Real Wind'	CCol EMar LLWG MNFA SApp SPol SRos
	'Red Butterfly' **new**	EMar
	'Red Flag'	CCol
	'Red Joy'	SApp
	'Red Precious' Ψ^{H4}	EGol MNFA MNrw SApp SMHy SRos
	'Red Ribbons'	CCol SDay SPol SRos
	'Red Ruby' **new**	ERCP
	'Red Rum'	CBgR EWll MBNS NBro WPnP
	'Red Torch'	CWsd
	'Red Volunteer'	EMar SPol SRos
	'Regency Dandy'	SApp
	'Renee' **new**	MNrw
	'Respighi'	SApp SRos
	'Return Trip'	SPol
	'Ribbonette'	EBee MBNS NMoo
	'Ringlets'	GSki MNFA
	'Riptide'	SApp
	'Robert Coe' **new**	SRos
	'Robin Coleman'	MNFA
	'Rocket City'	ELan SRos
	'Roger Grounds'	CCol SApp SPol
*	'Romantic Rose'	EMar MBNS NLar
	'Ron Rousseau'	SApp
	'Root Beer'	SRos WTin
	'Rose Emily'	SApp SDay SRos
	'Rose Festival'	WCAu
	'Rose Roland'	NBre
	'Rosella Sheridan'	SRos
	'Rosewood Flame'	SRos
	'Rosewood Rainbows End' **new**	SRos
	'Rosewood Snowflakes'	SRos
	'Roswitha' **new**	SPol
	'Rosy Returns'	MBNS MWea NLar NMoo
	'Royal Braid'	CPen EGle EPfP MBNS MNrw NCGa NLar SApp SPer WCot
	'Royal Charm'	SRos
	'Royal Corduroy'	SRos
	'Royal Crown'	MBNS
	'Royal Occasion' **new**	SRos
	'Royal Palace Prince'	EMar
	'Royal Prestige'	SApp
	'Royal Robe'	CTri SPhx
	'Royal Saracen'	SDay
	'Ruby Spider'	CCol SRos
	'Rudolf Seyer'	MBNS
	'Ruffled Antique Lavender'	WCAu
	'Ruffled Apricot'	CKel LBMP MAvo MBNS MNFA SDay SPad SPav SRos WCAu
	'Ruffles and Lace'	CCol
	'Rurbeck Dawn' **new**	CCol
	'Russell Prichard'	ERou
	'Russian Easter'	SRos
	'Russian Rhapsody'	CKel SApp SPol SRos
	'Rutilans'	CFee
	'Sabie'	SApp
	'Sabine Baur'	CHFP EBee EMar IBal IPot MBNS MWea WAul WCra
	'Sabra Salina'	SRos
	'Saffron Glow'	SDay
*	'Sagamore'	SApp
	'Salmon Sheen'	MNFA SDay SPer SRos
	'Sammy'	SDay
	'Sammy Russell'	More than 30 suppliers
	'Sandra Elizabeth'	SDay
	'Sandra Walker'	EGol
	'Santiago'	SPol
	'Sari'	SApp
	'Satin Clouds'	EGol

'Satin Glass'	MNFA
'Satin Glow'	ECha MLHP
'Scarlet Chalice'	SApp
'Scarlet Flame'	ECha WMoo
* 'Scarlet Oak'	LRHS MBri MNFA SRos
'Scarlet Orbit'	SApp SRos
'Scarlet Ribbons'	SPol
'Scarlock'	MNFA
'Scatterbrain'	CKel
'Schoeppinger Anfang'	EBee
'Scorpio'	CBgR CCol MNFA SPol
'Scotland'	IBal SApp
'Searcy Marsh'	EGol
'Sebastian'	SApp SRos
'Secret Splendor'	CCol SPol
'Selma Longlegs'	SRos
'Serena Sunburst'	CCol SPol SRos
'Serene Madonna'	CFir
'Serenity Morgan'	EBee EPfP MBNS
'Shaman'	SApp SRos
'Sherry Fair'	SApp
'Sherry Lane Carr'	SPol SRos
'Shimek September Morning' **new**	SPol
'Shogun'	MBNS
'Shooting Star'	CWsd SPla
'Shotgun'	SPol SRos
'Show Amber'	MBNS SApp SRos
'Significant Other'	SApp
'Silent Sentry'	CFir
'Silken Fairy'	EGol
'Silken Touch'	SApp SRos
'Siloam Amazing Grace'	SApp SDay SRos
'Siloam Angel Blush'	SDay
'Siloam Baby Talk'	EGle EGol ELon EMar LAst MNFA NBir SApp SRos WAul WHoo WMoo WPnP WTin
'Siloam Bertie Ferris'	MNFA SDay
'Siloam Bo Peep'	CCol EGol MNFA SApp WAul WTMC
'Siloam Brian Hanke'	SRos
'Siloam Button Box'	EBee EGol MBNS WAul
'Siloam Bye Lo'	EGol SDay
'Siloam Cinderella'	EGol SDay SRos
'Siloam David Kirchhoff'	EMar MBNS SDay SRos
'Siloam Doodlebug'	EGol SRos
'Siloam Double Classic' (d)	CCol EGol EMar SRos
'Siloam Dream Baby'	EPPr GBri MBNS NCGa
'Siloam Edith Sholar'	EGol LLWG
'Siloam Ethel Smith'	EGol MNFA SDay SPol SRos
'Siloam Fairy Tale'	CWat EGol
'Siloam Flower Girl'	SDay
'Siloam French Doll'	CCol MBNS NLar NRnb
'Siloam French Marble'	SRos
'Siloam Frosted Mint'	SApp
'Siloam Gold Coin'	SApp SDay
'Siloam Grace Stamile'	CFir EMar SApp SRos WGob
'Siloam Harold Flickinger'	SRos
'Siloam Jim Cooper'	SRos
'Siloam Joan Senior'	EGol MBNS
'Siloam John Yonski'	SDay
'Siloam June Bug'	EGol ELan LLWG MNFA SApp WCAu
'Siloam Justine Lee'	MBNS
'Siloam Kewpie Doll'	EGol
'Siloam Little Angel'	EGol SApp
'Siloam Little Fairy' **new**	LLWG
'Siloam Little Girl'	EGol SDay SRos
'Siloam Mama'	SApp SRos
'Siloam Merle Kent'	EMar MNFA SApp SDay SPol SRos
'Siloam New Toy'	EGol
'Siloam Nugget'	SApp
'Siloam Orchid Jewel'	EGol
'Siloam Paul Watts'	SPol SRos
'Siloam Peewee'	EGol

'Siloam Penny'	SApp
* 'Siloam Pink'	LAst
'Siloam Pink Glow'	EGle EGol SWat WAul
'Siloam Pink Petite'	EGol
'Siloam Plum Tree'	EGol SApp
'Siloam Pocket Size'	EGol MSte
'Siloam Powder Pink'	SApp
'Siloam Prissy'	EGol SApp
'Siloam Purple Plum'	EGol
'Siloam Queen's Toy'	SPol
'Siloam Ra Hansen'	SApp
'Siloam Red Ruby'	EGol
'Siloam Red Toy'	EGol MNFA
'Siloam Red Velvet'	EGol
'Siloam Ribbon Candy'	EGol SApp SDay
'Siloam Rose Dawn'	SApp SPol SRos
'Siloam Rose Queen'	SDay
'Siloam Royal Prince'	CMMP EBee EGle EGol EPfP MNFA NHol NRnb SApp SDay
'Siloam Shocker'	EGol MNFA
'Siloam Show Girl'	CMCo EGle EGol MBNS NCGa SApp
'Siloam Sugar Time'	EGol
'Siloam Sunburst' **new**	EMar
'Siloam Tee Tiny'	EGol LLWG
'Siloam Tinker Toy'	EGol
'Siloam Tiny Mite'	EGol SDay
'Siloam Toddler'	EGol
'Siloam Tom Thumb'	CBgR EGol EMar MBNS WCAu WGob
'Siloam Ury Winniford'	CHFP ECho EGol EMar EMil LLWG MBNS MCCP MNFA NBre NLar NMoo SApp WAul WHoo WPnP WTin
'Siloam Virginia Henson'	EGol LLWG MNFA SApp SRos WCAu
'Siloam Wendy Glawson'	SApp
'Silver Ice'	SApp SRos
'Silver Lance'	SRos
'Silver Quasar'	SRos
'Silver Trumpet'	EGle EGol
'Silver Veil'	WFar
'Sinbad Sailor' **new**	EMar
'Sir Blackstem'	ELon SApp SRos
'Sirius'	NHol
'Sirocco'	EBee WTin
'Sixth Sense' **new**	MAvo MBNS
'Slender Lady'	SDay SRos
'Smoky Mountain Autumn'	EMar MHar SApp SPol SRos
'Smoky Mountain Bell'	SApp
'Smuggler's Gold'	SApp
'Snappy Rhythm'	MNFA
'Snowed In'	SRos
'Snowy Apparition'	EBla EMar EWTr EWll MBNS MNFA MPop MSte MWea NHol SApp
'Snowy Eyes'	EGle EGol EMar GBuc IPot MBNS NCGa NHol NRnb SApp SWat WHrl
'So Lovely'	SApp
'Solid Scarlet'	SRos
'Someone Special'	SDay SPol SRos
'Song Sparrow'	GMac LRHS SApp WPer
'Sovereign Queen'	EGol
'Spacecoast Scrambled' **new**	EPfP MBNS
'Spacecoast Starburst'	EGle EMar MBNS NBro WCAu WCot
'Spanish Glow'	SRos
'Speak of Angels'	SApp
'Spider Breeder'	SApp
'Spider Man'	SApp SDay SRos WCAu
'Spider Miracle'	CCol MNFA SDay
'Spilled Milk'	SPol
'Spinne In Lachs'	SRos
'Spiral Charmer'	SApp

	'Spode'	SApp
	'Spring Ballerina'	SApp
	'Spring Willow Song'	SDay
	'Stafford'	More than 30 suppliers
	'Staghorn Sumach'	EBla EMar MPop NHol
	'Starling'	CFir CPar EGle EGol MNFA MSte NChi SApp WAul WCAu WSpi
	'Stars and Stripes'	MNFA
	'Startle'	CFir MBNS MNrw SPoG WCot
	'Statuesque'	WFar
	'Stella de Oro'	More than 30 suppliers
	'Stoke Poges' ♀H4	EBee EBla EGle EGoo EMFW EMar EPPr EPfP EPla LAst LBMP LHop LRHS LSRN MBNS MNFA NEgg NGdn SAga SApp SDay SPer SRos STes SWat WCAu
	'Stoplight'	CCol EBla ELon EMar SApp SDay SPol SRos
	'Strawberry Candy'	CMMP CWGN ECtt EMar EMil EPfP EWll LAst LLWG LSRN MBNS MBri NCGa NGdn NRnb SApp SPer SPet SPoG SRos WAul WCAu WHoo WHrl WSpi
	'Strawberry Fields Forever'	MBNS NLar SPol
	'Strawberry Swirl'	MNFA
I	'Streaker' B. Brown (v)	WCot
	'Streaker' McKinney	MNFA
	'Street Urchin' **new**	SPol
	'Strutter's Ball'	CPar EGle IPot MBNS MNFA NGdn NRnb SApp SDay SPer SRos SWat WAul WCAu WHoo WMnd
	'Sugar Cookie'	SApp SDay SRos
	'Summer Dragon'	EBee MBNS NMoo SPoG
	'Summer Interlude'	WCAu WMoo
	'Summer Jubilee'	SApp SDay
	'Summer Wine'	More than 30 suppliers
	'Sunday Gloves'	EGol SRos
	'Sunstar'	CCol
	'Super Purple'	CKel SApp
	'Superlative'	SApp SRos
	'Susan Weber'	SApp SRos
	'Suzie Wong'	MNFA SRos
	'Svengali'	SDay SPol
	'Sweet Harmony'	CCol
	'Sweet Pea'	EGol SDay
	'Taffy Tot'	SApp
	'Taj Mahal'	ELon SDay WFar
	'Tall Boy'	SApp
	'Tang'	LFur MBNS MNFA NMoo NOrc WCAu
	'Tangled Web' **new**	CCol
	'Tango Noturno'	SApp SPol
	'Tarantula'	SApp
	'Tasmania'	SPer
	'Techny Peach Lace'	SRos
	'Techny Spider'	SRos
	'Tejas'	CElw EBee MBNS NBre
	'Tender Shepherd'	EGol WCAu
	'Tennessee Flycatcher' **new**	SPol
	'Tetraploid Stella de Oro'	SDay
	'Tetrina's Daughter' ♀H4	CBgR EPfP NHol SApp SRos
	'Texas Sunlight'	WAul
	'Texas Toffee' **new**	SRos
	'Thai Silk'	SApp
	'Thanks a Bunch' **new**	SPol
	'Theresa Hall'	WFar
	'Thumbelina'	ECha MNFA
§	***thunbergii***	CAvo CWsd ECha EMon MNFA MNrw SMac WCAu
	- 'Ovation' **new**	MBNS
	'Thy True Love'	SApp SDay
	'Tigerling'	SRos
	'Tigger'	CDWL
	'Tilly Whim'	CCol
	'Time Lord'	EMar SApp SDay
	'Timeless Fire'	SApp SRos
	'Tinker Bell'	MSte SRos
	'Tiny Talisman'	SApp
	'Todd Monroe'	LLWG
	'Tom Collins'	SDay SRos
	'Tom Wise'	SPol SRos
	'Tomorrow's Song'	SApp
	'Tonia Gay'	SApp SPol SRos
	'Tootsie'	SDay
	'Tootsie Rose'	SPol SRos
	'Torpoint'	EBla EMar LRHS MBNS MNFA MRav NCob
	'Towhead'	EGol MRav
	'Toyland'	EGol EMar EPfP GSki MBNS NBir NGdn NLar NPri
	'Trahlyta'	CPar SApp SDay SPol SRos WTin
	'Trond'	SDay
	'Tropical Heat Wave'	SApp
	'True Glory'	SApp
	'True Grit'	SApp
	'Tuolumne Fairy Tale'	SPol
	'Tuscawilla Blackout'	SApp SRos
	'Tuscawilla Tigress'	CDWL ECho EMar NCGa SRos WAul
	'Tutankhamun'	MNFA
	'Tuxedo'	SApp SPol
	'Twenty Third Psalm'	WHal
	'Twist of Lemon'	SRos
	'Two Faces of Love'	SPol
	'Umbrella Parade' **new**	CCol
	'Uniquely Different'	SPol
	'Upper Class Peach'	SRos
	'Uptown Girl'	SRos
	'Valiant'	EMar MBNS
	'Vanilla Candy'	SRos
	'Varsity'	CPLG EGol GMac NBir SPer SRos WCAu
	'Veiled Beauty'	WCAu
	'Velvet Shadows'	SDay
	'Vera Biaglow'	MNFA SApp SDay SPol SRos
	'Vespers'	CAbP WFar
	vespertina	see *H. thunbergii*
	'Vi Simmons'	SRos
	'Victoria Aden'	IBal
	'Victorian Collar'	SApp
	'Victorian Ribbons'	SPol
	'Video'	SApp SRos
	'Vino di Notte'	EMar SRos
	'Vintage Bordeaux'	ELan SApp WAul
	'Violet Hour'	SDay
	'Viracocha'	SApp WMnd
	'Virgin's Blush'	SPer
	'Vision of Beauty'	SApp
	'Vohann'	SApp SRos
	'Waiting in the Wings'	SRos
	'Walking on Sunshine'	SApp SRos
	'War Paint'	SDay
	'Watchyl Dancing Spider' **new**	CCol
	'Water Witch'	CWat EGol SApp
	'Waxwing'	WPer
	'Wayside Green Imp'	EGle EGol MNrw MSte SApp
	'Wedding Band'	SRos
	'Wee Chalice'	EGol
	'Welchkins'	WAul
	'Welfo White Diamond'	SApp SPol
	'Well of Souls'	CCol
	'Wendy Glawson'	SApp
	'West Coast Blues'	CCol
	'Whichford' ♀H4	CMMP CSam EBee ECtt EGol ELan EMar EPla LAst LRHS MNFA NCob SPhx SPla SRos WCAu
	'Whiskey on Ice'	SApp
	'White Coral'	EMar LRHS LSRN MNFA NBro NEgg

'White Dish'	EGol
'White Edged Madonna'	EMar WHrl
'White Pansy'	SDay SRos
'White Star' **new**	LLWG
'White Temptation'	CFir CMMP EGol EPfP MBNS MNFA NCGa NGdn SApp SRos WAul WHoo WMnd
'White Tie Affair'	SApp SRos
'White Zone'	SRos
'Whooperee'	SRos
* 'Wide Eyed'	EPla MNFA
'Wild about Sherry'	SPol
'Wild Mustang'	CCol MBNS
'Wild One'	MNFA SApp
'Wild Welcome'	WCAu
'Wildfire Tango'	SApp
'Wilson Spider'	SApp SPol
'Wind Frills'	CCol SApp SDay
'Wind Song'	SApp SRos
'Window Dressing'	COIW EGol GMac
'Windsor Castle'	SApp
'Windsor Tan'	WCAu WCFE
'Wine Bubbles'	EGol SApp
'Wine Merchant'	EMar MNFA
'Wineberry Candy'	CPar EGle EPfP MBNS MLLN NLar WAul WCAu
'Winnetka'	WCAu
'Winnie' **new**	EMar
'Winnie the Pooh'	SDay
'Winsome Lady'	ECha EMar LRHS MBNS WHrl
'Winter Olympics'	SDay
'Wishing Well'	WCot
* 'Witch Hazel'	WCAu
'Women's Work'	SApp
'Wood Duck'	EGle SApp
'Woodside Velour' **new**	EMar
'Xia Xiang'	SRos
'Yabba Dabba Doo'	CCol EMar SPol SRos
'Yearning Love'	SApp
'Yellow Angel'	SApp
'Yellow Explosion'	SApp SRos
'Yellow Lollipop'	MNFA SApp SDay SRos
'Yellow Mantle'	MNFA
'Yellow Ribbon'	CCol
'Yellow Spider'	SApp
'Yellow Submarine' **new**	MBNS
'Yesterday Memories'	SRos
'Young Countess'	CMCo
'Zagora'	WCAu
'Zampa'	SDay
'Zara'	SPer
'Zarahemla' **new**	EMar

Hemiorchis (*Zingiberaceae*)

pantlingii	CKob

Hemiphragma (*Scrophulariaceae*)

heterophyllum	EBee

Hepatica ✿ (*Ranunculaceae*)

acutiloba	CArn CLAP EBee EBrs ECho GBuc GEdr LAma MAsh NBir NLar NSla WAbe WCru
americana	CLAP EBee EBrs ECho EHrv ELan GBuc LBBr MAsh NBir NLar WCru WPnP
angulosa	see *H. transsilvanica*
'Gyousei'	GBuc
henryi	EBee EPot LAma MAsh
insularis	CLAP SBla
- B&SWJ 859	WCru
maxima	GEdr NSla
- B&SWJ 4344	WCru
x ***media*** 'Ballardii'	EPot GBuc GEdr IBlr MNFA
- Blackthorn Group	SBla
- 'Harvington Beauty'	CFwr CLAP EHrv GBuc IBlr MAsh NBir WCot
- 'Millstream Merlin' (d) **new**	SBla
'Miyuki' (d)	GEdr
§ ***nobilis*** ΥH4	More than 30 suppliers
- var. ***asiatica***	MAsh
- blue-flowered	CDes ECho GAbr GBuc GEdr MAsh NLAp NSla NWCA SBla SRot WAbe WCru
- 'Cobalt'	CLAP ECho NLAp NSla WAbe
- 'Cremar'	GCrs MAsh
- dark blue-flowered	CLAP MAsh
- double pink-flowered	see *H. nobilis* 'Rubra Plena'
- 'Elkofener Resi' **new**	WCot
- var. ***japonica***	EPfP EWes GBuc GCrs LAma MAsh NBir SBla WCru
- - 'Akenezora' (d) **new**	GEdr
- - 'Asahi' (d) **new**	GEdr
- - 'Asahizuru' (d) **new**	GEdr
- - 'Dewa' (d) **new**	GEdr
- - 'Getsurin' (d) **new**	GEdr
- - 'Hakusetsu' (d) **new**	GEdr
- - 'Harukaze' (d) **new**	GEdr
- - 'Haruno-awayuki' (d) **new**	GEdr
- - 'Kagura' **new**	GEdr
- - 'Kougyoku' **new**	GEdr
- - 'Kouraku' **new**	GEdr
- - 'Kuetsu' **new**	GEdr
- - f. ***magna***	CStu
- - 'Orihime' **new**	GEdr
- - 'Saichou' **new**	GEdr
- - 'Sansetsu' **new**	GEdr
- - 'Shihou' **new**	GEdr
- - 'Shikouden' **new**	GEdr SBla
- - 'Shiun' **new**	GEdr
- - 'Shoujyouno-homare' **new**	GEdr
- - 'Suien' **new**	GEdr
- - 'Tamamushi' **new**	GEdr
- - 'Touhou' **new**	GEdr
- - 'Touryoku' **new**	GEdr
- - 'Usugesyou' **new**	GEdr
- - 'Yuzuru' **new**	GEdr
- var. ***japonica*** x ***iyamatuta***	MAsh
- 'Landquart Marble'	NLAp
- large, pale blue-flowered	NLAp
- lilac-flowered	MTho NLAp SBla
- mottled leaf	CSsd ECho EHrv MTho
- Picos strain	SBla
- pink-flowered	CAby CLAP ECho EPot GCrs MAsh NLar NWCA SBla SIng SRot
* - var. ***pyrenaica***	EBee GBin GBuc LEdu MAsh NSum
* - - 'Apple Blossom'	CLAP GCrs MAsh NBir WAbe
- 'Pyrenean Marbles'	CLAP
- red-flowered	ECho NLAp WAbe
- Rene's form	WFar
- var. ***rubra***	CLAP ECho NLAp NMen NSla
§ - 'Rubra Plena' (d)	ECha EPot MAsh MHom NSla
- 'Tabby'	ECho
- violet-flowered	MAsh SBla
- white-flowered	CLAP ECho GCrs MAsh NLAp NMen NSla SBla SIng SRot WAbe WCru
§ ***transsilvanica*** ΥH4	CLAP CMea EBee ECho GAbr GBuc GCrs LAma LHop LRHS MAsh NMen SBla WAul WCot WCru WHal WTin
- 'Ada Scott'	GEdr WSHC
- 'Blue Eyes' **new**	CTca EBee EBrs ECho
- 'Blue Jewel'	CFir CLAP CTca EBee EBrs ECho GCrs GEdr NLar NMen SMeo WPnP
- blue-flowered	IBlr MAsh

- 'Buis'	CBod CLAP CTca EBee EBrs ECho EPot GCrs GEdr MAsh MHom NLAp NLar SPhx WPnP
- 'Eisvogel'	CLAP CTca EBrs ECho GEdr NMen
- 'Elison Spence' (d)	ECha GEdr IBlr MAsh SBla
- 'Lilacina'	ECha ECho GEdr MAsh NSla
- 'Loddon Blue'	IBlr
- pink-flowered	CLAP CTca EBrs MAsh SBla
- white-flowered	ECho MAsh
- 'Winterfreude'	MAsh
triloba	see *H. nobilis*
yamatutai	EBee EBrs MAsh

Heptacodium (*Caprifoliaceae*)

jasminoides	see *H. miconioides*
§ ***miconioides***	CAbP CBcs CGHE CMCN CPLG CPMA CPle CSpe CTri EBee ELan EPfP GQui IDee IMGH LRHS MBlu MBri MCCP MGos NEgg NPal SMad SPoG WBVN WCot WMou WPGP WPat WSHC

Heptapleurum see *Schefflera*

Heracleum (*Apiaceae*)

candicans	EBee EMan
- BWJ 8157	WCru
hemsleyanum new	EBee
lanatum 'Washington Limes' (v)	EBee EMan EPPr EWes
lehmannianum	CBct EBee EMan NBPC NSti WCot
moellendorfii	EBee
sphondylium 'Hogin the Limelight' new	CNat
- pink	CNat

Herbertia (*Iridaceae*)

§ ***lahue***	CDes CHHB CStu EBrs ECho LRHS WPGP

Hereroa (*Aizoaceae*)

odorata	EShb EWin

Hermannia (*Sterculiaceae*)

candicans	see *H. incana*
erodioides JCA 15523	CPBP
flammea	SPlb
§ ***incana***	CHal
pinnata	CPBP WAbe
pulchella	CPBP NWCA WAbe
stricta	CPBP NWCA WAbe

Hermodactylus (*Iridaceae*)

§ ***tuberosus***	CAby CArn CAvo CBgR CFFs CHar CSpe CStu CTri CWCL EBee EBrs ECGP ECha ECho LAma LRHS SBch SMeo SPhx STes WCot WTin
- BS 348	WCot
- MS 76	WCot
- MS 729	WCot
- MS 731	WCot
- MS 821	WCot
- MS 964	WCot
- PB	WCot

Herniaria (*Illecebraceae*)

glabra	CArn GPoy MSal NGHP SIde

Herpolirion (*Anthericaceae*)

novae-zealandiae	ECou

Hertia see *Othonna*

Hesperaloe (*Agavaceae*)

funifera	XPep
parviflora	CTrC EMan LEdu SChr WCot XPep

Hesperantha (*Iridaceae*)

§ ***baurii***	CLyd CPBP CStu EBee EBrs ECho GBuc GGar NLar NMen WAbe
buhrii	see *H. cucullata* 'Rubra'
coccinea	see *Schizostylis coccinea*
cucullata	EBee EBrs WHil
* - 'Rubra'	NWCA
grandiflora	ECho GGar
huttonii	EBee ECho EMan MWrn NBir NCGa NEgg
mossii	see *H. baurii*
woodii	CFir

Hesperis (*Brassicaceae*)

lutea	see *Sisymbrium luteum*
matronalis	More than 30 suppliers
- ***alba***	see *H. matronalis* var. *albiflora*
§ - var. ***albiflora***	More than 30 suppliers
- - 'Alba Plena' (d)	CAbP CCge CElw CMea CSpe EBee ECtt ELan EMan GBuc LRHS LSou MNrw NBir NCGa NCob WBrk WCot WCra WFar
- - 'Edith Harriet' (d/v)	LSou LTwo WTMC
- double-flowered (d)	NCob NGdn WBor
- 'Frogswell Doris'	CBow LDai
- 'Lilacina'	CMea SWat
- 'Lilacina Flore Pleno' (d)	CCge NBre
steveniana	SMrm

Heterolepis (*Asteraceae*)

aliena	GFai SGar

Heteromeles (*Rosaceae*)

arbutifolia	see *H. salicifolia*
§ ***salicifolia***	EShb

Heteromorpha (*Apiaceae*)

arborescens	SPlb

Heteropolygonatum (*Convallariaceae*)

Og 93054 new	SBla
roseolum	EBee

Heteropyxis (*Myrtaceae*)

natalensis	EShb

Heterotheca (*Asteraceae*)

jonesii	WLin
mariana	see *Chrysopsis mariana*
pumila	NWCA WLin
§ ***villosa***	SPet WCot
- 'Golden Sunshine'	EBee

Heuchera ✿ (*Saxifragaceae*)

'Amber Waves'PBR	More than 30 suppliers
§ ***americana***	CEnt ECha MRav NBir SMHy
- Dale's strain	CChe EBee IBal IFoB LFur MNrw NLar SPlb SPur SWvt WGor WHrl WMnd WPnP WTMC WWeb
- 'Harry Hay'	CDes EPPr MSte NDov WCot WPGP WSHC
- 'Ring of Fire'	CHar EBee EBla EGle ENot EPfP GKev IArd IBal LHop LRHS MDun MGos MSte NCGa NMyG NPri NSti SApp SDnm SPav SPla SPoG SWvt WCot WFar WPnP
'Amethyst Myst'	CMMP COlW EBee ENot EPfP ERas GSki LRHS MBNS MGos NCob NEgg NLar NPri SDnm SMeo SPav SPer SPoG SRkn SRot WFar WGor
'Baby's Breath'	ECho
'Beauty Colour'	More than 30 suppliers

	'Black Beauty'	CBcs CBct EBee EWll GCai LSou NLar NPri SRot STes WGor
	'Black Bird' **new**	SJoo
*	'Black Velvet'	CDWL EBee EPfP NBre
	'Blackbird' ♀H4	EBee MBNS SApp SDnm SPav SRkn SWvt WMnd
	'Blood Red'	NBhm SJoo
	'Blood Vein'	CBow MBNS MWrn NBre
	'Blushing Bride'	NRnb
	Bressingham hybrids	CWib ENot IFoB LBMP LRHS MLHP NBir NBlu NMir SEND SPer SPet SRms WFar WPer
	'Burgundy Frost' ♀H4	WCot
	'Can-can' ♀H4	More than 30 suppliers
	'Canyon Duet'	EBee LRHS MBNS MSte NOrc
	'Canyon Pink'	NRnb NSti
	'Cappuccino'	CBct EBee ECtt ELan IBal MBNS MBnl MLLN NBro NPri NRnb SDnm SPav SWal SWvt WCFE WFar WWeb
	'Caramel'	CBow CWCL CWGN EBee EGle EPfP ERou GKev LAst LFur LSou LTwo MBNS MBnl MBri MNrw NBPC NCob NGdn NSti SHBN SJoo SMad SPer SPoG WBrk WCot
	'Cascade Dawn'	EBee ECtt ENot GBuc IBal LAst LBMP LHop LRHS MRav MSte NBir NGdn NLar SPav SPer WBrk WCot WFar
	'Champagne Bubbles' PBR	EBee MBNS NPri SJoo SPoG WCot
	'Cherries Jubilee' PBR	CAbP CFir CHar EBee EBla GMaP LRHS MBNS MBnl MGos MLLN NCGa NEgg NPri SHar SPav WBor WBrk WGor
	'Chinook' **new**	GCai
	chlorantha	NBre
	'Chocolate Ruffles' PBR	More than 30 suppliers
	'Chocolate Veil' ♀H4	EPfP SHar WWeb
	'Cinnabar Silver' **new**	GCai SJoo
	'City Lights'	SJoo
	'Color Dream'	IBal SHBN
	coral bells	see *H. sanguinea*
	'Coral Bouquet'	EBee EMan GBri GQue LAst LSou MBNS MLLN WCot WCra
	'Coral Cloud'	MRav
	Crème Brûlée = 'Tnheu041' (Dolce Series)	CBcs CBct CSpe CWCL EBee ECtt EWll GCai LAst LBMP LHop LRHS LTwo MBri MGos MPop MWea NPri SDnm SJoo SPoG SRot STes SVil WGor
	'Crème Caramel' **new**	SHar
	'Crimson Curls'	LRHS SPoG SWvt
	'Crispy Curly'	MBNS MWrn NBre NRnb WRHF
	cylindrica	EBee EPfP MBNS MRav MSte NBre WPer
	- var. ***alpina***	NWCA
	- 'Brownfinch'	SMHy
§	- 'Greenfinch'	CFee EBee ECha EGle ELan EPfP ERou GKev IBal LBMP LRHS MLHP MRav NBir NOrc SPav SPer SPoG SWat WCAu WFar WMnd WPer
	'David'	CBow
	'Dennis Davidson'	see *H.* 'Huntsman'
	Ebony and Ivory = 'E and I' PBR	More than 30 suppliers
I	'Eco Magnififolia'	CLAP
	'Eden's Aurora'	EBee SHBN WMnd
	'Eden's Joy'	MBNS
	'Eden's Mystery'	ECtt NBPN WWeb
	elegans	WCot
	'Emperor's Cloak'	CEnt CHar CSsd EKen LEdu LSou MGol NDlv NLar SWal SWvt WMnd WMoo WRHF
	'Emperor's Cloak' green	CEnt
	'Fandango' **new**	GCai
	'Fantasia' **new**	CBow SJoo
	'Firebird'	NBir NVic
	Firefly	see *H.* 'Leuchtkäfer'
	'Fireworks' PBR ♀H4	CBow CHFP EBee EPPr ERas MBNS MLLN NCob NLar NPri SAga SHar SPer SPla WBor WBrk WCot WFar WGor
	'Florist's Choice'	CAbP EBee IBal MBNS MNFA NRnb SHar WCot
	'Frosted Violet' **new**	CBow
	'Ginger Ale' **new**	GCai SJoo
	glauca	see *H. americana*
	'Green Ivory'	LRHS MRav NSti SBch
	'Green Spice'	CBct EBee EWll GBin LHop LSou MBNS NPri SPav SPer SPoG SRot WGor WSpi
	'Greenfinch'	see *H. cylindrica* 'Greenfinch'
	grossulariifolia	MBNS WPer
	'Gypsy Dancer' (Dancer Series) **new**	ENot LBuc SJoo
	'Helen Dillon' (v)	CBow EBee EMan GCra IBal LAst MLLN NBir NPri SPer SPla SWvt WFar
	'Hercules' PBR	EBee ECtt EPfP MBNS
	hispida	MSte WPer
	'Hollywood'	CBow ENot GCai LBuc NBhm WCot
§	'Huntsman'	ECha ELan GBuc MBNS MRav WFar WMnd
	'Ibis'	EBee
	'Jubilee'	EBee
	Key Lime Pie = 'Tnheu042' (Dolce Series)	CBcs CBct CHVG EBee EWll GCai LAst LHop LRHS MBnl MBri MGos MWea NPri SDnm SJoo SPoG SRot STes SVil WGor
	'Lady in Red'	MBNS NBre
§	'Leuchtkäfer'	CEnt COlW CWat EBee ECtt GBuc GMaP IBal LAst LBMP LRHS MHer MRav MWat NBir NEgg NMir NOrc SPer SPlb SRms SWat WFar WMnd WMoo WPer WPtf
	Licorice = 'Tnheu044' (Dolce Series)	EBee ECtt EWll GCai LRHS MBri MGos MPop NPri SDnm SJoo SPoG SRot SVil WGor
	'Lime'	LSou
	'Lime Rickey' (Rainbow Series)	CBow EBee ENot GCai LBuc NBhm NLar SJoo
	'Little Tinker'	CHid LAst LSou MBNS NBir SPhx STes WBor WBrk
	'Magic Color' **new**	CBow
	'Magic Wand' PBR ♀H4	CAbP EBee LRHS MBNS SHar WCot
	'Marmalade'	EBee EKen ENot GCai LBuc SJoo
	'Mars'	EPfP MBNS NSti SPav WCot
	maxima	EMon
	'Mercury'	MBNS NMoo SPav WCot
	'Metallica'	LRav MWat MWrn NLar WMoo
	micans	see *H. rubescens*
	micrantha	EBee MLHP SRms
	- var. ***diversifolia***	EPla ETod LBMP LRHS SPer SPla
	Bressingham Bronze = 'Absi' PBR	WFar
N	- - 'Palace Purple'	More than 30 suppliers
	- 'Martha Roderick'	WCot
§	- 'Ruffles'	EPPr LRHS
	'Mini Mouse'	EWes
	'Mint Frost' PBR	EBee ECtt ELan ENot EPfP EWTr GAbr GKev GSki LAst LFur LHop LRHS MGos MLLN MRav NGdn NHol NPri NRnb SDnm SPav SPer SPoG SWvt WCot WFar
	'Molly Bush' ♀H4 **new**	WCot
	'Monet'	see *H. sanguinea* 'Monet'
	'Montrose Ruby'	NBre
	'Mother of Pearl'	ECtt
	'Neptune'	EPfP MBNS NMoo SPav

Neueste hybrids	LRav
'Northern Fire'	MBNS
'Oakington Jewel'	EBee ELan LRHS SHBN WSpi
'Obsidian'[PBR]	CHar CRez CSpe EBee EGle ENot GBri GCai IPot LFur LSRN MBnl MSte MWea NBPC NBPN NRnb NSti SHar SJoo SPer SPoG WCot WFar WPnP
'Painted Lady'	GBuc
* 'Palace Purple Select'	CTri CWat CWib IBal LAst SHBN SWvt
parishii NNS 93-384	NWCA
'Peach Flambé'	CBow EBee GCai MWea NBhm SJoo
'Peachy Keen'	NBhm WCot
'Peppermint Spice' (21st Century Collection Series) <u>**new**</u>	SJoo
'Persian Carpet'	CHEx EBee ECha ECtt EHrv GMaP GSki IBal LHop LRHS MDun MLLN NBir NGdn NPri NSti SDnm SWvt WBVN WCot WFar WPtf
'Petite Marbled Burgundy'	CHFP EBee ECtt EGle EWTr GBri GKev IBal LAst LTwo MSte NDov NGdn NLar NPri NSti SWvt WAul WCot WCra WFar
'Petite Pearl Fairy'	CAbP CBct CBow CMea EBee EGle ELan EMil GSki MSte NCGa NGdn NLar NSti SPla SWvt WCot WFar WGor WHoo
'Petite Pink Bouquet'	CBct EBee ECtt EMan GSki IBal MBNS NLar SJoo SPla WCot WWeb
'Petite Ruby Frills'	WWeb
'Pewter Moon'	CBcs EBee ECtt ELan EMil EPfP LAst LCro LRHS MGos MRav NBir SDnm SHBN SPer WBrE WBrk WFar WMnd WTin
'Pewter Veil'[PBR]	EBee EPfP LAst MBNS NCGa NPri SPer SPoG WFar WMnd
pilosissima	EBee NBre
'Pink Lipstick'	GCai
§ 'Pluie de Feu'	CFir EBee ECtt EPfP GBri MBNS MRav WSpi
'Plum Pudding'[PBR]	More than 30 suppliers
'Prince'	CDWL EBee EBrs EKen EPfP LSRN MBNS NBPN NMoo SApp SJoo SMer SPoG SRkn SWvt WPtf
'Prince of Silver'	IBal MBNS NMoo
pringlei	see *H. rubescens*
* x ***pruhonicana*** Doctor Sitar's hybrids	SRms
pubescens	EBee GBri
pulchella	CBow CPBP CSam CSsd EBee EDAr LRHS MBNS MHer SBch SRms
- JCA 9508	NMen
'Purple Mountain Majesty'	EBee MBNS NBPN NCGa SJoo WBrk WCot
'Purple Petticoats' 🏆H4	CBcs EBee EPfP GCai MDun MLHP MLLN NBre NCGa NCob NDlv NGdn NLar NPri SHar SPer SRot WFar WSpi
'Quick Silver'	EBla GSki MNFA NBir SJoo SMer SWvt WFar
'Quilter's Joy' 🏆H4	NBre
'Rachel'	CAbP CMea CSev CWCL EBee ECtt EGle ELan EPla GMaP IBal IFoB LRHS MRav MWat NBir NPri SPer SPla SPoG SRGP SWvt WAul WBrk WFar WTin
Rain of Fire	see *H.* 'Pluie de Feu'
'Raspberry Ice'	NRnb
'Raspberry Regal' 🏆H4	ECtt EGle MLLN MRav NBir NEgg NSti SJoo SWvt WAul WFar
'Red Spangles'	EPfP LRHS MBNS MWrn NBir
'Regina' 🏆H4	CAbP EBee ECGP ECtt ENot EPfP IBal LSRN MBNS NBro SHar SPoG SWvt WFar WWeb
richardsonii	MNrw
'Robert'	MBNS
Rosemary Bloom = 'Heuros'[PBR]	LRHS
'Royal Velvet'	WCot
§ ***rubescens***	CAbP ECho MTho NBro NMen WPer WThu
'Ruby Veil'	EBee SPoG
'Ruffles'	see *H. micrantha* 'Ruffles'
'Sancyl'	SRms
§ ***sanguinea***	CSBt LRHS MRav NBir WPer
- 'Alba' 🏆H4	EMon EWTr
- 'Geisha's Fan'	CBow COIW EBee EKen IBal NBhm NGdn SHar SPer SWvt
§ - 'Monet' (v)	CBow EBee ENot EPfP MBNS MLHP NSti SJoo
- var. ***pulchra***	CPBP
- 'Ruby Bells' <u>**new**</u>	NPri SGar SPoG
- 'Sioux Falls'	EWes NBre WPnP
§ - 'Snow Storm' (v)	CBow ELan EPfP MGos MRav SPer SPlb WFar WMnd
- 'Taff's Joy' (v)	CBow EMon EWes
- 'White Cloud' (v)	EBee NBre SRms WPer
'Saturn'	EBee MBNS NMoo NSti
'Scarlet Flame'	EBee
'Schneewittchen'	EPfP MRav
'Scintillation' 🏆H4	ECtt NBre SRms
'Shamrock'	GCai NBre
'Silver Indiana'[PBR]	EBee LSRN SPoG
'Silver Lode'	NRnb
'Silver Scrolls'[PBR]	More than 30 suppliers
'Silver Shadows'	ETod MBrN SJoo
'Silver Streak'	see x *Heucherella* 'Silver Streak'
'Snow Storm'	see *H. sanguinea* 'Snow Storm'
'Snowfire' (v) <u>**new**</u>	GCai
'Sparkling Burgundy' <u>**new**</u>	GCai SJoo
'Starry Night'	GCai SHar
'Stormy Seas'	More than 30 suppliers
'Strawberries and Cream' (v)	EHrv WHer
'Strawberry Candy'[PBR]	CBow EBee GCai LAst LSou MBri MWea NCGa NEgg NPri SPer SPoG SRkn
'Strawberry Swirl'	CHar EBee EBla ECtt EWTr GMaP LAst MLLN MRav MSte NBir NDov NLar NPri NSti SPoG SWat SWvt WCAu WCot WFar WOVN WPtf
'Swirling Fantasy'[PBR]	CBow EPfP ERou EShb NMoo SJoo
'Tango' <u>**new**</u>	GCai
'Van Gogh'	MBNS SJoo SPoG
'Veil of Passion'[PBR]	NBre SHar
'Velvet Night'	CBow EBee EMan ENot EPfP EWsh IBal LRHS MBNS NBPC NBPN NBir NBre NRnb SHar SJoo SPoG WFar WMnd WPtf
'Venus'	EBrs ECtt EMan ERou GAbr LFur LSou MBNS MWgw NGdn NMRc SHBN SJoo SPur WBrE WBrk WCot WHoo WWlt
'Vesuvius'[PBR]	NRnb
villosa	ECha MRav
- 'Autumn Bride'	EBee EWTr LAst WRHF
- 'Brownies' <u>**new**</u>	MBNS
- var. ***macrorhiza***	EShb NBre WMnd WPnP
- 'Royal Red'	ECha GBuc WSpi
'White Marble'	SHar
'White Spires'	SHar
'Winter Red'	EBee LAst MBNS SPur WCAu
'Yeti'	WPnP
'Zabelliana'	GBri

x *Heucherella* (*Saxifragaceae*)

alba 'Bridget Bloom'	EBee EBla EBrs ECGP ECha ELan GMaP LBMP MRav NOrc NPri SRms WCAu WFar WHoo
§ - 'Rosalie'	CBow EBla ECha GKev LRHS MBNS MBri MRav MSte NBir NBro NPro SPlb WBrk WFar WMoo
'Birthday Cake' **new**	SJoo
'Burnished Bronze' PBR	CBct CBow CHVG EBee EBla GCai LSou MLLN MSte NBro NCGa NEgg NGdn NLar SDnm SHar SPav SPoG SRot STes SWvt WCot WFar
'Chocolate Lace'	EBee EKen MLLN NRnb SHar SJoo
'Cinnamon Bear'	EBee SJoo
'Dayglow Pink' PBR	CBct EBla EPPr EShb GCai GMaP MBri NBro NCGa NEgg SHar SRkn SRot WFar WGor
Gold Strike = 'Hertn041'	CBow EWll GCai SJoo SVil WGor
'Heart of Darkness'	NRnb
'Kimono' PBR ♀H4	More than 30 suppliers
'Ninja' PBR	see *Tiarella* 'Ninja'
'Party Time' **new**	SJoo
'Pink Frost'	EBla
Pink Whispers = 'Hertn042'	CBow LFur SJoo SVil
'Quicksilver'	CBcs CBct EBee EBla EHrv EMil GBuc GMaP LAst MSte NGdn NPri NSti SPer SWvt WCAu WCot WFar
'Ring of Fire'	WFar
§ 'Silver Streak'	CBow EBee EBla EPPr GSki LFur MSte MWgw NBro NCGa SJoo SPla SPoG SWvt WFar WMoo
'Stoplight'	CBow CSpe ECGP EGle ENot GCai LFur LSou MBNS MBnl NBhm NCGa NGdn SJoo SPer SPoG WCot WCra
'Sunspot' (v)	EKen EMil ENot EPfP GCai LRHS MGos NMyG NSti SHar SJoo SPoG WBor WCot
tiarelloides ♀H4	EPfP LRHS WMnd
§ 'Viking Ship' PBR	More than 30 suppliers

Hexastylis see *Asarum*

Hibanobambusa (*Poaceae*)

'Kimmei'	EBee
tranquillans	CMCo EBee EFul EPla MBrN MMoz MMuc MWht SDry WPGP
- 'Shiroshima' (v) ♀H4	CAbb CDTJ CDoC CGHE CPMA EAmu EBee ENBC EPla ERod LPal MAsh MAvo MBrN MCCP MMoz MWht NMoo NPal NVic SApp SDry WNor WPGP

Hibbertia (*Dilleniaceae*)

aspera	CBcs CCCN CPLG CPle CRHN EBee WFar WSHC
§ ***cuneiformis***	MAsh
pedunculata	ECou
procumbens	ITim WAbe
§ ***scandens*** ♀H1	CBcs CCCN CHEx CHll CRHN ECou ELan SOWG
stricta	ECou
tetrandra	see *H. cuneiformis*
* ***venustula***	ECou
volubilis	see *H. scandens*

Hibiscus ✿ (*Malvaceae*)

acetosella 'Red Shield'	CSpe EShb LSou
cannabinus	SIde
coccineus	CPLG EShb MSte SOWG
fallax	CHll
hamabo	ELan
huegelii	see *Alyogyne huegelii*
leopoldii	SPer SRms
manihot	see *Abelmoschus manihot*
'Moesiana'	MBri
moscheutos	CArn CFir CHEx MSte
- 'Galaxy'	EShb WHil
- 'Pyrenees Pink' **new**	EMil GBin
mutabilis	SOWG
paramutabilis	EWes SMad
rosa-sinensis	EBak EShb LRHS MBri SOWG
- 'All Aglow'	SOWG
- 'Bimbo'	SOWG
- 'Casablanca'	MBri
- 'Cockatoo'	SOWG
- 'Cooperi' (v) ♀H1	CHal SOWG
- Full Moon = 'Monoon' (d)	SOWG
- 'Gina Marie'	SOWG
- 'Great White'	SOWG
- 'Hawaiian Sunset'	SOWG
- 'Holiday'	MBri
- 'Jewel of India'	SOWG
- 'Kardinal'	MBri
- 'Kim Ellen'	SOWG
- 'Kinchen's Yellow'	SOWG
- 'Koeniger'	MBri
- 'Lady Flo'	SOWG
- 'Lemon Chiffon' (d)	SOWG
- 'Molly Cummings'	SOWG
- 'Mrs Andreasen'	SOWG
- 'Norman Lee'	SOWG
- 'Pink Mist'	SOWG
- 'Sprinkle Rain'	SOWG
- 'Tarantella'	SOWG
- 'Ten Thirty Seven'	SOWG
- 'Thelma Bennell'	SOWG
- 'Tivoli'	MBri
- 'Weekend'	SOWG
- 'Wings Away'	SOWG
sabdariffa	MSal
schizopetalus ♀H1	MJnS SOWG
sinosyriacus	EPfP
- 'Lilac Queen'	LRHS SPoG WPGP
- 'Ruby Glow'	MGos WPGP
syriacus	MNHC SPet WFar WNor
- 'Admiral Dewey' (d)	MGos SPla
- 'Aphrodite'	CPMA EBee LRHS MRav
- 'Ardens' (d)	CEnd CSBt EMui EPfP LAst MAsh MGos NLar SPer
- Blue Bird	see *H. syriacus* 'Oiseau Bleu'
- 'Boule de Feu' (d)	ELan SEND
- 'Bredon Springs' ♀H4	ENot MRav
- 'Caeruleus Plenus' (d)	MGos
- 'China Chiffon'	ENot
- 'Coelestis'	MGos SPer
- 'Diana' ♀H4	EBee EMil ENot EPfP EQua LRHS MGos MRav NPri SLon
- 'Dorothy Crane'	CEnd LRHS MAsh MGos SBra
- 'Duc de Brabant' (d)	CSBt EBee EMui EPfP SHBN SPer
- 'Elegantissimus'	see *H. syriacus* 'Lady Stanley'
- 'Freedom' **new**	EMil
- 'Hamabo' ♀H4	CDul CSBt CTri EBee ECho EMil ENot EPfP LAst LCro LPan LRHS LSRN MAsh MBri MGos MWat NLar SCoo SHBN SLim SPer SPla SPoG SWvt WFar
- 'Helene'	ELan ENot EQua LRHS LSRN MAsh MBlu MRav
- 'Jeanne d'Arc' (d)	EMil SLon
§ - 'Lady Stanley' (d)	EBee ECho LRHS MAsh MGan SCoo SPer
- Lavender Chiffon = 'Notwoodone' PBR ♀H4	EBee ELan EMil ENot EPfP EWes LRHS MGos NPri SCoo SPer SPoG
- 'Lenny' ♀H4	ENot MGos
- 'Leopoldii'	EQua NBlu
- 'Marina'	EMui EPfP MRav

- 'Meehanii' misapplied — see *H. syriacus* 'Purpureus Variegatus'
- 'Meehanii' (v) ♀H4 — CDul CEnd CSBt EMil ENot EPfP LRHS MAsh MBri MGos SCoo SPer SPla SPoG
- 'Monstrosus' — EBee NLar
§ - 'Oiseau Bleu' ♀H4 — More than 30 suppliers
- Pink Giant = 'Flogi' — CDul EBee ECho ELan EPfP EQua LRHS MBri MGos MWat SLon SPer
§ - 'Purpureus Variegatus' (v) — CSBt EMil LAst MGos SPoG
- 'Red Heart' ♀H4 — CEnd CSBt CTri EBee ECho ELan EPfP LAst LRHS MAsh MBri MCCP NBlu NLar NPri SBra SPer SPla SPoG SRms SWvt WCFE
- Rosalbane = 'Minrosa' — EBee
- 'Roseus Plenus' (d) — ECho
- Russian Violet = 'Floru' — CBcs CEnd EBee ELan EPfP LRHS MGos
- 'Sanchon Yo' — ENot EPfP
- 'Souvenir de Charles Breton' new — EMil
- 'Speciosus' — EMui SLon SPer
- 'Totus Albus' — CSBt ECho SPoG
- 'Variegatus' — see *H. syriacus* 'Purpureus Variegatus'
- White Chiffon = 'Notwoodtwo'PBR ♀H4 — EBee ELan EMil ENot EPfP EWes LRHS LSRN MGos MRav SCoo SPer SPoG
- 'William R. Smith' ♀H4 — EBee ELan LAst MAsh MSwo SHBN SLon SPer
- 'Woodbridge' ♀H4 — More than 30 suppliers

trionum — CSpe SBch WKif
- 'Sunny Day' — ELan

hickory, shagbark see *Carya ovata*

Hieracium (*Asteraceae*)

aurantiacum — see *Pilosella aurantiaca*
brunneocroceum — see *Pilosella aurantiaca* subsp. *carpathicola*
§ ***glaucum*** — WEas
§ ***lanatum*** — CSpe ECho MDKP NBir WEas WRos
maculatum — see *H. spilophaeum*
pilosella — see *Pilosella officinarum*
praecox — see *H. glaucum*
scullyi — EPPr
§ ***spilophaeum*** — EMar GGar LRHS NBid NPer WOut WPer WRos
- 'Leopard' — CEnt CSsd EBee EMan SGar WWeb
umbellatum — WOut
villosum — CSpe EBee ECho GGar LRHS MDun MNFA NBro WHer WLin WRos
waldsteinii — MDKP
welwitschii — see *H. lanatum*

Hierochloe (*Poaceae*)

occidentalis — CBig
odorata — CBig ELau GAbr GFor GPoy MGol XIsg

Hieronymiella (*Amaryllidaceae*)

aurea RCB/Arg M-4 — WCot

hildaberry see *Rubus* 'Hildaberry'

Himalayacalamus (*Poaceae*)

asper — CDTJ CGHE EBee EPla ERod WPGP
§ ***falconeri*** — CBrm CEnt EFul EPfP EPla MAsh MMoz SDix WPGP
§ - 'Damarapa' — CDTJ EPla MMoz WDyG
§ ***hookerianus*** — CAbb EPla
porcatus — CGHE WPGP

Himantoglossum (*Orchidaceae*)

hircinum — SHdy

x *Hippeasprekelia* (*Amaryllidaceae*)

'Red Beauty' — CFwr EBrs

Hippeastrum (*Amaryllidaceae*)

BC&W 5154 — CStu
x ***acramannii*** — WCot
advenum — see *Rhodophiala advena*
'Amoretta' new — LRHS
'Amputo' — LRHS
'Apple Blossom' — EBrs LAma LRHS MBri SGar
bifidum — see *Rhodophiala bifida*
'Blossom Peacock' (d) — EBrs
'Calimero' — EBrs
'Charisma' — EBrs
'Chico' — LRHS
'Christmas Gift' — EBrs
'Clown' — EBrs
'Double Record' (d) — EBrs
'Elvas' — EBrs
'Emerald' — LRHS
'Fairytale' — EBrs MBri
gracile 'Pamela' — CStu
'Grandeur' — LRHS
'Hercules' — LRHS MBri
'Inca' — LAma
'Jewel' (d) — EBrs MBri
'Jungle Star' — EBrs
'La Paz' new — LRHS
'Lady Jane' — LRHS MBri
'Lemon Lime' — EBrs LAma
'Lima' LAma — LRHS
'Lovely Garden' new — LAma
'Ludwig Dazzler' new — LRHS
'Mary Lou' (d) — EBrs
'Merengue' — EBrs
'Minerva' new — LRHS
'Mount Blanc' new — LRHS
papilio ♀H1 — CTca IHer LAma
* - 'Butterfly' — LRHS MMHG
'Papillon' — LCro
'Philadelphia' (d) — EBrs LRHS
'Picotee' — EBrs LAma
'Pink Floyd' — EBrs
'Pink Star' — EBrs
'Red Lion' — EBrs LRHS
'Red Peacock' (d) — LRHS
'Roma' new — LRHS
'Ruby Meyer' — LCro LRHS
* 'San Antonio Rose' — CDes WCot
'Scarlet Baby' new — LRHS
'Solomon' — EBrs
striatum — WCot
stylosum — EBrs
'Toughie' — CDes CSpe EMan WCot WPGP
'Unique' (d) — EBrs
'Vera' — LRHS
vittatum — CBgR EBrs
'White Dazzler' — LAma
'White Peacock' (d) new — LRHS
'Yellow Goddess' — EBrs EShb

Hippocrepis (*Papilionaceae*)

§ ***comosa*** — CRWN XPep
§ ***emerus*** — CBgR CCCN CMHG CPLG EBee ELan EPfP LAst LHop MBri MGos NLar SPoG STre WRHF WSHC WSpi XPep

Hippolytia (*Asteraceae*)

§ ***herderi*** — EMan EOHP

Hippophae (*Elaeagnaceae*)

rhamnoides 𝕐H4	CArn CBcs CBrm CCVT CDul CLnd CRWN CSBt CTri EBee ECrN ELan EMac EPfP LBuc MBar MBlu MCoo NWea SPlb WFar WHCG WMou XPep
– 'Askola' (f)	MGos
– 'Frugna' (f)	CAgr
– 'Hergo' (f)	CAgr MBri MCoo
– 'Hikal Dafo' (m)	CAgr
– 'Hikul' new	EMil
– 'Juliet' (f)	CAgr
– 'Leikora' (f)	CAgr ELan MBlu MCoo MGos NLar SPer
– 'Matt' (m) new	MCoo
– 'Pollmix' (m)	CAgr ELan MBlu MBri MGos NLar SPer
– 'Romeo' (m)	CAgr
salicifolia	CAgr
– GWJ 9221	WCru

Hippuris (*Hippuridaceae*)

vulgaris	CBen EHon EMFW NPer WFar WMAq

Hirpicium (*Asteraceae*)

armerioides	NWCA

Histiopteris (*Dennstaedtiaceae*)

incisa	WRic

Hoheria ✿ (*Malvaceae*)

§ ***angustifolia***	CBcs CTho ECou EPfP SSpi
'Borde Hill'	CPMA CWsd ECou EPfP LRHS SSpi SSta WHCG WPat
'County Park' new	ECou
glabrata	CBcs CWsd ECou EPfP GGar NPal WPGP
– 'Silver Stars'	EPfP
'Glory of Amlwch' 𝕐H3	CAbb CDul CPMA CSam CTho CWsd ECou EPfP MRav SSpi WKif WPGP WSpi
'Hill House'	CHll
'Holbrook'	CSam
§ ***lyallii*** 𝕐H4	CBcs CCCN CDoC CPLG ECou ELan EPfP IDee LRHS LSRN SHBN SSpi SSta WBod WBor
– 'Chalk Hills' new	ECou
– 'Swale Stream' new	ECou
microphylla	see *H. angustifolia*
populnea	CBcs CCCN SGar
– 'Alba Variegata' (v)	CBcs CDoC CTrC ECou SMad
– 'Moonlight'	CDoC SPoG
– 'Purple Shadow' new	ECou
– 'Sunshine' (v)	CDoC SPoG SSta
– 'Variegata' new	ECou
'Purple Delta'	ECou
sexstylosa	CAbb CDoC CDul CHEx CHid CMHG CTri EBee ECou ELan EPfP IMGH ISea LHop LRHS MDun MGos SPur SSta SWvt WGer
– 'Pendula'	CBcs
– 'Stardust' 𝕐H4	More than 30 suppliers
* – 'Sunburst'	NEgg

Holarrhena (*Apocynaceae*)

pubescens	CCCN

Holboellia (*Lardizabalaceae*)

angustifolia	MBri NLar WCru
chapaensis HWJ 1023	WCru
coriacea	CBcs CHEx CHll CSam EBee EPfP LEdu LRHS MDun MGos MRav NLar SAPC SArc SBra SOWG SPer SSta WCru
– purple-flowered	WCru
fargesii DJHC 506	WCru
grandiflora B&SWJ 8223	WCru
– HWJ 1024	WCru
latifolia	CBcs CBrm CHEx CRHN CSBt CSam CTrG CTri EBee ELan EPfP ERea LRHS MTPN NLar SAPC SArc SBra SEND SLPl SLim SOWG SPer SPoG WCFE WFar WPGP
– HWJK 2014	WCru
– SF 95134	ISea

Holcus (*Poaceae*)

lanatus	WSFF
mollis 'Albovariegatus' (v)	CWCL EAlp EBee ECha ELan EPPr EPfP GMaP GSki LRHS MBar NBid NBro NGdn NHol NPer NSti SMer SPer SPlb SPoG STre WEas WFar WLin WMoo WPer WTin XIsg
– 'Jackdaw's Cream' (v) new	EPPr
– 'White Fog' (v)	CChe EBee EHul EPPr LLWG MBlu NHol SApp WFar

Holmskioldia (*Verbenaceae*)

sanguinea	EShb

Holodiscus (*Rosaceae*)

discolor	CBcs CDul CPle EBee ELan EPfP EWes GQui IDee LRHS MBlu MRav NBlu NSti SHBN SLon SMad SPer SPlb SPoG SSpi SSta WBVN WHCG
– var. ***ariifolius***	EPfP EWTr
dumosus	NLar WPGP

Homalocladium (*Polygonaceae*)

§ ***platycladum***	CHal

Homeria (*Iridaceae*)

breyniana	see *H. collina*
– var. ***aurantiaca***	see *H. flaccida*
§ ***collina***	ECho ERos
§ ***flaccida***	EBrs ECho
ochroleuca	EBrs ECho

Homoglossum see *Gladiolus*

Hoodia (*Asclepiadaceae*)

flava new	LToo

Hordeum (*Poaceae*)

brachyantherum	CBig
chilense	EBee
jubatum	CBig CBod CHrt CKno CSpe CWCL CWib EAlp EGoo EPla EWes LHop MBnl MWat NChi NDov NGdn NHol SEND SIng SPoG WRos XIsg

Horkeliella (*Rosaceae*)

purpurascens NNS 98-323	WCot

Horminum (*Lamiaceae*)

pyrenaicum	EBee ECho EMan GAbr GKev SBla SRms WFar WMoo WOut WPer WPtf WTin
– pale blue	MDKP MSte

horseradish see *Armoracia rusticana*

Hosta ✿ (*Hostaceae*)

AGSJ 302	CDes
'A Many-Splendored Thing'	IBal
'Abba Dabba Do' (v)	EGol EMic EPGN LBuc NMyG SApp

'Abba Showtime' **new**	IBal
'Abby' (v)	EGol EMic EPGN IBal MBNS NMyG SApp
'Abiqua Ariel'	EMic SApp
'Abiqua Blue Crinkles'	EMic NBir
'Abiqua Blue Edger' **new**	EMic
'Abiqua Drinking Gourd'	EBee EGol EMic EPGN GBin GSki IBal MHom MIDC NMyG SApp
'Abiqua Ground Cover'	EGol
'Abiqua Moonbeam' (v)	CFir EMic EPGN IBal MSwo NGdn NMyG SApp
'Abiqua Recluse'	EGol SApp
'Abiqua Trumpet'	EGol IBal NGdn NLar NMyG SApp
aequinoctiiantha	EGol
albomarginata	see *H. sieboldii* 'Paxton's Original'
§ 'Albomarginata' (*fortunei*) (v)	CBcs CWib EBee ECho EGol EMic EQua GSki MBar MNrw NBir NMyG SHBN SPoG SWvt WBrE
'Alex Summers'	EBee EMic IBal NBhm
'Allan P. McConnell' (v)	EGol EMic EPGN GCra WHal WIvy
'Allegan Fog' (v)	EGol EMic IBal
'Alligator Shoes' (v)	EGol IBal
'Alpine Aire'	EMic
'Alvatine Taylor' (v)	EGol EMic
'Amanuma'	EGol EMic IBal MHom
'Amber Maiden' (v)	EGol
'Amber Tiara'	EMic
'American Dream' (v)	EBee EGol EMic EPGN IBal NMyG
'American Halo'	EMic IBal MIDC NBPC NLar
'American Sweetheart'	IBal
'Amy Elizabeth' (v)	EGol EMic IBal
'Angel Feathers' (v)	EGol
'Ann Kulpa' (v)	EMic EPGN IBal NMyG
'Anne' (v)	EGol EMic IBal
'Anne Arett' (*sieboldii*) (v)	EPGN
'Antioch' (*fortunei*) (v)	ECho EGol EMic GQue IBal MIDC MRav MSte NMyG NRnb WFar
'Aoki' (*fortunei*)	EMic EPGN NHol
'Aphrodite' (*plantaginea*) (d)	CFir EBee EGol EHrv EMic IBal LSou MBNS MHom MSte NCGa NCob NGdn NLar NMoo SApp SPer SPoG WCot WGwG
'Apollo'	NNor
'Apple Court'	SApp
'Apple Green'	EMic IBal
'Apple Pie'	SApp
'Aqua Velva'	EGol
'Archangel'	EGol
'Argentea Variegata' (*undulata*)	see *H. undulata* var. *undulata*
'Aristocrat' (Tardiana Group) (v)	EGol EMic EPGN IBal NMyG SApp
'Asian Beauty' **new**	EGol
'Aspen Gold' (*tokudama* hybrid)	SApp
'August Beauty'	EMic
'August Moon'	More than 30 suppliers
aureafolia	see *H.* 'Starker Yellow Leaf'
'Aureoalba' (*fortunei*)	see *H.* 'Spinners'
'Aureomaculata' (*fortunei*)	see *H. fortunei* var. *albopicta*
* 'Aureomarginata' ambig. (v)	CPrp GAbr GKev GSki NEgg
'Aureomarginata' (*montana*) (v)	CSBt EGol ELan EMic EPGN EWsh GMaP IBal MIDC NEgg NGdn NHol NLar NMyG SPla WFar WTin
§ 'Aureomarginata' (*ventricosa*) (v) ♀H4	ECha EGol EHon EMic EPfP IBal LRHS MBri MIDC MWat MWgw NGdn NVic SApp WFar WTin
'Aureostriata' (*tardiva*)	see *H.* 'Inaho'
'Aurora Borealis' (*sieboldiana*) (v)	EGol
'Austin Dickinson' (v)	EGol EMic IBal LBuc
'Azure Snow'	EGol
'Babbling Brook'	EGol
'Baby Bunting'	EGol EMic EPGN IBal MBNS MIDC NBro NLar NPro
'Ballerina'	EGol
'Banana Boat' (v)	EGol IBal
'Band of Gold' **new**	IBal
'Banyai's Dancing Girl'	EGol EMic
'Barbara Ann' (v)	EMic EPGN IBal MBri
'Barbara White'	EGol IBal
'Bea's Colossus'	SApp
'Beauty Little Blue' **new**	EGol
'Beauty Substance'	EGle EGol EMic EPGN NMyG
'Bedford Blue' **new**	IBal
bella	see *H. fortunei* var. *obscura*
'Bennie McRae'	EGol
'Betcher's Blue'	EGol
'Betsy King'	EBee EGol MRav NHol NMyG
'Bette Davis Eyes'	EGol
'Betty'	EGol IBal
'Bianca'	SApp
'Big Boy' (*montana*)	EGol NNor
'Big Daddy' (*sieboldiana* hybrid) (v)	More than 30 suppliers
'Big Mama'	CDWL EGol IBal LRHS MBNS NBhm NLar
'Bigfoot'	EGol
'Bill Brinka' (v)	EGol EMic
'Bill Dress's Blue'	IBal
'Birchwood Blue'	EGol
'Birchwood Elegance'	SApp
§ 'Birchwood Parky's Gold'	CMHG EBee EGol EMic EPfP GMaP LBMP LRHS MBNS MIDC NCob NGdn NHol NOak SApp SHBN SMrm
'Birchwood Ruffled Queen'	EGol EMic
'Bitsy Gold'	EGol IBal
'Bitsy Green'	EGol
'Black Beauty'	EGol EPGN
'Black Hills'	CWib EGol IBal MBNS NMyG
'Blackfoot'	EGol
'Blaue Venus'	EGol
'Blazing Saddles' **new**	IBal MIDC
'Blonde Elf'	EGol EMic IBal MBNS NEgg NGdn NMyG SApp
'Blue Angel' misapplied	see *H. sieboldiana* var. *elegans*
'Blue Angel' (*sieboldiana*) ♀H4	More than 30 suppliers
'Blue Arrow'	EGol EPGN SApp
'Blue Beard'	IBal
'Blue Belle' (Tardiana Group)	EGol EMic MSte NGdn NPro WHoo WTin
'Blue Blazes'	LRHS
'Blue Blush' (Tardiana Group)	EGol NGdn WTMC
'Blue Boy'	CWsd EGol EMic EWes NHol NMyG
'Blue Cadet'	CBcs ECho EGol EMic EMil GEdr GSki IBal IFoB LAst MBar MLHP NBir NGdn NLar NMyG NOak NRnb SApp SBod SHBN SPoG WCAu WFar WMnd
'Blue Canoe'	IBal SApp
'Blue Chip'	EMic EPGN IBal
'Blue Clown'	IBal
'Blue Cup' (*sieboldiana*)	MRav
'Blue Danube' (Tardiana Group)	EGol EMic MHom
'Blue Diamond' (Tardiana Group)	EGol EMic EPGN IBal WFar
'Blue Dimples' (Tardiana Group)	EGol EMic IBal LRHS MBNS NMoo
'Blue Edger'	CTca NBir
'Blue Eyes' **new**	IBal
'Blue Flame' **new**	IBal

'Blue Heart' (*sieboldiana*)	EMic
'Blue Ice'(Tardiana Group)	EGol EPGN IBal
'Blue Impression'	EMic
'Blue Jay' (Tardiana Group)	EGol IBal
'Blue Lady'	EMic
'Blue Mammoth' (*sieboldiana*)	EGol EMic LRHS
'Blue Monday'	EMic
'Blue Moon' (Tardiana Group)	EGol EMic EPGN EPfP IBal MBNS MHom NGdn NHol WAul
'Blue Mountains'	LBuc
'Blue Mouse Ears'	EGol EMic EPGN IBal
'Blue Seer' (*sieboldiana*)	EGol EMic IBal
'Blue Shadows' (*tokudama*) (v)	EPGN IBal LRHS MIDC MWgw SApp SHBN
'Blue Skies'(Tardiana Group)	EGol IBal MHom SApp
'Blue Umbrellas' (*sieboldiana* hybrid)	CDWL ECho EGol ELan EMic EPGN EPfP GSki IBal LRHS MHom MIDC MPop NGdn NHol NLar NMyG
'Blue Veil' **new**	EGol
'Blue Vision'	EMic EPGN LRHS
'Blue Wedgwood' (Tardiana Group)	CPrp EBee ECho EGol ELan EMic GSki IBal LAst LCro MIDC NGdn NHol NMyG SApp SPla SPoG WHil WTMC
'Blütenwunder'	SApp
'Bob Olson' (v) **new**	EGol IBal
'Bobbie Sue' (v)	EGol
'Bold Edger' (v)	EGol
'Bold Ribbons' (v)	EGol EMic GAbr WTin
'Bold Ruffles' (*sieboldiana*)	EGol LRHS SApp
'Bolt out of the Blue' **new**	EMic IBal
'Bonanza'	EMic
'Border Bandit' (v)	EGol
'Borwick Beauty' (*sieboldiana*) (v)	EMic NGdn NLar NMyG
'Bountiful'	EGol EMic
'Bouquet'	EGol
'Bread Crumbs' **new**	IBal
'Brenda's Beauty' (v)	EGol
'Bressingham Blue'	CDWL CPrp EBee ECho ECtt EGol IBal LRHS MIDC MRav MWat NMyG SPoG SWvt WCAu WFar WMnd WTMC
'Brigadier'	EGol
'Bright Glow' (Tardiana Group)	EGol
'Bright Lights' (*tokudama*) (v)	ECho EGol EMic EPGN IBal LAst NGdn NMyG WTMC
'Brim Cup' (v)	EBee EGol EMic EPGN IBal LAst MBNS MBri MIDC NBro NGdn NMyG NOrc NRnb SApp SPer
'Brooke'	EGol EMic IBal NMyG
'Brother Ronald' (Tardiana Group)	EGol EMic IBal LRHS SApp
'Bruce's Blue'	EGol GSki
'Buckshaw Blue'	EGol EPGN MDKP NBir NGdn NPro WTMC
'Bunchoko'	IBal
'Burke's Dwarf'	IBal
'Butter Rim' (*sieboldii*) (v)	EGol
'Cadillac' (v)	MIDC
'Caliban'	SApp
'Calypso' (v)	EGol EMic EPGN IBal LBuc
'Camelot'(Tardiana Group)	EGol EMic IBal LRHS NGdn
'Cameo' **new**	EMic IBal
'Canadian Blue'	EMic WTMC
'Candy Hearts'	CMHG CSam CWsd EGol EMic EPGN MHom MWat WTin
capitata B&SWJ 588	WCru
'Captain Kirk' (v)	EBee IBal NMyG
caput-avis	see *H. kikutii* var. *caput-avis*
'Carder Blue' **new**	EMic

'Carnival' (v)	EGol EMic EPGN IBal MIDC NBPC NCGa NEgg
'Carol' (*fortunei*) (v)	EGol EMic EWsh IBal LAst MBNS MPop MSte NEgg NMyG NNor SApp WHal
'Carolina Blue'	IBal
'Carousel' (v)	EGol
'Carrie Ann'	see *H.* 'Carrie'
§ 'Carrie' (*sieboldii*) (v)	EGol
'Cascades' (v)	EGol EMic EPGN IBal
'Cat's Eyes' (v)	EGol EMic EPGN IBal
'Celebration' (v)	EGol ELan EMic EPGN LRHS MDKP WHal
'Celestial' **new**	IBal
'Center of Attention'	EMic IBal
'Challenger'	EMic
'Change of Tradition' (*lancifolia*) (v)	EMic
'Chantilly Lace' (v)	EGol EMic IBal NMyG SApp WTin
'Chartreuse Waves'	EGol
'Chartreuse Wiggles' (*sieboldii*)	IBal LRHS NHar
'Cheatin Heart'	EGol IBal
'Chelsea Babe' (*fortunei*) (v)	EGol IBal
'Cherish'	EGol EMic IBal
'Cherry Berry' (v)	CMHG CRez EGol EMic EPGN IBal MBNS MIDC MWgw NBro NCob NEgg NGdn NLar NMyG NPro NRnb SApp SRGP SVil WAul WBor
'Cherub' (v)	EGol
* 'China' (*plantaginea*)	EMic
'Chinese Sunrise' (v)	CWsd EGol EMic EPGN IBal LBuc MBNS MHom NHol NMyG WHal WHil
'Chiquita'	EGol
§ 'Chôkô Nishik' (*montana*) (v)	EGle EGol EMic EPGN EQua EWsh IBal MIDC NGdn NMyG NNor SApp SPoG
'Choo Choo Train' **new**	EGol
'Christmas Candy'	EMic EPGN GAbr IBal NBhm NCob
'Christmas Pageant' (v) **new**	IBal
'Christmas Tree' (v)	CMMP ECho EGle EGol EMic EPGN GBri IBal IFoB IPot LRHS MIDC NEgg NGdn NMyG NRnb SApp SVil WTMC
'Cinnamon Sticks'	IBal
'Citation' (v)	EGol
'City Lights'	EGol EMic NEgg
clausa var. ***normalis***	EGol GQui LRHS NBir NGdn NLar NMyG
'Cliffords Forest Fire' **new**	EMic
'Climas' **new**	IBal
'Cody'	IBal
'Collector's Banner' **new**	EGol
'Collector's Choice'	EGol
'Color Glory' (v)	CBgR CDWL EGle EGol EMic EPGN GAbr IBal LAst NBPC NCGa NEgg NGdn NLar NMyG SApp SPer WAul WTMC
'Colossal'	EGol EMic
'Columbus Circle' (v)	EGol
'Cookie Crumbs' (v)	IBal
'Coquette' (v)	EGol EMic
'Corkscrew'	IBal
'Corona' (v)	EMic
'Cotillion' (v)	EGol IBal SApp
'County Park'	EGol EMic IBal
'Cracker Crumbs' (v)	EGol EMic EPGN IBal
'Cream Cheese' (v)	EGol
'Cream Delight' (*undulata*)	see ***H. undulata*** var. ***undulata***
'Crepe Soul' (v)	EGol IBal
'Crepe Suzette' (v)	EGol EPGN LRHS
'Crested Reef'	EGol EMic NMyG

	'Crested Surf' (v)	EGol EMic EPGN IBal
	'Crinoline Petticoats' **new**	EGol
§	***crispula*** (v) Υ^{H4}	EGol EHon EMic EPfP MBar MCot MHom MRav NChi NCob NMyG SHBN
	'Crown Jewel' (v)	EPGN
	'Crown Prince' (v)	EGol EPGN
§	'Crowned Imperial' (*fortunei*) (v)	CWat EMic NHol
	'Crumples' (*sieboldiana*)	EGol
	'Crusader' (v)	EGol EMic EPGN IBal LRHS NMyG SApp WFar
	'Cupboard Love'	SApp
	'Cupid's Dart' (v)	EGol
	'Curlew' (Tardiana Group)	EGol IBal
	'Cutting Edge' **new**	IBal
	'Dance with Me' **new**	EMic IBal
	'Dancing in the Rain' (v)	EBee EMic ERou IBal MBNS NBro SPoG
	'Dark Star' (v)	EGol EPGN SApp
	'Dawn'	EGol IBal
	'Daybreak'	ECho EGol EMic EPGN LAst LRHS MBri NBro SApp WTMC
	'Day's End' (v)	EGol
	'Deane's Dream'	EMic IBal
	decorata	EGol EMic MBar
	'Deep Blue Sea'	IBal
	'Delia' (v)	EPGN
	'Delta Dawn'	IBal
	'Devon Blue'(Tardiana Group)	CPrp EGol
	'Devon Giant'	EMic
	'Devon Green'	CTca EMic EPGN GBri IBal IPot MHom MLLN MSte NBro NCob NEgg NGdn NLar NMyG NNor NPro SApp WAul WFar WHal
	'Dew Drop' (v)	EGol EMic IBal NMyG
	'Diamond Tiara' (v)	EGol EMic EPGN IBal LAst LRHS MBNS MIDC NGdn NMyG
	'Diana Remembered'	EGol EMic EPGN IBal MBNS WBor
	'Dick Ward'	EMic IBal
	'Dimple'	EMic
	'Dixie Chick' (v)	IBal
	'Domaine de Courson'	EMic IBal WFar
	'Don Stevens' (v)	EGol
	'Donahue Piecrust'	EGol
	'Dorset Blue' (Tardiana Group)	EGol EMic EPGN GSki IBal LRHS
	'Dorset Charm' (Tardiana Group)	EGol
	'Dorset Flair' (Tardiana Group)	EGol EMic IBal
	'Doubloons'	EGol EMic
	'Dream Queen' (v)	EMic IBal
	'Dream Weaver' (v)	CWib EBee EGol EMic IBal MNrw NBro NGdn NMyG SPer
	'Dress Blues' **new**	EMic IBal
	'Drummer Boy'	EGol EMic
	'Duchess' (*nakaiana*) (v)	EGol
	'DuPage Delight' (*sieboldiana*) (v)	EGol IBal NGdn NLar
	'Dust Devil' (*fortunei*) (v)	EGol IBal
	'Dylan's Dillie' (v) **new**	IBal
	'Earth Angel' (v)	EGol EMic IBal
	'Edge of Night'	EMic
	'El Capitan' (v)	EGol EMic EPGN LRHS
	'El Niño'^{PBR} (Tardiana Group) (v)	CWGN EMic EPGN IBal MHom MIDC MNrw MSte NBro NGdn NMyG
§	***elata***	EBee EGol EMic GKev SApp
	'Elatior' (*nigrescens*)	EMic
	'Eldorado'	see *H.* 'Frances Williams'
	'Eleanor Lachman' (v)	EGol EMic IBal
	'Eleanor Roosevelt' **new**	IBal
	'Elegans'	see *H. sieboldiana* var. *elegans*

	'Elfin Power' (*sieboldii*) (v)	EGol
	'Elisabeth'	NMyG
	'Elizabeth Campbell' (*fortunei*) (v)	EGol EMic IBal MSte
	'Ellen'	EMic
	'Ellerbroek' (*fortunei*) (v)	EGol EMic GSki
	'Elsley Runner'	EGol
	'Elvis Lives'	EDAr EGol EKen EMic GBin IBal LAst MCCP NGdn NLar NMyG NNor NPro
	'Emerald Carpet'	EGol
	'Emerald Necklace' (v)	EGol
	'Emerald Skies'	EGol
	'Emerald Tiara' (v)	EGol EMic EPGN LRHS MIDC MLHP NMyG SVil WTin
	'Emeralds and Rubies'	EGol EMic IBal
	'Emily Dickinson' (v)	EBee EGol IBal NEgg SApp SPad
	'Enterprise' **new**	IBal
	'Eric Smith' (Tardiana Group)	EGol EMic EPGN IBal MHom NMyG WFar
	'Eric Smith Gold'	ENot
	'Eric's Gold' **new**	EPGN
	'Eskimo Pie' (v)	EBee EMic IBal
	'Eternal Flame'	IBal
	'Evelyn McCafferty' (*tokudama* hybrid)	EGol
	'Evening Magic' (v)	EGol
	'Eventide' (v)	EGol
	'Everlasting Love' (v)	EGol
	'Excitation'	EGol
	'Fair Maiden' (v)	EGol IBal
	'Faithful Heart' (v)	EMic IBal
	'Fall Bouquet' (*longipes* var. *hypoglauca*)	EGol
	'Fall Emerald'	EMic
	'Fallen Angel'	IBal
	'Falling Waters' (v)	EGol IBal
	'Fan Dance' (v)	EGol
	'Fantabulous' (v)	EPGN IBal
	'Fantastic' (*sieboldiana* hybrid)	EGol LRHS
	'Fantasy Island' (v)	IBal
	'Fatal Attraction'	IBal
	'Feather Boa'	EGol IBal
	'Fenman's Fascination'	EMic
	'Fire and Ice' (v)	More than 30 suppliers
	'Fire Island'	EGol EMic IBal
	'Fireworks' (v)	EBee EMic EPGN IBal MBNS NBro NMyG SPoG
	'First Frost' (v)	EMic IBal
	'Five O'Clock Shadow' (v)	IBal
	'Five O'Clock Somewhere' (v)	IBal
	'Flame Stitch' (*ventricosa*) (v)	EGol EMic
	'Flemish Sky' **new**	EMic IBal
	'Floradora'	EGol EMic IBal NMyG
	'Flower Power'	EGol
	fluctuans	ECho
	'Fool's Gold' (*fortunei*)	EMic IBal
	'Forest Fire'	EPGN IBal MBNS MIDC NMyG SPoG
	'Forest Shadows'	EMic IBal
	'Formal Attire' (*sieboldiana* hybrid) (v)	EGol EMic IBal LRHS
	'Forncett Frances' (v)	EGol IBal
	'Fortis'	see *H. undulata* var. *erromena*
	fortunei	CMMP EGol EMic GKev MIDC NHol NNor WEas WFar
§	- var. ***albopicta*** Υ^{H4}	More than 30 suppliers
	- - f. ***aurea*** Υ^{H4}	CMHG ECha EGol ELan EPla LRHS MBar MIDC NLar NMyG SPla SRms WFar WHal WWeb
	- - - dwarf	EMic
§	- var. ***aureomarginata*** Υ^{H4}	More than 30 suppliers

	- var. ***gigantea***	see *H. montana*
	- var. ***hyacinthina*** $\mathbb{Y}^{H4}$	ECho EGol EMic EPfP IBal LRHS MBar MRav NMyG NRnb SHBN WFar WPtf WWeb
	- - variegated	see *H.* 'Crowned Imperial'
§	- var. ***obscura***	ECho EGol EMic WLin
	- var. ***rugosa***	EMic
	'Fountain'	NHol
	'Fourth of July'	EGol
	'Fragrant Blue'	EBee ECho EGol EMic IBal LRHS NBro NGdn NMyG SMac SPoG
	'Fragrant Bouquet' (v)	CMHG CWib ECho EGol ELan EMic EPGN IBal LRHS NCGa NEgg NGdn NHol NLar NMyG SVil WPtf
	'Fragrant Dream'	EMic EPfP IBal NLar
	'Fragrant Fire' **new**	EMic IBal
	'Fragrant Gold'	EGol
	'Fragrant King'	IBal
	'Fragrant Star'	EMic IBal
	'Fragrant Surprise' (v)	IBal
	'Fran Godfrey'	EPGN
	'Francee' (*fortunei*) (v) $\mathbb{Y}^{H4}$	More than 30 suppliers
§	'Frances Williams' (*sieboldiana*) (v) $\mathbb{Y}^{H4}$	More than 30 suppliers
	'Frances Williams Improved' (*sieboldiana*) (v)	CTca EGol EPfP MWat NEgg
	Frances Williams' seedlings	NSti
	'Freising' (*fortunei*)	EBee
	'Fresh' (v)	EGol EPGN SApp
	'Fried Bananas'	EGol EMic
	'Fried Green Tomatoes'	ECho EGol EMic GBin MIDC NLar NMyG
	'Fringe Benefit' (v)	EGol EMic GAbr SApp
	'Frosted Dimples' **new**	EMic IBal
	'Frosted Jade' (v)	CWib EBee EGol EMic EPGN NLar NMyG SApp SRGP WTin
	'Fujibotan' (v)	EGol IBal
	'Fulda'	EGol
	'Gaiety' (v)	EGol EPGN
	'Gaijin' (v)	EGol IBal SApp
	'Gala' (*tardiflora*) (v)	NMyG
	'Galaxy'	IBal
	'Gay Blade' (v)	EGol SApp
	'Gay Feather' (v)	EMic IBal LAst NMyG SApp
	'Gay Search' (v)	EPGN IBal
	'Geisha' (v)	CWCL EGol EPGN IBal MBNS MCCP NGdn NMyG NPro WHal
	'Gene's Joy'	EPGN
	'Ghost Spirit'	EBee IBal
	'Gigantea' (*sieboldiana*)	see *H. elata*
	'Gilt By Association'	IBal
	'Gilt Edge' (*sieboldiana*) (v)	EMic NMyG
	'Ginko Craig' (v)	More than 30 suppliers
	'Glass Hearts' **new**	EMic
	glauca	see *H. sieboldiana* var. *elegans*
	'Glitter' **new**	EMic
	'Glockenspiel'	EGol
I	'Gloriosa' (*fortunei*) (v)	EGol WFar
	'Glory'	EGol
	'Goddess of Athena' (*decorata*) (v)	EGol
	'Gold Drop' (*venusta* hybrid)	ECho EGol EMic IBal NHol
	'Gold Edger'	CMea CPrp EGol ELan EMar EMic EPfP ERos GEdr GMaP LCro LRHS MIDC MRav MSte NBir NEgg NGdn NHol NMyG NNor NSti SApp SPer SPla WFar WLin WTin
§	'Gold Haze' (*fortunei*)	EGol EMic EPGN IBal MHom NBir NCGa NHol NMyG
	'Gold Leaf' (*fortunei*)	EGol
	'Gold Regal'	EBee EGol EMic EPGN MHom MSte NMyG WFar WMnd
	'Gold Rush'^{PBR}	NMyG
	'Gold Standard' (*fortunei*) (v)	More than 30 suppliers
	'Goldbrook' (v)	EGol IBal WTin
	'Goldbrook Galleon' **new**	IBal
	'Goldbrook Gayle' (v) **new**	EGol
	'Goldbrook Gaynor'	EGol IBal
	'Goldbrook Genie'	EGol IBal
	'Goldbrook Ghost' (v)	EGol
	'Goldbrook Girl'	EGol IBal
	'Goldbrook Glamour' (v)	EGol IBal
	'Goldbrook Glimmer' (Tardiana Group) (v)	EGol IBal
	'Goldbrook Gold'	EGol IBal
	'Goldbrook Grace'	EGol IBal
	'Goldbrook Gratis' (v)	EGol IBal
	'Goldbrook Grayling'	EGol IBal
	'Goldbrook Grebe'	EGol IBal
	'Golden Age'	see *H.* 'Gold Haze'
	'Golden Anniversary'	NHol WTMC
	'Golden Bullion' (*tokudama*)	EGol GBri
	'Golden Decade'	EGol
	'Golden Fascination'	EGol
	'Golden Friendship'	EGol
	'Golden Gate' **new**	EGol
	'Golden Guernsey' (v)	EMic
	'Golden Isle'	EGol IBal
	'Golden Meadows'^{PBR}	EPGN IBal NCob
	'Golden Medallion' (*tokudama*)	CMHG EGol ELan IBal MBNS NEgg NGdn NHol NMyG SHBN WFar
	'Golden Nakaiana'	see *H.* 'Birchwood Parky's Gold'
	'Golden' (*nakaiana*)	see *H.* 'Birchwood Parky's Gold'
	'Golden Oriole'	EGol
	'Golden Prayers'	ECtt IBal MIDC NLar WFar WHal
	'Golden Prayers' (*tokudama*)	ECtt EGol ELan EPGN ERos GSki LRHS MIDC MRav NBir NBro NGdn NHol NMyG NOrc SPla WSHC
	'Golden Scepter'	EGol EMic EPGN MPop NHol NMyG SApp SMer WFar
	'Golden Sculpture' (*sieboldiana*)	EGol LRHS
	'Golden Spider'	EGol EMic
	'Golden Sunburst' (*sieboldiana*)	CPrp EGol ELan EMic GSki IBal NEgg NGdn NHol WFar
	'Golden Tiara' (v) $\mathbb{Y}^{H4}$	More than 30 suppliers
	'Golden Waffles'	CMHG NEgg
	'Goldpfeil'	EMic
	'Goldsmith'	EGol SApp
	'Good as Gold'	EMic EPGN NMyG
	'Gosan Gold Mist'	EMic
	'Gosan Leather Strap' **new**	IBal
	'Gosan' (*takahashii*)	EGol
	gracillima	EPGN IBal NRya
	'Granary Gold' (*fortunei*)	EGol EPGN LRHS
	'Grand Finale'	IBal
	'Grand Marquee' (v)	EMic IBal
	'Grand Master'	EGol IBal MDKP SApp
	'Grand Prize' (v) **new**	IBal
	'Grand Slam' **new**	EGol
	'Grand Tiara' (v)	EGol EPGN IBal NMyG SApp
	'Gray Cole' (*sieboldiana*)	EGol EMic IBal LBuc NMyG
	'Great Arrival' **new**	IBal
	'Great Expectations' (*sieboldiana*) (v)	More than 30 suppliers
	'Great Lakes Gold' **new**	IBal
	'Green Acres' (*montana*)	EGle EMic LEdu MSte SMeo WFar
	'Green Angel' (*sieboldiana*)	EGol
	'Green Dwarf'	NWCA WFar
	'Green Eyes' (*sieboldii*) (v)	EGol
	'Green Fountain' (*kikutii*)	EGol EMic MIDC MSte
	'Green Gold' (*fortunei*) (v)	EMic
	'Green Piecrust'	EGol
	'Green Sheen'	EGol EPGN NMyG

'Green Velveteen'	EGol
'Green with Envy' (v)	EGol EMic IBal
'Grey Ghost'	IBal
'Grey Piecrust'	EGol IBal
'Ground Cover Trompenburg'	SApp
'Ground Master' (v)	CMHG COIW EBee ECho ECtt EGol ELan ENot EPfP GCra GMaP GSki IBal IFoB LRHS MBri MRav MSwo NBro NGdn NHol NMyG NSti WFar WWeb
'Ground Sulphur'	EGol
'Guacamole' (v)	CBgR EGle EGol EMic EPGN EPfP IBal IPot MIDC NGdn NLar NMyG SApp SVil WAul WTin
'Guardian Angel' (*sieboldiana*)	EGol EMic EPGN IBal
'Gum Drop'	EMic
'Gun Metal Blue'	EGol
'Gypsy Rose' **new**	EBee EMic EPGN NMyG
'Hadspen Blue' (Tardiana Group)	More than 30 suppliers
'Hadspen Hawk' (Tardiana Group)	EGol IBal NMyG SApp
Hadspen Heron (Tardiana Group)	EGol MHom MWat NMyG WCot
'Hadspen Nymphaea'	EGol IBal
'Hadspen Rainbow'	IBal
'Hadspen Samphire'	CWsd EGol EMic EPGN MHom NBir
'Hadspen White' (*fortunei*)	EGol EMic
'Hakujima' (*sieboldii*)	EGol
§ 'Halcyon' (Tardiana Group) $\mathbb{Y}^{H4}$	More than 30 suppliers
'Halo'	EGol
'Hampshire County' (v) **new**	IBal
Happiness' (Tardiana Group)	EGol EMic MHom MRav NMyG
'Happy Hearts'	EGol EMic
'Harlequin'	SApp
'Harmony' (Tardiana Group)	EGol EMic
'Harry van de Laar'	EMic IBal
'Harry van Trier'	EMic
'Hart's Tongue'	IBal
'Harvest Glow'	EGol
'Harvest Moon'	ECtt
'Heart Ache'	EGol
'Heart and Soul' (v)	EGol
'Heartleaf'	EMic
'Heart's Content' (v)	EGol
'Heartsong' (v)	EGol EMic NMyG
'Heideturm'	EBee
'Helen Doriot' (*sieboldiana*)	EGol EMic
helonioides misapplied f. ***albopicta***	see *H. rohdeifolia*
'Herifu' (v)	EGol
'Hertha' (v)	EMic
'Hidden Cove' (v)	EGol IBal
'High Kicker' **new**	EGol
'High Society' **new**	IBal
'Hi-ho Silver' (v)	EPGN IBal
'Hilda Wassman' (v)	EGol
'Hirao Elite'	IBal
'Hirao Majesty'	EGol
'Hirao Splendor'	EGol NMyG
'Hirao Supreme'	EGol
'His Honor' (v) **new**	IBal
'Holly's Honey' **new**	EGol
'Holstein'	see *H.* 'Halcyon'
'Honey Moon'	EGol
'Honeybells' $\mathbb{Y}^{H4}$	More than 30 suppliers
'Honeysong' (v)	EGol EMic EPGN
'Hoosier Harmony' (v)	EGol EMic
'Hoosier Homecoming'	SApp
'Hope' (v)	EGol EMic IBal
'Hotspur' (v)	EGol EMic IBal
'Hyacintha Variegata' (*fortunei*) (v)	CMHG GBri NNor
'Hydon Gleam'	EGol EMic
'Hydon Sunset' (*nakaiana*)	CMHG CMMP CMea ECtt EGol EMic EPGN GCra IBal MIDC NHol NMyG NOak NRya NSti WHal WMnd WPtf WTin
hypoleuca	EGol WLin
'Ice Cream' (*cathayana*) (v)	EGol
'Iced Lemon' (v)	EMic IBal
'Illicit Affair'	EMic IBal
'Ilona' (v)	EGol
§ 'Inaho'	EGol EPGN NMyG
'Inca Gold'	EGol IBal
'Independence' (v)	EMic IBal NBro NMyG
'Independence Day' (v)	EPGN
'Inniswood' (v)	CWib EGle EGol EPGN EPfP IBal IPot LRHS MBNS MBri NBro NGdn NLar NRnb NSti SApp WMnd
'Invincible'	EGle EGol EMic EPGN IBal LAst LRHS MBNS MIDC NGdn NLar NMyG NNor NRnb SApp SVil WTin
'Iona' (*fortunei*)	ECho EGol EMic EPGN NMyG
'Irische See'(Tardiana Group)	EGol
'Iron Gate Glamour' (v)	EGol
'Iron Gate Special' (v)	EMic
'Island Charm' (v)	EGol EMic EPGN IBal NBhm NLar SApp
'Iwa Soules'	EGol
'Jack of Diamonds'	IBal
'Jade Cascade'	EGol ELan EMic MSte NBir NEgg NHol NLar NMyG SApp SMrm WLin WOVN
'Jade Scepter' (*nakaiana*)	EGol EMic
'Jadette' (v)	EGol GBin
'Janet Day' (v)	EMic
'Janet' (*fortunei*) (v)	EBee EGol GMaP NGdn NHol
'Japan Girl'	see *H.* 'Mount Royal'
'Jester'	SApp
'Jewel of the Nile' (v)	EMic IBal
'Jim Mathews'	IBal
'Jimmy Crack Corn'	EGol EMic IBal
'John Wargo' **new**	EGol
'Jolly Green Giant' (*sieboldiana* hybrid)	EMic
'Joseph'	EGol EMic IBal
'Josephine' (v)	NNor
'Journeyman'	EGol EMic IBal
'Joyce Trott' (v)	IBal
'Judy Rocco' **new**	IBal
'Julia' (v)	EGol EMic IBal
'Julie Morss'	ECho EGol EMic EPGN GMaP IBal MHom MWat NMyG SApp
'Jumbo' (*sieboldiana*)	EMic
June' ^{PBR} (Tardiana Group) (v) $\mathbb{Y}^{H4}$	More than 30 suppliers
'June Beauty' (*sieboldiana*)	EWsh
'June Fever' (Tardiana Group)	EMic IBal NBhm NBro NLar NMoo
'Just So' (v)	EGol EMic IBal
'Kabitan'	see *H. sieboldii* var. *sieboldii* f. *kabitan*
'Kabuki' **new**	IBal
'Karin' ^{PBR}	EMic
'Katherine Lewis' (Tardiana Group) (v)	ECtt EMic IBal
'Kath's Gold'	SIng
'Kelsey'	EGol EMic

'Key Lime Pie' **new**	IBal
'Ki Nakafu Otome' (*venusta*) **new**	IBal
I 'Kifukurin' (*pulchella*) (v)	EGol EMic
'Kifukurin Ubatake' (*pulchella*) (v)	EGol EPGN IBal
kikutii	EGol EMic NWCA WTin
§ - var. ***caput-avis***	EGol EMic
- var. ***polyneuron***	EGol SApp
- var. ***pruinosa***	SApp
- var. ***tosana***	EGol
§ - var. ***yakusimensis***	CPBP EGol EMic GBin IBal
'Kimbotan' (v) **new**	EGol
'Kinbotan' **new**	IBal
'King James'	IBal
'Kingfisher' (Tardiana Group)	EGol
§ 'Kirishima'	EPGN SIng
'Kiwi Black Magic'	IBal
'Kiwi Blue Baby'	IBal
'Kiwi Blue Ruffles'	IBal
'Kiwi Blue Sky'	IBal
'Kiwi Canoe'	IBal
'Kiwi Cream Edge' (v)	EMic
'Kiwi Forest'	IBal
'Kiwi Fruit'	SApp
'Kiwi Full Monty' (v)	EMic IBal MPop
'Kiwi Gold Rush'	IBal
'Kiwi Hippo' **new**	IBal
'Kiwi Jordan'	IBal
'Kiwi Leap Frog'	IBal
'Kiwi Minnie Gold'	IBal
'Kiwi Parasol'	IBal
'Kiwi Spearmint'	IBal
'Kiwi Splash'	IBal
'Kiwi Sunlover'	IBal
'Kiwi Sunshine'	IBal
'Kiwi Treasure Trove'	IBal
kiyosumiensis	NHol
'Klopping Variegated' (v)	EGol
'Knockout' (v)	EGol EPGN IBal MBNS MIDC MNrw NBPC NBro NEgg NGdn NLar NMyG NNor NRnb SApp
'Komodo Dragon' **new**	WTin
'Korean Snow'	IBal
'Koriyama' (*sieboldiana*) (v)	EMic IBal LBuc
'Krossa Regal' ♀^{H4}	More than 30 suppliers
'Krugerrand' **new**	IBal
'Lacy Belle' (v)	EGol EMic IBal NBro NGdn NMyG NPro NRnb
'Lady Godiva' **new**	IBal
'Lady Guinevere'	EMic IBal
'Lady Helen'	EMic
'Lady Isobel Barnett' (v)	ECho EMic IBal NMyG SApp
laevigata	EGol SApp
'Lake Hitchock'	EGol IBal
'Lakeside Accolade'	NMyG
'Lakeside April Snow' (v)	EMic
'Lakeside Baby Face' (v)	IBal
'Lakeside Black Satin'	EMic IBal
'Lakeside Blue Cherub'	EMic IBal
'Lakeside Cha Cha' (v)	EGol EMic
'Lakeside Coal Miner'	EMic IBal
'Lakeside Cupcake' (v)	EMic IBal
'Lakeside Delight' **new**	EPGN
'Lakeside Dragonfly' (v)	IBal
'Lakeside Elfin Fire' **new**	EMic
'Lakeside Kaleidoscope'	EGol EMic IBal LBuc
'Lakeside Legal Tender' **new**	IBal
'Lakeside Little Gem'	IBal
'Lakeside Little Tuft' (v)	IBal
'Lakeside Lollipop'	EMic
'Lakeside Looking Glass'	EMic IBal
'Lakeside Love Affaire' **new**	EMic
'Lakeside Meter Maid' (v)	IBal
'Lakeside Miss Muffett' (v) **new**	IBal
'Lakeside Neat Petite'	EGol IBal
'Lakeside Ninita' (v)	EGol EMic EPGN IBal NMyG
'Lakeside Premier'	EGol EMic
'Lakeside Rhapsody' (v)	IBal
'Lakeside Roy El' (v)	IBal
'Lakeside Shoremaster' (v)	IBal
'Lakeside Small Fry' (v)	IBal
'Lakeside Spruce Goose' (v)	IBal
'Lakeside Symphony' (v)	EGol
'Lakeside Zinger' (v)	EMic IBal
lancifolia ♀^{H4}	CMHG CTca EBee ECha ECho EGol EHrv ELan EMic GMaP MIDC MRav NGdn NHol NMyG NSti SApp SBod SRms WAul WGwG WTin
'Last Dance' (v) **new**	IBal
'Leather Sheen'	EGol EMic EPGN
'Lederhosen' **new**	IBal
'Lee Armiger' (*tokudama* hybrid)	EGol
'Lemon Delight'	EGol EMic EPGN NMyG
'Lemon Frost'	IBal
'Lemon Lime'	EGol EMic IBal MHom MNrw NMyG NPro SIng WBrk WIvy WPat WTin
'Lemonade'	GBin
'Leola Fraim' (v)	EGol EMic IBal NMyG
'Leviathan'	EMic
'Liberty'^{PBR} (v)	EGol EPGN IBal NBro
* ***lilacina***	WFar
'Lily Pad'	EPGN
'Lime Piecrust'	EGol
'Lime Shag' (*sieboldii* f. *spathulata*)	MIDC
'Limey Lisa'	EMic EPGN IBal
'Little Aurora' (*tokudama* hybrid)	EGol EMic EPGN IBal
'Little Black Scape'	EGol EMic EPGN EWTr GBin IBal LSRN MBNS MHom NCob NEgg NGdn NHol NLar NMyG NPro SIng SPoG
'Little Blue' (*ventricosa*)	EGol
'Little Bo Beep' (v)	EGol
'Little Caesar' (v)	EGol EMic EPGN IBal
'Little Doll' (v)	EGol
'Little Jim' (v)	MIDC
'Little Miss Magic' **new**	IBal
'Little Razor'	EGol
'LIttle Red Rooster' **new**	IBal NMyG
'Little Stiffy'	IBal
'Little Sunspot' (v)	EGol EMic IBal
'Little White Lines' (v)	EGol EPGN IBal
'Little Wonder' (v)	EGol EMic IBal
longipes	EGol SApp
longissima	CMHG EGol WCru
'Louisa' (*sieboldii*) (v)	ECha EGol MSte WIvy
'Love Pat' ♀^{H4}	CBgR CFir EBee EGol EMic EPGN EPfP GAbr GBin GSki IBal LAst MCCP MIDC MRav NGdn NMyG NNor SApp SPla SVil
'Loyalist'^{PBR} (v)	EMic EPGN NLar WFar
'Lucky Charm'	EMic
'Lucy Vitols' (v)	EGol EMic IBal
'Lunar Eclipse' (v)	EGol SApp
'Mack the Knife'	IBal
'Maekawa'	EGol EMic
'Magic Fire' (v) **new**	EPfP IBal
'Majesty'	EGol IBal NGdn
'Mama Mia' (v)	EGol EMic EPGN EQua GAbr IBal MBNS NBro SRGP
'Maraschino Cherry'	EGol EMic IBal NMyG NRnb
'Margin of Error' (v)	EGol EPGN NMyG

	'Marginata Alba' misapplied	see *H. crispula*, *H.* 'Albomarginata'
	'Marginata Alba' ambig. (v)	ECha
	'Marilyn'	EGol LRHS
	'Marquis' (*nakaiana* hybrid)	EGol
	'Maruba' (*longipes* var. *latifolia*)	EGol
	'Mary Joe'	EMic
	'Mary Marie Ann' (*fortunei*) (v)	EGol EMic EPGN IBal NMyG
	'Masquerade' (v)	EGol EMic EPGN IBal NHar WFar WHal
	'May' **new**	IBal
	'Mediovariegata' (*undulata*)	see *H. undulata* var. *undulata*
	'Medusa' (v)	EGol IBal WCot
	'Memories of Dorothy' **new**	IBal
	'Mentor Gold'	EGol
	'Metallic Sheen'	LRHS
	'Midas Touch'	EGol NEgg NHol NLar
	'Middle Ridge'	NHol
	'Midwest Gold'	MHom SApp
	'Midwest Magic' (v)	CWib EGol EMic IBal NLar
	'Mildred Seaver' (v)	EGol EMic IBal NMyG
	'Millennium'	EMic
	'Millie's Memoirs' (v)	EGol
	'Ming Jade'	SApp
	'Minnie Bell' (v)	EGol
	'Minnie Klopping'	EMic
	minor misapplied f. ***alba***	see *H. sieboldii* var. *alba*
§	***minor*** Maekawa	EBee EGol EMic EPGN EPot ERos GEdr GGar GSki MTho NHol NMyG WCot WFar
	- from Korea	EGol
	- Goldbrook form	EGol IBal
	'Minor' (*ventricosa*)	see *H. minor* Maekawa
	'Minuteman' (*fortunei*) (v)	ECho EGle EMic EPGN EPfP GAbr GBin IBal IPot LAst LRHS MBNS MIDC MSte NBPC NCGa NGdn NMyG NNor NOrc NRnb SApp SHBN SPla WFar WGor WTMC WTin
	'Mississippi Delta' **new**	EMic
	'Moerheim' (*fortunei*) (v)	ECho EGol EMic EPGN IBal LRHS MBar MIDC NHol WHal WLin WTMC
N	***montana***	CWib ECho EGol EMic NHol WBrE
	- B&SWJ 4796	WCru
	- B&SWJ 5585	WCru
	- f. ***macrophylla***	EGol
	'Moon Glow' (v)	EGol NMyG
	'Moon River' (v)	EGol EMic EPGN NMyG SApp
	'Moon Shadow' (v)	EGol
	'Moon Waves'	EGol
	'Moonbeam'	NRnb WTMC
	'Moonlight' (*fortunei*) (v)	EBee EGol EMic EPGN GMaP NMyG SApp
	'Moonlight Sonata'	EGol EMic
	'Moonstruck' (v)	EGol EMic EPGN IBal
	'Morning Light'[PBR]	EBee EGol EMic EPGN EPfP IBal MBNS MBri NBhm NBro NGdn NMoo NMyG SApp WBor
	'Moscow Blue'	EGol EMic LRHS
	'Mount Everest'	EMic IBal
	'Mount Fuji' (*montana*)	EGol
	'Mount Hope' (v)	EGol
	'Mount Kirishima' (*sieboldii*)	see *H.* 'Kirishima'
§	'Mount Royal' (*sieboldii*)	NHol
	'Mount Tom' (v)	EGol IBal
	'Mountain Snow' (*montana*) (v)	CWat ECho EGol EMic LRHS NMyG SApp WTMC
	'Mountain Sunrise' (*montana*)	EGol
	'Mr Big'	MBNS
	'Mrs Minky'	EBrs EMic

	'Munchkin' (*sieboldii*)	WPat
	'My Friend Nancy' (v) **new**	EGol
	'Myerscough Magic'	MSte
	'Naegato'	SApp
	nakaiana	EBee EMic GEdr NDlv
	'Nakaimo'	NHol
	'Nameoki'	NHol
	'Nana' (*ventricosa*)	see *H. minor* Maekawa
§	'Nancy Lindsay' (*fortunei*)	CTri EGol EMic NGdn SApp WTMC
	'Nancy Minks'	EMic IBal
	'Neat and Tidy'	IBal
	'Neat Splash' (v)	CWCL NBir NHol
	'New Wave'	EGol
	'Niagara Falls'	CFir EGol EPGN GBin IBal NGdn
	'Nicola'	EGol EMic EPGN IBal MHom NMyG
	'Night before Christmas' (v)	CFir CMMP EBee ECho EGle EGol EPGN IBal IPot LAst MIDC MNrw MPop NBro NCGa NEgg NGdn NHol NMyG NNor NRnb SApp SHBN SPla SRGP WHoo WTMC WWeb
	nigrescens	EBee EGol EPGN GSki WBVN
	'Nokogiryama'	EGol EMic
	'North Hills' (*fortunei*) (v)	EBee EGol EMic GSki LRHS MPop MWgw NBir NCob NGdn SWvt
	'Northern Exposure' (*sieboldiana*) (v)	CFir EGol EMic IBal NGdn NMyG NRnb SApp SPoG
	'Northern Halo' (*sieboldiana*) (v)	ECho EGol EMic
	'Northern Lights' (*sieboldiana*)	EGol
	'Nouzang' **new**	IBal
	'Obscura Marginata' (*fortunei*)	see *H. fortunei* var. *aureomarginata*
	'Obsession'	EGol IBal
	'O'Harra' **new**	EGol
	'Okazuki Special'	EGol
	'Old Coot' **new**	IBal
	'Old Faithful'	EGol EMic
	'Old Glory'[PBR] (v)	EGol IBal
	'Olga's Shiny Leaf'	EGol EMic
	'Olive Bailey Langdon' (*sieboldiana*) (v)	EMic IBal
	'Olive Branch' (v)	EGol EMic IBal
	'Olympic Edger'	EMic IBal
	'Olympic Glacier' (v)	IBal
	'Olympic Sunrise' (v)	EMic
	'On Stage'	see *H.* 'Choko Nishiki'
	'On Stage' (*montana*)	see *H.* 'Choko Nishiki'
	'One Man's Treasure'	EMic EPGN IBal
	'Ophir'	IBal
	'Ops' (v)	IBal
	'Orange Marmalade'	EMic IBal
	'Oriana' (*fortunei*)	EGol IBal
	'Osprey' (Tardiana Group)	EGol LRHS
	'Oxheart'	EMic
	pachyscapa	EMic
	'Pacific Blue Edger'	CFir CMMP EGol EMic EPGN LAst MPop NGdn WAul
	'Pandora's Box' (v)	CWib EGol EMic EPGN GEdr NHar NMyG SApp WCot
	'Paradigm' (v)	EBee EGol EMic EPGN IBal NEgg NMyG
	'Paradise Backstage' (v)	EMic
	'Paradise Beach'	EMic
	'Paradise Glory' **new**	EMic
	'Paradise Joyce'[PBR]	EGol EMic EPGN IBal MIDC NLar NMyG
	'Paradise on Fire' (v)	EMic IBal
	'Paradise Power'[PBR]	EGol EMic IBal
	'Paradise Puppet' (*venusta*)	EMic EPGN
	'Paradise Red Delight' (*pycnophylla*)	EMic

'Paradise Standard' (d)	EMic
'Paradise Sunset' **new**	EGol EMic IBal
'Pastures Green'	EGol IBal
'Pastures New'	EGol EMic EQua MHom NHol NMyG SApp SPhx
'Pathfinder' (v)	EGol EMic IBal
'Patricia'	EMic
'Patrician' (v)	EGol EMic EPGN IBal NMyG
'Patriot' (v)	More than 30 suppliers
'Paul Revere' (v)	IBal
'Paul's Glory' (v)	EGol EMic EPGN EQua GBin GMaP IBal LAst LRHS MBri NBhm NGdn NMyG SApp SVil WTMC
'Peace' (v)	EGol EMic EPGN IBal
'Peanut'	IBal
'Pearl Lake'	EBee EGol EMic EWTr GEdr LRHS MHom MPop MSte MWat NBir NCob NGdn NHol NLar NMyG SApp SPhx SRGP WTin
'Peedee Absinth' **new**	EMic
'Peedee Gold Flash' (v)	NMyG
'Pelham Blue Tump'	EGol EMic
'Peppermint Ice' (v)	EGol
'Percy' **new**	IBal
'Permanent Wave'	EGol
'Peter Pan'	EGol EMic GBin
'Phantom'	SApp
'Phoenix'	EGol EMic GBin SApp
'Photo Finish' (v)	EGle EMic
'Phyllis Campbell' (*fortunei*)	see *H.* 'Sharmon'
'Picta' (*fortunei*)	see *H. fortunei* var. *albopicta*
'Piecrust Power'	EGol
'Piedmont Gold'	EGol EMic EPGN IBal MSte WTMC
'Pilgrim' (v)	EBee EGol ELan EMic EPGN IBal NBPC NBro NMyG SApp SMac SPoG WFar
'Pineapple Poll'	EMic EPGN MIDC MPop NMyG WTin
'Pineapple Upside Down Cake' (v)	EPGN IBal NBhm NBro NLar NMyG SPur WCot
'Pizzazz' (v)	CDWL EGle EGol EMic EPGN IBal MHom MIDC NGdn NHol NLar NMyG NRnb SApp SHBN WTMC
plantaginea	EGol EMic LEdu MHom NMyG SPhx SSpi WCru WKif WSpi
– var. ***grandiflora***	see *H. plantaginea* var. *japonica*
§ – var. ***japonica*** ♀H4	CDes CStu ECha EHrv EMic EPGN GSki IBal SApp WCAu WCFE WPGP
'Platinum Tiara' (v)	EMic EPGN IBal NBir NMyG
'Plug Nickel'	IBal
'Pooh Bear' (v)	EGol
'Popcorn' **new**	IBal
'Popo'	EGol EMic IBal
'Potomac Pride'	EPGN NMyG SApp
'Praying Hands' (v)	EGol EMic IBal
'Pretty Flamingo'	EMic IBal
'Prima Donna' **new**	EMic
'Primavera Primrose'	SApp
'Prince of Wales'	EMic IBal NMyG SApp SBra
'Princess of Wales' **new**	EBee
'Puck'	EGol
'Purple Dwarf'	EGol EMic NGdn NHol NLar WHal WIvy
'Purple Glory'	EMic
'Purple Passion'	EGol
'Purple Profusion'	EGol EMic
pycnophylla	EGol
'Queen Josephine' (v)	EGol EMic EPGN IBal IPot LAst MBNS MBri MHom NCGa NEgg NGdn NMyG NPro SApp SRGP WFar WTMC
'Queen of the Seas' **new**	IBal
'Quilting Bee'	EGol

'Radiant Edger' (v)	EGol EMic EPGN GCra IBal LRHS NHol
'Radio Waves'	IBal
'Rain Forest'	IBal
'Rainforest Sunrise' **new**	EMic IBal
'Raleigh Remembrance'	EGol
'Rascal' (v)	EGol EMic LRHS
'Raspberry Sorbet'	EGol EPGN
rectifolia	NHol NNor
'Red Neck Heaven' (***kikutii*** var. *caput-avis*)	EGol SApp WTin
'Red October'	CMHG CRez EBee EGol EMic EPGN EPfP GAbr GBin IBal MBNS MBri MCCP NEgg NGdn NLar NMoo NMyG
'Red Salamander'	EGol
'Regal Rhubarb' **new**	EMic IBal
'Regal Splendor' (v)	EGol EMFW EMic EPGN GSki IBal LRHS MHom NBro NCGa NGdn NHol NMyG SApp SHBN SPla WAul WMnd
'Reginald Kaye' **new**	EMic
'Remember Me'[PBR]	CWCL CWGN EDAr EGol ELan EMic EPGN IBal LAst LSRN MBNS MCCP MDun NCGa NCob NGdn NHol NLar NMyG NNor NRnb SApp SPoG WGor WWeb
'Resonance' (v)	EPGN NGdn NLar NPro WTMC
'Reversed' (*sieboldiana*) (v)	EBee EGol ELan EMic EPGN EPfP EWsh MDKP MIDC MSte NBro NGdn NHol NNor WHal WTMC
'Revolution'[PBR] (v)	CWGN CWib EBee EGle EGol EMic EPGN IBal IPot LSRN MBNS MBri MIDC NBPC NBro NCGa NCob NLar NMyG NOrc NRnb WAul
'Rhapsody' (*fortunei*) (v)	EGol EMic
'Rhapsody in Blue'	EGol
'Richland Gold' (*fortunei*)	EGol EMic EPGN NMyG
'Rim Rock' **new**	EMic
'Rippled Honey'	EMic EPGN IBal NCob NMyG NPro SApp
'Rippling Waves'	EGol EMic
'Rising Sun'	EGol
'Risky Business' (v)	IBal
'Robert Frost' (v)	EGol EMic IBal WTin
'Robin Hood' **new**	IBal
'Robusta' (*fortunei*)	see *H. sieboldiana* var. *elegans*
§ ***rohdeifolia*** (v)	EGol LRHS
– f. ***albopicta***	EGol ELan NHol
'Ron Damant'	EPGN
'Rosedale Golden Goose' **new**	IBal
'Rosedale Knox' **new**	IBal
'Rosemoor'	EGol
'Rotunda' **new**	EGol
'Rough Waters'	SApp
'Roxsanne'	EMic
'Royal Golden Jubilee'	EMic EPGN IBal NMyG
§ 'Royal Standard' ♀H4	More than 30 suppliers
'Royalty'	EGol
rupifraga	EGol
'Ryan's Big One'	IBal
§ 'Sagae' (v) ♀H3-4	EBee EBrs EGle EGol EMic EPGN EPfP IBal IPot MBri MHom MIDC MNrw MSte NEgg NGdn NMyG SPla SPoG WAul WFar WTMC
'Saint Elmo's Fire' (v)	CHid EGol EMic IBal NCGa NEgg SPla
'Saint Paul' **new**	IBal
'Saishu Jima' (*sieboldii* f. *spathulata*)	EPla NHol WCru
'Saishu Yahite Site' (v)	EGol
'Salute' (Tardiana Group)	EGol
'Samual Blue'	EGol

'Samurai' (*sieboldiana*) (v)	EBee EGol EMic IBal IPot LAst MRav NBir NBro NEgg NGdn NLar NRnb SApp
'Sarah Kennedy' (v)	EPGN
'Satisfaction' (v)	EMic
'Savannah'	EGol
'Sazanami' (*crispula*)	see *H. crispula*
'Scooter' (v)	EGol EMic EPGN NMyG
'Sea Bunny'	EGol
'Sea Dream' (v)	EGol EMic NMyG
'Sea Drift'	EGol
'Sea Fire'	EGol
'Sea Frolic' **new**	EGol
'Sea Gold Star'	EGol NMyG
'Sea Gulf Stream'	IBal
'Sea Hero'	EGol
'Sea Lotus Leaf'	EGol EMic NLar NMyG
'Sea Monster'	EGol
'Sea Octopus'	EGol
'Sea Sapphire'	EGol
'Sea Sunrise'	EPGN
'Sea Thunder' (v)	EGol EMic EPGN IBal
'Sea Yellow Sunrise'	EGol EMic IBal MPop SApp
'Second Wind' (*fortunei*) (v)	EMic EPGN NMyG
'Secret Love' **new**	IBal
'See Saw' (*undulata*)	EGol SApp
'Semperaurea' (*sieboldiana*)	GSki
'September Sun' (v)	EGol IBal LRHS NMyG
'Serena' (Tardiana Group)	SApp
'Serendipity'	EGol EMic MHom
'Shade Beauty' (v)	EGol
'Shade Fanfare' (v) ♀H4	CChe EBrs EGol ELan EMic EPGN EPfP GSki IBal LBMP LCro LRHS MBNS MBri MIDC MRav NBir NGdn NLar NMyG NSti SApp SPer WFar WMnd WTin
'Shade Master'	EGol NHol
'Shamoa'	SApp
§ 'Sharmon' (*fortunei*) (v)	CWat CWsd EGol EMic EPGN IBal MBNS NHol NMyG
'Sheila West'	EMic
'Shelleys' (v)	EGol IBal
'Sherborne Profusion' (Tardiana Group)	EMic IBal
'Sherborne Songbird' (Tardiana Group)	EGol IBal
'Sherborne Swan' (Tardiana Group)	EGol IBal
'Sherborne Swift' (Tardiana Group)	EGol
'Shere Khan' (v) **new**	EGol
'Shining Tot'	EGol
'Shiny Penny' (v)	EGol IBal
'Shirley Vaughn' (v)	EGol
'Shogun' (v)	EGol
'Showboat' (v)	EGol EMic IBal NMyG
sieboldiana	ECha ECho EGol ELan EMic EPfP GCra GMaP MRav NChi NHol SPer SPlb SRms WFar WGwG
§ - var. ***elegans*** ♀H4	More than 30 suppliers
- 'George Smith'	EMic IBal
sieboldiana x ***sieboldii*** f. ***kabitan*** **new**	CWsd
sieboldii	CBcs CWat NEgg
§ - var. ***alba***	EGol
§ - 'Paxton's Original' (v) ♀H4	CTca CWib EGol EHrv MBar SRms
§ - var. ***sieboldii*** f. ***kabitan*** (v)	EGol EPGN MIDC NMyG NSti SApp WTin
- - f. ***shiro-kabitan*** (v)	EGol EMic EPGN
'Silk Kimono' (v)	EGol
'Silver Bowl'	EGol
'Silver Crown'	see *H.* 'Albomarginata'
'Silver Lance' (v)	EGol EMic EPGN NMyG
'Silver Shadow' (v)	EMic EPGN IBal NCob NMyG WPtf
'Silver Spray' (v)	EGol IBal
'Silvery Slugproof' (Tardiana Group)	MWat NMyG SApp
'Sitting Pretty' (v)	EGol EPGN
'Sky Dancer' **new**	EMic IBal
'Sleeping Beauty' **new**	EMic IBal
'Slick Willie'	EGol
'Small Sum'	IBal
'Snow Cap' (v)	EBee EGle EGol EMic IBal MBri MIDC NEgg NGdn NLar NMoo NMyG NNor NPro SApp SHBN WAul WCra
'Snow Crust' (v)	EGol EMic LRHS
'Snow Flakes' (*sieboldii*)	EGol EPGN EPfP EWTr LRHS MBar NBro NGdn NHol NMyG NPro SBod SHBN WFar WGwG WTMC
'Snow White' (*undulata*) (v)	EGol
'Snowden'	CMHG ECha ECho EGol EMic EPGN ETod GMaP GMac IBal MWat NBir NCob NGdn NHol NMyG SApp SSpi WBrk WCru
'Snowstorm' (*sieboldii*)	NHol
'So Sweet' (v)	COIW CTca EBee EGol ELan EMFW EMic EMil EPGN GSki IBal LBMP MBri MHom MIDC MSte MSwo NBro NEgg NGdn NHol NMyG SPoG SRGP WSpi
'Solar Flare'	EGol
'Something Blue'	EMic
'Something Different' (*fortunei*) (v)	EGol EPGN
'Sparkling Burgundy'	EGol
'Sparky' (v)	EGol IBal
'Special Gift'	CTca EGol EMic
'Spilt Milk' (*tokudama*) (v)	EGol EMic EPGN IBal MPop WHoo
§ 'Spinners' (*fortunei*) (v)	ECha EGol EMic MPop
'Spinning Wheel' (v)	EGol
'Spring Fling' **new**	IBal
'Spritzer' (v)	EGol EMic NMyG SApp
'Squash Casserole'	EGol
'Squiggles' (v)	EGol
'Stained Glass'	EGol EMic EPGN IBal NGdn
'Starburst' (v)	EGol
§ 'Starker Yellow Leaf'	EMic
'Stenantha' (*fortunei*)	EMic
'Stenantha Variegated' (*fortunei*) (v)	NHol
'Step Sister' **new**	IBal
'Stetson' (v)	EGol
'Stiletto' (v)	CTca EBee EGol EHrv EMic EPGN GCra GEdr IBal IPot LAst LBMP MBNS MHom MIDC NBro NGdn NLar NMoo NMyG NNor NPro NRnb NSti SApp SDnm WAul WPtf
'Stirfry' **new**	EGol
'Stonewall' **new**	IBal
'Striptease' (*fortunei*) (v)	CDTJ EGol EMic EPGN GBin GQue IBal LAst MBNS MIDC NGdn NHol NLar NOrc NRnb SApp SHBN SMer SVil WFar WTMC
'Sugar and Cream' (v)	CMMP CWat ECho EGol EMic LAst LRHS MWat NGdn NRnb WTMC
'Sugar Daddy' **new**	EMic IBal
'Sugar Plum Fairy' (*gracillima*)	EGol
'Sultana' (v)	EMic IBal
'Sum and Substance' ♀H4	More than 30 suppliers
'Summer Breeze' (v)	EGol IBal
'Summer Fragrance'	EGol EMic LRHS NMyG
'Summer Joy' **new**	EMic
'Summer Music' (v)	CWCL EGle EGol EMic EPGN IBal MBNS MBri NMyG SApp

	'Summer Serenade' (v)	EGol EMic IBal
	'Sun Glow'	EGol
	'Sun Kissed' (v)	IBal
	'Sun Power'	ECho EGol EMic EPGN EPfP IBal LRHS MBNS MIDC NBro NGdn NLar NMyG NSti SApp SRGP
	'Sundance' (*fortunei*) (v)	EGol
*	'Sunflower'	NOak
	'Sunshine Glory' **new**	EGol
	'Super Bowl'	EGol
	'Super Nova' (v)	EGol EMic IBal SApp SPoG
	'Surprised by Joy' (v)	EGol EMic IBal
	'Sweet Bo Beep'	EGol
	'Sweet Bouquet' **new**	EMic
	'Sweet Home Chicago' (v)	EGol EMic IBal
	'Sweet Marjorie'	EGol
	'Sweet Sunshine' **new**	EGol
	'Sweet Susan'	EGol EMic MBNS SApp SPer SPoG
	'Sweet Tater Pie'	EGol
	'Sweetheart'	EMic
	'Sweetie' (v)	EGol EMic IBal SApp
	'Swirling Hearts'	EGol
	'Swoosh'	EPGN
	'Tall Boy'	CSev ECha EGol EPla MWgw NBir NNor
	'Tamborine' (v)	EGol EPGN NMyG SApp
	'Tango'^{PBR}	EMic IBal
	Tardiana Group	ECho EGol ELan MHom NGdn NHol
	tardiflora	CWsd EGol ERos SApp WCot WPGP
	tardiva	CWsd
	'Tattoo'^{PBR} (v)	CWGN EDAr EGol EMic EPGN IBal LSRN MBNS MIDC MNrw NLar NMoo NMyG SPoG
	'Tea and Crumpets' (v)	EPGN
	'Teaspoon'	EMic IBal
	'Temple Bells'	EGol
	'Temptation' **new**	EMic IBal
	'Tenryu'	EGol
	'Terry Wogan'	IBal
	'The Twister'	EGol EMic
	'Theo's Blue' **new**	EMic IBal
	'Thomas Hogg'	see *H. undulata* var. *albomarginata*
	'Thumb Nail'	ECha EGol EMic EPGN GSki IBal SApp
	'Thumbelina'	IBal
	'Thunderbolt' (*sieboldiana*)	EPGN IBal MBNS NCob NLar
	'Thunderbolt' (v)	EGol MIDC
	'Tick Tock' (v)	IBal
	'Tiny Tears'	CStu EGol EPGN IBal
	'Titanic'^{PBR}	IBal
	tokudama	EGol EMic LRHS MHom NBir NGdn NHol NNor NSti SApp WFar
§	- f. ***aureonebulosa*** (v)	EGol EMic EPGN IBal LRHS MSte NGdn NMyG NSti WMnd
	- f. ***flavocircinalis*** (v)	CBgR CPrp ECho EGol EMic EPGN GMaP IBal LRHS NBPC NBro NMyG SApp WFar WHoo WMnd
	'Tom Rex' **new**	IBal
	'Topscore'	NNor
	'Torchlight' (v)	EGol EMic LRHS
	tortifrons	IBal
	'Tortilla Chip'	IBal
	'Tot Tot'	EGol IBal
	'Touch of Class'^{PBR} (v)	EMic IBal
	'Touchstone' (v)	IBal NMyG SWvt
	'Toy Soldier'	EMic IBal
	'Trail's End'	EMic
	'Trill'	SApp
	'True Blue'	CBgR EBee EGol EMic GAbr IBal LAst NRnb SApp
	'Tsugaru Komachi' **new**	EMic
	'Turning Point' **new**	EGol
	'Tutu'	EGol MIDC
	'Twiggie' **new**	EMic
	'Twiggy'	SApp
	'Twilight' (*fortunei*) (v)	CDWL CWib EBee EGol EMFW EMic EPGN IBal MBNS NLar NRnb SApp SMer SWvt WRHF
	'Twilight Time' **new**	IBal
	'Twinkle Toes'	EGol
	'Twinkles'	MIDC
	'Twist of Lime' (v)	EGol
	'Ultramarine'	IBal
	'Ultraviolet Light'	EGol
	'Unchained Melody'	IBal
	undulata	ECha MIDC NNor WFar
§	- var. ***albomarginata***	More than 30 suppliers
§	- var. ***erromena*** Υ^{H4}	EHon EMic GMaP IBal MWgw NBid NHol SPer
§	- var. ***undulata*** (v) Υ^{H4}	EBee ECho EHrv ELan EMFW EPGN EPfP GMaP IBal LAst MIDC MRav MSwo NBlu NEgg NGdn NMyG NVic SIng SPer SPoG WEas WFar WWeb
	- var. ***univittata*** (v) Υ^{H4}	ECha EGol EPGN GKev IBal MHom NBir NPro WBrk WFar WMoo
	'Unforgettable' **new**	EMic
	'Urajiro Hachijo'	EGol
	'Urajiro' (*hypoleuca*)	EGol
	'Valentine Lace'	EBee EGol EMic
	'Van Wade' (v)	EGol EMic EPGN
	'Vanilla Cream' (*cathayana*)	EGol NMyG
	'Variegata' (*gracillima*)	see *H.* 'Vera Verde'
	'Variegata' (*tokudama*)	see *H. tokudama* f. *aureonebulosa*
	'Variegata' (*undulata*)	see *H. undulata* var. *undulata*
	'Variegata' (*ventricosa*)	see *H.* 'Aureomarginata'
	'Variegated' (*fluctuans*)	see *H.* 'Sagae'
	'Velvet Moon' (v)	IBal
	ventricosa Υ^{H4}	CBcs ECho EGol EGoo EMic EPfP GAbr GMaP MFOX MIDC MRav NHol SGar WBrk WCFE WFar
	- BWJ 8160 from Sichuan	WCru
	- var. ***aureomaculata***	EGol NBir NSti WFar
I	'Venucosa'	EGol EMic WFar
	'Venus Star'	EGol GSki NMyG
	venusta Υ^{H4}	CDes CSWP EBee ECho EDAr EGol EMic EPGN ERos GCra GCrs GEdr IBal MHer MRav NBir NMen NMyG NRya NSti SApp SMad SRot WEas WSHC WTMC WTin
	- B&SWJ 4389	WCru
	- dwarf	CSWP
	- ***yakusimensis***	see *H. kikutii* var. *yakusimensis*
§	'Vera Verde' (v)	EPGN GCra GQui IBal MHom NBir NMyG
	'Verna Jean' (v)	EGol
	'Veronica Lake' (v)	EGol EMic IBal WHal
	'Victory' **new**	IBal
	'Vilmoriniana'	EGol EMic
	'Viridis Marginata'	see *H. sieboldii* var. *sieboldii* f. *kabitan*
	Wagtail' (Tardiana Group)	EMic IBal
	'Wahoo' (*tokudama*) (v)	EGol
	'War Paint' **new**	IBal
	'Warwick Comet' (v) **new**	IBal
	'Warwick Curtsey' (v)	EGol EMic IBal
	'Warwick Delight' (v)	EGol EMic IBal
	'Warwick Edge' (v)	EGol IBal
	'Warwick Essence'	EGol EMic
	'Warwick Sheen'	IBal
	'Waving Winds' (v)	EGol
	'Waving Wuffles'	EMic
	'Wayside Blue'	EMic
	'Wayside Perfection'	see *H.* 'Royal Standard'
	'Weihenstephan' (*sieboldii*)	EGol EMic

'Weser'	EGol
'Wheaton Blue'	EMic MPop
'Whirlwind' (*fortunei*) (v)	CBcs CBgR CWib ECho EDAr EGol EMic EPGN GBin GQue IBal IPot MBri MIDC MNrw MSte NBro NEgg NGdn NMyG NNor NRnb SApp SVil WAul WMnd WTMC
'Whirlwind Tour' (v)	EGol
'Whiskey Sour'	IBal
'White Christmas' (*undulata*) (v)	EGle EGol EPGN EQua
'White Fairy' (*plantaginea*) (d)	IBal NMyG
'White Feather' (*undulata*)	EMic IBal NBir
'White Gold'	EGol NMyG
'White On' (Montana)	EMic
'White Tacchi'	EMon
'White Triumphator' (*rectifolia*)	EGol EMic EPGN GBin IBal NBPC NMyG
'White Trumpets'	EMic
'White Vision'	EGol
'Whoopee' (v)	MBNS
'Wide Brim' (v) ♀H4	More than 30 suppliers
'Wind River Gold'	EGol
'Windsor Gold'	see *H.* 'Nancy Lindsay'
'Winfield Blue'	CMHG EGol NEgg
'Winfield Gold'	EGol IBal
'Winsome' (v)	EGol IBal
'Wintersnow' new	EMic
'Wogon Giboshi'	see *H.* 'Wogon'
§ 'Wogon' (*sieboldii*)	CMMP EPGN GEdr GKev GMaP NDlv NHol NMen NSti
'Wogon's Boy'	EGol EPGN IBal
'Wolverine' (v)	EBee ECtt EGol EMic EPGN GAbr GEdr IBal LSou MBNS MHom MIDC NGdn NMyG WCot WLin
'Wrinkles and Crinkles'	EGol
'Wylde Green Cream'	EGol IBal
'Xanadu' (v)	IBal
'Yakushima-mizu' (*gracillima*)	EGol
* ***yakushimana***	GCrs NMen
'Yellow Boa'	EGol
'Yellow Edge' (*fortunei*)	see *H. fortunei* var. *aureomarginata*
'Yellow Edge' (*sieboldiana*)	see *H.* 'Frances Williams'
'Yellow River' (v)	ECho EGol EMic IBal MBri NEgg NGdn NMyG SApp
'Yellow Splash' (v)	ECha ECho EPGN LRHS MBNS MHom NMyG
'Yellow Splash Rim' (v)	EGol MBri NCGa NRnb
'Yellow Splashed Edged' (v)	EMic
'Yellow Submarine'	IBal
'Yin' (v)	IBal
yingeri	EGol SApp
- B&SWJ 546	WCru
'Yucca Ducka Do' new	EGol
'Zager Blue'	EMic
'Zager Green'	EMic
'Zager White Edge' (*fortunei*) (v)	EGol EMic NMyG SApp WTin
'Zounds'	CMHG EBee ECtt EGol ELan EMic EPGN EPfP EShb GSki IBal LRHS MDun MIDC MRav NHol NMyG NOak NOrc NSti SApp SHBN SPla WBor WFar

Hottonia (*Primulaceae*)

palustris	CDWL CWat EHon ELan EMFW NPer NSco NVic SWat WPnP

Houstonia (*Rubiaceae*)

caerulea misapplied	see *H. michauxii*
caerulea L.	ECho EDAr NPri SIng
- var. ***alba***	SPer SPlb
longifolia new	EWes
§ ***michauxii***	SPer SPoG
- 'Fred Mullard'	EPot EWes
serpyllifolia	ECho

Houttuynia (*Saururaceae*)

cordata	NEgg SDix SWat WFar
§ - 'Boo-Boo' (v)	EMan EPfP EPla EWin LBMP LSou NBro WFar
§ - 'Chameleon' (v)	More than 30 suppliers
- 'Fantasy'	EBee
- 'Flame' (v)	CBcs CWCL MAsh NCGa NPri SIng SMrm
- 'Flore Pleno' (d)	CBen EBee ECha EHon ELan EMFW EPfP EPla MCCP MRav NBir NPer SGar SIde SMac SPer SPlb SPoG SRms SWat WFar WPnP WTin
- 'Joker's Gold'	EBee EMan EPPr EPfP EPla EShb LBMP LSou NBro NVic SMrm
* - 'Pied Piper'	CDoC EBee ENot EPla EWin EWll LRHS
- 'Sunshine'	EBee
- 'Tequila Sunrise'	CHEx
- 'Terry Clarke'	see *H. cordata* 'Boo-Boo'
- 'Tricolor'	see *H. cordata* 'Chameleon'
- Variegata Group (v)	EBla NBro SIng

Hovenia (*Rhamnaceae*)

dulcis	CAgr CBcs CMCN EPfP EUnu ITer LEdu MBlu NLar WBVN

Howea (*Arecaceae*)

§ ***belmoreana*** ♀H1	LPal
§ ***forsteriana*** ♀H1	CCCN LPal LRHS MBri NScw XBlo

Hoya (*Asclepiadaceae*)

§ ***australis***	SOWG
bella	see *H. lanceolata* subsp. *bella*
carnosa ♀H1	CBcs CRHN EBak ELan EOHP MGol SRms SWal WWFP
* - 'Hindu Rope'	NPer
* - 'Krinkle'	NPer
- 'Red Princess'	MBri SAdn
- 'Tricolor'	NPer
- 'Variegata' (v)	MBri
cinnamomifolia	SOWG
* ***compacta*** 'Tricolor'	NPer
darwinii misapplied	see *H. australis*
imperialis	ERea
lacunosa	CCCN LRHS
§ ***lanceolata*** subsp. ***bella*** ♀H1	CHal ERea EShb SRms
linearis	SOWG
motoskei	ERea
multiflora	SOWG

huckleberry, garden see *Solanum scabrum*

Hugueninia (*Brassicaceae*)

alpina	see *H. tanacetifolia*
§ ***tanacetifolia***	NEgg

Humata (*Davalliaceae*)

tyermannii	CMen MPes WFib WRic

Humea see *Calomeria*

elegans	see *Calomeria amaranthoides*

Humulus (*Cannabaceae*)

japonicus	MSal
- 'Variegatus' (v)	EUnu
lupulus	CArn CBcs CRWN EPfP GPoy ILis MNHC MSal NGHP SIde WHer WSel

- 'Aureus' 🏆^{H4}	More than 30 suppliers
- 'Aureus' (f)	CRHN ELon GGar GKev MCCP MPRe SPla SPoG WCot WWFP
- 'Aureus' (m)	MCCP
* - ***compactus***	GPoy
- 'First Gold'^{PBR}	MNHC
- 'Fuggle'	CAgr GPoy SDea
- 'Golden Tassels' (f)	CAgr CBrm EBee ELon EMui EPfP LBuc LHop LRHS MAsh MBNS MBri MGos MPRe NGHP SBra SLim SMad SPoG WHlf WWeb
- (Goldings Group) 'Cobbs'	SDea
- - 'Mathons'	CAgr SDea
- 'Hallertauer'	SDea
- 'Hip-hop'	EMon
- var. ***neomexicanus***	EWes
- 'Prima Donna'	CAgr EBee EMui GBin LHop MBNS NLar SCoo SIde SPoG SWvt
- 'Taff's Variegated' (v)	EMon EWes MAvo WSHC
- 'Wye Challenger'	CAgr GPoy
- 'Wye Northdown'	CAgr SDea

Hunnemannia (*Papaveraceae*)

fumariifolia new	CSpe
- 'Sunlite' 🏆^{H4}	LRav

Huodendron (*Styracaceae*)

biaristatum new	WPGP
tibeticum	CBcs WPGP

Hutchinsia see *Pritzelago*

Hyacinthella (*Hyacinthaceae*)

acutiloba	ERos
dalmatica	ERos
dalmatica 'Grandiflora'	ECho WWst
glabrescens new	WCot
heldreichii	EBrs ECho ERos
lazuliria	ERos
leucophaea	EBrs ECho ERos WWst
lineata	WWst
millingenii	EBrs ECho ERos
pallens new	CTca EBrs ECho

Hyacinthoides (*Hyacinthaceae*)

§ ***hispanica***	EBrs IBlr NBir SPer
- 'Alba'	SPer
- subsp. ***algeriensis***	WCot
- 'Dainty Maid'	EBrs ECho WCot
- 'Excelsior'	EBrs ECho
- 'Miss World'	EBrs WCot
- 'Queen of the Pinks'	EBrs WCot
- 'Rose'	SPer
- 'Rosea'	CPom
- 'White City'	EBrs ECho WCot
§ ***italica*** 🏆^{H4}	SIng WShi
§ ***non-scripta***	CArn CAvo CBct CFFs CTca CTri EBrs ECho ENot EPot IBlr IHer LAma MHer NBir NMir SECG SHFr SPer SRms WHer WHil WPtf WShi
- 'Alba'	EBrs NBir WHil
- 'Bracteata'	CNat
- 'Chedglow'	CNat
- 'Rosea'	EBrs WHil
- 'Wavertree'	EBrs ECho
§ ***vicentina***	ERos
- 'Alba'	ERos

Hyacinthus ✿ (*Hyacinthaceae*)

amethystinus	see *Brimeura amethystina*
azureus	see *Muscari azureum*
comosus 'Plumosus'	see *Muscari comosum* 'Plumosum'
fastigiatus	see *Brimeura fastigiata*
multiflowered blue	CAvo CTca EBrs
multiflowered pink	CAvo CTca EBrs
multiflowered white	CAvo CTca EBrs
orientalis	EBrs SMeo
- 'Aiolos'	LRHS SPer
- 'Amethyst'	LAma
- 'Amsterdam'	LAma
- 'Anna Liza'	LRHS MBri
- 'Anna Marie' 🏆^{H4}	CAvo EBrs LAma LRHS MBri
- 'Atlantic' new	LRHS
- 'Ben Nevis' (d)	LAma
- 'Blue Festival'	LRHS SPer
- 'Blue Giant'	LAma
- 'Blue Jacket' 🏆^{H4}	EBrs LAma LRHS MBri
- 'Blue Pearl'^{PBR} new	SPer
- 'Blue Star'	LAma
- 'Carnegie'	CAvo EBrs ENot EPfP LAma LRHS SPer
- 'China Pink'	SPer
- 'City of Haarlem' 🏆^{H4}	EBrs EPfP LAma LRHS MBri
- 'Crystal Palace' (d)	LAma
- 'Delft Blue' 🏆^{H4}	CAvo CTca EBrs ENot EPfP LAma LRHS MBri SPer
- 'Fondant'	LAma LRHS
- 'General Köhler' (d)	LAma
- 'Gipsy Princess'	LAma
- 'Gipsy Queen' 🏆^{H4}	CTca EBrs LAma LRHS MBri SPer
- 'Hollyhock' (d)	LAma
- 'Jan Bos'	CTca EBrs ENot EPfP LAma LRHS MBri SPer
- 'Lady Derby'	LAma LRHS
- 'L'Innocence' 🏆^{H4}	CAvo EPfP LAma
- 'Odysseus'	LAma
- 'Ostara' 🏆^{H4}	EPfP LAma MBri
- 'Peter Stuyvesant'	EBrs LAma
- 'Pink Festival'	LRHS SPer
- 'Pink Pearl' 🏆^{H4}	CAvo EBrs EPfP LAma LRHS MBri
- 'Pink Royal' (d)	LAma
- 'Purple Sensation'^{PBR} new	EBrs
- 'Red Magic'	LAma
- 'Rosette' (d)	LAma
- 'Sky Jacket' new	LRHS
- 'Splendid Cornelia'	EBrs LRHS SPer
- 'Top Hit' new	SPer
- 'White Festival'	LRHS SPer
- 'White Pearl'	CAvo LAma LRHS MBri
- 'Woodstock'	CAvo EBrs LAma LRHS LSou SPer
- 'Yellow Queen' new	SPer

Hydrangea ✿ (*Hydrangeaceae*)

angustipetala	see *H. scandens* subsp. *chinensis* f. *angustipetala*
- f. ***formosana***	see *H. scandens* subsp. *chinensis* f. *formosana*
- f. ***macrosepala***	see *H. scandens* subsp. *chinensis* f. *macrosepala*
- f. ***obovatifolia***	see *H. scandens* subsp. *chinensis* f. *obovatifolia*
anomala subsp. ***anomala*** B&SWJ 2411	WCru
- - 'Winter Glow'	WCru
- subsp. ***glabra*** B&SWJ 3117	WCru
§ - subsp. ***petiolaris*** 🏆^{H4}	More than 30 suppliers
- - B&SWJ 6081 from Yakushima	WCru
- - B&SWJ 6337	WCru
§ - - var. ***cordifolia***	EBee MBNS NLar
§ - - - 'Brookside Littleleaf'	IClo NLar
- - dwarf	see *H. anomala* subsp. *petiolaris* var. *cordifolia*
- - 'Furuaziai'	WCru
* - - var. ***tiliifolia***	EBee EPfP WFar WSHC
- - - B&SWJ 8497	WCru
- - 'Yakushima'	WCru WPGP

*	- subsp. ***quelpartensis*** B&SWJ 8799	WCru
§	***arborescens***	CArn CPLG MRav WFar WPGP
	- 'Annabelle' ♀H4	More than 30 suppliers
	- 'Astrid Lindgren'	MAsh
§	- subsp. ***discolor***	WCru WPat
	- - 'Sterilis'	SHyH SPla WPGP
	- 'Grandiflora' ♀H4	CBcs CMac ELan EPfP LSRN MRav NBro NEgg SPer WCru WHCG WPGP WSHC
	- 'Hills of Snow'	MAsh
	- subsp. ***radiata***	CAbP CMil LRHS MAsh SSpi WFar WPGP
	- White Dome = 'Dardom'PBR **new**	MBri NBro
	aspera	CHEx CTri MGos SHyH SLon SSpi SSta WCru WKif WPGP
	- from Gongshan, China	WPGP
	- 'Anthony Bullivant'	LRHS MBri NLar SKHP SSpi WPat
	- Kawakamii Group	CHEx CMil CSpe EPla NLar SSpi WCru WPGP
	- - B&SWJ 1420	WCru
	- - B&SWJ 3462	WCru
	- - B&SWJ 6827	WCru
	- - B&SWJ 7025	WCru
	- - B&SWJ 7101	WCru
	- - 'August Abundance'	WCru
	- - 'September Splendour'	WCru
	- Kawakamii Group x ***involucrata***	WPGP
	- 'Macrophylla' ♀H3	CWib EPfP EWTr MRav NBlu NEgg NPal SHyH SMad SPer SPoG SSpi WCru WFar WPGP WSpi
	- 'Mauvette'	CMil MBlu NLar NPal SHyH SPer WCru WPGP
	- 'Peter Chappell'	CMil SSpi WPGP
§	- subsp. ***robusta***	SHyH SLPl WCru WPGP WSpi
	- 'Rocklon'	CMil NLar WCru WPGP
	- 'Rosthornii'	see *H. aspera* subsp. *robusta*
	- 'Sam MacDonald'	NEgg NLar SSpi WPGP WSpi
§	- subsp. ***sargentiana*** ♀H3	CAbb CBcs CEnd CHEx CMac EBee ELan EPfP IArd LRHS MAsh MBlu MBri MGos MRav NPal SHBN SHyH SPer SSpi SSta WAbe WCru WFar WKif WPGP
	- - large-leaved	WCot
	- subsp. ***strigosa***	CMil CPLG EPfP SKHP WCru WPGP
	- - B&SWJ 8201	WCru
	- 'Taiwan'	EQua MBri
	- 'Taiwan Pink'	EPfP NLar
	- 'Velvet and Lace'	LBuc LRHS NLar
§	- Villosa Group ♀H3	More than 30 suppliers
	cinerea	see *H. arborescens* subsp. *discolor*
	'Cohhii' **new**	ECre
	'Compact Red' **new**	ERas
	glandulosa B&SWJ 4031	WCru
	Goldrush = 'Nehyosh' (v) **new**	SPoG
§	***heteromalla***	CGHE CMHG CTrG EPfP SLPl SSpi WPGP
	- B&SWJ 2142 from India	WCru
	- B&SWJ 2602 from Sikkim	WCru
	- BWJ 7657 from China	WCru
	- HWJCM 180	WCru
	- HWJK 2127 from Nepal	WCru
	- SF 338	ISea
	- Bretschneideri Group	EPfP GQui MBlu NLar SHyH WBod WCru WFar
	- 'Fan Si Pan'	WCru
	- 'Snowcap'	EPfP GQui IArd SHyH SLPl SSpi WPGP
	- f. ***xanthoneura*** 'Wilsonii'	WKif
*	***heterophylla***	MGos

	hirta B&SWJ 5000	WCru
	indochinensis B&SWJ 8307	WCru
	integerrima	see *H. serratifolia*
	integrifolia	GGGa NLar WPGP
	- B&SWJ 022	WCru
	- B&SWJ 6967	WCru
	involucrata	CPLG EPfP LRHS MMHG SPer WCru
	- dwarf	WCru
	- 'Hortensis' (d) ♀H3-4	CMac CMil CPLG CPle EPfP MBri MGan MRav SDix SMad SPer SSpi WAbe WBod WCru WKif WPGP WSHC WSpi
*	- 'Plena' (d)	CLAP CMil GAbr LRHS MSte SKHP SPoG SSta WCot WCru WFar WPGP WTMC
*	- 'Sterilis'	EPfP
	- 'Viridescens'	SKHP SSpi WPGP WSpi
	lobbii	see *H. scandens* subsp. *chinensis*
	longipes	GQui WCru WPGP
	- BWJ 8188	WCru
	luteovenosa	IDee WCru WPGP
	- B&SWJ 5602	WCru
*	***macrocephala***	SKHP SSpi
	macrophylla	CTrG
	- 'AB Green Shadow'PBR	ENot SPoG
	- 'Adria' (H)	SHyH
	- 'All Summer Beauty' (H)	MAsh
	- Alpen Glow	see *H. macrophylla* 'Alpenglühen'
§	- 'Alpenglühen' (H)	CBcs CPLG CSBt ELan SHBN SHyH SRms WPGP
	- 'Altona' (H) ♀H3-4	CBcs CWSG EPfP IArd ISea LRHS MAsh MGos MRav NBir NPri SHyH SPer WPGP
	- 'Amethyst' (H/d)	CGHE MAsh WPGP
	- 'Ami Pasquier' (H) ♀H3-4	CDoC CMac CSBt CTri EBee ELan EPfP LRHS LSRN MAsh MRav MSwo SBod SCoo SGar SHyH SLim SPla SSpi SWvt WGer WPGP WWeb
*	- 'Aureomarginata' (v)	EPfP SHyH WCot
	- 'Aureovariegata' (L/v)	ELan
	- 'Ave Maria' (H) **new**	ERas MAsh
	- 'Ayesha' (H)	CBcs CBrm CDoC CDul CEnd CMHG CMac CPLG CWGN EBee ECtt ENot EPfP MAsh MGos MRav MWgw SDix SHBN SHyH SPer SPla SPoG SWvt WBor WPGP WWlt
	- 'Bachstelze' (L)	MAsh SSpi
	- 'Beauté Vendômoise' (L)	CGHE CMil NLar SSpi WPGP
	- 'Benelux' (H)	CBcs CWSG EMil SHyH
	- 'Bicolor'	see *H. macrophylla* 'Harlequin'
§	- 'Blauer Prinz' (H)	CSBt CSam MAsh SHBN SHyH
§	- 'Blauer Zwerg' (H)	ENot MGos
§	- 'Blaumeise' (Teller Series) (L)	CDoC CSBt EBee ENot EPfP EQua MAsh MBri MDKP MGos MRav NBlu NSti SCoo SHyH SLim SSpi SPoG SWvt WBod WGer WPGP WSpi WWeb
§	- 'Bläuling' (Teller Series) (L)	CDoC MAsh MGos NEgg SHyH WWeb
	- 'Blue Bonnet' (H)	CChe CSBt EPfP LSRN MWgw SHyH SPer WHen
	- Blue Butterfly	see *H. macrophylla* 'Bläuling'
	- Blue Dwarf	see *H. macrophylla* 'Blauer Zwerg'
	- Blue Prince	see *H. macrophylla* 'Blauer Prinz'
	- Blue Sky	see *H. macrophylla* 'Blaumeise'
	- Blue Tit	see *H. macrophylla* 'Blaumeise'
	- 'Blue Wave'	see *H. macrophylla* 'Mariesii Perfecta'
	- 'Bluebird' misapplied	see *H. serrata* 'Bluebird'
	- Bluebird	see *H. macrophylla* 'Bläuling'
	- 'Bodensee' (H)	MAsh MBri SPla WBVN
	- 'Bouquet Rose' (H)	CWib ECtt NBlu WBod
	- 'Bridal Bouquet' (H)	CDoC

- 'Brügg' (H) MAsh SHyH WPGP
- 'Brunette' see *H. macrophylla* 'Merveille Sanguine'
- 'Buchfink' (Teller Series) (L) SSpi WPGP
- Cardinal (L) see *H. macrophylla* 'Kardinal' (Teller Series) (L)
§ - 'Cardinal Red' (H) ECre
- 'Chaperon Rouge' (H) MAsh
- 'Colour Fantasy' **new** SPoG
- 'Cordata' see *H. arborescens*
- 'Dandenong' (L) **new** MAsh
- 'Decatur Blue' (H) **new** MAsh
- 'Deutschland' (H) CTri
- 'Domotoi' see *H. macrophylla* 'Setsuka-yae'
- Dragonfly see *H. macrophylla* 'Libelle'
* - 'Dwaag Pink' MRav
- 'Early Sensation' (H) MBri SPoG
- 'Eco Royal Velvet' **new** SKHP
- 'Eldorado' (H) SHyH
- Endless Summer = 'Bailmer' (H) **new** EBrs ENot EPfP LBuc LRHS
§ - 'Enziandom' (H) CBcs CSBt CWsd MAsh SHyH WAbe WBod WPGP
- Eternity Blue **new** EMil
- Eternity = 'Youmetwo' (H/d) **new** SPer SPoG
- 'Etoile Violette' **new** EQua
- 'Europa' (H) Υ^{H3-4} CBcs CMac CPLG CWSG EMil LRHS MGos MWgw SHyH WBod
- 'Faisan' **new** EQua
§ - 'Fasan' (Teller Series) (L) MAsh WPGP WSPU
- Firelight see *H. macrophylla* 'Leuchtfeuer'
- Fireworks see *H. macrophylla* 'Hanabi'
- Fireworks Blue see *H. macrophylla* 'Jōgasaki'
- Fireworks Pink see *H. macrophylla* 'Jōgasaki'
- Fireworks White see *H. macrophylla* 'Hanabi'
- 'Forever Pink' (H) MAsh
§ - 'Frau Fujiyo' (Lady Series) (H) CPLG LRHS
§ - 'Frau Katsuko' (Lady Series) (H) LRHS SPer
§ - 'Frau Mariko' (Lady Series) (H) LRHS
§ - 'Frau Nobuko' (Lady Series) (H) LRHS
§ - 'Frau Taiko' (Lady Series) (H) LRHS SPer
- 'Freudenstein' (H) MBri
- 'Frillibet' (H) CAbP CDoC EPfP WPGP
- 'Gartenbaudirektor Kuhnert' (H) SHyH SMer
§ - 'Générale Vicomtesse de Vibraye' (H) Υ^{H3-4} CDoC CEnd CMHG CTri CWSG EBee EPfP LRHS MAsh MBar NCGa SHBN SHyH SLim SPer SSpi WBVN WBod WPGP
- Gentian Dome see *H. macrophylla* 'Enziandom'
- 'Geoffrey Chadbund' see *H. macrophylla* 'Möwe'
- 'Gerda Steiniger' (H) MAsh SHyH
- 'Gertrud Glahn' (H) SHyH WFar
- 'Gimpel' (Teller Series) (L) **new** MAsh
- 'Glowing Embers' (H) IArd MBNS WPGP
- 'Goliath' (H) EPfP
§ - 'Grant's Choice' (L) SHyH
- Hamburg = 'Raham' (City-line Series) (L) CEnd CTri CWSG ECtt EPfP LRHS MAsh MGos MRav NEgg NPri SDix SHyH SLim WBod WBrE WFar WWeb
§ - 'Hanabi' (L/d) CDoC CLAP CMil ECre EPla EQua MBlu NLar
§ - 'Harlequin' (H) MAsh WCot WPGP
- 'Harry's Pink Topper' (H) MAsh
- 'Harry's Red' (H) **new** MAsh
- 'Hatsu-shime' NLar
- 'Heinrich Seidel' (H) CBcs WMoo
- 'Hobella'^{PBR} (Hovaria Series) (L) LBuc WBod
- 'Hobergine'^{PBR} (Hovaria Series) (H) SHyH
- 'Holstein' (H) MAsh MDun
- 'Homigo'^{PBR} (Hovaria) Series) (H SHyH
§ - 'Hörnli' (H) LAst
- 'Izu-no-hana' (L/d) CBcs CLAP CMil MAsh MBlu NLar SHyH SPoG SSpi WBor WPGP
- 'James Grant' see *H. macrophylla* 'Grant's Choice'
- 'Jofloma' NLar
§ - 'Jōgasaki' (L/d) CLAP CPLG MAsh MBlu NLar SHyH WPGP
- 'Joseph Banks' (H) CBcs CTri
§ - 'Kardinal' (Teller Series) (L) ERas MAsh
- 'Kardinal' (H) see *H. macrophylla* 'Cardinal Red' (H)
- 'King George' (H) CBcs CDoC CDul CSBt CWSG EBee LAst LRHS MAsh MBar MGos MRav MWat SHyH SLim SPer SPoG SWvt WFar WMoo WTel
§ - 'Klaveren' (L) CMil MAsh
- 'Kluis Superba' (H) CBcs CTri MAsh MRav SHyH
§ - 'Koningin Wilhelmina' (H) WTel
- 'La France' (H) CTri CWSG LRHS MBar MRav SHyH WFar
- 'Lady Fujiyo' see *H. macrophylla* 'Frau Fujiyo'
- Lady Katsuko see *H. macrophylla* 'Frau Katsuko'
- 'Lady Mariko' see *H. macrophylla* 'Frau Mariko'
- 'Lady Nobuko' see *H. macrophylla* 'Frau Nobuko'
- 'Lady Taiko Blue' see *H. macrophylla* 'Frau Taiko'
- 'Lady Taiko Pink' see *H. macrophylla* 'Frau Taiko'
- 'Lanarth White' (L) Υ^{H3-4} CBcs CBrm CDoC CSBt CTri EBee ELan EPfP MAsh MRav MSwo SBod SHBN SHyH SLPl SLim SPer SReu SRms SSpi WBod WBor WKif WPGP
- 'Lemon Wave' (L/v) NLar
§ - 'Leuchtfeuer' (H) EMil ENot MGos SHyH WBod WGer
§ - 'Libelle' (Teller Series) (L) CBcs CDoC CSBt EBee EPfP MAsh MGos MRav SBod SHyH SLim SPer SPoG SSpi WBVN WKif WSpi
- 'Lilacina' see *H. macrophylla* 'Mariesii Lilacina'
- 'Love You Kiss'^{PBR} (Hovaria Series) (L) SCoo SHyH SPoG
§ - 'Maculata' (L/v) ELan GQui SGar WBod WGwG
- 'Madame A. Riverain' (H) CWSG SHyH
- 'Madame Emile Mouillère' (H) Υ^{H3-4} More than 30 suppliers
- 'Madame Faustin Travouillon' (H) MAsh
- 'Maréchal Foch' (H) CTri
- 'Mariesii' (L) CMHG CSBt CTri ELan ISea LCro LRHS MSwo NEgg SDix SPer WGwG WKif
§ - 'Mariesii Grandiflora' (L) Υ^{H3-4} EBee ENot EPfP LCro LRHS MAsh MBar NBro NCGa NPri SHBN SHyH SPer SRms WFar WMoo WPGP
§ - 'Mariesii Lilacina' (L) Υ^{H3-4} EPfP MAsh SEND SLon SPer WKif WMoo WPGP
§ - 'Mariesii Perfecta' (L) Υ^{H3-4} More than 30 suppliers
- 'Mariesii Variegata' (L/v) CWib
- 'Masja' (H) EBee IArd LRHS MAsh MGos MRav MSwo NBro SHBN SHyH WWeb
- 'Mathilde Gütges' (H) CDoC MAsh SHyH SSpi WPGP WWeb

	- 'Max Löbner' (H)	SHyH
§	- 'Merveille Sanguine' (H)	CGHE CDoC CMil EMil IArd MBri MRav NLar WCot WLeb WPGP WPat
	- 'Messalina' (L)	ENot MGos
	- 'Mini Hörnli'	see *H. macrophylla* 'Hörnli'
	- 'Mirai'PBR (H) **new**	SHyH
	- 'Miss Belgium' (H)	CMac CTri MAsh
	- 'Mousmée' (L)	IArd MAsh SSpi
	- 'Mousseline' (H)	MAsh
§	- 'Möwe' (L) ♀H3-4	CDoC CEnd CMil CPLG EBee ECtt ENot LCro LHop MAsh NEgg SBod SCoo SDix SGar SHBN SHyH SLim SPer SRms SSpi SSta WPGP
	- 'Mrs W.J. Hepburn'	CSBt SHyH SPer
§	- 'Nachtigall' (Teller Series) (L)	MAsh SSpi
	- 'Niedersachsen' (H)	CDoC CTri MRav SHyH SMer WPGP
	- Nightingale	see *H. macrophylla* 'Nachtigall'
	- 'Nigra' (H) ♀H3-4	CBcs CChe CMil CPLG CWib ELan EPfP EPla GGGa MAsh MBri MGos SDix SHBN SHyH SPer WFar WGwG WLeb WPGP WSpi
	- 'Nikko Blue' (H)	CBcs CWSG EPfP MBar MDun NBlu NEgg
	- var. ***normalis*** (L)	CPLG
	- 'Papagei' (Teller Series) (L)	SPer
	- 'Parzifal' (H) ♀H3-4	CDul SHyH WPGP
	- 'Pfau' (Teller Series) (L)	SSpi
	- Pheasant	see *H. macrophylla* 'Fasan'
	- 'Pia' (H)	CBgR CDoC CPLG CSBt CStu ELan MGos MRav NWCA SLim SMad SPer SPla SRms WAbe WBor WCru WFar WPat
	- Pigeon	see *H. macrophylla* 'Taube'
	- 'Pink Wave' (L)	NPri
	- 'Prinses Beatrix' (H)	SHyH
	- 'Quadricolor' (L/v)	CAbb CMac CMil CPLG LRHS MRav SDix SGar SHBN SHyH SLim SPer SPla SPlb SRms WCot WHCG WSHC WWeb
	- Queen Wilhelmina	see *H. macrophylla* 'Koningin Wilhelmina'
	- 'R.F. Felton' (H)	CBcs SHyH
	- 'Red Baron'	see *H. macrophylla* 'Schöne Bautznerin'
	- 'Red Red'PBR (H) **new**	MAsh
	- Redbreast	see *H. macrophylla* 'Rotkehlchen'
	- 'Regula' (H)	SHyH
	- 'Renate Steiniger' (H)	ENot MGos SHyH WBod WGwG
	- 'Romance' **new**	SPoG
	- 'Rosita' (H)	EMil MAsh WFar
§	- 'Rotkehlchen' (Teller Series) (L)	CDoC CSBt EPfP NBlu SCoo SPlb SPoG SWvt WWeb
	- 'Rotschwanz' (Teller Series) (L)	CMil ERas MAsh SSpi WPGP
	- 'Sabrina'PBR (H)	CBcs ENot MAsh MBri MGos SPoG
	- 'Saint Claire' (H)	CBcs CPLG SHyH
	- 'Sandra' (Dutch Ladies Series) (L)	CBcs ENot MAsh
§	- 'Schneeball' (H)	ENot MAsh MGos
§	- 'Schöne Bautznerin'	ENot ERas MWea
	- 'Sea Foam' (L)	NBlu
	- 'Selina' (Dutch Ladies Series)	CBcs ENot MDKP MGos SPoG
	- 'Selma' (Dutch Ladies Series) (L)	CBcs ENot MBri
	- 'Semperflorens' (H)	MAsh
§	- 'Setsuka-yae' (L/d)	CMil
	- 'Sheila' (Dutch Ladies Series) (L)	CBcs MAsh MBri
	- 'Sibilla' (H)	CBcs EMil WPGP
	- Sister Therese	see *H. macrophylla* 'Soeur Thérèse'
	- Snowball	see *H. macrophylla* 'Schneeball'
§	- 'Soeur Thérèse' (H)	CSBt MAsh MGos SHyH SWvt WGwG WPGP
	- 'Soraya' (Dutch Ladies Series) (L)	CBcs
	- 'Souvenir du Président Doumer' (H)	MAsh
*	- 'Sunset' (L)	CBcs
	- 'Taiko' blue	see *H. macrophylla* 'Frau Taiko'
	- 'Taiko' pink	see *H. macrophylla* 'Frau Taiko'
§	- 'Taube' (Teller Series) (L)	CBcs CDoC CDul CPLG EBee EPfP GQui MAsh NBlu SCoo SWvt WWeb
	- Teller Blue	see *H. macrophylla* 'Blaumeise'
	- Teller Pink	see *H. macrophylla* 'Taube'
	- Teller Red	see *H. macrophylla* 'Rotkelchen'
	- Teller Rot	see *H. macrophylla* 'Rotkelchen'
N	- Teller variegated	see *H. macrophylla* 'Tricolor'
	- Teller Weiss	see *H. macrophylla* 'Libelle'
	- Teller White	see *H. macrophylla* 'Libelle'
	- 'Tokyo Delight' (L) ♀H3-4	CChe CDoC CGHE CLAP CPLG EBee MAsh SHyH WPGP
§	- 'Tricolor' (L/v)	CBcs CDoC CTri EBee EMil EQua ERas LAst LRHS MGos NEgg NPri SHyH SLon SPer SPoG WFar WKif WMoo
	- 'Trophée' (H)	SPoG
	- 'Val du Loir' (H)	CWSG
	- 'Variegata'	see *H. macrophylla* 'Maculata'
	- 'Veitchii' (L) ♀H3-4	CBcs CMHG CMil CPLG CSBt ENot EPfP MAsh MRav MSwo SDix SGar SHyH SPer SPoG SSpi WPGP WSpi
	- 'Vicomte de Vibraye'	see *H. macrophylla* 'Générale Vicomtesse de Vibraye'
	- 'Violetta' (H) **new**	MAsh
	- 'Westfalen' (H) ♀H3-4	CMac IArd SDix SPla
I	- 'White Lace' (L)	ELan SHyH
	- 'White Mop' (H)	CWib
	- 'White Wave'	see *H. macrophylla* 'Mariesii Grandiflora'
	- 'Zaunkönig' (Teller Series) (L) **new**	MAsh
	paniculata	CMCN LAst
	- B&SWJ 3556 from Taiwan	WCru
	- B&SWJ 5413 from Japan	WCru
	- 'Ammarin'	NLar WPat
	- 'Big Ben'	MBri
	- 'Brussels Lace'	CAbP CMil EBee LRHS LSRN MAsh MBri MRav NLar SHyH SPla SPoG SSpi WPat
	- 'Burgundy Lace'	CBcs MBlu MBri SHyH
	- Dart's Little Dot = 'Darlido'	WPat
	- 'Dharuma' **new**	LRHS
	- 'Everest'	CAbP LRHS MAsh SHyH
	- 'Floribunda'	CGHE ELan EPfP EWTr LRHS NEgg WBod WPGP
	- 'Grandiflora' ♀H4	More than 30 suppliers
	- 'Greenspire'	LRHS MBlu MBri
	- 'Harry's Souvenir'	MBri
	- 'Kyushu' ♀H4	More than 30 suppliers
	- 'Limelight'PBR	CBcs CMil EKen EMil EPfP EQua ERas EWTr GQui LBuc MAsh MBlu MBri MGos NHol NLar SHyH SKHP SRkn WBrE WFar WOVN WPat WSpi
	- 'Mount Aso'	CMil NLar WPGP
	- 'October Bride'	MBri NLar WPGP
	- 'Phantom'	GGGa LRHS MAsh MBlu MBri MDKP SHyH WPGP WPat WSpi
	- 'Pink Beauty'	MDKP
	- Pink Diamond = 'Interhydia' ♀H4	CAbP CBcs CDoC EBee ECrN ENot GQui LAst LHop LRHS LSRN MAsh MBlu MBri MGos MRav NLar NPri SHyH SMad SPla SSpi SSta WBod WFar WPGP WPat

- 'Pink Jewel'	CWib WPat
- Pinky Winky = 'Dvppinky'	EMil MGos NLar SPoG
- 'Praecox'	GQui MRav SLon SPer WPat
- 'Silver Dollar'	MAsh MBri
- 'Tardiva'	CBcs CChe CDoC CMac EPfP GQui LPan LRHS MAsh MGos MRav NBro NPri SDix SHyH SPer SRms WBod WFar WHCG WPGP WPat WWeb
- 'Unique' ♀H4	CBcs CBgR CBrm CDoC CGHE CMil EBee EPfP GQui LHop LRHS MAsh MBri MRav NBro SHyH SPer SPla SSpi WBod WFar WPGP WPat
- 'Waterfall'	CLAP
- 'White Lace'	MBlu
- 'White Lady'	CBcs MAsh
- 'White Moth'	CBcs NLar SHyH SKHP WBod WPat
petiolaris	see *H. anomala* subsp. *petiolaris*
§ 'Preziosa' ♀H3-4	More than 30 suppliers
quelpartensis	CRHN GQui
- B&SWJ 4400	WCru
quercifolia ♀H3-4	More than 30 suppliers
- 'Alice'	EPfP WPGP
- 'Alison'	EPfP
I - 'Amethyst' Dirr new	MBri
- 'Back Porch'	NLar
- 'Burgundy'	CBcs CPMA EPfP MBri NLar WPGP
- 'Flore Pleno'	see *H. quercifolia* Snowflake = 'Brido'
- 'Harmony'	CEnd CPMA EPfP IArd MBri NLar SSta WHCG WPGP WPat
- 'Lady Anne'	EBee WPGP
- 'Little Honey'	MAsh
* - 'Pee Wee'	CBcs CDoC CMil EMil EPfP LRHS MAsh NLar SHyH SLon SPoG SReu SSta WPGP WPat
- 'Sike's Dwarf'	CEnd CPMA EBee MGos NLar WPat WSpi
- Snow Queen = 'Flemygea'	CBcs CDoC CKno CPMA CSBt CWSG EBee ELan EPfP LCro MGos MRav MSte NLar SHyH SLim SPer SPla SWvt WFar WHCG WPGP WPat WSpi
- 'Snowdrift' new	CPMA
§ - Snowflake = 'Brido' (d)	CAbP CBcs CDoC CEnd CHar CMil CPMA CSPN CWGN EBee ELan EMil EPfP LRHS MAsh MGos MRav SLon SPer SPla SPoG SSpi SSta WBod WHCG WPGP WPat
- 'Tennessee Clone'	EBee MBri NLar
sargentiana	see *H. aspera* subsp. *sargentiana*
scandens B&SWJ 5523	WCru
- B&SWJ 5893	WCru
§ - subsp. ***chinensis***	CPLG CPle WFar
- - B&SWJ 1488	WCru
- - B&SWJ 3214	WCru
- - B&SWJ 3420	WCru
- - B&SWJ 3423 from Taiwan	WCru
- - BWJ 8000 from Sichuan	WCru
§ - - f. ***angustipetala***	WPGP
- - - B&SWJ 3454	WCru
- - - B&SWJ 3814	WCru
- - - B&SWJ 6038 from Yakushima	WCru
- - - B&SWJ 7121	WCru
§ - - f. ***formosana***	NLar
- - - B&SWJ 7097	WCru
§ - - f. ***macrosepala*** B&SWJ 3476	WCru
§ - - f. ***obovatifolia*** B&SWJ 3487b	WCru
- subsp. ***liukiuensis***	WCru
- - B&SWJ 6022	WCru
- 'Splash' (v)	CMil
seemannii	More than 30 suppliers
serrata	CPLG CWib WKif
- B&SWJ 4817	WCru
- B&SWJ 6241	WCru
- 'Acuminata'	see *H. serrata* 'Bluebird'
- 'Aigaku' (L)	CLAP CPLG WPGP
- Amacha Group	CGHE
- - 'Amagi-amacha' (L)	CMil
- - 'Ō-amacha'	CMil
- 'Amagyana' (L)	CGHE CPLG WPGP
- 'Belle Deckle'	see *H. serrata* 'Blue Deckle'
- 'Beni-gaku' (L)	CLAP CMil CPLG GGGa MAsh NBro NLar SHyH SMer WPGP
- 'Beni-yama' (L)	CGHE CMil WPGP
- 'Blue Billow' (L)	GGGa MAsh NLar
§ - 'Blue Deckle' (L)	CMHG CMac CWsd MAsh MRav SHyH SPla WPGP
§ - 'Bluebird' (L) ♀H3-4	More than 30 suppliers
- 'Diadem' (L) ♀H3-4	CMil CPLG EQua SDix WPGP
- dwarf white (L)	WCru
- Fuji Snowstorm	see *H. serrata* 'Fuji-no-shirayuki'
- 'Fuji Waterfall'	see *H. serrata* 'Fuji-no-taki'
§ - 'Fuji-no-shirayuki' (L/d)	CMil
§ - 'Fuji-no-taki' (L/d)	CAbP CMil LSou LTwo MSte NCGa SMad SPoG WBor WCot WCra
- 'Golden Showers' (L)	CMil GGGa MAsh
- 'Golden Sunlight'PBR (L)	CBcs CDoC SMad SPoG SWvt
- 'Graciosa' (L)	CMil MAsh WPGP
- 'Grayswood' (L) ♀H3-4	CBcs CEnd CMac CSBt CWSG EQua ERas GQui LRHS MAsh MBri MRav SDix SGar SHyH SPer SSpi WBor WKif WPGP
- 'Hallasan' misapplied	see *H. serrata* 'Maiko', 'Spreading Beauty'
- 'Hallasan' ambig. (L)	CMil
- 'Hime-benigaku' (L)	CLAP CMil
- 'Intermedia' (L)	CPLG NBro
- 'Kiyosumi' (L)	CDoC CEnd CGHE CLAP CMil CPLG ECre GGGa GQui WCru WPGP WSpi
- 'Klaveren'	see *H. macrophylla* 'Klaveren'
- 'Koreana' (L)	GGGa
- 'Kurenai' (L)	NLar SKHP SSpi
- 'Kurenai-nishiki' (L/v)	CMil
- 'Macrosepala' (L)	SHyH
§ - 'Maiko' (L)	IArd
- 'Midora' new	CPLG
- 'Miranda' (L) ♀H3-4	CBow CBrd CPLG CSam CWsd MAsh SHyH SSpi WFar
- 'Miyama-yae-murasaki' (L/d)	CGHE CLAP CMil LRHS MAsh SHyH SKHP WPGP
- 'Preziosa'	see *H.* 'Preziosa'
- 'Professeur Iida' (L)	WPGP
- 'Prolifera' (L/d)	CGHE CMil WPGP
- 'Ramis Pictis' (L)	ERas MAsh WPGP
- 'Rosalba' (L) ♀H3-4	CLAP CPLG EPfP SPer SPla WFar WSHC
- 'Shichidanka-nishiki' (L/d/v)	CBcs CDoC CGHE CPLG ECre LRHS SHyH WBor
- 'Shinonome' (L/d)	CLAP CMil GQui WPGP
- 'Shirofuji' (L/d)	CLAP CMil LRHS WPGP
- 'Shirotae' (L/d)	CMil WPGP
- 'Shōjō' new	MAsh
§ - 'Spreading Beauty' (L)	CMil WPGP
- var. ***thunbergii*** (L)	CMHG GQui WFar WPGP
* - - 'Plena' (L/d)	WCru
- 'Tiara' (L) ♀H3-4	CAbb CMil CWsd GGGa MAsh MBri NLar SDix SHyH SSpi WPGP WSHC
- 'Uzu-azisai'	WPGP
- 'Yae-no-amacha' (L/d)	CBcs SHyH WPGP
§ ***serratifolia***	CHEx EPfP EPla SPoG SSpi SSta WCru WFar WPGP

sikokiana CLAP
- B&SWJ 5035 WCru
- B&SWJ 5855 WCru
tiliifolia see *H. anomala* subsp. *petiolaris*
villosa see *H. aspera* Villosa Group
'Water Wagtail' new ERas
xanthoneura see *H. heteromalla*
'You and Me' new LBuc

Hydrastis (*Ranunculaceae*)
canadensis CArn COld GBuc GPoy WCru

Hydrocharis (*Hydrocharitaceae*)
morsus-ranae CDWL EHon EMFW NPer NSco SWat WPnP

Hydrocleys (*Limnocharitaceae*)
nymphoides XBlo

Hydrocotyle (*Apiaceae*)
asiatica see *Centella asiatica*
sibthorpioides CBow
- 'Crystal Confetti' CPLG EBee EMan EPPr EShb LLWG SIng WHer WMoo WPer
vulgaris EMFW

Hydrophilus (*Restionaceae*)
rattrayi CBig

Hydrophyllum (*Hydrophyllaceae*)
canadense CLAP EBee
macrophyllum new EBee
virginianum CLAP CPom EBee MSal

Hylomecon (*Papaveraceae*)
* ***erecta*** EBee
* ***hylomecoides*** WCru
§ ***japonica*** CDes CFwr CMea CPom EBee ECho ELan GBuc GCra GCrs GEdr GKev MSte NBir NDov NMen NRya SHGN WAbe WCru WFar WHil WPnP WTin

Hylotelephium see *Sedum*

Hymenanthera see *Melicytus*

Hymenocallis (*Amaryllidaceae*)
'Advance' CHHB EBrs ECho LAma LRHS
§ ***caroliniana*** ECho WCot
x ***festalis*** ♀H1 CPom ECho EPfP ERea IHer LAma LRHS MBri SPav WCot WFar
- 'Zwanenburg' EBrs ECho
harrisiana EBrs ECho LRHS WCot
latifolia new WCot
§ ***longipetala*** EBrs ECho LRHS WCot
occidentalis see *H. caroliniana*
'Sulphur Queen' ♀H1 CBgR CHHB EBrs ECho LRHS SPav WCot

Hymenolepis (*Asteraceae*)
parviflora see *Athanasia parviflora*

Hymenosporum (*Pittosporaceae*)
flavum SOWG

Hymenoxys (*Asteraceae*)
grandiflora see *Tetraneuris grandiflora*
§ ***hoopesii*** CWib EBee EBla EHrv ELan EPfP EShb EWTr GAbr GMaP GSki LCro LHop LRHS MNrw NBir NChi NEgg NPri NSti SECG SPer SPhx SRms WCot WFar WHoo WMnd WMoo WPer
torreyana CPBP

Hyophorbe (*Arecaceae*)
lagenicaulis LPal
verschaffeltii LPal

Hyoscyamus (*Solanaceae*)
albus CSpe MSal
niger CArn GPoy MSal

Hyparrhenia (*Poaceae*)
hirta XPep

Hypericum ✿ (*Clusiaceae*)
CC 4131 CPLG MGol
CC 4543 MGol
CC 4544 CPLG
acmosepalum WPGP WPat
aegypticum CLyd ECho ECtt EPot LRHS MHer NMen NWCA SBla SRot WAbe WFar WLin WOld WPat WPer XPep
androsaemum CArn CRWN EAro ECha ELan ELau MHer MRav MSal MSwo NPer NSco SHFr WMoo WOut
§ - 'Albury Purple' CElw EShb GBuc LDai MRav SGar WHrl WMoo WPtf
- 'Autumn Blaze' CBcs EQua MGos
§ - 'Dart's Golden Penny' EQua SPer
- 'Excellent Flair' MGos NLar
- 'Orange Flair' EQua MGos
§ - f. ***variegatum*** 'Mrs Gladis Brabazon' (v) EAro MWgw NBir NLar NScw NSti SBod SLon SPoG WHrl
'Archibald' EBee
athoum CLyd NBir WPat WThu
atomarium EBee WPGP
balearicum EHrv MTho SDry WAbe WPGP XPep
§ ***beanii*** WBod
bellum EBee SLon
- subsp. ***latisepalum*** SLon
buckleyi SBla
calycinum CBcs CDul CTri ECho ECrN ELan ENot EPfP LBuc MBar MGos MRav MWat NEgg NWea SHBN SWvt WGwG WMoo WTel
- 'Senior' EWin
cerastioides CTri CWib LBee LRHS SIng SPoG SRms WAbe WFar WPer
coris ECho EWes LRHS MTho MWat SRms
crux-andreae EBee
cuneatum see *H. pallens*
x ***cyathiflorum*** 'Gold Cup' CDoC CMac
x ***dummeri*** 'Peter Dummer' NLar WSpi
elatum see *H.* x *inodorum*
elodes EMFW
empetrifolium EBee ECho XPep
- 'Prostatum' see *H. empetrifolium* subsp. *tortuosum*
§ - subsp. ***tortuosum*** CLyd ECho EWes
§ ***forrestii*** ♀H4 EPfP LRHS WFar WPGP
- B&L 12469 WPGP
- Hird 54 WPGP
N ***fragile*** hort. see *H. olympicum* f. *minus*
frondosum 'Buttercup' NLar
- 'Sunburst' EPfP WFar
N 'Gemo' MGos
'Gold Penny' see *H. androsaemum* 'Dart's Golden Penny'
'Golden Beacon' CBow CElw EBee EMil EQua LAst LSou MAsh MGol NCGa NEgg NLar SMad SPer SPoG WCot WWeb
grandiflorum see *H. kouytchense*
henryi NPen

- L 753	SRms
'Hidcote' ♀H4	More than 30 suppliers
'Hidcote Variegated' (v)	CBow MAsh MCCP SLim SPer SRms WBrE WFar WWeb
hircinum subsp. ***cambessedesii***	LRHS
hirsutum	NMir
§ x ***inodorum***	EAro NBir
- 'Albury Purple'	see *H. androsaemum* 'Albury Purple'
- 'Dream' **new**	NLar
- 'Elstead'	EBee ECrN ECtt ELan EPfP MBar MGos MMHG MRav MWat NBlu SHBN SRms WHCG WSpi
- 'Hysan'	GGar
- 'Ysella'	MRav MSwo MTPN SDry
japonicum	ECho EWes
kalmianum	EWes
kamtschaticum	ECho
§ ***kiusianum*** var. ***yakusimense***	MBar MTho NPro
§ ***kouytchense*** ♀H4	CBcs CMCN EBee ECrN EPfP EQua EWes GQui LRHS MAsh MRav NLar SDry WBVN WCFE WHrl WPat WSpi
lancasteri	EBee EPfP LRHS MAsh SPoG WPat
leschenaultii misapplied	see *H.* 'Rowallane'
leschenaultii Choisy	CMCN
linarioides	EBee
maclarenii	EWes WPGP
Magical Beauty = 'Kolmbeau'PBR **new**	NLar
Magical Red = 'Kolmred'PBR **new**	NLar SPoG
x ***moserianum*** ♀H4	EBee ECrN ENot EPfP LBMP MBar MRav NPer SHBN SLon SPer SRms
§ - 'Tricolor' (v)	More than 30 suppliers
- 'Variegatum'	see *H.* x *moserianum* 'Tricolor'
'Mrs Brabazon'	see *H. androsaemum* f. *variegatum* 'Mrs Gladis Brabazon'
nummularium	NBir WAbe
oblongifolium	CPLG WCot
- CC 4546	GKev MGol
olympicum ♀H4	CEnt CHrt CTri ECha ECho ELan EPfP GMaP LRHS MBrN MWat SBla SHGN SIng SPer SRms WFar WHen XPep
- 'Grandiflorum'	see *H. olympicum* f. *uniflorum*
§ - f. ***minus***	CTri EBee ECho ECtt GKev SPlb SRms WFar WHrl WPer
§ - - 'Sulphureum'	CChe CPrp ECho EWes GMaP LRHS MLLN NBir SPer SRms WCFE WFar
§ - - 'Variegatum' (v)	CBow EWes LBee NBir NLAp SPoG WPat
§ - f. ***uniflorum***	ECho MBar NBro NPri NVic SEND
- - 'Citrinum' ♀H4	CBgR CMea EBee ECha ECtt EPfP LBee LRHS MRav MWat NBro NCGa NDlv NLAp SBla SPoG WCot WEas WHoo WKif WLin WPGP WPat
orientale	EWes SHGN
§ ***pallens***	ECho NMen
patulum var. ***forrestii***	see *H. forrestii*
- var. ***henryi*** Rehder & hort.	see *H. pseudohenryi*
- var. ***henryi*** Veitch ex Bean	see *H. beanii*
perforatum	CArn CBod CHby CWan EBee ELau EPfP EUnu GPoy MHer MNHC NMir SEND SIde WHer WJek WMoo WSel
- 'Elixir'	EUnu
- 'Topaz'	MSal
polyphyllum	see *H. olympicum* f. *minus*
- 'Citrinum'	see *H. olympicum* f. *minus* 'Sulphureum'
- 'Grandiflorum'	see *H. olympicum* f. *uniflorum*
- 'Sulphureum'	see *H. olympicum* f. *minus* 'Sulphureum'
- 'Variegatum'	see *H. olympicum* f. *minus* 'Variegatum'
prolificum	ECtt EPla GAbr MMHG WCFE
§ ***pseudohenryi*** L 1029	GBuc
pseudopetiolatum var. ***yakusimense***	see *H. kiusianum* var. *yakusimense*
quadrangulum L.	see *H. tetrapterum*
reptans misapplied	see *H. olympicum* f. *minus*
reptans Dyer	CMea ECho EWes
§ 'Rowallane' ♀H3	CPSs CTrC EPfP ISea SDix SHBN SMrm SSpi WBod
stellatum	EMon WFar
'Sungold'	see *H. kouytchense*
tenuicaule KR 743	ISea
§ ***tetrapterum***	CArn MSal NSco
tomentosum	XPep
trichocaulon	EWes WAbe WPat
uralum HWJ 520	WCru
xylosteifolium	SLon
yakusimense	see *H. kiusianum* var. *yakusimense*

Hypocalymma (*Myrtaceae*)

angustifolium	ECou SOWG
cordifolium 'Golden Veil' (v)	ECou

Hypocalyptus (*Papilionaceae*)

sophoroides	CPLG SPlb

Hypochaeris (*Asteraceae*)

maculata	WHer
radicata	NMir

Hypocyrta see *Nematanthus*

Hypoestes (*Acanthaceae*)

aristata	CPLG ERea EShb WHil
§ ***phyllostachya*** (v) ♀H1	MBri
- 'Bettina' (v)	MBri
- 'Carmina' (v)	MBri
- 'Purpuriana' (v)	MBri
- 'Wit' (v)	MBri
sanguinolenta misapplied	see *H. phyllostachya*

Hypolepis (*Dennstaedtiaceae*)

alpina	EAmu
millefolium	GGar WCot
punctata	EFer

Hypoxis (*Hypoxidaceae*)

hirsuta	CPen CWsd ECho
hygrometrica	EBrs ECho ECou NMen WAbe WThu
krebsii	ECho
parvula	CTca NMen
- var. ***albiflora***	EBrs ITim
§ - - 'Hebron Farm Biscuit'	ECho EWes GEdr SBla WAbe WFar
- pink-flowered	EBrs
* ***tasmanica***	EMan
villosa	ECho ERea

Hypoxis x *Rhodohypoxis* see x *Rhodoxis*

H. parvula x ***R. baurii***	see x *Rhodoxis hybrida*

Hypsela (*Campanulaceae*)

sp.	CFee
longiflora	see *H. reniformis*
§ ***reniformis***	EAlp ECho EDAr EMan GGar LAst LBee LRHS MRav NWCA SIng SPoG WFar
- 'Greencourt White'	ECho GBuc

Hypseocharis (*Oxalidaceae*)

	pimpinellifolia	WCot

Hyssopus ✿ (*Lamiaceae*)

	ambiguus	XPep
	officinalis	CArn CHby CSev ECha ELan ELau EPfP EUnu GPoy LBuc LRHS MBNS MBar MBri MHer MLHP MNHC MRav NGHP SGar SIde SPlb WGwG WPer XPep
	- f. ***albus***	CSev CWan EBee ECha ELau EPfP EWin GPoy MHer MNHC NGHP SBch SGar SHGN SIde SPlb WGwG WJek WPer WSel
	- subsp. ***aristatus***	CArn CBod CHrt CWan EBee ECho ELau GPoy LLWP MHer MNHC NChi SIde WEas WJek WSel
	- 'Blaue Wolke'	GBin
	- subsp. ***canescens***	EAro XPep
	- 'Roseus'	CEnt CHrt CSev EBee ECha ELau EPfP EWin GPoy LLWP MBNS MHer MNHC NGHP SBch SHGN SIde WGwG WJek WKif WPer
*	***schugnanicus***	EBee MHar

Hystrix (*Poaceae*)

	patula	CHrt CKno CPLG EMon EPPr EShb GFor ILad LLWP MCCP MMoz MNrw NHol NOak SHFr SPlb SWal WPer WRos WTin XIsg

Iberis (*Brassicaceae*)

	aurosica 'Sweetheart'	GEdr
	candolleana	see *I. pruitii* Candolleana Group
	commutata	see *I. sempervirens*
	'Correvoniana'	WEas
	'Dick Self'	LRHS
	gibraltarica	ECho EWin LRav NPri SRms WGor
	- 'Betty Swainson'	CHrt GBri SMrm
	'Golden Candy'	CHVG CRez EAlp SPoG WFar
§	***pruitii*** Candolleana Group	ECho WAbe WFar
	saxatilis	ECho EDAr LRHS XPep
	- ***candolleana***	see *I. pruitii* Candolleana Group
	semperflorens	WCFE WSPU XPep
§	***sempervirens*** 🏆H4	CBcs CTri CWib ECho ELan EPfP IFoB LAst MHer MWat NBlu NBro NEgg NHol NOrc NPri NVic SEND SRms SWal WBrE WCFE WFar WHoo WPer
	- 'Compacta'	ECho
	- 'Little Gem'	see *I. sempervirens* 'Weisser Zwerg'
	- 'Pygmaea'	ECho NMen SBla
	- Schneeflocke	see *I. sempervirens* 'Snowflake'
§	- 'Snowflake' 🏆H4	ECho EPfP GAbr GEdr IFoB LRHS LRav NBlu SBch SPer SPoG SWvt WFar WRHF
	- Snowflake	see *I. sempervirens* 'Snowflake'
§	- 'Weisser Zwerg'	CMea CPLG ECha ECho ECtt ELan LAst LBee LRHS MHer MRav NMen NRya SBla SPoG SRms WAbe WHoo

Idesia (*Flacourtiaceae*)

	polycarpa	CAbP CBcs CDul CMCN CWoW EPfP IDee LHop NLar NPen SSpi WBVN WFar WPGP WPat

Ilex ✿ (*Aquifoliaceae*)

N	x ***altaclerensis***	SHHo STop
	- 'Atkinsonii' (m)	SHHo WWHy
	- 'Balearica'	SHHo
	- 'Barterberry' (f)	WWHy
	- 'Belgica' (f)	SHHo
§	- 'Belgica Aurea' (f/v) 🏆H4	CBcs CDoC CPMA CSBt CTho EBee EPfP EQua ERas LRHS MBar MBri MSwo NHol NWea SHBN SHHo WFar WWHy
	- 'Camelliifolia' (f) 🏆H4	CDul CSBt CTho EBee ELan EPfP IFoB MBlu MBri MWat NLar NWea SHHo SPla STop WFar WSpi WWHy
	- 'Golden King' (f/v) 🏆H4	More than 30 suppliers
	- 'Hendersonii' (f)	SHHo WWHy
	- 'Hodginsii' (m) 🏆H4	CTri ECot MBar MRav SEND SHHo WFar WWHy
	- 'Howick' (f/v)	SHHo
	- 'James G. Esson' (f)	SHHo
	- 'Jermyns' (m) **new**	SHHo
	- 'Lady Valerie' (f/v)	SHHo WWHy
	- 'Lawsoniana' (f/v) 🏆H4	CDoC CSBt CSam EBee ELan EPfP LRHS MAsh MBar MBri MRav MWat NBlu NHol NWea SHBN SHHo SLim SLon SPer SPla SPoG SRms WBVN WFar WPat WTel WWHy
	- 'Maderensis Variegata'	see *I. aquifolium* 'Maderensis Variegata'
	- 'Marnockii' (f)	SHHo WWHy
	- 'Moorei' (m)	SHHo
	- 'Mundyi' (m)	SHHo
	- 'N.F. Barnes' (f) **new**	SHHo
	- 'Purple Shaft' (f)	EQua MRav SHHo
	- 'Ripley Gold' (f/v)	MAsh NHol SHHo STop WWHy
	- 'Silver Sentinel'	see *I.* x *altaclerensis* 'Belgica Aurea'
	- 'W.J. Bean' (f)	SHHo
	- 'Wilsonii' (f)	EBee EPfP LPan SHHo WWHy
	aquifolium 🏆H4	More than 30 suppliers
	- 'Alaska' (f)	CDoC CMCN EMil ENot LAst LBuc NBlu NHol NLar NSti SHHo STop SWvt WFar WWHy
	- 'Amber' (f) 🏆H4	CTri EQua SHHo SMad WWHy
	- 'Angustifolia' (f)	EPla MAsh WCFE WFar WWHy
	- 'Angustifolia' (m or f)	EPfP MBar MWat SHHo SPoG WBVN WFar
	- 'Angustimarginata Aurea' (m/v)	SHHo
	- 'Argentea Longifolia' **new**	WWHy
§	- 'Argentea Marginata' (f/v) 🏆H4	More than 30 suppliers
§	- 'Argentea Marginata Pendula' (f/v)	CDoC CTri ELan EMil EPfP LPan LRHS MAsh MRav NHol NLar SHHo SRms WFar WPat WWHy
	- 'Argentea Pendula'	see *I. aquifolium* 'Argentea Marginata Pendula'
	- 'Argentea Variegata'	see *I. aquifolium* 'Argentea Marginata'
	- 'Atlas' (m)	CBcs CDoC LBuc WWHy
	- 'Aurea Marginata' (f/v)	CDul CTho EBee LBuc MGos NBlu NEgg NHol NWea SBod SCoo SHBN SHHo WCFE WFar WPat
	- 'Aurea Marginata Pendula' (f/v)	CDoC MAsh NHol NLar WPat
	- 'Aurea Marginata Stricta' (f/v)	WWHy
	- 'Aurea Ovata'	see *I. aquifolium* 'Ovata Aurea'
	- 'Aurea Regina'	see *I. aquifolium* 'Golden Queen'
	- 'Aureovariegata Pendula'	see *I. aquifolium* 'Weeping Golden Milkmaid'
	- 'Aurifodina' (f)	IMGH SHHo WWHy
§	- 'Bacciflava' (f)	CBcs CDoC CDul CSBt CTho CTri EBee ECrN ELan ENot EPfP MBar

		MBlu MBri MGan MGos MRav NBlu NEgg NHol NWea SHHo SPer SRms SWvt WCFE WFar WWHy
	- 'Bella' (f)	SHHo
	- 'Bokrijk'	SHHo
	- 'Bowland' (f/v)	MAsh NHol
	- 'Cookii' (f)	SHHo WWHy
	- 'Crassifolia' (f)	CWib EPla SHHo SMad WWHy
	- 'Crispa' (m)	EBee MBlu NHol SHHo WWHy
	- 'Crispa Aureomaculata'	see *I. aquifolium* 'Crispa Aureopicta'
§	- 'Crispa Aureopicta' (m/v)	SHHo WWHy
	- 'Elegantissima' (m/v)	SCoo SHHo WWHy
	- 'Ferox' (m)	CDul ELan EPfP LRHS SHHo STop WGwG WWHy
	- 'Ferox Argentea' (m/v) Υ^{H4}	More than 30 suppliers
*	- 'Ferox Argentea Picta' (m/v)	LRHS WFar WWHy
	- 'Ferox Aurea' (m/v)	CDoC CPMA CSBt CWib EBee ELan EPfP LAst MAsh NHol SHHo SPla WWHy
§	- 'Flavescens' (f)	EBee EMil EPfP NHol SHHo
	- 'Frogmore Silver' **new**	EQua SHHo
	- 'Fructu Luteo'	see *I. aquifolium* 'Bacciflava'
	- 'Gold Flash' (f/v)	EBee LRHS MAsh MBri MGos NBlu NHol SHHo WWHy
	- 'Golden Hedgehog'	SHHo SPoG WWHy
	- 'Golden Milkboy' (m/v)	EBee ELan EPfP MBlu MGos SHHo SPoG WPat WWHy
§	- 'Golden Queen' (m/v) Υ^{H4}	CDoC CDul CWSG CWib EBee LRHS MGos NBir NHol NWea SHHo SPer SRms WPat WWHy
	- 'Golden Tears'	SHHo WWHy
	- 'Golden van Tol' (f/v)	CBcs CDoC CLnd CSBt CTri EBee ECrN ELan ENot EPfP IMGH LAst LRHS MAsh MBar MBlu MGos MSwo NHol SCoo SHBN SHHo SRms WWHy WWeb
§	- 'Green Pillar' (f)	EPfP MBar SHHo WWHy
	- 'Green Spire'	see *I. aquifolium* 'Green Pillar'
	- 'Handsworth New Silver' (f/v) Υ^{H4}	More than 30 suppliers
	- 'Harpune' (f)	SHHo WWHy
§	- 'Hascombensis'	CDoC LHop MGos NHol NMen WFar WWHy
	- 'Hastata' (m)	CWib IArd WWHy
	- 'Ingramii' (m/v)	SHHo WWHy
	- 'Integrifolia' **new**	WWHy
	- 'J.C. van Tol' (f/m) Υ^{H4}	More than 30 suppliers
	- 'Latispina' (f)	SHHo WWHy
	- 'Laurifolia Aurea' (m/v)	SHHo
	- 'Lichtenthalii' (f)	IArd SHHo
	- 'Madame Briot' (f/v) Υ^{H4}	CDoC CDul CSBt CTri CWib EBee ELan ENot EPfP ERas IMGH LAst LBuc LRHS MAsh MBar MBri MRav MSwo NEgg NHol NWea SCoo SHHo SPer SRms SWvt WFar WMoo WWHy
§	- 'Maderensis Variegata' (m/v)	SHHo
	- 'Monstrosa' (m)	SHHo
	- 'Moonlight' **new**	EQua
	- moonlight holly	see *I. aquifolium* 'Flavescens'
	- 'Myrtifolia' (m)	ELan EPfP LPan MBar MBlu MGos MRav NBlu NLar SCoo SHHo SPoG WFar WWHy
	- 'Myrtifolia Aurea' (m/v)	SPoG SWvt WFar
§	- 'Myrtifolia Aurea Maculata' (m/v) Υ^{H4}	CBgR CBrm CDoC CSam EBee ELan EPfP IMGH LAst LRHS MAsh MBri MRav NEgg NHol NWea SHHo SMad SPer SPoG SWvt WFar WPat WWHy
	- 'Myrtifolia Aureovariegata'	see *I. aquifolium* 'Myrtifolia Aurea Maculata'
	- 'Ovata' (m)	WWHy
§	- 'Ovata Aurea' (m/v)	SHHo WWHy
	- 'Pendula' (f)	EPfP SHHo
	- 'Pendula Mediopicta'	see *I. aquifolium* 'Weeping Golden Milkmaid'
§	- 'Pyramidalis' (f) Υ^{H4}	CDoC CDul CEnd CSBt CTho CTri EBee ELan IFoB LRHS MAsh MBar MBri MGan MGos NBlu NHol NLar NWea SHHo SPer SRms WFar WMoo WWHy
	- 'Pyramidalis Aureomarginata' (f/v)	CDoC LRHS MBri MGos NLar SHHo WBor
	- 'Pyramidalis Fructu Luteo' (f) Υ^{H4}	MBar NWea SHHo
	- 'Recurva' (m)	SHHo WWHy
	- 'Rubricaulis Aurea' (f/v)	CBgR NHol SHHo STop WWHy
	- 'Scotica' (f)	SHHo WWHy
	- Siberia = 'Limsi'^{PBR} (f)	EBee SHHo WWHy
	- 'Silver King'	see *I. aquifolium* 'Silver Queen'
	- 'Silver Lining' (f/v)	SHHo STop
	- 'Silver Milkboy' (f/v)	ELan LRHS MBNS MBlu MGos WFar WWHy
	- 'Silver Milkmaid' (f/v)	CBgR CDoC CWSG EBee EPfP LAst LRHS MAsh MBar MRav NEgg NHol SHBN SHHo SLim SPer SPla SPoG SWvt WMoo WWHy
§	- 'Silver Queen' (m/v) Υ^{H4}	More than 30 suppliers
	- 'Silver Sentinel'	see *I.* x *altaclerensis* 'Belgica Aurea'
	- 'Silver van Tol' (f/v)	CDoC ELan IMGH LAst LRHS NHol NLar NPer NWea SHHo SMer WFar WWHy WWeb
	- 'Somerset Cream' (f/v)	CPMA CWib NLar WWHy
§	- 'Watereriana' (m/v)	MAsh SHHo
	- 'Waterer's Gold'	see *I. aquifolium* 'Watereriana'
§	- 'Weeping Golden Milkmaid' (f/v)	SHHo WPat
	x ***aquipernyi***	SHHo
	- Dragon Lady = 'Meschick' (f)	LPan MBri NLar SHHo WWHy
	- 'San Jose' (f)	CMCN SHHo
	x ***attenuata***	WFar
	- 'Sunny Foster' (f/v)	CMCN ENot EPla MGos SHHo WFar
§	***bioritsensis***	CMCN CTri NWea
	buergeri	CMCN
	cassine	CMCN
	- var. ***angustifolia***	STop
	centrochinensis **new**	CBcs
	China Boy = 'Mesdob' **new**	SHHo
	China Girl = 'Mesog' **new**	SHHo
	chinensis misapplied	see *I. purpurea*
	ciliospinosa	CMCN WPGP
	colchica	CMCN SHHo
	corallina	CBcs CMCN
	cornuta	ERom LPan LRHS SHHo WFar
*	- 'Aurea'	SHHo
	- 'Burfordii' (f)	SHHo
§	- 'Dazzler' (f)	LPan SHHo
	- 'Fine Line' (f)	SHHo
	- 'Ira S. Nelson' (f/v)	SHHo
	- 'O. Spring' (f/v)	SHHo WSpi
	- 'Rotunda' (f)	SHHo
I	- 'Willowleaf' (f)	SHHo
	crenata	CMCN CTri ERom GCra MBar MGos SAPC SArc SHHo WFar WNor
	- 'Akagi'	WFar
	- 'Aureovariegata'	see *I. crenata* 'Variegata'
	- 'Cole's Hardy' (f)	SHHo
	- 'Convexa' (f) Υ^{H4}	EMil EPfP IMGH LPan MBar MBri MRav MSwo NBlu NHol NWea WFar WGwG WPat
	- 'Convexed Gold'	EMil MBri SPoG
	- 'Fastigiata' (f)	CDoC CEnd ECrN EPfP EPla LAst LRHS MAsh MBNS MBar MBri

		MGos NBlu NLar SCoo SHHo SPer SPoG WBod WFar
	- 'Fukarin'	see *I. crenata* 'Shiro-fukurin'
*	- 'Glory Gem' (f)	CBcs LPan
	- 'Gold Tips'	MGos
	- 'Golden Gem' (f) ♀H4	More than 30 suppliers
	- 'Green Hedge'	EMil LBuc
	- 'Green Island' (m)	SHHo
	- 'Green Lustre' (f)	SHHo
	- 'Helleri' (f)	CMCN EPfP EPla MBar SBla SHHo WPat
	- 'Hetzii' (f)	NLar SHHo
	- 'Ivory Hall' (f)	EPla
*	- 'Kobold'	SHHo
	- 'Korean Gem'	SHHo
	- 'Luteovariegata'	see *I. crenata* 'Variegata'
	- 'Mariesii' (f)	CMac IMGH MBlu SBla SIng
I	- 'Pyramidalis' (f)	NHol NWea
	- 'Shiroe' **new**	IClo
§	- 'Shiro-fukurin' (f/v)	CMCN CMHG ELan EPfP LAst LRHS MAsh SHHo
	- 'Sky Pencil' (f)	CMCN
	- 'Snowflake'	see *I. crenata* 'Shiro-fukurin'
	- 'Stokes' (m)	EMil NHol NLar
§	- 'Variegata' (v)	CMCN CMac EPla LRHS MBar SPoG
	'Dazzler'	see *I. cornuta* 'Dazzler'
	decidua	CMCN
	dimorphophylla	CBcs CDoC CMCN CMac SHHo SMad
	- 'Somerset Pixie'	SHHo
	'Doctor Kassab' (f)	CMCN SHHo
	'Drace' (f)	SHHo
	'Elegance' (f)	WFar
	fargesii	CPne
	ficoidea	CMCN
	glabra	SHHo
	'Good Taste' (f)	SHHo WFar WWHy
	hascombensis	see *I. aquifolium* 'Hascombensis'
	hookeri	SHHo
	'Indian Chief' (f)	MBlu SMad WFar
	insignis	see *I. kingiana*
	'John T. Morris' (m)	SHHo
§	***kingiana***	WFar WPGP
	x ***koehneana***	CDul ELan
	- 'Chestnut Leaf' (f) ♀H4	CCVT CDoC CLnd CMCN EMil EPfP EQua IClo MBri MRav SHHo SMad WFar WLeb WPGP WWHy
	- 'Wirt L. Winn' **new**	WWHy
	latifolia	CBcs CHEx CMCN EMil SHHo SMad WPGP
	'Lydia Morris' (f)	CSam SHHo WFar
	'Mary Nell' (f)	SHHo
	maximowicziana var. ***kanehirae***	WWHy
	x ***meserveae***	SHHo
	- Blue Angel = 'Conang' (f)	CBcs CDoC CDul EBee ELan EMil EPfP IFoB IMGH LPan MBar MBri MLan MWat NBlu NEgg NHol NWea SHHo SPoG SRms WFar WPat WWHy
	- Blue Maid = 'Mesid' (f)	EWTr WWHy
	- Blue Prince = 'Conablu' (m)	CBcs CBrm CDoC EBee GKev LBuc LPan MBar MBlu NBlu NHol NWea SHBN SHHo SLim SPoG WFar WWHy
	- Blue Princess = 'Conapri' (f)	CBcs CBrm ECrN ENot EPfP LBuc LPan MBar MBlu MRav NBlu NHol NSti NWea SCoo SHBN SHHo SLim SPer SPoG WWHy
	- Golden Girl = 'Mesgolg' (f)	WWHy
	- 'Goliath' (f) **new**	WWHy
	myrtifolia	CMCN ECot MLan MRav NEgg NPri
	'Nellie R. Stevens' (f)	EBee LPan NWea SCoo WWHy
	opaca	CMCN
	paraguariensis	EOHP
	pedunculosa	CMCN
	perado latifolia	see *I. perado* subsp. *platyphylla*
	- subsp. ***perado***	CBcs
§	- subsp. ***platyphylla***	CBcs CHEx CMCN MBlu SAPC SArc SHHo WWHy
	pernyi	CMCN CMac CTrG CTri EPfP LRHS SHHo SLon WFar WPic WWHy
	- var. ***veitchii***	see *I. bioritsensis*
§	***purpurea***	CMCN SPla
	'Pyramidalis'	see *I. aquifolium* 'Pyramidalis'
	rugosa	WWHy
	'September Gem' (f)	CMCN
	serrata	CMen
	suaveolens	CMCN
	verticillata	CMCN IMGH WFar
	- (f)	EPfP NLar NWea WFar
	- (m)	EPfP NLar
	- 'Christmas Cheer' (f)	WFar
	- 'Jim Dandy' (m)	MBlu
	- 'Maryland Beauty' (f)	CPMA MBlu
	- 'Southern Gentleman' (m)	CPMA MBlu
	- 'Winter Red' (f)	CMCN CPMA MBlu
	vomitoria	CMCN EShb SHHo
	x ***wandoensis***	CMCN SHHo WWHy
	'Washington' (f)	SHHo WWHy
	yunnanensis	CMCN SHHo

Iliamna see *Sphaeralcea*

Illicium (*Illiciaceae*)

	anisatum	CArn CBcs CFwr CWsd EPfP MBri NLar SSpi WFar WPGP WSHC
	floridanum	CBcs CFwr EBee EPfP MBri NLar SKHP SSpi SSta WPat
I	- 'Compactum'	WPGP
	- 'Halley's Comet'	NLar
	henryi	CGHE CMCN CMHG CPLG CWib EBee EPfP MBri NLar SKHP SSpi WPGP WSHC
	aff. ***henryi***	CBcs
	mexicanum	SKHP
	parviflorum	SKHP
	simonsii	CExc
	- BWJ 8024	WCru

Ilysanthes see *Lindernia*

Impatiens ✿ (*Balsaminaceae*)

	CC 4980 **new**	CPLG
	apiculata	CKob MDKP
	arguta	CDes CFir CLAP CPLG CPom CSpe EBee EMan EShb LSou MCCP MDKP WCru WPGP WPrP
	auricoma	EBak SHFr
	- 'Jungle Gold' **new**	LSou
	auricoma x ***bicaudata***	WDib
	balfourii	EHrv EMan EMon NBir
	(Butterfly Series) Butterfly Cherry = 'Butly Cher' **new**	LSou
	- Butterfly Deep Pink = 'Butly DePink' **new**	LSou WGor
	- Butterfly Lavender = 'Butly Laver' **new**	WGor
	- Butterfly Lilac = 'Butly Lilla' **new**	LSou
	- Butterfly Salmon Eye = 'Butly Saley' **new**	LSou
	congolensis	CCCN EPfP
	cristata	CPLG
	'Diamond Rose'	CHal

double-flowered (d)	EBak
flanaganae	WPrP
forrestii	CLAP
aff. ***forrestii*** new	WPrP
'Fusion Sunset' new	LSou
glandulifera 'Candida'	EMon
- 'Mien Ruys'	EMon
gomphophylla new	CFir
(Harmony Series) Harmony Dark Red = 'Danhardkrd'	LAst WGor
- Harmony Lavender	LAst
- Harmony Light Pink ' = 'Danharltpk	LAst
- Harmony Margenta = 'Danharmgta'	LAst LSou
- Harmony Orange Blaze = 'Danharoblaze'	LAst WGor
- Harmony Raspberry Cream	LAst WGor
- Harmony Salmon = 'Danharsal'	LAst WGor
- Harmony Violet = 'Danharvio' new	WGor
hawkeri	see *I. schlechteri*
hians	SHFr
keilii	WDib
kerriae B&SWJ 7219	WCru
kilimanjari subsp. ***kilimanjari*** new	CSpe
kilimanjari x ***pseudoviola***	CFee CKob CPLG CSpe LSou
langbianensis HWJ 1054 new	WCru
longiloba B&SWJ 6623	WCru
macrophylla B&SWJ 10157 new	WCru
'Madame Pompadour'	CHal
New Guinea Group	see *I. schlechteri*
niamniamensis	CHll CTca EBak ERea EShb WCot WDib
- 'Congo Cockatoo'	CDTJ CDoC CHEx CHal EOHP MJnS NPer SHFr SRms
- 'Golden Cockatoo' (v)	CDTJ CDoC CHal EBak EShb MJnS
noli-tangere new	WSFF
omeiana	CFir CHEx CKob CLAP CPLG CPom CSpe CWsd EBee EMan EPPr EShb ITer LHop MCCP MNrw SBch WBor WCot WCru WLin WPGP WPrP WSHC
- DJHC 98492	CWsd
- silver-leaved	CHEx CKob CLAP CSpe EMan LFur LSou MCCP MDKP MHar WCot WPGP WPrP
parasitica	WDib
platypetala B&SWJ 9722 new	WCru WPrP
pseudoviola	SHFr
puberula	WPrP
- HWJK 2063	WCru
'Raspberry Ripple'	CHal
§ ***schlechteri***	EBak MBri NBlu
sodenii	CDTJ CKob CSpe EShb SBHP SHFr
stenantha	CFir WPrP
sulcata	SHFr
sultani	see *I. walleriana*
tinctoria	CDoC CFir CGHE CHEx CHll CKob CPLG CSpe EBee EMon EShb GCra LFur MCCP MNrw WCot WCru WPGP WPrP WWlt
- subsp. ***elegantissima***	CFee
tuberosa	WDib
uniflora	CFir CPLG CSpe LHop LSou MCCP MDKP WPrP
Velvetea = 'Secret Love'PBR	SHFr
violeta B&SWJ 6608	WCru
walkeri	CFee
§ ***walleriana***	EBak MBri
- 'Dapper Dan' (Duet Series) (d/v)	CHal
- (Fiesta Series) 'Burgundy Rose'PBR (d)	LAst
- - Fiesta Appleblossom = 'Balfieplos' (d)	LAst NPri SVil
- - Fiesta Olé Frost = 'Balolefro' (d)	NPri
- - Fiesta Olé Peppermint = 'Balolepep' (d/v)	SVil
- - Fiesta Olé Rose = 'Balolerose'PBR	NPri
- - Fiesta Olé Salmon = 'Balolesal' (d)	NPri
- - Fiesta Olé Stardust = 'Balolestop' (d)	NPri
- - Fiesta Sparkler Cherry = 'Balfiespary' (d)	NPri
- - Fiesta Stardust Lavender = 'Balfiesala'PBR	LAst
- - 'Lavender Orchid'PBR (d)	NPri
- - 'Pink Ruffle'PBR (d)	LAst
- - 'Salsa Red' (d)	LAst
- - 'Sparkler Rose'PBR (d)	NPri
- 'Peach Ice' (Summer Ice Series) (d/v)	CHal
- (Tempo Series) 'Meloblue'	LAst
- - 'Meloda'	LAst
- - 'Melody'	LAst
- - 'Shocking Pink'	LAst

Imperata (*Poaceae*)

brevifolia	CBrm
cylindrica	CMen MGol MSal
- 'Red Baron'	see *I. cylindrica* 'Rubra'
§ - 'Rubra'	More than 30 suppliers

Incarvillea (*Bignoniaceae*)

arguta	EBee EShb GKev LPio MGol SBla
brevipes	see *I. mairei*
compacta	MDKP
- ACE 1455	EBee
- BWJ 7620	WCru
delavayi	More than 30 suppliers
- 'Alba'	see *I. delavayi* 'Snowtop'
- 'Bees' Pink'	CSpe EBee EBrs ECho GBuc GGar SHGN
§ - 'Snowtop'	CDWL EBee EBrs ECho ECrN ELan ENot EPfP EPot ERou GBuc GMaP LAst MDun MLLN NEgg NLar NRnb SPer SPla SWvt WBrE WFar WPGP
forrestii	EBee ECho GKev LPio
grandiflora	EBee ELan GCrs MGol SBla
himalayensis 'Frank Ludlow'	GBuc SBla
- 'Nyoto Sama'	GBuc
lutea BWJ 7784	WCru
§ ***mairei***	EBee EBrs ECho EGoo EMan GCrs GEdr GSki LHop LPio LRHS MLLN NLar WPer
- SDR 1531	GKev
- SDR 3028	GKev
- var. ***mairei***	EPot GBuc
- - CLD 101	GCrs
- - f. ***multifoliata***	see *I. zhongdianensis*
olgae	CBrm EBee EMan EShb GSki LPio MLLN NLar NWCA SHGN

sinensis 'Cheron'	CSpe EBee
younghusbandii	EBee
§ ***zhongdianensis***	CPBP ERos GBri GBuc GCrs GEdr GKev MDKP MGol NWCA WAbe
- BWJ 7692	WCru
- BWJ 7978	WCru

Indigofera (*Papilionaceae*)

CC 4536	MGol
amblyantha ♀H4	CBcs CHar EBee ELon EPfP IDee IMGH LHop LRHS MAsh MBlu MBri NLar SBod SDry SEND SKHP SPlb SPoG SSpi WKif WSHC WSpi
australis	EUnu SOWG
balfouriana BWJ 7851	WCru
cassioides	WCru
cytisoides	GFai
decora f. ***alba***	EPfP MBri
dielsiana	CWGN EPfP MWea WKif WPGP
'Dosua'	SLPl
frutescens	CPLG
gerardiana	see *I. heterantha*
hebepetala	CPLG EPfP WPGP WSHC
§ ***heterantha*** ♀H4	More than 30 suppliers
- CC 4537	MGol
himalayensis **new**	EBee SKHP
- Yu 10941	WPGP
- 'Silk Road' **new**	LBuc MBri
kirilowii	EBee EPfP MBri NLar SKHP SOWG WPGP WSHC
pendula	EPfP IDee MAsh SSpi WPGP WSHC
- B&SWJ 7741	WCru
potaninii	EPfP MGol SHBN SKHP
pseudotinctoria	CPLG EPfP LRav MBri MGol NLar SRms WFar
splendens **new**	EPfP MBri
subverticillata	WPGP WSHC
tinctoria	CArn MSal

Indocalamus (*Poaceae*)

latifolius	EBee EPPr EPla ERod LPal MMoz MMuc MWht NLar SDry
- 'Hopei'	EPla
longiauritus	EPla SDry
solidus	see *Bonia solida*
§ ***tessellatus*** ♀H4	CAbb CDoC CEnt CGHE CHEx CMCo EAmu EBee EFul ENBC EPfP EPla ERod LCro MBri MCCP MMoz MWht NGdn NMoo SMad WDyG WFar WMoo WPGP WPnP
- f. ***hamadae***	CMCo EPla ERod MMoz MWht SDry

Inula ✿ (*Asteraceae*)

acaulis	WCot
afghanica	EBee
barbata	MLLN NBre
britannica var. ***chinensis***	NBre
candida	XPep
crithmoides	WHer XPep
dysenterica	see *Pulicaria dysenterica*
ensifolia	CBcs ELan EPfP LEdu MLLN MRav MSte MTho NBro NWCA SLPl WCAu WFar
- 'Compacta'	ECho
- 'Gold Star'	EBee ECho EMan EPfP MLLN MNFA MWat MWgw NBid NBir SMer SPet WFar WMnd WPer
glandulosa	see *I. orientalis*
helenium	CArn CHby COld CPrp CSev EBee ELau EUnu GPoy ILis LEdu MHer MLLN MNHC MSal NBid NGHP NMir SECG SPoG SRms WCAu WGwG WHer WMoo WPer WSel
- 'Goliath'	MLLN
helianthus-aquatilis	MLLN
hirta	MLLN NBre WPer
hookeri	More than 30 suppliers
- GWJ 9033	WCru
macrocephala misapplied	see *I. royleana*
macrocephala Boiss. & Kotschy ex Boiss.	MLLN
magnifica	More than 30 suppliers
- 'Sonnenstrahl' ♀H4	SPhx
oculus-christi	EBee EWes MLLN NBre WPtf
- MESE 437	EPPr
* 'Oriental Star'	GAbr WHil
§ ***orientalis***	CHrt CKno COlW EBee EPfP MBri MNFA MWat NBre SHGN SMad SPet SPoG WBrE WCAu WFar WLin WMnd WPGP WPer WSel
racemosa	EMon EPla EShb EWes GBin IBlr MGol MNrw MSte NBid NSti SPlb SRms WFar
- 'Sonnenspeer'	GMac NBre NLar SLPl WPer WPtf
rhizocephala	ECho MDKP WPer
§ ***royleana***	CEnt EDAr GBuc GMac MDKP MNrw MRav MSte NBre NLar
salicina	EBee
verbascifolia	ECho

Iochroma (*Solanaceae*)

§ ***australe***	CHEx CHll CKob CPle CSpe LRav SGar SHFr SOWG
§ - 'Andean Snow'	CHll CKob CPLG EShb
§ - 'Bill Evans'	CPLG EShb
cyaneum	CCCN CDoC CKob CPLG CTri ERea SHFr SOWG
- 'John Miers' **new**	CKob
- purple-flowered	CHll
§ - 'Trebah'	CDTJ CKob ERea
gesnerioides 'Coccineum'	CCCN CHll CKob
§ ***grandiflorum***	CCCN CDoC CHEx CHll CKob CSev SGar SOWG
'Purple Haze' **new**	CKob
violaceum hort.	see *I. cyaneum* 'Trebah'
warscewiczii	see *I. grandiflorum*

Ipheion (*Alliaceae*)

'Alberto Castillo'	More than 30 suppliers
dialystemon	CStu EBee EBrs ECho EPot LPio SBla WAbe
hirtellum **new**	EBee EBrs WCot
'Jessie' **new**	EBee EBrs ECho EPot LAma NMin SPhx WCot WHil
'Rolf Fiedler' ♀H2-3	More than 30 suppliers
sellowianum	MAsh SCnR WCot
§ ***uniflorum***	CFFs CSpe CStu CTri EBee EBrs ECha ECho LAma LEdu MNrw MRav NMen SIng SPer SRms WAbb WAul WCot WFar WPer WPnP WTin
- 'Album'	CPom EBee EBrs ECha ECho EPot ERCP ERos EWes LAma LPio LRHS MAsh MRav MTho SBla SIng SPhx WCot WHal WHil WPnP
- 'Charlotte Bishop'	More than 30 suppliers
- 'Froyle Mill' ♀H4	More than 30 suppliers
- 'Wisley Blue' ♀H4	More than 30 suppliers
yellow-flowered **new**	CDes

Ipomoea (*Convolvulaceae*)

sp. **new**	CWib
acuminata	see *I. indica*
alba	CCCN
batatas 'Ace of Spades'	EUnu
- 'Blackie'	CSpe EMan EShb EUnu WCot WFar
- 'Margarita'	EUnu
- 'Pink Frost' (v)	EMan EShb EUnu
'Cameo Elegance' (v)	LSou

carnea	CCCN SOWG
coccinea (L.) A. Gray var. ***hederifolia***	see *I. hederifolia*
§ ***hederifolia***	CCCN
x ***imperialis*** 'Sunrise Serenade' **new**	CCCN
§ ***indica*** ♀H1	CCCN CHEx CHal CHll EMan EPfP ERea EShb LRHS MJnS MPRe SOWG
learii	see *I. indica*
§ ***lobata***	CSpe LBMP LRHS LSou SGar
'Milky Way' **new**	CCCN
muellerii	CCCN
x ***multifida***	CSpe
nil	LRav
purpurea	LBMP
- 'Feringa' **new**	LRHS
- 'Grandpa Otts' **new**	LRHS
- 'Kniola's Purple-black'	CSpe SBch
- 'Shira' **new**	LRHS
quamoclit	CSpe
tricolor	WGwG
tuberosa	see *Merremia tuberosa*
versicolor	see *I. lobata*

Ipomopsis (*Polemoniaceae*)

§ ***aggregata***	NPol
rubra	EBee NPol

Iresine (*Amaranthaceae*)

herbstii	CHal EBak ERea
- 'Aureoreticulata'	CHal
- 'Brilliantissima'	CHal SMrm
lindenii ♀H1	CHal
'Shiny Rose Purple' **new**	LBuc

Iris ✿ (*Iridaceae*)

CLD 1399	NHol
'Aah Soo' (TB) **new**	EFam
'Abbey Road' (TB)	WCAu
'About Town'	EFam
'Abracadabra' (SDB)	SMrm
'Acadian Miss' (La)	WCAu
'Ace' (MTB) **new**	ESgI
'Acoma' (TB)	EFam WCAu
'Action Front' (TB)	EBee EHrv ETod IPot LAst MSte MWgw NEgg NGdn SCoo SDnm SPla WCra WWeb
'Actress' (TB)	CWGN ECGP ETod IPot LBuc LSRN MSte SPet SPla WCra
acutiloba subsp. ***lineolata*** **new**	SBla WWst
'Adobe Rose' (TB)	ESgI
'Adrienne Taylor' (SDB) ♀H4	WCAu WPen
'After Dark' **new**	CKel
'After Hours' (TB) **new**	ERou
'After the Dawn' (TB) **new**	LRHS
'After the Storm' (TB)	ECho EFam
'Afternoon Delight' (TB)	ESgI MRav WCAu
'Agatha Christie' (IB)	WCAu
'Agatha Dawson' (Reticulata/v)	EMon
'Aggressively Forward' (TB)	WCAu
'Ahead of Times' (TB)	EFam
'Air Up There' (TB)	CIri
'Airy Fancy' (Spuria) **new**	ESgI
albicans ♀H4	CMea EBrs ECho EPot LEdu WCAu
albomarginata	WWst
'Alcazar' (TB)	EPfP LSRN NMoo SWat WEas WFar WMnd
'Aldo Ratti' (TB)	ESgI
'Alexia' (TB) ♀H4 **new**	CKel
'Alice Harding' (TB)	ESgI
'Alien Mist' (TB)	EFam WCAu
'Alison Elizabeth'	WAul
'Alizes' (TB) ♀H4	CIri ESgI WAul WCAu
'All American' (TB)	EFam
'All Lit Up' (TB)	EFam
'All Right' (IB)	NZep
'Allegiance' (TB)	WCAu WEas
'Allison Elizabeth' (BB) ♀H4	CIri
'Alpine Journey' (TB)	EFam ESgI
'Alpine Lake' (MDB)	WCAu
'Alpine Twilight' (TB)	EFam
'Alsterquelle' (SDB)	WTin
'Altruist' (TB)	EFam WCAu
'Amadora' (TB)	CKel
'Amagita' (CH) **new**	CWsd
'Amain' (TB)	EFam
'Amas' (TB)	WCAu
'Ambassadeur' (TB)	EBee WHlf
'Amber Queen' (DB)	EBee ECtt ELan ERos MSte MWat MWgw NBir NEgg NMen SPer SPla SPoG WWeb
'Amber Snow' (TB)	EFam
'Ambroisie' (TB)	ESgI ETod
'Amelia Chynoweth' (TB) **new**	CKel
'American Patriot' (IB)	WCAu
'America's Cup' (TB)	WCAu
'Amethyst Dancer'	EFam
'Amethyst Flame' (TB)	ECho ENot ERou ESgI NBre SRms WCAu
'Amherst' (SDB)	EFam
'Amherst Blue' (SDB)	SIri
'Amherst Bluebeard' (SDB)	SIri
'Amherst Caper' (SDB)	WCAu
'Amherst Jester' (BB)	SIri WAul
'Amherst Moon' (SDB)	SIri WCAu
'Amherst Purple Ribbon' (SDB)	SIri WCAu
'Amherst Sweetheart' (SDB)	SIri WCAu
'Amigo' (TB)	ESgI
'Amphora' (SDB)	ERos GBuc
'Ancient Echoes' (TB) **new**	ESgI
'Andalou' (TB)	ESgI
'Andy Dandy' (La)	MBri
'Angel Unawares' (TB)	WCAu
'Angelic' (SDB)	WCAu
'Angelic Wings' (TB)	EFam
'Angel's Tears'	see *I. histrioides* 'Angel's Tears'
anglica	see *I. latifolia*
'Anna Belle Babson' (TB)	ESgI
'Anna Marie' (TB)	EFam
'Annabel Jane' (TB)	CKel COIW ELon WCAu
'Anne Elizabeth' (SDB)	ERos
'Annikins' (IB) ♀H4	CKel
'Anniversary Celebration' (TB)	CKel
'Antarctique' (IB)	ESgI
'Anthology' (TB)	EFam
'Antigone' (TB)	ESgI
'Anvil of Darkness' (TB)	CIri WAul
'Anxious' (TB)	EFam
'Anything Goes' (TB) **new**	WAul
'Apache Warrior' (IB)	ERou
aphylla	WCAu
- subsp. ***fieberi***	WCot
'Apollo' (Dut)	EBrs
'Appledore' (SDB)	ERos
'Appointer'	GBin
'Apricorange' (TB) ♀H4	CKel
'Apricot Drops' (MTB) ♀H4	ESgI WAul WCAu
'Apricot Frosty' (BB)	ESgI
'Apricot Silk' (IB)	CWGN
'Apricot Skies' (BB)	NZep

	'Arab Chief' (TB)	CKel
	'Arabi Pasha' (TB)	ESgI WCAu
	'Arabian Story'	EFam
*	'Arabic Night' (IB)	WCAu
	'Archie Owen' (Spuria)	WCAu
	'Arctic Fancy' (IB) ♀H4	CKel
	'Arctic Snow' (TB)	WCAu
	'Arctic Wine' (IB)	WCAu
	'Arden' (BB)	EFam
	arenaria	see *I. humilis*
	'Argument'	WWst
	'Argus Pheasant' (SDB)	ESgI WCAu
	'Arlene's Other Love'	EFam
	'Armageddon' (TB)	ESgI
	'Arnold Velvet' (SDB)	EFam
	'Art Deco' (TB)	SIri
	'Art School Angel' (TB)	CIri
	'Artful' (SDB)	WCAu
	'Artistic Gold' (TB)	EFam
	'Artist's Whim' (TB)	EFam
	'Ask Alma' (IB)	ESgI NZep WAul WCAu
	'Asteroid Zone' (TB)	EFam
	'Astrid Cayeux' (TB)	ESgI
*	'Atlantique' (TB)	CKel
	'Attention Please' (TB)	CKel ELan
§	***attica***	CPBP EPPr EPot ERos LEdu LRHS LTwo NRya NWCA WAbe WLin WThu
	– lemon	CPBP WThu
§	***aucheri*** ♀H2	EBrs ECho EPot GKev LEdu WWst
	'Aunt Corley' (TB)	CIri
	'Aunt Josephine' (TB)	ESgI
	'Aunt Martha' (BB)	MBri WCAu
	'Aurean' (IB)	CKel
	'Auroralita' (SDB)	EFam
	'Austrian Sky' (SDB)	CSam EBee ENot MBNS MSte NEgg STes WCAu
	'Autumn Apricot' (TB)	EFam
	'Autumn Bugler' (TB)	EFam
	'Autumn Circus' (TB)	EFam WAul WCAu
	'Autumn Clouds' (TB)	EFam
	'Autumn Echo' (TB)	EFam ESgI SPet
	'Autumn Encore' (TB)	WBor WHlf
	'Autumn Jester' (SDB) **new**	EFam
	'Autumn Leaves' (TB)	ESgI WCAu
	'Autumn Maple' (SDB)	EFam ESgI
	'Autumn Mists' (TB)	EFam
	'Autumn Orangelite' (TB)	EFam
	'Autumn Thunder' (TB)	EFam
	'Autumn Tryst' (TB)	EFam ESgI WCAu
	'Avalon Sunset' (TB)	ESgI
	'Avanelle' (IB)	ERou NBre
	'Awesome Blossom' (TB) **new**	ESgI
	'Az Ap' (IB)	COIW EBee ELon NZep WCAu WGwG
	'Aztec Sun' (TB)	SIri
	'Babbling Brook' (TB)	SPoG
	'Baboon Bottom' (BB)	WCAu
	'Baby Bengal' (BB)	WCAu
	'Baby Blessed' (SDB)	EFam NZep SRGP WCAu
	'Baby Prince' (SDB)	EFam ESgI
	'Baccarat' (TB)	WCAu
	'Back in Black' (TB)	CKel
	'Bahloo' (TB)	EFam
	'Bajazzo' (La)	WCAu
	bakeriana	EBrs ECho IHer LRHS NMin
	'Bal Masqué' (TB)	ESgI
	baldschuanica	WWst
	'Ballerina' (TB)	NBir
	'Ballerina Blue' (TB)	ERou
	'Ballet Lesson' (SDB) ♀H4	CIri
	'Ballyhoo' (TB)	WCAu
	'Bamba' (SDB)	EFam
	'Banana Cream'	EFam
	'Banbury Beauty' (CH) ♀H3	CLAP
	'Banbury Gem' (CH)	CSam SPhx
	'Banbury Melody' (CH)	CFee
	'Banbury Ruffles' (SDB)	ESgI NMen WCAu
	'Bandera Waltz' (TB)	WCAu
	'Bang' (TB)	CKel
	'Bangles' (MTB)	WCAu
	'Bantam Prince' (SDB) **new**	EFam
	'Bar de Nuit' (TB)	ESgI
	'Barbara's Kiss' (Spuria)	CIri
	barbatula BWJ 7663	WCru
	'Barletta' (TB)	WCAu
	'Barn Dance' (TB)	EFam
	'Baroque Prelude' (TB)	CKel
	'Batik' (BB)	LRHS WCAu WCot
	'Bayberry Candle' (TB)	ESgI MWea WAul WCAu
	'Be a Devil' (TB)	EFam
	'Be Mine' (TB)	EFam
	'Be My Baby' (BB)	WCAu
	'Beauty Mark' (SDB)	NZep
	'Becalmed' (IB)	EFam
	'Bedford Lilac' (SDB) ♀H4	NZep
	'Bedtime Story' (IB)	EBee GBri SSvw SWat WCot
	'Bee's Knees' (SDB) ♀H4	WAul
	'Before the Storm' (TB)	CKel ESgI MSte WCAu
	'Beguine' (TB)	ESgI
	'Being Busy' (SDB)	ESgI
	'Bel Azur' (IB)	CBgR ESgI
	'Bel Esprit' (TB) **new**	ESgI
	'Bellboy' (MTB)	NZep
	'Belvi Cloud' (TB)	EFam
	'Belvi Queen' (TB)	EFam MNrw
N	'Benton Arundel' (TB)	ECha
	'Benton Cordelia' (TB)	ESgI
	'Benton Dierdre' (TB)	ELon SRms
	'Benton Nigel' (TB)	WCAu
	'Benton Sheila' (TB)	CFee
	'Berkeley Gold' (TB)	CSBt EBee ECtt ELan EPfP EWes EWsh NEgg NOrc NVic SCoo SHBN SPer SWat WCAu
	'Berlin Tiger' ♀H4	EPPr SApp WCAu
	'Berry Blush' (TB)	EFam
	'Bess Bergin' (TB)	EFam
	'Best Bet' (TB)	EFam ESgI LRHS WCAu
	'Best Man' (TB)	EFam
	'Bethany Claire' (TB)	EFam ESgI
	'Betty Cooper' (Spuria)	ESgI WAul WCAu
	'Betty Simon' (TB)	CKel ESgI ETod
	'Beverly Sills' (TB)	ESgI LRHS MRav SRGP WCAu
	'Bewilderbeast' (TB)	WCAu
	'Bianco' (TB)	ERou WCAu
	'Bibury' (SDB) ♀H4	EFam WCAu
	'Big Dipper' (TB)	SIri
	'Big Melt' (TB)	CKel
	'Big Money' (CH) ♀H3	GBuc
	'Big Squeeze' (TB)	CIri
	biglumis	see *I. lactea*
	'Billionaire' (TB)	EFam
	'Bishop's Robe' (TB)	SSvw
N	'Black Beauty' (Dut)	EPfP LRHS
	'Black Beauty' (TB)	SPer WFar
	'Black Gamecock' (La)	CFir CWCL EPPr MBNS NBPN NBro NMoo NOrc WCAu WMAq
	'Black Hills' (TB)	EBee ENot WCAu
	'Black Ink' (TB)	COIW
	'Black Knight' (TB)	NGdn SMer SPoG
	'Black Night' (IB)	MWea SRGP
	'Black Sergeant' (TB) ♀H4 **new**	CKel
	'Black Stallion' (MDB)	ESgI
	'Black Suited' (TB)	CIri
	'Black Swan' (TB)	ECha ECtt ELan ENot EPfP ESgI EShb EWTr LAst LSRN MBri MSte

		NBre SDnm SHBN SPer SPla WCAu WCra WEas WWeb
	'Black Taffeta' (TB)	CKel
	'Black Tie Affair' (TB)	ESgI MSte WCAu
	'Black Ware' (TB)	EFam
	'Blackbeard' (BB) ♀H4	CKel WCAu
	'Blackcurrant' (IB)	CIri
	'Blackout' (TB)	EFam ESgI LRHS
	'Blast' (IB)	CKel
	'Blatant' (TB)	EFam ESgI WCAu
	'Blazing Light' (TB)	ESgI
	'Blazing Saddles' (TB)	EMic NZep
	'Blenheim Royal' (TB)	ESgI WCAu
	'Blessed Again'	EKen
	'Blessed Again' (IB)	EFam EKen
	'Blessed Assurance' (IB)	EFam
	'Blitz' (SDB)	EFam NZep
	'Blitzen' (IB)	WCAu
	'Blood Covenant' (SDB)	NZep
	'Blousy Blouse'	EFam
	'Blue Ballerina' (CH) ♀H3	GBuc
	'Blue Crusader' (TB)	CIri WCAu
	'Blue Denim' (SDB)	ECho ECtt EPfP GMaP MBNS MRav NBir NBro NMoo SMrm WCAu WCot WHoo WTin
	'Blue Eyed Blond' (IB)	ERou MWea WCAu
	'Blue Eyed Brunette' (TB)	ESgI WCAu
	'Blue Fin' (TB)	EFam WCAu
	'Blue For You'	EFam
	'Blue Hendred' (SDB)	NBir WCAu
	'Blue Horizon' (TB)	ERos
	'Blue Lamp' (TB)	CKel
	'Blue Line' (SDB) ♀H4	NBre NZep
	'Blue Luster' (TB) ♀H4	ESgI
	'Blue Moonlight' (TB)	EFam
	'Blue Mystery'	WWst
	'Blue Note Blues' (TB)	WCAu
	'Blue Pigmy' (SDB)	CWat ERos MBNS MWat MWgw NEgg NMen NSti SPer SPet WWeb
	'Blue Pools' (SDB)	MBri MSte NBir NZep WTin
	'Blue Reflection' (TB)	ESgI
	'Blue Rhythm' (TB)	CKel EFam ELan ELon EPfP ERou GMaP LCro MRav MSte NBre NMoo SCoo SPer SPhx WAul WCAu WMnd
	'Blue Sapphire' (TB)	ESgI SHBN WCAu
	'Blue Shimmer' (TB)	CSBt CWGN EBee ECha ELan ENot EPfP ESgI ETod MSte NCGa NGdn SHBN SPer SPet SPla SPoG SWat WCAu WCra
	'Blue Staccato' (TB)	CKel ESgI WCAu
	'Blue Suede Shoes' (TB)	ESgI
	'Blue Velvet' (TB)	WMoo
	'Blue Warlsind'	WWst
	'Blueberry Filly' (IB)	CIri
	'Bluebird Wine' (TB)	WCAu
	'Bob Nichol' (TB) ♀H4	CKel
	'Bodacious' (TB)	EFam ESgI
	'Bohemia Sekt' (TB)	CKel
	'Bohemian' (TB)	ESgI
	'Boisterous' (BB)	WCAu
	'Bold Gold' (TB)	EFam
	'Bold Look' (TB)	ESgI
	'Bold Pretender' (La)	EPfP MBNS MBri
	'Bold Print' (IB)	EBee ELon SPoG WAul WCAu WCra
	'Bollinger'	see *I.* 'Hornpipe'
	'Bonnie Davenport' (TB)	CIri
	'Bonus Bucks' (TB)	CKel
	'Bonus Mama' (TB)	EFam
	'Boo' (SDB)	CKel NZep WCAu
	'Bouzy Bouzy' (TB)	ESgI
	bracteata	CPBP GBuc WPer
	- JCA 13427	CLAP
	'Braggadocio' (TB)	WCAu
	'Braithwaite' (TB)	CKel EBee ELan ENot ERou ESgI IPot MBnl MSte NBre SHBN SPer SPur SRms SWat WAul WCAu
	'Brannigan' (SDB)	MBri NBir NSti WPen
	'Brasilia' (TB)	NBir NBre
	'Brass Tacks' (SDB)	EFam NZep WCAu
	'Brassie' (SDB)	ERos MBNS NBro NMoo SHGN SMrm
	'Brave New World' (TB)	CIri
	'Brazilian Holiday' (TB) **new**	WAul
	'Breakers' (TB) ♀H4	CKel ESgI WCAu
	'Breezy Blue' (SDB)	WCAu
§	'Bride' (DB)	NBlu WMnd
	'Bride's Halo' (TB)	WCAu
	'Brigantino' (BB)	ESgI
	'Bright Button' (SDB)	CKel ESgI
	'Bright Chic' (SDB)	ESgI
	'Bright Child' (SDB)	WCAu
	'Bright Fire' (TB)	SIri
	'Bright Moment' (SDB)	EFam EPPr
	'Bright Vision' (SDB)	ESgI NZep
	'Bright White' (MDB)	CKel ECho ERos MBNS NMen
N	'Bright Yellow' (DB)	MRav
	'Brighteyes' (IB)	SRms
	'Brilliant Excuse' (TB)	NZep
	'Brindisi' (TB)	ESgI WCAu
	'Brise de Mer' (TB)	ESgI
	'Broadleigh Carolyn' (CH) ♀H3	CWsd
	'Broadleigh Dorothy' (CH)	GGar
	'Broadleigh Joan' (CH)	CWsd
	'Broadleigh Mitre' (CH)	CElw
	'Broadleigh Peacock' (CH)	CElw CWsd IBal
N	'Broadleigh Rose' (CH)	CElw CWsd EHrv EPyc GBuc MBrN MRav SAga SApp SIri SMrm WSHC
	'Broadleigh Sybil' (CH)	GCrs
	'Broadleigh Victoria' (CH)	GBuc
	'Broadway' (TB)	NZep
	'Broadway Baby' (IB)	ESgI WAul
	'Broadway Doll' (BB)	EFam
	'Broadway Star' (TB)	ERou
	'Brom Bones' (SDB)	EFam
	'Bromyard' (SDB) ♀H4	WCAu
	'Bronzaire' (IB) ♀H4	CKel EFam ESgI WCAu WGwG
	'Bronze Beauty Van Tubergen' (*boogiana* hybrid)	EPfP LRHS NBir SAga SPer WFar
	'Bronzed Aussie' (TB)	CIri
	'Bronzed Violet' (TB) **new**	CKel
	'Brother Carl' (TB)	EFam
N	'Brown Chocolate' (TB)	WCAu
	'Brown Duet' (TB)	EFam
	'Brown Lasso' (BB) ♀H4	LRHS WCAu
	'Brown Trout' (TB)	NBir
N	'Brummit's Mauve' (TB)	WCAu
	'Brussels' (TB) **new**	ESgI
	bucharica misapplied	see *I. orchioides* Carrière
	bucharica ambig.	CTca EBrs ECho GCrs IHer NWCA WBor WHil WWst
§	***bucharica*** Foster ♀H3-4	CBgR CMdw CPom CPrp CSam EBee EBrs ECho EPfP EPot EWTr GKev LAma LRHS WCAu
	- 'Princess' **new**	CTca EBrs ECho LRHS
N	- 'Sanglok'	WWst
	- 'Top Gold' **new**	EBrs ECho WWst
N	- 'Yellow Dushanbe'	ELon
	bucharica* x *orchioides	WWst
	'Buckwheat' (TB)	EFam SIri
	'Buddy Boy' (SDB)	WCAu
	'Bugles and Horns' (TB)	EFam
	'Bugsy' (MDB) **new**	ESgI
	'Buisson de Roses' (TB)	ESgI
	bulleyana	ECho EPot GKev MGol NEgg NWCA SRms WAbe WCot

	– ACE 2296	EBee GBuc
	– black-flowered	EBee GKev
	'Bumblebee Deelite' (MTB) $\mathbb{Y}^{H4}$	CKel NZep WCAu
	'Burgundy Brown' (TB)	NZep
	'Burgundy Bubbles' (TB)	CIri
	'Burgundy Party' (TB)	ESgI
	'Burka' (TB) **new**	ESgI
	'Burnt Toffee' (TB)	ESgI WAul
	'Busy Being Blue' (TB)	EFam
	'Butter Pecan' (IB)	WCAu
	'Buttercup Bower' (TB)	WCAu
	'Buttercup Charm' (MDB)	NZep
	'Buttered Popcorn' (TB)	SMer
	'Buttermere' (TB)	SRms
	'Butterpat' (IB)	EFam ESgI NZep
	'Butterscotch Carpet' (SDB)	EFam WCAu
	'Butterscotch Kiss' (TB)	CSBt EBee ECGP ELan LDai MBNS MRav MWgw NBir NEgg SDnm SHBN SPer
	'Button Box' (SDB)	NZep
	'Bye Bye Blues' (TB)	EFam
	'Cabaret Royale' (TB)	ESgI WCAu
	'Cable Car' (TB)	CKel ESgI
	'Cahoots' (SDB)	EFam
	'Caliente' (TB)	CWGN EKen EPfP ESgI MRav SPet WBor WCAu
	'California Style' (IB)	ESgI NZep
	'Californian Gold' **new**	ERou
§	Californian hybrids	CAby CElw CPBP CWCL EPot GCra NBir WBor WCFE WCot
	'Calliope Magic'	EFam
	'Calm Stream' (TB) $\mathbb{Y}^{H4}$	CKel
	'Cambridge Blue'	see *I.* 'Monspur Cambridge Blue'
	'Camelot Rose' (TB)	WCAu
	'Cameo Blush' (BB)	EFam
	'Cameo Wine' (TB)	ECtt EFam EPPr ESgI
	'Cameroun' (TB)	ESgI
	'Campbellii'	see *I. lutescens* 'Campbellii'
	canadensis	see *I. hookeri*
	'Canaveral' (TB)	EFam
	'Candy Clouds' (TB)	WCAu
	'Candy Queen' (SDB) **new**	EFam
	'Candyland' (BB)	EFam
	'Candylane' (MTB)	CKel
	'Cannington Bluebird' (TB)	WCAu
	'Cannington Skies' (IB)	EFam
	'Cantab' (Reticulata)	CAvo CFFs EBrs ECho EPot GBin GKev LAma LHop LRHS SPer SPhx
	'Cantina' (TB)	EFam
	'Capricious' (TB)	ESgI
	'Capricorn Cooler' (TB)	EFam
	'Captain Gallant' (TB)	WCAu
	'Captain Indigo' (IB) **new**	CKel
	'Caption' (TB)	ESgI
	'Captive' (IB)	EFam
	'Caramba' (TB)	WCAu
	'Carats' (SDB)	EFam
	'Carenza' (BB) **new**	CKel
	'Carilla' (SDB)	ERos
	'Carnaby' (TB)	ESgI MBri WCAu
	'Carnival Song' (TB)	WCAu
	'Carnival Time' (TB)	CWGN EBee ECGP EShb IPot LAst LBuc LDai MBNS SPer WAul WCra
	'Carnton' (TB)	WEas
N	'Carolyn' (CH)	CFir
	'Carolyn Rose' (MTB) $\mathbb{Y}^{H4}$	NBre NZep
	'Caronte' (IB)	ESgI
	'Carriwitched' (IB)	CKel
	'Cascade Sprite' (SDB)	SRms
	'Cast A Spell'	EFam
	'Cat's Eye' (SDB)	CIri
N	'Cedric Morris'	EWes WEas
	'Celebration Song' (TB)	ESgI WAul WCAu
	'Celestial Flame' (TB) **new**	LRHS
	'Celestial Glory' (TB)	WCAu
	'Celestial Happiness' (TB)	EFam
	'Celsius' (SDB)	EFam
	'Cerdagne' (TB) **new**	ESgI
	'Certainly Certainly' (TB)	EFam
	chamaeiris	see *I. lutescens*
	'Champagne Elegance' (TB)	EFam ESgI NBir WAul WCAu
	'Champagne Encore' (IB)	ESgI
	'Champagne Frost' (TB)	EFam WCAu
	'Champagne Music' (TB)	WCAu
	'Champagne Waltz' (TB)	EFam
	'Chance Beauty' (SpecHybrid) $\mathbb{Y}^{H4}$	WCAu
	'Change of Pace' (TB)	ESgI WCAu
	'Chanted' (SDB)	EFam EPPr ESgI WCAu
	'Chanteuse' (TB)	SWat
	'Chantilly' (TB)	CMil EBee ECGP ELan EPfP MAvo MRav MSte NBir NEgg NGdn SDnm SPer SWat WFoF
	'Chapeau' (TB)	ESgI WCAu
	'Chapel Bells' (TB)	CKel
	'Charlotte Maria' (TB) **new**	CKel
	'Chartreuse Ruffles' (TB)	ECtt
	'Char-true' (Spuria)	WCAu
	'Chasing Rainbows' (TB)	WCAu
	'Chaste White' (TB)	EFam ESgI
	'Chatter' (TB)	EFam
	'Cheerful One' (TB)	CIri
	'Cheers' (IB)	NZep
N	'Cherished' (TB)	EBee GBin SMer
	'Cherokee Lace' (Spuria)	WTin
	'Cherry Blossom Special' (TB)	CIri
	'Cherry Garden' (SDB)	CElw CKel EBee ECtt EFam EGoo EHrv ELan EPfP EWes LEdu MBNS MBri MRav MSte NBir NGdn NMRc NMoo NSti NWCA SMrm WAul WCot WEas WPen
	'Cherry Glen' (TB)	CIri
	'Cherry Smoke' (TB)	WCAu
	'Cherub Tears' (SDB)	NZep WCAu
	'Cherub's Smile' (TB)	ESgI
	'Chickasaw Sue' (BB)	EFam
	'Chickee' (MTB) $\mathbb{Y}^{H4}$	CKel NZep
	'Chicken Little' (MDB)	EBee NMoo
	'Chief Moses' (TB)	WCAu
I	'Chieftain' (SDB)	MRav
	'China Dragon' (TB)	SWat
	'China Moon' (TB) **new**	WAul
	'China Seas' (TB)	NBre
	'Chinese Empress' (TB)	EFam
	'Chinook Winds' (TB) **new**	ESgI
	'Chivalry' (TB)	ESgI WTin
	'Chocolate Vanilla' (TB)	ESgI WCAu
	'Chorus Girl' (TB)	CKel
	'Christmas Angel' (TB)	WCAu
	'Christopher Columbus' (TB)	EFam
	chrysographes $\mathbb{Y}^{H4}$	More than 30 suppliers
I	– 'Black Beauty'	CFir ECho EPfP
I	– 'Black Knight'	CMdw EDAr ELon EPfP GBuc GCra GGar ITim LCro LHop MDun MHer MSte NBid NChi NLar SHGN SMad SWat WBor WGwG WMnd
	– black-flowered	More than 30 suppliers
	– blue-flowered **new**	EDAr
	– 'Ellenbank Nightshade'	CBgR GMac
N	– 'Inshriach'	GBuc LEdu WAbe
N	– 'Kew Black'	CDes ECho EShb LEdu NBir NChi NEgg NHol NWCA WHer WHil
	– 'Mandarin Purple'	GBuc GMac MBri SPer SWat WMoo
	– red	ECho
	– 'Rob'	ECho

§	– 'Rubella'	ECho GCra MSte WFar WPrP
	– 'Rubra'	see *I. chrysographes* 'Rubella'
N	– 'Tsiri'	NWCA
	chrysographes* x *forrestii	NBir
	chrysophylla	GBuc
	– JCA 13233	CLAP
	'Chubby Cheeks' (SDB)	CKel WCAu
	'Chuck Waltermire' (TB)	EFam
	'Chuckwagon' (TB) new	ESgI
	'Church Stoke' (SDB)	WCAu
N	'Cider Haze' (TB)	CKel
	'Cimarron Rose' (SDB)	EFam EPPr ESgI NZep WCAu
	'Cinnabar Red' (Spuria)	WAul
	'Cinnamon Apples' (MDB)	ESgI
	'Cinnamon Roll' (Spuria)	WCAu
	'Cinnamon Stick' (Spuria)	CIri
I	'City Lights' (TB)	EFam WCAu
	'Clairette' (Reticulata)	LAma NMin
	'Clara Garland' (IB) ♀H4	CKel EFam WCAu
	'Clarence' (TB)	EFam ESgI WCAu
	clarkei	CPrp GBin GQue WCot WFar
	– B&SWJ 2122	WCru
	– CC 2751	NWCA
	– CC 4181	MGol
	'Class Act' (TB)	EFam
	'Classic Bordeaux' (TB)	CIri
	'Classic Hues' (TB) new	ESgI
	'Classic Look' (TB)	ESgI
	'Classico' (TB)	EFam
	'Clay's Caper' (SDB)	NBre
	'Clear Morning Sky' (TB) ♀H4	CIri EPfP
N	'Cleo' (TB)	CKel NBir NSti
	'Cleo Murrell' (TB)	ESgI
	'Cliffs of Dover' (TB)	CKel EFam EKen ESgI MCot SGar SIri SRms
N	'Climbing Gold'	ECho
	'Close Shave' (TB)	CIri
	'Close Your Eyes' (TB)	EFam
	'Cloud Fire'	EFam
	'Cloud Mistress' (IB)	ESgI
	'Cloud Pinnacle' (IB) new	CKel
	'Cloudcap' (TB)	SRms
	'Cloudia' (TB)	EFam
	'Cloudless Sunrise' (TB)	ERou
	'Clyde Redmond' (La) ♀	WMAq
	'Coalignition' (TB)	WCAu
	'Codicil' (TB)	ESgI WCAu
	'Colette Thurillet' (TB)	ESgI WCAu
	collettii	EBee EBrs ECho
	'Colonial Gold' (TB)	WCAu
	'Color Brite' (BB)	EFam
	'Color Tart' new	LRHS
	'Colorific' (La)	EPPr EPfP MBri NBro NMoo
	'Colortrak' (TB) new	ERou
	'Colorwatch' (TB)	EFam
	'Combo' (SDB)	CKel
	'Come to Me' (TB)	EFam
	'Coming Up Roses' (TB)	WCAu
	'Compact Buddy' (MDB)	ESgI
	'Con Fuoco' (TB)	ESgI
	'Concertina' (IB)	CIri
	'Confetti' (TB)	MBri
	confusa ♀H3	CAbP CAby CHEx CSev EShb GBin LEdu SAPC SArc SEND SMad WBrk WFar WPic WRos WWst
N	– 'Martyn Rix'	CBct CDes CFwr CGHE CHEx CHid CLAP CPen CPou CSev CSpe EBee EMan EPfP IGor LFur MAvo MHer SChr WCot WFar WGwG WHil WHrl WMnd WPGP WPer WPic WPrP WSHC
	'Conjuration' (TB)	EFam ESgI WCAu
	'Connect The Dots' (MTB)	WCAu
	'Conspiracy' (TB)	CIri
	'Constant Wattez' (IB)	CKel EBee ERou ESgI NLar
	'Consummation' (MTB)	NZep
	'Cool Melodrama' (SDB) new	EFam
	'Cool Treat' (BB) ♀H4	CIri
	'Copatonic' (TB)	ESgI WCAu
	'Copper Classic' (TB)	ESgI NZep WCAu
	'Cops' (SDB)	ESgI NZep
	'Coquetterie' (TB)	ESgI
	'Coral Chalice' (TB)	EFam LRHS
	'Coral Charmer' (TB)	EFam
	'Coral Joy' (TB)	EFam
	'Coral Point' (TB)	EFam WCAu
	'Coral Strand' (TB)	WCAu
	'Cordoba' (TB)	WCAu
	'Corn Harvest' (TB)	EFam NZep
	'Corps de Ballet' (TB)	CIri
	'Cosmic Dance' (TB) new	ERou
	'Countess Zeppelin' (Spuria) new	ESgI
	'County Town Red' (TB)	CIri SIri
	'Court Magician' (SDB)	SIri
	'Cozy Calico' (TB)	ESgI WCAu
	'Crackles' (TB) new	CKel
	'Cranapple' (BB) ♀H4	WAul WCAu
	'Cranberry Crush' (TB)	LRHS WCAu
	'Cranberry Sauce' (TB)	CIri
	'Cream and Peaches' (SDB)	SIri
	'Cream Beauty' (Dut)	EBrs
	'Cream Pixie' (SDB)	EFam WCAu
	'Cream Soda' (TB) ♀H4	CKel
	'Creative Stitchery' (TB)	EFam
	'Creme d'Or' (TB)	EFam ESgI
	'Crème Glacée' (TB)	ESgI
	cretensis	see *I. unguicularis* subsp. *cretensis*
	'Cricket Lane' (SDB)	NZep
	'Crimson Tiger' (TB)	EFam
	'Crinoline' (TB)	CKel
	'Crispette' (TB)	WCAu
	'Crispin' (SDB) new	EWTr
	cristata ♀H4	CPBP GBuc LEdu NHar NLar NPro SIng SRms WCru
	– 'Alba'	CWsd ERos LRHS NWCA WAbe
	cristata* x *lacustris	NMen
	croatica new	ESgI
	crocea ♀H4	CPLG GBin MGol
	'Croftway Lemon' (TB)	COIW ELon
	'Cross Current' (TB)	WCAu
	'Cross Stitch' (TB)	EFam NZep
	'Crowned Heads' (TB)	CKel ESgI WCAu
	'Crownette' (SDB) new	CKel
	'Crushed Velvet' (TB)	WCAu
	'Crystal Glitters' (TB)	ESgI
	cuniculiformis	MGol
	– ACE 2224	GBuc
	'Cup Cake' (MDB)	ESgI
	'Cup Race' (TB)	WCAu
	'Cupid's Cup' (SDB)	ESgI
	'Curlew' (IB)	WCAu
	'Curtain Up' (TB)	EFam
	'Cute Orange Horn' (TB)	EFam
	'Cutie' (IB)	ERou ESgI NZep WAul WCAu
	'Cyanea' (DB)	ECho EFam
	cycloglossa	CPBP EBrs ECho EPot LEdu LRHS SBla WWst
	'Daffodil Cloud'	EFam
	'Dance Away' (TB)	ESgI WCAu
	'Dance for Joy' (TB)	EFam
	'Dancer's Veil' (TB)	CHar ECtt ERou ESgI IPot MRav NBre NVic SMer WCAu
	'Dancin'' (IB)	NZep
	'Dancing Gold' (MTB)	NZep
	'Dandy Candy' (TB)	CIri

	danfordiae	CAvo CBcs CFFs CTca EBrs ECho EPfP EPot GKev LAma LRHS SPet WFar WGwG WLin
	'Danger' (TB)	ESgI
	'Dante's Inferno' (TB)	EFam
	'Dardanus' (AB)	CFwr CMea EBrs ECho EPot ERCP LEdu LRHS
	'Dark Avenger' (SDB)	CIri
	'Dark Blizzard' (IB)	NZep
	'Dark Crystal' (SDB)	EFam ESgI
	'Dark Rosaleen' (TB) 𝕐H4	NBre
	'Dark Spark' (SDB)	WCAu
	'Dark Twilight'	EFam
	'Dark Vader' (SDB)	ESgI WCAu
	'Darkling' (SDB)	EFam
	'Dash Away' (SDB)	ESgI SIri
	'Dashing' (TB)	EFam
	'Daughter of Stars' (TB)	CIri
	'Dauntless' (TB)	ESgI
	'David Guest' (IB)	CKel
	'Dawn of Fall' (TB)	EFam
	'Dawning' (TB)	ESgI
	'Dazzle Me' (SDB)	WCAu
	'Dazzling Gold' (TB)	ESgI WCAu
	'Death by Chocolate' (SDB)	CIri ESgI
§	***decora***	NWCA WCot
	'Deep Black' (TB)	CKel EHrv ELan EPfP IPot LAst LSRN MAvo MBNS MCot MRav MSte NOrc SDnm SHBN SWat WAul WCAu
	'Deep Caress' (TB)	ESgI
	'Deep Dark Secret' (TB)	CIri
	'Deep Pacific' (TB)	MBri WCAu
	'Deep Purple' (TB)	LAst
	'Deep Space' (TB)	WCAu
	'Deft Touch' (TB)	CKel WCAu
	'Deity' (TB)	EFam
	delavayi 𝕐H4	CAby EBee ECho EWes GBin GMaP IBlr MLLN NEgg NLAp
	- SDR 50	GKev
	'Delicate Lady' (IB) 𝕐H4	CKel
	'Delta Butterfly' (La)	WMAq
	'Demelza' (TB)	CKel
	'Demon' (SDB)	CKel SMrm
	'Denys Humphry' (TB)	CKel WCAu
	'Depth of Field' (TB)	ERou
	'Deputé Nomblot' (TB)	ESgI
	'Derwentwater' (TB)	SRms WCAu
	'Desert Country' (SDB)	EFam
	'Desert Dream' (AB)	GAbr GGar
	'Desert Echo' (TB)	SPet
	'Desert Orange' (SDB) **new**	EFam
	'Desert Song' (TB)	CKel EFam WCAu
	'Designer Gown' (TB)	ERou
	'Destry Rides Again' (TB)	EFam
	'Devil May Care' (IB)	CIri
	'Diabolique' (TB)	CIri
	'Diamond Doll' (BB)	EFam
	'Diligence' (SDB) 𝕐H4	CKel
	'Distant Roads' (TB)	WCAu
	'Ditto' (MDB)	EFam
	'Divine' (TB)	CKel
	'Dixie Darling' (TB)	ESgI
	'Dixie Pixie' (SDB)	WCAu WTin
	'Doctor No' (TB)	EFam
	'Dolce Acqua' (TB)	CIri
	'Dolly Madison' (TB)	ESgI
	'Don Juan' (TB)	ESgI
	'Donegal' (IB)	EFam
	'Doodads' (TB)	WCAu
	'Doodle Strudel'	EFam
	'Doozey' (MDB)	ESgI
	'Dorcas Lives Again' (TB)	EFam
	'Double Byte' (SDB)	EFam
	'Double Espoir' (TB)	ESgI
	'Double Lament' (SDB)	ERos
	'Double Time' (TB)	EFam
	'Doublemint' (TB) **new**	EFam
	douglasiana 𝕐H4	CPen ECho EShb GKev MLLN NEgg NWCA SKHP SMac WFar WTin
	- 'Amiguita' (CH)	CFir EBee
	'Dovedale' (TB) 𝕐H4	EFam WCAu
	'Dover Beach' (TB)	SGar
	'Draco' (TB)	ESgI
	'Drake Carne' (TB) **new**	CKel
	'Drama Queen' (TB)	CIri
	'Drambuie' (SDB) **new**	EFam
	'Dream Indigo' (IB)	CKel WCAu
	'Dream Lover' (TB) **new**	ESgI
	'Dreamsicle' (TB)	SIri
	'Dresden Candleglow' (IB)	WCAu
	'Dress Circle' (Spuria)	CIri
	'Drum Song' (IB)	EFam
	'Dualtone' (TB)	CKel
	'Dude Ranch' (TB)	CIri
	'Duke of Earl' (TB)	EFam
	'Dunlin' (MDB)	ERos NBir NMen
	'Dural White Butterfly' (La)	CHid CSpe LAst NCGa
	'Dusky Challenger' (TB)	CKel ERou ESgI LCro MRav SCoo WAul WCAu
	'Dutch Chocolate' (TB)	ESgI ETod LCro WCAu
	'Dwight Enys' (TB) 𝕐H4	CKel
	'Dynamite' (TB)	CIri WAul
	'Eagle Control' (TB)	EFam
	'Eagle's Flight' (TB)	CKel
	'Earl of Essex' (TB)	EFam LRHS WCAu
	'Early Frost' (IB)	CKel EPPr LCro WAul
	'Early Light' (TB) 𝕐H4	ESgI WCAu
	'Earthborn' (TB)	CIri
	'Earthborne' (TB)	EFam
	'East Indies' (TB)	WCAu
	'Easter Tide' (La)	WCAu
	'Eastertime' (TB)	ECtt ESgI
	'Echo Beach' (TB)	EFam
	'Echo de France' (TB)	ESgI
	'Ecstatic Echo' (TB)	ESgI
	'Ecstatic Night' (TB)	WCAu
	'Edge of Winter' (TB)	CKel SIri
	'Edith Wolford' (TB)	CIri EBee ESgI GBin MWea SRGP WCAu WCot WCra
N	'Ed's Blue' (DB)	ELan
	'Edward' (Reticulata)	EBrs ECho EPfP EPot GKev LAma LRHS WCAu WFar
	'Edward of Windsor' (TB)	CMil ELan GMaP MSte NLar SDnm SRGP WCAu WMnd
	'Eggnog' (TB)	EFam
	'Egyptian' (TB) **new**	EFam
	'Eileen Louise' (TB) 𝕐H4	EFam WCAu
	'Elainealope' (TB)	EFam
	'Eleanor Clare' (IB) 𝕐H4	CKel LCro
	'Eleanor Hill' (Spuria)	WAul
	'Eleanor's Pride' (TB)	CKel EFam ESgI WCAu
	'Electrique' (TB)	WCAu
	elegantissima	see *I. iberica* subsp. *elegantissima*
	'Elizabeth Arden' (TB)	CKel
	'Elizabeth of England' (TB)	CWCL GKev SPet SRGP
	'Elizabeth Poldark' (TB)	ESgI WCAu
	'Ellenbank Damselfly'	CBgR GMac
	'Ellenbank Sapphire'	GMac
	'Elsa Sass' (TB)	ESgI
	'Emmanuel' (TB)	EFam
	'Empathy' (Spuria) **new**	CIri
	'Empress of India' (TB)	EBee
	'Enchanted Gold' (SDB)	NZep
	'Encircle' (CH)	GBuc
	'Encre Bleue' (IB)	ESgI
	'English Charm' (TB)	EFam ESgI WAul WCAu
	'English Cottage' (TB)	COlW EBee EFam ELon MWat NLar WCAu
	'English Knight' (TB)	EFam

	'Ennerdale' (TB)	SRms
	'Ennoble' (TB)	CIri ESgI
§	***ensata*** 𝕐H4	CBcs CDWL CHEx COIW ECGP ELan EMFW ENot EPfP EWTr GKev GSki LCro LRHS MNrw MWat NBro NCob NEgg NGdn NLar SPlb SRms SWal SWat WCAu WCFE WFar WPer
N	- 'Activity'	CSBt GSki NBro NGby SHar WFar WPrP
	- 'Alba'	ECha MWat
	- 'Alcho-no-kagalaku' **new**	CBow
	- 'Aldridge Prelude'	WAul
	- 'Aldridge Snow Maiden' 𝕐H4 **new**	WBIS
	- 'Aldridge Visitor' 𝕐H4 **new**	WBIS
	- 'Alpine Majesty' 𝕐	CIri
	- 'Aoigata'	CPrp
	- 'Apollo'	CBen
	- 'Artist'	NBro
	- 'August Emperor'	CBgR EKen NBhm
	- 'Azuma-kagami'	CBgR CFir EBee EKen ELan NCGa
	- 'Barr Purple East' 𝕐H4	CPrp
	- 'Beni-tsubaki'	ESgI WAul
I	- 'Blue King'	GSki MBlu NBro
I	- 'Blue Peter'	CBen
	- 'Blue Prince'	CBen
N	- 'Blush'	NBro
	- 'Caprician Butterfly' 𝕐H4	CMHG EPfP ESgI EWTr GAbr GBin GSki NBhm NMoo SMrm WAul WCAu
N	- 'Carnival Prince'	CFir NBro SBod WFar WMoo WPnP
	- 'Cascade Crest'	WAul
	- 'Cascade Spice'	WAul
	- 'Center of Interest'	NCGa
	- 'Chico Geisho'	ESgI WAul
	- 'Chiyodajō'	CKel
	- 'Crepe Paper'	WFar
N	- 'Cry of Rejoice'	EBee ECho EWll GBri NBhm NBre NBro SWat WAul WCAu WFar
	- 'Crystal Halo'	CIri
	- 'Dace'	EBee GBin
I	- 'Darling'	CPen CSam EBee ECho EPfP EWTr GSki IBlr MBNS MLHP NBro NLar SRGP SWat WAul WCAu WFar WMoo WPnP WTMC
	- 'Diomedes' **new**	ESgI
	- 'Dramatic Moment'	GBuc WFar
N	- 'Eden's Blue Pearl'	CHid CMMP EBee EGle GBin IPot NBro
N	- 'Eden's Blush'	EBee MLHP WAul
N	- 'Eden's Charm'	CAby EGle ELan GBin NBro NHol SPet WAul WHil
N	- 'Eden's Delight'	NHol
N	- 'Eden's Harmony'	EBee NBro WAul WTMC
N	- 'Eden's Paintbrush'	EBee EGle ELan EPfP NBro WTMC
N	- 'Eden's Picasso'	CFir EBee EGle ELan EPfP IPot NBro WHil WTMC
N	- 'Eden's Purple Glory'	CHid EGle GBin NBro WCot WTin
N	- 'Eden's Starship'	CFir EBee
	- 'Electric Rays'	WAul
I	- 'Emotion'	EBee EWTr NBro NGby WAul WFar WPnP
	- 'Flashing Koi'	ESgI
	- 'Flying Tiger' 𝕐H4	WBIS
I	- 'Fortune'	EHrv WAul
	- 'Fractal Blue'	CIri
	- 'Freckled Geisha'	CIri
	- 'Frilled Enchantment' 𝕐H4	WAul
*	- 'Galathea'	EBee
	- 'Geisha Gown'	SWal
	- 'Gei-sho-mi'	CPrp
N	- 'Gipsy'	EBee WAul
	- 'Give-me-Patience' 𝕐H4	WBIS
N	- 'Gracieuse'	CBgR CPen EBee EGle ELan EPfP GBin MBri NBro NLar SWat WAul WFar WMoo WPnP
	- 'Gusto'	CMHG CPen EBee EPfP IPot LDai NBhm NBro NMoo
	- 'Hana-aoi'	IBlr
	- 'Happy Awakening'	GSki
	- 'Haru-no-umi'	CKel
	- 'Hatsu-shimo'	IBlr
	- 'Hegira'	WAul
	- 'Hercule'	CPrp EGle GAbr NBir WTMC
	- Higo hybrids	IBlr
	- Higo white	SPer
	- 'Himatsuri'	CMHG
N	- 'Hokkaido'	CBen ESgI IBlr
	- 'Hue and Cry' 𝕐H4	ESgI WAul
	- hybrids	EHon ESgI
	- 'Iapetus' **new**	ESgI
	- 'Imperial Magic' 𝕐H4	WBIS
*	- 'Innocence'	CKel EHrv NBre NGby NLar SWat WAul WFar WMoo
	- 'Iso-no-nami'	EBee EWll MBlu NBro WAul WPrP WTMC
	- 'Jacob's Coat' **new**	NCot
	- 'Jitsugetsu'	CFir CMHG NMoo SPoG
N	- 'Jodlesong'	EBee WFar
	- 'Kalamazoo'	WFar
	- 'Katy Mendez' 𝕐H4	WAul WBIS
	- 'Kiyo-tsura'	CKel
	- 'Kiyozuru' **new**	EPfP
N	- 'Kogesho'	EBee EPfP GBuc NBro NLar NMoo WAul
N	- 'Koh Dom'	SPer
	- 'Kongo San'	WFar
	- 'Kuma-funjin'	IBlr
	- 'Kumo-no-obi'	CPrp EBee LRHS NBro SWat WAul WCAu
	- 'Kunshikoku' **new**	NLar
N	- 'Laced'	SPer
	- 'Lady in Waiting' **new**	NLar
N	- 'Laughing Lion'	CPen CRez EBee EBla NBro NOrc WAul WFar WMoo
	- 'L'Idéal'	CPen
	- 'Light at Dawn'	CMHG CPen EGle EPfP LDai NBPC NBhm NBro SPoG WAul WFar WMoo
N	- 'Lilac Blotch'	SPer
	- 'Lorenzaccio'	CIri
I	- 'Loyalty'	EBla ECho SRGP WFar
	- 'Manadzuru'	IBlr
	- 'Mancunian' 𝕐H4	CKel
I	- 'Mandarin'	CBen
	- 'Midnight Stars'	WAul
	- 'Midnight Whispers'	WAul
	- 'Mist Falls' **new**	ESgI
N	- 'Momozomo'	LTwo NBhm NBro NLar SPoG
§	- 'Moonlight Waves'	CMHG CPrp EBla EGle ELan EMFW EPPr EPfP EShb EWll GAbr GBuc GCra GGar GMaP GMac MBri MSte NBro NEgg NGdn NHol SPla SWat WAul WCAu WFar WTMC
	- 'Murasame' 𝕐H4	CMHG SPoG
	- 'Narihira'	IBlr
	- 'Ocean Mist'	CHid CMHG CPen EBee NBro NMoo
	- 'Oku-banri'	CHEx CPrp EShb IBlr
	- 'Oriental Eyes'	EBee GAbr GBin NGdn NLar NMoo WAul WCAu
	- pale mauve	NBir SPer
	- 'Pastel Princess'	WAul
	- 'Peacock'	EBee
	- 'Pin Stripe'	MBri NBro NLar NMoo SPoG SWat WAul WMoo

	- 'Pink Frost'	CBgR CPrp EBee EGle ELan EPPr EPfP EWll NBro NHol WAul WFar WTMC WTin
	- 'Pinkerton'	CIri
	- 'Pleasant Earlybird'	WAul
	- 'Pleasant Journey'	EHrv
	- 'Prairie Frost'	EBee EPfP NLar SMrm
	- 'Prairie Noble'	EBee NBro NLar WHil
N	- 'Purple Glory'	ELan
	- purple-flowered	SPer
I	- 'Red Dawn'	CBen
	- 'Reign of Glory'	WAul
	- 'Returning Tide' ♀H4	WBIS
I	- 'Reveille'	NBro SWat WAul WPtf
	- 'Rivulets of Wine'	CIri
§	- 'Rose Queen' ♀H4	CBen CDWL COlW CPrp CSam EBee ECha EGle EHon ELan EMFW EPfP ESgI EShb GBuc GCra GMaP MRav NBir NBro NGdn SPer WAbe WAul WFar WMoo WPnP WTMC
	- 'Rose Tower'	CMHG
I	- 'Royal Banner'	EBee NBro WAul WFar
	- 'Royal Crown'	ECho
	- 'Royal Pageant'	CMHG EBee NBPC NBro SIri
I	- 'Ruby King'	GSki WAul
	- 'Ruffled Dimity' **new**	IPot NBPC
	- 'Sandsation'	CIri
	- 'Sapphire Star'	CKel
	- 'Sea of Amethyst'	ESgI
I	- 'Sensation'	CMHG CPen CWCL ECho EWTr MBri SPoG SWat WAul WCAu WPrP
N	- 'Shihainami'	IBlr
	- 'Shiro-nihonkai'	EBee SPoG
	- 'Snowy Hills'	WAul
	- 'Sorcerer's Triumph'	EBee GBin
	- 'Southern Son' ♀H4 **new**	ESgI WBIS
	- var. ***spontanea***	SPet SWat WAbe
	- - B&SWJ 1103	WCru
	- - B&SWJ 8699	WCru
	- 'Springtime Melody'	WAul
I	- 'Star'	CBen
	- 'Summer Storm' ♀H4	CKel SPer WBIS
N	- 'Teleyoshi'	SHar
	- 'The Great Mogul' ♀H4	CKel
	- 'Tideline'	CIri
	- 'Variegata' (v) ♀H4	More than 30 suppliers
N	- 'Velvety Queen'	CPrp EPPr WAul
	- 'Vintage Festival' ♀H4	WBIS
	- 'Waka-murasaki'	EBee EGle EWll MBNS NBro
	- 'White Ladies'	CSBt SWat
	- white-flowered	WFar
	- 'Wine Ruffles'	LSRN SIri SMrm
	- 'Yako-no-tama'	WMoo
	- 'Yamato Hime'	CMHG EPfP NLar NMoo
N	- 'Yedo-yeman'	WFar
	- 'Yezo-nishiki'	GBin NBro SBod WHil
N	- 'Yu Nagi'	SPer
	enstata 'Umi-kaze' **new**	NLar
	'Entertainer' (TB)	EFam
	'Epicenter' (TB)	WCAu
	'Eramosa Enigma' **new**	EFam
	'Eramosa Miss' (BB) **new**	EFam
	'Eramosa Skies' (SDB)	WCAu
	'Eramosa Snowball' (SDB) **new**	EFam
	'Erect' (IB)	CKel EFam
	'Esoteric' (SDB)	ESgI
	'Etched Apricot' (TB)	WCAu
	'Eternal Bliss' (TB)	EFam
	'Eternal Prince' (TB)	EFam
	'Evening Dress' (Spuria)	CIri
	'Evening Pond' (MTB)	CKel
	'Ever After' (TB)	ESgI
	'Ever Ready' (SDB) **new**	EFam
	'Evergreen Hideaway' (TB)	CIri

	'Everything Plus' (TB)	ERou ESgI WCAu
	'Exclusivity' (TB)	CIri
	'Exotic Gem' (TB)	WCAu
	'Exotic Isle' (TB)	ESgI NZep
	'Eye Magic' (IB) ♀H4	CKel EFam
	'Eye Shadow' (SDB)	WCAu
	'Eyebright' (SDB) ♀H4	WCAu
	'Faenelia Hicks' (La)	WMAq
	'Fairy Meadow' (TB)	EFam
	'Fakir's Fire' (MTB)	NZep
	'Falcon's Crest' (Spuria)	CIri
	'Fall Fiesta' (TB)	ESgI
	'Fall Primrose' (TB)	EFam
	'Fallin'' (TB)	EFam
	'Falling in Love' (TB)	EFam
	'Famecheck Andrew'	EFam
	'Famecheck Christmas Snow' (TB)	EFam
	'Famecheck Cream Tea' (TB)	EFam
	'Famecheck Dream' (TB)	EFam
	'Famecheck Forever Lemon' (IB)	EFam
	'Famecheck Lemon Repeater' (TB)	EFam
	'Famecheck Muriel' (MTB)	EFam
	'Famecheck Paul'	EFam
	'Famecheck Perpetual Joy' (TB)	EFam
	'Famecheck Pink' (TB)	EFam
	'Famecheck Ruddy Toes' (MTB)	EFam
	'Famecheck Showoff' (TB)	EFam
	'Famecheck Spearhead'	EFam
	'Famecheck Taste o' Honey' (MTB)	EFam
	'Famecheck Thelma' (MTB)	EFam
	'Fancy Woman' (TB)	WAul WCAu
	'Fanfaron' (TB)	EFam ESgI
	'Faraway Places' (TB)	WCAu
	'Fashion Lady' (MDB)	ECho
	'Fatal Attraction' (TB)	WCAu
	'Feature Attraction' (TB)	WCAu
	'Feed Back' (TB)	EFam
	'Feminine Charm' (TB)	WCAu
	'Ferrous Fantasy' (TB)	CIri
	'Festive Skirt' (TB)	CKel WCAu
	'Feu du Ciel' (TB) ♀H4	ESgI
	'Fierce Fire' (IB) ♀H4	CKel
	filifolia var. ***latifolia*** SF 332	SKHP
	'Film Festival' (TB)	ESgI
	'Finalist' (TB) **new**	WAul
	'Fingest' **new**	MSte
N	'Fire and Flame' (TB)	NBir
	'Firebug' (IB)	ESgI
	'Firecracker' (TB)	MRav WCAu
	'Fireside Glow' (TB)	EFam
	'First Interstate' (TB)	ESgI WCAu
	'First Movement' (TB) **new**	ESgI
	'First Romance' (SDB)	SIri
	'First Violet' (TB)	WCAu
	'Flambé' (IB) **new**	WAul
	'Flaming Victory' (TB)	ESgI
	'Flammenschwert' (TB)	ERou
	'Flareup' (TB)	WCAu
	'Flashing Beacon' (MTB)	NZep
	flavescens	ESgI WCAu
	'Flavours' (BB)	WCAu
	'Fleur Collette Louise' (La)	CIri
	'Flight of Fantasy' **new**	CKel
	'Flight to Mars' (TB)	CIri
	'Flirting' (SDB)	EFam
	'Flirty Mary' (SDB)	MSte
	'Floorshow' (TB)	EFam

§	'Florentina' (IB/TB) ♀H4	CArn CHby COlW EGoo ESgI GPoy ILis MHer MNHC MRav NBid NBir SIde WAul WCAu WGwG WPic
	'Flower Shower' (SDB)	EFam
	'Flumadiddle' (IB)	CKel
	foetidissima ♀H4	More than 30 suppliers
	- 'Aurea'	WCot
	- ***chinensis***	see *I. foetidissima* var. *citrina*
§	- var. ***citrina***	CAby CBre CFir CSsd EGle ENot EPla GAbr GCra GSki IBlr MRav NBid SChr WCot WEas WHoo
	- 'Fructu Albo'	GSki MBNS WCot
	- var. ***lutescens***	CHid EPPr IBlr
N	- 'Moonshy Seedling'	CSWP EGol
	- 'Variegata' (v) ♀H4	CElw CHar ECtt EGle EHrv EPfP GMaP MCCP NBir NCob NPer SBch WCAu WCot WHil
	- yellow-seeded	WCot WTin
	'Fogbound' (TB)	CIri
	'Fondation Van Gogh' (TB)	ESgI
	'Foolish Fancy' (TB)	SIri
	'For Mary' (TB)	CIri
	'Forest Light' (SDB)	ESgI
	'Forever Blue' (SDB) **new**	EFam
	'Forever Gold' (TB)	EFam
	'Forever Trevor' (CH) **new**	SPhx
	'Forever Yours' (TB)	EFam WAul
	'Forge Fire' (TB)	ESgI
	formosana	ECho
	- B&SWJ 3076	WCru
	forrestii ♀H4	CHid CMHG ECho EPfP EWTr GAbr GCra GCrs GKev IBlr LRHS MBri MHer NBir NBro NCob NGdn NHol SAga SMac SRot WAbe WHer WPtf
	'Fort Apache' (TB)	ESgI EWes
	'Fortunata' (TB)	EFam
	'Fortune Teller' **new**	CKel
	fosteriana	NWCA WWst
	'Fourfold Blue' **new**	WBIS
	'Foxy Lady' (TB)	EFam ESgI
	'Frank Elder' (Reticulata)	EBrs ECho EPot ERos LAma LRHS MRav MTho NMen WCAu
	'Frans Hals' (Dut)	EBrs GKev MAvo MMHG MNrw WCot
	'French Rose' (TB)	CKel
	'Fresh Image' (IB)	WCAu
	'Fresh Start' (SDB)	WAul
	'Fresno Calypso' (TB)	ESgI WCAu
	'Fringe Benefits' (TB)	WCAu
	'Frison-roche' (TB)	ESgI
	'Frisounette' (TB) **new**	ESgI
	'Fritillary Flight' (IB) ♀H4	CKel LCro
	'Frivolité' (TB)	ESgI
	'Frontier Marshall' (TB)	NMoo
	'Frost and Flame' (TB)	ECtt ELan ENot EPfP ERou EWll LCro MBri MRav MSte NEgg NGdn NLar SHBN SPer SPla SWat
	'Frosted Biscuit' (TB) ♀H4 **new**	CKel
	'Frosted Velvet' (MTB)	EFam WAul WCAu
	'Frosty Jewels' (TB)	ESgI
	'Full Impact' (TB)	CIri
	fulva ♀H3	CDes CPrp CWsd EBee GSki NBir NBro NSti WBor WCot WLin WTin
	x ***fulvala*** ♀H4	CAby CDes CFir CWsd EBee EPPr EWes GBin NBir NSti
	- 'Violacea'	EBee WCot
	'Furnaceman' (SDB)	ERos MBri
	'Fuzzy' (MDB)	ERos
	'Gala Gown' (TB)	WCAu
	'Galathea'	see *I. ensata* 'Galathea'
	'Gallant Moment' (TB)	SIri
	'Galleon Gold' (SDB)	CKel NZep

	'Galway' (IB)	SIri
	'Garden Bride'	EFam
	'Garden Grace' (TB)	EFam
	'Garnet Robe' (TB) **new**	LCro
	'Gay Parasol' (TB)	LRHS MSte
	'G'day Mate' (TB)	EFam
N	'Gelbe Mantel' (Sino-Sib)	CHid CLAP EBee NBir NBro NGdn NHol NSti WFar
	'Gemstar' (SDB)	WCAu
	'Gentius' (TB)	WMnd
	'Gentle' (SDB)	WCAu
	'Gentle Grace' (SDB)	ESgI
	'George' (Reticulata) ♀H4	CAvo CFFs CPrp ECho EPfP EPot ERos GAbr GCrs GKev LHop LRHS MMHG MSte NMin WHoo
	'George Smith' (TB) **new**	ESgI
	'Gerald Darby'	see *I.* x *robusta* 'Gerald Darby'
	germanica ♀H4	EGoo LCro LEdu WCAu WGwG
	- 'Firebreather'	ERou
	- var. ***florentina***	see *I.* 'Florentina'
N	- 'Mel Jope'	NBir
	- 'Nepalensis'	EGoo
N	- 'The King'	WCAu
	'Ghost Train' (TB)	CIri
	'Gibson Girl' (TB)	EFam WCAu
	'Gilded' (TB)	EFam
	'Ginger Swirl' (TB)	EFam
	'Gingerbread Castle' (TB)	WCAu
	'Gingerbread Man' (SDB)	CMea EHrv ERos ESgI MBrN MWea NMen SMrm SWal WCAu WHoo WLin
	'Glacier' (TB)	ECho
	'Glacier King' (TB)	EFam
	'Glad Rags' (TB)	ESgI NZep
	'Gladys Austin' (TB) **new**	EFam
	'Glam' (IB)	EFam WCAu
	'Glorious Day' (IB)	EFam
	'Glowing Seraphin' (TB)	EFam
	'Glowing Smile' (TB)	CIri
	'Gnu Rayz' (IB)	CIri
	'Gnus Flash' (TB)	WCAu
	'Go Between' (TB)	WCAu
	'Godfrey Owen' (TB)	CKel WCAu
	'God's Handiwork' (TB)	EFam
	'Godsend' (TB)	CKel EFam WCAu
	'Going My Way' (TB)	ERou ESgI SIri STes WCAu
	'Gold Burst' (TB)	EFam
	'Gold Country' (TB)	EFam ESgI
	'Gold Galore' (TB)	EFam
	'Gold Mania' (Spuria)	CIri
	'Gold of Autumn' (TB)	CKel SMrm
	'Gold Reprise' (TB)	EFam
	'Goldberry' (IB)	WCAu
	'Golden Alien' (TB)	CIri
	'Golden Alps' (TB)	SRms WCAu
	'Golden Child' (SDB)	EFam ESgI
	'Golden Ecstasy' (TB)	EFam
	'Golden Encore' (TB)	CKel EFam WCAu
	'Golden Fair' (SDB)	NBir
	'Golden Forest' (TB)	LRHS WCAu
	'Golden Inmortal' (TB)	EFam
	'Golden Muffin' (IB)	NZep
	'Golden Panther' (TB)	CIri
	'Golden Planet' (TB)	CKel
	'Golden Violet' (SDB)	ESgI
	'Goldkist' (TB)	CIri
	goniocarpa	EBee WAbe
	- var. ***grossa***	EBee
	'Good Fairy' (TB)	EFam
	'Good Looking' (TB)	ESgI WCAu
	'Good Show' (TB)	WAul WCAu
	'Good Vibrations' (TB)	SIri
	'Goodbye Heart' (TB)	ESgI
	'Gordon' (Reticulata)	CAvo CFFs CSam EBrs ECho EPot GKev LAma LRHS WFar

	gormanii	see *I. tenax*
	'Gosh' (SDB)	CKel
	'Gossip' (SDB)	ESgI
	'Gothic' (TB)	EFam
	gracilipes	SIng
	gracilipes* x *lacustris	GEdr WAbe
	graeberiana	EBrs ECho EPot WWst
	- white fall	LRHS WWst
	- yellow fall	EBee EBrs ECho LRHS WWst
	graminea ♀H4	CAvo CMHG CPrp EBee ECha ECho EHrv ELan EPPr EPfP ERos IBlr LLWP LRHS NBir NCot NEgg NMen NSti NWCA SMac SPer WAbe WAul WCAu WCot WFar WHoo
	- var. ***pseudocyperus***	GBin SDys
	graminifolia	see *I. kerneriana*
	'Granada Gold' (TB)	SRms
	'Grand Baroque' (TB)	EFam
	'Grape Adventure' (TB)	EFam
	'Grape Jelly' (TB)	WCAu
	'Grape Reprise' (TB)	EFam
	'Grapelet' (MDB)	ERos NZep WCAu
	'Grapeshot' (TB)	CIri
	'Great Gatsby' (TB)	CKel EFam
	'Great Lakes' (TB)	ESgI
	'Grecian Goddess' (TB)	EFam
	'Grecian Skies' (TB)	ESgI
	'Green and Gifted' (TB)	EFam
	'Green Ice' (TB)	CKel MRav
	'Green Prophecy' (TB)	CKel
	'Green Spot' (SDB) ♀H4	CBgR CKel CWGN EBee ECtt EHrv ELan ENot EPfP EWTr GBuc MRav MWat NBir NCob NEgg NHol NLar NMen NWCA SBla SPer WCAu WCFE
	'Green Streak' (TB)	CIri
	'Gringo' (TB)	WCAu
	'Gudrun' (TB)	ESgI
	'Gwyneth Evans' (BB) ♀H4 **new**	CKel
	'Gypsy Beauty' (Dut)	EBrs LRHS MMHG SPer WHil
	'Gypsy Boy' (SDB)	NZep
	'Gypsy Caravan' (TB)	LRHS
	'Gypsy Jewels' (TB)	CKel ESgI
	'Gypsy Romance' (TB) ♀H4	ESgI WCAu
	'Habit' (TB)	WCAu
	'Hafnium' (SDB) **new**	CKel
	'Hagar's Helmet' (IB)	EFam
	'Halloween Pumpkin' (TB)	EFam
	'Halo in Pink' (TB)	EFam
	halophila	see *I. spuria* subsp. *halophila*
	'Hand Painted' (TB)	EFam
	'Handshake' (TB)	CIri
	'Happenstance' (TB) **new**	ESgI
	'Happy Birthday' (TB)	ESgI
N	'Happy Border' (BB)	WCAu
	'Happy Mood' (IB) ♀H4	EFam NBre WCAu
	'Happy Pal' (TB)	EFam
	'Harbor Blue' (TB)	MWat SWat WCAu
	'Hareknoll' **new**	NWCA
	'Harlequinade' (BB)	EFam
	'Harlow Gold' (IB)	ESgI NZep
	'Harmony' (Reticulata)	CAvo CFFs EBrs ECho EPfP EPot GKev LAma LRHS MBri WFar
	'Harriette Halloway' (TB)	CPen EBee EShb ETod GMaP LSRN MAvo MBNS MSte NLar SMrm SPet SRGP WCot
	hartwegii	ECho
	'Harvest King' (TB)	ESgI
	'Harvest of Memories' (TB)	EFam ESgI
	'Haute Couture' (TB)	WCAu
	'Haviland' (TB)	SIri
	'Hawaiian Halo' (TB)	EFam
	'Hazelnut Delight' (TB)	CIri
	'Headcorn' (MTB) ♀H4	WAul
	'Headlines' (TB)	WCAu
	'Heather Carpet' (SDB)	WCAu
	'Heather Sky' (TB)	CIri
	'Heavenly Days' (TB)	WCAu
	'Heaven's Bounty' (BB)	EFam
	'Heepers' (SDB) **new**	EFam
	'Helen Boehm' (TB)	ESgI
	'Helen Collingwood' (TB)	ESgI
	'Helen K. Armstrong'	EFam
	'Helen McGregor' (TB)	ESgI
	'Helen Proctor' (IB)	ESgI WCAu
	'Helen Traubel' (TB)	WCAu
	'Helge' (IB)	COIW ECho ERou NBre SWat
	'Hellcat' (IB)	NZep WAul WCAu
	'Hello Darkness' (TB) ♀H4	CIri ESgI WCAu
	'Hemstitched' (TB)	EFam
	'Hercules' (Reticulata)	NMin
	'Here's Heaven' (TB)	EFam
	'Hey There' (MDB) **new**	ESgI
	'Hickory Leaves' (Spuria)	CIri
	'Hidden World' (TB) **new**	LRHS
	'High Barbaree' (TB)	WCAu
	'High Blue Sky' (TB)	WCAu
	'High Command' (TB)	CKel EFam
	'High Energy' (TB)	EFam
	'High Ho Silver'	EFam
	'High Roller' (TB)	CIri
	'High Waters' (TB)	EFam
	'Highland Games' (TB)	CIri
	'Highline Amethyst' (Spuria)	WAul
	'Highline Halo' (Spuria)	WCAu
	'Hindenburg' (TB)	EFam
	'Hindu Magic' (TB)	WCAu
	'Hippie' (SDB) **new**	EFam
	'Hissy-Fit' (IB)	CKel
	histrio subsp. ***aintabensis***	EBrs ECho EPot LAma
	histrioides	ECho GCrs WAbe WWst
§	- 'Angel's Tears'	CTca EBrs ECho ERos LRHS NMen NMin WWst
	- 'Lady Beatrix Stanley'	EBrs ECho ERCP LRHS NMen NMin
N	- 'Major'	CDes LAma NMin
N	- 'Michael Tears'	WWst
	- var. ***sophenensis***	EBrs
	'Hocus Pocus' (SDB)	EPPr WAul
	'Holden Clough' (SpecHybrid) ♀H4	CTca ELan EMFW EPfP EPla EWTr GBuc GCra GMaP GSki LEdu LRHS MRav MWgw NBir NCob NEgg NGdn NSti WAul WCAu WEas WFar WHer WLin WPen WPrP WSHC WTin
	'Holden's Child' **new**	WBIS
	x ***hollandica*** hort.	EBrs
	'Hollywood Blonde' (TB)	EFam
	'Holy Fire' (TB)	CIri
	'Holy Night' (TB)	CKel
	'Honey Behold' (SDB)	CKel
	'Honey Glazed' (IB)	ESgI NZep WAul WCAu
	'Honey Scoop' (TB)	EFam
	'Honeyplic' (IB) ♀H4	SIri WAul WCAu
	'Honington' (SDB)	EFam WCAu
	'Honky Tonk Blues' (TB)	CKel ESgI WAul
	'Honky Tonk Hussey' (BB) **new**	CKel
	'Honorabile' (MTB)	WCAu
	hoogiana ♀H3	EBrs ECho EPot GKev LRHS
N	- 'Gypsy Beauty'	WFar
	- 'Purpurea'	EBrs ECho
§	***hookeri***	CSam CStu ELan GEdr IGor WAbe WCot
	- RBS 0233	CStu

	hookeriana	CTca
§	'Hornpipe' (TB)	WCAu
	'Hot Fudge' (IB)	EPPr
	'Hot Gossip' (TB)	WCAu
	'Hot Jazz' (SDB)	WCAu
	'Hot Spice' (IB)	WCAu
	'Hotseat' (SDB)	EFam
	'Howard Weed' (TB)	EBee
	'Howdy Do' (TB)	EFam
	'Huckleberry Fudge' (TB) **new**	WAul
	'Hugh Miller' (TB)	WCAu
	'Hula Doll' (MDB)	NMen
	'Hula Honey' (TB)	EFam
	'Hula Moon' (TB) **new**	ESgI
§	***humilis***	CGra
	hyrcana	EBrs ECho
	'I Bless' (IB)	EFam
	'I Do' (TB)	EFam NZep
	'I Repeat' (TB) **new**	ESgI
	'I Seek You' (TB)	ESgI
	iberica	ECho
§	- subsp. ***elegantissima***	CMea EBrs EPot WWst
	- subsp. ***iberica***	WWst
§	- subsp. ***lycotis***	WWst
	'Ice Dancer' (TB) Υ^{H4}	CKel
	'Ice Wings' (BB)	WCAu
	'Iced Tea' (TB)	CIri
	'Ida' (Reticulata)	LAma
	'Ila Crawford' (Spuria) Υ^{H4}	WCAu
	illyrica	see *I. pallida*
	'Imagine Me' (TB)	EFam
	'Imbue' (SDB)	EFam ESgI
	'Immortal Hour' (TB)	WCAu
	'Immortality' (TB)	CKel CWGN EFam EKen ESgI LRHS MSte WCAu
	'Imperator' (Dut)	ECho
	'Imperial Bronze' (Spuria)	WAul WCAu
	'Impetuous' (BB) Υ^{H4}	CKel EFam
	'Imprimis' (TB)	ESgI WCAu
	'In a Flash' (IB)	WCAu
	'In Limbo' (IB) **new**	CKel
	'In Love' (TB)	EFam
	'In Reverse' (TB) **new**	CKel
	'In the Stars' (TB)	EFam
	'In Town' (TB)	ESgI
	'Incoscente' (TB)	ESgI
	'Indeed' (IB)	CBgR EFam
	'Indian Chief' (TB)	ESgI GBin SPur WCAu
	'Indian Idyll' (IB) **new**	CKel
	'Indian Pow Wow' (SDB)	CSev
N	'Indiana Sunset' (TB)	CKel
	'Indigo Flight' (IB)	CKel
	'Indigo Princess' (TB)	CKel
	'Indiscreet' (TB)	EFam WCAu
	'Infernal Fire' (TB)	CIri
	'Infinite Grace' (TB)	ESgI
	'Innocent Heart' (IB) Υ^{H4}	WCAu
	'Innocent Pink' (TB) **new**	ESgI
	'Innocent Star' (TB)	EFam
	innominata	CWCL ECha ECho GGar IBlr LHop LRHS NBir NBro NEgg NMen NPal SRms SWal WBVN WOut
	- JCA 13225	CLAP
	- apricot	CPrp IBlr
	- Ballyrogan hybrids	IBlr
I	- 'Clotted Cream' **new**	ECha
N	- 'Spinners'	CWsd
	- yellow	CAvo NMen NRya
	'Instructor' (TB) **new**	ERou
	'Interpol' (TB)	ESgI WCAu
	'Invitation' (TB)	EFam ESgI
	'Irish Doll' (MDB)	WCAu
	'Irish Moss' (SDB)	WAul
	'Irish Tune' (TB)	ESgI
	'Island Sunset' (TB)	EFam SIri
	'Isoline' (TB)	ESgI
	'Istanbul' (TB)	EFam
	'It's Magic' (TB)	EFam
	'J.S. Dijt' (Reticulata)	CAvo CFFs EBrs ECho EPfP EPot GKev LAma LRHS MBri MGos
	'Jabal' (SDB)	SIri
	'Jane Phillips' (TB) Υ^{H4}	More than 30 suppliers
	'Janet Lane' (BB)	CKel
	'Jangles' (IB)	WCAu
	'Janice Chesnik' (Spuria)	ESgI
	'Janine Louise' (TB) Υ^{H4} **new**	CKel
	japonica Υ^{H3}	CHEx ECho EHrv NPer WAul WFar WOut
	- B&SWJ 8921	WCru
	- 'Aphrodite' (v)	WTin
	- 'Bourne Graceful'	CAby CWsd WCAu
	- 'Ledger'	CHll CKel CPLG CPrp CSpe ECha EHrv ELan EPfP IGor MRav SHom SIri SMad WPGP
I	- 'Purple Heart'	CAvo
N	- 'Rudolph Spring'	CPen
I	- 'Snowflake'	CAvo
§	- 'Variegata' (v) Υ^{H3}	CAvo CBow CHEx CKel CPrp CSpe ECha EHrv ELon GGar LRHS NBro NPer SAPC SAga SArc SPoG WAul WEas WFar WHil WPGP
	'Jasper Gem' (MDB)	ERos NBir
	'Jaunty Jean'	EFam
	'Jay Kenneth' (IB)	CBgR
	'Jazz Festival' (TB)	WCAu
	'Jazz Maid'	EFam
	'Jazzamatazz' (SDB)	ESgI WCAu
	'Jazzed Up' (TB)	WCAu
	'Jean Cayeux' (TB)	ESgI
	'Jean Guymer' (TB)	EFam ESgI NBir WCAu
	'Jeanne Price' (TB)	SCoo WCAu
	'Jenny Grace' **new**	SIri
	'Jephthah's Daughter' (TB)	EFam
	'Jeremy Brian' (SDB) Υ^{H4}	WCAu
	'Jersey Lilli' (SDB)	WCAu
	'Jesse Lee' (SDB) **new**	CKel
	'Jesse's Song' (TB)	EFam ESgI NZep WCAu
	'Jester' (TB)	EFam
	'Jewel Baby' (SDB)	CKel NZep
	'Jeweler's Art' (SDB)	WCAu
	'Jigsaw' (TB)	ESgI
	'Jitterbug' (TB)	EHrv LRHS WCAu
	'Joanna' (TB)	NLar
	'Joanna Taylor' (MDB)	ERos NMen NZep WCAu
N	'Joe Elliott' (CH)	EGle
	'John' (IB)	CKel EFam WAul
	'Joy Boy' (SDB)	ESgI
	'Joyce' (Reticulata)	EBrs ECho EPot GKev LAma LRHS MBri SGar
	'Joyce Terry' (TB)	ESgI LRHS
	'Joyful' (SDB)	ESgI
	'Jubilant Spirit' (Spuria)	EBee EWes
	'Jubilé Rainier III' (TB)	CIri
	'Jubilee Gem' (TB)	CKel
	'Jud Paynter' (TB) **new**	CKel
	'Juicy Fruit' (TB)	EFam WCAu
	'Julia Vennor' (TB)	CKel
	'July Sunshine' (TB)	EFam
	'June Prom' (IB)	LRHS SRGP WCAu
	'June Rose' (IB) **new**	WAul
	'Jungle Fires' (TB)	WCAu
	'Jungle Shadows' (BB)	MRav NBir WCAu
	'Jungle Warrior' (SDB) **new**	CKel
	'Jurassic Park' (TB)	CIri ESgI WAul WCAu
	'Juris Prudence' (TB)	ESgI
	'Just Dance' (IB)	EFam ESgI
	'Just Jennifer' (BB)	WCAu

	kaempferi	see *I. ensata*
	'Kaibab Trail' (Spuria)	CIri
	'Kangchenjunga' (TB)	ESgI
	kashmiriana	CBcs
	'Katharine Hodgkin' (Reticulata) $\mathbb{Y}^{H4}$	More than 30 suppliers
	'Katie-Koo' (IB) $\mathbb{Y}^{H4}$	CKel
	'Katmandu' (TB)	EFam
	'Katy Petts' (SDB)	ESgI NZep WCAu
	'Kayleigh-Jayne Louise' (TB)	CKel
	'Keeping up Appearances' (TB)	WCAu
	'Kelway Renaissance' (TB)	CKel
	'Ken's Choice' (TB) $\mathbb{Y}^{H4}$	CKel
	'Kent Pride' (TB)	EBee ECha EPPr EPfP ESgI ETod IPot MRav MSte MWat SGar SHBN SIri SPer SPoG SWat WAul WCAu WCra WTin WWlt
	'Kentucky Bluegrass' (SDB)	WCAu
§	***kerneriana*** $\mathbb{Y}^{H4}$	ERos GBuc LRHS MLLN NBir NEgg WPen
	'Kernewek' (TB)	EFam
	'Kevin's Theme' (TB)	CIri WCAu
	'Kildonan' (TB)	WCAu
	'Kilt Lilt' (TB)	WCAu
	'King's Rhapsody' (TB)	EFam
	'Kirkstone' (TB)	WCAu
	'Kissing Circle' (TB)	EFam ESgI
	'Kitt Peak' (Spuria) $\mathbb{Y}^{H4}$	CIri
	'Kiwi Capers' (SDB)	NZep
	'Kiwi Slices' (SDB)	ESgI
	'Klingon Princess' (SDB) **new**	EFam
	'Knick Knack' (MDB)	CPBP EBee ECho ELan ERos ETod GAbr GCrs LBee LRHS MRav MSte NEgg NMen SDnm SPla SPoG WHil
	kolpakowskiana	WWst
	'Kona Nights' (BB)	ESgI
	korolkowii	WWst
	'La Nina Rosa' (BB)	WCAu
	'La Senda' (Spuria)	WCAu WCot
	'La Vie en Rose' (TB)	ESgI
	'Laced Cotton' (TB)	ERou ESgI WCAu
	'Laced Lemonade' (SDB)	MBri
§	***lactea*** $\mathbb{Y}^{H4}$	EPot NWCA
	lacustris $\mathbb{Y}^{H4}$	NMen NWCA WAbe
	'Lady Emma' (MTB)	EFam
	'Lady Essex' (TB)	EFam WCAu
	'Lady Friend' (TB)	EFam ERou ESgI WCAu
	'Lady Gale' (IB) **new**	CKel
	'Lady Ilse' (TB)	WCAu
	'Lady in Red' (SDB)	ESgI
	'Lady Mohr' (AB)	CKel WCAu
	'Lady of Fatima' (TB)	ESgI
	'Lady Snowflake' (TB)	SPet
	laevigata $\mathbb{Y}^{H4}$	CDWL CWat ECha ECho EGle EHon ELan EMFW EPfP GSki MRav NBro NPer SEND SGar SPer SWat WCAu WFar WMAq WMoo WPnP WShi
	- var. ***alba***	CBen ECha ECho EHon ELan EPfP SWat WAbe WFar WMoo
	- 'Albopurpurea'	CDWL EMFW WTMC
	- 'Atropurpurea'	IBlr
	- 'Colchesterensis'	CBen CDWL CWat EMFW NGdn NPer SNin SWat WMAq WTMC
I	- 'Dorothy'	NGdn
N	- 'Dorothy Robinson'	CWat SWat WPnP
	- 'Elegant'	see *I. laevigata* 'Weymouth Elegant'
	- 'Elgar'	WMAq
	- 'Midnight'	see *I. laevigata* 'Weymouth Midnight'
N	- 'Plum Purple'	EGle
	- 'Regal'	CDWL CWat
I	- 'Reveille'	EGle
	- 'Rose Queen'	see *I. ensata* 'Rose Queen'
I	- 'Snowdrift'	CBen CDWL CWat EHon EMFW NBir NGdn NPer SNin SPer SWat WCAu WFar WMAq WPnP WTMC
	- 'Surprise'	see *I. laevigata* 'Weymouth Surprise'
	- 'Variegata' (v) $\mathbb{Y}^{H4}$	CBen CBow CDWL CMea CWat ECha ECho EHon EMFW EPfP EPla LRHS MHar NBro NGdn NPer SPer SWat WMAq WMoo WPnP WTin
	- 'Weymouth'	see *I. laevigata* 'Weymouth Blue'
§	- 'Weymouth Blue'	CBen
§	- 'Weymouth Elegant'	CBen
§	- 'Weymouth Midnight'	CBen CFir CMil EHon SNin SWat
	- 'Weymouth Nearly'	CBen
§	- 'Weymouth Surprise'	CBen
N	'Langport Chapter' (IB)	CKel ESgI LCro
N	'Langport Chief' (IB)	CKel
N	'Langport Claret' (IB)	CKel ESgI LCro
N	'Langport Curlew' (IB)	CKel ESgI
N	'Langport Duchess' (IB)	CKel ESgI WTin
N	'Langport Fairy' (IB)	CKel ESgI
N	'Langport Finch' (IB)	NBir
N	'Langport Flame' (IB)	CKel ESgI LCro WTin
N	'Langport Flash' (IB)	EFam
N	'Langport Haze' (IB)	ESgI
N	'Langport Hope' (IB)	CKel ESgI
N	'Langport Jane' (IB)	CKel
N	'Langport Lady' (IB)	CKel
N	'Langport Lord' (IB)	ESgI LCro
	'Langport Minstrel' (IB)	CKel ESgI LCro
N	'Langport Pearl' (IB)	CKel
	'Langport Phoenix' (IB)	CKel
N	'Langport Pinnacle' (IB)	CKel
N	'Langport Robe' (IB)	ESgI
N	'Langport Smoke' (IB)	CKel
	'Langport Snow' (IB)	CKel
N	'Langport Song' (IB)	ESgI
N	'Langport Star' (IB)	CKel ESgI LCro
	'Langport Storm' (IB)	CKel EBee EMil ESgI MBri MRav MSte NGdn SHBN WAul WTin
N	'Langport Sun' (IB)	CBgR CKel EFam ESgI SMrm
N	'Langport Swift' (IB)	CKel
	'Langport Sylvia' (IB)	CKel
N	'Langport Tartan' (IB)	CKel
N	'Langport Violet' (IB)	CKel ESgI
	'Langport Vista' (IB)	CKel
	'Langport Warrior' (IB)	CKel
	'Langport Wren' (IB) $\mathbb{Y}^{H4}$	CKel CMdw EFam EPfP ESgI IPot LCro LRHS MBri NBir SMrm SPhx WAul WEas WPen WTin
	'Lark Rise' (TB) $\mathbb{Y}^{H4}$	CKel
	'Larry Gaulter' (TB)	WCAu
	'Las Vegas' (TB)	WCAu
	'Lascivious Dreams' (TB)	EFam
	'Latest Style'	EFam
§	***latifolia*** $\mathbb{Y}^{H4}$	ECho IHer WShi
	- 'Duchess of York'	ECho EPot
	- 'Isabella'	EBee EBrs EPot SMeo
	- 'King of the Blues'	EBrs ECho EPot GKev
	- 'Mansfield'	EBee EBrs EPot GKev SMeo
	- 'Montblanc'	EBee EBrs EPot
	- 'Queen of the Blues' (Eng)	ECho EPot
	'Latin Lark' (TB) **new**	ESgI
	'Latin Rock' (TB)	WCAu
§	***lazica*** $\mathbb{Y}^{H4}$	CAbP CPen CPrp CSpe EBee EMan EMon EPPr EPfP EPot ESgI EWsh GGar GKev IBlr LEdu LRHS MRav MSte NBir NCGa NSti SIng WAbe WEas WPGP WSpi
	- 'Joy Bishop'	WCot
	- 'Richard Nutt'	ELon WCot

N	– 'Turkish Blue'	CPrp GBin IBlr
	'Leah Traded' (BB)	EFam
	'Leda's Lover' (TB)	ESgI
	'Legato' (TB)	EFam
	'Lemon Brocade' (TB)	ESgI MBri WCAu
	'Lemon Dilemma' (Spuria)	CIri
	'Lemon Fever' (TB)	ESgI
	'Lemon Flare' (SDB)	EFam MRav SRms WCAu
	'Lemon Ice' (TB)	EBee LBuc SPer
	'Lemon Lyric' (TB)	EFam ESgI
	'Lemon Mist' (TB)	ESgI
	'Lemon Peel' (IB)	CKel
	'Lemon Pop' (IB)	WCAu
	'Lemon Puff' (MDB)	WCAu
	'Lemon Tree' (TB)	WCAu
	'Lenna M' (SDB)	CKel ECho
	'Lenora Pearl' (BB)	ESgI WCAu
	'Lent A. Williamson' (TB)	GMaP
	'Lenten Prayer' (TB)	CIri
	'Leprechaun Delight' (SDB)	EFam
	'Leprechaun's Purse' (SDB)	WCAu
	'Let's Elope' (IB)	ESgI WCAu
	'Letter From Paris'	EFam
	'Liaison' (TB) **new**	LRHS
	'Light Beam' (TB)	EFam
	'Light Cavalry' (IB)	ESgI NZep
	'Light Laughter' (IB)	WCAu
	'Lightning Streak' (TB) **new**	LRHS
	'Lilac and Lavender' (SDB)	NZep
	'Lilac Stitchery' (TB)	EFam
	'Lilla's Gloves'	EFam
	'Lilla's Stripes'	EFam
	'Lilli-white' (SDB)	CKel CWat EBee EHrv ELan ENot MBNS MRav MWgw NEgg SPoG WCAu
	'Lilting' (TB)	EFam
	'Lima Colada' (SDB)	NBre SMrm
	'Limelight' (TB)	SRms
	'Linesman' (SDB)	NZep
	'Lingering Love' (TB)	WCAu
	'Liqueur Crème' (TB)	EFam
N	'Little Amoena'	ERos NMen
	'Little Bev' (SDB)	EFam
	'Little Black Belt' (SDB)	NZep SIri
	'Little Blackfoot' (SDB)	ESgI WCAu WHoo
	'Little Blue-eyes' (SDB)	ESgI
	'Little Bluets' (SDB)	ESgI
	'Little Dandy' (SDB)	WCAu
	'Little Dream' (SDB)	WCAu
	'Little Episode' (SDB)	ESgI NZep WCAu
	'Little Firecacker' (SDB) **new**	EFam
	'Little John' (TB)	WCAu
	'Little Rosy Wings' (SDB)	CPBP EFam ERos
	'Little Shadow' (IB)	ENot MRav SRms
	'Little Sheba' (AB)	WCAu
	'Little Showoff' (SDB)	EFam ESgI WAul
	'Little Snow Lemon' (IB)	EFam NZep
	'Little Tilgates' (CH) ♀H3	WCot
	'Live Jazz' (SDB)	NZep WCAu
	'Llanthony' (SDB)	WCAu
	'Local Color' (TB) **new**	ESgI WAul
	'Lodore' (TB)	SRms WCAu
	'Logo' (IB)	WCAu WGwG
	'Lois Parrish' (TB)	CIri
	'Lollipop' (SDB)	EFam ESgI SIri
	longipetala	EWes NBir
	'Lookin' Good' (IB)	NZep
	'Lookingglass Eyes' (Spuria)	CIri
	'Loop the Loop' (TB)	EBee EPfP ERou LRHS NBre SCoo SPoG SWat WCra
	'Loose Valley' (MTB) ♀H4	SIri WCAu
	'Lord Warden' (TB)	ECGP LDai MSte SPet WAul WCAu
	'Loreley' (TB)	ESgI
	'Lorenzaccio de Medecis' (TB)	ESgI
	'Lorilee' (TB)	ESgI
	'Lothario' (TB)	WCAu WFoF
	'Loud Music' (TB)	WCAu
	'Louis d'Or' (TB) ♀H4	CIri
	'Louvois' (TB)	ESgI
	'Love for Leila' (Spuria) ♀H4	CIri
	'Love the Sun' (TB)	EFam ESgI
	'Lovebird' (TB)	EFam
	'Lovely Again' (TB)	EFam MRav WCAu
	'Lovely Fran' (TB)	EFam
	'Lovely Leilani' (TB) **new**	ESgI
	'Lovely Light' (TB)	MBri
	'Lover's Charm' (TB)	WCAu
	'Love's Tune' (IB)	SRGP
	'Loveshine' (SDB)	NZep
	'Low Ho Silver' (IB)	EFam WCAu
	'Loyalist' (TB) **new**	SIri
	'Lucky Devil' (Spuria)	CIri
	'Lucy's Gift' (MTB) ♀H4	WAul
	'Lugano' (TB)	ESgI
	'Luli-Ann' (SDB) ♀H4	CKel
	'Lullaby of Spring' (TB)	CKel WCAu
	'Lumalite' (SDB)	WAul
	'Lumière d'Automne' (TB)	ESgI
	'Luminosity' (TB)	EFam
	'Luna di Miele' (BB)	ESgI
	'Lunar Frost' (IB)	SIri
	'Lurid' (TB)	EFam
§	***lutescens*** ♀H4	EBrs ECho EPot ERos GCra GEdr NSla WAbe XPep
§	– 'Campbellii'	ERos MSte NMen
	– subsp. ***lutescens***	WLin
§	– 'Nancy Lindsay'	WCAu
	lycotis	see *I. iberica* subsp. *lycotis*
	'Lyrique' (BB) **new**	CKel
	'Ma Mie' (IB)	ESgI
	maackii	GSki
	macrosiphon	GKev
	'Madame Maurice Lassailly' (TB)	ESgI
	'Madeira Belle' (TB)	ESgI WCAu
	'Magharee' (TB)	ESgI
	'Magic Bubbles' (IB) ♀H4	CIri
	'Magic Kingdom' (TB)	EFam
	'Magic Man' (TB)	EBee
	'Magic Memories'	EFam
	'Magic Palette'	EFam
	magnifica ♀H3-4	EBrs ECho GKev LEdu NPri NWCA WWst
N	– 'Agalik'	CMea EBrs GKev LRHS
	– 'Alba'	EBrs GKev WWst
	'Maiden' (TB)	EFam
	'Maisie Lowe' (TB)	ESgI
	'Making Eyes' (SDB)	ESgI WCAu
	'Mallow Dramatic' (TB)	WCAu
I	'Mandarin' (TB)	ESgI
	'Mandarin Purple' (Sino-Sib)	CDes EBee GGar IBlr NGdn NHol
	mandshurica	CPBP
	'Mango Entree' (TB)	CIri
	'Mango Kiss' (SDB)	EFam
	'Many Moons Tales' (TB)	EFam
	'Maple Madness' (SDB) **new**	EFam
	'Maple Treat' (TB)	EFam
	'Mara' (IB) **new**	CKel
	'Marcel Turbat' (TB)	ESgI
	'Marche Turque' (TB)	ESgI
	'Marco Polo' (TB)	ESgI
	'Margarita' (TB)	WCAu
	'Margrave' (TB)	SIri WCAu
	'Marguérite' (Reticulata/v)	EBrs ECho ERCP LRHS
	'Marhaba' (MDB)	ERos
	'Marilyn Holloway' (Spuria)	ECha WCAu

	'Marita' (SDB) **new**	EFam
	'Marmalade Skies' (BB)	EFam NZep WCAu
	'Maroon Moon' (TB)	CIri
	'Martyn Rix'	see *I. confusa* 'Martyn Rix'
	'Mary Constance' (IB) Υ^{H4}	CKel
	'Mary Frances' (TB)	ESgI WCAu
	'Mary McIlroy' (SDB) Υ^{H4}	CKel WTin
	'Mary Randall' (TB)	WCAu
	'Mastery' (TB)	CIri
	'Matinata' (TB)	CKel
	'Matrix' (TB)	EFam
	'Maui Moonlight' (IB) Υ^{H4}	CKel EFam ERou ESgI NZep WAul
	'Maui Surf' (BB) Υ^{H4}	WAul
	'Mauna Loa Fire' (TB)	CIri
	'Mauvelous' (TB)	EFam
	'May Melody' (TB)	WCAu
	'Maya Mint' (MDB) **new**	LTwo
	'McKellar's Grove' (TB)	CIri
	'Meadow Court' (SDB)	CKel ERos NBro WCAu
	'Media Luz' (Spuria)	WCAu
	'Medway Valley' (MTB) Υ^{H4}	SIri WAul WCAu
	'Meg's Mantle' (TB) Υ^{H4}	CKel
	'Melbreak' (TB)	WCAu
	'Melissa Sue' (TB)	EFam
	mellita	see *I. suaveolens*
	- var. ***rubromarginata***	see *I. suaveolens*
	'Melon Honey' (SDB)	CKel NZep WCAu WHoo
	'Memo' (IB)	EFam
	'Memphis Delight' (TB)	WCAu
	'Men in Black' (TB)	WCAu
	'Menton' (SDB)	CKel
	'Mer du Sud' (TB) Υ^{H4}	ESgI SCoo
	'Merebrook Blue Lagoon' (La) **new**	WMAq
	'Merebrook Lemon Maid' (La) **new**	WMAq
	'Merebrook Rusty Red' (La) **new**	WMAq
	'Merebrook Snowflake' (La) **new**	WMAq
	'Merit' (MTB)	EFam WCAu
	'Merlot' (TB)	CIri
	'Mescal'	EFam
	'Mesmerizer' (TB)	CIri EFam ESgI WCAu
	'Metaphor' (TB)	WCAu
	'Mezza Cartuccia' (IB)	ESgI
	'Michael Paul' (SDB) Υ^{H4}	ESgI
	'Michael's Angel'	WWst
	'Midday Blues' (IB)	NZep
	'Midnight Caller' (TB)	EFam
	'Midnight Moonlight' (TB)	CIri
	'Midnight Oil' (TB)	WCAu
	'Midnight Pacific' (TB)	EFam
	'Mil Byers' (TB)	EFam
	milesii Υ^{H4}	CDes CPLG CPou GBuc IGor NBir NEgg WCot WPer
	- CC 4590	CHid MGol
	'Millennium Falcon' (TB)	CIri WAul
	'Millennium Sunrise' (TB)	WCAu
	'Ming' (IB)	WCAu
	'Mini Big Horn' (IB)	CIri
	'Mini Champagne' (BB)	EFam
	'Mini Might' (SDB) Υ^{H4}	EFam
	'Minneopa' (Spuria) **new**	ESgI
	'Miss Carla' (IB)	NBre
	'Miss Mauve' (IB)	CIri
	'Miss Nellie' (BB)	CKel
	'Miss Scarlett' (BB)	EFam
	'Mission Sunset' (TB)	EHrv WCAu
	'Missouri Iron Ore' (Spuria)	CIri
	'Missouri Orange' (Spuria)	CIri
	'Missouri Rainbows' (Spuria)	CIri

	missouriensis Υ^{H4}	EBee IGor NBid
§	- 'Tollong' Υ^{H4}	MSte
	'Mister Matthew' (TB) Υ^{H4} **new**	CKel
	'Mister Roberts' (SDB)	ESgI NZep
	'Mistigri' (IB)	CBgR WAul
	'Mme Chereau' (TB)	ESgI WCAu
	'Mme Louis Aureau' (TB)	ESgI
*	'Mohogang Mountain' (TB)	EFam
	'Moonbeam' (IB) **new**	CKel
	monnieri	NLar SDix
	'Monsieur' (TB) **new**	ESgI
	Monspur Group	WCot
§	'Monspur Cambridge Blue' (Spuria) Υ^{H} [4]	WCAu
	'Monty's Sweet Blue' (TB)	EFam
	'Moon Journey' (TB)	SIri
	'Moon Sparkle' (IB)	CKel LCro
	'Moonlight' (TB)	EFam WCot
	'Moonlight Waves'	see *I. ensata* 'Moonlight Waves'
	'Moonlit Waves' (TB)	CKel
	'Morning Show' (IB)	CWGN EBee
	'Morning's Blush' (SDB) Υ^{H4}	CIri
	'Morwenna' (TB) Υ^{H4}	CKel EFam WCAu
	'Mote Park' (MTB)	CIri SIri
	'Mother Earth' (TB)	ESgI LRHS
	'Mountain Brook' **new**	LLWG
	'Mrs Horace Darwin' (TB)	CFir SWat WMnd
	'Mrs Nate Rudolph' (SDB)	EBee MBri SMrm
	'Mrs Tait' (Spuria)	NChi
	'Mulberry Rose' (TB)	CFee
	'Mulled Wine' (TB)	EFam ESgI
	'Murmuring Morn' (TB)	WCAu
	'Music Box' (SDB)	NZep
	'My Friend Jonathan' (TB)	EFam
	'My Ginny' (TB)	CIri
	'My Honeycomb' (TB)	WCAu
	'My Kayla' (SDB)	ESgI
N	'My Seedling' (MDB)	ERos NMen
	'Mystic Lover' (TB)	EFam
	'Naivasha' (TB)	CKel
	'Nancy' (TB)	SApp
	'Nancy Hardy' (MDB)	ERos NMen
	'Nancy Lindsay'	see *I. lutescens* 'Nancy Lindsay'
	'Nanny' (SDB)	SIri
	'Naples' (TB) **new**	ESgI
	narcissiflora	CFir EBee
	'Nashborough' (TB)	WCAu
	'Natascha' (Reticulata)	EBrs ECho EPot LAma LRHS SPhx WLin
	'Natchez Trace' (TB)	ERou
	'Natural Grace'	EFam
	'Navajo Jewel' (TB)	ESgI LRHS WCAu
	'Near Myth' (SDB)	WCAu
	'Nectar' (IB)	ESgI WAul
	'Needlecraft' (TB)	EFam NBre
	'Needlepoint' (TB)	ESgI
	'Neige de Mai' (TB)	ESgI
*	'Nel Jupe' (TB)	ERou
	nepalensis	see *I. decora*
	nertschinskia	see *I. sanguinea*
N	'New Argument' (Juno)	WWst
	'New Centurion' (TB)	WCAu
	'New Idea' (MTB)	ESgI WCAu
	'New Leaf' (TB)	EFam WCAu
	'New Snow' (TB)	WCAu
	'Nibelungen' (TB)	EPfP ERou MWea NBre WFar
	'Nice n' Nifty' (IB)	NZep WTin
	'Nicola Jane' (TB) Υ^{H4}	CKel
	nicolai	WWst
	'Nigerian Raspberry' (TB)	WCAu
	'Night Edition' (TB)	ESgI
	'Night Game' (TB)	WCAu
	'Night Owl' (TB)	CKel ELan ESgI SPet WHlf

	'Night Ruler' (TB)	ESgI WCAu
	'Night Shift' (IB)	NBre
	'Nightfall' (TB)	EBee
	'Nights of Gladness' (TB)	ESgI
I	'Ninesprings Strain' **new**	SNin
	'Nineveh' (AB)	WCAu
	'Noces Blanches' (IB)	ESgI
	'Noon Siesta' (TB)	ESgI
	'Nora Eileen' (TB)	CKel
	'Northern Flame' (TB)	EFam
	'Northwest Pride' (TB)	WCAu
	'Novemberfest' (SDB) **new**	EFam
	'Nut Ruffles' (SDB)	WAul
	'O Shenandoah' (TB)	EFam
	'Obsidian' (TB)	CIri
	'Ocean Depths' (TB) **new**	ESgI
	'Ocelot' (TB) **new**	ESgI
	'Ochraurea' (Spuria)	NGdn NSti
	'Ochre Doll' (SDB)	CKel
	ochroleuca	see *I. orientalis* Mill.
	'O'Cool' (IB)	CKel
	'October' (TB)	EFam
	'October Storm' (IB)	EFam
	odaesanensis	EBee
	'Off Broadway' (TB)	EFam
	'Oktoberfest' (TB)	EFam ESgI
	'Ola Kalá' (TB)	ECGP ESgI GMaP LCro MSte MWat NBre NEgg NLar SPer SPoG SPur WCAu
	'Old Black Magic' (TB)	ESgI
	'Olive Reflection'	EFam
	'Olympiad' (TB)	ERou ESgI
	'Olympic Challenge' (TB)	ESgI WCAu
	'Olympic Torch' (TB)	EFam ESgI WCAu
	'Ominous Stranger' (TB)	ESgI WCAu
	'On Edge' (TB) **new**	ERou
	'One Desire' (TB)	NZep WCAu
	'Opalette' (IB)	EFam
	'Open Sky' (SDB)	NZep SIri
	'Orageux' (IB)	CBgR ESgI WAul
	'Orange Caper' (SDB)	EGoo ESgI GBuc MRav MSte MWat NEgg NLar NZep WCAu WWeb
	'Orange Cordial' (SDB) **new**	EFam
	'Orange Dawn' (TB) ♀H4	EFam
	'Orange Design' (SDB) **new**	EFam
	'Orange Gumdrops' (SDB) **new**	EFam
	'Orange Harvest' (TB)	EFam
	'Orange Order' (TB)	WCAu
N	'Orange Plaza'	ECho NMen
	'Orange Popsicle' (TB)	EFam
	'Orange Tiger' (SDB)	EFam NZep WCAu
	'Orangerie'	EFam
	'Orchardist' (TB)	CKel
	'Orchid Cloud' (TB)	EFam
	'Orchidarium' (TB)	CKel
	'Orchidea Selvaggia' (TB)	ESgI
	orchioides misapplied	see *I. bucharica* Foster
§	***orchioides*** Carrière	CMea CSam ECho ELan ERos NWCA WLin
N	- 'Urungachsai'	EPot WWst
	'Oregold' (SDB)	NZep WCAu
	'Oregon Skies' (TB)	ESgI ETod
N	'Oriental Argument' (Juno)	WWst
	'Oriental Baby' (IB)	CKel WAul
	'Oriental Beauty' (TB)	GBri MAvo
	'Oriental Beauty' (Dut)	EBrs GKev LRHS SPer WCot WFar
	'Oriental Glory' (TB)	WCAu
	orientalis Thunb.	see *I. sanguinea*
	orientalis ambig.	EPyc
§	***orientalis*** Mill. ♀H4	EPPr MSte MWgw SGar SPer WBVN WCAu WDyG
	- 'Alba'	see *I. sanguinea* 'Alba'
	'Orinoco Flow' (BB) ♀H4	CHar CKel EFam ESgI WCAu
	'Orloff' (TB)	ESgI

	'Osage Buff' (TB)	CKel
	'Osaka' (TB)	CIri
	'Out Yonder' (TB)	WCAu
	'Ovation' (TB)	ESgI
	'Over Easy' (SDB) **new**	CKel
	'Overjoyed' (TB)	WCAu
	'O'What' (SDB)	EFam ESgI
	'Owyhee Desert' (TB)	WCAu
	'Oxford Tweeds' (SDB)	ESgI
	'Ozone Alert' (TB)	CIri
	Pacific Coast hybrids	see *I.* Californian hybrids
	'Pacific Mist' (TB)	WCAu
	'Pacific Panorama' (TB)	ESgI
	'Pacific Tide' (TB)	EFam
	'Pagan Dance' (TB)	EFam WCAu
	'Pagan Goddess' (TB)	EFam
	'Pagan Princess' (TB)	WCAu
	'Paint It Black' (TB)	ETod
	'Painted Clouds' (TB)	LRHS
	'Painter's Choice' (Spuria)	CIri
	'Pale Primrose' (TB)	WCAu
	'Pale Shades' (IB) ♀H4	CKel ERos
	'Palissandro' (TB)	ESgI
§	***pallida***	EBee EGoo ESgI GMaP GSki MCCP MRav MSte MWat SIng WCAu WMnd
§	- 'Argentea Variegata' (TB/v)	CBcs CWCL CWGN EBee EBrs ECha ECho EHrv ENot EPfP GGar GMaP GSki LAst LRHS MBrN MBri MLLN MNFA MRav MWgw NBir NCiC NSti SPer SPoG WAul WCot WCra
	- 'Aurea'	see *I. pallida* 'Variegata' hort.
	- 'Aurea Variegata'	see *I. pallida* 'Variegata' hort.
	- var. ***dalmatica***	see *I. pallida* subsp. *pallida*
§	- subsp. ***pallida*** ♀H4	CKel ECha ELan MBri MWgw SDix SPer
	- 'Variegata' misapplied	see *I. pallida* 'Argentea Variegata'
§	- 'Variegata' hort. (v) ♀H4	More than 30 suppliers
	pallida* x *tectorum	GSki
	'Palo Pinto' (TB)	EFam
	'Palomino' (TB)	WCAu
	'Paltec' (IB)	CPou EBee
	'Pane e Vino' (TB)	ESgI
	'Pansy Top' (SDB)	SIri
	'Paprika Fono's' (TB)	EFam
	'Paradise' (TB)	CKel
	'Paradise Bird' (TB) ♀H4	EFam
	'Paradise Saved' (TB)	EFam
	paradoxa	EBrs ECho SBla WWst
	- f. ***choschab***	SBla
	'Party Dress' (TB)	CWGN EBee ELan EMan ENot LAst LCro LRHS MBNS MBnl MRav NBir NEgg NGdn NLar SMer SPer SPoG SRms SWat WCFE WCot WCra WWeb
	'Passion Flower' (TB)	EFam
	'Passionata'	EFam
	'Passport' (BB)	ECho
	'Pastel Charm' (SDB)	CMMP GBin MSte SMrm STes WMnd
	'Pastel Delight' (SDB)	NZep
	'Patches' (TB)	ESgI
	'Patina' (TB)	ECtt ESgI ETod WAul WCAu
	'Patterdale' (TB)	NBir NBre NVic WCAu
	'Paul Black' (TB)	CIri
	'Pauline' (Reticulata)	EBrs ECho EPfP EPot GKev LAma LRHS WFar
	'Peaceful Waters' (TB)	ECtt EFam
	'Peacetime' (TB)	WCAu
	'Peach Brandy' (TB)	EFam
	'Peach Everglow' (TB)	EFam
	'Peach Eyes' (SDB)	CKel ERos
	'Peach Float' (TB)	WCAu
	'Peach Melba' (TB)	ESgI

	'Peach Petals' (BB)	NZep
	'Peach Picotee' (TB)	EFam ESgI
	'Peach Reprise' (BB)	EFam
	'Peach Spot' (TB)	WCAu
	'Peaches ala Mode' (BB)	WCAu
	'Pearls of Autumn' (TB)	EFam WCAu
	'Pearly Dawn' (TB)	EBee ECha MCot MSte NEgg SPer SRGP SSvw SWat WAul WCot
	'Pegaletta'	EPPr NBro
	'Peggy Chambers' (IB) Υ^{H4}	EFam SMrm
	'Pele' (SDB)	EFam ESgI WCAu
	'Penny Anne' (BB)	EFam
	'Penny Royal' (BB) **new**	SKHP
	'Pepita' (SDB) **new**	SIri
	'Pepper Blend'	EFam
	'Peppermint Twist' (SDB)	NZep
	'Perfume Counter' (TB)	EFam
	'Perfume Shop' (IB) **new**	CKel
	'Persian Berry' (TB)	LRHS WCAu
	'Pet' (SDB)	NZep
	'Peter James' (SDB) Υ^{H4}	CIri
	'Phaeton' (TB)	CIri
	'Pharaoh's Daughter' (IB)	SIri WAul
	'Pheasant Feathers' (TB)	CIri
	'Phil Keen' (TB) Υ^{H4}	CKel EFam
	'Picacho Peak' (Spuria)	CIri
N	'Picadee'	EPfP GBuc NCob
	'Picante' (TB)	CIri
	'Piero Bargellini' (TB)	ESgI
	'Pigmy Gold' (IB)	EBee ENot ERos
	'Pineapple Poll' (TB)	EFam
	'Pinewood Amethyst' (CH)	CAby CDes
	'Pinewood Delight' (CH)	CDes
	'Pink Attraction' (TB)	EFam ESgI
	'Pink Bubbles' (BB)	WAul
	'Pink Charm' (TB)	CWGN EMan EPfP IPot LBuc LRHS SPet WAul WCra
	'Pink Confetti' (TB)	ESgI
	'Pink Fawn' (SDB)	ESgI
	'Pink Formal' (TB)	ESgI
	'Pink Horizon' (TB)	EPfP WFar
	'Pink Kitten' (IB)	NZep WCAu WGwG
	'Pink Parchment' (BB) Υ^{H4} **new**	CKel
	'Pink Pele' (IB) **new**	ESgI
	'Pink Pussycat' (TB)	MBri
	'Pink Ruffles' (IB)	CHar
	'Pink Swan' (TB)	ESgI
	'Pink Taffeta' (TB)	ESgI
	'Pinkness' (TB)	EFam
	'Pinky Dinky'	EFam
	'Pinnacle' (TB)	CKel ERou ESgI SWat WCAu
	'Piper's Tune' (IB)	SMrm
	'Pipes of Pan' (TB)	ESgI MRav WCAu
	'Pirate's Patch' (SDB)	ESgI
	'Pirate's Quest' (TB)	EFam
	'Piroska' (TB) Υ^{H4}	ESgI
	'Piu Blue' (TB)	ESgI
	'Pixie' (Reticulata) Υ^{H4}	EBrs ECho ELan EPot LRHS SPer
	'Pixie' (DB)	GKev
	'Pixie Flirt' (MDB)	ERos
	planifolia	SBla SKHP
*	- f. ***alba***	EBrs ECho WWst
	'Pleased as Punch' (IB)	EFam
	'Pledge Allegiance' (TB)	ESgI GSki SIri WCAu
	plicata	WCAu
	'Pluie d'Or' (TB)	ESgI
	'Plum Lucky' (SDB)	SIri
	'Plum Wine' (TB)	CKel
	'Poco Taco' (SDB)	WAul
	'Poem of Ecstasy' (TB)	WCAu
	'Poetess' (TB)	WCAu
	'Pogo' (SDB)	CWGN ECtt EFam ELan ENot EPfP EPot ETod GBuc GMaP MBNS MMHG MRav NBir NWCA SRms
	'Polar Queen' (TB)	EFam
	'Pond Lily' (TB)	ESgI WCAu
	'Pookanilly' (IB)	ESgI
	'Portfolio' (TB) **new**	ESgI
	'Portrait of Amy' (TB)	EFam
	'Posh' (IB)	EFam
	'Powder Blue Cadillac' (TB)	CKel
	'Precious Heather' (TB) Υ^{H4}	CKel
	'Presby's Crown Jewel' (TB)	CIri
	'Presence' (TB)	EFam SIri
	'Presumption'	EFam
	'Pretender' (TB)	LRHS WCAu
	'Pretty Please' (TB)	ESgI
	'Prince Indigo' (TB)	MRav
	'Prince of Burgundy' (IB) Υ^{H4}	WCAu
	'Prince of Earl' (TB)	EFam
	'Princess Beatrice' (TB)	WCAu
	'Princess Pittypat' (TB)	EFam
	'Princess Sabra' (TB) Υ^{H4}	CKel
	'Princesse Caroline de Monaco' (TB)	ESgI
	'Priscilla of Conrinth' (TB)	EFam
	prismatica	EBee WTin
	- ***alba***	IGor
	'Professor Blaauw' (Dut) Υ^{H4}	EBrs EPfP
	'Progressive Attitude' (TB)	CIri EFam WCAu
	'Protocol' (IB)	CKel EFam
	'Proud Tradition' (TB)	SIri WCAu
	'Provencal' (TB)	CKel ECtt ESgI ETod WAul WCAu
	'Proverb' (Spuria)	WCAu
	'Prudy' (BB) Υ^{H4}	CKel
	pseudacorus Υ^{H4}	More than 30 suppliers
	- B&SWJ 5018 from Japan	WCru
	- 'Alba'	EBee GBin LAst LRHS NGdn
	- var. ***bastardii***	CBgR CWat EBee ECha ELon EMFW ESgI IGor NPer SLon SMHy SPer WBrk WFar WMoo WTin
	- cream	EGol NBir WAul
N	- 'Crème de la Crème'	GBin
	- 'Esk'	GBin
N	- 'Flore Pleno' (d)	CBgR EBee EBrs ECho EMFW EPPr ESgI GCra GSki NLar NPer WBrk WCot WFar WPnP
I	- 'Golden Fleece'	SPer
	- 'Golden Queen'	IGor
	- 'Roccapina'	GBin
	- 'Roy Davidson' Υ^{H4}	CBgR CDWL CKel CPrp EMFW ESgI GBin IBlr WFar WHil WPtf WTin
N	- 'Sulphur Queen'	WCot
	- 'Sun Cascade'	WBIS
N	- 'Tiger Brother'	SIri WBrk
N	- 'Turnipseed'	ESgI WTin
	- 'Variegata' (v) Υ^{H4}	More than 30 suppliers
	- white-flowered, from Lake Michigan **new**	WTin
	pseudopumila	ERos
	'Puddy Tat' (SDB)	CIri
	'Pulsar' (TB)	EFam
	pumila	CPBP EDAr GKev GSki LRHS MHer NMen NWCA WLin
	- 'Alba' (DB)	CPBP
	- ***atroviolacea***	CKel ESgI SMrm WMnd
	- subsp. ***attica***	see *I. attica*
	- blue-flowered	SWal
N	- 'Gelber Mantel'	NBir
N	- 'Lavendel Plicata'	EBee NBro NGdn
	- 'Violacea' (DB)	MBri SRms
	- yellow	GAbr SWal
	'Pumpin' Iron' (SDB)	CKel ESgI MSte

	'Pumpkin Center' (SDB)	NZep
	'Punkin' (TB)	EFam
	'Puppy Love' (MTB)	NZep
	purdyi	GBuc
	'Pure Allure' (SDB) ♀^{H4}	NZep
	'Purple Duet' (TB)	EFam
	'Purple Gem' (Reticulata)	EBrs ECho EPfP EPot LAma LHop LRHS
	'Purple Sensation' (Dut)	ECho
	'Quaker Lady' (TB)	ESgI SIri WCAu
	'Quark' (SDB)	CKel NZep
	'Quasar' (TB)	EFam
	'Quechee' (TB)	CPen EBee EPfP ETod GMaP IPot LBuc LDai MBNS MCot MRav MSte MWat MWgw NLar SHBN SWat WAul WCra WSpi
	'Queen in Calico' (TB)	ESgI WCAu
	'Queen of May' (TB)	ESgI
	'Queen's Circle' (TB)	CIri
	'Queen's Ivory' (SDB)	WCAu
	'Queen's Prize' (SDB)	SIri
	'Quiet Times' (TB) **new**	ERou
	'Quietly' (SDB)	EFam
	'Radiant Angel' (TB)	EFam
	'Radiant Apogee' (TB)	ECtt ESgI
	'Rain Dance' (SDB) ♀^{H4}	ESgI NZep WCAu
	'Rainbow Goddess' (TB)	EFam
	'Rainbow Rim' (SDB)	ESgI
	'Rajah' (TB)	EBee EHrv ELan EPfP EShb GMaP LSRN MMHG MRav MSte NOrc SCoo SHBN SPer SPet SPla SPoG SPur WCra WMnd
	'Rameses' (TB)	ESgI
	'Rancho Rose' (TB)	CKel
	'Rare Edition' (IB)	CKel EFam ESgI LCro MBri NBre NZep WAul WCAu
	'Rare Quality' (TB) **new**	WAul
	'Rare Treat' (TB)	NZep WCAu
	'Raspberry Acres' (IB)	MRav WCAu
	'Raspberry Blush' (IB) ♀^{H4}	CKel CPar EFam EPfP LAst MCot MRav NBre NZep SHBN SWat WAul WCAu
	'Raspberry Fudge' (TB)	WCAu
	'Raspberry Jam' (SDB)	NZep
	'Raven Hill' (TB)	WCAu
	'Raven Rock' (TB) **new**	ERou
	'Razoo' (SDB)	CKel
	'Real Coquette' (SDB)	SIri
	'Recurring Dream' (TB)	EFam
	'Red At Night' (TB) **new**	WAul
	'Red Atlast' (MDB)	ESgI
	'Red Canyon Glow' (TB)	CIri
	'Red Duet' (TB)	EFam
	'Red Flash' (TB)	ESgI
	'Red Hawk' (TB)	CIri
	'Red Heart' (SDB)	ESgI GMaP MRav WTin
	'Red Lion' (TB)	NZep
	'Red Oak' (Spuria)	ESgI WCAu
	'Red Orchid' (IB)	ELan ERou NBlu NBre WCAu
	'Red Revival' (TB)	EFam MRav WCAu
N	'Red Rum' (TB)	CKel
	'Red Tornado' (TB)	ESgI
	'Red Zinger' (IB)	ESgI NZep WAul
	'Redelta' (TB)	EFam
	'Redwood Supreme' (Spuria)	GSki WAul
	'Regal Surprise' (SpecHybrid) ♀^{H4}	WAul
§	***reichenbachii***	CPBP CSsd ERos LBee LTwo NWCA WHil WThu
	- NS 700	CPou
	'Reincarnation' (TB)	EFam
	'Remember Spring' (TB)	EFam
	'Renown' (TB)	ESgI
	'Repartee' (TB)	ESgI

	reticulata ♀^{H4}	CBcs CTca EBrs ECho ELan EPfP LRHS MBNS SPer SPet WCAu WFar WGwG
	- 'Spring Time'	EBrs ECho LAma LRHS
N	- 'Violet Queen'	EBrs ECho
	'Return to Bayberry' (TB)	CIri
	'Returning Chameleon' (TB)	EFam
	'Returning Peace' (TB)	EFam
	'Rime Frost' (TB)	EFam WCAu
	'Ringer' (SDB)	ESgI
	'Ringo' (TB)	ESgI MRav WCAu
	'Rip City' (TB) **new**	ESgI
	'Ripple Chip' (SDB)	NZep WTin
	'Rippling Waters' (TB)	ESgI
	'Rive Gauche' (TB)	ESgI
	'River Avon' (TB) ♀^{H4}	CKel WCAu
	'Rivulets of Pink' (Spuria)	CIri
§	x ***robusta*** 'Dark Aura' ♀^{H4}	WBIS WTin
§	- 'Gerald Darby' ♀^{H4}	More than 30 suppliers
	'Rock Star'	EFam
	'Rockabye' (SDB)	WAul
§	'Rocket' (TB)	GMaP IPot LBuc MRav MSte NBir NBre NEgg SPer
	'Role Model' (TB)	LRHS WCAu
	'Roman Emperor' (TB)	EFam
	'Roman Rhythm' (TB)	WCAu
	'Romantic Evening' (TB)	ESgI WAul WCAu
	'Romantic Mood' (TB)	CKel
	'Romp' (IB)	CKel
	'Rondo' (TB) **new**	ECtt
	'Roney's Encore' (TB)	EFam
	'Rosalie Figge' (TB)	EFam ESgI WCAu
	'Rose Queen'	see *I. ensata* 'Rose Queen'
	'Rose Violet' (TB)	WCAu
	'Rosemary's Dream' (MTB)	NBre SMrm
	rosenbachiana	EBrs ECho WWst
I	- 'Sina'	WWst
N	- 'Varzob'	WWst
	'Roseplic' (TB)	ESgI
	'Rosette Wine' (TB)	ESgI WCAu
	'Rosy Veil' (TB)	ESgI
	'Rosy Wings' (TB)	ESgI
	'Roulette' (TB)	MBri
N	'Roy Elliott'	NMen SIng
	'Royal Contrast' (SDB) ♀^{H4}	NZep
	'Royal Courtship' (TB) **new**	ESgI
	'Royal Crusader' (TB)	WCAu
	'Royal Elegance' (TB)	EFam SIri
	'Royal Intrigue' (TB)	SIri
	'Royal Magician' (SDB)	WTin
	'Royal Overtime' (SDB) **new**	EFam
	'Royal Summer' (TB)	EFam
	'Royal Tapestry' (TB)	NBre
	'Royal Yellow' (Dut)	LRHS
	'Royalist' (TB)	CKel
	'Rubacuori' (TB)	ESgI
	'Ruban Bleu' (TB)	ESgI
	'Rubistar' (TB)	ESgI
	'Ruby Chimes' (IB)	ESgI WCAu
	'Ruby Contrast' (TB)	WCAu
	'Ruby Eruption' **new**	EFam
	'Ruby Morn' (TB)	CIri
	rudskyi	see *I. variegata*
	'Ruffled Canary' (Spuria)	WCAu
	'Ruffled Revel' (SDB)	SIri
	'Russet Crown' (TB) **new**	CKel
	'Rustic Cedar' (TB)	ESgI WCAu
	'Rustic Dream' (TB)	CIri
	'Rustic Royalty' (TB)	CIri
	'Rustler' (TB)	ESgI WAul WCAu
	'Rusty Dusty' (SDB)	NZep
	'Ruth Black' (TB)	WCAu

	ruthenica	EChо ERos GBin NMen
	- var. ***nana***	EBee
	- - L 1280	SBla
	'Ryan James' (TB)	CKel
	'Sable' (TB)	EBee EHrv ELan ESgI ETod GMaP LBuc MBri MRav MSte MWat NGdn NOrc SCoo SEND SHBN SPer WAul WCAu WCra
	'Sable Night' (TB)	CHar CKel ESgI
	'Sager Cedric' (TB)	WCAu
	'Sahara Sands' (Spuria)	ECha
	'Saint Crispin' (TB)	EPfP ESgI GCra GMaP MPop MRav MSte MWgw SPer SPet SPoG WWeb
	'Sally Jane' (TB)	WCAu
	'Salonique' (TB)	ERou ESgI NBlu NBre NLar WCAu WFar
	'Saltwood' (SDB)	NBre SIri
	'Sam Carne' (TB)	WCAu
	'San Francisco' (TB)	ESgI
	'San Leandro' (TB)	MBri
	'Sand Princess' (MTB)	SIri
	'Sandstone Sentinel' (BB)	CIri
	'Sandy Caper' (IB)	WCAu WTin
	'Sangone' (IB)	ESgI
§	***sanguinea*** ♀H4	MGol WBVN
§	- 'Alba'	IBlr WCot
	- 'Nana Alba'	GBin IBlr SIri
§	- 'Snow Queen'	More than 30 suppliers
	'Santana' (TB)	ECtt
	'Sapphire Beauty' (Dut)	EPfP LRHS MAvo
	'Sapphire Gem' (SDB)	CKel EFam ESgI WAul WCAu
	'Sapphire Hills' (TB)	WCAu
	'Sapphire Jewel' (SDB)	EPPr NZep
	'Sarah Taylor' (SDB) ♀H4	EFam WCAu
	'Sarajaavo' (AB)	CKel
	sari	EBrs ECho SBla
	'Sass with Class' (SDB)	CKel EFam WTin
	'Satin Gown' (TB)	WCAu
	'Saturday Night Live' (TB)	CIri ESgI
	'Saxon' (TB)	EFam
	'Saxon Princess' (TB)	EFam
	'Scented Bubbles' (TB)	EFam
	schachtii	CGra
	- purple-flowered	SBla
	'Scottish Warrior' (TB)	EFam
	'Scribe' (MDB)	NBir WCAu
	'Sea Monster' (SDB)	EPPr SIri
	'Sea Power' (TB)	CIri
	'Sea Wisp' (La)	EPPr EWTr NBro
	'Seafire' (SDB)	CIri
	'Season Ticket' (IB)	ESgI
	'Second Look' (TB)	EFam
	'Second Opinion' (MTB)	NZep
	'Second Show' (TB)	EFam
	'Second Wind' (TB) **new**	ECtt
	'Secretariat'	EFam
	'Self Evident' (MDB) **new**	LTwo
	'Semola' (SDB)	ESgI
	'Seneca Rebound' (SDB)	EFam
	'Senlac' (TB)	ERou NLar SMer WMnd
	'Senor Frog' (SDB)	ESgI
	'September Frost' (TB)	EFam
	'September Replay'	EFam
	serbica	see *I. reichenbachii*
	'Serene Moment' (TB)	SIri
	'Serengeti Spaghetti' (TB)	CIri
	'Serenity Prayer' (SDB)	WCAu
	'Set To Music'	EFam
	setosa ♀H4	CTri CWCL EAlp EBee ECho EKen EMFW EPfP ERos GCra GKev GMaP IGor LRHS MHer MLan MNrw NDlv NEgg NGdn NLAp SPer WCot WSpi
	- RBS 0233	ITer MGol
	- ***alba***	MBri MSte NLar SIng
	- var. ***arctica***	EBee EMon EPot GBuc LEdu MHer NMen NWCA WHoo WPer
	- subsp. ***canadensis***	see *I. hookeri*
	- dwarf	see *I. hookeri*
§	- 'Hondoensis'	MSte
	- 'Hookeri'	see *I. hookeri*
	- 'Kirigamini'	see *I. setosa* 'Hondoensis'
	- var. ***nana***	see *I. hookeri*
	'Seuver Fourses' **new**	WBIS
*	'Sevenly Seven' (TB)	EFam
	'Severn Side' (TB) ♀H4	CKel
	'Shakespeare's Sonnet' (SDB)	ESgI
	'Shameless' (IB)	NBre
	'Shampoo' (IB)	CKel SIri WAul WCAu
	'Sheer Ecstasy' (TB)	CIri
	'Sheila Ann Germaney' (Reticulata)	EBrs ECho EPot GCrs NMen WWst
	'Shelford Giant' (Spuria) ♀H4	NEgg
	'Shepherd's Delight' (TB)	WCAu
	'Sherbet Lemon' (IB) ♀H4	CKel EFam WCAu WGwG
	'Sherwood Pink' (TB)	EFam
	'Sherwood Primrose' (TB) ♀H4	EFam
	'Shindig' (SDB)	EFam WCAu
	'Shocking Blue' **new**	WWst
	'Shoot the Moon' (TB)	EFam
	'Short Distance' (IB)	SIri
	'Showman' (TB)	ERou
	shrevei	see *I. virginica* var. *shrevei*
	'Shurton Inn' (TB)	CKel WCAu
	'Shy Violet' (SDB)	NZep
	sibirica ♀H4	CMHG COIW CWat EDAr EHon ESgI GAbr LAma LAst LLWP MHer MLHP NChi NCob NEgg NVic SIng SPlb SPoG WBVN WBrE WBrk WEas WFar WHer WHoo WMoo WShi WTel WWeb
	- 'Ann Dasch'	EBee WLin
	- 'Annemarie Troeger' ♀H4	EBee NBre
	- 'Anniversary'	CDes CLAP CMdw EBee LRHS MBNS WLin
	- 'Atlantic Crossing' **new**	SIri WAul
	- 'Atoll'	SIri
	- 'Baby Sister'	CAby CMHG EBee EBla EGle GAbr GBin LRHS MBri NBre NBro SWat WAul
	- 'Begin the Beguine' **new**	WBIS
	- 'Berlin Bluebird'	SMHy SPhx
	- 'Berlin Chrytosa' **new**	WBIS
	- 'Berlin Ruffles' ♀H4	CIri
	- 'Berlin Sky'	ESgI
	- 'Bickley Cape'	EBee
	- 'Blaue Milchstrasse' ♀H4	GBin WBIS
	- 'Blaumacher'	GBuc
	- 'Blue Burgee'	ECha
I	- 'Blue Butterfly'	ELan EPfP NGdn SHBN
N	- 'Blue Emperor'	EBee
	- 'Blue King'	CHid CKel EBee EBla EGle ELan EPfP GMaP MBNS MDun MRav NBro NGdn NMoo SPer SPoG WLin WMnd WMoo
	- 'Blue Meadow Fly'	EBee
	- 'Blue Mere'	WLin
	- 'Blue Moon'	WFar
	- 'Blue Pennant'	EBee GBin
	- 'Blue Reverie'	CPen EPPr ESgI
N	- 'Blue Sceptre'	IBlr
	- 'Blue Seraph'	GBin
	- 'Blueberry Fair'	CIri
	- 'Bournemouth Ball Gown' **new**	SIri
	- 'Bournemouth Beauty' ♀H4	CIri

	– 'Bridal Jig'	EBee
	– 'Butter and Sugar' Υ^{H4}	More than 30 suppliers
	– 'Caesar'	ERou SDys SRms WLin
	– 'Caesar's Brother'	CBgR CHid EBee EGle ELan EMil ERou IBlr LCro LRHS MNFA NBro SPer SPet SWal SWat WCAu
	– 'Camberley'	WLin
	– 'Cambridge' Υ^{H4}	CAby CPrp EBee EBla ECGP MNFA MSte NBre SBch SWat WCAu WFar WWlt
	– 'Canonbury Belle'	WLin
	– 'Chartreuse Bounty'	EBee EGle EMan ERou EWes GAbr GBin GQue ITim LAst MBNS MBri MLLN NBPC NLar NMoo NPri NSti WPtf WWeb
N	– 'Chateuse Belle'	WBrE
	– 'Circle Round'	CSpe EPPr SPhx
	– 'Clee Hills'	WLin
	– 'Cleedownton' Υ^{H4}	WBIS WLin
	– 'Cleve Dodge'	ESgI SIri
	– 'Cool Spring'	WLin
	– 'Coquet Waters'	NBid WLin
	– 'Coronation Anthem'	NEgg WAul
	– cream	see *I. sibirica* 'Primrose Cream'
	– 'Dance Ballerina Dance'	CFir CWCL EBee ERou EWTr GBri GQue MLLN MNFA NBPC NCGa NMoo SMrm SPoG SWat WFar WPtf
	– 'Dancing Nanou'	NBre SWat
	– 'Dark Circle'	EBee
	– 'Dark Desire'	LLWG MRav
	– 'Dear Delight'	EPPr
	– 'Dear Dianne'	CKel ECha NBre
	– 'Dewful'	WFar
	– 'Dirigo Black Velvet'	CIri
	– 'Double Standards'	CIri
	– 'Dreaming Green'	WLin
	– 'Dreaming Spires' Υ^{H4}	ESgI SIri WCot WLin
	– 'Dreaming Yellow' Υ^{H4}	CBre CFee EBee ECha EGle EHon EMan EPfP EShb GMac LLWG MNFA MRav MWgw NBro NChi NGdn SApp SBch SHBN SPer WCAu WCra WMoo
	– 'Ego'	CAby CAvo CHid CWsd ECha EWTr GAbr GBin GMac GSki NBro NCGa NGby SWat WLin WMoo WPen WPrP
	– 'Ellesmere'	NGdn WLin
	– 'Emma Ripeka'	WAul WLin
	– 'Emperor'	CWat ERou MSte MWgw NBre NSti SMrm SWat
	– 'Eric the Red'	IBlr
	– 'Ewen'	CBgR CHVG CHid CLAP CMdw CPou CSam EBee EGle GBin GBuc IBlr MNFA MNrw NGdn SWat WCot WFar WPrP WWlt
	– 'Exuberant Encore' Υ^{H4}	WCAu
	– 'Flight of Butterflies'	More than 30 suppliers
	– 'Fourfold Lavender'	EBee GSki MBri WAul
	– 'Fourfold White'	ESgI LRHS
	– 'Gatineau'	CDes CLAP EBee GBuc
N	– 'Gerbel Mantel'	GBin SHBN SPet WFar
	– 'Glanusk' Υ^{H4}	WBIS
	– 'Grand Junction'	WLin
	– grey	SApp
	– 'Gull's Wing'	EBee
	– 'Harpswell Hallelujah'	EBee
	– 'Harpswell Happiness' Υ^{H4}	CHVG CLAP CPrp EBee EGle EPfP EPyc GBin GCra MBri SWat WAul WMoo
	– 'Harpswell Haze'	ECha WMoo
	– 'Heavenly Blue'	SPer WLin
	– 'Helen Astor'	CDes CHVG CLAP CMea CSam CTri EBee EGle EShb MBNS MHar MRav SApp SWat
N	– 'Himmel von Komi'	GBin
	– 'Hohe Warte' Υ^{H4} **new**	WBIS
	– 'Hubbard'	CMMP CPen ERou EShb GBin MNrw NBro NHol WHrl
	– 'Illini Charm'	CHid CPen GSki NBro SSvw WFar WMoo
	– 'Jewelled Crown'	CPen WFar
	– 'Jugendtraum' **new**	WBIS
	– 'Kabluey'	CIri
	– 'Kent Arrival' **new**	SIri WAul
	– 'Lady Vanessa'	CPou EBee EGle EPPr ERou EWTr GAbr GBin GMac LBuc MBNS MRav NBro NMoo NSti WAul WHil
	– 'Langthorns Pink'	CMdw EGle ELan MRav
	– 'Laurenbuhl'	CPLG WLin
	– 'Lavender Bounty'	CHid EBee EBla EGle NBre NBro SPet WCAu
	– 'Lavender Light'	WLin
	– 'Limeheart'	CPou CSev EGle ELan ERou
	– 'Little Blue'	EBee
	– 'Little Sister'	GBuc
N	– 'Little Twinkle Star'	EBee GBin NPro WFar
	– 'Mabel Coday'	WLin
	– 'Mad Magenta'	WCAu
	– 'Marcus Perry'	MSte
	– 'Marilyn Holmes'	EBee EGle WCot
	– 'Marlene Ahlburg'	WLin
	– 'Marshmallow Frosting'	WFar
§	– 'Melton Red Flare'	CMHG CPen EBee EBla EHon ELan EPPr EShb GBin LRHS MBNS SDys WCAu WCra WFar
	– 'Memphis Memory'	CHFP ELan GBin GCra NGdn SPer WHoo
	– 'Mesa Pearl'	CIri
	– 'Moon Silk'	EBee EPyc GBin GGar
	– 'Mountain Lake'	CPen CSam EPPr GBin LRHS SBch SWat WCAu WSpi
	– 'Mrs Rowe'	CDes CFee CPou EBee EBla EGle EPPr GBuc LLWP MRav MSte MWat SWat WCAu WFar WLin WPtf
	– 'Mrs Saunders'	WLin
	– 'My Love'	WLin
	– 'Navy Brass'	EGle GBuc NBre
	– 'Night Breeze'	SIri
	– 'Niklas Sea'	GBin
	– 'Nora Distin'	WLin
	– 'Nottingham Lace'	EBee SWat WLin
	– 'Oban' Υ^{H4}	ESgI GBuc GMac
	– 'Orville Fay'	GMac WCot WFar
	– 'Ottawa'	CPou ECGP ELan ERou LRHS MBNS SWat WFar
	– 'Outset'	EBee GSki SSvw
I	– 'Pageant'	WCot
I	– 'Painted Desert'	EBee
	– 'Papillon'	CAvo CHVG CTri EBee EBla ECtt EGle ELan EPPr ERou LHop LRHS MAvo MNFA NBir NBro NCob NGdn NHol NSti SApp SPer STes SWat WFar WLin WPer WPnP
N	– 'Pearl Queen'	MTPN WFar
	– 'Peg Edwards'	EBee
	– 'Percheron'	ESgI SIri
	– 'Perfect Vision' Υ^{H4}	MBri
	– 'Perry's Blue'	More than 30 suppliers
I	– 'Perry's Favourite'	CFee
	– 'Perry's Pigmy'	GBuc WLin
	– 'Persimmon' misapplied	see *I. sibirica* 'Tycoon'
	– 'Persimmon' ambig.	CFir CHid EBee EBla ECtt EGle EMFW ERou GCra LRHS MNFA MWat NMoo SWat WFar WMoo WRHF
N	– 'Phosphorflamme'	WLin
	– 'Pink Haze'	CHar EBee EGle EMan EPfP ERou ESgI GBin MAvo MBri MLLN MNFA NBro NMoo NSti SPoG SPur WAul WHrl

	- 'Pirate Prince'	NPer WCra WHoo
	- Plant World hybrids	MDKP SWal
	- 'Plissee' ♀H4	GBin
	- 'Pounsley Purple'	CPou
§	- 'Primrose Cream'	WCot
	- 'Prussian Blue' ♀H4	GBin WBIS
	- 'Purple Cloak'	MSte
	- 'Purple Mere'	WFar WLin
N	- 'Red Flag'	NHol
	- 'Reddy Maid'	WCAu
	- 'Redflare'	see *I. sibirica* 'Melton Red Flare'
N	- 'Regality'	CWCL EWTr GBin MBNS MHer MMuc NBro SHBN SHGN
	- 'Regency Belle' ♀H4	SIri
	- 'Rikugi-sakura'	EBla EMan GBin LTwo NBPC NBhm NBro WCot
	- 'Roanoke's Choice'	CElw EBee EWes GBin NCGa WHrl
	- 'Roaring Jelly'	WCAu
	- 'Roger Perry'	CFee
	- 'Rosselline' ♀H4	WBIS WLin
	- 'Royal Blue'	ECha GBuc SWat
	- 'Ruby Wine'	CPen EWll LEdu
	- 'Ruffled Velvet' ♀H4	More than 30 suppliers
	- 'Savoir Faire'	ECha
	- 'Sea Horse'	GBuc NCot WLin
	- 'Sea Shadows'	ESgI NBir WCAu
	- 'Seren Wib'	WLin
	- 'Shaker's Prayer' ♀H4	WAul
	- 'Shall We Dance' ♀H4	WAul WBIS
	- 'Shirley Pope' ♀H4	CAby EBee GAbr GBin GMac GQue NCGa NMoo NSti SMeo SPhx WAul WCot WFar WMoo
	- 'Shirley's Choice'	SIri
	- 'Showdown'	EBee ECtt EGle GMaP NHol SAga SHBN SWat WCAu WFar
	- 'Shrawley'	WCAu
	- 'Sibirische Nacht' **new**	WBIS
	- 'Silberkante'	WLin
	- 'Silver Edge' ♀H4	More than 30 suppliers
	- 'Simple Gifts' ♀H4	CIri
	- 'Sky Wings'	ECha MArl WMoo
	- 'Smudger's Gift' ♀H4	WLin
	- 'Snow Queen'	see *I. sanguinea* 'Snow Queen'
	- 'Snowcrest'	CBre GMac WLin
	- 'Snowflake' **new**	CSsd
	- 'Soft Blue' ♀H4	CDes EBee LLWG NBre WBIS
N	- 'Southcombe White'	CWsd GBin GBuc MHar NGdn SIri
	- 'Sparkling Rosé'	More than 30 suppliers
	- 'Splashdown' (Sino-Sib)	SWat
	- 'Star Cluster'	WFar
	- 'Steve'	CHVG CPar EBee EWes GMac MLLN MNFA NBro NCGa SWat WAul
	- 'Steve Varner'	SIri WFar
	- 'Strawberry Fair'	CIri
	- 'Summer Sky'	CBre SWat WAul WCAu WCot WTin
	- 'Super Ego'	WCot WTin
	- 'Superba'	WLin
	- 'Sutton Valence' **new**	SIri WAul
	- 'Tal-y-Bont'	WFar WLin
	- 'Tanz Nochmal'	GBin
	- 'Teal Velvet'	ECha GMac GSki SIri WCAu WFar
	- 'Tealwood'	WLin
	- 'Temper Tantrum'	CKel
	- 'Thelma Perry'	WLin
	- 'Tornado Rose'	CIri
	- 'Tropic Night'	CHVG CSam CTri EBee EBla ECtt EHrv EMFW EMan EPPr EPla ERou GBuc GSki LAst LCro LRHS MNFA MRav NCob NGdn NRya NSti SHBN SPer SWat WAul WCAu WFar WWeb
§	- 'Tycoon'	CHid EBee EShb GBin GBuc IBlr LRHS MNFA NChi NHol SPer WCra
	- 'Valda'	EBee
	- 'Velvet Night'	ECtt WBrE
	- 'Vi Luihn'	CBcs ECha EPPr WMoo
	- 'Viel Creme' ♀H4 **new**	WBIS
N	- 'Violet Skies'	EBee GBin
	- 'Visual Treat'	SIri
	- 'Walter'	EBee
	- 'Wealden Butterfly' ♀H4 **new**	SIri WAul
	- 'Wealden Mystery' **new**	WAul
	- 'Wealden Skies' **new**	SIri WAul
	- 'Welcome Return'	CElw CHVG EBee ERou GBin GQue IPot MBNS NBro NMoo SWat WFar WMoo
N	- 'Welfenfürstin'	GBin
	- 'Welfenprinz' ♀H4	WBIS WLin
I	- 'White Queen'	EBla ESgI SSvw SWat WBrE
I	- 'White Swan'	LAst
	- 'White Swirl' ♀H4	More than 30 suppliers
	- 'White Triangles'	SIri
	- 'Wisley White'	MWgw NBre SPer
	- 'Zweites Hundert'	NBre
	'Sibirica Alba'	CBrm ECha EDAr EPfP EShb GAbr LLWP MHer SIng SWat WBrk WCFE WFar
	'Sibirica Baxteri'	CFee
	sibirica 'Über den Wolken' **new**	NCot
	sichuanensis	CExc EBee
	sieboldii	see *I. sanguinea*
	'Sierra Blue' (TB)	ESgI
	'Sierra Grande' (TB)	EFam WCAu
	'Sign of Leo' (TB)	EFam
	'Silent Strings' (IB)	MBri
	'Silicon Prairie' (TB)	ESgI
	'Silk Romance' (TB)	EFam
	'Silkirim' (TB)	CKel
	'Silver Dividends' (TB)	EFam
	'Silver Screen' (TB)	EFam
	'Silverado' (TB)	CKel ESgI WCAu
	'Silvery Beauty' (Dut)	LRHS NBir SPer WFar
	sindjarensis	see *I. aucheri*
	'Sindpers' (Juno) ♀H3	WWst
	'Sinister Desire' (IB)	WCAu
	sintenisii ♀H4	CHid CPBP EBrs ECho NWCA WTin
	- HH&K 172	CMdw
	'Sir Michael' (TB)	ESgI
	'Sister Helen' (TB)	EFam
	'Siva Siva' (TB)	MRav WCAu
	'Skating Party' (TB)	CKel ESgI
	'Skiers' Delight' (TB)	NBre WCAu
	'Skookumchuck' (TB)	EFam
	'Sky and Sun' (TB)	CIri
	'Sky Hooks' (TB)	EFam
	'Skye Blue' (TB)	EFam
	'Skyfire' (TB)	ESgI MWea
	'Skyline' (Juno)	WWst
	'Skyship' (TB)	CIri
	'Slap Bang' (SDB)	ESgI
N	'Smart Girl' (TB)	CKel SMrm
	'Smell the Roses' (SDB)	EFam NZep
	'Smokey Dream' (TB)	CKel
	'Sneezy' (TB)	WCAu
	'Snow Fiddler' (MTB)	NZep
	'Snow Plum' (IB)	SIri
	'Snow Season' (SDB) **new**	EFam
	'Snow Tracery' (TB)	MBri
	'Snow Troll' (SDB)	WCAu
	'Snowbrook' (TB)	WCAu
	'Snowcone' (IB)	ESgI
	'Snowdrift' (*laevigata*)	see *I. laevigata* 'Snowdrift'
	'Snow-in-Summer' (TB)	EFam
	'Snowmound' (TB)	CKel ESgI WCAu
	'Snowy Owl' (TB) ♀H4	CKel WCAu
	'Soaring Kite' (TB)	WCAu

	'Social Event' (TB)	ESgI WCAu
	'Soft Caress' (TB)	WCAu
	'Solid Mahogany' (TB)	EFam MRav WCAu
	'Solstice' (TB)	EFam
	'Sombrero Way' (TB)	EFam
	'Somerset Blue' (TB) ♀H4	CKel WCAu
N	'Somerset Vale' (TB)	SMrm
	'Somerton Brocade' (SDB)	CKel
	'Somerton Dance' (SDB)	CKel
	'Son of Sun' (Spuria)	CIri
	'Sonata in Blue' (TB)	EFam
	'Song of Norway' (TB)	ECtt EPPr ESgI NZep SIri WAul WCAu
	'Sonoran Sands' (IB)	CIri
	'Sonoran Señorita' (Spuria) ♀H4	CIri
	'Sopra il Vulcano' (BB)	ESgI
	'Sostenique' (TB)	ESgI WCAu
	'Soul Power' (TB)	ERou
	'Sound of Gold' (TB)	EFam
	'Southern Clipper' (SDB)	MBri
	'Southern Spy' (TB)	EFam
	'Sovereign Crown' (TB)	EFam
	'Space Mist' (TB)	EFam
	'Spanish Coins' (MTB)	NZep
	'Sparkplug' (SDB)	ESgI
	'Sparks Fly' (SDB)	WCAu
	'Spartan' (TB)	CKel
	'Spatzel' (TB)	EFam
	'Special Feature' (TB)	EFam
	'Speed Limit' (TB)	EFam
	'Spellbreaker' (TB)	ESgI
	'Spice Lord' (TB)	WCAu
	'Spiced Custard' (TB)	ESgI
	'Spiced Tiger' (TB)	WCAu
	'Spinning Wheel' (TB)	SIri
	'Spirit of Fiji' (TB)	EFam
	'Spirit of Memphis' (TB)	EFam
	'Splash of Red' (SDB)	NZep
	'Splashacata' (TB)	CIri
	'Spot of Tea' (MDB)	ESgI
	'Spreckles' (TB)	ESgI
	'Spring Festival' (TB)	WCAu
	'Spun Gold' (TB)	ESgI
	spuria	CPou ELan GSki NEgg WBVN
	- subsp. ***carthaliniae***	GBin WPer
§	- subsp. ***halophila***	GBin WCAu
	- subsp. ***maritima***	EMan
	- subsp. ***ochroleuca***	see *I. orientalis* Mill.
	- subsp. ***spuria***	GBuc
	x ***squalens***	WCAu
	'Stairway to Heaven' (TB)	CIri ESgI WAul WCAu
	'Staplehurst' (MTB) ♀H4	SIri WAul
	'Star Performer' (TB)	EFam
	'Star Prince' (SDB)	ESgI
	'Star Shine' (TB)	ESgI WCAu
	'Starcrest' (TB)	ESgI WAul
	'Stardate' (SDB) **new**	CKel
	'Starfrost Pink' (TB)	EFam
	'Starring' (TB)	CIri
	'Stars and Stripes' (TB) **new**	EFam
	'Starship' (TB)	EFam ESgI
	'Starship Enterprise' (TB)	CIri LRHS
	'Starwoman' (IB) **new**	WAul
	'Staten Island' (TB)	ESgI MBri SRms WCAu WTin
	'Status Seeker' (TB)	WCAu
	'Stella Polaris' (TB)	ELon
	'Stellar Lights' (TB)	MSte WCAu
	stenophylla	SBla
	'Stepping Out' (TB) ♀H4	EBee EPfP ESgI EShb GBin IPot LDai LRHS MWea MWgw NBre WAul WCAu
	'Stinger' (SDB) ♀H4	CIri
	'Stingray' (TB)	EFam ESgI
	'Stitch in Time' (TB)	WCAu
	'Stockholm' (SDB)	CKel NZep WPen
	stolonifera	EBrs ECho
	- 'Sina Dark'	WWst
	- 'Vera'	LRHS
	- 'Zwanenburg Beauty'	EBrs ECho
	'Storm Center' (TB)	SIri
	'Stormy Circle' (SDB)	WCAu
	'Stormy Night' (TB)	EFam
	'Strawberry Love' (IB) ♀H4	CKel
	'Strawberry Sensation' (TB)	NZep
	'Strictly Jazz' (TB)	EFam WCAu
	'Strozzapretti' (TB)	CIri
	'Study In Black' (TB)	WCAu
	stylosa	see *I. unguicularis*
§	***suaveolens***	CPou NMen WIvy
	- 'Rubromarginata'	ERos
*	- var. ***violacea***	NMen NWCA WLin
	subbiflora	WCot
	subbiflora x ***timofejewii***	WCot
	subdichotoma	EBee
	'Sugar' (IB)	NSti WCAu
	'Sugar Blues' (TB)	EFam
	'Sugar Snaps' (IB)	EFam
	'Suky' (TB)	EFam
	'Sultan's Palace' (TB)	ECho ESgI LRHS NBPC SMer WBor WSpi
	'Sumatra' (TB)	ESgI
	'Summer Green Shadows' (TB)	EFam
	'Summer Holidays' (TB)	EFam
	'Summer Luxury' (TB)	NZep
	'Summer's Smile' (TB)	ESgI
	'Sun Doll' (SDB) ♀H4	CKel EFam NZep
	'Sun King' (TB)	EFam
	'Sunchime' (SDB)	EFam
	'Sundown Red' (IB)	NBir
	'Sunmaster' (TB)	EFam
	'Sunny and Warm' (TB)	CKel
	'Sunny Dawn' (IB) ♀H4	CKel EFam
	'Sunny Disposition' (TB)	EFam
	'Sunny Honey' (IB)	NZep
	'Sunny Red Wine'	GBin
	'Sunny Smile' (SDB)	EFam
	'Sunny Tyke' (MDB)	EFam
	'Sunrise in Sonora' (Spuria) ♀H4	CIri
	'Sunset Colors' (Spuria) ♀H4	CIri
	'Sunset Point' (TB)	CIri
	'Sunshine Boy' (IB)	CKel
	'Sunshine Isle' (SDB)	NZep
	'Superstition' (TB) ♀H4	ELan EPPr ESgI GBin LCro LRHS NBPN SIri SMrm SSvw WCAu WCot
	'Supreme Sultan' **new**	ETod
	'Supreme Sultan' (TB)	EFam ESgI WAul WCAu
	'Susan Bliss' (TB)	CRez EBee ELan EPfP ESgI GMaP MBNS NBre WCAu
	'Susan Gillespie' (IB) ♀H4 **new**	CKel
	susiana	LAma
	svetlanae	WWst
	'Swain' (TB)	ESgI
	'Swaledale' (TB)	WCAu
	'Swazi Princess' (TB)	CKel ESgI WCAu
	'Sweet Kate' (SDB) ♀H4	WCAu
	'Sweet Lena' (TB)	ESgI
	'Sweet Musette' (TB)	EFam WCAu
	'Sweeter than Wine' (TB)	ESgI WCAu
	'Sweetheart Ring' (TB)	EFam
	'Swingtown' (TB)	WCAu
	'Sybil' (TB)	GBin GCra NHar
	'Sylvan' (TB)	EFam
	'Sylvia Murray' (TB)	WCAu
	'Symphony' (Dut)	ECho NBir

'Syncopation' (TB) ESgI WCAu
'Tahitian Pearl' (TB) CIri
'Talish' (Reticulata) WWst
'Talk' (SDB) EFam
'Tall Chief' (TB) WCAu
N 'Tanex' ECho
'Tang Fizz' (TB) EFam
'Tangerine Sky' (TB) SCoo WCAu
'Tangfu' (IB) ESgI
'Tantara' (SDB) WTin
'Tanzanian Tangerine' (TB) WCAu
'Tarheel Elf' (SDB) ESgI WTin
'Tarn Hows' (TB) SRms WCAu
'Tarot' (BB) ♀H4 EFam
'Tatiana' (TB) EFam
'Taverlae' LRHS
'Tchin Tchin' (IB) **new** WAul
'Tea Leaves' (TB) EFam
tectorum CAby CSWP CSsd ERos GBin GKev GSki NWCA
- BWJ 8191 WCru
- 'Alba' CPBP ERos MHar WThu
- 'Variegata' misapplied see *I. japonica* 'Variegata'
- 'Variegata' ambig. (v) EBee EMan MRav NSti SPoG WFar
'Teesdale' (TB) EFam
'Temple Gold' (TB) CKel NPer
'Temple Meads' (IB) EFam ESgI WCAu
'Templecloud' (IB) ♀H4 CHar CKel LCro
'Tempting Fate' (TB) WAul
§ ***tenax*** CLAP CPBP ECho GBuc GEdr GSki NWCA
'Tender Years' (IB) WAul
'Tennessee Gentleman' (TB) EFam
'Tennessee Vol' (TB) EFam
'Tennison Ridge' (TB) EFam WCAu
tenuissima GBuc
- subsp. ***tenuissima*** CPBP NMen
'Terra Rosa' (TB) CIri
'Terre de Feu' (TB) ESgI SIri
'Thais' (TB) ESgI
'That's Red' (MTB) WCAu
'The Bride' see *I.* 'Bride'
'The Red Douglas' (TB) ESgI
'The Rocket' see *I.* 'Rocket'
'Theatre' (TB) ESgI
'Then Again' (TB) EFam
'Third Charm' (SDB) EFam
'Thornbird' (TB) ♀H4 CIri EFam ESgI WCAu
'Three Cherries' (MDB) ECho
'Three Seasons' (TB) EFam
'Thrice Blessed' (SDB) EFam
'Thriller' (TB) ESgI WCAu
thunbergii see *I. sanguinea*
'Thunder Echo' (TB) ESgI
'Thundering Hills' (TB) **new** CKel
'Tickle Me' (MDB) WCAu
'Tiffany' (TB) WTin
'Tiffany Time' (TB) EFam
'Tiger Butter' (TB) ESgI
'Tiger Honey' (TB) WCAu
'Tiger's Eye' **new** EPfP
tigridia EBee WCot
'Tiki Bird' (Sino-Sib) CIri
'Tillamook' (TB) WCAu
'Time Piece' (TB) CKel
'Time Traveller' (TB) CIri
'Ting Tang' (SDB) EFam
tingitana var. ***fontanesii*** EBee WPGP
'Tinkerbell' (SDB) CPBP MSte NBir NGdn
'Tintinara' (TB) ♀H4 CKel
'Tiny Freckles' (MDB) NZep
'Tir Na Nog' (TB) CIri
'Titan's Glory' (TB) ♀H4 ELon ESgI MRav WAul WCAu WCot
'To the Point' (TB) WCAu
'Toasted Watermelon' (TB) CIri WCAu
'Tol-long' see *I. missouriensis* 'Tollong'
'Tom Johnson' (TB) CIri WCAu
'Tom Tit' (TB) WCAu
'Tomingo' (SDB) WCAu
'Tomorrow's Child' (TB) ESgI
'Toots' (SDB) WTin
'Top Flight' (TB) ELan LAst MSte SHBN SMrm SRms
N 'Topolino' (TB) CKel SAga
'Topsy Turvy' (MTB) NBre
'Total Eclipse' (TB) SRms
'Total Recall' (TB) EFam
'Toucan Tango' (TB) CIri
'Touch of Mahogany' (TB) WCAu
'Touch of Spring' (TB) EFam
'Tracy Tyrene' (TB) ESgI
'Trapel' (TB) **new** ESgI
'Travelling North' (TB) EFam
'Treccia d'Oro' (TB) **new** ESgI
'Trencavel' (TB) **new** ESgI
'Trenwith' (TB) CKel
'Trick or Treat' (TB) EFam
'Trillion' (TB) CIri
'Triple Whammy' (TB) EFam ESgI
'Triplet' **new** WAul
'True Navy' (SDB) WCAu
'Tu Tu Turquoise' (SDB) NZep
tuberosa see *Hermodactylus tuberosus*
'Tumultueux' (TB) ESgI
'Tut's Gold' (TB) ECtt ESgI WCAu
'Tweety Bird' (SDB) EFam
'Twice Told' (TB) EFam
'Twin' WWst
'Two Rubies' (SDB) NZep
typhifolia EBee NEgg
'Tyrian Dream' (IB) WCAu
§ ***unguicularis*** ♀H4 More than 30 suppliers
- 'Abington Purple' CPen WCot
- 'Alba' CAvo
N - 'Bob Thompson' EBee
- subsp. ***carica*** J&JA 600.416 **new** NWCA
- - var. ***angustifolia*** WSHC
§ - subsp. ***cretensis*** CAby CWsd ECho EPPr EPot NMen SHGN WAbe WCot
- - 'Mount Ida' SBla
- - white-flowered SBla
N - 'Diana Clare' WCot
- 'Kilndown' WFar
- var. ***lazica*** see *I. lazica*
N - 'Marondera' CAvo
- 'Mary Barnard' ♀H4 CAvo CFee CHar CMea CPen CPou CSam ECGP ECha ECho EHrv GEdr IBlr NBir NMen SBla SHBN WAbe WCot WMnd
N - 'Oxford Dwarf' EBee ECho
N - 'Palette' ELan
§ - 'Walter Butt' CAvo ECGP ECha ECho NBir SBla WFar WLin WSHC
'Up Dancing' (TB) EFam
uromovii GBuc MArl
'Ursula Warleggan' (TB) **new** CKel
'Vague a l'Ame' (TB) ESgI
'Valimar' (TB) WCAu
'Vamp' (IB) CKel EPPr SIri WAul
'Vandal Spirit' (TB) ESgI
'Vanity' (TB) ♀H4 ESgI WCAu
'Vanity's Child' (TB) ERou WCAu
§ ***variegata*** ♀H4 CMea EGoo MSte WCAu WCot
- var. ***reginae*** MSte WCAu
I - - 'Davidowii' **new** MSte
'Vegas Heat' (BB) CIri
'Vegas Showgirl' (SDB) NZep
'Veneer' (TB) CIri

	'Verity Blamey' (TB)	CKel
	verna	ERos NHol
	versicolor ♀H4	More than 30 suppliers
	- 'Claret Cup'	CPou
	- 'Kermesina'	CDWL CWat EBee ECha EHon ELan EMFW ESgI GBuc GGar IBlr MGos NBlu NPer NSti SRms SWat WBrk WEas WFar WMAq WMoo WPnP
	- 'Mysterious Monique'	CDWL CMdw CWat CWsd LLWG WAul
	- 'Party Line'	SIri
	- purple	GSki
	- var. ***rosea***	LLWG
	'Vert Galant' (TB)	ESgI
	'Vibrant' (TB)	ESgI WCAu
	'Vibrations' (TB)	ESgI
	vicaria	EBrs ECho EPot LEdu WWst
	- 'Hodji-obi-Garm' **new**	LRHS WWst
I	- 'Sina'	WWst
	'Victoria Falls' (TB)	EFam ESgI WCAu
	'Vinho Verde' (IB) ♀H4	CKel LCro
	'Vino Rosso' (SDB)	ESgI
	'Vintage Press' (IB)	WCAu
	'Vintage Year' (Spuria)	WCAu
	'Violet Beauty' (Reticulata)	ECho EPot ERCP GKev LAma LRHS SPhx
	'Violet Classic' (TB)	WCAu
	'Violet Harmony' (TB) **new**	ESgI
	'Violet Icing' (TB) ♀H4	CKel EFam
	'Violet Minuet' **new**	WBIS
	'Violet Music' (TB)	EFam
	'Violet Returns' (TB)	EFam
	'Violet Rings' (TB)	WCAu
	'Viper' (IB)	CIri
	'Virginia Bauer' (TB)	EFam
	virginica **new**	LLWG
	- 'De Luxe'	see *I.* x *robusta* 'Dark Aura'
§	- var. ***shrevei***	WCAu
	'Vitafire'	ECtt SIri
	'Vitality' (IB)	ELon ESgI
	'Vive la France' (TB)	ESgI
	'Vizier' (TB)	WCAu
	'Voila' (IB)	ESgI NZep
	'Volts' (SDB)	CKel EFam
	'Voluminous' (TB)	CIri
	'Volute' (TB)	ESgI
	'Wabash' (TB)	ELan ESgI WCAu WTin
	'Wake Up' (SDB) **new**	EFam
	'Walker Ferguson' (Spuria)	WCAu
	'Walter Butt'	see *I. unguicularis* 'Walter Butt'
	'Waltz Across Texas' (TB)	EFam
	'War Chief' (TB)	ESgI WCAu
	'War Sails' (TB)	SIri WCAu
	warleyensis	WWst
	'Warl-sind' (Juno)	WWst
	'Warranty' (TB)	WCAu
	'Warrior King' (TB)	WCAu
	'Waterboy' (SDB)	NZep
	'Watercolor' (SDB)	NZep
	wattii	CExc EBee MGol
	'Way to Go' (TB)	CIri
	'Wedding Candles' (TB)	WCAu
	'Wedding Vow' (TB)	CKel
	'Wedgwood' (Dut)	NBre
	'Welch's Reward' (MTB) ♀H4 **new**	CKel ESgI
	'Westar' (SDB) ♀H4	CKel NZep
	'Westwell' (SDB)	WCAu
	'Wheels' (SDB)	WTin
	'Whispering Spirits' (TB)	CIri
	'White City' (TB)	ECGP EFam EPfP ESgI GMaP MRav MWat NPer SCoo SDnm SHBN SIri SPer SPoG SRms SWat WAul WCAu WMnd
N	'White Cliffs of Dover'	NEgg
	'White Excelsior' (Dut)	ECho
	'White Knight' (TB)	EBee ELan EPfP NBre WMnd
	'White Lightning' (TB)	EFam
	'White Reprise' (TB)	ESgI
	'White Superior' (Dut)	NBir
	'White Wine' (MTB)	WCAu
	'Whiteladies' (IB) ♀H4	EFam
	'Whitewater River' (Spuria)	CIri
	'Whole Cloth' (TB) **new**	ESgI
	'Whoop 'em Up' (BB)	EFam NZep WFar
	'Why Not' (IB)	NZep
	'Widdershins' (TB)	CIri
N	'Wild Echo' (TB)	CKel
	'Wild Jasmine' (TB)	WCAu
	'Wild Ruby' (SDB)	CKel
	'Wild West' (TB)	CKel
	willmottiana	WWst
	- 'Alba'	EBrs ECho EPot WWst
	'Willowmist' (SDB)	EFam
	wilsonii ♀H4	EBee GBin GBuc NEgg WBVN
	'Windsurfer' (TB)	EFam
	'Winemaster' (TB)	SIri
	winogradowii ♀H4	CAvo EBrs ECho EPot ERos GCrs LAma NMen NMin WAbe
	'Winter Crystal' (TB) ♀H4 **new**	CKel
	'Winter Olympics' (TB)	CMil EBee ESgI EShb LBuc MRav
	'Wirral Gold' (IB)	EFam
	'Wisteria Sachet' (IB)	WCAu
	'Witching' (TB)	EFam WCAu
	'Wizard of Id' (SDB)	NZep WTin
	'Wondrous' (TB)	EFam ESgI
	'Words and Music' (TB)	EFam
	'Worlds Beyond' (TB)	WCAu
	'Wyckhill' (SDB)	WCAu
	'Wyoming Cowboys' (Spuria) ♀H4	CIri
	'Xillia' (IB) **new**	CKel
	xiphioides	see *I. latifolia*
	xiphium	EBrs ECho
	- var. ***lusitanica***	SKHP
	'Xmas Fires' (TB)	EFam
	'Yaquina Blue' (TB)	ESgI WCAu
	'Yes' (TB)	ESgI WCAu
	'Young Blood' (IB)	WCAu
	'Youth Dew' (TB)	EFam
	'Yo-yo' (SDB)	EPPr SIri
	'Yvonne Pelletier' (TB)	WCAu
	'Zambezi' (TB)	EFam
	'Zantha' (TB)	ESgI WCAu
	zenaidae	WWst
	'Zero' (SDB) ♀H4	CKel
	'Zinc Pink' (BB)	WCAu
	'Zipper' (MDB)	ESgI WCAu

Isatis (*Brassicaceae*)

	tinctoria	CArn CBod CHby COld CRWN CSev EOHP EUnu GPoy ILis LRHS MHer MNHC MSal NVic SECG SIde SPav WHer WJek WSel
	- var. ***indigotica*** **new**	EUnu

Ischyrolepis (*Restionaceae*)

	ocreata	WNor
§	***subverticillata***	CBig CCtw CHEx CTrC EAmu

Ismene see *Hymenocallis*

Isolepis (*Cyperaceae*)

§	***cernua***	CBrm CHal CMil CWat EAlp EBee EMFW EPfP MBri NOak SCoo WDyG WFar WMAq WPrP

Isoloma see *Kohleria*

Isomeris see *Cleome*

Isoplexis (*Scrophulariaceae*)

canariensis CAbb CBcs CCCN CDTJ CHEx CHll CHrt CPLG CRHN CSpe EBee ECre EMan EWll SAga SHFr SPlb WCFE
* **cernua** NHol
chalcantha CDTJ
isabelliana CCCN CDTJ EBee EShb LDai
sceptrum CCCN CDTJ CHEx CHVG CHll CPLG CRHN CSpe ECre SAPC SArc SHFr WPGP
– pink CDes WPGP

Isopogon (*Proteaceae*)

anemonifolius new SPlb
anethifolius SPlb

Isopyrum (*Ranunculaceae*)

biternatum GBuc NLar
nipponicum CLAP WCru WSHC
thalictroides WAbe

Isotoma (*Campanulaceae*)

sp. LAst SWvt
§ **axillaris** CHrt CSpe LRHS NPer SBch SCoo SPer SPet SPoG
– 'Fairy Carpet' EMan NPri SRms
fluviatilis CBrm ECou NLar NSfd
– white ECou
'Sapphire Star' LRHS

Itea (*Escalloniaceae*)

chinensis WPGP
ilicifolia ♀H3 More than 30 suppliers
* **illicifolia** 'Rubrifolia' new LRHS MAsh SPoG
japonica 'Beppu' MGos SLPl
virginica CAbP CBcs CMCN EBee ECrN ELan MBlu MRav SLon SPer WBVN WFar WOrn
§ – 'Henry's Garnet' CDoC CEnd CMCN CMHG CPMA CWSG CWoW EBee ECrN EPfP EWTr GAbr LAst LEdu LRHS MBri MGos MWgw NLar NPri SLim SPoG SRGP SSpi SWvt WGwG
– Little Henry = 'Sprich'PBR CBgR EBee ELan IClo LAst NLar
– 'Long Spire' CPMA MBri
– 'Merlot' CPMA LRHS MGos NLar
– 'Sarah Eve' CMCN CPMA EBee NLar SRGP
– 'Saturnalia' NLar
– 'Shirley's Compact' NLar
– Swarthmore form see *I. virginica* 'Henry's Garnet'
yunnanensis CPLG

Itoa (*Flacourtiaceae*)

orientalis SF 92300 ISea

Ixia (*Iridaceae*)

'Blue Bird' CFir EBrs ECho LAma WHil
'Castor' CPrp EBrs ECho WHil
conferta var. **ochroleuca** WCot
flexuosa WCot
'Giant' EBrs ECho WHil
'Hogarth' CPrp ECho LAma WHil
'Holland Glory' ECho WHil
hybrids EBrs
'Mabel' EBrs ECho WCot WHil
maculata WCot
'Marquette' ECho
monadelpha WCot
paniculata WCot
'Panorama' ECho WHil
pumilio WCot
purpureorosea 'Saldanha' ECho
'Rose Emperor' ECho LAma WHil
'Spotlight' ECho WHil
thomasiae WCot
'Venus' CFir EBrs ECho LAma WHil
viridiflora CBow EDif WCot
'Vulcan' ECho
'Yellow Emperor' EBrs ECho WCot WHil

Ixiolirion (*Ixioliriaceae*)

montanum CHFP CHHB CMea CPBP ECho
pallasii see *I. tataricum*
§ **tataricum** CPrp CStu CTca EBee EBrs ECho EMan LAma LEdu MBri NWCA SBch WHil
– var. **ixiolirioides** new EBee
– Ledebourii Group CAvo CFFs EBee

Ixora (*Rubiaceae*)

chinensis 'Apricot Queen' SOWG
'Golden Ball' SOWG
'Pink Malay' SOWG

J

Jaborosa (*Solanaceae*)

integrifolia CAby CDes CFir CPLG CStu EBee ELan GEdr LFur WAul WCot WCru WPGP XPep

Jacaranda (*Bignoniaceae*)

acutifolia misapplied see *J. mimosifolia*
§ **mimosifolia** CBcs CHll ELan ERea EShb GQui LRav MBri MGol MGos MPRe SOWG SPlb

Jacobinia see *Justicia*

Jaltomata (*Solanaceae*)

procumbens new EUnu

Jamesbrittenia (*Scrophulariaceae*)

'Cinderella Strawberry' new CSpe

Jamesia (*Hydrangeaceae*)

americana CBcs CPle IDee MBri NLar

Jasione (*Campanulaceae*)

§ **heldreichii** GAbr LRHS MWrn SBla SRms
jankae see *J. heldreichii*
§ **laevis** CArn EBee ECho ECot EWTr GAbr LRHS MDKP MGol SRms WGwG WWFP
§ – 'Blaulicht' CBrm CCge CFis CMHG CTca CWib EBee ECha EPfP LRHS MBNS MBri MLan MNFA MWat MWrn NBPC NBlu NEgg NLar SPla SPlb WMoo WWeb
– Blue Light see *J. laevis* 'Blaulicht'
– 'Sangster' CPLG
montana CSam EBee ECho EDAr WFar WPnn WSFF
perennis see *J. laevis*

Jasminum (*Oleaceae*)

CC 4728 CPLG
affine see *J. officinale* f. *affine*
angulare ♀H1 CRHN ERea EShb SOWG
azoricum ♀H1 CCCN CRHN ELan EPfP ERea EShb NPal XPep
beesianum More than 30 suppliers

bignoniaceum WSHC
blinii see *J. polyanthum*
dispermum CPLG CRHN
floridum EBee EWes NScw XPep
fruticans CMac CPle EBee EPfP EPla NScw XPep
grandiflorum misapplied see *J. officinale* f. *affine*
grandiflorum L. XPep
- 'De Grasse' ♀H1 CRHN ERea EShb SOWG
humile CEnt CPLG EQua GSki IMGH MGos MHer SHFr WFar WKif
- var. *glabrum* see *J. humile* f. *wallichianum*
§ - 'Revolutum' ♀H4 More than 30 suppliers
§ - f. *wallichianum* B&SWJ 2559 WCru
§ *laurifolium* f. *nitidum* ERea EShb
§ *mesnyi* ♀H2-3 CEnt CMac CRHN CSBt CTri CWib EBak EBee ELan EPfP ERas ERea IGor SAga SBra SLim SOWG SPer STre WSHC XPep
multipartitum EShb
- bushy CSpe
nitidum see *J. laurifolium* f. *nitidum*
§ *nudiflorum* ♀H4 More than 30 suppliers
- 'Argenteum' see *J. nudiflorum* 'Mystique'
- 'Aureum' EBee ELan EPfP EPla LRHS MAsh MRav NHol NSti SLim SPer SPla SPoG WCot WPat
§ - 'Mystique' (v) ELan LRHS LSou MAsh NLar SLon SPer SPoG WCot WPat
odoratissimum ERea EShb SOWG
officinale ♀H4 More than 30 suppliers
§ - f. *affine* CBcs CRHN CSPN CSam CTri CWSG CWib EBee ELan ENot EPfP LAst MAsh MGan MRav MWgw NCGa NHol SCoo SDix SLim SRms WCru WFar
§ - 'Argenteovariegatum' (v) ♀H4 More than 30 suppliers
- 'Aureovariegatum' see *J. officinale* 'Aureum'
§ - 'Aureum' (v) CChe CDoC CMac CWSG CWib EBee ECtt ELan EPfP EPla LRHS MAsh MBri MHer MLan MWgw NBir NHol SCoo SHBN SLim SLon SMad SPer SPoG SRms WHCG WMoo WPat
- 'Clotted Cream' CBcs CCCN EBee EPfP LAst LBuc LCro LRHS LSRN MAsh MBri MGos MWea NHol NLar SBra SCoo SLim SPer SPoG WBod WPat
- 'Crûg's Collection' B&SWJ 2987 WCru
- Fiona Sunrise = 'Frojas'PBR More than 30 suppliers
- 'Grandiflorum' see *J. officinale* f. *affine*
- 'Inverleith' ♀H4 CDoC CWSG EBee ELan EPfP IArd LBMP LHop LRHS MAsh MBNS MBri MCCP MLan MRav NEgg SCoo SLim SMac SPer SPoG WFar WSHC
- 'Variegatum' see *J. officinale* 'Argenteovariegatum'
parkeri CBcs CBgR CFee CMea CTri EBee ECho EPfP EPot GEdr GMaP IMGH LHop MBNS NLar NMen NWCA SBla SIng SPla WAbe WFar WPat XPep
§ *polyanthum* ♀H1-2 CArn CBcs CPLG CRHN CSBt CTri EBak EBee ELan EPfP ERea ERom EShb LCro LRHS MBri NBlu NPal SBra SLim SOWG SPer SRms WPGP XPep
primulinum see *J. mesnyi*
reevesii hort. see *J. humile* 'Revolutum'
sambac ♀H1 CHII CRHN ELan EPfP EShb SOWG XPep
- 'Grand Duke of Tuscany' (d) ERea EShb SOWG
- 'Maid of Orleans' (d) ♀H1 EShb SOWG
sieboldianum see *J. nudiflorum*
stenalobium new SOWG
x *stephanense* More than 30 suppliers

Jatropha (*Euphorbiaceae*)

podagrica ♀H1 LToo

Jeffersonia (*Berberidaceae*)

diphylla CArn CElw CLAP EBee EBrs ECho EHrv EPot GBuc GGar GSki LAma LEdu LRHS MDun MNFA MSal MTho NBir NMen NMyG SMad WAbe WCru WFar WPnP
dubia CFir CLAP ECho EPot EWes GBuc GCrs GEdr LEdu LRHS NBir NHar NMen NSla SBla WAbe WCru
- B&SWJ 984 WCru
- 'Alba' EHrv SBla

jostaberry see *Ribes* x *culverwellii*

Jovellana (*Scrophulariaceae*)

punctata CCCN CDoC CPLG CPSs CPle EBee IBlr MBlu
repens CFir EBee
sinclairii CHII CPLG EBee ECou IBlr LTwo WCru
violacea ♀H3 CAbP CAbb CBcs CCCN CDoC CHEx CPLG CPSs CPle CTrC CWib EBee EMil GGGa GGar IBlr ITim SAPC SArc SDry SMad WBod WCru WPGP WPic WSHC WWlt

Jovibarba ✿ (*Crassulaceae*)

§ *allionii* CMea CTca CTri CWil ECha EPot GAbr LBee MHer NHol NPri SBla SIng STre WAbe WFar WHal WHoo WIvy WPer WTin
- 'Oki' CWil
allionii x *hirta* CWil GAbr NHol NMen SDys SFgr
§ *arenaria* CWil GAbr NMen SIng
- from Passo Monte Crocecar Nico CWil
'Emerald Spring' CTca CWil EPem NMen SFgr
§ *heuffelii* ECho LRHS NHol NMen NWCA WIvy WPer
- 'Aga' NHol WIvy
- 'Aiolos' EPem NHol
- 'Alemene' NHol
- 'Almkroon' NHol
- 'Angel Wings' CWil NHol NMen
- 'Apache' CWil
- 'Aquarius' CWil WIvy
- 'Artemis' NHol
- 'Aurora' NHol
- 'Be Mine' CTca CWil
- 'Beacon Hill' CWil WIvy
- 'Belcore' CWil WIvy
- 'Benjamin' CWil NHol
- 'Bermuda' WIvy
- 'Bermuda Sunset' NHol
- 'Big Red' NHol
- 'Blaze' CWil
- 'Brandaris' NHol SDys
- 'Brocade' NHol WIvy
- 'Bronze Ingot' CWil
- 'Bronze King' WIvy
- 'Bulgarien' CWil
- 'Cakor' new NHol
- 'Cameo' WIvy
§ - 'Cherry Glow' CWil NHol

- 'Chocoleto'	WTin
- 'Cleopatra'	NHol
- 'Copper King'	CWil WIvy
- 'Dunbar Red'	NHol
- 'Fandango'	CWil MHom WIvy
- 'Gento'	NHol
- 'Geronimo'	NHol
- 'Giuseppi Spiny'	MHom NHol WIvy WTin
- var. ***glabra***	LBee WHoo
- - from Anabakanak	CWil MHom NHol WTin
- - from Anthoborio	CWil NMen WIvy WTin
- - from Backovo	NHol
- - from Galicica	NHol
- - from Haila, Montenegro/Kosovo	CWil NHol NMen SFgr WIvy
- - from Jakupica, Macedonia	CWil WIvy
- - from Ljuboten	CWil NHol NMen WTin
- - from Osljak	CWil
- - from Pasina Glava	CWil
- - from Rhodope	CWil MHom NHol
- - from Treska Gorge, Macedonia	CWil NMen WTin
- - from Vitse, Greece	WIvy
§ - - 'Cameo'	NHol
- 'Gold Rand'	NHol
- 'Grand Slam'	CWil
- 'Green Land'	CWil
- 'Greenstone'	CMea CWil MHom NHol NMen WIvy WTin
- 'Harmony'	CWil NHol
- 'Henry Correvon'	CWil EPem
- var. ***heuffelii***	CWil
- 'Hot Lips'	CWil
- 'Hystyle'	WIvy
- 'Ikaros'	NHol
- 'Inferno'	MHom NHol
- 'Iole'	WIvy
- 'Ithaca'	NHol
- 'Iuno'	CWil NHol
- 'Jade'	CWil NMen WIvy
- 'Kapo'	WIvy
- var. ***kopaonikensis***	CWil LBee MHom NMen
- 'Mary Ann'	MHom WIvy
- 'Miller's Violet'	CWil WIvy WTin
- 'Mink'	CWil
- 'Minuta'	CWil NHol NMen WIvy WTin
- 'Mystique'	CMea CWil LBee NMen WIvy
- 'Nannette'	CWil
- 'Nobel'	NHol
- 'Opele'	NHol
- 'Orion'	CWil NHol NMen
- 'Pink Skies'	CWil WIvy
- 'Prisma'	CWil WIvy WTin
- 'Purple Haze'	WIvy
- 'Red Rose'	CWil WIvy
- 'Serenade'	CWil
- 'Springael's Choice'	CWil
- 'Sundancer'	WIvy
- 'Sungold'	NHol
- 'Suntan'	CWil NHol WIvy
- 'Sylvan Memory'	CWil
- 'Tan'	CWil NHol WTin
- 'Torrid Zone'	WIvy WTin
- 'Tuxedo'	CWil
- 'Vesta'	CWil
- 'Violet'	SDys WIvy
§ ***hirta***	CHal CWil GAbr GKev NHol NMen SBla SFgr STre WPer
- from Wintergraben	EPem SIng SPlb
§ - subsp. ***borealis***	CWil NDlv NHol
- subsp. ***glabrescens***	GKev LRHS SIng
- - from Belianske Tatry	CWil NDlv
- - from High Tatra	EPem
- - from Smeryouka	CWil EPem SIng
- var. ***neilreichii***	LRHS MHom WBVN
- 'Preissiana'	CTca CWil EPem LBee NDlv NHol NMen SFgr SIng WIvy WTin
§ ***sobolifera***	CHEx CTca CWil EDAr EPot NHol NMen SFgr SIng SPlb WAbe WHal WIvy WPer
- 'August Cream'	CWil LBee LRHS
- 'Green Globe'	CWil LRHS SDys WTin
- 'Miss Lorraine'	CWil SFgr

Juanulloa (*Solanaceae*)

aurantiaca	see *J. mexicana*
§ ***mexicana***	SOWG

Jubaea (*Arecaceae*)

§ ***chilensis***	CBrP CDoC CPHo EAmu LPJP LPal MJnS MPRe NPal SAin SChr
spectabilis	see *J. chilensis*

Juglans ✿ (*Juglandaceae*)

§ ***ailanthifolia***	CMCN CTho ECrN EGFP IDee
- var. ***cordiformis*** 'Brock' (F)	CAgr
- - 'Campbell Cw1' (F)	CAgr
- - 'Campbell Cw3' (F) new	CAgr
- - 'Fodermaier' seedling	CAgr
- - 'Rhodes' (F)	CAgr
ailanthifolia x ***cinerea***	see *J.* x *bixbyi*
§ x ***bixbyi***	CAgr WGWT
cathayensis (F)	WGWT
- B&SWJ 6778	WCru
cinerea (F)	CMCN EGFP WGWT
- 'Beckwith' (F) new	CAgr
- 'Booth' seedlings (F)	CAgr
- 'Craxezy' (F)	CAgr
- 'Kenworthy' seedling	CAgr
- 'Myjoy' (F) new	CAgr
§ ***elaeopyren***	EGFP WGWT
hindsii	WGWT
x ***intermedia***	WGWT
mandschurica	EGFP WGWT
microcarpa	WGWT
- subsp. ***major***	see *J. elaeopyren*
nigra (F) Υ^{H4}	More than 30 suppliers
- 'Bicentennial' (F) new	CAgr
- 'Emma Kay' (F)	CAgr WGWT
- 'Laciniata'	CMCN MBlu WGWT
- 'Student Orchard' (F) new	WGWT
- 'Thomas' (F)	CAgr
- 'Weschke' (F)	CAgr
'Paradox'	WGWT
'Red Danube' (F)	WGWT
regia (F) Υ^{H4}	More than 30 suppliers
- 'Abbotbad' (F)	WGWT
- 'Axel' (F)	WGWT
- 'Broadview' (F)	CAgr CDoC CDul CEnd CTho ECrN EMui ERea GTwe LRHS MBlu MBri MCoo MGos MNHC SCoo SDea SGFT SKee SPoG WGWT WOrn
- 'Buccaneer' (F)	CAgr CDul CTho ECrN GTwe LRHS SDea SGFT SKee WGWT
- 'Coenen' (F)	WGWT
- 'Corne du Périgord' (F)	CAgr
- 'Ferjean' (F)	CAgr
- 'Fernette'^{PBR} (F)	CAgr MCoo
- 'Fernor'^{PBR} (F)	CAgr MCoo
- 'Franquette' (F)	CAgr CDoC ECrN EMil GTwe LRHS MCoo
- 'Hansen' (F)	CAgr WGWT
- 'Laciniata'	CMCN WGWT
- 'Lara' (F)	CAgr GTwe MCoo WGWT
- 'Leopold' (F)	WGWT
- 'Lu Guang' (F)	WGWT

- 'Majestic' (F) new	EMui
- 'Mayette' (F)	CAgr ECrN
- 'Metcalfe' (F)	WGWT
- 'Meylannaise' (F)	CAgr
- number 16 (F)	CAgr WGWT
- 'Parisienne' (F)	CAgr EMil
- 'Pedro' (F)	WGWT
- 'Pendula'	WGWT
- 'Plovdivski' (F)	CAgr WGWT
- 'Proslavski' (F)	CAgr CDul WGWT
- 'Purpurea'	CMCN MBlu MBri WGWT
- 'Rita' (F)	CAgr WGWT
- 'Ronde de Montignac' (F)	CAgr
- 'Saturn' (F) new	CAgr
- 'Soleze' (F)	CAgr WGWT
- 'Sorrento' (F) new	CCCN
- 'Ssang Sung'	WGWT
- 'Tremlett's Giant' (F)	WGWT
- 'Zhong Lin' (F)	WGWT
sieboldiana	see *J. ailanthifolia*

jujube see *Ziziphus jujuba*

Juncus (*Juncaceae*)

sp. new	XIsg
acutiflorus	NSco
acutus	GFor XPep
* ***balticus*** 'Spiralis'	CTrC ECho
bulbosus	CNat CRWN
'Curly Gold Strike' (v)	ELon EPPr LLWG SPoG
§ ***decipiens*** 'Curly-wurly'	CBcs CDWL CDes CFee CKno CMea CMil CSpe EBee EMon EPfP EPla EWes GFor GGar LAst LHop LRHS MBrN NOak SMac SPla SWal SWat WHal WPGP WPnP WRos
- 'Spiralis'	see *J. decipiens* 'Curly-wurly'
I - 'Spiralis Nana'	NWCA
effusus	CHEx CRWN CWat EHon EMFW GFor LCro MNHC NPer NSco NSti SWat WMAq XIsg
- 'Carman's Japanese' new	CKno
- 'Gold Strike' (v)	CWCL EMan EPla EWes EWin LHop NOak
§ - f. ***spiralis***	CBen CFee CSpe CStu CWat EHon ELan EMFW EMon EPfP EPla GAbr GFor GKev GMaP NBlu NHol NOak SLim SPer SPlb WBor WFar WHal WMAq WMoo WPGP WPnP XIsg
- - 'Limelight' (v) new	EAlp
§ - - 'Unicorn'PBR	CBgR EBee EPPr EWin MWgw SApp SPoG
- - 'Yellow Line'PBR (v)	CPen EBee
ensifolius	CDWL CDes CKno CPen CWat EBee EMFW EWes GFor MAvo MMHG NHol NNor NPer WFar XIsg
filiformis 'Spiralis'	CBgR CBig CBrm EBee EWin GFor GKev MAvo SApp
inflexus	CBen CRWN CWat EHon GFor NHol NSco SWat XIsg
- 'Afro'	CBgR CBig CKno EAlp EBee ELan EMan EMon EPfP EWin MAvo MBrN MCCP NBro NOak SPlb WHal
pallidus	EBee EPPr NBid NNor
patens 'Carman's Gray'	CBcs CFee CKno CRez CWCL EBee EMan EPPr EPla GQue LRHS MAvo MCCP MMoz NGdn NHol NNor NOak SAga SApp WMoo XIsg
- 'Elk Blue'	CKno
'Silver Spears'	MCCP
'Unicorn'PBR	see *J. effusus* f. *spiralis* 'Unicorn'
xiphioides	CKno EPla MHar NHol
- JLS 8609LACA	EPPr

Junellia (*Verbenaceae*)

azorelloides F&W 9344	WAbe
micrantha F&W 9389	WAbe
sylvestrii F&W 2705	WAbe
wilczekii	WFar
- F&W 7770	NWCA

Juniperus ✿ (*Cupressaceae*)

chinensis	CMac CMen SEND
- 'Aurea' 🏆H4	CBcs CKen CMac ECho EHul EOrn LCon MBar MGos SPoG
§ - 'Blaauw' 🏆H4	CDoC CMac CMen ECho EHul EOrn LCon LLin MBar MGos SCoo SHBN SPoG STre WEve WFar
- 'Blue Alps'	CDoC ECho EHul EOrn IMGH LCon MBar MBri MGos NEgg NHol NLar SCoo SEND SLim WEve WFar
- 'Blue Point'	MBar MGos
- 'Densa Spartan'	see *J. chinensis* 'Spartan'
- 'Echiniformis'	CKen EOrn
- 'Expansa Aureospicata' (v)	CDoC CKen CMac CRob ECho EHul EOrn EPfP LCon LLin MBar MGos SLim SPoG SRms
§ - 'Expansa Variegata' (v)	CDoC CMac CRob CWib ECho EHul EOrn EPfP IMGH LCon LLin MAsh MBar MGos SCoo SMer SPoG SRms WFar WMoo WTel
- 'Ferngold'	MGos
- 'Globosa Cinerea'	MBar
- 'Japonica'	EOrn MBar SMer
§ - 'Kaizuka' 🏆H4	ECho EHul EOrn LBee LCon LRHS MBar NLar SCoo SLim SMad SMer SPoG STre XPep
- 'Kaizuka Variegata'	see *J. chinensis* 'Variegated Kaizuka'
- 'Keteleeri'	MBar
- 'Kuriwao Gold'	see *J.* x *pfitzeriana* 'Kuriwao Gold'
- 'Obelisk' 🏆H4	ECho EHul LCon LRHS MBar MGos
- 'Oblonga'	CDoC ECho EHul MBar STre
§ - 'Parsonsii'	MBar SHBN STre WCFE
- 'Plumosa'	MBar
- 'Plumosa Albovariegata' (v)	EOrn MBar
§ - 'Plumosa Aurea' 🏆H4	EHul EOrn LCon MBar WFar
- 'Plumosa Aureovariegata' (v)	CKen EOrn MBar
- 'Pyramidalis' 🏆H4	CDoC CRob ECho EHul EPfP IMGH LCon LLin SCoo SPoG SRms WFar
- 'Pyramidalis Variegata'	see *J. chinensis* 'Variegata'
- 'Robust Green'	CRob ECho EOrn LCon MBar SCoo SPoG
- 'San José'	CDoC CMen ECho EHul EOrn LLin MAsh MBar SCoo SLim
§ - var. ***sargentii***	CMen STre
- 'Shimpaku'	CKen CMen EOrn MBar NLar
§ - 'Spartan'	EHul
- 'Stricta'	CSBt EHul LBee LRHS MAsh MBar MGos NBlu SLim SPla
- 'Stricta Variegata'	see *J. chinensis* 'Variegata'
- 'Sulphur Spray'	see *J.* x *pfitzeriana* 'Sulphur Spray'
- 'Torulosa'	see *J. chinensis* 'Kaizuka'
§ - 'Variegata' (v)	MBar
§ - 'Variegated Kaizuka' (v)	CBrm ECho EHul EOrn LCon MBar SPoG WFar
communis	CArn CRWN CTrG EHul GPoy ITim MHer MNHC MSal NLar NWea SIde
- (f)	SIde
- 'Arnold'	CDul LLin MBar MGos
- 'Arnold Sentinel'	CKen
- 'Atholl'	CKen
I - 'Aureopicta' (v)	MBar
- 'Barton'	ECho MBar MGos NHol

	- 'Berkshire'	CKen CRob WThu
	- 'Brien'	CDoC CKen
	- 'Brynhyfryd Gold'	CKen CRob
§	- var. ***communis***	ECho MBar NEgg
	- 'Compressa' Υ^{H4}	More than 30 suppliers
§	- 'Constance Franklin' (v)	ECho EHul LLin MBar STre
	- 'Corielagan'	CKen MBar NLar
	- 'Cracovia'	CKen EHul
	- var. ***depressa***	ECho GPoy MBar
	- 'Depressa Aurea'	CKen CMac CSBt ECho EHul LBee LCon LLin LRHS MBar MGos SHBN SPoG WFar
	- 'Depressed Star'	CRob ECho EHul MBar
	- 'Derrynane'	EHul
	- 'Effusa'	CKen
	- 'Gelb'	see *J. communis* 'Schneverdingen Goldmachangel'
	- 'Gold Ball'	LBee
	- 'Gold Cone'	CKen CSli ECho EHul EPfP LBee LCon LLin LRHS MAsh MBar MGos NEgg NHol SLim SMer SPoG WFar
	- 'Golden Showers'	see *J. communis* 'Schneverdingen Goldmachangel'
	- 'Goldenrod'	MGos
	- 'Green Carpet' Υ^{H4}	CDoC CKen CRob ECho EHul EOrn EPfP IMGH LBuc LCon LLin LRHS MAsh MBar MBri NEgg NHol SCoo SLim SMer SPoG WCFE WEve
	- 'Haverbeck'	CKen
	- var. ***hemispherica***	see *J. communis* var. *communis*
	- 'Hibernica' Υ^{H4}	CBrm CDoC CDul CSBt CTri ECho ECrN EHul EOrn EPfP IMGH LAst LBee LCon LLin LPan LRHS MBar MGos NWea SHBN SLPl SLim SMer SPer SPla SPoG WBrE WEve WOrn
	- 'Hibernica Variegata'	see *J. communis* 'Constance Franklin'
	- 'Hornibrookii' Υ^{H4}	CMac ECho EHul EOrn LLin MBar MGos SBod SHBN SMer SRms STre
	- 'Horstmann'	MBar NLar SCoo
I	- 'Horstmann's Pendula'	CDoC ECho LCon LLin
	- 'Kenwith Castle'	CKen
	- 'Prostrata'	WFar
	- 'Pyramidalis'	SPlb
	- 'Repanda' Υ^{H4}	CBcs CDoC CMac CRob CSBt CWib ECho EHul EPfP GGar LAst LCon LLin MAsh MBar MGos NWea SCoo SLim SMer SPer SPla SPoG SRms WBVN WEve WFar
§	- 'Schneverdingen Goldmachangel'	CRob ECho EOrn LLin MBri MGos NHol SLim
	- 'Sentinel'	CDoC ECho EHul EPfP LCon LRHS MBar NBlu NEgg NHol SLim WCFE WEve
	- 'Sieben Steinhauser'	CKen
	- 'Silver Mist'	CKen
	- 'Spotty Spreader' (v)	SLim SPoG
	- Suecica Group	EHul MBar NLar NWea SLPl
	- 'Suecica Aurea'	EHul EOrn
	- 'Wallis'	NHol
	- 'Zeal'	CKen
	conferta	see *J. rigida* subsp. *conferta*
	- var. ***maritima***	see *J. taxifolia*
	davurica	EHul
	- 'Expansa'	see *J. chinensis* 'Parsonsii'
	- 'Expansa Albopicta'	see *J. chinensis* 'Expansa Variegata'
	- 'Expansa Variegata'	see *J. chinensis* 'Expansa Variegata'
	deppeana 'Silver Spire'	MBar
	excelsa subsp. ***polycarpos*** new	CMen
	foetidissima	CMen
	x ***gracilis*** 'Blaauw'	see *J. chinensis* 'Blaauw'
	'Grey Owl' Υ^{H4}	ECho EHul ELan EPfP LCon MBar NWea SCoo SLim SLon SRms STre WFar
	horizontalis	ECho NWea
§	- 'Andorra Compact'	LPan MBar NLar SCoo
	- 'Bar Harbor'	CKen CMac ECho EHul MBar MGos
§	- 'Blue Chip'	CKen CRob ECho EHul ELan EOrn EPfP LBee LCon LLin LRHS MAsh MBar MGos NBir NBlu NEgg SCoo SLim SPer SPoG XPep
	- 'Blue Moon'	see *J. horizontalis* 'Blue Chip'
	- 'Blue Pygmy'	CKen
	- 'Blue Rug'	see *J. horizontalis* 'Wiltonii'
	- 'Douglasii'	CKen CMac EHul MBar
	- 'Emerald Spreader'	CKen ECho EHul ELan LLin MBar
	- 'Glacier'	CKen
	- Glauca Group	CMac ECho EHul LLin MBar MGos NWea SMer SPer SPoG WEve
	- 'Glomerata'	CKen MBar
	- 'Golden Carpet'	ECho ELan EOrn EPfP IMGH LBuc LLin MGos NBlu NEgg NLar SPer SPoG WEve
	- 'Golden Spreader'	CDoC ECho
	- 'Grey Pearl'	CKen ECho EHul
	- 'Hughes'	CMac ECho EHul LBee LLin LRHS MBar MGos SBod SPla
	- Icee Blue = 'Monber'	CKen CRob LCon NLar SLim SPoG
	- 'Jade River'	ECho EHul GBin LRHS MGos SLim SPer SPoG
	- 'Jade Spreader'	ECho
	- 'Limeglow'	CKen ECho MAsh NLar SCoo SLim
	- 'Mother Lode'	CKen
	- 'Neumann'	CKen EOrn
	- 'Plumosa Compacta'	see *J. horizontalis* 'Andorra Compact'
	- 'Prince of Wales'	CRob EHul LLin LPan LRHS MAsh MGos NLar SCoo SLim XPep
	- var. ***saxatalis*** E.Murray	see *J. communis* var. *communis*
	- 'Turquoise Spreader'	CSBt ECho EHul LLin MBar SCoo
	- 'Variegata' (v)	MBar
	- 'Venusta'	see *J. virginiana* 'Venusta'
	- 'Villa Marie'	CKen
	- 'Webber'	MBar
§	- 'Wiltonii' Υ^{H4}	CDul EHul EOrn MGos NBlu
	- 'Winter Blue'	LBee LCon LRHS SLim SPer
	- 'Youngstown'	CMac CRob CSWP ECho LLin MBar MGos SBod WFar
	- 'Yukon Belle'	CKen
N	x ***media***	see *J.* x *pfitzeriana*
	- 'Plumosa Aurea'	see *J. chinensis* 'Plumosa Aurea'
§	x ***pfitzeriana***	CDul ECho
	- 'Armstrongii'	EHul
	- 'Blaauw'	see *J. chinensis* 'Blaauw'
	- 'Blue and Gold' (v)	CKen ECho EHul LLin MBar NEgg SHBN SPer
	- 'Blue Cloud'	see *J. virginiana* 'Blue Cloud'
§	- 'Carbery Gold'	CBcs CDoC CMac CRob CSBt CSli ECho EHul EOrn LBee LCon LLin LRHS MAsh MBar MGos NHol SCoo SLim SPoG WEve WFar
	- 'Gold Coast'	CDoC CKen CRob CSBt ECho EHul EPfP LBee LRHS MAsh MBar MBri MGos MWat NHol NLar SLim SPer SPla WEve
	- Gold Sovereign = 'Blound'PBR	LBee LCon MAsh MGos NHol SMer
	- 'Gold Star'	SLim
*	- 'Golden Joy'	LCon SCoo SLim SPoG
	- 'Golden Saucer'	MBar SCoo
	- 'Goldkissen'	CRob MGos NLar
§	- 'Kuriwao Gold'	CMac ECho EHul LBee MBar MGos NHol NLar SCoo SMer STre WEve WFar
	- 'Milky Way' (v)	SCoo SPoG
	- 'Mint Julep'	CSBt ECho EHul IMGH LAst LBee LCon LLin LPan LRHS MBar MGos NBlu SCoo SLim SPer WBrE WEve WFar WMoo

	- 'Mordigan Gold'	WEve
	- 'Old Gold' ♀H4	CKen CMac ECho EHul EOrn EPfP IMGH LBee LCon LRHS MAsh MBar MGos NBlu NEgg NHol NWea SCoo SLim SMer SPer SPlb SPoG SRms WEve WFar WTel
	- 'Old Gold Carbery'	see *J.* x *pfitzeriana* 'Carbery Gold'
	- 'Pfitzeriana'	see *J.* x *pfitzeriana* 'Wilhelm Pfitzer'
	- 'Pfitzeriana Aurea'	CBcs CMac CSBt ECho EHul EPfP LCon LRHS MBar MBri MGos NBlu NEgg NWea SHBN SPoG WEve WFar WOrn
	- 'Pfitzeriana Compacta' ♀H4	CMac ECho EHul MBar SCoo
	- 'Pfitzeriana Glauca'	EHul IMGH LCon LRHS MBar SCoo
	- 'Richeson'	MBar
	- 'Silver Cascade'	EHul
§	- 'Sulphur Spray' ♀H4	CSBt CWib ECho EHul EOrn EPla LAst LCon LLin LRHS MAsh MBar MGos NEgg NHol SEND SLim SPer SPla SPoG SRms WBVN WCFE WEve WFar WMoo WTel
§	- 'Wilhelm Pfitzer'	ECho EHul EPfP MBar NWea
	phoenicea	XPep
§	***pingii*** 'Glassell'	CDoC ECho MBar NLar
§	- 'Pygmaea'	ECho EOrn MBar
§	- var. ***wilsonii***	CDoC CKen ECho EHul EOrn GGar MBar NEgg
	procumbens 'Bonin Isles'	LLin LRHS SLim
	- 'Nana' ♀H4	CDoC CKen CMac CRob CSBt ECho EHul EOrn EPfP IMGH LAst LBee LCon LLin LRHS MAsh MBar MGos MWat NEgg NHol SCoo SHBN SLim SPla SPoG WCFE WEve WFar
	recurva 'Castlewellan'	EOrn LCon MGos NLar
	- var. ***coxii***	CDoC CMac ECho EHul EOrn GGGa LCon LLin MAsh MBar MGos NEgg SRms
§	- 'Densa'	CDoC CKen ECho EHul EOrn MBar NHol SHBN
	- 'Embley Park'	EHul MBar
	- 'Nana'	see *J. recurva* 'Densa'
	rigida	CMen EHul LLin MBar NLar
§	- subsp. ***conferta***	CRob ECho LBee LCon MBar MWat SEND SLim SPer SPoG STre WEve
*	- - 'Blue Ice'	CKen ECho EOrn LLin SPoG WFar
	- - 'Blue Pacific'	CRob ECho EHul MBar NLar SPoG WFar
	- - 'Blue Tosho'	CRob ECho LCon SLim SPoG
	- - 'Emerald Sea'	EHul
	- - 'Schlager' **new**	SLim
	- - 'Silver Mist'	CKen
	sabina	ECho NWea
§	- 'Blaue Donau'	ECho EHul MBar
	- Blue Danube	see *J. sabina* 'Blaue Donau'
	- 'Broadmoor'	EHul
	- 'Buffalo'	EHul
	- Cupressifolia Group	MBar
	- 'Hicksii'	CMac MBar
	- 'Knap Hill'	see *J.* x *pfitzeriana* 'Wilhelm Pfitzer'
	- 'Mountaineer'	see *J. scopulorum* 'Mountaineer'
	- 'Rockery Gem'	ECho EHul EOrn SLim SPla SPoG WEve WGor
	- 'Skandia'	CKen
	- 'Tamariscifolia'	CBcs CMac CWib ECho ECrN EHul LBee LCon LLin LRHS MAsh MBar MGos NBlu NEgg NWea SHBN SLim SMer SPer SPoG WCFE WEve WFar WTel
	- 'Tripartita'	see *J. virginiana* 'Tripartita'
	- 'Variegata' (v)	ECho EHul MBar
	sargentii	see *J. chinensis* var. *sargentii*
	scopulorum	CKen MBar
	- 'Blue Arrow'	More than 30 suppliers
	- 'Blue Banff'	CKen
	- 'Blue Heaven'	ECho EHul MAsh MBar SRms
	- 'Blue Pyramid'	EHul
	- 'Boothman'	EHul
	- 'Moonglow'	EHul MBar
§	- 'Mountaineer'	EHul
	- 'Mrs Marriage'	CKen
	- 'Repens'	MBar MGos
	- 'Silver Star' (v)	ECho EHul MBar MGos
	- 'Skyrocket'	CBcs CDul CMac CSBt CTri CWib ECho ECrN EHul EPfP GEdr LAst LBee LCon MBar MGos NBlu NEgg NHol NWea SBod SEND SMer SPlb WBVN WCFE WEve WFar
	- 'Springbank'	EHul LBee LRHS MAsh MBar WCFE
	- 'Tabletop'	MBar
	- 'Tolleson's Blue Weeping'	SIFN
	- 'Wichita Blue'	EHul EPfP SEND WEve
§	***squamata***	WBVN
	- 'Blue Carpet' ♀H4	More than 30 suppliers
	- 'Blue Spider'	CKen ECho LRHS MBar SCoo SLim SPoG
	- 'Blue Spreader'	ECho NEgg
	- 'Blue Star' ♀H4	More than 30 suppliers
	- 'Blue Star Variegated'	see *J. squamata* 'Golden Flame'
	- 'Blue Swede'	see *J. squamata* 'Hunnetorp'
	- 'Chinese Silver'	ECho EHul MBar SLim
	- 'Dream Joy'	CKen LCon SCoo SLim
	- var. ***fargesii***	see *J. squamata*
	- 'Filborna'	CKen ECho LBee MBar MWat SLim SMer
	- 'Glassell'	see *J. pingii* 'Glassell'
§	- 'Golden Flame' (v)	CKen
	- 'Holger' ♀H4	CBrm CDoC CDul CMac CRob CSBt ECho EHul EOrn EPfP EPla LBee LCon LLin LRHS MAsh MBar MGos SCoo SLim SPoG WEve
§	- 'Hunnetorp'	ECho EOrn MBar NHol
	- 'Loderi'	see *J. pingii* var. *wilsonii*
	- 'Meyeri'	CBcs ECho EHul EOrn IMGH MBar NWea SCoo SPoG STre WFar WTel
	- 'Pygmaea'	see *J. pingii* 'Pygmaea'
	- 'Wilsonii'	see *J. pingii* var. *wilsonii*
§	***taxifolia***	CDoC CRob ECho EOrn IMGH LBee
	virginiana	CPne
§	- 'Blue Cloud'	EHul MBar SLim WEve WGor
	- 'Burkii'	EHul
	- 'Frosty Morn'	CKen ECho EHul MBar WFar
	- 'Glauca'	CSWP EHul NWea
	- 'Golden Spring'	CKen
	- 'Helle'	see *J. chinensis* 'Spartan'
	- 'Hetzii'	CMac ECho EHul MBar NLar NWea WFar
	- 'Hillii'	MBar
	- 'Hillspire'	EHul
	- 'Nana Compacta'	MBar
	- Silver Spreader = 'Mona'	CKen EHul SCoo
	- 'Staver'	EHul
	- 'Sulphur Spray'	see *J.* x *pfitzeriana* 'Sulphur Spray'
§	- 'Tripartita'	MBar
§	- 'Venusta'	CKen

Jurinea (Asteraceae)

dolomiaea CC 4268	MGol
glycacantha	LRHS

Jurinella see *Jurinea*

Jussiaea see *Ludwigia*

Justicia (*Acanthaceae*)

sp.	LSou MJnS
aurea	EShb MJnS
§ ***brandegeeana*** ♀H1	CCCN CHal EShb MBri SOWG
- 'Lutea'	see *J. brandegeeana* 'Yellow Queen'
- variegated (v)	MJnS
§ - 'Yellow Queen'	CHal EShb
§ ***carnea***	CHal CSev EBak ERea EShb MBri MJnS SMad SOWG
guttata	see *J. brandegeeana*
'Nørgaard's Favourite'	MBri
'Penrhosiensis'	EShb
pohliana	see *J. carnea*
rizzinii ♀H1	CCCN CHll CPle CSev ERea EShb SMad SOWG
spicigera	ERea EShb
suberecta	see *Dicliptera suberecta*

K

Kadsura (*Schisandraceae*)

sp.	CMac
japonica	CBcs CMen EShb IDee MGol WPGP
- B&SWJ 1027	WCru
- 'Fukurin' (v)	IClo NLar
- 'Shiromi'	EPfP
- 'Variegata' (v)	CCCN EPfP EShb LRHS SBra WSHC
- white fruit	EPfP NLar

Kaempferia (*Zingiberaceae*)

rotunda	CBct CKob LAma

Kalanchoe (*Crassulaceae*)

beharensis ♀H1	CAbb CCCN CDTJ CHal EShb LToo MBri
- 'Fang' new	CDTJ
- 'Rusty'	CDTJ CSpe
blossfeldiana	LRHS
- 'Variegata' (v)	CHal
daigremontiana	CHal EShb SRms
§ ***delagoensis***	CCCN CHal EShb STre
fedtschenkoi	CHal EShb STre
laciniata	EShb
manginii ♀H1	CDoC
marmorata ♀H1 new	EShb
orgyalis	EShb
pubescens	EShb
pumila ♀H1	CHal EMan ERea EShb EWin SBch SPet WEas
rhombopilosa	EShb
sexangularis	EShb
'Tessa' ♀H1	MBri MLan SPet SRms STre WCot
thyrsiflora 'Bronze Sculpture'	CBct CSpe EWll
tomentosa ♀H1	CHal EShb SHFr SPet WEas
tubiflora	see *K. delagoensis*

Kalimeris (*Asteraceae*)

§ ***incisa***	EBee GMac MRav WBor WFar WMoo WTin
- 'Alba'	EBee ECha NLar NRnb SSvw WFar
- 'Blue Star'	EBee ECha EMil ENot EWll LHop MWea NLar NRnb WFar
- 'Charlotte'	CSam EBee EWes NBre NDov NGby
- 'Madiva'	EBee ECha
* - 'Variegata' (v)	NBre
integrifolia	ECha WTin
intricifolia	NBre
§ ***mongolica***	EBee ECha NBre WFar WPer WSHC
§ ***pinnatifida***	EBee EPPr WCot
- 'Hortensis'	CBod NBPC NSti WHil
§ ***yomena*** 'Shogun' (v)	CEnt EBee ECha ELan EMil EMon ENot EPPr EPfP GBuc GEdr MLLN MWgw NBir NPri NRnb SAga SMer SPer WBor WFar WSHC
- 'Variegata'	see *K. yomena* 'Shogun'

Kalmia ✿ (*Ericaceae*)

angustifolia ♀H4	GKev MBar NBlu SRms WFar
- f. ***rubra*** ♀H4	CBcs CBrm CDoC CSBt ELan EPfP LRHS MAsh MGos NDlv NEgg NVic SHBN SPer SPoG SReu SRot SSta WFar WPat WSpi
latifolia ♀H4	CBcs CEnd CPSs CTrG ELan EMil EPfP MBar MGos MLan NBlu NEgg NWea SPer SPlb SReu SSpi SSta SWvt WBod WBrE WFar WGer WNor WSpi
- 'Alpine Pink'	LRHS MAsh SRot WSpi
- 'Carousel'	ECho EPfP GGGa MGos NDlv WFar WGob
- 'Elf'	ECho GEdr LRHS MAsh MGos MLea WBod WFar
- 'Freckles' ♀H4	ECho ELan EPfP GEdr GGGa LRHS MAsh NDlv SPoG WFar
- 'Fresca'	ECho WGob
- 'Galaxy'	GGGa
- 'Heart of Fire'	GGGa LRHS
- 'Keepsake'	GGGa
- 'Little Linda' ♀H4	ECho GEdr GGGa GKev LRHS MAsh NDlv
- 'Minuet'	CBcs CDoC CDul CWSG ECho EPfP GEdr GGGa ISea LRHS MAsh MGos MLan MLea MWea NDlv SPoG SSpi SWvt WBrE WFar
- f. ***myrtifolia***	ECho GEdr GKev LRHS MLea WFar WGob
- 'Nancy'	GEdr WBod WFar
- 'Olympic Fire' ♀H4	CEnd EPfP GGGa LRHS MAsh MBri MGos MRav NHol SSpi
- 'Ostbo Red'	CBcs CDoC CDul CPSs CSBt ECho EMil EPfP GEdr GGGa ISea LRHS MGos MLea NDlv NHol SHBN SPer SPoG SReu SSpi SSta SWvt WBod WFar
- 'Peppermint'	GGGa
- 'Pink Charm' ♀H4	ECho GGGa GWCH LRHS MAsh
- 'Pink Frost'	ECho GGGa ISea MBri NHol NLar WFar
- 'Quinnipiac'	NHol
- 'Raspberry Glow'	GGGa
- 'Richard Jaynes'	ECho GEdr LRHS WBod WBrE WFar
- 'Sarah'	ECho GGGa LRHS MAsh SSpi
- 'Silver Dollar'	GGGa
- 'Snowdrift'	ECho GEdr GGGa GKev LRHS NDlv NLar SSpi WBod WFar
§ ***microphylla***	GGGa
polifolia	CBcs ECho MBar NLAp SKHP SPer WPat WThu
- var. ***compacta***	WSHC
- 'Glauca'	see *K. microphylla*
- f. ***leucantha***	GGGa NLAp WPat WThu

Kalmia x *Rhododendron* see *Rhododendron*

K. latifolia x ***R. williamsianum***, 'Everlasting'	see *Rhododendron* 'Everlasting'

Kalmiopsis (*Ericaceae*)

leachiana ♀H4	GCrs
- 'Glendoick'	GGGa LTwo MDun
* - 'Shooting Star'	LTwo WAbe

x *Kalmiothamnus* (*Ericaceae*)

ornithomma 'Cosdon'	WThu
- 'Haytor'	WAbe

Kalopanax (*Araliaceae*)

pictus	see *K. septemlobus*
§ ***septemlobus***	CBcs CDul CFwr CHEx CLnd ELan EPfP EWTr GBin NEgg NLar WBVN WOVN
- var. ***lutchuensis*** B&SWJ 5947	WCru
- var. ***maximowiczii***	CDoC EPfP MBlu NBee NLar WCot

Keckiella (*Scrophulariaceae*)

corymbosa	SBla

Keiskea (*Lamiaceae*)

japonica new	EBee

Kelseya (*Rosaceae*)

uniflora	CGra WAbe

Kennedia (*Papilionaceae*)

beckxiana	SOWG
coccinea	CCCN WHil
nigricans	CCCN EBee ERea EShb SOWG
prostrata	SPlb
rubicunda	CCCN CHal CRHN ERea

Kentia (*Arecaceae*)

belmoreana	see *Howea belmoreana*
forsteriana	see *Howea forsteriana*

Kentranthus see *Centranthus*

Kerria (*Rosaceae*)

japonica misapplied, single	see *K. japonica* 'Simplex'
- (d)	see *K. japonica* 'Pleniflora'
- 'Albescens'	WFar
- 'Buttercup'	MBri
- 'Golden Guinea' 🏆H4	CChe CPLG CWSG EBee ECtt ELan EPfP EWTr LRHS MAsh MGos MNrw MRav MSwo SCoo SPer SRms SWal SWvt WFar WWeb
§ - 'Picta' (v)	CDul CWib EBee ELan EPfP LAst LRHS MBar MGos MRav MSwo SGar SLim SLon SPer SPoG SRms WFar WSHC WTel WWeb
§ - 'Pleniflora' (d) 🏆H4	More than 30 suppliers
§ - 'Simplex'	CPLG CSBt EShb NWea WFar WTel
- 'Variegata'	see *K. japonica* 'Picta'

Khadia (*Aizoaceae*)

sp.	CStu
acutipetala new	CCCN

Kickxia (*Scrophulariaceae*)

spuria	MSal

Kirengeshoma (*Hydrangeaceae*)

palmata 🏆H4	More than 30 suppliers
- dwarf	CDWL WCot
- Koreana Group	CLAP CPLG EBee EGle EHrv ELan EMan EPfP EWTr GSki IPot LAst MBri MDun MRav NBir NCGa NRnb SMad SPer SPhx WCot WCru WFar WGwG WHil WOVN WTMC

Kitaibela (*Malvaceae*)

vitifolia	CFee EBee EDAr ELan EMan EMon EUnu LRav NBHF NBid NEgg SDnm SGar SPav SPlb WPer WTMC

Kitchingia see *Kalanchoe*

kiwi fruit see *Actinidia deliciosa*

Kleinia (*Asteraceae*)

articulata	see *Senecio articulatus*
grantii	ERea EShb
repens	see *Senecio serpens*
senecioides	WEas
stapeliiformis 🏆H1	EShb

Knautia (*Dipsacaceae*)

§ ***arvensis***	CArn CBgR CHll CRWN MHer MLLN MNHC NLan NLar NMir NPri NSco SECG SPer WFar WHer WMoo WSFF WSHC
- 'Rachael'	CElw
dipsacifolia	NDov SHar
§ ***macedonica***	More than 30 suppliers
- 'Crimson Cushion'	CSpe ECtt GAbr GBri LSou NPri SPav WCra WFar
- 'Mars Midget'	More than 30 suppliers
- Melton pastels	CChe EBee EGoo ENot EPfP EShb LBMP LSRN LSou MGos MNHC MWrn NCob NPer SPav SPet SPoG SRot SWal SWat SWvt WFar WWeb
- pink	CSam WWlt
- red	CWib MNHC NCob
- 'Red Dress'	EMon
- short	ECtt EHrv NCob NCot NDov STes WTMC WWlt
- tall, pale	NDov SPhx
sarajevensis	EBee MAvo
§ ***tatarica***	NBre

Knightia (*Proteaceae*)

excelsa	CBcs

Kniphofia ✿ (*Asphodelaceae*)

'Ada'	CMdw EWTr EWes MLLN MRav SMrm
'Alcazar'	CBcs CDes EBee EBla ECot ECtt ENot EPfP GGar LPio LRHS LSRN MBri MHer MRav MSte NCGa NPri SPoG SWvt WFar WMnd WPGP WSpi WWeb
'Amber'	NBre
'Amsterdam'	MWat
'Apple Court'	NBir
'Apricot'	CMdw EPla SMHy SMrm
'Apricot Souffle'	EBee MLLN WCot WPGP WPrP
'Atlanta'	CPne EMon LRHS
'Barton Fever'	EBee WCot
baurii	WCot
'Bees' Flame'	EBee
'Bee's Gold'	ERou WCAu
'Bees' Lemon'	More than 30 suppliers
'Bees' Sunset' 🏆H4	CAvo CDes EGle GAbr GBri GBuc MNrw MRav MWgw NBir WCot WHil WPGP WPrP WSpi WTMC
* ***bicolor***	ECtt WCot WPrP
'Border Ballet'	CBrm EDAr EQua ERou EWTr LBMP LHop LRHS NBir NBre NBro NLar SWat WFar
brachystachya	CPou ELon GBin SPlb WCot
'Bressingham Comet'	CWsd EBee EBrs ECtt EMan EPfP LRHS MAvo MBri MRav NBir WPGP
'Bressingham Gleam'	EBrs SMrm WCot
Bressingham hybrids	NBir
Bressingham Sunbeam = 'Bresun'	EBee GSki NBir WCot
Bridgemere hybrids	WFar
'Brimstone' 🏆H4	More than 30 suppliers

	bruceae new	CPou
	buchananii	CDes
	'Buttercup' ♀H4	CAvo WSHC WSpi WTin
	'C.M. Prichard' misapplied	see *K. rooperi*
	'C.M. Prichard' Prichard	WCot
	'Candlelight'	CDes CMdw COIW CWsd EBee ECtt LPio NBre SDys WPGP
*	'Candlemass'	EBee EBrs LPio
	caulescens ♀H3-4	More than 30 suppliers
	- 'Coral Breakers'	CAby CBct EBee ECGP ECtt GBin MLLN MSte WCot WTMC
	- from John May	WCot
	citrina	CFir CFwr EBee EDAr EPfP GKev LAst LRHS MBrN NBre NChi NLar WCot
	'Cobra'	CDes EBrs LRHS MRav NBhm WCot WHil
	'Comet'	ECtt
	'Corallina'	WFar
	'Dingaan'	CAbb CAvo CPou EBee ECtt EMan EPPr ERou GBin GMac GQue GSki LFur MAvo MNrw NBir NEgg NPri SAga SDnm SPav WBrk WCot WFar
	'Doctor E.M. Mills'	CSam
	'Dorset Sentry'	CAbP CAbb CMdw CSam EBee EBla ECtt EGle EMan EMar GBuc GSki LAst LPio MEHN MLLN MNrw MSte NBir NCGa NEgg NLar NMyG NOrc SAga STes WCot WFar
	'Dropmore Apricot'	CMMP SPav
	'Drummore Apricot'	CMHG ECha EGle ELan EMan EWll LAst LSou MLLN MRav MSte NBir NSti SAga SDnm WCot WFar WPGP WPrP WTMC
I	'Earliest of All'	EBee GSki LRHS
	'Early Buttercup'	CTca EBee ECot EPfP EQua GBri MRav WCot WFar
	ensifolia	CDTJ CPne CPou ECtt GSki NGdn SRms WMnd
	'Ernest Mitchell'	MRav SMrm WCot
	Express hybrids	NBre NLar
	'Fairyland'	ECGP NGBl WBrk WFar WTin
	'False Maid'	SMHy
*	'Fat Yellow'	MWgw
	fibrosa	CFir
	'Fiery Fred'	CMil EBee EBrs ELan LRHS MRav NBre SMrm WCot
	'First Sunrise'	EBee ERou
	'Flamenco'	CChe CFwr EDAr EWll EWsh NBre NEgg NGdn SMac SPet WOut WRHF WTMC WWeb
	'Flaming Torch'	ECha
	foliosa	LRHS SChr SMrm
	'Frances Victoria'	WCot
	galpinii misapplied	see *K. triangularis* subsp. *triangularis*
	galpinii Baker ♀H4	EBee GBri MRav NBre SRms WTMC
*	'Géant'	XPep
	'Gilt Bronze'	EBee LFur WCot
	'Gladness'	EBee ECtt GSki LFur MRav NBir NBre WCot WPrP
	'Goldelse'	CWsd EBee NBir WCot
	'Goldfinch'	CMdw CSam CWsd MRav SMHy
	gracilis	LEdu
	'Green and Cream'	MNrw
	'Green Jade'	CDes CFir CMdw CSpe EBee ECha EPfP ERou GBri GQue LPio MRav MSte NBir NBro NLar NSti SEND SGar WCAu WCot WFar WTin
	'Green Lemon'	NBre
	'H.E. Beale'	MRav SMrm WCot
	'Hen and Chickens'	WCot
	hirsuta	CFir CPou CSam ELan EMan EShb LPio MSte SPad WCot
	- JCA 3.461.900	WCot
	- 'Traffic Lights'	EBee ERou EWll LFur LSou MGol NBhm WHil
	'Hollard's Gold'	WCot
	'Ice Queen'	CAvo CFir CPar CSam CSev EBee EBrs ECtt EPPr ERou GBri LPio MBri MRav MSte NBro NCGa NChi NGdn SMad SWvt WBrE WCAu WCot WTin
	ichopensis	CDes GBuc WPGP
	'Ingénue'	WCot
	'Innocence'	EBrs NBre
	'Jane Henry'	CDes WPGP
	'Jenny Bloom'	More than 30 suppliers
	'John Benary'	CAvo CFFs CHar CPou CSam CTca EBee ECtt EGle ERou GAbr GMaP GSki IGor LHop LPio MAvo MLLN MSte NBir NEgg NGdn SPer SPoG WCot WFar WKif WLin WTin
	'Johnathan'	WCot
	laxiflora	CPou EBee MGol SKHP WPGP
	'Lemon Ice'	WCot
	'Light of the World'	see *K. triangularis* subsp. *triangularis* 'Light of the World'
	linearifolia	CPou CTrC GCra GGar MLLN MNrw SHom SPlb WCot
	'Little Elf'	CWsd SDys WSHC
	'Little Maid'	More than 30 suppliers
	'Lord Roberts'	EBee ECha ENot LPio MRav SDix SPav WCot
	'Luna'	SMrm WCot
	'Lye End'	SMrm
	macowanii	see *K. triangularis* subsp. *triangularis*
	'Maid of Orleans'	CWsd WCot
	'Mermaiden'	CMHG CSam EBee ECtt GMac GSki LAst MNrw NCob WCot WFar
	'Minister Verschuur'	EBee ENot GSki LRHS MBri NBre WFar WMnd WSpi
	'Modesta'	EBee WPGP
	'Molten Lava'	EBee
	'Mount Etna'	EBee WCot WPGP
	multiflora	CTca EBee ECtt LFur WCot
	'Nancy's Red'	More than 30 suppliers
	nelsonii	see *K. triangularis* subsp. *triangularis*
	'Nobilis'	see *K. uvaria* 'Nobilis'
	northiae	CFir CHEx CPou CTca CWsd EBee ECtt EWes GBin LEdu LPio MAvo MBNS MNrw NBhm SAPC SArc SPlb SPoG WCru WGwG WMnd WPGP
	'November Glory'	WCot
I	'Old Court Seedling'	WCot WPrP
	'Orange Torch'	CPou
	'Painted Lady'	CAbP CSam CTri EBee ECtt GMaP GMac MBnl MBri MRav NCGa NPri SMHy SPoG WBrk
	parviflora	CPou
	pauciflora	EBee EMan ERos LHop SDys WCot
	'Percy's Pride'	More than 30 suppliers
	'Pfitzeri'	SRms
	porphyrantha	WCot
	x ***praecox***	GAbr WCot
	'Primulina' Bloom	CPou EMar LRHS
	'Prince Igor'	CFir EBee GAbr MLHP MWea NBir SMad WCot WHrl
	pumila	GSki
	'Ranelagh Gardens'	SArc
	'Rich Echos' new	WCot

	ritualis	EDAr LSou MAvo NLar WCot WLin WPGP
§	***rooperi*** ♀H4	More than 30 suppliers
I	- 'Torchlight'	CAbb CPne CTca EBee
	'Royal Castle'	CFwr MRav NBir NEgg NOrc NPri WFar
	'Royal Standard' ♀H4	CBcs EBee EBla ELan ENot EPfP ERou EShb GBri GSki LAst LCro LRHS MNrw MRav NLar NPri SHBN SPoG SRms SWvt WCot WFar WMnd WSpi WWeb
	rufa	CPou
	'Safranvogel'	WCot
	'Samuel's Sensation' ♀H4	CFir EBee EBrs ELan GBri GGar GSki LFur LRHS MBnl MNFA MRav NEgg NLar SHBN WCot WTMC
	sarmentosa	CPou EBee SPlb WCot WPGP XPep
	'September Sunshine'	MRav
	'Sherbet Lemon'	CHid CTca EBee ECtt EPPr GQue LFur MLLN MNrw STes WBrk WCot
	'Shining Sceptre'	CFwr CSam EBee ECha ECtt ERou LRHS MLLN MRav MSte MWat NCGa NLar SGar SMad SSvw SWvt WAul WCot WEas
	'Springtime'	WCot
	'Star of Baden Baden'	NBir SMad WCAu WCot
	'Strawberries and Cream'	CAvo CBcs CFir CPen CWCL EBee ECha ENot EPfP GQue LAst LPio MSte NPri SAga SPer WCot
	stricta	CTrC WCot
	'Sunbeam'	NBir
	'Sunningdale Yellow' ♀H4	CDes CMdw COIW CPou EBee EBla ECha EHrv EMan ERou GMaP MLHP MWat SMHy SPer SRms WCot WEas WHoo WPGP
	'Tawny King'	More than 30 suppliers
	'Tetbury Torch'PBR	EBee EBla EMan LRHS SMrm WWeb
	thodei	CPou
	thomsonii var. ***snowdenii*** misapplied	see *K. thomsonii* var. *thomsonii*
	- var. ***snowdenii*** ambig.	CPou CWsd MGol SKHP WPGP
§	- var. ***thomsonii***	CDes CFir ECha EMan EMar LPio MGol SKHP SMHy WCot WHal WPrP WWlt
	- - triploid variety	GSki
	'Timothy'	More than 30 suppliers
	'Toffee Nosed' ♀H4	COIW CPar EBee EBla ECGP ECtt EGle EPfP ERou GBin GBri GWWP LAst LPio MBnl MRav MWat NBir NBro NEgg NSti SMHy SPav WAul WCot WMnd WPrP
	'Torchbearer'	EBee NBre WCot WFar
	triangularis	CMHG EPfP EShb GSki LRHS SAga WFar
§	- subsp. ***triangularis***	COIW CWCL EBee ENot EPfP GBuc ITer LAst LRHS LSRN MRav SRms SWat WBrE WPrP
§	- - 'Light of the World'	CDes CHar CSpe CTca EBee ECtt EHrv ENot GAbr GSki LAst LPio LRHS MLLN NBPC NBir NCGa NChi NEgg NLar SPav SPoG SWvt WBrk WCot WCra WFar WGwG WTMC
	'Tubergeniana'	WCot
	'Tuckii'	SRms
	typhoides	NBir SPlb
	tysonii	SPlb
	uvaria	CBig CPou CTrC EMil GSki LCro LRHS MNHC NBir NPri NVic SRms WCot WHoo WMnd WPnP WTMC
	- 'Grandiflora' **new**	WSpi
§	- 'Nobilis' ♀H4	More than 30 suppliers
	'Vanilla'	CFir EBee EMan GSki LAst MBNS MRav NGdn NLar WAul WTMC
	'Vincent Lepage' **new**	NBhm
	'Wol's Red Seedling'	CAby CFir CHFP EBee ECtt EGle LSou MAvo NCGa SPoG WGwG
	'Wrexham Buttercup'	CDes CSam EBee ECtt GAbr GBri GMaP GMac GSki IPot LSRN MAvo MLLN MNFA MRav WBVN WCot WHal WHoo WPrP WSpi WTMC
	'Yellow Cheer'	LRHS
	'Yellowhammer'	CSam EBee ECha NBre WFar WPrP
	'Zululandii'	WCot

Knowltonia (*Ranunculaceae*)

	filia	CPLG

Kochia see *Bassia*

Koeleria (*Poaceae*)

	cristata	see *K. macrantha*
	glauca	More than 30 suppliers
§	***macrantha***	CBig EAlp GFor NBre NLar NNor XIsg
	vallesiana	EMon MNrw

Koelreuteria (*Sapindaceae*)

	bipinnata	CMCN LEdu
	paniculata ♀H4	More than 30 suppliers
	- 'Coral Sun'	CGHE MBlu MBri NLar WPat
	- 'Fastigiata'	EBee EPfP LRHS MBlu MBri NPal SCoo SPoG SSpi WHar
	- 'Rosseels'	MBlu MGos NEgg NLar
	- 'September' **new**	MBri

Kohleria (*Gesneriaceae*)

	'Clytie'	MBri
	'Cybele' **new**	EABi
	'Dark Velvet'	CHal WDib
	eriantha ♀H1	CHal EShb MBri WDib
	'Jester' ♀H1	CHal EABi WDib
	'Red Ryder' **new**	EABi
	'Ruby Red' **new**	WDib
	'Strawberry Fields' ♀H1	MBri
	warscewiczii ♀H1	CHal EABi LRHS WDib

Kolkwitzia (*Caprifoliaceae*)

	amabilis	CPLG CSBt CTri ELan EMil EPfP LPan MAsh MGan MGos NWea SPlb SRms WCFE WHCG WHar WMoo WNor WTel
	- 'Maradco'	CPMA EBee EMil EPfP LRHS MAsh MRav NLar NPro SCoo SPoG SSta WPat WSpi
	- 'Pink Cloud' ♀H4	More than 30 suppliers

Krascheninnikovia (*Chenopodiaceae*)

§	***lanata***	XPep

kumquat see *Fortunella*

Kunzea (*Myrtaceae*)

	ambigua	CPLG CTrC ECou SOWG SPlb
	- pink-flowered **new**	ECou
	- prostrate **new**	ECou
	'Badja Carpet'	WAbe
	baxteri	ECou EUnu SOWG
	capitata	SOWG
	ericifolia	SPlb
§	***ericoides***	ECou GGar SOWG
	- 'Auckland'	ECou
	- 'Bemm'	ECou
	parvifolia	ECou SOWG
	pomifera	ECou

L

Lablab (*Papilionaceae*)

§	***purpureus***	LSou
	- 'Ruby Moon'	CSpe LRav

+ *Laburnocytisus* (*Papilionaceae*)

	'Adamii'	CDul CLnd CPMA EBee ELan EMil EPfP LBuc LPan LSRN MBlu MGos NLar SMad

Laburnum ✿ (*Papilionaceae*)

	alpinum	EPfP GGar NEgg NWea SPlb
§	- 'Pendulum'	CDoC CDul CLnd EBee ELan EMil EPfP LPan LRHS LSRN MAsh MBar MBri MGos NBlu NEgg SBLw SBod SCrf SLim SPer SPoG WOrn
§	***anagyroides***	CDul CWib ECrN EMac ISea NWea SBLw SEND SRms WBVN
	- var. ***alschingeri***	MBlu MGos
§	- 'Pendulum'	NEgg
	'Pendula'	see *L. alpinum* 'Pendulum', *L. anagyroides* 'Pendulum'
	vulgare	see *L. anagyroides*
	x ***watereri*** 'Vossii' ♀H4	More than 30 suppliers

Lachenalia ✿ (*Hyacinthaceae*)

	algoensis new	WCot
§	***aloides***	CBow CGrW CStu CTca EBrs ECho MBri
	- var. ***aurea*** ♀H1	CTca EBrs ECho LRHS MSte SBch WCot
I	- var. ***luteola***	ECho
	- 'Nelsonii'	ECho LRHS WCot
	- 'Pearsonii'	EBrs ECho LRHS
	- var. ***quadricolor*** ♀H1	CGrW CTca EBrs ECho GAbr IHer LRHS WCot
§	***bulbifera*** ♀H1	CTca EBrs ECho MBri
	carnosa	WCot
	contaminata ♀H1	EBrs ECho LRHS WCot
	elegans	EBrs ECho
	'Fransie'PBR new	EBrs
	gillettii	EBrs ECho
	hirta	EBrs ECho
	juncifolia	EBrs ECho
	'Lemon Ripple' new	WCot
	liliiflora	EBrs ECho
	maximilianii new	EBrs
	mediana	EBrs ECho
	montana new	EBrs
	mutabilis	EBrs ECho LRHS WCot
	'Namakwa' (African Beauty Series) new	CTca EBrs WHil
	namaquensis	CTca EBrs ECho
	namibiensis new	CTca EBrs
	neilii	WCot
	'Nova' new	EBrs
	orchioides var. ***glaucina***	CGrW ECho WCot
	orthopetala	EBrs ECho WCot
	pallida	EBrs ECho
	peersii	CGrW
	pendula	see *L. bulbifera*
	pusilla	ECho
	pustulata ♀H1	CTca EBrs ECho LRHS WCot
	- blue-flowered	CGrW CHHB CTca EBrs ECho
	- yellow-flowered new	EBrs ECho
	reflexa	EBrs ECho WCot
	'Robijn'	CGrW EBrs ECho WCot WHil
	'Rolina'	EBrs ECho WCot
	'Romaud'	EBrs ECho WCot
	'Romelia'PBR	EBrs ECho WCot WHil
	'Ronina'	EBrs ECho WCot
	'Rosabeth'	EBrs WCot WHil
	rubida	EBrs ECho WCot
	'Rupert' (African Beauty Series)	CGrW CTca EBrs ECho WCot WHil
	splendida	ECho
	thomasiae new	EBrs
	tricolor	see *L. aloides*
	unicolor	ECho WCot
	unifolia	EBrs ECho
	violacea	EBrs ECho WCot
	viridiflora ♀H1	CGrW ECho LRHS WCot
	zeyheri	WCot

Lactuca (*Asteraceae*)

	alpina	see *Cicerbita alpina*
	lessertiana	EBee
	perennis	CSpe CWan EBee GSki LSou MBri MHar MTho NDov NLar NSti SPla SPoG WCFE WCot WHer WHrl
	virosa	CArn MSal

Lagarosiphon (*Hydrocharitaceae*)

§	***major***	CBen CDWL EHon EMFW EPfP NBlu WFar WMAq

Lagarostrobos (*Podocarpaceae*)

§	***franklinii***	CDoC CTrG LLin STre WPic
	- 'Fot' (f) new	WThu
	- 'Picton Castle' (m) new	WThu

Lagerstroemia (*Lythraceae*)

	fauriei B&SWJ 6023 new	WCru
	indica ♀H1	CCCN CMen CPle EPfP ERom EShb IDee MWya SBLw SEND SPlb
	- Little Chief hybrids	EShb
	- Petite Pinkie = 'Monkie'	MPRe
	- 'Red Imperator'	CBcs SEND
	- 'Rosea'	CBcs LPan SEND
	- 'Rubra'	MPRe

Lagunaria (*Malvaceae*)

	patersonii	CHll WPGP XPep

Lagurus (*Poaceae*)

	ovatus ♀H3	CHrt CKno CWCL EAlp EGoo MGol SAdn SBch

Lambertia (*Proteaceae*)

	formosa	ECou

Lamiastrum see *Lamium*

Lamium ✿ (*Lamiaceae*)

	from Turkey	CStu
	album	CArn GWCH NMir
	- 'Friday' (v)	CBow EMan NBir NBre WHer WHil
	flexuosum	EPPr NBre
§	***galeobdolon***	CArn CNat CTri CWib MHar MHer MSal NSco SMac SRms WBrE
	- 'Hermann's Pride'	CBcs COIW CTca EBee ECtt EPfP GMaP LAst LBMP LRHS MAvo MBri MWgw MWrn NBir NCob NMir SAga SMad SPer SPla SRms SWvt WFar WHil WHoo WMoo
	- 'Kirkcudbright Dwarf'	EBee EWes GBin NBre
§	- subsp. ***montanum*** 'Florentinum'	CHal CHrt CSBt CWan EBee ECha EMan EPfP LBMP MMuc MRav SPer WBrk WCAu WFar WPer
§	- 'Silberteppich'	ECha ELan EMan EMar MRav MTho
	- 'Silver Angel'	EMan NBre
	- Silver Carpet	see *L. galeobdolon* 'Silberteppich'
	- 'Variegatum'	see *L. galeobdolon* subsp. *montanum* 'Florentinum'

garganicum	WTMC
- subsp. ***garganicum***	CPom EWes GBri WPer
- subsp. ***pictum***	see *L. garganicum* subsp. *striatum*
- subsp. ***reniforme***	see *L. garganicum* subsp. *striatum*
§ - subsp. ***striatum***	SBla
luteum	see *L. galeobdolon*
maculatum	CArn CHrt EGoo SEND SHFr SRms WFar
- 'Album'	EBee ELan EPfP LBMP SHar SPer SRms
- 'Anne Greenaway' (v)	CBow EBee EWes GBri SPet
§ - 'Aureum'	CArn COIW EBee ECha ECho EGoo ELan LAst MTho SPet SWvt WFar WHil WPer
- 'Beacon Silver'	CArn CEnt COIW CWib EBee ECha ECho ELan ENot EPfP GGar LCro LRHS MHer MLHP NCob NSti SPer SPet SPlb SRGP SRms SWvt WCAu WEas WFar WPer WWeb
- 'Beedham's White'	NBir NSti
- 'Brightstone Pearl'	EGoo EWes
- 'Cannon's Gold'	ECha ECtt ELan EPPr EWes EWin GBuc MHer SWvt WFar
- 'Chequers' ambig.	EBee EWin LBMP LRHS NBre SPer SPla
- 'Dingle Candy'	CBgR
- 'Elaine Franks'	CSam
- 'Elisabeth de Haas' (v)	CBow EWes NBre
- 'Forncett Lustre'	CBgR EBee EWes EWin
- 'Forncett White Lustre'	NBre
- 'Gold Leaf'	see *L. maculatum* 'Aureum'
- Golden Anniversary = 'Dellam'^{PBR} (v)	EBee ELan LAst NBro NGdn SPla SPoG WFar WHil
- 'Golden Nuggets'	see *L. maculatum* 'Aureum'
- 'Golden Wedding'	ECho
- 'Ickwell Beauty' (v)	EBee GBri
- 'James Boyd Parselle'	CBgR CBow CSam EBee EWin MLLN NBre WHal WRHF
- 'Margery Fish'	SRms
- 'Pink Nancy'	CSpe EGoo SWvt WFar
- 'Pink Pearls'	CHrt CSBt EBee ECho NBre NCiC SHar SPet WFar WMoo
- 'Pink Pewter'	CTca EBee ECGP ECha ECtt ELan EPfP EShb GGar GMaP LBMP LRHS MAvo NGdn NSti SMac SPer SPla SPlb WBrE
- 'Red Nancy'	EBee
§ - 'Roseum'	CWib EBee ELan EPfP GGar GMaP LBMP MRav MWat MWgw NChi SGar SPer WCAu WPer
- 'Shell Pink'	see *L. maculatum* 'Roseum'
- 'Silver Shield'	EBee EWes
- 'Sterling Silver'	EBee NBre WPer
- 'White Nancy' Υ^{H4}	More than 30 suppliers
- 'Wootton Pink'	GBuc MBri MHer NBir NLar SSvw SWvt WCra WEas
microphyllum	WAbe
orvala	CCVN CSpe EBee EBrs ECha ECtt EHrv ELan EMon EPPr EWTr LEdu MAvo MNFA MRav MSte NCGa NChi NSti SMac SMad SPhx WCAu WCru WFar WHer WPGP WPer WTin
- 'Album'	CBod EBee EHrv ELan EMon EPPr LEdu MSte NLar SGar SHar SMrm WHer WPtf WTin
- pink-flowered **new**	CSpe
- 'Silva'	CSam EMan EMon EPPr GBin LEdu NBre NGby WSHC
sandrasicum	CPBP CStu EBee SBla WAbe

Lampranthus (*Aizoaceae*)

sp.	EDAr
aberdeenensis	see *Delosperma aberdeenense*
aurantiacus	CBcs CHEx SPet
'Bagdad'	CHEx
blandus	CBcs CCCN
'Blousey Pink'	CHEx
§ ***brownii***	CBcs CCCN CHEx CHal CStu ECho ELan EWin SEND SPet WPnn
coccineus	SPet
deltoides	see *Oscularia deltoides*
edulis	see *Carpobrotus edulis*
falcatus	CPLG
glaucus	CStu SEND
haworthii	CHal
multiradiatus	GGar SEND
oscularis	see *Oscularia deltoides*
roseus	CCCN CHEx EAlp EWin LRHS SPet
spectabilis	CBcs CCCN CHal CStu SAPC SArc SPet WBrE
- 'Tresco Apricot'	CCCN
- 'Tresco Brilliant'	CCCN CHEx SPet
- 'Tresco Fire'	CCCN CDoC CHal
- 'Tresco Orange'	CCCN
- 'Tresco Peach'	CCCN CHal CStu WAbe
- 'Tresco Red'	CCCN
- white-flowered	CStu
'Sugar Pink'	CHEx

Lamprothyrsus (*Poaceae*)

hieronymi	EBee

Lancea (*Scrophulariaceae*)

tibetica	EBee NWCA

Lantana (*Verbenaceae*)

'Aloha' (v)	CHal
camara	CArn ELan EPfP EShb MBri SRms XPep
- 'Kolibri'	EWin LAst
- orange-flowered	CCCN SWal
- pink-flowered	CCCN
- red-flowered	CCCN
- 'Snow White'	LAst
- 'Sonja'	LAst
- variegated	EShb
- white-flowered	CCCN EShb
- yellow-flowered	EShb NPri
'Goldsome'	EWin LAst
'Ingersheimer'	EWin
§ ***montevidensis***	CHal EShb XPep
- RCB/Arg AA-1	WCot
- 'Boston Gold'	CHal
'Schneeflocke'	EWin
sellowiana	see *L. montevidensis*
'Spreading Sunset'	SOWG
violet-flowered	SEND

Lapageria (*Philesiaceae*)

rosea Υ^{H3}	CBcs CCCN CHll CKob CPLG CPne CRHN EPfP EPla EShb GQui MDun NLar NSla SAdn SHBN WGwG WNor WPGP
- var. ***albiflora***	CRHN SAdn
- 'Flesh Pink'	CPLG CRHN
- 'Nash Court'	ECot EMil

Lapeirousia (*Iridaceae*)

anceps	CStu
cruenta	see *Anomatheca laxa*
divaricata	CStu
laxa	see *Anomatheca laxa*

Lapsana (*Asteraceae*)

communis 'Inky'	CNat EUnu

Lardizabala (*Lardizabalaceae*)

biternata	see *L. funaria*
§ ***funaria***	CTrG

Larix (*Pinaceae*)

	decidua ♀H4	CBcs CCVT CDoC CDul CMen CRWN CSBt ECho ECrN ELan EMac EPfP EWTr LCon MBar MGos NBlu NEgg NWea SHBN SPer SPlb WEve WFar WMou
	- 'Autumn Gold Weeping'	NHol
	- 'Corley'	CKen ECho LLin MBlu
	- 'Croxby Broom'	CKen
§	- var. ***decidua***	WFar
	- 'Globus'	ECho LRHS NHol SLim
	- 'Horstmann Recurved'	ECho LLin LRHS NLar SCoo SLim SPoG
	- 'Krejci'	NLar SLim
	- 'Little Bogle'	CKen ECho MAsh NHol
	- 'Oberförster Karsten'	CKen ECho
	- 'Pendula'	CBcs ECho WEve
	- 'Puli'	CEnd ECho LCon LLin LRHS MAsh MBlu MGos NHol NLar SCoo SLim SPer SPoG WEve
	x ***eurolepis***	see *L.* x *marschlinsii*
	europaea Lam. & DC.	see *L. decidua* var. *decidua*
	europaea Middend.	see *L. sibirica*
	gmelinii 'Tharandt'	CKen ECho
§	***kaempferi*** ♀H4	CDoC CDul CLnd CMen CSBt CTri ECho ECrN ELan EMac EPfP LBuc LCon LPan LRHS MAsh MBar NEgg NWea SCoo SLim SPer STre WEve WFar WMou WNor
	- 'Bambino'	CKen
	- 'Bingman'	CKen
	- 'Blue Ball'	CKen ECho LLin NLar WEve
	- 'Blue Dwarf'	CKen ECho LCon LLin LPan LRHS MAsh MBar MGos NBlu SCoo SLim SPoG WEve
	- 'Blue Haze'	CKen
	- 'Blue Rabbit'	CKen CTho
	- 'Blue Rabbit Weeping'	ECho LCon LLin MGos NHol SCoo SLim WEve
	- 'Cruwys Morchard'	CKen
	- 'Cupido'	ECho LLin NHol SLim
	- 'Diane'	CEnd CKen ECho EPfP LCon LLin LRHS MAsh MBar MBlu MGos NHol NLar SBLw SLim SPoG WEve WFar
	- 'Elizabeth Rehder'	CKen ECho NLar
	- 'Grant Haddow'	CKen
	- 'Green Pearl'	ECho
	- 'Grey Green Dwarf'	NHol
	- 'Grey Pearl'	CKen ECho LLin NLar
	- 'Hanna's Broom'	LCon NLar SLim
	- 'Hobbit'	CKen
	- 'Jakobsen'	LCon
*	- 'Jakobsen's Pyramid'	LLin LRHS MAsh NHol SCoo SLim SPoG
	- 'Nana'	CKen ECho GBin LLin NLar SLim
I	- 'Nana Prostrata'	CKen ECho
	- 'Pendula'	CDul CEnd EBee ECho ECrN EPfP LLin LRHS MAsh MBar MBlu MGos NHol NLar SBLw SPer SPoG WEve
	- 'Peve Tunnis' new	NLar
	- 'Pulii'	ECho SBLw
	- 'Stiff Weeping'	CTri ECho LCon MAsh MBlu NLar SCoo SLim
	- 'Swallow Falls'	CKen
	- 'Varley'	CKen ECho
	- 'Walter Pimven'	NLar
	- 'Wehlen'	CKen
	- 'Wolterdingen'	CKen ECho LCon MBlu NLar SLim
	- 'Yanus Olieslagers'	CKen
	laricina 'Arethusa Bog'	CKen ECho MBlu
	- 'Bear Swamp'	CKen ECho
	- 'Bingman'	CKen
	- 'Hartwig Pine'	CKen ECho
	- 'Newport Beauty'	CKen ECho
	leptolepis	see *L. kaempferi*
§	x ***marschlinsii***	CSBt ECho ECrN GBin NWea WMou
	- 'Domino'	CKen ECho LLin
	- 'Gail'	CKen ECho
	- 'Julie'	CKen SLim
	- 'Newport 17'	NLar
	russica	see *L. sibirica*
§	***sibirica***	MBar
	sukaczevii	see *L. sibirica*
	'Varied Directions'	SCoo SLim

Larrea (*Zygophyllaceae*)

tridentata	CArn

Larryleachia (*Asclepiadaceae*)

cactiformis new	LToo
perlata new	LToo

Laserpitium (*Apiaceae*)

halleri	EBee
siler	CArn EBee GBin NDov NLar SMHy SPlb WSHC WSpi

Lasiagrostis see *Stipa*

Lasiospermum (*Asteraceae*)

bipinnatum	SPlb

Lastreopsis (*Dryopteridaceae*)

glabella	WRic
microsora	WRic

Latania (*Arecaceae*)

loddigesii	EAmu LPal
verschaffeltii	LPal

Lathyrus ✿ (*Papilionaceae*)

	albus	CEnd
§	***articulatus***	ELan
§	***aureus***	CDes CPom CSsd EBee EDAr EMon GBuc MNFA MTho NBir NChi NSti NWCA SMeo WCAu WEas WFar WHal WHil WPat
	azureus misapplied	see *L. sativus*
	chilensis	CSsd EBee LSou NLar
	chloranthus	CSpe SPav
	cirrhosus	CDes EBee EMon WPGP
	clymenum articulatus	see *L. articulatus*
	cyaneus misapplied	see *L. vernus*
	cyaneus (Steven) K.Koch	SAga
*	- 'Alboroseus'	MTho SWat
	davidii	EBee EMon EWes WSHC
	filiformis	WSHC
	fremontii hort.	see *L. laxiflorus*
§	***gmelinii***	NLar
	- 'Aureus'	see *L. aureus*
	grandiflorus	CSev EMon NLar SBla SMrm SSvw SWat WCot
	heterophyllus	EMon MNrw NLar
	hirsutus	WGwG
	inermis	see *L. laxiflorus*
	japonicus	SPhx
	laevigatus	NLar
	latifolius ♀H4	CArn CRHN CRWN CTca EPfP GAbr LAst LCro LRav MWat NBid NBlu NPer SDnm SPoG SRms SWal WBVN WBor WBrk WEas WFar WHer WPer
§	- 'Albus' ♀H4	EBee ELan EMan NBHF SPav SPhx SRms WEas
	- 'Blushing Bride'	SPav WCot WSel
	- deep pink	MHer NLar NSti
	- pale pink	NSti

	- Pink Pearl	see *L. latifolius* 'Rosa Perle'
	- 'Red Pearl'	ECtt ELan EPfP ERou GAbr LCro MBri MWgw NPri NRnb SPav SPer SPlb SPoG SSvw WFar WPer WWeb
§	- 'Rosa Perle' Υ^{H4}	CBcs CTri EBee ECtt ERou EShb LCro LHop MBri MLHP MNHC MRav MSte NBir NEgg NLar NPer NPri NRnb SBra SPav SPer SSvw WCAu WMoo WWeb
	- Weisse Perle	see *L. latifolius* 'White Pearl'
	- 'White Pearl' misapplied	see *L. latifolius* 'Albus'
§	- 'White Pearl' Υ^{H4}	More than 30 suppliers
§	***laxiflorus***	CAby CDes CPom EBee LHop MCCP MHar MNrw MTho NChi WBVN WPGP
	linifolius	EMon NLar WCot WPGP
	luteus (L.) Peterm.	see *L. gmelinii*
	- 'Aureus'	see *L. aureus*
	maritimus	NLar WHil
	montanus	GPoy
	nervosus	CSpe EBee EWes MTho SBla SRms WOut
	neurolobus	CPLG CPom ITer
	nevadensis new	WHil
	niger	CFee CSpe EDAr EMon GBuc GMac LHop LSou MCot MHer MLLN NLar NRnb SHFr WFar WHil
	odoratus	EWll NBlu
	- 'Cupani'	CHrt
	- 'Dancing Queen' new	MPet
	- 'King Size Navy Blue'	LCro
	- 'Lightening' new	MPet
	- 'Matucana'	CSpe MWat SBch
	- 'Painted Lady'	LCro
	palustris	NLar
	polyphyllus	NSti
	pratensis	NMir NSco SECG WSFF
	pubescens	CRHN GBuc MPet
	roseus	WSHC
	rotundifolius Υ^{H4}	MNrw MTho NLar WFar WHoo
	- 'Tillyperone'	CFwr EMon EPPr
§	***sativus***	CSpe CWCL ECho ELan SBch
	- var. ***azureus***	see *L. sativus*
	sylvestris	CAgr CBgR CPLG EBee EMon MHer MLLN MNrw MSte MWgw NLar SBch WBrk
	tingitanus	CRHN WGwG
	- 'Roseus'	CRHN SBch
	transsilvanicus	CPom
	tuberosus	CAgr MNrw WCot
	'Tubro'	EMon SHar
	venetus	CPom EBee MNrw WSHC
§	***vernus*** Υ^{H4}	More than 30 suppliers
	- 'Alboroseus' Υ^{H4}	More than 30 suppliers
	- var. ***albus***	CDes EBee ECho EWes WCot WPGP
	- ***aurantiacus***	see *L. aureus*
	- 'Caeruleus'	CDes EMon LHop MNFA SPhx WPGP
*	- 'Cyaneus'	SAga SWat WCot
	- 'Flaccidus'	CAby EBee EGle EMon SMeo WCot WTin
	- 'Rainbow'	CBgR GAbr NWCA
	- 'Rosenelfe'	CDes CMea EBee EDAr EMan EWin GBuc MDKP SBod WCot WHal WPGP
	- f. ***roseus***	EBee ECha MRav NBir SRms WCot WCru
	- 'Spring Melody'	EBee MRav WCot WPat
	- 'Subtle Hints'	EMon

Laurelia (*Monimiaceae*)

§	***sempervirens***	CBcs WPGP
	serrata	see *L. sempervirens*

Laurentia see *Isotoma*

Laurus (*Lauraceae*)

§	***azorica***	CBcs WFar
	canariensis	see *L. azorica*
	nobilis Υ^{H4}	More than 30 suppliers
	- f. ***angustifolia***	CSWP EPla GQui MBlu MHer NGHP NLar SAPC SArc SDry SPoG WPGP WSel
	- 'Aurea' Υ^{H4}	CBcs CBrm CDul CSBt EBee ELan ELau EMil EPfP GQui LHop LRHS MAsh MBlu MGos SBLw SLim SLon SMad SPer SPoG SWvt WFar WJek WMoo WPat WSel
	- clipped pyramid	MGos NBlu
	- 'Crispa'	MRav
	- 'Sunspot' (v)	WCot

Lavandula ✿ (*Lamiaceae*)

	'After Midnight'	see *L.* 'Avonview'
	'Alba' ambig.	CArn CSev CWib MHrb SAdn SIde SPer SWat WEas WPer
	'Alba'	see *L.* x *intermedia* 'Alba'
	x ***allardii*** (Gaston Allard Group) 'African Pride'	XPep
§	***angustifolia***	CArn CHEx CSBt CWib EBee ELau ENot EPfP EUnu GPoy LBMP LBuc LCro LRHS MBar MBri MGos MHer NBlu NGHP NPer SAll SHBN SLim SMer SPlb SWal WFar XPep
	- 'Alba' misapplied	see *L. angustifolia* 'Blue Mountain White'
	- 'Alba'	CChe CWan EAro ECho ELau ENot EPfP GPoy LBuc LSRN MHer MNHC MRav MSwo NGHP NMen SAll SLon SPlb WFar WSel XPep
	- 'Alba Nana'	see *L. angustifolia* 'Nana Alba'
	- 'Arctic Snow'	CBcs CChe CEnt CWan ENor LAst LBMP MBri MHrb MSwo NGHP NLLv SDnm SPer SPoG WLav
	- 'Ashdown Forest'	CWan ECho ELau EMil MAsh MHer MHrb MLHP MNHC NGHP NPri SAdn SBch SDow SIde WHoo WJek WLav WSpi
	- 'Backhouse Purple' new	SDow
	- 'Beechwood Blue' Υ^{H4}	CWCL MHrb SDow WLav
	- Blue Cushion = 'Lavandula Schola'^{PBR}	EMil ENot EPfP LRHS LSRN MHrb SDow SMer WFar WLav
	- 'Blue Ice'	CWSG ENor MGos SDow WLav
	- 'Blue Mountain'	ITim MHrb WLav
§	- 'Blue Mountain White'	NLLv SDow WLav
	- 'Blue River'^{PBR}	WFar WLav
	- 'Blue Scent' new	EMil
§	- 'Bowles Early'	CSam CWan NGHP SAga SMer WFar WLav XPep
	- 'Bowles Grey'	see *L. angustifolia* 'Bowles Early'
	- 'Bowles Variety'	see *L. angustifolia* 'Bowles Early'
	- 'Cedar Blue'	CSev CWan EAro ECho EGoo ELau EMil EPfP MHer NGHP SDow SHDw SIde SPla WFar WLav
	- 'Coconut Ice'	CWSG EMil NGHP NLLv NTHB SJoo WLav WSpi
	- 'Compacta'	MHrb SDow WLav
	- 'Crystal Lights'	EMil
	- 'Dwarf Blue'	EMil EWin WFar XPep
	- 'Eastgrove Dome'	WEas
	- 'Eastgrove Nana'	see *L. angustifolia* 'Eastgrove Dome'
	- 'Erbalunga'	XPep
	- 'Folgate'	CArn CBcs ELau EMil LAst MHer MHrb MNHC NGHP SAll SDow SIde WFar WHoo WLav WMnd WSel WTel XPep
	- 'Fring A'	SDow
	- 'Granny's Bouquet'	SJoo WSpi
§	- 'Hidcote' Υ^{H4}	More than 30 suppliers

	- 'Hidcote Pink'	CArn CEnt CWib EBee ECho LSRN MHer MNHC MRav MWat NGHP SDow SPer WFar WHen WKif WMnd WPer WSel XPep
	- 'Hidcote Superior'	NChi WWeb
	- 'Imperial Gem' Υ^{H4}	More than 30 suppliers
	- 'Jean Davis'	see *L. angustifolia* 'Rosea'
§	- 'Lady'	CWSG NPer SBch SEND SHDw SWal WPer
	- 'Lady Ann'	EMil MHer MHrb NLLv NTHB SDow WLav
	- 'Lavender Lady'	see *L. angustifolia* 'Lady'
	- 'Lavenite Petite'	ENor EPfP LRHS LSRN LTwo MAsh MHrb NGHP NLLv NLar SDow SPoG SVil WLav WWeb
	- Little Lady = 'Batlad'^{PBR}	CRez EBee EMil EWsh LAst LRHS LSRN MAsh MHer MHrb MSwo NGHP NLLv NLar NPri SAll WLav
	- Little Lottie = 'Clarmo' Υ^{H4}	CWCL CWSG EMil ENot EPfP EWin LAst MAvo MHer SCoo SDow SIde SMer SWvt WLav
	- 'Loddon Blue' Υ^{H4}	CEnt ECho EMil EPfP LRHS NGHP SAdn SDow SIde WHoo WLav
§	- 'Loddon Pink' Υ^{H4}	CWan EBee ECho ELan EMil ENot EPfP GMaP LAst LRHS MAsh MBri MLHP MNHC MRav NGHP NPri SAdn SMer WEas WFar WHoo WLav WPGP
	- 'Lumières des Alpes'	XPep
	- 'Maillette'	EWin MHrb NGHP SDow SIde WLav XPep
	- 'Matheronne'	XPep
	- 'Melissa Lilac'	CBcs LRHS MAsh MHrb NPri SDow SJoo WLav
	- 'Middachten'	SAga
	- 'Miss Donnington'	see *L. angustifolia* 'Bowles Early'
	- 'Miss Katherine'^{PBR} Υ^{H4}	CSBt CWCL EBee ELan EMil ENor EPfP LAst LHop LRHS LSRN MAsh MHer MHrb MNHC NBPC NGHP NLar SDow SMer SPer SPoG SVil WLav
	- Miss Muffet = 'Scholmis' Υ^{H4}	CWCL EBee EMil LTwo NLLv SDow WLav
	- 'Munstead'	More than 30 suppliers
§	- 'Nana Alba' Υ^{H4}	More than 30 suppliers
	- 'Nana Atropurpurea'	WSel
	- 'No 9'	SDow
	- 'Peter Pan'	CWCL EMil LSRN MHrb NGHP SDow SMer WLav
	- 'Princess Blue'	CSBt CWCL EAro ELan EMil ENor EShb LRHS MAsh NPri SAga SAll SDow SIde SMer WFar WLav WPer WWeb XPep
	- 'Rêve de Jean-Claude'	WLav XPep
§	- 'Rosea'	More than 30 suppliers
	- 'Royal Purple'	CArn CBcs EBee EMil ENor EWes LRHS NGHP NTHB SAdn SAll SDow SIde SWvt WLav XPep
	- 'Saint Jean' **new**	SDow
	- 'Silver Mist' **new**	SJoo
	- 'Twickel Purple'	CBcs CHrt CSBt CWCL CWSG EBee ENot EPfP EWin LHop LRHS LSRN MAsh MNHC MRav NGHP NPri NTHB SDix SDow SIde SMer SPer SPla SWvt WFar WLav WSel XPep
	- 'Walberton's Silver Edge'	see *L.* x *intermedia* Walberton's Silver Edge
	'Aphrodite'	WLav
	aristibracteata	MHer WLav
§	'Avonview'	CBcs CWCL MHer NGHP SDow WHoo WLav
	'Badsey Starlite'	WLav
	'Ballerina'	MHrb SDow
§	'Bee Brilliant'^{PBR}	NGHP SJoo SPoG WLav
§	'Bee Cool'^{PBR}	EBee MHer MHrb NGHP NLLv SJoo SPoG WLav
§	'Bee Happy'	CWan EMil NGHP SHGN SJoo SPoG WLav
§	'Bee Pretty'	NGHP
	(Bella Series) 'Bella Purple' **new**	EMil
	- 'Bella Rose' **new**	EMil
	- 'Bella Rouge' **new**	EMil
	- 'Bella White' **new**	EMil
	'Blue Star'	EBee EPfP EWin MAvo NGHP SAll WFar WGwG
	'Bowers Beauty'	LRHS MAsh WLav
	buchii var. ***buchii***	SDow WLav XPep
	- var. ***gracilis***	CSpe
	Butterfly Garden = 'Avenue'^{PBR}	CWSG
	'Cambridge Lady'	see *L. angustifolia* 'Lady'
	canariensis	ERea EShb MHer MHrb SDow WLav XPep
	x ***chayforae*** 'Silver Sands' **new**	ENor ENot LSRN SBra SPoG
	x ***chaytorae***	CArn
	- 'Gorgeous'	MAsh SDow
	- 'Kathleen Elizabeth'	XPep
	- 'Richard Gray' Υ^{H3-4}	CArn CCge EBee EMil LRHS LSRN MAsh MHer MHrb MNHC NGHP SAga SDnm SDow SSvw WAbe WLav WMnd XPep
§	- 'Sawyers' Υ^{H4}	More than 30 suppliers
	x ***christiana***	MAsh MHer MHrb NGHP SDow SHDw WGwG WJek WLav XPep
	'Cornard Blue'	see *L.* x *chaytorae* 'Sawyers'
	dentata	CArn CEnt CSev EAro EShb MNHC NEgg NGHP SAdn SDry SGar SMer XPep
§	- var. ***candicans***	CSev LHop MHer MHrb MNHC NLLv SBch SDow SPer WLav XPep
	- - 'Pure Harmony'	WLav
	- var. ***dentata*** 'Dusky Maiden'	CWCL MHrb SDow WLav
	- - 'Linda Ligon' (v)	CBow EWin MHrb NGHP WGwG WHer WJek WLav XPep
	- - 'Monet'	MHrb NGHP
	- - 'Ploughman's Blue'	CWCL MHrb WLav
	- - f. ***rosea***	MHrb SDow WLav
	- - 'Royal Crown' Υ^{H2-3}	EMil MHer WFar WLav XPep
	- - 'Royal Standard'	SHBN
	- - 'Silver Queen'	WLav
	- silver	see *L. dentata* var. *candicans*
	'Devonshire Compact'	CHar CSBt CWCL EMil EWin LSou MHer NGHP NTHB SBch WJek
	'Fathead'	CBcs CBgR CSBt EBee ELan EPfP LAst LCro LRHS LSRN MAsh MHer MHrb MLan MNHC NGHP NPri SAdn SCoo SDow SLim SPer SPet SPoG WBrE WJek
	x ***ginginsii*** 'Goodwin Creek Grey'	MHer MHrb NLLv SDow WGwG WJek WLav XPep
	'Hazel'	WLav
	'Helmsdale'^{PBR}	More than 30 suppliers
	heterophylla misapplied	see *L.* x *heterophylla* Gaston Allard Group
	heterophylla 'Devantville-Cuche'	WJek WLav XPep
§	- Gaston Allard Group	CArn CPLG CSev EWin MHer NGHP NLLv SDow WLav WSel XPep
	'Hidcote Blue'	see *L. angustifolia* 'Hidcote'
§	x ***intermedia***	EWin SPla WFar
	- 'Abrialii'	NLLv SDow WLav XPep
§	- 'Alba' Υ^{H4}	CBcs CMea CWan MHer SAga SDow SGar SMer XPep
*	- 'Alexis'	WLav XPep
	- 'Arabian Night'	see *L.* x *intermedia* 'Impress Purple', 'Sussex'

	- 'Bogong'	WLav
§	- Dutch Group	CArn CSBt CWan CWib ENot EPfP EWTr LCro LRHS MAsh MBar MRav MSwo SAga SCoo SDow SGar SLim SPer SWat WFar WHen WPer XPep
	- 'Edelweiss'	EAro EMil EWin MAvo MRav NGHP NLLv SDow WLav XPep
	- 'Fragrant Memories'	ELau EMil EPfP EWin MAsh MHrb NPri SAga SDow SIde SMer WLav
*	- 'Futura'	XPep
	- Goldburg = 'Burgoldeen'PBR (v)	CBow CSBt ELan EMil ENot EPfP LAst MCCP MGos MRav NGHP NLLv SPav SPer SPla SPoG WLav WWeb
	- 'Grappenhall' misapplied	see *L.* x *intermedia* 'Pale Pretender'
	- 'Grey Hedge'	CWan EMil NGHP SAga WLav
	- 'Gros Bleu'	SDow WLav
	- 'Grosso'	CBcs CEnt CSam CSev CTri EAro EBee ELan ELau EMil EPfP LCro MHer MHrb MLHP MNHC MRav NGHP SAdn SAll SCoo SDow SSvw SWvt WFar WJek WSel XPep
	- 'Hidcote Giant' ♀H4	EPfP LRHS MHrb NPer SAdn SAga SDow SPer WKif WLav WSel XPep
§	- 'Impress Purple'	MNHC SDow WLav XPep
	- 'Jaubert'	XPep
	- 'Julien'	XPep
	- 'Lullingstone Castle'	CBod EAro ELau EMil LHop NGHP SAga SDow WGwG WJek WLav WRHF WSPU
	- 'Old English'	MHrb SDow
	- Old English Group	CArn CBod ELau WHoo WJek WLav WSel
§	- 'Pale Pretender'	CArn CEnd CSBt CSam CTri CWSG EAro EBee ELau EMil EUnu LCro MRav MSwo NGHP SMer SPer WFar WMnd WPer WPnn WSel XPep
	- 'Seal'	CArn CPrp EAro EBee ELau MHer MHrb MNHC NGHP SAga SDow SPer SPoG WFar WHCG WMnd WPer XPep
	- 'Sumian'	WLav XPep
	- 'Super'	XPep
§	- 'Sussex'	ELau MHrb MNHC NGHP SDow WLav WWeb XPep
N	- 'Twickel Purple'	CArn CWSG CWib ELau EWes LAst LSRN NGHP SMrm SWat WJek WMnd
§	- Walberton's Silver Edge = 'Walvera' (v)	CBow CRez CWCL ENor EShb LBuc LRHS MAsh MGos NPri SCoo SDow SIde SJoo SPoG
	'Jean Davis'	see *L. angustifolia* 'Rosea'
	lanata ♀H3	CArn ECha GPoy MHer MHrb NWCA SDow SDry SHFr WLav XPep
§	***latifolia***	CArn NHol XPep
I	'Lavender Lace'	CWSG NGHP SCoo
	'Loddon Pink'	see *L. angustifolia* 'Loddon Pink'
	'Madrid Blue'	see *L.* 'Bee Happy'
	'Madrid Pink'	see *L.* 'Bee Pretty'
	'Madrid Purple'	see *L.* 'Bee Brilliant'
	'Madrid White'	see *L.* 'Bee Cool'
	mairei	XPep
	'Marshwood'PBR	CTri EBee EPfP LRHS MRav SAdn SCoo SDow SIde SJoo SLim SMer SPer SPla
	minutolii	MHrb SDow XPep
	multifida	CArn EUnu LDai MHer NLLv WLav XPep
	- 'Blue Wonder'	GGar
*	- 'Tizi-n-Test'	XPep
	officinalis	see *L. angustifolia*
	'Passionné'	CWSG EBee EMil MAsh NGHP SJoo WLav
	pedunculata subsp. ***lusitanica***	WLav
§	- subsp. ***pedunculata*** ♀H3-4	More than 30 suppliers
	- - 'James Compton'	CWib EBee ECha LRHS MAsh SLim WLav
	- - 'Wine'	CBcs WLav
	- subsp. ***sampaiana***	WLav
	- - 'Purple Emperor'	CWSG LRHS SJoo SPoG WLav
	- - 'Roman Candles'	WLav
	- 'Whero Iti'	SDow
§	***pinnata***	CArn CHrt CSev EPfP EShb EWin MHer MHrb MNHC NEgg SDow SDry SPoG XPep
	'Pippa White'	NLLv
	'Pretty Polly'	CBcs ENor NBPC SDow WLav
	pterostoechas pinnata	see *L. pinnata*
	pubescens	XPep
	'Pukehou'	ENor EPfP LRHS MAsh MHrb NLLv SDow SJoo WLav WPat
	'Regal Splendour'PBR	CWCL EBrs ELan ENor EPfP LCro LRHS LSRN MAsh MBri MGos MHrb NBPC NGHP NLLv NPri SDow SPoG WLav
	'Rocky Road'	CWSG ENor LBuc LCro LRHS LSRN MAsh MBri MGos MHrb NGHP NLLv SDow SPav SPoG WLav
	'Rosea'	see *L. angustifolia* 'Rosea'
	rotundifolia	MHer SDow XPep
	'Roxlea Park'PBR	CChe CWCL ENor MHrb NGHP WLav
	'Russian Anna' **new**	EMil
	'Saint Brelade'	CWCL CWan EPfP EWin MAsh NGHP NLLv SDow WLav
	'Silver Edge'	see *L.* x *intermedia* Walberton's Silver Edge
	'Somerset Mist'	WLav
N	***spica***	see *L. angustifolia*, *L. latifolia*, *L.* x *intermedia*
	- 'Hidcote Purple'	see *L. angustifolia* 'Hidcote'
	- 'Pink Perfume'	LSou
	stoechas ♀H3-4	More than 30 suppliers
	- var. ***albiflora***	see *L. stoechas* subsp. *stoechas* f. *leucantha*
	- 'Anouk' **new**	SPoG
	- (Barcelona Series) 'Barcelona Pink' **new**	EMil
	- - 'Barcelona Purple' **new**	EMil
	- - 'Barcelona Rose' **new**	EMil
	- - 'Barcelona White' **new**	EMil
	- 'Blueberries and Cream'	LRHS MAsh SCoo
	- (Coco Series) 'Coco Deep Pink' **new**	EMil
	- - 'Coco Deep Purple' **new**	EMil
	- - 'Coco Deep Rose' **new**	EMil
	- - 'Coco Deep White on Blue' **new**	EMil
	- 'Fragrant Butterfly'	LSou
	- 'Lace'	SPoG WLav
	- subsp. ***luisieri*** 'Tickled Pink'	CWCL ELan ENor MHrb NGHP SDnm SPav
	- 'Papillon'	see *L. pedunculata* subsp. *pedunculata*
	- subsp. ***pedunculata***	see *L. pedunculata* subsp. *pedunculata*
	- 'Rocky Red'	ENot
	- 'Saint Marc'	EBee
§	- subsp. ***stoechas*** f. ***leucantha***	CArn CHrt CSBt CSev CWib ECha ELau EPfP LAst LRHS MBri MSwo NChi SDow SPla WAbe WFar WOut
	- - - 'Snowman'	CBcs CChe CSBt CWan EBee EMil ENor EPfP LAst LCro LRHS MHer

	MHrb MTPN MWat NGHP NPri SAdn SLim SPer SPoG SVil SWvt WFar WWeb
- - 'Liberty'	NGHP NLLv SDow SPoG WLav
- - 'Lilac Wings'	ENor LRHS LSRN LTwo MBri NGHP SJoo WLav
- - 'Provençal'	LRHS MBri
- - 'Purple Wings'	LRHS MBri SJoo SVil
- - f. ***rosea*** 'Kew Red'	More than 30 suppliers
- 'Victory'	SPoG
'Sugar Plum'	SHGN WLav
'Tiara'	ENor LCro MAsh MBri NBPC NGHP NLLv NPri SDow SJoo SLim SVil WLav
'Van Gogh'	MHrb SDow
vera misapplied	see *L.* x *intermedia* Dutch Group
vera DC.	see *L. angustifolia*
viridis	CArn CChe CSev ELan ELau EPfP LRHS MAsh MHer MNHC NGHP NLLv NPer SDow SGar SPla WAbe WJek WKif WLav XPep
'Willow Vale' ♀H3-4	CMea CTri EBee ELan EPfP LRHS LSRN MAsh MHer MHrb MLHP NCGa NLLv SAdn SAga SDow SPav SPhx SWvt WEas WJek WPGP WSPU WWeb
'Willowbridge Calico'PBR	CWSG EMil NEgg WLav

Lavatera (*Malvaceae*)

arborea	LEdu SChr WHer
- 'Rosea'	see *L.* x *clementii* 'Rosea'
- 'Variegata' (v)	CBow CDTJ CSsd ELan EMan EWin LSou NPer NSti SBod SDix SEND SGar WCot WEas WHer
bicolor	see *L. maritima*
cachemiriana	EQua GBuc LSou NPer WPer
Chamallow = 'Inovera'	EBee ENot LBuc LSRN MAsh NPri
x ***clementii*** 'Barnsley'	More than 30 suppliers
- 'Barnsley Baby'	LBuc LRHS MAsh NLar NPer NPri
- 'Blushing Bride'	CDoC EBee EPfP LRHS MAsh MBri MGos NLar NPri SBod SPer SPla SPoG
- 'Bredon Springs' ♀H3-4	CChe CDoC CWSG EBee ECha ECtt EMil ENot EPfP GBri LHop LRHS LSRN MAsh MBri MNHC MSwo MWgw NBlu NHol NScw SBod SLim SMer SPer SPla SWvt WFar WHar WWeb
- 'Burgundy Wine' ♀H3-4	More than 30 suppliers
- 'Candy Floss' ♀H3-4	EBee EPfP LRHS MBar MGos NLar NPer SAdn
- 'Kew Rose'	CDoC CTri EBee EMil EPfP LRHS MAsh MSwo NPer SLim SPla SRms WWeb
- 'Lavender Lady'	ECtt EPPr EQua NPer
- 'Lisanne'	LRHS MAsh MHer MNrw MSwo NHol NPri SEND SMrm WRHF
- 'Mary Hope'	LRHS MAsh
- Memories = 'Stelav'	CHid EBee ELan EPfP LRHS MAsh NEgg NLar SLim
- 'Pavlova'	CDoC CPLG LRHS MAsh NPri SMrm
- 'Poynton Lady' (v)	MGos
§ - 'Rosea' ♀H3-4	CBcs CDul CSBt CWSG EBee ECtt ENot EPfP GGar LRHS LSRN MAsh MBar MGos MNHC MWat NEgg NPri SBod SLon SPer SPoG WBVN WBod WFar WTel WWeb XPep
- 'Shorty'	WFar
§ - 'Wembdon Variegated' (v)	NPer
'Grey Beauty'	MAsh
§ ***maritima*** ♀H2-3	CDoC CHrt CMHG CPLG CRHN EBee ECtt ELan EPfP IFoB LHop MAsh SDry SPer SPoG SWvt WCFE WFar WHCG WKif WSHC XPep
- ***bicolor***	see *L. maritima*
- 'Princesse de Lignes'	MGos XPep
N ***olbia***	CTri LAst SPlb SRms XPep
- 'Eye Catcher'	EBee LRHS MBNS MSwo NEgg NLar SPer SPoG SWal
- 'Lilac Lady'	EBee ECha ELan EPfP LRHS LSou MAsh MBNS MCCP MWgw NCGa NLar SLim SPer WFar WKif WWeb
§ - 'Pink Frills'	EBee EQua LRHS MBar MBri MGos MNrw NPri SDry SMrm SPla WWlt
'Peppermint Ice'	see *L. thuringiaca* 'Ice Cool'
'Pink Frills'	see *L. olbia* 'Pink Frills'
'Rosea'	see *L.* x *clementii* 'Rosea'
'Summer Kisses'PBR	MBri
'Sweet Dreams'PBR	LRHS MBri NLar
tauricensis	NLar
N ***thuringiaca***	NNor WFar
§ - 'Ice Cool'	ECha ECtt LAst LRHS MBar MGos MHer NRnb WCot WFar WKif WWeb
- 'Red Rum'	GBin LBuc LRHS LTwo MAsh MBri NHol NLar NPri SPoG
'Variegata'	see *L.* x *clementii* 'Wembdon Variegated'
'White Angel'PBR	LRHS NLar
'White Satin'PBR	LHop MBri SPoG

Lecanthus (*Urticaceae*)

peduncularis	CHEx

Ledebouria (*Hyacinthaceae*)

adlamii	see *L. socialis*
concolor	EShb
cooperi misapplied	see *L. socialis*
§ ***socialis***	CBgR CHal CSWP CSev CSpe CStu EBrs ECho ELan EMan EPem ERos EShb GGar ITim LEdu LHop LToo NBir NCGa NLAp SBHP SBch WPGP WPrP
violacea	see *L. socialis*

x *Ledodendron* (*Ericaceae*)

§ 'Arctic Tern' ♀H4	CDoC CSBt CTri ECho GCrs GGar GQui LMil LRHS MAsh MBar MDun MGos MLea NHol NWCA SPer WBod WCwm

Ledum (*Ericaceae*)

§ ***groenlandicum***	MBar MLea SPer WFar WGer WSHC
- 'Compactum'	MAsh NLar SPoG WFar
macrophyllum	CFir
palustre	COld GGGa GPoy NLar
- subsp. ***decumbens***	GCrs

Leea (*Leeaceae*)

coccinea	see *L. guineensis*
§ ***guineensis***	MBri

Leersia (*Poaceae*)

oryzoides	EBee

Legousia (*Campanulaceae*)

pentagonica 'Midnight Stars' **new**	CSpe

Leiophyllum (*Ericaceae*)

buxifolium ♀H4	EPfP GCrs LRHS NLar WThu
- var. ***hugeri***	GBin NLar
- 'Maryfield'	WAbe

Lembotropis see *Cytisus*

Lemna (*Lemnaceae*)

gibba	CWat NPer
minor	CWat EHon EMFW NPer SWat

polyrhiza	see *Spirodela polyrhiza*
trisulca	CWat EHon EMFW NPer SWat

lemon balm see *Melissa officinalis*

lemon grass see *Cymbopogon citratus*

lemon see *Citrus limon*

lemon verbena see *Aloysia triphylla*

Leonotis (*Lamiaceae*)

leonitis	see *L. ocymifolia*
leonurus	CBcs CCCN CDMG CDTJ CHEx CHll CMdw CTrC ENot EShb EWes LRHS NSti SMad SPoG WSHC
- var. ***albiflora***	CPLG
nepetifolia var. ***nepetifolia*** 'Staircase'	SDnm SPav WRos
§ ***ocymifolia***	CPLG EBee EShb LSou WPGP
- var. ***ocymifolia***	EMan SPlb
- var. ***raineriana***	CHll

Leontice (*Berberidaceae*)

albertii	see *Gymnospermium albertii*

Leontochir (*Amaryllidaceae*)

ovallei new	CCCN

Leontodon (*Asteraceae*)

autumnalis	NMir
hispidus	NMir
§ ***rigens***	EBee EDAr EMan GBri GBuc MLHP MNrw NBid SDix SMad SMrm WFar WMoo WPrP WRos
- 'Girandole'	see *L. rigens*

Leontopodium (*Asteraceae*)

alpinum	CArn CTri CWan CWib ECho GKev LRHS NWCA SBla SIng SPlb SPoG SRms WPer
- 'Mignon'	CMea ECho EWes GEdr SIng WAbe WFar WHoo
- subsp. ***nivale***	GKev WPat
coreanum	EBee GKev
kamtschaticum	ECho
§ ***ochroleucum*** var. ***campestre***	EShb MDKP NLar WPer
palibinianum	see *L. ochroleucum* var. *campestre*
pusillum SAQE79	WAbe

Leonurus (*Lamiaceae*)

artemisia	see *L. japonicus*
cardiaca	CArn CWan EGoo EMan EMon GPoy LEdu MHer MSal SECG SIde WSel
- 'Crispa'	EMan EMon
§ ***japonicus***	MSal
macranthus	EFEx
- var. ***alba***	EFEx
sibiricus misapplied	see *L. japonicus*
sibiricus L.	CPom MSal SHGN SMad SPav

Leopoldia (*Hyacinthaceae*)

comosa	see *Muscari comosum*
spreitzenhoferi	see *Muscari spreitzenhoferi*
tenuiflora	see *Muscari tenuiflorum*

Lepechinia (*Lamiaceae*)

chamaedryoides	CHll CPLG
floribunda	CPle CSev
ganderi NNS 03-362	WCot
hastata	CBrd CMdw CPom EBee MWea XPep
salviae	CDTJ CDoC CPLG CPne EMan WBor

Lepidium (*Brassicaceae*)

campestre	CArn
latifolium	CArn MSal
peruvianum	MSal
ruderale	MSal
virginicum	MSal

Lepidothamnus (*Podocarpaceae*)

§ ***laxifolius***	WThu

Lepidozamia (*Zamiaceae*)

hopei	LPal
peroffskyana	CBrP LPal

Leptecophylla (*Epacridaceae*)

§ ***juniperina***	ECou
- 'Nana'	WThu
§ - subsp. ***parvifolia***	ECou

Leptinella (*Asteraceae*)

§ ***albida***	CStu
§ ***atrata***	ECho EDAr
- subsp. ***luteola***	EBee ECho MBrN WAbe
'County Park'	ECho ECou EDAr
§ ***dendyi***	ECho ECou EDAr EWes MHer NLAp NMen NSla WMAq
dioica	CTrC GBin
filicula	ECou
hispida	see *Cotula hispida*
§ ***minor***	ECou EDAr WMoo
pectinata var. ***sericea***	see *L. albida*
- subsp. ***villosa*** CC 475	NWCA
§ ***potentillina***	CTri EBee ECha ECho EWsh MBNS MRav MWgw NLar NRya SRms WPer WPtf
§ ***pyrethrifolia***	ECho EDAr GGar NLAp NMen SIng
- 'Macabe'	ECou
§ ***rotundata***	ECou
§ ***serrulata***	ECho MBar
§ ***squalida***	ECha ECho EDAr GBin GGar MBar NRya NSti STre
§ - 'Platt's Black'	CPBP CStu EBee ECha ECho EDAr EMan EShb EWes GEdr GGar GKev LEdu LRHS NLAp NSti NWCA SBch SIng SPet WFar WHoo WMoo WPat WPer WPrP WPtf WWFP
traillii	GGar

Leptocarpus (*Restionaceae*)

paniculatus new	LLWG
similis	CTrC
- BR 70	GGar

Leptocodon (*Campanulaceae*)

gracilis HWJK 2155	WCru

Leptodactylon ✿ (*Polemoniaceae*)

pungens	NLAp

Leptospermum (*Myrtaceae*)

'Centaurus' PBR	CWSG MNHC
citratum	see *L. petersonii*
* ***compactum***	CPLG
'Confetti'	ECou
'Copper Sheen' new	CBcs
'County Park Blush'	ECou
cunninghamii	see *L. myrtifolium*
'Electric Red' (Galaxy Series)	CBrm CWSG MNHC SLim WCot
ericoides	see *Kunzea ericoides*
flavescens misapplied	see *L. glaucescens*
flavescens Sm.	see *L. polygalifolium*
§ ***glaucescens***	CMHG ECou GGar

§ ***grandiflorum***	CTrG CWsd ELan EPfP GGar ISea LRHS SOWG SSpi WSHC
grandifolium	ECou
'Green Eyes'	ECou
'Havering Hardy'	ECou
humifusum	see *L. rupestre*
juniperinum	CTrC SPlb
laevigatum 'Yarrum'	ECou
§ ***lanigerum***	CBcs CMHG CPLG CTri ECou EPfP GGar ISea MGol SLim SOWG SPoG
- 'Cunninghamii'	see *L. myrtifolium*
- 'Wellington'	ECou
liversidgei	CChe ECou
macrocarpum	SOWG
minutifolium	ECou
morrisonii	ECou
§ ***myrtifolium***	CTri ECou EPla EWes GGar NLAp SDry SOWG SPer WPat
- 'Newnes Forest'	ECou
myrtifolium x ***scoparium***	ECou
nitidum	CTrC ECou GGar SOWG SPlb
- 'Cradle'	ECou
obovatum	CMHG
§ ***petersonii***	CArn ECou EOHP EShb EWin MHer SOWG
- 'Chlorinda'	ECou
phylicoides	see *Kunzea ericoides*
'Pink Falls'	ECou
'Pink Surprise'	ECou SOWG
§ ***polygalifolium***	ECou GGar MGol SPlb SRms
prostratum	see *L. rupestre*
pubescens	see *L. lanigerum*
'Red Cascade'	SWvt
rodwayanum	see *L. grandiflorum*
rotundifolium	CTrC ECou
§ ***rupestre*** ♀H4	CDoC CTri ECou EPot GGar MBar SDry SPlb SRms WFar WSHC
rupestre x ***scoparium***	ECou
scoparium	CArn CDul ECou ELau ERom EUnu MGol MNHC SPlb
- 'Adrianne'	ELan EPfP
- 'Autumn Glory'	CSBt CWSG ISea SLim
- 'Avocet'	ECou
- 'Black Robin'	SOWG
- 'Blossom' (d)	CBcs ECou SOWG WGer
- 'Boscawenii'	CBcs
- 'Burgundy Queen' (d)	CBcs CSBt ECou GGar
- 'Chapmanii'	CMHG CTrG GGar
- 'Coral Candy'	SOWG WGer
- 'County Park Pink'	ECou
- 'County Park Red'	ECou
- 'Dove Lake'	WAbe
- 'Elizabeth Jane'	GGar
- 'Essex'	ECou
- 'Fantasia'	ECou
- 'Fred's Red'	NLAp WPat
- 'Gaiety Girl' (d)	CSBt
- 'Grandiflorum'	WGer
- var. ***incanum*** 'Keatleyi' ♀H3	ECou SOWG
- - 'Wairere'	ECou
- 'Jubilee' (d)	CBcs CSBt ISea
- 'Kerry'	CAbP LRHS
- 'Leonard Wilson' (d)	CTri ECou EWes
- 'Lyndon'	ECou
- 'Martini'	CDoC CSBt CTrG SOWG WBor WWeb
- 'McLean'	ECou
- (Nanum Group) 'Huia'	CBcs
- - 'Kea'	CBcs CSBt ECou GGar MRav WGer
- - 'Kiwi' ♀H3	CAbP CBcs CCCN CDoC CDul CSBt CWSG ECou ELan EPfP EPot EWes GQui LRHS MAsh MDun SLim SPla WFar WGer
- - 'Kompakt'	EPot
- - 'Nanum'	ECou NMen SBod SIng
- - 'Pipit'	EPot EWes ITim WAbe
- - 'Tui'	CSBt CTrC
- 'Nichollsii' ♀H3	CTrC CTri GQui SOWG WSHC
- 'Nichollsii Nanum' ♀H2-3	CMea EPot ITim NLAp SIng SRms WPat WThu
- 'Pink Cascade'	CBcs CSBt CTri CWib GGar SLim
- 'Pink Damask'	SWvt
- 'Pink Splash'	ECou
- var. ***prostratum*** hort.	see *L. rupestre*
- 'Red Damask' (d) ♀H3	More than 30 suppliers
- 'Red Falls'	CBcs CPLG ECou SOWG
- 'Redpoll'	ECou
- 'Rosy Morn'	ISea
* - 'Ruby Wedding'	ELan EPfP LRHS MAsh SPla SPoG
- var. ***scoparium***	GGar
- 'Silver Spire'	SOWG
- 'Snow Flurry'	CBcs CTrC ENot MRav SBod SLim SPoG
- 'Sunraysia'	CSBt
- 'Winter Cheer'	CBcs LRHS WCot WWeb
- 'Wiri Joan' (d)	CBcs
- 'Wiri Kerry' (d)	SRGP
- 'Wiri Linda'	CBcs
- 'Wiri Sandra'	SRGP
- 'Zeehan'	ECou
sericeum	SOWG
'Silver Sheen' ♀H3	CEnd ECou ELan EPfP NLar SLon SPoG WPGP
'Snow Column'	ECou
spectabile	SOWG
sphaerocarpum	ECou
turbinatum	ECou
- 'Thunder Cloud'	ECou
'Wellington Dwarf'	ECou

Leschenaultia (*Goodeniaceae*)

'Angels Kiss'	ECou
biloba	ECou
- 'Big Blue'	SOWG
- 'Sky Blue'	ECou
'Blue Moon'	ECou
'Carnival'	ECou
* 'Eldorado'	SOWG
formosa red-flowered	ECou
- 'Scarlett O'Hara'	SOWG
- yellow-flowered	ECou
hirsuta	SOWG
pink-flowered	ECou
'Prima'	ECou

Lespedeza (*Papilionaceae*)

bicolor	CAgr CBcs CMen MGol NPal SEND WFar WHCG
- 'Yakushima'	CMen MGol NEgg NLar
buergeri	MBri NLar WSHC
capitata	MSal
floribunda	CMen
japonica	SPlb
thunbergii ♀H4	CBcs CMen CWib EBee ELan EMil EPfP IDee IMGH LHop LRHS MAsh MBlu MBri MGos NBlu SLon SOWG SPer SSpi SSta WFar WHCG WPGP WSHC
- 'Albiflora'	EPfP MBri
- 'Avalanche' **new**	NLar
- 'Pink Fountain' **new**	MBri
- 'Summer Beauty'	CBcs CDul EPfP MBri MGos NLar
tiliifolia	see *Desmodium elegans*

Lesquerella (*Brassicaceae*)

alpina	NWCA

Leucadendron (Proteaceae)

argenteum	CCCN CHEx CTrC SPlb
daphnoides	EShb SPlb
eucalyptifolium	CTrC EShb SPlb
galpinii	CTrC
'Inca Gold'	CBcs CTrC
'Maui Sunset'	CTrC
'Mrs Stanley'	CTrC
'Safari Sunset'	CAbb CBcs CCCN CDoC CTrC IDee LRHS WGer
salignum 'Early Yellow'	CAbb CTrC
- 'Fireglow'	CAbb CBcs CDoC CTrC IDee
strobilinum	CDoC CTrC
tinctum	EShb

Leucanthemella (Asteraceae)

§ ***serotina*** ♀H4	More than 30 suppliers
- 'Herbststern'	CFir NLar WDyG

Leucanthemopsis (Asteraceae)

§ ***alpina***	ECho
hosmariensis	see *Rhodanthemum hosmariense*
§ ***pectinata***	NSla
radicans	see *L. pectinata*

Leucanthemum ✿ (Asteraceae)

atlanticum	see *Rhodanthemum atlanticum*
catananche	see *Rhodanthemum catananche*
'Dipsy Daisy' **new**	WPer
graminifolium	EBee NBre WPer
hosmariense	see *Rhodanthemum hosmariense*
mawii	see *Rhodanthemum gayanum*
maximum misapplied	see *L.* x *superbum*
§ ***maximum*** (Ramond) DC.	NBro NPer WSpi
* - ***nanus***	WWeb
- ***uliginosum***	see *Leucanthemella serotina*
nipponicum	see *Nipponanthemum nipponicum*
§ x ***superbum***	EWsh MHer MLHP NBlu NVic SMac WFar
§ - 'Aglaia' (d) ♀H4	More than 30 suppliers
- 'Alaska'	CAni CPLG EBee EBla GMac LAst LEdu LHop LRHS MCot NGdn SPer SPur SWal SWvt WBor WFar WPer WRHF
- 'Amelia'	EBee NBre
- 'Anita Allen' (d)	CAni CElw CFee CPou EBee EBla MAvo NBre WCot WFar WPer
- 'Anna Camilla'	CAni
- 'Antwerp Star'	NBre NLar WBrk
- 'Banwell'	CAni
- 'Barbara Bush' (v/d)	EBee ECtt ELan ENot EPla ERou EShb GSki LAst LSou MBNS MDKP MFOX NBir NCob NEgg SPla SPoG SRGP SWvt WHil WWeb
§ - 'Beauté Nivelloise'	CAni CPrp EBla ECtt EPfP ERou MAvo MDKP MHar MLLN MMuc NBPC NBre NLar NPri SPoG SWat WCot WFar WPer WPrP WSpi
- 'Becky'	EBee ECha EPfP MAvo NBre NPro SPoG WHil
- 'Bishopstone'	CAni CSam EBee ELan ERou MAvo NBre WEas WPer
- 'Christine Hagemann'	CAni CPrp EBee MAvo MDKP MRav WAul WHoo
- 'Cobham Gold' (d)	CAni CElw CWCL EMan NBre NOrc
- 'Coconut Ice'	WPer
- 'Colwall'	CAni
- 'Crazy Daisy'	CAni CElw CMMP CTri CWib NBHF NBre NCob NLar SWal WHrl WRHF WSpi
- 'Devon Mist'	CAni
- 'Droitwich Beauty'	CAni EBee MAvo WCFE WHil WHoo WTel
- 'Duchess of Abercorn'	CAni CSam
- 'Dwarf Snow Lady'	NBre
- 'Easton Lady'	CAni
- 'Eclipse'	CAni MAvo
- 'Edgebrook Giant'	CAni MAvo
- 'Edward VII'	CAni
- 'Eisstern'	MAvo
- 'Elworthy Sparkler' **new**	CElw MAvo
- 'Esther Read' (d)	More than 30 suppliers
- 'Etoile d'Anvers'	EBee XPep
§ - 'Everest'	CAni CSam EBee NBre SRms
- 'Exhibition'	NBre
- 'Fiona Coghill' (d)	CAni CElw CMil EBee EBla ECtt EGle GBri LBMP MAvo MBnl MDKP MLLN NChi NGdn WCot WHil WHoo
- 'Firnglanz'	CAni CFwr GBin MAvo
- 'Goldrush' **new**	SPoG WRHF
- 'Gruppenstolz'	CAni GBin
- 'H. Seibert'	CAni CElw CEnt EBla MAvo
- 'Harry'	CAni
- 'Highland White Dream'PBR	ENot WFar WWeb
- 'Horace Read' (d)	CAni CElw CHar CMea CMil ELan EMon ERea MBri NBir SAga SBch WEas WPer WSpi
- 'Jennifer Read'	CAni CElw ERea MAvo WCot
§ - 'John Murray' (d)	CAni EBee EShb EWes GSki LRHS LSou MAvo NBir WAbb WCot WFar WHrl WTel
- 'Little Miss Muffet'	EBee EBla EPPr GBin GBri LBMP LRHS NCob NPro
- 'Little Princess'	see *L.* x *superbum* 'Silberprinzesschen'
- 'Majestic'	CAni
- 'Manhattan'	CAni CFwr CMdw EBee EBla EBrs EWes GBin GBuc LRHS NBre
- 'Margaretchen'	CAni MAvo
- 'Marion Bilsland'	CAni MBnl MDKP NChi
- 'Marion Collyer'	CAni
- 'Mayfield Giant'	CAni CTri ERou WPer
- 'Mount Everest'	see *L.* x *superbum* 'Everest'
- 'Octopus'	CAni EBee MAvo
- 'Old Court'	see *L.* x *superbum* 'Beauté Nivelloise'
- 'Phyllis Smith'	More than 30 suppliers
- 'Polaris'	EBee EShb NBre WMoo WSpi
- 'Rags and Tatters'	CAni EBee EWes MAvo
- 'Schneehurken'	CAni COlW EBee EBla MAvo SPoG STes
- 'Shaggy'	see *L.* x *superbum* 'Beauté Nivelloise'
§ - 'Silberprinzesschen'	CAni CPrp EBee EBla EPfP LRHS NMir NPri SPlb SRms WFar WHen WMoo WPer
- 'Silver Spoon'	EWll GBri WPer
- 'Snow Lady'	COlW EBee EShb LRHS NMir NPer NPri SPet SRms WFar WHen WWeb
- 'Snowcap'	EBee EBla EBrs ECha ENot EPfP EPla GSki LCro LRHS MBNS MBri MRav NEgg NGdn SPer SPla SWvt WCAu WTin
- 'Snowdrift'	CAni CMMP EBee EDAr EGoo MAvo NBre NPri WCot WHil WPer WWeb
§ - 'Sonnenschein'	More than 30 suppliers
- 'Starburst' (d)	SRms WHen
- 'Stina'	EBee
- 'Summer Snowball'	see *L.* x *superbum* 'John Murray'
- 'Sunny Killin'	CAni WTin
- 'Sunny Side Up'PBR	EBee ECtt EWes MBNS MLLN NLar
- Sunshine	see *L.* x *superbum* 'Sonnenschein'

§ - 'T.E. Killin' (d) 🏆[H4]	CElw CKno CPrp CSam EBee EBla EBrs ECha ECtt EGle EMan EPfP GMaP GSki LAst LBMP LHop LRHS MBnl MRav NChi WCAu WCot WFar WSpi
- 'White Iceberg' (d)	CAni WPer
- 'White Knight'	MWea NBre
- 'Wirral Pride'	CAni CCVN CHar EBee EGle ERou MAvo MBnl MBri NPri WCra WMnd
§ - 'Wirral Supreme' (d) 🏆[H4]	More than 30 suppliers
'Tizi-n-Test'	see *Rhodanthemum catananche* 'Tizi-n-Test'
§ ***vulgare***	CArn CBgR CRWN EPfP GWCH LEdu MHer MNHC NLan NMir NPri NSco SBch SECG SIde WBVN WBrk WHen WHer WJek WShi
- 'Avondale' (v)	MAvo NGdn
- 'Filigran'	CAby EShb GMac NBre SIde
§ - 'Maikönigin'	CBgR EBee GAbr NBre NNor WHrl
- May Queen	see *L. vulgare* 'Maikönigin'
- 'Sunny'	CBre EBla EWes
'White Knight'	MBri MCCP

Leucocoryne (*Alliaceae*)

alliacea	ECho
'Andes'	EBrs ECho
'Caravelle'	EBrs ECho
hybrids	EBrs ECho
ixioides	ECho
* - ***alba***	EBrs ECho
purpurea 🏆[H1]	CGrW EBrs ECho LRHS

Leucogenes (*Asteraceae*)

grandiceps	NSla WAbe
leontopodium	EPot GEdr GGar NLAp NSla WAbe
tarahaoa	WAbe

Leucojum (*Amaryllidaceae*)

aestivum	CBcs CFee EBee EBrs ECho EPfP GCrs LAma LHop LRHS MDun NHol SPer SRms WBVN WBor WCot WEas WFar WLin WShi
- 'Gravetye Giant' 🏆[H4]	More than 30 suppliers
autumnale	see *Acis autumnalis*
longifolium	see *Acis longifolia*
roseum	see *Acis rosea*
tingitanum	see *Acis tingitana*
trichophyllum	see *Acis trichophylla*
valentinum	see *Acis valentina*
vernum 🏆[H4]	CBgR CPLG CStu CTca EBrs ECho EHrv ELan EPfP EPot GCrs GKev LAma LRHS MDun MNrw MRav NHol NMen SPhx SRms WAbe WCot WFar WHer WShi
- var. ***carpathicum***	CLAP EBrs ECha ECho EHrv GEdr MRav NMen WAbe
- 'Podpolozje'	CHHB
- var. ***vagneri***	CLAP EBee ECha EHrv EMon GEdr LFox LHop NPol WSHC WTin

Leucophyllum (*Scrophulariaceae*)

frutescens	SOWG XPep
minus	XPep

Leucophysalis (*Solanaceae*)

sinensis BWJ 8093 new	WCru

Leucophyta (*Asteraceae*)

§ ***brownii***	CStu ECou EMan EShb EWin LAst XPep

Leucopogon (*Epacridaceae*)

§ ***colensoi***	GCrs MBar MBri NLar NWCA WBod WPat
ericoides	GKev MBar
§ ***fasciculatus***	ECou
§ ***fraseri***	ECou GCrs GEdr WThu
§ ***parviflorus***	ECou

x *Leucoraoulia* (*Asteraceae*)

hybrid (*Raoulia hectorii* x *Leucogenes grandiceps*)	SIng WAbe
§ ***loganii***	CPBP NSla NWCA WAbe

Leucosceptrum (*Lamiaceae*)

canum	CPLG CTrG
- GWJ 9424	WCru
stellipilum var. ***formosanum***	WSHC
- - B&SWJ 1804	WCru
- var. ***tosaense*** B&SWJ 8892	WCru

Leucospermum (*Proteaceae*)

cordifolium	SOWG
'Scarlet Ribbon'	CCCN CTrC

Leucothoe (*Ericaceae*)

axillaris 'Curly Red'[PBR]	CBcs CWSG EBee ELan EMil ENot EPfP LBuc LRHS MAsh MGos NLar SPoG
- 'Scarletta'	see *L.* Scarletta = 'Zeblid'
Carinella = 'Zebekot'	MBri MGos SPoG
davisiae	EPfP
§ ***fontanesiana*** 🏆[H4]	CMac EPfP LRHS NEgg STre
- SDR 2249	GKev
- 'Nana'	LRHS
- 'Rainbow' (v)	More than 30 suppliers
- 'Rollissonii' 🏆[H4]	MBar MRav SRms
keiskei	EPfP LRHS
- 'Minor'	SSta
- 'Royal Ruby'	CWSG EBee EPfP MGos NCGa NHol NLar SPoG WFar WMoo
Lovita = 'Zebonard'	CEnd CSam LRHS MBri MGos MRav NCGa NLar SCoo
populifolia	see *Agarista populifolia*
racemosa	NLar
Red Lips = 'Lipsbolwi'[PBR]	CDoC EBee ENot MGos NBPN NLar NScw
§ Scarletta = 'Zeblid'	More than 30 suppliers
walteri	see *L. fontanesiana*

Leuzea (*Asteraceae*)

centaureoides	see *Stemmacantha centaureoides*
* ***conifera macrocephala***	WAbe

Levisticum (*Apiaceae*)

officinale	CArn CBod CHby CHrt CPrp CSev ELau EUnu GPoy LEdu MBar MHer MNHC NBid NBlu NGHP SDix SECG SIde SPlb SWat WBrk WHer WPer WSel
I - 'Magnus'	ELau

Lewisia ✿ (*Portulacaceae*)

'Archangel'	NRya
Ashwood Carousel hybrids	CPBP ECho GCrs MAsh NHar
'Ashwood Pearl'	MAsh
'Ben Chace'	MAsh
Birch strain	CBcs ECho ELan
brachycalyx 🏆[H2]	CGra ECho EWes MTho
cantelovii	MAsh
columbiana	ITim MAsh NWCA WAbe
- 'Alba'	GCrs MAsh NLAp WAbe
- 'Rosea'	GCrs MAsh NLAp NSla WAbe WGor
- subsp. ***rupicola***	LTwo MAsh NDlv WLin
- subsp. ***wallowensis***	MAsh NMen WGor

congdonii	MAsh
'Constant Comment'	NBhm
cotyledon ΨH4	ECho GKev LRHS LTwo MNrw WBrE WFar WPat
- J&JA 12959	NWCA
- f. ***alba***	EDAr LHop MAsh NWCA
- 'Ashwood Ruby'	MAsh
- Ashwood strain	CTri CWCL ECho ENot EPfP EWes LBee LRHS LSou MAsh SRms WGor
- Crags hybrids	SRms
- 'Fransi'	EDAr NLar
- var. ***howellii***	LTwo SRms WGor
- hybrids	ECho EDAr GGar GKev ITim LHop NBlu SIng SPoG WBVN WGor
- 'John's Special'	GCrs
- magenta	EDAr MAsh WGor
- 'Praline' (d)	EDAr
§ - 'Regenbogen' mixed	WGor WPer
- 'Snowstorm' **new**	GKev
- Sunset Group ΨH4	EAlp LAst MHer NLar NWCA SRms WPer WRHF
- 'White Splendour'	SIng
'George Henley'	ECho EPfP EWes MAsh NMen NRya SIng WAbe
glandulosa NNS 02-210	NWCA
leeana	MAsh
'Little Peach'	CBrm EDAr GCrs ITim MSte SIng WPer
'Little Plum'	CMea CPBP EDAr EPfP GCrs GKev ITim MAsh MDKP MSte NCGa NDlv NLar NRya NSla NWCA SIng WGor WPer
§ ***longipetala***	NSla
§ ***nevadensis***	ECho ERos GEdr GGar ITim LRHS MAsh MNrw MTho NMen NRya NWCA SRms SRot WHoo WLin WPer
- ***bernardina***	see *L. nevadensis*
- 'Rosea'	EPot GCrs MAsh NWCA WAbe
oppositifolia	EDAr ITim MAsh
'Pinkie'	CPBP EDAr GCrs ITim LTwo MAsh NLAp NMen
pygmaea	CGra EAlp ECho EDAr EWes GCrs GEdr GGar GKev ITim LAst LRHS MAsh MHer NBir NLAp NMen NRya WAbe WPer
- ***alba***	GKev
- subsp. ***longipetala***	see *L. longipetala*
Rainbow mixture	see *L. cotyledon* 'Regenbogen' mixed
'Rawreth'	LTwo WAbe
rediviva	ECho EWes GCrs GEdr GKev ITim NLAp NWCA WAbe
- Jolon strain	WGor
- subsp. ***minor***	CGra WAbe
serrata	MAsh
sierrae	EDAr MAsh WPer
stebbinsii	NWCA
'Trevosia'	MAsh
tweedyi ΨH2	CGra EPfP GCrs ITim LHop LRHS MAsh NBir NWCA SIng WGor
- 'Alba'	GCrs ITim LRHS MAsh
- 'Elliott's Variety'	MAsh WGor
- 'Rosea'	LHop LRHS SIng WGor

Leycesteria (*Caprifoliaceae*)

crocothyrsos	CAbP CArn CBcs CBgR CHEx CHid CWib EBee ELan EPfP EShb GQui MFOX NBid SLon SMad SPoG WFar WSHC
formosa ΨH4	More than 30 suppliers
- brown-stemmed	IFoB
- Golden Lanterns = 'Notbruce'PBR	CDoC EBee EMil ENot EPfP EPla EQua IDee LBuc MBri MGos MMHG NLar NPri SCoo SPoG
- 'Golden Pheasant' (v)	CPMA ERas
- 'Purple Rain'	EBee EMil EQua EWes MBri NLar
'Smouldering Embers' **new**	WLeb

Leymus (*Poaceae*)

from Falkland Islands	EPPr
§ ***arenarius***	More than 30 suppliers
condensatus 'Canyon Prince'	CKno
hispidus	see *Elymus hispidus*
'Niveus'	EHul
§ ***racemosus***	CHrt LRav

Lhotzkya see *Calytrix*

Liatris (*Asteraceae*)

aspera	GSki NBre WPer
elegans	GSki NBre NLar SPlb WPer
lancifolia	EBee
ligulistylis	EBee GSki NBPC NBre NLar WPer
punctata	NBre
pycnostachya	CFis CRWN EBee MHar MLLN NLar SRms WPer
- 'Alexandra'	EBee
scariosa 'Alba'	EBee NBPC NLar WPer
- 'Gracious'	CPLG EWll
- 'Magnifica'	CBcs
§ ***spicata***	More than 30 suppliers
- 'Alba'	COlW CPrp CSBt EBee ECha ECtt ELan ENot EPfP EShb GSki LAma LAst LEdu LSRN MNFA MNrw NEgg NGdn NRnb SPer SPlb WBrE WCAu WHoo WPer
- ***callilepis***	see *L. spicata*
- 'Floristan Violett'	CBrm EBee EHrv EPPr EPfP GMaP LBMP LRHS MHer MWgw MWrn NEgg SCoo SPlb SPoG SWvt WFar WGwG WMnd WMoo WPer WWeb
- 'Floristan Weiss'	CArn CBrm CElw COlW EBee EBrs EHrv ELau EMar EPPr EPfP GBuc GMaP LBMP LRHS MHer MRav MWgw MWrn NCGa NPri SPla SPoG SWvt WFar WGwG WMnd WMoo WPer WWeb
- Goblin	see *L. spicata* 'Kobold'
§ - 'Kobold'	More than 30 suppliers

Libertia ✿ (*Iridaceae*)

sp.	WPGP
HCM 98.089	CDes EBee
'Amazing Grace'	CDes EBee IBlr SBch WPGP
Ballyrogan hybrid	IBlr
* ***breunioides***	CPLG
caerulescens	CBgR CCVN CDMG CPLG EBee ECho EDAr EMan ERos GKev GSki IFoB IGor NBid NBir NLar NRnb SBch SGar SMad SMrm WCot WFar WHer WKif WMoo WPGP
chilensis	see *L. formosa*
elegans	CPLG GBuc IBlr
§ ***formosa***	More than 30 suppliers
- brown-stemmed	IBlr IFoB
grandiflora ΨH4	More than 30 suppliers
- stoloniferous	GGar
ixioides	CBcs CKno EBee EBrs ECha ECho ECou EMan EShb GSki IBlr LEdu MAvo NGdn NSti SBod WCFE WFoF WPGP WPic WRHF WSpi WWeb
- hybrid	SDix
- 'Tricolor'	CPen EBee EMan GBuc GGar IBlr SPer WMoo WPat
'Nelson Dwarf'	ECho
paniculata	CPLG WSHC
peregrinans	More than 30 suppliers

– East Cape form IBlr
– 'Gold Leaf' CBcs CBgR CBow CCCN CElw CPrp CTri CWil CWsd EHrv IBlr LAst SMad WCot WCru WFar WHoo WPic WTMC
* ***procera*** CPLG CSpe EBee EPla IBlr LEdu SKHP WPGP WSHC
pulchella CWsd IBlr
– Tasmanian form ECho
sessiliflora CElw CFee EBee ECho IBlr NBir WFar WPGP
– RB 94073 SMad
Shackleton hybrid IBlr
'Taupo Sunset'[PBR] **new** CHid CMil ETod GBin SKHP

Libocedrus (*Cupressaceae*)

chilensis see *Austrocedrus chilensis*
decurrens see *Calocedrus decurrens*

Libonia see *Justicia*

Licuala (*Arecaceae*)

grandis MBri
spinosa LPal

Ligularia ✿ (*Asteraceae*)

B&SWJ 2977 WCru
BWJ 7686 from China WCru
CC 4911 MGol
amplexicaulis GWJ 9404 WCru
'Britt Marie Crawford'[PBR] More than 30 suppliers
'Cheju Charmer' LEdu WCru
clivorum see *L. dentata*
§ ***dentata*** CPLG EBee ECtt EPfP LBMP MMuc NBro NEgg NGby NLar SRms SWat WBVN WFar WWeb
– 'Dark Beauty' CBcs ERou EWll GSki IBal NBre WMnd
– 'Desdemona' 🏆H4 More than 30 suppliers
– 'Dunkellaubig' MBNS
– 'Enkelrig' MBNS
– 'Orange Princess' NPer WPer
– 'Orange Queen' NBre WFar WWeb
– 'Othello' More than 30 suppliers
– 'Sommergold' EBee ECha GSki WFar
§ ***fischeri*** CBct GSki LEdu NBre WCot WPer
– B&SWJ 1158 WFar
– B&SWJ 2570 WCru
– B&SWJ 4478 WCru
– B&SWJ 5540 WCru
– B&SWJ 5841 WCru
§ 'Gregynog Gold' 🏆H4 CBct EBee ECha EGle EMFW EPfP ERou GAbr GMaP GSki LRHS MRav MWgw NBro NCGa NCob NEgg NGdn NOrc SDnm SPav SPer WCru WFar
x ***hessei*** EBee GMaP GSki NLar SWat WFar WPnP
hodgsonii CKno EBee EBla EPPr GSki LEdu MBri MSte WFar WPer
intermedia WFar
– B&SWJ 606a WCru
japonica CHar EBee ECha GCra GSki LEdu NLar WFar WPnP
– B&SWJ 2883 WCru
– 'Rising Sun' WCru
aff. ***kaialpina*** B&SWJ 5806 WCru
– B&SWJ 6185 EBee
'Laternchen' EBee NBro NMoo
'Little Rocket'[PBR] GBin NBro
macrophylla WFar
x ***palmatiloba*** see *L.* x *yoshizoeana* 'Palmatiloba'
§ ***przewalskii*** 🏆H4 More than 30 suppliers
– 'Light Fingered' NBre
sachalinensis EBee
sibirica CSam GAbr GSki NLar WFar WLin WMoo WPer WPnP
– B&SWJ 5806 WCru
– var. ***speciosa*** see *L. fischeri*
smithii see *Senecio smithii*
soldanella **new** EBee
speciosa see *L. fischeri*
stenocephala EBee EMil MCot NBro NLar SWat WFar
– B&SWJ 283 WCru
– BWJ 7964 from China **new** WCru
'Sungold' CBct CSam EBee EBla GBin NCGa NGdn WCot WPnP
tangutica see *Sinacalia tangutica*
'The Rocket' 🏆H4 More than 30 suppliers
tsangchanensis NEgg
tussilaginea see *Farfugium japonicum*
– 'Aureo-maculata' see *Farfugium japonicum* 'Aureomaculatum'
veitchiana CBct CHEx EBee EBla EMFW EPfP GAbr GGar GKev LAst LEdu MSte NCGa NCob NEgg SDnm SPav SWat WCAu WFar WPnP WTMC
vorobievii CHar EBee EKen GSki MBNS NLar WLin
'Weihenstephan' LRHS MBri
wilsoniana CBct CHEx EBee ECtt ERas MLLN MRav NBre SDnm SPav SWat WCAu WFar
§ x ***yoshizoeana*** 'Palmatiloba' CFir CHEx EBee EBla ELan EPla EWTr GSki LEdu LRHS MRav NSti SDnm SPav SPhx SWat WCot WFar WPnP
'Zepter' EBee EBla GBuc MBri NLar WCot WFar

Ligusticum (*Apiaceae*)

lucidum CDul CMCN EBee EPfP MSal SEND SPhx WFar WPGP
– subsp. ***lucidum*** CSpe
porteri MSal
§ ***scoticum*** CArn CSpe ECrN EKen EOHP EWTr EWes GPoy ILis ITer MDKP MHer MSal NLar NSti WFar WHrl WJek WOut WPtf
striatum B&SWJ 7259 WCru

Ligustrum ✿ (*Oleaceae*)

chenaultii see *L. compactum*
§ ***compactum*** NLar
§ ***delavayanum*** EPfP EQua ERom LPan MBar MGos SAPC SArc SBLw STrG WFar WSpi
ibota NLar
ionandrum see *L. delavayanum*
japonicum CHEx ECrN LPan SBLw SEND SPer WFar XPep
I – 'Aureum' MGos
– 'Coriaceum' see *L. japonicum* 'Rotundifolium'
* – 'Coriaceum Aureum' **new** EMil
– 'Macrophyllum' EPfP MAsh
§ – 'Rotundifolium' CAbP CBcs CDoC CDul CHEx CPLG CPle EBee ELan EMil EPfP EPla LRHS MAsh MGos MRav SBod SCoo SMad SPer SPoG WCFE WFar
– 'Silver Star' (v) CPMA EBee MGos NLar SLon
§ – 'Texanum' EWes NLar
lucidum 🏆H4 CDoC CSBt CTri ECrN ELan LAst MBar MGos MRav MSwo NLar NWea SAPC SArc SPer SWvt WBVN WFar XPep
– 'Aureovariegatum' (v) NEgg
– 'Excelsum Superbum' (v) 🏆H4 CAbP CBcs CDul CLnd CPMA ELan EPfP LAst LPan LRHS MAsh

	MBar MGos NBlu SBLw SPer SPoG SSpi
- 'Golden Wax'	CAbP CPMA IDee MRav
- 'Tricolor' (v)	CPMA EBee ELan EPfP LRHS NLar SHBN SPer SPla SSpi SWvt WFar
obtusifolium 'Darts Perfecta'	SLPl
- var. ***regelianum***	WFar
ovalifolium	CBcs CCVT CChe CDoC CDul CHll CLnd CSBt CTri ECrN EMac EPfP LBuc LCro LRHS MBar MBri MGos MSwo NBlu NWea SBLw SLim SPer SWvt WMou
§ - 'Argenteum' (v)	CBcs CDoC CDul CPLG CTri CWib EBee ECrN LBuc LRHS MAsh MBar MBri MWat NBlu NEgg NHol SLim SPer SPla SPoG SWvt WFar WTel
- 'Aureomarginatum'	see *L. ovalifolium* 'Aureum'
§ - 'Aureum' (v) ♀H4	More than 30 suppliers
- 'Lemon and Lime' (v)	EBee EMil MGos SCoo SWvt
- 'Variegatum'	see *L. ovalifolium* 'Argenteum'
quihoui ♀H4	ECre ELan EPfP IDee MBri MWea SDix SKHP SLon SMad SPer SSpi WFar WHCG WPat
sempervirens	EPfP NLar SLon
sinense	CMCN EPfP MRav WFar
- 'Multiflorum'	CPLG CWib WFar
- 'Pendulum'	EPla
- var. ***stauntonii***	NLar
- 'Variegatum' (v)	CBgR CPMA EBee EPla EWes LHop MRav SPer
- 'Wimbei'	EPla WFar
strongylophyllum	CDoC WFar
texanum	see *L. japonicum* 'Texanum'
tschonoskii	NLar
undulatum 'Lemon Lime and Clippers'	EBee NLar SLim SPoG WMoo
'Vicaryi'	CPMA EBee ELan EMil EPfP EPla EQua EWTr IArd LRHS MAsh MBar MGos NPro SPer SPla WFar
vulgare	CBcs CCVT CDul CRWN CTri CWan ECrN EMac EPfP LAst LBuc MSwo NWea SHFr SWvt WBVN WMou WSFF XPep
- 'Atrovirens' **new**	EMac
- 'Aureovariegatum' (v)	CNat
- 'Lodense'	MBar

Lilium ✿ (*Liliaceae*)

Chen Yi 1	WCot
'Acapulco' (VIId)	EBrs LAma
African Queen Group (VIa) ♀H4	EBrs ECot GBuc LAma SCoo SPer WFar
- 'African Queen' (VIa)	CSut EBrs EPfP LRHS MCri SPer
albanicum	see *L. pyrenaicum* subsp. *carniolicum* var. *albanicum*
'Algarve' **new**	MBri
amabile (IX)	LRHS
- 'Luteum' (IX)	LRHS WWst
'Amber Gold' (Ic)	CLAP
America = 'Holean' (Ia)	IBal
amoenum (IX)	EBee EPot
'Apeldoorn' (Ic)	LRHS MCri NNor
'Aphrodite' (Ia/d)	EBrs
'Apollo' (Ia) ♀H4	EBrs GBuc GKev LAma LRHS MBri
'Arena' (VIIb)	EPfP LRHS SCoo SPer WFar
'Ariadne' (Ic)	CLAP
* Asiatic hybrids (VI/VII)	LAma NGdn SGar
auratum (IX)	CHHB EBee EBrs ECho EFEx EPfP GBuc
- 'Gold Band'	see *L. auratum* var. *platyphyllum*
§ - var. ***platyphyllum*** (IX)	GBuc MCri SBch
- Red Band Group (IX)	WFar
- var. ***virginale*** (IX)	LRHS WWst
'Avignon' (Ia)	LRHS MCri
'Bach' **new**	MBri
Backhouse hybrids (II)	CLAP
bakerianum (IX)	GEdr LAma
- var. ***aureum***	CHHB EBee WWst
- var. ***delavayi*** (IX)	CHHB LAma
- var. ***roseum*** **new**	CHHB
- var. ***rubrum***	LAma
'Barbara North' (Ic)	CLAP
'Barbaresco' (VII)	SCoo SPer
'Barcelona' (Ia)	MNrw NNor
Bellingham Group (IV)	CLAP GBuc GEdr
'Bergamo' (VIId)	EPfP LEdu SCoo WFar
'Bianco Uno'	MBri
'Black Beauty' (VIId)	CAvo CFFs CLAP EBrs EPfP ERCP GBuc GGar LAma LCro LRHS MCri MSte NNor
'Black Bird'	NBPN
'Black Dragon' (VIa)	MCri
'Black Jack'PBR	IBal NBPC NBPN
'Black Tie' **new**	MCri
'Blazing Dwarf' (Ia)	MBri
'Bright Pixie'	IBal
'Bright Star' (VIb)	LAma MCri
'Bronwen North' (Ic)	CLAP
brownii (IX)	EBee EBrs ECho LAma MCri WWst
- var. ***australe*** (IX) B&SWJ 4082	WCru
bulbiferum	ECho GBuc
- var. ***croceum*** (IX)	ECho
Bullwood hybrids (IV)	CLAP
'Bums' (Ia/d)	EMon
'Butter Pixie'PBR (Ia)	IBal LAma WGor
callosum	EBee
§ ***canadense*** (IX)	GBuc LAma WWst
- var. ***coccineum*** (IX)	CLAP GBuc WWst
- var. ***flavum***	see *L. canadense*
'Cancun' (Ia)	EPot LRHS
candidum (IX) ♀H4	CArn CAvo CBcs CHar CTca CTri EBrs ECha EHrv ELan EPfP EPot ERCP IBal IHer LAma LRHS MAvo MCri MHer NGHP SPer WBrE WCot WHil WSpi
- 'Plenum' (IX/d)	EMon
carniolicum	see *L. pyrenaicum* subsp. *carniolicum*
'Casa Blanca' (VIIb) ♀H4	CAvo CFFs CSut CTca EBrs EPfP GBuc GKev IBal LAma LRHS MCri NBir SCoo SPer WFar
'Casa Rosa' (V)	CSWP MCri NBir SWat
'Centrefold'	GBuc NNor
cernuum (IX)	CHHB CLAP EBee EBrs ECho LAma MCri SPer WPrP
* - 'Album'	CHHB EBrs SPer
'Chianti' (Ia)	CSut
'Chinook' (Ia)	NNor
'Chippendale' (Ic)	CLAP
'Cinnabar' (Ia)	MCri
Citronella Group (Ic)	EBrs ECho LAma LRHS MCri NNor WFar
columbianum (IX)	CLAP EBrs ECho GBuc GCrs GEdr NMen
- B&SWJ 9564	WCru
- dwarf (IX)	EBrs ECho NMen
'Compass' (Ia)	MBri
'Con Amore' (VIIb)	LRHS SCoo SPer WFar
'Conca d'Or'PBR NNS 03-377	WWst
'Connecticut King' (Ia)	EPfP LAma MCri
'Coral Butterflies'	CLAP
'Corina' (Ia)	GBuc NNor SGar
'Costa Del Sol' **new**	EBrs
'Côte d'Azur' (Ia)	EPot GKev LAma LRHS NNor SBch SRms WGor
'Coulance' (VIId)	EBrs
'Courier'PBR **new**	CAvo CFFs

x ***dalhansonii*** (IX)	CLAP WCot
§ - 'Marhan' (II)	CLAP EBee GCrs
§ ***dauricum*** (IX)	EBee GCrs
davidii (IX)	CLAP EBee EBrs ECho GEdr LAma MCri WCru
§ - var. ***willmottiae*** (IX)	CLAP EBee WCot
'Denia' (Ib)	IBal SPoG
'Diabora'	GBuc
distichum	EBee
- B&SWJ 794	WCru
'Dizzy'	LRHS MCri
'Doeskin' (Ic)	CLAP
duchartrei (IX)	CLAP EBee EBrs ECho ERCP GBuc GCrs GEdr LAma NSla SMac WAbe WCru
§ 'Ed' (VII)	EBee LAma NNor
'Eileen North' (Ic)	CLAP GBuc
'Electric' (Ia)	LRHS NNor
'Ellen Willmott' (II)	CLAP
'Elodie' PBR **new**	CAvo CFFs
'Enchantment' (Ia)	IBal LAma MBri NNor
'Eros'	CLAP
'Eurydike' (Ic)	CLAP
'Evelina'	EBrs LRHS
'Everest' (VIId)	NNor
'Fairest' (Ib-c/d)	CLAP
'Fancy Joy'	MBri
fargesii (IX)	CExc EBee GEdr
'Farolito'	LBuc LRHS
'Fata Morgana' (Ia/d) ♀H4	EBrs EPfP LRHS SCoo
'Feuerzauber' (Ia)	SPer
'Fire King' (Ib)	ECGP LAma MCri NBir SCoo WFar
formosanum (IX)	EBee EBrs ECho GBin GMac LFur MAsh MCri WCot
- B&SWJ 1589	WCru
- var. ***pricei*** (IX)	CMea EBrs ECho EDAr ELan ENot EPot GEdr GGar LBee LRHS MHer MNrw NLAp NMen NWCA SCoo SRot WBVN WHer WPer
- 'Snow Queen' (IX)	CHHB MCri
- 'White Swan' (IX)	GBuc
'Fresco' (VII)	ECho
'Garden Party' (VII) ♀H4	EBrs LRHS WFar
'Gibraltar' (Ia)	MCri
'Glossy Wings'	GBuc NNor
'Golden Joy'	MBri
'Golden Melody' (Ia)	MCri
Golden Splendor Group (VIa) ♀H4	CFwr EBrs LAma LRHS MCri SCoo SMeo SPer SWat
'Gran Cru' (Ia) ♀H4	EBrs EWll MCri NNor SPad
'Gran Paradiso' (Ia)	MCri SRms
grayi (IX)	CLAP
'Green Magic' (VIa)	MCri NNor
hansonii (IX)	CLAP EBee EBrs ECha ECho GEdr IBlr LAma MCri
- B&SWJ 4756	WCru
'Heloma' (Ia) **new**	EBrs
henryi (IX) ♀H4	CAvo CFFs CFwr CLAP CSWP EBee EBrs ECho EPfP IHer ITer LAma LRHS MCri SMeo SPhx WCot WCru WPrP
- var. ***citrinum***	CLAP ECho
'Hit Parade' (VII)	LAma
x ***hollandicum***	MCri
'Honeymoon'	SPoG WWeb
'Hotlips'	EPfP LRHS SPer
'Ibarra' **new**	MCri
Imperial Silver Group (VIIc)	LAma
'Inzell' (Ia)	EBrs
'Jacqueline'	CFwr EBrs GKev LRHS
'Jacques S. Dijt' (II)	CLAP
japonicum (IX)	EFEx WCru
- 'Albomarginatum' (IX)	GEdr WWst
'Journey's End' (VIId)	GBuc LAma LRHS NNor
§ 'Joy' (VIIb) ♀H4	LAma LRHS MCri NNor
'Karen North' (Ic)	CLAP
§ ***kelleyanum*** (IX)	CLAP GBuc
- NNS 02-227	WWst
- NNS 98-373	WCot WWst
kelloggii (IX)	WCot
- NNS 03-379	WWst
kesselringianum	EBrs
'King Pete' (Ib) ♀H4	EBrs
'Kiss Proof' (VIIb)	LRHS
'Lady Alice' (VI)	CLAP EBrs NBPC
'Lady Bowes Lyon' (Ic) **new**	CWsd
§ ***lancifolium*** (IX)	CArn CHEx CHid CTca GBin WBVN WBrk WFar
- B&SWJ 539	WCru
* - ***album***	WBor
- Farrer's form	EBee LFur WCot
- var. ***flaviflorum*** (IX)	CLAP EBee EBrs GBuc GCrs MCri MSte
- 'Flore Pleno' (IX/d)	CLAP CMil CSWP CSam CTca EBee EBrs EMon EPPr GAbr GBuc GSki ITer LHop LRHS MHer NBir NSti WBrk WCot WCru WFar WHil WTin
* - var. ***forrestii*** (IX) **new**	MCri
- Forrest's form (IX)	CLAP CPMA
- var. ***fortunei*** (IX) B&SWJ 4352	WCru
- var. ***splendens*** (IX) ♀H4	EBee EBrs ECho EPfP GKev LAma LRHS MCri NNor WBor
'Landini'	NBPN
lankongense (IX)	CLAP GEdr ITim LAma MCri
'Last Dance' (Ic)	CLAP
'Le Rêve'	see *L.* 'Joy'
leichtlinii	CHHB CLAP EBee EBrs ECho EPot IHer MCri
- B&SWJ 4519	WCru
- var. ***maximowiczii***	EBee
'Lemon Pixie' PBR (Ia)	LAma
leucanthum (IX)	EBee LAma
- var. ***centifolium*** (IX)	EBee MCri WCru WWst
lijiangense	GEdr
'Lollypop' (Ia)	EBrs EPfP LRHS MNrw NNor SCoo
longiflorum (IX) ♀H2-3	EBee EBrs ECho LAma LCro LRHS MCri SCoo
- B&SWJ 4885	WCru
§ - 'Carmel'	IBal
- 'Memories'	MBri SPoG
- 'Mount Carmel'	see *L. longiflorum* 'Carmel'
§ - 'White American' (IX)	CSWP EBrs EPfP LRHS SPer
lophophorum (IX)	CHHB EBee EPot ITer LAma WCru WWst
'Lovely Girl' (VIIb)	EBrs
'Luxor' (Ib)	EBrs EPfP EWll LRHS MCri NBir SPer
mackliniae (IX)	CLAP CWCL EBee EBrs ECho GBuc GCra GCrs GEdr GGGa GMaP GMac IBlr ITim NMen NWCA SBla WAbe WBVN WHal
- deep pink-flowered **new**	GGGa
- robust habit	GGar WWst
x ***maculatum*** var. ***davuricum***	see *L. dauricum*
- Japanese double (IX)	EMon
'Magento' (1a) **new**	LRHS
'Marco Polo' (Ia)	LEdu SCoo WFar
'Marhan'	see *L.* x *dalhansonii* 'Marhan'
martagon (IX) ♀H4	More than 30 suppliers
- var. ***album*** (IX) ♀H4	CAvo CFFs CLAP CSWP EBee EBrs ECGP ECha EHrv ELan EPfP EPot GBuc GEdr LAma LCro LRHS MTho MWgw NBir NChi SPhx SRms WAbe WCot WShi
- var. ***cattaniae*** (IX)	MCri WCot
- - 'The Moor' (IXb/d) **new**	SKHP
- 'Inshriach' (IX)	WCot

	Name	Suppliers
	- 'Plenum' (IX/d)	EMon WCot
*	- var. ***rubrum*** new	MWgw
	'Maxwill' (Ic)	CLAP EBrs
	medeoloides (IX)	CLAP EBee EBrs ECho EFEx EPot GBuc GCrs GGGa NMen WCot
	'Mediterrannee' (VIIb/d)	LRHS
	'Menton'	MCri
	michiganense (IX)	CSWP GBuc GCrs
	'Milano' (Ia)	MCri
	'Miss Lucy'[PBR] (d)	CSut LRHS
	'Miss Rio' (VII)	LRHS SCoo
	'Mona Lisa' (VIIb/d)	EBrs EPfP EPot IBal LAma LAst LRHS MBri NNor WBVN WFar
§	***monadelphum*** (IX)	CLAP CWsd EBee EBrs ECho EPot GBuc GCra LAma NLar SPhx
	- pale yellow-coloured	WWst
	'Mont Blanc' (Ia)	NBir
	'Montana'	LRHS
	'Monte Negro' (Ia)	EBrs IBal
	'Montreal' (VIIb) new	LRHS
	'Montreux' (Ia)	LAma
	'Mr Ed'	see *L.* 'Ed'
	'Mr Ruud'	see *L.* 'Ruud'
	'Mrs Backhouse'	see *L.* 'Mrs R.O. Backhouse'
§	'Mrs R.O. Backhouse' (II)	CLAP CTca EBee EBrs GEdr MSte
	'Muscadet'[PBR] (VII)	CSut EBrs LEdu LRHS
§	***nanum*** (IX)	EBee EBrs ECho GBuc GCrs GEdr GGGa LAma NMen WCru WHal WWst
	- AGS/ES	WWst
	- ex EMAK new	NMen
	- from Bhutan (IX)	EBee EBrs ECho GBuc GCrs GEdr NMen WCru
	- var. ***flavidum*** (IX)	EBee EBrs GEdr NMen
	nepalense (IX)	CBcs CFwr CHid CLAP CSWP CTca EBee EBla EBrs ECho EPot ERCP GCrs GEdr GGar IHer ITer LAma LHop LRHS MCri MDun NCob SBla SSvw WCot WCru WFar WPnP
	- B&SWJ 2985	WCru
	nobilissimum (IX)	EFEx
	'Noblesse' (VII)	LRHS
	'Novo Cento' ♀[H4]	MCri
	'Odeon'	MCri
	'Olivia' (Ia)	EBrs LAma MCri NNor
	Olympic Group (VIa)	MCri
	'Orange Pixie' (Ia)	EPfP IBal MCri SCoo WGor
	'Orange Triumph' (Ia)	EPfP NNor
	'Orania'[PBR] (VIII) new	CAvo CFFs MCri
	'Orestes' (Ib)	CLAP
	oriental hybrids	EBrs
*	Oriental Superb Group	NGdn
§	***oxypetalum*** (IX)	EBee GCrs GGGa WWst
	- var. ***insigne*** (IX)	CLAP EBee EBrs ECho EPot GBin GBuc GCrs GEdr GGGa GGar NMen NSla WCru WHal
	'Painted Pixie' (Ia)	IBal
	'Pan' (Ic)	CLAP
	papilliferum	EBrs ECho LAma
	pardalinum (IX) ♀[H4]	CHHB CLAP CWCL EBee EBrs ECho ELan EPot GKev LRHS MSte NSla WBVN WCot WCru WHal WPnP
	- var. ***giganteum*** (IX)	CLAP EPfP LCro MCri MNrw SPer WTin
	- subsp. ***pardalinum*** (IX) NNS 00-488	WCot WWst
	- - NNS 02=228	WWst
	- subsp. ***shastense*** (IX)	CLAP EBee GCrs NMen WCot WWst
	- - NNS 98-374	WWst
	- - NNS 00-490	WCot
	- subsp. ***shastense*** x ***vollmeri***	WWst
	parryi (IX)	GBuc
	- NNS 03-384	WWst
	parvum (IX)	ECho GBuc GCrs
	'Peach Butterflies' (Ic/d)	CLAP
	'Peach Pixie' (Ia)	NBir NNor SCoo
	'Peggy North' (Ic)	CLAP
	philippinense (IX)	EBee EWin MCri
	- B&SWJ 4000	WCru
	Pink Perfection Group (VIa) ♀[H4]	CAvo CFFs EBrs EPfP ERCP LAma LRHS MCri NNor SBch SCoo SPer SWat WFar
	'Pink Pixie'[PBR] (Ia)	IBal MCri SGar
	'Pink Tiger' (Ib)	CLAP EBrs GKev LRHS MCri NNor WGor
	'Pink Twinkle' new	EBrs
	polyphyllum CC 4570	WWst
	primulinum (IX)	WWst
	- var. ***ochraceum***	CLAP LAma WWst
§	***pumilum*** (IX) ♀[H4]	CLAP CTca EBee EBrs ECho EPot ERCP GBuc GKev ITer LAma LRHS MCri MSte MTho WAul WCot WPrP
	- 'Golden Gleam' (IX)	WWst
	pyrenaicum (IX)	CLAP EBee EBrs ECho GGar IBlr LTwo MCri MFOX WCot WPGP WShi
§	- subsp. ***carniolicum*** (IX)	EBee MCri
§	- - var. ***albanicum*** (IX)	CLAP EBee GCrs
	- subsp. ***pyrenaicum*** var. ***pyrenaicum*** (IX)	CLAP
	- - var. ***rubrum*** (IX)	GEdr WCot
	'Raspberry Butterflies' (Ic/d)	CLAP
	'Red Carpet' (Ia)	EBrs LRHS MCri NBir NNor WGor
	'Red Dutch' (VIII) new	ERCP
	'Red Dwarf' (Ia)	IBal
	'Red Night' (I)	LRHS
	'Red Rum'	MBri
	'Red Tiger' (Ib)	CLAP
	'Red Twinkle'	CFwr EBrs LRHS
	'Red Velvet' (Ib)	CLAP
	regale (IX) ♀[H4]	More than 30 suppliers
	- 'Album' (IX)	CAvo CFFs CSWP EBee EBrs GBuc LAma LCro LRHS MCri NNor SBch SCoo SGar SPur WFar WHil
§	- 'Royal Gold' (IX)	EPfP MCri
	'Reinesse' (Ia)	IBal MBri
	'Roma' (Ia)	EWll LAma LRHS NBir
	'Rosefire' (Ia)	MCri NNor
	'Rosemary North' (I)	CLAP
	Rosepoint Lace Group (Ic)	CLAP
	'Rosita' (Ia)	MCri WFar
	rosthornii	CExc EBee GBuc GEdr WCot WCru WWst
	'Royal Gold'	see *L. regale* 'Royal Gold'
	rubellum (IX)	EFEx GBuc
§	'Ruud' (VII)	EPfP LAma LRHS
	sachalinense RBS 0235	CStu EPPr
	'Salmon Twinkle'	EBrs WFar
	'Sam' (VII) ♀[H4]	EPfP GBuc LAma LRHS
	sargentiae (IX)	CExc CLAP EBrs GBuc GCrs GGGa MCri NMen WCot WCru
	- Cox 7099	EBee
	sempervivoideum (IX)	EBrs ECho GEdr LAma
	shastense	see *L. kelleyanum*
	'Shocking'[PBR] new	MCri
	'Siberia'[PBR]	EBrs
	'Silly Girl' (Ia)	MCri NNor
§	'Snow Crystal' (I)	EPfP IBal
	souliei (IX)	CExc EBee
	speciosum (IX)	CHHB NSla
	- B&SWJ 4847	WCru
	- var. ***album*** (IX)	CHHB EBee EBrs GBuc LEdu LRHS MCri MWgw NBir NNor SBch
	- var. ***gloriosoides*** (IX)	CHHB EBrs EPot LAma WCot
	- var. ***roseum*** (IX)	GBuc NNor

– var. ***rubrum*** (IX)	CFwr CLAP EBee EBrs ECha GBuc LAma LRHS MCri NBir NLar SPer WPrP
§ – 'Uchida' (IX)	MCri NNor SBch
'Sphinx' (Ia/d)	WCot
'Staccato' (Ia)	MCri
'Star Gazer' (VIIc)	CSut EBrs ECot ELan IBal LAma LAst LRHS MCri NNor SCoo SPer WFar WGor
'Starfighter' (VIId)	EBrs IBal LRHS MCri
'Sterling Star' (Ia)	CLAP EPfP MCri NNor
Stones = 'Holebobo'	LRHS NNor
'Sulphur King' new	WCot
sulphureum	EBee LAma MAsh MCri NLAp WWst
'Sun Ray' (Ia)	LRHS MCri
superbum (IX)	CLAP EBee ECho GBuc GEdr LAma WCot WCru WPGP
'Sutton Court' (II)	CLAP
'Sweet Lord' new	EBrs
'Sweet Surrender' (I)	EBrs LRHS MCri NNor
szovitsianum	see *L. monadelphum*
taliense (IX)	ECho GBuc GEdr LAma MCri WCru
tenuifolium	see *L. pumilum*
'Theseus' (Ic)	CLAP
Tiger Babies Group	CLAP WSPU
'Tiger White' (Ic)	CLAP
tigrinum	see *L. lancifolium*
'Tinkerbell' (Ic)	CLAP
'Tom Pouce' (VIIa/b) new	LRHS
'Touch' new	MCri
'Triumphator' new	CFFs MCri
tsingtauense (IX)	CLAP
– B&SWJ 519	WCru
'Uchida Kanoka'	see *L. speciosum* 'Uchida'
'Vermeer' (Ia/b) new	EBrs EWll
'Victory Joy' new	MBri
'Viking' new	WThu
'Viva' (Ic)	CLAP
vollmeri (IX)	CLAP GCrs NMen WCru WWst
– JCA 1.500.901	WWst
– NNS 00-490	EBee
wallichianum (IX)	EBee EBrs ECho EPot GBuc LAma
'White American'	see *L. longiflorum* 'White American'
'White Butterflies' (Ic/d)	CLAP
'White Dwarf' (Ia) new	EBrs GKev
'White Henryi' (VId)	CLAP EBee
'White Kiss' (Ia/d)	LRHS
I 'White Lace' (Ic/d)	CLAP
'White Mountain' (VIIc)	SPer
'White Paradise' (V)	SCoo
'White Pixie' (I)	see *L.* 'Snow Crystal'
'White Tiger' (Ib)	CLAP
'White Twinkle' (Ia/b) new	EBrs
wigginsii (IX)	CLAP EBee GEdr MCri
– 00-493NNS RTO	WWst
willmottiae	see *L. davidii* var. *willmottiae*
'Woodriff's Memory' (VIIb) new	EBrs
xanthellum var. ***luteum***	GEdr WWst
Yellow Blaze Group (Ia)	EPfP
'Yellow Bunting' (I)	WWst
'Yellow Star' (Ib)	EBrs EWll LRHS NNor
yunnanense	EBee

lime see *Citrus aurantiifolia*

lime, djeruk see *Citrus amblycarpa*

lime, Philippine see x *Citrofortunella microcarpa*

Limnanthes (*Limnanthaceae*)

douglasii ♀H4	CArn CHrt EPfP LRav SECG SIde SIng

Limnophila (*Scrophulariaceae*)

aromatica	MSal

Limoniastrum (*Plumbaginaceae*)

monopetalum	XPep

Limonium (*Plumbaginaceae*)

bellidifolium	EBee ECha EDAr SBla WEas WHoo WPer WTin XPep
binervosum	WAbe
'Blauer Diamant'	NBre
chilwellii	EBee ECGP EMan MSte NCGa SPoG
cosyrense	CMea CStu MHer NMen WAbe WPer
dumosum	see *Goniolimon tataricum* var. *angustifolium*
gmelinii	EBee MLLN SPlb WPer
* – subsp. ***hungaricum***	NLar
gougetianum	WPer
latifolium	see *L. platyphyllum*
minutum	MNHC SPoG
perezii	EShb
§ ***platyphyllum***	More than 30 suppliers
– 'Robert Butler'	EBee ECGP EMan LRHS MRav MSte NCGa SPoG SRGP
– 'Violetta'	EBee ECGP ECha ELan EMan EPfP ERou LAst LRHS MBri MMHG MRav NCGa NOrc SPer WCAu WHoo WSHC
pruinosum	XPep
speciosum	see *Goniolimon incanum*
tataricum	see *Goniolimon tataricum*
vulgare	WHer XPep

Linanthastrum see *Linanthus*

Linanthus (*Polemoniaceae*)

nuttallii subsp. ***floribundus***	CPBP

Linaria (*Scrophulariaceae*)

aeruginea	CSpe
– subsp. ***nevadensis*** 'Gemstones'	LRHS
alpina	CSpe ECho ECtt GGar MTho NRya SRms WEas
anticaria 'Antique Silver'	EBee ECha GBuc LAst LSou MRav NEgg SSvw WPGP WWeb
Blue Lace = 'Yalin'	EBee LAst LSou NPri SMrm SPoG
capraria	CPBP
cymbalaria	see *Cymbalaria muralis*
§ ***dalmatica***	CEnt CHrt CSpe EBee ECha ELan EPPr ERou MHar MNFA NBid NBro NPri SBch SHGN SPhx WCFE WCot WKif WMoo WPer
dalmatica x ***purpurea*** new	WCot
x ***dominii*** 'Carnforth'	CBre CPom LSou NBre NBro SBch SHar WCot
– 'Yuppie Surprise'	CHid EMan LAst NBir SWvt WCot WPGP WSpi
genistifolia	MDKP
– subsp. ***dalmatica***	see *L. dalmatica*
'Globosa Alba'	see *Cymbalaria muralis* 'Globosa Alba'
hepaticifolia	see *Cymbalaria hepaticifolia*
japonica	WCot
* ***lobata alba***	ECho SPlb
nevadensis 'Grenada Sol'	MWea
origanifolia	see *Chaenorhinum origanifolium*
pallida	see *Cymbalaria pallida*
pilosa	see *Cymbalaria pilosa*
purpurea	CAby CBgR COlW CTri EBee EHrv ELan EPfP IFoB LBMP MHer

	MNHC MWgw NBro NPer NPri NSti SECG SRms WCAu WCot WHen WMoo WPer
- 'Alba'	see *L. purpurea* 'Springside White'
- 'Canon Went'	More than 30 suppliers
- 'Radcliffe Innocence'	see *L. purpurea* 'Springside White'
§ - 'Springside White'	CBgR CElw COIW CPom EBee ECha ECtt EMan GBuc LBMP MBri MSte NBir NPri SBch SPhx SSvw WAul WCAu WCot WPer
- 'Thurgarton Beauty'	MDKP
repens	CPom MNrw WCot WHer
reticulata 'Red Velvet'	CSpe
x ***sepium*** new	WCot
'Toni Aldiss'	SPhx
triornithophora	CEnt CFir CSpe EBee ECha EMan GBuc IGor LBMP MNFA MWrn SEND WKif WMoo WPer WPtf
- 'Pink Budgies'	CDMG LSou
- purple	ELan MHar STes WMoo
tristis	CEnt
vulgaris	CArn ELau GWCH LDai MDKP MHer MNHC NMir NPri NSco SECG WHer WJek
- 'Peloria'	CNat MDKP WCot
'Winifrid's Delight'	EPfP NBre

Lindelofia (*Boraginaceae*)

anchusoides misapplied	see *L. longiflora*
anchusoides (Lindl.) Lehm.	EPPr GBri NBid
§ ***longiflora***	CFir GBuc GCra LRHS MLLN NBid

Lindera (*Lauraceae*)

aggregata	CBcs
benzoin	CAgr CBcs CMCN EPfP LRHS MBri MSal NLar SSpi
communis	WPGP
erythrocarpa	CBcs CPLG EPfP
- B&SWJ 6271	WCru
megaphylla	CBcs CHEx
obtusiloba ♀H4	CAbP EPfP WNor
- var. ***heterophylla***	ISea
praecox	EPfP WPGP
reflexa	CGHE EPfP NLar WPGP
strychnifolia	EPfP
umbellata var. ***membranacea*** B&SWJ 6227	WCru

Lindernia (*Scrophulariaceae*)

grandiflora	EBee ECou LLWG SIng

Linnaea (*Caprifoliaceae*)

borealis	CStu ILis MHar WAbe
- subsp. ***americana***	NHar NWCA

Linum ✿ (*Linaceae*)

africanum	EShb
alexeenkoanum	WLin
alpinum	SHGN
arboreum ♀H4	SBla WAbe WKif WPat
- NS 529	NWCA
campanulatum	WThu
- 'Sulphur'	LSou
capitatum	NSla
dolomiticum	WPat
flavum	CTri EPfP XPep
- 'Compactum'	EBee ECho GAbr SBla SRms
'Gemmell's Hybrid' ♀H4	CDes CLyd CMea ECho EPot EWes GKev LRHS MDKP NBir NMen SBla WAbe WPat
leonii	LRHS
monogynum	CDes CSsd ECou SBla
§ - var. ***diffusum***	ECou
- 'Nelson'	see *L. monogynum* var. *diffusum*
narbonense	CMdw CSam ECGP LBMP LDai LRHS NLar SBch SRms
- 'Heavenly Blue'	ERou WHen
§ ***perenne***	CArn CRWN CTri EBee ECha ELan EPfP ERou GMaP LRHS MHer MNFA MNHC NMir SIde SPer SRms WCAu WPer XPep
- 'Album'	EBee ECha ELan EPfP ERou MNFA NLar SPer WHen WPer
- subsp. ***alpinum*** 'Alice Blue'	CPBP SBla
§ - 'Blau Saphir'	EBee EShb LAst LRHS MLLN MRav MWat NLar SRms SWal WHen WWeb
- Blue Sapphire	see *L. perenne* 'Blau Saphir'
- 'Diamant'	EBee EWin LRHS
- 'Himmelszelt'	LBMP NLar SMrm
- subsp. ***lewisii***	EBee NBir WAbe
- 'Nanum Diamond'	EShb NLar
- 'Nanum Sapphire'	see *L. perenne* 'Blau Saphir'
- 'White Diamond'	NCob
punctatum new	WAbe
sibiricum	see *L. perenne*
suffruticosum	CPBP
- subsp. ***salsoloides*** 'Nanum'	SBla WPat
- - 'Prostratum'	GBuc
uninerve new	WAbe
usitatissimum	CRWN MHer SIde

Lippia (*Verbenaceae*)

alba	MSal
canescens	see *Phyla nodiflora* var. *canescens*
chamaedrifolia	see *Verbena peruviana*
citriodora	see *Aloysia triphylla*
dulcis	CArn CFir EOHP EUnu LRav MSal SPad
nodiflora	see *Phyla nodiflora*
repens	see *Phyla nodiflora*

Liquidambar ✿ (*Hamamelidaceae*)

acalycina	CLnd CPMA EBee ELan EPfP LPan LRHS MAsh MBlu MGos MRav NLar SCoo SIFN SSpi SSta WNor WPGP WPat
- 'Burgundy Flush'	CPMA
formosana	CEnd CMCN EBee ECrN EPfP IMGH LPan MBlu MGos NPen SPer SSpi SSta WNor WPGP
- B&SWJ 6855	WCru
- Monticola Group	CPMA EPfP SIFN SSta
orientalis	CMCN CPMA EPfP LPan SSta
styraciflua	More than 30 suppliers
- 'Andrew Hewson'	CLnd CPMA LRHS MAsh NLar SCoo SPoG SSpi SSta
- 'Anja'	CPMA MBlu SSta
- 'Anneke'	CPMA LRHS SSta
- 'Aurea'	see *L. styraciflua* 'Variegata' Overeynder
- 'Aurea Variegata'	see *L. styraciflua* 'Variegata' Overeynder
- 'Aurora'	CPMA SLim
- 'Burgundy'	CLnd CPMA CTho NHol SSta WPGP WPat
- 'Fastigiata'	MBlu
- 'Festeri'	CEnd MAsh SSta WPat
- 'Festival'	CPMA MBlu SBLw SSta
- 'Frosty' (v) new	CPMA
- 'Globe'	see *L. styraciflua* 'Gum Ball'
- 'Golden Treasure' (v)	CMCN CPMA LRHS MGos NLar SSpi WPat
§ - 'Gum Ball'	CEnd CLnd CMCN CPMA EPfP EWes LTwo MBri MGos NLar SCoo SMad SSta WPat

- Happidaze = 'Hapdell'	CEnd CPMA NLar WPat
- 'Jennifer Carol'	CPMA NLar
- 'Kia'	CAbP CEnd CPMA MAsh WPat
- 'Kirsten'	CPMA
- 'Lane Roberts' ♀H4	CDoC CDul CLnd CMCN CTho EBee EPfP LPan LRHS MAsh MBlu MGos MLan NEgg NLar SCoo SMad SPoG SReu SSta WPGP WPat
- 'Manon' (v)	CDoC CEnd CPMA EMil LPan NBhm
- 'Midwest Sunset'	WPGP WPat
- 'Moonbeam' (v)	CEnd CMCN CPMA EBee MAsh NLar SLim SSta WPat
- 'Moraine'	CMCN CPMA SBLw
- 'Naree'	CMCN CPMA NLar
- 'Oconee'	CEnd EPfP MAsh WPat
- 'Paarl' (v)	CMCN CPMA
- 'Palo Alto'	CEnd CPMA LRHS LTwo MAsh NHol SBLw SCoo SMad SSta WPGP WPat
- 'Parasol'	CEnd CPMA NLar SSta
- 'Pendula'	CLnd CMCN CPMA LRHS SSta
- 'Penwood'	CPMA NLar SSta
- 'Rotundiloba'	CMCN CPMA EPfP SIFN SSta WPat
- 'Schock's Gold' new	CPMA
- 'Silver King' (v)	CDul CLnd CMCN CPMA EBee ECrN EMil EPfP IMGH LRHS MBlu MBri MGos NLar SCoo SKHP SLim SPer SPoG SSta WPat
- 'Slender Silhouette' new	CAbP LRHS SPoG
- 'Stared'	CEnd CLnd CPMA LPan MBri SCoo WPGP WPat
- 'Thea'	CAbP CPMA LRHS MBlu SSta
§ - 'Variegata' Overeynder (v)	CBcs CDul CLnd CPMA EBee ELan EMil EPfP LPan LRHS MAsh MBlu MDun MGos NEgg SLim SPer SPoG SSta WPat
- 'White Star' (v) new	CPMA
- 'Worplesdon' ♀H4	More than 30 suppliers

Liriodendron ✿ (*Magnoliaceae*)

'Chapel Hill'	MBlu
chinense	CBcs CDul CGHE CLnd CMCN CPLG CTho EPfP MBlu SKHP SSpi WFar WPGP WPat
'Doc Deforce's Delight'	MBlu
tulipifera ♀H4	More than 30 suppliers
- 'Ardis'	CMCN NLar SSpi
- 'Arnold'	CMCN
- 'Aureomarginatum' (v) ♀H4	More than 30 suppliers
- 'Aureum'	CMCN
- 'Crispum'	CMCN
- 'Fastigiatum'	CDoC CDul CEnd CLnd CMCN CTho EBee ECrN ELan EPfP IMGH LPan LRHS MBlu MBri MGos NPal SBLw SPer SPoG SSta WOrn WPat
- 'Glen Gold'	CEnd CMCN IArd MBlu MGos NLar
- 'Mediopictum' (v)	CMCN CTho MBlu
- 'Purgatory' new	MBri
- 'Roodhaan'	NLar

Liriope ✿ (*Convallariaceae*)

from Vietnam	WPGP
HWJ 590 from Vietnam	WPGP
'Big Blue'	see *L. muscari* 'Big Blue'
'Blue Spire' new	WBod
§ ***exiliflora***	CEnd CLAP EBee EGle NLar WFar
- 'Ariaka-janshige' (v)	SWat
§ ***gigantea***	CLAP EBee GSki SWat
graminifolia misapplied	see *L. muscari*
hyacinthifolia	see *Reineckea carnea*
kansuensis	ERos
koreana	EBee EPPr
- B&SWJ 8821	WCru
'Majestic'	CBct CHar EBee EGle ERou GSki MBri SPla WBor WFar WHoo
'Minnow' new	WCot
§ ***muscari*** ♀H4	More than 30 suppliers
- B&SWJ 561	WCru
- 'Alba'	see *L. muscari* 'Monroe White'
§ - 'Big Blue'	CBct CBrm CKno CLAP COIW CPrp EBee ENot EPPr EPfP EShb EWTr GSki LEdu LHop LRHS MRav NLar SWvt WBor WCFE WMoo
- 'Christmas Tree'	CPrp EPPr WHoo WMoo
- 'Evergreen Giant'	see *L. gigantea*
- 'Gold-banded' (v)	CPrp EBee EGle EPfP LLWG MBNS NSti SHBN WFar WSpi
- 'Goldfinger'	EPla WPGP
- 'Ingwersen'	CBgR CPrp EBee EBrs ECho LBMP NMRc SMeo WHoo WLeb WPnP
- 'John Burch' (v)	CBct CLAP CPrp EBee ELon EShb LHop MBNS MCCP NLar SMad WLeb WSpi
- 'Majestic' misapplied	see *L. exiliflora*
§ - 'Monroe White'	CBgR CEnd CLAP CPrp EBee ECha ECho EGle EHrv ENot EPfP ERou EWTr GSki LAst LEdu MRav NLar SBod SMac SPer SPet SPla SWat WAul WCra WFar WSpi
- 'Okina' (v)	WCot
- 'Paul Aden'	EPfP WPGP
- 'Royal Purple'	CBct CHar CLAP EBee ENot EPPr EPfP GQue GSki NBPC NGdn NLar SPla WBor WLeb
- 'Silver Ribbon'	CLAP CPrp EBee EPfP EShb GSki NSti SMad SPer WPGP
- 'Silvery Midget' (v)	CPrp
- 'Superba'	WCot
- 'Variegata' (v)	More than 30 suppliers
- variegated, white-flowered (v)	CBcs CDes CFir ECho
- 'Webster Wideleaf'	GSki WHoo
'New Wonder'	EHrv LEdu
platyphylla	see *L. muscari*
'Samantha'	CPrp ECha
spicata	EBee ECho ERos SWat WWeb
- 'Alba'	CPLG ECho MRav MTho WTin
§ - 'Gin-ryu' (v)	CBct CBgR CCge CHar CLAP COIW CSpe EBee ECho ECtt EPPr EWes GBuc GSki LEdu LSRN MAvo MCCP MSte NLar SLPl SPer WBrk WCot WPGP
- 'Silver Dragon'	see *L. spicata* 'Gin-ryu'

Lisianthius (*Gentianaceae*)

russelianus	see *Eustoma grandiflorum*

Listera (*Orchidaceae*)

ovata	WHer

Litchi (*Sapindaceae*)

chinensis	CCCN

Lithocarpus ✿ (*Fagaceae*)

edulis	CBcs CGHE CHEx CPLG SArc WPGP
henryi new	CExc
pachyphyllus	CBcs

Lithodora (*Boraginaceae*)

§ ***diffusa***	ECho SGar SRot WWlt
- 'Alba'	CTri ECho EPfP GKev LRHS MGos SGar SPer SPoG WFar
- 'Baby Barbara'	GKev
- 'Cambridge Blue'	ECho SPer
- 'Compacta'	ECho EWes NWCA WAbe WPat
§ - 'Grace Ward' ♀H4	ECho GAbr MGos MWya NHol SBod WAbe WFar WPat

§ - 'Heavenly Blue' 🏆H4	More than 30 suppliers
- 'Inverleith'	ECho EWes WFar
- 'Pete's Favourite'	SRGP WAbe
- 'Picos'	CMea ECho EPot GCrs NMen WAbe WFar WPat
- 'Star' PBR	CMHG EPfP GGar LRHS NLar SBod SCoo SIng SPer SPoG SRot
fruticosa	CArn XPep
graminifolia	see *Moltkia suffruticosa*
x ***intermedia***	see *Moltkia* x *intermedia*
§ ***oleifolia*** 🏆H4	ECho EPot LRHS NBir NMen SBla WPat
rosmarinifolia	CSpe
zahnii	ECho EPot WPat
- 'Azureness' **new**	WAbe

Lithophragma (*Saxifragaceae*)

parviflorum	CDes CMea CPom EBee EWes MSte MTho NBir NLar NRya NWCA WBor WCru WFar WPnP

Lithospermum (*Boraginaceae*)

diffusum	see *Lithodora diffusa*
doerfleri	see *Moltkia doerfleri*
erythrorhizon	MSal
'Grace Ward'	see *Lithodora diffusa* 'Grace Ward'
'Heavenly Blue'	see *Lithodora diffusa* 'Heavenly Blue'
officinale	CArn GPoy MSal NMir
oleifolium	see *Lithodora oleifolia*
purpureocaeruleum	see *Buglossoides purpurocaerulea*

Litsea (*Lauraceae*)

glauca	see *Neolitsea sericea*

Littonia (*Colchicaceae*)

modesta	CRHN EBrs ECho EShb ITer

Livistona (*Arecaceae*)

australis	EAmu LPal
chinensis 🏆H1	CBrP CPHo EAmu LPJP LPal MPRe SAin
decipiens	CPHo CTrC EAmu LPal
mariae	EAmu LPal
nitida	CKob

Lloydia (*Liliaceae*)

delavayi **new**	EBee
ixiolirioides	EBee
oxycarpa	EBee
serotina	EBee
tibetica	EBee
yunnanensis	CExc EBee

Loasa (*Loasaceae*)

triphylla var. ***volcanica***	EWes GCra WSHC

Lobelia (*Campanulaceae*)

B&SWJ 8220 from Vietnam	WCru
RCB/Arg S-4	WCot
'Alice'	WDyG
angulata	see *Pratia angulata*
bridgesii	CPLG CPle EShb GGar STes WPGP WRos
§ ***cardinalis*** 🏆H3	CArn CBen CHEx CRWN EBla EHon ELau EMFW EPfP ERou EWsh GAbr GMaP MSal NBlu NPer SMer SPer SPet SPlb SRms SWat SWvt WEas WFar WMAq
- 'Bee's Flame'	CFir CPrp CWGN EBee EMan ERou GBuc LBMP MCot MLLN MRav MSte NBre SWat
§ - 'Elmfeuer'	CFwr CMHG EBee ERou EShb EWin LAst MBNS MSte MWat NGby NLar NPri SMrm SPlb SWvt WFar
- 'Eulalia Berridge'	CAby CSam CWsd EBee EGle GBuc SMrm WDyG WFar WMoo WSHC
- subsp. ***graminea*** var. ***multiflora***	CFir
- 'Illumination'	GBuc
§ - 'Queen Victoria' 🏆H3	More than 30 suppliers
- 'Russian Princess' purple-flowered	see *L.* x *speciosa* 'Russian Princess'
chinensis **new**	LLWG
'Cinnabar Deep Red'	see *L.* x *speciosa* 'Fan Tiefrot'
'Cinnabar Rose'	see *L.* x *speciosa* 'Fan Zinnoberrosa'
Compliment Blue	see *L.* x *speciosa* 'Kompliment Blau'
Compliment Deep Red	see *L.* x *speciosa* 'Kompliment Tiefrot'
Compliment Purple	see *L.* x *speciosa* 'Kompliment Purpur'
Compliment Scarlet	see *L.* x *speciosa* 'Kompliment Scharlach'
coronopifolia	EShb
dortmanna	EMFW
erinus Big Blue = 'Weslobigblue' PBR	LAst LSou
- Blue Star = 'Wesstar' PBR	LAst
- 'Kathleen Mallard' (d)	CCCN ECtt LAst SWvt
- 'Pink Star' **new**	LSou
- 'Richardii'	see *L. richardsonii*
excelsa	CPle EBee EShb GCra GGar LSou MTPN NCGa NRnb NSfd SBHP SPav SPoG WFar WSHC
- B&SWJ 9513	WCru
Fan Deep Red	see *L.* x *speciosa* 'Fan Tiefrot'
'Fan Deep Rose'	see *L.* x *speciosa* 'Fan Orchidrosa'
'Flamingo'	see *L.* x *speciosa* 'Pink Flamingo'
'Forncett Merry'	NBre
fulgens	see *L. cardinalis*
- Saint Elmo's Fire	see *L. cardinalis* 'Elmfeuer'
x ***gerardii***	see *L.* x *speciosa*
gibberoa	CHEx WHil
'Gladys Lindley' **new**	EBee
grandidentata F&M 133 **new**	WPGP
'Hadspen Purple' PBR	see *L.* x *speciosa* 'Hadspen Purple'
inflata	CArn EBee EOHP GPoy MSal NSfd
kalmii	EShb
- 'Blue Shadow'	CStu EBla LAst NBlu WPtf
'La Fresco'	EBee
laxiflora	CHid MTho SAga SHom SPet
- B&SWJ 9064	WCru
- var. ***angustifolia***	CHEx CPrp CSam ECtt EShb MSte SBod SDnm SHFr SMrm SPav SPoG SRms WHil WPrP WWlt XPep
'Lena'	SWat
lindblomii	CFee CStu GSki
linnaeoides	SPlb
'Lipstick'	WWlt
longifolia from Chile	CFee
lutea	see *Monopsis lutea*
'Martha'	EBee
pedunculata	see *Pratia pedunculata*
perpusilla	see *Pratia perpusilla*
polyphylla	ECtt EShb NCGa NRnb NSfd
preslii	SPlb
'Queen Victoria'	see *L. cardinalis* 'Queen Victoria'
§ ***richardsonii*** 🏆H1+3	ECtt LAst NBlu SWvt
seguinii B&SWJ 7065	WCru
- var. ***doniana*** CC 3673	WRos
sessilifolia	CDWL CPLG EBee EGle GBuc NEgg WCot WPer
- B&L 12396	EMon
siphilitica	More than 30 suppliers

	- 'Alba'	CEnt CSam EBee EBla EPfP EShb MLLN NRnb SPav SPoG SRms SWat SWvt WCAu WFar WHoo WHrl WMnd WMoo WPer
	- blue-flowered	CSpe SWat SWvt
	- 'Rosea'	MNrw
	'Sonia'	SWat
§	x ***speciosa***	CEnt CHFP CSam LAst MHer NBre SMHy SWat WBor WFar WHil WMoo WSHC
	- 'Butterfly Blue'	CBcs CChe CWsd EBee LFur NEgg SPla
	- 'Butterfly Rose'	EGle SRot
	- 'Cherry Ripe'	CPrp CWsd EPfP GCra NHol WEas
	- 'Cranberry Crown'	NRnb
	- 'Cranberry Crush'PBR	NRnb SHar
	- dark	CMHG EBee EGle
	- 'Dark Crusader'	CDWL CPrp CTca CWsd EBee ECGP ECtt EGle ELan EMan EMar EShb LAst LBMP LRHS LSou NHol SBch SMrm SPla SWat WEas WMnd
	- 'Fan Blue' **new**	WHil
	- 'Fan Burgundy'	CEnt CSpe CWCL EWll WHil
§	- 'Fan Orchidrosa' ♀H3-4	EShb NGdn SRot WHil
	- 'Fan Scharlach' ♀H3-4	CFwr EHon EShb MGos NLar SBch SGar SHar SRot SWvt WDyG WHil
§	- 'Fan Tiefrot' ♀H3-4	CBen CBrm CChe CDWL CWsd ERou MWea NBlu NCGa NGdn SHar SMHy SRms SWat SWvt WPer
§	- 'Fan Zinnoberrosa' ♀H3-4	CEnt CFir CMMP EHon ERou LAst LRHS MFOX MHar SRms SRot SWvt WMoo WPer
	- 'Grape Knee-high'	EBee EPfP ERou GCra LSRN LSou NCGa NRnb SPoG
§	- 'Hadspen Purple'PBR	CDWL CWCL CWGN EBee EBrs EGle ELan EPfP EWTr IPot LAst LSRN MBri MCCP MCot MWea NCGa NCob NSti SHar SPoG SRkn SWat WOVN
	- 'Kimbridge Beet'	CMac
§	- 'Kompliment Blau'	CFir CWat ERou LRHS SWvt WPer
	- 'Kompliment Pale Pink' **new**	EShb
§	- 'Kompliment Purpur'	ERou EShb MNrw SWvt
§	- 'Kompliment Scharlach' ♀H3-4	CBcs CSWP CSpe CTca CWsd EBee EMil EPfP ERou EShb LBBr LFur LHop LRHS MBNS MNrw NHol NPer SWvt WFar WMnd WPer WWlt
§	- 'Kompliment Tiefrot'	ERou EWll MNrw MWat SWvt WPer
	- 'Monet Moment'	CBow EBee EBla ERou EWes LSou NBre NCGa NRnb SPoG WSpi
	- 'Pauline'	ECtt
	- 'Pink Elephant' ♀H4	CBow CChe CSWP CWCL CWsd EBee GCra MDKP NBre SHar WFar WWeb
§	- 'Pink Flamingo'	CBen CMMP CPLG EBee EBla LRHS SPer SWat WFar WSHC WShi
	- 'Purple Towers'	EBee NBre
	- purple-flowered	EWin
	- red-flowered	EWin
	- 'Rosencavalier'	EBee LRHS NGby WFar
	- 'Ruby Slippers'	CBcs CWCL EBee ECtt ELan EMan EPfP ERou IPot LAst LSRN MBri MWea NCGa SPoG WFar
I	- 'Russian Princess' purple-flowered	CDWL CMHG CPrp CSam CTri CWCL EBee ECtt ELan ENot EWTr LAst LBMP LRHS MBri MCCP MCot MHer MWgw NBre NCGa NEgg NHol NRnb SPer SPoG WCAu WFar WMnd WWeb
	- 'Sparkle deVine'	WFar
	- 'Tania'	More than 30 suppliers
	- Tresahor Series	CHEx
§	- 'Vedrariensis'	CBen CDWL CPrp CWCL CWib EBee EBla ELan EPfP EShb EWTr GGar MHar NBlu NGdn SGar SHFr SMeo SPer SRms STes SWvt WCAu WEas WFar WHil WHoo WMnd
	- 'Wildwood Splendor'	NBre WFar
	- 'Will Scarlet'	EWin
	tomentosa	EShb
	treadwellii	see *Pratia angulata* 'Treadwellii'
	tupa	More than 30 suppliers
	- JCA 12527	MTPN WCot
	- Archibald's form	CPLG NRnb
	- dark orange	SMrm
	urens	WPGP
	valida	EBee EWin LHop SGar SWvt WFar
	- 'True Blue' **new**	SVil
	vedrariensis	see *L.* x *speciosa* 'Vedrariensis'
	White Star = 'Weslowei'PBR	LAst
	'Zinnoberrosa'	see *L.* x *speciosa* 'Fan Zinnoberrosa'

Lobularia (*Brassicaceae*)

maritima	XPep

Loeselia (*Polemoniaceae*)

mexicana	CHII

loganberry see *Rubus* x *loganobaccus*

Loiseleuria (*Ericaceae*)

procumbens from Japan	GCrs

Lomandra (*Lomandraceae*)

confertifolia	ECou
- 'Wingarra' **new**	GBin
hystrix	SPlb
'Little Con'	CBcs
'Little Pal'	CBcs
longifolia	ECou LEdu SPlb
- 'Kulnura'	ECou
- 'Orford'	ECou
- 'Tanika'	EBee EPPr GBin GGar LRHS

Lomaria see *Blechnum*

Lomatia (*Proteaceae*)

	ferruginea	CBcs CDoC CHEx CTrG CWsd EPfP SAPC SArc SKHP WCru
	fraseri	EPfP LHop SKHP SSpi
	longifolia	see *L. myricoides*
§	***myricoides***	CBcs CCCN CDoC CHEx CPSs CTrG EBee ELan EPfP LRHS MBri NLar SAPC SArc SLon SSpi WPGP
	silaifolia	CDoC EPfP
	tinctoria	CBcs CDoC CHEx CPSs EPfP LRHS NLar SArc SSpi

Lomatium (*Apiaceae*)

dissectum	NBhm
grayi	EMan
utriculatum	MSal

Lonicera ✿ (*Caprifoliaceae*)

	B&SWJ 2654 from Sikkim	WCru
	from China	WCru
§	***acuminata***	EBee LRHS WGwG WPnP
	- B&SWJ 3480	WCru
	alberti	GBin MBNS MRav SLon WGwG WHCG
	alseuosmoides	EBee GBin IArd IDee SAga SBra SLon SPla SPoG WCru WPGP WSHC WWeb

§ x ***americana*** (Miller) K. Koch	CBcs CRHN CWoW EPfP LRHS MAsh MGos MRav NWea SDix SGar SLim SPla WGwG WMoo
x ***americana*** misapplied	see *L.* x *italica*
§ x ***brownii*** 'Dropmore Scarlet'	More than 30 suppliers
- 'Fuchsioides' misapplied	see *L.* x *brownii* 'Dropmore Scarlet'
- 'Fuchsioides' K. Koch	NSti WSHC
caerulea	MRav STre WHCG
- var. ***altaica***	LEdu
- var. ***edulis***	CAgr LEdu
- subsp. ***kamtschatica***	CAgr NLar
§ ***caprifolium*** Ψ[H4]	CDoC CRHN CWoW EBee ELan EPfP LBuc LFol LRHS MBar MLan NBea SBra SHBN SPer WCot
- 'Anna Fletcher'	CRHN CSPN MBNS NHaw SBra SLim WCFE
- 'Inga'	SBra
- f. ***pauciflora***	see *L.* x *italica*
chaetocarpa	CPle WSHC
chamissoi	NLar
§ ***chrysantha***	CMCN
'Clavey's Dwarf'	see *L.* x *xylosteoides* 'Clavey's Dwarf'
'Copper Beauty'[PBR] new	CWGN SBra
crassifolia new	WCot
deflexicalyx	EPfP NLar
'Early Cream'	see *L. caprifolium*
elisae	EBee ENot NLar SSpi WPat
etrusca	IDee LAst MRav WWeb XPep
- 'Donald Waterer' Ψ[H4]	CRHN EBee EPfP LHop LRHS NLar SPla WFar WGor
- 'Michael Rosse'	EBee ELan EMil IArd LRHS MBNS MSte SBra SKHP SRms
- 'Superba' Ψ[H4]	CRHN EBee ECrN ECtt ELan EPfP LRHS MLLN NLar SBra SEND SLim SPer SPla WFar WSHC
flexuosa	see *L. japonica* var. *repens*
fragrantissima	More than 30 suppliers
gibbiflora Maxim.	see *L. chrysantha*
giraldii misapplied	see *L. acuminata*
giraldii Rehder	EBee EPfP MAsh MRav SBra SLim WCru
glabrata	SCoo SLim
- B&SWJ 2150	WCru
'Golden Trumpet'	CWGN MAsh SKHP
gracilis	MBlu
grata	see *L.* x *americana* (Miller) K. Koch
x ***heckrottii***	CDoC CMac CRHN CSBt EBee ECtt MBar MGan MGos NBea NBlu NLar NSti
- 'Gold Flame'	CBgR CDul EBee ELan ENot EPfP LAst LBuc LCro LPan LRHS MAsh MBar MBri MGos MRav NBea NBlu NEgg SBra SHBN SLim SMer SPer SRms WBod WFar WMoo WSHC WWeb
§ ***henryi***	More than 30 suppliers
- B&SWJ 8109	WCru
- Sich 1489	WPGP
- 'Copper Beauty'	CFir EBee EQua LAst LHop MAsh MBlu MGos MRav NBPN NCGa NLar SPoG WPGP
- var. ***subcoriacea***	see *L. henryi*
hildebrandiana	CCCN EMil ERea EShb SOWG WPGP XPep
'Hill House'	CHll
'Honey Baby'[PBR]	EBee EBrs MAsh MBlu MBri MGos MRav NHol SBra SPoG WPat
implexa	MAsh NHol WSHC XPep
insularis	see *L. morrowii*
involucrata	CFee CMCN CMHG CPLG CPMA CPle CWib GQui LHop MBNS MBar MBlu NHol SMac SPer WBod WCFE WFar
- var. ***ledebourii***	CBgR CPle EBee ELan EPfP LAst NHol SDys WTel
§ x ***italica*** Tausch Ψ[H4]	CBgR CMac CRHN CSam CTri CWSG ECtt LAst LBMP LEdu LFol MBri MSwo MWgw NPer NSti SBra SCoo SLim SPer SPet WFar WPnn WTel
x ***italica*** ambig.	LFol LHop NBea NPer SBra SEND
§ - Harlequin = 'Sherlite'[PBR] (v)	CSPN ENot EPfP LAst LCro LHop LRHS LSRN MGos NBea NCGa NSti SBra SGar SLim SPer SPlb SPoG SWvt WWeb
japonica	CMen
§ - 'Aureoreticulata' (v)	CDul CMac CWib EBee ECrN ELan ENot EPfP MAsh MBNS MBar MBri MGos MRav NPer SGar SHBN SPet SRms STre WEas WFar WHen WMoo WTel
- 'Cream Cascade'	CWoW EBee EMil LAst MAsh MGos MLLN MSwo NLar SBra SCoo
- 'Dart's Acumen'	CRHN
- 'Dart's World'	EBee MAsh MBri SPla WFar
- 'Halliana' Ψ[H4]	More than 30 suppliers
- 'Hall's Prolific'	More than 30 suppliers
- Honeydew = 'Hinlon' new	ENot
§ - 'Horwood Gem' (v)	CWoW EBee ECtt LFol MGos NLar NPro SCoo WFar
- 'Maskerade' new	IBlr
- 'Mint Crisp'[PBR] (v)	CBow CFwr CSBt CWGN CWoW EBee ECrN ELan ENot EPfP LAst LRHS LSRN MBri MGos NLar SPer SPoG SWvt WFar WMoo WPat
- 'Peter Adams'	see *L. japonica* 'Horwood Gem'
- 'Red World'	EBee
§ - var. ***repens*** Ψ[H4]	More than 30 suppliers
- 'Variegata'	see *L. japonica* 'Aureoreticulata'
korolkowii	CBgR CPMA CSam CWoW EBee EPfP MAsh MBNS MBri NBir SLon SPla WHCG WLeb WPat WSHC
- var. ***zabelii*** misapplied	see *L. tatarica* 'Zabelii'
- var. ***zabelii*** (Rehder) Rehder	ELan
maackii	CHll CMCN CPMA EBee EPfP MBri MRav NLar WHCG
* ***macgregorii***	CMCN
'Mandarin'	CDoC CWSG EBee ELan ENot LBuc LRHS MAsh MBlu MGos NCGa NLar SBra SCoo SLim SPer SPoG SSta SWvt WSpi
maximowiczii var. ***sachalinensis***	NLar
§ ***morrowii***	CMCN
myrtillus	NLar
nitida	CBcs CCVT CDul CMen CSBt CTri ECrN EMac EPfP MRav NBlu NWea SHBN SPer SPoG STre WBVN WFar WHar WHen
- 'Baggesen's Gold' Ψ[H4]	More than 30 suppliers
- 'Cumbrian Calypso' (v)	NPro
- 'Eden Spring'	NPro
- Edmée Gold = 'Briloni'[PBR]	EBee MAsh MBri
- 'Elegant'	LBuc
- 'Ernest Wilson'	MBar
- 'Fertilis'	SPer
- 'Hohenheimer Findling'	NLar
- 'Lemon Beauty' (v)	CDoC CSBt CWan EBee EPfP EPla EShb LAst LHop MBNS MBar MBri MGos MNHC NBir NHol NScw SLPl SPer SPoG SRGP SWvt WFar WHar WMoo WWeb
- 'Lemon Queen'	CWib ELan MSwo

	- 'Lemon Spreader'	CBcs LBuc
§	- 'Maigrün'	CBcs EMil EPfP EWTr LBuc MBri MSwo NPro SPer SWvt WFar
	- Maygreen	see *L. nitida* 'Maigrün'
	- 'Red Tips'	CWan EBee EMil EPfP EPla MBNS MGos NHol WFar WMoo WWeb
	- 'Silver Beauty' (v)	CMHG CWib EBee ECrN EPfP LAst LHop MBar MGos MLHP MRav MSwo NHol NSti SAga SGar SPer SPlb SPoG SRms SWvt WFar WMoo
*	- 'Silver Cloud'	NHol
	- 'Silver Lining'	see *L. pileata* 'Silver Lining'
	- 'Twiggy' (v)	CDoC EMil LBuc LHop MAsh MBrN NHol NLar NPro WCot WLeb WRHF
	nummulariifolia	XPep
	periclymenum	CArn CDul CRWN CTri GPoy MDun MHer MLHP MRav NLar NSco NWea SHFr SPlb WHCG WPnn WSFF
	- 'Belgica' misapplied	see *L.* x *italica*
	- 'Belgica'	More than 30 suppliers
	- 'Florida'	see *L. periclymenum* 'Serotina'
	- 'Graham Thomas' ♀H4	More than 30 suppliers
	- 'Harlequin'PBR	see *L.* x *italica* Harlequin
	- 'Heaven Scent'	CWoW LBuc MGos MNHC NLar SBra WFar WPnn
	- 'Honey Bush' new	CWGN
	- 'Honeybush'	CDoC CPMA CPle CSPN MAsh MBlu MBri NHol NPri SLim WMoo WWeb
	- 'La Gasnérie'	EBee SBra SLim WPnn
	- 'Munster'	CWoW EBee WPnn WSHC
	- 'Red Gables'	CSam CWan CWoW EBee MBNS MGos MRav MSte NLar SBra SCoo SEND SLim SPla WCot WGor WKif WPat WPnn
	- 'Scentsation'PBR	MAsh MBri SCoo
N	- 'Serotina' ♀H4	More than 30 suppliers
	- - EM '85	ENot
*	- ***sulphurea***	WFar
	- 'Sweet Sue'	CRHN CSPN CWoW EBee ECtt ELan EPfP LAst LBuc LFol LRHS MAsh MBNS MBri MGos MLHP MLan MSte MSwo NCGa NEgg NSti SBra SCoo SPoG SWvt WFar WMoo WPnP WWeb
	- 'Winchester'	EBee
	pileata	CBcs CCVT CDul CSBt CTri EBee ECrN ELan EPfP LBuc MBar MGos MRav MSwo NBlu NHol NPer NWea SPer SPoG SRms STre WBVN WCFE WFar WHar WTel
	- 'Moss Green'	CDoC
	- 'Pilot'	SLPl
§	- 'Silver Lining' (v)	EPla SAga
	- 'Stockholm'	SLPl
	x ***purpusii***	CBgR CDoC CPSs CRHN CTri CWSG CWib EBee ECrN EPfP EWTr LAst MBNS MBar MGos MWat NBea SLim SPer SPla SRms WBod WFar WHCG WSHC WTel
	- 'Winter Beauty' ♀H4	More than 30 suppliers
	pyrenaica	CPle
	quinquelocularis f. ***translucens***	MBlu
	ramosissima	NLar
	rupicola var. ***syringantha***	see *L. syringantha*
	saccata	CPMA EPfP
	sempervirens ♀H4	CRHN CSBt EPfP MBNS NBea SBra WFar WSHC
	- 'Dropmore Scarlet'	see *L.* x *brownii* 'Dropmore Scarlet'
	- 'Leo'	CSPN CWGN
N	- f. ***sulphurea***	EBee EPfP LRHS NBea WSHC
	- - 'John Clayton'	SBra
	setifera	CPle
	- 'Daphnis'	EPfP
	similis var. ***delavayi*** ♀H4	CChe CRHN CSPN CSam CWGN EBee ECrN ELan EPfP IClo LRHS MAsh MBri MLan MRav NBea NSti SBra SDix SEND SLPl SPla SPoG WCot WFar WPGP WSHC
	'Simonet'	EBee SBra
	standishii	CBcs CTri EBee MGos MRav SPer WFar WHCG
	- 'Budapest'	MBlu MBri MGos NEgg WPat
	stenantha	NLar
	'Stone Green'	MGos
	subaequalis	SKHP WPGP
§	***syringantha***	More than 30 suppliers
	- 'Grandiflora'	GQui SLon
	tatarica	CMCN CWib EBee MRav WFar WHCG WTel
	- 'Alba'	CPMA
	- 'Arnold Red'	CBcs EBee ELan EMil EPfP MBlu MHer NBlu NLar XPep
	- 'Hack's Red'	CWib EBee EMil EPfP EWTr GQui LHop LSou MRav MWea SAga SKHP SWvt WCot WFar WHCG
§	- 'Zabelii'	EPfP
	x ***tellmanniana***	More than 30 suppliers
	- 'Joan Sayers'	EBee MBNS SBra SCoo SLim WCFE WWeb
	thibetica	MBlu SPer WFar
	tragophylla ♀H4	CBcs CDoC CSBt EBee ELan EPfP IDee LRHS MAsh MBNS MBlu MBri MRav NSti SBra SCoo SLim SPer SPoG SSpi SWvt WSHC
	- 'Maurice Foster'	EBee EMil
*	- 'Pharaoh's Trumpet'	EBee ERea LRHS MAsh MBri SSpi SSta
	webbiana	ELan
	x ***xylosteoides***	MRav WFar
§	- 'Clavey's Dwarf'	EBee MBlu NHol SLPl
	xylosteum	CArn NLar WFar

Lopezia (*Onagraceae*)

	racemosa	CSpe SHFr

Lophatherum (*Poaceae*)

	gracile	CPLG LRav

Lophomyrtus (*Myrtaceae*)

§	***bullata***	CAbP CTrC ECou GQui SPer WFar
	- 'Matai Bay'	CBcs CTrC EBee
§	x ***ralphii***	MHer WPic
	- 'Gloriosa' (v)	CDoC CPle CTrC
	- 'Kathryn'	CBcs CDoC CPLG EBee EMil IDee NLar SKHP SPoG SSpi
	- 'Little Star' (v)	CBcs CDoC CTrC GBri LRHS SKHP SPoG WPat
	- 'Multicolor' (v)	CBcs CTrC EMil
	- 'Pixie'	CAbP CBcs CDoC CTrC SPoG WPat
	- 'Red Dragon'	CBcs CTrC EBee EMil GBri IDee LSou MAsh WFar WPat
	- 'Red Pixie'	CDoC
	- 'Sundae' (v)	CPLG
§	- 'Traversii' (v)	MGos SPoG
	- 'Tricolor' (v)	WFar
	- 'Variegata' (v)	MHer
	- 'Wild Cherry'	CBcs CTrC EBee

Lophosoria (*Dicksoniaceae*)

	quadripinnata	CDTJ CFir WRic

Lophospermum (*Scrophulariaceae*)

§	***erubescens*** ♀H2-3	CHEx CHal CRHN EBee EUnu MSte SBch SGar WPtf

'Magic Dragon' MCCP
§ 'Red Dragon' CSpe EShb SBch SGar
§ ***scandens*** CCCN CRHN ELan
§ - 'Pink Ice' SOWG

loquat see *Eriobotrya japonica*

Loropetalum (*Hamamelidaceae*)

chinense CMCN CPen CWib CWoW SSpi
- 'China Pink' **new** CBcs
- 'Ming Dynasty' CAbP CPen EBee EMil MAsh MGos MPRe SSta
- f. ***rubrum*** CMen CPLG CWib
- - 'Blush' CBgR CPMA CWoW
- - 'Burgundy' CBcs WCot
- - 'Daybreak's Flame' CBcs CPMA CPen NBPN SPoG SSta WGob
- - 'Fire Dance' CAbP CBcs CBgR CDoC CHll CPMA CPen EBee ENot IDee MGos SPoG SSpi SSta SWvt WBrE WFar WGwG
- - 'Pipa's Red' CPen SPoG
- - 'Zhuzhou Fuchsia' CWoW
- 'Snowdance' CAbP
- 'Tang Dynasty' CPen EMil MGos SSta

Lotus (*Papilionaceae*)

berthelotii CCCN CFee CHEx CSpe ECtt ELan EOHP ERea EWin MCot SPet SPoG
- deep red-flowered ♀H1+3 SWvt
berthelotii x ***maculatus*** ♀H1+3 CCCN
corniculatus CArn GWCH MCoo MHer NLan NMir NSco NTHB SECG SIde WSFF XPep
- 'Plenus' (d) MTho NLar WPer
creticus SHFr
cytisoides XPep
* 'Fire Vine' (*berthelotii* x *maculatus*) EShb LAst NPri
'Gold Flash' CHEx LAst
hirsutus ♀H3-4 More than 30 suppliers
- 'Brimstone' (v) CWib ECtt EGoo EWin LHop LSou SPer SWvt
- dwarf LHop
- 'Fréjorgues' XPep
- 'Little Boy Blue' **new** MAsh SPoG
- 'Lois' EBee LHop MDKP MWgw WPGP WSPU
maculatus EOHP EWin SHFr SOWG SPet
maritimus EBee EWll SHFr SPhx SRot
mascaensis misapplied see *L. sessilifolius*
pedunculatus see *L. uliginosus*
pentaphyllus NLar XPep
- subsp. ***herbaceus*** XPep
'Red Flash' LAst
§ ***sessilifolius*** ERea
tetragonolobus SRot
§ ***uliginosus*** NMir NSco WSFF

lovage see *Levisticum officinale*

Ludwigia (*Onagraceae*)

grandiflora WMAq

Luetkea (*Rosaceae*)

pectinata NRya WAbe

Luma (*Myrtaceae*)

§ ***apiculata*** ♀H3 More than 30 suppliers
§ - 'Glanleam Gold' (v) ♀H3 More than 30 suppliers
- 'Variegata' (v) CMHG CTri ISea SAga SLim
§ ***chequen*** CBcs CFee EBee GGar IDee LEdu MHer NLar WBrE WCwm WFar WJek WMoo WPic XPep

Lunaria (*Brassicaceae*)

§ ***annua*** CTca GAbr GWCH MNHC MWgw NPri SIde SWat WHer WSFF
- var. ***albiflora*** ♀H4 MWgw NBir SWat
I - - 'Alba Variegata' (v) CCge CSpe EMar MWgw WBrk WHil WTin
- 'Corfu Blue' **new** CSpe
- 'Luckington' CNat
- 'Munstead Purple' CSpe
* - 'Stella' WHen
- 'Variegata' (v) IBlr MTho NBir SWat WEas WHer
- violet-flowered NBir WFar
biennis see *L. annua*
rediviva CCge CSpe EBee ECGP ECha EMon EPPr EPla GAbr GCra GGar IBlr MRav MSte NBid NChi NPer NSti SMeo SPhx WCot WEas WFar WHen WHer WPGP
- 'Partway White' CMil

Lupinus ✿ (*Papilionaceae*)

'African Sunset' CWCL
albifrons XPep
'Amber Glow' CWCL
'Animal' **new** CWCL
'Approaching Storm' SMrm
'Apricot Spire' CWCL
arboreus ♀H4 More than 30 suppliers
- ***albus*** CSpe CWib NRnb SHGN
- 'Barton-on-Sea' CBgR EWin NRnb SPla
- blue-flowered CBgR CBrm CFwr CHar CWCL CWib ECGP ERou EWTr MAsh MCCP MNHC NBPC NLar NPri SEND SPer SPlb SPoG SWvt WFar WHer
- 'Blue Boy' ELan SPla
- 'Blue Spire' **new** MBri
- cream-flowered ECGP
- 'Mauve Queen' CHEx EWin NRnb SHGN SSvw
- mixed CArn
- prostrate EWin MDKP MMHG
- 'Snow Queen' EWin MAsh MCCP SPer SPoG
- 'Sulphur Yellow' ERou EWin SHGN SWvt
- white-flowered CWCL CWib GGar
- yellow-flowered GGar MAsh MLHP
- yellow and blue-flowered SRkn
arboreus x ***variicolor*** CHid MLHP
arcticus CSpe EBee EDif
'Aston Villa' CWCL
'Avalon' CWCL
'Baby Doll' CWCL
'Bagpuss' **new** CWCL
Band of Nobles Series ♀H4 ECtt MAvo WFar
'Beryl, Viscountess Cowdray' EMon
'Bishop's Tipple' CWCL EWes
'Blossom' **new** CWCL
'Blue Moon' CWCL
'Blue Streak' CWCL
'Blueberry Pie' CWCL
bogotensis B&SWJ 10761 **new** WCru
'Bruiser' CWCL
'Bubblegum' CWCL
'Captain Scarlet' CWCL
'Casanova' CWCL
'Cashmere Cream' CWCL
'Chameleon' **new** CWCL
chamissonis CHid CHll CSpe CWCL EBee EHrv EMan EWes LHop LRHS MAsh MTho SDry SGar SPer SPla SPoG WFar WPtf
'Chandelier' CBcs CSBt CTri EBee ECtt ELan ENot EPfP ERou LRHS MBri MRav

		MWat NEgg NMir NPri SMer SPer SPoG SWal SWvt WBVN WCAu WFar WHen WHil WMnd WWeb
	'Cherry Belle'	CWCL
	'Copperlight'	CWCL
	'Desert Sun'	CWCL
	'Dolly Mixture'	CWCL
	'Dreaming Spires'	CWCL
	'Dumpty'	CWCL
	'Dwarf Lulu'	see *L.* 'Lulu'
	Gallery Series	CSBt ENot LAst SCoo SGar SPlb WFar
	- 'Gallery Blue'	ECtt ENot EPfP GAbr LCro LSRN LSou NCGa NDlv NLar NNor NPri NVic SCoo SPoG WFar
	- 'Gallery Pink'	EPfP LCro LRHS LSou NCGa NDlv NLar NPri NVic SCoo SPla SPoG WFar
	- 'Gallery Red'	CBrm ECtt ENot EPfP GAbr LCro LRHS MLHP NBlu NCGa NDlv NLar NPri NVic SCoo SPla SPoG WFar
	- 'Gallery Rose'	LSRN
	- 'Gallery White'	ENot EPfP GAbr LRHS NBlu NDlv NLar NPri NVic SCoo SPla SPoG WFar
	- 'Gallery Yellow'	CBrm ECtt EPfP GAbr LCro LRHS LSou NBlu NCGa NDlv NLar NPri NVic SCoo SPla SPoG
	'Garden Gnome'	LRav WMoo
	'Gladiator' **new**	CWCL
	'Imperial Robe' **new**	CWCL
	'Ivory Chiffon'	CWCL
	'Lady Penelope'	CWCL
	littoralis	NRnb
§	'Lulu'	ECtt ENot LAst LRHS MRav MWat NBlu SPer SPoG SWvt WFar WMoo WRHF
	'Manhattan Lights'	CWCL NLar
	'Masterpiece' **new**	CWCL
	Minarette Group	CTri ECtt SPet SPoG SRms WFar
	'Mrs Perkins'	SMrm
	mutabilis	NRnb
	'My Castle'	CBcs CSBt CTri EBee ECtt ELan ENot EPfP ERou LRHS LSRN MBri MNHC MRav MWat NEgg NMir NPri SPer SPoG SWal SWvt WBVN WCAu WFar WHen WHil WMnd WMoo WWeb
	'Neptune' **new**	CWCL
	'Noble Maiden' (Band of Nobles Series)	More than 30 suppliers
	nootkatensis	LDai
	'Pauly'	CWCL
	'Persian Slipper'	CWCL NLar
	'Pink Cadillac'	CWCL
	'Plum Duff'	CWCL
	'Plummy Blue'	EDif LSou MCCP MWea
	'Polar Princess'	CWCL ERou EWes GBin SWat
	polyphyllus	EBee
	propinquus	CEnt
	'Queen of Hearts'	CWCL
	'Rainbow Select'	NRnb
	'Red Arrow'	CWCL
	'Red Rum'	CWCL
	'Redhead' **new**	CWCL
	x ***regalis*** 'Morello Cherry'	CWib MWrn
	'Rote Flamme'	EWes
	'Ruby Lantern'	CWCL
	Russell hybrids	CSBt ENot EPfP LAst LHop MHer MLHP MNHC NBlu SECG SPet SPlb SRms SWvt WFar
	'Saffron'	CWCL
	'Saint George'	CWCL
	'Salmon Star'	CWCL
	'Sand Pink'	CWCL EWes
	'Sherbert Dip'	CWCL
	'Silk Rain'	CWCL
	'Snowgoose'	CWCL
	'Sparky'	CWCL
	'Storm'	CWCL
	'Tequila Flame'	CWCL
	'Terracotta'	CWCL
I	'Texas Bonnet' **new**	CWCL
	texensis	CSpe
	- 'Almo Fire' **new**	CWCL
	'The Chatelaine' (Band of Nobles Series)	More than 30 suppliers
	'The Governor' (Band of Nobles Series)	More than 30 suppliers
	'The Page' (Band of Nobles Series)	CBcs EBee ELan ENot EPfP ERou LRHS LSRN MBri MNHC MRav MWat NEgg NMir NPri SPer SPoG SWal SWvt WBVN WFar WMnd WMoo WWeb
	'Thor'	CWCL
	'Thundercloud'	CDes SMrm
	'Tutti Frutti'	WHil WRos
	variicolor	CHid CPLG CSpe
	versicolor	CArn CSpe CSsd EMan LDai MEHN MLLN SMad WBrk WHoo WPtf
	Woodfield hybrids **new**	MAvo

Lutzia (*Brassicaceae*)

	cretica	XPep

Luzula (*Juncaceae*)

	alpinopilosa	CBig EPPr GBin GFor XIsg
	x ***borreri***	EPPr
	- 'Botany Bay' (v)	ECtt EPPr EPla GBin NHol WMoo
	forsteri	CBgR
	lactea	EPPr
	lutea **new**	GFor
	luzuloides	CBig GFor GQui NBre NLar WPer XIsg
	- 'Schneehäschen'	EMon GBin LBBr MWgw
	maxima	see *L. sylvatica*
	nivalis	EWTr GAbr
	nivea	More than 30 suppliers
	- 'Lucius' **new**	XIsg
	pilosa	CBgR EPla NNor
	- 'Igel'	EBee GBin SLPl
	purpureosplendens	EMon
	'Ruby Stiletto'	EBee
	rufa	ECou
§	***sylvatica***	CHEx CRWN CSWP ELan EPPr EPfP EPla LEdu MLLN MMoz MRav NBro NOrc WFar WHer WPGP WShi XIsg
	- 'A. Rutherford'	see *L. sylvatica* 'Taggart's Cream'
	- from Tatra Mountains, Czechoslovakia	EPPr
	- 'Aurea'	CHEx CHar CHrt CKno CSWP ECha ECrN EHul EPGN EPPr EPfP EPla LAst LBMP LRHS MBar MBri MMoz MRav NBid NSti SApp SPla STre WCot WFar WLeb WMoo
	- 'Aureomarginata'	see *L. sylvatica* 'Marginata'
I	- 'Auslese'	CBig EBee EPPr GBin GFor NLar NNor WMoo
	- 'Barcode' (v)	CNat
	- 'Bromel'	EBee
	- 'Hohe Tatra'	CBcs CBgR CBrm CElw CMea CPrp EBee ECtt EMon EPPr EPfP EWes EWsh GBin GMaP MBNS MCCP MWgw NBro NGdn NHol NVic SPer SPla SPoG WFar WHil WPGP WPnP
§	- 'Marginata' (v)	More than 30 suppliers
*	- f. ***nova***	EPPr

- 'Select'	XIsg
§ - 'Taggart's Cream' (v)	CElw EBee EMar EPla GGar NBid NHol SApp WDyG WLeb WMoo WPrP
- 'Tauernpass'	CBgR EPPr EPla NHol SMac
- 'Wäldler'	EPPr MBNS NHol
- 'Waulkmill Bay'	SLPl
ulophylla	CBig CFir CTrC EAlp ECou EDAr GEdr GFor NBre NLar NWCA XIsg

Luzuriaga (*Philesiaceae*)

radicans	CCCN CFee ERos IBlr WCru WFar WSHC
- MK 92	SSpi

Lychnis (*Caryophyllaceae*)

alpina	EBee ECho EDAr EPfP GKev GMaP NBlu NEgg NNor NPri NVic SGar WFar WPer
- 'Alba'	GKev NBir
- 'Rosea'	NBir
- 'Snow Flurry'	EDAr GKev NCGa NLar
§ x ***arkwrightii***	ECha ELan NBre NNor SRot WFar
- 'Orange Zwerg'	CWCL EBee LAst LSou NEgg WHal WHlf WWeb
- 'Vesuvius'	CBcs EBee EPfP EShb LAst LBMP LRHS MNrw NBPN NBir NBlu NNor SPav SPer SPoG SRms STes SWal WMnd WPer
chalcedonica 🏆^{H4}	More than 30 suppliers
- var. ***albiflora***	CEnt EBee LAst LRHS MWgw NBro SPer WBrk WFar WHen WMoo WPer
- - 'Snow White'	ECtt SMer
- 'Carnea'	EBrs EShb EWsh NBre SPhx WBrk WPer
- 'Dusky Pink'	LSou
- 'Dusky Salmon'	MDKP MGol NBPC NDlv
- 'Flore Pleno' (d)	EBee ECha ELan ERou EShb MBri MLLN NLar WCot WFar
- 'Morgenrot'	MCCP NNor
- 'Pinkie'	ELan NLar SBod WLin
- 'Rauhreif'	EBee EShb NBre
- 'Rosea'	EBee EPfP NBir WFar WHen WHrl WMoo WPer
* - 'Salmonea'	ECtt GBri MWea NBir SRms WCAu
- salmon-pink-flowered	COIW
- 'Summer Sparkle Pink'	SWal
- 'Summer Sparkle Red'	SWal
- 'Summer Sparkle White'	SWal
cognata	CDes EBee GMac MDKP
- B&SWJ 4234	WCru
§ ***coronaria*** 🏆^{H4}	More than 30 suppliers
- 'Abbotswood Rose'	see *L.* x *walkeri* 'Abbotswood Rose'
- 'Alba' 🏆^{H4}	More than 30 suppliers
- 'Angel's Blush'	EBee GAbr MBnl MDKP NBir SPav SPer WRHF
- Atrosanguinea Group	CBre EBee ERou GMaP IBlr LRHS MBnl MRav NCot NEgg NPri SPer SPoG
- 'Cerise'	MArl MDKP NBir WRHF
- 'Dancing Ladies'	WMnd
- Gardeners' World = 'Blych' (d)	EBee GBri LSou NGdn NSti SBla SPer SPhx WCot WTMC
- 'Hutchinson's Cream' (v)	NPro
- Oculata Group	CMHG CSpe EBee ECtt EGoo ERou GCra LEdu MTho NPri SGar SPav SPlb SPoG SWal WFar WHen WMoo WTin
§ ***coronata*** var. ***sieboldii***	NBre
dioica	see *Silene dioica*
flos-cuculi	CArn CBen CEnt CHrt CPom CRWN CSam EBee ECho EHon EHrv EMFW EPfP LEdu MHer MMuc MSal NBre NLan NMir NPri SECG SGar WHen WHer WMAq WMoo WPnP WSFF
- var. ***albiflora***	CBre EBee EMFW MLLN NBro NLar SSvw WHer WMnd WMoo WOut
- Jenny = 'Lychjen' (d)	EBrs GBri
* - 'Little Robin'	ECho EDAr
- 'Nana'	CSpe ECho EDAr GAbr NLar WPer
- 'White Robin'	CBod CEnt CTca EBee EWTr GBri LRHS NPri WHil
flos-jovis 🏆^{H4}	CAby CEnt EBee EPfP LRHS NLar NPri SBch SRms WMoo WPer
- 'Hort's Variety'	EBrs MRav SBla WSHC
- 'Minor'	see *L. flos-jovis* 'Nana'
§ - 'Nana'	NWCA
- 'Peggy'	CMMP EBee EGoo GMaP LRHS MCCP NBre NCGa NLar WWeb
fulgens	NBre
x ***haageana***	EBee LRHS NBre NLar NWCA SRms WRHF WSpi
'Hill Grounds'	EBee MAvo WCot
lagascae	see *Petrocoptis pyrenaica* subsp. *glaucifolia*
miqueliana	NBre NLar WGwG WMoo
- 'Variegated Lacy Red' (v)	EBee
'Molten Lava'	CFir EBee ECho LRHS MHer MRav NBre NLar SGar WPer WWeb
nutans	MSal
* ***sikkimensis***	NBre
'Terry's Pink'	EBee MLLN NCGa WFar WHil
§ ***viscaria***	CArn CEnt ECha GCra LDai MSal NCiC NNor SBch SGar SHGN WCot WFar WMoo WTin
- 'Alba'	EBee ECha MLLN NBre NBro NNor
- ***alpina***	see *L. viscaria*
§ - subsp. ***atropurpurea***	CMea ECtt LRav LSou MHar NBre SRms SSvw WHrl WOut
- 'Feuer'	CKno EBee NCGa NEgg NLar NVic WMoo
- 'Firebird'	EWes NBre
- 'Plena' (d)	EBee MDun NEgg
- 'Schnee'	MSte
- 'Splendens'	EPfP EQua MNFA SPad SPet
- 'Splendens Plena' (d) 🏆^{H4}	CAby CHar EBee GMac MArl MWgw NBre NBro WEas WFar
§ x ***walkeri*** 'Abbotswood Rose' 🏆^{H4}	IBlr WBrk
wilfordii	EShb NEgg SHar
§ ***yunnanensis***	EBee GKev MSte NBid SIng SPav SPhx WMoo WPer
- ***alba***	see *L. yunnanensis*

Lycianthes (*Solanaceae*)

rantonnetii	see *Solanum rantonnetii*

Lycium (*Solanaceae*)

barbarum	EUnu EWes MBri NBlu SMad
chinense	CArn CMen NLar
cf. ***cinereum***	EUnu
europaeum	XPep

Lycopodium (*Lycopodiaceae*)

clavatum	GPoy

Lycopsis see *Anchusa*

Lycopus (*Lamiaceae*)

americanus	EBee MSal
europaeus	CArn ELau GPoy MHer MSal WGwG WHer
lucidus	MSal
virginicus	COld MSal SDys

Lycoris (*Amaryllidaceae*)

albiflora	CHHB EBrs ECho WCot
aurea	EBee EBrs ECho LRHS WHil
haywardii	WCot
radiata	CHHB EBee EBrs ECho GBin GSki LRHS WHil
sanguinea	EBrs ECho LRHS
- var. ***kiusiana*** new	EBee
shaanxianensis new	EBee
sprengeri	CHHB EBee EBrs ECho
squamigera	EBee EBrs ECho LRHS WHil

Lygodium (*Schizaeaceae*)

japonicum	NBid WFib WRic

Lygos see *Retama*

Lyonia (*Ericaceae*)

ligustrina	LRHS NLar
mariana	NLar

Lyonothamnus (*Rosaceae*)

floribundus subsp. ***aspleniifolius***	CAbb CCCN CDoC CGHE CPLG CPSs EBee NLar SAPC SArc SGar SKHP SMad SSpi WBor WFar WPGP

Lysichiton (*Araceae*)

americanus ♀H4	More than 30 suppliers
americanus x ***camtschatcensis***	ECha SSpi
camtschatcensis ♀H4	CBcs CBen CDWL CFwr CLAP CWat EBee ECha EHon ELan EMFW EPfP GAbr ITer ITim MDun MRav NEgg NOrc NPer SMad SPer SSpi SWat SWvt WCot WFar WPnP WShi

Lysimachia ✿ (*Primulaceae*)

B&SWJ 8632 from Korea	WCru
§ ***atropurpurea***	CArn CHar CSpe EAro EBee EGle ELan EPfP LHop LRHS MNFA SMad SPer SPlb SPoG STes WCot WFar WMnd WRos WSpi
- 'Beaujolais'	CBod CEnt ECGP LRHS LSRN MBNS MCot NBPC NPri SMeo SPav SRkn WWeb WWlt
- 'Geronimo'	CSpe LRav
barystachys	EBee GMac MGol MRav MWrn SHar SMac SMer WFar WOut
candida	WCot
ciliata	CMHG CPLG EBee ECha ELan GMaP MNrw NEgg NGdn NSti SWat WCAu WCot WFar WMnd WOut WPer
§ - 'Firecracker' ♀H4	More than 30 suppliers
- 'Purpurea'	see *L. ciliata* 'Firecracker'
clethroides ♀H4	More than 30 suppliers
- 'Geisha' (v)	CBow EBee LSou MBNS SPer SPoG WCot
- 'Lady Jane'	CBrm MWrn SRms
§ ***congestiflora***	NPer SHFr SPet
- HWJ 846	WCru
- 'Golden Falls'	LAst NEgg
- 'Outback Sunset'PBR (v)	ECtt EWin LAst NBlu NPri
ephemerum	More than 30 suppliers
fortunei	EBee MWat SMac
henryi	EWes
hybrida	EBee WCot
japonica var. ***minutissima***	CFee CStu
lichiangensis	CPLG EBee GKev GSki MBNS MGol MLLN NRnb SGar SHFr WMoo WPer
lyssii	see *L. congestiflora*
mauritiana	EWin
- B&SWJ 8815	WCru
melampyroides	WCot
minoricensis	CArn EBee EEls EHrv ELan EMan EWin LFur MBNS SWat WPer WSpi
nemorum	WPer
- subsp. ***azorica*** new	WCot
- 'Pale Star'	CBre
nummularia	CHal COIW CSBt CTri CWat ECtt EHon EPfP EShb GPoy MBar SHFr SWat WBrk WCot
- 'Aurea' ♀H4	More than 30 suppliers
paridiformis	WCot
- var. ***stenophylla***	EBee WCot WPGP
- - DJHC 704	CDes
punctata misapplied	see *L. verticillaris*
punctata L.	More than 30 suppliers
§ - 'Alexander' (v)	More than 30 suppliers
- 'Gaulthier Brousse'	EBee WCot
- Golden Alexander = 'Walgoldalex'PBR (v)	CBct EKen ELon MBNS MBnl MBri NEgg NHol NLar SPer SPoG
- 'Golden Glory' (v)	WCot
- 'Ivy Maclean' (v)	CRez EBee EMan EWin LSou SWvt WCot
- 'Senior'	EMil
- 'Sunspot'	EBee NBre
- 'Variegata'	see *L. punctata* 'Alexander'
- ***verticillata***	see *L. verticillaris*
'Purpurea'	see *L. atropurpurea*
pyramidalis	CPLG
quadrifolia	EBee
serpyllifolia	ECtt
Snow Candles = 'L9902'PBR	EBee GBin LHop LSou
taliensis BWJ 7797	WCru
thyrsiflora	CBen EBee EHon EMFW NPer SWat WCot WHer WMAq
§ ***verticillaris***	CTri WCot
vulgaris	CArn CRWN NSco SIde WCot WFar WMoo WPer
- subsp. ***davurica***	WCot
yunnanensis	CDMG CDes CPLG EKen EMan GKev GMaP MDKP MGol MHar NRnb SGar WPer WPtf

Lysionotus (*Gesneriaceae*)

* ***carniolica***	CStu
gamosepalus B&SWJ 7241	WCru
aff. ***kwangsiensis*** HWJ 643	WCru
'Lavender Lady'	CSpe
pauciflorus	CDes SKHP WAbe
- B&SWJ 189	WCru
- B&SWJ 303	WCru
- B&SWJ 335	WCru
serratus new	MWea

Lythrum (*Lythraceae*)

alatum	EShb NBre
anceps	EBee NBre NLar SPhx
salicaria	CArn CBen CBrm CKno CPLG CRWN CWat EBee EHon EMFW LBMP MHer MLHP MNHC MSal NBro NLan SECG SPlb SRms SWat WBrk WFar WHer WMoo WPnP WSFF WShi WWlt
- 'Blush' ♀H4	More than 30 suppliers
- 'Brightness'	CDWL
§ - 'Feuerkerze' ♀H4	More than 30 suppliers
- Firecandle	see *L. salicaria* 'Feuerkerze'
- 'Happy'	NHol SMrm
- 'Lady Sackville'	CDWL EBee ECtt EGle EMFW GBuc GMaP LRHS MBNS MCot NDov SSvw WCAu WTMC WTel

- 'Morden Pink'	CChe CPrp EBee EGle MBri MDKP MSte NCob NGby SPhx WFar WPtf WSHC
- 'Prichard's Variety'	CKno EBee WPGP
- 'Red Gem'	NEgg
- 'Robert'	More than 30 suppliers
- 'Robin'	EBee SPoG
- 'Rose'	ELan NBir NEgg SWvt
- 'Rosencaule'	EBee
- 'Stichflamme'	NCob
- 'Swirl'	EBee ECtt EGle LLWG MDKP NBre NDov WFar
- 'The Beacon'	CMHG EBee EMFW EMan MDKP SRms
- 'Zigeunerblut'	CKno CMHG EBee EGle MDKP MRav MSte NGby NLar SPhx SWat
virgatum	CMHG EPPr NDov SMHy SPhx WMoo WOut WSHC
- 'Dropmore Purple'	CDWL CHar COlW CSBt CSam EBee ECtt EGle EPPr ERou LBMP LHop LRHS MBri MDKP MRav MSte NCob NDov SAga SMer SPhx WCAu WFar WPtf
- 'Rose Queen'	ECha ECtt EMan MDKP MRav NDov SMHy WFar WPer
- 'Rosy Gem'	CMMP CWan EBee ECtt EPfP GMaP GMac MBNS MWat MWgw NBPC NBid NBro SECG SRGP SRms SWal SWvt WFar WHoo WPer WWeb
- 'The Rocket'	CMMP CSam CTri EBee EGle EPfP ERou LAst LRHS MRav NBro NDov NEgg SMer SPer SWvt

Lytocaryum (*Arecaceae*)

§ ***weddellianum*** ♀H1	LPal MBri

M

Maackia (*Papilionaceae*)

amurensis	CBcs CDul CMCN EBee ELan EPfP IDee IMGH LRav MBri MWea WBVN WNor
- var. ***buergeri***	CLnd GBin
chinensis	CBcs CMCN MBlu MBri NLar
tashiroi new	CBcs

Macbridea (*Lamiaceae*)

caroliniana	WPGP

mace, English see *Achillea ageratum*

Macfadyena (*Bignoniaceae*)

uncata	SOWG
§ ***unguis-cati***	CCCN CRHN EShb MJnS XPep

Machaeranthera (*Asteraceae*)

bigelovii	NBre WPer

Machaerina (*Cyperaceae*)

rubiginosa 'Variegata' (v)	CDWL CKno

Machilus see *Persea*

Mackaya (*Acanthaceae*)

§ ***bella*** ♀H1	CHII ERea EShb SOWG

Macleania (*Ericaceae*)

ericae	WCot

Macleaya (*Papaveraceae*)

cordata misapplied	see *M.* x *kewensis*
§ ***cordata*** (Willd.) R. Br. ♀H4	CArn COlW CWCL EBee ELan EPfP EWsh LHop LRHS MBri MLHP MWgw NBir NDov NOrc NPri SPer SPhx SPlb SRms SWal WCAu WCot WFar WMnd WMoo WPer
- 'Celadon Ruffles'	GBin
§ x ***kewensis***	EBee EDAr GAbr LBMP MBri WHoo WPGP
- 'Flamingo' ♀H4	CPrp EBee ECha EQua GBuc MRav NEgg NGdn SBch SWvt
§ ***microcarpa***	CDMG MGol SGar SWat WSel
- 'Kelway's Coral Plume' ♀H4	CBcs CKno CSam EBee ECha EHrv ELan EPfP ERou GKev GMaP LCro LRHS LSRN MBri MGos MRav MWat NBro NCGa NEgg NGdn SPer SPoG SWvt WBrE WCot WFar WMnd
- 'Spetchley Ruby'	EBee GBin MRav NDov SPhx WCot
'Plum Tassel'	WCot

Maclura (*Moraceae*)

pomifera	CAgr CArn CBcs CMCN IDee MGol NLar SPlb WFar WPGP XPep
- 'Pretty Woman'	NLar
tricuspidata	CAgr CPle

Macrodiervilla see *Weigela*

Macropiper (*Piperaceae*)

§ ***excelsum***	CHEx ECou

Macrozamia (*Zamiaceae*)

communis	CBrP CKob LPal WNor
diplomera	CBrP
dyeri	see *M. riedlei*
glaucophylla	CBrP
johnsonii	CBrP
lucida	CBrP
miquelii	CBrP LPal
moorei	CBrP ETod LPal
mountperiensis	CBrP
§ ***riedlei***	CBrP LPal

Maddenia (*Rosaceae*)

hypoleuca	NLar

Maesa (*Myrsinaceae*)

japonica	CPLG
montana	CPLG

Magnolia ✿ (*Magnoliaceae*)

acuminata	CBcs CLnd CMCN EPfP IClo IDee IMGH NBhm NLar NPal
- 'Golden Glow'	CBcs
* - 'Kinju'	CEnd NLar
- 'Koban Dori'	CBcs CPMA CTho ECho EMil
§ - var. ***subcordata***	EBee NEgg NLar
§ - - 'Miss Honeybee'	SSpi
'Advance'	CPMA
'Albatross'	CBcs CDoC CEnd CTho SKHP SSpi WPGP
'Alixeed'	CBcs
'Ambrosia'	CBcs CPMA
amoena	CBcs CSdC WNor
- 'Multiogeca'	CBcs CWib
'Ann' ♀H4	CBcs CPLG CSdC CTrh MGos NLar SSpi
'Anticipation'	CEnd
'Apollo'	CDoC CEnd CPMA MBri SKHP SSpi
ashei	see *M. macrophylla* subsp. *ashei*
'Athene'	CBcs CDoC CMHG CPMA
'Atlas'	CBcs CDoC CEnd CMHG CPMA CTho LMil WPGP

	Name	Suppliers
	'Banana Split'	CBcs SSpi
	'Betty' ♀H4	CBcs CDoC CDul CSdC IDee LPan MGos NLar NScw SLim SSta WBod WFar WOrn
	'Big Dude'	CBcs CEnd CMCN IArd IClo SSpi
	biondii	CBcs NLar WNor WPGP
	'Black Beauty' **new**	CBcs
	'Black Tulip'	ENot EPfP LRHS MGos NPri SCoo SPoG SSpi WBod
	x ***brooklynensis***	NPal
	- 'Evamaria'	CBcs CTho
	- 'Hattie Carthan'	CBcs WPGP
	- 'Woodsman'	CBcs NLar SSta
	- 'Yellow Bird'	CBcs CDoC CEnd CMCN CPMA CTho EBee ENot EPfP LRHS MAsh MBlu MBri MDun MGos MLan NLar NPal WGer
	'Butterbowl' **new**	CBcs
	'Butterflies'	CBcs CDoC CEnd CMHG CPMA CTho EBee ELan EMil EPfP ISea LHyd LMil LRHS MAsh MDun NLar SHBN SSpi SSta WBVN WBod WFar WGob WPGP WSpi
	'Caerhays Belle'	CBcs CPMA ECho MBri NLar SSpi
	'Caerhays New Purple'	CLnd ECho
	'Caerhays Surprise'	CBcs CPMA SKHP
	campbellii	CBcs CMCN ELan EPfP ISea LRHS MDun SSpi WFar WPic
	- Alba Group	CBcs CEnd MGos WFar WPGP
	- - 'Ethel Hillier'	CBcs
I	- - 'Trelissick Alba'	CTho
	- 'Betty Jessel'	CPMA CTho
	- 'Darjeeling'	CBcs CDoC ECho EMil MBri SKHP
	- 'Lamellan Pink'	CTho
	- 'Lamellan White'	CTho
	- subsp. ***mollicomata***	CEnd CHEx EPfP ISea WFar
	- - 'Lanarth'	CBcs CEnd SKHP SSpi WBod
	- - 'Maharanee'	CBcs
	- - 'Peter Borlase'	CBcs CDoC CTho
	- (Raffillii Group) 'Charles Raffill'	CAbP CBcs CDoC CDul CLnd EBee ELan EPfP LMil MAsh MBri MDun MGos MLan SHBN SKHP SLim SPer WHCr WPGP
	- - 'Kew's Surprise'	CBcs CDoC CPMA
	- 'Sidbury' **new**	CBcs MBri
	'Candy Cane'	LPan WPGP
	Chameleon	see *M.* 'Chang Hua'
§	'Chang Hua'	CPMA MBri MDun NLar
	'Charles Coates'	CSdC MDun NLar WPGP
	China Town = 'Jing Ning'	MDun
	'Columbus'	CPMA CSdC SSpi WPGP
	'Coral Lake'	MDun
	cordata	see *M. acuminata* var. *subcordata*
	- 'Miss Honeybee'	see *M. acuminata* var. *subcordata* 'Miss Honeybee'
	cylindrica misapplied	see *M.* 'Pegasus'
	cylindrica ambig.	CBcs
	cylindrica Wilson	CMCN EPfP IArd IDee SSpi
	'Daphne'	CBcs
	'Darrell Dean'	CPMA CTho WPGP
	'David Clulow'	CBcs CPMA CTho ECho ENot SKHP
	dawsoniana	CMCN EBee EPfP IMGH NLar WSpi
	- 'Clarke'	SKHP
	'Daybreak'	CBcs SSpi
	dealbata	see *M. macrophylla* subsp. *dealbata*
	delavayi	CBcs CBrP CHEx CMCN EPfP LRHS SAPC SArc
§	***denudata*** ♀H3-4	CBcs CDul CMCN CTho CWib EMil EPfP ISea LMil LPan LRHS MGos NLar SSpi SSta WBod WFar WNor
	- 'Dubbel'	CBcs MDun SKHP

	Name	Suppliers
	- 'Forrest's Pink'	CBcs
	- Fragrant Cloud = 'Dan Xin'	CPMA CWib MBri MDun NLar
	- 'Gere'	CBcs
	- Yellow River = 'Fei Huang'	CBcs CEnd CWib EBee MBri MDun NLar SKHP SMad SPoG SSpi WOrn
	'Elizabeth' ♀H4	More than 30 suppliers
	'Eskimo'	MBri SKHP SSpi
	'Felix Jury'	CBcs ELan ENot
	'Fireglow'	CBcs CTho
	'Frank Gladney'	CPMA CTho
	'Frank's Masterpiece'	MDun
	'Full Eclipse'	WPGP
	'Galaxy' ♀H4	CBcs CDoC CEnd CMCN CSdC EBee ECho EPfP EWTr IArd IMGH ISea LCro LMil LRHS MBar MBri MDun MGos MSte NBhm SLim SSpi SSta WBrE WGob WPGP
	'George Henry Kern'	CBcs CDoC EMil ERas IArd IDee ISea LBuc LRHS MBri MSte NLar SSpi SSta WCFE WFar WGob
	globosa	CPLG EBee SKHP WFar WGob WPGP
	'Gold Crown'	SSpi
	'Gold Star'	CBcs CDoC CEnd CMCN CPMA CSdC CTho LPan LRHS MAsh MBlu MBri MGos NLar NPal SPoG SSpi WOrn
	'Golden Endeavour'	MDun
	'Golden Gift'	CPMA SSpi
	'Golden Sun'	CBcs CPMA MBri NLar
	grandiflora	CMCN CWib EPfP LAst LCro LEdu LRHS MGos MRav MWya NBlu NLar SAPC SArc SHBN WFar WNor WOrn
	- 'Blanchard'	CBcs CPMA
	- 'Bracken's Brown Beauty'	MBri
	- 'Charles Dickens'	CBcs CPMA
	- 'Edith Bogue'	CDul CPMA ECho EQua MAsh MBri MGos NLar WBVN WGob
	- 'Exmouth' ♀H3-4	More than 30 suppliers
	- 'Ferruginea'	CBcs CPMA EBee MGos NBea
	- 'Francois Treyve'	EMil EPfP EQua
	- 'Galissonnière'	CBcs CWib ECrN EPfP ERom IMGH LPan LRHS MGos NBlu SLim SSpi SWvt WFar WPGP
I	- 'Gallissonnière Nana'	LPan SBLw
	- 'Goliath'	CBcs CDul CEnd CHEx CPSs ELan EPfP LCro LPan SBra SSpi WPGP
	- 'Harold Poole'	CBcs CPMA
	- 'Kay Paris'	SKHP
	- 'Little Gem'	CBcs CDoC CPMA ELan EPfP LRHS MGos NLar SKHP SSpi
	- 'Mainstreet'	CBcs CPMA
	- 'Monland'	CBcs
	- 'Monlia'	CBcs CPMA
	- 'Nannetensis'	CPMA EQua
	- 'Overton'	CBcs CPMA
	- 'Praecox' **new**	MWya
	- 'Russet'	CBcs CPMA
	- 'Saint Mary'	CBcs CPMA
	- 'Samuel Sommer'	CPMA SAPC SArc
	- 'Symmes Select'	CBcs CPMA
	- 'Undulata'	WGer
	- 'Victoria' ♀H3-4	CBcs CDoC CDul CPMA CTho ELan EPfP LHyd LMil LRHS MAsh MBlu MGos SLim SPoG SReu SSpi SSta WFar WGob WPGP
	'Green Bee'	CBcs
	'Green Mist' **new**	CBcs
	'Heaven Scent' ♀H4	More than 30 suppliers
	'Helen Fogg'	WPGP
	heptapeta	see *M. denudata*
§	'Hong Yur'	CEnd CPMA MDun
	'Hot Flash'	CBcs CPMA

	hypoleuca	see *M. obovata* Thunb.
	'Ian's Red'	CBcs CPMA
	'Indian Tapestry' **new**	MBri
	'Iolanthe'	CBcs CEnd CGHE CMCN CMHG CPMA CSdC CTho ECho ELan MAsh MGos NBhm NHol NLar SPer SSpi SSta WFar WPGP
	'J.C. Williams'	CBcs CDoC CPMA CTho
	'Jane' ♀^{H4}	CDoC CSdC ELan EPfP LMil LRHS MAsh MBri MGos SHBN SPer
	'Jersey Belle'	CPMA
	'Joe McDaniel'	CPMA CSdC MLan NLar SSpi WBod
	'Jon Jon'	CPMA MBri
	'Judy'	EMil NEgg NLar
	x ***kewensis*** hort. ex Pearce 'Wada's Memory'	see *M. salicifolia* 'Wada's Memory'
	kobus	CBcs CDul CLnd CMCN CPLG CSBt CTho EBee EPfP IMGH LPan MDun MWya NMoo SBLw SLdr SPer WFar WGob WNor
	- var. ***borealis***	CPMA
	- 'Esveld Select' **new**	MBri SSpi
	- 'Janaki Ammal'	CPMA
§	- 'Norman Gould'	CDoC EPfP MBri NLar NScw SSta WGer
	'Lamellan Surprise'	CTho
	'Leda'	CMCN SSpi
	'Legacy'	NLar
	'Legend' **new**	EPfP
§	***liliiflora***	CBcs MBar NBlu
§	- 'Nigra' ♀^{H4}	More than 30 suppliers
	- 'Oldfield'	WPGP
*	'Limelight'	CBcs CSdC
	x ***loebneri***	CBcs LRHS WNor
	- 'Ballerina'	CDoC MBri NLar
	- 'Donna'	CBcs MGos NLar SSpi WGer
	- 'Leonard Messel' ♀^{H4}	More than 30 suppliers
	- 'Merrill' ♀^{H4}	CBcs CMCN CMHG CTho CTrh CWib EBee ELan EPfP ISea LMil LPan LRHS MAsh MBri MGos MWat SPer SReu SSpi SSta WBVN WBod WCwm WFar WGob WPGP
	- 'Pink Perfection'	MDun
	- 'Snowdrift'	NLar SSta
	- 'Wildcat' **new**	CBcs
	- 'Willow Wood' **new**	CPMA
	'Lois' **new**	CBcs ENot SKHP SSpi
	'Lombardy Rose' **new**	MBri
§	***lotungensis***	NLar
	macrophylla	CBcs CBrP CHEx CMCN EPfP IClo IDee MBlu SAPC SArc WNor WPGP
§	- subsp. ***ashei***	SKHP WNor
	- subsp. ***ashei*** x ***virginiana*** **new**	CPMA
§	- subsp. ***dealbata***	WBod
	'Manchu Fan'	CBcs CMCN CPMA CSdC ECho EMil IArd MDun NLar SSpi
	'Margaret Helen'	CPMA ECho
	'Mark Jury'	CBcs
	'Maryland'	CPMA CWib EQua SSta
	'Maxine Merrill'	IDee SSpi
	'May to Frost' **new**	CBcs
	'Milky Way' ♀^{H4}	CBcs CDoC CGHE CMHG CPMA CTho LRHS MGos SKHP SSpi WPGP
	'Moon Spire' **new**	CBcs
	'Moondance' **new**	CBcs
	'Nimbus'	CPMA
	obovata Diels	see *M. officinalis*
§	***obovata*** Thunb. ♀^{H4}	CBcs CMCN CPMA CTho EPfP IDee IMGH MDun MGos MLan NLar SSpi SSta WPGP
§	***officinalis***	CBcs CMCN EPfP NLar WBVN WFar
	- var. ***biloba***	CGHE EPfP NLar SSpi WPGP
	'Peachy'	CBcs NLar
§	'Pegasus'	CEnd SSpi
	'Peppermint Stick'	CBcs CSdC ECho MGos SSta
	'Peter Smithers'	CBcs CPMA CTho WFar
	'Phelan Bright'	CSdC
	'Phillip Tregunna'	CBcs CTho SSpi
	'Pickard's Sundew'	see *M.* 'Sundew'
	'Pinkie' ♀^{H4}	EMil EPfP LRHS MBri MGos NLar SSpi SSta WGer WGob
	'Pirouette'	SKHP SSpi
	'Princess Margaret'	CBcs CDoC CPMA ECho SSpi
	x ***proctoriana***	CAbP CDoC CGHE CPLG CSdC EBee EPfP LMil NLar SKHP WPGP
	x ***proctoriana*** Gloster form	NLar
I	x ***proctoriana*** 'Proctoriana'	LMil
	'Purple Platter' **new**	CBcs
	'Purple Sensation'	CBcs CPMA
	quinquepeta	see *M. liliiflora*
	'Randy'	CBcs EPfP MGos
	'Raspberry Ice'	CBcs CDoC CMHG CPLG CSam CSdC CTho EBee EPfP ISea LMil LRHS MAsh NLar SLim WFar WGob
	'Ricki'	CBcs CSdC EMil EPfP LBuc MBlu MGos NLar SPoG WFar
	rostrata	CGHE EBee ELan SKHP SSpi WPGP
	'Rouged Alabaster'	CDoC
	'Royal Crown'	CBcs CDoC CSdC EMil EQua MRav NBhm NLar SLim WGer
	'Ruby'	CBcs CPMA ECho MGos
	'Ruth'	CBcs
	salicifolia ♀$^{H3-4}$	CBcs CMCN EPfP ISea LRHS SSpi SSta WSpi
	- 'Jermyns'	SSpi
	- upright	WPGP
§	- 'Wada's Memory' ♀^{H4}	CDoC CMCN CMHG CPMA CTho ELan EPfP IClo LMil LRHS MAsh MBri MLan MSte NBea NLar NVic SPer SSpi SSta WFar WGob
	- 'Windsor Beauty'	SSpi
	sargentiana var. ***robusta***	CBcs CBrd CEnd CMCN EBee ELan EPfP IMGH ISea LMil MDun MGos SPer SSpi SSta WFar
	- var. ***robusta*** 'Blood Moon'	SSpi
	- - 'Multipetal'	CBrd
	- - 'Trengwainton Glory'	SKHP SSpi
	'Satisfaction'	MBri
	'Sayonara' ♀^{H4}	CBcs CPMA ECho EPfP MBri SSpi WPGP
	'Schmetterling'	see *M.* x *soulangeana* 'Pickard's Schmetterling'
	'Serene'	CBcs CEnd CMHG CPMA ECho LMil MBri MGos SSpi SSta
	'Shirazz'	CBcs CPMA SSpi
	sieboldii	More than 30 suppliers
	- B&SWJ 4127	WCru
	- from Korea, hardy	GGGa
	- 'Colossus'	MBri SSpi
	- 'Genesis'	SSpi
	- 'Michiko Renge'	MBri NLar
	- 'Pride of Norway' **new**	CBcs
	- subsp. ***sinensis***	CBcs CDoC CLnd CMCN CPMA CSam CTho ELan EPfP GCra GGGa IMGH LRHS MBlu MDun MWya SSpi SSta WCwm WGer
	'Solar Flair' **new**	CBcs
	x ***soulangeana***	More than 30 suppliers
§	- 'Alba'	CBcs CDoC CEnd CSBt CTri EPfP GKev LCro LPan LRHS MGos NBlu SLim SPer WBVN WFar WOrn WSpi

	- 'Alba Superba'	see *M.* x *soulangeana* 'Alba'
	- 'Alexandrina'	CBcs EPfP NLar
	- 'Amabilis'	MLan WGob
	- 'Brozzonii' ♀H3-4	CDoC EPfP ERas LRHS MBri MGos NLar SSpi WBVN
	- 'Burgundy'	CBcs CDoC ISea MGos WFar
	- 'Lennei' ♀H3-4	CBcs CDoC CEnd CMCN CSBt EBee EPfP IMGH LRHS MAsh MBri MGos MSwo NBea NHol NPri SHBN SLim SPer SRms WFar WNor WOrn
	- 'Lennei Alba' ♀H3-4	CBcs CDoC CMCN CSdC LRHS SPer SSpi WFar WGob WSpi
	- 'Nigra'	see *M. liliiflora* 'Nigra'
	- 'Pickard's Ruby'	CBcs MDun SMad
§	- 'Pickard's Schmetterling'	CDoC CSdC LMil MAsh
	- 'Pickard's Sundew'	see *M.* 'Sundew'
	- 'Picture'	CBcs CDoC CTri NLar WGob
	- Red Lucky	see *M.* 'Hong Yur'
	- 'Rubra' misapplied	see *M.* x *soulangeana* 'Rustica Rubra'
§	- 'Rustica Rubra' ♀H3-4	CBcs CDoC CMCN CSBt CTri EBee ECrN ELan EMui EPfP IMGH ISea LAst LMil LRHS LSRN MAsh MBri MDun MGos SHBN SPer SReu SSpi SSta WBod WFar WGob WPGP WPic
	- 'San José'	CBcs LMil LRHS MAsh MBri MDun NLar WFar
	- 'Verbanica'	LMil LRHS MAsh NLar
	'Spectrum'	CBcs CEnd CPMA CSdC IArd IDee LMil MBri MGos NLar SKHP SSpi WPGP
	sprengeri	CWib WNor
	- 'Copeland Court'	CBcs
	- var. ***diva***	CBcs CEnd NLar SSpi WPGP
	- - 'Burncoose'	CBcs CDoC
	- - 'Claret Cup'	WBod
	- - 'Eric Savill'	CBcs CTho SKHP SSpi SSta WPGP
	- - 'Lanhydrock'	CBcs CTho SSpi
	- - 'Westonbirt'	WPGP
	- 'Marwood Spring'	CMHG
	'Star Wars' ♀H4	CBcs CDoC CEnd CPMA CSdC CTho ECho EMil ENot EPfP LMil MAsh MBri MDun MGos MLan NLar SPoG SSpi SSta WBod WGer WPGP
	'Stellar Acclaim'	MDun
	stellata ♀H4	More than 30 suppliers
	- 'Centennial'	CBcs CDoC CTho MBri NLar WFar
	- 'Chrysanthemiflora'	LMil
	- 'Jane Platt'	CBcs ELan ENot EWes MBri MDun MGos SKHP SSpi
	- f. ***keiskei***	CEnd CSdC MAsh
	- 'King Rose'	CBcs CDoC CSdC EPfP ISea LAst LRHS MAsh MSte MWat NPen SLdr SPer SPla
	- 'Norman Gould'	see *M. kobus* 'Norman Gould'
	- 'Rosea'	CMCN CTho ELan GKev LPan LRHS MDun MGos MRav MSwo NLar SHBN SPoG WBod
I	- 'Rosea Massey'	GBin WFar
	- 'Royal Star'	More than 30 suppliers
	- 'Scented Silver'	CSdC
	- 'Waterlily' ♀H4	CBcs CMCN ELan EPfP GKev IMGH ISea LAst LRHS LSRN MAsh NLar SLdr SLim SPer SPla SPoG SSpi SSta WFar WGob WPGP
	'Summer Solstice'	CBcs CPMA
	'Sunburst'	CBcs MDun
	'Sundance'	CBcs CPMA MDun MGos NLar
§	'Sundew'	CBcs CDoC EBee EPfP EQua IArd MGos NLar WBVN WBod
	'Sunsation' **new**	CBcs
	'Sunspire' **new**	CBcs
	'Susan' ♀H4	More than 30 suppliers
	'Susanna van Veen'	CBcs MBri
	x ***thompsoniana***	CMCN EPfP IDee NLar SSpi
	'Thousand Butterflies'	CBcs CPMA
	'Tina Durio'	CBcs SSpi
	'Todd Gresham'	CPMA WPGP
	'Todd's Forty Niner' **new**	CBcs
	'Tranquility'	MDun SSpi
	'Trewidden Belle'	CEnd
	tripetala	CBcs CHEx CLnd CMCN CPLG CTri EBee ELan EPfP GGGa IMGH LPan MDun MLan NLar SKHP SSpi SSta WBod WPGP
	'Ultimate Yellow' **new**	CBcs
	x ***veitchii***	CDul CSBt EPfP SSta
	- 'Isca'	CBcs
	- 'Peter Veitch'	CBcs CTho
	virginiana	CMCN CPMA EPfP LRHS SSpi WPGP
	- 'Havener'	IArd
	- 'Henry Hicks'	SSpi
	- 'Moonglow'	CPMA
	'Vulcan'	CBcs CEnd CMCN CMHG CPMA CTho ENot MAsh MBlu MBri MDun NHol
	x ***watsonii***	see *M.* x *wieseneri*
§	x ***wieseneri***	CBcs CGHE CMCN CPMA EBee ELan EPfP IDee LRHS MBlu SKHP SSpi WBVN WFar WGob WPGP
	- 'Aashild Kalleberg'	CBcs SSpi
	wilsonii ♀H4	More than 30 suppliers
	- 'Gwen Baker'	CEnd
	'Yellow Fever'	CBcs CMCN CPMA CTho ECho EMil MDun SSta WBod
	'Yellow Lantern'	CAbP CBcs CDoC CEnd CMCN CSdC EBee EPfP IDee LMil LRHS MAsh MBlu NBea NLar NPal SPoG SSpi SSta
	zenii	CSdC
	- 'Pink Parchment'	CBcs CPMA

x *Mahoberberis* (*Berberidaceae*)

aquisargentii	CPle EBee ECrN EMil EPfP MRav NHol SEND SLon SPoG WFar WPGP
'Dart's Desire' **new**	NLar
'Dart's Treasure'	EPla WFar
'Magic'	MGos NLar
miethkeana	MBar SRms

Mahonia ✿ (*Berberidaceae*)

	F&M 178 **new**	WPGP
	F&M 193	WPGP
§	***aquifolium***	CBcs CDul CPLG CTrG EBee ECrN EMac ENot LAst MBar MGan MGos MRav NBlu NWea SHBN SPer SPlb SReu WFar
	- 'Apollo' ♀H4	CBcs CMac CWib EBee ECrN ELan EMil EPfP LHop LRHS LSRN MAsh MBar MBlu MBri MGos MRav NBlu NEgg NPri SCoo SMer SPer SPoG WPat
	- 'Atropurpurea'	ELan EPfP EPla LRHS NBPN NEgg NLar SPer SPla SPoG
*	- 'Cosmo Crawl'	MGos
	- 'Exception'	EBee
	- 'Fascicularis'	see *M.* x *wagneri* 'Pinnacle'
	- 'Green Ripple'	CPMA EPfP MBri MGos NLar WFar
	- 'Orange Flame'	CPMA EPfP MBlu MBri NLar
	- 'Smaragd'	CBcs CDoC CMac ELan EPfP LRHS LSRN MAsh MBlu MGos MRav SLPl WHCG
	- 'Versicolor'	EPla MBlu
	bealei	see *M. japonica* Bealei Group
	bodinieri	NLar

confusa	CDoC CGHE EPla NLar SKHP SSpi WFar WPGP
fortunei	EPla NLar WSHC
- 'Winter Prince'	NLar
gracilipes	CGHE EBee EPfP EPla MBlu MDun NLar SLon WPGP WSPU
gracilis new	WPGP
japonica ♀H4	More than 30 suppliers
§ - Bealei Group	CBcs CDul CSBt EBee ELan EPfP EPla LAst LRHS MAsh MBar MGan MGos MRav MSwo NEgg NHol NPer NScw SCoo SLim SMer SPoG SWvt WBor WFar WGwG WWeb
- 'Gold Dust'	MBri SPer
- 'Hiemalis'	see *M. japonica* 'Hivernant'
§ - 'Hivernant'	MGos NBlu WOrn
leschenaultii B&SWJ 9535	WCru
lomariifolia ♀H3	CBcs CHEx EPfP EWes LRHS SAPC SArc SDry SSpi SSta WSpi
x ***media*** 'Buckland' ♀H4	CAbP CBcs CDul CMac CSBt CSam CWSG EBee EMil EPfP ERas LAst LHop LRHS MDun MRav NWea SDix SHBN SPer SRms WPat
- 'Charity'	More than 30 suppliers
- 'Faith'	EPla EQua
- 'Hope'	NLar
- 'Lionel Fortescue' ♀H4	CBcs CBrm CEnd CMac CPSs CSBt CSam CWSG EBee ELan EPfP ISea LHop LRHS MAsh MGos MRav NCGa SMad SPer SPoG SSpi WBVN WFar
- 'Underway' ♀H4	CSam EPfP LRHS NLar
- 'Winter Sun' ♀H4	More than 30 suppliers
nervosa	CBcs EPfP EPla MBlu MRav NLar SKHP SPer WCru WPat
- B&SWJ 9562	WCru
oiwakensis B&SWJ 3660	WCru
pallida	WPGP
pinnata misapplied	see *M.* x *wagneri* 'Pinnacle'
pinnata ambig.	EPfP EPla MBar
pumila	WCru
repens	EPla NLar
- 'Rotundifolia'	EPla
x ***savilliana***	EPla MBlu WPGP
- 'Commissioner'	CWib
trifoliolata var. ***glauca***	CEnd CPMA NLar
x ***wagneri*** 'Fireflame'	EPla WSpi
- 'Hastings Elegant'	CPMA NLar
- 'Moseri'	EPla NLar SSpi WPat
§ - 'Pinnacle' ♀H4	ELan EMil EPfP EPla LRHS MAsh MGos MLan SPer SPoG
- 'Sunset'	CPMA EPla MBlu NLar
- 'Undulata'	EPfP MBlu NEgg NLar SRms WHCG

Maianthemum (*Convallariaceae*)

atropurpureum	EBee WCru
bicolor	CDes MBri
bifolium	CAvo CBct CDes CHid CPLG EBee EBrs ECho EPot GBuc GCra LEdu MNrw MTho NBro NMen SRms WCru WPGP WPnP WTin
§ - subsp. ***kamtschaticum***	CAvo CLAP CPom CWsd EBee ECha EHrv NLar NRya SMac WCot WTin
- - B&SWJ 4360	WCru WPrP
* - - var. ***minimum***	WCru
canadense	EBee EBrs ECho GGar NBid NMen WCru
* ***chasmanthum***	EBee EPPr LRHS
dilatatum	see *M. bifolium* subsp. *kamtschaticum*
flexuosum B&SWJ 9069	WCru
- B&SWJ 9255	WCru
formosanum	WCot
- B&SWJ 349	WCru
forrestii	WCru
fuscum	GBin WCru
ginfushanicum new	EBee
henryi	EBee ECho WCru
japonicum	EBee ECho SBla
- B&SWJ 1179	WCru
lichiangense new	SBla
oleraceum	CBct ECho GBin GEdr LEdu WCot
- B&SWJ 2148	WCru
paniculatum new	EBee
purpureum	EBee
§ ***racemosum*** ♀H4	More than 30 suppliers
- subsp. ***amplexicaule***	CAvo GBin
- - 'Emily Moody'	CFwr CPou EBee ELan SKHP SMad WPGP
- dwarf	ECho
- 'Wisley Spangles' new	MBri
salvinii	LEdu
- B&SWJ 9000	WCru
aff. ***scilloideum*** B&SWJ 10215 new	WCru
stellatum	CAvo CBct EBee EBrs ECha ECho EPPr EPla EPot GEdr GKev LEdu LHop MLLN NChi NMyG SMac WCru WPnP WTin
szechuanicum	EBee GEdr WCru
tatsiense	CAby ECho WCru
trifolium	EBee ECho

Maihuenia (*Cactaceae*)

poeppigii	SIng SPlb
- JCA 2.575.600	WCot

Maireana (*Chenopodiaceae*)

georgei	SPlb

Malacothamnus (*Malvaceae*)

fremontii	MDKP

Malcolmia (*Brassicaceae*)

littorea	XPep

Malephora (*Aizoaceae*)

crocea var. ***purpureocrocea***	XPep

Mallotus (*Euphorbiaceae*)

japonicus	CPLG
- B&SWJ 6852	WCru

Malus ✿ (*Rosaceae*)

§ 'Adirondack'	CDoC CWSG EBee EMui EPfP LRHS MAsh MBri MGos MLan NLar SCoo SLim SPoG
'Admiration'	see *M.* 'Adirondack'
x ***adstringens*** 'Almey'	ECrN
- 'Hopa'	CDul CLnd
- 'Simcoe'	CLnd CTho
'Aldenhamensis'	see *M.* x *purpurea* 'Aldenhamensis'
'Amberina'	CLnd
* ***arborescens***	CLnd CTho
x ***atrosanguinea*** 'Gorgeous'	CCAT CDul CLnd CTho CWSG EBee ECrN GTwe LRHS MAsh MGan MGos MSwo NBlu SCoo SKee SLim SPer SPoG WBod WJas WOrn
baccata	CDul CLnd CMCN CTho GTwe NWea SCoo SEND WNor
- 'Dolgo'	CCAT CDoC CTho SKee
- 'Gracilis'	SBLw
- 'Lady Northcliffe'	CLnd CTho SFam
- var. ***mandshurica***	CTho
aff. ***baccata***	NWea
- MF 96038	SSpi

§	***bhutanica***	CDul CLnd CTho EPfP SCrf SPer WNor
	brevipes	CLnd CTho MBri SCoo
	'Butterball'	CLnd CTho ECrN EMui EPfP MAsh MBlu SCoo SKee SLim SPoG WJas
	'Candymint Sargent' **new**	CLnd
	'Cave Hill' **new**	CLnd
*	'Cheal's Weeping'	ECrN LAst NBea
	'Comtessa de Paris'	MAsh
	'Coralburst'	MBri
	coronaria var. ***dasycalyx*** 'Charlottae' (d)	CDul CLnd EBee EPfP SPer SPur
	- 'Elk River'	LRHS MAsh MBri SCoo
	'Crimson Brilliant'	CLnd
	'Crittenden'	CLnd ECrN MAsh MRav SLim
*	'Directeur Moerlands'	CCVT CDoC EBee ECrN EMil EPfP IArd MGos SPur WJas
	domestica (F)	ECrN WMou
	- 'Acklam Russet' (D)	SKee
	- 'Acme' (D)	ECrN MCoo SDea SKee
	- 'Adams's Pearmain' (D)	CCAT CTho ECrN EMui ERea GBut GTwe LRHS MAsh SDea SFam SKee WJas WOrn
	- 'Admiral' (D)	ECrN
	- 'Akane' (D)	SDea
	- 'Alfriston' (C)	CAgr SKee
§	- 'Alkmene' (D) ♀H4	ECrN SDea SKee
	- 'All Doer' (D/C/Cider)	CTho
	- 'Allen's Everlasting' (D)	GTwe SDea SKee
	- 'Allington Pippin' (D)	CSBt CTho CTri ECrN SDea SKee WJas
	- Ambassy = 'Dalil'PBR (D) **new**	SGFT SLon
	- 'American Mother'	see *M. domestica* 'Mother'
	- 'Ananas Reinette' (D)	ECrN SKee
	- 'Anna Boelens' (D)	SDea
	- 'Annie Elizabeth' (C)	CAgr CCAT CTho CWib ECrN GTwe LAst MCoo SDea SFam SKee WJas
	- 'Anniversary' (D)	SDea
	- 'Api Rose' (D)	SKee WJas
	- 'Ard Cairn Russet' (D)	ECrN GTwe SDea SKee
	- 'Aromatic Russet' (D)	SKee
	- 'Arthur Turner' (C) ♀H4	CCAT CCVT CDoC CTri ECrN EMui GBut GTwe LBuc SCrf SDea SFam SKee WJas
	- 'Ashmead's Kernel' (D) ♀H4	CAgr CCAT CSBt CTho CTri CWib ECrN EMui EPfP ERea GTwe LBuc LRHS MAsh MRav MWat NWea SCrf SDea SFam SGFT SKee WHar WJas WOrn
	- 'Ashton Bitter' (Cider)	CCAT CTho GTwe
	- 'Ashton Brown Jersey' (Cider)	CCAT
	- 'Autumn Pearmain' (D)	SDea WJas
	- 'Baker's Delicious' (D)	CCAT ECrN SDea SKee
	- 'Ball's Bittersweet' (Cider)	CCAT CTho
	- 'Balsam'	see *M. domestica* 'Green Balsam'
	- 'Banana Pippin'	CEnd
	- 'Banns' (D)	ECrN
	- 'Bardsey' (D) **new**	CAgr LBuc MCoo WGwG
	- 'Barnack Beauty' (D)	CTho SKee
	- 'Barnack Orange' (D)	SKee
	- 'Baumann's Reinette' (D)	SKee
	- 'Baxter's Pearmain' (D)	ECrN SDea SKee
	- 'Beauty of Bath' (D)	CAgr CCAT CCVT CDoC CDul CTho CTri CWib ECrN EMui GBut GTwe LAst LBuc SDea SFam SKee WJas
	- 'Beauty of Hants' (D)	ECrN SKee
	- 'Beauty of Kent' (C)	SDea SKee
	- 'Beauty of Moray' (C)	GBut GQui SKee
	- 'Bedwyn Beauty' (C)	CTho

	- 'Beeley Pippin' (D)	GTwe SDea SKee
	- 'Bell Apple' (Cider/C)	CCAT CTho
	- 'Belle de Boskoop' (C/D) ♀H4	CAgr CCAT ECrN GTwe LCro MCoo SDea SKee
	- 'Belvoir Seedling' (D/C)	SKee
	- 'Bembridge Beauty' (F)	SDea
	- 'Ben's Red' (D)	CAgr CCAT CEnd CTho
	- 'Bess Pool' (D)	SDea SFam WJas
	- 'Bewley Down Pippin'	see *M. domestica* 'Crimson King' (Cider/C)
	- 'Bickington Grey' (Cider)	CTho
	- 'Billy Down Pippin' (F)	CTho
	- 'Bismarck' (C)	CCAT ECrN SKee
	- 'Black Dabinett' (Cider)	CCAT CEnd CTho
	- 'Black Tom Putt' (C/D)	CTho
	- 'Blenheim Orange' (C/D) ♀H4	More than 30 suppliers
	- 'Blenheim Red'	see *M. domestica* 'Red Blenheim'
	- 'Bloody Ploughman' (D)	ECrN GBut GTwe LRHS SKee
	- 'Blue Pearmain' (D)	SDea SKee
	- 'Blue Sweet' (Cider)	CTho
	- BoleroPBR	see *M. domestica* Bolero = 'Tuscan'
§	- Bolero = 'Tuscan'PBR (D/Ball)	ECrN ENot LRHS SDea SKee
	- 'Boston Russet'	see *M. domestica* 'Roxbury Russet'
	- 'Bountiful' (C)	CAgr CCAT CDoC CSBt CTri CWib ECrN EMui GTwe LBuc MBri SDea SGFT SKee SPoG WBVN WHar
	- 'Bow Hill Pippin' (D)	SKee
	- 'Braddick Nonpareil' (D)	SKee
	- 'Braeburn' (D)	CCAT CSut ECrN EMui ERea LAst LRHS MAsh MNHC SCrf SDea SGFT SKee
	- 'Braintree Seedling' (D)	ECrN
	- 'Bramley's Seedling' (C) ♀H4	More than 30 suppliers
	- 'Bramley's Seedling' clone 20	CDoC EMui MAsh MBri NLar SCoo SDea SPoG WHar
	- 'Bread Fruit' (C/D)	CEnd CTho
	- 'Breakwell's Seedling' (Cider)	CCAT CTho
	- 'Bridgwater Pippin' (C)	CCAT CTho WJas
	- 'Broad-eyed Pippin' (C)	SKee
	- 'Broadholm Beauty'	EMui
	- 'Brown Snout' (Cider)	CCAT CTho
	- 'Brownlees Russet' (D)	CAgr CCAT CTho CTri GTwe MCoo NWea SDea SFam SKee
	- 'Brown's Apple' (Cider)	CCAT GTwe
	- 'Broxwood Foxwhelp' (Cider)	CCAT
	- 'Burn's Seedling' (D)	CTho
	- 'Burr Knot' (C)	ECrN SKee
	- 'Burrowhill Early' (Cider)	CTho
	- 'Bushey Grove' (C)	SDea SKee
	- 'Buttery Do'	CTho
	- 'Cadbury' **new**	CCAT
	- 'Calville Blanc d'Hiver' (D)	SKee
	- 'Cambusnethan Pippin' (D)	GBut GQui SKee
	- 'Camelot' (Cider/C)	CCAT
	- 'Cap of Liberty' (Cider)	CCAT
	- 'Captain Broad' (D/Cider)	CCAT CEnd CTho
	- 'Captain Kidd' (D)	EMui
	- 'Captain Smith' (F)	CEnd
	- 'Carlisle Codlin' (C)	GBut GTwe NLar NWea SDea
	- 'Catherine' (C)	ECrN
	- 'Catshead' (C)	CAgr CCAT ECrN GQui SDea SKee WJas
	- 'Cellini' (C/D)	SDea SKee
	- 'Charles Ross' (C/D) ♀H4	More than 30 suppliers
	- 'Charlotte'PBR (C/Ball)	LRHS MGos SDea
	- 'Chaxhill Red' (Cider/D)	CCAT CTho
	- 'Cheddar Cross' (D)	CAgr CTri ECrN

	Cultivar	Suppliers
	– 'Chelmsford Wonder' (C)	ECrN SKee
	– 'Chisel Jersey' (Cider)	CCAT CTri
	– 'Chivers Delight' (D)	CAgr CCAT CSBt ECrN EMui GTwe MCoo SDea SKee WJas
	– 'Chorister Boy' (D)	CTho
	– 'Christmas Pearmain' (D)	CTho ECrN GTwe SDea SFam SKee
	– 'Cider Lady's Finger' (Cider)	CCAT
	– 'Claygate Pearmain' (D) 🏆H4	CCAT CTho CTri ECrN GTwe MCoo SDea SFam SKee WJas
	– 'Clopton Red' (D)	ECrN
	– 'Clydeside'	GQui
	– 'Coat Jersey' (Cider)	CCAT
	– 'Cockle Pippin' (D)	CAgr CTho SDea
	– 'Coeur de Boeuf' (C/D)	SKee
	– 'Coleman's Seedling' (Cider)	CTho
	– 'Collogett Pippin' (C/Cider)	CCAT CEnd CTho
	– 'Colonel Vaughan' (C/D)	SKee
	– 'Cooper's Seedling' (C)	SCrf
	– 'Cornish Aromatic' (D)	CAgr CCAT CTho ECrN GTwe LRHS SCrf SDea SFam SKee WJas
	– 'Cornish Gilliflower' (D)	CAgr CCAT CTho ECrN EMui LRHS MCoo SDea SFam SKee WJas WOrn
	– 'Cornish Honeypin' (D)	CTho
	– 'Cornish Longstem' (D)	CAgr CEnd CTho
	– 'Cornish Mother' (D)	CEnd CTho
	– 'Cornish Pine' (D)	CEnd CTho SDea SKee
	– 'Coronation' (D)	SDea SKee
	– 'Corse Hill' (D)	CCAT CTho
	– 'Cortland' (D)	SKee
	– 'Costard' (C)	GTwe SKee
	– 'Cottenham Seedling' (C)	ECrN SKee
	– 'Coul Blush' (D)	GBut SKee
	– 'Court of Wick' (D)	CAgr CCAT CTho ECrN SKee
	– 'Court Pendu Plat' (D)	CAgr CCAT LBuc MWat NWea SDea SFam SKee WJas WOrn
	– 'Court Royal' (Cider)	CCAT
	– 'Cow Apple' (C)	CCAT
	– 'Cox Cymraeg' (D) **new**	WGwG
	– 'Cox's Orange Pippin' (D)	CBcs CCAT CCVT CDul CMac CSBt CTri CWib ECrN EMui ENot GTwe LAst LCro LRHS MAsh MWat NBlu NEgg NPri SCrf SDea SFam SKee SPer WJas WOrn
	– 'Cox's Pomona' (C/D)	SDea SKee WJas
	– 'Cox's Rouge de Flandres' (D)	SKee
	– 'Cox's Selfing' (D)	CDoC CTri CWSG CWib EMui EPfP ERea GTwe LBuc MAsh MBri MGan MGos MNHC NBlu SCrf SDea SGFT SKee SPoG WHar WJas
	– 'Crawley Beauty' (C)	CAgr CCAT GTwe SDea SFam SKee WJas
	– 'Crawley Reinette' (D)	SKee
	– 'Crimson Beauty of Bath' (D)	CAgr
	– 'Crimson Bramley' (C)	CCAT LAst
	– 'Crimson Cox' (D)	SDea
§	– 'Crimson King' (Cider/C)	CAgr CCAT
	– 'Crimson King' (D)	CAgr
	– 'Crimson Queening' (D)	SKee WJas
	– 'Crimson Victoria' (Cider)	CTho
	– Crispin	see *M. domestica* 'Mutsu'
§	– 'Crowngold' (D)	EMui GTwe
	– 'Curl Tail' (D)	SKee
	– 'Cutler Grieve' (D)	SDea
	– Cybèle = 'Delrouval' **new**	LBuc
	– 'Dabinett' (Cider)	CCAT CTho CTri EMui GTwe SCrf SDea SKee WOrn
	– 'D'Arcy Spice' (D)	CAgr CCAT ECrN EMui EPfP MCoo SDea SFam SKee
	– 'Dawn' (D)	SKee
	– 'Deacon's Blushing Beauty' (C/D)	SDea
	– 'Deacon's Millennium'	SDea
	– 'Decio' (D)	SKee
	– 'Delprim' (D)	SKee
	– 'Devon Crimson Queen' (D)	CTho
	– 'Devonshire Buckland' (C)	CEnd CTho
	– 'Devonshire Crimson Queen' (D)	SDea
	– 'Devonshire Quarrenden' (D)	CAgr CCAT CEnd CTho ECrN GBut SDea SFam SKee WJas
	– 'Diamond Jubilee' (D)	SKee
	– 'Discovery' (D) 🏆H4	More than 30 suppliers
	– 'Doctor Hare's' (C)	WJas
	– 'Doctor Harvey' (C)	ECrN SFam
	– 'Doctor Kidd's Orange Red'Red'	see *M. domestica* 'Kidd's Orange Red'
	– 'Don's Delight' (C)	CTho
	– 'Dove' (Cider)	CCAT
	– 'Downton Pippin' (D)	SKee WJas
	– 'Dredge's Fame' (D)	CTho
	– 'Duchess's Favourite' (D)	SKee
	– 'Dufflin' (Cider)	CCAT CTho
	– 'Duke of Cornwall' (C)	CTho
	– 'Duke of Devonshire' (D)	CTho CTri SDea SFam SKee WJas
	– 'Duke of Gloucester' (C)	WJas
N	– 'Dumeller's Seedling'	see *M. domestica* 'Dummellor's Seedling'
	– 'Dumelow's Seedling'	see *M. domestica* 'Dummellor's Seedling'
§	– 'Dummellor's Seedling' (C) 🏆H4	CCAT SDea SKee
	– 'Dunkerton Late Sweet' (Cider)	CCAT CTho EMil
	– 'Dunn's Seedling' (D)	SDea
§	– 'Dutch Mignonne' (D)	ECrN SKee
	– 'Dymock Red' (Cider)	CCAT
	– 'Early Blenheim' (D/C)	CCAT CEnd CTho
	– 'Early Bower' (D)	CEnd
	– 'Early Julyan' (C)	GBut GQui SKee WJas
	– 'Early Victoria'	see *M. domestica* 'Emneth Early'
	– Early Windsor = 'Alkmene'	see *M. domestica* 'Alkmene'
	– 'Early Worcester'	see *M. domestica* 'Tydeman's Early Worcester'
	– 'East Lothian Pippin' (C)	GQui SKee
	– 'Easter Orange' (D)	GTwe SKee
	– 'Ecklinville' (C)	SDea SKee WJas
	– 'Edith Hopwood' (D)	ECrN
	– 'Edward VII' (C) 🏆H4	CCAT CDoC GTwe SCrf SDea SFam SKee WJas
	– 'Egremont Russet' (D) 🏆H4	More than 30 suppliers
	– 'Ellis' Bitter' (Cider)	CCAT CTho GTwe SKee
	– 'Ellison's Orange' (D) 🏆H4	CAgr CCAT CDul CSBt CTri CWib ECrN EMui EPfP GBut GTwe LAst LBuc LRHS NEgg NWea SDea SFam SKee WHar WJas WOrn
	– 'Elstar' (D) 🏆H4	CWib ECrN EMui GTwe LAst MRav NBlu SDea SKee
	– 'Elton Beauty' (D)	SDea
§	– 'Emneth Early' (C) 🏆H4	CAgr ECrN EMui GBut GTwe SDea SFam SKee WJas WOrn
	– 'Empire' (D)	LAst SKee
	– 'Encore' (C)	SDea
	– 'English Codlin'	CCAT CTho CTri
	– 'Epicure'	see *M. domestica* 'Laxton's Epicure'
	– 'Ernie's Russet' (D)	SDea
	– 'Eros' (D)	ECrN
	– 'Esopus Spitzenburg' (D) **new**	SKee
	– 'Essex Pippin' (D)	ECrN

- 'Evening Gold' (C)	SDea
- 'Eve's Delight' (D)	SDea
- 'Excelsior' (C)	ECrN
- 'Exeter Cross' (D)	CCAT ECrN SDea SFam
- 'Fair Maid of Devon' (Cider)	CAgr CCAT CEnd CTho
- 'Fairfield' (D)	CTho
- 'Falstaff'^{PBR} (D) ♀^{H4}	CAgr CCAT CCVT CDoC ECrN EMui EPfP GTwe MGos SCoo SDea SKee WBVN WJas
- 'Farmer's Glory' (D)	CAgr CTho
- 'Fearn's Pippin' (D)	SKee
- 'Fiesta'^{PBR} (D) ♀^{H4}	More than 30 suppliers
- 'Fillbarrel' (Cider)	CCAT
- 'Firmgold' (D)	SDea
- 'Five Crowns' (D)	SKee
- 'Flame' (D)	ECrN
- 'Flamenco'^{PBR}	see *M. domestica* 'Obelisk'
§ - 'Flower of Kent' (C)	CCAT SCrf SDea SKee
- 'Flower of the Town' (D)	SKee
- 'Forfar'	see *M. domestica* 'Dutch Mignonne'
- 'Forge' (D)	CAgr SDea SKee
- 'Fortune'	see *M. domestica* 'Laxton's Fortune'
- 'Francis' (D)	ECrN
- 'Frederick' (Cider)	CCAT CTho
- 'French Crab' (C)	SDea
- 'Freyberg' (D)	SKee
- 'Fuji' (D)	SDea SKee
- 'Gala' (D)	CSBt EMui GTwe LAst NEgg NPri SCoo SCrf SDea SFam SGFT SKee WHar
§ - 'Gala Mondial' (D)	WJas
- 'Gala Royal'	see *M. domestica* 'Royal Gala'
- 'Galloway Pippin' (C)	GBut GQui GTwe SKee
- 'Garnet' (D)	ECrN
- 'Gascoyne's Scarlet' (D)	CCAT SDea SFam SKee
- 'Gavin' (D)	CAgr GBut SDea SKee
- 'Genesis II' (D/C)	SDea
- 'Genet Moyle' (C/Cider)	CCAT CTri WJas
- 'George Carpenter' (D)	SDea SKee
- 'George Cave' (D)	CTho ECrN GBut GTwe MCoo SDea SFam SKee WJas
- 'George Neal' (C) ♀^{H4}	CAgr SDea SFam
- 'Gilliflower of Gloucester' (D)	CTho
- 'Gin' (Cider)	CCAT
- 'Gladstone' (D)	CAgr CTho SKee WJas
§ - 'Glass Apple' (C/D)	CCAT CEnd CTho
- 'Glockenapfel' (C) **new**	SKee
- 'Gloria Mundi' (C)	SDea SKee
- 'Gloster '69' (D)	NBlu SDea SKee
- 'Gloucester Royal' (D)	CTho
- 'Gloucester Underleaf'	CTho
- 'Golden Ball'	CTho
- 'Golden Bittersweet' (D)	CAgr CTho
- 'Golden Delicious' (D) ♀^{H4}	CDul CSBt CSut CWib ECrN EMui ENot EPfP LAst MGan NBlu SCrf SDea SKee SPer WHar WOrn
- 'Golden Glow' (C)	SDea
- 'Golden Harvey' (D)	CAgr CCAT
- 'Golden Jubilee'	CEnd
- 'Golden Knob' (D)	CCAT CTho
- 'Golden Noble' (C) ♀^{H4}	CAgr CCAT CDoC CTho CTri ECrN GTwe MCoo SDea SFam SKee WOrn
- 'Golden Nugget' (D)	CAgr
- 'Golden Pippin' (C)	CAgr CCAT GBut SKee
- 'Golden Reinette' (D)	GTwe SKee
- 'Golden Russet' (D)	CAgr ECrN GTwe SDea SKee
- 'Golden Spire' (C)	GBut MCoo SDea SKee
- 'Gooseberry' (C)	SKee
- 'Goring' (Cider)	CTho
- 'Grand Sultan' (D)	CCAT
- 'Granny Smith' (D)	CDul CLnd CWib ECrN GTwe LAst NPri SCrf SDea SKee SPer WHar
- 'Gravenstein' (D)	CCAT GQui SDea SFam SKee
§ - 'Green Balsam' (C)	CTri
- 'Green Harvey' (D/C)	SKee
- 'Green Kilpandy Pippin' (C)	GQui
- 'Greensleeves'^{PBR} (D) ♀^{H4}	CAgr CCAT CDoC CSBt CTri CWSG CWib ECrN EMui GTwe LAst MGan MGos NEgg SDea SGFT SKee SPoG WHar WJas WOrn
- 'Greenup's Pippin' (D)	GBut
- 'Grenadier' (C) ♀^{H4}	CAgr CCAT CDoC CSBt CTri ECrN EMui GBut GTwe LRHS MGos NEgg SDea SGFT SKee WJas WOrn
- 'Halstow Natural' (Cider)	CAgr CTho
- 'Hambledon Deux Ans' (C)	SDea SKee
- 'Hangy Down' (Cider)	CCAT CTho
- 'Harbert's Reinette' (D) **new**	SKee
§ - 'Harry Master's Jersey' (Cider)	CCAT CTho CTri SDea SKee
- 'Harvester' (D)	CTho
- 'Harvey' (C)	SDea SKee
- 'Hawthornden' (C)	GBut GQui GTwe SKee
- 'Hereford Cross' (D)	SKee
- 'Herefordshire Beefing' (C)	WJas WOrn
- 'Herefordshire Russet'^{PBR}	EMui LBuc LRHS MAsh MBri MCoo SKee WOrn
- 'Herring's Pippin' (D)	GTwe SDea SKee
- 'Heusgen's Golden Reinette' (D)	SKee
- 'High View Pippin' (D)	SKee
- 'Histon Favourite' (D)	SKee
- 'Hoary Morning' (C)	CCAT CTho ECrN SDea SKee
- 'Hocking's Green' (C/D)	CAgr CCAT CEnd CTho
- 'Holland Pippin' (C)	SKee
- 'Hollow Core' (C)	CAgr CTho
- 'Holstein' (D)	CTho SDea SKee
- 'Honey Pippin' (D)	ECrN SKee
- 'Hood's Supreme' (D)	GBut
- 'Horneburger Pfannkuchen' (C)	SKee
- 'Horsford Prolific' (D)	ECrN ERea
- 'Howgate Wonder' (C)	CAgr CCAT CCVT CDoC CDul CSBt CWib ECrN EMui GBut GTwe LAst LBuc LRHS MAsh MGan NPri SCrf SDea SFam SKee SPer WBVN WHar WJas
- 'Hubbard's Pearmain' (D)	ECrN SKee
- 'Hunt's Duke of Gloucester' (D)	CTho
- 'Idared' (D) ♀^{H4}	CWib ECrN SDea SKee
- 'Improved Dove' (Cider)	CCAT
- 'Improved Keswick' (C/D)	CEnd CTho
- 'Improved Lambrook Pippin' (Cider)	CCAT CTho CTri
- 'Improved Redstreak' (Cider)	CTho
- 'Ingrid Marie' (D)	SDea SKee WJas
- 'Irish Peach' (D)	CAgr CCAT ECrN GBut GTwe MCoo SDea SFam SKee WJas
- 'Isaac Newton's Tree'	see *M. domestica* 'Flower of Kent'
- 'Isle of Wight Pippin' (D)	SDea
- 'Isle of Wight Russet' (D)	SDea
- 'Jackson's'	see *M. domestica* 'Crimson King'
- 'James Grieve' (D) ♀^{H4}	More than 30 suppliers
- 'Jerseymac' (D)	SDea
- 'Jester' (D)	ECrN GTwe SDea SKee
- 'Jimbo'	LRHS
- 'John Standish' (D)	CAgr CCAT CTri GTwe SCrf SDea
- 'John Toucher's'	see *M. domestica* 'Crimson King' (Cider/C)

- 'Johnny Andrews' (Cider)	CAgr CCAT CTho
- 'Johnny Voun' (D)	CEnd CTho
- 'Jonagold' (D) ♀H4	CTri CWib ECrN EMil EMui GTwe LAst SCrf SDea SFam SKee SPer WJas
- 'Jonagold Crowngold'	see *M. domestica* 'Crowngold'
§ - 'Jonagored'PBR (D)	SDea SKee
- 'Jonared' (D)	GTwe
- 'Jonathan' (D)	SDea SKee
- 'Jordan's Weeping' (C)	GTwe SDea WJas
- 'Josephine' (D)	SDea
- 'Joybells' (D)	SKee
- 'Jubilee'	see *M. domestica* 'Royal Jubilee'
- 'Jumbo'	LBuc MAsh MBri MCoo SKee
- 'Jupiter'PBR (D) ♀H4	CCAT CDul CSBt CTri CWib ECrN GTwe LAst NPri SCoo SDea SKee WJas WOrn
- 'Kandil Sinap' (D)	SKee
- 'Kapai Red Jonathan' (D)	SDea
- 'Karmijn de Sonnaville' (D)	SDea
§ - 'Katja' (D)	CAgr CCAT CCVT CDoC CTri CWib ECrN EMui EPfP GBut GTwe LAst LBuc MAsh SCoo SDea SKee SPer WHar WJas WOrn
- Katy	see *M. domestica* 'Katja'
- 'Kent' (D)	ECrN EMui GTwe MCoo NLar SCrf SDea SKee
- 'Kentish Fillbasket' (C)	SKee
- 'Kentish Pippin' (C/Cider/D)	SKee
- 'Kerry Pippin' (D)	SKee
- 'Keswick Codlin' (C)	CTho ECrN GBut GTwe MCoo NLar NWea SDea SKee WJas
§ - 'Kidd's Orange Red' (D) ♀H4	CAgr CCAT CTri ECrN EMui GQui GTwe LAst LBuc LRHS SCrf SDea SFam SKee WJas
- 'Kill Boy'	CTho
- 'Killerton Sharp' (Cider)	CTho
- 'Killerton Sweet' (Cider)	CTho
- 'King Byerd' (C/D)	CCAT CEnd CTho
- 'King Luscious' (D)	SDea
§ - 'King of the Pippins' (D) ♀H4	CCAT CTho CTri ECrN GBut GTwe LCro MCoo SCrf SDea SFam SGFT SKee WOrn
- 'King Russet' (D) ♀H4	SDea
- 'King's Acre Bountiful' (C)	WJas
- 'King's Acre Pippin' (D)	CCAT SDea SFam WJas
- 'Kingston Bitter' (Cider)	CTho
- 'Kingston Black' (Cider/C)	CCAT CEnd CTho CTri ECrN GTwe SDea SKee
- 'Kirton Fair' (D)	CTho
- 'Knobby Russet' (D)	SKee
- 'Lady Henniker' (D)	CCAT CTho ECrN GTwe SDea WJas
- 'Lady Lambourne' (C/D)	EMil
- 'Lady of the Wemyss' (C)	GBut GQui SKee
- 'Lady Sudeley' (D)	CTho SDea SKee
- 'Lady's Finger' (C/D)	CEnd
- 'Lady's Finger of Offaly' (D)	SDea
- 'Lake's Kernel' (D)	CTho
- 'Lamb Abbey Pearmain' (D)	SKee
- 'Lamb's Seedling' (D)	SKee
- 'Lane's Prince Albert' (C) ♀H4	CAgr CCAT CSBt ECrN EMui GBut GTwe MGos MRav MWat SCoo SCrf SDea SFam SKee WHar WJas WOrn
- 'Langley Pippin' (D)	SDea
§ - 'Langworthy' (Cider)	CCAT CTho
- 'Lass o' Gowrie' (C)	GBut GQui SKee
§ - 'Laxton's Epicure' (D) ♀H4	CAgr CDul ECrN GTwe LAst SDea SFam SKee WJas
§ - 'Laxton's Fortune' (D) ♀H4	CCAT CDul CMac CSBt CTri CWib ECrN EMui GBut GTwe LAst SCrf SDea SFam SKee WHar WJas
- 'Laxton's Pearmain' (D)	MCoo
- 'Laxton's Rearguard' (D)	WJas
- 'Laxton's Royalty' (D)	SDea
§ - 'Laxton's Superb' (D)	CBcs CCAT CCVT CDoC CSBt CTri CWib ECrN EMui ENot GTwe LAst LBuc LRHS MCoo MGan NEgg NPri NWea SCrf SDea SKee SPer WHar WJas WOrn
- 'Leathercoat Russet' (D)	CAgr CCAT SKee
- 'Lemon Pippin' (C)	CCAT ECrN SDea SKee WJas
- 'Lemon Pippin of Gloucestershire' (D)	CTho
- 'Lewis's Incomparable' (C)	SKee
- 'Liberty' (D)	GBut SDea
- 'Limberland' (C)	CTho
- 'Limelight' (D)	EMui LRHS MBri MCoo SCoo SKee
- 'Linda' (D)	SKee
- 'Link Wonder'	CEnd
§ - 'Loddington' (C)	SKee
- 'Lodgemore Nonpareil' (D)	SKee
- 'Lodi' (C)	SDea
- 'London Pearmain' (D)	ECrN
- 'London Pippin' (C)	CAgr CTho
- 'Longkeeper' (D)	CAgr CEnd CTho
- 'Longstem' (Cider)	CTho
- 'Lord Burghley' (D)	GTwe SDea SKee
- 'Lord Derby' (C)	CAgr CCAT CDul CMac CTho CWib ECrN EMui GBut GTwe LAst MBri SCrf SDea SFam SKee
- 'Lord Grosvenor' (C)	SKee
- 'Lord Hindlip' (D)	GTwe SDea SFam WJas
- 'Lord Lambourne' (D) ♀H4	CAgr CCAT CCVT CDoC CDul CSBt CTri CWib ECrN EMui EPfP GTwe LAst LRHS MCoo MWat SCoo SCrf SDea SFam SKee SPer WBVN WHar WJas WOrn
- 'Lord of the Isles' (F)	CAgr CCAT
- 'Lord Stradbroke' (C)	ECrN SKee
- 'Lord Suffield' (C)	CTri ECrN
- 'Love Beauty' (D)	GBut
- 'Lucombe's Pine' (D)	CAgr CEnd CTho ECrN
- 'Lucombe's Seedling' (D)	CTho
- 'Lynn's Pippin' (D)	ECrN
- 'Mabbott's Pearmain' (D)	SDea
- 'Maclean's Favourite' (D)	ECrN
- 'Madresfield Court' (D)	SDea SKee WJas
- 'Maggie Sinclair' (D)	GBut GQui
- 'Major' (Cider)	CCAT
- 'Maldon Wonder' (D)	ECrN
- 'Malling Kent' (D)	EMui SDea SFam
- 'Maltster' (D)	SKee WJas
- 'Manaccan Primrose' (C/D)	CEnd
- 'Manks Codlin' (C)	GBut
- 'Margil' (D)	CCAT GTwe SDea SFam SKee
- 'May Queen' (D)	SDea SFam WJas
- 'Maypole'PBR (D/Ball)	LRHS MGos SDea WJas
- 'Maypole 2000' (C/Ball)	ENot
- 'McIntosh' (D)	SKee
- 'Melba' (D)	SKee
- 'Melon' (D)	SDea
- 'Melrose' (D)	ECrN GTwe
- 'Merchant Apple' (D)	CCAT CTho CTri
- 'Mère de Ménage' (C)	GBut SFam
- 'Meridian'PBR (D)	CAgr CDoC ECrN EMui MBri SDea SGFT SKee
- 'Merton Beauty' (D)	SKee
- 'Merton Knave' (D)	GTwe SDea SFam
- 'Merton Russet' (D)	SDea
- 'Merton Worcester' (D)	ECrN SDea SKee

– 'Michaelmas Red' (D)	GTwe SKee WJas
– 'Michelin' (Cider)	CCAT CTri GTwe SDea SKee WOrn
– 'Miller's Seedling' (D)	GTwe SKee WJas
– 'Millicent Barnes' (D)	SDea
– 'Mollie's Delicious' (D)	SKee
– 'Monarch' (C)	CAgr CCAT CTri ECrN GBut GTwe SDea SFam SKee
– see 'Mondial Gala'	see *M. domestica* 'Gala Mondial'
– 'Monidel'PBR	ECrN
– 'Morgan's Sweet' (C/Cider)	CCAT CEnd CTho CTri SDea SKee\
– 'Moss's Seedling' (D)	SDea
§ – 'Mother' (D) 𝕐H4	CAgr CCAT CDoC CTri ECrN GTwe SCrf SDea SFam SKee
§ – 'Mutsu' (D)	CCAT CTri ECrN GTwe SCrf SDea SKee
– 'Nancy Jackson' (C)	SKee
– 'Nant Gwrtheryn' (D) **new**	WGwG
– 'Nasona' (D) **new**	SKee
– 'Nettlestone Pippin' (D)	SDea
– 'Newton Wonder' (D/C) 𝕐H4	CAgr CCAT CDoC CMac CSBt CTho CTri CWib ECrN EMui GTwe LAst LBuc MCoo SCrf SDea SFam SKee WJas WOrn
– 'Newtown Pippin' (D)	SDea
– 'Nigde' (D) **new**	SKee
– 'Nine Square' (D)	CCAT CTho
– 'Nittany Red' (D)	SDea
– 'No Pip' (C)	CTho
– 'Nolan Pippin' (D)	ECrN
– 'Nonpareil' (D)	SKee
– 'Norfolk Beauty' (C)	ECrN SKee
– 'Norfolk Beefing' (C)	ECrN ERea LRHS SDea SFam SKee
– 'Norfolk Royal' (D)	CDoC ECrN ERea GTwe SDea SKee
– 'Norfolk Royal Russet' (D)	ECrN ERea GBut
– 'Norfolk Summer Broadend' (C)	SKee
– 'Norfolk Winter Coleman' (C)	SKee
– 'Northcott Superb' (D)	CTho
– 'Northern Greening' (C)	SKee
§ – 'Northwood' (Cider)	CCAT CTho
– 'Nutmeg Pippin' (D)	ECrN SDea
– Nuvar Freckles (D)	SKee
– Nuvar Gold (D)	SKee
– Nuvar Golden Elf	SKee
– Nuvar Golden Hills (D)	SKee
– Nuvar Home Farm (D)	SKee
– Nuvar Long Harvest (D)	SKee
– Nuvar Melody (D)	SKee
– Nuvar Red Gloss (D)	SKee
– 'Oaken Pin' (C)	CCAT CTho
§ – 'Obelisk'PBR (D)	ENot MCoo NPri SDea SKee
– 'Old Pearmain' (D)	SDea SKee
– 'Old Somerset Russet' (D)	CCAT CTho
– 'Opal' (D)	ECrN
– 'Opalescent' (D)	SKee
– 'Orange Goff' (D)	SKee
– 'Orkney Apple' (F)	SKee
– 'Orleans Reinette' (D)	CAgr CCAT CTho CTri CWib ECrN GBut GTwe LBuc LRHS MWat SCrf SDea SFam SKee WJas
– 'Oslin' (D)	GBut SKee
– 'Owen Thomas' (D)	CTri
– 'Paignton Marigold' (Cider)	CTho
– 'Pascoe's Pippin' (D/C)	CTho
– 'Paulared' (D)	SKee
– 'Payhembury' (C/Cider)	CAgr CTho CTri
– 'Pear Apple' (D)	CAgr CEnd CTho
– 'Pearl' (D)	ECrN SDea
– 'Peasgood's Nonsuch' (C) 𝕐H4	CAgr CCAT CDoC ECrN GTwe MAsh MGan SCrf SDea SFam SKee SLon WJas WOrn

– 'Pendragon' (D)	CTho
– 'Penhallow Pippin' (D)	CTho
– 'Pépin Shafrannyi' (D) **new**	SKee
– 'Peter Lock' (C/D)	CAgr CEnd CTho NWea
– 'Peter's Pippin' (D)	SDea
– 'Peter's Seedling' (D)	SDea
– 'Pethyre' (Cider) **new**	CCAT
– 'Pig's Nose Pippin' (D)	CEnd
– 'Pig's Nose Pippin' Type III (D)	CAgr CTho
– 'Pig's Snout' (Cider/C/D)	CCAT CEnd CTho
– 'Pine Apple Russet' **new**	CAgr
– 'Pine Golden Pippin' (D)	SKee
– 'Pitmaston Pine Apple' (D)	CCAT CTho CTri ECrN LAst LRHS MAsh MCoo SCrf SDea SFam SKee WJas WOrn
– 'Pitmaston Russet Nonpareil' (D)	SKee
– 'Pixie' (D) 𝕐H4	CCAT CWib EMui GTwe LRHS SDea SFam SKee WJas
– 'Plum Vite' (D)	CAgr CTho CTri
– 'Plympton Pippin' (C)	CEnd CTho CTri
– Polka = 'Trajan'PBR (D/Ball)	ENot LRHS MGos SDea SKee
– 'Polly' (C/D)	CEnd
– 'Polly Whitehair' (C/D)	CCAT CTho SDea
– 'Poltimore Seedling'	CTho
– 'Pomeroy of Somerset' (D)	CCAT CTho CTri
– 'Ponsford' (C)	CAgr CCAT CTho
– 'Port Allen Russet' (C/D)	GQui
– 'Port Wine'	see *M. domestica* 'Harry Master's Jersey'
– 'Porter's Perfection' (Cider)	CCAT
– 'Princesse'	ECrN EMui SDea SKee
– 'Profit' **new**	CTho
– 'Quarry Apple' (C)	CTho
– 'Queen' (C)	CAgr CTho ECrN SKee
– 'Queen Cox' (D)	CTri ECrN EMui SDea SGFT SKee SLon
– 'Queen Cox' self-fertile	CSut CWib EMui SDea
– 'Queens' (D)	CTho
– 'Quench' (D/Cider)	CTho
– 'Radford Beauty'	MCoo
– 'Rajka' (D)	SKee
– 'Red Alkmene' (D)	MBri
– 'Red Belle de Boskoop' (D)	CAgr
§ – 'Red Blenheim' (C/D)	SKee
– 'Red Bramley' (C)	CWib
– 'Red Charles Ross' (C/D)	SDea
– 'Red Delicious' (D)	SCrf
– 'Red Devil' (D)	CAgr CTri CWSG ECrN EMui ENot GTwe LAst MAsh MBri MGan MNHC NLar SCoo SDea SGFT SKee SPoG WHar WJas
– 'Red Ellison' (D)	CCAT CTho CTri ERea GTwe SDea
– 'Red Elstar' (D)	SCrf
– 'Red Falstaff'PBR (D)	CAgr CCAT CDoC ECrN EMui ERea LBuc LRHS MBri MCoo NBlu NLar SGFT SKee SPoG WBVN WHar
– 'Red Fuji' (D)	SDea
– 'Red Jersey' (Cider)	CCAT
– 'Red Joaneting' (D)	SKee
– 'Red Jonagold'PBR	see *M. domestica* 'Jonagored'
– 'Red Jonathan' (D)	SDea
– 'Red Miller's Seedling' (D)	ECrN SCrf SDea
– 'Red Rattler' (D)	CTho
– 'Red Robin' (F)	CEnd
– 'Red Roller' (D)	CTho

– 'Red Ruby' (F)	CTho
– 'Red Victoria' (C)	GTwe
– 'Red Windsor'	EMui LRHS MAsh SCoo SKee SPoG
– 'Redcoat Grieve' (D)	SDea
– 'Redsleeves' (D)	CAgr ECrN GTwe SDea SKee
– 'Redstrake' (Cider)	CCAT
– 'Reine des Reinettes'	see *M. domestica* 'King of the Pippins'
– 'Reinette d'Obry' (Cider)	CCAT
– 'Reinette du Canada' (D)	SKee
– 'Reinette Rouge Etoilée' (D)	SDea
– 'Reverend Greeves' (C)	SDea
– 'Reverend McCormick' **new**	CTho
– 'Reverend W. Wilks' (C)	CAgr CCAT CDoC CTri ECrN EMui LAst LRHS MAsh MWat SCrf SDea SFam SKee WJas WOrn
– 'Ribston Pippin' (D) ♀H4	CCAT CTho CTri CWib ECrN ERea GBut GTwe LRHS MCoo MWat SCrf SDea SFam SKee WJas WOrn
– 'Rival' (D)	CAgr SDea WJas
– 'Rome Beauty' (D)	SDea
– 'Rosemary Russet' (D) ♀H4	CAgr CCAT CTho GBut GTwe MCoo SCrf SDea SFam SKee
– 'Ross Nonpareil' (D)	CAgr GTwe SDea SKee
– 'Rosy Blenheim' (D)	ECrN
– 'Rough Pippin' (D)	CCAT CEnd
– 'Roundway Magnum Bonum' (D)	CAgr CTho SDea
§ – 'Roxbury Russet' (D)	SKee
§ – 'Royal Gala' (D) ♀H4	ECrN EMui LAst SDea SLon
§ – 'Royal Jubilee' (C)	CCAT
– 'Royal Russet' (C)	CEnd ECrN SDea
– 'Royal Snow' (D)	SKee
– 'Royal Somerset' (C/Cider)	CCAT CTho CTri
– 'Rubinette' (D)	ECrN EMil MGos SDea
– 'Saint Cecilia' (D)	SDea
§ – 'Saint Edmund's Pippin' (D) ♀H4	CTho ECrN ERea GTwe MCoo SCrf SDea SFam SKee
– 'Saint Edmund's Russet'	see *M. domestica* 'Saint Edmund's Pippin'
– 'Sam Young' (D)	CAgr SKee
– 'Sandlands' (D)	SDea
– 'Sandringham' (C)	ECrN SKee
– 'Sanspareil' (D)	CAgr SKee
– 'Saturn'	CAgr CTri EMui GBut GTwe SDea SGFT SKee SPoG
– 'Saw Pits' (F)	CAgr CEnd
– 'Scarlet Nonpareil' (D)	SDea SKee
– 'Scotch Bridget' (C)	GBut NBid SCoo SKee WOrn
– 'Scotch Dumpling' (C)	GBut GTwe MCoo
– 'Scrumptious'^{PBR} (D)	CAgr CDoC ENot ERea LBuc LRHS MAsh MBri MLan NBlu NLar NWea SCoo SKee SPer SPoG WHar
– 'Seabrook's Red' (D)	ECrN
– 'Seaton House' (C)	GBut
– 'Sercombe's Natural' (Cider)	CTho
– 'Severn Bank' (C)	CCAT CTho
– 'Sheep's Nose' (C)	CCAT SDea SKee
– 'Shenandoah' (C)	SKee
– 'Sidney Strake' (C)	CAgr CEnd
– 'Sir Isaac Newton's'	see *M. domestica* 'Flower of Kent'
– 'Sir John Thornycroft' (D)	SDea
– 'Slack Ma Girdle' (Cider)	CCAT CTho
– 'Smart's Prince Arthur' (C)	SDea
– 'Snell's Glass Apple'	see *M. domestica* 'Glass Apple'
– 'Somerset Lasting' (C)	CTri
– 'Somerset Redstreak' (Cider)	CCAT CTho CTri GTwe
– 'Sops in Wine' (C/Cider)	CCAT CTho
– 'Sour Bay' (Cider)	CAgr CTho
– 'Sour Natural'	see *M. domestica* 'Langworthy'
– 'Spartan' (D)	CCAT CDoC CSBt CTri CWib ECrN EMui GTwe LAst LRHS MGan MGos NEgg NPri SCoo SCrf SDea SFam SKee SPer SPoG WJas WOrn
– 'Spencer' (D)	CTri ECrN SKee
– 'Spotted Dick' (Cider)	CTho
– 'Stable Jersey' (Cider)	CCAT
– 'Stamford Pippin' (D)	SDea
– 'Stanway Seedling' (C)	ECrN
– 'Star of Devon' (D)	CCAT CEnd SDea
– 'Stark' (D)	SDea
– 'Starking' (D)	ECrN
– 'Starkrimson' (D)	SKee
– 'Stembridge Cluster' (Cider)	CCAT
– 'Stembridge Jersey' (Cider)	CCAT
– 'Steyne Seedling' (D)	SDea
– 'Stirling Castle' (C)	CAgr GBut GQui GTwe SKee
– 'Stobo Castle' (C)	GBut GQui SKee
– 'Stockbearer' (C)	CTho
– 'Stoke Edith Pippin' (D)	WOrn
– 'Stoke Red' (Cider)	CCAT CTho
– 'Stone's'	see *M. domestica* 'Loddington'
– 'Stoup Leadington' (C)	SKee
– 'Strawberry Pippin' (D)	CTho WJas
– 'Striped Beefing' (C)	ECrN
– 'Sturmer Pippin' (D)	CCAT CDul CSBt CTri ECrN GTwe SCrf SDea SFam SKee WJas
* – 'Sugar Apple'	CTho
– 'Sugar Bush' (C/D)	CTho
– 'Sugar Loaf'	see *M. domestica* 'Sugar Apple'
– 'Summer Golden Pippin' (D)	SKee
– 'Summer Stubbard' (D)	CCAT
– 'Summerred' (D)	ECrN EMil
– 'Sunburn' (D)	ECrN
– 'Sunnydale' (D/C)	SDea
– 'Sunrise'^{PBR} (D)	EMui SKee
– 'Sunset' (D) ♀H4	More than 30 suppliers
– 'Suntan' (D) ♀H4	CCAT CWib ECrN EMil GTwe LAst MWat SDea SKee
– 'Superb'	see *M. domestica* 'Laxton's Superb'
– 'Surprise' (D)	GTwe
– 'Swaar' (D) **new**	SKee
– 'Sweet Alford' (Cider)	CCAT CTho ECrN
– 'Sweet Bay' (Cider)	CAgr CTho
– 'Sweet Caroline' (D)	ECrN
– 'Sweet Cleave' (Cider)	CTho
– 'Sweet Coppin' (Cider)	CCAT CTho CTri
– 'Sweet Ermgaard' (D)	ECrN
– 'Sweet Society' (D)	EMui LBuc LRHS MCoo
– 'Tale Sweet' (Cider)	CCAT CTho
– 'Tamar Beauty' (F)	CEnd
– 'Tan Harvey' (Cider)	CCAT CEnd CTho
– 'Tare de Ghinda' **new**	SKee
– 'Taunton Cross' (D)	CAgr
– 'Taunton Fair Maid' (Cider)	CCAT CTho
– 'Taylor's' (Cider)	CCAT SDea
– 'Ten Commandments' (D/Cider)	CCAT SDea
– Tentation = 'Delblush'^{PBR} (D) **new**	SLon
– 'Tewkesbury Baron' (D)	CTho
– 'The Rattler' (F)	CEnd
– 'Thomas Jeffrey' (D) **new**	GBut
– 'Thomas Rivers' (C)	SDea
– 'Thorle Pippin' (D)	GBut SKee
– 'Tidicombe Seedling' (D)	CTho
– 'Tom Putt' (C)	CAgr CCAT CCVT CTho CTri CWib ECrN GTwe LBuc SDea SKee WJas WOrn
– 'Tommy Knight' (D)	CAgr CCAT CEnd CTho

	- 'Topaz' (D)	SKee
	- 'Totnes Apple' (D)	CTho
	- 'Tower of Glamis' (C)	GBut GQui GTwe SKee
	- Town Farm Number 59 (Cider)	CTho
	- 'Tregonna King' (C/D)	CCAT CEnd CTho
	- 'Tremlett's Bitter' (Cider)	CCAT CTho SDea
	- 'Trwyn Mochyn' (C) **new**	WGwG
	- 'Twenty Ounce' (C)	GTwe WJas
§	- 'Tydeman's Early Worcester' (D)	CAgr CLnd CWib ECrN GTwe SDea SKee WJas
	- 'Tydeman's Late Orange' (D)	ECrN EMil EMui GTwe LAst LRHS MCoo SDea SFam SKee WOrn
	- 'Upton Pyne' (D)	CCAT CTho SCrf SDea SKee
	- 'Vallis Apple' (Cider)	CCAT CTho
	- 'Veitch's Perfection' (C/D)	CTho
	- 'Venus Pippin' (C/D)	CEnd
	- 'Vicar of Beighton' (D)	ECrN ERea
	- 'Vicary's Late Keeper' **new**	CTho
	- 'Vickey's Delight' (D)	SDea
	- 'Vileberie' (Cider)	CCAT
	- 'Vista-bella' (D)	ECrN SDea
	- 'Wagener' (D)	ECrN SDea SKee
	- 'Waltham Abbey Seedling' (C)	ECrN
	- Waltz = 'Telamon'^{PBR} (D/Ball)	LRHS MGos SDea SKee
	- 'Warner's King' (C) Υ^{H4}	CCAT CTho CTri SCrf SDea SKee WJas
	- 'Warrior'	CTho
	- 'Wealthy' (D)	SDea
	- 'Wellington' (C)	see *M. domestica* 'Dummellor's Seedling' (C)
	- 'Wellington' (Cider)	CAgr CTho
§	- 'Wellspur' (D)	GTwe
	- 'Wellspur Red Delicious'	see *M. domestica* 'Wellspur'
	- 'Welsh Russet' (D)	SDea
	- 'West View Seedling' (D)	ECrN
	- 'Wheeler's Russet' (D)	GBut
	- 'White Alphington' (Cider)	CTho
	- 'White Close Pippin' (Cider)	CTho
	- 'White Jersey' (Cider)	CCAT
	- 'White Joaneting' (D)	CCAT GBut GTwe
	- 'White Melrose' (C)	GBut GTwe LRHS MCoo SDea
	- 'White Paradise'^{PBR} (C)	GBut
	- 'White Transparent' (C/D)	SDea SKee
	- 'Whitpot Sweet' (F)	CEnd
	- 'Wick White Styre' (Cider)	CTho
	- 'William Crump' (D)	CCAT CTho ECrN SDea SFam WJas
	- 'Winston' (D) Υ^{H4}	CAgr CCAT CSBt CTri ECrN GTwe MAsh MCoo NWea SCrf SDea SFam
	- 'Winter Banana' (D)	ECrN SDea SKee
	- 'Winter Gem' (D)	CAgr CCAT CDoC ECrN EMil EMui ERea LBuc LRHS MBri MGos SDea SGFT SKee SPoG WBVN
	- 'Winter Lawrence'	CTho
	- 'Winter Lemon' (C/D)	GQui SKee
	- 'Winter Majetin' (C)	ECrN
	- 'Winter Peach' (D/C)	CAgr CEnd CTho ECrN
	- 'Winter Pearmain' (D)	SKee
	- 'Winter Quarrenden' (D)	SDea
	- 'Winter Queening' (D/C)	SDea
	- 'Winter Stubbard' (C)	CTho
	- 'Woodbine'	see *M. domestica* 'Northwood'
	- 'Woodford' (C)	ECrN
	- 'Woolbrook Pippin' (D)	CAgr CCAT CEnd CTho
	- 'Woolbrook Russet' (C)	CCAT CTho ECrN
	- 'Worcester Pearmain' (D) Υ^{H4}	More than 30 suppliers
	- 'Wormsley Pippin' (D)	ECrN
	- 'Wyatt's Seedling'	see *M. domestica* 'Langworthy'
	- 'Wyken Pippin' (D)	CCAT ECrN GTwe SDea SFam SKee WJas
	- 'Yarlington Mill' (Cider)	CCAT CTho CTri SDea SKee
	- 'Yellow Ingestrie' (D)	MAsh SFam SKee WHar WJas
	- 'Yellow Styre' (Cider)	CTho
	- 'Zabergäu Renette' (D)	SKee
	'Donald Wyman'	CLnd NLar SCoo
	'Echtermeyer'	see *M.* x *gloriosa* 'Oekonomierat Echtermeyer'
	'Evelyn'	MAsh
§	'Evereste' Υ^{H4}	More than 30 suppliers
	florentina	CLnd CMCN CTho EBee EPfP LTwo SLon SSpi
	- 'Rosemoor' **new**	EBee
	floribunda Υ^{H4}	More than 30 suppliers
	'Fontana'	MGos
	'Gardener's Gold'	CEnd CTho
§	x ***gloriosa*** 'Oekonomierat Echtermeyer'	CCAT SDea WJas
	'Golden Gem'	CCAT EBee EPfP GTwe LRHS MAsh SKee SLim
	'Golden Hornet'	see *M.* x *zumi* 'Golden Hornet'
	'Harry Baker'	EMui ERea LRHS MAsh MBlu NLar SCoo SLim
	'Hillieri'	see *M.* x *scheideckeri* 'Hillieri'
	hupehensis Υ^{H4}	CCAT CCVT CDul CEnd CLnd CMCN CSBt CTho CTri EBee ECrN EPfP GTwe LRHS MBlu MGos MRav SCrf SFam SHBN SLPl WMou WPGP WPat
	'Hyde Hall Spire'	LRHS MBri MGos SCoo
	'Indian Magic' **new**	CLnd
§	'John Downie' (C) Υ^{H4}	More than 30 suppliers
	'Kaido'	see *M.* x *micromalus*
	kansuensis	CLnd EPfP MBri WCwm
	'Laura'	CWSG ECrN EMui EPfP LRHS MAsh MBlu MGos NLar SCoo SKee SPoG
	'Lisa' **new**	CLnd
	x ***magdeburgensis***	CCVT CDul CLnd CSBt
	'Mandarin'	MAsh
	'Marshal Ôyama'	CTho MBlu
	'Mary Potter'	CLnd CTho
§	x ***micromalus***	CLnd NLar
	x ***moerlandsii***	CLnd
	- 'Liset'	CDul CEnd CLnd CWib EBee ECrN MBri NEgg SCoo SFam SPer SPoG WFar WJas
§	- 'Profusion'	CBcs CDul CLnd CTri CWSG EBee ECrN ELan ENot LAst LCro LRHS MGan MGos MRav MSwo NEgg NWea SCrf SHBN SPer WBVN WFar WJas
	- 'Profusion Improved'	CCAT CEnd CSBt CWSG MBri MWat SCoo SKee WOrn
	'Molten Lava' **new**	CLnd
	niedzwetzkyana	see *M. pumila* 'Niedzwetzkyana'
	Nuvar Carnival	SKee
	Nuvar Dusty Red	SKee
	Nuvar Marble	SKee
	Nuvar Pearl	SKee
	Nuvar Red Lantern	SKee
	orthocarpa	CLnd
	Perpetu	see *M.* 'Evereste'
	'Pink Glow'	CLnd EMui LRHS MAsh MBlu NLar SCoo SLim SPoG
	'Pink Mushroom'	LRHS NLar SCoo
	'Pink Perfection'	CDoC CEnd CLnd ECrN ENot LRHS SHBN SKee SPer
	Pom'Zaï = 'Courtabri'	CDoC
	'Pond Red' **new**	CLnd
	'Prairie Fire'	MAsh MBri SCoo
	prattii	CLnd CTho EPfP

	'Princeton Cardinal'	CLnd EBee MAsh SCoo
	'Professor Sprenger'	see *M.* x *zumi* 'Professor Sprenger'
	'Profusion'	see *M.* x *moerlandsii* 'Profusion'
	prunifolia 'Pendula'	MGan
	pumila 'Cowichan'	CLnd ECrN
	- 'Dartmouth'	CCAT CDul CLnd CSBt CSam CTri ECrN NEgg SFam
	- 'Montreal Beauty'	CLnd SCoo WJas WOrn
§	- 'Niedzwetzkyana'	CLnd
§	x ***purpurea*** 'Aldenhamensis'	CCAT CLnd SDea WOrn WSpi
	- 'Eleyi'	CDul CLnd ECrN LAst MGan NWea
	- 'Lemoinei'	CLnd ECrN EWTr
	- 'Neville Copeman'	CCVT CDoC CDul CLnd EBee ECrN EWTr MBlu MGos SPur WJas
	- 'Pendula'	see *M.* x *gloriosa* 'Oekonomierat Echtermeyer'
	'R.J. Fulcher'	CLnd CTho
	'Ralph Shay'	CLnd
	'Red Barron'	CLnd
	'Red Glow'	CLnd EBee ECrN MAsh WJas
	'Red Jade'	see *M.* x *scheideckeri* 'Red Jade'
	'Red Obelisk'	LRHS MBri SCoo SPoG WBod
	'Red Peacock' **new**	CLnd
	'Robinson'	CLnd MAsh SPoG
§	x ***robusta***	CLnd CTri GTwe LRHS LSRN NWea SCrf SLon
	- 'Red Sentinel' ♀H4	More than 30 suppliers
	- 'Red Siberian'	ECrN SDea SHBN SPer
	- 'Yellow Siberian'	CLnd SPer
	'Royal Beauty' ♀H4	CDoC CDul CLnd CWib EBee ENot EPfP GTwe LAst LRHS MBri MGos MSwo SCoo SCrf SGFT SPer WBod WHar WOrn
	'Royalty'	More than 30 suppliers
	'Rudolph'	CCAT CCVT CDul CLnd EBee ECrN LBuc LRHS MAsh MGos SCoo SLim SPer SPoG WJas WOrn
	'Ruth Ann'	CLnd
	sargentii	see *M. toringo* subsp. *sargentii*
	'Satin Cloud'	CLnd
§	x ***scheideckeri*** 'Hillieri'	CCAT CDul CLnd ECrN MAsh SFam
§	- 'Red Jade'	More than 30 suppliers
	Siberian crab	see *M.* x *robusta*
	sieboldii	see *M. toringo*
	- 'Wooster'	CLnd
	sikkimensis	WHCr
	- B&SWJ 2431	WCru
	'Silver Drift'	CLnd SCoo
	'Snowcloud'	CCAT CDul CLnd EBee ECrN LRHS MAsh MBlu SLim SPer WOrn
	spectabilis	CLnd
	'Street Parade'	CLnd SCoo
	'Striped Beauty'	CLnd CTho
	x ***sublobata***	CLnd
	'Sun Rival'	CCAT CCVT CDoC CDul CEnd CLnd CSBt CWSG EMui EPfP GTwe LRHS MAsh MBri MGos SCoo SLim SPoG WHar WJas WOrn
	sylvestris	CArn CCVT CDul CLnd CRWN CTri ECrN EMac ENot EPfP LBuc MRav NBee NWea WMou
§	***toringo***	CCAT CLnd CTho ECrN EPfP MBri SSpi WSHC
	- var. ***arborescens***	CTho
§	- subsp. ***sargentii***	CDul CLnd CMCN CTho ECrN ENot LAst MBri MGos MRav NWea SFam SPer WNor
	- - 'Tina'	CLnd
	- 'Scarlett'	IArd LRHS MAsh MBri SCoo
	toringoides	see *M. bhutanica*
	- 'Mandarin'	MBri NLar SCoo SSpi
	transitoria ♀H4	CCAT CDoC CDul CEnd CLnd CTho EBee ECrN ELan EMil EPfP LRHS MAsh MBlu MBri NWea SCoo SSpi WPGP
	- 'Thornhayes Tansy'	CAbP CTho WSpi
	trilobata	CCAT CLnd CTho EBee EMil EPfP LRHS MBlu MBri MGos SCoo SPoG
	- 'Guardsman'	MAsh MBri NLar SCoo SSpi
	tschonoskii ♀H4	More than 30 suppliers
	'Van Eseltine'	CCAT CDul CLnd CSBt CWSG CWib EBee ECrN EPfP GTwe LRHS MAsh MBri MWat NEgg SFam SPer SPoG WJas WPat
	'Veitch's Scarlet'	CDul CLnd CSBt GTwe SFam
	Weeping Candied Apple = 'Weepcanzam' **new**	CLnd
	'White Star'	CCVT CDoC CDul CLnd CSBt CWSG ECrN SCoo SLim SPoG
	'Winter Gold'	CDoC CDul CLnd SCrf SPoG
	'Wisley Crab'	CLnd EMil GTwe SDea SFam SKee
	yunnanensis	EPfP
	- var. ***veitchii***	CTho
	x ***zumi*** var. ***calocarpa***	CLnd CTho
§	- 'Golden Hornet' ♀H4	More than 30 suppliers
§	- 'Professor Sprenger'	CLnd CSam EPfP SCoo

Malva (*Malvaceae*)

	alcea	CAgr EPfP
	- var. ***fastigiata***	CArn ERou EShb LRHS MBri NBro SPer SRms WPer
	bicolor	see *Lavatera maritima*
	'Gibbortello'	CCge
	moschata	CAgr CArn CBcs CHrt CPrp CRWN CSev EBee ECtt ELan EPfP ERou MHer MNHC NBlu NMir SIde SPer SPlb SWat WGwG WHer WMoo
	- f. ***alba*** ♀H4	More than 30 suppliers
	- - 'Pirouette'	WHen
	- 'Pink Perfection'	EShb
	- 'Romney Marsh'	see *Althaea officinalis* 'Romney Marsh'
	- ***rosea***	EPfP GMaP LAst NBlu NCot NEgg NPer SPoG SWvt WWeb
	pusilla **new**	CCCN
	'Sweet Sixteen' **new**	NLar
	sylvestris	CAgr CArn GWCH MNHC NBro NMir NSco SMad SWat WHer WJek WMoo
	- 'Bardsey Blue'	WGwG
	- 'Brave Heart'	EShb GBri NLar SPav SWvt WOut
I	- 'Magic Hollyhock' (d)	SGar
	- Marina = 'Dema' PBR	ELan NLar
	- subsp. ***mauritiana***	EBee EPfP GBri MBri NPer WMoo
	- - 'Bibor Fehlo'	CSpe EWin
	- 'Mystic Merlin'	EBee SPav
	- 'Perry's Blue'	NPer
	- 'Primley Blue'	CElw EBee ECha ECtt ELan EPfP GBri GMaP MRav MTho NBPC NBlu NGdn NPer NSti SMad SPer WFar WSpi
	- 'Zebrina'	EBee GBri LDai LSou NGdn NPer NPri SPer SWvt WBrE WMoo
	verticillata 'Crispa'	CAgr

Malvastrum (*Malvaceae*)

x ***hypomadarum***	see *Anisodontea* x *hypomadara* (Sprague) D.M. Bates
lateritium	More than 30 suppliers

Malvaviscus (*Malvaceae*)

arboreus	CHII CKob LEdu XPep
- var. ***mexicanus***	CKob CPLG
- pink-flowered	CKob

mandarin see *Citrus reticulata*

Mandevilla (*Apocynaceae*)

§	***x amabilis***	CCCN
	– 'Alice du Pont' ♀^{H1}	CBcs CCCN CRHN CSpe ELan ERea EShb MJnS SOWG
	x amoena	see *M. x amabilis*
	boliviensis ♀^{H1}	CCCN ELan SOWG
§	***laxa*** ♀^{H2}	CCCN CHEx CHll CSpe ELan ERea EShb SAga SHFr SOWG WCot WHrl WSHC
	sanderi	CCCN EShb MBri MJnS
	– 'Rosea'	CSpe ERea NScw
	splendens ♀^{H1}	CCCN EPfP LRHS SOWG
	suaveolens	see *M. laxa*

Mandragora (*Solanaceae*)

	autumnalis	CFwr CWan ITer LEdu MGol MSal NLar WCot
	caulescens	CFir EBee WSpi
§	***officinarum***	CFwr EEls GCrs GPoy LEdu MGol MHer MSal NGHP SMad

Manettia (*Rubiaceae*)

	inflata	see *M. luteorubra*
§	***luteorubra***	CCCN ELan WCot

Manfreda see *Agave*

Mangifera (*Anacardiaceae*)

indica	CCCN

Manglietia (*Magnoliaceae*)

chevalieri HWJ 533	WCru
conifera	SSpi WPGP
insignis	CBcs CHEx NLar SKHP SSpi WPGP
yuyuanensis	CBcs

Maranta (*Marantaceae*)

leuconeura var. ***erythroneura*** ♀^{H1}	EShb XBlo
– var. ***kerchoveana*** ♀^{H1}	CHal LRHS MBri XBlo

Margyricarpus (*Rosaceae*)

§	***pinnatus***	CFee CPLG CPle CSpe GEdr GGar MMHG NWCA WPer
	setosus	see *M. pinnatus*

Mariscus see *Cyperus*

marjoram, pot see *Origanum onites*

marjoram, sweet see *Origanum majorana*

marjoram, wild, or oregano see *Origanum vulgare*

Marrubium (*Lamiaceae*)

§	***bourgaei*** var. ***bourgaei***	CFee EBee ECha EGoo EMan EWin
	'All Hallow's Green'	GBuc LHop LRHS MRav MWgw SLon SPoG WOut
	candidissimum	see *M. incanum*
	cylleneum	ECha
	friwaldskyanum	XPep
§	***incanum***	EBee EGoo NCGa WEas
	libanoticum	ECha WPer
	pestalloziae	EBee
	supinum	CArn XPep
	vulgare	CArn CPrp CWan ELau GPoy GWCH MHer MNHC SECG SIde WHer WPer WSel
	– 'Green Pompon'	ELau NLar

Marshallia (*Asteraceae*)

grandiflora	CDes EBee
trinerva	EBee WHil

Marsippospermum (*Juncaceae*)

gracile	ECou

Mascarena see *Hyophorbe*

Massonia (*Hyacinthaceae*)

depressa	CStu
echinata	CStu WCot
aff. ***echinata***	CStu
jasminiflora **new**	WCot
pustulata	CStu WCot

Mathiasella (*Apiaceae*)

bupleuroides	EBee LSou
– 'Green Dream' **new**	WCot

Matricaria (*Asteraceae*)

	chamomilla	see *M. recutita*
	maritima	see *Tripleurospermum maritimum*
	parthenium	see *Tanacetum parthenium*
§	***recutita***	CArn GPoy MNHC
	tchihatchewii	XPep

Matteuccia (*Woodsiaceae*)

	intermedia	see *Onoclea intermedia*
	orientalis	CLAP ERod GGar MAsh MPes MWgw NGby NLar NOrc SKHP WFar WRic
	pensylvanica	CLAP EMon ITim NHol WRic
	struthiopteris ♀^{H4}	More than 30 suppliers
	– 'Bedraggled Feathers'	EMon
*	– 'Depauperata'	CLAP
	– 'Erosa' **new**	EMon
	– 'Jumbo'	CCCN CLAP

Matthiola (*Brassicaceae*)

§	***fruticulosa***	EBee EWin
	– 'Alba'	CDes EBee EWin WPGP
	– subsp. ***perennis***	NWCA WHal
	incana	CHrt LRHS MArl NLar SBHP SPad WCFE WPer WRHF
	– ***alba***	ELan LSou NBir SPav WBVN WCot WPtf WSpi
	– purple-flowered	LSou SPhx WCot
	sinuata	GGar
	thessala	see *M. fruticulosa*
	white-flowered, perennial	CArn CHrt CMil CSev CSpe ECGP ERou LRav MAvo MSte NPer SEND SMeo SPhx WEas

Maurandella (*Scrophulariaceae*)

§	***antirrhiniflora***	EWld LRHS

Maurandya (*Scrophulariaceae*)

§	***barclayana***	CDTJ CHll CSpe ITer MBri SGar WRos
	– ***alba***	CSpe
	'Bridal Bouquet'	CCCN LSou
	erubescens	see *Lophospermum erubescens*
	lophantha	see *Lophospermum scandens*
	lophospermum	see *Lophospermum scandens*
	'Pink Ice'	see *Lophospermum scandens* 'Pink Ice'
	'Red Dragon'	see *Lophospermum* 'Red Dragon'
§	'Victoria Falls'	SOWG

Maytenus (*Celastraceae*)

boaria	CMCN EPfP IDee LEdu NLar SAPC SArc WFar WPGP
disticha	LEdu
magellanica	WFar

Mazus (*Scrophulariaceae*)

	miquelii	EBee
	reptans	EBee ECho EDAr EPfP GEdr NPer NWCA WBVN
	- 'Albus'	EBee ECho EMFW LAst LLWG SPlb
	- 'Blue' **new**	EAlp

Mecardonia (*Scrophulariaceae*)

	'Goldflake'	CCCN EWin LSou NPri

Meconopsis ✿ (*Papaveraceae*)

	aculeata	GGGa
	baileyi	see *M. betonicifolia*
	Ballyrogan form	GEdr IBlr
	x ***beamishii***	GBuc
§	***betonicifolia*** Υ^{H4}	More than 30 suppliers
	- var. ***alba***	CWCL EBee ELan EPfP GBuc GCra GGGa GKev GMaP ITim NChi NCob NEgg NLar NSum SPer SPoG SRms
	- 'Glacier Blue'	GCra
	- 'Hensol Violet'	GBuc GCra GCrs GGGa ITim NLar NSum
	cambrica	CHrt CPLG CTri EBee EHrv ELan EMar EPfP GGar NCot NHol NPri SGar SIng WAbe WBrk WFar WHen WHer WPnP WPtf
	- 'Anne Greenaway' (d)	WCot
	- var. ***aurantiaca***	LSou SBch
	- ***flore-pleno*** (d)	GBuc MTho NBid WCot
	- - orange (d)	NBid NBir NPen WCot WHen
§	- 'Frances Perry'	GBuc IBlr WCot WFar WRos
	- 'Rubra'	see *M. cambrica* 'Frances Perry'
	chelidoniifolia	GCra IBlr IGor NBid WCru WFar
	x ***cookei*** **new**	GMac
	- 'Old Rose' **new**	GCrs
	'Dalemain' **new**	GMac
	delavayi	GGGa
	dhwojii	NEgg
	discigera HWJK 2282	WCru
	(Fertile Blue Group) 'Blue Ice'	see *M.* (Fertile Blue Group) 'Lingholm'
N	- 'Lingholm'	CAby CLAP CPLG CPne CSam EBee EShb GBuc GCra GCrs GEdr GGGa GGar GKev GMaP ITer LHop MDun MSte NCGa NChi NEgg NGdn NHar NHol NSum WPGP WPnP
N	George Sherriff Group	EBee GBuc GCra GEdr IBlr NBir
N	- 'Ascreavie'	GCrs GMaP
N	- 'Branklyn' ambig.	CGHE GBri IBlr WFar WPGP
N	- 'Huntfield'	GCrs GMaP
N	- 'Jimmy Bayne'	GBuc GCrs GEdr GGGa GMaP
N	- 'Spring Hill'	GBuc IBlr
N	***grandis*** misapplied	see *M.* George Sherriff Group
N	***grandis*** ambig.	CHar CWCL EGle GEdr ITim MNrw NEgg NSla SPoG SRms WAbe WSpi
	grandis Prain	EBee
	- from Sikkim	GCrs
	- GS 600	see *M.* George Sherriff Group
	- GWJ 9275	WCru
	- HWJK 2304	WCru
	- 'Alba'	GAbr
	- Balruddery form	GGGa
	grandis x ***regia***	GBuc
	horridula	GGGa MTho NEgg NLar
	- BWJ 7983	WCru
	- HWJK 2293	WCru
N	(Infertile Blue Group) 'Bobby Masterton'	GBuc GCra GCrs
N	- 'Crewdson Hybrid'	GBuc GCrs GMaP NLar
N	- 'Cruickshank'	GCrs
N	- 'Dawyck'	see *M.* (Infertile Blue Group) 'Slieve Donard'
N	- 'Mrs Jebb'	GBuc GCra GCrs GMaP
N	- 'Slieve Donard' Υ^{H4}	GBri GBuc GCra GCrs GMaP IBlr
	integrifolia	GGGa GGar
	'Keillour'	GKev
	Kingsbarns hybrids	GGGa
	latifolia	NEgg
	napaulensis	CSam EBee ENot GAbr GCra GEdr GGGa GGar GKev LHop LRHS MDun NChi NEgg NLar NSum SPoG WCAu WMoo
	- GWJ 9264	WCru
	- pink-flowered	CBcs CWCL NEgg NGdn WPGP
	- red-flowered	CBcs GBuc ITim MDun
	nudicaulis	see *Papaver nudicaule*
	'Ormswell' ambig.	GBuc IBlr
	paniculata	GGGa ITim MDun NBir NEgg WAbe
	- GWJ 9312	WCru
	- HWJK 2167	WCru
	- HWJK 2315	WCru
	- from Ghunsa, Nepal	CLAP WAbe
	- ginger foliage	GEdr MDun
	pseudointegrifolia	GCra GGGa NEgg
	punicea	GBin GCrs GGGa
	quintuplinervia Υ^{H4}	CLAP GCra GCrs GGGa GMaP IGor NBir NChi NSla NSum WHal
	- 'Kaye's Compact'	GBuc
	regia	GAbr LHop NLar WMoo
	x ***sarsonsii***	NSum
	x ***sheldonii*** misapplied (fertile)	see *M.* Fertile Blue Group
	x ***sheldonii*** misapplied (sterile)	see *M.* Infertile Blue Group
N	x ***sheldonii*** ambig.	CBcs CBow CHar EBee ENot EPot GAbr GBuc ITim LAst MBri MDun NBir SPer SPoG SRms WBod WCru WFar
	x ***sheldonii*** G. Taylor	NPer
	simplicifolia	GGGa NEgg
	superba	GBuc GGGa NEgg
	villosa	CPLG GBuc GCra GGGa IBlr WCru
	wallichii misapplied	see *M. wallichii* Hook.
§	***wallichii*** Hook.	CMil GGGa NEgg NLar
	- GWJ 9400	WCru
	'Willie Duncan'	GMaP ITim

Medicago (*Papilionaceae*)

	arborea	CArn SEND SPlb XPep
	sativa	NLar WHer WSFF

Medinilla (*Melastomataceae*)

	magnifica Υ^{H1}	CCCN LRHS MBri

medlar see *Mespilus germanica*

Meehania (*Lamiaceae*)

	cordata	CDes CLAP EBee NLar
	fargesii	CDes CLAP
	urticifolia	EBee EPPr MHar MSte WSHC WTMC
	- B&SWJ 1210	WCru
	- 'Wandering Minstrel' (v)	CDes CLAP EBee EMan WCot

Melaleuca (*Myrtaceae*)

	acerosa	SOWG
	acuminata	SPlb
	alternifolia	CArn ECou ELau EOHP EShb GPoy MGol MHer MSal NTHB SOWG SPlb WHer
	armillaris	CBgR CCCN CDoC IDee SGar SOWG SPlb
	- pink-flowered	SOWG
	blaeriifolia **new**	ECou
	bracteata	ECou
	citrina	SOWG
	coccinea	SOWG

cuticularis	SPlb
decora	SOWG
decussata	ECou SOWG SPlb
elliptica	SOWG
ericifolia	CTri SOWG SPlb
filifolia	SOWG
fulgens	SOWG SPlb
- apricot-flowered	SOWG
* - 'Hot Pink'	SOWG
- purple-flowered	SOWG
gibbosa	CPLG EBee ECou IDee SKHP SOWG WSHC
holosericea misapplied	see *M. smartiorum*
huegelii	SOWG
hypericifolia	CPLG ECou SOWG SPlb
incana	EBee SOWG
lateritia	ECou SOWG
leucadendra	MSal
linariifolia	ECou SPlb
nesophila	ECou EShb IDee SOWG SPlb
pentagona var. *subulifolia* new	ECou
platycalyx	SOWG
pulchella	SOWG
pungens	SPlb
pustulata	ECou EShb SOWG
radula	SOWG
* *rosmarinifolia*	SOWG
§ *smartiorum*	SOWG
spathulata	SOWG
squamea	EBee IDee SPlb WBrE
* *squarmania*	SOWG
squarrosa	CPLG ECou SOWG SPlb
thymifolia	ECou SOWG SPlb
viridiflora	GQui
wilsonii	ECou IDee SOWG

Melandrium see *Vaccaria*

rubrum	see *Silene dioica*

Melanoselinum (*Apiaceae*)

§ *decipiens*	CArn CHEx CHrt CSpe EBee ERCP EWes ITer SKHP SPhx WPGP

Melasphaerula (*Iridaceae*)

graminea	see *M. ramosa*
§ *ramosa*	CBre CStu ERos WPrP

Melia (*Meliaceae*)

§ *azedarach*	CArn CBcs CCCN EBee ELau EShb LRav WPGP
- B&SWJ 7039	WCru
- var. *japonica*	see *M. azedarach*

Melianthus (*Melianthaceae*)

comosus	CDTJ EBee EShb EUnu EWes LPio NLar SPhx SPlb WCot WGwG WOut
elongatus	CPne EShb
major ♀H3	More than 30 suppliers
minor	CDTJ CFir CHid LPio
villosus	CBod CBow CDTJ CFir EBee EShb EUnu EWes LPio MCCP SGar SPlb SPoG WOut

Melica (*Poaceae*)

altissima 'Alba'	MLHP
- 'Atropurpurea'	More than 30 suppliers
ciliata	CBig EBee GFor MMoz NLar NNor SSvw WMnd WRos XIsg
- subsp. *taurica*	EPPr MAvo
macra	EPPr SApp
nutans	CBig CWCL EAlp EPPr EPla EWsh GBin GFor GWCH NLar NWCA SBch WRos XIsg
penicillaris	EBee EPPr MAvo WPer XIsg
persica	EPPr MAvo XIsg
transsilvanica	CBig EPPr GFor NBre NNor XIsg
- 'Atropurpurea'	EBee SPer
- 'Red Spire'	CBig CWib EShb LRav MBNS SMad WMoo
uniflora	CBig GFor XIsg
- f. *albida*	ECha EGoo EPPr LBBr MAvo MHar SLPl WCot
- 'Variegata' (v)	CBre CWsd EBee ECha ELon EPPr EPla EShb LBMP MBri MMoz NGdn WCot WMoo WTin

Melicope (*Rutaceae*)

ternata	ECou

Melicytus (*Violaceae*)

alpinus	ECou
angustifolius	ECou
crassifolius	ECou EPla WFar
obovatus	ECou NLar
ramiflorus	CHEx ECou

Melilotus (*Papilionaceae*)

officinalis	CArn GPoy NSco SIde WHer WSel
- subsp. *albus*	CArn

Melinis (*Poaceae*)

nerviglumis	CKno
- 'Savannah' new	CSpe CWib
roseus	EHul

Meliosma (*Meliosmaceae*)

cuneifolia	CBcs NLar
parviflora B&SWJ 8408	WCru

Melissa (*Lamiaceae*)

officinalis	CAgr CArn CHal CHrt CPbn CTri EDAr ELau EUnu GMaP GPoy LCro MBar MBri MHer MNHC SECG SIde SPlb SWal WBrk WPer XPep
- 'All Gold'	CArn CBre CPbn CPrp CSev ECha EGoo ELan ELau EUnu NBid NSti NVic SPoG WMoo
§ - 'Aurea' (v)	CArn CBgR CFee CPLG CPrp CSev ELan ELau EUnu GCra GMaP GPoy LRHS MBar MBri MHer MNHC MRav MWgw NBid NBro NGHP NPri SIde SPer SPoG SRms WFar WMnd WMoo
* - 'Compacta'	CPbn GPoy MHer
- 'Lime Balm' new	CPbn
- 'Quedlinburger Niederliegende'	CArn CPbn
N - 'Variegata' misapplied	see *M. officinalis* 'Aurea'

Melittis (*Lamiaceae*)

melissophyllum	CBrm CFir CPom EBee EMan EMon LPio LSou MGol MRav MSte NChi NMen SRms SSvw WAbb WCAu WCot WCra
- subsp. *albida*	EBee EMon LPio WCot
- pink	CFwr EMon
- 'Royal Velvet Distinction'PBR	CPen EBee MRav

Melliodendron (*Styracaceae*)

xylocarpum	CBcs IArd IDee

Menispermum (*Menispermaceae*)

canadense	CTri GPoy MGol MSal SHBN
davuricum	MGol MSal NLar

Menstruocalamus (*Poaceae*)

sichuanensis	WPGP

Mentha ✿ (*Lamiaceae*)

	angustifolia ambig.	CPbn SIde
	angustifolia Corb.	see *M.* x *villosa*
	angustifolia Host	see *M. arvensis*
	aquatica	CArn CBen CPbn CWat EHon ELau EMFW EPfP GPoy LCro MHer MNHC NPer NSco SIde SPlb SWal SWat WFar WHer WMAq WMoo WPnP WSFF
§	- var. ***crispa***	CPbn SIde
	- krause minze	see *M. aquatica* var. *crispa*
	- 'Mandeliensis'	CPbn
§	***arvensis***	CArn CPbn ELau MHer MSal NSco SIde WHer WJek
	- 'Banana'	CPbn LSou MHer MNHC NGHP
	- var. ***piperascens***	MSal SIde
§	- - 'Sayakaze'	CArn CPbn ELau
	- var. ***villosa***	CPbn
	asiatica	CPbn ELau MHer SIde WHer
	'Betty's Slovakian'	CPbn
	Bowles' mint	see *M.* x *villosa* var. *alopecuroides* Bowles mint
*	***brevifolia***	CPbn SIde WHer
	cervina	CBen CDWL CPbn CWat EHon EMFW MHer NLar SIde SWat WJek
*	- ***alba***	CDWL CPbn LLWG MHer NLar WMAq
I	'Chocolate Peppermint'	MNHC NBir SECG
	citrata	see *M.* x *piperita* f. *citrata*
	'Clarissa's Millennium'	CPbn SIde
	cordifolia	see *M.* x *villosa*
	corsica	see *M. requienii*
	crispa L. (1753)	see *M. spicata* var. *crispa*
	crispa L. (1763)	see *M. aquatica* var. *crispa*
	crispa ambig. x (x ***piperita***)	CPbn EDAr
	'Dionysus'	CPbn SIde
	x ***dumetorum***	CPbn
	'Eau de Cologne'	see *M.* x *piperita* f. *citrata*
	eucalyptus mint	CPbn ELau MHer NGHP WGwG
	gattefossei	CArn CPbn ELau
	x ***gentilis***	see *M.* x *gracilis*
§	x ***gracilis***	CArn CHby CPbn ELau GWCH NGHP NPri SIde WJek
	- 'Aurea'	see *M.* x *gracilis* 'Variegata'
§	- 'Variegata' (v)	CHrt CPbn CPrp CSev CWan ECha ELau EMar GGar GPoy ILis MBar MHer MNHC NBlu NPri NVic SPlb WFar WHer WPer WSel
	haplocalyx	CArn ELau MSal SIde
*	'Hillary's Sweet Lemon'	CPbn ELau MHer SIde
	'Julia's Sweet Citrus'	CPbn MHer SIde
*	***lacerata***	CPbn SIde
	lavender mint	CArn CPbn CPrp CWan ELau EMan EOHP GPoy MHer NGHP NTHB WJek
§	***longifolia***	CAgr CPbn CPrp CWan ELau SBch SIde SPlb WEas WHer WJek WPer WSel
	- Buddleia Mint Group	CArn CPbn EBee ELau EMan EUnu GGar MHer MRav NGHP SECG SIde WSel
	- dwarf	CPbn
	- subsp. ***schimperi***	CPbn SIde WJek
	- silver-leaved	CArn CPbn ELau GWCH MHer MNHC NLar WOut
*	- 'Variegata' (v)	CPbn CPrp ELau WJek
	Nile Valley mint	CArn CBod CPbn CPrp ELau SHDw SIde
	x ***piperita***	CArn CHby CHrt CPbn CSev CWan ECha ELau GGar GPoy ILis LHop MBri MHer NBlu NGHP NPri NVic SPlb SWal WPer
*	- alba	CArn CPbn MHer WGwG

	- 'Black Mitcham'	CArn CPbn
	- black peppermint	CAgr CHby CPbn EPfP GWCH MNHC NBir NBlu NGHP NHol NLar NTHB SBch SWal WGwG
§	- f. ***citrata***	CArn CHby COIW CPbn CPrp CTri ECha ELau EOHP GGar GMaP GPoy MBar MBri MHer MNHC NBir NBlu NGHP SHDw SIde SPlb STre WGwG WPer WSel
*	- - 'Basil'	CHrt CPbn CPrp CWan ELau MHer MNHC MRav NBlu NGHP NHol NTHB SBch SHDw SIde WGwG WJek
	- - 'Bergamot'	CPbn
	- - 'Chocolate'	CArn CPbn CPrp CWan ELau EMan EPfP EUnu GGar ILis MHer MNHC NGHP NPri SHDw SIde WGwG WJek WMoo WPer
	- - 'Grapefruit'	CPbn CPrp CTca CWan ILis LFol LSou NGHP SWal WGwG WJek
	- - 'Lemon'	CPbn CPrp CWan ELau EMan GPoy MBri MHer MNHC NGHP SBch SHDw SIde WGwG WJek WPer WSel
	- - 'Lime'	CHrt CPbn CPrp CWan EMan ILis LSou MHer NGHP NPri SHDw SIde SPlb WGwG WJek
	- - 'Orange'	CPbn EUnu MHer MNHC NGHP WDyG WOut
	- - 'Reverchonii'	CPbn SIde
	- - 'Swiss Ricola'	EUnu MHer SIde
	- 'Logee's' (v)	CPbn CWan EBee EMan EWes MNHC NBlu NGHP NHol NPri NTHB SIde WHer WJek
	- f. ***officinalis***	CPbn ELau SIde
	- var. ***ouweneellii*** Belgian mint	CPbn SIde
	- 'Reine Rouge'	CPbn SIde
	- 'Swiss'	NGHP NLar
I	- Swiss mint	CArn CPbn CPrp SECG WGwG WOut
	pulegium	CArn CHby COIW CPbn CPrp CRWN CSev CTri CWan ELau EMFW GPoy MHer MNHC SIde SPlb SRms SWal WHer WJek WPer
	- 'Upright'	CArn CBod CPbn GPoy MHer MNHC NTHB SHDw SIde WJek WPer WSel
§	***requienii***	More than 30 suppliers
	rotundifolia misapplied	see *M. suaveolens*
	rotundifolia (L.) Hudson	see *M.* x *villosa*
	rubra var. ***raripila***	see *M.* x *smithiana*
	'Russian' curled leaf	CPbn
	'Russian' plain leaf	CPbn
	'Sayakarze'	see *M. arvensis* var. *piperascens* 'Sayakaze'
§	x ***smithiana***	CAgr CArn CPbn CPrp CWan ELau EOHP GPoy ILis MHer MNHC NBir NBlu NGHP NPri SBch WHer WPer
	- 'Capel Ulo' (v)	ELau WHer
§	***spicata***	CArn CHby CHrt COIW CPbn CPrp CSev CTri CWan GPoy ILis LCro LFol MBar MBri MHer NBlu NGHP NHol SPlb SRms SWal WHer WJek WPer
	- Algerian fruity	CPbn EUnu SIde
	- 'Austrian'	CPbn
*	- 'Brundall'	CPbn ELau ILis SIde
*	- var. ***crispa***	CArn CPbn CPrp CWan ECha ELau EOHP GGar LEdu LHop MHer MNHC NGHP NHol NPri SIde SPlb WCot WPer WSel
	- - 'Moroccan'	CArn CPbn CPrp CSev ELau EUnu GAbr GGar GPoy LEdu MHer

	MNHC NGHP NPri NVic SHDw SIde STre WJek WSel
- - 'Persian'	CPbn
- 'Guernsey'	CPbn SHDw SIde
- 'Irish' new	CPbn
- 'Kentucky Colonel'	CPbn
- 'Mexican'	CArn CPbn
- 'Newbourne'	CPbn ELau SIde
- 'Pharoah'	CArn CPbn
- 'Rhodos'	CPbn
- 'Russian'	CPbn EWin NGHP NHol NTHB SIde
- 'Small Dole' (v)	SHDw
- 'Spanish Furry'	CPbn MHer SIde
- 'Spanish Pointed'	CPbn ELau SIde
- 'Tashkent'	CArn CHby CPbn ELau GWCH MHer MNHC NGHP SHDw SIde WGwG WJek WOut
- subsp. ***tomentosa***	CPbn
* - 'Variegata' (v)	CPbn SHDw WGwG
- 'Verte Blanche'	CPbn
§ ***suaveolens***	CAgr CArn CHby CPbn CWan ELau GMaP GPoy GWCH ILis MBri MHer MNHC NGHP NPri SIde SPlb SWal WBrk WPer WSFF
* - 'Grapefruit'	EWin NGHP NPri
- 'Jokka'	CPbn EBee
* - 'Mobillei'	CPbn SIde WJek
* - 'Pineapple'	WGwG
- subsp. ***timija***	CPbn ELau SIde WJek
- 'Variegata' (v)	CArn CHrt COIW CPbn CPrp CTri ECha ELau GMaP GPoy LCro MBar MBri MHer MNHC MRav MWgw NBlu NGHP NHol NPri NVic SIde SPlb SRms WHer WPer
'Sweet Pear'	CPbn EUnu LSou
sylvestris L.	see *M. longifolia*
* ***verona***	CPbn MHer
§ x ***villosa***	CArn CPbn SIde
§ - var. ***alopecuroides*** Bowles mint	CAgr CBre CHrt CPbn CPrp ELau EMan GGar GPoy ILis MHer MNHC NBir NGHP SIde STre SWat WGwG WHer WJek
viridis	see *M. spicata*

Mentzelia (*Loasaceae*)

decapetala new	CSpe

Menyanthes (*Menyanthaceae*)

trifoliata	CBen CWat EHon ELau EMFW GPoy MCCP NPer NSco NVic WBVN WFar WHal WMAq WPnP

Menziesia (*Ericaceae*)

alba	see *Daboecia cantabrica* f. *alba*
ciliicalyx	SSpi
- ***lasiophylla***	see *M. ciliicalyx* var. *purpurea*
- var. ***multiflora***	CStu EPfP GGGa MDun
§ - var. ***purpurea***	GGGa
ferruginea	SSta
'Ulva'	GGGa

Mercurialis (*Euphorbiaceae*)

perennis	GPoy MGol NSco WHer WShi

Merendera (*Colchicaceae*)

attica	EBrs ECho
eichleri	see *M. trigyna*
filifolia	ECho
§ ***montana***	EBrs ERos WIvy WThu
pyrenaica	see *M. montana*
raddeana	see *M. trigyna*
sobolifera	WCot WFar
§ ***trigyna***	CHHB EBrs ECho

Merremia (*Convolvulaceae*)

pinnata	MSal
§ ***tuberosa***	SOWG

Mertensia (*Boraginaceae*)

ciliata	CMdw CPom LRHS MNrw NBid SWat WLin
maritima	CSpe EWll GMaP GPoy MSal
- subsp. ***asiatica***	see *M. simplicissima*
pterocarpa	see *M. sibirica*
pulmonarioides	see *M. virginica*
§ ***sibirica***	CLAP CSpe EBee NChi NDlv NLar NPri SMrm SPhx SPlb
§ ***simplicissima***	CMea CWCL EBee ECho EMan MNrw NBir SGar SPhx SPlb WFar WHoo
§ ***virginica*** ♀H4	CArn CLAP CPrp EBee EBrs ECho ELan EPfP EPot EWTr GMac LAma NBid NBir NLar NMyG NPri NWCA SMrm SPoG SRms STes WCru WFar
viridis	SPhx

Merwilla (*Hyacinthaceae*)

§ ***plumbea***	WCot

Merxmuellera see *Rytidosperma*

Meryta (*Araliaceae*)

sinclairii	CHEx

Mesembryanthemum (*Aizoaceae*)

'Basutoland'	see *Delosperma nubigenum*
brownii	see *Lampranthus brownii*

Mespilus (*Rosaceae*)

germanica (F)	CBcs CDul CLnd CTri EBee ECrN ELan IDee MWat NLar NScw SBLw SDnm SHBN SLon WFar WMou WOrn
- 'Bredase Reus' (F)	SKee
- 'Dutch' (F)	SDea SFam SKee
- 'Large Russian' (F)	CAgr ERea GTwe
- 'Macrocarpa'	SKee
- 'Monstrous' (F)	SDea
- 'Nespoli del Giappone' new	WSpi
- 'Nottingham' (F)	More than 30 suppliers
- 'Royal' (F)	CAgr MBri MCoo SCoo SKee
- 'Westerveld' (F)	SKee

Metapanax see *Pseudopanax*

Metaplexis (*Asclepiadaceae*)

japonica B&SWJ 8459	WCru

Metarungia (*Acanthaceae*)

longistrobus	GFai

Metasequoia (*Cupressaceae*)

glyptostroboides ♀H4	More than 30 suppliers
- 'Emerald Feathers'	ECho LLin WEve
- 'Fastigiata'	see *M. glyptostroboides* 'National'
- 'Gold Rush'	More than 30 suppliers
- 'Green Mantle'	ECho EHul
- 'Matthaei Broom' new	NLar SLim
- 'Miss Grace' new	SLim
§ - 'National'	ECho
- 'Sheridan Spire'	CEnd WPGP
- 'Spring Cream'	ECho LLin NLar WEve
- 'Waasland' new	LRHS SLim
- 'White Spot' (v)	ECho LLin SLim WEve

Metrosideros (*Myrtaceae*)

carminea	CTrC

§ ***excelsa*** CHEx CHll CTrC CTrG EBak ECou SHFr
- 'Aurea' ECou
- 'Fire Mountain' CTrC
- 'Parnell' CBcs
- 'Scarlet Pimpernel' SOWG
- 'Spring Fire' CBcs CCCN
- 'Vibrance' CTrC

kermadecensis ECou
- 'Red and Gold' CDoC CTrC
- 'Variegata' (v) CBcs CDoC CTrC ECou MLan

lucida see *M. umbellata*

'Moon Maiden' SOWG

'Pink Lady' CTrC

robusta CBcs CHEx
- ***aureovariegata*** EShb

x ***subtomentosa*** 'Mistral' ECou

'Thomasii' SOWG

tomentosa see *M. excelsa*

§ ***umbellata*** CBcs CHEx CPLG CTrC EBee ECou EShb GGar

villosa SOWG
- 'Tahiti' CBcs

Meum (*Apiaceae*)

athamanticum CSev CSpe CWsd EBee EDAr EGle EHrv EMan GPoy LRHS MAvo MRav MSal MTho NBid NCGa NChi NSti SGar WFar WHil WPer WPrP WTin

Michauxia (*Campanulaceae*)

campanuloides EWld SPad

laevigata WCot

tchihatchewii CCCN CSpe EBee GKev WBor

Michelia (*Magnoliaceae*)

'Allspice' **new** SKHP

cavalerieri CBcs

champaca CCCN ERea

chapensis CBcs SSpi
- HWJ 621 WCru

compressa CCCN EPfP

doltsopa CBcs CGHE CHEx EBee ECre EMil EPfP SSpi SSta WPGP
- 'Silver Cloud' CBcs

figo CAbb CBcs CCCN CDoC EPfP ERea MBri SKHP SSpi SSta WPGP
- var. ***crassipes*** SSpi
- var. ***figo*** SSpi

foveolata CBcs SSpi
- var. ***cinerascens*** WPGP

'Jack Fogg' **new** SKHP

macclurei CBcs SSpi WPGP

martinii CBcs

maudiae CAbb CBcs CDoC CGHE CPLG EBee EPfP ISea NLar SKHP SSpi WPGP

odora **new** CWib

yunnanensis CBcs SKHP SSpi WPGP

Microbiota (*Cupressaceae*)

decussata 🏆^{H4} CBcs CDoC CKen CMac CRob CSBt ECho EHul EOrn EPla LBee LCon LLin LRHS MAsh MBar MGos MWat NHol NWea SLim SPoG WCFE WEve WFar
- 'Gold Spot' NLar SLim
- 'Jakobsen' CDoC CKen
- 'Trompenburg' CKen

Microcachrys (*Podocarpaceae*)

tetragona CDoC ECho ECou EHul EOrn IDee LCon LLin SCoo SIng

Microcitrus (*Rutaceae*)

australasica (F) **new** ERea

§ ***papuana*** (F) **new** ERea

Microcoelum see *Lytocaryum*

weddelianum see *Lytocaryum weddellianum*

Microlaena see *Ehrharta*

Microlepia (*Dennstaedtiaceae*)

speluncae MBri

strigosa CCCN CLAP LRHS LTwo MPes WRic

Micromeria (*Lamiaceae*)

chamissonis GPoy

corsica see *Acinos corsicus*

croatica NMen

dalmatica XPep

fruticosa CArn EWin XPep

graeca CArn XPep

rupestris see *M. thymifolia*

§ ***thymifolia*** NMen SPlb

viminea see *Satureja viminea*

Microseris (*Asteraceae*)

ringens hort. see *Leontodon rigens*

Microsorum (*Polypodiaceae*)

diversifolium see *Phymatosorus diversifolius*

scolopendria Green Wave = 'Vp003'PBR **new** MPes

Microstrobos (*Podocarpaceae*)

fitzgeraldii CKen

niphophilus ECou

Microtropis (*Celastraceae*)

petelotii HWJ 719 WCru

Mikania (*Asteraceae*)

araucana LSou

§ ***dentata*** MBri

ternata see *M. dentata*

Milium (*Poaceae*)

effusum COld
- 'Aureum' 🏆^{H4} More than 30 suppliers
- var. ***esthonicum*** EBee EPPr NHol XIsg
- 'Yaffle' (v) CBre CFir CKno CNat CRez EBee ECha EGle EPPr LEdu MCCP MWat SPoG SSvw WCot WLeb

Millettia (*Papilionaceae*)

japonica 'Hime Fuji' NLar

murasaki-natsu-fuji see *M. reticulata*

§ ***reticulata*** CPLG

Milligania (*Asteliaceae*)

densiflora IBlr

Mimosa (*Mimosaceae*)

pudica CArn CCCN CDTJ LRHS

Mimulus (*Scrophulariaceae*)

'A.T. Johnson' NVic

'Andean Nymph' see *M. naiandinus*

§ ***aurantiacus*** 🏆$^{H2\text{-}3}$ CElw CFee CHal CPle CSpe CTri EBak EBee ECtt EPot EWTr LHop MHar NBir NPer SAga SDnm SDry SGar SHFr SMrm SPet SPlb SPoG WAbe

§ - var. ***puniceus*** CPle CSpe CTri EBee EDif EMan EWin LAst LHop LRHS LSou MHar SAga SBHP SDry SHom SMrm SRkn

- 'Pure Gold'	EBee EDif
- 'Tangerine'	EBee EDif
x ***bartonianus***	see *M.* x *harrisonii*
bifidus	MHar
- 'Tapestry'	CSpe
- 'Trish'	CSpe SAga
- 'Verity Buff'	EBee EDif
§ - 'Verity Purple'	EDif
- 'Wine'	see *M. bifidus* 'Verity Purple'
x ***burnetii***	ECho SRms
cardinalis ♀H3	CDWL EBee EHon ELan EPfP MNrw MTho SHFr SPer WBor WCot WFar WHil WMoo WPer WPnP
- NNS 95-344	EMan
- 'Dark Throat'	SGar
- 'Red Dragon'	SBHP
cupreus	GKev
- 'Minor'	ECho
- 'Whitecroft Scarlet' ♀H4	ECho ECtt ELan EPfP LRHS LSou MHer SRms WPer
eastwoodiae new	CPBP
'Eleanor'	ECtt EMan LSou SAga SHom SMrm
glutinosus	see *M. aurantiacus*
- ***atrosanguineus***	see *M. aurantiacus* var. *puniceus*
- ***luteus***	see *M. aurantiacus*
§ ***guttatus***	CWat EMFW NPer NSco SECG SRms WMoo WPer WPnP
§ - 'Richard Bish' (v)	CBow EMan EShb MCCP
§ x ***harrisonii***	EBee EMan EPfP EWes EWin LSou
'Highland Orange'	ECho EPfP SPlb SPoG WGor WPer
'Highland Pink'	ECho EPfP NBlu SPlb SPoG WGor WPer
'Highland Red' ♀H4	ECho ECtt EPfP GAbr GGar NBlu SPlb SPoG SRms WFar WHen WPer
'Highland Yellow'	ECho ECtt EDAr NBlu SPlb SPoG WFar WHen WPer
hose-in-hose (d)	CDWL NPer
'Inca Sunset'	EWes
langsdorffii	see *M. guttatus*
lewisii ♀H3	CHll EBee EShb MTho NWCA SPav SPer SRms WPer
longiflorus subsp. ***calycinus*** new	SKHP
luteus	CBen CWat EHon EPfP GKev NPer NSco SHFr SPlb WBrk WFar WMAq
- 'Variegatus' misapplied	see *M. guttatus* 'Richard Bish'
- 'Variegatus' ambig. (v)	NPer
* 'Major Bees'	EPfP
'Malibu Ivory'	MDKP
'Malibu Orange'	EPfP
'Malibu Red'	MDKP
minimus	ECho
moschatus	EBee
§ ***naiandinus*** ♀H3	CMMP EBee GKev LRHS SPlb SRms WFar
- C&W 5257	WRos
'Orange Glow'	EPfP WHal
orange hose-in-hose (d)	NBir
'Orkney Lemon'	NSti
'Popacatapetl'	CHll EBee EDif EMan LHop LSou MHar MSte SAga SBHP SMrm WAbe
primuloides	CEnt ECho EWes SIng SPlb
'Puck'	ECho ECtt LRHS
'Quetzalcoatl'	LSou SAga SMrm
ringens	CBen CWat EBee EDif EHon EMFW EPfP GBri NBir NPer SPlb SRms WFar WHil WMAq WMoo WPer
'Threave Variegated' (v)	EBee EMan EWin GBuc MRav NBir WFar
tilingii	ECho EShb
'Western Hills'	MLLN
'Wine Red'	see *M. bifidus* 'Verity Purple'
'Wisley Red'	ECho ECot SRms
'Yellow Velvet'	ECho

Mina see *Ipomoea*

Minuartia (*Caryophyllaceae*)

capillacea	ECho
caucasica	see *M. circassica*
§ ***circassica***	NWCA WPer
laricifolia	LRHS
parnassica	see *M. stellata*
§ ***recurva***	WLin
§ ***stellata***	EAlp EPot NDlv NMen SIng
- NS 758	NWCA
§ ***verna***	EAlp ECho EDAr NMen NVic
- subsp. ***caespitosa***	CTri ECho
- - 'Aurea'	see *Sagina subulata* var. *glabrata* 'Aurea'

mint, apple see *Mentha suaveolens*

mint, Bowles see *M.* x *villosa var. alopecuroides*

mint, curly see *M. spicata var. crispa*

mint, eau-de-Cologne see *M.* x *piperita f. citrata*

mint, ginger see *M.* x *gracilis*

mint, horse or long-leaved see *M. longifolia*

mint, pennyroyal see *M. pulegium*

mint, peppermint see *M.* x *piperita*

mint, round-leaved see *M. suaveolens*

mint (spearmint) see *M. spicata*

Mirabilis (*Nyctaginaceae*)

jalapa	CArn CDTJ CHrt CPLG CStu EBrs EPfP EShb LAma LEdu LRHS LRav MBri MSal SBod SEND SHFr SRms WHil
- 'Buttermilk'	CCCN
- white-flowered	CSpe

Miscanthus ✿ (*Poaceae*)

capensis	CBig SPlb
chejuensis B&SWJ 8803 new	WCru
flavidus B&SWJ 6749	WCru
floridulus misapplied	see *M.* x *giganteus*
floridulus ambig.	NLar NOak WFar WPrP
floridulus Warb. ex K. Schum. & Lauterb. HWJ 522	WCru
§ x ***giganteus***	CFwr CHar CKno EBee ELon EPPr EWsh GAbr MAvo MCCP MMoz MMuc NBea NVic SApp SDix SEND SMad SPlb WCot WFar WSpi XIsg
- 'Gilt Edge' (v)	CBow CKno EPPr EWsh MAvo SApp
- 'Gotemba' (v)	EPPr EWes EWsh MAvo
'Golden Bar'	ECha GBuc
'Gotemba Gold'	SApp
'Mount Washington'	SApp
nepalensis	CBig CBod CBrm CEnt CHrt CKno CMil CPLG ECre EPGN EWes LEdu MAvo SDix SMrm WPrP WTin
- B&SWJ 2302	WCru

	- CC 3619	WRos
	oligostachyus	CBig NGdn
§	- 'Afrika'	CBig CFwr CKno CPen EBee
I	- 'Nanus Variegatus' (v)	CDes CKno EPPr EWes LEdu MAvo MMoz WCot WPGP
	'Pos'	SApp
§	'Purpurascens'	CKno CPrp ECha EHrv EHul EPla EShb EWsh GSki LAst LRHS LSRN MAvo MBnl MBrN MMoz MWgw NOak SWal WBor WSpi WTin XIsg
	sacchariflorus misapplied	see *M.* x *giganteus*
	sacchariflorus ambig.	More than 30 suppliers
	- 'Robustus' **new**	CHVG
	sinensis	CBig CEnt CHEx CHrt CTri EBla GFor LEdu MGol MMoz MNHC MWrn NLar NOak WMoo WRos XIsg XPep
	- 'Adagio'	CBig CFwr CKno CPen EBee EGle EPPr GBin LEdu NDov SMHy WCot WPrP
	- 'Afrika'	see *M. oligostachyus* 'Afrika'
	- 'Arabesque'	CBig CBrm CFwr EBee EGle EPPr MMoz NLar SApp
	- 'Augustfeder'	CFwr CPen EGle EPPr LEdu LRHS XIsg
	- 'Autumn Light'	CFwr CKno CPen CRez EBrs EPPr
	- 'Ballerina'	CFwr CPen
	- 'Blütenwunder'	CFwr CKno CPen CRez EBee EGle IPot
	- 'China'	More than 30 suppliers
	- var. ***condensatus***	CBig LSou XIsg
	- - 'Cabaret' (v)	CBod CBrm CDes CFwr CHEx CHar CKno CPen CRez CWCL EBee EPPr EPla EPyc IPot LEdu LRHS LSRN MBri MSte NOak NOrc SMad SPoG SRos WCot WHal WMoo
	- - 'Central Park'	see *M. sinensis* var. *condensatus* 'Cosmo Revert'
§	- - 'Cosmo Revert'	CBig CPen EBee LEdu MMoz WDyG WSpi
	- - 'Cosmopolitan' (v) ♀H4	More than 30 suppliers
	- - 'Emerald Giant'	see *M. sinensis* var. *condensatus* 'Cosmo Revert'
	- 'David'	CPen CRez EBee EPPr LEdu MBNS
	- 'Dixieland' (v)	CBig CBrm CFwr CKno EGle ELan EPPr EWsh LEdu MMoz SApp
	- 'Emmanuel Lepage'	CFwr CPen EPPr
	- 'Etincelle'	EPPr
	- 'Ferner Osten'	More than 30 suppliers
	- 'Feuergold'	MSte
	- 'Flamingo' ♀H4	More than 30 suppliers
	- 'Flammenmeer'	CFwr CPen
	- 'Gaa'	SApp
	- 'Gearmella'	CBig EGle EWsh LEdu LRHS MGol
	- 'Gewitterwolke' ♀H4	CBig CFwr CKno EGle NDov SMHy SPhx
	- 'Ghana' ♀H4	CFwr CKno CPen EBee EGle ELon GBin SMHy
	- 'Giraffe'	CDes CFwr CKno CPen EBee LEdu WPGP
	- 'Gnome'	CKno CPen EBee EPPr MMHG
	- 'Gold Bar' (v)	CBow CChe CElw CFwr CKno CMHG CMea EBee ECha ECtt EMil EPPr LEdu LFur LSou MBNS NCGa SMad SPer SPoG WBVN WCot WGwG WMoo XIsg
	- 'Goldfeder' (v)	CFwr CPen
	- 'Goliath'	CBig CFwr CPen EBee EPPr GBin IPot LBMP LEdu LRHS MBNS WFar WPnP WPrP XIsg
	- 'Gracillimus'	More than 30 suppliers
	- 'Graziella'	CEnd CFwr CHar CKno CWib EAlp EBee EBla EGle EHrv EPPr EPfP EPla LCro LEdu LRHS MBri MMoz MSte NDov NGdn NOak NOrc SLPl SMeo SPer WPGP WPrP WTMC
	- 'Grosse Fontäne' ♀H4	CBig CBrm CKno EBee EBla EGle ELan EPGN EPPr EPla EWsh LEdu LRHS SMHy WAul WMoo XIsg
	- 'Haiku'	CFwr CKno CPen EPPr GBin NDov SPhx WPrP
	- 'Helga Reich'	CBig EBee SApp
	- 'Hercules'	CBig CPen EPPr MAvo MMoz SApp
	- 'Hermann Müssel'	CFwr CPen EBee GBin NDov SMHy SPhx
	- 'Hinjo' (v)	CDes CElw CFwr CKno CSpe EBee ECha ECtt EPPr EWsh GBin LBBr LEdu LFur LSou MBri SApp SPoG WCot WPGP WPrP
I	- 'Jubilaris' (v)	EWes
	- 'Juli'	CBig CSsd GBin WPrP WSpi
	- 'Kaskade' ♀H4	CBig CBrm CFwr CKno CWCL EBee EBrs EGle EPGN EPPr EPla IPot LEdu LRHS MAvo MMoz MSte SApp SMeo SMrm WFar WMoo XIsg
	- 'Kirk Alexander' (v)	MAvo SApp
	- 'Kleine Fontäne' ♀H4	More than 30 suppliers
	- 'Kleine Silberspinne' ♀H4	More than 30 suppliers
	- 'Krater'	CBig CFwr CKno EBee EBrs EPPr LEdu MBrN SMeo SWat XIsg
	- 'Kupferberg'	CFwr
§	- 'Little Kitten'	CBig CDes CFwr CKno CPen CSpe EBee EGle EPPr EPla EWsh LEdu MBar MGol MSte SMad SPoG WPGP
	- 'Little Zebra' (v)	CKno EBee ENot EPPr EPfP LRHS MGos NOak SPoG
	- 'Malepartus'	More than 30 suppliers
	- 'Morning Light' (v) ♀H4	More than 30 suppliers
	- new hybrids	CBcs EHul LRav NScw
	- 'Nippon'	CBig CBow CElw CHrt CKno CPrp EBee EBla EGle EPPr EPla EWsh LEdu LHop LRHS MCCP MMoz NDov NGdn NOrc SDys SPer WPGP WSpi XIsg
	- 'Nishidake'	CFwr CPen EBee XIsg
	- 'November Sunset'	CBig EBrs EPPr EWes IPot MMoz
	- 'Poseidon'	EPPr LBBr MAvo SDys XIsg
	- 'Positano'	CBig CKno EBee EPPr MMoz WPGP
	- 'Professor Richard Hansen'	CFwr CKno CPen GBin NDov WPrP
	- var. ***purpurascens*** misapplied	see *M.* 'Purpurascens'
	- 'Pünktchen' (v)	CBig CBrm CFwr CKno CPen CWCL EAlp EBee ECha EGle EPPr EPla GBin LEdu MAvo MSte SApp SMHy SMrm SPhx WFar WPnP WTin XIsg
	- 'Rigoletto' (v)	EPPr SApp
	- 'Roland'	CBig CFwr CKno CPen EBee GBin SPhx
	- 'Roterpfeil'	CFwr CPen SMHy SMeo
	- 'Rotfeder' **new**	XIsg
	- 'Rotfuchs'	CFwr CPen EBee MGos MSte SAga SPhx WFar
	- 'Rotsilber'	More than 30 suppliers
I	- 'Russianus' **new**	EWsh
	- 'Samurai'	CFwr EPPr GMaP GQue MAvo
	- 'Sarabande'	CBig CBrm CFwr CKno EBee ECha EGle EHul ELan EPPr EWsh IPot LRHS MSte NDov SApp SMHy WFar WGwG WMoo XIsg
	- 'Septemberrot' ♀H4	CFwr CHVG CKno COlW CPrp CRez EBee LEdu SPoG
§	- 'Silberfeder' ♀H4	More than 30 suppliers

- 'Silberpfeil' (v)	EWsh MSte
- 'Silberspinne'	CBig CMdw EBla EGle EPla ERas LEdu LRHS MCCP MWat NDov NGdn SAga SApp SMHy SMeo SPlb WAul XIsg
- 'Silberturm'	CFwr CKno COIW EBee SPoG
- Silver Feather	see *M. sinensis* 'Silberfeder'
- 'Sioux'	CBig CFwr CKno EBee EBrs EGle EPPr EPla EShb EWsh GBin LEdu LRHS MBri MMoz MSte SPer WOVN WTin XIsg
- 'Sirene'	CBig CFwr CKno EBee EGle EPGN EPPr EPla LEdu LRHS MBNS MBlu WFar WPrP XIsg
- 'Slavopour'	EPla
- 'Spätgrün'	CFwr EPla
- 'Strictus' (v) ♀H4	More than 30 suppliers
- 'Tiger Cub' (v)	CBig CWCL EBee SApp
- 'Undine' ♀H4	CFwr CKno CMea CPrp CSam EBee EBla ECha EGle EHrv ELan EPGN EPla EWsh LEdu LRHS MLLN MMoz MSte SHFr SPla WPrP XIsg
- 'Variegatus' (v)	More than 30 suppliers
- 'Vorläufer'	CBrm CFwr CKno CPen EWsh LEdu SAga
- 'Wetterfahne'	CFwr EGle LEdu
§ - 'Yaku-jima'	CFwr CRez CSam EBee ECha EGle SPoG XIsg XPep
- 'Yakushima Dwarf'	CElw CEnd CFwr CHVG CKno CPLG CWCL EAlp EBee EGle EHrv EPPr EPfP EPla GBin IArd LEdu LHop LRHS MWgw NGdn NSti SApp SPhx SPla SWal WCot WMoo WPGP WTin
- 'Zebrinus' (v) ♀H4	More than 30 suppliers
- 'Zwergelefant'	CBig CFwr MMoz SMHy
I 'Spartina'	SApp
tinctorius 'Nanus Variegatus' misapplied	see *M. oligostachyus* 'Nanus Variegatus'
transmorrisonensis	CBig CHid CKno EBee ELan EPPr GBin GFor LRav MAvo MBri MMoz NDov NNor NOak SAdn SApp SMad SWal WTin
- B&SWJ 3697	WCru
yakushimensis	see *M. sinensis* 'Yaku-jima', *M. sinensis* 'Little Kitten'

Mitchella (*Rubiaceae*)

repens	CBcs GBin WCru
undulata B&SWJ 4402	WCru

Mitella (*Saxifragaceae*)

breweri	CHid CSam EBee GGar MAvo MRav MSte NHol NSti SHFr SMac SRms WEas WFar WMoo WTin
caulescens	ECha NBro NHol WMoo
diphylla	EBee EPPr
formosana	EPPr
- B&SWJ 125	WCru
japonica B&SWJ 4971	WCru
kiusiana	CLAP
- B&SWJ 5888	WCru
makinoi	CLAP EBee
- B&SWJ 4992	WCru
ovalis	EBee EPPr
pauciflora B&SWJ 6361	WCru
pentandra	WMoo
stylosa B&SWJ 5669	WCru
yoshinagae	GEdr SBch WMoo
- B&SWJ 4893	CHid WCru WPrP WPtf

Mitraria (*Gesneriaceae*)

coccinea	CBcs CEnt CMac CPLG CPle CTrG CWib ECho ELan EShb MBlu MDun SArc SLon SPer SSpi WPic
- Clark's form	CSam CTrC EBee GGar LAst MDun NLar WBor
- from Lake Puyehue	CBcs CDoC CFee EBee EMil ERea GAbr GQui LRHS MAsh MGos SWvt WAbe WCru WCwm WFar WPGP WSHC
- 'Lake Caburgua'	CSpe EWld GGar IArd NSti

Moehringia (*Caryophyllaceae*)

muscosa **new**	WCot

Molinia (*Poaceae*)

altissima	see *M. caerulea* subsp. *arundinacea*
caerulea	CBig CRWN CWib EHul EPPr GFor LAst MBlu SPhx
§ - subsp. ***arundinacea***	CAby CBig CKno CWCL ECha EPPr GFor MBNS NLar SApp SLPl WPer
- - 'Bergfreund'	CKno CSam EPGN EPPr EWsh MAvo NDov SApp SMHy SPhx WDyG WMoo WPrP WTin XIsg
- - 'Cordoba'	CBig CKno EPPr GBin NDov SMHy SPhx
- - 'Fontäne'	CBig CPen CSam EPPr EWsh GQue LEdu MSte NDov NNor SApp SPhx XIsg
- - 'Karl Foerster'	CKno CSpe EBee EGle EHul EPGN EPPr EPfP EWsh GBin GMaP LEdu MAvo MMoz MSte NBid NDov NHol SApp SPhx SWat WCAu WCot WFar WMoo WPnP XIsg
- - 'Louise' **new**	XIsg
- - 'Poul Petersen' **new**	EPPr SPhx
- - 'Skyracer'	CBig CChe CFwr CKno COIW CPrp CSam EBee EPPr EWsh GBri GQue LBBr MAvo MBri MMoz NDov SMHy SMad SPhx WCot WFar WMoo XIsg
- - 'Transparent'	More than 30 suppliers
- - 'Windsaule'	CBig CKno EBee EPPr NDov SPhx
- - 'Windspiel'	CBrm CKno CSam CWCL EBee ECha EGle EMil EMon EPGN EPPr EWsh LEdu MAvo MWgw NDov SApp SPhx SWal WCAu WCot WMoo WPGP WTin XIsg
- - 'Zuneigung'	CBig CKno CSam EPPr MAvo NDov SApp SPhx XIsg
- subsp. ***caerulea***	CMdw
- - 'Carmarthen' (v)	CElw EBee EPGN EPPr MAvo SApp WHal WPnP WPrP
- - 'Claerwen' (v)	ECha EPPr GBuc SMHy SPhx WMoo
- - 'Coneyhill Gold' (v)	EPPr
- - 'Dauerstrahl'	CKno EBee EPPr GBin GQue MAvo NDov NHol
- - 'Edith Dudszus'	CKno CWCL EBee ECha EGle EPPr EWsh GQue LEdu LRHS MAvo MBrN MBri MMoz NDov NGdn NHol SApp SMHy SPer SPhx WLeb WMoo WPGP WWeb XIsg
- - 'Heidebraut'	CBig CWsd EAlp EBee EGle EHul EPGN EPPr EWsh GBin GQue LRHS MWgw NBro NCGa NDov SApp SPhx WFar WMoo WPnP XIsg
- - 'Moorflamme'	CBig CBrm CKno CSam EPPr MAvo SPhx
- - 'Moorhexe'	More than 30 suppliers
- - 'Overdam' **new**	NDov
- - 'Strahlenquelle'	CElw CKno CSam EBee EGle ELan EMon EPGN EPPr EPla GBin LRHS MAvo MMoz MSte NBro NCGa NDov SPhx WPGP XIsg
- - 'Variegata' (v) ♀H4	More than 30 suppliers

litoralis	see *M. caerulea* subsp. *arundinacea*

Molopospermum (*Apiaceae*)

peloponnesiacum	CAby CSpe EBee EMan ITer LEdu MLLN NLar SPhx WBor WCru WSHC

Moltkia (*Boraginaceae*)

§ ***doerfleri***	CPle NChi
graminifolia	see *M. suffruticosa*
§ x ***intermedia*** ♀H4	CMea WAbe WFar
petraea	LTwo WAbe WLin WPat
§ ***suffruticosa***	NBir

Moluccella (*Lamiaceae*)

laevis 'Pixie Bells' new	CSpe

Momordica (*Cucurbitaceae*)

balsamina	MSal
charantia	MSal

Monachosorum (*Adiantaceae*)

henryi new	WRic

Monadenium (*Euphorbiaceae*)

lugardiae	MBri
'Variegatum' (v)	MBri

Monarda (*Lamiaceae*)

'Adam'	LRHS MLLN MSte NBre WCAu WSHC
'Amethyst'	EBee ECtt EWes SIde
'Aquarius'	EBee EMar ERou LAst LRHS MSte MWgw NCob NGHP NHol NPro NSti SPla SPoG SRGP WAul WCAu WFar WWlt
austromontana	see *M. citriodora* subsp. *austromontana*
'Baby Spice'	EBee NCob
§ 'Balance'	CWCL EAro EBee ECtt EMan EPPr EPfP MRav NBro NCob NDov NGHP NGdn NHol NSti SMeo SPhx SPla SPoG SRGP WCAu WFar WHil WPGP WSHC WWlt
'Beauty of Cobham' ♀H4	CHar CPrp EBee ECha ELan EPfP ERou GMaP LCro LHop LRHS MBri MHer MSte NGHP NHol NLar NPri NRnb SMad SPer SPhx WBor WWlt
'Blaukranz'	NBre
§ 'Blaustrumpf'	CElw EBee ECtt GBri MSte NCob NLar SPer WLin
Blue Stocking	see *M.* 'Blaustrumpf'
Bowman	see *M.* 'Sagittarius'
bradburyana	EShb LTwo NBre NLar
'Cambridge Scarlet' ♀H4	More than 30 suppliers
'Capricorn'	ERou GBuc LRHS MSte NBre
'Cherokee'	GBri NCob NHol SPhx WFar
citriodora	CArn ECtt EUnu GPoy LRHS MNHC MSal NSti SIde SPlb SRms SWat WJek WSel
§ - subsp. ***austromontana***	CSpe EAro NBir SBch SGar SIde WFar WPer
'Comanche'	EHrv EPfP EWes NCob NDov WFar
'Croftway Pink' ♀H4	More than 30 suppliers
I 'Dark Ponticum'	NCob
didyma	CArn CHar EPfP MSal NBro NGHP SWat WBrE WJek
- 'Duddiscombe'	CPrp CSam CWCL
- 'Goldmelise'	CFwr NBre NGHP WMoo
'Elsie's Lavender'	EBee EGle GBri GBuc MAvo NDov NLar SAga SPhx WAul
'Fireball'PBR	CHFP CWCL EBee ECtt LTwo MBnl NCob NLar WHil
§ 'Fishes'	CHVG EBee ECtt EHrv ELan EPPr EWes LAst MAvo MRav MSte MWgw NCob NDov NGHP NHol NLar NRnb SPla SRGP STes WFar WSHC WWlt
fistulosa	CArn CWan EUnu GPoy MNHC MSal MWrn WJek WMoo WPer
- f. ***albescens***	EBee
'Gardenview Scarlet' ♀H4	CWCL EBee EBrs ECtt EWes GBri GCra GQue LRHS MBri MDKP MWat NCGa NChi NDov NGHP NGby NLar NSti SMrm SPhx WHlf WPer WRHF
Gemini	see *M.* 'Twins'
'Gewitterwolke'	CSam GBin IPot
'Hartswood Wine'	NHol SMad
'Heidelerche'	EPPr
'Jacob Cline'	GBin NBre NCob NDov
'Kardinal'	EBee EMil GBin NHol
'Lambada'	SPav
Libra	see *M.* 'Balance'
'Lilac Queen'	NCob
'Loddon Crown'	CFwr CHar COlW EBee ECtt GQue LRHS MBri MDKP NCob NGHP NHol NLar SIde SMer WFar WSHC
'Mahogany'	CHar EBee ELan ERou GBri GMaP LRHS MLHP NCGa NChi NCob NGHP SMad SPer WSHC WSpi
'Marshall's Delight' ♀H4	CElw CPrp EBee ECtt EWes LSou NCob NGHP NHol NLar NRnb SGar SMrm WCAu WHil
'Melissa'	EBee EGle EMil NBre
menthifolia	EAro EBee LSou SMrm
'Mohawk'	CKno CWCL EBee ECtt EHrv EMan EPPr ERou LRHS MWat MWgw NChi NCob NDov NHol NOrc WCAu WHil
'Mrs Perry'	EWes NGHP
'Neon'	NDov SPhx
'On Parade'	EBee ECGP ECtt EMar EWll MSte NCob NHol
'Ou Charm'	CWCL EBee EPPr ERou EWes GBri LCro LRHS MLLN MWat MWrn NDov NGHP NLar WFar
'Panorama'	EAro ECtt MSal NHol NLar SGar SPad SPlb WMoo WPer
'Panorama Red Shades' (Panorama Series)	CFwr CWib EAro MNHC MWrn NGHP
Petite Delight = 'Acpetdel'PBR	CAbP CBcs CRez EBee ECtt ELan ENot EPfP GBin LHop LRHS MDun NBir NCob NDov NEgg NGHP NGdn NHol NLar SPla SPoG WAul WFar WLin WWeb
'Petite Pink Supreme'	EBee EPfP MBnl MLLN
'Pink Supreme'PBR	CHFP EMar NCob NLar
'Pink Tourmaline'	EBee NDov NGby NHol NMyG SMad SMrm SPhx WFar
Pisces	see *M.* 'Fishes'
'Poyntzfield Pink'	GPoy
Prairie Night	see *M.* 'Prärienacht'
§ 'Prärienacht'	CHar CPrp CSBt CSam EBee ECha ELan EMar EPfP ERou LHop MHer MLLN NBPC NBro NGHP NGdn NHol NRnb NVic SPer SPlb SRms STes SWvt WEas WFar WPer WSHC
punctata	CArn CBod CWCL EAro EBee EDAr ELan EMan EUnu GSki LRHS MLLN MNFA MSal MWrn NGdn SDnm SMrm SPav SPer SWat WCFE WMoo
- 'Fantasy'	CFwr NGHP
'Purple Ann'	NCGa NDov
'Raspberry Wine'	ECtt GBri
'Ruby Glow'	CWCL EBee EHrv EMan EMar IPot LRHS MArl NCGa NDov NHol SMad SPhx WFar

§ 'Sagittarius' — EBee EKen EMan LRHS MWgw NChi NCob NGdn NHol SPla SPur SRGP WCAu
'Saxon Purple' — NDov NLar
§ 'Schneewittchen' — More than 30 suppliers
'Scorpion' — CWCL EAro EBee ECtt EHrv ELan EPPr LRHS MRav MSte MWgw NBPC NBir NCob NDov NHol NOrc NPri NPro SPhx SRGP SWvt WCAu WPGP WSHC
'Sioux' — EHrv EWes GBuc LRHS WFar
'Snow Maiden' — see *M.* 'Schneewittchen'
'Snow Queen' — CSam EAro EBee ECtt EMar EPPr LBMP LRHS MWat MWgw NCob NHol NLar NPro SHar SPla SPur STes
Snow White — see *M.* 'Schneewittchen'
'Squaw' ♀H4 — More than 30 suppliers
'Talud' ♀H4 — NDov
§ 'Twins' — CMil CPrp CWCL EBee EPPr ERou LRHS MLLN NGHP NHol NRnb SWat SWvt WCAu WLin WSHC
'Velvet Queen' — LSou
'Vintage Wine' — CWCL ECtt GBri NCob NDov WCot WFar WLin
'Violacea' — NHol
'Violet Queen' ♀H4 — EAro EBee EBrs EWes LBMP LRHS NBre NCob NHol NPro WCAu WFar WHil

Monardella (*Lamiaceae*)

linoides subsp. ***stricta*** — NWCA
macrantha — CPBP
nana subsp. ***arida*** — CPBP
- subsp. ***tenuiflora*** — CPBP
odoratissima — CArn

Monochoria (*Pontederiaceae*)

§ ***hastata*** — LLWG

Monopsis (*Campanulaceae*)

§ ***lutea*** — EWin LRav
Midnight = 'Yagemon'PBR — LAst

Monstera (*Araceae*)

deliciosa (F) ♀H1 — MBri SRms XBlo
- 'Variegata' (v) ♀H1 — MBri SRms

Montbretia see *Crocosmia*

x ***crocosmiiflora*** — see *Crocosmia* x *crocosmiiflora*
pottsii — see *Crocosmia pottsii*

Montia (*Portulacaceae*)

australasica — see *Neopaxia australasica*
perfoliata — see *Claytonia perfoliata*
sibirica — see *Claytonia sibirica*

Moraea (*Iridaceae*)

alpina — GCrs
alticola — CPne CWsd EBee EBrs ECho GCrs GGar WCot WPGP
- CDL 181 — CStu
§ ***aristata*** — WCot
§ ***bellendenii*** — WCot
bipartita — WCot
comptonii — CPBP WCot
elegans — CPBP
§ ***fugax*** — WCot
gawleri — WCot
gigandra new — WCot
glaucopsis — see *M. aristata*
huttonii — CCCN CFir CPBP CSpe CWsd EBee EDif EPPr GSki SMad WBVN WCot WLin WPic WSHC
iridioides — see *Dietes iridioides*
longifolia Sweet — see *M. fugax*
loubseri — WCot
lurida — WCot
moggii — CStu
natalensis — SBla
pavonia var. ***lutea*** — see *M. bellendenii*
polyanthos — EBee
polystachya — EBrs ECho LRHS
spathacea — see *M. spathulata*
§ ***spathulata*** — CAby CDes CPLG EBee EMan ERos GMac LEdu SKHP WCot
tricolor — CPBP
tulbaghensis — WCot
vegeta — CPBP ERea WCot
villosa — WCot

Moricandia (*Brassicaceae*)

moricandioides — CSpe

Morina (*Morinaceae*)

* ***afghanica*** — GAbr
alba — GCra NChi
bulleyana — see *M. nepatensis* var. *delavayi*
longifolia — More than 30 suppliers
§ ***nepatensis*** var. ***delavayi*** new — EBee
persica — EWes GBuc LPio MHar NLar WHoo
polyphylla — GPoy

Morisia (*Brassicaceae*)

hypogaea — see *M. monanthos*
§ ***monanthos*** — EPot GMaP MBar NLAp NWCA SRot WFar
- 'Fred Hemingway' — ECho GCrs ITim LRHS NDlv NMen NSla SIng WAbe WThu

Morus ✿ (*Moraceae*)

alba — CAgr CArn CBcs CDul CLnd CMCN CMen CTho CWib ECrN ELan EPfP ERea GTwe LBuc LCro MGos SBLw SHBN WFar
- 'Macrophylla' — CMCN NLar SMad
- 'Pendula' — CBcs CDoC CDul CEnd CLnd CTho CTri ECrN ELan EPfP ERea GTwe LAst LPan LRHS MAsh MBlu MBri MLan MWya NLar SBLw SCoo SHBN SLim SPer SPoG WOrn
- 'Platanifolia' — MBlu SBLw
- var. ***tatarica*** — CAgr LEdu NLar
§ ***bombycis*** — LPan SBLw
'Capsrum' (F) new — CAgr
'Carmen' (F) new — CAgr
'Illinois Everbearing' (F) — CAgr ECrN
'Italian' (F) new — CAgr
'Ivory' (F) new — CAgr
kagayamae — see *M. bombycis*
latifolia 'Spirata' — NLar
nigra (F) ♀H4 — More than 30 suppliers
§ - 'Chelsea' (F) — CAgr CEnd CTho CTri EMui EPfP ERea GTwe LRHS MBri MGan MGos MLan MWya NWea SCoo SGFT SKee SPer SPoG WPGP
- 'Jerusalem' — MAsh
- 'King James' — see *M. nigra* 'Chelsea'
- 'Large Black' (F) — EMui
- 'Wellington' (F) — CEnd LPan
rubra — NLar
- 'Nana' — MBri

Mosla (*Lamiaceae*)

dianthera — EMan EWld MNrw WHil

Muehlenbeckia (*Polygonaceae*)

astonii — CBcs ECou
australis — ECou

	axillaris misapplied	see *M. complexa*
§	***axillaris*** Walp.	CBcs CTri ECou EPla GGar SDry
	- 'Mount Cook' (f)	ECou
	- 'Ohau' (m)	ECou
§	***complexa***	CBcs CDoC CHEx CPLG CTrC CTri CWib EBee ECou EPla EShb LRHS MCCP MWgw NSti SAPC SArc SBra SDry SLim SLon SMac SWvt WCFE WPGP WSHC XPep
	- (f)	ECou
	- 'Nana'	see *M. axillaris* Walp.
	- var. ***trilobata***	CHEx CTrC EBee EPla IBlr SSta WDyG XPep
	- 'Ward' (m)	ECou
	ephedroides	ECou
	- 'Clarence Pass'	ECou
*	- var. ***muricatula***	ECou
	gunnii	ECou
	platyclados	see *Homalocladium platycladum*

Muhlenbergia (*Poaceae*)

capillaris	CBig CKno XIsg
dubia	CKno
japonica 'Cream Delight' (v)	CPen EBee LEdu
lindheimeri	XIsg
mexicana	CBig EBee EPPr GFor LEdu WPGP XIsg
rigens	CBig CKno SApp XPep

Mukdenia (*Saxifragaceae*)

acanthifolia	CLAP WCru
rossii	CDes CLAP EBee ELon EMon EPla LEdu MSte NLar NMyG SMac SMad WCot WCru WHil WPGP WTMC WThu WTin
- 'Crimson Fans'	CLAP NBhm NMyG
- dwarf	CLAP
- 'Ōgon'	CLAP
- variegated	EMon

mulberry see *Morus*

Murraya (*Rutaceae*)

*	***elliptica***	SOWG
	exotica	see *M. paniculata*
	koenigii	EOHP GPoy
§	***paniculata***	CArn CPLG ERea

Musa ✿ (*Musaceae*)

	from Tibet	CKob
	from Yunnan, China	see *M. itinerans* 'Yunnan'
§	***acuminata***	MBri
	- 'Bordelon'	CKob
§	- 'Dwarf Cavendish' (AAA Group) (F) 🏆^{H1}	CKob EAmu ELan EPfP LRHS MJnS MPRe NLar NScw SPer WBVN XBlo
	- 'Grand Nain' x ***acuminata*** 'Zebrina'	EAmu
	- 'Williams' (AAA Group) (F)	EAmu
	- 'Zebrina' 🏆$^{H1+3}$	CDTJ CKob EAmu LRHS MJnS XBlo
	balbisiana	CKob EAmu MJnS
	basjoo 🏆$^{H3-4}$	More than 30 suppliers
	- 'Little Prince' **new**	MPRe
I	- 'Rubra' **new**	CAbb CCCN EAmu
	- 'Sakhalin'	CKob SAdn
	beccarii	CKob
	'Burmese Blue'	CKob MJnS
	'Butuhan' (*balbisiana* x *textilis*)	CKob
	'Cavendish Super Dwarf'	MJnS
	'Cavendish Zan Moreno'	MJnS
	cavendishii	see *M. acuminata* 'Dwarf Cavendish'
§	***coccinea*** 🏆^{H1}	MJnS XBlo
	ensete	see *Ensete ventricosum*
	(Fe'i Group) 'Utafan' (F)	MNHC
	'Helen' **new**	ETod
	hookeri	see *M. sikkimensis*
*	***iterans glaucum*** **new**	CDTJ
§	***itinerans*** 'Yunnan'	CKob EAmu ITer MJnS
§	***lasiocarpa***	CAbb CBct CDTJ CDWL CDoC CHEx CHll CKob EAmu ERea EShb ETod IDee LCro LRHS MBri MJnS NPal NScw WCot WGwG
	laterita	CKob
	mannii	CKob
	nana misapplied	see *M. acuminata* 'Dwarf Cavendish'
	nana Lour.	see *M. acuminata*
	ornata 🏆^{H1}	CCCN ERea LPal MJnS XBlo
	- 'African Red'	CKob
	- 'Macro'	CKob
	- 'Purple'	CKob
	x ***paradisiaca***	MJnS
	- 'Ele-ele' (AAB Group) (F)	CKob
	- Goldfinger = 'Fhia-01' (AAAB Group) (F)	CKob
	- 'Hajaré' (ABB Group) (F)	CKob
	- 'Malbhog' (AAB Group) (F)	CKob
	- 'Ney Poovan' (AB Group) (F)	CCCN EAmu MJnS NPal
	- 'Orinoco' (ABB Group) (F)	CKob EAmu
	- 'Rajapuri' (AAB Group) (F)	CKob EAmu MJnS
	'Royal Purple' (*ornata* hybrid)	CKob
*	***rubinea***	CKob MJnS
	'Saba' ambig. (F)	CKob
§	***sikkimensis***	CDTJ CDoC CKob EAmu ELan EShb ETod EWes IDee LPJP LRHS MJnS SChr XBlo
	- 'Red Tiger'	CCCN CKob
	'Tropicana'	XBlo
	uranoscopus misapplied	see *M. coccinea*
	velutina 🏆$^{H1+3}$	CCCN CKob EAmu ETod MJnS
*	'Violacea' (*ornata* hybrid)	LPal

Muscari ✿ (*Hyacinthaceae*)

	PF	NWCA
	ambrosiacum	see *M. muscarimi*
	anatolicum **new**	EBrs ECho
	armeniacum 🏆^{H4}	CTca CTri EBrs ECho EGoo EPfP ERos LRHS MBri MCot SRms WCot WFar WShi
	- 'Argaei Album'	EBrs ECho EPot LAma
	- 'Atlantic' **new**	EBrs LRHS
	- 'Babies Breath'	see *M.* 'Jenny Robinson'
	- 'Blue Pearl'	EBrs ECho GKev LRHS
	- 'Blue Spike' (d)	EBrs ECho ENot EPfP LAma LRHS MBri NBir NBlu SPer WCot WGwG
	- 'Cantab'	EBrs ECho GKev
	- 'Christmas Pearl' 🏆^{H4}	CStu EBrs ECho WCot
	- 'Dark Eyes'	CTca EBrs ECho EPfP LRHS SPer WFar WHil
	- 'Early Giant'	ECho
	- 'Fantasy Creation'	EBrs ECho EPot SPer
	- 'Heavenly Blue'	ECho
	- 'New Creation'	ECho
	- 'Saffier' 🏆^{H4}	CGrW EBrs ECho LAma WCot
	- 'Valerie Finnis'	More than 30 suppliers
*	***auchadra***	ERos
	aucheri 🏆^{H4}	ECho ERos LAma MSte NRya
*	- var. ***bicolor***	WCot
	- 'Blue Magic'	EBrs ECho EPot
	- 'Mount Hood'	EBrs ECho ERCP

§	- 'Tubergenianum'	EBrs ECho
§	***azureum*** ♀H4	CAvo CBgR CFFs CHar CTca EBrs ECho EGoo ELan EPfP ERos GMaP LAma LEdu NMen NWCA SPhx WCot
	- 'Album'	CBgR CSsd CTca EBla EBrs ECho ERos LAma LRHS SPhx WCot
	'Baby's Breath'	see *M.* 'Jenny Robinson'
	'Blue Dream' **new**	EBrs ECho
	'Blue Eyes'	EBrs ECho WCot
	'Blue Star' **new**	EBrs ECho
	botryoides	EBrs ECho ERos LAma LEdu
	- 'Album'	CAvo CFFs CMea CTri EBla EBrs ECho ENot EPfP LAma LBMP MBri SPer SRms WBor WCot WShi
	caucasicum	ECho ERos WCot
	chalusicum	see *M. pseudomuscari*
§	***comosum***	CArn CHHB EBrs ECho EPfP LEdu LRHS NWCA WRos
*	- 'Album'	ECho
	- 'Monstrosum'	see *M. comosum* 'Plumosum'
	- 'Pinard'	EBrs ECho ERos
§	- 'Plumosum'	CAvo CTca EBla EBrs ECho EMon EPfP EPot LAma LEdu MAvo MBri SBch WAul WCot WHil
	dionysicum	CTca EBrs ECho
	- HOA 8965	WCot
	grandifolium	ERos
	- JCA 689.450	WCot
	- var. ***populeum***	ERos
§	'Jenny Robinson' ♀H4	CHHB CMil ECho EHrv SCnR SMad SMrm WCot
	latifolium ♀H4	CAvo CFFs CMea CTca EBla EBrs ECho ENot GGar LAma LRHS MAvo MLLN NBPN NChi SBch SPer SPhx WCot WHoo WTin
*	- 'Blue Angels'	NBir
§	***macrocarpum***	CAvo CBgR CMea CTca EBee EBrs ECha ECho EPot ERos LAma WAbe WCot
	- 'Golden Fragrance' PBR	CBgR CHHB CMil CPom EBrs ECho EPot ERCP LRHS
	mirum	ECho
	moschatum	see *M. muscarimi*
§	***muscarimi***	CAvo CBgR CHHB CStu EBrs ECho ERCP LAma LEdu NWCA WCot
	- var. ***flavum***	see *M. macrocarpum*
§	***neglectum***	CSWP EBrs ECho ERos LAma SEND WShi WWst
	pallens	CHHB EBrs ECho ERos LRHS NWCA WCot
	paradoxum	see *Bellevalia paradoxa*
	parviflorum	EBrs ECho ERos
§	***pseudomuscari*** ♀H4	EBrs ECho ERos WCot
	racemosum	see *M. neglectum*
	'Sky Blue'	EBrs ECho WCot
§	***spreitzenhoferi***	EBrs ECho ERos
	'Superstar'	EBrs ECho LEdu WCot
§	***tenuiflorum***	ECho WCot
	tubergenianum	see *M. aucheri* 'Tubergenianum'
	weissii	ERos
	'White Beauty'	ECho

Muscarimia (*Hyacinthaceae*)

ambrosiacum	see *Muscari muscarimi*
macrocarpum	see *Muscari macrocarpum*

Musella see *Musa*

lasiocarpa	see *Musa lasiocarpa*

Mussaenda (*Rubiaceae*)

erythrophylla	MJnS
incana	EShb
philippica	MJnS

Musschia (*Campanulaceae*)

wollastonii	CHEx

Mutisia (*Asteraceae*)

clematis	CRHN
'Glendoick'	GGGa
ilicifolia	CPle LRHS MTPN WSHC

Myoporum (*Myoporaceae*)

debile	see *Eremophila debilis*
laetum	CDoC CHEx CPLG CTrC XPep
parvifolium	XPep

Myosotidium (*Boraginaceae*)

§	***hortensia***	CAbb CBct CGHE CHEx CHid CTrC EBee ECre EHrv ELan EPfP EWes GAbr GBin GBuc GGar GKev ITer LAst LHop MDun NCob NCot NWCA SKHP WBor WCot WCru WGwG WPGP
	- white-flowered	WNor
	nobile	see *M. hortensia*

Myosotis (*Boraginaceae*)

	from Eyre Mountains, New Zealand **new**	NWCA
	alpestris 'Ruth Fischer'	NBir NMen
*	***aquatica***	NSco
	arvensis	GWCH SECG
	australis	NWCA
	capitata	ECou GCrs
	colensoi	ECou NMen NWCA
	explanata	NMen
	macrantha **new**	GBin
	palustris	see *M. scorpioides*
	pulvinaris	CPBP
	rakiura	SBch
§	***scorpioides***	CBen CWat EHon EMFW EPfP NGdn SCoo SPer SPlb SRms SWat WEas WMAq WMoo WPnP
	- 'Alba'	CDWL
	- 'Ice Pearl' **new**	CBen
	- Maytime = 'Blaqua' (v)	CDWL NBir
	- 'Mermaid'	CBen CWat ECha EHon EMFW EPfP LLWG LRHS SBch SDix SWat WFar WPer WPnP
	- 'Pinkie'	CDWL CWat EMFW NGdn SWat
	- 'Snowflakes'	CWat EMFW SWat
	sylvatica	CRWN NBlu NMir
	'Unforgettable' (v) **new**	CBow EBee NBro NCob

Myrceugenia (*Myrtaceae*)

ovata	CTrG
planipes	CTrG

Myrica (*Myricaceae*)

californica	CPle LEdu WPGP
cerifera	CArn NLar
gale	CAgr CRWN EMil GPoy MCoo MGos NLar SWat WFar WSpi
pensylvanica	ELau LEdu NLar

Myricaria (*Tamaricaceae*)

germanica	NLar

Myriophyllum (*Haloragaceae*)

propinquum	EMFW
spicatum	CDWL EHon EMFW NSco WMAq
verticillatum	EHon SCoo

Myrrhidendron (*Apiaceae*)

donnellsmithii B&SWJ 9099	WCru
- B&SWJ 10484	WCru

Myrrhis (*Apiaceae*)

odorata	CArn CBod CBre CHby CSev EBee ECha ELau EUnu GPoy ILis MHer MNHC MSal NBid NBlu NPri SIde WAul WBrk WEas WHer WPer WSel WWFP
- 'Forncett Chevron'	LEdu

Myrsine (*Myrsinaceae*)

africana	CPLG CPle CWib SBLw XPep
divaricata	CTrC IDee
nummularia	GGar WLin WThu

Myrteola (*Myrtaceae*)

§ nummularia	EPot ISea NMen WThu

Myrtus (*Myrtaceae*)

apiculata	see *Luma apiculata*
bullata	see *Lophomyrtus bullata*
chequen	see *Luma chequen*
communis 𝕐H3	More than 30 suppliers
* - 'Alhambra'	XPep
- 'Baetica'	XPep
* - 'Cascade'	XPep
- 'Flore Pleno' (d)	ELau XPep
- 'Jenny Reitenbach'	see *M. communis* subsp. *tarentina*
* - 'La Clape'	XPep
* - 'La Clape Blanc'	XPep
- 'Microphylla'	see *M. communis* subsp. *tarentina*
- 'Nana'	see *M. communis* subsp. *tarentina*
§ - subsp. ***tarentina*** 𝕐H3	More than 30 suppliers
- - 'Compacta'	CStu LBuc NLar WSel
* - - 'Granada'	XPep
- - 'Microphylla Variegata' (v)	CBcs CPle GQui MHer NGHP SPer STre WJek WSel
- - pink-flowered	XPep
I - - 'Variegata'	CPLG EPla SBLw XPep
* - - 'Vieussan'	XPep
- 'Tricolor'	see *M. communis* 'Variegata'
§ - 'Variegata' (v)	More than 30 suppliers
dulcis	see *Austromyrtus dulcis*
'Glanleam Gold'	see *Luma apiculata* 'Glanleam Gold'
lechleriana	see *Amomyrtus luma*
luma	see *Luma apiculata*
nummularia	see *Myrteola nummularia*
* ***paraguayensis***	CTrC
x ***ralphii***	see *Lophomyrtus* x *ralphii*
'Traversii'	see *Lophomyrtus* x *ralphii* 'Traversii'
ugni	see *Ugni molinae*
* ***variegata*** 'Penlee' (v)	CTrG

N

Nabalus (*Asteraceae*)

albus	see *Prenanthes alba*

Nananthus (*Aizoaceae*)

vittatus	WAbe

Nandina (*Berberidaceae*)

domestica 𝕐H3	More than 30 suppliers
- B&SWJ 4923	WCru
- 'Fire Power' 𝕐H3	More than 30 suppliers
- 'Gulf Stream' **new**	CBcs
- 'Harbor Dwarf'	LRHS SKHP WFar
- var. ***leucocarpa***	EPla MBlu NLar
- 'Little Princess'	EPla
- 'Nana'	see *N. domestica* 'Pygmaea'
- 'Nana Purpurea'	CDul EPla
- 'Orhime'	NLar
§ - 'Pygmaea'	CBct CMen
- 'Richmond'	CBcs CEnd CPMA CSBt EBee ELan EPfP LRHS MAsh MGos NVic SBod SHBN SLim SPer SPla SPoG SRGP SRkn WFar
- 'Wood's Dwarf'	MGos

Nannorrhops (*Arecaceae*)

ritchieana	LPal
- blue-leaved **new**	SAin
- green-leaved **new**	SAin

Napaea (*Malvaceae*)

dioica	EBee EMan WCot

Narcissus ✿ (*Amaryllidaceae*)

'Abstract' (11a)	CQua
'Accent' (2) 𝕐H4	CQua LRHS
'Achduart' (3)	CQua
'Achentoul' (4)	CQua
'Achnasheen' (3)	CQua
'Acropolis' (4)	CQua EBrs EPfP IHer
'Actaea' (9) 𝕐H4	CQua CTca EBrs MBri
'Acumen' (2)	CQua
'Admiration' (8)	CQua
'Advocat' (3)	CQua
'African Sunset' (3)	IRhd
'Agnes Mace' (2)	IRhd
'Ahwahnee' (2)	CQua IRhd
'Ainley' (2) **new**	CQua
'Aintree' (3)	CQua
'Aircastle' (3)	CQua
'Akepa' (5)	CQua
'Albatross' (3)	CQua WShi
I ***albidus*** subsp. ***occidentalis*** (13)	ERos
'Albus Plenus Odoratus'	see *N. poeticus* 'Plenus' ambig.
'Alpine Winter' (1)	IRhd
'Alston' (2)	IRhd
'Alto' (2)	IRhd
'Altruist' (3)	CQua
'Altun Ha' (2)	CQua IRhd
'Amazing Grace' (2)	IRhd
'Amber Castle' (2)	CQua
'Ambergate' (2)	EBrs LAma
'American Heritage' (1)	CQua IRhd
'American Robin' (6)	CQua
'American Shores' (1)	CQua IRhd
'Amstel' (4)	CQua
'Andalusia' (6)	ERos
'Angel' (3)	CQua
'Angel Eyes' (a) **new**	EBrs
'Angel Face' (3)	CQua IRhd
'Angelito' (3)	IRhd
Angel's Tears	see *N. triandrus* subsp. *triandrus* var. *triandrus*
'Angel's Wings' (2)	CQua
'Angkor' (4)	CQua
'An-gof' (7)	CQua
'Apotheose' (4)	CQua LRHS
'Applins' (2)	IRhd
'April Love' (1)	CQua
'April Snow' (2)	CQua
'April Tears' (5) 𝕐H4	NMin
'Aranjuez' (2)	CQua
'Arctic Gem' (3)	CQua
'Arctic Gold' (1) 𝕐H4	CQua LAma
'Ardress' (2)	CQua
'Ardview' (3)	IRhd
'Argent' (4) **new**	CAvo
'Argosy' (1)	CQua
'Arid Plains' (3)	IRhd
'Arish Mell' (5)	CQua
'Arkle' (1) 𝕐H4	CQua

	'Arleston' (2)	IRhd
	'Armidale' (3)	IRhd
	'Armoury' (4)	CQua
	'Arndilly' (2)	CQua
	'Arpege' (2)	CQua
	'Arran Isle' (2)	IRhd
	'Arthurian' (1)	IRhd
	'Arwenack' (11a)	CQua
	'Ashmore' (2)	CQua IRhd
	'Ashton Wold' (2)	CQua
	'Asila' (2)	IRhd
	'Assertion' (2)	IRhd
§	***assoanus*** (13)	EBrs ECho EPot ERos LAma NMen NMin SPhx
	'Astropink' (11a)	CQua
§	***asturiensis*** (13) ♀H3-4	CSam ECho IBlr MNrw NMin SPhx
	- 'Navarre' (I)	WCot
	asturiensis x ***cyclamineus***	NMen
	'Atricilla' (11a)	IRhd
	'Auchrannie' (2)	IRhd
	'Audubon' (2)	CQua
	'Auntie Eileen' (2)	CQua
	'Auspicious' (2)	IRhd
	'Autumn Gold' (7) **new**	EBrs
	'Avalanche' (8) ♀H3	CQua EBrs LEdu
	'Avalanche of Gold' (8)	CQua
	'Avalon' (2)	CQua
	'Azocor' (1)	IRhd
	'Baby Moon' (7)	CMea CQua CTca EBrs EPot GKev ITim LAma LEdu LRHS LSou MBrN MBri NHol NMin SPer
	'Badanloch' (3)	CQua
	'Badbury Rings' (3) ♀H4	CQua
	'Balalaika' (2)	CQua
	'Baldock' (4)	CQua
	'Ballinamallard' (3)	IRhd
	'Ballydorn' (9) **new**	IRhd
	'Ballygarvey' (1)	CQua
	'Ballygowan' (3)	IRhd
	'Ballyrobert' (1)	CQua
	'Baltic Shore' (3)	IRhd
	'Balvenie' (2)	CQua
	'Bambi' (1)	ERos
	'Bandesara' (3)	CQua IRhd
	'Bandit' (2)	CQua
	'Banstead Village' (2)	CQua
	'Bantam' (2) ♀H4	CQua ERos
	'Barlow' (6)	CQua
	'Barnesgold' (1)	IRhd
	'Barnsdale Wood' (2)	CQua
	'Barnum' (1) ♀H4	IRhd
	'Barrett Browning' (3)	EBla EBrs LRHS
	'Bartley' (6)	CQua
	'Bath's Flame' (3)	CAvo CQua WShi
	'Bear Springs' (4)	IRhd
	'Bedruthan' (2)	CQua
	'Beersheba' (1)	CQua EBrs
	'Belbroughton' (2)	CQua
	'Belcanto' (11a)	CQua
	'Belfast Lough' (1)	IRhd
	'Bell Rock' (1)	CQua
	'Bell Song' (7)	CAvo CFFs CMea CQua CTca EBrs EPfP ERos LEdu LRHS LSou NHol SPer
	'Bella Vista' (2) **new**	LRHS
	'Ben Aligin' (1)	CQua
	'Ben Hee' (2) ♀H4	CQua
	'Berceuse' (2)	CQua IRhd
	'Bere Ferrers' (4)	CQua
	'Bergerac' (11a)	CQua
	'Berlin' (2)	ERos
	'Bernardino' (2)	CQua
	'Beryl' (6)	CAvo CQua EBrs ERos LRHS NMin
	'Best Seller' (1)	SPer

	'Bethal' (3)	CQua
	'Betsy MacDonald' (6)	CQua
	'Biffo' (4)	CQua
	'Bikini Beach' (2)	IRhd
	'Bilbo' (6)	CQua
	'Binkie' (2)	CQua SPer
	'Birdsong' (3)	CQua
	'Birma' (3)	EFam LAma
	'Birthday Girl' (2)	IRhd
	'Bishops Light' (2)	CQua
	'Blair Athol' (2)	CQua
	'Blarney' (3)	CQua
	'Blisland' (9)	CQua
	'Blossom' (4)	CQua
	'Blossom Lady' (4)	CQua
	'Blue Danube' (1)	IRhd
	'Blushing Lady' (7) **new**	EBrs
	'Blushing Maiden' (4)	CQua
	'Bob Spotts' (2)	CQua
	'Bobbysoxer' (7)	CQua ERos MTho
	'Bobolink' (2)	CQua
	'Bodelva' (2)	CQua
	'Bodwannick' (2)	CQua
	'Bold Prospect' (1)	CQua
	'Bon Viveur' (11a)	IRhd
	'Bosbigal' (11a)	CQua
	'Boscastle' (7)	CQua
	'Boscoppa' (11a)	CQua
	'Boslowick' (11a) ♀H4	CQua
	'Bosmeor' (2)	CQua
	'Bossa Nova' (3)	CQua
	'Bossiney' (11a)	CQua
	'Bosvale' (11a)	CQua
	'Bouzouki' (2)	IRhd
	'Boyne Bridge' (1)	IRhd
	'Brandaris' (11a)	CQua
	'Bravoure' (1) ♀H4	CQua
	'Brentswood' (8)	CQua
	'Bridal Crown' (4) ♀H4	EBrs EPfP LAma SPer
	'Bright Flame' (2)	CQua
	'Brindaleena' (2)	IRhd
	'Brindle Pink' (2)	IRhd
	'Broadland' (2)	CQua
	'Broadway Star' (11b)	EBrs LAma
	'Brodick' (3)	CQua IRhd
	'Brookdale' (1)	CQua
	'Broomhill' (2) ♀H4	CQua
	broussonetii (13)	EBrs ECho
	'Budock Bells' (5)	CQua
	'Budock Water' (2)	CQua
	'Bugle Major' (2)	CQua
	bulbocodium (13) ♀H3-4	CStu EBrs GKev ITim LBee LEdu LRHS NWCA SBch SPer SPhx SRms WLin
§	- subsp. ***bulbocodium*** var. ***citrinus*** (13)	EPot SSpi
	- - var. ***conspicuus*** (13)	CArn CHar CPMA CQua CTca EBrs ECho EPfP EPot ERos GCrs GEdr ITim LAma MSSP NMen NRya SBch SGar WCot
§	- - var. ***graellsii*** (13)	NSla
	- - var. ***nivalis*** (13)	EBrs ECho EPot ERos
	- - var. ***pallidus*** (13)	ERos
§	- - var. ***tenuifolius*** (13)	CStu NMen
	- var. ***mesatlanticus***	see *N. romieuxii* subsp. *romieuxii* var. *mesatlanticus*
	- subsp. ***praecox*** (13)	ECho WCot
	- - var. ***paucinervis*** (13)	EBrs ECho GCrs
	- subsp. ***romieuxii***	see *N. romieuxii*
I	- subsp. ***viriditubus*** (13)	ERos
	'Bunchie' (5)	CQua
	'Bunclody' (2)	CQua
	'Bunting' (7) ♀H4	CQua
	'Burning Bush' (3)	IRhd
	'Burntollet' (1)	CQua

'Busselton' (3)	IRhd
'Butterscotch' (2)	CQua
'By George!' (2) **new**	EBrs
'C.J. Backhouse' (2) **new**	CQua
'Cabernet' (2)	IRhd
'Cacatua' (11a)	IRhd
'Cadgwith' (2)	CQua
'Cairntoul' (3)	CQua
'Calamansack' (2)	CQua
calcicola (13)	CWoo ERos
'California Rose' (4)	CQua IRhd
'Camellia' (4)	EFam
'Camelot' (2) ♀H4	CQua EPfP SPer
'Cameo Angel' (2)	CQua
'Cameo King' (2)	CQua
'Camoro' (10)	GCrs NMen
'Campernelli Plenus'	see *N.* x *odorus* 'Double Campernelle'
'Campion' (9)	CQua IRhd
'Canaliculatus' (8)	CArn CQua CTca EBrs ECho EPfP ERos GKev LAma LRHS MBri SPer WGwG
canaliculatus Gussone	see *N. tazetta* subsp. *lacticolor*
'Canary' (7)	CQua
'Canarybird' (8)	CQua WShi
'Canasta' (11a)	CQua
'Canisp' (2)	CQua
'Cantabile' (9) ♀H4	CQua CTca
cantabricus (13)	EBrs ECho EPot GCrs SPhx
- subsp. ***cantabricus*** (13)	ERos
- - var. ***foliosus*** (13) ♀H2	EBrs ECho GKev NMen SCnR
'Canticle' (9)	IRhd
'Capax Plenus'	see *N.* 'Eystettensis'
'Cape Cornwall' (2)	CQua
'Cape Helles' (3)	IRhd
'Cape Point' (2)	IRhd
'Capisco' (3)	CQua
'Caramba' (2)	CQua
'Carbineer' (2)	CQua EFam
'Carclew' (6)	CQua
'Cardiff' (2) **new**	CQua
'Cardinham' (3)	CQua
'Cargreen' (9)	CQua
'Carib Gipsy' (2) ♀H4	CQua IRhd
'Caribbean Snow' (2)	CQua
'Carlton' (2) ♀H4	CQua EBrs EFam LAma
'Carnearny' (3)	CQua
'Carnkeeran' (2)	CQua
'Carnkief' (2)	CQua
'Carnyorth' (11a)	CQua
'Carole Lombard' (3)	CQua
'Carwinion' (2)	CQua
'Cassata' (11a)	EBrs EFam EPfP LAma NBir
'Castanets' (8)	IRhd
'Casterbridge' (2)	CQua IRhd
'Catalyst' (2)	IRhd
'Catistock' (2)	CQua
'Causeway Sunset' (2)	IRhd
'Cavalryman' (3)	IRhd
'Cavendish' (4)	IRhd
'Caye Chapel' (3)	CQua
'Cazique' (6)	CQua
x ***cazorlanus*** (13)	ITim
'Ceasefire' (2)	IRhd
'Cedar Hills' (3)	CQua
'Cedric Morris' (1)	CDes CElw CLAP ECha EHrv NCGa NDov SMrm
'Celestial Fire' (2)	CQua
'Celtic Gold' (2)	CQua
'Centannées' (11b)	EBrs
'Centrefold' (3)	CQua
'Cha-cha' (6)	CQua
'Chanson' (1)	IRhd
'Chanterelle' (11a)	EBla LAma
'Chapman's Peak' (2)	IRhd
'Charity May' (6) ♀H4	CQua
'Charleston' (2)	CQua
'Chasseur' (2)	IRhd
'Chaste' (1)	CQua IRhd
'Chat' (7)	CQua
'Cheer Leader' (3)	CQua
'Cheerfulness' (4) ♀H4	CAvo CFFs CQua EBrs LAma LRHS MBri
'Cheesewring' (3)	CQua
'Cheetah' (1)	CQua IRhd
'Chelsea Girl' (2)	CQua
'Cheltenham' (2)	CQua
'Chenoweth' (2)	CQua
'Chérie' (7)	CQua
'Cherish' (2)	CQua
'Cherrygardens' (2)	CQua IRhd
'Chesapeake Bay' (1)	CQua
'Chesterton' (9) ♀H4	CQua
'Chickadee' (6)	CQua
'Chickerell' (3)	CQua
'Chief Inspector' (1)	IRhd
'Chiloquin' (1)	CQua
'China Doll' (2)	CQua
'Chinchilla' (2)	CQua IRhd
'Chingah' (1)	IRhd
'Chinita' (8)	CQua
'Chipper' (5) **new**	NMin
'Chit Chat' (7) ♀H4	CQua EBrs EPot ERos LRHS
'Chobe River' (1)	IRhd
'Chorus Line' (8)	IRhd
'Churston Ferrers' (4)	CQua
'Chy Noweth' (2)	CQua
'Chysauster' (2) **new**	CQua
'Cisticola' (3)	IRhd
citrinus	see *N. bulbocodium* subsp. *bulbocodium* var. *citrinus*
'Citron' (3)	CQua
'Citronita' (3)	CQua
'Clare' (7)	CQua IRhd NMin
'Claverley' (2)	CQua
'Clearbrook' (2)	CQua
'Clouded Yellow' (2)	CQua IRhd
'Clouds Hill'	CQua
'Clouds Rest' (2)	IRhd
'Codlins and Cream'	see *N.* 'Sulphur Phoenix'
'Coldbrook' (2)	CQua
'Colin's Joy' (2)	CQua
'Colleen Bawn'	CAvo CQua EBrs
'Colley Gate' (3)	CQua
'Colliford' (2)	CQua
'Colorama' (11a)	CQua
'Colourful' (2)	IRhd
'Columbus' (2)	CQua
'Colville' (9)	CQua
'Comal' (1)	CQua
'Compressus'	see *N.* x *intermedius* 'Compressus'
'Compton Court' (3)	IRhd
concolor	see *N. triandrus* subsp. *triandrus* var. *concolor*
'Conestoga' (2)	CQua IRhd
'Confuoco' (2)	EFam
'Congress' (11a)	CQua
* 'Connie Number 1'	CStu
'Conowingo' (11a)	CQua
'Conspicuus' ambig.	CQua LAma
'Content' (1) **new**	CQua
'Cool Autumn' (2)	CQua
'Cool Crystal' (3)	CQua
'Cool Evening' (11a)	CQua IRhd
'Cool Pink' (2)	CQua
'Cool Shades' (2)	CQua
'Coolmaghery' (2)	IRhd
'Coombe Creek' (6)	CQua
'Copper Nob' (2)	IRhd
'Copper Rings' (3)	CQua

'Copperfield' (2)	CQua
'Coral Fair' (2)	CQua
'Corbiere' (1)	CQua IRhd
cordubensis (13)	EBrs ECho
'Cornet' (6)	CQua
'Cornish Chuckles' (12)	CBgR CQua CTca
'Cornish Sun' (2) **new**	CQua
'Cornish Vanguard' (2)	CQua
'Cornsilk' (11a)	CQua
'Coroboree' **new**	IRhd
'Corofin' (3)	CQua
'Coromandel' (2)	IRhd
'Corozal' (3)	CQua
'Cosmic Dance' (3)	IRhd
'Cotinga' (6)	CQua EBrs NMin
'Countdown' (2)	CQua
'Coverack Glory' (2) **new**	CQua
'Crackington' (4) 🏆^{H4}	CQua IRhd
'Craig Stiel' (2)	CQua
'Creag Dubh' (2)	CQua
'Creed' (6)	CQua
'Crenver' (3)	CQua
'Crevenagh' (2)	IRhd
'Crewenna' (1)	CQua
'Crill' (7)	CQua
'Crimson Chalice' (3)	CQua IRhd
'Cristobal' (1)	CQua
'Crock of Gold' (1)	CQua
'Croesus' (2)	CQua
'Crofty' (6)	CQua
'Croila' (2)	CQua
'Crowndale' (4)	CQua IRhd
'Crugmeer' (11a)	CQua
'Cryptic' (1)	CQua IRhd
'Crystal Star' (2)	CQua
cuatrecasasii (13)	ERos
'Cudden Point' (2)	CQua
'Cul Beag' (3)	CQua
'Culmination' (2)	CQua
'Cultured Pearl' (2)	CQua
'Cupid's Eye' (3)	CQua
'Curlew' (7)	CQua EBrs
'Curly' (2)	EBrs
cyclamineus (13) 🏆^{H4}	CPom CWCL CWoo CWsd EPot GCrs MSSP SCnR SRms WAbe
'Cyclope' (1)	CQua
cypri (8)	CQua
'Cyros' (1)	CQua
'Dailmanach' (2)	CQua IRhd
'Dailmystic' (2)	IRhd
'Dallas' (3)	CQua
'Dambuster' **new**	IRhd
'Damson' (2)	CQua
'Dan du Plessis' (8)	CQua
'Dancing Queen' (2)	IRhd
'Dardanelles' (2)	IRhd
'Dateline' (3)	CQua
'David Alexander' (1)	CQua
'David Mills' (2)	CQua
'Dawn Call' (2)	IRhd
'Dawn Run' (2)	IRhd
'Dawn Sky' (2)	CQua
'Daydream' (2) 🏆^{H3}	CQua EBrs
'Daymark' (8)	CQua
'Dayton Lake' (2)	CQua
'Debutante' (2)	CQua
'December Bride' (11a)	CQua
'Delia' (6)	IRhd
'Délibes' (2)	SPer
'Dell Chapel' (3)	CQua
'Delnashaugh' (4)	CQua EBrs LAma LRHS NHol
'Delos' (3)	CQua
'Delphin Hill' (4)	IRhd
'Delta Flight' (6)	IRhd
'Demand' (2)	CQua

'Demeanour' **new**	IRhd
'Demmo' (2)	CQua
'Dena' (3)	IRhd
'Denali' (1)	IRhd
'Derryboy' (3)	IRhd
'Descant' (1)	IRhd
'Desdemona' (2) 🏆^{H4}	CQua
'Desert Bells' (7)	CQua
'Desert Orchid' (2)	CQua
'Dick Wilden' (4)	EBla EBrs
'Dickcissel' (7) 🏆^{H4}	CQua EBrs ERos LEdu
'Dimity' (3)	CQua
'Dimple' (9)	CQua
'Diversity' (11a)	IRhd
'Doctor Hugh' (3) 🏆^{H4}	CQua IRhd
'Doctor Jazz' (2)	CQua
'Dolly Mollinger' (11b)	EBla EBrs
'Doombar' (1)	CQua
'Dora Allum' (2)	CQua
'Dorchester' (4)	CQua IRhd
'Double Campernelle'	see *N.* x *odorus* 'Double Campernelle'
'Double Fashion' (4)	EBrs
double pheasant eye	see *N. poeticus* 'Plenus' ambig.
double Roman	see *N.* 'Romanus'
'Double White' (4)	CQua CTca
'Doubleday' (4)	CQua IRhd
'Doublet' (4)	CQua
'Doubtful' (3)	CQua
'Dove Wings' (6) 🏆^{H4}	CQua
'Dover Cliffs' (2)	CQua
'Downlands' (3)	CQua
'Downpatrick' (1)	CQua
'Dragon Run' (2)	CQua
'Drama Queen' (11a)	IRhd
'Drumbeg' (2)	IRhd
'Drumlin' (1) 🏆^{H4}	IRhd
dubius (13)	EBrs ECho EPot
'Duiker' (6)	IRhd
'Duke of Windsor' (2)	EFam
'Dulcimer' (9)	CQua
'Dunadry Inn' (4)	IRhd
'Dunkeld' (2)	CQua
'Dunkery' (4)	CQua IRhd
'Dunley Hall' (3)	CQua IRhd
'Dunmurry' (1)	CQua
'Dunskey' (3)	CQua
'Dupli Kate' (4)	IRhd
'Dusky Lad' (2)	IRhd
'Dusky Maiden' (2)	IRhd
'Dutch Delight' (2)	IRhd
'Dutch Master' (1) 🏆^{H4}	CQua EBrs LAma LRHS
'Early Bride' (2)	CQua
'Early Splendour' (8)	CQua
'Earthlight' (3)	CQua
'Easter Bonnet' (2)	EBla SPer
'Easter Moon' (2)	CQua
'Eastern Dawn' (2)	CQua
'Eastern Promise' (2)	CQua
'Eaton Song' (12) 🏆^{H4}	CQua
'Eddy Canzony' (2)	CQua
'Edenderry' (1)	IRhd
'Edgbaston' (2)	CQua
'Edge Grove' (2)	CQua
'Edward Buxton' (3)	CQua LRHS
'Egard' (11a)	CQua LRHS
'Egmont King' (2)	CQua
'Eland' (7)	CQua
'Elburton' (2)	CQua
'Electrus' (11a)	IRhd
elegans (13)	EBrs ECho
'Elf' (2)	CQua
'Elfin Gold' (6)	CQua IRhd
'Elizabeth Ann' (6)	CQua
'Elka' (1)	CAvo CBgR CQua NMin

	'Ella D' (2)	CQua
	'Ellen' (2) **new**	LRHS
	'Elphin' (4)	CQua
	'Elrond' (2)	CQua
	'Elven Lady' (2)	CQua
	'Elvira' (8)	CQua
	'Emerald Pink' (3)	CQua
	'Emily' (2)	CQua
	'Eminent' (3)	CQua
	'Emperor's Waltz' (6)	CQua IRhd
	'Empress of Ireland' (1) ♀H4	CQua EBrs IHer IRhd
	'English Caye' (1)	CQua
	'Ensemble' (4)	CQua
	'Enterprise' (4) **new**	CQua
	'Epona' (3)	CQua
	'Erlicheer' (4)	CQua EBrs
	'Escapee' (2)	IRhd
	'Estrella' (3)	CQua
	'Ethereal Beauty' (2)	IRhd
	'Ethos' (1)	IRhd
	'Etincelante' (11a)	EBrs
	'Euryalus' (1)	CQua
	'Eve Robertson' (2)	CQua
	'Evening' (2)	CQua
	'Evesham' (3)	IRhd
	'Exotic Beauty' (4) **new**	EBrs
	'Eyeglass' (3)	IRhd
	'Eyelet' (3)	IRhd
	'Eype' (4)	IRhd
	'Eyrie' (3)	IRhd
§	'Eystettensis' (4)	ECha ERos GCrs IBlr
	'Fair Head' (9)	CQua
	'Fair Prospect' (2)	CQua
	'Fair William' (2)	CQua
	'Fairgreen' (3)	CQua
	'Fairlawns' (3)	CQua
	'Fairmile' (3)	CQua
	'Fairy Chimes' (5)	CBgR CQua NMin
	'Fairy Footsteps' (3)	CQua IRhd
	'Fairy Island' (3)	CQua
	'Fairy Spell' (3)	IRhd
	'Fairy Tale' (3)	CQua
	'Falconet' (8) ♀H4	CBgR CQua EBrs ERos
	'Falmouth Bay' (3)	CQua
	'Falstaff' (2)	CQua
	'Famecheck Giant'	EFam
	'Famecheck Luck' (2)	EFam
	'Famecheck Silver' (11b)	EFam
	'Far Country' (2)	CQua
I	'Fashion' (11b)	CQua
	'Fashion Model' **new**	IRhd
	'Fastidious' (2)	CQua
	'February Gold' (6) ♀H4	CAvo CFFs EBrs EPfP EPot ERos LAma LRHS MBri NBir SGar SPer SRms WShi
	'February Silver' (6)	EBrs EPot LAma SMeo
	'Felindre' (9)	CQua
	'Feline Queen' (1)	IRhd
	'Feock' (3)	CQua
	fernandesii (13)	EBrs ECho ERos NMin SCnR WThu
	'Ferndown' (3)	CQua IRhd
	'ffitch's Folly' (2)	CQua
	'Fidelity' (1) **new**	LRHS
	'Filoli' (1)	CQua IRhd
	'Finchcocks' (2)	CQua
	'Fine Gold' (1)	CQua
	'Fine Romance' (2)	CQua
	'Finlandia' (1)	CQua
	'Fiona MacKillop' (2)	IRhd
	'Fire tail' (3) **new**	CQua WShi
	'First Born' (6)	CQua
	'First Formal' (3)	CQua
	'Flambards Village' (4)	CQua
	'Flirt' (6)	CQua

	'Florida Manor' (3)	IRhd
	'Flower Drift' (4)	EPfP
	'Flower Record' (2)	LAma LRHS SPer
	'Flycatcher' (7)	CQua
	'Flying Colours' (4)	IRhd
	'Flying High' (3)	CQua
	'Foff's Way' (1) **new**	CQua
	'Foresight' (1)	CQua EFam
	'Forge Mill' (2)	CQua
	'Fortissimo' (2)	EBrs
	'Fortune' (2)	CQua EFam LAma MBri
	'Foundling' (6) ♀H4	CQua
	'Foxhunter' (2) **new**	CQua
	'Fragrant Breeze' (2)	EBrs
	'Fragrant Rose' (2)	CQua EBrs IRhd
	'Francolin' (1)	IRhd
	'Frank' (9)	IRhd
	'Freedom Rings' (2)	CQua
	'Freedom Stars' (11a)	IRhd
	'Fresco' (11a)	IRhd
	'Fresh Lime' (1)	CQua
	'Fresno' (3)	IRhd
	'Frogmore' (6)	CQua
	'Front Royal' (2)	CQua
	'Frosted Pink' (2)	IRhd
	'Frostkist' (6)	CQua
	'Frou-frou' (4)	CQua
	'Frozen Jade' (1)	CQua
	'Fruit Cup' (7)	CQua EPfP
	'Fulwell' (4)	CQua
	'Furbelow' (4) **new**	CQua
	'Furnace Creek' (2)	IRhd
	'Fynbos' (3)	IRhd
	gaditanus (13)	ERos
	'Galilee' (3)	EBrs
	'Gamebird' (1)	IRhd
	'Garden News' (3)	IRhd
	'Garden Princess' (6)	EBrs LRHS
	'Gay Cavalier' (4)	CQua
	'Gay Kybo' (4) ♀H4	CQua
	'Gay Song' (4)	CQua
§	***gayi*** (13)	CQua
	'Geevor' (4)	CQua
	'Gellymill' (2)	CQua
	'Gemini Girl' (2)	CQua
	'George Leak' (2)	CQua
	'Georgie Girl' (6)	CQua
	'Geranium' (8) ♀H4	CQua EBrs EPfP LAma LEdu LRHS SMeo SPer
	'Gettysburg' (2)	CQua
	'Gillan' (11a)	CQua
	'Gin and Lime' (1) ♀H4	CQua
	'Gipsy Moon' (2)	CQua
	'Gipsy Queen' (1)	CBgR CQua GCrs NMin
	'Gironde' (11)	CQua
	'Glacier' (1)	CQua
	'Glen Cassley' (3)	CQua
	'Glen Clova' (2)	CQua
	'Glendermott' (2)	CQua
	'Glenside' (2)	CQua
	'Glissando' (2)	CQua
	'Gloriosus' (8)	CQua
	'Glover's Reef' (1)	CQua
	'Glowing Pheonix' (4)	CQua
	'Glowing Red' (4)	CQua
	'Goff's Caye' (2)	CQua IRhd
	'Golant' (2)	CQua
	'Gold Bond' (2)	CQua IRhd
	'Gold Charm' (2)	CQua
	'Gold Convention' (2) ♀H4	CQua IRhd
	'Gold Ingot' (2)	IRhd
	'Gold Medallion' (1)	CQua
	'Gold Top' (2) **new**	CQua
	'Golden Amber' (2)	CQua
	'Golden Aura' (2) ♀H4	CQua

	'Golden Bear' (4)	CQua
§	Golden Bells Group	CAvo CFFs CMea CPom CQua CSam CSsd CWCL EBrs ECho EPot GMaP LBBr LRHS MBri NHol SPer
	'Golden Bells'	see *N.* Golden Bells Group
	'Golden Cheer' (2)	CQua
	'Golden Cycle' (6)	CQua
	'Golden Dawn' (8) ♀H3	CQua EBrs EPfP
	'Golden Ducat' (4)	CQua LAma MBri NBir
	'Golden Flute' (2)	IRhd
	'Golden Gamble' (11a)	IRhd
	'Golden Halo' (2)	CQua
	'Golden Harvest' (1)	CQua EBrs LAma SPer
	'Golden Incense' (7)	CQua
	'Golden Jewel' (2) ♀H4	CQua
	'Golden Joy' (2)	CQua
	'Golden Lady' (1) **new**	LRHS
	'Golden Lion' (1) **new**	CQua
	'Golden Marvel' (1)	CQua
	'Golden Orbit' (4)	CQua
	'Golden Phoenix' (4)	CQua WShi
	'Golden Quince' (12)	CQua
	'Golden Rain' (4)	CQua
	'Golden Rapture' (1) ♀H4	CQua
	'Golden Sheen' (2)	CQua
	'Golden Splash' (11a)	IRhd
	'Golden Spur' (1)	CQua LAma
	'Golden Strand' (2)	IRhd
	'Golden Torch' (2)	CQua
	'Golden Vale' (1) ♀H4	CQua
	'Goldfinger' (1) ♀H4	CQua IRhd
	'Goldhanger' (2)	CQua
	'Golitha Falls' (2)	CQua
	'Good Measure' (2)	CQua
	'Goonbell' (2)	CQua
	'Gorran' (3)	CQua
	'Gossmoor' (4)	CQua
	graellsii	see *N. bulbocodium* subsp. *bulbocodium* var. *graellsii*
	'Grand Monarque'	see *N. tazetta* subsp. *lacticolor* 'Grand Monarque'
	'Grand Opening' (4)	IRhd
	'Grand Primo Citronière' (8)	CBgR CQua
	'Grand Prospect' (2)	CQua
	'Grand Soleil d'Or' (8)	CQua EBrs LAma NHol
	'Great Expectations' (2)	CQua
	'Greatwood' (1)	CQua
	'Green Howard' (3)	EBrs
	'Green Lodge' (9)	IRhd
	'Greenlet' (6)	CBgR CQua MSte
	'Greenodd' (3)	CQua
	'Greenpark' (9)	IRhd
	'Grenoble' (2)	CQua
	'Gresham' (4)	CQua IRhd
	'Gribben Head' (4)	CQua
	'Groundkeeper' (3)	IRhd
	'Grullemans Senior' (2)	EFam
	'Gulliver' (3)	CQua
	'Gunwalloe' (11a)	CQua
	'Guy Wilson' (2)	CQua
	'Gwennap' (1)	CQua
	'Gwinear' (2)	CQua
	'Hacienda' (1)	CQua
	'Half Moon Caye' (2) **new**	CQua
	'Halley's Comet' (3)	CQua IRhd
	'Halloon' (3) **new**	CQua
	'Halzephron' (2)	CQua
	'Hambledon' (2) ♀H4	CQua
	'Hampton Court' (2)	CQua
	'Happy Dreams' (2)	IRhd
	'Happy Fellow' (2)	CQua
	'Happy Valley' (2)	IRhd
	'Harbour View' (2)	IRhd
	'Harmony Bells' (5)	CQua

'Harp Music' (2)	IRhd
'Harpers Ferry' (1)	CQua
'Hartlebury' (3)	CQua
'Hawangi' (3)	IRhd
'Hawera' (5) ♀H4	CAvo CFFs CQua CTca EBrs ECGP EGoo EPfP EPot GKev LAma LEdu LRHS LSou MBri SPer SPhx WHal WLin
'Heamoor' (4) ♀H4	CQua
hedraeanthus (13)	EBrs ECho
- SG 13	WCot
'Helford Dawn' (2)	CQua
'Helford Sunset' (2)	CQua
'Helios' (2)	CQua
hellenicus	see *N. poeticus* var. *hellenicus*
henriquesii	see *N. jonquilla* var. *henriquesii*
'Henry Irving' (1)	CQua
'Hero' (1)	CQua
'Heslington' (3)	CQua
'Hexameter' (9)	CQua
'Hexworthy' (3)	CQua
'Hicks Mill' (1)	CQua
'High Society' (2) ♀H4	CQua IRhd
'Highfield Beauty' (8) ♀H4	CQua
'Highgrove' (1)	CQua
'Highlite' (2)	CQua
'Hilda's Pink' (2)	CQua
'Hill Head' (9)	IRhd
'Hillstar' (7) ♀H4	CMea CQua EBrs IRhd LRHS MSte
hispanicus (13)	EBrs ECho
'Hocus Pocus' (3)	IRhd
'Holly Berry' (2)	CQua
'Hollypark' (3)	IRhd
'Holme Fen' (2)	CQua
'Home Fires' (2)	CQua
'Homestead' (2) ♀H4	IRhd
'Honey Pink' (2)	CQua
'Honeybird' (1)	CQua
'Honeyorange' (2)	IRhd
'Honolulu' (4)	CQua
'Hoopoe' (8) ♀H4	CQua EBrs LRHS
'Horace' (9)	CQua
'Horn of Plenty' (5)	CQua EBrs
'Hornpipe' (1)	IRhd
'Hospodar' (2)	CQua
'Hot Gossip' (2)	CQua
'Hotspur' (2)	CQua
'Hugh Town' (8)	CAvo CQua
'Hullabaloo' (2)	IRhd
humilis misapplied	see *N. pseudonarcissus* subsp. *pseudonarcissus* var. *humilis*
'Hunting Caye' (2)	CQua
'Huntley Down' (1)	CQua
'Ice Chimes' (5)	CQua
'Ice Dancer' (2)	CQua
'Ice Diamond' (4)	CQua
'Ice Follies' (2) ♀H4	CQua EBrs EFam LAma MBri NBir SPer
'Ice King' (4)	EBla EBrs NBir SPer
'Ice Wings' (5) ♀H4	CAvo CFFs CQua EBrs EPot ERos MSte NMin WLin WShi
'Idless' (1)	CQua
'Immaculate' (2)	CQua
'Inara' (4)	CQua
'Inbal' (8) **new**	EBrs
'Inca' (6)	CQua
'Inchbonnie' (2)	CQua
'Independence Day' (4)	CQua
'Indian Chief' (4)	EFam
'Indian Maid' (7) ♀H4	CQua IRhd
'Indora' (4)	CQua
'Inner Glow' (2)	IRhd
'Innisidgen' (8)	CQua
'Innovator' (4)	IRhd
'Inny River' (1)	IRhd

'Interim' (2)	CQua
x ***intermedius*** (13)	CQua ERos
§ – 'Compressus' (8)	CQua
'Intrigue' (7) Υ^{H4}	CQua IRhd LRHS SPer
'Invercassley' (3)	CQua
'Ipi Tombi' (2)	EBrs ERos
'Ireland's Eye' (9)	CQua
'Irene Copeland' (4)	CQua
'Irish Fire' (2)	CQua
'Irish Light' (2)	CQua
'Irish Linen' (3)	CQua
'Irish Luck' (1)	CQua
'Irish Minstrel' (2) Υ^{H4}	CQua
'Irish Wedding' (2)	CQua
'Isambard' (4)	CQua
'Islander' (4)	CQua
'Ita' (2)	IRhd
'Itzim' (6) Υ^{H4}	CAvo CQua EBrs ECho ERos GCrs LRHS SPer
'Jack Snipe' (6) Υ^{H4}	CAvo CFFs CQua EBrs ECGP ECho EPfP EPot ERos LAma LRHS MBri MSte WCra WShi
'Jack Wood' (11a)	CQua
'Jackadee' (2)	IRhd
'Jake' (3)	IRhd
'Jamage' (8)	CQua
'Jamaica Inn' (4)	CQua CTca
'Jambo' (2)	IRhd
'Jamboree' (2)	CQua
'Jamestown' (3)	IRhd
'Janelle' (2)	CQua
'Jantje' (11a)	CQua
'Javelin' (2)	IRhd
'Jeanine' (2)	CQua
'Jeanne Bicknell' (4)	CQua
'Jedna' (2)	CQua
'Jenny' (6) Υ^{H4}	CFFs CMea CQua CTca EBla EBrs EPot ERos LAma LEdu NBir WShi
'Jersey Carlton' (2) **new**	CQua
'Jersey Roundabout' (4) **new**	CQua
'Jersey Torch' (4) **new**	CQua
'Jetfire' (6) Υ^{H4}	CMea CQua CTca EBrs ECho EPfP EPot ERos LAma LRHS LSou NHol SPer
'Jimmy Noone' (1) **new**	CQua
'Jim's Gold' (2)	CQua
'Jodi' (11b) **new**	IRhd
'Jodi's Sister' (11a)	IRhd
'John Daniel' (4)	CQua
'John Lanyon' (3)	CQua
'John's Delight' (3)	CQua
x ***johnstonii***	EBrs ECho NMin
– 'Queen of Spain' (10)	CAvo
jonquilla (13) Υ^{H4}	CAvo CQua EBrs EPot ERos LAma LEdu LRHS SPhx WLin WShi
§ – var. ***henriquesii*** (13)	CQua EBrs ECho NMin SCnR SPhx
'Joppa' (7)	CQua
'Joy Bishop'	see *N. romieuxii* 'Joy Bishop'
'Joybell' (6)	CQua
'Juanita' (2)	EPfP LRHS SPer
'Jules Verne' (2)	CQua
'Julia Jane'	see *N. romieuxii* 'Julia Jane'
'Jumblie' (12) Υ^{H4}	CQua EBrs EPfP EPot ERos GGar LAma MBri SPer
juncifolius	see *N. assoanus*
'June Lake' (2)	CQua IRhd
'Kabani' (9)	CQua
'Kalimna' (1)	CQua
'Kamau' (9)	IRhd
'Kamms' (1)	CQua
'Kamura' (2)	CQua
'Kanchenjunga' (1)	CQua
'Kathy's Clown' (6)	CQua
'Katie Heath' (5) **new**	EBrs LRHS
'Katrina Rea' (6) **new**	CQua
'Kaydee' (6) Υ^{H4}	CQua IRhd NMin
'Kea' (6)	CQua
'Keats' (4)	CQua
'Kebaya' (2)	CQua
'Kelly Bray' (1) **new**	CQua
'Kenellis' (10)	CBgR CQua EBrs EPot GEdr MSte
'Kernow' (2)	CQua
'Kidling' (7)	CQua EBrs ECho
'Killara' (8)	CQua
'Killearnan' (9)	CQua
'Killigrew' (2)	CQua
'Killivose' (3)	CQua
'Kiltonga' (2)	IRhd
'Kilworth' (2)	CQua EFam
'Kimmeridge' (3)	CQua
'King Alfred' (1)	CQua EPfP SPer
'King Size' (11a)	LRHS
'Kinglet' (7)	CQua
'King's Grove' (1) Υ^{H4}	CQua
'Kings Pipe' (2)	CQua
'Kingscourt' (1) Υ^{H4}	CQua
'Kissproof' (2)	EBla EBrs
'Kit Hill' (7)	CQua CTca
'Kitten' (6)	CQua
'Kitty' (6)	ERos
'Kiwi Magic' (4)	CQua IRhd
'Kiwi Solstice' (4)	CQua
'Kiwi Sunset' (4)	CQua
'Knocklayde' (3)	CQua
'Knowing Look' (3)	IRhd
'Kokopelli' (7) Υ^{H4}	CQua EBrs NMin
'Korora Bay' (1)	IRhd
'La Argentina' (2)	EFam
'La Riante' (3)	CQua
'Ladies' Choice' (7)	IRhd
'Ladies' Favorite' (7)	IRhd
'Lady Ann' (2)	IRhd
'Lady Be Good' (2)	CQua
'Lady Eve' (11a)	IRhd
'Lady Margaret Boscawen' (2)	CQua
'Lady Serena' (9)	CQua
'Lake Tahoe' (2)	IRhd
'Lalique' (3)	CQua
'Lamanva' (2)	CQua
'Lamlash' (2)	IRhd
'Lancaster' (3)	CQua
'Langarth' (11a)	CQua
'Lapwing' (5)	ERos IRhd
'Larkelly' (6)	ERos
'Larkhill' (2)	CQua
'Larkwhistle' (6) Υ^{H4}	EBrs ERos LAma LRHS
'Las Vegas' (1)	EBrs
'Latchley' (2)	CQua CTca
'Lauren' (3)	IRhd
'Lavender Lass' (6)	CQua
'Lavender Mist' (2) **new**	CQua
'Lazy River' (1) **new**	CQua
'Leading Light' (2)	CQua
'Lee Moor' (1)	CQua CTca
'Lemon Beauty' (11b)	CQua CTca EBla SPer
'Lemon Drops' (5) Υ^{H4}	CQua EBrs EPot ERos LRHS MSte SPhx
'Lemon Grey' (3)	IRhd
'Lemon Silk' (6)	CMea CQua EBrs ECho NMin SPhx
'Lemon Snow' (2)	IRhd
'Lemonade' (3)	CQua
'Lennymore' (2)	CQua IRhd
'Lewis George' (1)	CQua
'Libby' (2)	IRhd
'Liberty Bells' (5)	CQua EBrs LAma MBri
'Liebeslied' (3)	CQua
'Life' (7)	CQua
'Lighthouse' (3)	CQua

'Lighthouse Reef' (1)	CQua IRhd
'Lilac Charm' (6)	CQua IRhd
'Lilac Mist' (2)	CQua
'Lilliput' ambig.	CQua
'Limbo' (2)	CQua IRhd
'Limehurst' (2)	CQua
'Limpopo' (3)	IRhd
'Lindsay Joy' (2)	CQua
'Lingerie' (4) ♀H4	NZep
'Lintie' (7)	CQua EBrs ERos LEdu
'Lisbarnett' (3)	IRhd
'Lisnamulligan' (3)	IRhd
'Lisnaruddy' (3)	IRhd
'Little Beauty' (1) ♀H4	CBgR CQua EBrs ECho EPot ERos LAma MBrN NMin
'Little Dancer' (1)	CQua
'Little Gem' (1) ♀H4	CAvo CBgR CFFs CQua EBrs LAma LRHS SPer
'Little Jewel' (3)	CQua
'Little Karoo' (3)	IRhd
'Little Rosie' (2)	IRhd
'Little Rusky' (7)	CQua NMin
'Little Sentry' (7)	CQua
'Little Soldier' (10)	CQua
'Little Spell' (1)	CQua EBrs
'Little Witch' (6)	CQua EBrs ECho EPot ERos LAma WShi
'Littlefield' (7)	CQua
'Liverpool Festival' (2)	CQua
'Lobularis'	see *N. pseudonarcissus* 'Lobularis'
lobularis misapplied	see *N. nanus*
lobularis Schultes	see *N. obvallaris*
'Loch Alsh' (3)	CQua IRhd
'Loch Assynt' (3)	CQua
'Loch Brora' (2)	CQua
'Loch Coire' (3)	CQua
'Loch Fada' (2)	CQua
'Loch Hope' (2)	CQua
'Loch Leven' (2)	CQua
'Loch Lundie' (2)	CQua
'Loch Maberry' (2)	CQua
'Loch Naver' (2)	CQua
'Loch Owskeich' (2) ♀H4 **new**	CQua
'Loch Stac' (2)	CQua
'Logan Rock' (7)	CQua
'Lordship' (1)	CQua
'Lorikeet' (1)	CQua NZep
'Lothario' (2)	LAma MBri
'Lough Gowna' (1)	IRhd
'Lough Ryan' (1)	IRhd
'Loveny' (2)	CQua
'Lubaantun' (1)	CQua
'Lucifer' (2)	CAvo CQua WShi
'Lucky Chance' (11a)	IRhd
'Lundy Light' (2)	CQua
'Lynher' (2) **new**	CQua
'Lyrebird' (3)	CQua
'Lyric' (9)	CQua
'Lysander' (2)	CQua
x ***macleayi*** (13)	CQua NMin
'Madam Speaker' (4)	CQua
'Magician' (2)	IRhd NZep
'Magna Carta' (2)	CQua
'Magnet' (1)	LAma
'Magnificence' (1)	CQua
'Mai's Family' (6)	CQua
'Majarde' (2)	EFam
'Majestic Star' (1)	CQua
'Mallee' (11a)	IRhd
'Malvern City' (1) **new**	CQua LRHS
'Mamma Mia' (4) **new**	IRhd
'Manaccan' (1)	CQua
'Mangaweka' (6)	CQua
'Manly' (4) ♀H4	CQua LRHS

'Mantle' (2)	CQua
'Marieke' (1) **new**	EBrs
'Marilyn Anne' (2)	CQua
'Marjorie Hine' (2)	CQua
'Marjorie Treveal' (4)	CQua
'Marlborough' (2)	CQua
'Marlborough Freya' (2)	CQua
'Marshfire' (2)	CQua
'Martha Washington' (8)	CQua
'Martinette' (8)	CQua EBrs MBri
'Martinsville' (8)	CQua
marvieri	see *N. rupicola* subsp. *marvieri*
'Mary Copeland' (4)	CQua LAma
'Mary Kate' (2)	CQua IRhd
'Mary Lou' (6)	IRhd
'Mary Veronica' (3)	CQua
'Marzo' (7)	CQua IRhd
'Matador' (8)	CQua IRhd
'Mawla' (1)	CQua
'Max' (11a)	CQua
'Maximus' ambig.	CQua
'Maya Dynasty' (2)	CQua
'Mayan Gold' (1)	IRhd
'Mazzard' (4)	CQua
'Media Girl' (2)	IRhd
x ***medioluteus*** (13)	CQua NMin
'Melancholy' (1)	CQua
'Melbury' (2)	CQua
'Meldrum' (1)	CQua
'Memento' (1)	CQua
'Menabilly' (4)	CQua
'Men-an-Tol' (2)	CQua
'Menehay' (11a) ♀H4	CQua IRhd
'Merida' (2)	IRhd
'Merlin' (3) ♀H4	CQua LAma
'Merry Bells' (5)	CQua
'Merrymeet' (4)	CQua
'Mersing' (3) **new**	CQua
'Merthan' (9)	CQua
'Midas Touch' (1)	CQua
'Midget'	CAvo CBgR CFFs CQua CStu ECho EPot ERos GKev LAma
'Mike Pollock' (8)	CQua
'Millennium Sunrise' (2)	CQua
'Millennium Sunset' (2)	CQua
'Millgreen' (1)	LRHS
'Milly's Magic' (2)	CQua
'Minicycla' (6)	EBrs GCrs MSSP
minimus misapplied	see *N. asturiensis*
'Minnow' (8) ♀H3	CAvo CFFs CMea CQua EBrs ECho EPfP ERos GKev LAma LRHS MBri NBir NBlu SPer SPhx WLin
minor (13) ♀H4	CQua EBrs ECha ECho EPot GCrs LAma LRHS SPhx WCot WShi
– var. ***pumilus*** 'Plenus'	see *N.* 'Rip van Winkle'
– Ulster form	IBlr MSSP
'Mint Julep' (3) ♀ **new**	EBrs LRHS
'Minute Waltz' (6)	CQua
'Miss Klein' **new**	NMin
'Miss Muffitt' (1)	CBgR CQua
'Mission Bells' (5) ♀H4	CQua IRhd
'Mission Impossible' (11a)	CQua
'Misty Dawn' (3)	IRhd
'Misty Glen' (2) ♀H4	CQua
'Misty Moon' (3)	CQua
'Mite' (6) ♀H4	CBgR CMea CQua EPot ERos LAma NMin
'Mithrel' (11a)	CQua
'Mitylene' (2)	CQua
'Mitzy'	NMin
'Modern Art' (2)	EBrs
'Mondragon' (11a)	CQua EBrs EFam
'Mongleath' (2)	CQua
'Monks Wood' (1)	CQua
'Monksilver' (3)	CQua

	'Montclair' (2)	CQua
	'Montego' (3)	CQua
	'Moon Dream' (1)	CQua
	'Moon Ranger' (3)	CQua IRhd
	'Moon Rhythm' (4)	IRhd
	'Moon Shadow' (3)	CQua
	'Moon Tide' (3)	IRhd
	'Moon Valley' (2)	IRhd
	'Moonstruck' (1)	CQua
	'Morab' (1) **new**	CQua
	'Moralee' (4)	IRhd
	'Morvah Lady' (5) **new**	CQua
§	***moschatus*** (13) $\mathbb{Y}^{H4}$	CHHB CQua EBrs ECho EPot LAma LRHS NMin WCot WShi
	- 'Cernuus Plenus' (4)	CAvo CQua
	'Mother Catherine Grullemans' (2)	EFam
	'Motmot'	CQua
	'Mount Fuji' (2)	CQua
	'Mount Hood' (1) $\mathbb{Y}^{H4}$	EBrs EPfP LAma LRHS NBir SPer
	'Mount Rainier' (1)	CQua
	'Movie Star' (2)	IRhd
	'Mowser' (7)	CQua
	'Mr Julian' (6)	CQua
	'Mrs Langtry' (3)	CQua WShi
	'Mrs R.O. Backhouse' (2)	CQua EBla WShi
	'Mullion' (3)	CQua
	'Mulroy Bay' (1)	CQua IRhd
	'Multnomah' (2) **new**	LRHS
	'Murlough' (9)	CQua
	'Muscadet' (2)	CQua
	'My Sunshine' (2)	CQua
	'Mystic' (3) **new**	CQua
	'Naivasha' (2)	IRhd
	'Namraj' (2)	CQua
	'Nancegollan' (7)	CQua
	'Nangiles' (4)	CQua
	'Nanpee' (7)	CQua
	'Nansidwell' (2)	CQua
	'Nanstallon' (1)	CQua
§	***nanus***	CWCL
	- 'Midget' (1) **new**	EBrs
	'Nederburg' (1)	IRhd
	'Nelly' ambig.	CQua
	'Nether Barr' (2)	IRhd
§	***nevadensis*** (13)	ERos SBla
	'New Hope' (3)	CQua
	'New Life' (3)	CQua
	'New Penny' (3)	CQua IRhd
	'New-baby' (7)	CQua EBrs EPfP LRHS
	'Newcastle' (1)	CQua
	'Newcomer' (3)	CQua
	'Night Music' (4)	CQua
	'Nightcap' (1)	CQua
	'Niveth' (5)	CQua
	nobilis var. ***nobilis*** (13)	NMin
	'Nonchalant' (3)	CQua IRhd
	'Norma Jean' (2)	CQua
	'Nor-nor' (2)	ERos
	'North Rim' (2)	CQua
	'Northern Sceptre' (2)	IRhd
	'Noss Mayo' (6)	CQua
	'Notre Dame' (2) $\mathbb{Y}^{H4}$	CQua IRhd
	'Numen Rose' (2)	IRhd
	Nylon Group (10)	EBrs EPot GEdr
	- yellow (10)	ECho
	'Oadby' (1)	CQua
	'Obdam' (4)	EBla EBrs LRHS SPer
	'Obelisk' (11a)	CQua
	obesus (13)	EBrs ERos WCot
	'Obsession' (2)	CQua
§	***obvallaris*** (13) $\mathbb{Y}^{H4}$	CArn CAvo CFFs CQua CTca EBrs ECho EPot ERos IHer LRHS SBch SGar SMeo SPer WHer WShi
	'Ocarino' (4)	CQua

	'Ocean Blue' (2)	IRhd
	'Odd Job'	CQua
	x ***odorus*** (13)	EBrs IHer LRHS WShi
§	- 'Double Campernelle' (4)	CQua ECho SBch SPer WShi
	- 'Rugulosus'	see *N.* 'Rugulosus'
	'Oecumene' (11a)	CQua
	old pheasant's eye	see *N. poeticus* var. *recurvus*
	'Orange Monarch' (2)	EFam
	'Orange Queen' (3)	EBrs LRHS
	'Orange Walk' (3)	CQua IRhd
	'Orangery' (11a)	CTca EBla EBrs EFam LAma
	'Orchard Place' (3)	CQua
	'Oregon Pioneer' (2)	IRhd
	'Orkney' (2) **new**	CQua
	'Ormeau' (2) $\mathbb{Y}^{H4}$	CQua
	'Oryx' (7) $\mathbb{Y}^{H4}$	CQua IRhd
	'Osmington' (2)	CQua
	'Ouma' (1)	CQua
	'Outline' (2)	IRhd
	'Ouzel' (6)	CQua
	'Oykel' (3)	CQua
	'Oz' (12)	CQua ERos
	pachybolbus **new**	EBrs
	'Pacific Coast' (8) $\mathbb{Y}^{H4}$	CQua ECho LAma NMin
	'Pacific Mist' (11a)	CQua
	'Pacific Princess' (3)	CQua
	'Pacific Rim' (2)	IRhd
	'Painted Desert' (3)	CQua
	'Pale Sunlight' (2)	CQua
§	***pallidiflorus*** (13)	ECha
	'Palmares' (11a)	CQua
	'Pamela Hubble' (2)	CQua
	'Pampaluna' (11a)	CQua
	'Panache' (1)	CQua
	'Panorama Pink' (3)	IRhd
	'Paper White'	see *N. papyraceus*
	'Paper White Grandiflorus' (8)	CQua MBri SPer
	'Papillon Blanc' (11b)	EBrs
	'Papua' (4) $\mathbb{Y}^{H4}$	CQua
§	***papyraceus*** (13)	CQua CStu LAma
	- subsp. ***panizzianus***	CQua
	'Paradigm' (4)	IRhd
	'Parisienne' (11a)	EBla
	'Park Springs' (3)	CQua
	'Parkdene' (2)	CQua
	'Party Time' (2)	IRhd
	'Passionale' (2) $\mathbb{Y}^{H4}$	CQua LAma NBir
	'Pastiche' (2)	CQua
	'Patabundy' (2)	CQua
	'Pathos' (3)	IRhd
	'Patois' (9)	CQua IRhd
	'Patrick Hacket' (1) **new**	CQua
	'Pay Day' (1)	CQua
	'Peach Prince' (4)	CQua
	'Peacock' (2)	IRhd
	'Pearl Wedding' (3)	CQua
	'Pearlax'	see *N.* 'Perlax'
	'Pearlshell' (11a)	CQua
	'Peeping Tom' (6) $\mathbb{Y}^{H4}$	EBrs ECho ERos LAma SPer SRms
	'Peggy's Gift' (3)	IRhd
	'Pemboa'	CQua
	'Pencrebar' (4)	CAvo CQua CTca EBrs EPot ERos LAma NMin NMyG SPer WShi
	'Pend Oreille' (3)	CQua
	'Pengarth' (2)	CQua
	'Penjerrick' (9)	CQua
	'Penkivel' (2) $\mathbb{Y}$	CQua
	'Pennance Mill' (2)	CQua
	'Pennine Way' (1)	CQua
	'Pennyfield' (2)	CQua
	'Penpol' (7)	CQua
	'Penril' (6)	CBgR CQua ERos
	'Penstraze' (7)	CQua
	'Pentewan' (2) **new**	CQua LRHS

	Name	Suppliers
	'Pentille' (1)	CQua
	'Pentire' (11a)	CQua
	'Penvale'	CQua
	'Peppercorn' (6)	CQua
	'Percuil' (6)	CQua
	'Perdredda' (3)	CQua
	'Perimeter' (3)	CQua
	'Peripheral Pink' (2)	CQua
§	'Perlax' (11a)	CQua
	'Permissive' (2)	IRhd
	'Personable' (2)	CQua
	'Petanca' **new**	IRhd
	'Petillant' (3) **new**	EBrs
	'Petit Four' (4)	EBla EBrs LAma
	'Petrel' (5)	CQua EBrs EPot LEdu MSte SPer SPhx WLin
	'Phalarope' (6)	CQua
	'Phantom' (11a)	CQua
	'Phil's Gift' (1)	CQua
	'Phinda' (2)	IRhd
	'Phoenician' (2)	CQua
	'Picoblanco' (2)	CQua NMin
	'Pigeon' (2)	CQua
	'Pincambo' (2)	IRhd
	'Pineapple Prince' (2) 🏆H4	CQua
	'Pink Angel' (7)	CQua EBrs
	'Pink Champagne' (4)	CQua EBrs
	'Pink Charm' (2)	EBrs
	'Pink Evening' (2)	CQua
	'Pink Formal' (11a)	CQua
	'Pink Gilt' (2)	IRhd
	'Pink Glacier' (11a)	CQua
	'Pink Holly' (11a)	CQua
	'Pink Ice' (2)	CQua
	'Pink Pageant' (4)	CQua IRhd
	'Pink Paradise' (4)	CQua EBrs IRhd
	'Pink Perry' (2)	IRhd
	'Pink Sapphire' (2)	CQua
	'Pink Silk' (1)	CQua IRhd NZep
	'Pink Smiles' (2)	SPer
	'Pink Surprise' (2)	CQua
	'Pink Tango' (11a)	CQua
	'Pipe Major' (2)	CQua EPfP SPer
	'Pipers Barn' (7)	CQua
	'Piper's End' (3)	CQua
	'Pipestone' (2)	CQua
	'Pipit' (7) 🏆H4	CAvo CFFs CQua CTca EBrs ECho EPfP ERos GKev LAma LEdu MBri MNrw NBir SPer SPhx WShi
	'Piraeus' (4)	IRhd
	'Pismo Beach' (2)	CQua
	'Pistachio' (1) **new**	EBrs
	'Pitchroy' (2)	CQua
	'Pitt's Diamond' (3) **new**	CQua
	'Pixie's Sister' (7) 🏆H4	CQua NMin
	poeticus (13)	CAvo LRHS WHer
§	- var. ***hellenicus*** (13)	CQua
	- old pheasant's eye	see *N. poeticus* var. *recurvus*
	- var. ***physaloides*** (13)	CHHB CQua EBrs ECho SPhx
N	- 'Plenus' ambig. (4)	CQua EBrs EPot GQui WShi
	- 'Praecox' (3)	CQua
§	- var. ***recurvus*** (13) 🏆H4	CArn CFFs CMea CQua CTca EBrs ECGP ECho EPfP EPot IHer LAma NBir SMeo SPer WShi
	'Poet's Way' (9)	CQua
	'Pol Crocan' (2)	CQua IRhd
	'Pol Dornie' (2)	CQua
	'Pol Voulin' (2)	CQua IRhd
	'Polar Ice' (3)	CMea EBrs LAma
	'Polgooth' (2)	CQua
	'Polly's Pearl' (8)	CQua
	'Polruan'	CQua
	'Poltreen'	CQua
	'Polwheveral' (2)	CQua
	'Pooka' (3)	IRhd
	'Poppy's Choice' (4)	CQua
	'Pops Legacy' (1)	CQua IRhd
	'Port Patrick' (3)	IRhd
	'Port William' (3)	IRhd
	'Porthchapel' (7)	CQua
	'Portloe Bay' (3)	CQua
	'Portrush' (3)	CQua
	'Potential' (1)	CQua
	'Powerstock' (2)	IRhd
	'Prairie Fire' (3)	CQua IRhd
	'Preamble' (1)	CQua
I	'Precocious' (2) 🏆H4	CQua LRHS
	'Premiere' (2)	CQua
	'Presidential Pink' (2)	CQua
	'Pretty Baby' (3)	CQua
	'Primrose Beauty' (4)	CQua
	'Princeps' (1)	CQua
	'Princess Zaide' (3)	CQua
	'Princeton' (3)	CQua
	'Prism' (2)	CQua
	'Problem Child' **new**	IRhd
	'Probus' (1)	CQua
	'Professor Einstein' (2)	EBrs EPfP
	'Prologue' (1)	CQua
	'Prototype' (6)	IRhd
	'Proud Fellow' (1)	IRhd
	'Prussia Cove' (2) **new**	CQua
	pseudonarcissus (13) 🏆H4	CQua CTca EBrs LAma SPhx WHer WShi
	- subsp. ***gayi***	see *N. gayi*
§	- 'Lobularis'	CArn CAvo CQua EBrs ECho EPot ERos MBri SPer
	- subsp. ***moschatus***	see *N. moschatus*
	- subsp. ***nevadensis***	see *N. nevadensis*
	- subsp. ***nobilis***	see *N. nobilis*
	- subsp. ***pallidiflorus***	see *N. pallidiflorus*
§	- subsp. ***pseudonarcissus*** var. ***humilis*** (13)	EBrs ECho
	'Pueblo' (7)	EBrs ERos LRHS SPer WShi
	'Pulsar' (2)	IRhd
	pumilus (13)	EBrs ECho EPot ERos LRHS
	'Punchline' (7) 🏆	CQua
	'Puppet' (5)	CQua
	'Purbeck' (3) 🏆H4	CQua IRhd
	'Quail' (7) 🏆H4	CPBP CQua CTca EBrs EPfP ERos LAma LRHS LSou MBri SPer
	'Quasar' (2) 🏆	CQua NZep
	Queen Anne's double daffodil	see *N.* 'Eystettensis'
	'Queen Juliana' (1)	CQua
	'Queen Mum' (1) **new**	CQua
	'Queen's Guard' (1)	IRhd
	'Quick Step' (7)	CQua IRhd
	'Quiet Hero' (3)	IRhd
	'Quiet Man' (1)	IRhd
	'Quiet Waters' (1)	CQua
	'Quince' (12)	CQua LRHS LSou MSte
	'Radiant Gem' (8)	CQua
	radiiflorus (13) **new**	NMin
	'Radjel' (4)	CQua
	'Rainbow' (2) 🏆H4	CQua SPer
	'Rame Head' (1)	CQua
	'Rameses' (2)	CQua
	'Rapture' (6) 🏆H4	CQua EBrs IRhd NMin
	'Rashee' (1)	CQua
	'Raspberry Ring' (2)	CQua
	'Rathowen Gold' (1) **new**	CQua
	'Ravenhill' (3)	CQua
	'Rebekah' (4)	CQua
	'Recital' (2)	CQua
I	'Red Coat'	CQua
	'Red Era' (3)	CQua
	'Red Reed' (1)	IRhd
	'Red Socks' (6)	CQua

	'Refrain' (2)	CQua
	'Regal Bliss' (2)	CQua
	'Reggae' (6) 🏆H4	CQua EBrs IRhd LRHS
	'Rembrandt' (1)	CQua
	'Rendezvous Caye' (2)	CQua
	'Replete' (4)	CQua EBla EBrs LRHS
	'Reprieve' (3)	CQua
	requienii	see *N. assoanus*
	'Ribald' (2)	IRhd
	'Ridgecrest' (3)	IRhd
	rifanus	see *N. romieuxii* subsp. *romieuxii* var. *rifanus*
*	'Rijnveld's Early Bicolor' **new**	CAvo
	'Rijnveld's Early Sensation' (1) 🏆H4	CAvo CFFs CMea CQua EBrs ECha ERos WCot
	'Rikki' (7)	CQua ERos NMin
	'Rima' (1)	CQua
	'Rimmon' (3)	CQua
	'Ring Fence' (3)	IRhd
	'Ringhaddy' (3)	IRhd
	'Ringing Bells' (5)	CQua
	'Ringleader' (2)	CQua
	'Ringmaster' (2)	CQua
	'Ringmer' (3)	CQua
	'Rio Bravo' (2)	IRhd
	'Rio Gusto' (2)	IRhd
	'Rio Lobo' (2)	IRhd
	'Rio Rondo' (2)	IRhd
	'Rio Rouge' (2)	IRhd
§	'Rip van Winkle' (4)	CAvo CFFs CQua CSWP CTca EBla EBrs EPot ERos IHer LAma LRHS MBri NHol WHal WShi
	'Rippling Waters' (5) 🏆H4	CQua EBrs ECGP EPot ERos LAma
	'Ristin' (1)	CQua
	'Rival' (6)	CQua
	'River Dance' (2)	IRhd
	'River Queen' (2)	CQua IRhd
	'Rockall' (3)	CQua
	'Rockery White' (1) **new**	NMin
	'Roger' (6)	CQua
	'Romance' (2) 🏆H4	EBrs LAma
§	'Romanus' (4)	CQua CTca
§	***romieuxii*** (13) 🏆H2-3	CPBP EPot ERos ITim LRHS SBch SChr SCnR WAbe WCot
	- JCA 805	EPot
	- SF 370	WCot
	- subsp. ***albidus*** (13)	ECho WCot
§	- - var. ***zaianicus*** (13)	EBrs ECho SPhx
	- - SB&L 82	WCot
	- 'Atlas Gold'	SCnR
§	- 'Joy Bishop' ex JCA 805 (10)	EPot ERos SCnR
§	- 'Julia Jane' ex JCA 805 (10)	EBrs ECho EPot ERos GEdr LRHS NMin SCnR SPhx
*	- 'Prolific' (10)	CLyd
	- subsp. ***romieuxii***	EBrs ECho SPhx WCot
§	- - var. ***mesatlanticus*** (13)	CStu ERos
§	- - var. ***rifanus*** (13)	EBrs SPhx
	- - B 8929	WCot
	- 'Treble Chance' (10)	EPot
	'Rosannor Gold' (11a)	CQua
	'Roscarrick' (6)	CQua
	'Rose Gold' (1)	IRhd
	'Rose of May' (4)	CQua WShi
	'Rose of Tralee' (2) **new**	CQua
	'Rose Royale' (2)	CQua
	'Rose Umber' (2)	IRhd
	'Rosemerryn' (2)	CQua
	'Rosemoor Gold' 🏆H4	CQua LRHS
	'Rosevine' (3)	CQua
	'Roseworthy' (2)	EBla ERos
	'Roxton' (4)	IRhd
	'Royal Armour' (1)	LRHS
	'Royal Ballet' (2)	CQua
	'Royal Connection' (8)	CQua
	'Royal Marine' (2)	CQua
	'Royal Princess' (3)	CQua
	'Royal Regiment' (2)	CQua
	'Rubh Mor' (2)	CQua
	'Ruby Rose' (4)	IRhd
	'Ruby Wedding' (2)	IRhd
	'Rubythroat' (2)	CQua
	'Ruddy Rascal' (2)	IRhd
§	'Rugulosus' (7) 🏆H4	CQua EBrs ECho ERos
*	'Rugulosus Flore Pleno' (d)	CHHB EBrs ECho LRHS
	rupicola (13)	CQua CWoo EBrs ERos GCrs MSSP NMen NMin NSla NWCA SCnR
§	- subsp. ***marvieri*** (13) 🏆H2	ERos
§	- subsp. ***watieri*** (13)	CWsd ERos GCrs NMin SPhx
	'Rustom Pasha' (2)	CQua
	'Rytha' (2)	CQua
	'Saberwing' (5)	CQua
	'Sabine Hay' (3)	CQua
	'Sabrosa' (7)	NMin
	'Sailboat' (7) **new**	EBrs LRHS LSou
	'Saint Agnes' (8)	CQua
	'Saint Budock' (1)	CQua
	'Saint Day' (5)	CQua
	'Saint Dilpe' (2)	CQua
	'Saint Keverne' (2) 🏆H4	CQua
	'Saint Keyne' (8)	CQua
	'Saint Patrick's Day' (2)	CQua EBla LAma SPer
	'Saint Peter' (4) **new**	CQua
	'Saint Piran' (7)	CQua
	'Salakee' (2)	CQua
	'Salcey Forest' (1)	CQua
	'Salmon Trout' (2)	CQua
	'Salome' (2) 🏆H4	CQua EBla EBrs EPfP LAma LRHS NBir
	'Salute' (2)	CQua
	'Samantha' (4)	CQua
	'Samba' (5)	ERos
	'Sancerre' (11a)	CQua
	'Sandycove' (2)	CQua IRhd
	'Santa Claus' (4)	CQua
	'Sargeant's Caye' (1)	CQua
	'Satsuma' (1)	CQua
	'Saturn' (3)	CQua
	'Saturnalia' **new**	IRhd
	'Savoir Faire' (2)	IRhd
	scaberulus (13)	CStu EPot ERos
	'Scarlet Chord' (2)	CQua
	'Scarlet Elegance' (2)	CQua
	'Scarlet Gem' (8)	NHol
	'Scarlett O'Hara' (2)	CQua
	'Scented Breeze' (2)	IRhd
	'Scilly Spring' (8)	CAvo
	'Scilly White' (8)	CQua
	'Scorrier' (2)	CQua
	'Scrumpy' (2)	CQua
	'Sea Dream' (3)	CQua
	'Sea Green' (9)	CQua
	'Sea Legend' (2)	CQua
	'Sea Princess' (3)	CQua
	'Sea Shanty' (2)	IRhd
	'Seagull' (3)	CAvo CQua ECho LAma WShi
	'Sealing Wax' (2)	CQua
	'Segovia' (3) 🏆H4	CMea CQua EBla EBrs EPot ERos LAma LRHS NHol NMin SCnR SPer
	'Selma Lagerlöf' (2)	EFam
	'Sempre Avanti' (2)	LAma MBri
	'Seraglio' (3)	CQua
	'Serena Beach' (4)	IRhd
	'Serena Lodge' (4) 🏆H4	CQua IRhd
	serotinus (13)	EBrs ECho EPot
	'Sextant' (6)	CQua
	'Shangani' (2)	IRhd

'Sheelagh Rowan' (2)	CQua IRhd
'Sheer Joy' (6)	IRhd
'Sheleg' (8) **new**	EBrs
'Shepherd's Hey' (7)	CQua
'Sherborne' (4) 🏆	CQua
'Sherpa' (1)	IRhd
'Sheviock' (2)	CQua
'Shindig' (2)	IRhd
'Shining Light' (2)	CQua
'Shortcake' (2)	CQua
'Shrimp Boat' (11a)	IRhd
'Siam' (2)	EFam
'Sidley' (3)	CQua IRhd
'Signorina' (2)	IRhd
'Silent Valley' (1) 🏆H4	CQua
'Silk Cut' (2)	CQua
'Silkwood' (3)	CQua
'Silver Bells' (5)	CQua IRhd
'Silver Chimes' (8)	CAvo CFFs CQua CTca EBrs ECho EPfP ERos LAma NBir
'Silver Convention' (1)	CQua
'Silver Crystal' (3)	IRhd
'Silver Kiwi' (2)	CQua
'Silver Minx' (1)	CQua
'Silver Plate' (11a)	CQua
'Silver Shell' (11a)	CQua
'Silver Standard' (2)	CQua
'Silver Surf' (2)	CQua IRhd
'Silversmith' (2)	CQua
'Silverthorne' (3)	CQua
'Silverwood' (3)	CQua IRhd
'Singing Pub' (3)	IRhd
'Sinopel' (3)	EBrs LAma
'Sir Samuel' (2)	CQua
'Sir Watkin' (2)	CAvo CQua
'Sir Winston Churchill' (4) 🏆H4	CQua EPfP LAma SPer
'Skerry' (2)	CQua
'Skilliwidden' (2) 🏆	CQua
'Skywalker' (2)	IRhd
'Slieveboy' (1)	CQua
'Slipstream' (6)	IRhd
'Small Fry' (1)	CQua
'Small Talk' (1)	CQua NMin
'Smiling Maestro' (2) **new**	CQua
'Smiling Twin' (11a) **new**	EBrs
'Smokey Bear' (4)	CQua
'Smooth Sails' (3)	CQua
'Snipe' (6) **new**	CQua NMin
'Snoopie' (6)	CQua
'Snowcrest' (3)	CQua
'Snowshill' (2)	CQua
'Soft Focus' (2)	IRhd
'Solar System' (3)	IRhd
'Solar Tan' (3)	CQua IRhd
'Solera Reserva' **new**	IRhd
'Solferique' (2)	CQua
'Soloist' (2)	IRhd
'Sonata' (9)	CQua
'Songket' (2)	CQua
'Soprano' (2)	CQua IRhd
'Sorcerer' (3)	CQua
'South Street' (2)	CQua
'Spaniards Inn' (4)	CQua CTca
'Sparkling Tarts' (8)	CQua
'Sparnon' (11a)	CQua
'Sparrow' (6)	CQua
'Special Envoy' (2) 🏆H4	CQua
'Speenogue' (1)	IRhd
'Spellbinder' (1) 🏆H4	CQua EFam MBri
'Sperrin Gold' (1)	IRhd
'Spin Doctor' (3)	IRhd
'Spindletop' (3) 🏆H4	IRhd
'Spirit of Rame' (3)	CQua
'Split Image' (2)	IRhd
'Split Vote' (11a)	IRhd
'Sportsman' (2)	CQua
'Spring Dawn' (2)	LCro LRHS LSou SPer
'Spring Joy'	ERos
'Spring Morn' (2)	IRhd
'Spring Pride' (2) **new**	LRHS
'Stainless' (2)	EBrs MSte
'Stann Creek' (1)	CQua
'Stanway' (3)	CQua IRhd
'Star Glow' (2)	CQua
'Star Quality' (3)	IRhd
'Starfire' (7)	CQua
'State Express' (2)	CQua
'Steenbok' (3)	IRhd
'Stella' (2)	WShi
'Stenalees' (6) **new**	CQua
'Step Forward' (7)	ERos
'Stilton' (9)	CQua
'Stinger' (2)	CQua
'Stint' (5) 🏆H4	CQua
'Stocken' (7)	CQua ERos
'Stoke Charity' (2)	CQua
'Stoke Doyle' (2)	CQua
'Stormy Weather' (1)	CQua
'Stratosphere' (7) 🏆H4	CQua
'Strines' (2)	CQua
'Suave' (3)	CQua
'Sugar and Spice' (3)	CQua
'Sugar Bird' (2)	IRhd
'Sugar Cups' (8)	CQua
'Sugar Loaf' (4)	CQua
'Sugarbush' (7)	EBrs
'Suisgill' (4)	CQua
§ 'Sulphur Phoenix' (4)	CQua WShi
'Summer Solstice' (3)	IRhd
'Sun Disc' (7) 🏆H4	CMea CQua EBrs ECho EPot ERos LAma LSou MBri NMin SPer
'Sunday Chimes' (5)	CQua
'Sundial' (7)	CQua EBrs ECho EPot ERos LAma LRHS
'Sunrise' (3)	CQua
'Sunstroke' (2)	CQua
'Suntory' (3)	CQua
'Suntrap' (2)	IRhd
'Surfside' (6) 🏆H4	CQua EBrs ERos LRHS
'Surprise Packet' **new**	IRhd
'Surrey' (2)	CQua
'Suzie Dee' (6)	IRhd
'Suzie's Sister' (6)	IRhd
'Suzy' (7) 🏆H4	LAma
'Swaledale' (2)	CQua
'Swallow' (6) **new**	CQua
'Swallow Wing' (6)	IRhd
'Swanpool' (3)	CQua
'Swanvale' (1)	CQua
'Swedish Fjord' (2)	CQua
'Sweet Blanche' (7)	CQua
'Sweet Harmony' (2)	EBrs
'Sweet Lorraine' (2)	CQua
'Sweet Sue' (3)	CQua
'Sweetness' (7) 🏆H4	CAvo CFFs CMea CQua CTca EBrs LAma SPer WShi
'Swing Wing' (6)	CQua
'Sydling' (5)	CQua
I 'Sylph' (1)	CQua
'Tahiti' (4) 🏆H4	CQua EBrs EPfP LAma
'Tamar Fire' (4) 🏆H4	CQua CTca
'Tamar Lad' (2)	CQua CTca
'Tamar Lass' (3)	CQua CTca
'Tamar Snow' (2)	CQua
'Tamara' (2)	CQua SPer
'Tangent' (2)	CQua
'Tarlatan' (10)	ERos
'Tasgem' (4)	CQua
'Taslass' (4)	CQua

'Tater-Du' (5)	CQua
tazetta (13) **new**	EBrs
§ - subsp. ***lacticolor*** (13)	CBgR CQua EBrs LRHS
§ - - 'Grand Monarque' (8)	CQua
* - var. ***odoratus***	CQua
- subsp. ***papyraceus***	see *N. papyraceus*
'Teal' (1)	CQua
'Tehidy' (3)	CQua
§ 'Telamonius Plenus' (4)	CAvo CQua IGor WCot WShi
'Temba' **new**	IRhd
'Temple Cloud' (4)	IRhd
tenuifolius	see *N. bulbocodium* subsp. *bulbocodium* var. *tenuifolius*
'Terracotta' (2)	CQua IRhd
'Terrapin' (3)	IRhd
'Tête-à-tête' (12) ♀H4	CAvo CFFs CHar CMea CQua CTca EBrs EPfP EPot ERos LAma LRHS LSou MBri MNHC NBlu SPer WHal
'Thalia' (5)	CAvo CFFs CMea CQua CTca EBrs EPfP ERos GKev LAma LEdu LRHS MBri MSte NBir NHol SPer WShi
'The Alliance' (6) ♀	CQua
'The Grange' (1)	CQua
'The Knave' (6)	CQua
'Thistin' (1)	IRhd
'Thoresby' (3)	CQua
'Thoughtful' (5)	CQua
'Tibet' (2)	CQua
'Tideford' (2)	CQua
'Tidy Talk' **new**	IRhd
'Tiercel' (1)	CQua
'Tiffany Jade' (3)	CQua
'Tiger Moth' (6)	CQua
'Timolin' (3)	CQua
'Tinderbox' (2)	IRhd
'Tiritomba' (11a)	CQua
'Tittle-tattle' (7)	CQua
'Toby' (2)	ERos
'Toby the First' (6)	CQua EBrs
'Tommora Gold' (2)	CQua
'Tommy White' (2)	CQua
'Top Hit' (11a)	CQua
'Topolino' (1) ♀H4	CAvo CFFs CQua EBrs EPot LAma SGar
'Torianne' (2)	CQua
'Torridon' (2)	CQua
'Toscanini' (2)	EFam
'Toto' (12) ♀H4	CFFs CQua LRHS MBri
'Tracey' (6) ♀H4	CQua EBrs LAma
'Treasure Chest' (1) **new**	IRhd
'Trebah' (2) ♀H4	CQua
'Treble Two' (7)	CQua
'Trecara' (3)	CQua
'Trefusis' (1)	CQua
'Trehane' (6)	CQua
'Trelawney Gold' (2)	CQua
'Trelissick'	CQua
'Tremough Dale' (11a) **new**	CQua
'Trena' (6) ♀H4	CBgR CQua EBrs NMin
'Tresamble' (5)	CBgR CMea CQua EBrs LAma
'Trevaunance' (6)	CQua
'Treverva' (6)	CQua
'Treviddo' (2)	CQua
'Trevithian' (7) ♀H4	CQua EBla EBrs GGar LAma WLin
'Trewarvas' (2)	CQua
'Trewirgie' (6)	CQua
'Trewoon' (4) **new**	CQua
triandrus var. ***albus***	see *N. triandrus* subsp. *triandrus* var. *triandrus*
§ - subsp. ***triandrus*** var. ***concolor*** (13)	EBrs ECho
§ - - var. ***triandrus*** (13)	CWCL EBrs ECho SPhx
'Tricollet' (11a)	EBrs
'Trident' (3)	CQua

'Tripartite' (11a) ♀H4	CQua EBrs NMin NZep
'Triple Crown' (3) ♀H4	CQua IRhd
'Tristram' (2)	CQua
'Tropic Isle' (4)	CQua
'Tropical Heat' (2)	IRhd
'Trousseau' (1)	CQua
'Troutbeck' (3)	CQua
'Tru' (3)	CQua
'Trueblood' (3)	IRhd
'Trumpet Warrior' (1) ♀H4	CQua IRhd
'Tryst' (2)	CQua
'Tudor Minstrel' (2)	CQua
'Tuesday's Child' (5) ♀H4	CQua ERos
'Tullynagee' (3)	IRhd
'Turncoat' (6)	CQua
'Tutankhamun' (2)	CQua
'Tweeny' (2)	CQua
'Twink' (4)	CQua
'Tyee' (2)	CQua
'Tyrara' **new**	CQua
'Tyrian Rose' (2)	CQua IRhd
'Tyrone Gold' (1) ♀H4	CQua IRhd
'Tyrree' (1)	IRhd
'Ulster Bank' (3)	CQua
'Ulster Bride' (4)	CQua
'Uncle Duncan' (1)	CQua IRhd
'Unique' (4) ♀H4	CQua EBla LAma
'Unsurpassable' (1)	CQua LAma
'Upalong' (12)	CQua
'Upshot' (3)	CQua
'Urchin' (2)	IRhd
'Utiku' (6)	CQua
'Val d'Incles' (3)	CQua IRhd
'Valdrome' (11a)	CQua EBla
'Valinor' (2)	CQua
'Van Sion'	see *N.* 'Telamonius Plenus'
'Vanellus' (11a)	IRhd
'Veneration' (1)	CQua
'Verdin' (7)	CQua
'Verger' (3)	LAma MBri
'Vernal Prince' (3) ♀H4	CQua
'Verona' (3) ♀H4	CQua
'Verran Rose' (2)	IRhd
'Vers Libre' (9)	CQua
'Vice-President' (2)	CQua
'Vickie Linn' (6)	IRhd
'Victoria' (1) **new**	CQua
'Victorious' (2)	CQua
'Vigil' (1) ♀H4	CQua
'Viking' (1) ♀H4	CQua
'Violetta' (2)	CQua
'Virginia Waters' (3)	CQua
viridiflorus (13)	WCot
'Volcanic Rim' **new**	IRhd
'Vulcan' (2) ♀H4	CQua
'W.P. Milner' (1)	CAvo CFFs CQua EBla EBrs EPfP EPot LAma NMin WLin WShi
'Wadavers' (2)	CQua
'Waif' (6)	CQua
'Waldon Pond' (3)	CQua
'Waldorf Astoria' (4)	CQua IRhd
'Walton' (7)	CQua
'War Dance' (3)	IRhd
'Warbler' (6)	CQua LAma NMin
'Warmington' (3)	CQua
'Watamu' (3)	IRhd
'Waterperry' (7)	EBrs LAma
'Watership Down' (2)	CQua
watieri	see *N. rupicola* subsp. *watieri*
'Wavelength' (3)	IRhd
'Waxwing' (5)	CQua
'Wayward Lad' (3)	IRhd
'Wee Bee' (1)	CQua
'Weena' (2)	CQua

'Welcome' (2)	CQua
'Westward' (4)	CQua
'Whang-hi' (6)	CQua ERos
'Wheal Bush' (4)	CQua
'Wheal Coates' (7) 🏆H4	CQua
'Wheal Honey' (1)	CQua
'Wheal Jane' (2)	CQua
'Wheal Kitty' (7)	CBgR CQua ERos
'Wheatear' (6)	CQua IRhd SPhx
'Whetstone' (1)	CQua
'Whisky Galore' (2)	CQua
'Whisky Mac' (2)	CQua
'White Emperor' (1)	CQua
'White Empress' (1)	CQua
'White Lady' (3)	CAvo CQua LAma WShi
'White Lion' (4) 🏆H4	CQua EFam LAma LRHS NHol
'White Majesty' (1)	CQua
'White Marvel' (4)	CBgR CQua EBrs
'White Medal' (4) **new**	EBrs
'White Nile' (2)	CQua
'White Prince' (1)	CQua
'White Star' (1)	CQua
'Wicklow Hills' (3)	CQua
'Widgeon' (2)	CQua
'Wild Honey' (2) **new**	CQua
'Will Scarlett' (2) **new**	CQua
willkommii (13)	EBrs ERos GCrs NMin
'Wind Song' (2)	CQua
'Winged Victory' (6)	CQua
'Winholm Jenni' (3)	CQua
'Winifred van Graven' (3)	CQua
'Winter Waltz' (6)	CQua
'Witch Doctor' (3)	IRhd
'Witch Hunt' (4)	IRhd
'Wodan' (2)	EFam
'Woodcock' (6)	CQua
'Woodland Prince' (3)	CQua
'Woodland Star' (3)	CQua
'Woodley Vale' (2)	CQua
'Woolsthorpe' (2)	CQua
'Xit' (3)	CAvo CFFs CMea CQua EBrs EPot NMin SCnR SPhx
'Xunantunich' (2)	CQua IRhd
'Yellow Belles' (5)	IRhd
'Yellow Cheerfulness' (4) 🏆H4	EBrs EPfP LAma LRHS MBri
'Yellow Minnow' (8)	CQua
'Yellow River' (1)	LAma
'Yellow Wings' (6) **new**	EBrs ECho
'Yellow Xit' (3)	CQua NMin
'Yoley's Pond' (2) **new**	CQua
'York Minster' (1)	CQua IRhd
'Young American' (1)	CQua
'Young Blood' (2)	CQua IRhd
'Yum-Yum' (3)	IRhd
zaianicus	see *N. romieuxii* subsp. *albidus* var. *zaianicus*
'Zekiah' (1)	CQua
'Zion Canyon' (2)	CQua
'Ziva' (8)	CAvo CFFs EBrs NHol

Nardostachys (*Valerianaceae*)

grandiflora	GPoy

Nardus (*Poaceae*)

stricta	CRWN

Nassauvia (*Asteraceae*)

revoluta **new**	GKev

Nassella (*Poaceae*)

cernua	CBig EBee
lepida	CBig
pulchra	CBig
tenuissima	see *Stipa tenuissima*
trichotoma	CChe CHrt CMea CWsd EMon EPPr EWsh LRHS MCCP SLim SPoG WHal WPGP WRos

Nasturtium (*Brassicaceae*)

'Banana Split' **new**	CCCN
officinale	CPrp EMFW SWat WHer

Nauplius (*Asteraceae*)

sericeus **new**	CSpe

Nautilocalyx (*Gesneriaceae*)

pemphidius	WDib

nectarine see *Prunus persica var. nectarina*

Nectaroscordum (*Alliaceae*)

sp. **new**	WFoF
bivalve	ERos
koelzii **new**	EBee
§ ***siculum***	More than 30 suppliers
§ - subsp. ***bulgaricum***	CTca EBee EBrs ECha EMar EPfP EPot ERos GSki IBlr LBMP LRHS MDun MNrw NBid NGHP SPhx WAbb WBrE WCot WCra WTin
tripedale	EBee WCot

Neillia (*Rosaceae*)

affinis	CDul EBee EPfP LAst LTwo MBri NBid NLar NPro SCoo WBVN WHCG
longiracemosa	see *N. thibetica*
sinensis	CMCN MRav
§ ***thibetica***	CBcs CDul CPLG CPle EBee ECrN ELan EMil EPfP IDee MAsh MLHP MRav NEgg NPri SLim SLon SMad SPer SSpi SSta SWvt WBod WBor WFar WPat WSpi
thyrsiflora var. ***tunkinensis*** HWJ 505	WCru

Nelumbo (*Nelumbonaceae*)

'Baby Doll'	CDWL
'Chawan Basu'	CDWL
'Debbie Gibson'	CDWL
'Momo Botan'	CDWL
'Mrs Perry D. Slocum'	CDWL
nucifera	XBlo
- 'Shiroman'	CDWL

Nematanthus (*Gesneriaceae*)

'Apres'	WDib
'Black Magic'	CHal WDib
'Christmas Holly'	WDib
'Freckles'	WDib
§ ***gregarius*** 🏆H1	CHal EBak WDib
§ - 'Golden West' (v)	CHal WDib
- 'Variegatus'	see *N. gregarius* 'Golden West'
'Lemon and Lime'	WDib
radicans	see *N. gregarius*
'Tropicana' 🏆H1	CHal WDib

Nemesia (*Scrophulariaceae*)

Amelie = 'Fleurame'	LRHS SPer SPoG
(Aromatica Series) Aromatica Compact White = 'Balarcomwit'PBR	NPri
- Aromatica True Blue = 'Balartublue'PBR	NPri
Blue Lagoon = 'Pengoon'PBR (Maritana Series)	LAst LSRN SCoo SMrm SPoG WGor
'Bluebird'	see *N.* Bluebird = 'Hubbird'
§ Bluebird = 'Hubbird'PBR	CHll

	Blushing Bride = 'Yablush'PBR	LSou
§	***caerulea***	ECtt MWgw WPer
	- 'Joan Wilder' (clonal)	ECtt WSPU
N	- 'Joan Wilder' (seed raised)	see *N. caerulea* lilac/blue
§	- lilac/blue-flowered	WPer
	Candy Girl = 'Pencand'PBR (Maritana Series)	SCoo
	Celine = 'Fleurcel'	SPoG
	Claudette = 'Fleurcla' **new**	SPoG
§	***denticulata*** ♀H3-4	CHal CHar CPrp ECGP ECtt EPfP LHop LRHS MArl MAvo SCoo SGar SPer SPoG SRms WBrE WFar WFoF WWeb
	- 'Celebration'	LRHS WWeb
	- 'Confetti'	see *N. denticulata*
	- 'Maggie' **new**	LBuc
	'Fleurie Blue'	LRHS
	foetens	see *N. caerulea*
	'Fragrant Cloud'PBR	CChe ELan EPfP LRHS LSou MCCP MNrw NEgg SPer SPla
	'Fragrant Gem'	LSRN SHGN
	fruticans misapplied	see *N. caerulea*
	'Golden Eye'	EPfP LBuc LSRN LSou SHGN SVil
	Honey Girl = 'Penhon'PBR (Maritana Series)	LAst LSRN SCoo SPoG WGor
	'Ice Blue'	SPoG
	'Ice Cool'	SPoG
	Ice Pink = 'Fleuripi'	SPoG
	'Innocence' ♀H3	CHal CPrp EBee EMan EWin LAst MArl MHar SCoo
I	'Innocence Improved'	LSou
	Karoo Blue = 'Innkablue'PBR	CSpe LSou SCoo
	Karoo Pink = 'Innkapink'PBR	LSou NPri
	'Lemon Drop' **new**	LSou SVil
	'Melanie'PBR	see *N.* Melanie = 'Fleuron'
§	Melanie = 'Fleuron'PBR ♀H3	EPfP LRHS
	'Orchard Blue'	EBee EPfP EWin
	'Pensky'	SCoo
	'Pippa Manby'	ECtt LAst
	'Rose Wings'	EPfP
	Sugar Girl = 'Pensug'PBR (Maritana Series)	EPfP LAst LSRN LSou SMrm SPoG
	'Sugar Plum'	EPfP LBuc
	(Sunsatia Series) Sunsatia Banana = 'Intraibana'PBR	LAst LHop
	- Sunsatia Blackberry = 'Inuppink'PBR	LHop SCoo SVil
	- Sunsatia Coconut = 'Intraiwhi'PBR	NPri
	- Sunsatia Cranberry = 'Intraired'PBR	LAst NPri SCoo
	- Sunsatia Lemon = 'Intraigold'PBR	NPri SCoo
	- Sunsatia Mango = 'Inupyel'PBR **new**	LHop
	- Sunsatia Peach = 'Inupcream'PBR	LAst NPri SCoo SVil
	sylvatica	CSpe SHGN
	'Tanith's Treasure'	EMan
	umbonata misapplied	see *N. caerulea* lilac/blue
	Vanilla Mist = 'Grega'PBR	EPfP LBuc
	'White Wings'PBR	EPfP
	'Wisley Vanilla'	LRHS SPoG

Nemophila (*Hydrophyllaceae*)

	menziesii 'Penny Black'	CSpe

Neodypsis (*Arecaceae*)

	decaryi	see *Dypsis decaryi*

Neolitsea (*Lauraceae*)

	glauca	see *N. sericea*
§	***sericea***	CBcs SSpi

Neomarica (*Iridaceae*)

	caerulea	CDes SKHP WCot
	gracilis	WPGP

Neopanax see *Pseudopanax*

Neopaxia (*Portulacaceae*)

§	***australasica***	ECou EDAr
	- bronze-leaved	see *N. australasica* 'Ohau'
	- 'Lyndon'	ECou
§	- 'Ohau'	ECou EDAr

Neoregelia (*Bromeliaceae*)

	carolinae	MBri
§	- (Meyendorffii Group) 'Flandria' (v)	MBri
	- - 'Meyendorffii'	MBri XBlo
	- f. ***tricolor*** (v) ♀H1	CHal MBri
	Claret Group	MBri
	'Hojo Rojo'	XBlo
	'Marconfos'	XBlo

Neoshirakia (*Euphorbiaceae*)

	japonica	CMCN MBri WPGP
	- B&SWJ 8744	WCru

Neottianthe (*Orchidaceae*)

	cucullata	EFEx

Nepenthes (*Nepenthaceae*)

	alata	CSWC
	alata x ***ventricosa***	SHmp
	ampullaria	CSWC
	bongso **new**	SHmp
	x ***coccinea***	MBri
	densiflora **new**	SHmp
	fusca	CSWC
	fusca x ***maxima***	SHmp
	x ***hookeriana***	CSWC
	khasiana	SHmp
	lowii	SHmp
	maxima x ***mixta***	SHmp
	rafflesiana	CSWC
	'Rebecca Soper' **new**	SHmp
	sanguinea	SHmp
	spectabilis	SHmp
	stenophylla	SHmp
	truncata highland form **new**	SHmp

Nepeta (*Lamiaceae*)

	CC 4610	MGol WCot
	'Blue Beauty'	see *N. sibirica* 'Souvenir d'André Chaudron'
	bucharica	GBuc WOut
*	***buddlejifolium***	NBre NLar
*	- 'Gold Splash'	NBre
	camphorata	MLLN MSte NBre SAga SIde
	cataria	CArn CPrp CTri ELau EUnu GPoy MHer MNHC MSal NBro NGHP NPri NTHB SECG SIde WHer WMoo WPer WSel XPep
§	- 'Citriodora'	CArn CHar CPrp EAro EBee ELan ELau EUnu GPoy MHer MNHC MSal NGHP SHGN SIde WHer WSel
	citriodora Dum.	see *N. cataria* 'Citriodora'
	clarkei	EAro EBee EPPr EWTr LEdu MDKP MMHG MSte NDov SBod SEND SIde SWat WMoo WPer WSpi

curviflora	EUnu
'Dropmore'	EBee EWin XPep
§ x ***faassenii*** ♀H4	More than 30 suppliers
- 'Alba'	EBee ECtt EPfP LAst NBre NGHP NLar SHGN WFar
- 'Blauknirps'	NBre
- 'Kit Cat'	EBee LCro MSte NDov NGby
glechoma 'Variegata'	see *Glechoma hederacea* 'Variegata'
govaniana	CSam CWCL EBee ECha EHrv ELan EPfP GCra GMaP LAst LHop LRHS MRav MWgw NBid NBro NDov NGdn NSti SGar SPoG STes WCAu WFar WHil WMnd WMoo WPer
grandiflora	EBee MRav NBre SIde WFar WHer WOut
- 'Blue Danube'	NDov
- 'Bramdean'	CMea CSam EBee ECtt EMan EWes EWin MBri MHar MRav NCGa NDov SBch SPhx WKif WOut
- 'Dawn to Dusk'	More than 30 suppliers
- 'Pool Bank'	EBee ECtt EMan EWes LSou NBre NCGa NGby SGar SIde
- 'Wild Cat'	CSam EBee EPfP MBri MSte NBPC SPhx WFar
hederacea 'Variegata'	see *Glechoma hederacea* 'Variegata'
italica	EBee SHar SIde
laevigata	EBee
lanceolata	see *N. nepetella*
latifolia	NBre SIde
- 'Super Cat' new	EBee
'Lilac Cloud'	NBir
* ***longipes*** hort.	More than 30 suppliers
macrantha	see *N. sibirica*
* ***magnifica*** new	WOut
melissifolia	EBee SBch WPer XPep
mussinii misapplied	see *N.* x *faassenii*
mussinii Spreng.	see *N. racemosa*
§ ***nepetella***	EBee GBri LBMP MGol NBir NChi WFar WOut WPer
nervosa	CArn CKno CSpe EBee ECha ELan EPfP ERou LAst LRHS MBri MHer MNHC MSte NBro NPri NSti SPer STes WFar WPer WSHC WSpi WWeb
- 'Blue Carpet'	CSpe
- 'Blue Moon'	EBee LRHS NBid
- 'Forncett Select'	CSam EMan MRav NBre SDys SMrm
§ ***nuda***	CPom CSam EAro EBee ECha ECtt MDKP MFOX MLLN SIde WFar XPep
- subsp. ***albiflora***	EBee ECha
* - 'Anne's Choice'	EBee MSte
* - 'Grandiflora'	NBre NLar WMoo
- 'Isis'	EBee
- 'Purple Cat'	GBin GMac LSou LTwo NCGa WCot WFar
- 'Snow Cat'	EBee GBin LSou MDKP MSte NCGa SMeo SPhx WCot
pannonica	see *N. nuda*
parnassica	CDMG CSam EBee ECtt EShb EWsh LRHS MWgw NBPC NEgg NLar SBod SIde SMad SPav SPoG WCot WFar WMnd WMoo XPep
phyllochlamys	CPBP EBee NCGa
'Porzellan'	CPrp EBee EMan EWin LAst MSte NCGa SMrm WOut
§ ***prattii***	CSpe EBee ERou MWat NCGa NLar SBod SIde SPla STes WPer WSpi
§ ***racemosa*** ♀H4	CArn CHby CPbn CSev ELau EPfP EUnu LRHS MNHC MRav SIde WMoo WPtf XPep
- ***alba***	WFar
- 'Amelia'	WOut
- 'Blue Ice'	GBuc SIde
- 'Grog'	EBee EWin SIde WSpi
- 'Leporello' (v)	EPPr
- 'Little Titch'	CBod CPrp EBee EMan EPfP EShb LAst LRHS MNFA MSte NLar SAga SIde SMrm SPla SPoG SWat WFar WSHC WSpi WWeb
- 'Snowflake'	CBcs CMea EBee ELan EPfP EShb GMaP LBMP LRHS MHer MSte NBir SAga SIde SPer SPla SPoG SWvt WCAu WFar WSel XPep
- 'Superba'	EMon GBuc NBre WFar
- 'Walker's Low'	More than 30 suppliers
* 'Rae Crug'	EWes
reichenbachiana	see *N. racemosa*
§ ***sibirica***	COIW EBee ECha ELan EPfP GMac LBMP LEdu LRHS MHer MRav NBid NBro NCGa NDov NPri SBch WCot WFar WHal WPer WPtf
§ - 'Souvenir d'André Chaudron'	CSam CSpe CWCL EBee ECtt EHrv ELan EPfP ERou GMaP LAst LEdu LHop LRHS MAvo MBri MLLN MNrw MRav NCob SAga SMad SPer SPoG WCAu WCot WEas WFar WHoo WSpi
sintenisii	CSWP NBre
'Six Hills Giant'	More than 30 suppliers
stewartiana	CPom EAro GBuc LDai MLLN NCGa NEgg NLar STes WMoo
- ACE 1611	GBuc
- BWJ 7999	WCru
subsessilis	More than 30 suppliers
- 'Candy Cat'	EBee EHrv MBri MDKP SBHP
- 'Cool Cat'	EBee ECGP MBri MDKP MSte NLar NPro SMrm SPhx WFar
- Nimbus = 'Yanim' new	EBee SPoG
- pink-flowered	CAby ECha EGle GBuc MLLN MSte
- 'Sweet Dreams'	CHar CKno EBee ECtt EMil EWin GBri LBMP LEdu MBri MDKP MGol MRav NBPC NGby NLar NPro NSti SHar SPhx WCAu WFar WMnd WWeb
tenuifolia	MSal
transcaucasica	CArn
- 'Blue Infinity'	NBre NLar WMnd WMoo
troodii	MDKP SIde
tuberosa	CBod CSam CSpe EAro EBee ECha EDAr EKen EShb GBuc LRHS MAvo MHer MRav SBch SIde SMad SPav SPhx STes WCot WHoo WLin WMnd WMoo WPtf XPep
'Veluws Blauwtje'	EBee
yunnanensis	CDes EBee EMan EPPr LEdu SPhx WHil WOut

Nephrolepis (*Oleandraceae*)

biserrata 'Macho' new	MPes
cordifolia	MBri WRic
duffii new	MPes
exaltata ♀H2	ERea
- 'Bostoniensis'	MBri
- 'Fluffy Ruffles' ♀H1 new	MPes
- 'Montana' new	MPes
- 'Smithii'	MBri
- 'Smithii Linda'	MBri
- 'Teddy Junior'	MBri MPes
falcata f. ***furcans*** new	MPes

Nephrophyllidium (*Menyanthaceae*)

crista-galli	IBlr

Nerine ✿ (*Amaryllidaceae*)

'Afterglow'	ECho LAma SGar

	'Albivetta'	CAby CBgR CFwr CPen EBee EBrs ECho EPot
	angustifolia	CPen
	'Aries' new	WCot
	'Audrey'	WCot
	'Aurora'	WCot
	'Berlioz'	WCot
	'Blanchefleur'	WCot
	bowdenii ♀H3-4	More than 30 suppliers
	- 'Alba'	CStu ECho ELan EShb LRHS SCoo SMHy
	- 'Codora'	CBgR CCCN CPen ECho EShb LHop LSou SPer
	- 'E.B. Anderson'	WCot
	- 'Kinn McIntosh'	WCot
	- 'Manina'	CMdw MSte WCot
	- 'Marjorie' new	EMal WCot
	- 'Mark Fenwick'	CBcs EBee ECha ERas MSte WCot WOld
	- 'Marnie Rogerson'	CPne MSte SMHy WCot
§	- 'Mollie Cowie' (v)	EBee EMon IBlr MAvo WCot WCru WHil
	- pale pink striped darker	CDes
	- 'Pink Triumph'	CAbP CBcs EBee EBla EBrs ECho EShb GBuc GQui IBlr LAma LRHS MSte MWgw NHol SChr SPer SPla WCot WHoo
	- 'Porlock'	EBee
	- 'Quinton Wells'	SPhx
	- 'Variegata'	see *N. bowdenii* 'Mollie Cowie'
	- Washfield form	SMHy
	- 'Wellsii'	CDes CMil EBee GSki MAvo WCot
	'Canasta'	WCot
	corusca 'Major'	see *N. sarniensis* var. *corusca*
	crispa	see *N. undulata*
	filamentosa	EBrs ECho
	filifolia	CPen ECho ERos ITim MNrw MTho SChr WAbe WCot WHil
	flexuosa	CPne CWsd GSki MRav
	- 'Alba'	CAvo CBgR CPen CStu CWsd EBee EBrs ECha EPot EWTr GSki LRHS MRav MSte SPhx WAbe WCot
	'Fucine'	CDes EBee
	'Hera'	EMon MSte SPhx WCot
	hesseoides new	WCot
*	***hirsuta***	EBee EBrs
	humilis	CStu CWsd EBrs
	- Breachiae Group	CStu SBch
	'Jenny Wren'	WCot
	'King of the Belgians'	ECho LAma WCot
	'Kodora'	EBee EBrs
	krigei	CPen
	'Lady Havelock Allen'	WCot
	'Mansellii'	IHer WCot
	'Maria'	WCot
	masoniorum	CStu ERos MTho SBch SChr WCot
	'Miss Cator'	WCot
	'Nikita'	CFwr CPen EBee EBrs ECho MSte
	'November Cheer'	CTca ECho
	peersii	WCot
	'Plymouth'	SChr
	pudica	SBch
	- pink-flowered	WCot
	'Purple Prince' new	LRHS
	'Red Pimpernel'	ECho LAma
	rehmannii new	EBrs
	'Rose Princess' new	LRHS
	'Rushmere Star'	CDes SChr WCot
	'Salmon Supreme' new	LRHS
	sarniensis ♀H2-3	CFwr CPne EBee EBrs ECha EPot IHer LRHS MSte WCot
*	- 'Alba'	WCot
§	- var. ***corusca***	CStu LAma
	- - 'Major'	EBrs SChr WCot
	- var. ***curvifolia*** f. ***fothergillii***	WCot
	- late, dull red-flowered	CDes
	'Stephanie'	CBgR CFwr EBee EBrs ECho EShb LAma LHop LRHS LSou SBch SPer WFar WHoo
§	***undulata***	CBgR CCCN CPne CSut CTca EBee EBrs ECha ECho EPot ERos LAma LRHS LSou MSte SPer WCot WHil
*	- 'Alba'	SPhx
	'Vicky'	WCot
	'Virgo'	CTca ECho
	'White Swan'	ECho LAma
	'Zeal Candy Stripe'	CFir
	'Zeal Colour Break'	SChr
	'Zeal Giant' ♀H3-4	CAvo CFFs CFir CPne NGby
	'Zeal Grilse'	CDes CPne
	'Zeal Salmon'	CPne
	'Zeal Silver Stripe'	CFir

Nerium ✿ (*Apocynaceae*)

	oleander	CAbb CArn CTri EBak EBee EEls ELan EShb LRHS MJnS NLar SArc SChr SPer SPoG SRms SWal
	- 'Agnes Campbell'	XPep
*	- 'Alassio'	XPep
	- 'Album'	EEls
	- 'Album Maximum'	XPep
	- 'Album Plenum' (d)	EEls XPep
*	- 'Almodovar'	XPep
	- 'Alsace'	EEls XPep
	- 'Altini'	EEls XPep
	- 'Angiolo Pucci'	EEls XPep
*	- 'Apache'	XPep
*	- 'Aquarelle'	XPep
*	- 'Arad'	XPep
*	- 'Aramis' (d)	XPep
*	- 'Argunista'	XPep
*	- 'Arizona'	XPep
*	- 'Art Déco'	XPep
*	- 'Atlas'	XPep
*	- 'Barcelona'	XPep
	- 'Belle Hélène'	XPep
	- 'Bousquet d'Orb'	EEls
	- 'Calypso'	XPep
*	- 'Campane'	XPep
	- 'Cap Saint Vincent'	XPep
§	- 'Carneum Plenum' (d)	EEls XPep
*	- 'Caro'	XPep
	- 'Cavalaire' (d)	EEls XPep
*	- 'Cheyenne'	XPep
*	- 'Christine'	XPep
*	- 'Clare'	SOWG
*	- 'Claudia'	XPep
	- 'Commandant Barthélemy'	XPep
	- 'Cornouailles'	EEls XPep
*	- 'Dimona'	XPep
	- 'Docteur Golfin'	EEls
	- 'Dottore Attilio Ragionieri'	XPep
	- 'East End Pink'	XPep
	- 'Ed Barr'	XPep
*	- 'Elat'	XPep
	- 'Emile Sahut'	EEls XPep
	- 'Emilie'	EEls
*	- 'Eole'	XPep
	- 'Eugenia Fowler' (d)	XPep
*	- 'Feuille d'Eucalyptus'	XPep
*	- 'Fiesta Pienk'	XPep
*	- 'Fiesta Rodi'	XPep
	- 'Flavescens Plenum' (d)	EEls EShb XPep
	- 'Framboise'	XPep
*	- 'Galipette' (d)	XPep
*	- 'Garlaban'	XPep

	- 'Géant des Batailles' (d)	EEls SOWG
	- 'General Pershing' (d)	XPep
	- 'Grandiflorum'	XPep
*	- 'Haïfa'	XPep
	- 'Hardy Red'	EEls XPep
*	- 'Harriet Newding'	XPep
	- 'Hawaii'	EEls XPep
*	- 'Icare'	XPep
*	- subsp. ***indicum***	XPep
*	- 'Isabelle'	EEls
	- 'Isle of Capri'	EEls SOWG XPep
	- 'Italia'	XPep
	- 'J.R. '	EEls XPep
*	- 'Jack'line'	XPep
	- 'Jannoch'	EEls XPep
*	- 'Jardin du Luxembourg'	XPep
*	- 'Jordan Valley'	XPep
*	- 'La Fontaine'	XPep
	- 'Lady Kate'	XPep
	- 'Lane Taylor Sealy'	XPep
*	- 'Lisou'	XPep
	- 'Louis Pouget' (d)	EEls XPep
	- 'Madame Allen' (d)	EEls XPep
*	- 'Madame de Billy'	XPep
	- 'Magaly'	XPep
	- 'Maguelone'	XPep
*	- 'Mainate'	XPep
	- 'Maresciallo Graziani'	EEls XPep
	- 'Margaritha'	EEls XPep
	- 'Marie Gambetta'	EEls XPep
	- 'Marie Mauron'	XPep
	- subsp. ***mascatense***	XPep
*	- 'Massif de l'Etoile'	XPep
*	- 'Maurin des Maures'	XPep
*	- 'Mer Egée'	XPep
	- 'Minouche'	XPep
*	- 'Mishna'	XPep
	- 'Mont Blanc'	EEls XPep
*	- 'Mont Rose'	XPep
*	- 'Monts Saint Cyr'	XPep
	- 'Moshav'	XPep
	- 'Mrs Burton' (d)	XPep
	- 'Mrs Magnolia Willis Sealy' (d)	XPep
	- 'Mrs Roeding'	see *N. oleander* 'Carneum Plenum'
	- 'Mrs Swanson' (d)	XPep
	- 'Mrs Trueheart'	XPep
	- 'Mrs Willard Cooke'	XPep
	- 'Nana Rosso'	EEls XPep
*	- 'Natou'	XPep
	- 'Navajo'	XPep
*	- 'Neguev'	XPep
*	- 'Nomade'	XPep
	- 'Oasis'	EEls XPep
	- subsp. ***oleander***	EEls XPep
*	- 'Osiris'	XPep
	- 'Papa Gambetta'	EEls XPep
*	- 'Pasadena'	XPep
	- 'Petite Pink'	EEls MPRe XPep
	- 'Petite Red'	EEls MPRe XPep
	- 'Petite Salmon'	EEls XPep
*	- 'Petite White'	XPep
	- 'Pietra Ligure'	XPep
	- 'Pink Beauty'	XPep
*	- 'Pirate Des Caraïbes'	XPep
	- 'Porto'	XPep
	- 'Professeur Granel' (d)	EEls XPep
	- 'Professeur Parlatore'	XPep
	- 'Provence' (d)	EEls SOWG XPep
*	- 'Rivage'	XPep
	- 'Rosa Bartolini'	XPep
	- 'Rosario' (d)	XPep
	- 'Rose des Borrels'	EEls XPep
*	- 'Rose des Vents' (d)	XPep
	- 'Rosée du Ventoux' (d)	EEls SOWG
	- 'Roseum'	EEls
	- 'Roseum Plenum' (d)	CRHN EEls XPep
	- 'Rosita'	EEls XPep
*	- 'Rossignol'	XPep
*	- 'Rubis' (d)	XPep
*	- 'Sabra'	XPep
*	- 'Sainte Beaume'	XPep
*	- 'Sainte Victoire'	XPep
*	- 'Santa Fe'	XPep
*	- 'Sausalito'	XPep
	- 'Scarlet Beauty'	XPep
	- 'Sealy Pink'	EEls XPep
*	- 'Simie'	XPep
*	- 'Snowflake'	SOWG
	- 'Soeur Agnès' (d)	EEls XPep
*	- 'Soeur Elisabeth' (d)	XPep
	- 'Soleil Levant'	EEls XPep
*	- 'Solfège'	XPep
*	- 'Sophie'	XPep
	- 'Souvenir d'Emma Schneider'	EEls XPep
	- 'Souvenir des Iles Canaries'	EEls XPep
	- 'Splendens' (d)	SOWG
	- 'Splendens Foliis Variegatis' (d)	XPep
	- 'Splendens Giganteum' (d)	EEls XPep
	- 'Splendens Giganteum Variegatum' (d/v)	EEls
*	- 'Tamouré' (d)	XPep
*	- 'Tavira'	XPep
	- 'Tiberias'	XPep
	- 'Tito Poggi'	EEls XPep
*	- 'Toulouse'	XPep
	- 'Vanilla Cream'	CBcs SPoG
	- 'Variegatum' (v) ♀H1+3	EShb
	- 'Variegatum Plenum' (d/v)	CBow WCot
*	- 'Vénus'	XPep
	- 'Villa Romaine'	EEls XPep
*	- 'Ville d'Aubagne'	XPep
	- 'Ville de Carpentras' (d)	EEls XPep
	- 'Virginie'	XPep
*	- 'Zoulou'	XPep

Nertera (*Rubiaceae*)

balfouriana	ECou
granadensis	EShb MBri

Neviusia (*Rosaceae*)

alabamensis	CBcs NLar

Nicandra (*Solanaceae*)

physalodes	CArn CHby EUnu ILis MSal NVic WRos
- 'Splash of Cream' (v)	CCCN EUnu LSou
- 'Violacea'	CSpe SRms SWvt

Nicotiana (*Solanaceae*)

acaulis new	CPBP
alata	SPhx
- 'Grandiflora'	LRav
alata* x *mutabilis	EBee
glauca	CHll CPLG CSpe EBee EShb EWes EWin LDai LFur LRav MGol MSte NLar SDnm SPav
'Hopleys'	CSpe
knightiana	CSpe EBee EWin
langsdorffii ♀H3	CSpe EBee EMan EMon EWin GBri LPio LRav SDnm SPav WEas
- 'Cream Splash' (v)	EBee EWin LSou
'Lime Green' ♀H3	CSpe
mutabilis	CHll CHrt CSpe EBee EWin LDai MWea SBch SPhx WBor WPGP
rustica	EBee

suaveolens	CBre MSte
sylvestris 𝕐H3	CDTJ CHEx CSpe CWSG EBee ELan EMan EPfP LCro SBch SDnm SEND SMrm SPav SWvt WEas WGwG
– pink-flowered **new**	CDTJ
tabacum	CArn SPav
– var. ***macrophylla*** **new**	CDTJ
'Tinkerbell' **new**	CSpe

Nidularium (*Bromeliaceae*)

flandria	see *Neoregelia carolinae* (Meyendorffii Group) 'Flandria'
innocentii	XBlo

x *Niduregelia* (*Bromeliaceae*)

§ 'Surprise'	MBri

Nierembergia (*Solanaceae*)

caerulea	see *N. linariifolia*
frutescens	see *N. scoparia*
hippomanica	see *N. linariifolia*
§ ***linariifolia*** 𝕐H1	CAbP EBee EHrv EMan
§ ***repens***	CStu ECho EDAr LRHS NLar
rivularis	see *N. repens*
§ ***scoparia***	XPep
– 'Mont Blanc'	LRHS
– 'Purple Robe'	LRHS

Nigella (*Ranunculaceae*)

papillosa 'African Bride' **new**	CSpe
– 'Midnight'	CSpe

Nigritella see *Gymnadenia*

Nipponanthemum (*Asteraceae*)

§ ***nipponicum***	CDes CWan EBee ECho EWin GMac LAst MNrw NSti SRms WBrk WCot

Noccaea see *Thlaspi*

Nolina (*Dracaenaceae*)

bigelovii	CBrP
longifolia	EAmu WCot
microcarpa	XPep
nelsonii **new**	EAmu
texana	CTrC NWCA

Nomocharis (*Liliaceae*)

aperta	CExc CPLG EBee EBrs ECho EHrv EPot GBuc GCra GCrs GEdr GGar GKev ITim LAma MLul WCru
– ACE 2271	GCrs WWst
– CLD 229	GBuc WWst
– CLD 482	GEdr
– CLD 524	WWst
– KGB 777	GEdr
farreri	EBee EBrs ECho WCru
x ***finlayorum***	EBee EBrs ECho GBuc GEdr ITim
mairei	see *N. pardanthina*
meleagrina	EBee EBrs ECho EPot GBuc GEdr LAma MLul NLAp WAbe WWst
nana	see *Lilium nanum*
oxypetala	see *Lilium oxypetalum*
§ ***pardanthina***	CWsd GBuc GGGa GGar NSla WAbe
– CLD 1490	EHrv GCrs WWst
– f. ***punctulata***	EBee GBuc GGGa WCru WWst
saluenensis	EBee EBrs ECho GCrs GGGa WAbe WCru WWst

Nonea (*Boraginaceae*)

lutea	LSou MLLN NOrc NSti SMad WHal WRos

Nothochelone see *Penstemon*

Nothofagus ✿ (*Fagaceae*)

§ ***alpina***	CDul CLnd CMCN NWea WMou WNor WPGP
antarctica	More than 30 suppliers
cunninghamii	IArd STre WNor
dombeyi	CBcs CDoC CDul CLnd CTho EBee EPfP IClo LHyd SAPC SArc STre WNor WPGP WSpi
fusca	CDoC MGos
menziesii	CBcs CTrC
nervosa	see *N. alpina*
obliqua	CDoC CDul CLnd CMCN NWea STre WMou WNor
procera misapplied	see *N. alpina*
procera Oerst.	see *N. alpina*
solanderi	CAbb
– var. ***cliffortioides***	CBcs

Notholaena see *Cheilanthes*

Notholirion (*Liliaceae*)

bulbuliferum	EBee EBrs ECho EPot GBuc GCra GKev WAbe
campanulatum	EBee EBrs WWst
– SDR 310	GKev
macrophyllum	EBee EBrs ECho EPot GBri GBuc GCrs GEdr GKev
thomsonianum	EBee EBrs GCrs

Nothopanax see *Polyscias*

Nothoscordum (*Alliaceae*)

bivalve	CStu
gracile	CFir CPLG EBee WPrP
inodorum	EBee GBuc
neriniflorum	see *Caloscordum neriniflorum*
strictum	EBee ECho

Notospartium (*Papilionaceae*)

carmichaeliae	ECou
– 'Hodder'	ECou
– 'Seymour'	ECou
glabrescens	ECou
– 'Ben More'	ECou
– 'Woodside'	ECou
glabrescens x ***torulosum***	ECou
'Joy'	ECou
torulosum	ECou
– 'Blue Butterfly'	ECou
– 'Malvern Hills'	ECou

Nuphar (*Nymphaeaceae*)

japonica	CDWL
– var. ***variegata*** (v)	NLar
lutea	EHon EMFW LCro NSco SCoo SWat WFar
– subsp. ***advena***	EMFW
pumila	CDWL

Nuxia (*Buddlejaceae*)

congesta	EShb
floribunda	EShb

Nylandtia (*Polygalaceae*)

spinosa	SPlb

Nymphaea ✿ (*Nymphaeaceae*)

'Afterglow' (T/D)	CDWL
alba (H)	CBen CRWN CWat EHon EMFW EPfP LCro NSco SCoo SWat WFar WMAq
'Alba Plenissima' (H)	WPnP

	'Albatros' misapplied	see *N.* 'Hermine'
§	'Albatros' Latour-Marliac (H)	CDWL SWat WPnP
	'Albert Greenberg' (T/D)	CDWL
*	'Albida'	CDWL WMAq XBlo
	'Almost Black' (H)	CDWL
	'Amabilis' (H)	CBen CDWL EMFW SWat WMAq
	'American Star' (H)	CWat EMFW SWat WMAq
	'Andreana' (H)	CDWL CWat LLWG SWat
	'Anne Emmet' (T/D) **new**	CDWL
	'Arabian Nights' (T/D)	CDWL
	'Arc-en-ciel' (H)	CDWL SCoo SWat WMAq
	'Atropurpurea' (H)	CBen CDWL EMFW LLWG SWat WMAq
	'Attraction' (H)	CBen CDWL EHon EMFW EPfP NBlu NPer SCoo SWat WMAq XBlo
	'Aurora' (H)	CDWL EMFW LCro SWat WMAq WPnP
	'Barbara Davies' (H)	LLWG
	'Barbara Dobbins' (H)	CDWL LLWG
	'Bateau' (H)	LLWG
	'Berit Strawn' (H)	CDWL
	'Berthold' (H)	CBen
	'Betsy Sakata' (H)	LLWG
	'Blue Beauty' (T/D)	CBen
	'Blue Horizon' (T/D)	CDWL
	'Brakeleyi Rosea' (H)	WMAq
	'Burgundy Princess' (H)	CDWL CWat
	candida (H)	CBen EHon EMFW WMAq
	'Candidissima' (H)	CDWL SWat
§	***capensis*** (T/D)	XBlo
	'Carolina Sunset' (H)	LLWG
	'Caroliniana' (H)	CDWL
	'Caroliniana Nivea' (H)	CBen CDWL EHon EMFW
	'Caroliniana Perfecta' (H)	CBen SWat
	'Celebration' (H)	LLWG
	'Charlene Strawn' (H)	CWat EMFW LLWG SWat WMAq
	'Charles de Meurville' (H)	CBen CDWL EMFW NPer WMAq
	'Château le Rouge' (H)	LLWG
	'Colonel A.J. Welch' (H)	CBen EHon EMFW LCro NPer SCoo SWat WFar WMAq WPnP
	'Colorado' (H)	CDWL LLWG
	colorata	see *N. capensis*
	'Colossea' (H)	CBen CWat EMFW WPnP
	'Comanche' (H)	CBen EMFW NPer WMAq
	'Conqueror' (H)	EMFW IArd SCoo SWat WFar
	'Danieda'	SWat
§	'Darwin' (H)	CBen CDWL CWat SWat WMAq
	'David' (H)	CWat
	'Denver' (H)	LLWG
	'Director George T. Moore' (T/D)	CDWL
	'Ellisiana' (H)	CBen CDWL EMFW LLWG SWat
	'Escarboucle' (H) 🏆^{H4}	CBen CDWL CWat EHon EMFW LCro NLar NPer SCoo SWat WMAq WPnP XBlo
	'Esmeralda' (H)	SWat
	'Evelyn Randig' (T/D)	CDWL
	'Excalibur'	CDWL
§	'Fabiola' (H)	CBen CDWL EHon EMFW EPfP SCoo WFar WMAq
	'Fire Crest' (H)	CBen CDWL EHon EMFW NBlu SCoo SWat WFar WMAq
	'Froebelii' (H)	CBen CDWL CWat EHon EMFW LCro SWat WFar WMAq WPnP
	'Galatée' (H)	CDWL
	'Geisha Girl'	CDWL
	'General Pershing' (T/D)	CDWL
	'Georgia Peach' (H)	CDWL LLWG
	'Gladstoneana' (H) 🏆^{H4}	CBen CWat EHon EMFW LCro NPer SCoo SWat WMAq
	'Gloire du Temple-sur-Lot' (H)WMAq	CBen CDWL EHon EMFW SWat
	'Gloriosa' (H)	CBen CDWL SCoo SWat WFar
	'Gold Medal' (H)	CBen LLWG
	'Golden West' (T/D)	CDWL
	'Gonnère' (H) 🏆^{H4}	CBen CDWL CWat EHon EMFW EPfP LCro SWat WMAq WPnP
	'Graziella' (H)	SWat WMAq WPnP
	'Green Smoke' (T/D)	CDWL
	'Gypsy' (H)	LLWG
	'H.C. Haarstick' (T/N)	CDWL
	'Hal Miller' (H)	LLWG
	'Hassell' (H)	LLWG
	'Helen Fowler' (H)	CDWL EMFW SWat WMAq
	x ***helvola***	see *N.* 'Pygmaea Helvola'
§	'Hermine' (H)	CBen CDWL EMFW SWat WMAq
	'Highlight' **new**	LLWG
	'Hollandia' misapplied	see *N.* 'Darwin'
	'Hollandia' Koster (H)	SWat
	'Indiana' (H)	CBen CDWL EMFW WMAq
	'Inner Light' **new**	LLWG
	'Irene Heritage' (H)	CBen
	'Jack Wood' (T/D)	CDWL
	'James Brydon' (H) 🏆^{H4}	CBen CDWL CWat EHon EMFW EPfP NLar NPer SCoo SWat WFar WMAq WPnP
	'Jean de Lamarsalle' (H)	LLWG
§	'Joanne Pring' (H)	SWat
	'Joey Tomocik' (H)	CBen CDWL CWat LLWG SCoo WMAq
	'June Alison' (T/D)	CDWL
	'King of Siam' (T/D)	CDWL
	'Lactea' (H)	CDWL LLWG
	'Laura Strawn' (H)	LLWG
	'Laydekeri Alba'	CDWL
	'Laydekeri Fulgens' (H)	CBen CDWL EMFW SWat WMAq
	'Laydekeri Lilacea' (H)	CBen CDWL SWat WMAq
	'Laydekeri Purpurata' (H)	CDWL EMFW SWat
	'Laydekeri Rosea' misapplied	see *N.* 'Laydekeri Rosea Prolifera'
§	'Laydekeri Rosea Prolifera' (H)	CBen
	'Lemon Chiffon' (H)	CDWL
	'Lemon Mist' **new**	LLWG
	'Limelight'	SWat
	'Little Sue' (H)	CDWL LLWG
	'Livingstone' (H)	LLWG
	'Luciana'	see *N.* 'Odorata Luciana'
	'Lucidia' (H)	CBen CDWL EMFW SWat WMAq
	'Madame de Bonseigneur' (H)	CDWL
	'Madame Ganna Walska' (T/D)	CDWL
	'Madame Wilfon Gonnère' (H)	CBen CDWL CWat EHon EMFW LCro SWat WMAq WPnP
	'Marliacea Albida' (H)	CBen CDWL CWat EHon EMFW LCro SWat WFar WMAq WPnP XBlo
	'Marliacea Carnea' (H)	CBen CDWL EHon EMFW EPfP LCro NBlu NPer SCoo SWat WFar WMAq
§	'Marliacea Chromatella' (H) 🏆^{H4}	CBen CDWL CWat EHon EMFW EPfP NLar SCoo SWat WFar WMAq WPnP XBlo
	'Marliacea Rosea' (H)	EMFW SWat WMAq XBlo
	'Maroon Beauty' (T/N)	CDWL
	'Mary' (H)	LLWG
	'Masaniello' (H)	CBen CDWL EHon EMFW EPfP SWat WMAq
	'Maurice Laydeker' (H)	CDWL LLWG
	'Maxima'	see *N.* 'Odorata Maxima'
	'Mayla'	LLWG
§	'Météor' (H)	CBen CWat EMFW LCro WMAq
	'Midnight' (T/D)	CDWL
	'Millennium Pink'	CDWL
	'Moorei' (H)	CBen CDWL EHon EMFW SWat WMAq
	'Mrs George C. Hitchcock' (TN)	CDWL
	'Mrs George H. Pring' (T/D)	CDWL

	'Mrs Martin E. Randig' (T/D)	CDWL
	'Mrs Richmond' misapplied	see *N.* 'Fabiola'
	'Mrs Richmond' Latour-Marliac (H)	SWat XBlo
	'Neptune' (H)	LLWG
	'Newchapel Beauty'	WMAq
	'Newton' (H)	CDWL LLWG SWat WMAq
	'Nigel' (H)	EMFW LLWG SWat
	'Norma Gedye' (H)	CBen CWat SWat WMAq
	'Odalisque' (H)	EMFW
§	***odorata*** (H)	CBen EHon SCoo WMAq
§	- var. ***minor*** (H)	CBen CDWL EMFW SWat WFar WMAq
	- 'Pumila'	see *N. odorata* var. *minor*
	- subsp. ***tuberosa*** (H)	CBen
	'Odorata Alba'	see *N. odorata*
§	'Odorata Luciana' (H)	EMFW
§	'Odorata Maxima' (H)	WMAq
	'Odorata Sulphurea' (H)	CDWL EHon LCro NBlu SWat WFar WPnP
§	'Odorata Sulphurea Grandiflora' (H)	CBen CDWL EMFW SCoo SWat XBlo
	'Odorata William B. Shaw'	see *N.* 'W.B. Shaw'
	'Orange Commanche'	CDWL
	'Pam Bennett' (H)	CBen
	'Pamela' (T/D)	CBen
	'Panama Pacific' (T/D)	XBlo
	'Patio Joe'	CDWL LLWG
	'Paul Hariot' (H)	CDWL CWat EHon EMFW SWat WMAq WPnP
	'Peace Lily' **new**	LLWG
	'Peach Glow' **new**	LLWG
	'Peaches and Cream' (H)	CDWL
	Pearl of the Pool (H)	SWat
	'Perry's Baby Red' (H)	CBen CDWL CWat LLWG SCoo WMAq
	'Perry's Double White' (H)	CBen
	'Perry's Fire Opal' (H)	CDWL
	'Perry's Pink' (H)	SWat WMAq
	'Perry's Viviparous Pink' (H)	CBen
	'Perry's Yellow Sensation'	see *N.* 'Yellow Sensation'
	'Peter Slocum' (H)	CDWL EMFW SWat
	'Phoebus' (H)	CDWL SWat
	'Picciola' (H)	LLWG
	pink hybrid	CDWL
	'Pink Opal' (H)	CBen CDWL CWat EMFW
	'Pink Panache' **new**	CDWL
	'Pink Pumpkin' (H)	LLWG
	'Pink Sensation' (H)	CBen CDWL EMFW LLWG SWat WMAq
	'Pink Sparkle' (H)	LLWG
	'Pöstlingberg' (H)	LLWG
	'Princess Elizabeth' (H)	EHon LLWG
	'Pygmaea Alba'	see *N. tetragona*
§	'Pygmaea Helvola' (H) ♀H4	CBen CDWL CWat EHon EMFW LCro NBlu NLar NPer SCoo SWat WMAq WPnP
	'Pygmaea Rubis' (H)	EHon SWat WMAq
	'Pygmaea Rubra' (H)	CBen CDWL CWat EMFW LCro NBlu NLar NPer SCoo WMAq WPnP
	'Ray Davies' (H)	EMFW LLWG
	'Red Spider' (H)	CWat
	'Rembrandt' misapplied	see *N.* 'Météor'
	'Rembrandt' Koster (H)	CDWL
	'René Gérard' (H)	CBen CDWL CWat EHon EMFW SWat WFar WMAq WPnP
	'Rosanna Supreme' (H)	LLWG SWat
	'Rose Arey' (H)	CBen CDWL EHon EMFW SCoo SWat WMAq
	'Rose Magnolia' (H)	CDWL SWat
§	'Rosea' (H)	CBen
	'Rosennymphe' (H)	CBen LCro SWat WFar WMAq
	'Rosy Morn' (H)	LLWG
	'Saint Louis Gold' (T/D)	CDWL
	'Seignouretti' (H)	EMFW
	'Sioux' (H)	CBen CDWL EHon EMFW NBlu NPer SWat WMAq XBlo
	'Sir Galahad' (T/N)	CDWL
	'Sirius' (H)	CBen CDWL EMFW LLWG SWat
	'Snow Princess'	WPnP
	'Solfatare' (H)	LLWG
	'Somptuosa' (H)	EPfP
	'Splendida' (H)	WMAq
	'Starbright' **new**	LLWG
	'Steven Strawn' (H)	LLWG
	'Sunny Pink'	CDWL LLWG
	'Sunrise'	see *N.* 'Odorata Sulphurea Grandiflora'
§	***tetragona*** (H)	CBen CDWL CWat EHon NBlu WFar WMAq
	- 'Alba'	see *N. tetragona*
	- 'Johann Pring'	see *N.* 'Joanne Pring'
	'Texas Dawn' (H)	CDWL LLWG WMAq
	'Thomas O'Brian'	LLWG
	'Tina' (T/D)	CDWL
	'Tuberosa Flavescens'	see *N.* 'Marliacea Chromatella'
	'Tuberosa Richardsonii' (H)	EHon EMFW WFar
	tuberosa 'Rosea'	see *N.* 'Rosea'
	'Vésuve' (H)	CDWL EMFW LLWG SWat
	'Virginalis' (H)	LLWG SWat WMAq
	'Virginia' (H)	LLWG
§	'W.B. Shaw' (H)	CBen EHon EMFW SWat WMAq WPnP
	'Walter Pagels' (H)	CDWL EMFW LLWG WMAq
	'Weymouth Red' (H)	CBen
	'White Delight' (T/D)	CDWL
	'White Sultan' (H)	LLWG
	'William Falconer' (H)	CBen CDWL CWat EMFW SWat
	'Wow' (H)	CDWL
	'Yellow Commanche'	CDWL
	'Yellow Dazzler' (T/D)	CDWL
	'Yellow Princess' (H)	CDWL
§	'Yellow Sensation' (H)	CBen
	'Yul Ling' (H)	LLWG SWat
	'Zeus'	CDWL

Nymphoides (*Menyanthaceae*)

	peltata	CWat EMFW EPfP NLar NPer NSco SCoo SWat WFar WMAq WPnP
§	- 'Bennettii'	EHon

Nyssa (*Cornaceae*)

	aquatica	CTho SSpi SSta
	sinensis ♀H4	CAbP CBcs CDoC CMCN CTho ELan EPfP IDee LRHS MAsh MBlu SPer SReu SSpi SSta WNor
	- Nymans form	EPfP LRHS
	- Savill form	SIFN
	sylvatica ♀H4	More than 30 suppliers
	- 'Autumn Cascades'	EPfP MBlu NLar WPGP
	- 'Jermyns Flame'	CAbP EPfP LRHS MAsh MBri SSpi
	- 'Miss Scarlet' (f) **new**	NLar
	- 'Red Red Wine'	CGHE EPfP MBlu WPGP
	- 'Sheffield Park'	CAbP EPfP LRHS MAsh SSpi
	- 'Windsor'	EPfP LRHS MAsh SSpi
	- 'Wisley Bonfire'	CAbP CGHE EBee ECrN EPfP LRHS MAsh MBri NLar SKHP SPoG SSpi WPGP

O

Oakesiella see *Uvularia*

Ochagavia (*Bromeliaceae*)

§	sp.	CHEx CPne NPal SAPC SArc
	carnea	WCot
	elegans	WPGP

* ***rosea***	CHEx

Ochna (*Ochnaceae*)

serrulata	CCCN

Ocimum (*Lamiaceae*)

'African Blue'	CArn CBod ELau EOHP EWin GPoy LSou MHer NBlu NGHP SPoG
§ ***americanum***	NGHP
- 'Meng Luk'	see *O. americanum*
- 'Spice'	see *O.* 'Spice'
basilicum	CArn CSev GPoy LRHS NBlu NPri SIde SWat WPer WSel
- 'Anise'	see *O. basilicum* 'Horapha'
- 'Ararat'	NGHP
- ***camphorata***	see *O. kilimandscharicum*
* - 'Cinnamon'	LRHS MNHC MSal NGHP SHDw WJek WSel
- 'Genovese'	ELau MHer MNHC NGHP NVic
- 'Glycyrrhiza'	see *O. basilicum* 'Horapha'
- 'Green Globe'	MNHC NGHP
- 'Green Ruffles'	EPfP LRHS MNHC WJek WSel
- 'Holy'	see *O. tenuiflorum*
§ - 'Horapha'	CArn MHer MNHC MSal NGHP SIde WJek
* - 'Horapha Nanum'	NGHP WJek
- 'Magic Mountain'	EWin
- 'Mrs Burns' **new**	NGHP
- 'Napolitano'	CBod MHer NGHP SIde SWat WJek
- var. ***purpurascens***	CArn CSev MNHC NBlu SIde
- - 'Dark Opal'	CBod MNHC NGHP SHDw WJek WSel
- - 'Purple Ruffles'	EPfP LRav MNHC SIde SWat WJek WSel
- - 'Red Rubin'	LRav MHer MNHC WJek
- var. ***purpurascens*** x ***kilimandscharicum***	CSpe GPoy
- 'Thai'	see *O. basilicum* 'Horapha'
canum	see *O. americanum*
x ***citriodorum***	CArn LRHS MNHC MSal NGHP SHDw SIde WJek WSel
- 'Lime'	LSou MNHC NGHP WJek
- 'Siam Queen'	LRHS MHer WJek
gratissimum	ELau MHer
§ ***kilimandscharicum***	GPoy
minimum	CArn CBod CSev ELau LRHS MHer MNHC NBlu NGHP SIde WJek WPer WSel
sanctum	see *O. tenuiflorum*
§ 'Spice'	NGHP
'Spicy Globe'	WJek
§ ***tenuiflorum***	CArn GPoy LRHS LRav MNHC MSal NGHP SHDw SIde WJek

Odontonema (*Acanthaceae*)

schomburgkianum	CCCN

Oemleria (*Rosaceae*)

cerasiformis	CBcs CBgR CPLG CPle EPfP EPla NLar SSpi WCot WEas WHCG WSHC

Oenanthe (*Apiaceae*)

aquatica 'Variegata' (v)	EMFW
javanica 'Flamingo' (v)	CBen EBee ELan EMan EMon EPfP GGar LEdu MBNS NBro SGar WFar WMAq WPer WSHC

Oenothera ✿ (*Onagraceae*)

from South America	MTho
§ ***acaulis***	CSpe MNrw SBch SBri SGar SPhx WRos
- ***alba***	MDKP WCot
§ - 'Aurea'	WPer
- 'Lutea'	see *O. acaulis* 'Aurea'
'Apricot Delight'	EBee EMan ENot LRHS MAvo MBNS STes WMnd WMoo
§ ***biennis***	CArn COld CSev CWan ELan EUnu GPoy LCro LEdu MDun MHer NBro NGHP SECG SGar SIde SPhx WBrk WEas WFar WHer WJek WPer WSFF
caespitosa subsp. ***caespitosa*** NNS 93-505	NWCA
* ***campylocalyx***	EUnu LDai
childsii	see *O. speciosa*
cinaeus	see *O. fruticosa* subsp. *glauca*
'Colin Porter'	CCge CSsd EBur NWCA WHrl WMoo WPer
'Copper Canyon' **new**	MBNS
'Crown Imperial'	CChe EBee MCCP SHar SPer SPoG
'Crown of Gold' **new**	ELan SPoG
drummondii	XPep
§ ***elata*** subsp. ***hookeri***	EWes NBre WPer
erythrosepala	see *O. glazioviana*
'Finlay's Fancy'	LEdu WCru
§ ***fruticosa***	CSam NLar SPlb
- 'African Sun'[PBR]	EBee ECtt EWes SBod SRot
- 'Camel' (v)	EGle EMan LDai LHop MDKP MFOX NEgg NPro SMrm WHil WHrl
- Fireworks	see *O. fruticosa* 'Fyrverkeri'
§ - 'Fyrverkeri' ♀H4	More than 30 suppliers
§ - subsp. ***glauca*** ♀H4	CElw CHrt COlW EPfP ERou GSki MDKP MNrw MWgw NEgg SPer SRms WEas WPer
- - 'Erica Robin' (v)	CBct CMea CPrp EBee ECtt EGle EMon EPla GBuc LAst LHop MRav NEgg NGdn SAga SMad SMrm SPla SPoG SRGP SRot WCAu WCot WHoo WPGP
- - 'Frühlingsgold' (v)	CBct EShb
- - Solstice	see *O. fruticosa* subsp. *glauca* 'Sonnenwende'
§ - - 'Sonnenwende'	CBre CElw CEnt EBee EBrs LRHS MLLN NLar NPro SPad WLin WMoo WTel
- - 'Sunspot' (v)	GBuc
- Highlight	see *O. fruticosa* 'Hoheslicht'
§ - 'Hoheslicht'	EBee
- 'Lady Brookeborough'	MRav
- 'Michelle Ploeger'	EGle NBre NCGa
- 'Silberblatt' (v)	CBow EBee LSou WAul
- 'Yellow River'	CElw EBee LRHS WWeb
- 'Youngii'	EBee EPfP ERou LEdu MCCP MLLN WPer
glabra misapplied	ECha NSti SIng
glabra Miller	see *O. biennis*
§ ***glazioviana***	CWan EUnu MNHC NBir WFar WHrl WPer
hookeri	see *O. elata* subsp. *hookeri*
kunthiana	CEnt ECho EMan ERou MDKP MHer MWea NWCA WMnd WMoo WPer
- 'Glowing Magenta'	EAlp EBee LSou SHGN
lamarckiana	see *O. glazioviana*
'Lemon Sunset'	CSsd CWan EBee LSou NGHP SWat WMoo
linearis	see *O. fruticosa*
'Longest Day'	LEdu LRHS MArl MBrN WWeb
§ ***macrocarpa*** ♀H4	More than 30 suppliers
- subsp. ***fremontii*** 'Silver Wings'	LBMP MBri
- 'Greencourt Lemon'	SPhx
- subsp. ***incana***	CMea CSam CSpe NBre SMad
macrosceles	NBre
* ***minima***	MDKP WLin
missouriensis	see *O. macrocarpa*

muricata	NBre
oakesiana	EBee SPhx
odorata misapplied	see *O. stricta*
odorata Hook. & Arn.	see *O. biennis*
odorata Jacquin	CArn
- cream-flowered	CSpe
- 'Sulphurea'	see *O. stricta* 'Sulphurea'
organensis	CDes EBee MLLN NBre WPGP
pallida	SWat
- 'Innocence'	LRHS MBNS NBre WPer
'Penelope Hobhouse'	CBct GBuc LSou
§ ***perennis***	EBee NBre NPro SRms WBVN WEas WPer
pumila	see *O. perennis*
rosea	CEnt
'Silky Orchid' **new**	SWal
§ ***speciosa***	CMHG EBee EWin LAst NBre SEND SPer SWat WFar WPer XPep
* - 'Alba'	EBee EWes XPep
- 'Ballerina'	LHop WCFE
- var. ***childsii***	see *O. speciosa*
- 'Pink Petticoats'	ECha EShb NPer SWat
- 'Rosea'	ECho LEdu LRHS SPlb SWat WPer
- 'Siskiyou'	CHrt CPrp CSpe EBee ENot EPfP GBuc LBMP LEdu LRHS NPri SCoo SGar SHar SIng SMad SMrm SPer SRot SWat
- Twilight = 'Turner01' (v)	SPoG
- 'Woodside White'	SMrm
§ ***stricta***	CHar CHrt CMea CSam EBee ECGP EGoo SIng WBrk WPer
* - 'Moonlight'	SGar SIng
§ - 'Sulphurea'	CHar CMHG CMil EGoo ELan EMan MNFA MWgw NPer SBch SGar SMrm WAbb WCot WPer
'Summer Sun'	EBee LBMP LRHS MSte NBre SPoG
syrticola	NBre
taraxacifolia	see *O. acaulis*
tetragona	see *O. fruticosa* subsp. *glauca*
- var. ***fraseri***	see *O. fruticosa* subsp. *glauca*
- 'Sonnenwende'	see *O. fruticosa* subsp. *glauca* 'Sonnenwende'
versicolor	WCFE
- 'Sunset Boulevard'	CHrt CPom CSpe CWCL EBee GBuc LDai MHer MWrn NGHP SBod SGar SMrm SPer SWal WMoo WPer WWeb

Olea (*Oleaceae*)

europaea (F)	More than 30 suppliers
- subsp. ***africana***	CTrC WPGP XPep
- 'Aglandau' (F)	CAgr ERea
- 'Bouteillan' (F)	CAgr ERea
- 'Cailletier' (F)	CAgr
- 'Chelsea Physic Garden' (F)	WPGP
§ - 'Cipressino' (F)	ERea LPan SBLw XPep
- 'El Greco' (F)	CBcs ERea
- subsp. ***europaea*** var. ***sylvestris***	XPep
- 'Frantoio' (F)	CAgr MCoo
- 'Pyramidalis'	see *O. europaea* 'Cipressino'
* - 'Sativa' (F)	EMui

Olearia ✿ (*Asteraceae*)

albida misapplied	see *O.* 'Talbot de Malahide'
albida Hook. f.	GGar
- var. ***angulata***	CBcs CTrC
algida	ECou GGar
arborescens	GGar GSki
argophylla	CPLG ECou GGar
avicenniifolia	CBcs CMac CPLG ECou GGar
canescens	CPne
capillaris	CDoC CPle ECou GGar SDry WCwm
chathamica	GGar
§ ***cheesemanii***	CBcs CDoC CMHG CPLG CPle CTrC CWsd GGar NLar SPer
coriacea	ECou
'County Park'	ECou
erubescens	CDoC CPLG
floribunda	CPle GGar
frostii	GGar IDee
furfuracea	ECou
glandulosa	ECou GGar
gunniana	see *O. phlogopappa*
x ***haastii***	More than 30 suppliers
- 'McKenzie'	ECou
hectorii	ECou
§ 'Henry Travers'	CBcs CDoC CPLG CPle EPfP GGar GQui IClo MDun
ilicifolia	CDoC CPle EBee EPfP GGar GSki LRHS SDry
§ ***ilicifolia*** x ***moschata***	CPle GGar WKif
insignis	see *Pachystegia insignis*
lacunosa	IClo MDun
ledifolia	GGar
lepidophylla	ECou
- silver-leaved	ECou
lirata	ECou GGar
macrodonta ♀H3	More than 30 suppliers
- 'Intermedia'	GGar
- 'Major'	GGar SHBN
- 'Minor'	CBcs CDoC CMac CTrC ELan EPfP GGar GQui SPlb WFar WSpi
minor	CBcs
x ***mollis*** misapplied	see *O. ilicifolia* x *O. moschata*
x ***mollis*** (Kirk) Cockayne	CPle GQui WSHC
- 'Zennorensis' ♀H3	CBcs CCCN CDoC EPfP GGar IArd IDee ISea MDun SDry SOWG WEas WGer WPGP
moschata	GGar NLar
moschata x ***nummularifolia*** **new**	GGar
myrsinoides	CPLG
nummularifolia	CBcs CDoC CHll CTrC CTri EBee ECou EPfP EPla GGar ISea SDry SEND SPer STre WBod WFar WKif WTel
- var. ***cymbifolia***	ECou WGer
- hybrids	ECou
- 'Little Lou'	ECou
odorata	CPLG ECou ISea NLar WFar WHCG
oleifolia	see *O.* 'Waikariensis'
paniculata	CBcs CDoC CMHG CPLG CTrC CTri EBee EPfP GGar GSki IClo ISea SDry SLon WGer
§ ***phlogopappa***	CSBt CTri ECou GGar WBrE
- 'Comber's Blue'	CBcs CCCN EPfP GGar LRHS LSRN NCGa SCoo SKHP SPer WBod
§ - 'Comber's Pink'	CBcs CBrm CCCN CDoC CPLG EPfP GGar ISea LRHS LSRN NCGa NPer SAga SCoo SPer WBod WEas WKif WLeb WWeb
- pink-flowered	CTrG
- 'Rosea'	see *O. phlogopappa* 'Comber's Pink'
- Splendens Group	CDul WFar
I - var. ***subrepanda*** (DC.) J.H. Willis	CPle CTrC GGar LEdu SEND
ramulosa	CDoC CPLG CPle CTrC
- 'Blue Stars'	ECou GGar
- var. ***ramulosa***	ECou
- 'White Stars'	ECou
rani misapplied	see *O. cheesemanii*
rani Druce	ISea
* ***rossii*** **new**	CTrC
x ***scilloniensis*** misapplied	see *O. stellulata* DC.
x ***scilloniensis*** Dorrien-Smith ♀H3	CCCN CChe GGar XPep

- 'Compacta'	CBcs
- 'Master Michael'	CCCN CDoC EPfP LRHS MRav NLar SBod SOWG SPer SPoG SRGP WEas WKif WSHC WWeb
semidentata misapplied	see *O.* 'Henry Travers'
solandri	CDoC CHEx CMac CSam EBee ECou EPla GGar IDee LRHS SDix SDry SEND SHFr SPer STre XPep
- 'Aurea'	CBcs GQui
stellulata misapplied	see *O. phlogopappa*
§ ***stellulata*** DC.	CBrm CPLG CSBt CTrG CWSG CWib ECou EPfP ISea LRHS MWat SAga SCoo SDix SGar SOWG SPer SPla WEas WFar WHCG WPic
- 'Michael's Pride'	CPLG
- var. ***rugosa***	ECou
§ 'Talbot de Malahide'	CDoC GGar
traversii	CBcs CDoC CMHG CSBt CTrC EBee GGar LRHS SEND WGer WHer XPep
- 'Tweedledum' (v)	CBow CDoC CTrC CWib ECou GGar
virgata	CCCN CHEx ECou GGar GQui GSki LEdu MCot WCot XPep
- var. ***laxiflora***	CTrC WHer
- var. ***lineata***	CDoC CPLG ECou GGar NLar SEND WSHC
- - 'Dartonii'	CBcs CDoC EBee ECou GGar LRHS MBlu SLPl
viscosa	CPle GGar
§ 'Waikariensis'	CMHG CPLG CPle CTrC CWsd ECou GGar IDee LRHS MBri SEND SLon WCFE WGer

Oligoneuron see *Solidago*

olive see *Olea europaea*

Olsynium (*Iridaceae*)

§ ***douglasii*** ♀H4	CMea EDAr EPot GCrs GEdr LTwo NMen NRya SIng WAbe WCot
- 'Album'	CMea GCrs GEdr NMen NRya NSla SIng WHal
- dwarf	GEdr
- var. ***inflatum***	EWes
§ ***filifolium***	NWCA
§ ***junceum***	MDKP WCot WPGP
- JCA 12289	MTho
lyckolmii	WCot

Olyra (*Poaceae*)

latifolia new	EBee
- F&M 70	WPGP

Omphalodes (*Boraginaceae*)

cappadocica ♀H4	CElw CEnt EBee ECha EPot IFoB LBMP LEdu LRHS NBro NCGa NCob NPer NSum NWCA SGar SPer SRms SWat WBrk
- 'Anthea Bloom'	GBuc IBlr NEgg
- 'Blueberries and Cream' (v)	WCot
- 'Cherry Ingram' ♀H4	More than 30 suppliers
- 'Cherry Ingram' variegated (v)	CFir
- 'Lilac Mist'	CElw CLAP EBee EPot LLWP MRav NCob SBch SRms SSvw SWat SWvt WGwG WPnP WTin
- 'Parisian Skies'	CElw CLAP
- 'Starry Eyes'	More than 30 suppliers
kuzinskyanae	SBla
§ ***linifolia*** ♀H4	CMea CSpe MCot NMen SBch WHil
- ***alba***	see *O. linifolia*
lojkae	SBla
luciliae	CLAP WThu
nitida	CPom EMon GGar NRya
verna	More than 30 suppliers
- 'Alba'	More than 30 suppliers
- 'Elfenauge'	CMil EGle EMon EPPr GBin NBir NRya SSvw WCot
- ***grandiflora***	WCot

Omphalogramma (*Primulaceae*)

delavayi	EBee GKev
forrestii	CExc EBee
vinciflorum	EBee

Oncostema see *Scilla*

onion see *Allium cepa*

Onixotis (*Colchicaceae*)

stricta	CPLG
triquetra	WCot

Onobrychis (*Papilionaceae*)

viciifolia	EBee EMan MSal SECG WSHC

Onoclea (*Woodsiaceae*)

§ ***intermedia***	EMon
sensibilis ♀H4	More than 30 suppliers
- copper-leaved	CHEx CWsd WPGP

Ononis (*Papilionaceae*)

fruticosa new	NLar
repens	CArn MSal NMir
rotundifolia	CPom MSal
spinosa	EBee EWin LRav MHer MSal NMir WFar WPer WSpi XPep

Onopordum (*Asteraceae*)

acanthium	CArn CBct CHrt EBee EBrs ECha ELan EPfP GAbr GMaP GWWP MHer MWat MWgw NBid NCGa NEgg NVic SIde SPoG WBor WCAu WCot WFar WHer WHil WMnd WSpi
arabicum	see *O. nervosum*
bracteatum	WPer
illyricum	WCot
§ ***nervosum*** ♀H4	CArn CSpe SAga SRms WFar
turcicum new	EBee

Onosma (*Boraginaceae*)

alborosea	CMdw CSev EBee ECha EGoo EMan GBri GCra GEdr GKev SAga WEas WKif WPGP
echioides	SSvw
helvetica	EMan
rigida	CMea
taurica ♀H4	CMdw NBir

Onychium (*Adiantaceae*)

contiguum	WAbe
japonicum	EFer GQui SRms WAbe

Ophiopogon ✿ (*Convallariaceae*)

BWJ 8244 from Vietnam	WCru
'Black Dragon'	see *O. planiscapus* 'Nigrescens'
bodinieri	CBct ECho ERos EWes LEdu SMac WRHF
- B&L 12505	CLAP EBee EPPr EPla
aff. ***caulescens*** HWJ 590	WCru
chingii	EBee EPPr EPla LEdu SCnR
* - 'Crispum'	CRez
formosanus	CPrp GBin
- B&SWJ 3659	EBee WCru
'Gin-ryu'	see *Liriope spicata* 'Gin-ryu'
graminifolius	see *Liriope muscari*

	intermedius	CBct EBee EPla ERos MSte WCot WPGP
	- GWJ 9387	WCru
	- HWJK 2093	WCru
§	- 'Argenteomarginatus'	ECho ERos EWes WPGP
	- ***parviflorus***	NSti
	- 'Variegatus'	see *O. intermedius* 'Argenteomarginatus'
§	***jaburan***	EBee ECho EShb LEdu MSte NHol WMoo
	- 'Variegatus'	see *O. jaburan* 'Vittatus'
§	- 'Vittatus' (v)	CMHG CPrp CSBt ECho ELan EPPr EPfP EShb EWes GSki LEdu MCCP MGos SAga WCot WFar WSpi
	japonicus	ECho EPPr EPfP EPla EShb GSki LEdu NLAp NSti XPep
	- B&SWJ 1842	WCru
	- 'Albus'	CLAP ECho NHol
	- 'Compactus'	CDoC CStu EBee SMac SPla WPGP
	- 'Kigimafukiduma'	CBgR CPen MBNS MRav NHol SPad WCot WSpi
	- 'Kyoto'	EPPr GSki NLAp
	- 'Minor'	CBct CEnd CKno CSBt EBee EPPr EPfP EPla NLar SMac WPGP
	- 'Nanus Variegatus' (v)	CDes EBee EMon NChi WHil
	- 'Nippon'	CPrp ECho EPPr GGar LAst MWgw
*	- 'Tama-ryu Number Two'	ECho EPPr
*	- 'Variegatus' (v)	CDTJ CKno CPrp ECho LEdu SLPl
	malcolmsonii B&SWJ 5264	WCru
	planiscapus	CEnd CFee CKno CMHG CPLG CSWP CSam CSev CStu EBee ECho EPPr EPla EShb GAbr MNHC MSte MTho NBro SPla STre WBVN WMoo
*	- 'Albovariegatus'	SPoG
	- 'Green Dragon'	ELan
	- ***leucanthus***	EPPr WCot
	- 'Little Tabby' (v)	CBow CDes CLAP CSpe EBee ECho EPla MDKP MMoz NPro WCot WDyG WHal WHrl WPGP WTin
*	- ***minimus***	ECho ERos
§	- 'Nigrescens' ♀H4	More than 30 suppliers
	- 'Silver Ribbon'	ECho MDKP SGar
	scaber B&SWJ 1871	WCru
	'Spring Gold'	CMil EBee EMon
	'Tama-hime-nishiki' (v)	EMon
	wallichianus	CStu EMar EPPr EPla GGar NLar SGar WCot WPGP
	- GWJ 9387	WCru

Ophrys (*Orchidaceae*)

	apifera	CFir NLAp SHdy WHer
	bombyliflora	NLAp
	fuciflora	SHdy
	holoserica new	NLAp
	insectifera	SHdy
	speculum new	NLAp
	sphegodes new	NLAp SHdy

Oplismenus (*Poaceae*)

§	***africanus*** 'Variegatus' (v) ♀H1	CHal
	hirtellus 'Variegatus'	see *O. africanus* 'Variegatus'

Opopanax (*Apiaceae*)

	chironium	LEdu

Opuntia ✿ (*Cactaceae*)

	compressa	see *O. humifusa*
§	***humifusa***	CDTJ SChr SMad
	microdasys	SWal
	- var. ***albospina***	SWal
	ovata new	WCot
§	***polyacantha***	LPJP SChr SPlb
	rhodantha	see *O. polyacantha*

orange, sour or Seville see *Citrus aurantium*

orange, sweet see *Citrus sinensis*

Orbea (*Asclepiadaceae*)

§	***variegata*** ♀H1	EShb

Orchis (*Orchidaceae*)

	anthropophora	EFEx SHdy
	elata	see *Dactylorhiza elata*
	foliosa	see *Dactylorhiza foliosa*
	fuchsii	see *Dactylorhiza fuchsii*
	graminifolia	GEdr
	laxiflora	see *Anacamptis laxiflora*
	maculata	see *Dactylorhiza maculata*
	maderensis	see *Dactylorhiza foliosa*
	majalis	see *Dactylorhiza majalis*
§	***mascula***	CWsd WHer
	morio	see *Anacamptis morio*
	purpurea new	SHdy
	simia new	SHdy

oregano see *Origanum vulgare*

Oreomyrrhis (*Apiaceae*)

	argentea	NMen

Oreopteris (*Thelypteridaceae*)

§	***limbosperma***	SRms WRic

Oresitrophe (*Saxifragaceae*)

	rupifraga	WCru

Origanum ✿ (*Lamiaceae*)

	acutidens	XPep
	amanum ♀H2-3	CPBP EBee ECho EGle EWes LRHS MDKP NBir NMen SBla WAbe WHoo WPat
	- var. ***album***	ECho SBla WAbe WPat
	x ***applii***	ELau
	'Barbara Tingey'	CPBP CSpe CWCL ECho ELan EWes ITim LBee LRHS MNrw MSte MTho NWCA SBla SMeo SPhx WAbe WCFE WHoo
	'Bristol Cross'	EBee ECha MHer
	'Buckland'	EBee ECho EPot LRHS MHer MSte NMen NWCA SBla SPhx WAbe WPat WSHC
	caespitosum	see *O. vulgare* 'Nanum'
§	***calcaratum***	ECho EMan LRHS MTho SBla WAbe WPat
	creticum	see *O. vulgare* subsp. *hirtum*
	dictamnus	CArn ECho EEls EPot GPoy LRHS LTwo MDKP NWCA SBla SHDw WAbe WJek WLin XPep
	'Dingle Fairy'	CMMP EBee ECho EGoo EMan EPot EWes MHer MLLN MMHG MNrw MTho NBir NWCA SBch SIde SIng SRot WGwG WMoo
	'Emma Stanley'	WAbe
	'Erntedank'	EBee
	'Frank Tingey'	ECho LTwo
	'Fritz Kummert'	NCGa
	'Gold Splash'	EPfP SIde WMoo
	heracleoticum L.	see *O. vulgare* subsp. *hirtum*
	'Hot and Spicy'	EWin NPri
§	x ***hybridinum***	SBla WPat
	'Ingolstadt'	SAga SPhx
	'Kent Beauty'	More than 30 suppliers
	'Kent Beauty Variegated' (v)	ECho

	kopetdaghense	XPep
	laevigatum ♀H3	CArn CMHG ECho ELan EPfP MHar MHer NBro NMir NPer NWCA SGar SIde WMoo WPer WSHC XPep
	- 'Herrenhausen' ♀H4	More than 30 suppliers
	- 'Hopleys'	More than 30 suppliers
	- 'Purple Charm'	EBee EDAr MNHC NBre WSpi
	- 'Springwood'	NWCA
	majorana	CArn CSev ELan ELau GWCH MHer MNHC MSal SIde SWal SWat WJek WPer WSel XPep
I	- 'Aureum'	SWal
	- Pagoda Bells = 'Lizbell'PBR	LHop WHoo
	'Marchants Seedling'	SMHy
	microphyllum	CFee EDAr LRHS MAsh MTho NMen SBla SIng SMeo XPep
	minutiflorum	ECho LTwo
	'Norton Gold'	CBre EBee ECha EPot EWin GBuc LRHS MHer NBre NPer SIde
	'Nymphenburg'	CFee CSam EBee EMan LSou MHer MSte NCob SIde SMrm WCru WHer WSpi
	onites	CArn CHby CWan ELau ILis MHer MNHC MSal NBlu SIde SPlb WBrk WGwG WHer WJek WPer WSel XPep
	- 'Noa'	EWin
	'Phoenix Seedling' new	SPhx
	'Pilgrim'	EWsh SIde
	pulchellum	see *O.* x *hybridinum*
	'Purple Cloud'	NBir
	'Rosenkuppel'	CMea CPrp EBee ECha ELan EPot LHop MHer MLHP MRav MSte NCGa NGHP SMad SMeo SMrm SPer SPhx SPla SPlb WLin WMoo WSpi WTel XPep
	'Rotkugel'	CAby CMHG CPrp CWsd EBee EGle EWin LSou MSte SPhx WCru
	rotundifolium ♀H4	ECho ELan MDKP MHer NBir SBch SBla WAbe
	- hybrid	MDKP
	scabrum	CArn
	- subsp. ***pulchrum***	CStu XPep
	- - 'Newleaze'	LHop SBch WHoo
	sipyleum	SBla
	syriacum	XPep
	'Tinpenny Pink'	WTin
	tournefortii	see *O. calcaratum*
	tytthanthum	EMon XPep
	villosum	see *Thymus villosus*
	virens	CArn ILis MCCP
	vulgare	CArn CHrt CRWN CSev CWan ECho EDAr GMaP GPoy MBar MHer MNHC NBro NLan NMir NPri SEND SGar SIde SPlb SWal WHer WPer WSFF XPep
	- from Israel	ELau
	- 'Acorn Bank'	CArn CBod CPrp CWan EBee EGoo EShb EUnu EWes EWin MHer MNHC NHol NLar SAga SIde WGwG WHer WJek
	- var. ***album***	CElw
	- 'Aureum' ♀H4	More than 30 suppliers
	- 'Aureum Crispum'	CBgR CPrp CWan ECha EGoo ELau GAbr GPoy ILis NBid NBlu NGHP SBch SIde SWat WJek WSel
	- 'Compactum'	CArn CMea CPrp CSev EBee ECha EGoo ELau GPoy ILis LEdu MHar MHer MNHC NCob NGHP SAga SBla SIde SPlb SWat WAbe WGwG WHoo WMoo WPer WSel WTMC WTin
	- 'Corinne Tremaine' (v)	NBir WHer
	- 'Country Cream' (v)	More than 30 suppliers
	- ***formosanum*** B&SWJ 3180	WCru
§	- 'Gold Tip' (v)	CBgR CEnt CMea CSev EBee ELau ILis MHer MNHC NGHP NPri SIde SPlb SWat WFar WHer
	- 'Golden Shine'	CMMP EBee EWes EWin NGHP
§	- subsp. ***hirtum***	CArn CHby GPoy LEdu MSal SPlb WJek WPer XPep
	- - 'Greek'	CBod CEnt CPrp CWan ELau EUnu GWCH MHer MNHC NGHP WGwG
§	- 'Nanum'	ECho LRHS WJek
	- 'Nyamba'	GPoy
	- 'Polyphant' (v)	CSev EBee EDAr EGle EMan LSou MLLN NBir WBrE WJek WMoo WSel
	- 'Thumble's Variety'	CBgR CBod CElw CMea CPrp EBee ECha EGle EGoo EPot LHop LRHS MBri MHer MRav NCob NGHP NHol SIde SSvw SWat WEas WMnd WMoo WSpi XPep
	- 'Tomintoul'	GPoy
	- 'Variegatum'	see *O. vulgare* 'Gold Tip'
	- 'White Charm'	NHol
	'White Cloud'	EBee
	'Z'Attar'	MHer SIde

Orixa (*Rutaceae*)

	japonica	EPfP NLar WFar WPGP
	- 'Variegata' (v)	EBee EPfP LRHS LTwo NLar SPoG

Orlaya (*Apiaceae*)

	grandiflora	CBre CHrt CSpe LPio MAvo SBch WCot WFar WHal

Ornithogalum (*Hyacinthaceae*)

	arabicum	CBgR EBrs ECho EPfP LAma LRHS MBri MLLN SPhx WCot
	arcuatum	CHHB WCot
	arianum new	EBee EBrs ECho
	balansae	see *O. oligophyllum*
	caudatum	see *O. longibracteatum*
	chionophilum	EBee EBrs ECho
	comosum	ECho
	dubium ♀H1	CBgR CHHB EBrs ECho WCot
	exscapum	CStu ECho
	fimbriatum	EBee EBrs ECho
*	***kotschyanum*** new	GCrs
	lanceolatum	CHHB WCot
§	***longibracteatum***	CHEx CStu EBee ECho EPem SChr WGwG WPrP
	magnum	CAvo CFFs CMea CSsd EBee EBrs ECho ERCP LRHS MNrw SPur WCot
	- 'Saguramo'	EBrs
	montanum	ECho
	'Mount Everest'	ECho
	'Mount Fuji'	EBrs ECho
	nanum	see *O. sigmoideum*
	narbonense	CHHB EBee EBrs ECho GBuc LRHS SPhx WCot
	nutans ♀H4	CAvo CBgR CFFs CFwr CMea CStu EBee EBrs ECho EMon EPfP EPot LAma LBMP MAvo MEHN MLLN MNrw NMen NWCA SMeo SPhx WAul WBrk WCot WFar WPer
§	***oligophyllum***	CBgR CHHB CMea CStu EBee EBrs ECho EPfP EPot ERCP MNrw NWCA SMeo WCot
§	***orthophyllum***	CStu EBrs WCot
	platyphyllum	EBrs
	ponticum	CHHB ECho ERos
	pyramidale	CDes CSpe EBee EBrs ECho EPot LRHS MNrw WCot

	pyrenaicum	CAvo CFFs CStu EBee ECha ERos WCot WShi
	reverchonii	CAvo CDes EBee EBrs ECho ERos WCot
	saundersiae	EBee EBrs ECho
	schmalhausenii	WWst
	sibthorpii	see *O. sigmoideum*
§	***sigmoideum***	CStu EBrs ECho WAbe
	sintenisii	CHHB EBee EBrs LRHS
	sphaerocarpum	WCot
	tenuifolium	see *O. orthophyllum*
	- subsp. ***aridum***	WWst
	thyrsoides ♀H1	CCCN EBrs ECho EPfP ERCP LAma SPet
	ulophyllum new	EBee EBrs ECho
	umbellatum	CAvo CFFs CTri EBrs ECho ELan EMon EPfP GAbr GPoy LAma LHop LRHS MBri MNrw NMen SPer SRms WBVN WFar WPer WShi
	unifolium	ECho

Orobanche (*Scrophulariaceae*)

	sp. new	SKHP

Orontium (*Araceae*)

	aquaticum	CBen CDWL CWat EHon EMFW NLar NPer SWat WMAq WPnP

Orostachys (*Crassulaceae*)

	furusei	EMan WCot WFar
	iwarenge	CStu
§	***spinosa***	CStu EMan EWes NMen WCot WFar

Oroxylum (*Bignoniaceae*)

	indicum	CArn

Orphium (*Gentianaceae*)

	frutescens	EShb

Orthrosanthus (*Iridaceae*)

	chimboracensis	CDes CFir EMan MDKP MGos MWea NLar WFar WLin WPGP WPer
	- B&SWJ 10234	WCru
	- JCA 13743	CPou
	laxus	CFir EBee ECou EPau ERos EWsh GBuc GMac MAvo NEgg SMad WHrl
	multiflorus	CBct CDes CElw CWCL EBee ITim WPGP
	polystachyus	CCVN CPle CRez CSpe EBee EMan ERos MAvo MWea SSvw WHrl WSHC

Oryzopsis (*Poaceae*)

	hymenoides	LEdu MAvo
	lessoniana	see *Anemanthele lessoniana*
	miliacea	CBig CHar CHrt CKno CSpe EBee ECha EPPr EWsh GFor ITer LDai SMHy WCot WPGP
	paradoxa	EPPr

Oscularia (*Aizoaceae*)

§	***deltoides*** ♀H1-2	CCCN CStu EWin WCot WEas

Osmanthus (*Oleaceae*)

	armatus	CAbP CTri EPfP MWya NLar WFar
§	x ***burkwoodii*** ♀H4	More than 30 suppliers
§	***decorus***	CBcs CSBt CTri EBee ELan EPfP EWTr MGos MRav NLar SPer SPla WBod WFar WSpi
	delavayi ♀H4	More than 30 suppliers
	- 'Latifolius'	EPfP LRHS SLon WFar
	forrestii	see *O. yunnanensis*
	x ***fortunei***	CPLG EPfP LTwo MGos SLPl WFar
	fragrans	SLon
	- 'Latifolius' new	CBcs
	- f. ***thunbergii***	CBcs
§	***heterophyllus***	CBcs CDul EBee ENot EPfP EWTr MBar MGan MRav MWya NLar SPer SReu SRms SSta WFar XPep
§	- all gold	CAbP CDoC EMil LAst MBlu SMer SPer SPla SPoG
	- 'Argenteomarginatus'	see *O. heterophyllus* 'Variegatus'
§	- 'Aureomarginatus' (v)	CBcs CDoC CHar CMHG CSBt EBee EPfP ISea LRHS MWya SHBN SLon SPer SPoG
	- 'Aureus' misapplied	see *O. heterophyllus* all gold
	- 'Aureus' Rehder	see *O. heterophyllus* 'Aureomarginatus'
§	- 'Goshiki' (v)	More than 30 suppliers
N	- 'Gulftide' ♀H4	CDoC EBee ECrN EPfP LRHS MGos NLar SCoo WFar
	- 'Kembu' (v) new	NLar
	- 'Myrtifolius'	NLar
	- 'Ogon'	MBar
	- 'Purple Shaft'	CAbP ELan EPfP LRHS MAsh NHol
	- 'Purpureus'	CAbP CBcs CBgR CDoC CDul CMHG CSam CWib EBee ECrN EPfP LRHS MBri MGos MRav NHol SCoo SDry SLim SLon SPer SSpi WWeb
	- 'Rotundifolius'	CBcs NLar
	- Tricolor	see *O. heterophyllus* 'Goshiki'
§	- 'Variegatus' (v) ♀H4	More than 30 suppliers
	ilicifolius	see *O. heterophyllus*
	rigidus	NLar
	serrulatus	CAbP NLar WPGP
	suavis	EPfP LRHS NLar
§	***yunnanensis***	EBee EPfP LRHS MBlu NLar SAPC SArc WFar WPGP

x *Osmarea* (*Oleaceae*)

	burkwoodii	see *Osmanthus* x *burkwoodii*

Osmaronia see *Oemleria*

Osmitopsis (*Asteraceae*)

	asteriscoides	GFai

Osmorhiza (*Apiaceae*)

	aristata B&SWJ 1607	WCru

Osmunda ✿ (*Osmundaceae*)

	sp.	CCCN
	cinnamomea ♀H4	CCCN CFwr CLAP CMil CPrp CWCL EWes GBin MAsh MPes NMyG WPGP WRic
	claytoniana ♀H4	CLAP CMil CRez EPfP MAsh MPes NBid NHol NLar NMyG NVic WCru WPnP WRic
	japonica	GBin
	lancea	NLar
	regalis ♀H4	More than 30 suppliers
	- 'Cristata' ♀H4	CFwr CLAP ELan EWTr GBin MBri MPes MRav NBid NHol NLar WFib WPGP WRic
	- 'Purpurascens'	More than 30 suppliers
	- var. ***spectabilis***	CCCN CLAP WRic
	- 'Undulata'	ELan NHol WFib

Osteomeles (*Rosaceae*)

	schweriniae	EMan
	- B&L 12360	CPle
	subrotunda	MBri

Osteospermum ✿ (*Asteraceae*)

	'African Queen'	see *O.* 'Nairobi Purple'
	'Almach' PBR (Springstar Series)	LSou

'Arctur'PBR — LAst
Banana Symphony = 'Sekiin47' (Symphony Series) — CBcs CCCN LSou SPoG
barberae misapplied — see *O. jucundum* (Phillips) Norlindh
'Blackthorn Seedling' — see *O. jucundum* 'Blackthorn Seedling'
'Blue Streak' — CCCN
'Brickell's Hybrid' — see *O.* 'Chris Brickell'
'Buttermilk' ♀H1+3 — CCCN CHal ELan SMrm WWlt
'Cannington John' — GCra
'Cannington Roy' — CCCN CMHG COlW CSam ECtt EPfP EWin LSRN SPoG
'Castor' — LAst
caulescens misapplied — see *O.* 'White Pim'
§ 'Chris Brickell' — CHal MSte WHil
ecklonis — CCCN CDTJ CHll CTri GGar GMaP IBlr ISea MHer NBro NGdn WPer
- var. ***prostratum*** — see *O.* 'White Pim'
'Edna Bond' — WEas
fruticosum — XPep
I - 'Album' — XPep
'Gemma'PBR (Springstar Series) — MBNS SMrm WGor
'Giles Gilbey' (v) — CCCN CHal CPLG MBNS
'Gold Sparkler' (v) — SMrm
'Gweek Variegated' (v) — CCCN
'Helen Dimond' — LBuc WWeb
'Hopleys' ♀H3-4 — MHer MWrn SEND
'Irish' — EPot IGor LSou MWrn
§ ***jucundum*** (Phillips) Norlindh ♀H3-4 — CChe CEnt CMHG CMea CPLG CTri CWCL ECha EPfP LRHS LSRN MLHP MNrw MRav NBir NChi NEgg NGdn NPer SEND SPlb SRms WBVN WHen WWeb
§ - 'Blackthorn Seedling' ♀H3-4 — CMea GBuc NGdn SAga
- var. ***compactum*** — CHEx CLyd CPBP ELan EPfP EShb GGar MBri MHar NLar NPer SMrm SPoG SPur WAbe WHen WHoo WLin
- 'Jackarandum' — MDKP
§ - 'Killerton Pink' — WPer
§ - 'Langtrees' ♀H3-4 — LHop SMrm
Kalanga Rosy = 'Aksinto'PBR (Cape Daisy Series) — LRHS
'Keia'PBR (Springstar Series) — CCCN LAst LSou
'Killerton Pink' — see *O. jucundum* 'Killerton Pink'
§ 'Lady Leitrim' ♀H3-4 — CCCN CHEx CHrt ECha EPfP EShb GBri GCra GGar IBlr LHop LSRN MBnl MWrn NPer SAga SPoG SSvw WAbe WFar WWeb
'Langtrees' — see *O. jucundum* 'Langtrees'
'Lemon Symphony'PBR (Symphony Series) — CBcs CFir LAst SVil
'Malindi'PBR (Cape Daisy Series) **new** — SGar
Milk Symphony = 'Seiremi' (Symphony Series) — CCCN CFir SVil
'Mirach' (Springstar Series) — LSou
§ 'Nairobi Purple' — CCCN CDoC CFee CHEx CHal CPLG ELan
Nasinga Cream = 'Aknam'PBR (Cape Daisy Series) — CCCN
Nasinga Purple = 'Aksullo'PBR — LRHS
oppositifolium — CCCN
Orange Symphony = 'Seimora'PBR (Symphony Series) — CBcs CCCN LSou SMrm SPoG SVil
Orania Terracotta = 'Akterra' (Cape Daisy Series) — SGar
'Pale Face' — see *O.* 'Lady Leitrim'
Peach Symphony = 'Seitope'PBR (Symphony Series) — CBcs
'Peggyi' — see *O.* 'Nairobi Purple'
I 'Pink Superbum' — CHEx
'Pink Whirls' ♀H1+3 — CCCN CHal
'Pollux'PBR (Springstar Series) — MBNS
'Port Wine' — see *O.* 'Nairobi Purple'
'Seaside'PBR (Side Series) — EPfP
'Serenity Cream' (Serenity Series) **new** — SVil
'Silver Sparkler' (v) ♀H1+3 — CCCN CDTJ ELan EShb EWin MBNS MHer WBrE
Sonja = 'Sunny Sonja'PBR — EPfP
'Sparkler' — CCCN CHEx MSte
Springstar Series — EShb
'Stardust'PBR — LBuc LRHS NPer SCoo SPoG
'Sunny Alex'PBR — LRHS
'Sunny Amanda'PBR — LSou SRGP WGor
'Sunny Amelia' — LAst SRGP
'Sunny Cecil'PBR — LRHS SRGP
'Sunny Dark Martha'PBR — EPfP LAst LRHS
'Sunny Flora'PBR — SRGP
'Sunny Martha'PBR — LAst
'Sunny Mary'PBR — LAst LSou SRGP WGor WRHF
'Sunny Nathalie' — LAst SRGP
'Sunny Philip'PBR — SRGP
'Sunny Plum Serena'PBR — SRGP
'Sunny Serena'PBR — LAst LRHS SRGP
'Sunny Stephanie'PBR — LAst SRGP
'Sunny Zara'PBR — SRGP
* 'Superbum' — CHEx
I 'Superbum' x 'Lady Leitrim' — CHEx
'Svelte' — MSte
'Tauranga' — see *O.* 'Whirlygig'
(Tradewinds Series) Tradewinds Deep Purple = 'Oste Deeppur' — SVil
- Tradewinds Light Purple = 'Oste Lightpur' **new** — SVil
- Tradewinds Pink Bicolour = 'Oste Pinkbic'PBR **new** — SVil
- Tradewinds Pure Yellow = 'Oste Yel' **new** — SVil
- Tradewinds White with Blue Eye = 'Oste Whitey'PBR **new** — SVil
'Tresco Peggy' — see *O.* 'Nairobi Purple'
'Tresco Pink' — CCCN IBlr
'Tresco Purple' — see *O.* 'Nairobi Purple'
'Uranus' — SRGP
'Vega' — LAst
'Weetwood' ♀H3-4 — CCCN CMHG CPLG ECtt EPot EShb EWin LHop MBNS MBri MHer MLHP MSte NLar SAga SPoG WAbe WEas WFar WWeb
§ 'Whirlygig' ♀H1+3 — CCCN CHal MHer
§ 'White Pim' ♀H3-4 — CDTJ CHll CMHG ELan ELon GBuc LCro MAvo NPer SDix SPer SPhx SPoG XPep
'Wildside'PBR (Side Series) — EShb
'Wine Purple' — see *O.* 'Nairobi Purple'
Wisley hybrids — WEas
'Wisley Pink' — EPyc
'Zaurak'PBR (Springstar Series) — CBcs CCCN EShb LAst LSou WGor
'Zimba'PBR — ELan
'Zulu'PBR (Cape Daisy Series) — CCCN

Ostrowskia (*Campanulaceae*)

magnifica MTho

Ostrya (*Corylaceae*)

carpinifolia CBcs CDul CLnd CMCN CTho CWib EBee ECrN EMil EPfP EWTr LRHS MBar MBlu NLar SBLw WNor
japonica CDul CMCN NLar
virginiana CMCN EPfP IClo WNor

Otanthus (*Asteraceae*)

maritimus XPep

Othonna (*Asteraceae*)

capensis CHal
cheirifolia CMea CSam EGoo ELan EMan EWes MFOX NBir SDry WBrk WCot WEas WPer XPep

Othonnopsis see *Othonna*

Ourisia (*Scrophulariaceae*)

x ***bitternensis*** 'Cliftonville Roset' new WAbe
caespitosa GCrs GGar IBlr NMen NRya
– var. ***gracilis*** GEdr IBlr NMen
§ ***coccinea*** EBee ELon EMan GAbr GBuc GCra GEdr GGar GKev GMac IBlr LRHS NBir NMen NRya NWCA WAbe
crosbyi GEdr GGar IBlr
crosbyi x ***macrocarpa*** IBlr
elegans see *O. coccinea*
lactea IBlr
'Loch Ewe' CPLG GAbr GBuc GEdr GGar IBlr MDun WCru WPGP
macrocarpa IBlr
macrophylla EBee EWld GBin GBuc GGar GKev IBlr IGor LTwo WAbe
macrophylla x ***modesta*** IBlr
microphylla WAbe
* – f. ***alba*** WAbe
modesta IBlr
polyantha F&W 8487 CPBP WAbe
– 'Cliftonville Scarlet' CPBP SBla WAbe WFar
'Snowflake' Υ^{H4} GAbr GBin GCrs GEdr IBlr MDun NBir NLAp NMen WAbe

Oxalis (*Oxalidaceae*)

F&W 8673 CPBP
acetosella CHid CRWN MHer NSco SIng WHer WShi
– var. ***subpurpurascens*** MMHG SIng WCot
adenophylla Υ^{H4} More than 30 suppliers
– 'Brenda Anderson' ITim
– dark MTho
adenophylla x ***enneaphylla*** see *O.* 'Matthew Forrest'
anomala EBrs ECho EMan ERos WCot
arborescens CHEx
§ ***articulata*** EMan MTho NPer SEND WCot
– 'Alba' LRHS WCot
– 'Aureoreticulata' MTho
– 'Festival' WCot
'Beatrice Anderson' GCrs LRHS MTho NMen WAbe
bowiei CHHB CPBP CStu EBee EBrs ECho EPot
– 'Amarantha'^{PBR} EBee EBrs ECho
'Bowles' White' MTho
brasiliensis CPBP CStu ECho EPot MTho NMen
brick-orange-flowered WCot
chrysantha WAbe
compacta F&W 8011 CPBP
corniculata var. ***atropurpurea*** MTho
'Dark Eye' GCrs
deppei see *O. tetraphylla*
§ ***depressa*** CStu CTri EBee EBrs ECho EPot EWes GEdr GSki LTwo MTho NBir NEgg NLAp NMen NRya NSla SIng SRms WBrE WFar
– 'Irish Mist' CStu EBee EBrs ECho
* ***eckloniana*** var. ***sonderi*** EBee EBrs ECho WCot
enneaphylla Υ^{H4} CElw ECho EMan EPot GCrs GGar GMaP LRHS MTho NMen NRya
– F&W 2715 CPBP
– 'Alba' CPBP ECho ERos GBuc GCrs GGar ITim NMen NSla WAbe WIvy
– 'Lady Elizabeth' CPBP
– 'Minutifolia' ERos GCrs LRHS LTwo MTho NMen NRya NSla WIvy
* – 'Minutifolia Rosea' CGra
– 'Rosea' CStu EBrs EPot ERos GKev MTho NRya NSla
– 'Ruth Tweedie' CGra NLAp NSla
– 'Sheffield Swan' CGra CStu ECho NMen NSla WAbe
europaea GWCH
falcatula WCot
'Fanny' CStu EBee EBrs ECho
floribunda misapplied see *O. articulata*
fourcadei WCot
geminata NBir
gigantea CSpe
glabra CPBP WAbe
'Gwen McBride' CGra GCrs SBla WAbe
hedysaroides CCCN
'Hemswell Knight' NMen
hirta CPBP EPot MTho
– 'Gothenburg' CPBP EBee ECho EMan ERos MTho NMen
imbricata CPBP EPot LTwo
inops see *O. depressa*
'Ione Hecker' Υ^{H4} CGra CLyd CPBP EBrs ECho EPot ERos GCrs GEdr GGar GKev GMaP ITim LRHS MTho NHar NLAp NMen NRya NSla NWCA WAbe WIvy WLin
* ***karroica*** EBee EBrs ECho NMen WCot
§ ***laciniata*** CGra ERos GCrs ITim MTho NHar NMen NSla WAbe
– hybrid seedlings NHar
– 'Seven Bells' WAbe
lactea double see *O. magellanica* 'Nelson'
lasiandra EBee EBrs EPot ERos
§ ***lobata*** CPBP CStu EBee EBrs ECho EMan ERos EWes LHop LRHS MTho WAbe WFar
loricata EBrs ECho NMen
magellanica CPom CSpe CTri EAlp ECho EDAr GGar LBee MTho NPro SIng SPlb WFar WMoo WPer
– 'Flore Pleno' see *O. magellanica* 'Nelson'
§ – 'Nelson' (d) CPLG CSpe CStu EBee ECho EDAr EMan EWes GBuc GGar GMac LBee LRHS MTho NBir NPer WMoo WPer WPnP WPrP WPtf
massoniana CHHB EBee EBrs ECho SBla SIng WAbe
§ 'Matthew Forrest' NMen WAbe
megalorrhiza CPLG SChr
§ ***melanosticta*** CHHB CStu EBrs EDAr EMan EPot GCrs LTwo SIng
monophylla EBee EBrs ECho
nahuelhuapiensis F&W 8469 CPBP
namaquana WCot
obtriangulata new EBrs ECho

obtusa	CLyd CStu EBee EBrs ECha ECho MTho SCnR WCot
- apricot	WCot
oregana	CDes CHid CRez EBee ELon GBuc GGar WCot WCru WPGP WPrP WSHC
- f. ***smalliana***	EWes WCru
palmifrons	CPBP EPot MTho
patagonica	EBrs ECho EPot ERos GCrs NMen
perdicaria	see *O. lobata*
polyphylla	EBee EBrs ECho
- var. ***heptaphylla*** **new**	SIng
- var. ***pentaphylla***	EPot
§ ***purpurea***	EBrs ECho MWea WAbe
- 'Ken Aslet'	see *O. melanosticta*
regnellii	see *O. triangularis* subsp. *papilionacea*
rosea misapplied	see *O. rubra*
§ ***rubra***	EBee EBrs WBrE
semiloba	EBrs ECho EMan WCot
speciosa	see *O. purpurea*
squamata	NLAp WPat
squamosoradicosa	see *O. laciniata*
succulenta Barnéoud	CHll CSpe
'Sunny'	EBrs
'Sunset Velvet'	CHal LAst SVil
'Superstar'	NMen WAbe
§ ***tetraphylla***	CAgr CMMP EBee EBrs ECho GSki LAma LRHS MTho NEgg NPer
* - ***alba***	ECho
- 'Iron Cross'	CHEx CHHB CPLG EBee EBrs ECho EPot GSki LAma MMHG NBir WBVN WPer
'Tima'	CPBP
tortuosa **new**	WCot
triangularis	CAgr CCCN CHEx CHal CStu CTca ECGP ECho EOHP EShb LAma MAvo NBir NBlu NEgg NPer WBrE WFar
- 'Birgit'	EBee ECho
- 'Cupido'	EBee ECho GGar WPer
- 'Mijke'	EBee EBrs ECho
§ - subsp. ***papilionacea*** ♀H1	EBee EBrs EMan GSki LAma LRHS MMHG NEgg
- - 'Atropurpurea'	CSpe EBee LHop WBVN
* - - ***rosea***	EBee EMan WCot
- subsp. ***triangularis***	CHHB EBee EBrs
truncatula **new**	SIng
tuberosa	EUnu GGar GPoy ILis LEdu
- 'Fat White'	EUnu
- pink-flowered	EUnu
- red-flowered	EUnu
'Ute'	CGra CLyd CPBP GEdr NSla SBla
valdiviensis	EDAr EMan MDKP
versicolor ♀H1	CHHB CPBP CStu EBee EBrs ECho EMan EPot ERos ITer MTho NMen SBla SCnR WAbe WCot
- 'Clove Ball'	WPtf
vulcanicola	CCCN CStu LSou SDix WDyG
- 'Burgundy' **new**	NPri
zeekoevleyensis	WCot

Oxycoccus see *Vaccinium*

Oxydendrum (*Ericaceae*)

arboreum	CAbP CBcs CDoC CEnd CMCN EPfP IDee IMGH LRHS MBri NLar SCoo SSpi SSta WFar WNor WOrn WPGP
- 'Chameleon'	EBee EPfP MAsh SPer SPoG SSpi SSta

Oxygraphis (*Ranunculaceae*)

§ ***glacialis*** **new**	EBee

Oxypetalum (*Asclepiadaceae*)

caeruleum	see *Tweedia caerulea*

Oxyria (*Polygonaceae*)

digyna	CAgr GGar NLar WHer

Oxytropis (*Papilionaceae*)

borealis var. ***viscida***	CPBP
hailarensis var. ***chankaensis***	CPBP
lambertii	LTwo
megalantha	EMan
oreophila var. ***juniperina*** **new**	CPBP
purpurea	EMan LTwo NWCA
shokanbetsuensis	EMan LTwo

Ozothamnus (*Asteraceae*)

§ ***coralloides*** ♀H2-3	ECou EPot GCrs NDlv NHar NWCA SIng WAbe
§ 'County Park Silver'	EWes GEdr ITim MDKP NDlv NLAp NWCA WLin WPat
§ ***hookeri***	CDoC CMdw EBee ECou GGar MBrN MRav NLar NWCA SPer WJek WPat
§ ***ledifolius*** ♀H4	CDoC CMHG CPle EBee ELan EPfP GGar LRHS MBri NBir SLon SPer WHCG WPat WSHC
§ ***rosmarinifolius***	CBcs CDoC CPLG CTrG EBee ELan EPfP GGar LRHS MSwo MWat SPer WBod WEas WFar WHCG XPep
- 'Kiandra'	ECou
- 'Silver Jubilee' ♀H3	CBcs CDoC CEnd CEnt CHEx CPLG CSBt CTrG EBee ELan EPfP LRHS MAsh MBri MGos MRav MSwo NEgg NSti SLim SLon SPer SPlb SPoG SRkn WFar WHCG WKif XPep
scutellifolius	ECou
§ ***selago***	ECou NDlv WCot WThu
- 'Minor'	ITim WAbe
§ - var. ***tumidus***	ITim SIng WThu
'Sussex Silver'	EWin
'Threave Seedling'	CDoC ELan GBin LRHS SKHP SPer
§ ***thyrsoideus***	CPLG WFar

P

Pachyphragma (*Brassicaceae*)

§ ***macrophyllum***	CPom CSev EBee ECGP ECha EGle EHrv ELan IBlr LRHS MNFA NCiC NLar NMRc NSti WCru WEas WMoo WPGP WSHC

Pachyphytum (*Crassulaceae*)

hookeri **new**	EPem
oviferum	SChr

Pachypodium (*Apocynaceae*)

brevicaule **new**	LToo
lamerei ♀H1	LToo
lealii subsp. ***saundersii***	LToo
namaquanum	LToo
rosulatum var. ***gracilius***	LToo
succulentum	LToo

Pachysandra (*Buxaceae*)

axillaris	CLAP SKHP
- BWJ 8032	WCru
procumbens	CLAP EBee EHrv EPla NLar SKHP WCot WCru

stylosa	EPla MRav NLar
terminalis	CSBt CTri EBee ECha ECrN ELan ENot EPfP LBuc LCro LRHS MBar MGos MRav MSwo NEgg NHol NWea SHBN SLim SMer SPer SPlb SReu WBrE WCFE WHar WWeb
- 'Green Carpet' ♀H4	CBcs CDoC COfW CSam CWib EBee ECot EGol ELan EPfP EWTr GMaP LAst LBMP LHop LRHS LSRN MBar MBri MGos MSwo NBlu NPro SMac SPer SPla SPoG SWvt WCAu
- 'Green Sheen'	ECha MGos WFar
- 'Variegata' (v) ♀H4	More than 30 suppliers

Pachystachys (*Acanthaceae*)

lutea ♀H1	CHal ERea EShb LRHS MBri MJnS

Pachystegia (*Asteraceae*)

§ ***insignis***	GGar
rufa	CPle

Pachystima see *Paxistima*

Packera (*Asteraceae*)

§ ***aurea***	ECha MSal SKHP WMoo

Paederia (*Rubiaceae*)

scandens	CPLG WCru WSHC
- HWJ 656	WCru
- var. ***mairei*** B&SWJ 989	WCru

Paederota (*Scrophulariaceae*)

§ ***bonarota***	CLyd
lutea	CDes NWCA

Paeonia ✿ (*Paeoniaceae*)

'Age of Gold' (S)	WCAu
albiflora	see *P. lactiflora*
'Alley Cat'	WAul
'America'	MBri WCAu
'Angelet'	CKel
'Angelo Cobb Freeborn'	WCAu
anomala	CFir EBee EGle MHom MPhe NLar NSla WCot
§ - var. ***anomala*** **new**	EBee
- var. ***intermedia***	EBrs EGle
- subsp. ***veitchii***	see *P. veitchii*
'Argosy'	WCAu
arietina	see *P. mascula* subsp. *arietina*
'Athena'	GBin
'Auten's Red'	WCAu
'Avant Garde'	ECha
bakeri	EBee
banatica	see *P. officinalis* subsp. *banatica*
'Banquet' (S)	WCAu
beresovskii	EBrs
'Black Monarch'	WCAu
'Black Panther' (S)	WCAu
'Black Pirate' (S)	CKel WCAu
'Blaze'	GMaP WCAu
Blue and Purple Giant	see *P. suffruticosa* 'Zi Lan Kui'
'Bolero' **new**	CHFP
'Bridal Icing'	WCAu
'Bride's Dream' **new**	GBin
broteroi	EBrs MHom SKHP
'Buckeye Belle'	CKel EBee GBin MBri MHom MNrw MSte MWea NBPN SPhx SPoG SWat WAul WCAu
'Burma Midnight'	GBin
'Burma Ruby'	GBin WCAu
cambessedesii ♀H2-3	CAby CSpe EBee EBrs EGle EPot GCrs GKev LHop LRHS MTho NBir NLar NMen NSla NWCA SRot SSpi WAbe WCot
'Carol'	WCAu
caucasica	see *P. mascula* subsp. *mascula*
x ***chamaeleon***	EBee EBrs
'Cheddar Royal'	GBin
'Cherry Ruffles'	WCAu
'China Pink'	MBri
'Chinese Dragon' (S)	CKel WCAu
'Claire de Lune'	GBin LCro MBri WCAu WCot
'Claudia'	WCAu
'Coral Charm'	GBin WCot
'Coral Fay'	GBin MSte WCAu
'Coral 'n' Gold'	WCAu
'Coral Sunset'	EBee GBin
'Coral Supreme'	GBin WCot
corallina	see *P. mascula* subsp. *mascula*
Crimson Red	see *P. suffruticosa* 'Hu Hong'
'Crusader'	WCAu
'Cytherea'	MHom WCAu
'Dancing Butterflies'	EBee LRHS LSRN WCAu
daurica	see *P. mascula* subsp. *triternata*
'Dawn Glow'	WCAu
decomposita	GBin MPhe
decora	see *P. peregrina*
'Defender'	WCAu
delavayi (S) ♀H4	More than 30 suppliers
- BWJ 7775	WCru
- from China (S)	MPhe
- var. ***angustiloba*** f. ***alba*** **new**	EBrs
§ - - f. ***angustiloba*** (S)	SSpi
- - - ACE 1047	EPot
- - - 'Coffee Cream' **new**	CKel
§ - - f. ***trollioides*** (S)	EBrs WCAu
- var. ***atropurpurea***	see *P. delavayi* var. *delavayi* f. *delavayi*
§ - var. ***delavayi*** f. ***delavayi***	NEgg
§ - - f. ***lutea*** (S)	CDul CSpe EBee EPfP GKev LEdu LFur LRHS MAsh MGos MLan NLAp SAga SHBN SLon SPhx SPoG SRms STre WAul WFar WHar WHoo WPic WTin
- hybrid (S)	CPLG NEgg
- var. ***ludlowii***	see *P. ludlowii*
- var. ***lutea***	see *P. delavayi* var. *delavayi* f. *lutea*
- 'Mrs Sarson'	CSpe GBin MCCP SWat
- Potaninii Group	see *P. delavayi* var. *angustiloba* f. *angustiloba*
- Trollioides Group	see *P. delavayi* var. *angustiloba* f. *trollioides*
delavayi x ***delavayi*** var. ***delavayi*** f. ***lutea***	ELan
delavayi x ***suffruticosa*** **new**	SSpi
Drizzling Rain Cloud	see *P. suffruticosa* 'Shiguregumo'
'Early Glow'	GBin
'Early Scout'	GBin MHom WAul WCAu
'Early Windflower'	EGle GBin WCAu
'Eastgrove Ruby Lace'	WEas
'Eden's Perfume'	NLar SHBN
'Elizabeth Foster'	WCAu
'Ellen Cowley'	WCAu
emodi	EBrs LPio SPhx
'F. Koppius' **new**	CKel
'Fairy Princess'	GBin WAul WCAu
'Firelight'	WCAu
'Flame'	EBee EBrs EWTr GBin MNrw MSte MWea SPer WAul WCAu WCot
Fragrance and Beauty	see *P. suffruticosa* 'Lan Tian Yu'
§ Gansu Mudan Group (S)	CKel EBrs MHom MPhe
- 'Bai Bi Fen Xia' (S)	MPhe
- 'Bai Bi Lan Xia' (S)	MPhe
- 'Bai Zhang Bing' (S)	IPPs
- 'Cheng Xin' (S)	MPhe
- 'Fen He' (S)	IPPs MPhe

	– 'Feng Xian' (S)	MPhe
	– 'Hei Xuan Feng' (S)	MPhe
	– 'Huang He' (S)	MPhe
	– 'Lan Hai Yiu Bo' (S)	MPhe
	– 'Lan He' (S)	IPPs MPhe
	– 'Li Xiang' (S)	MPhe
	– 'Lian Chun' (S)	MPhe
	– 'Mei Gui Sa Jin' (S)	IPPs
	– 'Xue Hai Bing Xin' (S)	IPPs
	– 'Xue Hai Dan Xin' (S)	IPPs
	– 'Xue Lian' (S)	MPhe
	– 'Zi Ban Bai' (S)	IPPs
	– 'Zi Guan Yu Zhu'	IPPs
	– 'Zi He' (S)	IPPs
	'Gaugin' (S)	WCAu
	'Gold Standard'	GBin WAul
	'Golden Bowl'	CKel
	'Golden Glow'	WCAu
	'Golden Isles'	CKel
	'Golden Thunder'	CKel
	Green Dragon Lying on a Chinese Inkstone	see *P. suffruticosa* 'Qing Long Wo Mo Chi'
	'Hei Hua Kui'	see *P. suffruticosa* 'Hei Hua Kui'
	'Hesperus' (S)	WCAu
	'High Noon' (S)	CKel LCro MAsh MPhe NBPC SPer SWat WCAu
	'Ho-gioku'	GBin
	'Hoki'	CKel
	'Honor'	WCAu
	'Horizon'	GBin
§	'Huang Hua Kui' (S)	CKel
	'Illini Belle'	GBin
	'Illini Warrior'	WAul WCAu
	'Isani Gidui'	see *P. lactiflora* 'Isami-jishi'
	japonica misapplied	see *P. lactiflora*
	japonica ambig.	GEdr
	japonica (Makino) Miyabe & Takeda	EBee
	'Jean E. Bockstoce'	WCAu
	'Joseph Rock'	see *P. rockii*
	'Joyce Ellen'	GBin WCAu
	'Kamikaze' **new**	CKel
§	***kavachensis***	EBee EBrs EGle
	kevachensis	see *P. kavachensis*
	'Kinkaku'	see *P.* x *lemoinei* 'Souvenir de Maxime Cornu'
	'Kinko'	see *P.* x *lemoinei* 'Alice Harding'
	'Kinshi'	see *P.* x *lemoinei* 'Chromatella'
	'Kintei'	see *P.* x *lemoinei* 'L'Espérance'
	'Koikagura' **new**	CKel
	'Kokamon'	CKel
	'Kun Shan Ye Guang'	CKel
§	***lactiflora***	EBee EHrv MPhe WWst
	– 'A.F.W. Hayward'	CKel
	– 'Abalone Pearl'	GBin
	– 'Adolphe Rousseau'	CBcs EBee LCro NBlu WCAu
*	– 'Afterglow'	CKel
	– 'Agida'	GBin MRav
	– 'Agnes Mary Kelway'	CKel
I	– ***alba*** **new**	CExc
	– 'Albert Crousse'	CBcs CKel GBin NBir NBlu SWat WCAu
	– 'Alexander Fleming'	CHFP EBee ECot MWea MWgw NBir SWat WBrE WCAu WHoo
	– 'Algae Adamson'	CKel
	– 'Alice Harding'	GBin WCAu
	– 'Amibilis'	WCAu
	– 'Amo-no-sode'	WCAu
	– 'Angel Cheeks'	WCAu
	– 'Anna Pavlova'	CKel MRav
	– 'Antwerpen'	ERou MBri WCAu
	– 'Arabian Prince'	CKel
	– 'Argentine'	SHBN WCAu
	– 'Asa Gray'	CKel
	– 'Auguste Dessert'	CKel EBee GBin MWea WCAu WCot

§	– 'Augustin d'Hour'	CKel EBee ERou
	– 'Aureole'	CKel MRav
	– 'Avalanche'	EBee GBin NBPC NLar SMrm SPur
	– 'Ballerina'	CKel MRav
	– 'Barbara'	CKel WCAu
	– 'Baroness Schröder'	ELan GBin
	– 'Barrington Belle'	EPfP GBin MBri MSte WAul
	– 'Barrymore'	CHFP CKel
	– 'Beacon'	CKel
	– 'Beatrice Kelway'	CKel
	– 'Belle Center'	GBin WCAu
	– 'Best Man'	MBNS WCAu
	– 'Bethcar'	CKel
	– 'Better Times'	WCAu
	– 'Big Ben'	GBin WCAu
	– 'Bing Qing'	IPPs
	– 'Blaze of Beauty'	CKel
	– 'Bluebird'	CKel
	– 'Blush Queen'	ELan WCAu
	– 'Border Gem'	MRav
	– 'Bouchela'	EBee
	– 'Boule de Neige'	EWll
	– 'Bower of Roses'	CKel
	– 'Bowl of Beauty' Υ^{H4}	More than 30 suppliers
	– 'Bowl of Cream'	EBee GBin SHBN SWat SWvt WCAu
	– 'Bracken'	CKel
	– 'Break o' Day'	WCAu
	– 'Bridal Gown'	GBin WCAu
	– 'Bridal Veil'	CKel
	– 'Bridesmaid'	CKel MRav
	– 'British Beauty'	CKel MRav
	– 'Bunker Hill'	CKel EBee GBin MBri SPer SWvt WCAu
	– 'Butter Bowl'	GBin MBri WCAu
	– 'Canarie'	MBri
	– 'Candeur'	CKel EBee
	– 'Cang Long'	CKel
	– 'Captivation'	CKel
	– 'Carnival'	CKel
	– 'Caroline Allain'	CKel
	– 'Carrara'	GBin
	– 'Cascade'	CKel
	– 'Catherine Fontijn'	CHFP CKel EBee GBin WCAu
	– 'Charles' White'	EBee EGle EPfP GBin NBPC WCAu
	– 'Charm'	WCAu
	– 'Cheddar Charm'	WAul WCAu
	– 'Cheddar Cheese'	MBri
	– 'Cheddar Gold' Υ^{H4}	MBri
	– 'Cherry Hill'	WCAu
	– 'Chestine Gowdy'	CKel
	– 'Chief Wapello'	GBin
	– 'Chun Xiao'	CKel
	– 'Claire Dubois'	CKel ERou GBin WCAu
	– 'Cora Stubbs' **new**	MBNS
	– 'Cornelia Shaylor'	WCAu
	– 'Couronne d'Or'	WCAu
	– 'Crimson Glory'	CKel
	– 'Dandy Dan'	WCAu
	– 'Dawn Crest'	CKel EBee
	– 'Dayspring'	CKel
	– 'Daystar'	MRav
	– 'Decorative' **new**	CKel
	– 'Delachei'	CKel
	– 'Denise'	MRav
	– 'Dinner Plate'	MBri SPer WCAu WCot
	– 'Do Tell'	GBin NLar SPer WCAu
	– 'Docteur H. Barnsby'	CKel
	– 'Doctor Alexander Fleming'	CKel SWat SWvt
	– 'Dominion'	CKel
	– 'Don Juan' **new**	CKel
	– 'Doreen'	CFir EBee GBin MBri MRav SHBN SHar WCAu
	– 'Doris Cooper'	WCAu
	– 'Dorothy Welsh'	CKel

- 'Dragon' CKel
- 'Dresden' WCAu
- 'Duchesse de Nemours' 🏆H4 More than 30 suppliers
- 'Duchesse d'Orléans' WCAu
- 'Edouard Doriat' WCAu
- 'Edulis Superba' CKel EBee EGle ELan ENot LEdu LRHS MBNS NMoo NPer SHar SMer SPur WCAu
- 'Elizabeth Stone' CKel
- 'Ella Christine Kelway' CKel
- 'Elsa Sass' WCAu
- 'Emma Klehm' GBin WCAu
- 'Emperor of India' CKel MRav
- 'Enchantment' CKel
- 'English Princess' CKel
- 'Ethereal' CKel
- 'Evelyn Tibbets' GBin
- 'Evening Glow' CKel
- 'Evening World' CKel
- 'Fairy's Petticoat' WCAu
- 'Fashion Show' CKel
- 'Félix Crousse' 🏆H4 CBcs CHFP CKel CTri ELan EMil ENot EPfP ERou EWsh GMaP LAst MBNS MRav MSte MWgw NBir SMrm SPoG SPur SRms SWat WCAu
- 'Felix Supreme' GBin
- 'Fen Chi Jin Yu' CKel
- 'Fen Yu Nu' IPPs
- 'Festiva Maxima' 🏆H4 CHFP CKel CTri CWCL EBee ECot ELan EPfP ERou GBin LRHS MBri MSte MWgw NEgg NLar SHBN SPer SPla SRms SWat SWvt WAul WCAu WHoo
- 'France' CKel
- 'Fuji-no-mine' GBin
- 'Garden Lace' GBin
- 'Gardenia' EBee EBrs EKen EPfP GBin SHBN
- 'Gay Paree' GBin NLar SPer WCAu
- 'Gayborder June' CKel WCAu
- 'Gene Wild' WCAu
- 'Général MacMahon' see *P. lactiflora* 'Augustin d'Hour'
- 'General Wolfe' CKel
- 'Germaine Bigot' CKel WCAu
- 'Gertrude' GBin
- 'Gilbert Barthelot' WCAu
- 'Gleam of Light' CKel MBri
- 'Globe of Light' GBin
- 'Gloriana' WCAu
- 'Glory Hallelujah' WCAu
- 'Glowing Candles' WCAu
- 'Go-Daigo' GBin
- 'Golden Fleece' WCAu
- 'Green Lotus' WAul
- 'Guidon' WCAu
- 'Gypsy Girl' CKel
- 'Hakodate' CKel
- 'Heartbeat' CKel
- 'Helen Hayes' WCAu
- 'Henri Potin' GBin
- 'Henry Bockstoce' GBin
- 'Her Grace' CKel
- 'Her Majesty' NBir
- 'Herbert Oliver' CKel
- 'Hermione' **new** CKel
- 'Hiawatha' WCAu
- 'Hit Parade' WCAu
- 'Honey Gold' ELan GBin SHBN SPoG WAul WCAu
- 'Huang Jin Lun' CKel IPPs
- 'Hyperion' CKel
- 'Immaculée' EBee GBin MBri SMer SPoG WSpi
- 'Inspecteur Lavergne' CKel EBee LAst MBri MWea SPer WAul WCAu WCot
- 'Instituteur Doriat' CKel GBin MBri WCAu

§ - 'Isami-jishi' GBin
- 'Jacorma' CFir GBin WHoo
- 'Jacques Doriat' CKel
- 'James Pillow' WCAu
- 'Jan van Leeuwen' EBee EPfP ERou GBin WCAu WSpi
- 'Jappensha-Ikhu' GBin
- 'Jeanne d'Arc' CKel
- 'Jewel' CKel
- 'Jin Chi Yu' CKel
- 'Jin Dai Wei' IPPs
- 'John Howard Wigell' WCAu
- 'Joseph Plagne' CKel
- 'Joy of Life' CKel
- 'June Morning' CKel
- 'June Rose' WCAu
- 'Kansas' CHFP EBee ELan ERas ERou GBin MBri NMoo WCAu WCot WFar
- 'Karen Gray' GBin WCAu
- 'Karl Rosenfield' CKel CSBt EBee ECot EGle ENot EPfP LAst LCro LRHS MSte NEgg SPer SPla SPoG SRms SWvt WFar WHoo
- 'Kathleen Mavoureen' CKel
- 'Kelway's Betty' CKel
- 'Kelway's Brilliant' CKel
- 'Kelway's Circe' CKel
- 'Kelway's Daystar' CKel
- 'Kelway's Exquisite' CKel
- 'Kelway's Glorious' CSam EBee EPfP ERou GBin MBNS NLar SMrm SPoG WCAu
- 'Kelway's Lovely' CKel
- 'Kelway's Lovely Lady' CKel
- 'Kelway's Majestic' CKel
- 'Kelway's Scented Rose' CKel
- 'Kelway's Supreme' CKel SWat
- 'King of England' GBin
- 'Knighthood' CKel
- 'Kocho-jishi' CKel

§ - 'Koningin Wilhelmina' GBin MNrw
- 'Krinkled White' EBee EWTr GBin MBri MHom MRav MWgw NCGa NLar SHar SMeo WAul WCAu WCot
- 'La Belle Hélène' CKel
- 'La France' GBin
- 'La Lorraine' CKel
- 'Lady Alexandra Duff' 🏆H4 CKel EBee EPfP GBin MRav MWea SCoo SRms SWvt WCAu
- 'Lady Kate' WCAu
- 'Lady Ley' CKel
- 'Lady Mayoress' CKel
- 'Lady Orchid' WCAu
- 'Lancaster Imp' GBin WAul
- 'Langport Triumph' CKel
- 'Laura Dessert' 🏆H4 EBee EPfP ERou GBin MBri MWea MWgw SHBN WCAu
- 'Le Cygne' GBin
- 'Le Jour' MBri
- 'L'Eclatante' CKel EBee GBin
- 'Legion of Honor' CKel WCAu
- 'Lemon Ice' CKel
- 'Lemon Queen' GBin
- 'L'Etincelante' GBin LCro
- 'Lian Tai' IPPs
- 'Lights Out' GBin
- 'Lillian Wild' WCAu
- 'Little Medicineman' CElw GBin NBhm
- 'Liukrecija' GBin
- 'Lois Kelsey' WCAu
- 'Longfellow' CKel
- 'Lora Dexheimer' WCAu
- 'Lord Calvin' WCAu
- 'Lord Kitchener' CKel GBin
- 'Lorna Doone' CKel
- 'Lotus Queen' GBin NLar WCAu

- 'Louis Barthelot'	WCAu
- 'Louis Joliet'	ELan MSte
- 'Lowell Thomas'	WCAu
- 'Lyric'	CKel
- 'Madame Calot'	ERas SRms WCAu
- 'Madame Claude Tain'	MBri
- 'Madame de Verneville'	CKel WCAu
- 'Madame Ducel'	CKel WCAu
- 'Madame Emile Debatène'	CWCL EBee LBuc NMoo NOrc SHBN SPoG WCAu
- 'Madame Jules Dessert'	WCAu
- 'Madelon'	CKel WCAu
- 'Maestro'	GBin
- 'Magic Orb'	CKel
- 'Margaret Truman'	CKel WCAu
- 'Marguérite Gerard'	WCAu
- 'Marie Crousse'	WCAu
- 'Marie Lemoine'	CKel WCAu WCot
- 'Marietta Sisson'	WCAu
- 'Mary Brand'	WCAu
- 'Masterpiece'	CKel
- 'Merry Mayshine'	GBin WCAu
- 'Midnight Sun'	MBri WCAu
- 'Minnie Shaylor'	WCAu
- 'Mischief'	WCAu
- 'Miss America'	EPfP GBin MBri WCAu
- 'Miss Eckhart'	CKel EBee ERou GBin WCAu
- 'Miss Mary'	EPfP LAst SHar
- 'Mister Ed'	GBin WCAu
- 'Mistral'	CHFP CKel MBri
- 'Mo Zi Ling'	WCAu
- 'Monsieur Jules Elie' ♀H4	CKel EBee EPfP ERou GBin LAst MBri MHom NBPC SMer SPer SPla WAul WCAu WHoo
- 'Monsieur Martin Cahuzac'	CFir GBin WCAu
- 'Moon of Nippon'	EBee
- 'Moon River'	EPfP GBin SHBN
- 'Moonglow'	WCAu
- 'Mother's Choice'	GBin SHBN WCAu
- 'Mr G.F. Hemerik'	CKel GBin MBri WCAu
- 'Mr Thim'	WCAu
- 'Mrs Edward Harding'	WCAu
- 'Mrs F.J. Hemerik'	WCAu
- 'Mrs Franklin D. Roosevelt'	GBin WCAu
- 'Mrs J.V. Edlund'	WCAu
- 'Mrs Livingston Farrand'	WCAu
- 'My Pal Rudy'	GBin WCAu
- 'Myrtle Gentry'	GBin
- 'Nancy Nicholls'	WCAu
- 'Nancy Nora'	SPer
- 'Nice Gal'	WCAu
- 'Nick Shaylor'	GBin WCAu
- 'Nippon Beauty'	EBee EGle GBin NBPC NLar SPhx SPoG
- 'Ornament'	CKel
- 'Orpen'	CKel
- 'Paola'	CKel
- 'Paul Bunyan'	GBin
- 'Paul M. Wild'	NLar WCAu
- 'Peche'	EBee
* - 'Pecher'	CWCL NMoo NPer SMrm WSpi
- 'Peregrine'	CKel
- 'Peter Brand'	GBin
- 'Philippe Rivoire'	WCAu
- 'Philomèle'	WCAu
- 'Pico'	WCAu
- 'Pillow Talk'	EBee ERas GBin WCAu
- 'Pink Cameo'	EBee NLar SHBN SPoG WCAu WCot
- 'Pink Giant'	WCAu
- 'Pink Lemonade'	WCAu
- 'Pink Parfait'	GBin SPer WCAu WCot
- 'Pink Princess'	MBri WCAu

- 'Polar King'	WCAu
- 'Port Royale'	CKel
- 'President Franklin D. Roosevelt'	SWat WCAu
- 'Président Poincaré'	CKel SWat
- 'President Taft'	see *P. lactiflora* 'Reine Hortense'
- 'Primevere'	EBee EPfP EWll GBin LAst MBNS MSte NLar NMoo SHBN SHar SMrm SPer SPoG SPur WCAu
- 'Qi Hua Lu Shuang'	CKel IPPs
- 'Qing Wen'	CKel
- 'Queen of Sheba'	WCAu
- 'Queen Victoria'	GBin
- 'Queen Wilhelmina'	see *P. lactiflora* 'Koningin Wilhelmina'
- 'Raoul Dessert'	WCAu
- 'Raspberry Sundae'	ELan ERou GBin MAvo MRav NLar SPer WCAu
- 'Red Dwarf'	CKel
- 'Red Emperor'	WCAu
- 'Red Rover' **new**	CKel
- 'Red Sarah Bernhardt'	ELan
§ - 'Reine Hortense'	CKel GBin MRav WCAu
- 'Renato'	GBin
- 'Richard Carvel'	WCAu
- 'Ruth Cobb'	WCAu
- 'Sante Fe'	EPfP SHBN WCAu
- 'Sarah Bernhardt' ♀H4	More than 30 suppliers
- 'Scarlet O'Hara'	GBin
- 'Schaffe'	GBin
- 'Sea Shell'	GBin NLar SHar
- 'Sha Jin Guan Ding'	IPPs
- 'Shawnee Chief'	WCAu
- 'Shen Tao Hua'	CKel
- 'Shimmering Velvet'	CKel SAga
- 'Shirley Temple'	CHFP CKel CWCL EBee ELan GBin GMaP LCro MBNS MRav MSte MWgw SPoG WCAu WCot
- 'Silver Flare'	CKel
- 'Soft Salmon Joy'	GBin
- 'Solange'	CKel EBee GBin NCGa NLar SPoG WCAu
- 'Sorbet'	CWCL EBee EPfP NLar NMoo NPer SMrm WCAu
- 'Starlight'	WCAu
- 'Strephon'	CKel
- 'Sweet Melody'	GBin WCAu
- 'Sweet Sixteen'	WCAu
- 'Sword Dance'	EBee EGle EWll GBin SPoG WSpi
- 'Taff'	EBee
- 'Tamate-boko'	WCAu
- 'The Mighty Mo'	GBin
- 'Thérèse'	WCAu
- 'Tom Eckhardt'	GBin SPer
- 'Top Brass'	EBee GBin MRav WCAu
- 'Toro-no-maki'	WCAu
- 'Translucient'	CKel
- 'Victoire de la Marne'	EBee
- 'Violet Dawson'	GBin
- 'Vogue'	EBee GBin SWvt WCAu
- 'Walter Faxon'	GBin
- 'West Elkton'	GBin
- 'Westerner'	GBin WCAu
- 'White Angel'	SPoG
- 'White Ivory'	WCAu
- 'White Rose of Sharon'	CKel
- 'White Wings'	CBcs CKel CTri EBee EGle ELan EPfP EWTr GBin LCro MAvo MSte MWea NSti SPer SWat SWvt WAul WCAu WCot
- 'Whitleyi Major' ♀H4	WCot
- 'Wiesbaden'	WCAu
- 'Wilbur Wright'	GBin WCAu
- 'Wladyslawa'	EBee EBrs WCot
- 'Wu Hua Long Yu'	IPPs

	- 'Xue Feng'	CKel
	- 'Yan Fei Chu Yu'	CKel
	- 'Yan Zi Dian Yu'	CKel IPPs
	- 'Yu Cui He Hua'	IPPs
	- 'Zhu Sha Dian Yu'	CKel
	- 'Zi Die Xian Jin'	IPPs
	- 'Zi Feng Chao Yang'	IPPs
	- 'Zus Braun'	EBee
	- 'Zuzu'	GBin WAul WCAu
	x ***lagodechiana***	EBrs
	'Late Windflower'	EBrs ECha EGle GCra LPio MHom
	x ***lemoinei*** (S)	GBin WHal
§	- 'Alice Harding' (S)	CKel SPer WCAu
§	- 'Chromatella' (S)	CKel LAma
§	- 'L'Espérance' (S)	LAma WCAu
§	- 'Souvenir de Maxime Cornu' (S)	CKel EMui ENot LAma LCro LRHS MGos MPhe WCAu
	lithophila	see *P. tenuifolia* subsp. *lithophila*
	lobata 'Fire King'	see *P. peregrina*
	'Lois Arleen'	WCAu
§	***ludlowii*** (S) AGM	More than 30 suppliers
	lutea	see *P. delavayi* var. *delavayi* f. *lutea*
	- var. ***ludlowii***	see *P. ludlowii*
	macrophylla	MPhe
	'Magenta Gem'	WAul
	'Mai Fleuri'	WCAu
	mairei	CExc CFir EBee MPhe WCot
	'Marchioness' (S)	CKel WCAu
	mascula	EBee EPfP LHop LTwo NBir NLar WCot
	- from Samos	SSpi
	- from Sicily	MPhe
§	- subsp. ***arietina***	MWat WEas WKif
	- - 'Northern Glory'	WCAu
	- subsp. ***hellenica***	EBee EBrs MHom
	- - from Sicily	MPhe
§	- subsp. ***mascula***	EBee EBrs EGle GBin MHom NLar WCot
	- - from Georgia	MPhe WPGP
§	- subsp. ***russoi***	CAby EBrs EGle GBin SSpi WCot WThu
	- - from Sardinia	MPhe
	- - 'Reverchoni'	EBee EBrs MHom
§	- subsp. ***triternata***	CLAP EBee EBrs EGle LFur MHom MPhe MWgw NLar WBor WCot
	- - from Crimea	WPGP
	'Mikuhino Akebono'	CKel
	mlokosewitschii ♀H4	CBct CKel CSpe EBee EBrs ECha ECho EGle GCrs ITer LHop LPio LRHS MAvo MHom MNrw MPhe MWat MWgw NBir NChi NMen SBla WCot WEas WHoo WPGP WSpi WTin
	- 'Fedora' **new**	EBrs
	mollis	see *P. officinalis* subsp. *villosa*
	'Montezuma'	MBri WCAu
	'Moonrise'	WCAu
	'My Love' **new**	GBin
	'Nymphe'	CKel EBee EPfP MRav WAul WCAu
	obovata ♀H4	CFir EBee EBrs EGle MPhe MSal SSpi
	- var. ***alba*** ♀H4	CExc EBrs EPot GBin GCrs GEdr GKev WEas WThu
	- var. ***willmottiae***	EBee MHom MPhe
	officinalis	CMil EGle EWsh GCra GPoy NEgg SBla
	- WM 9821 from Slovenia	MPhe
	- 'Alba Plena'	CPou EWTr GMaP MRav MSte NEgg SWvt WCAu
	- 'Anemoniflora Rosea' ♀H4	CKel EBee EGle EPfP GBin MBri MHom SWvt WCAu
§	- subsp. ***banatica***	EBrs GKev MHom MPhe WCAu
	- 'China Rose'	GBin WCAu
	- 'Lize van Veen'	GBin WCAu
	- 'Mutabilis Plena'	EBee IBlr WCAu
	- 'Rosea Plena' ♀H4	CKel EBee ECtt EPfP GBin GMaP LAst LHop MRav NEgg SPer SWat SWvt WCAu
	- 'Rosea Superba Plena'	EWTr NEgg SPoG WCAu
	- 'Rubra Plena' ♀H4	CPou CTri CWCL EBee EBrs ECtt EMil EPfP GAbr GBin GCra GMaP LAst LHop MBri MHom MRav NEgg NGdn SHBN SPer SPoG SRms SWat SWvt WAul WCAu WCot WFar
§	- subsp. ***villosa***	CKel CMdw EBee EBrs ELan GAbr GBin NLar SEND WCAu
	'Oriental Gold'	CKel
	ostii (S)	CExc CKel MPhe
§	- 'Feng Dan Bai' (S)	CKel EBee GBin IPPs MPhe NBlu WCAu WSpi
	papaveracea	see *P. suffruticosa*
	'Paula Fay'	EBee EPfP GBin MRav NLar WCAu
	'Peachy Rose'	GBin
	Peony with the Purple Roots	see *P. suffruticosa* 'Shou An Hong'
§	***peregrina***	CAby CHFP EBrs ECho GBin MHom MPhe MWgw NLar NSla SBla SSpi WCAu
	- 'Fire King'	GBin
§	- 'Otto Froebel' ♀H4	GBin MHar NLar WCAu WCot WSpi
	- 'Sunshine'	see *P. peregrina* 'Otto Froebel'
	'Phoenix White' (S)	MBlu
	'Pink Hawaiian Coral'	GBin SHar WCot
	'Postilion'	GBin WCAu
	potaninii	see *P. delavayi* var. *angustiloba* f. *angustiloba*
	'Prairie Charm' **new**	GBin
	'Prairie Moon'	GBin NLar
	'Red Charm'	EBrs GBin MBNS MBri MHom SHBN SPhx SPoG WCAu WSpi
	'Red Glory'	GBin
	'Red Magic'	EBee NBPC NLar SMrm WSpi
	'Red Red Rose'	WCAu
	'Renown' (S)	CKel
	'Requiem'	GBin WCAu
	'Robert W. Auten'	WCAu
§	***rockii*** (S)	CKel CSpe EPfP MPhe NLar SBla WCot WSpi
	- 'Bing Shan Xue Lian' (S)	IPPs MPhe
	- 'He Ping Lian' (S)	MPhe
	- 'Hong Guan Yu Dai'	IPPs
	- 'Hong Lian' (S)	IPPs MPhe
	- 'Hui He' (S)	MPhe
	- hybrid	see *P.* Gansu Mudan Group
	- subsp. ***linyanshanii***	MPhe
	- 'Shu Sheng Peng Mo' (S)	MPhe
	- 'Tian Bai Xue'	IPPs
	- 'Zi Die Ying Feng' (S)	MPhe
	'Roman Gold'	CKel
	romanica	see *P. peregrina*
	'Rose Garland'	WCAu
	'Roselette'	GBin WCAu
	Rouge Red	see *P. suffruticosa* 'Zhi Hong'
	'Roy Pehrson's Best Yellow'	GBin
	ruprechtiana	EBee EBrs
	russoi	see *P. mascula* subsp. *russoi*
	'Scarlett O'Hara'	GBin SHar SPer SPoG WCAu
	Shandong Red Lotus	see *P. suffruticosa* 'Lu He Hong'
	'Shimano-fuji'	CKel
	'Showanohokori' **new**	CKel
	'Silver Dawn'	GBin
	sinensis	see *P. lactiflora*
	sinjianensis	see *P. anomala* var. *anomala*
	x ***smouthii***	MBri
	'Soshi'	GBin
	'Stardust'	WCAu

	steveniana	EBrs EGle GBin MHom MPhe NLar
§	***suffruticosa*** (S)	CWib ELan GBin IPPs MGos MPhe NBlu WBVN
	- 'Akashigata' (S)	CKel
	- 'Alice Palmer' (S)	CKel
	- 'Bai Yu' (S)	CBcs
	- 'Bai Yulan' (S)	LTwo
	- Best-shaped Red	see *P. suffruticosa* 'Zhuan Yuan Hong'
	- Bird of Rimpo	see *P. suffruticosa* 'Rimpo'
	- Black Dragon Brocade	see *P. suffruticosa* 'Kokuryû-nishiki'
	- Black Flower Chief	see *P. suffruticosa* 'Hei Hua Kui'
	- Brocade of the Naniwa	see *P. suffruticosa* 'Naniwa-nishiki'
	- 'Cardinal Vaughan' (S)	CKel LCro
	- Charming Age	see *P. suffruticosa* 'Howki'
	- 'Dou Lu' (S)	CBcs CKel IPPs MPhe
	- Double Cherry	see *P. suffruticosa* 'Yae-zakura'
	- 'Duchess of Kent' (S)	CKel LCro
	- 'Duchess of Marlborough' (S)	CKel LCro
	- 'Er Qiao' (S)	CBcs CKel MPhe
	- Eternal Camellias	see *P. suffruticosa* 'Yachiyo-tsubaki'
	- 'Fen Qiao' (S)	CBcs
	- 'Feng Dan Fen' (S)	IPPs
	- 'Feng Dan Zi' (S)	IPPs
	- Flight of Cranes	see *P. suffruticosa* 'Renkaku'
	- Floral Rivalry	see *P. suffruticosa* 'Hana-kisoi'
	- 'Fuji Zome Goromo' (S)	CKel
*	- 'Glory of Huish' (S)	CKel
	- 'Godaishu' (S)	CKel LAma LRHS MPhe SPer
	- 'Guan Shi Mo Yu' (S)	MPhe
§	- 'Hakuojisi' (S)	CKel ENot WCAu
§	- 'Hana-daijin' (S)	LAma LRHS WCAu
§	- 'Hana-kisoi' (S)	CKel GBin LAma MPhe WCAu
	- 'Haru-no-akebono' (S)	CKel
§	- 'Hei Hua Kui' (S)	IPPs MPhe
§	- 'Higurashi' (S)	ENot
§	- 'Howki' (S)	WCAu
§	- 'Hu Hong' (S)	EBee WCAu WSpi
	- Jewel in the Lotus	see *P. suffruticosa* 'Tama-fuyo'
	- Jewelled Screen	see *P. suffruticosa* 'Tama-sudare'
	- 'Jia Ge Jin Zi' (S)	CKel
	- 'Jitsugetsu-nishiki' (S)	CKel
	- 'Jiu Zui Yang Fei' (S)	IPPs
	- 'Joseph Rock'	see *P. rockii*
	- Kamada Brocade	see *P. suffruticosa* 'Kamada-nishiki'
§	- 'Kamada-fuji' (S)	CKel LAma WCAu
§	- 'Kamada-nishiki' (S)	CKel
§	- 'Kaow' (S)	CKel MAsh NBlu WCAu
	- King of Flowers	see *P. suffruticosa* 'Kaow'
	- King of White Lions	see *P. suffruticosa* 'Hakuojisi'
*	- 'Kingdom of the Moon' (S)	LRHS
	- 'Kinkaku'	see *P.* x *lemoinei* 'Souvenir de Maxime Cornu'
	- 'Kinshi'	see *P.* x *lemoinei* 'Alice Harding'
	- 'Kokucho'	CKel
§	- 'Kokuryû-nishiki' (S)	CKel GBin LAma SPer SPoG
	- 'Koshi-no-yuki' (S)	CKel
	- 'Lan Bao Shi' (S)	IPPs
	- 'Lan Fu Rong' (S)	CBcs MPhe
	- 'Lan Hu Die' (S)	IPPs
§	- 'Lan Tian Yu' (S)	MPhe
§	- 'Lu He Hong' (S)	WCAu
	- Magnificent Flower	see *P. suffruticosa* 'Hana-daijin'
	- 'Mikasayama' (S)	MPhe
	- 'Montrose' (S)	CKel
*	- 'Mrs Shirley Fry' (S)	CKel
	- 'Mrs William Kelway' (S)	CKel
	- 'Muramatsu-zakura' (S)	ENot
§	- 'Naniwa-nishiki' (S)	CKel
	- 'Nigata Akashigata' (S)	CKel
	- Pride of Taisho	see *P. suffruticosa* 'Taisho-no-hokori'
§	- 'Qing Long Wo Mo Chi' (S)	CKel IPPs WCAu
	- 'Reine Elisabeth' (S)	CKel
§	- 'Renkaku' (S)	CKel LCro LRHS MAsh NBlu SPer WCAu
§	- 'Rimpo' (S)	CKel ENot EPfP GBin LAma MPhe SPer
	- subsp. ***rockii***	see *P. rockii*
	- 'Rou Fu Rong' (S)	EBee MPhe WCAu WSpi
	- 'Sheng Hei Zi' (S)	CBcs
§	- 'Shiguregumo' (S)	CKel
	- 'Shimadaigin' (S)	CKel MAsh MPhe NBlu
	- 'Shimane-chojuraku' (S)	CKel
	- 'Shimane-hakugan' (S)	CKel
	- 'Shimane-seidai' (S)	CKel
	- 'Shimanishiki'	CKel SPer
*	- 'Shimanojuji'	SPer
	- 'Shin Shima Kagayaki'	CKel
	- 'Shintoyen' (S)	CKel
§	- 'Shou An Hong' (S)	MPhe
	- 'Sumi-no-ichi' (S)	CKel LCro
	- 'Superb' (S)	CKel
§	- 'Taisho-no-hokori' (S)	CKel LRHS WCAu
§	- 'Taiyo' (S)	CKel ENot EPfP LAma LRHS MPhe
§	- 'Tama-fuyo' (S)	CKel LAma
§	- 'Tama-sudare' (S)	CKel LCro SPer WCAu
	- The Sun	see *P. suffruticosa* 'Taiyo'
	- Twilight	see *P. suffruticosa* 'Higurashi'
	- Wisteria at Kamada	see *P. suffruticosa* 'Kamada-fuji'
	- 'Wu Jin Yao Hui' (S)	CBcs MPhe WCAu
	- 'Wu Long Peng Sheng' (S)	CKel GBin MPhe WCAu WSpi
	- 'Xiao Tao Hong' (S)	CBcs
	- 'Xue Ta' (S)	CKel
§	- 'Yachiyo-tsubaki' (S)	CKel ENot LAma WCAu
§	- 'Yae-zakura' (S)	LAma MAsh NBlu WCAu
	- 'Yan Long Zi Zhu Pan' (S)	CKel
	- 'Yin Hong Qiao Dui' (S)	CKel
	- 'Yomo-zakura' (S)	LRHS
	- 'Yoshinogawa' (S)	CKel ENot EPfP LRHS
	- 'Yu Ban Bai' (S)	IPPs
	- 'Zha Sha Lei'	GBin
	- 'Zhao Fen' (S)	IPPs MPhe NBPC NPer
§	- 'Zhi Hong' (S)	CKel
	- 'Zhu Sha Lei' (S)	CKel EBee IPPs MPhe WSpi
*	- 'Zhuan Yuan Hong' (S)	WSpi
	- 'Zi Er Qiao' (S)	CKel IPPs MPhe
§	- 'Zi Lan Kui' (S)	CKel
	'Sunshine'	see *P. peregrina* 'Otto Froebel'
	'Taiheko' **new**	CKel
	'Ten' i' **new**	CKel
	tenuifolia	CLAP CSpe EBee EGle LFur LPio MDun MHom MWea NCGa NMen NSla SPoG WBor WCAu WCot WGwG WSpi
	- subsp. ***carthalinica***	MPhe
§	- subsp. ***lithophila***	MHom MPhe WWSt
	- 'Plena'	EBrs GEdr LPio NBhm NLar
	- 'Rosea'	EBrs MHom
	'Thunderbolt' (S)	WCAu
	tomentosa	CMil MHom MPhe WWSt
	turcica	GBin
	'Vanilla Twist'	WAul
§	***veitchii***	CAby EBrs EPfP GBin GKev GMaP LPio MHom MTho NBid NDlv NLar NMen SSpi WCAu WSpi
	- from China	MPhe
	- 'Alba'	SPhx
	- var. ***woodwardii***	CLyd CMdw CMil EBrs ECho EGle ERos GBin GCra GCrs GGar GKev LPio MRav MTho NSla NWCA SSpi WCAu WCot WHoo
I	- - 'Alba' **new**	EBrs
	'Vesuvian'	CKel WCAu
	'Walter Mains'	WCAu
	White Phoenix	see *P. ostii* 'Feng Dan Bai'
	'Wine Angel'	GBin
	wittmanniana	EBrs GBin NLar WCAu WCot

§ 'Yao Huang' (S)	CBcs IPPs MPhe WCAu
Yao's Yellow	see *P.* 'Yao Huang'
'Yellow Crown'	GBin SHar WCAu
'Yellow Dream'	SCoo WCAu WCot
'Yellow Emperor'	WCot
Yellow Flower of Summer	see *P.* 'Huang Hua Kui'

Paesia (*Dennstaedtiaceae*)

scaberula	CDes CLAP CWil NBir SSpi WAbe

Paliurus (*Rhamnaceae*)

spina-christi	CArn CBcs CPle IDee NLar SLon XPep

Pallenis (*Asteraceae*)

§ ***maritima***	CCCN XPep
- 'Golden Dollar'	NPri

Panax (*Araliaceae*)

ginseng	EBee GKev GPoy
japonicus	EBee WCru
- BWJ 7932	WCru
quinquefolius	GPoy MSal
sambucifolius	CPLG

Pancratium (*Amaryllidaceae*)

maritimum	CHHB CTca EBee EBrs ECho GKev IHer LRHS WCot

Pandanus (*Pandanaceae*)

utilis	EAmu LPal

Pandorea (*Bignoniaceae*)

jasminoides	CHal CHll CRHN CSpe CTri EBak EBee ECot EPfP EShb LRHS SOWG
- 'Alba'	EShb
§ - 'Charisma' (v)	CBcs CBow CHll EBee EMil EPfP EShb LSou SOWG SPoG WCot WSPU
- 'Lady Di'	CHEx ERea SOWG WCot
- 'Rosea'	MJnS
- 'Rosea Superba' ♀H1	CBcs CHEx CRHN EBee ERea SBod WSPU
- 'Variegata'	see *P. jasminoides* 'Charisma'
lindleyana	see *Clytostoma calystegioides*
pandorana	CRHN EBee ERea IDee LRHS MAsh SAdn SLim
- 'Golden Showers'	CBcs CCCN CMdw CRHN EBee ERea EShb MRav SLim SOWG SPoG

Panicum (*Poaceae*)

bulbosum	EAlp EPPr EPla
clandestinum	EBee EPPr EPla EWes LEdu MCCP NPro
miliaceum	EGle
- 'Purple Majesty' **new**	CWib
- 'Violaceum'	CBig CSpe GKev
'Squaw'	CPrp LRHS NOrc XIsg
virgatum	CBig CRWN CTri ECha GFor LCro LRav NBre WPer XIsg XPep
- 'Blue Tower'	CKno EGle EPPr SApp SPhx
- 'Cloud Nine'	CBig CKno CPen CRez EBee EGle EPPr LHop MAvo NDov NLar SApp SMHy SPhx WHal XIsg
- 'Dallas Blues'	CBig CKno CPen CPrp EBee ECha EPPr EWes EWsh MAvo MRav MSte MWgw NOak SApp SMHy SPer WFar WMoo XIsg
- 'Hänse Herms'	CBig CBrm CKno CRez EAlp EBee EGle LPio MAvo SApp SPhx SPla SPoG WFar XIsg
- 'Heavy Metal'	More than 30 suppliers
- 'Heiliger Hain'	CFwr EBee MWea NCGa XIsg
I - 'Kupferhirse'	CBig CKno EBee EPPr
- 'Northwind'	CBig CKno CPen EBee EPPr MAvo NDov SApp SMHy SPhx WFar XIsg
- 'Pathfinder'	SApp
- 'Prairie Sky'	CBig CKno CRez CWCL EBee EGle ELon EPPr GBin LEdu LPio MAvo MBri MWgw NLar SApp SMHy SPhx WPGP XIsg
- 'Red Cloud'	CBig CKno EGle
- 'Rehbraun'	CRez CSBt EBee EGle EPPr EWsh LEdu LPio NGdn NOak SAga SApp SPhx SWal WCAu WFar WTin XIsg
- 'Rotstrahlbusch'	CBig CKno CPrp CWib EBee EGle EPPr MAvo MBri MSte NBea NOrc SMad SPer SWal WCot WPGP XIsg
- 'Rubrum'	CKno CSBt EBee ECha ECot ELan ENot EPPr EPfP LLWG LRHS MAvo MRav MWgw SApp SDix SHBN SPer SPla STes WMoo WPrP
- 'Shenandoah'	CAbb CBig CBrm CKno CPen CRez CWCL EBee ECha EGle EPPr EPfP EShb EWsh GBin IPot LCro LPio MAvo MBNS MBri NDov SApp SMHy SMad SPhx WBor WMoo WPrP XIsg
- 'Squaw'	CHar CKno CPrp CWCL CWib EAlp EBee EGle EPPr EWsh IPot LCro LPio MBri MSte MWgw NDov SApp SMad SWal WCot WDyG WFar WPnP WPrP WTin WWeb
- 'Strictum'	CBig EBee EHul EMil EPPr EWes LEdu NLar SApp SMHy SMeo SPhx WMoo XIsg
- 'Warrior'	CBrm CHar CKno CPrp EBee EGle EPPr EPfP EWsh GFor LEdu LHop LPio LRHS MBri MRav MWgw NCGa NDov NGdn NNor SAga SApp SWal WFar WLin WMoo WPGP WPnP WWlt

Papaver ✿ (*Papaveraceae*)

aculeatum	SPhx
alboroseum	LRHS
'Alpha Centauri' (Super Poppy Series)	SWat WHoo
alpinum L.	CSpe ECho LRHS SIng SPet SRms SWat WFar
- 'Famecheck Double Orange' (d)	EFam
- 'Flore Pleno' (d)	NBir
amurense	CHVG LEdu NLar SHGN SWat
anomalum album	CSpe
apokrinomenon	ELan
atlanticum	EBee EWin GBuc LDai MLan NBre NBro SPlb WPtf
- 'Flore Pleno' (d)	CSam CSpe MCCP NBre NBro WBrk WFar
'Aurora' (Super Poppy Series)	SWat
'Beyond Red' (Super Poppy Series)	SWat
bracteatum	see *P. orientale* var. *bracteatum*
'Bright Star' (Super Poppy Series)	SWat
burseri	SRot
'Cathay' (Super Poppy Series)	SWat
'Celebration' (Super Poppy Series)	SWat
commutatum ♀H4	CSpe CWCL ELan SWat WEas
corona-sancti-stephani	SWat
'Danish Flag' **new**	CWCL
'Eccentric Silk' (Super Poppy Series)	SWat
fauriei	GKev WRos

§	'Fire Ball' (d)	ECha IGor LHop MLLN NBre NBro NLar SHGN SWat WMnd WRHF
	'Harlequin' (Super Poppy Series)	SWat
	'Heartbeat' (Super Poppy Series)	SWat
	heldreichii	see *P. pilosum* subsp. *spicatum*
	x ***hybridum*** 'Flore Pleno' (d)	NSti SWat
	involucratum	NWCA
	'Jacinth' (Super Poppy Series)	SWat WHoo
	lateritium	CHid CPou SRms
	- 'Fire Ball'	see *P.* 'Fire Ball'
	- 'Nanum Flore Pleno'	see *P.* 'Fire Ball'
	'Lauffeuer'	SWat
	'Medallion' (Super Poppy Series)	SWat WHoo
§	***miyabeanum***	CSpe ECho ELan GAbr LRHS NBlu NWCA WEas WFar WPer WTMC
	- ***album***	ECho
	- ***tatewakii***	see *P. miyabeanum*
	nanum 'Flore Pleno'	see *P.* 'Fire Ball'
§	***nudicaule***	ELan NEgg WPer
	- 'Aurora Borealis' **new**	CSpe
	- Champagne Bubbles Group	EWll GWCH LRHS SWat WFar
	- Constance Finnis Group	GBuc MCot
	- var. ***croceum*** 'Flamenco'	LRHS
	- Garden Gnome Group	see *P. nudicaule* Gartenzwerg Series
§	- Gartenzwerg Series	COlW CSpe EMil GAbr MBri NBlu NEgg NLar SPlb WFar WGor
	- 'Illumination' **new**	MBri
	- 'Matador'	NEgg
	- 'Pacino'	EMil EWin EWll GBuc LRHS NLar SPet SPoG SRms WFar WWeb
	- 'Solar Fire Orange' Υ^{H4}	EWll
	- 'Summer Breeze Orange' Υ^{H4}	MBri NPri
	- 'Summer Breeze Yellow'	NPri
	- Wonderland Series	EHrv LBMP SPet
	- - 'Wonderland Orange'	NPri
	- - 'Wonderland Pink Shades'	NPri
	- - 'Wonderland White'	NPri
	- - 'Wonderland Yellow'	NPri
	orientale	CBcs EPfP LAst NBlu NNor SRms SWal SWat WBor WBrE WFar WPer
	- 'Abu Hassan'	SWat
	- 'Aglaja' Υ^{H4}	CElw EBee ECtt GAbr GBin LAst LPio MNFA MSte NCot NEgg NRnb NSti SAga SPhx SPoG SWat WCot WCra WHoo WLin
	- 'Aladin'	NBre NRnb SWat
	- 'Ali Baba'	NBre SWat
	- 'Alison'	SWat
	- 'Allegro'	CMea CSBt EBee ECtt GAbr GMaP IBal LAst LCro LRHS MBNS MBri MHer MRav MWgw NCGa NGdn NVic SPer SPlb SWat SWvt WBVN WCAu
	- 'Arc de Triomphe'	EBee
	- 'Arwide'	SWat
	- 'Aslahan'	ECha ELon MRav NBre SWat
	- 'Atrosanguineum'	NBre SWat
	- 'Avebury Crimson'	MWat SWat
	- 'Baby Kiss'	CFwr EBee MAvo
	- 'Ballkleid'	ECha SWat
	- 'Beauty Queen'	CCge EBee ECha ECot GMac LPio LRHS MRav NGdn SDix SWat
	- 'Bergermeister Rot'	SWat
	- 'Big Jim'	ELon SPla SWat
	- 'Black and White' Υ^{H4}	CDes CSpe EBee ECha EGle EHrv ELan EPfP ERou GMaP LBMP LCro LRHS MAvo MRav NBPC SApp SPer SPla SWat WCAu
	- 'Blackberry Queen'	EBee SWat
	- 'Blickfang'	NBre SWat
	- 'Blue Moon'	WHal
	- 'Bobbile' **new**	ECha
	- 'Bolero'	NCGa NLar WCot
	- 'Bonfire'	CAby EHrv NCob NRnb
	- 'Bonfire Red'	EBee LRHS SWat WCAu
§	- var. ***bracteatum*** Υ^{H4}	CWsd ECha NBir SMHy SWat WMoo
	- 'Brilliant'	EBee LRHS MWat NBre NGdn NLar SWat WFar WMoo
	- 'Brooklyn'	EBee ECtt EMan ERou IPot LPio MAvo MBri NBre SWat
	- 'Burning Heat' **new**	SPer
	- 'Carmen'	MNrw NBPC NCGa NLar WCot
*	- 'Carneum'	LRHS NBre NLar SPoG
	- 'Carnival'	CMil EBee NBre NLar SWat
	- 'Castagnette'	NLar WCot
	- 'Catherina'	EBee NBre NRnb SWat
	- 'Cedar Hill'	EBee EMar EWes GMac LRHS MRav NBre NRnb SWat
	- 'Cedric Morris' Υ^{H4}	CSpe ECha EGle ELan EPPr ERou GMac LFur LPio MRav MSte SMrm SPhx SWat WCot WHoo WMnd
	- 'Central Park'	CFwr EBee
	- 'Charming'	CAby CCge CPar EBee EMar LRHS MNFA MWat NGdn SPhx SWat
	- 'Checkers'	CTri LRav MLHP SEND
	- 'China Boy'	SWat WHrl WWeb
	- 'Choir Boy'	CEnt EBee ECtt EGle NLar NRnb SGar SPoG STes SWat WHrl WMoo
	- 'Clochard'	EBee SPoG
	- 'Coral Reef'	EBee EWll LEdu MHer MLHP NEgg SAga SMeo SWat WHer WMoo
	- 'Corrina'	EBee NBre SWat
	- 'Curlilocks'	CPar EBee ECtt ELan ELon EPfP ERou IBal LRHS MRav MWat NRnb SAga SPer SPoG SRms SWat SWvt WCot WHoo
	- 'Derwisch'	NBre SWat
*	- 'Diana'	SWat
	- 'Domino'	GMac MWea NBPN NCGa STes
	- double orange (d)	IBal
	- 'Double Pleasure' (d)	EBee ECtt IBal NBre NLar NMoo SWat WHrl
	- 'Doubloon' (d)	EBee ERou NBre NGdn NRnb SWat WFar
	- 'Dwarf Allegro'	GBuc WMnd
	- 'Effendi' Υ^{H4}	EBee IPot NBre SPhx SWat
	- 'Elam Pink'	EGle MLLN SWat WCot
	- 'Erste Zuneigung'	ECha EGle ELon SPhx SWat
	- 'Eskimo Pie'	SWat
	- 'Eyecatcher'	NCGa
	- 'Fancy Feathers'	EBee ECtt IPot MAvo MWea NBhm WHlf
	- 'Fatima'	CDes CMil NBre SWat WHrl WWeb
	- 'Feuerriese'	SWat
	- 'Feuerzwerg'	SWat
	- 'Fiesta'	CAby NBre SMeo SWat
	- 'Firefly'	WCot
	- 'Flamenco'	ECtt SWat
	- 'Flamingo'	SWat
	- 'Forncett Summer'	CTca EBee EMar ERou GMac LPio MRav NBre NGby NGdn SPer STes SWat WCAu WCot
	- 'Frosty' **new**	SHar
	- 'Garden Glory'	CPar EBee ECtt GCra GMac LRHS LSRN NBre NRnb SMrm SWat WCAu WTMC
	- 'Garden Gnome'	ENot SPet
	- 'Glowing Embers'	CSpe ERou LRHS SWat
	- 'Glowing Rose'	MDKP NBre SWat

- Goliath Group	ECha ELan ELon IBal LRHS MAvo MRav NBro NVic SAga SDix SRms SWat WFar WMnd
- - 'Beauty of Livermere'	More than 30 suppliers
- 'Graue Witwe'	CAby CMil EBee EGle GBuc LFur SApp SMHy SWat WHrl WTin
- 'Halima'	NBre SWat
- 'Harlem'	CHFP CSpe CWCL EBee EMar IPot MAvo MBri NBPN NLar SWat WCAu WHrl
- 'Harlem Louvre'	SMrm
- 'Harvest Moon' (d)	CAby EBee ECtt ERou IBal LCro LRHS NEgg NPer SPad SPhx SWat WHal WHil
- 'Heidi'	SWat
- 'Hewitt's Old Rose'	NBre WCot
- 'Hula Hula'	ECha ELon SWat
- 'Indian Chief'	CMHG EPfP ERou GMac IPot LPio LRHS MSte NBPC NBro NMoo NPer SPoG WCAu WFar WHil
- 'Joanne'	NLar
- 'John III' ΨH4	EBee LPio SPhx SWat
- 'John Metcalf'	EBee EMan EPPr LPio LRHS MLLN MRav NBre NSti SMrm SWat WCAu WCot WSpi
- 'Juliane'	CAby EBee ECha EGle GMac MNFA MSte NSti SPhx SWat WCot WTin
- 'Karine' ΨH4	CDes CElw CHar CSam CSpe EBee EBrs ECha EGle ELan EPPr EPfP GMaP GMac LCro LPio LRHS MNFA MWgw NPri SMHy SPhx SPoG SWat WCAu WHoo WTMC WTin WWeb
- 'Khedive' (d) ΨH4	EBee SWat
- 'King George'	GBuc SWat
- 'King Kong'	NCGa NLar
- 'Kleine Tänzerin'	CMil CSam ECha EMar ERou GBri GMac LRHS MLLN MRav MWgw NBre NGdn NPri NSti SPoG SWat WCAu WCot WWeb
- 'Kollebloem'	NBre SWat
- 'Lady Frederick Moore'	EBee GMac LPio LRHS MLLN NBre SWat
- 'Lady Roscoe'	NBre SWat
- 'Ladybird'	EBee ENot ERou LRHS MSte NBre SPoG
- 'Lambada'	SWat
- 'Lauren's Lilac'	CAby CMdw EBee ELon LPio LRHS NBre SMeo SPhx SWat
- 'Leuchtfeuer' ΨH4	CDes EBee ECha NBre SMHy SPhx SWat
- 'Lighthouse' ΨH4	SWat
- 'Lilac Girl'	CElw CSpe ECha ECtt EGle EWll GMaP GMac LHop LPio MSte NLar NSti SApp SPhx STes SWat WCot WHoo WHrl
- 'Louvre'	EBee EHrv MAvo MBri NLar SPoG WGwG
- 'Maiden's Blush'	NBre NGby NSti SWat
- 'Mandarin'	EBee NBhm NMoo
- 'Manhattan'	More than 30 suppliers
- 'Marcus Perry'	EBee ENot EPfP ERou EWes GMaP LCro LRHS NEgg NPri NRnb SPoG SWat WCAu WFar
- 'Mary Finnan'	CTca EBee NBre SWat
- 'Master Richard'	SWat
- 'May Queen' (d)	EShb EWes IBlr LRHS MRav NBre NBro NCGa NSti SWat WCot WHrl WPnn
- 'May Sadler'	EBee ENot NBre NRnb SWat
- 'Midnight'	ERou NBre SWat
- 'Miss Piggy'	CElw EBee IPot
- 'Mrs H.G. Stobart'	SWat
- 'Mrs Marrow's Plum'	see *P. orientale* 'Patty's Plum'
- 'Mrs Perry'	More than 30 suppliers
- 'Nanum Flore Pleno'	see *P.* 'Fire Ball'
- 'Noema'	SWat
- 'Orange Glow'	NBre NMoo NPri NRnb SWat WMoo
- 'Orangeade Maison'	NBre SWat
- 'Oriana'	LRHS NBre SWat
- 'Oriental'	SWat
- 'Pale Face'	ERou SWat
- 'Papillion'	EBee WPtf
§ - 'Patty's Plum'	More than 30 suppliers
- 'Perry's White'	More than 30 suppliers
- 'Peter Pan'	CAby MLLN NBre SWat
- 'Petticoat'	ECtt ELan NBre SWat
- 'Picotée'	EBee EBrs ECtt EHrv ELan EPfP ERou IBal LBMP LCro LPio LRHS MBri MRav NBPC NBro NCGa NCob NGdn NMoo SPer SPhx SPoG SWat SWvt WBrE WCAu WFar
- 'Pink Lassie'	NBre SWat
- 'Pink Panda'	SWat
- 'Pink Ruffles' PBR	EBee EMan ERou SPoG SWat
- 'Pinnacle'	CAby CDes CSWP EBee ELon ERou LRHS NGdn NPri SWat WFar
- 'Pizzicato'	CEnt CMea CPar CWib EHrv ERou LRHS MBri MNHC NPer SGar SPet SWat WFar WMoo WRHF
- 'Pizzicato White'	NBre NRnb
- 'Place Pigalle' **new**	CSpe EBee EHrv EPfP ERou LHop LPio LSou MAvo MBri MWea NBPC NGdn NOrc SPer WCra
- 'Polka'	SWat
- 'Prince of Orange'	SWat WHil
- Princess Victoria Louise	see *P. orientale* 'Prinzessin Victoria Louise'
- 'Prinz Eugen'	CMil EBee NBre SWat
§ - 'Prinzessin Victoria Louise'	CSWP EBee EGoo EPfP EShb GAbr GMaP IBal LAst LRHS MBri MDun MLLN NCGa NGdn NPri SSvw SWat WBVN WBrk WFar WPer
- 'Prospero'	NBre
- 'Queen Alexandra'	EHrv MCot NGdn NLar
- 'Raspberry Queen'	CDes CMea EBee ECtt EGle ELan ERou GMaP GMac LCro LRHS MArl MRav NCGa NPri NSti SApp SPhx STes SWat WBor WCot WCra WFar WHal WHoo WMnd WTin
- 'Raspberry Ruffles'	NBre SPhx SWat
- 'Rembrandt'	CAby ECot EHrv EMil ERou LRHS MDKP NBre NMoo NPri SWat WPer
- 'Rose Queen'	NBre WCot
- 'Rosenpokal'	EBee LRHS NGdn NRnb SWat
- 'Roter Zwerg'	ECha SWat
- 'Royal Chocolate Distinction'	CElw CMil CSpe CWCL EBee ECtt ELon EPPr EPfP ERou GBri IPot LCro LFur LPio MAvo MWea NBPC NBPN NLar NPri NSti SPoG SWat
- 'Royal Wedding'	CCge CHFP CTca CTri EBee ERou EShb LHop LRHS MBri MDun MHer NGdn NLar NPri NRnb SMad SMrm SPer SPla SPoG SSvw SWat WCot WFar WMoo WSpi WWeb
* - 'Saffron'	CAby CElw CMil SWat
- 'Salmon Glow' (d)	CBcs CRez IBal NRnb SSvw SWat WFar WPer
- 'Salome'	SWat
- scarlet	NCot
- 'Scarlet King'	LRHS NBre NEgg NOrc SWat
- 'Scarlett O'Hara' (d) **new**	EPfP NPri
- 'Showgirl'	EBee MLLN NBre SWat
* - 'Silberosa'	ECha SWat
- 'Sindbad'	CAby ECtt ELon GMac LRHS MAvo MRav NRnb SPhx SWat

- 'Snow Goose'	CAby NBre SPhx SWat WHoo
- 'Spätzünder'	NBre SWat
- 'Springtime'	EWes GMac LAst LRHS MRav NGdn NLar SWat WCAu WTMC WTin
- 'Staten Island'	EBee ECtt ERou MBri MNrw
- 'Stokesby Belle'	MWgw NBre
- Stormtorch	see *P. orientale* 'Sturmfackel'
§ - 'Sturmfackel'	ERou IBal NBre SWat
- 'Suleika'	NBre SWat
- 'Sultana'	ECha ELon ERou GMac MWat SWat WCAu
- 'The Promise'	NBre SWat
- 'Tiffany'	CBow CMil CSpe EBee ECtt ERou EWTr GMac LPio LSou MWgw NCGa NCot NLar SMad SPer SPla SPoG SSvw STes SWat WCot WCra WGwG
- 'Trinity'	SWat
- 'Turkish Delight'	CAby CElw EBrs ECtt ELon ENor EPfP ERou GMac LRHS MLLN MRav MSte MWat NBid NBir NPri NRnb SMer SPhx SRGP STes SWat SWvt WCAu WFar WMnd WTMC
- 'Tutu'	ERou IBal SWat
- 'Türkenlouis'	CHar CMHG CSpe EBee ECGP ECtt ENot EPfP ERou GCra GMaP GMac IBal LBMP LRHS SPer SPoG STes SWat WCAu WFar WTin WWlt
- 'Victoria Dreyfuss'	SWat
- 'Viola'	SWat
- 'Violetta' **new**	SWat
- 'Walking Fire'	MNrw
- 'Water Babies'	SWat
- 'Watermelon'	CMil EBrs ECtt ERou IPot LRHS MAvo MLLN MWat NBPC NPri NSti SMeo SPer STes SWat WBor WCAu WFar WHoo WTMC
- 'White Karine' **new**	GMac
- 'White King'	NBre
- 'Wild Salmon'	NBre
- 'Wisley Beacon'	NBre SWat
- 'Wunderkind'	EBee ECtt EMan IBal MNrw SWat WCAu
'Party Fun'	CSpe NEgg WWeb
paucifoliatum	CDes NBre
pilosum	EBee EMan GBuc SRms SWat WTin
§ - subsp. ***spicatum***	CMea ECGP ECha EGle GAbr LHop MSte NBir NChi STes WCot WMoo
rhaeticum	GKev NBre
'Rhapsody in Red' (Super Poppy Series)	SWat
rhoeas	CArn GPoy LCro WJek
- Angels' Choir Group (d)	SWat
- Mother of Pearl Group	CSpe SWat
rupifragum	CEnt CHrt CPLG CSsd ECha GAbr MLLN NPol SGar SWal WCot WEas WFar WHrl WPer WPnn WTMC
- 'Double Tangerine Gem'	see *P. rupifragum* 'Flore Pleno'
§ - 'Flore Pleno' (d)	CSWP CSpe LSou MBri NBre NChi WCFE WHen WHrl WMoo
- 'Tangerine Dream'	IBal LSRN MCCP MDun NEgg
sendtneri	WLin
'Serena' (Super Poppy Series)	SWat
'Shasta' (Super Poppy Series)	SWat WHoo
somniferum	CArn CWCL GPoy MSal SWat
- 'Black Beauty' (d)	CSpe SWat
- 'Black Paeony'	CWCL SBch
- 'Flemish Antique'	CWCL SWat
- (Laciniatum Group) 'Swansdown' (d)	CSpe
- var. ***paeoniiflorum*** (d)	CWCL SWat
- 'Pink Chiffon'	SWat WEas
- 'White Cloud' (d)	CWCL SWat
'Tequila Sunrise' (Super Poppy Series)	SWat
'The Cardinal'	NBre
thianschanicum	SPhx
triniifolium	CSpe MWea
'Vesuvius' (Super Poppy Series)	SWat
'Viva' (Super Poppy Series)	SWat

Parabenzoin see *Lindera*

Parachampionella see *Strobilanthes*

Paradisea (*Asphodelaceae*)

liliastrum ♀H4	CHid EBee ECho EPPr ERos GEdr IGor SRms WBVN WHoo WSHC
- 'Major'	ECho GSki SPhx
lusitanica	CBrm CDes CHid CMHG CPom CPrp CSam CSpe CWsd EBee ECho ERos GMac IBlr SMHy SWal WBVN WCot WPGP WThu WTin WWeb

Parahebe (*Scrophulariaceae*)

'Betty'	GGar
x ***bidwillii***	MHer NDlv NWCA SRms SRot
- 'Kea'	CFee ECou ECtt MDKP SRot WPer
canescens	ECou
§ ***catarractae***	CHar CMHG CPLG CTri CWib EBee ECho ECou EPfP GCra GGar MLHP MNrw MWat NBro SPoG WAbe WBrE WFar WHen WKif WMnd WPer
- from Chatham Island	EWes
- 'Baby Blue'	CAbP EPfP
- blue-flowered	CHar SPer
- 'County Park'	ECou
- 'Cuckoo'	ECou NHol
§ - 'Delight' ♀H3	CPLG ECho ECou EWes GGar GMaP GQue LHop LRHS MHer NEgg NHol NPer SDix SHFr SRot STre WEas WFar WHen
- subsp. ***diffusa***	ECho ECou ERas NPer NVic NWCA
- - 'Annie'	ECou NHol
- garden form	ECha SBla
- subsp. ***martinii***	ECou
- 'Miss Willmott'	ECho NPri NVic SBch SPer SPlb WBVN WBod WPer
- 'Porlock Purple'	see *P. catarractae* 'Delight'
- 'Rosea'	CEnt ECho WFar
- white-flowered	CPom CSpe ECho LHop MLHP NChi WBVN WPer
decora	CPLG
densifolia	see *Chionohebe densifolia*
§ ***formosa***	WHCG
- erect	GGar
'Gillian'	SWal WPer
'Greencourt'	see *P. catarractae* 'Delight'
§ ***hookeriana***	GGar ITim NBlu
§ - var. ***olsenii***	ECou GGar
'Jean' **new**	GGar
'Joy'	ECou EWes
'Julia'	GGar
linifolia	CTri
§ ***lyallii***	ECGP ECho ECou GMaP LAst MBar MHer MMuc MSwo MWat NChi NDlv NEgg NHol NPol NWCA SBla SPlb SRms WAbe WKif
- 'Baby Pink'	EPfP
- 'Clarence'	ECou
- 'Glacier'	ECou
- 'Julie-Anne' ♀H3	CAbP ECou EPfP GMaP LRHS

- 'Rosea' CTri WPer
- 'Summer Snow' ECou
'Mervyn' CTri ECho MDKP NDlv WHen WPer
olsenii see *P. hookeriana* var. *olsenii*
§ ***perfoliata*** ♀H3-4 More than 30 suppliers
- dark blue-flowered GBuc SMad
- 'Pringle' CAbP EPfP LRHS
'Snowcap' CDoC EBee EPfP LRHS SPlb

Parajubaea (*Arecaceae*)

cocoides LPJP LPal

Parakmeria see *Magnolia*

lotungensis see *Magnolia lotungensis*

Paranomus (*Proteaceae*)

reflexus EShb

Paraquilegia (*Ranunculaceae*)

adoxoides see *Semiaquilegia adoxoides*
§ ***anemonoides*** CPLG GCrs GKev SBla WAbe WLin
grandiflora see *P. anemonoides*

Paraserianthes (*Mimosaceae*)

distachya see *P. lophantha*
§ ***lophantha*** ♀H1 CHEx CRHN EBak ERea IDee LRav SAPC SArc SOWG

Parasyringa see *Ligustrum*

x *Pardancanda* (*Iridaceae*)

norrisii CFir CPen EBee EMan EWes GSki LRHS
- 'Dazzler' CHFP EShb

Pardanthopsis (*Iridaceae*)

dichotoma EBee EWes

Parietaria (*Urticaceae*)

judaica GPoy MSal WHer WSFF

Paris ✿ (*Trilliaceae*)

Chen Yi 8 WCot
Chen Yi 14 WCot
axialis new CHHB EBee
bashanensis CExc CHHB EBee NLAp WCru
chinensis EBee WCru
- B&SWJ 265 from Taiwan WCru
cronquistii CLAP GKev MLul
daliensis new CExc EBee
delavayi CHHB EBee WCru
- var. ***delavayi*** new MLul
- var. ***petiolata*** CHHB EBee
fargesii CHHB EBee LAma MLul WCru
- var. ***brevipetalata*** WCru
- var. ***petiolata*** CHHB EBee WCru
forrestii WCru
* ***hubeiensis*** new CExc EBee
incompleta CAvo CLAP GCrs SBla SSpi WCru
japonica SBla WCru
lancifolia B&SWJ 3044 from Taiwan WCru
luquanensis CHHB EBee MLul
mairei CHHB EBee WCru
marmorata CExc EBee EBrs WCru
polyphylla CArn CBct CFir CLAP EBee EBrs ECho GEdr GGar ITer LAma MLul MNFA MNrw WAbe WCot WCru WFar WPnP WSpi WWst
- B&SWJ 2125 WCru
- HWJCM 475 WCru
- var. ***alba*** CFir CHHB GKev
- var. ***stenophylla*** CFir CHHB CLAP EBee GEdr LAma MLul NLAp WCru
- var. ***yunnanensis*** EBee
* - - ***alba*** EBee
quadrifolia CAby CArn CFir CHHB CLAP GPoy NMen SPhx SSpi WCot WCru WHer WPGP WPnP WShi WTin
tetraphylla WCru
thibetica CFir CLAP EBee WCru
- var. ***apetala*** CHHB EBee WCru
- var. ***thibetica*** CHHB EBee GEdr
vaniotii new EBee
verticillata CLAP EBee GEdr LAma WCru

Parochetus (*Papilionaceae*)

§ ***africanus*** ♀H2 CHid ELon GBuc
communis misapplied see *P. africanus*
communis ambig. CBcs CFee CPLG NPer
communis Buch.-Ham. ex D. Don CC 3660 WRos
- B&SWJ 7215 Golden Triangle WCru
- from Himalaya EBee GCra
- - HWJCM 526 WCru
* - 'Blue Gem' CCCN CWCL EWin
- dark GGar

Paronychia (*Illecebraceae*)

argentea CLyd WPat WPer
§ ***capitata*** CLyd CTri EAlp SRms WPer
kapela SMad SPlb WPer
- 'Binsted Gold' (v) CBow LRHS WPer
§ - subsp. ***serpyllifolia*** GBin NRya XPep
nivea see *P. capitata*
serpyllifolia see *P. kapela* subsp. *serpyllifolia*

Parrotia (*Hamamelidaceae*)

persica ♀H4 More than 30 suppliers
- 'Biltmore' new CPMA
- 'Burgundy' CPMA NLar
- 'Felicie' CPMA EPfP NLar
- 'Jodrell Bank' CPMA MBlu MBri NLar
§ - 'Lamplighter' (v) CPMA
- 'Pendula' CMCN CPMA EPfP
- 'Vanessa' CBcs CDoC CMCN CPMA EWes MBlu MBri MGos NLar SLPl WFar WMou WOrn WPat
- 'Variegata' see *P. persica* 'Lamplighter'

Parrotiopsis (*Hamamelidaceae*)

jacquemontiana CBcs CPMA MBlu NLar NPal SSpi

Parrya (*Brassicaceae*)

menziesii see *Phoenicaulis cheiranthoides*

parsley see *Petroselinum crispum*

Parsonsia (*Apocynaceae*)

capsularis CPLG ECou
heterophylla ECou

Parthenium (*Asteraceae*)

integrifolium CArn GPoy MSal
* ***virginicum*** new SPhx

Parthenocissus (*Vitaceae*)

TH CHEx
§ ***henryana*** ♀H4 More than 30 suppliers
himalayana CBcs CPLG
- CC 4519 EWld MGol
- 'Purpurea' see *P. himalayana* var. *rubrifolia*
§ - var. ***rubrifolia*** CWCL EBee ELan LRHS MAsh MWgw NEgg NLar SLim SLon SPoG WCru WFar
inserta NLar
laetevirens NLar
§ ***quinquefolia*** ♀H4 More than 30 suppliers

	– var. ***engelmannii***	CBcs EBee LAst LBuc MGos NBlu SPer WCFE
	– 'Guy's Garnet'	WCru
	– 'Star Showers' (v)	EBee
	semicordata B&SWJ 6551	WCru
	striata	see *Cissus striata*
	thomsonii	see *Cayratia thomsonii*
§	***tricuspidata*** ♀H4	CWib EBee ECtt EPfP LAst MGos SMer SPer SReu WFar WWeb
	– 'Beverley Brook'	CMac EBee ERas LBuc MBri NLar SBod SBra SPer SPla SRms WFar
	– 'Crûg Compact'	CGHE WCru
	– 'Fenway Park'	ENot LBuc MBlu MBri SPoG
	– 'Ginza Lights' **new**	ENot
	– 'Green Spring'	CBcs EBee ERas IArd MGos NEgg NLar
	– 'Lowii'	CMac EBee ECot EPfP ERas LBuc LRHS MBlu MGos MRav NLar SBra SLon
	– 'Purpurea'	MBlu
	– 'Robusta'	CHEx EBee LCro LPan MBNS XPep
§	– 'Veitchii'	More than 30 suppliers

Pasithea (*Anthericaceae*)

	caerulea	WCot

Paspalum (*Poaceae*)

	glaucifolium	CElw LEdu WDyG
	quadrifarium	CKno CMHG EPPr LDai WCot WPrP XIsg
	– RCB/Arg RA-5-5	EBee

Passerina (*Thymelaeaceae*)

	montana	NWCA

Passiflora ✿ (*Passifloraceae*)

	RCB/Arg R-7	WCot
	actinia	CPas CRHN
	adenopoda	CPas
	'Adularia'	CCCN CPas LRHS
	alata (F) ♀H1	CCCN CPas LRHS MJnS
	– 'Shannon' (F)	CPas
	x ***alatocaerulea***	see *P.* x *belotii*
	allantophylla	CPas
	'Allardii'	CCCN CPas EShb LRHS
	amalocarpa	CPas
	ambigua	CPas
§	'Amethyst' ♀H1	CCCN CPas CRHN CSPN CWoW EAmu EBee EMil LHop LRHS LSRN MAsh MJnS MRav SBra SLim SPad SPla SPoG WFar WPGP WPat WWeb
	amethystina misapplied	see *P.* 'Amethyst'
§	***amethystina*** Mikan	CBcs CPas ECre ERea LRHS
	ampullacea (F)	CPas
	'Anastasia'	CCCN
	'Andy'	CCCN
	'Anemona'	CPas
	anfracta	CPas
	'Angelo Blu'	CCCN CPas
	antioquiensis misapplied	see *P.* x *exoniensis*
	antioquiensis ambig.	CBcs CDoC CPas CRHN ERea LRHS SOWG
	antioquiensis ambig. x ***mixta***	CTrC
	antioquiensis ambig. x (x ***exoniensis*** 'Hill House') **new**	CHll
	antioquiensis Karst ♀H2	CHll ISea
	apetala	CPas
	arbelaezii	CPas
	arida var. ***pentaschista*** **new**	CPas
	x ***atropurpurea***	CCCN CPas
§	***aurantia***	CPas LRHS
	auriculata	CPas
	'Aurora' **new**	CPas
	banksii	see *P. aurantia*
	'Barborea'	CPas
§	x ***belotii***	CCCN CPas EQua EShb LRHS
	– 'Impératrice Eugénie'	see *P.* x *belotii*
	bicornis **new**	CPas
	biflora Lamarck	CPas LRHS
	'Blaumilch' **new**	CPas
	'Blue Bird'	CCCN CPas
	'Blue Moon'	CCCN CPas
	boenderi	CPas
	bogatensis	CPas
	brevifila **new**	CPas
	'Byron Beauty'	CCCN CPas
	'Cacita' **new**	CPas
§	***caerulea*** ♀H3	More than 30 suppliers
	– 'Clear Sky'	CPas NBlu
	– 'Constance Elliott'	More than 30 suppliers
	– ***rubra***	CSBt LRHS MGos WFar
	x ***caeruleoracemosa***	see *P.* x *violacea*
	capsularis	CPas
	chinensis	see *P. caerulea*
	cincinnata	CPas
	cinnabarina	CPas
	citrifolia	CCCN CPas
	citrina	CPas LRHS SOWG
	cobanensis	CPas
	coccinea (F)	CPas LRHS
	colinvauxii	CPas
	x ***colvillii***	CHll CPas
	conzattiana	CPas
	'Coordination'	CCCN
§	***coriacea***	CPas LRHS
	costaricensis	CPas
	crenata	CPas
	'Crimson Trees' **new**	CCCN
	cuneata	CPas
§	– 'Miguel Molinari'	CPas
	cuprea	CPas
I	'Curiosa'	CPas LRHS
	cuspidifolia	CPas
	'Debby'	CPas
	x ***decaisneana*** (F)	CCCN CPas
	dioscoreifolia	CPas
	discophora	CPas
	'Eclipse'	CPas
	'Eden'	CCCN EAmu LBuc LCro LRHS MBri NLar SBra SCoo SLim SPoG SRkn
	edulis (F)	CAgr CCCN CPas GPoy LRHS MJnS
	– 'Crackerjack' (F)	ERea
	– f. ***flavicarpa*** (F)	CPas
	– 'Golden Nugget' (F)	CPas
	– 'Norfolk' (F)	CPas
	– 'Panama Gold' **new**	CPas
	– 'Pink Cheek' **new**	CPas
	– 'Possum Purple' **new**	CPas
	eichleriana	CPas
	elegans	CPas
	'Elizabeth' (F)	CPas
	'Empress Eugenie'	see *P.* x *belotii*
	'Excel'	CPas
§	x ***exoniensis*** ♀H1	CHll CPas CRHN EBee ECre LRHS
	exura	CPas
	'Fairylights' **new**	CCCN
	filipes	CPas
	'Fledermouse'	CPas
	'Flying V'	CCCN CPas
	foetida	CPas SOWG
	– var. ***galapagensis***	CPas
	– var. ***hastata*** **new**	CPas
	– var. ***hirsuta*** (F)	CPas
	– var. ***hirsutissima***	CPas
I	***gabrielliana***	CPas

	garckei	CPas
	gibertii	CPas EShb
	gilbertiana	CPas WFar
	glandulosa	CPas
	'Golden Glow' **new**	LBuc
	gracilis	CPas
	gritensis	CPas
	guatemalensis	CPas
	hahnii	CPas EAmu
	helleri	CPas
	herbertiana (F)	CPas
	holosericea	CPas
	incana	see *P. seemannii*
	incarnata (F)	CAgr CArn CPas EShb MSal SPlb
	'Incense' (F) ♀H1	CCCN CPas LRHS SLim SPlb WFar
	indecora	CPas
	'Inspiration' **new**	CPas
	'Inverleith'	CPas
	jatunsachensis	CPas
	'Jeanette'	CPas
	'Jelly Joker'	CCCN CPas
	jorullensis	CPas
	juliana	CPas
	kalbreyeri	CPas
	karwinskii	CPas
	'Kate Adie'	CPas
	kermesina	CPas
	x ***kewensis***	CCCN CPas
	'Lady Margaret'	CPas EShb LRHS
	lancearia	CPas
	lancetellesis	CPas
	laurifolia (F)	CPas SLim
§	***ligularis*** (F)	CPas LRHS
	'Lilac Lady'	see *P.* x *violacea* 'Tresederi'
	lobata	CPas
	loefgrenii	CPas
	lourdesae	see *P. cuneata* 'Miguel Molinari'
	lowei	see *P. ligularis*
	lutea	CPas
	macrophylla	CPas
	maliformis (F)	CHll CPas
	manicata (F)	CPas EShb
	'Maria'	CCCN
	'Mary Jane' **new**	CCCN
	matthewsii	CPas
	'Mavis Mastics'	see *P.* x *violacea* 'Tresederi'
	mayana	see *P. caerulea*
	membranacea (F)	CPas
	menispermifolia	see *P. pilosa*
	microstipula	CPas
	miersii	CPas
	misera	CPas
	mixta (F)	CCCN
	- B&SWJ 10756	WCru
*	- var. ***pinanga***	CPas
	mollissima (F) ♀H1	CAgr CBcs CCCN CHll CPas CRHN ERea EShb LRHS SOWG SPlb
	moluccana	CPas
	mooreana	CPas
	morifolia	CPas EShb
	mucronata	CPas
	multiflora	CPas
	murucuja	CCCN CPas
	naviculata	CPas
	- RCB/Arg P-12	WCot
	nephrodes	CPas
	'New Incense'	CPas
	nigradenia	CPas
	oblongata	CPas
	obtusifolia	see *P. coriacea*
	oerstedii	CPas
	- var. ***choconiana***	CPas
	onychina	see *P. amethystina* Mikan
	organensis	CPas
	'Oriental Sunset' **new**	CPas
	ornitheura	CPas
	pallida **new**	CPas
	palmeri	CPas
I	***pardifolia***	CPas
	parritae	CPas
	penduliflora	CPas
	perakensis	CPas
	perfoliata	CPas
	'Peter Lawerence' **new**	CCCN
	phoenicea	CPas
§	***pilosa***	CPas
	pilosicorona	CPas
	'Pink Jewel'	CPas
	'Pink Polka Dot' **new**	CPas
	pinnatistipula (F)	EUnu
	x ***piresiae***	CCCN CPas LRHS
	pittieri	CPas
	platyloba	CPas
*	***pseudo-oerstedii***	CPas
	punctata	CPas
	'Pura Vida'	CPas LRHS
	'Pura Vida 1' **new**	CPas
	'Pura Vida 2' **new**	CPas
	'Purple Haze'	CCCN CPas CRHN CWib EAmu EBee LRHS SLim WWeb
	'Purple-heart' **new**	CPas
	quadrangularis (F) ♀H1	CCCN CHll CPas CWSG ERea LRHS MJnS
	quinquangularis	CBcs CPas
	racemosa ♀H2	CPas EBee ERea LAst LRHS MNHC SLim SOWG
	reflexiflora	CPas
	resticulata	CPas
	rovirosae	CPas LRHS
	rubra	CCCN CPas SLim
*	***rufa***	CPas
	sagastegui	CPas
	'Saint Rule'	CPas
	'Sancap' **new**	CPas
	sanguinolenta	CPas LRHS
	'Sapphire'	CPas
	'Sarah Aimee'	CPas LRHS
§	***seemannii***	CPas
	serratifolia	CPas
	sexflora	CPas
	sexocellata	see *P. coriacea*
	'Simply Red'	CPas LRHS
	'Smythiana'	CPas EShb
	sprucei	CPas
	standleyi	CPas
	'Star of Bristol' ♀H2	CPas EAmu SBra SLim
	'Star of Clevedon'	CPas
	'Star of Kingston'	CPas
	'Star of Surbiton'	CPas LRHS
	stipulata	CPas
	suberosa	CPas
	sublanceolata **new**	CPas
	subpeltata	CPas LRHS
	subpurpurea	CPas
	subrotunda	CPas
	'Sunburst'	CCCN CHEx CPas LRHS
	talamancensis	CPas
	tenuifila	CPas
	tetrandra	CPLG CPas ECou
	tiliifolia **new**	CPas
	'Tinalandia' **new**	CPas
	x ***tresederi***	see *P.* x *violacea* 'Tresederi'
	trialata	CPas
	tricuspis	CPas
	tridactylites	CPas
	trifasciata	CCCN CPas EShb
	triloba	CPas
	tripartita	CPas
	trisecta	CPas
	tuberosa	CPas

tulae	CPas LRHS
umbilicata	CPas SKHP WCru
urbaniana	CPas
vespertilio	CPas
§ x ***violacea*** ♀H1	CBcs CPas CRHN WFar
- 'Dedorina'	CPas
- 'Eynsford Gem'	CCCN CPas
- 'Lilac Lady'	see *P.* x *violacea* 'Tresederi'
§ - 'Tresederi'	CPas WFar
- 'Victoria'	CPas CSBt EBee LRHS SLim
vitifolia (F)	CPas LRHS SOWG
- 'Scarlet Flame' (F)	CPas LRHS
'White Lightning' new	LBuc
xiikzodz	CPas
yucatanensis	CPas
zamorana	CPas

passion fruit see *Passiflora*

passion fruit, banana see *Passiflora mollissima*

Patersonia (*Iridaceae*)

occidentalis	SPlb

Patrinia (*Valerianaceae*)

gibbosa	EMan LRHS MBNS MGol WFar WMoo WPnP
- B&SWJ 874	WCru
intermedia	WLin
scabiosifolia	CDes CHll CMea CSpe CWsd EBee ECha ECtt EGle EWsh GAbr GBuc GSki MLLN MNFA NBir NCGa NDov NLar NPri NSti SPhx SPoG SSvw WAul WFar WHoo WMoo WPGP WSHC
- B&SWJ 8740	WCru
- 'Nagoya'	MNrw
triloba	ECho EDAr GBuc GCrs GEdr LRHS LSou MGol SMac WBVN WFar WMoo WPnP
* - 'Minor'	ECho
- var. ***palmata***	WDyG WFar WMoo
villosa	CPLG EBee NDov NGdn NLar SSvw

Paulownia (*Scrophulariaceae*)

catalpifolia	CBcs EBee EGFP EPla NLar WPGP
elongata	CBcs EGFP NLar WPGP
fargesii Osborn	see *P. tomentosa* 'Lilacina'
fortunei	CBcs CHEx MBlu NPal SPlb WBVN WNor WPat
- Fast Blue = 'Minfast' new	EBee EMil EPfP LSRN SLon
kawakamii	WPGP
- B&SWJ 6784	WCru
taiwaniana B&SWJ 7134	WCru
tomentosa ♀H3	More than 30 suppliers
- 'Coreana'	CHll
- - B&SWJ 8503	WCru
§ - 'Lilacina'	CBcs

Pavonia (*Malvaceae*)

hastata	EShb
missionum	EShb
multiflora Jussieu ♀H1	ERea
* ***volubilis*** new	CCCN

paw paw (false banana) see *Asimina triloba*

paw paw (papaya) see *Carica papaya*

Paxistima (*Celastraceae*)

canbyi	NLar WThu

peach see *Prunus persica*

pear see *Pyrus communis*

pear, Asian see *Pyrus pyrifolia*

pecan see *Carya illinoinensis*

Pedicularis (*Scrophulariaceae*)

axillaris	EBee
- SDR 1745	GKev
longiflora var. ***tubiformis***	EBee GKev
rex	EBee
rhinanthoides subsp. ***tibetica***	EBee GKev
superba	GKev

Peganum (*Zygophyllaceae*)

harmala	CArn EMan MGol MHer MSal

Pelargonium ✿ (*Geraniaceae*)

'A Happy Thought'	see *P.* 'Happy Thought'
'A.M. Mayne' (Z/d)	WFib
'Abba' (Z/d)	WFib
'Abel Carrière' (I/d)	SPet
abrotanifolium (Sc)	CRHN LPio MBPg MHer SSea WFib XPep
'Abundance' (Sc)	LDea MBPg
acerifolium misapplied	see *P. vitifolium*
acetosum	LPio MHer MSte SHFr
* - 'Variegatum' (v)	LPio MSte SSea
'Acushla by Brian' (Sc)	MBPg MWhe
'Ada Green' (R)	LDea WFib
'Adagio' (Dw)	ESul
'Adam's Quilt' (Z/C)	WEas
'Adele' (Min/d)	ESul
'Ade's Elf' (Z/St)	NFir SSea
'Aerosol' (Min)	ESul
'Ailsa' (Min/d)	ESul
'Ainsdale Beauty' (Z)	SSea WFib
'Ainsdale Claret' (Z)	SSea
'Ainsdale Eyeful' (Z)	SSea WFib
'Ainsdale Glasnost' (Z)	SSea
'Ainsdale Happiness' (Z/d)	SSea
'Ainsdale Sixty' (Z)	SSea
'Akela' (Min)	ESul
'Alan West' (Z/St)	SSea
alchemilloides	CRHN LPio NCiC
'Alcyone' (Dw/d)	ESul WFib
'Alde' (Min)	ESul MWhe NFir SSea WFib
'Aldenham' (Z)	WFib
'Aldham' (Min)	ESul WFib
'Aldwyck' (R)	ESul LDea WFib
'Alex Kitson' (Z)	WFib
'Alex Mary' (R)	ESul SSea
'Algenon' (Min/d)	ESul WFib
I 'Alice' (Min)	WFib
'Alice Greenfield' (Z)	NFir SSea
'Alison' (Dw)	ESul
'Alison Wheeler' (Min/d)	MWhe
'All My Love' (R)	LDea
'Alma' (Dw/C)	ESul
'Almond' (Sc)	MBPg
'Almost Heaven' (Dw/Z/v)	MWhe
'Alpine Glow' (Z/d)	MWhe
'Altair' (Min/d)	ESul
'Amari' (R)	WFib
'Amazon' (R)	ESul
'Ambrose' (Min/d)	ESul WFib
Amelit = 'Pacameli'PBR (I/d)	LAst LSou WGor
'American Prince of Orange' (Sc)	MBPg
'Amethyst' (R)	ESul LDea SCoo SPet WFib

§	Amethyst = 'Fisdel'PBR (I/d) Υ^{H1+3}	ECtt LDea LVER MWhe NPri
	'Amour' (R)	ESul
I	'Amy' (Dw)	WFib
	'Andersonii' (Z/Sc)	MBPg MHer
	'Andrew Salvidge' (R)	LDea
	'Androcles' (A)	LDea
	'Angel Josie' (A)	LAst
	'Angela' (R)	ESul LDea
	'Angela Read' (Dw)	ESul
	'Angela Thorogood' (R)	ESul
	'Angela Woodberry' (Z)	WFib
	Angeleyes Series (A)	LAst MWhe SSea
	- Angeleyes Bicolor = 'Pacbicolor'PBR (A)	LAst NPri WHlf
	- Angeleyes Burgundy = 'Pacburg'PBR (A)	LAst LSou MPes SSea WHlf
	- Angeleyes Daphne (A)	LAst
	- Angeleyes Josie (A)	LAst
	- Angeleyes Light = 'Paceyes'PBR (A)	LAst LSou
	- Angeleyes Randy (A)	LAst LSou SSea
	- Angeleyes Velvet Duet (A) **new**	LAst
	- Angeleyes Viola = 'Pacviola'PBR (A)	LAst
	'Angelique' (Dw/d)	ESul LVER NFir WFib
	'Anglia' (Dw)	ESul
	'Ann Field' (Dw/d)	ESul
	'Ann Hoystead' (R) Υ^{H1+3}	ESul NFir WFib
	'Ann Redington' (R)	ESul
	'Anna' (Dw)	ESul
	'Anna Scheen' (Min)	ESul
	'Anne' (I/d)	WFib
	'Annsbrook Aquarius' (St)	ESul NFir
	'Annsbrook Beauty' (A/C)	ESul MBPg NFir WFib
	'Annsbrook Capricorn' (St/d)	ESul
	'Annsbrook Fruit Sundae' (A)	LDea
	'Annsbrook Jupitor' (Z/St)	ESul NFir
	'Annsbrook Mars' (St/C)	ESul
	'Annsbrook Peaches' (Min)	ESul
	'Annsbrook Pluto' (Z/St)	ESul
	'Annsbrook Rowan' (Min)	ESul
	'Annsbrook Squirrel' (Min)	ESul
	'Annsbrook Venus' (Z/St)	ESul
	'Anthony Ayton' (R)	ESul
	Anthony = 'Pacan' (Z/d)	LAst
	(Antik Series) Antik Orange = 'Tikorg' PBR (Z) Υ^{H1+3}	LVER
	- Antik Pink = 'Tikpink' PBR (Z)	LVER
	- Antik Salmon = 'Tiksal' PBR (Z)	LVER
	- Antik Violet = 'Tikvio' PBR (Z)	LVER
	'Antoine Crozy' (ZxI/d)	WFib
	'Antoinette' (Min)	ESul
	'Antonnia Scammell' (St/d)	ESul
	'Apache' (Z/d) Υ^{H1+3}	CHal WFib
	'Aphrodite' (Z)	ECtt
	'Apollo' (R)	ESul
	appendiculatum **new**	LPio
	'Apple Betty' (Sc)	MBPg WFib
	'Apple Blossom Rosebud' (Z/d) Υ^{H1+3}	CStu ECtt EShb ESul LAst LVER MBri MCot MWhe SSea WBrk WFib
	'Appledram' (R)	LDea
	'Apri Parmer' (Min)	ESul
	'Apricot' (Z/St)	ESul LAst WGor
	'Apricot Queen' (I/d)	LDea
	'Apricot Star'	MSte MWhe
	'April Hamilton' (I)	LDea WFib
	'April Showers' (A)	LDea WFib
	'Aquarell' (R)	ESul
	Arcona 2000 = 'Klecona'PBR	LAst LSou
	'Arctic Frost'	WFib
§	'Arctic Star' (Z/St)	ESul LVER NFir SSea WBrk WFib
	'Ardens'	CSpe EBee ESul LHop LPio MCot MHer MSte NCiC NCob NFir NSti SMrm SSea SWvt WCot WEas WFib WGwG
	'Ardwick Cinnamon' (Sc)	ESul LDea MBPg NFir WFib
	aridum	LPio
	'Aries' (Min)	MWhe
	Aristo Apricot = 'Regapri' (R) **new**	LAst WGor
	Aristo Beauty = 'Regbeauty' (R) **new**	LAst LSou
	Aristo Clara Schumann (R) **new**	LAst
	Aristo Claret = 'Regros'PBR (R) **new**	LAst
	Aristo Lavender = 'Reglav'PBR (R) **new**	LAst WGor
	Aristo Red Velvet = 'Regvel' (R) **new**	LAst
	Aristo Schoko = 'Regschoko' (R) **new**	LAst
	Aristo Violet = 'Regvio'PBR (R) **new**	LAst
	'Arnside Fringed Aztec' (R)	LDea WFib
	'Aroma' (Sc)	MBPg
	'Arthington Slam' (R)	LDea
	'Arthur Biggin' (Z)	MWhe
	'Ashby' (U/Sc)	LVER MBPg NFir SSea
	'Ashfield Jubilee' (Z/C)	NFir
	'Ashfield Monarch' (Z/d) Υ^{H1+3}	MWhe NFir SSea
	'Ashfield Serenade' (Z) Υ^{H1+3}	SSea WFib
	'Ashley Stephenson' (R)	WFib
	'Askham Fringed Aztec' (R) Υ^{H1+3}	ESul LDea SSea WFib
	'Askham Slam' (R)	LDea
	asperum Ehr. ex Willd.	see *P.* 'Graveolens'
	'Asperum'	MBPg
	'Astrakan' (Z/d)	SSea
	'Athabasca' (Min)	ESul
§	'Atomic Snowflake' (Sc/v)	CArn CHal CTca ESul LDea MBPg MHer MSte MWhe SDnm SIde SPet SSea WFib
	'Atrium' (U)	WFib
	'Attar of Roses' (Sc) Υ^{H1+3}	CArn CHal CHrt CRHN CTca ESul LAst LDea LVER MBPg MHer MSte MWhe NFir NPri SDnm SIde SSea WBrk WFib WGwG
	'Attraction' (Z/Ca/d)	SSea
	'Aubusson' (R)	ESul
	'Auntie Billie' (A)	LDea
	'Aurelia' (A)	LDea
	'Aurora' (Z/d)	LAst LSou LVER MWhe SSea
	'Aurore' (U)	see *P.* 'Unique Aurore'
	australe	CRHN LPio SBch SChr WFib
	'Australian Bute' (R)	ESul LSou LVER
	'Australian Mystery' (R/Dec)	CSpe ESul LPio MSte NFir SAga WFib
	'Autumn' (Z/d)	MWhe
	'Autumn Colours' (Min)	ESul
	'Autumn Haze' (R)	ESul
	'Avril'	ESul
	'Aztec' (R) Υ^{H1+3}	ESul LDea LVER MSte NFir SSea WFib
	'Baby Bird's Egg' (Min)	ESul WFib
	'Baby Brocade' (Min/d)	ESul WFib
	'Baby Harry' (Dw/v)	WFib
	'Baby Helen' (Min)	ESul
	'Baby James' (Min)	ESul

'Baby Snooks' (A)	ESul LDea MWhe
'Babylon' (R)	ESul SSea
'Badley' (Dw)	ESul
Balcon Imperial	see *P.* 'Roi des Balcons Impérial'
'Balcon Lilas'	see *P.* 'Roi des Balcons Lilas'
'Balcon Rose'	see *P.* 'Hederinum'
'Balcon Rouge'	see *P.* 'Roi des Balcons Impérial'
'Balcon Royale'	see *P.* 'Roi des Balcons Impérial'
I 'Ballerina' (Min)	WFib
'Ballerina' (Z/d)	MWhe
'Ballerina' (R)	see *P.* 'Carisbrooke'
'Bandit' (Min)	ESul
'Banstead Beacon'	LVER
'Banstead Beauty' **new**	LVER
'Banstead Village' (Z)	LVER
'Bantam' (Min/d)	ESul WFib
'Barbara Houghton' (Dw/d) **new**	WFib
§ 'Barbe Bleu' (I/d)	ECtt LCro LDea LVER MWhe NFir SSea WFib
'Barcelona' (R)	ESul
'Barham' (Min/d)	ESul
'Barking' (Min/Z)	ESul NFir
barklyi	LFur
'Barnston Dale' (Dw/d)	ESul NFir
'Bath Beauty' (Dw)	CSpe WEas
'Baylham' (Min)	ESul
Beach = 'Fisbea' (I/d)	NPri
'Beacon Hill' (Min)	ESul
'Beatrice Cottington' (I/d)	WFib
'Beatrix' (Z/d)	LVER
'Beau Geste' (R)	ESul
'Beauty of Diane' (I/d)	LDea
'Beauty of Eastbourne' misapplied	see *P.* 'Lachskönigin'
'Beidermeier' (R)	ESul
'Belinda Adams' (Min/d) 🏆H1+3	MWhe NFir
Belladonna = 'Fisopa' (I/d)	ECtt SCoo
'Belvedere' (R)	ESul
'Bembridge' (Z/St/d)	SSea WFib
'Ben Franklin' (Z/d/v) 🏆H1+3	ESul MWhe NFir SSea
'Ben Matt' (R)	WFib
'Ben Nevis' (Dw/d)	ESul LVER
'Ben Picton' (Z/d)	WFib
'Bentley' (Dw)	ESul
'Berkswell Blush' (A) **new**	LDea
'Berkswell Carnival' (A)	LDea
'Berkswell Champagne' (A) **new**	LDea
'Berkswell Dainty' (A)	LDea
'Berkswell Debonair' (A)	LDea
'Berkswell Gaiety' (A)	LDea
'Berkswell Lace' (A)	LDea
'Berkswell Pixie' (A)	LDea
'Berkswell Sparkler' (A) **new**	LDea
'Berkswell Windmill' (A) **new**	LDea
Bernardo = 'Guiber'PBR (I/d)	LAst NBlu WGor
'Bernice Ladroot'	LDea
'Beromünster' (Dec)	ESul LDea MHer MSte NFir SAga SSea WFib
'Bert Pearce' (R)	ESul LDea WFib
'Beryl Gibbons' (Z/d)	MWhe
'Beryl Read' (Dw)	ESul
'Beryl Reid' (R)	ESul LDea WFib
'Berylette' (Min/d)	ESul
'Bess' (Z/d)	ESul
'Bette Shellard' (Z/d/v)	MWhe NFir
'Betty Merry' (R)	LDea
'Betty Read' (Dw)	ESul
'Betty West' (Min/d)	ESul
betulinum	LPio SSea WFib
'Betwixt' (Z/v)	SSea
'Bianca' (Min/d)	ESul
'Bi-coloured Startel' (Z/St/d)	MWhe
'Big Apple' (Sc)	MBPg
'Bildeston' (Dw/C)	ESul NFir WFib
'Bill West' (I)	SSea WFib
'Billie Read' (Dw/d)	ESul
'Bingo' (Min)	ESul
'Bird Dancer' (Dw/St) 🏆H1+3	CHal ESul LVER MHer MSte MWhe NFir SHFr SSea WBrk
'Birdbush Andy Pandy' (Sc)	MBPg
'Birdbush Bella' (Sc) **new**	MBPg
'Birdbush Blush' (Sc)	MBPg
'Birdbush Bold and Beautiful' (Sc)	MBPg
'Birdbush Bramley' (Sc)	MBPg
'Birdbush Chloe' (St)	MBPg
'Birdbush Claire Louise' (Sc) **new**	MBPg
'Birdbush Dawndew' (Sc) **new**	MBPg
'Birdbush Eleanor' (Z)	MBPg WFib
'Birdbush Julie Anne' (Sc) **new**	MBPg
'Birdbush Lemon and Lime' (Sc)	MBPg
'Birdbush Lemonside' (Sc)	MBPg
'Birdbush Linda Creasey' (Sc) **new**	MBPg
'Birdbush Matty'	MBPg
'Birdbush Miriam' (Sc) **new**	MBPg
'Birdbush Nutty' (Sc)	MBPg
'Birdbush Pinky and Perky' (U)	MBPg
'Birdbush Sweetness' (Sc)	MBPg
'Birdbush Too Too O' (Sc)	MBPg
'Birdbush Velvet' (Sc)	MBPg
'Birthday Girl' (R)	WFib
'Bitter Lemon' (Sc)	ESul MBPg
'Black Butterfly'	see *P.* 'Brown's Butterfly'
'Black Knight' (R)	CSpe EShb LVER MSte
'Black Knight' Lea (Dw/d/c)	ESul MSte NFir
'Black Magic' (R)	NPri
'Black Night' (A)	ESul MBPg
'Black Pearl' (Z/d)	LVER
'Black Prince' (R/Dec)	NFir WFib
'Black Top' (R)	ESul
'Black Velvet' (R)	ESul LDea MCot
'Black Vesuvius'	see *P.* 'Red Black Vesuvius'
'Blackdown Delight' (Z)	NFir
'Blackdown Sensation' (Dw/Z)	NFir
'Blakesdorf' (Dw)	ESul MWhe
Blanca = 'Penwei'PBR (Dark Line Series) (Z/d)	LAst LSou LVER NBlu
Blanche Roche = 'Guitoblanc' (I/d)	LAst LSou NBlu SCoo
§ 'Blandfordianum' (Sc)	LDea LPio MHer MSte
'Blandfordianum Roseum' (Sc)	LDea
'Blaze Away'	SSea
'Blazonry' (Z/v)	MWhe WFib
'Blendworth' (R)	LDea
'Blooming Gem' (Min/I/d)	LDea
'Blue Beard'	see *P.* 'Barbe Bleu'
'Blue Orchid' (R)	ESul
Blue Sybil = 'Pacblusy'PBR (I/d)	LAst LSou LVER
'Blue Wine'	LAst
Blue Wonder = 'Pacbla'PBR (Z/d)	LAst LSou WGor
'Bluebeard'	see *P.* 'Barbe Bleu'

Blue-Blizzard = 'Fisrain'PBR (I)	SCoo
'Blush Petit Pierre' (Min)	ESul
'Blushing Bride' (I/d)	LDea
'Blushing Emma' (Dw/d)	ESul
'Bob Hall' (St)	ESul
'Bob Newing' (Min/St) **new**	WFib
'Bobberstone' (Z/St)	LVER WFib
'Bold Appleblossom' (Z)	SSea WFib
'Bold Carmine' (Z/d)	NFir
'Bold Carousel' (Z/d) **new**	WFib
'Bold Dawn' (Z)	NFir
'Bold Flame' (Z/d)	SSea WFib
'Bold Limelight' (Z/d) **new**	WFib
'Bold Pixie' (Dw/d) **new**	WFib
'Bold Sunrise' (Z/d)	LVER NFir
'Bold Sunset' (Z/d)	LVER NFir WFib
'Bold White' (Z)	NFir
'Bolero' (U) ♀H1+3	LVER MSte NFir SSea WFib
'Bon Bon' (Min/St)	WFib
'Bonito' (I/d)	LVER
'Bonnie Austin' (St)	ESul
'Bonny' (Min/St)	ESul
'Bosham' (R)	ESul LDea WFib
'Botham's Surprise'	MHer
'Both's Snowflake' (Sc/v)	GGar MBPg
bowkeri	LFur WFib
'Brackenwood' (Dw/d) ♀H1+3	ESul LVER NFir
'Bramford' (Dw)	ESul
'Braque' (R)	LDea
Bravo = 'Fisbravo'PBR (Z/d)	LAst MWhe WFib
'Break o' Day' (R)	LDea WEas
'Bredon' (R) ♀H1+3	ESul
'Brenda' (Min/d)	ESul WFib
'Brenda Hyatt' (Dw/d)	ESul WFib
'Brenda Kitson' (Z/d)	LVER MWhe
'Brettenham' (Min)	ESul
'Briarlyn Beauty' (A)	LDea MBPg MWhe SSea
'Briarlyn Moonglow' (A)	ESul LDea SSea
'Bridesmaid' (Dw/d)	ESul NFir WFib
'Bridgwater' (R)	ESul
'Bright Eyes' ambig. (Dw)	WFib
'Brightstone' (Z/d)	WFib
'Brightwell' (Min/d)	ESul
'Brilliant' (Dec)	MBPg MHer WFib
'Brilliantine' (Sc)	ESul MBPg MHer WFib
'Bristol' (Z/v)	SSea
'Britannia' (R)	LDea
'Brixworth Boquet' (Min/C/d)	MWhe
'Brixworth Charmer' (Z/v)	MWhe
'Brixworth Melody' (Z/v)	MWhe
'Brixworth Pearl' (Z)	MWhe WFib
'Brixworth Rhapsody' (Z/v)	MWhe
'Brixworth Starlight' (I/v)	MWhe
'Brockbury Scarlet' (Ca)	WFib
'Bronze Corinne' (Z/C/d)	SPet
'Bronze Queen' (Z/C)	MWhe
'Bronze Velvet' (R)	LDea
'Brook's Purple'	see *P.* 'Royal Purple'
'Brookside Betty' (Dw/C/d)	ESul
'Brookside Bolero' (Z)	ESul
'Brookside Candy' (Dw/d)	ESul
'Brookside Champagne' (Min/d)	ESul
'Brookside Fiesta' (Min/d)	ESul
'Brookside Flamenco' (Dw/d)	ESul MWhe WFib
'Brookside Primrose' (Min/C/d)	ESul MWhe NFir WFib
'Brookside Rosita' (Min)	ESul
'Brookside Serenade' (Dw)	ESul WFib
'Brookside Spitfire' (Dw/d)	ESul

§ 'Brown's Butterfly' (R)	ECtt EShb ESul LDea LPio NFir SSea WFib
'Bruni' (Z/d)	MWhe
'Brunswick' (Sc)	ESul LDea MBPg MHer MSte SSea WFib
'Bucklesham' (Dw)	ESul
'Bullfinch' (R)	ESul
'Bumblebee' (Dw)	ESul
'Burgenlandmädel' (Z/d)	LVER
'Burstall' (Min/d)	ESul
'Bushfire' (R) ♀H1+3	ESul LDea WFib
'Butley' (Min)	ESul
'Butterfly' (Min/v)	ECtt NPri
Butterfly = 'Fisam'PBR (I)	SCoo
'Button 'n' Bows' (I/d)	WFib
caffrum	LPio
'Cal'	see *P.* 'Salmon Irene'
'California Brilliant' (U)	MBPg
'Calignon' (Z/St) **new**	WFib
'Cameo' (Dw/d)	MWhe
'Camphor Rose' (Sc)	ESul LDea MBPg MHer NFir SSea
'Can-can' (I/d)	WFib
'Candy' (Min/d)	ESul
'Candy Kisses' (D)	ESul
Candy Rose = 'Pacdy'	LAst
canescens	see *P.* 'Blandfordianum'
'Capel' (Dw/d)	ESul
capitatum	LPio MBPg MHer WFib
'Capri' (Sc)	MBPg WFib
'Capricorn' (Min/d)	ESul
'Captain Starlight' (A)	CRHN ESul LDea LVER MBPg MHer NFir SSea WFib
'Caravan' (A)	LDea
'Cardinal'	see *P.* 'Kardinal'
'Cardington' (St/Dw)	ESul
'Carefree' (U)	LPio MSte NFir WFib
'Cariboo Gold' (Min/C) ♀H1+3	ESul
§ 'Carisbrooke' (R) ♀H1+3	ESul LDea SSea WEas WFib
'Carl Gaffney'	LDea
'Carmel' (Z)	WFib
'Carnival' (R)	see *P.* 'Marie Vogel'
'Carol' (R)	ESul
'Carol Gibbons' (Z/d)	LVER MWhe NFir WFib
'Carol Helyar' (Z/d)	WFib
'Carole Munroe' (Z/d)	LVER
'Caroline' (Dec)	ESul
'Caroline Plumridge' (Dw)	ESul
'Caroline Schmidt' (Z/d/v)	CHal LAst LVER MSte MWhe NFir SSea WBrk WFib
'Carolyn' (Dw)	ESul
'Carolyn Hardy' (Z/d)	WFib
Cascade Lilac	see *P.* 'Roi des Balcons Lilas'
Cascade Pink	see *P.* 'Hederinum'
Cascade Red	see *P.* 'Red Cascade'
'Catford Belle' (A) ♀H1+3	CHal CSpe ESul LDea MWhe SSea WFib
'Cathay' (Z/St)	ESul MWhe NFir SSea
'Catherine Wheels' (Z/St)	LVER
'Cathy' (R)	NFir
caucalifolium subsp. ***caucalifolium***	LPio
- subsp. ***convolvulifolium***	LPio WFib
'Celebration' (Z/d)	ESul
'Cézanne' (R)	ESul LDea LVER MCot WFib
'Chantilly Claret' (R)	LDea
'Chantilly Lace' (R)	ESul LDea
'Charity' (Sc) ♀H1+3	CHal EOHP ESul LDea MBPg MCot MHer MSte MWhe NFir SSea WBrk WFib
'Charlie Boy' (R)	LDea
'Charlotte Amy' (R)	LDea
'Charlotte Bidwell' (Min)	ESul
'Charlotte Bronte' (Dw/v)	WFib

	'Charm' (Min)	ESul
	'Charmay Adonis'	NFir
	'Charmay Alf' (A)	LDea
	'Charmay Aria' (A)	LDea
	'Charmay Bagatelle' (A)	LDea
	'Charmay Electra' (A)	LDea
	'Charmay Marjorie' (A)	LDea
	'Charmay Snowflake' (Sc/v)	ESul MBPg
	'Chattisham' (Dw/C)	ESul NFir
	'Chelmondiston' (Min/d)	ESul MWhe
	'Chelsea Diane' (Min)	LVER
	'Chelsea Gem' (Z/d/v) ♀H1+3	LVER NFir WFib
	'Chelsea Morning' (Z/d)	WFib
	'Chelsea Star' (Z/d/v)	LVER
	'Chelsworth' (Min/d)	ESul
	'Chelvey' (R)	LDea
	'Cherie' (R)	ESul LDea
	'Cherie Bidwell' (Dw/d/v)	ESul
	'Cherie Maid' (Z/v)	SSea
	'Cherry' (Min)	WFib
	'Cherry Baby' (Dec)	NFir
	'Cherry Cocktail' (Z/d/v)	MWhe NFir
	'Cherry Hazel Ruffled' (R)	ESul LDea
	'Cherry Orchard' (R)	ESul LDea SSea WFib
	'Cherry Sundae' (Z/d/v)	ESul
	'Cheryldene' (R)	LDea
	'Chew Magna' (R)	WFib
	'Chi-Chi' (Min)	ESul
	'Chieko' (Min/d)	MWhe WFib
	'Chime' (Min/d)	ESul
	'China Doll' (Dw/d)	WFib
	'Chinz' (R)	CSpe NFir
	'Chocolate Drops' (Z)	LVER
§	'Chocolate Peppermint' (Sc)	CHal CHrt CRHN CSev EAro ESul LDea MBPg MHer MNHC MWhe NFir SIde SSea WBrk WFib
	'Chocolate Tomentosum'	see *P.* 'Chocolate Peppermint'
	'Chrissie' (R)	ESul WFib
	'Christina Beere' (R)	LDea
	'Christopher Ley' (Z)	LVER
	'Cindy' (Dw/d)	ESul WFib
	'Citriodorum' (Sc) ♀H1+3	LDea MBPg MCot MHer WFib
	'Citronella' (Sc)	CRHN LDea MBPg MHer MSte MWhe SSea WFib
	citronellum (Sc)	LPio MBPg
	'Clara Read' (Dw)	ESul
	'Claret Rock Unique' (U)	LDea MBPg MSte WFib
	'Clarissa' (Min)	ESul
	'Clatterbridge' (Dw/d)	ESul LVER NFir
	'Claude Read' (Dw)	ESul
	'Claudette' (Min)	ESul
	'Claudius' (Min)	ESul
	'Claydon' (Dw/d)	ESul NFir
	'Claydon Firebird' (R)	ESul
	'Clorinda' (U/Sc)	CHal CHrt CRHN EShb ESul LVER MBPg MCot MHer MSte SIde SSea WFib
	'Clorinda Variegated'	see *P.* 'Variegated Clorinda'
	'Clown' (R)	ESul
	'Coconut Ice' (Dw)	ESul LVER
	'Coddenham' (Dw/d)	ESul LVER WFib
§	'Colonel Baden-Powell' (I/d)	LDea WFib
	'Colwell' (Min/d) **new**	WFib
	'Concolor Lace'	see *P.* 'Shottesham Pet'
	'Confetti' (R)	ESul
	'Conner' (Min)	ESul
	'Contrast' (Z/C/v)	LAst LRHS MBri MPes MWhe NEgg SCoo SPoG SSea WFib
	'Cook's Peachblossom'	WFib
	'Copdock' (Min/d)	ESul
	'Copthorne' (U/Sc) ♀H1+3	CRHN ESul LDea LVER MBPg MHer MSte SSea WFib

	'Coral Frills' (Min/d)	ESul
	'Coral Reef' (Z/d)	LVER
	cordifolium	CRHN WFib
	coriandrifolium	see *P. myrrhifolium* var. *coriandrifolium*
	'Cornell' (I/d)	ECtt WFib
	'Corsair' (Z/d) ♀H1+3	MWhe
	'Corvina' (R)	WFib
	'Cotta Lilac Queen' (I/d)	LVER
	'Cottenham Beauty' (A)	ESul LDea NFir
	'Cottenham Belle' (A)	ESul
	'Cottenham Bliss' (A)	ESul
	'Cottenham Charm' (A)	ESul LDea
	'Cottenham Cynthia Haird' (A)	ESul
	'Cottenham Delight' (A)	ESul LDea NFir
	'Cottenham Gem' (A)	ESul
	'Cottenham Glamour' (A)	ESul NFir
	'Cottenham Harmony' (A)	ESul LDea
	'Cottenham Jubilee' (A)	ESul LDea MHer
	'Cottenham Mervyn Haird' (A)	ESul
	'Cottenham Star' (A)	ESul
	'Cottenham Surprise' (A)	ESul LDea MBPg MSte MWhe NFir
	'Cottenham Treasure' (A)	ESul LDea
	'Cottenham Wonder' (A)	ESul
	'Cotton Candy' (Min/d)	ESul
	'Cottontail' (Min)	ESul WFib
	cotyledonis	WFib
	'Countess of Scarborough'	see *P.* 'Lady Scarborough'
	'Country Girl' (R)	SPet
	'Cover Girl' (Z/d)	WFib
	'Cowes' (St/Min/d)	ESul
	'Cramdon Red' (Dw)	WFib
	'Cransley Blends' (R)	ESul LDea
	'Cransley Star' (A)	LDea MWhe WFib
	'Cream 'n' Green' (R/v)	LSou NFir
	'Creamery' (d)	MWhe WFib
	'Creamy Nutmeg' (Sc/v)	CArn CHal CHrt EShb ESul LDea MHer MWhe NFir SSea
	'Creeting St Mary' (Min)	ESul
	'Creeting St Peter' (Min)	ESul
	'Crescendo' (I/d)	ECtt
	'Crimson Fire' (Z/d)	MBri MWhe
	'Crimson Unique' (U) ♀H1+3	CRHN CSpe MBPg MHer SSea WFib
§	***crispum*** (Sc)	CHrt GPoy LDea MBPg MCot
§	- 'Golden Well Sweep' (Sc/v)	MBPg NFir WFib
	- 'Major' (Sc)	ESul MBPg WFib
	- 'Minor' (Sc)	MBPg MHer
	- 'Peach Cream' (Sc/v)	CHal ESul MBPg MWhe WFib
	- 'Prince Rupert' (Sc)	MBPg
	- 'Variegatum' (Sc/v) ♀H1+3	CHal CRHN GGar GPoy LDea LVER MBPg MHer MWhe NFir SIde SPet SSea WFib
	crithmifolium	MHer
	'Crock O Day' (I/d)	LVER
	'Crocketta' (I/d/v)	LVER NFir SSea
	'Crocodile' (I/C/d)	ECtt EShb LDea LVER MHer MWhe NFir SSea SWal WFib
	'Crowfield' (Min/d)	ESul WFib
	'Crowfoot Rose' (Sc)	EAro MBPg
	'Crown Jewels' (R)	LDea
	'Crystal Palace Gem' (Z/v)	LAst LRHS LVER MWhe WFib
	'Crystal West' (Min/St)	ESul
	cucullatum	ESul LPio SSea WFib
	- 'Flore Plenum'	MHer WFib
	'Culpho' (Min/C/d)	ESul
	'Cupid' (Min/Dw/d)	WFib
	'Cyril Read' (Dw)	ESul
§	'Czar' (Z/C)	SCoo
	'Dainty Maid' (Sc)	ESul GGar MBPg NFir SAga SSea
	'Dale Queen' (Z)	WFib

'Dallimore' (Dw)	ESul
'Danielle Marie' (A)	LDea
'Danton' (Z/d) **new**	WFib
'Daphne' (A)	LAst
'Dark Ascot' (Dec)	ESul
'Dark Lady' (Sc)	MBPg
'Dark Red Irene' (Z/d)	MWhe WFib
'Dark Secret' (R)	CSpe ESul LDea MSte WFib
'Dark Venus' (R)	ESul LDea WFib
'Darmsden' (A) ♀H1+3	ESul LDea NFir SSea
'David John' (Dw/d)	ESul
'David Mitchell' (Min/Ca/d)	ESul
'Davina' (Min/d)	ESul MWhe WFib
'Dawn Star' (Z/St)	ESul NFir
'Deacon Arlon' (Dw/d)	ESul LVER MWhe
'Deacon Avalon' (Dw/d)	WFib
'Deacon Barbecue' (Z/d)	ESul MWhe WFib
'Deacon Birthday' (Z/d)	ESul LVER MWhe WFib
'Deacon Bonanza' (Z/d)	ESul LVER MWhe WFib
'Deacon Clarion' (Z/d)	ESul WFib
'Deacon Constancy' (Z/d)	ESul MWhe
'Deacon Coral Reef' (Z/d)	ESul MWhe WFib
'Deacon Finale' (Z/d)	ESul LVER
'Deacon Fireball' (Z/d)	ESul LVER MWhe WFib
'Deacon Flamingo' (Z/d)	ESul MWhe WBrk
'Deacon Gala' (Z/d)	ESul MWhe WFib
'Deacon Golden Bonanza' (Z/C/d)	ESul WFib
'Deacon Golden Gala' (Z/C/d)	ESul
'Deacon Golden Lilac Mist' (Z/C/d)	ESul WFib
'Deacon Jubilant' (Z/d)	ESul MWhe
'Deacon Lilac Mist' (Z/d)	ESul LVER MWhe WFib
'Deacon Mandarin' (Z/d)	ESul MWhe WFib
'Deacon Minuet' (Z/d)	ESul MWhe NFir WFib
'Deacon Moonlight' (Z/d)	ESul LVER MWhe
'Deacon Peacock' (Z/C/d)	ESul MWhe WFib
'Deacon Picotee' (Z/d)	ESul MWhe WFib
'Deacon Regalia' (Z/d)	ESul MHer MWhe WFib
'Deacon Romance' (Z/d)	ESul MWhe
§ 'Deacon Summertime' (Z/d)	ESul MWhe WFib
'Deacon Sunburst' (Z/d)	ESul LVER MWhe
'Deacon Suntan' (Z/d)	ESul MWhe
'Deacon Trousseau' (Z/d)	ESul LVER MWhe WFib
'Dean's Delight' (Sc)	LDea MBPg
'Debbie' (A)	LDea MBPg
'Debbie Parmer' (Dw/d)	ESul
'Debbie Thrower' (Dw)	ESul
'Deborah Miliken' (Z/d)	ESul WFib
'Decora Impérial' (I)	LAst LVER
'Decora Lavender'	see *P.* 'Decora Lilas'
§ 'Decora Lilas' (I)	ECtt LAst LVER SPet
'Decora Mauve'	see *P.* 'Decora Lilas'
'Decora Pink'	see *P.* 'Decora Rose'
'Decora Red'	see *P.* 'Decora Rouge'
§ 'Decora Rose' (I)	ECtt LAst SPet
'Decora Rouge' (I)	ECtt LAst SPet
'Deerwood Darling' (Min/v/d)	WFib
'Deerwood Don Quixote' (A)	MWhe
'Deerwood Lavender Lad' (Sc)	ESul LDea MBPg MHer SSea WFib
'Deerwood Lavender Lass'	ESul LDea LPio MBPg MHer
'Deerwood Pink Puff' (St/d)	WFib
'Delightful' (R)	WFib
'Delilah' (R)	LDea
'Delli' (R)	NPer WFib
'Delta' (Min/d)	ESul
'Denebola' (Min/d)	ESul
'Dennis Hunt' (Z/C) **new**	NFir
denticulatum	MHer SSea
§ – 'Filicifolium' (Sc)	CHal CRHN CTca EShb ESul LDea LPio LVER MBPg MHer MNHC SSea WFib
'Diana Hull'	MBPg
'Diane' (Min/d)	ESul
'Diane Louise' (d)	SSea
'Dibbinsdale' (Z)	ESul NFir
dichondrifolium (Sc)	LPio LVER MBPg NCiC NFir WFib
dichondrifolium x ***reniforme*** (Sc)	ESul NFir
'Didi' (Min)	ESul
'Dingley Bell'	MWhe
'Dinky' (Min/d)	ESul
'Display' ambig. (Dw/v)	WFib
'Distinction' (Z)	LAst MHer MPes MWhe NFir SPoG SSea WFib
'Doctor A. Chipault' (I/d)	LDea
'Dollar Bute' (R)	ESul
'Dolly Read' (Dw)	ESul
'Dolly Varden' (Z/v) ♀H1+3	ESul LDea MWhe NFir SSea WFib
x ***domesticum*** 'Royalty White' (R)	LAst
'Don's Helen Bainbridge' (Z/C)	NFir
'Don's Mona Noble' (Z/C)	NFir
'Don's Richard A. Costain' (Z/C)	NFir
'Don's Seagold' (Z/C)	NFir
'Don's Shiela Jane' (Z/C/d)	NFir
'Don's Southport' (Z/v)	NFir
'Don's Stokesley Gem' (Z/C)	NFir
'Don's Swanland Girl' (Min)	ESul
'Don's Whirlygig' (Z/C)	NFir
'Dorcas Brigham Lime' (Sc)	CSpe EAro SAga
'Dorcus Bingham' (Sc)	MBPg
'Doris Frith' (R)	LDea
'Doris Hancock' (R)	WFib
'Doris Shaw' (R)	ESul
'Dorothy May' (A)	LDea
'Double Grace Wells' (Min/d)	ESul
'Double New Life' (Z/d)	CHal
'Double Pink' (R/d) **new**	WFib
'Dovedale' (Dw/C)	ESul WFib
'Downlands' (Z/d)	WFib
'Dragon's Breath' (Z/St)	LVER
'Dresden China' (R)	ESul LDea
'Dresden White' (Dw)	WFib
'Dresdner Amethyst' (I/d)	LAst
Dresdner Apricot = 'Pacbriap'[PBR] (I/d)	LVER
'Dubonnet' (R)	LDea SSea
'Duchess of Devonshire' (U)	WFib
'Duke of Edinburgh'	see *P.* 'Hederinum Variegatum'
'Dulcie' (Min)	ESul
'Dunkery Beacon' (R)	ESul WFib
'Dusty Rose' (Min)	ESul
'E. Dabner' (Z/d)	WFib
'Earl of Chester' (Min/d) ♀H1+3	WFib
'Earliana' (Dec)	ESul LDea
'Earlsfour' (R)	LDea MSte
'Easter Morn' (Z/St)	SSea
'Easter Promise' (R)	ESul
echinatum	CSpe LPio MBPg MHer SSea
– 'Album'	LPio WFib
– 'Miss Stapleton'	see *P.* 'Miss Stapleton'
'Eclipse' (I/d)	MWhe
'Eden Gem' (Min/d)	WFib
'Edith Stern' (Dw/d)	ESul
'Edmond Lachenal' (Z/d)	WFib
'Edwards Michael' (A)	LDea

'Eileen' (Min/d)	ESul
'Eileen Postle' (R) 🏆H1+3	WFib
'Eileen Stanley' (R)	LDea
'Elaine' (R)	LDea
'Elaine Thompson' (R)	LDea
Elbe Silver = 'Pensil' (I)	LAst NFir SCoo
'Elegance Burgundy'	LAst
'Elizabeth Angus' (Z)	SSea WFib
'Elizabeth Read' (Dw)	ESul
'Ella Martin' (St)	ESul
'Elmfield' (St/Min/d)	ESul
'Elmsett' (Dw/C/d)	ESul LVER NFir WFib
'Elna' (Min)	ESul
elongatum	SHFr SSea
'Els' (Dw/St)	ESul LVER WBrk
'Elsi' (I x Z/d/v)	LVER WFib
'Elsie Gillam' (St)	ESul LVER WFib
'Elsie Hickman' (R)	ESul LDea
'Elsie Portas' (Z/C/d)	ESul
'Embassy' (Min)	ESul WFib
Emilia = 'Pactina'	LAst LSou WGor
'Emma Game' (Z/St) **new**	WFib
'Emma Hössle'	see *P.* 'Frau Emma Hössle'
'Emma Jane Read' (Dw/d)	ESul MWhe NFir WFib
'Emmy Sensation' (R)	LDea
'Emperor Nicholas' (Z/d)	MWhe
'Ena' (Min)	ESul
'Encore' (Z/d/v)	LVER MWhe NFir
endlicherianum	LPio NBhm WCot WWFP
'Endsleigh' (Sc)	MBPg
'Enid Brackley' (R)	ESul
'Eroica 2000'	LAst
'Erwarton' (Min/d)	ESul NFir
'Escapade' (Min/d)	ESul
'Eskay Gold' (A)	WFib
'Eskay Jewel' (A) **new**	WFib
'Eskay Sugar Candy' (A) **new**	WFib
'Eskay Verglo' (A) **new**	WFib
'Evelyn' (Min)	ESul
Evening Glow = 'Bergpalais'^{PBR}	LAst LVER
'Evka'^{PBR} (I/v)	LAst LVER NBlu NFir SCoo SSea
'Excalibur' (Z/Min/v)	LVER
'Explosive' (I)	NPri
exstipulatum	EShb SSea WEas XPep
'Eyes Randy' (A)	LAst
'Fair Dinkum' (Z/v)	ESul MWhe NFir
'Fair Ellen' (Sc)	ESul LDea MBPg MHer WFib
'Fairlee' (DwI)	WFib
'Fairy Lights' (Dw/St)	ESul NFir
'Fairy Orchid' (A)	ESul LDea WFib
'Fairy Queen'	LDea MHer
'Falkenham' (Min)	ESul
'Falkland Brother' (Z/C/v)	WFib
'Falkland Hero' (Z/v)	NFir
'Fallen Angel' (Z/St)	LVER
'Fandango' (Z/St)	ESul MWhe NFir WFib
'Fanny Eden' (R)	WFib
'Fantasia' white-flowered (Dw/d) 🏆H1+3	ESul MWhe WFib
'Fareham' (R) 🏆H1+3	LDea MSte WFib
'Feneela' (Dw/d)	ESul
'Fenland' (R)	ESul
'Fenton Farm' (Dw/C)	ESul NFir WFib
'Fern Mint' (Sc)	MBPg
'Festal' (Min/d)	ESul
'Feuerriese' (Z)	LVER
'Fiat Queen' (Z/d)	WFib
'Fiery Sunrise' (R)	ESul LDea
'Fiesta' (I/d)	LDea
'Fifth Avenue' (R)	CSpe ESul LPio MSte WFib
'Filicifolium'	see *P. denticulatum* 'Filicifolium'
'Fir Trees Audrey B' (St)	NFir
'Fir Trees Big Show' (I/v)	NFir
'Fir Trees Eileen' (St)	NFir
'Fir Trees Ele' (A/v)	NFir
'Fir Trees Flamingo' (Dw)	NFir
'Fir Trees Jack' (Z/Dw)	NFir
'Fir Trees John Grainger' (Z/v)	NFir
'Fir Trees Mark' (R/Dec/v)	NFir
'Fir Trees Nan' (R/Dec)	NFir
'Fir Trees Roseberry Topping' (Dw)	NFir
'Fir Trees Ruby Wedding' (C)	NFir
'Fir Trees Silver Wedding' (Z/C/d)	NFir
'Fir Trees Sparkler' (Min/C)	NFir
'Fire Dancer' (R)	ESul
'Fire Dragon' (Z/St/d)	SSea
'Fireball'^{PBR}	LAst LSou
'Firebrand' (Z/d)	LVER
'Firefly' (Min/d)	ESul
'Firestone' (Dw)	ESul
(Fireworks Series)	LAst
Fireworks Cherry = 'Fiwocherry'^{PBR} (Z) **new**	
- Fireworks Cherry-white = 'Fiwocher'^{PBR} (Z)	LAst SSea
- Fireworks Light Pink = 'Fiwopink'^{PBR} (Z)	LAst
- Fireworks Red-white = 'Fiworewhi'^{PBR} (Z) **new**	LAst
- Fireworks Salmon = 'Fiwosal'^{PBR} (Z)	LAst
- Fireworks Scarlet = 'Fiwoscarl'^{PBR} (Z) **new**	LAst
- Fireworks White = 'Fiwowit'^{PBR} (Z)	LAst
'First Blush' (R)	WFib
'First Love' (Z)	NFir
'Fistaneon'^{PBR} (Z/d)	LAst
Flair = 'Fisberno' (I)	NPri
'Flakey' (I/d/v) 🏆H1+3	ESul LDea NFir
'Flamingo' **new**	LVER
'Flarepath' (Z/C/v)	NFir
'Flash' (Min)	ESul
'Flecks' (Min/St)	ESul
'Fleur-de-lys' (A)	LDea
'Fleurette' (Min/d)	CHal ESul MWhe
'Fleurisse' (Z)	WFib
'Flirt' (Min)	WFib
'Floral Cascade' (Fr/d)	SSea
'Floria Moore' (Dec)	ESul NFir SAga SSea
'Flower Basket' (R/d)	ESul LDea NFir
'Flower of Spring' (Z/v) 🏆H1+3	CHal MWhe SSea
'Flowton' (Dw/d)	ESul
'Foxhall' (Dw)	ESul
Foxy = 'Pacfox' **new**	LAst LSou
fragrans **new**	EAro
Fragrans Group (Sc)	CHal CRHN CSev CTca ESul GPoy LVER MBPg MHer MNHC MWhe SDnm SPet SSea WFib XPep
§ - 'Fragrans Variegatum' (Sc/v)	CSev ESul MBPg MWhe NFir WBrk WFib
- 'Snowy Nutmeg'	see *P.* (Fragrans Group) 'Fragrans Variegatum'
'Fraiche Beauté' (Z/d)	WFib
'Francis Gibbon' (Z/d)	WFib
'Francis James' (Z)	WFib
'Francis Kelly' (R)	ESul
'Francis Parrett' (Min/d) 🏆H1+3	ESul MWhe WFib

	'Francis Read' (Dw/d)	ESul
	'Frank Headley' (Z/v) ♀H1+3	CHal EShb ESul LAst LRHS LVER MPes MSte MWhe NPer NVic SAga SCoo SDnm SIde SSea WBrk WFib
§	'Frau Emma Hössle' (Dw/d)	ESul LVER MWhe WFib
	'Freak of Nature' (Z/v)	ESul MHer MWhe NFir SSea WFib
	'Frensham' (Sc)	ESul LDea MBPg MHer WFib
	'Freshfields Suki' (Dw)	NFir
	'Freshwater' (St/C)	ESul MWhe SSea WFib
	'Freston' (Dw)	ESul
	'Friary Wood' (Z/C/d)	ESul NFir WFib
	'Friesdorf' (Dw/Fr)	ESul LVER MHer MWhe NFir WBrk WFib
	'Frills' (Min/d)	ESul MWhe NFir
	'Fringed Angel' (A)	CFee
	'Fringed Apple' (Sc)	LDea MBPg
	'Fringed Aztec' (R) ♀H1+3	ESul LDea LVER NFir SPet SSea WFib
	'Fringed Jer'Ray' (A)	LDea
	'Fringed Petit Pierre' (Min)	MWhe
	'Fringed Rouletta' (I)	LDea
	'Frosty' misapplied	see *P.* 'Variegated Kleine Liebling'
	'Frosty Petit Pierre'	see *P.* 'Variegated Kleine Liebling'
	'Frou Frou' **new**	LVER
	'Fruity' (Sc)	MBPg
	frutetorum	MBPg
	fruticosum	EShb LPio WFib
	'Frühlingszauber Lila' (R)	ESul
	'Fuji' (R)	NFir
	fulgidum	CSpe EShb LFur LPio NFir WFib
	'Funny Girl' (R)	ESul
	'Fynn' (Dw)	ESul
	'Gabriel' (A)	ESul LDea MBPg
	'Galilee' (I/d) ♀H1+3	LDea LVER
	Galleria Sunrise = 'Sunrise' (R)	ESul LDea LVER WEas
	'Galway Girl' (Sc)	MBPg
	'Galway Star' (Sc/v) ♀H1+3	MBPg MHer WBrk WFib
	'Garland' (Dw/d)	ESul
	'Garnet' (Z/d)	ESul
	'Garnet Rosebud' (Min/d)	ESul LVER WFib
	'Gartendirektor Herman' (Dec)	ESul LAst NFir SSea WFib
	'Gaudy' (Z)	WFib
	'Gay Baby' (DwI)	ESul LDea MWhe
	'Gay Baby Supreme' (DwI)	ESul
	'Gemini' (Z/St/d)	ESul MWhe NFir SSea WFib
	'Gemma' (R)	ESul NFir
	'Gemma Jewel' (R) ♀H1+3	ESul
	'Gemma Rose' (R)	LDea
I	'Gemstone' (Min)	ESul
	'Gemstone' (Sc) ♀H1+3	LDea MBPg MHer NFir WBrk
	'Genie' (Z/d)	MWhe WFib
	'Gentle Georgia' (R)	WFib
	'Geofbar' (R)	ESul
	'Geoff May' (Min)	ESul
	'Georgia' (R)	WFib
	'Georgia Mai Read'	ERea
	'Georgia Peach' (R)	ESul WFib
	'Georgie' (R)	LDea
	'Georgina Blythe' (R) ♀H1+3	WFib
	'Geo's Pink' (Z/v)	MWhe
	'Geosta'	LAst
	'Gerald Portas' (Dw/C)	ESul
	'Gerald Wells' (Min)	ESul LVER
	'Geraldine' (Min)	ESul
	'Gesa' **new**	LAst
	'Gess Portas' (Z/v)	ESul
	'Ghost Storey' (Z/C)	NFir
	'Giant Butterfly' (R)	ESul
	'Giant Oak' (Sc)	ESul MBPg MSte
	gibbosum	LFur LPio MHer SSea WFib
	'Gilda' (R/v)	LDea

	'Gill' (Min/Ca)	ESul
	'Ginger Frost' (Sc/v)	WFib
	'Ginger Rogers' (Z)	NFir
	'Glacier Claret' (Z)	WFib
	'Glacis' PBR (Quality Series) (Z/d)	LAst LSou
	'Gladys Evelyn' (Z/d)	WFib
	'Gladys Stevens' (Min/d)	ESul
	'Gladys Weller' (Z/d) **new**	WFib
	glaucum	see *P. lanceolatum*
	'Gleam' (Z/d)	LVER
	'Glen Sheree' (R)	ESul
	'Gloria Pearce' (R)	ESul LDea SSea
	'Glowing Embers' (R)	ESul LDea SSea
§	***glutinosum***	MBPg WFib
	'Goblin' (Min/d)	ESul LVER WFib
	'Godfreys Pride' (Sc)	MBPg
	'Godshill' (R)	LDea
	'Goesta' (Z/d)	LSou
	'Gold Star' (Z/St/C)	ESul
	Golden Angel PBR	see *P.* 'Sarah Don'
	'Golden Baby' (Dw/I/C)	ESul LDea NFir WFib
	'Golden Brilliantissimum' (Z/v)	ESul MWhe SSea WFib
	'Golden Butterfly' (Z/C)	ESul
	'Golden Chalice' (Min/v)	ESul MWhe NFir WFib
	'Golden Clorinda' (U/Sc/C)	CRHN LDea MBPg MHer NFir SSea
	'Golden Ears' (Dw/St/C)	ESul MWhe NFir NPer WFib
	'Golden Edinburgh' (I/v)	WFib
	'Golden Everaarts' (Dw/C)	ESul
	'Golden Fleece' (Dw/C/d)	ESul
	'Golden Gates' (Z/C)	ESul
	'Golden Harry Hieover' (Z/C) ♀H1+3	ESul MBri MHer SSea
	'Golden Lilac Gem' (I/d)	WFib
	'Golden Petit Pierre' (Min/C)	ESul SSea
	'Golden Princess' (Min/C)	WFib
	'Golden Princess' (R)	SSea
	'Golden Roc' (Min/C)	ESul
	'Golden Square' (Dw/St) **new**	WFib
	'Golden Staphs' (Z/St/C)	ESul MHer NFir SSea WFib
	'Golden Stardust' (Z/St)	ESul LVER
	'Golden Wedding' (Z/d/v)	MWhe NFir
	'Golden Well Sweep'	see *P. crispum* 'Golden Well Sweep'
	'Goldilocks' (A)	ESul
	'Gooseberry Leaf'	see *P. grossularioides*
	'Gordano Midnight' (R)	LDea
	'Gordon Quale' (Z/d) **new**	WFib
	'Gosbeck' (A)	SSea WFib
	'Gossamer Carnival' (Z/d)	NFir
	'Gothenburg' (R)	ESul
	'Gottweig' (Z)	ESul
	'Grace' (A)	LDea
	'Grace Thomas' (Sc) ♀H1+3	LDea MBPg MHer WFib
	'Grace Wells' (Min)	ESul WFib
	'Grand Duchess' (R)	LDea
	'Grand Slam' (R)	ESul LDea LVER NFir WFib
	'Grandad Mac' (Dw/St)	ESul NFir SSea
	grandiflorum	LPio MHer WFib
	'Grandma Fischer'	see *P.* 'Grossmutter Fischer'
	'Grandma Ross' (R)	ESul
	'Grandma Thompson' (R)	ESul
	'Granny Hewitt' (Min/d)	ESul
	graveolens	LDea LPio SBch
§	'Graveolens' (Sc)	CHal ESul GPoy LVER MBPg MHer MWhe SSea WFib
	'Great Bricett' (Dw/d)	ESul
	'Green Ears' (Z/St)	ESul
	'Green Eyes' (I/d)	MHer
	'Green Goddess' (I/d)	LDea
	'Green Gold Petit Pierre' (Min)	ESul

'Green Lady' (Sc)	MBPg
'Green Silver Galaxy' (St)	ESul
'Green Woodpecker' (R)	LDea SSea
§ 'Greengold Kleine Liebling' (Min/C/v)	ESul
'Greengold Petit Pierre'	see *P.* 'Greengold Kleine Liebling'
'Greetings' (Min/v)	ESul MBri SSea WFib
'Grey Lady Plymouth' (Sc/v)	ESul LDea MBPg MCot MHer NFir WFib
'Grey Sprite' (Min/v)	ESul WFib
§ 'Grossmutter Fischer' (R)	LDea
§ ***grossularioides***	EOHP MBPg MHer
- 'Coconut'	MBPg
'Grozser Garten' (Dw)	ESul
'Grozser Garten Weiss' (Dw)	ESul
'Guardsman' (Dw)	ESul
Guido = 'Kleugudo' (Z/d)	LAst NBlu
'Gwen' (Min/v)	MWhe NFir
'Hadleigh' (Min)	ESul
'Halo' (R)	ESul
§ 'Hannaford Star' (Z/St)	NFir WFib
'Hansen's Pinkie' (R)	LDea
'Hansen's Wild Spice' (Sc)	LPio MBPg
'Happy Appleblossom' (Z/v/d)	NFir SSea
'Happy Birthday' (Z/T)	LVER
(Happy Face Series) Happy Face Amethyst = 'Penrad'^{PBR} (I)	LAst
- Happy Face Mex = 'Pacvet'^{PBR} (I)	LAst LSou LVER
- Happy Face Scarlet = 'Penhap'^{PBR} (I)	LAst
- Happy Face Velvet Red = 'Pachafvel' (I) **new**	LAst LSou
- Happy Face White = 'Pacfali' (I)	LAst
§ 'Happy Thought' (Z/v) 🏆H1+3	CHal ESul LAst LVER MBri MWhe NFir NVic SCoo SSea WFib
'Happy Valley' (R)	ESul
'Harbour Lights' (R)	ESul LDea WFib
'Harewood Slam' (R)	ESul LDea MSte WFib
'Harkstead' (Dw)	ESul
'Harlequin' (Dw)	ESul
'Harlequin Alpine Glow' (I/d)	MWhe
'Harlequin Mahogany' (I/d)	LDea LVER MWhe
'Harlequin Picotee' (I/d)	LDea
'Harlequin Pretty Girl' (I x Z/d)	LVER MWhe WFib
'Harlequin Rosie O'Day' (I)	LDea MWhe WFib
'Harlequin Ted Day' (I/d)	LDea
Harmony (Z/Dw)	LVER
'Harvard' (I/d)	WFib
'Harvey' (Z)	MWhe
'Havenstreet' (Dw/St)	ESul
'Hayley Charlotte' (Z/v)	MWhe
'Hazel' (R)	WFib
'Hazel Anson' (R)	LDea
'Hazel Barolo' (R)	LDea
'Hazel Birkby' (R)	LDea
'Hazel Burtoff' (R)	ESul LDea
'Hazel Candy' (R)	ESul
'Hazel Carey' (R)	LDea
'Hazel Cerise' (R)	LDea
'Hazel Cherry' (R)	ESul LDea MSte WFib
'Hazel Chick' (R)	ESul
'Hazel Choice' (R)	ESul LDea NFir
'Hazel Dean' (R)	NFir
'Hazel Glory' (R)	LDea
'Hazel Gowland' (R)	LDea
'Hazel Gypsy' (R)	ESul LDea
'Hazel Harmony' (R)	ESul LDea
'Hazel Henderson' (R)	LDea
'Hazel Herald' (R)	ESul LDea
'Hazel Orchid' (R)	ESul
'Hazel Perfection' (R)	NFir
'Hazel Ripple' (R)	ESul
'Hazel Rose' (R)	LDea
'Hazel Satin' (R)	LDea
'Hazel Star' (R)	ESul WFib
'Hazel Stardust' (R)	ESul LDea NFir
'Hazel Wright' (R)	LDea SSea
§ 'Hederinum' (I)	LSou LVER
§ 'Hederinum Variegatum' (I/v)	CHal SPet WFib
'Heidi' (Min/d)	ESul
'Helen Christine' (Z/St)	ESul LVER MWhe NFir WFib
'Helena' (I/d)	LDea MWhe
'Hemingstone' (A)	LDea
'Hemley' (Sc)	LDea MBPg
'Henhurst Gleam' (Dw/d)	ESul
'Henley' (Min/d)	ESul
'Henry Weller' (A)	ESul MBPg MWhe NFir WFib
'Hermanus Show' (Sc)	MBPg
'Hermione' (Z/d)	CHal MWhe WFib
'High Fidelity' (R)	ESul
'Highfields Appleblossom' (Z)	LVER
'Highfields Attracta' (Z/d)	WFib
'Highfields Ballerina' (Z/d)	LVER
'Highfields Candy Floss' (Z/d)	LVER NFir
'Highfields Charisma' (Z/d)	LVER
'Highfields Contessa' (Z/d)	WFib
'Highfields Delight' (Z)	WFib
'Highfields Fancy' (Z/d)	LVER NFir
'Highfields Festival' (Z/d)	MWhe NFir WFib
'Highfields Flair' (Z/d)	LVER
'Highfields Melody' (Z/d)	WFib
'Highfields Orange' (Z)	MWhe
'Highfields Pride' (Z)	WFib
'Highfields Prima Donna' (Z/d)	LVER MWhe
'Highfields Sugar Candy' (Z/d)	LVER WFib
'Highfields Symphony' (Z)	LVER WFib
'Highfields Vogue' (Z)	LVER
'Hilbre Island' (Z/C/d)	NFir
'Hildegard' (Z/d)	CHal
'Hills of Snow' (Z/v)	CHal MBri MHer SSea WFib
'Hillscheider Amethyst'^{PBR}	see *P.* Amethyst = 'Fisdel'
'Hindoo' (RxU)	CSpe LVER NFir SSea WFib
'Hindoo Rose' (U)	NFir
'Hintlesham' (Min)	ESul
hirtum	LPio
hispidum	LPio MBPg MHer
'Hitcham' (Min/d)	ESul WFib
'Holbrook' (Dw/C/d)	ESul NFir WFib
'Hollywood Star' (Z) **new**	EBrs
'Honeywood Lindy' (R)	ESul LDea
'Honeywood Margaret' (R)	ESul
'Honeywood Suzanne' (Min/Fr)	ESul LVER NFir
'Honneas' (Dw)	ESul
'Honnestolz' (Dw)	ESul
'Hope Valley' (Dw/C/d) 🏆H1+3	ESul MWhe NFir
'Horace Parsons' (R)	ESul WFib
'Horace Read' (Dw)	ESul
'Horning Ferry' (Dw)	ESul
'House and Garden' (R)	NFir
'Hula' (U x R)	MHer
'Hulda Conn' (Z/Ca/d)	WFib
'Hulverstone' (Dw/St)	ESul
'Hunter's Moon' (Z/C)	NFir
'Hurdy-gurdy' (Z/d/v)	ESul MWhe
'Ian Read' (Min/d)	ESul

	'Icecrystal'PBR (Sweetheart Series) (Z/d)	LAst
	'Icing Sugar' (I/d)	ESul LDea SSea WFib
	ignescens	MBPg
	'Immaculatum' (Z)	WFib
	'Imperial'PBR (R)	LAst
	'Imperial Butterfly' (A/Sc)	CRHN ESul GGar LDea LVER MBPg MSte MWhe NFir SSea WFib
	'Inca' (R)	ESul
	Ingres = 'Guicerdan'PBR (I/d) ♀H1+3	LAst LSou
	'Inspiration' (R)	ESul
	ionidiflorum	CBgR CSpe EShb LPio MBPg MHer XPep
	'Ipswich Town' (Dw/d)	ESul
	'Irene' (Z/d) ♀H1+3	WFib
	'Irene Collet' (R)	LDea
	'Irene Toyon' (Z) ♀H1+3	WFib
	'Isabell' (Quality Series) (Z/d)	LAst LSou NBlu
	'Isidel' (I/d) ♀H1+3	WFib
	'Islington Peppermint' (Sc)	LPio MBPg WFib
	'Isobel Eden' (Sc)	LDea MBPg
	'Ivalo' (Z/d)	MWhe WFib
	'Ivory Snow' (Z/d/v)	ESul LVER MWhe NFir SSea WFib
	'Jack of Hearts' (I x Z/d)	WFib
	'Jack Simmons' (Dw) **new**	ESul
	'Jack Wood' (Z/d)	NFir WFib
§	'Jackie' (I/d)	EShb LVER MBri WFib
	'Jackie Gall'	see *P.* 'Jackie'
	'Jackie's Gem' (I/d)	MWhe
	'Jackpot Wild Rose' (Z/d)	WFib
	'Jacqui Caws' (Dw) **new**	ESul
	'Jake Brougham' (St) **new**	ESul
	'Jane Biggin' (Dw/C/d)	ESul MWhe
	'Janet Dean' (R)	LDea
	'Janet Hofman' (Z/d)	WFib
	'Janet Kerrigan' (Min/d)	ESul MWhe WFib
	'Jasmin' (R)	ESul LDea
	'Jaunty' (Min/d)	ESul
	'Jayne' (Min/d)	ESul
	'Jayne Eyre' (Min/d)	CHal ESul MWhe NFir WFib
	'Jazzy' (Min/St)	ESul
	'Jean Bart' (I)	LVER
	'Jean Caws' (Z/St) **new**	WFib
	'Jeanetta' (R)	LDea
	'Jeanie Hunt' (Z/C/d) **new**	NFir
§	'Jeanne d'Arc' (I/d)	WFib
	'Jenifer Read' (Dw)	ESul
	'Jennifer' (Min)	ESul
	'Jennifer Strange' (R)	ESul
	'Jericho' (Z/St/v)	ESul LVER
	'Jer'Ray' (A)	ESul LDea MBPg MWhe NFir SSea WFib
	'Jessel's Unique' (U)	LDea MHer MSte SPet SSea
	'Jessica'	LVER
	'Jewel' (Z/d)	LAst
	'Jewel'PBR (R)	ESul LAst
	'Jimbar' (R)	ESul
	'Jinny Reeves' (R)	ESul LDea
	'Jip's Freda Burgess' (Z/C/d) **new**	NFir
	'Jip's Rosy Glow' (Min/d) **new**	NFir
	'Joan Cashmere' (Z/d)	ESul
	'Joan Fontaine' (Z)	WFib
	'Joan Hayward' (Min)	ESul
	'Joan Morf' (R)	ESul LDea NFir SSea WFib
	'Joan of Arc'	see *P.* 'Jeanne d'Arc'
	'Joan Sharman' (Min)	ESul
	'Joanna Pearce' (R)	LDea
	'John Thorp' (R)	LDea
	'John's Angela'	LVER
	'John's Pride' (Dw)	MBri NFir SSea
	'Joseph Haydn' (R)	ESul LDea MSte
	'Joseph Paul' (R)	SSea
	'Joseph Wheeler' (A)	ESul LDea MWhe
	'Joy' (R) ♀H1+3	ESul LDea LRHS LSou NFir WFib
	'Joy' (I)	SPet
I	'Joy' (Z/d)	LAst LVER SSea
	'Joy Lucille' (Sc)	CSev ESul LDea MBPg
	'Joyful' (Min)	ESul
	'Jubilant' (R)	ESul
	'Judy Read' (Dw)	ESul
	'Julia' (R) ♀H1+3	LDea
	'Juliana' (R)	LAst LDea
	'Julie Bannister' (R)	ESul
	'Julie Smith' (R)	ESul LDea WFib
	'June Filbey' (R)	LDea
	'Jungle Night' (R)	ESul
	'Juniper' (Sc)	MBPg MHer WFib
	'Jupiter' (R)	ESul
	'Just Beth' (Z/C/d) **new**	NFir
	'Just Joss' (Dw/d) **new**	NFir
	'Just Rita' (A)	SSea
	'Just William' (Min/C/d)	ESul WFib
	'Kamahl' (R)	ESul WFib
§	'Kardinal' (Z/d)	SPet
	'Karl Hagele' (Z/d)	WFib
	'Karl Offenstein' (R)	ESul
	'Karmin Ball'	WFib
	karrooense Knuth	MHer
	'Karrooense'	see *P. quercifolium*
	'Kathleen' (Min)	ESul
	'Kathleen Gamble' (Z)	WFib
	'Kathryn' (Min)	ESul
	'Kathryn Portas' (Z/v)	ESul
	'Kathy Kirby' (R)	ESul
	'Katie' (R)	LDea
	'Katie Hillier' (R)	LDea
	'Katrine'	LAst LSou WGor
	'Kayleigh Aitken' (R)	NFir
	'Kayleigh West' (Min)	ESul SSea
	'Keepsake' (Min/d)	ESul WFib
	'Keith Vernon' (Z)	NFir SSea
	'Kelly Brougham' (St/dw)	ESul
	'Ken Lea' (Z/v)	ESul
	'Ken Salmon' (Dw/d)	ESul
	'Kenny's Double' (Z/d)	WFib
	'Kensington' (A)	LDea
	'Kerensa' (Min/d)	ESul WFib
	'Kershy' (Min)	ESul
	'Kesgrave' (Min/d)	ESul LVER WFib
	'Kettlebaston' (A) ♀H1+3	LDea WFib
	'Kewense' (Z)	EShb
	'Kimono' (R)	ESul NFir
	'Kinder Gaisha' (R)	NFir
	'King Edmund' (R)	ESul LDea NFir
	'King of Balcon'	see *P.* 'Hederinum'
	'King of Denmark' (Z/d)	LVER WFib
	'King Solomon' (R)	LDea WFib
	'Kirton' (Min/d)	ESul
§	'Kleine Liebling' (Min)	ESul MWhe WFib
	'Knaves Bonfire' (R)	ESul
	'Korcicum' (Sc)	MBPg
	'Krista' (Min/d)	ESul WBrk WFib
	'Kyoto' (R)	NFir
	'Kyra' (Min/d)	ESul WFib
	'La France' (I/d) ♀H1+3	LDea MWhe WFib
	'La Paloma' (R)	ESul WFib
	'Laced Mini Rose Cascade' (I)	NFir
	Laced Red Mini Cascade = 'Achspen' (I)	NFir
§	'Lachskönigin' (I/d)	LVER SPet WFib
	'Lady Cullum' (Z/C/v)	MWhe
	'Lady Ilchester' (Z/d)	WFib
	'Lady Love Song' (R)	ESul LSou NFir WFib
	'Lady Mary' (Sc)	ESul MBPg MHer

'Lady Mavis Pilkington' (Z/d)	WFib
'Lady Plymouth' (Sc/v) 🏆H1+3	CHal CHrt CRHN CSpe CStu CTca EPfP EShb ESul GGar LDea LPio LRHS LVER MBPg MHer MNHC MSte MWhe NFir SPet SSea WBrk WFib
Lady Ramona = 'Klep01007'PBR (Z/d)	LAst
§ 'Lady Scarborough' (Sc)	ESul LDea LPio MBPg MHer WFib
'Lady Scott' (Sc)	MBPg
'Lady Woods' (Z)	SSea
laevigatum	MHer
'Lakeland' (I)	ESul SSea
'Lakis' (R)	LDea
'Lamorna' (R)	ESul LDea
'Lancastrian' (Z/d)	WFib
§ ***lanceolatum***	LPio MHer
'Langley' (R)	ESul LDea
'Lanham Lane' (I)	LDea
'Lanham Royal' (Dw/d)	ESul
'Lara Aladin' (A)	LDea MBPg
'Lara Ballerina'	NFir
'Lara Candy Dancer' (Sc) 🏆H1+3	CRHN ESul LDea MBPg MHer WBrk WFib
'Lara Jester' (Sc)	MBPg MHer WFib
'Lara Maid' (A) 🏆H1+3	CHrt MWhe WFib
'Lara Nomad' (Sc)	LDea MBPg
'Lara Starshine' (Sc) 🏆H1+3	EAro ESul LPio MBPg MHer NFir SSea WBrk WFib
'Lara Waltz' (R/d)	WFib
'Lark' (Min/d)	ESul
'Larkfield' (Z/v)	SSea
N 'Lass o' Gowrie' (Z/v)	ESul LVER MSte MWhe NFir
'Latte Coffee' (R)	ESul
'Laura Parmer' (Dw/St)	ESul
'Laura Wheeler' (A)	ESul LDea MWhe
'Laurel Hayward' (R)	WFib
'Lauren Alexandra' (Z/d) **new**	WFib
Lauretta = 'Pacamla'PBR (Quality Series) (Z/d)	LAst LSou
Lavenda = 'Penlava' PBR (Dark Line Series) (Z/d)	LAst LSou
'Lavender Grand Slam' (R) 🏆H1+3	ESul LDea LVER NFir
'Lavender Harewood Slam' (R)	ESul LDea
'Lavender Mini Cascade'PBR	see *P.* Lilac Mini Cascade
'Lavender Sensation' (R)	WFib
'Lavender Wings' (I)	LDea
'Lawrenceanum'	ESul LPio WFib
'Layham' (Dw/d)	ESul
'L'Elégante' (I/v) 🏆H1+3	CHal LAst LDea LVER MWhe SSea WEas WFib
'Lemon Air' (Sc)	ESul MBPg
'Lemon Crisp'	see *P. crispum*
'Lemon Fancy' (Sc)	LDea LVER MBPg MHer MWhe NFir WFib
'Lemon Kiss' (Sc)	MBPg
'Lemon Meringue' (Sc)	MBPg
'Lemon Toby' (Sc)	MBPg
'Len Chandler' (Min)	ESul
'Lenore' (Min/d)	ESul
'Leo' (Min)	ESul
'Leonie Holbrow' (Min)	ESul
'Lesley Judd' (R)	ESul
'Leslie Salmon' (Dw/C)	MWhe
'Lesmona'	LAst LSou
'Lessland'	LVER
Lila Compakt-Cascade	see *P.* 'Decora Lilas'
Lilac Cascade	see *P.* 'Roi des Balcons Lilas'
'Lilac Domaine de Courson' (Sc)	MBPg
'Lilac Domino'	see *P.* 'Telston's Prima'
'Lilac Elaine' (R)	LDea
'Lilac Gem' (Min/I/d)	LDea MWhe
'Lilac Gemma' (R)	ESul
'Lilac Jewel' (R)	ESul
'Lilac Joy' (R)	ESul LVER
§ Lilac Mini Cascade = 'Lilamica'PBR (I)	ESul LAst LDea LVER NFir
'Lili Marlene' (I)	SPet
'Lilian' (Min)	ESul LAst LSou
'Lilian Pottinger' (Sc)	CArn CHal CRHN ESul LDea MBPg MHer MWhe NFir SSea
'Lilian Woodberry' (Z) **new**	WFib
'Limelight' (Z/v)	SSea
'Limoneum' (Sc)	CSev LDea MBPg MHer
'Linda' (R)	ESul
'Lindsey' (Min)	ESul
'Lipstick' (St)	WFib
'Lisa' (Min/C)	ESul WFib
'Lisa Jo' (St/v/Dw/d)	WFib
'Little Alice' (Dw/d) 🏆H1+3	ESul MWhe NFir WFib
'Little Blakenham' (A)	ESul LDea
'Little Fi-fine' (Dw/C)	ESul
'Little Gem' (Sc)	LDea MBPg MHer MWhe SSea WFib
'Little Jim' (Min/d)	NFir
'Little Jip' (Z/d/v)	LVER NFir WFib
'Little Margaret' (Min/v)	ESul
'Little Primular' (Min)	ESul
'Little Rascal' (A)	LDea
'Little Spikey' (St/Min/d)	ESul WFib
'Lively Lady' (Dw/C)	ESul SSea
'Lizzie Hillier' (R) **new**	LDea
lobatum	LPio
'Lollipop' (Z/d)	LAst
longicaule	LPio MBPg
longifolium **new**	LPio
'Lord Baden-Powell'	see *P.* 'Colonel Baden-Powell'
'Lord Bute' (R) 🏆H1+3	CSpe ECtt EShb ESul GGar LAst LCro LDea LRHS LVER MHer MSte NCiC NFir NPer SAga SDnm SIde SMer SMrm SPet SSea WEas WFib WPen
'Lord Constantine' (R)	LDea
'Lord de Ramsey'	see *P.* 'Tip Top Duet'
'Lord Roberts' (Z)	WFib
Lorena = 'Pacdala'PBR (Dark Line Series) (Z/d)	LAst WGor
'Loretta' (Dw)	ESul
'Lorna' (Dw/d)	ESul
'Lorraine' (Dw)	ESul
Lotus = 'Floscala' (Z/d)	LAst
'Lotusland' (Dw/St/C)	LAst LSou NFir WFib
'Louise' (Min)	ESul
I 'Louise' (R)	ESul NFir
'Louise Waddington' (Min/St)	ESul
'Love Song' (R/v)	ESul LDea LSou NFir SSea WFib
'Love Story' (Z/v)	ESul
'Loveliness' (Z)	WFib
* 'Loverly' (Min/d)	ESul
'Lovesdown' (Dw/St)	ESul
'Lowood' (R)	ESul
'Lucie Caws' (St/d)	ESul
'Lucilla' (Min)	ESul
'Lucinda' (Min)	ESul
'Lucy' (Min)	ESul
'Lucy Gunnett' (Z/d/v)	ESul MWhe NFir
'Lucy Jane' (R)	ESul LDea
'Lulu' (I/d)	NPri
Luna = 'Fisuna' (I/d)	NPri
luridum	WCot
'Lustre' (R)	ESul
'Lyewood Bonanza' (R)	ESul LDea WFib
'Lynne Valerie' (A)	LDea

'Lyric' (Min/d)	ESul WFib
'Mabel Grey' (Sc) ♀H1+3	CHal CRHN CSev CSpe EShb ESul LPio LVER MBPg MHer MSte MWhe NFir NPer SBch SIde SSea WFib
§ 'Madame Auguste Nonin' (U/Sc)	CHrt ESul LVER MBPg MHer NFir WFib
'Madame Butterfly' (Z/d/v)	ESul MWhe NFir
'Madame Crousse' (I/d) ♀H1+3	WFib
'Madame Fournier' (Dw/C)	ESul
'Madame Layal' (A)	MHer MSte NFir WFib
'Madame Margot'	see *P.* 'Hederinum Variegatum'
'Madame Salleron' (Min/v) ♀H1+3	LAst LDea LRHS LSou LVER MPes MSte
'Madame Thibaut' (R)	LDea MSte
'Madge Taylor' (R)	NFir
'Magaluf' (I/C/d)	SSea
'Magda' (Z/d)	ESul
'Magic Lantern' (Z/C)	NFir
'Magic Moments' (R)	ESul
'Magnum' (R)	WFib
'Maid of Honour' (Min)	ESul
'Maiden Petticoat'	LAst SAga
'Maiden Rosepink' (R)	LAst
'Maiden Sunrise'	LAst
'Mairi' (A)	LDea WFib
'Mandala' **new**	LVER
'Mandarin' (R)	ESul
'Mangles' Variegated' (Z/v)	WFib
'Mantilla' (Min)	ESul
'Manx Maid' (A)	ESul LDea NFir
'Maple Leaf' (Sc)	MBPg
'Marble Sunset'	see *P.* 'Wood's Surprise'
'Marchioness of Bute' (R/Dec)	EMan LDea LVER MSte NFir SSea WFib
'Maréchal MacMahon' (Z/C)	SSea
'Margaret Parmenter' (I/C)	ESul
'Margaret Pearce' (R)	LDea
'Margaret Salvidge' (R)	LDea
'Margaret Soley' (R) ♀H1+3	LDea WFib
'Margaret Thorp'	LVER
'Margaret Waite' (R)	ESul WFib
'Margery Stimpson' (Min/d)	ESul WFib
'Maria Wilkes' (Z/d)	WFib
'Marie Rober' (R)	ESul
'Marie Rudlin' (R)	LVER SSea
'Marie Thomas' (Sc)	LDea MBPg SBch SSea
§ 'Marie Vogel' (R)	ESul MSte
Marimba = 'Fisrimba'^{PBR}	NPri SCoo
'Marion' (Min)	ESul
'Mariquita' (R)	WFib
'Marja' (R)	LDea
'Mark' (Dw/d) **new**	WFib
'Marmalade' (Min/d)	ESul MWhe WFib
'Marquis of Bute' (R/v)	ESul LVER NFir
'Marquita' (R)	ESul
'Martha Parmer' (Min)	ESul
'Martin Parrett' (Min/d)	WFib
'Martin's Splendour' (Min)	ESul
'Martlesham' (Dw)	ESul
'Mary' (R)	ESul
'Mary Caws' (Dw/Z/d)	ESul
'Mary Ellen Tanner' (Min/d)	ESul
'Mary Harrison' (Z/d) **new**	WFib
'Mary Read' (Min)	ESul
'Mary Webster' (Min)	ESul
'Masquerade' (R)	ESul SPet
'Masquerade' (Min)	ESul
'Master Paul' (Z/v)	ESul
'Maureen' (Min)	ESul LVER NFir
'Mauve Beauty' (I/d)	WFib
Maxime = 'Fismaxi'^{PBR} (I/d)	NPri

'Maxime Kovalevski' (Z)	WFib
'Maxine' (Z/C)	NFir
'May Day' (R)	LDea WFib
'May Magic' (R)	ESul NFir WFib
'Mayfield County Girl' (R)	ESul
'Mayor of Seville' (Z/d)	WFib
'Meadowside Dark and Dainty' (St)	WFib
'Meadowside Fancy' (Z/d/C)	LVER
'Meadowside Harvest' (Z/St/C)	NFir WFib
'Meadowside Julie Colley' (Dw)	NFir
'Meadowside Mahogany' (Z/C)	LVER
'Meadowside Mardi Gras' (Dw/d)	NFir
'Meadowside Midnight' (St/C)	MHer MWhe SHFr WFib
'Meadowside Orange' (Z/d)	LVER
'Medallion' (Z/C)	SSea
'Meditation' (Min)	ESul
'Medley' (Min/d)	MWhe WFib
'Megan Hannah' (Dw/c/d) **new**	NFir
'Meike' (R)	ESul
'Melanie' (R)	ESul LDea
'Melanie' (Min)	ESul
* 'Melissa' (Min)	ESul
'Melissa' (R)	ESul
Meloblue = 'Penblue'	NBlu
'Melody'^{PBR} (Tempo Series) (Z/d)	LAst
Melosilver = 'Penber' (Tempo Series) (Z/d/v)	LAst SPoG
'Memento' (Min/d)	ESul WFib
'Mendip' (R)	WFib
'Mendip Anne' (R)	NFir
'Mendip Barbie' (R)	NFir
'Mendip Blanche' (R)	NFir
'Mendip Candy Floss' (R)	ESul
'Mendip Lorraine' (R)	ESul
'Menorca' (Dw/C/d) **new**	ESul WFib
'Meon Maid' (R)	ESul LDea WFib
'Mere Casino' (Z)	WFib
'Mere Greeting' (Z/d)	MWhe WFib
'Mere Sunglow' (R)	LDea
'Merlin' (Sc)	MBPg
'Merry-go-round' (Z/C/v)	MWhe
'Mexica Katrine'	LAst
'Mexica Tomcat' (I/d)	LAst LSou WGor
'Mexically Rose' (R)	ESul
'Mexican Beauty' (I)	CHal WFib
'Mexicana'	see *P.* 'Rouletta'
'Mexicanerin'	see *P.* 'Rouletta'
'Michael' (A)	ESul LDea MHer NFir
'Michelle' (Min/C)	LDea
'Michelle West' (Min)	ESul WFib
'Midas Touch' (Dw/C/d)	ESul
'Mikado' (R)	ESul
'Milden' (Dw/Z/C)	ESul NFir
'Millbern Choice' (Z)	MWhe
'Millbern Clover' (Min/d)	ESul MWhe
'Millbern Engagement' (Min/d)	MWhe
'Millbern Peach' (Z)	MWhe
'Millbern Serenade'	MWhe
'Millbern Sharna' (Min/d)	ESul MWhe
'Millbern Skye' (A)	MWhe
Millennium Dawn (Dw)	LVER
'Millfield Gem' (I/d)	LVER WFib
'Millfield Rose' (I/d)	LVER MWhe
'Mimi' (Dw/C/d)	ESul
'Mina Lorenzen' (R)	ESul

	'Minah's Cascade' (Z/d)	LVER
	'Mini-Czech' (Min/St)	ESul LVER
	'Minnie' (Z/d/St)	ESul LVER WBrk
	'Minstrel Boy' (R)	CSpe ESul LDea NFir SSea WFib
	'Minuet' (Z/d)	SSea
	'Minx' (Min/d)	WFib
	'Miranda' (Dw)	ESul
	'Miranda Deep Salmon' **new**	WGor
	'Miss Australia' (R/v)	LDea MBPg
	'Miss Burdett Coutts' (Z/v)	ESul LVER MHer MWhe SSea WFib
	'Miss Flora' (I)	MWhe
	'Miss McKinsey' (Z/St/d)	LVER NFir
	'Miss Muffett' (Min/d)	WFib
§	'Miss Stapleton'	LPio MHer SSea WFib
	'Miss Wackles' (Min/d)	ESul
	'Misterioso' (R)	WFib
	'Mistress' (Z/C)	NFir
	'Misty Morning' (R)	WFib
	'Modesty' (Z/d)	WFib
	'Mohawk' (R)	ESul LDea LVER NFir WFib
	'Mole'	see *P.* 'The Mole'
	Molina = 'Fismoli'[PBR] (I/d)	NPri
	'Mollie' (R)	CSpe
	'Mona Lisa'[PBR]	ESul
	'Monarch' (Dw/v)	ESul
	'Monica Bennett' (Dw)	ESul
	'Monkwood Charm' (R)	ESul
	'Monkwood Rhapsody' (R)	ESul
	'Monkwood Rose' (A)	LDea NFir
	'Monkwood Sprite' (R)	ESul LDea SMrm
	'Monsal Dale' (Dw/C/d)	ESul
	'Monsieur Ninon' misapplied	see *P.* 'Madame Auguste Nonin'
§	'Monsieur Ninon' (U)	CRHN MSte WFib
	'Mont Blanc' (Z/v)	ESul LVER MWhe WFib
	'Montague Garabaldi Smith' (R)	WFib
	'Moon Maiden' (A)	CSpe ESul LDea WFib
	'Moor' (Min/d)	ESul
	'Moppet' (Min/d)	ESul
	'Morello'[PBR] (R)	ESul
	'More's Victory' (U/Sc)	SSea
	'Morning Cloud' (Min/d)	ESul
	'Morval' (Dw/C/d) ♀H1+3	ESul LVER MWhe WFib
	'Morwenna' (R)	ESul LDea LPio MHer MSte NFir WFib
	'Mosaic Gay Baby' (I/v/d)	WFib
	'Mosaic Silky' (Z/C/d/v)	LVER
	'Mountie' (Dw)	ESul
	'Mozart' (R)	ESul
	'Mr Everaarts' (Dw/d)	ESul MWhe
	'Mr Henry Apps' (Dw/C/d)	MWhe
	'Mr Henry Cox' (Z/v) ♀H1+3	ESul LVER MHer MWhe NFir WFib
	'Mr Wren' (Z)	CHal LVER MWhe SSea WFib
	'Mrs Cannell' (Z)	WFib
	'Mrs Dumbrill' (A)	ESul LDea LVER
	'Mrs Farren' (Z/v)	MWhe
	'Mrs G.H. Smith' (A)	ESul LDea MBPg MSte MWhe NFir SSea WFib
	'Mrs G. Morf' (R)	SSea
	'Mrs Innes Rogers' (R)	ESul
	'Mrs J.C. Mappin' (Z/v) ♀H1+3	SSea
	'Mrs Kingsbury' (U)	WFib
	'Mrs Langtry' (R)	LDea
	'Mrs Martin' (I/d)	WFib
	'Mrs McKenzie' (Z/St)	WFib
	'Mrs Morf' (R)	LDea NFir
	'Mrs Parker' (Z/d/v)	ESul LRHS LVER MWhe NFir WFib
	'Mrs Pat' (Dw/St/C)	MWhe NFir SSea
	'Mrs Pollock' (Z/v)	LAst LRHS LSou LVER MWhe NEgg NVic SCoo SSea WBrk WFib

	'Mrs Quilter' (Z/C) ♀H1+3	LVER MBri MHer MWhe NVic SSea WFib
	'Mrs Salter Bevis' (Z/Ca/d)	ESul WFib
	'Mrs Strang' (Z/d/v)	LVER MWhe SSea
	'Mrs Tarrant' (Z/d)	CHal
	'Mrs Taylor' (Sc)	MBPg
	'Mrs W.A.R. Clifton' (I/d)	LDea WFib
	multicaule	LPio
	- subsp. ***multicaule***	EShb
	mutans	WFib
§	'Mutzel' (I/v)	LVER NFir
	'My Chance'	NFir SSea WFib
	'My Choice' (R)	LDea
	myrrhifolium	LPio
§	- var. ***coriandrifolium***	CSpe LPio WFib
	'Mystery' (U) ♀H1+3	LPio LVER MBPg NFir SAga SSea WFib
	'Müttertag' (R)	MSte
	'Nacton' (Min)	ESul
	'Nancy Grey' (Min)	ESul NFir
	'Nancy Mac' (St)	ESul
	'Narina' (I)	SCoo
	'Natalie' (Dw)	ESul
	'Naughton' (Min)	ESul
	'Needham Market' (A)	ESul LDea MSte WFib
	'Neene' (Dw)	ESul
	'Neil Clemenson' (Sc)	MBPg WFib
	'Nell Smith' (Z/d)	WFib
	'Nellie' (R)	ESul LDea
	'Nellie Green' (R)	LDea
	'Nellie Nuttall' (Z)	WFib
	'Nervosum' (Sc)	ESul MBPg
	'Nervous Mabel' (Sc) ♀H1+3	ESul LDea LPio MBPg MHer WBrk WFib
	'Nettlecombe' (Min/St)	ESul
	'Nettlestead' (Dw/d)	ESul LVER
	'Nettlestone' (Dw/d)	ESul
	'Nettlestone Star' (Min/St)	ESul
	'New Day' (A)	LDea
	'New Life' (Z)	ESul MWhe
	'Newbridge' (St/Min/d)	ESul
	'Newton Rigg' (Sc)	MBPg
	'Newtown' (Min/St)	ESul
	'Nicola Buck' (R)	LDea NFir
	'Nicor Star' (Min)	ESul WFib
	'Nikki' (A)	LDea
	'Nimrod' (R)	LDea
	'Noche' (R)	ESul LDea
	'Noel' (Z/Ca/d)	WFib
	'Noele Gordon' (Z/d)	LVER WFib
	'Noir' (R)	SSea
	'Nono' (I)	WFib
	'Norrland' (Z/d)	LVER
	'Nostra'	LAst LSou
	oblongatum	LPio NFir
	'Occold Embers' (Dw/C)	ESul NFir
	'Occold Lagoon' (Dw/d)	ESul
	'Occold Orange Tip' (Min/d)	ESul
	'Occold Profusion' (Dw/d)	ESul NFir
	'Occold Shield' (Dw/C/d)	ESul LAst LRHS NFir SDnm WBrk WFib
	'Occold Tangerine' (Z)	WFib
	'Occold Volcano' (Dw/C/d)	WFib
	'Odyssey' (Min)	WFib
	odoratissimum (Sc)	CHal ESul GPoy LDea MBPg MHer NFir SSea WFib
	'Offton' (Dw)	ESul
	'Old Orchard' (A)	LDea SSea
	'Old Rose' (Z/d)	WFib
	'Old Spice' (Sc/v)	ESul LDea MBPg MHer NFir SSea SWal WFib
	'Oldbury Duet' (A/v)	ESul LAst LDea LSou LVER MBPg MHer MWhe NFir SSea
	'Olga Shipstone' (Sc)	MBPg

	'Olivia' (R)	WFib
	'Onalee' (Dw)	ESul WFib
	'Opera House' (R)	WFib
	'Orange' (Z/St)	MBPg
	'Orange Fizz' (Sc)	ESul MHer MNHC SDnm WBrk
	'Orange Fizz' (Z/d)	LDea
	'Orange Imp' (Dw/d)	ESul
	'Orange Parfait' (R)	WFib
I	'Orange Princeanum' (Sc)	MBPg
	'Orange Ricard' (Z/d)	MWhe
	'Orange Ruffy' (Min)	ESul
	'Orangeade' (Dw/d)	LVER WFib
	'Orchid Clorinda' (Sc)	MBPg WFib
	'Orchid Paloma' (Dw/d)	ESul
	'Oregon Hostess' (Dw)	ESul
	'Oriental Delight' (R) **new**	ESul
	'Orion' (Min/d)	ESul MWhe SSea WFib
	'Orsett' (Sc) ♀H1+3	LDea LVER MBPg
	'Osna' (Z)	LAst
	'Otto's Red' (R)	NFir
	'Our Gynette' (Dec)	NFir SSea
	'Oyster' (Dw)	ESul
	PAC cultivars	see under cultivar name
	'Paclai'	LAst
	'Paddie' (Min)	ESul
	'Pagoda' (Z/St/d)	ESul LVER MHer MSte MWhe WFib
	'Paisley Red' (Z/d)	NFir WFib
	'Pam Craigie' (R)	LDea
	'Pamela' (R)	ESul
	'Pamela Vaughan' (Z/St) **new**	WFib
	'Pampered Lady' (A)	LDea NFir
	panduriforme	LPio MBPg WFib
	papilionaceum	CHEx CRHN LPio MCot MHer WEas WFib
	'Parisienne' (R)	ESul LDea WFib
	'Parmenter Pink' (Min)	ESul
	'Party Dress' (Z/d)	MWhe WFib
	'Pat Hannam' (St)	WFib
	'Paton's Unique' (U/Sc) ♀H1+3	CHal CRHN EShb LVER MBPg MHer MSte NFir SPet WFib
	'Patricia Andrea' (T)	ESul LVER NFir NPer WFib
	'Patricia Read' (Min)	ESul
	'Paul Crampel' (Z)	CHal MHer WFib
	'Paul Gunnett' (Min)	MWhe
	'Paul West' (Min/d)	ESul
	'Pauline' (Min/d)	ESul MWhe SSea
	'Pauline Harris' (R)	LDea
	'Pax' (R)	LDea
	'Peace' (Min/C)	ESul WFib
	'Peace Palace' (Dw)	ESul
	'Peach Princess' (R)	ESul NFir SSea
	'Peaches' (Z)	LAst LSou
	'Peaches and Cream' (R)	MBPg
	'Peacock'	LDea
	'Pearly Queen' (Min/d)	ESul
	'Pebbles' (Z/Min)	LVER
	'Peggy Clare' (Dw/St)	ESul
	'Peggy Sue' (R)	ESul LDea LVER
	'Peggy West' (Min/C/d)	SSea
	PELFI cultivars	see under cultivar name
	peltatum	LPio SPhx WFib
	'Penny' (Z/d)	MWhe WFib
	'Penny Dixon' (R)	NFir
	'Penny Lane' (Z)	WFib
	'Penny Serenade' (Dw/C)	ESul
	'Pensby' (Dw)	ESul
	'Penve'PBR (Quality Series) (Z/d)	LAst
	'Peppermint Lace' (Sc)	MBPg
	'Peppermint Scented Rose' (Sc)	MBPg
	'Peppermint Star' (Z/St)	ESul SSea
	'Perchance' (R)	SSea
	'Percival' (Dw/d)	MWhe
	'Perfect' (Z)	WFib
	Perlenkette Orange = 'Orangepen'PBR (Quality Series) (Z/d)	LAst LSou
	'Perlenkette Sabine' (Quality Series) (Z/d)	LAst LSou
	'Pershore Princess'	WBrk
	'Persian King' (R)	LDea
	'Persian Ruler' (Min)	ESul
	'Persimmon' (Z/St)	WFib
	'Petals' (Z/v)	MSte
	'Peter Beard' (Dw/d)	ESul
	'Peter Godwin' (R)	ESul LDea WFib
	'Peter Read' (Dw/d)	ESul
	'Peter's Choice' (R)	ESul LDea SSea WFib
	'Peter's Luck' (Sc) ♀H1+3	ESul MBPg
	'Petit Pierre'	see *P.* 'Kleine Liebling'
	'Petite Blanche' (Dw/d)	SSea WFib
	'Philomel' (I/d)	SPet
	'Phlox New Life' (Z)	ESul
	'Phyllis' (Z)	LDea
	'Phyllis' (U/v)	ESul LVER MBPg MHer NFir SSea
	'Phyllis Brooks' (R)	ESul
	'Phyllis Read' (Min)	ESul
	'Phyllis Richardson' (R/d)	ESul LDea LVER
	'Picotee'	SSea
	'Pin Mill' (Min/d)	ESul
	'Pink Aura' (Min/St)	ESul SSea
	'Pink Aurore' (U)	MHer MSte WFib
	'Pink Blush' (Min/St) **new**	ESul
	'Pink Bonanza' (R)	ESul LDea WFib
	'Pink Bouquet' (R)	ESul
	'Pink Capitatum'	see *P.* 'Pink Capricorn'
§	'Pink Capricorn' (Sc)	CHrt CRHN ESul MBPg MHer MWhe SDnm WBrk WFib
	'Pink Carnation' (I/d)	LDea
	'Pink Cascade'	see *P.* 'Hederinum'
	'Pink Champagne' (Sc)	CRHN ESul MBPg MCot MHer
	'Pink Dolly Varden' (Z/v)	SSea WFib
	'Pink Domaine de Courson' (Sc)	MBPg
	'Pink Flamingo' (R)	LDea
	'Pink Fondant' (Min/d)	ESul WFib
	'Pink Fringed Aztec' (R)	SSea
	'Pink Gay Baby'	see *P.* 'Sugar Baby'
	'Pink Golden Ears' (Dw/St/C)	ESul
	'Pink Golden Harry Hieover' (Z/C)	ESul
	'Pink Happy Thought' (Z/v)	LAst MWhe SDnm SSea WFib
	'Pink Ice' (Min/d)	ESul NFir
	'Pink Margaret Pearce' (R)	ESul
	'Pink Mini Cascade'	see *P.* 'Rosa Mini-cascade'
	'Pink Needles' (Min/St)	ESul WFib
	'Pink Paradox' (Sc)	LDea MBPg
	'Pink Rambler' (Z/d)	MWhe WFib
	'Pink Raspail' (Z/d)	SSea
	'Pink Rosebud' (Z/d)	WFib
	'Pink Snow' (Min/d)	ESul
	'Pink Splash' (Min/d)	ESul
	'Pink Tiny Tim' (Min)	ESul
	Pink-Blizzard = 'Fispink' (I)	NPri
	'Pippa' (Min/Dw)	ESul
	'Pixie' (Min)	ESul
	'Playmate' (Min/St)	ESul WFib
	'Plum Rambler' (Z/d)	EShb SSea WFib
	'Poetesse' (A)	LDea
	'Polestar' (Min/St)	ESul
	'Polka' (U)	ESul LVER MBPg MHer NFir SSea WBrk WFib
	'Pompeii' (R)	ESul LDea NFir SSea WFib
	'Poquita' (Sc)	MBPg
	'Porchfield' (Min/St)	ESul
	'Portsmouth' (R)	ESul

	'Potter Heigham' (Dw)	ESul
	'Powder Puff' (Dw/d)	WFib
	'Praeludium Scarlet' **new**	WGor
	'Presto' (Dw/St)	ESul MWhe
	'Preston Park' (Z/C)	WFib
	'Pretty Girl' (I)	LDea MCot
	'Pretty Petticoat' (Z/d)	WFib
	'Pretty Polly' (Sc)	LDea MBPg WFib
	'Pride of Exmouth'	CBgR CStu
	'Prim' (Dw/St/d)	ESul WFib
	'Prince Consort' (R)	LDea
	'Prince of Orange' (Sc)	CArn CHrt CRHN CSev CTca EOHP ESul GPoy LDea LVER MBPg MHer MSte MWhe NFir SIde SSea WFib
	'Princeanum' (Sc) 🏆$^{H1+3}$	MBPg MHer WFib
	'Princess Alexandra' (R)	SSea
	'Princess Alexandra' (Z/d/v)	ESul MWhe NFir
	'Princess Anne' (Z)	MSte
	'Princess Josephine' (R)	LDea WFib
	'Princess of Balcon'	see *P.* 'Roi des Balcons Lilas'
	'Princess of Wales' (R)	ESul LDea LVER WFib
	'Princess Virginia' (R/v)	ESul LDea SSea WFib
	'Priory Salmon' (St/d)	EShb ESul
	'Priory Star' (St/Min/d)	ESul WFib
	'Prospect' (Z/d)	MWhe
	'Prosperity' (Sc)	LDea MBPg
	pseudoglutinosum	WFib
	'Pungent Peppermint' (Sc)	MBPg
	'Purple Ball'	see *P.* Purpurball
	'Purple Emperor' (R)	ESul LDea WFib
	'Purple Flare' (St)	ESul
	'Purple Heart' (Dw/St/C)	ESul NFir
	'Purple Muttertag' (R)	ESul
I	'Purple Radula Rosea' (Sc)	MBPg
	'Purple Rambler' (Z/d)	ESul MWhe
	'Purple Rogue' (R) **new**	WFib
	'Purple Unique' (U/Sc)	EShb ESul LDea MCot MHer MSte NFir SSea WFib
§	Purpurball (Z/d)	LAst
§	Purpurball 2 = 'Penbalu'^{PBR} (Quality Series) (Z/d)	LAst LSou
	'Pygmalion' (Z/d/v)	SSea WFib
	'Quakeress' (R)	ESul
	'Quakermaid' (Min)	ESul
	'Quantock' (R)	ESul WFib
	'Quantock Beauty' (A)	ESul LDea MWhe
	'Quantock Blonde' (A)	LDea
	'Quantock Candy' (A)	NFir
	'Quantock Classic' (A) **new**	NFir
	'Quantock Cobwebs' (A)	NFir
	'Quantock Darren' (A)	NFir
	'Quantock Dragonfly' (A)	NFir
	'Quantock Jayne' (A)	ESul
	'Quantock Kendy' (A)	ESul LDea NFir
	'Quantock Kirsty' (A)	LDea NFir
	'Quantock Louise' (A) **new**	NFir
	'Quantock Marjorie' (A)	ESul LDea MBPg MWhe NFir
	'Quantock Matty' (A)	ESul LDea MWhe NFir
	'Quantock May' (A)	LDea NFir
	'Quantock Medoc' (A)	ESul LDea MBPg
	'Quantock Millennium' (A)	ESul LDea MBPg NFir
	'Quantock Mr Nunn' (A)	NFir
	'Quantock Philip' (A)	ESul MBPg
	'Quantock Plume' (A)	MBPg
	'Quantock Rita' (A)	MWhe
	'Quantock Rory' (A)	LDea
	'Quantock Rose' (A)	ESul LDea MBPg
	'Quantock Sapphire' (A)	LDea
	'Quantock Sarah' (A)	ESul
	'Quantock Shirley' (A)	ESul LDea
	'Quantock Star' (A)	LDea MBPg MWhe NFir
	'Quantock Star Gazer' (A/Sc)	NFir
	'Quantock Ultimate' (A)	ESul MBPg NFir
	'Quantock Variegated Matthew' (A/v) **new**	NFir
	'Quantock Victoria' (A)	ESul MBPg
	'Queen of Denmark' (Z/d)	WFib
	'Queen of Hearts' (I x Z/d)	LVER WFib
	'Queen of Sheba' (R)	LDea
	'Queen of the Lemons'	EAro
N	***quercifolium*** (Sc)	CHal CRHN CSev GPoy LPio MBPg MHer NFir WFib
	- variegated (v)	MBPg MHer
	quinquelobatum	CSpe LFur LPio
	'R.A. Turner' (Z/d)	WFib
	'Rachel' (Min)	ESul
	radens (Sc)	EPfP LPio WFib
	'Rads Star' (Z/St)	ESul NFir SSea WFib
	'Radula' (Sc) 🏆$^{H1+3}$	CSev ESul LDea MBPg MHer MNHC MWhe SSea WFib
	'Radula Roseum' (Sc)	MBPg SSea WFib
	'Ragamuffin' (Dw/d)	ESul MWhe
	'Rager's Pink' (Dw/d)	ESul
	'Rager's Star' (Dw)	ESul
	'Rager's Veri-Star' (Min/C)	ESul
	'Ragtime' (St)	NPri
	'Raphael' (A)	LDea
	'Raspberry Parfait' (R)	LDea
	'Raspberry Ripple' (A)	ESul LDea MWhe NFir SSea WFib
	'Raspberry Surprise' (R)	ESul LVER
	'Raspberry Yhu' (R)	ESul
	'Ray Bidwell' (Min)	ESul MWhe NFir WFib
	'Raydon' (Min)	ESul
	'Rebecca' (Min/d)	ESul WFib
I	'Rebecca' (Sc)	MBPg
	'Red Admiral' (Min/d/v)	ESul
§	'Red Black Vesuvius' (Min/C)	CHal ESul MWhe SSea WFib
	'Red Cactus' (St)	NFir
	'Red Capri' (Sc)	MBPg
§	'Red Cascade' (I) 🏆$^{H1+3}$	MWhe WFib
	'Red Galilee' (I/d)	MWhe
	'Red Glitter' (Dw/St) **new**	ESul
	'Red Glow' (Min)	ESul
	'Red Ice' (Min/d)	ESul MWhe NFir
	'Red Pandora' (Z)	LVER NFir WFib
	'Red Pimpernella'	LVER
	'Red Rambler' (Z/d)	CHal ESul LVER MWhe WBrk WFib
	'Red Robin' (Dw/2) **new**	WCot
	Red Satisfaction = 'Usredsat'^{PBR} (Z/d)	LAst
	'Red Silver Cascade'	see *P.* 'Mutzel'
	'Red Spider' (Dw/Ca)	EShb ESul WFib
	'Red Starstorm' (Dw/St) **new**	ESul
	'Red Startel' (Z/St/d)	MWhe WFib
	'Red Susan Pearce' (R)	ESul WFib
	'Red Sybil Holmes' (I)	LSou LVER
	Red Sybil = 'Pensyb'^{PBR} (I/d)	LAst LSou
	'Red Witch' (Dw/St/d)	ESul LVER SSea WFib
	Red-Blizzard = 'Fizzard'^{PBR} (I)	NPri SCoo
§	Red-Mini-Cascade = 'Rotemica' (I)	ESul LAst LDea LVER MWhe WFib
	'Redondo' (Dw/d)	ESul LVER MWhe
	'Reflections' (Z/d)	WFib
	'Reg 'Q'' (Z/C)	NFir
	Reggae Bright Red = 'Fip 202' (I) **new**	NPri
	'Regina' (Z/d)	LVER NFir WFib
	'Rembrandt' (R)	LDea LVER WFib
	'Renate Parsley'	EShb ESul LCro LPio MBPg MHer NFir WFib
	'Rene Roué' (Dw/d/v)	ESul NFir
	reniforme	LPio MBPg MHer SSea WFib
	'Retah's Crystal' (Z/v)	ESul LVER MWhe

	'Rhian Harris' (A)	LDea
	Rhodonit = 'Paccherry'^{PBR} (I/d)	LAst LSou
	'Richard Gibbs' (Sc)	GGar LDea MBPg MHer
	'Richard Key' (Z/d/C)	WFib
	'Ricky Promise' (A)	LDea
	'Ricky Ruby' (A)	LDea
	'Rietje van der Lee' (A)	ESul WFib
	'Rigel' (Min/d)	ESul LVER MWhe NFir
	'Rigi' (I/d)	MBri
	'Rigoletto' (I)	LDea NFir
	'Rimey' (St)	NFir
	'Rimfire' (R)	ESul LDea LVER MHer NFir WFib
	'Rio Grande' (I/d)	LDea LVER MWhe NFir SPet WFib
	'Rising Sun'	NFir
	'Rita Scheen' (A/v)	ESul LDea MWhe SSea
	'Ritchie' (R)	ESul
	'Robbie Hare' (R)	ESul
	'Robe' ^{PBR} (Quality Series) (Z/d)	LAst LVER
	'Rober's Lemon Rose' (Sc)	CRHN CTca ESul LDea MBPg MHer SIde SSea WBrk
	'Rober's Salmon Coral' (Dw/d)	ESul
	'Robert Fish' (Z/C)	ESul LRHS SCoo
	'Robert McElwain'	WFib
	'Robin' (Sc)	LDea LVER MBPg
	'Robin' (R)	LDea SSea
	'Robin's Unique' (U)	NFir SSea WFib
	'Robyn Hannah' (St/d)	NFir
	'Roger's Delight' (R/Sc)	MBPg
	'Rogue' (R)	ESul MSte WFib
	'Roi des Balcons'	see *P.* 'Hederinum'
§	'Roi des Balcons Impérial' (I) ♀$^{H1+3}$	MWhe
§	'Roi des Balcons Lilas' (I) ♀$^{H1+3}$	LSou MBPg MWhe WFib
	'Roi des Balcons Rose'	see *P.* 'Hederinum'
	'Roller's Echo' (A)	ESul LDea MWhe WFib
	'Roller's Pathfinder' (I/d/v)	LDea LVER
	'Roller's Pioneer' (I/v)	LDea LVER SSea
	'Roller's Satinique' (U) ♀$^{H1+3}$	LPio MBPg MHer SSea
	'Roller's Shadow' (A)	ESul LDea NFir
	'Rollisson's Unique' (U)	MBPg MHer MSte SSea WFib
	'Romeo' (R)	CSpe LVER
	Romy (I)	LDea
	'Rookley' (St/d)	ESul
	'Rosa Della Sera' **new**	LVER
§	'Rosa Mini-cascade' (I)	ESul LAst LVER MWhe NFir
	'Rosaleen' (Min)	ESul
	'Rosalie' (R)	ESul
	'Rose Bengal' (A)	CRHN ESul LDea MWhe WFib
	Rose Evka = 'Penevro'^{PBR} (Dw/I/v)	LAst NFir
	'Rose Irene' (Z/d)	MWhe
	'Rose Jewel' (R)	ESul
	'Rose of Amsterdam' (Min/d)	ESul WFib
	'Rose Paton's Unique' (U/Sc)	LDea
	'Rose Silver Cascade' (I)	LDea LVER MCot
	'Rosebud Supreme' (Z/d)	ESul WFib
	'Rosecrystal'^{PBR} (Sweetheart Series) (Z/d)	LVER
	'Rosemarie' (Z/d)	MWhe
	'Rosina Read' (Dw/d)	ESul
	'Rosmaroy' (R)	ESul LDea LVER NFir WFib
	'Rosy Dawn' (Min/d)	WFib
	'Rosy Morn' (R)	NFir
	'Rote Mini-cascade'	see *P.* Red-Mini-Cascade = 'Rotemica'
§	'Rouletta' (I/d)	ECtt LAst LDea LVER MWhe NBlu NPri WFib
	'Round Leaf Rose' (U)	MBPg
	'Rousillon' (R)	LDea
	'Royal Ascot' (R)	CHal ESul LDea MSte NFir SPet SSea
	'Royal Carpet' (Min/d)	ESul
	'Royal Court' (R)	LDea
	'Royal Decree' (R)	LDea
	'Royal Magic' (R)	LDea
	'Royal Norfolk' (Min/d)	ESul LVER MWhe NFir
	'Royal Oak' (Sc) ♀$^{H1+3}$	CRHN CSev EAro ESul LDea LVER MBPg MHer MNHC MWhe SGar SPet SSea WFib
	'Royal Opera' (R)	LDea
	'Royal Pride' (R)	LDea
*	'Royal Princess' (R) ♀$^{H1+3}$	LDea
§	'Royal Purple' (Z/d)	CHal LVER WFib
	'Royal Sovereign' (Z/C/d)	LDea
	'Royal Star' (R)	LDea
	'Royal Surprise' (R)	ESul LDea NFir
	'Royal Wedding' (R)	ESul
	'Royal Winner' (R)	LDea
	'Ruben' (d) **new**	LAst LSou
	'Rubi Lee' (A)	MWhe
	'Ruby' (Min/d)	ESul WFib
	Ruby Dream = 'Fisruby'^{PBR} (I)	NPri
	'Ruby Orchid' (A)	LDea NFir
	'Ruby Wedding' (Z)	ESul
	'Ruffled Velvet' (R)	SSea
	'Rushmere' (Dw/d)	ESul WFib
	'Rusty' (Dw/C/d)	ESul
	'Sabine'^{PBR} (Z/d)	LVER
	'Saint Elmo's Fire' (St/Min/d)	SSea WFib
	'Saint Helen's Favourite' (Min)	ESul
	Saint Malo = 'Guisaint'^{PBR} (I)	LAst
	'Sally Munro' (R)	LDea SSea
	'Sally Read' (Dw/d)	ESul
	'Salmon Beauty' (Dw/d)	WFib
	'Salmon Black Vesuvius' (Min/C)	ESul
§	'Salmon Irene' (Z/d)	WFib
	'Salmon Queen'	see *P.* 'Lachskönigin'
	'Salmon Startel' (Z/St/d)	MWhe
	salmoneum	SSea
	'Saltford' (R)	ESul
	'Samantha' (R)	ESul WFib
	'Samantha Stamp' (Dw/d/C)	WFib
	Samelia = 'Pensam'^{PBR} (Dark Line Series) (Z/d)	LAst LSou
	'Sammi Brougham' (Dw/Z)	ESul
	'Sammi Caws' (St)	ESul
	'Sancho Panza' (Dec) ♀$^{H1+3}$	CSpe ESul LDea LVER MBPg MHer MSte SSea WFib
	'Sandford' (Dw/St)	ESul
	'Sandown' (Dw/d)	ESul
	'Sandra Lorraine' (I/d)	WFib
	'Sanguineum'	CSpe
	'Santa Marie' (R)	LDea
	'Santa Paula' (I/d)	ECtt LDea
§	'Sarah Don'^{PBR} (A/v)	LSou WFib
	'Sarah Hunt' (Min/d)	NFir
	'Sarah Jane' (Sc)	MBPg
	'Sassa' ^{PBR} (Quality Series) (Z/d)	LAst LSou
	'Satsuki' (R)	ESul LDea NFir
	scabrum	MBPg
	'Scarlet Gem' (Z/St)	WFib
*	'Scarlet Kewense' (Dw)	ESul
	'Scarlet Nosegay'	CHal
I	'Scarlet O'Hara' (Z)	LVER
	'Scarlet Pet' (U)	CRHN ESul MBPg NFir
	'Scarlet Pimpernel' (Z/C/d)	ESul

'Scarlet Rambler' (Z/d)	EShb SSea WFib
'Scarlet Unique' (U)	CBgR CHrt CRHN LDea MSte SSea WFib
schizopetalum	WFib
§ 'Schneekönigin' (I/d)	ECtt LDea LVER MSte
§ 'Schottii'	LPio NFir WFib
x ***schottii***	see *P.* 'Schottii'
'Scottow Star' (Z/c) **new**	WFib
'Seaview Silver' (Min/St) **new**	WFib
'Seaview Sparkler' (Z/St) **new**	WFib
'Secret Love' (Sc)	LDea MBPg
'Seeley's Pansy' (A)	LDea MHer SAga WFib
'Sefton' (R) 🏆H1+3	ESul LDea WFib
'Selecta Royal Amethyst'	NBlu
'Selecta Royal Blue' (I)	LSou
'Selena' (Min)	LDea
'Semer' (Min)	ESul
* 'Serre de la Madone' (Sc)	WEas
'Shalfleet' (Min/St)	ESul
'Shalimar' (St)	MSte NFir
'Shanks' (Z)	NFir
'Shannon'	WFib
'Sharon' (Min/d)	ESul
'Sheila' (Dw)	ESul
'Shelley' (Dw)	ESul
'Sheraton' (Min/d)	MWhe
'Shimmer' (Z/d)	LVER MWhe
'Shirley Ash' (A)	LDea WFib
'Shirley Gillam' (Z/St/v)	ESul LVER
Shocking Pink = 'Pensho'PBR (Quality Series) (Z/d)	LAst
Shocking Violet = 'Pacshovi'PBR (Quality Series) (Z/d)	LAst LSou
'Shogan' (R)	NFir
'Shorwell' (Dw/C/d)	ESul
§ 'Shottesham Pet' (Sc)	ESul MBPg MHer
'Show Off' (Z)	LVER
'Shrubland Pet' (U/Sc)	LPio SSea
'Shrubland Rose' (Sc)	LPio SSea
'Sid' (R)	LDea
sidoides	CSpe EBee ERea ESul LCro LPio MBPg MCot MHer MWea NFir SMrm SPhx SSea WCot WEas WFib
- black-flowered	CSpe
- 'Sloe Gin Fizz'	CSpe LPio
Sidonia = 'Pensid'PBR (Dark Line Series) (Z/d)	LAst LSou WGor
'Sienna' (R)	ESul LDea NFir
'Sil Anne'PBR (Z) **new**	MPes
'Sil Baldo'PBR (Z) **new**	MPes
'Sil Claudio'PBR (Z) **new**	LAst MPes
'Sil Folke'PBR (I) **new**	MPes
'Sil Frauke'PBR (Z)	LAst LSou MPes
'Sil Friesia'PBR (Z)	LAst
'Sil Gesa'	LAst MPes
'Sil Herma'PBR (Z) **new**	MPes
'Sil Hero' (Z) **new**	MPes
'Sil Lara' (Z) **new**	MPes
'Sil Liske'PBR (Z) **new**	LAst LSou
'Sil Maxima' **new**	MPes
'Sil Mona'PBR (I) **new**	MPes
'Sil Niklas'PBR (Z) **new**	MPes
'Sil Onno'PBR (Z) **new**	MPes
'Sil Pia'PBR (I)	LAst LSou MPes
'Sil Raiko'PBR	LAst MPes
'Sil Renko'PBR (Z) **new**	MPes
'Sil Ruben'PBR (I) **new**	MPes
'Sil Rumika'PBR	LAst
'Sil Sören'	LAst LSou MPes
'Sil Tabea'PBR (I) **new**	MPes
'Sil Tedo'PBR (Z)	LAst LSou MPes
'Sil Teske'PBR (I)	LAst MPes
'Sil Tomke'PBR (I) **new**	LAst LSou MPes
'Sil Wilko' **new**	MPes
'Sil Wittje'PBR (I) **new**	MPes
'Silver Anne' (R/v)	ESul NFir
'Silver Dawn' (Min/St) **new**	ESul
'Silver Delight' (v/d)	WFib
'Silver Dusk' (Min/St) **new**	ESul
'Silver Glitter' (Dw/St) **new**	ESul
'Silver Kewense' (Dw/v)	ESul WFib
'Silver Leaf Rose' (Sc)	MBPg
'Silver Rimfire' (R)	ESul
'Silver Snow' (Min/St/d) **new**	ESul WFib
'Silver Wings' (Z/v)	ESul LVER MWhe SSea
'Silvia' (R)	ESul
'Simon Read' (Dw)	ESul
'Simplicity' (Z)	LVER
'Sir Colin' (Z)	SSea
'Skelly's Pride' (Z)	WFib
'Skies of Italy' (Z/C/d)	MBri MHer SSea WFib
'Small Fortune' (Min/d)	ESul
'Smuggler' (R)	LDea
'Snape' (Min)	ESul
'Sneezy' (Min)	ESul NFir
'Snow Cap' (MinI)	NFir
'Snow Flurry' (Sc)	MBPg WBrk
Snow Queen	see *P.* 'Schneekönigin'
'Snow White' (Min)	ESul
'Snowbaby' (Min/d)	ESul
'Snowberry' (R)	ESul
'Snowbright' (St/d)	ESul
'Snowdrift' (I/d)	LVER WFib
'Snowflake' (Min)	see *P.* 'Atomic Snowflake'
'Snowmass' (Z/d)	MWhe
'Snowstorm' (Z)	WFib
'Snowy Baby' (Min/d)	WFib
'Sofie'	see *P.* 'Decora Rose'
'Solent Waves' (R)	ESul LDea
'Solferino' (A)	ESul LDea
Solidor (I/d) 🏆H1+3	LDea NFir
Solo = 'Guillio' (Z/I)	LVER
'Somersham' (Min)	ESul WFib
'Something Else' (Z/St/d)	LVER
'Something Special' (Z/d)	LVER MWhe NFir WFib
'Sonata' (Dw/d)	ESul
'Sophie' (R)	ESul
Sophie Casade	see *P.* 'Decora Rose'
'Sophie Caws' (St)	ESul
'Sophie Dumaresque' (Z/v)	MBri MWhe NFir SSea WFib
'Sorcery' (Dw/C)	ESul MWhe
'Sound Appeal' (A)	ESul LDea MBPg
'South American Bronze' (R) 🏆H1+3	ESul LDea WFib
'South American Pink' (R)	ESul
'Southern Belle' (A)	LDea SSea
'Southern Belle' (Z/d)	WFib
'Southern Charm' (Z/v)	LVER
'Southern Cherub' (A)	LDea
'Southern Damsel' (R) **new**	ESul
'Southern Festival' (Dw) **new**	ESul
'Southern Flamenco' (R) **new**	ESul
'Southern Galaxy' (Min/St) **new**	ESul
'Southern Gem' (Min/d)	ESul
'Southern Michaela' (A) **new**	ESul
'Southern Peach' (Min/d)	ESul
'Southern Posy' (Dw) **new**	ESul
'Southern Purity' (Min) **new**	ESul
'Southern Rosina' (Dw) **new**	ESul

	'Southern Siewigy' (Dec) **new**	ESul
	'Souvenir' (R)	CHal ESul LDea SSea
	'Sowoma Lavender' (Sc)	MBPg
	'Spanish Angel' (A) 🏆[H1+3]	ESul LDea NFir SSea WFib
	'Spanish Banks' (Z/St/v)	ESul LVER
	'Sparkler' (Z)	LVER
	'Spellbound' (R)	WFib
	'Spital Dam' (Dw/d)	ESul
	'Spitfire' (Z/Ca/d/v)	ESul LVER WFib
	'Spithead Cherry' (R)	LDea
	'Splash Down'	SSea
§	'Splendide'	CRHN CSpe EShb ESul LPio MBPg MHer NFir SSea SWvt WCot WEas WFib
	'Splendide' white-flowered	LPio MBPg
	'Spotlite Hotline' (I)	LDea
	'Spotlite Winner' (I)	LDea
	'Spot-on-bonanza' (R)	ESul LDea NFir SSea WFib
	'Spring Bride' (R)	LDea
	'Spring Park' (A)	ESul MHer SSea WFib
I	'Springfield Alba' (R)	ESul
	'Springfield Ann' (R)	ESul
	'Springfield Black' (R)	ESul LDea LVER SSea
	'Springfield Charm' (R)	ESul
	'Springfield Joy' (R)	ESul
	'Springfield Pearl' (R)	ESul LDea
	'Springfield Purple' (R)	ESul
	'Springfield Unique' (R)	ESul LDea
	'Springtime' (Z/d)	MWhe WFib
I	'Springtime' (R)	ESul
	'Sprite' (Min/v)	MWhe
	'Sproughton' (Dw)	ESul
	'Stacey' (R)	ESul LDea
	'Stadt Bern' (Z/C)	LAst LSou LVER MBri MSte MWhe NFir
	'Stadt Bern' pink-flowered **new**	MPes
	'Stan Shaw' (R) **new**	LDea
	x ***stapletoniae***	see *P.* 'Miss Stapleton'
	'Star Flair' (St/Min/d)	ESul
	'Star Flecks' (st)	NFir
	'Star of Persia' (Z/Ca/d)	WFib
	'Star Storm' (St/d)	ESul
	'Starflecks' (St)	LVER
	'Starlet' (Ca)	WFib
	'Starlight' (R)	WFib
	'Starlight Magic' (A) 🏆[H1+3]	ESul LDea
	'Starry Eyes' (Dw)	ESul
	'Startel Salmon' (Z/St)	MHer
	'Stella Read' (Dw/d)	ESul
	'Stellar Arctic Star'	see *P.* 'Arctic Star'
	'Stellar Hannaford Star'	see *P.* 'Hannaford Star'
	'Stephen Read' (Min)	ESul
	'Stewart Meehan' (R)	LDea
	'Strawberries and Cream' (Z/St)	NFir
	'Strawberry Fayre' (Dw/St)	LVER WFib
	'Strawberry Sundae' (R)	ESul LDea MSte WFib
	'Stringer's Delight' (Dw/v)	ESul LVER
	'Stringer's Souvenir' (Dw/d/v)	SSea
	'Stuart Mark' (R)	LDea
	'Stutton' (Min)	ESul
	'Suffolk Agate' (R)	ESul
	'Suffolk Amethyst' (A)	ESul
	'Suffolk Coral' (R)	ESul
	'Suffolk Emerald' (A)	ESul
	'Suffolk Garnet' (Dec)	ESul MWhe
	'Suffolk Jade' (Min)	ESul
	'Suffolk Jet' (Min)	ESul
§	'Sugar Baby' (DwI)	ECtt ESul LAst LDea MBri WFib
	'Summer Cloud' (Z/d)	WFib
	'Summer Rose Lilac' (I)	NPri
	'Summertime' (Z/d)	see *P.* 'Deacon Summertime'

	'Sun Rocket' (Dw/d)	MWhe WFib
	'Sundridge Moonlight' (Z/C)	WFib
	'Sundridge Surprise' (Z) **new**	WFib
	'Sunraysia' (Z/St)	WFib
	'Sunridge Moonlight' (Dw)	NFir
	'Sunset Snow' (R)	ESul LVER NFir WFib
	'Sunspot' (Min/C)	NFir
	'Sunspot Kleine Liebling' (Min)	WFib
	'Sunspot Petit Pierre' (Min/v)	WFib
	'Sunstar' (Min/d)	ESul WFib
	'Super Rose' (I)	SPet
	'Super Rupert' (Sc)	MBPg
	'Supernova' (Z/St/d)	ESul MWhe WFib
	'Surcouf' (I)	WFib
	'Susan Hillier' (R)	LDea
	'Susan Payne' (Dw/d)	ESul LVER MHer
	'Susan Pearce' (R)	ESul LDea LVER
	'Susan Read' (Dw)	ESul
	'Susie 'Q'' (Z/C)	LVER MWhe SSea
	'Sussex Delight' (Min)	SPet
	'Sussex Gem' (Min/d)	ESul WFib
	'Sussex Lace'	see *P.* 'White Mesh'
	'Suzanne' **new**	LVER
	'Swainham Mellow Yellow' (Z)	LVER
	'Swan Lake' (Min)	ESul
	'Swanland Lace' (I/d/v)	WFib
	'Swedish Angel' (A)	ESul LDea MWhe NFir SSea WFib
	'Sweet Lady Mary' (Sc)	LDea MBPg
	'Sweet Mimosa' (Sc) 🏆[H1+3]	CHal CHrt CRHN CTca ESul LVER MBPg MHer MSte NFir SDnm SSea WBrk WFib
	'Sweet Miriam' (Sc)	LDea MBPg
	'Sweet Rosina' (Sc)	MBPg
	'Sweet Sixteen'	WFib
	'Sweet Sue' (Min)	ESul
	'Swilland' (A)	LDea LVER MWhe WFib
	'Sybil Bradshaw' (R)	LDea
	'Sybil Holmes' (I/d)	ECtt LAst LVER MBri MWhe NBlu SPet WFib
	'Sylbar' (R)	ESul
	'Sylvia' (R)	ESul
	'Sylvia Gale' (R)	ESul
	'Sylvia Marie' (d)	MWhe NFir
	'Taffety' (Min)	ESul WFib
	'Tamie' (Dw/d)	ESul MWhe NFir
	'Tammy' (Dw/d)	ESul MWhe
	'Tangerine' (Min/Ca/d)	ESul LVER SSea WFib
	'Tangerine Elf' (St)	WFib
	Tango Pink = 'Fisgopi'[PBR]	LAst
	'Tanzy' (Min)	ESul
	'Tapriz' (R)	ESul
	'Taspo' (R)	ESul
	'Tattingstone' (Min)	ESul
	'Tattoo' (Min)	ESul
	'Tavira' (I/d)	SPet
	'Tazi' (Dw)	ESul
	'Ted Dutton' (R)	ESul
	'Telstar' (Min/d)	ESul
§	'Telston's Prima' (R)	ESul LDea
	'Tenderly' (Dw/d)	ESul
	'Tenerife Magic' (MinI/d)	ESul
	tetragonum	CRHN EShb MBPg MHer SHFr SSea WFib
	'The Axe' (A)	LDea MWhe
	'The Barle' (A) 🏆[H1+3]	LDea MWhe WFib
	'The Boar' (Fr) 🏆[H1+3]	EShb LDea MSte SRms WFib
	'The Bray' (A)	LDea
	'The Creedy' (A)	LDea
	'The Culm' (A)	ESul LDea MSte SSea WFib
	'The Czar'	see *P.* 'Czar'

	'The Dart' (A)	LDea
	'The Heddon' (A)	LDea
	'The Joker' (I/d)	WFib
	'The Kenn-Lad' (A)	LDea
	'The Lowman' (A)	LDea SSea
	'The Lyn' (A)	ESul LDea MWhe
§	'The Mole' (A)	ESul LDea LVER MBPg MHer MSte SSea WFib
	'The Okement' (A)	LDea MSte MWhe SSea
	'The Otter' (A)	ESul LDea MWhe SSea
	'The Tamar' (A)	CFee LDea SSea
	'The Tone' (A) $\mathbb{Y}^{H1+3}$	LDea MWhe
	'The Yar' (Z/St) **new**	WFib
	'Thomas' (Sc)	MBPg
	'Thomas Earle' (Z)	WFib
	'Thomas Gerald' (Dw/C)	ESul
	'Tilly' (Min)	CHal NFir
	'Tim' (Min)	ESul
	'Timothy Clifford' (Min/d)	ESul MWhe
	'Tinkerbell' (A)	LDea
§	'Tip Top Duet' (A) $\mathbb{Y}^{H1+3}$	CHal ESul LAst LDea LRHS LSou LVER MHer MWhe NFir SSea WFib
	'Tirley Garth' (A) **new**	WFib
	'Tom Portas' (Dw/d)	ESul
	'Tomcat'^{PBR} (I/d)	LAst LVER SSea
	tomentosum (Sc) $\mathbb{Y}^{H1+3}$	CArn CHEx CHal CRHN CSev CSpe CTca EAro EShb ESul GPoy LDea LPio LVER MBPg MHer MNHC MWhe NFir SSea WFib
	- 'Chocolate'	see *P.* 'Chocolate Peppermint'
	'Tomgirl' (A)	LSou
	Tomgirl = 'Pactomgi'^{PBR} (IxZ/d)	LAst LVER
	'Tommay's Delight' (R)	LDea
	'Tony' (Min)	ESul
	'Topan' (R)	ESul
	'Topcliffe' (Dw/St)	ESul
	'Topscore' (Z/d)	WFib
	'Tornado' (R)	ESul NFir SAga WFib
	'Torrento' (Sc)	ESul LDea MBPg MHer WFib
	'Tortoiseshell' (R)	WFib
	'Tracy' (Min/d)	ESul NFir
	transvaalense	LPio NFir
	tricolor misapplied	see *P.* 'Splendide'
	tricuspidatum	CSpe LPio
	trifidum	LPio MBPg MHer SSea WFib
	'Trimley' (Dw/d)	ESul
	'Trinket' (Min/d)	WFib
	'Triomphe de Nancy' (Z/d)	WFib
	triste	EBee LFur LPio WFib
	'Trixie' (R)	LDea
	'Trudie' (Dw/Fr)	ESul LVER MHer SHFr WBrk WFib
	'Trulls Hatch' (Z/d)	MWhe
	'Tu Tone' (Dw/d)	ESul
	'Tuddenham' (Min/d)	ESul
	'Tuesday's Child' (Dw/C)	ESul
	'Tunias Perfecta' (R)	ESul
	'Turkish Coffee' (R)	ESul LVER NFir WFib
	'Turkish Delight' (Dw/C)	ESul MWhe NFir SSea WFib
	'Tuyo' (R)	WFib
	'Tweedle-Dum' (Dw)	ESul MWhe
	'Tweenaway' (Dw) **new**	ESul
	'Twinkle' (Min/d)	ESul WFib
	'Ullswater' (Dw/C)	ESul
§	'Unique Aurore' (U)	LVER MBPg MHer MSte
	'Unique Mons Ninon'	see *P.* 'Monsieur Ninon'
	'Unity' (Dw)	LVER
	'Urban White' (Dec) **new**	WFib
	urbanum	EShb
	'Urchin' (Min/St)	ESul MWhe NFir SHFr WFib
	'Ursula Key' (Z/c)	WFib
	'Ursula's Choice' (A) **new**	WFib
	'Val Merrick' (Dw/St) **new**	WFib
	'Valencia' (R)	ESul
	'Valentina' (Min/d)	ESul
	'Valentine'	ESul WFib
	'Vancouver Centennial' (Dw/St/C) $\mathbb{Y}^{H1+3}$	ESul LAst LRHS LVER MBri MHer MPes MWhe NFir SCoo SDnm SHFr SPoG SSea WFib
	'Vandersea'	EAro
	'Variegated Attar of Roses' (Sc/v)	MBPg
§	'Variegated Clorinda' (Sc/v)	WFib
	'Variegated Fragrans'	see *P.* (Fragrans Group) 'Fragrans Variegatum'
	'Variegated Joy Lucille' (Sc/v)	MBPg
§	'Variegated Kleine Liebling' (Min/v)	ESul SSea WFib
	'Variegated Madame Layal' (A/v) $\mathbb{Y}^{H1+3}$	WFib
	'Variegated Petit Pierre' (Min/v)	MWhe WFib
	'Vasco da Gama' (Dw/d)	ESul
	'Vectis Allure' (Z/St)	LVER
	'Vectis Dream' (St)	ESul
	'Vectis Fanfare' (St/d)	ESul
	'Vectis Finery' (St/d)	ESul
	'Vectis Glitter' (Z/St)	ESul LVER MWhe NFir SSea WFib
	'Vectis Pink' (Dw/St) **new**	WFib
	'Vectis Purple' (Z/d) **new**	WFib
	'Vectis Sparkler' (Dw/St)	ESul
	'Vectis Spider' (Dw/St)	ESul
	'Vectis Starbright' (Dw/St) **new**	WFib
	'Vectis Volcano' (Z/St) **new**	WFib
	'Velvet Duet' (A) $\mathbb{Y}^{H1+3}$	CHal LAst LDea LRHS LVER MBPg MWhe NFir SSea
	'Venus' (Min/d)	ESul
	'Vera Vernon' (Z/v)	SSea
	'Verdale' (A)	GGar LDea WFib
	'Verity Palace' (R)	ESul LDea WFib
	'Verona' (Z/C)	CHal MBri SSea
	'Verona Contreras' (A)	ESul LDea MWhe NFir WFib
	'Veronica' (Z/d)	MWhe
	'Vicki Town' (R)	WFib
	'Vicky Claire' (R)	CSpe ESul LDea NFir WFib
	Vicky = 'Pacvicky'^{PBR} (I)	LAst LSou
	'Vickybar' (R)	ESul
	Victor = 'Pacvi'^{PBR} (Quality Series) (Z/d)	LAst LSou
	'Victoria' (Z/d)	LAst LSou
	'Victoria Regina' (R)	ESul LDea
	'Viking Red' (Z)	MWhe
	'Village Hill Oak' (Sc)	ESul LDea MBPg MHer
	Ville de Dresden = 'Pendresd'^{PBR} (I)	LAst LSou
	'Ville de Paris'	see *P.* 'Hederinum'
	'Vina' (Dw/C/d)	ESul MWhe WFib
	'Vincent Gerris' (A)	ESul LDea MWhe
	Vinco = 'Guivin'^{PBR} (I/d)	LAst LSou WGor
	violareum misapplied	see *P.* 'Splendide'
	'Violet Lambton' (Z/v)	WFib
	'Violet Unique' (U)	CHrt
I	'Violetta' (R)	LDea WFib
	'Virginia' (R)	LDea SPet
	'Viscossisimum' (Sc)	MHer
	viscosum	see *P. glutinosum*
§	***vitifolium***	MBPg
	'Vivat Regina' (Z/d)	WFib
	'Voo Doo' (Dec)	ESul
	'Voodoo' (U) $\mathbb{Y}^{H1+3}$	CSpe EShb LAst LPio LSou MBPg MHer MSte NCiC NFir SSea WCot WFib
	'Wallace Fairman' (R)	LDea
	'Wallis Friesdorf' (Dw/C/d)	ESul MWhe
	'Wantirna' (Z/v)	ECtt MHer NFir SSea
	'Warrenorth Coral' (Z/C/d)	NFir SSea WFib
	'Warrenorth Thulite' **new**	LVER

'Warrion' (Z/d)	LVER SSea
'Washbrook' (Min/d)	ESul NFir
'Watersmeet' (R)	LDea
'Wattisham' (Dec)	LDea
'Waveney' (Min)	ESul
'Wayward Angel' (A) ♀H1+3	ESul LDea LVER MWhe SSea WFib
'Wedding Royale' (Dw/d)	ESul WFib
'Welcome' (Z/d)	WFib
'Welling' (Sc)	ESul LDea LVER MBPg MHer NFir
'Wendy' (Min)	LAst
'Wendy Jane' (Dw/d)	WFib
'Wendy Read' (Dw/d)	ESul MWhe WFib
'Wendy-O' (R)	LDea
'Wensum' (Min/d)	ESul
'Westdale Appleblossom' (Z/d/C)	ESul LVER SSea WBrk WFib
'Westerfield' (Min)	ESul
'Westside' (Z/d) new	WFib
'Westwood' (Z/St) new	WFib
'Wherstead' (Min)	ESul
'Whisper' (R)	WFib
'White Bird's Egg' (Z)	WFib
'White Boar' (Fr)	EShb MSte WFib
'White Bonanza' (R)	ESul WFib
'White Charm' (R)	ESul LDea
'White Chiffon' (R)	ESul LVER
'White Duet' (A)	LDea MWhe
'White Eggshell' (Min)	ESul LVER WFib
'White Feather' (Z/St)	MHer
'White Glory' (R) ♀H1+3	ESul NFir
'White Lively Lady' (Dw/C)	ESul
§ 'White Mesh' (I/v)	ECtt MBri
'White Prince of Orange' (Sc)	MBPg
'White Roc' (Min/d)	ESul
'White Truffle'	LAst
'White Unique' (U)	CHal CSpe LDea MBPg MHer MSte SPet SSea WFib
'White Velvet Duet' (A)	ESul
White-Blizzard = 'Fisbliz'PBR	NPri SCoo
'Wickham Lad' (R)	LDea
Wico = 'Guimongol'PBR (I/d)	LAst LSou WGor
'Wild Spice' (Sc)	LDea LVER
'Wildmalva' (Sc)	MBPg
'Wilf Vernon' (Min/d)	ESul
'Wilhelm Kolle' (Z)	WFib
'Wilhelm Langath'	MPes SCoo SDnm
'Willa' (Dec) new	WFib
'Winford Festival'	LVER
'Winnie Read' (Dw/d)	ESul
'Wirral Target' (Z/d/v)	ESul MWhe
'Wispy' (Dw/St/C)	ESul
'Witnesham' (Min/d)	ESul
'Wolverton' (Z) new	WFib
§ 'Wood's Surprise' (Min/I/d/v)	EShb ESul LDea MWhe
'Wooton's Unique'	CSpe
'Wordsworth'	MBPg
'Wroxham' (Dw)	ESul
'Wychwood' (A/Sc)	LDea MBPg
'Yale' (I/d) ♀H1+3	LDea MBri MSte MWhe WFib
'Yhu' (R)	ESul LDea NFir SMrm WFib
'Yolanda' (Dw/C)	ESul
'York Florist' (Z/d/v)	LVER
'Yvonne' (Z)	WFib
'Zama' (R)	ESul NFir
'Zena' (Dw)	ESul
'Zinc' (Z/d)	WFib
'Zoe' (A)	LDea
zonale	SSea WFib
'Zulu King' (R)	WFib
'Zulu Warrior' (R)	WFib

Peliosanthes (*Convallariaceae*)

monticola B&SWJ 5183	WCru

Pellaea (*Adiantaceae*)

andromedifolia new	WRic
atropurpurea	CLAP WFib
§ ***calomelanos***	WRic
falcata	CLAP MBri SEND WRic
hastata	see *P. calomelanos*
rotundifolia ♀H2	CHal CLAP LRHS LTwo MBri NMyG STre WRic
viridis	WRic
- var. ***macrophylla*** new	WRic

Pellionia see *Elatostema*

Peltandra (*Araceae*)

undulata	see *P. virginica*
§ ***virginica***	CDWL EBee EMFW NPer SWat

Peltaria (*Brassicaceae*)

alliacea	CSpe ECha GBin LEdu SAga

Peltiphyllum see *Darmera*

peltatum	see *Darmera peltata*

Peltoboykinia (*Saxifragaceae*)

§ ***tellimoides***	CCol CLAP EBee GEdr GKev MGol NBir SMac WBVN WFar WMoo
watanabei	CDes CLAP EBee GEdr LEdu NLar SMac WCru WFar WMoo WPGP

Pennantia (*Icacinaceae*)

baylisiana	ECou
corymbosa	ECou
- 'Akoroa'	ECou
- 'Woodside'	ECou

Pennellianthus see *Penstemon*

Pennisetum ✿ (*Poaceae*)

§ ***alopecuroides***	CEnd CHar CPrp CSBt CWCL EBee EHrv EPfP EPla GAbr GFor GKev GMaP LBMP LRHS MAvo MBrN MLLN NGdn SApp SLim SPer SPlb SPoG SWat SWvt WFar WHoo WWeb XIsg
- Autumn Wizard	see *P. alopecuroides* 'Herbstzauber'
- black	WSHC
- 'Black Beauty'	SMHy
- 'Cassian's Choice'	CBig CBrm CKno CSam ELon NCGa SMrm
- 'Caudatum'	CBig CKno CPen EBee SApp
- f. ***erythrochaetum*** 'Ferris'	EBee WCru
- 'Hameln'	More than 30 suppliers
§ - 'Herbstzauber'	CFir CKno CMdw CPen CPrp CSam EBee EGle EPfP LEdu LHop SPoG
- 'Little Bunny'	CKno CPen CWib EAlp EBee EBrs ELan EMan EPPr EPfP EQua LEdu LRHS NGdn SApp SWvt WBor XIsg
- 'Little Honey' (v)	CKno EBee EMan EPPr NLar SPla WCot XIsg
- 'Magic'	CPen MDKP
- 'Moudry'	CBig CBrm CKno CPen EAlp EBee WFar
- 'National Arboretum'	CBig CPen EPPr LEdu LLWG SApp SMad XIsg
- var. ***purpurascens***	CAby CBig CWCL
- f. ***viridescens***	CKno EBee ECha EGle ELan EMan EPPr EPfP EShb EWsh GFor LEdu LRHS MLLN MMoz MWgw NBPC SApp SWal XIsg

- 'Weserbergland' CBig CKno CSam EBee SApp
- 'Woodside' CBig CBrm CKno CPen CSam CWCL EMan EPPr EQua LEdu MBNS SApp SMad SPla
compressum see *P. alopecuroides*
flaccidum CSam EBee EHul EPPr
glaucum 'Jester' **new** LRav
- 'Purple Baron' **new** LRav
- 'Purple Majesty' CKno CSpe CWCL IPot LCro LRav MAvo MNrw NPri SCoo SMad SWal WPrP XIsg
incomptum LRHS NDov WHal XPep
- purple-flowered CBig CBrm CKno EBee MMoz
longistylum misapplied see *P. villosum*
macrostachyum 'Burgundy Giant' CBig MGos SMad
macrourum CBrm CElw CEnt CGHE CHrt CKno CSam CSpe CWCL EBee ECha EGle EPau EWsh LEdu LHop MAvo NDov SHom SMHy SMad SMrm SWal WCot WGwG WPGP XIsg
massaicum **new** SIng
- 'Red Buttons' see *P. thunbergii* 'Red Buttons'
orientale ♀H3 More than 30 suppliers
- 'Karley Rose'PBR CBig CKno CPen CRez EBee EGle EHrv EWes IPot LCro LLWG MAvo MBNS SPhx SSvw
I - 'Robustum' CDes SApp
- 'Shenandoah' SApp
* - 'Shogun' CKno CPen EBee MAvo WCot
- 'Tall Tails' CBig CKno COlW CPen EAlp EBee ECGP ECha EPPr EWes GFor IPot LBMP LEdu MAvo NBHF SMad WCot XIsg
'Paul's Giant' CKno SApp
rueppellii see *P. setaceum*
§ ***setaceum*** ♀H3 CBig CKno CPen CWib EShb LBMP MNrw SIde SWal XIsg XPep
- 'Eaton Canyon' CKno CPen EAlp
- 'Rubrum' ♀H4 More than 30 suppliers
§ ***thunbergii*** 'Red Buttons' CBig CKno CPen CRez EAlp EGle IPot LEdu LLWG MDKP
§ ***villosum*** ♀H3 More than 30 suppliers

pennyroyal see *Mentha pulegium*

Penstemon ✿ (*Scrophulariaceae*)

PC&H 148 EAro
P&C 150 CFee
RCB/Arg V-1 WCot
RCB/MO A-7 WCot
'Abberley' WEll WPer
'Abbeydale Blue' WEll
'Abbeydore' **new** SLon
'Abbotsmerry' MBNS SAga SGar SLon SPhx WEll WSPU
'Agnes Laing' LPen LRHS SLon SPlb WEll
albertinus see *P. humilis*
albidus WLin
§ 'Alice Hindley' ♀H3 More than 30 suppliers
alpinus EAro NEgg NOak
'Amy Gray' WEll
§ 'Andenken an Friedrich Hahn' ♀H4 More than 30 suppliers
§ ***angustifolius*** EBee MNrw SRms WEll
'Apple Blossom' misapplied see *P.* 'Thorn'
'Apple Blossom' ♀H3-4 More than 30 suppliers
aridus CPBP
arizonicus see *P. whippleanus*
'Ashton' CElw LPen SAga SLon WEll WSPU
attenuatus WLin
'Audrey Cooper' CChe SLon WEll
'Axe Valley Jessica' **new** WEll
'Axe Valley Mabel Alice' **new** WEll
'Axe Valley Penny Mitchell' WEll
'Axe Valley Pixie' CEnt
'Axe Valley Suzie' WEll
azureus CFir CPBP EBee GKev
'Baby Lips' LTwo
'Barbara Barker' see *P.* 'Beech Park'
§ ***barbatus*** CFee ECha EHrv ELan ELau EPfP MLan SECG SPer SPhx SRms WLin XPep
- 'Cambridge Mixed' LRHS LRav NBlu
- subsp. ***coccineus*** CBgR CMea EAro EBee EMon LPen LRHS MBNS MWat NChi NLar SPhx
- 'Iron Maiden' NBPC
- 'Jingle Bells' EPfP LPen MWgw NBPC SPav
- orange-flowered SMrm SPlb
- 'Peter Catt' LSou SMrm
- var. ***praecox*** CBgR MBNS WPer
- - f. ***nanus*** LRHS MSte SRms
- - - 'Rondo' CBrm MNFA NLar NWCA WBrE WWeb
'Beckford' CPrp EPfP EShb MBNS WCFE WEll WSPU
§ 'Beech Park' ♀H3 EBee ECtt ELan EWes IGor LPen LRHS MBNS NBir SAga WEll WHCG WSPU
§ ***berryi*** WLin
'Bisham Seedling' see *P.* 'White Bedder'
'Blackbird' More than 30 suppliers
'Blue Spring' misapplied see *P. heterophyllus* 'Blue Spring'
'Bodnant' LSou MBNS WEll WHoo WPer
bradburii see *P. grandiflorus*
'Bredon' CElw MBNS NChi SAga WBrk WEll WSPU
bridgesii see *P. rostriflorus*
'Burford Purple' see *P.* 'Burgundy'
'Burford Seedling' see *P.* 'Burgundy'
'Burford White' see *P.* 'White Bedder'
§ 'Burgundy' CHrt CSam CWCL EBee ECtt ENot GMaP GMac LLWP LPen LRHS MRav MWgw NBir NPer SAga SBch SGar SPoG SWal WFar WHCG WPer WSHC
caeruleus see *P. angustifolius*
caespitosus subsp. ***suffruticosus*** see *P. tusharensis*
californicus CPBP WAbe
calycosus EBee
§ ***campanulatus*** CEnt EAro ECtt EPfP EWes GEdr MLLN NDlv NMen NRnb SPoG SRms WEll WFar WPer WSPU
- PC&H 148 EMan GBri SGar SHFr WEll
- ***pulchellus*** see *P. campanulatus*
- ***roseus*** misapplied see *P. kunthii*
'Candy Pink' see *P.* 'Old Candy Pink'
cardinalis EBee
cardwellii EWes ITim SRms
cardwellii x ***davidsonii*** WAbe
'Carolyn Orr' (v) CBow EBee ECtt EMan LSou WEll
'Castle Forbes' EPyc GMac LPen MBNS MLLN WEll WHCG WPer
'Cathedral Rose' NPri
'Catherine de la Mare' see *P. heterophyllus* 'Catherine de la Mare'
* 'Centra' MBNS MLLN MWgw WEll
'Charles Rudd' CWCL EBee ECGP ECtt ERou LLWP LPen LRHS LSRN MBNS MLLN SBai SPav SRGP SWal SWvt WBrk WCot WEll WHCG WLin WWlt
§ 'Cherry' ♀H3 GMac LPen MBNS MHer SGar SHar SPla SPlb WHCG WPer WSPU
'Cherry Ripe' misapplied see *P.* 'Cherry'
§ 'Chester Scarlet' ♀H3 CWCL GBri GMac LPen MNrw MRav MSte SDix SGar SLon WEll WHCG WPer WSPU

	Name	Suppliers
	cinicola	LTwo
	cobaea	EBee GKev WPer
	comarrhenus cyaneus	see *P. cyaneus*
	'Comberton'	MBNS WEll WLin WSPU
	confertus	CTri CWGN EAro EBee ECho EPot LPen MBNS NChi NLAp NMen NWCA SGar SRms WBVN WEll WGwG WLin WPer
	'Connie's Pink' ΨH3	EBee ECtt ENot LPen MBNS MSte SLon WEll WHCG WLin WSPU
*	'Coral Pink'	SLon WEll
	'Cottage Garden Red'	see *P.* 'Windsor Red'
§	'Countess of Dalkeith'	CBcs EBee ECtt ELan ERou EWes LLWP LPen LRHS MLLN MNrw MRav SBai SGar SPer SPlb SWvt WCAu WCot WEll WFar WHCG WLin WSPU
	crandallii	CPBP WLin
	- subsp. ***atratus***	WLin
	- subsp. ***glabrescens***	WLin
§	- subsp. ***taosensis***	NWCA SMrm
	cristatus	see *P. eriantherus*
§	***cyaneus***	EBee
	davidsonii	ECho EWes NLAp SRms WAbe WFar
	- var. ***davidsonii***	CPBP SBla
§	- var. ***menziesii*** ΨH4	MDun SRms
	- - 'Broken Top Mountain'	CLyd
	- - 'Microphyllus'	LTwo WAbe WLin
	- var. ***praeteritus***	CGra MDKP
	'Dazzler'	CMMP CWCL ERou LPen NChi SAga SWal SWvt WEll WPer WSPU
§	***deaveri***	EBee
	'Devonshire Cream'	CWCL LPen LRHS MBNS WEll WHCG
	diffusus	see *P. serrulatus*
	digitalis	CRWN ECha EMan LPen MBNS NWCA SHar SPhx WFar WHCG WPer
§	- 'Husker Red'	More than 30 suppliers
	- 'Huskers Lilac'	see *Strobilanthes anisophylla*
	- 'Purpureus'	see *P. digitalis* 'Husker Red'
	- 'Ruby Tuesday'	CDes EBee EWes WPGP
	- white-flowered	SPhx SRms SWal
	discolor pale lavender-flowered	NBir WFar
	dissectus	SGar
§	'Drinkstone Red'	EGoo EPfP LPen NChi SDix WEll WHCG WPer WSPU
	'Drinkwater Red'	see *P.* 'Drinkstone Red'
	eatonii	NBPC
	'Edithae'	LPen SRms WEas WIvy
	'Elmley'	EBee MBNS MLLN NChi SAga WEll WSPU
§	***eriantherus***	CGra
	Etna = 'Yatna'	EBee ECtt EMil GKev LBMP LHop MAsh MBri NEgg WEll WHlf
	euglaucus	EBee EDAr LTwo
§	'Evelyn' ΨH4	CTri EBee ECha ELan EPfP EPot ERou LAst LRHS MBNS MHer MPop MRav NBir NWCA SPer SPet SPla SPlb SPoG SRGP SRms SWvt WFar WHCG WKif WPtf WSHC WSPU
	'Evelyn' x 'Papal Purple'	LPen SBch
	'Fanny's Blush'	CWGN SAga
	'Firebird'	see *P.* 'Schoenholzeri'
	'Flame'	LHop LPen LRHS MBNS SLon WEll WHCG WPer WSPU
	'Flamingo'	CPrp CWCL EBee ECtt EPfP ERou EWes LAst LPen LRHS MBNS MSte NBir NEgg SBai SPet SPoG SWvt WCFE WEll WFar WSPU
	'Froggery Cottage' **new**	WEll
	frutescens	LHop

	Name	Suppliers
	fruticosus	EBee EDAr MNrw NWCA WAbe WFar
§	- var. ***scouleri*** ΨH4	MAsh NLAp SRms WBVN WLin
	- - f. ***albus*** ΨH4	CSpe WAbe WIvy WKif
	- - 'Amethyst'	WAbe WBod WLin
	- - f. ***ruber***	NWCA
	- var. ***serratus***	SBla WLin
	- - 'Holly'	NMen SBla SHGN
	Fujiyama = 'Yayama'PBR	ECtt EMil LHop LRHS LSou MAsh MBri NEgg SGar WFar WHlf
	'Gaff's Pink'	WEll
	'Garden Red'	see *P.* 'Windsor Red'
	'Garnet'	see *P.* 'Andenken an Friedrich Hahn'
	gentianoides	MNrw NBro
	'Geoff Hamilton'	CElw CFwr CWoW LHop LPen LSRN MBNS SAga WEll
	'George Elrick'	LPen MBNS WEll WLin
§	'George Home' ΨH3	CWCL ECGP ECtt EWes LPen LRHS MBNS MLLN MSte SMrm WEll WHCG
	'Ghent Purple'	CFee
	'Gilchrist'	LRHS SGar SLon SPhx WEll WLin WWeb
	glaber	CEnt CMea EAro GMac LHop LLWP LPen LRHS LSRN MBNS MEHN SBai SHFr SMrm SPlb WEll WKif WPer
	- 'Roundway Snowflake'	SHar SPhx
	- white-flowered	SGar
	globosus	EDAr
	'Gloire des Quatre Rues'	CWCL
	gormanii	EAro SGar
	gracilis	WPer
§	***grandiflorus***	EAro EBee EDAr EShb
	- 'Prairie Snow'	EBee
	'Great Witley' **new**	WPer
	hallii	CGra EPot EWes LRHS WLin
	hartwegii ΨH3-4	EPyc LPen WHCG WPer WSPU
	- 'Albus'	LHop LPen LRHS MSte MWat NChi SGar WEll WHCG WSPU
	- 'Tubular Bells Rose'	NGBl SPet WEll
	'Helenetti' **new**	SDys
	heterodoxus	NWCA SGar
	- NNS 93-564	NWCA
§	***heterophyllus***	LCro LPen MNrw NBir NGBl NGdn SGar SPet SRkn SRms WAbe WEas WEll WHCG WKif WPer
	- 'Blue Eye'	WBrk
	- 'Blue Fountain'	CHar LPen MBNS WEll
	- 'Blue Gem'	CElw CTri LRHS NChi SIng SPla
§	- 'Blue Spring'	CBrm ECtt LPen LRHS MAsh MSte NBir NLar SAga SBla SPoG STes SWal WAbe
§	- 'Catherine de la Mare' ΨH4	CHar CPrp EBee ELan LHop LPen LRHS LSRN MHer MWat NBir NBro SAga SBch SMrm SPer SPla SRGP SWvt WBVN WEas WFar WKif WSPU WSpi
	- 'Electric Blue'	CElw MCCP NBlu NPri SGar SPhx
	- 'Heavenly Blue'	CSBt CTca CWCL EBee ECtt EPfP ERou EShb GMaP LAst LPen LRHS MBNS MDun MLHP MWat NPri SPav SPet SPoG SWal SWat SWvt WBrk WCra WEll WFar WMnd
	- 'Hergest Croft'	CElw WEll
	- 'Jeanette'	WCot WHoo
	- 'Les Holmes' **new**	WEll
	- subsp. ***purdyi***	EPyc WEll WHCG
	- 'Roehrslev'	LPen
	- 'True Blue'	see *P. heterophyllus*
	- 'Züriblau'	EBee GAbr LPen SPlb WWFP
§	'Hewell Pink Bedder' ΨH3	CBcs COlW EBee ECtt EPfP ERou GBri LPen LRHS MBNS MSte NBlu NEgg SBai SWal SWvt WEll WFar

		WHCG WHil WHoo WMnd WPer
		WSPU WWeb
	'Hewitt's Pink'	ECtt MBNS NEgg SLon WEll
	'Hidcote Pink' ♀H3-4	More than 30 suppliers
	'Hidcote Purple'	CElw CMMP NGdn SHar
*	'Hidcote White'	GBri MHer SWvt WEll
	'Hillview Pink'	SLon WEll WHil
	'Hillview Red'	WEll WHil
§	***hirsutus***	CEnt SGar WBVN WFar WPer
	- f. ***albiflorus***	CEnt NWCA
	- var. ***pygmaeus***	CLyd EBee ECho EDAr EShb MHer
		NMen NWCA SBla SGar SIng SPlb
		SRms SRot WAbe WHoo WPer
	- - f. ***albus***	NWCA SHGN WPer
	- - 'Purpureus'	WAbe
	'Hopleys Variegated' (v)	CBow CWGN EMan EWin MHer
		NBir SAga SPav SWvt WSPU WWeb
	'Hower Park'	MBNS
§	***humilis***	MLLN SRms
	- 'Pulchellus'	NWCA WLin
	isophyllus ♀H3-4	CHFP EPfP LPen LRHS WEll WFar
		WHCG WPer WPtf WSPU
	'James Bowden'	MBNS
	jamesii	EBee WHrl
	Jean Grace = 'Penbow'	CHar LRHS
	'Jessica' **new**	WCFE
	'John Booth'	MSte WEas WEll
	'John Nash' misapplied	see *P.* 'Alice Hindley'
	'John Nash'	MBNS MHer SRkn WEll
	'John Spedan Lewis'	SLon
	'Joy'	EPyc LPen MLLN MSte WEll WPer
	'June'	see *P.* 'Pennington Gem'
	'Kate Gilchrist' **new**	SLon
	Kilimanjaro = 'Yajaro'	EBee EMil LRHS LSou MAsh WEll
	'King George V'	More than 30 suppliers
	'Knight's Purple'	LPen MBNS WEll WHCG
	'Knightwick' ambig.	LPen SGar WEll WSPU
	'Knightwick'	MBNS WEll WPer
§	***kunthii***	EAro EBee EPPr GEdr LHop LLWP
		LPen MAsh MDKP MWea SAga
		WEll WHrl WOut WPer
	- upright	SGar
§	***laetus*** subsp. ***roezlii***	ECho EPot GCrs GGar LHop LRHS
		MAsh MBar MDun NDlv NLAp
		NSla SRms
§	'Le Phare'	EBee LPen LRHS MBNS SAga WEll
		WHCG WPer WSPU
	leiophyllus	WLin
	leonensis	EAro WLin
	'Lilac and Burgundy'	EBee ERou EWin LPen LRHS MBNS
		SAga SBai SWvt WEll WFar
	'Lilliput'	EPfP GBin LHop LRHS MAsh MBri
		SIng
	linarioides	LPen NLAp WLin WPat
	'Little Witley'	LPen MBNS WEll WHCG WPer
	'Lord Home'	see *P.* 'George Home'
	'Lucinda Gilchrist' **new**	SLon
	lyallii	EAro EHrv ELan LPen LSou MCCP
		MLLN SRms WPer WPtf
	'Lynette'	LPen LRHS MBNS SBch SPlb WEll
		WHCG WPer
	'Macpenny's Pink'	EBee EPyc LPen MBNS SAga WEll
§	'Madame Golding'	CWCL GMac LPen LRHS MBNS
		MNrw SGar SPlb SRkn WEll WHCG
		WPer
	'Malvern Springs'	MBNS WEll
	'Margery Fish' ♀H3	CElw EPyc ERou EWes LPen LRHS
		MNrw MSte SBai WEll WPer WSPU
	'Marilyn Ross'	SLon WEll WSPU
	'Maurice Gibbs' ♀H3	CBcs CChe CMMP EBee ECtt EPfP
		EPyc ERou EWTr EWes LPen LRHS
		LSRN MBNS MLLN NBPC NGdn
		SAga SBai SGar SPav SRGP SWal
		WEll WHCG WMnd WSPU
	menziesii	see *P. davidsonii* var. *menziesii*

	'Mesa'	CPBP
	Mexicali hybrids	CPBP EDAr LPen MLLN WFoF
		WLin
	x ***mexicanus*** 'Sunburst Ruby' **new**	EDAr
	'Midnight'	CHFP EBee ELan EPfP GBri LLWP
		LPen MRav MSte SAga SGar SWvt
		WCFE WCot WHCG WLin WMnd
		WPer WSPU WWeb
	'Mint Pink'	SGar
	'Modesty'	EPfP LPen LRHS MBNS WEll
		WHCG WPer WSPU
	'Mother of Pearl'	More than 30 suppliers
	'Mrs Golding'	see *P.* 'Madame Golding'
	'Mrs Miller'	ECtt LPen MBNS WEll
	'Mrs Morse'	see *P.* 'Chester Scarlet'
	multiflorus	LPen
§	'Myddelton Gem'	LPen LRHS MBNS MNrw MWat
		WCot WEll WFoF WHCG WSPU
	'Myddelton Red'	see *P.* 'Myddelton Gem'
	nemorosus NNS 00-572	EPPr
	neotericus	NWCA
	newberryi ♀H4	CGra NRnb SAga SBla WBVN WKif
		WLin WPat
	- subsp. ***berryi***	see *P. berryi*
	- f. ***humilior***	EPot
§	- subsp. ***sonomensis***	EPot GEdr WAbe WFar WLin
*	'Newbury Gem'	EBee EWin LSRN MBNS MLLN SBai
		SRGP SWal SWvt WEll WFar
	'Oaklea Red'	ECtt EPyc ERou SWat WEll
§	'Old Candy Pink'	CFee LPen MBNS MSte SBai SWvt
		WEll WPer WSPU
	'Old Silk'	WHil
	'Osprey' ♀H3	More than 30 suppliers
	ovatus	EBee ELan LPen MLLN NDlv SBla
		SGar SPhx SRms WLin WWeb
	'Overbury'	EBee LPen MBNS NChi WSPU
	pallidus	EBee
	palmeri	EAro EBee EMan LEdu MWea
	'Papal Purple'	CChe CMea ERou LLWP LPen
		LRHS MAsh MBNS MSte NBir NChi
		SLon SRms WEll WFar WHCG
		WSPU
	'Patio Bells Pink'	LPen MLHP MLLN WEll
	'Patio Bells Shell'	LRHS WHlf
	'Patio Coral'	ECtt WLin
	'Patio Wine'	ECtt SAga SLon WEll
	'Peace'	LPen LRHS MBNS MRav SLon WEll
		WHCG WSPU
	'Pearl'	EPyc
§	'Pennington Gem' ♀H3	CBcs ELan GBri GMac LHop LLWP
		LPen LRHS MHer MNrw MSte NBir
		NGdn SBai SWvt WEll WHCG WPer
		WSPU WWlt
	'Pensham Amelia Jane'	ECtt EPfP MBnl SRGP WHlf
	'Pensham Anniversary' **new**	WEll
	'Pensham Arctic Fox'	ECtt LHop MWea SAga SLon
	'Pensham Arctic Sunset'	SLon WEll WHrl
	'Pensham Avonbelle'	MBnl WEll
	'Pensham Barbara Dixon'	WEll
	'Pensham Bilberry Ice'	ECtt EPyc MLLN SPav WEll WMnd
	'Pensham Blackberry Ice'	CFir ECGP ECtt EPfP EPyc MBri
		MWea SPav WEll WMnd
	'Pensham Blueberry Ice'	CWGN CWoW EBee EPyc MBnl
		MBri MLLN SAga SPav WCra WEll
		WFar WMnd WWlt
	'Pensham Bow Bells'	WEll
	'Pensham Capricorn Moon'	EBee ECtt SAga SLon SRGP WEll
		WLin
	'Pensham Cassis Royale'	MLLN WEll
	'Pensham Charles Romer'	WEll
	'Pensham Claret'	WEll
	'Pensham Czar'	CAby ECtt MBnl WCra WHlf
	'Pensham Daybreak'	WEll
	'Pensham Dorothy Wilson'	EBee EPyc SRGP WEll

'Pensham Edith Biggs'	CWCL EBee ECtt EPfP SHGN WEll WFar
'Pensham Eleanor Young'	ECtt MBnl MWea SRGP WCra WEll WHlf
'Pensham Freshwater Pearl'	CElw CHVG SAga WEll
'Pensham Great Expectations'	EBee MLLN SAga WEll
'Pensham Just Jayne'	CElw CWoW EBee ECtt EPyc MBnl MLLN NPro SLon SRGP WCra WEll WMnd WSpi
'Pensham Kay Burton'	EPfP EPyc SRGP WEll WMnd
'Pensham Laura'	ECtt MBnl MWea SAga SRGP WEll WHlf
'Pensham Loganberry Ice'	MBnl MBri
'Pensham Marjorie Lewis'	EPyc SLon WEll WMnd
'Pensham Mary Ryan' **new**	WEll
'Pensham Mischief'	WEll
'Pensham Miss Wilson'	WEll
'Pensham Petticoat'	MBri WEll WWlt
'Pensham Plum Dandy'	WEll
'Pensham Plum Jerkum'	CWGN EBee ECtt EPyc MBri MLLN MWea SPoG WCra WEll WMnd
'Pensham Prolific'	WEll
'Pensham Raspberry Ice'	MBri MLLN SPav WEll WMnd
'Pensham Saint James's'	WEll
'Pensham Son of Raven'	WEll
'Pensham Tayberry Ice'	ECtt EPyc MBnl MBri MLLN SAga SGar WEll WMnd
'Pensham The Dean's Damson'	WEll
'Pensham Tiger Belle Coral'	NChi WEll WLin
'Pensham Tiger Belle Rose'	SAga SLon WEll
'Pensham Victoria Plum'	CTca CWoW SHar WEll
'Pensham Wedding Bells'	EBee MBri MWgw SPoG WEll WFar
'Pensham Wedding Day'	SRGP WHlf
perfoliatus	EBee
'Perrins Red'	MBNS WEll
'Pershore Anniversary'	WLin WSPU
'Pershore Carnival'	NPro WEll WSPU
'Pershore Fanfare'	LPen SAga WEll WHrl WLin WSPU
'Pershore Festival'	WSPU
'Pershore Pink Necklace'	LPen LRHS MLLN SBai SMrm SWvt WCot WEll WHCG WSPU WWeb
'Phare'	see *P.* 'Le Phare'
'Phyllis'	see *P.* 'Evelyn'
pinifolius ♀H4	CDMG CMea CTri ECho ECtt EDAr EPot GAbr GCrs GMaP LRHS NEgg NLAp SAga SBla SPoG SRms WBVN WEll WFar WHoo WLin WPat
- dwarf **new**	GKev
- 'Mersea Yellow'	CMea EBee ECho ECtt EDAr EPfP EPot GAbr GCrs GEdr GKev LHop LRHS NDlv NLAp NWCA SAga SBla SPlb SPoG WBVN WEll WFar WLin WPat WPer
- 'Wisley Flame' ♀H4	ECho EPfP EPot EWes GEdr NRya NWCA WEll
'Pink Bedder'	see *P.* 'Hewell Pink Bedder', 'Sutton's Pink Bedder'
'Pink Endurance'	ERou LPen MBNS MSte SRkn WEll WHCG WHal WPer WSPU
'Pink Ice'	WEll
'Pink Profusion'	MRav
'Pixie'	CPen
'Port Wine' ♀H3	CHFP CSam CTri CWCL CWoW EBee EPfP GMaP ISea LPen LRHS MLLN MWat NBPC NBir NChi SAga SBai SPla SPoG SWal WBrE WCot WEll WHCG WKif WMnd WPer WSPU
'Powis Castle'	ECtt EWes MHar WEll WPer WWlt
'Prairie Dusk'	LPen
'Prairie Fire'	EBee ERou LPen
* 'Prairie Pride'	LPen
'Priory Purple'	MBNS SLon WEll WHCG WHrl WLin WPer
procerus	ECho EDAr GBri MLLN NEgg SPhx SRms WEll WLin WPer
- var. ***brachyanthus***	WLin
§ - var. ***formosus***	EPot NMen WAbe WFar
- - NNS 01-345	NWCA
- 'Hawkeye'	CGra
§ - 'Roy Davidson' ♀H4	CMea EPot LBee LHop LRHS NLAp NMen SBla WAbe WEll WFar WLin
- var. ***tolmiei***	CElw EPot GEdr NMen
pruinosus	CPBP
pubescens	see *P. hirsutus*
pulchellus Greene	see *P. procerus* var. *formosus*
pulchellus Lindl.	see *P. campanulatus*
* ***pulcherrimus***	NBro
pumilus	SRms
'Purple and White'	see *P.* 'Countess of Dalkeith'
'Purple Bedder'	CHar CHrt COIW EBee EPfP ERou LPen LRHS LSRN MLHP MLLN MNrw MWat NBir NGdn SAga SBai SPav SPoG SRkn SWat SWvt WCFE WEll WFar WGor WHCG WHil WSPU
'Purple Passion'	CElw EBee EBrs EHrv EPfP EWes LPen LRHS WEll
'Purple Sea'	WEll
'Purpureus Albus'	see *P.* 'Countess of Dalkeith'
purpusii	ITim LTwo WAbe WLin
'Rajah'	LPen
'Raven' ♀H3	More than 30 suppliers
'Razzle Dazzle'	LPen LRHS MBNS SPlb WCot WEll WPer
'Red Ace'	MNrw WEll
'Red Emperor'	ECtt LPen MBNS MHar SPlb WEll WHCG WPer WSPU
'Red Knight'	CWCL GCra LPen LRHS MBNS
'Red Scarlet'	ISea
'Rich Purple'	EPyc LRHS MBNS SPlb
'Rich Ruby'	CHFP CWCL CWGN EBee EBrs ECtt EHrv ELan EPfP EWes LHop LLWP LPen LRHS MNrw NBir SBai SMer SPlb SRGP SWvt WCot WHCG WLin WPer WSPU
richardsonii	CStu EShb MNrw NWCA SRms WEll WPer
'Ridgeway Red'	MBNS WCFE WEll WSPU
roezlii Regel	see *P. laetus* subsp. *roezlii*
'Ron Sidwell'	SLon WEll WLin
§ ***rostriflorus***	CPBP
- NNS 03-094	NWCA
- NNS 95-407	WCot
'Rosy Blush'	LPen LRHS MBNS SAga SPlb WHCG
'Roundhay'	CFee NChi
'Roy Davidson'	see *P. procerus* 'Roy Davidson'
'Royal White'	see *P.* 'White Bedder'
'Rubicundus' ♀H3	CWCL CWGN EBee ECtt EHrv ELan EPfP ERou LHop LPen LRHS MAsh MBNS SAga SBai SMrm SPla SPoG SWvt WCot WEll WFar WHCG WMnd WSPU WWeb
'Ruby'	see *P.* 'Schoenholzeri'
'Ruby Field'	EPyc MWgw WCFE WEll WHCG
'Ruby Gem'	LPen LRHS MBNS
rupicola ♀H4	GCrs LHop LRHS NSla SBla WAbe WLin
- 'Albus'	LTwo NSla WAbe
- 'Conwy Lilac'	WAbe
- 'Conwy Rose'	WAbe
- 'Diamond Lake'	CMea
'Russian River'	EBee ECtt EPfP EPyc EWes EWin LHop LPen LRHS LSRN SBch SGar SPlb WHCG WPer WSPU
rydbergii	NLAp

*	Saskatoon hybrids	EBee
	Saskatoon hybrids rose	SLon
§	'Schoenholzeri' ♀H4	More than 30 suppliers
	scouleri	see *P. fruticosus* var. *scouleri*
§	***serrulatus***	CHFP EBee EWes GKev LHop MSte SGar SHFr WBVN WEll WHrl WKif
	- 'Albus'	GKev
	'Shell Pink'	LPen NChi WEll WPer
*	'Sherbourne Blue'	GBuc MBNS SAga SLon WCot WEll WPer
	'Shock Wave'	MCCP MSte SAga
	'Shot Silk'	WEll WSPU
*	'Shrawley'	WPer
	'Sissinghurst Pink'	see *P.* 'Evelyn'
	'Six Hills'	GBri SRms WAbe WLin WPat
	'Skyline'	EAro EPfP
	smallii	CDes CEnt CMHG CWoW EAro EBee EDAr EMan EPPr EShb EWes GKev LPen LSRN MCCP NBPC NWCA SGar SIng SMrm SPhx SPoG SWal WPGP WPer
	'Snow Storm'	see *P.* 'White Bedder'
	'Snowflake'	see *P.* 'White Bedder'
	'Son of Raven'	SAga WEll
	sonomensis	see *P. newberryi* subsp. *sonomensis*
	'Sour Grapes' misapplied	see *P.* 'Stapleford Gem'
§	'Sour Grapes' M. Fish ♀H3-4	More than 30 suppliers
	'Southcombe Pink'	LPen MLLN WEll WHCG
	'Southgate Gem'	LCro LPen LRHS MNrw MWat SWvt WEll WHCG
	'Souvenir d'Adrian Regnier'	EBee LPen MBNS WEll
	'Souvenir d'André Torres' misapplied	see *P.* 'Chester Scarlet'
	'Souvenir d'André Torres'	LLWP LPen WEll
§	'Stapleford Gem' ♀H3	More than 30 suppliers
	'Strawberry Fizz'	SLon
	strictus	EAro EBee EGoo EMan EPPr EShb LPen LRHS MBNS MCCP MLLN MNFA NLAp SGar SPoG SRms WPer WWeb
	Stromboli = 'Yaboli'	CElw EBee LBMP MBri WEll
	'Susie's Blue' **new**	WEll
	'Sutton's Pink Bedder'	LRHS MBNS SPlb WEll WSPU
	'Sylvia Buss'	LPen
	tall pink-flowered	see *P.* 'Welsh Dawn'
N	'Taoensis'	EWes MBNS SGar WEll
	taosensis	see *P. crandallii* subsp. *taosensis*
	teucrioides	EPot GEdr NLAp NWCA
	- JCA 1717050	CPBP
	'The Juggler'PBR	CChe EBee EPfP EWin LPen LRHS MBNS MLLN SPav WCra WFar WMnd
§	'Thorn'	CSpe CWGN EBee ECtt ELan ERou EShb LPen LRHS MLLN MNrw MSte MWat NBir SAga SBai SMrm SPer SPla SWal SWvt WHCG WLin WSPU WWeb
	'Threave Pink'	CPrp CWCL ERou LLWP MRav SEND SMrm SPer SWvt WEll WLin WMoo
	'Thundercloud'	WSPU
	'Torquay Gem'	GBuc LPen WCot WHCG WPer
	'True Sour Grapes'	see *P.* 'Sour Grapes' M. Fish
	'Tubular Bells Red'	NGBl
§	***tusharensis***	SBla
	utahensis	GBri SAga WKif
	venustus	GBuc MHar MNrw NCob SGar SRms SRot WRos
	'Vera'	WSPU
	Vesuvius = 'Yasius'	EBee ECtt EMil ENot EPfP EPyc GKev LSou MAsh MBri NEgg WEll WFar WHlf WRHF
	'Violet Dusk'	WPtf
	virens	CPBP GKev WLin WPer
	virgatus subsp. ***arizonicus***	see *P. deaveri*
	- 'Blue Buckle'	CBrm CPBP EBee EShb MBri NBir NLar NMyG WLin
	watsonii	EBee ELan EMan MLLN SRms
§	'Welsh Dawn'	CEnt LPen MBNS WEll WSPU
§	***whippleanus***	EAro GEdr LRav NRnb SPhx WAbb
	- 'Chocolate Drop'	EBee LSou SIng WRos
§	'White Bedder' ♀H3	More than 30 suppliers
	'Whitethroat' Sidwell	LPen LRHS MBNS SAga SLon WEll WHCG WSPU
I	'Whitethroat' purple-flowered	WPer
	wilcoxii	EBee NEgg
	'Willy's Purple'	MBNS SLon WEll
§	'Windsor Red'	COlW CTri EBee ECtt EPfP ERou LPen LRHS MBNS MPop MSte NBPC SAga SBai SGar SPoG SWal SWvt WCot WEll WGor WHCG WHil WSPU
	wislizeni	EPfP MLan SRms
	'Woodpecker'	CAby EBee MPop SPer SWal WEll WHil

Pentachondra (*Epacridaceae*)

	pumila	IBlr

Pentaglottis (*Boraginaceae*)

§	***sempervirens***	CArn EPfP MHer MSal WHen WHil

Pentagramma (*Adiantaceae*)

	triangularis	WRic

Pentapanax (*Araliaceae*)

	leschenaultii HWJK 2385	WCru

Pentapterygium see *Agapetes*

Pentas (*Rubiaceae*)

	lanceolata	CCCN CHal ELan EShb LRHS MBri

Peperomia (*Piperaceae*)

§	***argyreia*** ♀H1	MBri
	arifolia	CHal
	caperata	LRHS MBri
	clusiifolia	CHal
	- 'Variegata' (v)	CHal
	glabella	CHal
	- 'Variegata' (v)	CHal
	obtusifolia 'Jamaica'	MBri
	- (Magnoliifolia Group) 'Golden Gate' (v)	MBri
	- - 'Greengold'	CHal MBri
	- - 'USA' ♀H1	MBri
	- 'Tricolor' (v)	MBri
	orba 'Pixie'	MBri
I	- 'Pixie Variegata' (v)	MBri
	pulchella	see *P. verticillata*
	sandersii	see *P. argyreia*
	scandens ♀H1	MBri
	- 'Variegata' (v)	CHal MBri
§	***verticillata***	CHal

pepino see *Solanum muricatum*

peppermint see *Mentha piperita*

Perezia (*Asteraceae*)

	linearis	GBuc NLar
	recurvata	EPot NWCA

Pericallis (*Asteraceae*)

§	***lanata*** (L'Hér.) B. Nord.	CHll ELan EShb MBlu SAga SBch WPic

- Kew form — CRHN CSpe SAga
multiflora — LHop SAga
Senetti Series **new** — NPer

Perilla (*Lamiaceae*)

frutescens **new** — EUnu
§ - var. ***crispa*** ♀H2 — CArn
- green-leaved — MNHC
- var. ***nankinensis*** — see *P. frutescens* var. *crispa*
- var. ***purpurascens*** — CArn CSpe EUnu MNHC WJek
- 'Shizo Green' **new** — CSpe

Periploca (*Asclepiadaceae*)

graeca — CArn CBcs CMac CRHN ITer SLon SPoG WSHC
purpurea — WSHC
- B&SWJ 7235 — WCru
sepium — CPLG

Peristrophe (*Acanthaceae*)

speciosa — ECre ERea

Pernettya see *Gaultheria*

Perovskia (*Lamiaceae*)

abrotanoides — WBod XPep
atriplicifolia — CArn CBcs CMea MHer MNHC NSti WHCG WMnd WPer
- 'Little Spire' PBR — CHFP CMac CSpe ENot EWes GBin LBuc NLar SPad SPer SPoG WSHC
'Blue Haze' — EBrs SMHy
'Blue Spire' ♀H4 — More than 30 suppliers
'Filigran' — EGoo EMil EWin GBuc LBMP LRHS SKHP SPet SPoG WPat WSpi XPep
'Hybrida' — LRHS
'Longin' — XPep

Persea (*Lauraceae*)

ichangensis — CPLG
indica — CCCN CPLG WPGP
thunbergii — CBcs CHEx WPGP

Persicaria (*Polygonaceae*)

§ ***affinis*** — CBcs CBen CSBt EBee GAbr MBar MTho NBro NVic SWat WBor WBrE WBrk WCFE WFar WMoo WRHF
- CC 4423 — MGol
§ - 'Darjeeling Red' ♀H4 — More than 30 suppliers
- 'Dimity' — see *P. affinis* 'Superba'
§ - 'Donald Lowndes' ♀H4 — More than 30 suppliers
- 'Kabouter' — EBee GBin
§ - 'Superba' ♀H4 — More than 30 suppliers
alata — see *P. nepalensis*
alpina — SBch
amphibia — NSco SWat
§ ***amplexicaulis*** — CBre CHVG COld CPrp CSpe EBee ELan EMar EWTr EWes GMaP MHer MSte NChi NOrc SEND WBor WFar WMoo WRHF WTel WTin
- 'Alba' — CElw CHar CKno EBee ECha EMan EPPr EPla ERou GBuc LHop MLLN MSte NDov SMrm SPhx SWat WCAu WCot WFar WMnd WMoo WPnP WTin
- 'Arun Gem' — see *P. amplexicaulis* var. *pendula*
- 'Atrosanguinea' — CTri EBee ECha ELan EMFW EMan EPla ERou GGar LRHS MNFA MRav MWgw NBir NDov NEgg NVic SPer SRms SWat SWvt WCAu WFar WOld
- 'Blush Clent' — EBee WHoo WSPU WTin
- 'Clent Charm' — WSPU
- 'Cottesbrooke Gold' — EMan EMar LSou
- 'Early Pink Lady' **new** — EMon
- 'Firedance' — NDov SMHy SPhx SWat WCot
- 'Firetail' ♀H4 — More than 30 suppliers
- 'High Society' — EBee
- 'Inverleith' — CBre CDes CHar EBee ECha ECtt EPPr EPla EWll GGar GMaP GQue NDov WCot WMoo WPGP
I - 'Jo and Guido's Form' — EBee WFar
* - var. ***pendula*** — NBir WFar WMoo
- 'Pink Lady' — NLar
- 'Rosea' — CElw CKno CSam EBee ECha ELan EMan EPla MSte NBro NChi NDov NSti SDys SMeo SPhx SWat WCAu WDyG WFar WMoo WPGP WSpi
- 'Rosy Clent' — WSPU
- 'Rowden Gem' — EPla WMoo
- 'Rowden Jewel' — EPla
- 'Summer Dance' — EBee EMon NBre NLar
- Taurus = 'Blotau' — CElw CKno EBee EBrs EGle EPla ERou MBri MLLN NDov NLar SMHy WCAu WFar WPGP WPnP WTin
§ ***bistorta*** — CArn ELau GPoy LAst MHer MSal NBir NGHP NSco SRms SWat WDyG WSel
- subsp. ***carnea*** — EBee EBla ECha GGar LRHS MNFA NBir NDov WFar WMoo
- 'Hohe Tatra' — CDes CKno EBee EMan NDov WFar WMoo WTMC
§ - 'Superba' ♀H4 — More than 30 suppliers
bistortoides — MSal
campanulata — CElw EBee ECha ECtt EShb GAbr GBuc GGar GMaP NBid NBro SPer WFar WMoo WOld WRHF
- Alba Group — CElw EBee GGar NBro WHer WMoo
- var. ***lichiangense*** — GBin
- 'Madame Jigard' — GBin
- 'Rosenrot' — CBre CKno EMan GBuc NBir NHol NLar NSti SWat WFar WOld
- 'Southcombe White' — EPla GBri WPer
§ ***capitata*** — CHal CPLG EMan SHFr SIng SRms WEas WMoo XPep
- 'Pink Bubbles' — ECtt SPet SWvt
conspicua — EBee NBre
* ***elata*** — EMan EMar GBuc
* ***emodi*** — NBre
hydropiper 'Fastigiata' — CArn EUnu
§ ***longiseta*** — MSal
* ***macrophylla*** — EBee LDai WFar
microcephala — EWes MHer SMac
- 'Red Dragon' PBR — More than 30 suppliers
* ***milletii*** — CDes EBrs EWes GAbr GBuc MTho NLar WCAu WCru WFar
§ ***mollis*** — EBee WDyG WPGP
* ***nakaii*** — EBee
neofiliformis — EBee
§ ***nepalensis*** — EBee EPPr EShb SMad
§ ***odorata*** — CArn ELau EOHP EUnu GPoy ILis LRav MHer MNHC MSal NGHP NPri SHDw SIde WJek
orientalis — MSal
* ***polymorpha*** — CBct CDes CKno CSpe EBee ECha EGle EHrv ELan EMan EMon EPPr EWTr GMaP MRav NCGa NDov SMad SPhx SWat WCot WFar WHil WMoo WSpi WTin
polystachya — see *P. wallichii*
* ***regeliana*** — LRHS
§ ***runcinata*** — CPLG EBee EMar GGar NBid NBir NCob NLar WFar WHer WMoo WPer WPtf WTMC
- Needham's form — NBid
scoparia — see *Polygonum scoparium*

sphaerostachya Meisn.	see *P. macrophylla*
* ***tenuicaulis***	CBre CPLG CSpe EBee ECho EHrv EMon EPla GGar SBch WCot WCru WFar WMoo
§ ***tinctoria***	EOHP
§ ***vacciniifolia*** ♀H4	More than 30 suppliers
§ ***virginiana***	ECtt EMan MSal WMoo WTMC
- Compton's form	CBct EBee ECha EMan EMar EPPr EWin LDai NCob WAul WCot WTMC
- 'Filiformis'	EBee ECtt EWin GBin MHar WCot WDyG WHil WRos
- 'Lance Corporal'	EBee EPla NBre NCob NLar WMnd WMoo
- 'Moorland Moss'	WMoo
- Variegata Group	EBee ECha EMan MBNS WCot WMoo WOld
- - 'Painter's Palette' (v)	More than 30 suppliers
- white-flowered	EPPr NCob
vivipara	NLar WCot
§ ***wallichii***	EBee NBre NLar NSti SDix SWat WCot WMoo
§ ***weyrichii***	EBee EMon EPPr NBir NBro NLar WCot WFar WMoo

persimmon see *Diospyros virginiana*

persimmon, Japanese see *Diospyros kaki*

Petalostemon see *Dalea*

Petamenes see *Gladiolus*

Petasites (*Asteraceae*)

albus	EBee EMon GPoy GSki NBre NLar NSti
formosanus	LEdu
- B&SWJ 3025	WCru
fragrans	CNat EBee ELan EMon MHer NLar SWat WFar WHer
§ ***frigidus*** var. ***palmatus***	EBee EPla LEdu MWgw NBre NLar NSti WCru WPGP
- - JLS 86317CLOR	SMad
- - 'Golden Palms'	CAby EHrv NBre NSti SPur
hybridus	EMFW LEdu NSco SMad SWat WHer WMAq WSFF
japonicus	CBcs
- var. ***giganteus***	CArn CHEx ECha ELan EMon EPPr EPfP LEdu NVic SWat WCru WMoo WTMC
§ - - 'Nishiki-buki' (v)	CHEx CMCo EBee EMan EMon EPPr EPla ITer MFOX NSti SMad WBor WFar WPGP WTMC
- - 'Variegatus'	see *P. japonicus* var. *giganteus* 'Nishiki-buki'
- f. ***purpureus***	CDes CMCo EBee EMan EPPr EWes WCru WPGP
palmatus	see *P. frigidus* var. *palmatus*
paradoxus	CBgR CDes CLAP CMCo EMon EPPr EWes LEdu SMad WCot

Petrea (*Verbenaceae*)

volubilis	CCCN CHIl MJnS SOWG

Petrocallis (*Brassicaceae*)

lagascae	see *P. pyrenaica*
§ ***pyrenaica***	NWCA WAbe
- ***alba***	WAbe

Petrocoptis (*Caryophyllaceae*)

grandiflora new	GKev
pyrenaica	EBur SBch SBla SRms
§ - subsp. ***glaucifolia***	NBir NLar

Petrocosmea (*Gesneriaceae*)

B&SWJ 7249 from Thailand	WCru
duclouxii new	WAbe
kerrii	WAbe
- B&SWJ 6634	WCru
aff. ***martini*** B&SWJ 7249 new	WCru
minor new	SBla
rosettifolia new	WAbe
sericea new	WAbe

Petrophytum (*Rosaceae*)

cinerascens	SIng
§ ***hendersonii***	NHol SIng WAbe

Petrorhagia (*Caryophyllaceae*)

'Pink Starlets'	GBri LHop LRav SHGN
saxifraga ♀H4	CDMG EBur ECho EShb NPri SRms SWal WMoo WPer WPnn WPtf
- 'Rosette'	MTho

Petroselinum (*Apiaceae*)

§ ***crispum***	CArn CHrt CSev GPoy GWCH ILis LCro MBar MNHC NBlu NGHP SECG SIde SWal WPer WSel
- 'Bravour' ♀H4	ELau MHer
- 'Darki'	CSev NGHP NPri
- French	CArn ELau MHer MNHC NBlu NPri NVic WJek
- 'Italian'	see *P. crispum* var. *neapolitanum*
§ - var. ***neapolitanum***	ELau GWCH SIde
- 'Super Moss Curled'	NVic SWal
§ - var. ***tuberosum***	MHer MNHC SIde WHer
- variegated (v)	CNat
hortense	see *P. crispum*
tuberosum	see *P. crispum* var. *tuberosum*

Petteria (*Papilionaceae*)

ramentacea	NLar WBVN

Petunia (*Solanaceae*)

* 'Angels Blue'	LAst
'Bavarian Belle' new	LSou
(Cascadias Series) Blue Spark = 'Dancasblue'PBR	LAst
- Cascadias Yellow Eye = 'Dancasye'PBR ♀H3	LAst
Candyfloss = 'Kercan'PBR (Tumbelina Series)	LAst NPri
(Charlie's Angels Series) 'Charlie's Angels Blue' new	LAst
* - 'Charlie's Angels Pink'	LAst
- 'Charlie's Angels White'	LAst
'Chilli Red'	SVil
(Conchita Series) Conchita Blossom White = 'Conbloss'PBR	SVil
- Conchita Blueberry Frost = 'Conblue'PBR ♀H3	LSou SVil
- Conchita Evening Glow = 'Conglow'PBR ♀H3 new	SVil
- Conchita Pink Kiss = 'Mediopimo'PBR	LSou SVil
- Conchita Strawberry Frost = 'Constraw'PBR ♀H3	LSou SVil WGor
- Conchita Twilight Blue = 'Ustuni218'PBR	LSou SVil
(Conchita Doble Series) Conchita Doble Dark Blue = 'Condost169' PBR (d)	LAst

- Conchita Doble Lavender = 'Condost177' PBR (d) — LAst SVil
- Conchita Doble Orchid Lace = 'Ustuni131' PBR (d) — LAst
- Conchita Doble Pink = 'Condopink' PBR (d) — LAst SVil
- Conchita Doble Velvet = 'Ustuni140' PBR (d) — LAst
- Conchita Doble White = 'Condowhite' PBR (d) — LAst

(Doubloon Series) Doubloon Blue Star = 'Dandbblst' (d) — LAst
- Doubloon Pink Star = 'Dandbpkst' (d) — LAst

'Empaurea' **new** — LAst LSou SVil
'Fanfare Appleblossom' **new** — SVil
'Fanfare Flame' **new** — SVil
'Fanfare Pink' **new** — SVil
(Jamboree Series) Jamboree Blue Vein = 'Jam Bluin' PBR **new** — SVil
- Jamboree Burgundy = 'Jam Burg' PBR **new** — SVil
- Jamboree Lavender = 'Jam Laver' **new** — SVil
- Jamboree Plum Vein = 'Jam Pluin' **new** — SVil
- Jamboree Scarlet = 'Jam Scarl' PBR **new** — SVil

Julia = 'Kerjul' PBR (Tumbelina Series) — LAst NPri
Katrina (Tumbelina Series) — LAst
Margarita = 'Kermar' PBR (Tumbelina Series) — LAst
patagonica — CPBP WAbe
Pink Spark = 'Dancaspink' PBR (Cascadias Series) — LAst
Priscilla = 'Kerpril' PBR (Tumbelina Series) — LAst LSou NPri
* 'Purple Surprise' — LAst
Queen (Tumbelina Series) — LAst
'Ramblin' Red' — LAst
Rosella Improved = 'Kerrosim' PBR (Tumbelina Series) — LAst
Rosella = 'Kerros' (Tumbelina Series) — LAst
Sunray = 'Dancas110' **new** — SVil
(Supertunia Series) Supertunia Blushing Princess = 'Kakegawa S38' PBR — LAst LSou
- Supertunia Lavender Morn = 'Kakegawa S66' PBR — LAst
- Supertunia Lavender Pink = 'Kakegawa S37' PBR — LAst
- Supertunia Mystic Pink = 'Kakegawa S29' PBR — LAst
- Supertunia Royal Magenta = 'Kakegawa S36' PBR — LAst LSou SVil
- Supertunia Royal Velvet = 'Kakegawa S28' PBR — LAst
- Supertunia White = 'Kakegawa S30' PBR — LAst

(Surfinia Series) Surfinia Amethyst **new** — LSou
- Surfinia Baby Pinkmorn = 'Sunbapimo' PBR — LAst
- Surfinia Blue = 'Sunblu' — LAst LSou NBlu NPri WGor
- Surfinia Blue Vein = 'Sunsolos' PBR — LAst NPri WGor
- Surfinia Burgundy — LAst LSou NPri WGor
- Surfinia Crazy Pink = 'Sunrovein' — NPri
- Surfinia Double Purple = 'Keidopuel' PBR (d) — LAst
- Surfinia Hot Pink = 'Marrose' PBR — LAst LSou NBlu WGor
- Surfinia Lime = 'Keiyeul' PBR — LAst NBlu NPri
- Surfinia Pastel 2000 = 'Sunpapi' PBR — NPri WGor
- Surfinia Patio Blue = 'Keipabukas' PBR — LAst
- Surfinia Pink Ice = 'Hakice' PBR (v) — LAst NPri WGor
- Surfinia Pink Mini 2000 = 'Sunmipi' PBR — NBlu
- Surfinia Pink Vein = 'Suntosol' PBR ♀H3 — NBlu WGor
- Surfinia Purple = 'Shihi Brilliant' ♀H3 — LSou NBlu NPri WGor

* - Surfinia Purple Sunrise — LAst
- Surfinia Red = 'Keirekul' PBR — LAst NPri WGor
- Surfinia Rose Vein = 'Sunrove' PBR — LAst NPri
- Surfinia Sky Blue = 'Keilavbu' PBR ♀H3 — LAst NBlu NPri WGor
- Surfinia Soft Pink **new** — WGor
- Surfinia Vanilla = 'Sunvanilla' — LSou
- Surfinia Velvet **new** — LSou
- Surfinia Victorian Apricot = 'Sunapri' — LAst
- Surfinia Victorian Yellow — LAst LSou NPri WGor
- Surfinia White = 'Kesupite' — LAst NBlu

Peucedanum (*Apiaceae*)

japonicum — CSpe
- B&SWJ 8816B — WCru

ostruthium — EDAr GPoy
- 'Daphnis' (v) — CDes CElw CSpe EBee EGle EMan EMar EMon EPPr LEdu NChi NGby NLar NMRc NPro WCot WEas WHrl

siamicum B&SWJ 264 — WCru
verticillare — CArn CSpe EBee EDAr ITer MNFA NBid NChi NDov NLar SDix SMad SPhx WSHC

Phacelia (*Hydrophyllaceae*)

bolanderi — LDai
californica **new** — WOut

Phaedranassa (*Amaryllidaceae*)

BKBlount 2623 **new** — WCot
carmiolii — WCot
cinerea — EBrs
cloracra — WCot
dubia — ECho WCot
* ***montana*** — ECho
tunguraguae — EBrs ECho
viridiflora — EBrs ECho WCot WHil

Phaedranthus see *Distictis*

Phaenocoma (*Asteraceae*)

prolifera — SPlb

Phaenosperma (*Poaceae*)

globosa	CFwr CHrt CSam EBee EGle EPPr EShb EWes EWsh LEdu MAvo SPhx WBor WDyG WPGP WPrP

Phaiophleps see *Olsynium*

nigricans	see *Sisyrinchium striatum*

Phalaris (*Poaceae*)

arundinacea	EMFW EPla GFor MBNS MLan NNor SPlb SWat WTin XIsg
- 'Elegantissima'	see *P. arundinacea* var. *picta* 'Picta'
- var. ***picta***	CBen CDul CHEx CTri CWCL CWib EMFW LCro LRHS NBid NPer SApp SPoG WFar
- - 'Aureovariegata' (v)	CBcs CSWP MRav NGdn NPer SWat WMoo
- - 'Feesey' (v)	More than 30 suppliers
- - 'Luteopicta' (v)	EAlp EBee EGoo EPPr EPfP EPla WLeb WTin
- - 'Luteovariegata' (v)	EShb NGdn
§ - - 'Picta' (v) 🏆[H4]	COlW CPLG EBee ELan EPfP EPla GFor GWCH LEdu LRHS MBar MWgw NHol SPer SWal SWat WMoo XIsg
- - 'Streamlined' (v)	EAlp EPPr EPla EWsh SLPl WFar WMoo
- - 'Tricolor' (v)	CPen EBee EPla MBar

Phanerophlebia (*Dryopteridaceae*)

caryotidea	see *Cyrtomium caryotideum*
falcata	see *Cyrtomium falcatum*
fortunei	see *Cyrtomium fortunei*

Pharbitis see *Ipomoea*

Phaseolus (*Papilionaceae*)

caracalla	see *Vigna caracalla*
vulgaris 'Yin Yang'	LSou

Phegopteris (*Thelypteridaceae*)

§ ***connectilis***	EFer EMon SRms WRic
decursive-pinnata	CFwr CLAP CRez EMon GBri MPes NHol NLar SPoG WFib WRic WSpi

Phellodendron (*Rutaceae*)

amurense	CBcs CCCN CDul CMCN ELan EPfP LEdu NLar SBLw WBor WNor WPGP
- var. ***sachalinense***	LRHS
chinense	CMCN
japonicum new	EGFP
lavalleei	EPfP

Phenakospermum (*Strelitziaceae*)

guianense	XBlo

Philadelphus ✿ (*Hydrangeaceae*)

F&M 152	WPGP
'Albâtre' (d)	MBri
'Avalanche'	CMHG CPLG EBee LRHS NLar NPro SRms WFar WHCG
'Beauclerk' 🏆[H4]	CDoC CDul CMHG CSBt CTri EBee ECrN EPfP GQui LRHS MBri MGos MRav NBro NEgg NHol NWea SPer SPoG SReu SRms SWvt WHCG WKif
'Belle Etoile' 🏆[H4]	More than 30 suppliers
'Bicolore'	EBee MWya NLar WSpi
'Boule d'Argent' (d)	CMHG
'Bouquet Blanc'	EBee GQui MRav NLar SPer SPoG SRms WPat
brachybotrys	EPfP MRav WHCG
'Buckley's Quill' (d)	EBee ECrN EPfP EQua EWes MRav MWya
'Burfordensis'	EBee EPfP LAst MRav WPGP
'Burkwoodii'	LRHS
aff. ***calvescens***	MRav
- BWJ 8005	WCru
caucasicus	WPGP
coronarius	CDul CTri EPfP LBuc SGar SHBN SMer SPer XPep
- 'Aureus' 🏆[H4]	More than 30 suppliers
- 'Bowles' Variety'	see *P. coronarius* 'Variegatus'
§ - 'Variegatus' (v) 🏆[H4]	More than 30 suppliers
'Coupe d'Argent'	CPLG MRav
'Dame Blanche' (d)	EWTr LBuc LRHS MAsh MRav
delavayi	CGHE EPfP MBri NWea SChF SGar SSpi WCru WCwm WHCG WPGP
- EDHCH 97170	EPPr
- var. ***calvescens***	see *P. purpurascens*
- var. ***melanocalyx***	GCra WPGP
'Enchantement' (d)	MRav SDix WBod
§ 'Erectus'	CSBt CWib EBee ENot EPfP MAsh MGos MRav SPer SPla SPoG WHCG WPat WTel
'Frosty Morn' (d)	CBcs MBri MGos MRav NBro NEgg SPer SPla SPoG WGwG
incanus B&SWJ 8616	WCru
§ 'Innocence' (v)	CEnd CMac CPLG CWSG EBee ECrN ELan EPfP LAst LBMP LRHS MAsh MBri MGos MRav MSwo NBlu NEgg NPri NPro SAga SHBN SPer SPla SPoG SReu WFar WHCG WPat
'Innocence Variegatus'	see *P.* 'Innocence'
§ ***insignis***	MRav WBod
x ***lemoinei***	CDul CTri CWoW EWTr MGos MWat SHBN SMer WFar
- 'Erectus'	see *P.* 'Erectus'
I - 'Lemoinei'	NWea
'Lemon Hill'	NEgg
lewisii	CPLG
- L 1896	WPGP
maculatus 'Mexican Jewel'	SKHP WPGP
madrensis	LHop MRav
'Manteau d'Hermine' (d) 🏆[H4]	More than 30 suppliers
'Marjorie'	EBee
mexicanus	EBee
- 'Rose Syringa'	CGHE WPGP
microphyllus	CDul CMHG CPSs CWoW EBee ELan EPfP LAst LRHS MGos MRav NHol SLon SPer SReu SSpi WBVN WHCG WPat WSHC
- var. ***occidentalis***	NLar
'Miniature Snowflake' (d)	MAsh WPat
'Minnesota Snowflake' (d)	CBcs CMac EBee ECtt EQua EWes LBuc LRHS LSRN MRav NLar NPro SPur WFar
'Mont Blanc'	CBcs MRav WFar
'Mrs E.L. Robinson' (d)	CMac EBee ECtt LAst LBuc LRHS NLar WPat
'Natchez' (d)	CMac EBee ECtt WPat
'Oeil de Pourpre'	LBMP MRav
palmeri	WPGP
pekinensis	CPLG
'Perryhill'	MRav
'Polar Star' new	WBod
§ ***purpurascens***	EPfP EWes GQui MAsh MRav NEgg SLon WCwm WPGP WPat
- BWJ 7540	WCru
x ***purpureomaculatus***	MAsh MRav WPat
'Rusalka'	MWya
schrenkii	NLar WPGP
- B&SWJ 8465	WCru

§	'Silberregen'	CDul CMac EBee ECtt EPfP LAst MAsh MBar MBri MGos MMuc MRav NCGa NPro SHBN SMad SPoG SRms SWvt WBod WFar WPat WRHF
	Silver Showers	see *P.* 'Silberregen'
	'Snow Velvet'	EBee ECrN EPfP LRHS
	'Snowbelle' (d)	EBee LBMP MAsh MBri MWea NBro
	'Snowflake'	CWSG NMoo
	'Souvenir de Billiard'	see *P. insignis*
	subcanus	CPLG MRav
	'Sybille' ♀H4	CDul CMHG ECrN EPfP LRHS MBri MRav SDix SPer SPoG SRms SSpi WHCG WKif WPat WSHC WSpi
	tenuifolius	CMCN NLar
	tomentosus	CPLG WHCG WPGP
	- B&SWJ 2707	WCru
	- GWJ 9215	WCru
	'Virginal' (d)	More than 30 suppliers
	'Voie Lactée'	MRav
	White Rock = 'Pekphil'	CDoC CMac CPLG CWSG EBee EQua LAst LRHS LTwo MRav NMoo SLim SPer SPoG WPat
	'Yellow Cab'	MBri NLar SPoG

Philesia (*Philesiaceae*)

	buxifolia	see *P. magellanica*
§	***magellanica***	GGGa GSki SSpi WBod WCru
	- 'Rosea'	LRHS MAsh SPoG

Phillyrea (*Oleaceae*)

	angustifolia	CBcs CDul CGHE CMCN CSpe EBee ELan EPfP ERom MBri MGos SEND SLPl SPer SSpi WBVN WFar WSHC XPep
	- f. ***rosmarinifolia***	CCCN CPLG EBee ELan EPfP EPla LAst MBri NLar SLPl WFar WPGP XPep
	decora	see *Osmanthus decorus*
§	***latifolia***	CHEx CPLG CSpe EBee EGFP ELan EPfP LRHS MWea NLar SAPC SArc SLPl SSpi WFar WPGP XPep
I	- 'Rodrigueziensis'	WCFE
	media	see *P. latifolia*

Philodendron (*Araceae*)

	epipremnum	see *Epipremnum pinnatum*
	erubescens 'Burgundy' ♀H1	CHal LRHS
	- 'Red Emerald'	CHal
*	***rubra*** **new**	XBlo
	scandens ♀H1	CHal
	- 'Mica'	XBlo
	selloum	EAmu XBlo
	xanadu	XBlo

Philotheca (*Rutaceae*)

	buxifolia 'Cascade of Stars'	SOWG

Phlebodium (*Polypodiaceae*)

§	***aureum*** ♀H1	CSpe

Phleum (*Poaceae*)

	bertolonii	CRWN
	pratense	CBig GQue WOut WSFF

Phlomis ✿ (*Lamiaceae*)

*	***anatolica***	NLar XPep
*	- 'Lloyd's Variety'	CAbP CSam ELan LRHS MBri MSte SPer WCot WPen
	betonicoides B&L 12600	EPPr
	bovei subsp. ***maroccana***	SEND WHal XPep
	bracteosa	MGol
	cashmeriana	CBcs CHFP CPLG EBee ECha GAbr LCro LDai MGol MNFA NChi NDov NLar SKHP SMad SPoG WPtf WWlt
	chrysophylla ♀H3	CAbP EBee ECha ELan EPfP LRHS NLar SDix SDry SPer SPoG WCFE WSpi XPep
	crinita	EBee
	cypria	XPep
	'Edward Bowles'	CDul MRav NBid SDry SKHP SLPl SLon SWvt XPep
*	'Elliot's Variety'	CPLG
	fruticosa ♀H4	More than 30 suppliers
	- 'Butterfly'	XPep
	- white-flowered	ECrN
	grandiflora	SEND XPep
	herba-venti	XPep
	italica	More than 30 suppliers
	lanata ♀H3-4	CAbP ELan EPfP LRHS MSte NCGa NPro SDry SKHP SPer SPoG WEas WKif XPep
	- 'Pygmy'	CHVG MGos NPro SLon XPep
	'Le Sud'	XPep
	leucophracta	XPep
	- 'Golden Janissary'	WPGP XPep
	longifolia	EBee EGoo EPfP LHop LRHS LSou MGos NLar SKHP SPer WGer XPep
	- var. ***bailanica***	CSam EBee LRHS WFar WSPU
	lunariifolia	XPep
	lychnitis	MWrn XPep
	lycia	LRHS XPep
	macrophylla	SPhx
	monocephala	XPep
	purpurea	CAbP CPLG CSam EBee ELan EPfP LRHS MAsh MGol NBir WCot WOVN XPep
I	- ***alba***	EBee EPfP LHop SKHP XPep
	- subsp. ***almeriensis***	CMdw CPom XPep
	- subsp. ***caballeroi***	XPep
	rotata	EBee
§	***russeliana*** ♀H4	More than 30 suppliers
	samia Boiss.	see *P. russeliana*
	samia L.	CEnt CPom EBee LDai LHop MGol NChi NDov NGdn NLar SKHP WCot WFar WHal WPtf XPep
	- JMT 285	LRHS
	taurica	NChi WHoo
	tuberosa	More than 30 suppliers
	- 'Amazone'	CFir CKno EBee ECha EHrv EPfP ERou LCro LHop MRav NBid NCGa NEgg NOrc NSti SAga SMad SMrm WCAu WCot WFar WMnd WSpi WTMC
	- 'Bronze Flamingo'	CHFP EBee ECGP EHrv EPfP ERCP ERou EWin LAst MAvo MBri MRav NBHF NDov NOrc SKHP WMnd WPer WSpi
	viscosa misapplied	see *P. russeliana*
	viscosa Poiret	XPep

Phlox ✿ (*Polemoniaceae*)

	adsurgens ♀H4	ITim NCob WAbe
	- 'Alba'	NSla SBla WAbe
	- 'Mary Ellen' **new**	NHar
	- 'Oregon Blush'	NHar
	- 'Red Buttes'	CLyd ECho EPot NHar SBla
	- 'Wagon Wheel'	CWCL EBee ECho EPPr EPot EWes GGar GKev ITim LAst LRHS NSla SIng SMrm SPlb SRms SRot WAbe WCFE WFar
	alyssifolia	CPBP
	amplifolia	EBee NBre WFar
	x ***arendsii*** 'Anja'	CPrp NDov WCot
	- 'Babyface'	CFwr NDov NGdn WHoo

	- 'Early Star'	EBee
	- 'Eyecatcher'	CMMP NBro NCGa NGdn
	- 'Lilac Girl'	NBre
	- 'Lilac Star'	CFir LAst
	- 'Lisbeth'	WCot
	- 'Luc's Lilac'	CMHG CPrp EMar GBin LRHS LTwo NBro NCGa NDov NGdn SMeo SPhx STes WAul WWlt
§	- (Spring Pearl Series) 'Miss Jill'	CMMP CSsd EBee EGle NCob NHol WHoo WTin
§	- - 'Miss Jo-Ellen'	EGle GBri
§	- - 'Miss Karen'	EGle ERou NBro
§	- - 'Miss Margie'	EGle ERou GBri GMaP LAst NBir
§	- - 'Miss Mary'	ECtt EGle ELan GBri GMaP LAst MDKP NCGa NHol NPro STes
§	- - 'Miss Wilma'	ENot GMaP
	- 'Paul' **new**	WCot
	- 'Ping Pong'	CPrp EBee LDai NBPC NBre NBro NPro STes
	- 'Pink Attraction'	CFwr MNrw NBro NCGa
	- 'Purple Star'	CPrp EBee
	- 'Rosa Star'	CFir EBee LAst NBre
	- 'Sabine'	CFir EBee
	- 'Suzanne'	EBee
	austromontana	EPot GKev NWCA WLin
	'Bavaria' **new**	LTwo
	bifida	ECho
	- 'Alba'	ECho LSou LTwo WAbe WFar WLin
	- blue-flowered	ECho LRHS LSou SBla
	- 'Colvin's White'	SBla
	- 'Minima Colvin'	ECho ECtt EPot NLAp
	- 'Petticoat'	CLyd CMea CPBP EPot LRHS MDKP SBla WFar WLin
	- 'Ralph Haywood'	CLyd CMea CPBP EPot GBuc ITim NLAp WAbe WLin
	- 'Starbrite'	CLyd LRHS WFar
	- 'Thefi'	EWes LTwo MNrw
	borealis	see *P. sibirica* subsp. *borealis*
*	- ***arctica***	EAlp EPot
	bryoides	see *P. hoodii* subsp. *muscoides*
	caespitosa	ECho EWes NDlv NWCA
	- subsp. ***condensata***	see *P. condensata*
	canadensis	see *P. divaricata*
	carolina 'Bill Baker' ♀H4	More than 30 suppliers
	- 'Magnificence'	COlW CPrp EBee EGle EMon EWes GBuc GMac LAst LRHS MDKP MSte SMad STes WCot WSHC WTin
	- 'Miss Lingard' ♀H4	More than 30 suppliers
	'Charles Ricardo'	EWes GBuc LCro LSou SMrm WHoo
	'Chattahoochee'	see *P. divaricata* subsp. *laphamii* 'Chattahoochee'
§	***condensata***	ECho WPat
	covillei	see *P. condensata*
	'Daniel's Cushion'	see *P. subulata* 'McDaniel's Cushion'
§	***divaricata*** ♀H4	MSte SBod SHBN SPlb WCot WPer
	- 'Blue Dreams'	CFir ECtt EHrv GBuc LRHS MNrw MSte NCob SPla WFar WHal WPGP WWlt
	- 'Blue Perfume'	CMHG CMMP CPrp EBee ECtt LCro LSou NBro NCGa NLar SHGN
	- 'Clouds of Perfume'	CMMP CWCL EBee ECtt GBri GMaP LAst LCro LRHS LSRN MWgw NCGa NCob NMyG SBla SBod SMer SMrm STes SWat WFar
	- 'Dirigo Ice'	EHrv GBri LHop NLar SBla SIng WFar WRHF WSHC
	- 'Eco Texas Purple'	ECtt NCGa NCob NPro SAga SMrm WFar WPGP WWlt
	- 'Fuller's White'	CWCL ECtt
	- subsp. ***laphamii***	EGle EWes LCro WFar
§	- - 'Chattahoochee' ♀H4	CPrp CSpe CWCL EBee ECho ECtt ELan EPPr EPfP EPot EWes GBuc LCro LHop LRHS MRav NCGa NEgg NLAp SBla SIng SMer SMrm SPoG SRot WAbe WCFE WFar WHoo
	- - 'Chattahoochee Variegated' (v)	LRHS
§	- 'Louisiana Purple'	WSHC
	- 'May Breeze'	EBee ECho EGle EHrv GMaP LAst LCro LHop LRHS MNrw MSte MWgw NCGa NCob SIng SPla WFar WPGP WSHC WWlt
	- 'Plum Perfect'	EBee NBhm NBro SHar WPtf
*	- 'White Perfume'	CMHG CMMP CPrp CWCL EBee EWes GBri LAst LSou MBrN MDKP NBro NCGa NCob NLar NSti SHGN SMrm STes
	douglasii	NPol NWCA SRms
	- 'Apollo'	CTri ECho EPot LRHS LTwo NHar NMen SBla
	- 'Boothman's Variety' ♀H4	ECha ECho EDAr ELan EPfP EPot LRHS MLHP MWat NMen SPoG SRms WLin
	- 'Crackerjack' ♀H4	ECho ECtt EDAr ELan EPfP EPot GAbr GMaP LRHS MHer MLHP NBir NEgg NMen SIng SPoG SRGP WFar WLin
	- 'Eva'	CMMP CPBP ECho EDAr EPot GAbr GKev GMaP LIMB LRHS NBir NMen NPri NWCA SPoG WFar WLin
	- 'Galaxy'	ECho
	- 'Ice Mountain'	ECho ELan EPot GMaP NEgg NWCA SPoG SRot WFar
	- 'Iceberg' ♀H4	ECho EPot NMen WLin
	- 'Lilac Cloud'	EAlp EDAr NPro SHGN SIng
	- Lilac Queen	see *P. douglasii* 'Lilakönigin'
§	- 'Lilakönigin'	ECho WRHF
	- 'Napoleon'	CPBP ECho EPot LTwo NMen
	- 'Ochsenblut'	EAlp ECho EPot GEdr LTwo MHer MLHP NHar SIng
	- 'Red Admiral' ♀H4	EAlp ECho EWes GMaP NMen WCFE WFar
	- 'Rose Cushion'	ECho EDAr EWes MHer NMen
	- 'Rose Queen'	CLyd ECho
	- 'Rosea'	ECho EDAr ELan GMaP NMen NPol WBVN WFar
	- 'Silver Rose'	ECho EPot NWCA
	- 'Sprite'	SRms
	- 'Tycoon'	see *P. subulata* 'Tamaongalei'
	- 'Violet Queen'	ECho EWes WFar
	- 'Waterloo'	ECho EPot LIMB NMen
I	- 'White Admiral'	EPot LRHS LSRN NPro SIng
	'Fancy Feelings'	NBro NCob SPoG
	'Geddington Cross'	MWgw
	glaberrima 'Morris Berd'	EBee WPGP
	hendersonii	CGra
	hoodii	CPBP ECho EPot
§	- subsp. ***muscoides***	ECho
	'Junior Dance'	WWeb
	'Junior Dream'	WWeb
	'Junior Surprise' PBR	WWeb
	'Kelly's Eye' ♀H4	CMMP CPBP ECho EPot LRHS NBir NHar NMen SPoG WBVN WFar WLin
	kelseyi	ECho NWCA WAbe
	- 'Lemhi Purple'	CGra WLin
	- 'Rosette'	CLyd ECho EPot LIMB LRHS MDKP NMen WFar WLin WPer
	Light Pink Flame = 'Bareleven' PBR	ENot SPoG
	Lilac Flame = 'Barten' PBR **new**	ENot
	longifolia subsp. ***brevifolia***	CPBP WAbe
	'Louisiana'	see *P. divaricata* 'Louisiana Purple'

	Name	Suppliers
	maculata	NOrc WPer
	- 'Alpha' ♀H4	CHrt CMHG CMea CSam CWCL EBee ECha ECtt EMar EPfP ERou GCra GGar GMaP LRHS MRav MSte MWgw NBid NCGa NHol NOrc SPer SPla SWvt WAul WCAu WFar
	- 'Delta'	CWCL EBee EPfP ERou GBuc LRHS LSou NBPC NEgg NHol SMad SPer SWvt WBor WCAu WFar
	- 'Natascha'	More than 30 suppliers
	- 'Omega' ♀H4	CMHG CPLG CPrp CWCL EBee ECtt EPfP ERou GBuc GGar GMaP LRHS MRav MSte MWgw NBid NCGa NEgg NGdn NHol NLar SMad SPer SPla SWvt WAul WCAu WFar WSHC WSpi
	- 'Princess Sturdza' ♀H4	SDix
	- 'Reine du Jour'	GMac LSou MDKP MSte NDov SAga SMrm SPhx WHil WSHC
	- 'Rosalinde'	COIW CPrp CWoW EBee ECtt EMar ERou GBuc LRHS MRav MSte NCGa NCob NEgg NHol NLar SPla SPoG SRGP STes SWvt WCAu WFar WHil WSHC
	'Matineus'	SPhx
	'Millstream'	see *P.* x *procumbens* 'Millstream'
	'Millstream Jupiter'	ECho
	'Minnie Pearl' **new**	SKHP
	muscoides	see *P. hoodii* subsp. *muscoides*
	nivalis	CPBP NLAp
	- 'Jill Alexander'	CMea SAga
	- 'Nivea'	EPot LRHS LSou WAbe WLin
	paniculata	EMon GCra NBid NDov SDix SMeo SPhx WCot WOld WTin
	- 'A.E. Amos'	ERou
	- var. ***alba***	NDov SDix WCot WTin
	- 'Alba Grandiflora' ♀H4	EHrv GMaP NCob WEas WHoo
	- 'Albert Leo Schlageter' ♀H4	WHil
	- 'Amethyst' misapplied	see *P. paniculata* 'Lilac Time'
	- 'Amethyst' Foerster	CEnt CFir CFwr CSam EBee EGle EHrv EPfP ERou LCro NBir NBlu NEgg NOrc NPri SMer SWat WCAu WFar WLin
	- 'Antoinette Six'	CFwr
I	- 'Aureovariegata Undulata' (v)	WCot
	- 'Balmoral'	EBee ECtt EPfP GCra LCro LRHS MLHP MRav MSte NCob NSti SMer SWat SWvt WSpi
	- 'Barnwell'	SWat
	- 'Becky Towe'[PBR] (v)	CBow CFwr EBee ECGP EGle EKen LHop LRHS LTwo SPoG WCot
	- 'Betty Symons-Jeune'	CFwr
	- 'Bill Green'	LRHS
	- 'Blue Boy'	CFwr EBee EGle ERou GMaP LAst LRHS MDKP NBir NBro NChi NGby NGdn NLar NRnb STes WBrE WFar WHil WMnd
	- 'Blue Evening'	LSou NCob
	- 'Blue Ice' ♀H4	EBee ELan EMar LRHS NBro NCob NEgg SPhx SPla
	- 'Blue Paradise'	More than 30 suppliers
	- 'Blushing Bride'	SRms
	- 'Border Gem'	CBcs CFwr EBee ECtt ERou MRav MSte MWgw NChi NCob NEgg NHol NLar SDix SMer SPur SWat SWvt WBrk WCot
	- 'Branklyn'	LRHS WFar
	- 'Bressingham White'	LAst
	- 'Brigadier' ♀H4	CSam CTri EBee ECtt ELan GMaP LRHS MDKP NCob NEgg NGdn NVic SPer SPla SRms WCAu WFar

	Name	Suppliers
	- 'Bright Eyes' ♀H4	More than 30 suppliers
	- 'Burgi'	SDix
	- 'Candy Floss' **new**	MAvo MBnl NCob
	- 'Caroline van den Berg'	SRms
	- 'Cecil Hanbury'	ERou NBlu NLar SRms
	- 'Chintz'	MRav SRms
	- 'Cinderella'	CFwr CSBt ERou
§	- 'Cool of the Evening'	EBee SPhx WKif WWlt
	- Count Zeppelin	see *P. paniculata* 'Graf Zeppelin'
	- 'Danielle'	CFwr EBee MWea
	- 'Darwin's Choice'	see *P. paniculata* 'Norah Leigh'
	- 'David'	EBee EBrs ECha ECtt EGle ERou EShb IPot LCro LRHS NBid NBro NChi NCob NGby NGdn NHol NMoo NOrc NRnb SPhx SPoG SRGP STes WBor WCAu WCot WHil WHoo
	- 'Delilah'	NCob
	- 'Discovery'	EBee EHrv EWes IPot MCot NCob SPla STes SWat WCAu
	- 'Dresden China'	SWat
§	- 'Düsterlohe'	CBrm CSam EGle ERou GAbr GBuc GMac IPot LSou NBir NDov NLar NRnb NSti SMrm STes SWat WFar WHil WHoo
	- 'Eclaireur' misapplied	see *P. paniculata* 'Düsterlohe'
	- 'Eclaireur' Lemoine	NCob SWat
	- 'Eden's Crush'	CMMP NBre NRnb NVic
	- 'Eden's Flash'	EBee EGle ERou NRnb
	- 'Eden's Glory'	EGle NCGa NRnb
	- 'Eden's Glow'	NRnb WHil
	- 'Eden's Smile'	EBee ERou NRnb
	- 'Elisabeth' (v)	CFwr EBee LAst NRnb SRGP
	- 'Elizabeth Arden'	ERou MRav MSte NLar SWat
	- 'Empty Feelings'[PBR]	EBee EGle GBin NBro NCob WHil
	- 'Ending Blue'	NRnb
	- 'Etoile de Paris'	see *P. paniculata* 'Toits de Paris' Symons-Jeune
	- 'Europa'	EBee ELan EPfP ERou LRHS MBri MCot NBir NCob NEgg NGdn NHol NLar SPer SPla WCAu WFar
	- 'Eva Cullum'	CFwr EBee ECtt EGle GCra GMaP LRHS MArl MRav NBPC NBid NHol NMoo SMer SPer SPet SRGP SWat WCot WRHF
	- 'Eventide' ♀H4	CFwr CWCL EBee ECtt EPfP LBMP LCro LRHS MArl MCot MRav MWgw NCob SMer SPet SPur SWat WCAu WCot WWlt
	- 'Excelsior'	MRav
	- 'Fairy's Petticoat'	MWat
	- 'Ferris Wheel' **new**	NCob
	- 'Flamingo'	CFwr ERou LRHS MBrN NGby NLar SWvt
	- 'Franz Schubert'	CFwr CHrt CSam EBee EBrs ECtt EGle GCra GMac LCro LRHS MLHP MRav NBir NChi NGdn NLar NSti STes SWat SWvt WCot WKif WTel
§	- 'Frau Alfred von Mauthner'	COIW MBri
	- 'Frosted Elegance' (v)	ECtt LSou
	- 'Fujiyama'	see *P. paniculata* 'Mount Fuji'
	- 'Giltmine' (v) **new**	NCob
	- 'Glamis'	MWat
	- 'Goldmine'[PBR] (v)	CWCL ELan IBal MBnl MCCP NBro NCob SPoG WCot
§	- 'Graf Zeppelin'	CFwr ECtt ELan LBMP LRHS NGby SRms
	- 'Harlequin' (v)	CBcs CFwr CMil EBee ECha ERou GBuc GMaP LAst MBnl MCCP NBPC NBid NBro NCob NEgg NLar NSti SPer SPla SPoG STes WBVN WCAu WCot WFar WLin WTel WWlt
	- 'Hesperis'	CMdw EBee GBin NDov SMeo SMrm SPhx WFar

	- 'Iris'	CDes GBuc SRms
	- 'Jubilee'	CFwr CMMP NRnb
	- 'Judy'	CFwr NBro
	- 'Jules Sandeau'	CFwr LRHS MBri NCob
§	- 'Juliglut'	ERou MWea NCGa SWat WCot
	- July Glow	see *P. paniculata* 'Juliglut'
	- 'Katarina'	CElw ECtt EMar NLar WBor
	- 'Katherine'	CFwr NLar
	- 'Kirchenfürst'	MBri NBir SMrm SPoG
	- 'Kirmesländler'	CFwr EBee ERou LRHS MLLN NCob NLar SWat
	- 'Lady Clare'	SRms
	- 'Landhochzeit'	EBee GBin LRHS NCob
*	- 'Laura'	CMMP EBee ECtt EGle ERou EWTr IPot NBPC NBro NRnb NVic SMrm SPoG SRGP STes WCot WFar WHoo WMnd WRHF WWeb
§	- 'Lavendelwolke'	CSam EBee LCro NBir NCob NLar SWat
	- Lavender Cloud	see *P. paniculata* 'Lavendelwolke'
	- 'Le Mahdi' ♀H4	ELan MBrN MRav MWat SMeo SRms SWat
	- 'Lichtspel'	NDov SAga SMeo SPhx
§	- 'Lilac Time'	CFwr CSBt EBee EHrv EWll LAst MDKP MSte MWat NCob NMoo SMer SRGP SWat SWvt
	- 'Little Boy'	CElw ECtt EGle ERou LRHS LSou MDKP MNrw NLar SPoG STes WFar WHil WWeb
	- 'Little Laura'	CElw CMHG EBee LRHS MAvo MCCP MWea NLar NOrc WBor
	- 'Little Princess'	CFwr EGle ELon ERou NLar SPoG SRGP WMnd
	- 'Lizzy'PBR	ERou MBri MWea NLar
	- 'Look Again'	CFwr
	- 'Manoir d'Hézèques'	WCot
	- 'Mary Christine' (v)	EBee NBid
	- 'Mary Fox'	CSam
	- 'Mia Ruys'	ERou GMac MArl MBri MLHP MLLN SMrm
	- 'Midnight Feelings'	ERou LTwo NBPN NBro NCob NLar WCot
	- 'Mies Copijn'	GMaP WFar
	- 'Milly van Hoboken'	WKif
	- 'Miss Elie'	CMMP EGle ERou NGdn SPoG WFar WHoo
	- 'Miss Holland'	EGle LAst MWea NBPC NCGa NGdn NRnb
	- 'Miss Jessica'	ERou LAst
	- 'Miss Jill'	see *P.* x *arendsii* 'Miss Jill'
	- 'Miss Jo-Ellen'	see *P.* x *arendsii* 'Miss Jo-Ellen'
	- 'Miss Karen'	see *P.* x *arendsii* 'Miss Karen'
	- 'Miss Kelly'	CMMP CMdw EBee LRHS MWea SRGP WHoo
	- 'Miss Margie'	see *P.* x *arendsii* 'Miss Margie'
	- 'Miss Mary'	see *P.* x *arendsii* 'Miss Mary'
	- 'Miss Pepper'	CWCL EBee ERou NLar SMrm SRGP WBor WFar WHil WWlt
	- 'Miss Universe'	CMMP EGle MCCP NRnb SPoG WHil
	- 'Miss Wilma'	see *P.* x *arendsii* 'Miss Wilma'
	- 'Monica Lynden-Bell'	More than 30 suppliers
	- 'Mother of Pearl' ♀H4	EBee ELan EMar LCro LRHS MWat NCob NHol NVic SPer WFar WWlt
§	- 'Mount Fuji' ♀H4	More than 30 suppliers
	- 'Mount Fujiyama'	see *P. paniculata* 'Mount Fuji'
	- 'Mrs A.E. Jeans'	SRms
	- 'Natural Feelings'PBR	CSpe ELan GBin MCCP NBro NCob NLar SPoG WCot WTMC
	- 'Newbird'	SRms WHal
	- 'Nicky'	see *P. paniculata* 'Düsterlohe'
§	- 'Norah Leigh' (v)	More than 30 suppliers
	- 'Orange Perfection'	see *P. paniculata* 'Prince of Orange'
	- 'Othello'	EBee EBrs EKen EMar LRHS NChi NCob NSti WFar WMnd
	- 'Otley Choice'	CFwr EBee LRHS MHer MRav MSte MWat NCob NHol NLar NSti SCoo SPoG SWat
	- 'Otley Purple'	CFwr
	- 'P.D. Williams'	WCot
	- 'Pastorale'	WCot WTel
	- 'Pax'	EMon ERou SMeo SPhx
	- 'Pink Posie' (v)	MBri WFar
	- 'Pinky Hill'	CElw
	- 'Pleasant Feelings'PBR	NBro NCob
	- 'Popeye'	ECtt MBri NLar
§	- 'Prince of Orange' ♀H4	CBcs CFwr CSam EBee ECtt ELan EPfP ERou LRHS LSRN MRav MWat MWgw NBlu NCob NHol NPri NRnb SAga SPer SPoG SWvt WAul WCot WMnd
	- 'Prospero' ♀H4	CHar CSam EBee EHrv LBMP LCro MCot MRav MWgw NBid NEgg SMer SWat WTel
	- 'Rainbow'	CElw EGle
	- 'Red Feelings'PBR	NBro NCob SPoG
	- 'Red Indian'	MWat SMer
	- 'Red Riding Hood'	CFwr CWCL ECtt LAst NBPC WRHF
	- 'Rembrandt'	CFwr CPLG ERou GBri LRHS NBlu WCot
	- 'Rijnstroom'	CBcs CFwr EBee ECha ECot ERou LRHS SMer WFar WHil WSpi WTel
	- 'Robert Poore'	GBin NCob
	- 'Rosa Pastell'	CDes CFwr EGle EHrv ELon EMon GBri LSou NCob SPhx
	- 'Rowie'	NBid NCob WBor
	- 'Rubymine'PBR (v)	ERou NCob
	- 'San Antonio'	WFar
	- 'Sandringham'	CFwr EBee EHrv EPfP LRHS MArl MNrw MRav MSte NBir NHol SMer SPer SPoG SWvt WCAu WWlt
§	- 'Schneerausch'	SPhx
	- 'Septemberglut'	CFwr NLar
	- 'Silvermine' (v)	CBow LSou MCCP NBro SDnm
	- 'Sir Malcolm Campbell'	EBee WHil
	- 'Skylight'	EBee EHrv LRHS LSRN NBre NBro NVic SDix SPer WAul WLin
	- 'Snow White'	NBre NVic
	- Snowdrift	see *P. paniculata* 'Schneerausch'
	- 'Speed Limit 45'	WCot
	- 'Spitfire'	see *P. paniculata* 'Frau Alfred von Mauthner'
	- 'Starburst'	EBee NBro NGdn WCot WHil
	- 'Starfire' ♀H4	More than 30 suppliers
	- 'Steeple Bumpstead'	EBee EGle LSou NCGa NCob SPoG WCot WTMC
	- 'Tenor'	CDes CFir CTri CWCL EBee EPfP ERou LAst LRHS MDKP MSte NCob NGdn NHol NPri NRnb SMer SPla SPoG SWvt WBor WBrE WCAu WCot WFar
	- 'The King'	CElw EBee EGle GBri LRHS MAvo MDKP MSte NBro NGby SWat WBor WHil WSpi
	- 'Toits de Paris' misapplied	see *P. paniculata* 'Cool of the Evening'
§	- 'Toits de Paris' Symons-Jeune	SPhx WSHC
	- 'Uspekh'	CSam EBee EBrs ECGP EMar EPPr EShb EWes MDKP MSte NBro NCGa NCob NGdn NHol NOrc SAga SGar SPer WFar
	- 'Utopia'	CDes CSam NRnb SPhx
	- 'Van Gogh'	CMdw EHrv
	- 'Vintage Wine'	MSte
	- 'Violetta Gloriosa'	LCro SPhx
	- 'Wendy House' **new**	NCob

- 'Wenn Schon Denn Schon'	EBee GBin
- 'White Admiral' ♈H4	More than 30 suppliers
- White Flame = 'Bartwentynine' new	EBee
- 'Wilhelm Kesselring'	CHrt EBee ELon NBre SRGP WBor
- 'Windsor' ♈H4	CFwr EBee ECtt EPfP ERou GBri LRHS MLLN NEgg NHol NLar SCoo SMer SPoG SRms SWvt WCAu WFar WSpi
pilosa	ECha NPro WFar
Pink Flame = 'Bartwelve'PBR	EBee ENot SPoG
§ x ***procumbens*** 'Millstream' ♈H4	GAbr SBla
- 'Variegata' (v)	ECha ECho EPot LRHS MDKP SBla SPlb SRot WFar WLin WPat
Purple Flame = 'Barfourteen'PBR	EBee ENot SPoG
'Sandra'	LRHS
'Scented Pillow'	LRHS
§ ***sibirica*** subsp. ***borealis***	EDAr
'Sileniflora'	EAlp EPot
stolonifera	MNrw
I - 'Alba'	CBcs EBee EWin EWll
- 'Ariane'	CWCL ECha EPPr EWTr LSou MBri SBla WCFE WFar
I - 'Atropurpurea'	CBcs
- 'Blue Ridge' ♈H4	CBcs CFir CPLG CWCL EBee ECha ECtt EPfP EShb GBuc LAst LSRN MBri MRav SMer SRms WFar
- 'Bob's Motley' (v)	ECtt EMan LSou WCot
- compact	EPot
- 'Compact Pink'	WFar
- 'Fran's Purple'	CWsd EBee NBro WCFE WFar WPGP WSPU
- 'Home Fires'	CFwr EBee ECtt EPPr EPfP EWin EWll GAbr LEdu MNrw NBro NLar SAga SMrm SPlb WFar
- 'Mary Belle Frey'	CEnt EBee MSte WFar
- 'Montrose Tricolor' (v)	EPPr LHop NBro
- 'Pink Ridge'	EWll MBri MNrw NBir WRos
- 'Purpurea'	CWCL EBee EPPr EWin EWll LSou
- 'Violet Vere'	GBuc WFar
subulata	CBrm NWCA
- 'Alexander's Surprise'	CMea EAlp ECho EDAr EPfP EPot LBee LRHS NBir SPlb SPoG SRGP
- 'Amazing Grace'	CTri CWCL ECho EDAr EPfP EWes LHop LIMB LRHS MHer NLar SIng SPoG
- 'Apple Blossom'	EDAr NEgg NPro SPet SPoG SRms WFar
- 'Atropurpurea'	EDAr LIMB LRHS NBlu
- Beauty of Ronsdorf	see *P. subulata* 'Ronsdorfer Schöne'
- 'Betty'	ECtt
- 'Blue Eyes'	see *P. subulata* 'Oakington Blue Eyes'
- 'Bonita'	CPBP EAlp ECho EPot EWin LBee LRHS WBor WBrE
- 'Bressingham Blue Eyes'	see *P. subulata* 'Oakington Blue Eyes'
- 'Brightness'	ECho LRHS
- 'Brilliant'	ECho
- subsp. ***brittonii*** 'Rosea'	GEdr WFar
- 'Candy Stripe'	see *P. subulata* 'Tamaongalei'
- 'Christine Bishop'	LRHS
- 'Coral Eye'	EPfP
- 'Daisy Hill'	CPBP
- 'Drumm'	see *P. subulata* 'Tamaongalei'
- 'Emerald Cushion'	CSam CTri CWCL ECho ECtt EDAr GKev MDKP MHer WBVN WRHF
- 'Emerald Cushion Blue'	CBrm CPLG ECho EPfP LIMB NBir NMen NPri NPro SBla SGar SPlb WFar WLin WPer
- 'Fairy'	WPer
- 'Fort Hill'	NHar
- 'G.F. Wilson'	see *P. subulata* 'Lilacina'
* - 'Holly'	EPot NMen
- 'Jupiter'	ECho
- 'Kimono'	see *P. subulata* 'Tamaongalei'
§ - 'Lilacina'	CMea ECha ECho LRHS NLar SPoG SRGP
§ - 'Maischnee'	CMea CTri ECho ECtt EPfP GAbr LRHS MHer MWat NHol SIng SPlb WFar
- 'Marjorie'	CLyd ECho ECtt LBee MHer NBir NPri NWCA SMer SPoG WFar WRHF
- May Snow	see *P. subulata* 'Maischnee'
§ - 'McDaniel's Cushion' ♈H4	CPLG ECha ECho EDAr ELan EPfP EPot GAbr GKev ITim LAst LBee LHop LRHS MLHP NHar NMen NWCA SPlb SPoG WCFE WFar WTel
- 'Mikado'	see *P. subulata* 'Tamaongalei'
- 'Moonlight'	ECtt EDAr
- 'Nettleton Variation' (v)	EAlp ECho EDAr EPPr EPfP EPot EWes GKev LHop LRHS MDKP MHer SIng SPlb SPoG SRot WBrE
§ - 'Oakington Blue Eyes'	LRHS SRms
- 'Pink Pearl'	EWes
- 'Purple Beauty'	CWCL EPot GGar LIMB NHar SBla WFar WLin WSHC
- 'Red Wings' ♈H4	ECho ECtt EPfP LRHS NMen SPoG SRms
§ - 'Ronsdorfer Schöne'	EAlp EPot LBee LRHS NBir
- 'Samson'	LRHS SMer
- 'Scarlet Flame'	CMea CSam ECho EDAr ELan EPfP EPot MHer NEgg NHol NPri SRGP WFar
- 'Sensation'	SBla
- 'Snow Queen'	see *P. subulata* 'Maischnee'
§ - 'Tamaongalei'	CMea CPBP CTri EAlp ECho EDAr EPfP EPot EWes GGar GKev GMaP LRHS MHer MMuc NEgg NHol SBla SCoo SIng SPet SPoG SRGP SRms STes WBor WCFE WFar
- 'Temiskaming'	CTri ECGP ECho EDAr EWes GEdr LBee LRHS MLHP NMen SBla SPoG SRms WSHC
- 'Tschernobyl'	EPot
- violet seedling	CLyd
- 'White Delight'	EAlp ECho ECtt EDAr ELan LAst LBee NMen SPoG WBor WFar
'Sweet William'	LRHS SRGP
'Tiny Bugles'	CStu SBla

Phoebe (*Lauraceae*)

sheareri	WPGP

Phoenicaulis (*Brassicaceae*)

§ ***cheiranthoides***	LTwo

Phoenix (*Arecaceae*)

canariensis ♈H1+3	More than 30 suppliers
dactylifera (F)	EAmu ETod LPal MPRe
reclinata	CKob EAmu ETod LPJP NPal SAin
roebelenii ♈H1+3	CBrP CDoC ETod LCro LPal MBri NPal SAin
- 'Multistem' new	XBlo
rupicola	LPal
sylvestris	EAmu LPal SAin
theophrasti	CPHo EAmu LEdu LPJP LPal

Phormium ✿ (*Phormiaceae*)

'Alison Blackman'PBR	CBcs CBct CDoC CPen CSBt CTrC CWil EBee ENot IBal IBlr IClo ISea LHop LSRN MGos MPRe NScw SCoo SPoG

'Amazing Red'	CWil IBal IBlr
'Apricot Queen' (v)	CAbb CBcs CCCN CDoC CSBt CTrC CWil EBee EPfP GQui IBal IBlr LCro LRHS MBri MCCP MGos MWat NMoo NPal NPri SHBN SLim SPer SPoG SRkn WBod WFar WGwG WPat
Ballyrogan variegated (v)	IBlr
* 'Black Edge'	CWil IBlr MRav NPri
'Bronze Baby'	More than 30 suppliers
'Buckland Ruby'	CBct CDoC CWil MAsh
'Carousel'	IBal
colensoi	see *P. cookianum*
§ ***cookianum***	CTrC CWil ECre EPfP GGar IBlr MGos SAPC SArc SCoo SEND WFar WHil
- 'Alpinum Purpureum'	see *P. tenax* 'Nanum Purpureum'
- dwarf	IBlr SLPl
- 'Flamingo'	CBcs CCCN CDTJ CSBt CTrC CWil EBee ECre ELan EPfP IBal LRHS LSou MAsh MGos MJnS NBlu NScw SHBN SLim SPer SPoG SRkn WCot WPat
- 'Golden Wonder'	IBlr
- subsp. ***hookeri*** 'Cream Delight' (v) ♀H3-4	More than 30 suppliers
- - 'Tricolor' (v) ♀H3-4	More than 30 suppliers
* 'Copper Beauty'	NMoo WDyG
'Crimson Devil'	CBcs IBal NScw WFar
'Dark Delight'	CBcs EPPr IBlr
'Dazzler' (v)	IBlr LAst MGos SHBN WCot
§ 'Duet' (v) ♀H3	CCCN CDoC CSBt CWil EBee EPfP IBal IBlr LRHS MGos MPRe NLar SPla SWvt WFar
'Dusky Chief'	CSBt CWil IBal LRHS WPat
'Emerald Isle'	CDoC CWil
'Evening Glow' (v)	CBcs CCCN CPen CTrC EBee ELan EPfP ETod IBal IBlr LRHS MBri MGos MPRe MWgw NBlu SPla SPoG SRkn SWvt WCot WFar WGer WLeb WPat
'Firebird'	CBcs IBlr LSRN SAga SLon SWvt
'Fortescue's Bronze'	CWil
'Glowing Embers'	CBrm CTrC IBal WLeb
'Gold Ray'	CTrC EMil IBal IBlr MPRe NLar
'Gold Sword' (v)	CBcs CCCN CDoC CMHG CSBt CTrC CWil EBee IBal IBlr LRHS MAsh MBri MGos
'Green Sword'	CCCN
'Guardsman' (v)	IBlr
'Jack Spratt' (v)	CPen CWil ECou ELan IBal IBlr LRHS MSwo SAga SPoG SWvt WLeb WPrP
'Jester' (v)	More than 30 suppliers
'Limelight'	CWil SWvt
'Mahogany'	CWil
§ 'Maori Chief'	CSBt CWil EBee ELan EPfP IBal IBlr LRHS NMoo SHBN SWvt WFar WLeb WPat
'Maori Eclipse'	CPen CWil
'Maori Elegance'	CWil
§ 'Maori Maiden' (v)	CBcs CBrm CCCN CChe CDoC CDul CSBt CTrC CTri EBee ECre EPfP IBal LAst LRHS MBri MGos MRav SWvt WFar
§ 'Maori Queen' (v)	CBcs CCCN CChe CDTJ CDoC CPrp CSBt CTrC CWil ELan EPfP IBal IBlr LCro LRHS MAsh MBri MGos MSwo NBlu NMoo SCoo SPer SRkn SWvt WCot WFar WPGP
§ 'Maori Sunrise' (v)	More than 30 suppliers
'Margaret Jones'	CBcs CBct CCCN CWil EBee IBal SLim
'Merlot'	CWil
'Pink Jester' **new**	EMil
'Pink Panther' (v)	More than 30 suppliers
'Pink Stripe' (v)	CBcs CDoC CSBt CWil EBee ECrN ENot EQua IBal IBlr LRHS MBri NPal SHBN SPoG SWvt WCot WGer
'Platt's Black'	More than 30 suppliers
'Rainbow Chief'	see *P.* 'Maori Chief'
'Rainbow Maiden'	see *P.* 'Maori Maiden'
'Rainbow Queen'	see *P.* 'Maori Queen'
'Rainbow Sunrise'	see *P.* 'Maori Sunrise'
'Red Sensation'	CPen EPfP LRHS MAsh
I 'Rubrum'	CWil IBal NBlu
'Sea Jade'	CWil IBlr
'Stormy Dawn'	WCot
'Sundowner' (v) ♀H3	More than 30 suppliers
'Sunset' (v)	CBcs CCCN CChe CSBt IBlr IFoB SWvt
'Surfer' (v)	CBcs CTrC CWil IBlr LHop MCCP WBod WLeb
'Surfer Boy'	CSBt CWil LAst
'Surfer Bronze'	CCCN CPen CSBt CWil EBee ETod IBal LSou MGos WGer
'Surfer Green'	CCCN CDoC IBal MGos WHer
tenax ♀H4	More than 30 suppliers
- 'Atropurpureum'	CHEx IBal LAst
- 'Bronze'	CHEx CWil SWal SWvt
- 'Co-ordination'	CCCN CWil EPfP GBin IBal IBlr ISea LRHS
- 'Deep Purple'	CHEx
- 'Duet'	see *P.* 'Duet'
* - dwarf	IBlr SLPl
I - 'Giganteum'	CHEx
* - ***lineatum***	SEND
§ - 'Nanum Purpureum'	IBlr MSte SEND
- Purpureum Group ♀H3-4	More than 30 suppliers
- 'Radiance' (v)	CWil IBlr
- 'Rainbow Queen'	see *P.* 'Maori Queen'
- 'Rainbow Sunrise'	see *P.* 'Maori Sunrise'
- 'Variegatum' (v) ♀H3-4	CDTJ CSBt EBee EPfP ETod IBal IBlr LPal LRHS MGos NBlu NMoo SAPC SArc SEND SPer SRms WBrE WFar WHoo
- 'Veitchianum' (v)	CWil IBlr LRHS SPer
'Thumbelina'	CBcs CCCN CTri ERas IBal IClo IFoB MSte NBPN WPat
'Tom Thumb'	CWil GGar WDyG WPrP
'Wings of Gold'	ETod IBal
'Yellow Wave' (v) ♀H3	More than 30 suppliers

Photinia ✿ (*Rosaceae*)

arbutifolia	see *Heteromeles salicifolia*
beauverdiana	CSam CTho SRms WFar
- var. ***notabilis***	EPfP MBri NLar
§ 'Branpara'PBR	EBee
davidiana	CDul CSam CTri EBee ELan EPfP ISea MBar MRav NLar SPer SRms WBod WFar WNor
- 'Palette' (v)	More than 30 suppliers
- var. ***undulata***	CMHG
- - 'Fructu Luteo'	CAbP CMHG CSam CTrG EPfP EPla NLar SPoG WFar
- - 'Prostrata'	CMac CTri ELan EPfP EQua MBar MRav NLar WFar
x ***fraseri***	CMCN
- 'Birmingham'	CMac EBee EWes MAsh SRGP SRms WWeb
- 'Canivily'	EMil EWes MAsh MGos MWgw NLar SPoG
- 'Red Robin' ♀H4	More than 30 suppliers
- 'Red Select'	EQua WPat WWeb
- 'Robusta'	CMac EBee EPfP LRHS MAsh SWvt
I - 'Robusta Compacta'	MWea WFar
glabra	SArc
- B&SWJ 8903	WCru

§	– 'Parfait' (v)	CAbP ELan MAsh SDry SHBN SPer SPla SPoG WFar
	– 'Pink Lady'	see *P. glabra* 'Parfait'
	– 'Rubens'	ELan EPfP LRHS MAsh MRav SDry SPer SPla SSta WPat
	– 'Variegata'	see *P. glabra* 'Parfait'
	glomerata misapplied	see *P. prionophylla*
	lasiogyna	CMCN
	microphylla HWJ 564	WCru
	parvifolia	EPfP
§	***prionophylla***	CHEx
	'Redstart'	CAbP CBrm CMac CSam EBee EPfP LRHS MGos NEgg NPro SLon SPer SSta SWvt WMoo
§	***serratifolia***	CBcs CDul CHEx EBee EPfP LRHS MBri NLar SAPC SArc SDry SPer SPoG SSpi SSta WFar WPGP XPep
	serrulata	see *P. serratifolia*
	– Curly Fantasy = 'Kolcurl' **new**	EMil
	'Super Hedge'PBR	see *P.* 'Branpara'
	villosa ♀H4	CAbP CGHE CTho MBar NPal
	– B&SWJ 8877	WCru
	– var. ***laevis***	CPLG EPfP
	– f. ***maximowicziana***	EPfP

Phragmites (*Poaceae*)

	from Sichuan, China	EPPr
§	***australis***	CBen CDWL CRWN EMFW GFor NMir SWat WFar WMAq WPnP XIsg XPep
	– subsp. ***australis*** var. ***striatopictus***	EMon EPPr
	– – 'Variegatus' (v)	CBen CBrm CDWL CKno CNat CPLG CWCL CWat EBee ECGP EMFW EMon EPPr EPla EShb EWsh LLWG LRHS MMoz NBir NOak SHBN SLPl SMad WFar WHil WMoo
	– subsp. ***pseudodonax***	EMon EPPr XIsg
	communis	see *P. australis*
	karka	EPPr
	– 'Candy Stripe' (v)	CBen CDWL EPPr
	– 'Variegatus' (v)	LRav NLar

Phrynium (*Marantaceae*)

	pubinerve	CKob

Phuopsis (*Rubiaceae*)

§	***stylosa***	CHrt CSev CTri EBee ECha ELan EPfP EWsh GAbr GMaP IFoB LRHS MHer MLHP NBid NBro NChi SHFr SMer SPet SPoG SRms WBor WCAu WFar WMoo WPer
	– 'Purpurea'	CElw EBee MNrw MRav NChi

Phygelius ✿ (*Scrophulariaceae*)

	aequalis	CFee MNrw MRav SPla WMoo WPer
	– ***albus***	see *P. aequalis* 'Yellow Trumpet'
	– 'Aureus'	see *P. aequalis* 'Yellow Trumpet'
	– Cedric Morris form	SHom
	– 'Cream Trumpet'	see *P. aequalis* 'Yellow Trumpet'
	– 'Indian Chief'	see *P.* x *rectus* 'African Queen'
*	– 'Pink Trumpet'	CDoC CHEx EAro SCoo SMrm SPet
§	– 'Sani Pass'	CBcs CDoC CPom EBee ECtt ELon EPfP GBri LAst LRHS LSRN MBri MDun MRav NCGa NPri SCoo SLim SPer SPoG SRms SWvt WSpi
	– Sensation	see *P. aequalis* 'Sani Pass'
	– 'Trewidden Pink' ♀H4	CChe CWib EBee ELan EPfP ERou LAst LHop MAsh MHer NCiC NGdn SHFr SHom SLim SWal SWvt WBVN WFar WHoo WMnd WMoo WPGP
§	– 'Yellow Trumpet' ♀H3-4	More than 30 suppliers
§	***capensis*** ♀H3-4	CDul CPLG CWib ELan ENot EPfP GCra LCro MHer NLar SBch SGar SHom SPet SRms WFar WMnd WMoo WPer
	– CD&R	EWes WHil
	– ***coccineus***	see *P. capensis*
	– orange-flowered	LHop SHom
	Cherry Ripe = 'Blacher' **new**	ERou SBla
	'Golden Gate'	see *P. aequalis* 'Yellow Trumpet'
	Logan form	MCCP
	'Madame Aerts' **new**	WSHC
	New Sensation = 'Blaphy'PBR	EMil ERou MAsh SBla SPer SWvt
§	x ***rectus*** 'African Queen' ♀H3-4	More than 30 suppliers
	– 'Aylesham's Pride'	SHom
	– 'Devil's Tears' ♀H4	CBcs CDoC CFee EBee ECrN ELan EMil EPfP ERou GKev LAst MBNS MDun MNHC NEgg NHol SHom SLim SRot SWvt WBod WHoo WMnd WMoo WPGP WPer
	– 'Ivory Twist'PBR	LBuc LRHS SHom SPer
	– 'Jodie Southon'	LSou SHom
*	– 'Logan's Pink'	LSRN
	– 'Moonraker'	More than 30 suppliers
	– 'Pink Elf'	ELan SHom
	– 'Raspberry Swirl'PBR	EPfP LBuc MAsh SHom
	– 'Salmon Leap' ♀H4	CBcs CDoC CTri EBee ELan ENot EPfP ERou LAst LBMP LSRN MAsh MBNS NEgg SHFr SHom SLim SPlb SRot SWal SWvt WFar WHoo WMnd WMoo WPer WWeb
	– Somerford Funfair Apricot = 'Yapapr'	MAsh SWvt
	– Somerford Funfair Coral = 'Yapcor'	CDoC EBee LBMP LHop LRHS LSou MAsh MBri MJnS NLar SIng SLim SPav SPoG SRkn SWvt WGor
	– Somerford Funfair Cream = 'Yapcre'	EBee EPfP LBMP LHop LRHS LSou MAsh MBri NLar SGar SIng SLim SPav SRkn SWvt
	– Somerford Funfair Orange = 'Yapor'	EBee LBMP LHop LRHS MAsh MBri NLar SIng SLim SPav SPoG SWvt
	– Somerford Funfair Wine = 'Yapwin'	CBcs EBee ELan EShb LHop LSou MAsh MBri NLar SGar SIng SLim SPav SPoG SRkn SWvt
	– Somerford Funfair Yellow = 'Yapyel'	EBee LRHS MAsh SLim SPoG SWvt
	– 'Sunshine'	EBee ELan EMan EWes LAst LHop MAsh MDKP NCiC SHom SPoG SWal
	– 'Sweet Dreams'PBR	LBuc LRHS SHom
§	– 'Winchester Fanfare'	CSBt EBee ECtt ELan EMil ENot EPfP ERou GMaP LAst LBMP MRav MWat NCGa NChi NGdn NHol NVic SHom SLim SPer SPla SWvt WFar WGwG WMoo WPer WTin WWeb
	– 'Winton Fanfare'	see *P.* x *rectus* 'Winchester Fanfare'

Phyla (*Verbenaceae*)

	lanceolata **new**	LLWG
§	***nodiflora***	CStu ECha EEls EWin NWCA SBch SBla SEND SIng WPer XPep
§	– var. ***canescens***	WHal

Phylica (*Rhamnaceae*)

	arborea 'Superba'	CBcs CPLG IDee
	ericoides	CPLG

Phyllanthus (*Euphorbiaceae*)

	glaucus **new**	MBri

x *Phylliopsis* (*Ericaceae*)

'Coppelia' ♀H4	CWsd EPot GCrs GEdr GGGa GKev ITim LTwo WPat
hillieri 'Askival'	GCrs GGGa LSou WAbe
- 'Pinocchio'	GCrs ITim LRHS MDun NLar WAbe WPat
'Hobgoblin'	WAbe WPat
'Mermaid'	GGGa ITim WAbe WThu
'Puck'	WAbe
'Sprite'	GCrs WPat
'Sugar Plum'	CCCN CWSG EBee IDee ITim MDun NLAp NLar SSta SWvt WAbe WPat
'Swanhilde'	WAbe

Phyllitis see *Asplenium*

scolopendrium	see *Asplenium scolopendrium*

Phyllocladus (*Phyllocladaceae*)

aspleniifolius new	IDee
trichomanoides	CDoC CDul CTrC ECou LCon LLin
var. ***alpinus***	NLar

Phyllodoce (*Ericaceae*)

aleutica	ECho GCrs NDlv NMen SRms
aleutica* x *caerulea	GCrs
caerulea ♀H4	ECho NDlv
- ***japonica***	see *P. nipponica*
* - var. ***japonica***	WThu
- 'Viking'	GCrs
empetriformis	ECho GCrs MBar SRms
§ ***nipponica*** ♀H4	GCrs NMen WAbe
- var. ***oblongo-ovata***	GCrs NMen
tsugifolia	GCrs

Phyllostachys ✿ (*Poaceae*)

angusta	EPla MWht SDry
arcana	ENBC EPla SDry
- 'Luteosulcata'	CGHE EPla LPal MMoz MWht NLar NPal SDry WNor WPGP
§ ***atrovaginata***	EPla ERod SDry
aurea ♀H4	More than 30 suppliers
- 'Albovariegata' (v)	EBee EFul ENBC EPla MPRe SDry
- 'Flavescens Inversa'	EPla ERod MWht SDry
- 'Holochrysa'	CBrP CDul EFul EPla ERod MWht SDry WPGP
- 'Koi'	CGHE EFul EPla ERod LPal MMoz MWht NMoo NPal SDry WPGP
aureocaulis	see *P. aureosulcata* f. *aureocaulis*, *P. vivax* f. *aureocaulis*
aureosulcata	CWib EFul EMui EPfP EPla ERod LEdu LRHS MAsh MMoz MWht NMoo SBLw SDry WBVN WMoo
- f. ***alata***	see *P. aureosulcata* f. *pekinensis*
- 'Argus'	EPla
§ - f. ***aureocaulis*** ♀H4	More than 30 suppliers
- 'Harbin'	EPla ERod SDry
- 'Harbin Inversa'	EPla ERod
- 'Lama Temple'	EPla WPGP
§ - f. ***pekinensis***	EPla MMoz NLar SDry WPGP
- f. ***spectabilis*** ♀H4	More than 30 suppliers
bambusoides	CBcs EPla MLan SDix SDry
- 'Allgold'	see *P. bambusoides* 'Holochrysa'
- 'Castilloni Inversa'	CGHE EAmu EPla ERod ETod EWes LEdu LPal MMoz MWht SDry WPGP
- 'Castillonii'	CAbb CBcs EAmu EFul ENBC EPla ERod EWes LEdu LPal MMoz MWht NBea NMoo NPal SBLw SDix SDry SEND WOrn WPGP
§ - 'Holochrysa'	CDoC EPla ERod MGos MMoz MWht NMoo NPal SDry SEND WPGP
- Holochrysa	see *P. bambusoides* 'Holochrysa'
- 'Katashibo'	EPla
- 'Kawadana'	EPla ERod SDry
- f. ***lacrima-deae***	CAgr CDTJ CTrC EPfP EPla ETod
- 'Marliacea'	EPla ERod LPJP
- 'Subvariegata'	EPla SDry WPGP
- 'Sulphurea'	see *P. bambusoides* 'Holochrysa'
- 'Tanakae'	ENBC MMoz NLar NMoo SDry WPGP
- 'Violascens'	EPla NMoo
bissetii	More than 30 suppliers
circumpilis	EPla
congesta misapplied	see *P. atrovaginata*
decora	EAmu ENBC EPla ERod MMoz MWht NLar NMoo NPal SDry SEND WPGP
dulcis	CAgr CEnt EPfP EPla ERod LEdu LPJP MWht WDyG WPGP
§ ***edulis***	CDTJ CTrC EFul EPla ERod LRav MGol MMoz MWht SDry WPGP
- 'Bicolor'	SDry
§ - 'Heterocycla'	SDry XBlo
- f. ***pubescens***	see *P. edulis*
flexuosa	CEnt EFul EPfP EPla IMGH MWht SDry SEND WPGP
glauca	CDTJ EPla ERod ETod LCro MMoz MWht NLar NMoo NPal WDyG
- f. ***yunzhu***	EPla ERod MWht SDry
heteroclada	CDTJ NMoo SDry
- 'Solid Stem' misapplied	see *P. purpurata* 'Straight Stem'
heterocycla	see *P. edulis* 'Heterocycla'
- f. ***pubescens***	see *P. edulis*
humilis	CBcs CDul EBee ENBC EPla ERod MCCP MGos MMoz MWht NLar NMoo NPal SDry SEND
iridescens	EPla NLar SDry
lithophila	EPla
lofushanensis	EPla
makinoi	ERod
mannii	EPla MWht SDry
meyeri	EPla SDry
nidularia	EPla ERod MMoz SDry
- f. ***farcta***	EPla
§ - f. ***glabrovagina***	EPla
- smooth-sheathed	see *P. nidularia* f. *glabrovagina*
nigella	EPla
nigra ♀H4	More than 30 suppliers
- 'Boryana'	CAbb CBig CBrm CDoC CEnt CGHE EAmu EBee EFul ENBC EPfP EPla MAsh MGos MLan MMoz MWht NMoo SArc SDry SWvt WFar WMoo WPGP XIsg
- 'Fulva'	EPla
- 'Hale'	EPla
- f. ***henonis*** ♀H4	CAbb CBcs EAmu EFul EMil ENBC EPla ERod LPal MJnS MLan MMoz MWht NBea NLar NMoo SDry WDyG WPGP
* - 'Lactae Deae'	NScw
- 'Megurochiku'	EPla ERod SDry
- f. ***nigra***	EPla MLan SPer
- f. ***punctata***	CBrm CDoC EBee ENBC EPfP EPla ERod MAvo MLan MWht NGdn SDry SEND WDyG WMoo WPGP
- 'Tosaensis'	EPla
- 'Wisley'	EPla
nuda	ENBC EPla ERod MMoz MWht NLar NPal SDry
- f. ***localis***	EPla MWht SDry
parvifolia	EPla ERod MWht WPGP
platyglossa	EPla ERod WPGP
praecox	EPla ETod NMoo
- f. ***notata*** new	EPla
- f. ***viridisulcata***	EAmu EPla
propinqua	CAgr CBig CDoC CDul ENBC EPla ERod LEdu MMoz MWht NMoo
- 'Li Yu Gan'	EPla

§	***purpurata*** 'Straight Stem'	EPla MWht SDry
	rubicunda	EPla
	rubromarginata	EPla ERod MWht NLar SDry WPGP
	'Shanghai 3' **new**	EAmu ETod
	stimulosa	EPla ERod LPan MWht
	sulphurea	NMoo
	- 'Houzeau'	EPla ERod SDry
	- 'Robert Young'	EPla SDry
§	- f. ***viridis***	EPla ERod LPal MAsh MWht NMoo SDry
	violascens	CBcs EFul EPla ERod LPal MMoz MWht SDry WPGP
	virella	EPla
	viridiglaucescens	CAbb CBcs CDTJ CHEx EFul EPfP EPla ETod LPan MBrN MMoz MWht NLar SArc SDry SEND SPla
	viridis	see *P. sulphurea* f. *viridis*
	vivax	EFul EPfP EPla ERod GQui LEdu MJnS MMoz MPRe MWht NLar SDry WNor
§	- f. ***aureocaulis*** Υ^{H4}	More than 30 suppliers
	- - 'Huanwenzii'	CDTJ CGHE CTrC EAmu EFul EMui ENBC EPla ERod ETod MGos MMoz MWht NMoo NScw
	- 'Katrin'	LEdu
*	- 'Sulphurea' **new**	XBlo

x *Phyllothamnus* (*Ericaceae*)

	erectus	GCrs WAbe WPat

Phymatosorus (*Polypodiaceae*)

§	***diversifolius***	CGHE MPes SKHP WPGP

Phymosia (*Malvaceae*)

§	***umbellata***	CPLG CRHN ERea SOWG

Phyodina see *Callisia*

Physalis (*Solanaceae*)

	alkekengi Υ^{H4}	CTri EBee EPfP MLan MNHC NBir NLar SWvt WFar
	- var. ***franchetii***	More than 30 suppliers
	- - dwarf	NLar NRnb SPoG
	- - 'Gigantea'	CWCL ECGP GBuc NGBl NLar NRnb SPlb WHil
	- - 'Gnome'	EBee MBri NEgg
	- - 'Variegata' (v)	ECtt EMan EPla EWes MAvo NPro WOld
	angulata	EUnu
	- B&SWJ 7016	WCru
	campanula B&SWJ 10409 **new**	WCru
	edulis	see *P. peruviana*
§	***peruviana*** (F)	CCCN EUnu LRav SHDw

Physocarpus (*Rosaceae*)

	malvaceus	EWes
	monogynus	NLar
	opulifolius	CDul MSal
	- 'Dart's Gold' Υ^{H4}	More than 30 suppliers
	- 'Diablo d'Or' **new**	EMil
	- 'Diabolo'^{PBR} Υ^{H4}	More than 30 suppliers
§	- 'Luteus'	CDoC CMHG CSam CWib EPfP IMGH ISea MBar MDun MRav NEgg SPer SRms WBod WFar WMoo WPat
	- 'Tilden Park'	EBee
	ribesifolius 'Aureus'	see *P. opulifolius* 'Luteus'

Physochlaina (*Solanaceae*)

	orientalis	CAby CPom MSal NLar WAul

Physoplexis (*Campanulaceae*)

§	***comosa*** Υ^{H2-3}	ECho EWes ITim LRHS NMen NSla SBla WHoo

Physostegia (*Lamiaceae*)

	angustifolia	CSam NBre
§	***virginiana***	CSBt CTri GMaP LAst MBNS SGar SWat WBrk WFar WRHF
	- 'Alba'	CEnt COIW CSBt CTri EHrv EPfP EShb GBri GMaP LEdu LRHS MSte NLar NOrc NRnb SPet SPlb WEas WHrl
§	- 'Crown of Snow'	CDWL CFir CMMP EBee ECtt ERou MBNS MHer MRav MWat STes SWal SWvt WFar WHil WPer
	- 'Grandiflora'	CFir
	- 'Miss Manners'	EBee ECtt MSte MWgw SPer SRGP WHil
	- 'Olympic Gold' (v)	EBee EMan ENot MDKP MRav WRHF
	- pale pink-flowered	SWat
	- 'Red Beauty'	CFir EBee ERou LRHS MDKP SPla
	- 'Rose Queen'	COIW CTri MFOX MWat NBre WTin
	- 'Rosea'	CBcs CBrm EBee ERou IFoB MDKP NBPC NBre NPri NRnb SPad SWal SWvt WFar WHrl WPer
	- Schneekrone	see *P. virginiana* 'Crown of Snow'
	- 'Snow Queen'	see *P. virginiana* 'Summer Snow'
	- var. ***speciosa***	WFar
§	- - 'Bouquet Rose'	CDWL CPrp EBee ECha EHrv ENot EPfP LEdu LRHS MHer MNFA MRav MSte NBir NHol SMac SPer SWvt WAul WCAu WFar WGwG WMoo WRos WTel WWeb
	- - Rose Bouquet	see *P. virginiana* var. *speciosa* 'Bouquet Rose'
	- - 'Variegata' (v)	More than 30 suppliers
§	- 'Summer Snow' Υ^{H4}	CBcs CPrp EBee ECha ELan ENot EPfP IBal LHop LRHS MBri MNFA NCGa NHol SMer SPla SRms SWat WBrk WCAu WCot WFar WMnd
	- 'Summer Spire'	EBee EHrv ELan EMan LSou MSte NHol SMer WFar
	- 'Vivid' Υ^{H4}	More than 30 suppliers
	- 'Wassenhove'	EMon

Phyteuma (*Campanulaceae*)

	comosum	see *Physoplexis comosa*
	hemisphaericum	ECho
	humile	EDAr
	nigrum	ECho LRHS MNrw NBid NChi WCot WLin WPGP
	scheuchzeri	CEnt EBee ECho EPfP EWTr GEdr MHer NChi NEgg NOrc NPri NWCA SBch SBla SGar SMad SPhx SRms SRot WHoo
	sieberi	CPBP NBir
	spicatum	NBro

Phytolacca (*Phytolaccaceae*)

	acinosa	CPLG EWld GPoy MGol MSal NLar SWat WHil
	- HWJ 647	WCru
§	***americana***	CArn CHEx COld CPom CSev EBee ECha ELan ELau EMar EPfP GPoy MBNS MHer MSal NEgg NLar SIde SMad SRms SWat WAbb WCru WFar WJek WMnd WMoo WSHC
	- 'Silberstein' (v)	CBct EBee LDai MBNS MGol NEgg NLar WCot
	- 'Variegata'	WHil
	clavigera	see *P. polyandra*
	decandra	see *P. americana*
	dioica	CHEx CPLG LEdu
	esculenta	LEdu LHop
	icosandra B&SWJ 8988	WCru
	japonica B&SWJ 4897	WCru

	octandra	CPLG
	- B&SWJ 9514	WCru
§	***polyandra***	CPLG ECha NBid NBro NLar SRms WBor
	rivinoides B&SWJ 10264 **new**	WCru

Picea ✿ (*Pinaceae*)

§	***abies***	CCVT CChe CDul CLnd CSBt CTri CWib EHul EMac ENot EPfP LAst LBuc LRHS MBar MBri MGos NBlu NWea SCoo SLim SPer SPoG WBVN WEve WMou
	- 'Acrocona'	ECho EHul EOrn LCon LLin MAsh MBar MBlu MBri MGos NLar SCoo WEve
	- 'Archer'	CKen
	- 'Argenteospica' (v)	ECho NHol
	- 'Aurea'	ECho EOrn IMGH LLin WEve
	- 'Capitata'	CKen MAsh MBar NLar
	- 'Ceejay's Gem'	CDHC SCoo
	- 'Clanbrassiliana'	CDoC CKen ECho IMGH LCon MAsh MBar MGos NLar SCoo WEve WFar
	- Compacta Group	ECho LBee LRHS NEgg
I	- 'Congesta'	CKen
	- 'Crippsii'	CKen
I	- 'Cruenta'	CKen
	- 'Cupressina'	CKen
	- 'Diffusa'	CKen LCon MBar SCoo
	- 'Dumpy'	CKen LCon NLar
	- 'Elegans'	MBar
	- 'Ellwangeriana'	NLar
	- 'Excelsa'	see *P. abies*
	- 'Fahndrich'	CKen CMen
	- 'Finedonensis'	LCon MGos NHol NLar WEve
	- 'Formanek'	CDoC CKen CMen ECho LCon LLin NLar
	- 'Four Winds'	CAbP CKen NLar
	- 'Frohburg'	CDoC CKen ECho MBar MGos
	- 'Globosa'	ECho MBar
	- 'Globosa Nana'	ECho LAst MGos
	- 'Goblin'	NLar
	- 'Goldstart'	MGos
	- 'Gregoryana'	CKen CMac ECho IMGH MBar NDlv WAbe
	- 'Hasin'	NLar
	- 'Heartland Gem'	CKen
	- 'Himfa'	NLar
	- 'Horace Wilson'	CKen
	- 'Humilis'	CKen
	- 'Hystrix'	CRob LCon NLar
	- 'Inversa'	CKen EBrs ECho EHul EOrn LCon LLin MBar MBlu MBri MGos SLim WEve
	- 'J.W. Daisy's White'	see *P. glauca* 'J.W. Daisy's White'
	- 'Jana'	CKen
	- 'Kral'	CKen
	- 'Little Gem' ♀H4	CDoC CFee CKen CMac CMen ECho EHul EOrn GBin GEdr IMGH LBee LCon LLin LRHS MAsh MBar SCoo SLim SPer SPoG WEve WFar
	- 'Maxwellii'	EHul MBar
	- 'Mikulasovice'	NLar
	- 'Nana'	MBar NEgg
	- 'Nana Compacta'	CKen CRob EHul IMGH LAst LBee MBar WFar
	- 'Nidiformis' ♀H4	CDoC CKen CMac CRob CSBt CTri ECho EHul EOrn LAst LCon LLin MBar NBlu NHol NWea SCoo SLim SPer SPoG SRms WEve WFar
	- 'Norrkoping'	CKen
	- 'Ohlendorffii'	CKen ECho EHul LCon MBar MGos NLar SCoo
	- 'Pachyphylla'	CKen
	- 'Pendula Major'	SHBN
	- 'Procumbens'	MBar
	- 'Pumila'	EOrn
	- 'Pumila Nigra'	ECho EHul LCon LLin MBar MGos SLim SPoG
	- 'Pusch'	CKen CMen EBrs NLar
	- 'Pygmaea'	CKen ECho MBar MGos NLar
	- 'Reflexa'	ECho EHul GBin IMGH LCon NHol WEve
	- 'Repens'	ECho MBar MBlu
	- 'Rydal'	CBcs CDoC CDul CKen LCon MAsh MGos NLar WEve
	- 'Saint James'	CKen
	- 'Starý Smolivec' **new**	NLar
	- 'Tabuliformis'	MBar
	- 'Tufty'	EOrn
	- 'Vermont Gold'	CKen NLar SLim
	- 'Waldbrunn'	CKen ECho LCon LLin MAsh SPoG WEve
	- 'Waugh'	MBar
	- Will's Dwarf	see *P. abies* 'Wills Zwerg'
§	- 'Wills Zwerg'	MAsh SCoo
I	***alcoquiana*** 'Prostrata'	LCon MBar
	- var. ***reflexa***	MPkF
	breweriana ♀H4	More than 30 suppliers
	- 'Emerald Midget' **new**	NLar
	- 'Kohout's Dwarf' **new**	CKen
	engelmannii	CDul NWea
	- 'Compact'	EBrs
	- subsp. ***engelmannii***	CKen
	- 'Jasper' **new**	NLar
	glauca	CDul CTri NWea WEve
	- Alberta Blue = 'Haal'PBR	CDoC CKen CRob ECho EOrn LCon LLin LRHS MAsh SLim WEve WFar
	- var. ***albertiana*** 'Alberta Globe'	CDoC CRob CSBt ECho EHul EOrn IMGH LBee LCon LLin MAsh MBar MBri MGos NDlv NEgg NHol SAga SCoo SLim SPoG WEve WFar
	- - 'Conica'	More than 30 suppliers
	- - 'Gnome'	CKen WEve
	- - 'Laurin'	CDoC CKen CRob ECho EOrn LBee LCon LLin MAsh MBar MGos WEve
	- - 'Tiny'	CKen EOrn LCon LLin MBar WGor
	- 'Arneson's Blue Variegated' (v)	CDoC CKen LLin MAsh MBri SLim WEve WFar WGor
	- 'Blue Planet'	CKen LCon MGos NLar
	- 'Blue Wonder'	MBri
	- 'Coerulea'	CDul ECho LCon MBar
I	- 'Coerulea Nana'	ECho NLar
	- 'Cy's Wonder'	CKen
	- 'Echiniformis' ♀H4	CKen ECho LBee LRHS MBar MBri
	- 'Goldilocks'	CKen
§	- 'J.W. Daisy's White'	CBcs CKen CRob EBrs ECho EOrn LCon LLin LRHS MAsh MGos NLar SCoo SLim SPer SPoG WEve WFar WGor
I	- 'Julian Potts Monstrosa' **new**	NLar
	- 'Lilliput'	CKen ECho EHul EOrn LCon MBar MGos NLar WEve
§	- 'Nana'	CKen
	- 'Piccolo'	CBcs CKen ECho LRHS MAsh NHol SLim
	- 'Pixie'	CKen
	- 'Rainbow's End' (v)	CKen ECho MGos SLim WFar
	- 'Sander's Blue'	CKen CRob ECho EOrn LBee MBri SLim SPoG WEve WFar
	- 'Zuckerhut'	MBar MBri
	glehnii	LCon
	- 'Sasanosei'	CKen
	- 'Shimezusei'	CKen
	jezoensis	CKen CMen MGos NWea
	- 'Chinese Marl' **new**	NLar

– subsp. ***hondoensis***	CMen WNor
– 'Yatsabusa'	CKen CMen
koraiensis	CDul NWea
kosteri 'Glauca'	see *P. pungens* 'Koster'
likiangensis	CDul CMCN EPfP ISea LCon
– var. ***balfouriana***	see *P. likiangensis* var. *rubescens*
– var. ***purpurea***	see *P. purpurea*
§ – var. ***rubescens***	CDoC LCon NHol WOrn
mariana	LCon NWea
– 'Aureovariegata' (v)	ECho LCon WFar
– 'Austria Broom'	CKen
– 'Doumetii'	EOrn
– 'Fastigiata'	CKen EOrn
– 'Nana' ♀H4	CDoC CKen CMac CMen CRob ECho EHul EPfP GEdr IMGH LCon LLin LRHS MAsh MBar MNrw MWat NBlu NDlv NHol NWea SAga SCoo SEND SLim SPoG WBrE WEve WFar
I – 'Pygmaea'	CKen
x ***mariorika***	MBar
– 'Gnom'	MGos
– 'Machala'	ECho
morrisonicola new	CKen
obovata	LCon
– var. ***coerulea***	NLar NWea
omorika ♀H4	CBcs CDul CMCN EMac LBuc LCon LRav MBar MGos NWea SPer SPoG WCFE WEve WFar WMou WRHF
I – 'Aurea'	ECho
– 'Frohnleiten'	CKen
– 'Frondenberg'	CKen ECho
– 'Karel'	CKen NLar
– 'Minimax'	CKen ECho
– 'Nana' ♀H4	ECho EHul LBee LCon MAsh MBar MGos SCoo SLim WEve WFar
– 'Pendula' ♀H4	CDoC ECho LCon LRHS MBar MBlu NLar NPal SLim SPoG SSta
– 'Peve Tijn'	NLar
– 'Pimoko'	CKen LCon LLin MAsh MGos NLar SCoo
– 'Pygmy'	CKen
– 'Schneverdingen'	CKen
– 'Tijn'	CKen LCon SLim
– 'Treblitsch'	CKen NLar
orientalis ♀H4	CDul LCon LRav NWea WMou
– 'Aurea' (v) ♀H4	CMac ECho EHul ELan LCon LLin LPan MBar MBri MGos MLan NPri SCoo SHBN SLim
– 'Aureospicata'	CDoC CTho ECho MAsh MBlu SCoo WEve
– 'Bergman's Gem'	CKen
– 'Golden Start'	NLar
– 'Gowdy'	MBar NLar
– 'Jewel'	CKen NLar
– 'Kenwith'	CKen ECho
– 'Mount Vernon'	CKen
– Nana Group new	SCoo
– Pendula Group	MGos
– 'Professor Langner'	CKen LCon SLim
– 'Skylands'	CDoC CKen ECho ELan LCon LLin MAsh MBri MGos NHol NLar SLim SPoG WEve
– 'Tom Thumb'	CKen LCon NLar SLim
– 'Wittboldt'	MAsh
pungens	MBar WNor
– 'Baby Blueeyes'	ECho MPkF WFar
– 'Blaukissen'	CKen
– 'Blue Mountain'	ECho MPkF NScw
– 'Drayer'	ECho MPkF
– 'Edith'	EBrs MPkF SLim WFar
– 'Endtz'	EBrs ECho MPkF
– 'Erich Frahm'	CTri ECho LCon LRHS MAsh MBar MBri MGos MPkF MWya SLim WFar

– 'Fat Albert'	CDul CWib ECho LLin MGos NLar SLim WFar
– 'Frieda'	NLar SLim
– Glauca Group	CDul CLnd EMac EWTr GWCH LBee LCon MBar NWea SCoo SPoG WBVN WEve WFar WMou WOrn
– – 'Glauca Procumbens'	CMen NLar
§ – – 'Glauca Prostrata'	ECho EHul MBar WEve
– 'Glauca Globosa'	see *P. pungens* 'Globosa'
– 'Globe'	CKen CMen
I – 'Globosa' ♀H4	CBcs CDoC CKen CRob ECho EHul EOrn LBee LCon LLin MAsh MBar MBri MGos NPri SCoo SHBN SLim SPer SPoG SRms WEve WFar
I – 'Globosa Viridis'	ECho
– 'Gloria'	CKen
– 'Hoopsii' ♀H4	CDul CMac CRob CSBt ECho EHul EPfP LAst LCon LRHS MAsh MBar MGos MWya NBlu NWea SHBN SLim SWvt WEve WFar
– 'Hoto'	EHul EOrn LCon MBar MGos
– 'Hunnewelliana'	EOrn
– 'Iseli Fastigiate'	CRob ECho LCon LLin MAsh MBri MGos SCoo SLim WEve
– 'Iseli Foxtail' new	NLar
§ – 'Koster' ♀H4	CDoC CMac CRob CSBt ECho EHul EPfP LCon LLin MBar MGos NScw NWea SLim SPoG SRms WEve WFar
– 'Lucky Strike'	CDoC CKen ECho LCon LLin MGos NLar
– 'Maigold' (v)	CKen EBrs ECho LCon MAsh NLar SLim
– 'Moerheimii'	ECho EHul LCon MBar NLar WEve
– 'Montgomery'	CKen ECho LCon LLin MBar NLar WEve
– 'Mrs Cesarini'	CKen
– 'Nimety'	CKen NLar
– 'Oldenburg'	MBar NLar NWea
– 'Procumbens'	CKen LCon
– 'Prostrata'	see *P. pungens* 'Glauca Prostrata'
– 'Prostrate Blue Mist'	WEve
– 'Rovelli's Monument'	NLar
– 'Saint Mary's Broom'	CKen NLar
– 'Schovenhorst'	ECho EHul WFar
– 'Snowkiss'	ECho MPkF WFar
– 'Spek'	ECho MPkF
– 'Thomsen'	ECho EHul LCon MAsh NScw
– 'Thuem'	ECho EHul LLin MGos NDlv NLar WEve WFar
– 'Wendy'	CKen
§ ***purpurea***	LCon WEve
retroflexa	NWea
rubens	LCon NLar NWea WEve
schrenkiana	CMCN LCon
sitchensis	CDul LCon LRav NWea WMou
– 'Nana'	CDoC ECho LLin
– 'Papoose'	see *P. sitchensis* 'Tenas'
– 'Silberzwerg'	CKen ECho NLar SLim
– 'Strypemonde'	CKen
§ – 'Tenas'	CDoC CKen CRob EBrs ECho EOrn LCon MAsh NLar SLim
smithiana	CDul CTho EPfP ISea LCon NLar NWea
I – 'Aurea'	MGos
– 'Sunray'	LCon SIFN
wilsonii	CKen LCon NLar

Picrasma (*Simaroubaceae*)

ailanthoides	see *P. quassioides*
§ ***quassioides***	EPfP MBri WPGP

Picris (*Asteraceae*)

echioides	CArn WHer

Picrorhiza (*Scrophulariaceae*)

	kurrooa	GPoy

Pieris ✿ (*Ericaceae*)

	'Bert Chandler'	LRHS SSpi WSpi
	'Brouwer's Beauty'	SLim
	'Firecrest' ♀H4	CMHG CTrG SSpi
	'Flaming Silver' (v) ♀H4	More than 30 suppliers
	floribunda	MBar
	'Forest Flame' ♀H4	More than 30 suppliers
	formosa B&SWJ 2257	WCru
	- var. ***forrestii***	CDoC CWib ISea NWea
	- - 'Fota Pink'	WHar
	- - 'Jermyns'	MRav SHBN
	- - 'Wakehurst' ♀H3	CAbP CDul CSBt CTrG CTri CWSG EPfP LHyd LRHS MAsh MGos MRav NPen NWea SPer SPoG SSpi WBod WFar WSpi
	Havila = 'Mouwsvila' (v)	MAsh MGos NHol NLar WFar
	japonica	CBcs MAsh MBar MGos SArc SReu
	- 'Astrid' **new**	EMil
	- 'Bisbee Dwarf'	MBar NHol
	- 'Blush' ♀H4	LRHS MAsh MBri MGos NHol SHBN
	- 'Bonfire'	CEnd EBee ELan EMil ENot EQua LBuc LRHS MBri MGos NLar SPoG WCwm WHlf
	- 'Brookside Miniature'	NHol
	- 'Carnaval' (v)	CDoC CEnd CSBt CWib EBee ELan EMil ENot LBuc LRHS LSRN MAsh MGos NLar NPri SCoo SPer SPoG SWvt WFar
	- 'Cavatine' ♀H4	CMHG LRHS
§	- 'Christmas Cheer'	EQua MAsh NLar WFar WMoo
	- 'Cupido'	CDoC EMil MAsh MBar MBri MGos NHol NLar SPoG WBod WFar
	- 'Debutante' ♀H4	CBcs CWSG CWib EBee ELan EPfP LRHS MAsh MBri MDun MGos NHol NLar SCoo SPoG SSpi SWvt WFar
	- 'Don'	see *P. japonica* 'Pygmaea'
	- 'Dorothy Wyckoff'	CBcs CMHG CSBt CTrG CWSG LRHS MAsh MDun NDlv NHol SHBN SSta
	- 'Flaming Star'	ECot SWvt WBrE
	- 'Flamingo'	LRHS MAsh MBar MGos NDlv NHol
	- 'Grayswood' ♀H4	EPfP LRHS NHol WFar
I	- 'Katsura'	CBcs CDoC CMac EBee ELan EMil ENot EPfP LAst LBuc LRHS MAsh MBlu MBri MGos NLar SCoo SPer SPoG SRkn SSpi SSta WBod WGer
	- 'Little Heath' (v) ♀H4	More than 30 suppliers
	- 'Little Heath Green' ♀H4	CChe CDoC CSBt CTrG LHyd MAsh MBar MGos MMuc NDlv NEgg NHol SPer SPoG SSta SWvt WFar WMoo
	- 'Minor'	GKev MBar NHol WThu
	- 'Mountain Fire' ♀H4	More than 30 suppliers
	- 'Pink Delight' ♀H4	CAbP CDoC LRHS LSRN MAsh MBar MRav NEgg SHBN SPoG SRms WGwG
	- 'Prelude' ♀H4	CSBt CTrG CWSG EMil LRHS MAsh MBri MRav NHol NLar NMen NPen SPoG WAbe WBod WFar
	- 'Purity' ♀H4	CBcs CDoC CMHG CWSG EPfP LRHS MAsh MBar MGos NHol SMer SPer SPoG SReu SSta SWvt WBod WFar
§	- 'Pygmaea'	NHol SPoG SSta
	- 'Red Mill'	CEnd CSBt CWSG EPfP LRHS MAsh NEgg SPer SSpi WFar
	- 'Rosalinda'	MAsh NLar WFar
	- 'Rosea'	LHyd
	- 'Sarabande' ♀H4	LRHS MAsh MBar MBri NLar SPoG SSta WCwm
	- 'Scarlett O'Hara'	CSBt MGos NLar
	- 'Select'	MGos
	- 'Silver Mills'	MGos
	- 'Snowdrift'	LRHS
	- 'Spring Snow'	LRHS
	- Taiwanensis Group	CMHG EPfP GGar LRHS MAsh MBar MDun NLar NWea SRms SSta WFar
	- 'Temple Bells'	CSBt MGos SMer
	- 'Valley Rose'	CGHE CSBt ELan EPfP MAsh MGos NLar SPoG SSpi WFar WSpi
	- 'Valley Valentine' ♀H4	CBcs CDoC CDul CEnd CSBt CTrh CWSG CWib ENot EPfP LCro LRHS LSRN MAsh MBri MGos NDlv SCoo SLim SPer SPoG SReu SSta SWvt WBod WFar
	- 'Variegata' misapplied	see *P. japonica* 'White Rim'
	- 'Variegata' (Carrière) Bean (v)	CMHG EPfP LHyd MAsh MBar MGos NHol SHBN SPer SPoG SReu SSta WFar WHar
	- 'Wada's Pink'	see *P. japonica* 'Christmas Cheer'
	- 'White Pearl'	CAbP MAsh MGos
§	- 'White Rim' (v) ♀H4	CDul EPfP MAsh NEgg SPlb WFar
	- 'William Buchanan'	GCrs MBar NHol
	- var. ***yakushimensis***	NLar
	koidzumiana	CWsd SSta
	nana	MBar

Pilea (*Urticaceae*)

*	'Anette'	MBri
	cadierei ♀H1	CHal MBri
	depressa	CHal
	involucrata 'Norfolk' ♀H1	CHal
§	***microphylla***	CHal EBak EShb
	muscosa	see *P. microphylla*
	nummulariifolia	CHal
	peperomioides ♀H1	CHal CSev EPem
	repens	MBri

Pileostegia (*Hydrangeaceae*)

	viburnoides ♀H4	More than 30 suppliers
	- B&SWJ 3565	WCru

Pilosella (*Asteraceae*)

§	***aurantiaca***	CArn CHrt CMCo CRWN CSsd ELan MHer MWgw NBid NBlu NOrc NPri NSti SECG SIde WCAu WFar WHer WMoo WSFF
§	- subsp. ***carpathicola***	GGar
§	***officinarum***	NBlu NRya

Pilularia (*Marsileaceae*)

	globulifera	CBgR EFer

Pimelea (*Thymelaeaceae*)

	coarctata	see *P. prostrata*
	drupacea	ECou
	ferruginea	ECou
	- 'Magenta Mist'	SOWG
	filiformis	ECou
	ligustrina	GGar
§	***prostrata***	CBcs CTri ECho ECou EPot LRHS MBar SRot WPer
	- f. ***parvifolia***	ECou
	- Tennyson's form	SBla
	tomentosa	ECou

Pimpinella (*Apiaceae*)

	anisum	CArn MSal SIde WSel
	bicknellii	SPhx WCot WPGP

major 'Rosea'	CAby CDes CElw CMea CPLG CSpe EBee EDAr GQue LDai LHop LSou MAvo MLLN MNFA NCGa NChi NCob NDov NGdn SMrm SPhx WBor WCot WEas WFar WHal WPGP WTMC
niitakayamensis B&SWJ 6942	WCru
saxifraga	NBre NDov

pineapple see *Ananas comosus*

Pinellia (*Araceae*)

cordata	CHHB CPom EBee EMan LEdu MDKP MSte NMen SBla WCot WCru
- variegated	EBee
pedatisecta	CPom EBee GEdr LEdu LFur LPio MDKP WCot WPnP
pinnatisecta	see *P. tripartita*
ternata	CStu EBee EBrs GEdr LEdu MSal NMen WCot WWst
- B&SWJ 3532	WCru
§ ***tripartita***	CFee CPLG CPom CStu EBee ECho LFur MDKP MGol WAbe WBVN WCot WCru WPnP WPrP
- B&SWJ 1102	WCru
- 'Purple Face'	WCru

Pinguicula (*Lentibulariaceae*)

acuminata	SHmp
crassifolia	CHew
crassifolia* x *emarginata	SHmp
cyclosecta	CHew SHmp
ehlersiae	EFEx
esseriana	EFEx
grandiflora	CSWC EFEx GCra GCrs GEdr LRHS MCCP MGol NMen NRya NWCA WAbe WGwG
hemiepiphytica	CHew
heterophylla	CHew SHmp
jaumavensis	CHew
lauana	CHew SHmp
leptoceras	CFir
longifolia subsp. ***longifolia***	EFEx
macrophylla	CHew SHmp
macrophylla* x *zecheri	SHmp
moctezumae	SHmp
moranensis var. ***caudata***	EFEx
- ***moreana***	EFEx
- ***superba***	EFEx
* ***pilosa***	SHmp
primuliflora	CSWC
rotundiflora	CHew SHmp
vulgaris	EFEx
'Weser'	CSWC

pinkcurrant see *Ribes rubrum* (P)

Pinus ✿ (*Pinaceae*)

albicaulis	WNor
- 'Flinck'	CKen
- 'Nana'	see *P. albicaulis* 'Noble's Dwarf'
- 'No. 3' **new**	CKen
§ - 'Noble's Dwarf'	CKen
aristata	CAgr CDul CLnd EHul EOrn LCon LLin MAsh MBar MBlu MBri MGos SCoo STre WEve
- 'Cecilia'	CKen
- 'Kohout's Mini'	CKen
- 'Sherwood Compact'	CKen LCon NLar
- 'So Tight'	CKen
armandii	CAgr CDoC CDul CTrC GKev LCon
- 'Gold Tip'	CKen
attenuata	LCon
austriaca	see *P. nigra* subsp. *nigra*
N ***ayacahuite***	LCon
- F&M 100A	WPGP
balfouriana 'Dwarf Form'	CKen
banksiana	CDul CLnd LCon SCoo
- 'Arctis'	NLar
- 'Chippewa'	CKen ECho LLin
I - 'Compacta'	CKen
- 'H.J. Welch'	CKen
- 'Manomet'	CKen
- 'Neponset'	CKen
- 'Schneverdingen'	CKen NLar
- 'Schoodic'	ECho LLin NLar SLim
- 'Uncle Fogy'	ECho MGos NLar WEve
- 'Wisconsin'	CKen
bungeana	CDoC CDul CLnd CMCN CTho EPfP LCon LLin MBlu SLPl WEve WNor
- 'Diamant'	CKen
canariensis	EHul GGar IDee LCon
cembra	CAgr CDul CLnd EHul LCon MBar NLar STre WEve
- 'Aurea'	see *P. cembra* 'Aureovariegata'
§ - 'Aureovariegata' (v)	EBrs ECho LLin LRHS SCoo WEve
- 'Barnhourie'	CKen
- 'Blue Mound'	CKen
- 'Chalet'	CKen
- 'Compacta Glauca'	CDoC ECho MBri
- Glauca Group	SCoo
- 'Inverleith'	CKen
- 'Jermyns'	CKen
- 'King's Dwarf'	CKen
- 'Ortler'	CKen
- 'Roughills'	CKen
- 'Stricta'	CKen ECho
- witches' broom	CKen
cembroides	LCon
contorta	CBcs CDoC CDul LCon MBar MGos NWea WMou
- 'Asher'	CKen ECho SCoo
I - 'Compacta' **new**	SCoo
- 'Frisian Gold'	CKen LLin SLim
- var. ***latifolia***	CDul CLnd LCon LRav
- 'Spaan's Dwarf'	CKen ECho LCon LLin MBar MGos NLar SCoo SLim SPoG WEve
coulteri ♀H4	CDul CMCN CTho ECho EPfP LCon LLin SCoo SKHP WNor WThu
densiflora	CDul CMCN LEdu WNor
- SF 99088	ISea
- 'Alice Verkade'	CDoC CMen CRob ECho EHul LBee LCon LLin LRHS MAsh MBri SCoo SLim WEve WFar
- 'Aurea'	MBar MGos NLar SLim
- 'Golden Ghost' **new**	NLar
- 'Jane Kluis'	CKen ECho EHul LBee LCon LLin LRHS MBri NLar SCoo SLim WEve WFar
- 'Jim Cross'	CKen
- 'Low Glow'	CKen ECho LCon NLar NScw SLim
- 'Oculus-draconis' (v)	ECho LCon LLin MBar MGos NLar SLim WEve WFar
- 'Pendula'	CKen ECho EOrn LLin MBri NEgg SCoo SLim WEve WFar
- 'Pygmy'	LCon
* - 'Pyramidalis'	ECho
- 'Umbraculifera'	CDoC CMen ECho IMGH LCon LLin MAsh MBar MGos NLar SCoo SSta WEve WFar
I - 'Umbraculifera Nana'	ECho LLin
§ ***devoniana***	CBrP CDoC LCon LLin LRHS SLim
edulis	CAgr STre
- 'Juno'	CKen

engelmanii 'Glauca'	EBrs WFar
flexilis	CDul LCon NWea
- 'Firmament'	ECho LCon LLin SLim
- 'Glenmore Dwarf'	CKen
- 'Nana'	CKen
- 'Pendula'	LLin
- 'Tarryall' **new**	CKen
- 'Vanderwolf's Pyramid'	CRob MAsh NLar
- WB No 1	CKen
- WB No 2	CKen
greggii	CTho EPfP IDee
griffithii	see *P. wallichiana*
§ ***hartwegii***	CDul SKHP
§ ***heldreichii*** ♀H4	CDoC CDul ECho LCon LPan LRav MBar MGos SCoo WFar WNor
- 'Aureospicata'	LCon LLin MBar NLar WEve
- 'Compact Gem'	CDoC CKen EBrs ECho LBee LCon LLin LRHS MBar MBri MGos NLar SCoo SLim SSta WEve
- 'Dolce Dorme'	CKen NLar
- 'Groen'	CKen
- 'Kalous'	NLar
- var. ***leucodermis***	see *P. heldreichii*
- - 'Irish Bell' **new**	NLar
- - 'Pirin 7' **new**	NLar
- 'Malink'	CKen ECho SLim
- 'Ottocek'	CKen
- 'Pygmy'	CKen ECho
- 'Satellit'	CDoC CTri ECho EHul EMil EOrn LCon LLin LRHS MAsh MGos NLar SCoo SLim SPoG WEve
- 'Schmidtii'	see *P. heldreichii* 'Smidtii'
§ - 'Smidtii' ♀H4	CDoC CKen CRob ECho LCon LLin MAsh MBar MGos NLar SLim
- 'Zwerg Schneverdingen'	CKen NLar
jeffreyi ♀H4	CAgr CLnd CTho ISea LCon LRav MBar NWea WEve
- 'Joppi'	CKen CRob LCon SLim
koraiensis	SCoo SLim WNor
- 'Bergman'	CKen
- 'Dragon Eye'	CKen
- 'Jack Corbit'	CKen
- 'Shibamichi' (v)	CKen
- 'Silver Lining'	MAsh
- 'Silveray'	MAsh NLar SLim
- 'Silvergrey'	CKen
- 'Winton'	CKen NLar SLim
leucodermis	see *P. heldreichii*
magnifica	see *P. devoniana*
massoniana	WNor
monophylla	ECho LLin
montezumae misapplied	see *P. hartwegii*
montezumae ambig.	SAPC SArc WNor
monticola	CDul
- 'Pendula'	CKen MBar
- 'Pygmy'	see *P. monticola* 'Raraflora'
§ - 'Raraflora'	CKen
- 'Skyline'	MBar NLar WEve
- 'Strobicola'	LCon
- 'Windsor Dwarf'	CKen
mugo	CArn CBcs CChe CDul CSBt CTri EHul MBar MGos NWea WBor WBrE WEve WFar
- 'Allgau'	CKen
- 'Benjamin'	CKen ECho NLar SCoo
- 'Bisley Green'	ECho LLin WEve
- 'Brownie'	CKen
- 'Carsten'	CKen ECho LLin MGos SCoo SLim WEve
- 'Carsten's Wintergold'	LCon MAsh MBri NLar SCoo SPoG WEve
- 'Chameleon'	NLar
- 'Corley's Mat'	CKen ECho LLin NHol NLar SCoo SLim WEve

- 'Dachstein 3' **new**	NLar
- 'Devon Gem'	ECho SPoG
- 'Dezember Gold'	NLar SLim
- 'Flanders Belle'	ECho SCoo SLim
- 'Gnom'	CDul ECho EHul EOrn IMGH LCon LLin LRHS MBar MBri MGos SCoo WEve WFar
- 'Golden Glow'	CKen ECho LLin MBri NLar SCoo SLim
- 'Hesse'	ECho SCoo
- 'Hoersholm'	CKen ECho
- 'Humpy'	CKen CMen CRob ECho EOrn IMGH LBee LCon LLin LRHS MAsh MBar MBri MGos SCoo SLim WEve WFar
- 'Ironsides' **new**	CKen
- 'Jacobsen'	CKen NLar
- 'Janovsky'	CKen ECho SCoo
- 'Kamila' **new**	NLar
- 'Kissen'	CKen ECho LCon LLin MGos NLar WEve
- 'Klosterkotter'	ECho MGos NLar SCoo
- 'Kobold'	ECho NHol WFar
- 'Krauskopf'	CKen
- 'Laarheide'	CRob ECho SCoo WEve
- 'Laurin'	CKen ECho
- 'Little Lady' **new**	NLar
- 'Marand'	ECho LLin
- 'March'	CKen ECho EHul LLin
- 'Mini Mops'	CKen ECho NLar
- 'Minikin'	CKen MAsh
- 'Mops' ♀H4	CDoC CDul CMen CRob ECho EHul EPfP LBee LCon LLin LRHS MAsh MBar MBlu MGos NHol NPri SCoo SLim SPer SPoG SSta WEve WFar
- 'Mops Midget'	CRob ECho LBee LCon LLin MAsh WEve
- var. ***mughus***	see *P. mugo* subsp. *mugo*
§ - subsp. ***mugo***	EMac EOrn LBuc LPan MBar NBlu NWea WEve WFar
- 'Mumpitz'	CKen
- 'Ophir'	CBcs CDoC CDul CKen CMen CRob ECho EHul EOrn EPfP IMGH LAst LBee LCon LLin LRHS MBar MBri MGos SCoo SLim SPer SPla SSta WEve WFar
- 'Pal Maleter' (v)	CRob ECho LCon LLin MAsh NLar SCoo SLim SPoG WEve
- 'Paradekissen'	NLar
- 'Paul's Dwarf'	CKen NLar
- 'Picobello'	NLar SLim
- 'Piggelmee'	CKen ECho
- Pumilio Group ♀H4	CDoC CLnd ECho EHul EOrn GBin LCon LLin MBar MGos NBlu NHol NWea SCoo SHBN STre WBVN WFar WMoo WNor
- 'Pygmy'	ECho
- var. ***rostrata***	see *P. mugo* subsp. *uncinata*
- 'Rushmore'	CKen
- 'Schilderhaus' **new**	NLar
- 'Spaan'	CKen WEve
- 'Sunshine' (v)	CKen NLar
- 'Suzi'	CKen
- 'Tuffet'	ECho LLin MGos NLar
§ - subsp. ***uncinata***	LCon NWea SCoo SLim WFar
- - 'Grüne Welle'	CKen ECho NLar SLim
- - 'Paradekissen'	CKen NLar
- 'Varella'	CKen NLar SCoo SLim
- 'White Tip'	CKen ECho
- 'Winter Gold'	CKen EBrs ECho EHul EOrn EPfP LAst LCon LLin LPan MAsh MGos NLar SPoG SSta WEve WFar
- 'Winter Sun'	CRob ECho MAsh
- 'Winzig'	CKen

	- 'Zundert'	CKen ECho EHul LLin MBar MGos NLar WEve
	- 'Zwergkugel'	CKen
	muricata ♀H4	CDoC CDul CLnd LCon LRav MGos NWea
	nigra ♀H4	CBcs CDul CLnd CSBt CTri ECrN LCon MBar MGos SAPC SArc SCoo SHBN WBrE WEve WMou
	- var. ***austriaca***	see *P. nigra* subsp. *nigra*
	- 'Bambino'	CKen
	- 'Black Prince'	CKen EBrs ECho EOrn IMGH LBee LCon LLin LRHS MAsh MGos NLar SCoo SLim SPoG WEve WFar WGor
	- var. ***calabrica***	see *P. nigra* subsp. *laricio*
	- var. ***caramanica***	see *P. nigra* subsp. *pallasiana*
N	- 'Cebennensis Nana'	CKen
	- var. ***corsicana***	see *P. nigra* subsp. *laricio*
	- 'Frank'	CKen ECho NLar
	- 'Globosa'	ECho
	- 'Green Tower' **new**	NLar
	- 'Hornibrookiana'	CKen ECho GBin LLin NLar SCoo
	- 'Komet'	NLar SCoo
§	- subsp. ***laricio*** ♀H4	CDoC CDul CKen CSBt ECrN EMac GWCH LAst LBuc LCon LRav MBar MGos NWea SBLw WMou
	- - 'Bobby McGregor'	CKen ECho LLin
	- - 'Globosa Viridis'	ECho IMGH LLin NHol SLim WEve
	- - 'Goldfingers'	CKen ECho LLin NLar SLim WEve
	- - 'Moseri'	CKen ECho EOrn LLin SLim SSta
	- - 'Pygmaea'	CKen ECho EOrn WEve WFar
	- - 'Spingarn'	CKen ECho
	- - 'Talland Bay'	CKen ECho
	- - 'Wurstle'	CKen
	- subsp. ***maritima***	see *P. nigra* subsp. *laricio*
	- 'Nana'	LBee MBri
§	- subsp. ***nigra***	CCVT CDoC CLnd CTho LBuc LPan MGos NLar NWea WEve WFar
	- - 'Birte'	CKen
	- - 'Bright Eyes'	ECho EOrn IMGH LBee LCon LLin LRHS MAsh SCoo SLim SPoG WEve
	- - 'Helga'	CKen NLar SCoo
	- - 'Schovenhorst'	CKen ECho
	- - 'Skyborn' **new**	CKen
	- - 'Strypemonde'	CKen
	- - 'Yaffle Hill'	CKen ECho
	- 'Obelisk'	CKen NLar SCoo
§	- subsp. ***pallasiana***	CDul LCon NLar
	- 'Richard'	CKen NLar
	- 'Rondello' **new**	NLar
	- 'Spielberg'	NLar
	- 'Uelzen'	CKen
	oocarpa **new**	CDul
	palustris	CDoC CDul CLnd CTho LCon LLin LRHS MAsh SKHP SLim
	parviflora	CDul CTri STre WNor WThu
	- 'Adcock's Dwarf' ♀H4	CDoC CKen ECho LCon LLin MBar MGos NLar SCoo SLim SPoG
	- 'Aito-goyo'	CKen
	- Aizu-goyo Group	ECho LLin
	- 'Al Fordham'	CKen
	- 'Aoi'	CKen CMen
	- 'Ara-kawa'	CKen CMen
	- Azuma-goyo Group	CKen CMen
I	- 'Baasch's Form'	CKen MGos
	- 'Bergman'	ECho LCon MAsh MBar NLar
	- 'Blauer Engel'	CDoC ECho MGos
	- 'Blue Giant'	ECho
	- 'Bonnie Bergman'	CKen ECho LLin NLar WEve
	- 'Brevifolia'	NLar
	- 'Dai-ho'	CKen
	- 'Daisetsusan'	CKen
	- 'Doctor Landis Gold'	CKen ECho
	- 'Fatsumo'	CKen
	- 'Fukai' (v)	CKen MGos NLar
	- 'Fukiju'	CKen
	- Fukushima-goyo Group	CKen CMen WEve
	- 'Fuku-zu-mi'	CKen ECho LLin WEve
	- 'Fu-shiro'	CKen
	- 'Gin-sho-chuba'	CKen
	- Glauca Group	CDoC CMac CRob ECho EHul LCon LLin MBar MBlu MBri MGos NPal SPoG WEve WFar
I	- 'Glauca Nana'	CKen
	- 'Goldilocks'	CKen ECho NLar
	- 'Gyok-ke-sen'	CKen
	- 'Gyo-ko-haku'	CKen
	- 'Gyokuei'	CKen
	- 'Gyokusen Sämling'	CKen NLar
	- 'Gyo-ku-sui'	CKen CMen ECho LLin
	- 'Hagaromo Seedling'	CKen CMen ECho LLin MAsh NLar
	- 'Hakko'	CKen
	- 'Hatchichi'	CKen
	- 'Ibo-can'	CKen CMen
	- 'Ichi-no-se'	CKen
	- 'Iri-fune'	CKen
	- Ishizuchi-goyo Group	CKen
	- 'Ka-ho'	CKen ECho LLin
	- 'Kanrico'	CKen
	- 'Kanzan'	CKen
	- 'Kiyomatsu'	CKen
	- 'Kobe'	CKen ECho LLin WEve
	- 'Kokonoe'	CKen CMen LLin
	- 'Kokuho'	CKen
	- 'Koraku'	CKen
	- 'Kusu-dama'	CKen
	- 'Meiko'	CKen CMen ECho
	- 'Michinoku'	CKen
	- 'Momo-yama'	CKen
	- 'Myo-jo'	CKen
	- Nasu-goyo Group	CKen
	- 'Negishi'	CDoC CKen CMen CRob LCon LLin LPan MAsh MBri NLar SCoo SLim WEve
	- 'Nellie D.' **new**	NLar
	- 'Ogon-janome'	CKen SLim
	- 'Ossorio Dwarf'	CKen
	- 'Regenhold'	CKen
	- 'Richard Lee'	CKen
	- 'Ryo-ku-ho'	CKen
	- 'Ryu-ju'	CKen NLar
	- 'Sa-dai-jin'	CKen
	- 'San-bo'	CKen ECho MBar MGos
§	- 'Saphir'	CKen ECho
	- 'Schoon's Bonsai' **new**	NLar
	- 'Setsugekka'	CKen
	- 'Shika-shima'	CDoC CKen
	- 'Shimada' **new**	CKen
	- Shiobara-goyo Group	CKen
	- 'Shirobana'	NLar
	- 'Shizukagoten'	CKen
	- 'Shu-re'	CKen
	- 'Sieryoden'	CKen
	- 'Tani-mano-uki'	CKen
	- 'Tempelhof'	CTho MAsh MBar NBlu NLar
	- 'Templeflora'	MLan
	- 'Tenysu-kazu'	CKen
	- 'Tokyo Dwarf'	CKen
I	- 'Torulosa'	LLin
	- 'Tribune'	CDoC NLar
	- 'Watnong'	CKen
	- 'Zelkova'	CMen ECho LLin
	- 'Zui-sho'	CKen
	patula ♀H2-3	CBgR CDoC CDul CLnd CTrC LAst LCon LLin SAPC SArc SCoo SIFN SLim SPlb WEve WPGP
	peuce	CDoC CDul LCon LRav MBar NLar NWea
	- 'Arnold Dwarf'	CKen
	- 'Cesarini'	CKen

	- 'Thessaloniki Broom'	CKen
	pinaster 🏆H4	CBcs CDoC CDul CLnd EHul LCon
	pinea 🏆H4	CAgr CArn CDoC CKen CLnd CMac CTho ECrN ELau EPfP LCon LEdu LLin LPan LRHS LRav MGos NPri SAPC SArc SBLw SCoo SEND WEve WNor WPGP
	- 'Queensway'	CKen
	ponderosa 🏆H4	CDul CLnd CMCN LCon LRav NWea
	- var. ***scopulorum***	NWea
	pumila	CRob NEgg
	- 'Buchanan'	CKen ECho
	- 'Draijer's Dwarf'	CDoC ECho EOrn LLin SCoo SLim
	- 'Dwarf Blue'	ECho MAsh
	- 'Glauca' 🏆H4	CKen LLin MBar
	- 'Globe'	ECho LCon LLin MAsh MBri NLar
	- 'Jeddeloh'	CKen
	- 'Knightshayes'	CKen
	- 'Säntis'	CKen ECho
	- 'Saphir'	see *P. parviflora* 'Saphir'
	radiata 🏆H3-4	CBcs CDoC CDul CLnd CSBt CTrC CTri ECrN ELan LCon LLin LRHS LRav MNHC NBee NWea SAPC SArc SCoo SHBN SPer WEve
	- Aurea Group	CDoC CKen CTho ECho EOrn LCon LLin LRHS LRav MAsh NScw SCoo SLim WEve WFar
	- 'Bodnant'	CKen
	- 'Isca'	CKen ECho
	- 'Marshwood' (v)	CKen ECho LCon MGos SLim
	resinosa 'Don Smith'	CKen
	- 'Joel's Broom'	CKen
	- 'Quinobequin'	CKen
	rigida	LCon
	roxburghii	CDul IDee ISea LCon SKHP WPGP
	x ***schwerinii***	CDoC ECho LCon LRHS MAsh MBri
	- 'Wiethorst'	CKen NLar SLim
	sibirica 'Mariko'	CKen
	strobiformis	ISea LCon
	- 'Coronado'	CKen
	- 'Loma Linda'	CKen
	strobus	CBcs CDul CMen ISea LCon LPan MBar MGos NWea SLim WEve WFar WNor
§	- 'Alba'	MGos SLim
	- 'Amelia's Dwarf'	CKen
	- 'Anna Fiele'	CKen
	- 'Bergman's Mini'	CKen NLar
	- 'Bergman's Pendula Broom'	CKen
I	- 'Bergman's Sport of Prostrata'	CKen
	- 'Bloomer's Dark Globe'	CKen
	- 'Blue Shag'	ECho EOrn LLin MGos NLar SCoo SLim SPoG WEve
	- 'Cesarini'	CKen
	- 'Densa'	CKen ECho LCon MAsh
	- 'Dove's Dwarf'	CKen
	- 'Edel' **new**	NLar
	- 'Ed's Broom'	CKen
	- 'Elkins Dwarf'	CKen
	- 'Fastigiata'	CKen ECho GBin IMGH LLin MBri
	- 'Green Curls' **new**	CKen
	- 'Greg'	CKen ECho NLar
	- 'Hershey'	CKen
	- 'Hillside Gem'	CKen
	- 'Himmelblau'	LCon NLar SLim
	- 'Horsford'	CKen ECho LLin NLar SLim
	- 'Jericho'	CKen EOrn
	- 'Julian Pott'	CKen
	- 'Julian's Dwarf' **new**	CKen
	- 'Krügers Lilliput'	LCon LLin LRHS MBri NLar SLim
	- 'Louie'	CKen NLar SLim
	- 'Macopin'	ECho SCoo
	- 'Mary Butler'	CKen
	- 'Merrimack'	CKen ECho NLar
	- 'Minima'	CKen ECho EOrn LCon LLin LRHS MAsh MBar MBlu MBri MGos NLar SCoo SLim SPoG WEve WGor
	- 'Minuta'	CKen
	- 'Nana'	see *P. strobus* Nana Group
§	- Nana Group	LLin MGos NPri
	- 'Nivea'	see *P. strobus* 'Alba'
	- 'Northway Broom'	CKen ECho LCon LLin SLim
	- 'Ontario'	MBlu
	- 'Pendula'	CKen IDee
I	- 'Pendula Broom'	CKen
	- 'Prostrata' **new**	LLin
	- 'Radiata'	CTri EHul EPla LCon MBar SPoG
	- 'Reinshaus'	CKen ECho LLin
	- 'Sayville'	CKen
	- 'Sea Urchin'	CKen ECho NLar SLim
	- 'Secrest' **new**	NLar
I	- 'Tortuosa' **new**	NLar
	- 'Uncatena'	CKen
	- 'Verkade's Broom'	CKen
	- 'Wendy' **new**	NLar
	sylvestris 🏆H4	More than 30 suppliers
	- 'Abergeldie'	CKen
	- 'Alderly Edge'	CMen WEve WFar
	- 'Andorra'	CKen MAsh
§	- 'Argentea'	CMen ECho SLim
§	- Aurea Group 🏆H4	CDul CKen CMac CMen EBrs ECho EHul EPfP GBin IMGH LBee LCon LLin LRHS MAsh MBar MBri NPri SCoo SHBN SLim SPer SSta WEve
	- 'Aurea'	see *P. sylvestris* Aurea Group
	- 'Avondene'	CKen ECho
	- 'Bergfield'	CMen ECho NLar WEve
	- 'Beuvronensis' 🏆H4	CKen CLnd CMac CMen ECho EOrn IMGH LLin LRHS MGos NHol NLar SCoo SLim WEve
	- 'Bonna'	CLnd LCon SCoo SIFN SLim
	- 'Brevifolia'	MBar
	- 'Buchanan's Gold'	CKen
	- 'Burghfield'	CKen CMen ECho LLin WEve
	- 'Chantry Blue'	CDoC CMen CRob ECho EHul EOrn IMGH LBee LCon LLin LRHS MAsh MBar MGos NHol NLar SCoo SLim WEve WFar
	- 'Clumber Blue'	CKen
	- 'Compressa'	LLin SLim
	- 'Corley'	ECho LLin
	- 'Dereham'	CKen ECho LLin
	- 'Doone Valley'	CKen ECho LLin MGos SCoo WEve
	- 'Edwin Hillier'	see *P. sylvestris* 'Argentea'
	- Fastigiata Group	CDoC CDul CEnd CKen CMen CRob ECho EOrn IMGH LBee LCon LLin LRHS MAsh MBar MGos SCoo SLim SPoG WEve WFar
	- 'Frensham'	CKen ECho EOrn IMGH LCon LLin MAsh MGos SCoo WEve WFar
	- 'Globosa'	ECho LRHS WEve
	- 'Gold Coin'	CDoC CDul CKen CMen ECho EOrn EPfP LBee LCon LLin MAsh MGos NHol NLar SCoo SLim SPoG WEve WFar
	- 'Gold Medal'	CKen ECho LLin SIFN SLim WEve WFar
	- 'Grand Rapids'	CKen
	- 'Gwydyr Castle'	CKen
	- 'Hibernia'	CRob
	- 'Hillside Creeper'	CKen EBrs ECho LCon LLin SCoo SLim WEve
	- 'Humble Pie'	CKen
	- 'Inverleith' (v)	ECho EHul LCon LLin MBar MGos SCoo SLim SPoG WEve WFar

	– 'Jeremy'	CKen ECho LCon LLin NHol SCoo SLim SPoG WEve
	– 'John Boy'	CMen ECho LLin NLar
	– 'Kelpie'	ECho LLin SCoo SLim
	– 'Kenwith'	CKen ECho
	– 'Lakeside Dwarf'	CMen ECho LLin WEve
	– 'Lodge Hill'	CMen CRob ECho EOrn IMGH LCon LLin MAsh SCoo SLim WEve
	– 'Longmoor'	CKen ECho MGos NLar
	– 'Martham'	CKen CMen ECho LLin WEve
*	– 'Moseri'	CRob ECho LBee MAsh SPoG WEve
	– 'Munches Blue'	CKen
	– 'Nana' misapplied	see *P. sylvestris* 'Watereri'
	– 'Nana Compacta'	CMen LLin
§	– 'Nisbet's Gem'	CKen CMen ECho LLin
	– 'Padworth'	CMen LLin NLar
	– 'Peve Heiheks' **new**	NLar
	– 'Peve Miba'	NLar
I	– 'Pine Glen' **new**	CKen
	– 'Piskowitz' **new**	CKen
	– 'Pixie'	CKen ECho LLin MGos NLar
I	– 'Prostrata'	SCoo
	– 'Pulham'	ECho LLin WEve
	– 'Pygmaea'	SCoo SLim
	– 'Reedham'	ECho LLin WEve
	– 'Repens'	CKen
	– 'Saint George'	CKen
	– 'Sandringham'	ECho LLin WEve
	– 'Saxatilis'	CKen CMen ECho EOrn LCon LLin MAsh WEve
	– 'Scott's Dwarf'	see *P. sylvestris* 'Nisbet's Gem'
	– 'Scrubby'	ECho LLin NLar
	– 'Sentinel'	CKen ECho SLim
	– 'Skjak I'	CKen NLar
	– 'Skjak II'	CKen ECho LLin SCoo
	– 'Slimkin' **new**	CKen
	– 'Spaan's Slow Column'	CKen ECho SCoo SLim
	– 'Tabuliformis'	ECho LLin
	– 'Tage'	CKen ECho LLin WEve
	– 'Tanya'	CKen MAsh
	– 'Tilhead'	CKen ECho
	– 'Treasure'	CKen ECho LLin
	– 'Trefrew Quarry'	CKen
	– 'Variegata' (v)	MGos WEve
§	– 'Watereri'	CMac ECho EHul IMGH LAst LBee LCon LLin LPan MAsh MBar MBri NHol NPri SCoo SLim SPer WEve WFar
	– 'Westonbirt'	CKen CMen ECho EHul LLin WEve
	– 'Wishmoor'	ECho LLin WEve
	– 'Wolf Gold'	CKen ECho
	– 'Xawrey 1'	NLar
*	– 'Yaff Hill'	ECho
	tabuliformis	CDul LCon
	taeda	WPGP
	thunbergii	CDul CLnd CMen EHul LCon LLin MGos NWea STre WNor
	– 'Akame'	CKen CMen
	– 'Akame Yatsabusa'	CMen
	– 'Aocha-matsu' (v)	CKen CMen NLar
	– 'Arakawa-sho'	CKen CMen
	– 'Banshosho'	CKen CMen ECho MGos NLar SLim
	– 'Beni-kujaku'	CKen CMen
	– 'Compacta'	CKen CMen
	– var. ***corticosa*** 'Fuji' **new**	CMen
	– – 'Iihara' **new**	CMen
	– 'Dainagon'	CKen CMen
	– 'Eechee-nee'	CKen
	– 'Hayabusa' **new**	CMen
	– 'Iwai'	CMen
	– 'Janome'	CMen
	– 'Katsuga'	CMen
	– 'Kotobuki'	CKen CMen CRob LCon NLar WFar
	– 'Koyosho'	CMen
	– 'Kujaku'	CKen CMen
	– 'Kyokko'	CKen CMen
	– 'Kyushu'	CKen CMen
	– 'Miyajuna'	CKen CMen
	– 'Nishiki-ne'	CKen CMen
	– 'Nishiki-tsusaka'	CMen ECho
	– 'Oculus-draconis' (v)	CMen ECho LLin
	– 'Ogon'	CKen CMen LCon NLar SLim
	– 'Porky'	CKen CMen
§	– 'Sayonara'	CKen CMen ECho LLin MAsh NLar SCoo SLim
	– 'Senryu'	CKen CMen
	– 'Shinsho'	CKen CMen
	– 'Shio-guro'	CKen CMen MAsh
	– 'Suchiro Yatabusa'	CKen CMen ECho
	– 'Sunsho'	CKen CMen ECho
	– 'Taihei'	CKen CMen
I	– 'Thunderhead'	CKen CMen EBrs LCon MAsh NLar SLim
	– 'Yatsubusa'	see *P. thunbergii* 'Sayonara'
	– 'Ye-i-kan'	CKen
	– 'Yoshimura'	CMen
	– 'Yumaki'	CKen CMen ECho MGos SCoo
	uncinata	see *P. mugo* subsp. *uncinata*
	– 'Etschtal'	CKen
	– 'Jezek'	CKen SLim
	– 'Kostelnicek'	NLar
	– 'Leuco-like'	CKen
	– 'Offenpass'	CKen
	– 'Susse Perle'	CKen
	virginiana 'Wate's Golden'	CKen
§	***wallichiana*** ♀H4	More than 30 suppliers
	– SF 00001	ISea
	– 'Densa'	LPan NLar SLim
	– 'Nana'	CKen EHul LCon LLin MBar NLar SCoo SLim WEve
	– 'Umbraculifera'	LRHS MBri
	– 'Zebrina' (v)	LBee LCon MAsh MBar MGos NLar WEve
	yunnanensis	CDul CTho WNor

Piper (*Piperaceae*)

	auritum	GPoy
	betle	MSal
	excelsum	see *Macropiper excelsum*
	nigrum	MSal

Piptanthus (*Papilionaceae*)

	forrestii	see *P. nepalensis*
	laburnifolius	see *P. nepalensis*
§	***nepalensis***	CBcs CDul CMac CSBt CSpe EBee ECrN ELan EMil EPau EPfP GGar GKev LRHS MGos NBid SEND SGar SHBN SLon SOWG SPer SPoG SRms WBVN
	– B&SWJ 2241	WCru
	tomentosus	MMHG SDry WPGP

Pistacia (*Anacardiaceae*)

	chinensis	CBcs CMCN EPfP XPep
	lentiscus	CArn CBcs EAro MGos SEND XPep
	terebinthus	XPep

Pistia (*Araceae*)

	stratiotes	NPer SCoo

Pitcairnia (*Bromeliaceae*)

	bergii	CHII
	heterophylla	WCot

Pittosporum ✿ (*Pittosporaceae*)

	anomalum	ECou SDry
	– (f)	ECou

- (m)	ECou
- 'Falcon'	ECou
- 'Raven' (f)	ECou
- 'Starling' (m)	ECou
'Arundel Green'	CDoC CWSG EBee EJRN EMil EPfP LRHS MAsh NHol SDry SLim SRms SWvt
bicolor	ECou EShb GQui IDee SAPC SArc WBor WPGP
- 'Cradle' (f)	ECou
- 'Mount Field' (f)	ECou
buchananii	SGar WCwm
colensoi	ECou
- 'Cobb' (f)	ECou
- 'Wanaka' (m)	ECou
crassifolium	CCCN CHEx ECou WBrE WPGP XPep
- 'Compactum'	XPep
- 'Havering Dwarf' (f)	ECou
- 'Napier' (f)	ECou
- 'Variegatum' (v)	EShb WSPU
crassifolium x ***tenuifolium***	CWib ECou SWvt
'Craxten' (f)	CCCN ECou EJRN
'Crinkles' (f)	ECou
daphniphylloides B&SWJ 6789	WCru
'Dark Delight' (m)	ECou
divaricatum	ECou
'Emerald Lake' **new**	MGos
'Essex' (f/v)	ECou EJRN
eugenioides	CHEx CMHG CTrG GGar
- 'Mini Green'	CPen LSou NLar WBrE
- 'Platinum' (v)	CBcs CCCN MGos
- 'Variegatum' (v) ♀H3	CAbb CBcs CBrm CCCN CDoC CDul CHEx CPLG EBee EJRN EMil EPfP ERas GQui IArd ISea LRHS MBri MGos MPRe SHBN SLim SPer SPoG WGob WPGP WSHC WSPU
eugenoides 'Tens Gold'	CPen
'Garnettii' (v) ♀H3	More than 30 suppliers
heterophyllum	CPen ECou SHBN XPep
- 'Ga Blanca'	CPen
- variegated (v)	ECou WSHC
'Holbrook' (v)	CSam
'Humpty Dumpty'	ECou EJRN
illicioides var. ***angustifolium*** B&SWJ 6771	WCru
- var. ***illicioides*** B&SWJ 6712	WCru
lineare	ECou
§ 'Margaret Turnbull' (v)	CBcs CPen CTrC ECou EJRN EWes LSRN MBri MGos MPRe
michiei	ECou
- (f)	ECou
- (m)	ECou
- 'Jack' (m)	ECou
- 'Jill' (f)	ECou
'Nanum Variegatum'	see *P. tobira* 'Variegatum'
obcordatum	ECou
- var. ***kaitaiaense***	ECou
'Oliver Twist' **new**	SCoo
omeiense	ECou ECre EWes SKHP
'Peter Pan'	EJRN
phillyreoides	XPep
pimeleoides var. ***reflexum*** (m)	ECou
'Purple Princess'	ECou EJRN
ralphii	CCCN ECou WPGP
- 'Green Globe'	ECou SKHP XPep
- 'Variegatum' (v)	CGHE EMil EPla SKHP SSpi WPGP
* ***robustum***	EWes
'Saundersii' (v)	EQua
tenufolium 'Croxton'	CCCN

tenuifolium ♀H3	More than 30 suppliers
- 'Abbotsbury Gold' (f/v)	CAbb CBcs CCCN CChe CDoC CMac CSam CTri EBee ECou ELan EMil EWes GBri LRHS MPRe SAga SDry SEND SHBN SLim SPer SPla WBod WGob WSHC
- 'County Park'	CCCN WFar
- 'County Park Dwarf'	CPen ECou EJRN EQua MAsh WCru
- 'Deborah' (v)	ECou EJRN LSou
- 'Dixie'	CPen ECou
§ - 'Eila Keightley' (v)	CMHG EJRN SAga
- 'Elizabeth' (m/v)	CBcs CDoC CMac CPen CTrC EBee ECou EJRN EMil IArd ISea LRHS MBri MGos MPRe
- 'French Lace'	CBcs CCCN CPen EBee ECou EJRN EMil GKev IClo NLar SHBN WBrE WFar WWeb
- 'Gold Star'	CBcs CDoC CPen ECou ENot LRHS MGos NHol NPal SCoo SLim SPoG WFar WMoo
- 'Golden Cut'	NLar
- 'Golden King'	CCCN CDoC CMHG CMac CSBt EBee EJRN EPfP LRHS LSou NHol NScw SLim SPoG SRms WWeb
- 'Golden Princess' (f)	ECou EJRN
- 'Green Elf'	ECou EJRN
- 'Green Thumb'	CMac CWSG EBee LRHS
- 'Irene Paterson' (m/v) ♀H3	More than 30 suppliers
- 'James Stirling'	CCCN CPMA ECou EPfP LRHS
- 'John Flanagan'	see *P.* 'Margaret Turnbull'
- 'Limelight' (v)	CBcs CPen CSBt CSPN CWGN LRHS MGos NHol SPoG
- 'Loxhill Gold'	CAbP CCCN CPen EBee IArd LRHS LSou MGos NScw
- 'Marjory Channon' (v)	LRHS
- 'Mellow Yellow'	CAbP LRHS
- 'Moonlight' (v)	CBcs CTrC EBee SKHP
- 'Mountain Green'	CMac LSou MGos
- 'Nutty's Leprechaun'	CCCN IClo
- 'Pompom'	CCCN SRms
- 'Purpureum' (m)	CBrm CCCN CMac CSBt CSam CTri EBee ECou EPfP ISea LAst LRHS LSRN MBri MPRe MWgw SAga SCoo SDry SHBN SPer SPla SPoG SRms WGer WSHC
- 'Silver Haze'	ISea
- 'Silver Magic' (v)	CBcs CPen CSBt EJRN MGos
- 'Silver 'n' Gold'	LRHS
- 'Silver Princess' (f)	ECou EJRN
- 'Silver Queen' (f/v) ♀H3	More than 30 suppliers
- 'Silver Sheen' (m)	CBcs CPen EBee ECou LRHS MGos
- 'Stevens Island' **new**	CBcs
- 'Stirling Gold' (f/v)	ECou EPfP EWes
- 'Sunburst'	see *P. tenuifolium* 'Eila Keightley'
- 'Tandara Gold' (v)	CBrm CCCN CDoC CDul CTrC EBee ECou EJRN EPfP ERas IClo LRHS LSRN MGos MPRe SLim SPla SPoG WBrE WFar WGer WGob WWeb
- 'Tiki' (m)	CBcs CCCN CTrC ECou
- 'Tom Thumb' ♀H3	More than 30 suppliers
- 'Tresederi' (f/m)	CBrm CCCN CMac CTrC EBee ECou LRHS WFar
- 'Variegatum' (m/v)	CBcs CDoC CSBt EBee ECou EQua GBri GGar LAst LCro LRHS MGos SPoG SWvt
- 'Victoria' (v)	CBcs CCCN CDoC CPen CTrC EBee EMil MGos SPoG WFar
- 'Warnham Gold' (m) ♀H3	CMac CSBt CWib EBee ECou EJRN ELan EPfP GBri LRHS MCCP MGos SCoo SDry SLim SPer SPoG SSpi WAbe

– 'Wendle Channon' (m/v)	CCCN CMac CSBt CSam CTrC EBee ECot ECou EMil EPfP EQua LRHS NCGa NHol SLim WGob WSHC
– 'Wrinkled Blue'	LRHS MGos
tobira 🏆H3	More than 30 suppliers
– B&SWJ 4362	WCru
* – 'Cuneatum'	CWGN LHop SAga
* – 'Nanum'	CBcs CCCN CDoC EBee ECou ELan EPfP ERom ETod LPan MGos MPRe MWya SAPC SArc SLim SPer SPla SPoG WFar WGer XPep
§ – 'Variegatum' (v) 🏆H2-3	More than 30 suppliers
truncatum	ECre EWes XPep
* – 'Variegatum'	XPep
undulatum	CHEx ECou
viridiflorum	ECou EShb

Plagianthus (*Malvaceae*)

betulinus	see *P. regius*
divaricatus	CBcs CTrC ECou ECre WPGP
lyallii	see *Hoberia lyallii*
§ ***regius***	CBcs ECou

Plagiorhegma see *Jeffersonia*

Planera (*Ulmaceae*)

aquatica **new**	EGFP

Plantago (*Plantaginaceae*)

asiatica	MSal
– 'Variegata' (v)	EMan GBuc MBNS NBro
cynops	MTho XPep
lanceolata	NMir WSFF
– 'Ballydowling Variegated' (v)	EBee
– 'Bomi-noka'	CNat
– 'Dent's Downs Link' (v)	WCot
– 'Golden Spears'	CBre EBee NSti
– 'Keer's Pride' (v)	WCot
– 'Streaker' (v)	EBee ITer WCot
– 'White Whiskers' **new**	CNat
major 'Atropurpurea'	see *P. major* 'Rubrifolia'
– 'Bowles' Variety'	see *P. major* 'Rosularis'
– 'Frills'	CNat EBee
* – 'Karmozijn'	EMan
§ – 'Rosularis'	CArn CNat CSpe CSsd EBee EDAr EShb ILis ITer LEdu MHer MTho NBid NBro NChi NEgg SPav WCAu WHer
§ – 'Rubrifolia'	CArn CHid CSpe EBee EShb LCro LDai MHer NBid NBro NChi NEgg NSti WCAu WHer WMoo WPer
– 'Tony Lewis'	CNat
maritima	WHer
media	MHer
psyllium L.	CArn MSal
rosea	see *P. major* 'Rosularis'
uniflora Hook. f.	WCot

Platanthera (*Orchidaceae*)

bifolia	NLAp SHdy
hologlottis	EFEx
metabifolia	EFEx

Platanus ✿ (*Platanaceae*)

x ***acerifolia***	see *P.* x *hispanica*
§ x ***hispanica*** 🏆H4	CBcs CCVT CDul CLnd CMCN CTho EBee ECrN EMac EPfP EWTr LAst LBuc LPan MAsh MGos NWea SBLw SEND SHBN SPer WFar WMou
– 'Bloodgood'	SBLw
– 'Dakvorm'	SBLw
– 'Dortmund'	SBLw
– 'Pyramidalis'	CTho SBLw WOrn
– 'Suttneri' (v)	CEnd CTho WMou
occidentalis	NEgg
orientalis 🏆H4	CCVT CLnd CMCN CTho EBee EPfP LEdu NLar SBLw SDix SLPl WMou
– MSF 0028 from Sfendili, Crete	WPGP
§ – f. ***digitata*** 🏆H4	CDoC CDul CLnd CMCN CTho EPfP ERod MBlu SBLw SLPl WMou
– var. ***insularis***	CEnd WPGP
– 'Laciniata'	see *P. orientalis* f. *digitata*
– 'Minaret'	CDul EMil WMou
– 'Mirkovec'	CDoC MBri SMad SPer WMou

Platycarya (*Juglandaceae*)

strobilacea	CBcs CMCN EGFP EPfP NLar

Platycerium (*Polypodiaceae*)

alcicorne misapplied	see *P. bifurcatum*
§ ***bifurcatum*** 🏆H1	MBri
– 'Netherlands' **new**	MPes

Platycladus (*Cupressaceae*)

§ ***orientalis***	CDul
§ – 'Aurea Nana' 🏆H4	More than 30 suppliers
– 'Autumn Glow'	CKen CRob LRHS MAsh SCoo SPoG WGor
– 'Beverleyensis'	LLin NLar WEve
– 'Blue Cone'	MBar
– 'Caribbean Holiday'	MAsh
– 'Collen's Gold'	EHul EOrn MBar
– 'Conspicua'	CKen CWib ECho EHul LBee MAsh MBar
§ – 'Elegantissima' 🏆H4	CMac ECho EHul EOrn LBee LPan MBar
– 'Franky Boy'	CDHC LCon MGos NLar SLim SPoG
– 'Golden Pillar'	EOrn
– 'Golden Pygmy'	CKen EOrn MAsh
– 'Golden Wonder'	ECho
– 'Juniperoides'	ECho EHul MBar
– 'Kenwith'	CKen ECho
– 'Lemon 'n Lime'	ECho SCoo SPoG WEve
– 'Little Susie'	CRob
– 'Madurodam'	LLin MBar
– 'Magnifica'	ECho EHul
– 'Meldensis'	CDoC CTri ECho EHul MBar WTel
– 'Minima'	CRob ECho EHul WGor
– 'Minima Glauca'	CKen ECho MBar
– 'Mint Chocolate'	ECho LLin
– 'Purple King'	LCon SCoo SLim SPoG
I – 'Pyramidalis Aurea'	LBee LCon LRHS NBlu NHol SCoo WEve
– 'Rosedalis'	CKen CMac CSBt ECho EHul EPfP LBee LCon LLin LRHS MAsh MBar SCoo SLim SMer SPla SPoG WFar
– 'Sanderi'	ECho MBar WCFE
§ – 'Semperaurea'	CMac IMGH
– 'Shirley Chilcott'	LBee LCon MAsh
– 'Sieboldii'	EHul
– 'Southport'	LBee LCon LLin LRHS MAsh
– 'Summer Cream'	CKen EHul MBar
– 'Westmont' (v)	CKen CSBt EOrn

Platycodon ✿ (*Campanulaceae*)

grandiflorus 🏆H4	CArn CHFP CMea CTri EBee ECha ELau EPot GKev LHop MHer MNrw MSal NEgg SGar SIng SRms WGwG WHoo
– 'Albus'	EBee ECho EPfP LHop SPer SPla SWvt WHoo WOut WPer
– Apoyama Group AGM	CLyd CStu ECho GKev LBee LRHS NMen WHoo WPer

	- - 'Fairy Snow'	CBgR CMdw CStu EBee ECho ELan EShb GGar GKev ITim LBMP MBNS NBre WEas WHoo WSel
	- (Astra Series) 'Astra Blue'	CSpe ECho EPfP NEgg NSfd WHoo
	- - 'Astra Double Blue' (d)	CSpe NEgg NSfd
	- - 'Astra Pink'	ITim NSfd WHoo
	- - 'Astra White'	NSfd WHoo
	- 'Blaue Glocke'	NBre
	- 'Blue Pearl'	WHoo
	- 'Florist Rose'	MHar
	- 'Fuji Blue'	EBee NLar SPad SPet SPur WSel
	- 'Fuji Pink'	CBrm EBee ECho ELan EMar EPfP ERou LAst LBBr LHop MRav NEgg NLar SMad SMrm SPet SPoG SPur SWvt WCAu WLin WSel
	- 'Fuji White'	EBee ECho ELan ERou LAst NLar SMrm SPet SPur WCAu WSel
	- 'Hakone'	LAst LHop MRav SMrm WHoo
	- 'Hakone Blue'	CBgR ECho EShb ITim NBre NLar WLin
*	- 'Hakone Double Blue' (d)	EBee ECGP ELan EMar LRHS MBNS SPoG SRms WCAu
	- 'Hakone White'	CBgR CBrm CMdw CPBP EBee ECGP ECho EPfP ITim LAst MRav NGby NLar NMen SMad SPoG WHoo WLin
	- 'Mariesii' ♀H4	CBgR CPLG CSBt EBee ECho ECtt EMar EPfP ERou LAst LRHS MWgw NBir NEgg NMen SMrm SPer SPla SPlb SRms SWvt WEas WHoo WPer WSHC
	- ***mariesii albus***	WHoo
	- 'Misato Purple'	WSel
	- Mother of Pearl	see *P. grandiflorus* 'Perlmutterschale'
	- 'Park's Double Blue' (d)	WHoo
§	- 'Perlmutterschale'	CBgR CMMP EBee ECho EMar EPPr EPfP IPot LAst MBNS NEgg WAul WHoo
	- pink-flowered new	GKev
	- ***pumilus***	CStu EBee GKev NChi NWCA WHoo
	- ***roseus***	GKev NEgg
	- 'Sentimental Blue'	CWib EBee ECho EWin EWll NLar
	- 'Shell Pink'	see *P. grandiflorus* 'Perlmutterschale'
	- 'Zwerg'	CPBP EBee ECho EShb GMac LBMP NBre
*	***leweri*** new	GKev

Platycrater (*Hydrangeaceae*)

	arguta	WCru
	- B&SWJ 6266	WCru

Plecostachys (*Asteraceae*)

§	***serpyllifolia***	CHal

Plectranthus (*Lamiaceae*)

	from Puerto Rico	CArn
	ambiguus	EOHP
	- 'Manguzuku'	EOHP
	- 'Umigoye'	EOHP
	amboinicus	CArn CHal EOHP NHor NTHB WDyG
*	- 'Variegatus' (v)	EOHP EUnu
	- 'Well Sweep Wedgewood'	EOHP EUnu
	argentatus ♀H2	CBcs CDMG CDoC CHal CHrt CMdw CPLG CPom CSev CSpe EBee EMan EOHP EShb MSte SBch SDix SEND SGar SHFr WDyG WKif WWlt
	- 'Hill House' (v)	CHll CHrt CPne EMan EOHP EShb
	australis misapplied	see *P. verticillatus*
	behrii	see *P. fruticosus*
	Blue Angel = 'Edelblau'	EOHP
	caninus	NHor
	ciliatus	CPne CSpe EOHP SGar WWlt
	- 'All Gold'	CPne
	- 'Easy Gold'	CHal EOHP
	- 'Sasha'	CCCN CDoC CHal CHll ECtt EOHP EShb LAst LSou SAga SPet
	coleoides 'Marginatus'	see *P. forsteri* 'Marginatus'
	- 'Variegatus'	see *P. madagascariensis* 'Variegated Mintleaf'
	Cuban oregano	EOHP EWll
	dolichopodus	EOHP
	ecklonii	EOHP WDyG
	- NJM 02.010	WPGP
	- 'Medley-Wood'	EOHP
	ernstii	EOHP
	excisus	EOHP
§	***forsteri*** 'Marginatus'	CHal EOHP ERea SGar
	frederici	see *P. welwitschii*
§	***fruticosus***	CHal CPne
	- 'Frills'	EOHP
	- 'James'	EOHP
	hadiensis var. ***tomentosus*** 'Carnegie'	EOHP
	- - green-leaved	EOHP
I	- 'Variegata'	CPne
	hilliardiae	CPne
	madagascariensis	CPne EOHP
	- gold-leaved	EOHP
§	- 'Variegated Mintleaf' (v) ♀H1	CHal EOHP SHFr SPet SRms
	'Marble Ruffles' new	EOHP
	menthol-scented, large-leaved	EOHP
	- small-leaved	CStu EOHP MNHC
	neochilus	MCot
	'Nico'	CSpe EOHP
§	***oertendahlii*** ♀H1	CHal EBak EOHP
	- silver-leaved	EOHP
	- 'Uvongo'	CPne
	ornatus	EOHP MCCP NHor NScw
	- 'Pee Off'	EOHP MPes
	purpuratus	EOHP
	rehmannii	EOHP
	saccatus	CPne GFai
	- var. ***longitubus*** new	EBee
	'Scarlet Ribbon' new	LAst
	spicatus	EOHP
	- 'Nelspruit'	EOHP
	Swedish ivy	see *P. verticillatus*, *P. oertendahlii*
§	***thyrsoideus***	CHal ECre EOHP
§	***verticillatus***	CHal EOHP
	Vick's plant	EOHP EUnu LSou
§	***welwitschii***	NHor
	zatarhendii	EOHP
	zuluensis	CDoC CFee CHal CPne CSpe EOHP EShb SBch WOld
	- dark-leaved	EOHP
	- 'Symphony'	CFee

Pleioblastus ✿ (*Poaceae*)

	akebono	see *P. argenteostriatus* 'Akebono'
	argenteostriatus	CTrC
§	- 'Akebono'	CMCo SDry
§	- f. ***glaber*** (v)	MAsh MNHC SDry
§	- 'Okinadake' (v)	EPla
§	- f. ***pumilus***	CDoC CSam EBee ENot EPfP LPan LRHS MBlu MMoz MWht NHol SDry SPla SPlb WFar WNor WPat WPer
	auricomus	see *P. viridistriatus*
	- 'Vagans'	see *Sasaella ramosa*
§	***chino***	EPla SDry
	- f. ***angustifolius***	see *P. chino* 'Murakamianus'

	- var. ***argenteostriatus***	see *P. argenteostriatus* 'Okinadake'
	- f. ***aureostriatus*** (v)	EPla LEdu MGos MMoz SDry
	- f. ***elegantissimus***	CDoC CEnd CFir CGHE EBee ENBC EPla ERod MGos MMoz NMoo SDry SEND WMoo WPGP WPnP
	- var. ***hisauchii***	EPla
	- 'Kimmei'	EPla SDry
§	- 'Murakamianus'	SDry
	'Gauntlettii'	see *P. argenteostriatus* f. *pumilus*
	glaber 'Albostriatus'	see *Sasaella masamuneana* 'Albostriata'
	gramineus	EPla SDry
§	***hindsii***	EPla ERod GBin LPan MMoz NMoo SDry SEND
§	***humilis***	ELan ENBC LPan
	- var. ***pumilus***	see *P. argenteostriatus* f. *pumilus*
	kongosanensis 'Aureostriatus' (v)	EPla SDry
	linearis	CAbb CBcs CMCo EAmu EFul EPla ERod EShb LAst LPal MMoz MWht NMoo SDry WMoo WPGP
	longifimbriatus	see *Sinobambusa intermedia*
	oleosus	EPla SDry
§	***pygmaeus***	More than 30 suppliers
§	- 'Distichus'	EBee EFul EHul ENBC EPPr EPla LCro LRHS MGos MMoz MMuc MWht NGdn NLar NMoo SDry WMoo
§	- 'Mirrezuzume'	CPLG WFar
*	- var. ***pygmaeus*** 'Mini'	WCot
§	***simonii***	CMCo EBee EFul GBin LRHS MBNS MMoz MWht SDry SPoG
	- 'Variegatus' (v)	EPla MBar NGdn SDry SPer WPGP
§	***variegatus*** (v) 🏆^{H4}	More than 30 suppliers
	- 'Tsuboii' (v)	CAbb CBig CChe CDTJ CDoC CSBt EPPr EPla ERod GQui LAst LPJP LPal LRHS MBNS MBrN MBri MMoz MWht NMoo SDry WFar WMoo WPGP WPnP
	- var. ***viridis***	see *P. argenteostriatus* f. *glaber*
§	***viridistriatus*** 🏆^{H4}	More than 30 suppliers
	- 'Bracken Hill'	SDry
	- 'Chrysophyllus'	EPla MMoz SDry
	- f. ***variegatus*** (v)	CHEx SAga SWvt WMoo
	yixingensis new	EPla

Pleione ✿ (*Orchidaceae*)

	Adams gx new	LBut
	Alishan gx	NSpr
	- 'Merlin'	LBut
	- 'Mother's Day' new	LBut
	- 'Mount Fuji'	EPot LBut
	Asama gx 'Bittern'	LBut
	- 'Red Grouse'	LBut
	Askia gx	LBut
	aurita	EPot LBut NSpr
	Bandai-san gx	EPot LBut
	- 'Sand Grouse'	LBut
	x ***barbarae***	EPot LBut NSpr
	Barcena gx	LBut
	Berapi gx 'Purple Sandpiper'	LBut
	Brigadoon gx	LBut NSpr NWCA
	- 'Stonechat'	LBut
	- 'Woodcock'	LBut
	Britannia gx	LBut
	- 'Doreen'	EPot LBut
§	***bulbocodioides***	EPot ERos IHer LBut NSpr
	- Limprichtii Group	see *P. limprichtii*
	- 'New Forest' new	NSpr
	- Pricei Group	see *P. formosana* Pricei Group
§	- 'Yunnan'	EPot NSpr
	Captain Hook gx	EPot LBut
	chunii	EFEx LBut
	x ***confusa***	EPot LBut
	Danan gx	EPot LBut
	Deriba gx	EPot LBut
	Egmont gx 'Jay'	LBut
	Eiger gx	ERos LBut
	- cream	ERos LBut
	El Pico gx 'Goldcrest'	NSpr
	- 'Kestrel'	EPot
	- 'Pheasant'	LBut NSpr
	Erebus gx 'Quail'	LBut
	Erh Hai gx	NSpr
	Etna gx 'Bullfinch'	LBut
	Follifoot gx 'Princess Tiger'	NSpr
	formosana 🏆^{H2}	CKob CStu CTri EBrs ECho EFEx EPot GBuc LAma LEdu NCGa SIng WFar WPGP WPnP
	- Alba Group	CTri EBrs ECho SIng WFar
	- - 'Claire'	EPot ERos LBut NSpr
	- - 'Snow Bunting'	LBut
	- 'Avalanche'	EPot NSpr
	- 'Blush of Dawn'	LBut NWCA
	- 'Cairngorm'	NSpr
	- 'Chen'	SIng
	- 'Greenhill'	EPot LBut
	- 'Lilac Jubilee'	SIng
	- 'Little Winnie'	SIng
	- 'Lucy Diamond'	NSpr
	- 'Lulu'	SIng
	- 'Pitlochry'	LBut
	- 'Polar Sun'	SIng
§	- Pricei Group	EPot ERos SIng
	- - 'Oriental Grace'	LBut
	- - 'Oriental Splendour'	LBut
	- 'Red Spot'	EPot SIng
	- 'Snow White'	LBut
	forrestii	EBrs EFEx EPot LAma
	Fu Manchu gx	NSpr
	Fuego gx	NSpr WAbe
	'Ganymede' new	LBut
	Gerry Mundey gx	NSpr
	Giacomo Leopardi gx	NSpr
§	***grandiflora***	LBut
	Harlequin gx 'Norman' new	LBut
	Heathfield gx	NSpr
	Hekla gx	ERos NSpr
	- 'Partridge'	LBut
	humilis	LBut NSpr
	Irazu gx 'Wood Warbler'	LBut
	Jorullo gx	NSpr WAbe
	- 'Long-tailed Tit'	LBut
	Keith Rattray gx	NSpr
	- 'Kelty'	LBut
	Kenya gx	LBut
	- 'Bald Eagle' new	LBut
	Kilauea gx	EPot LBut
	- 'Curlew'	LBut
	Kohala gx	LBut
	Krakatoa gx	LBut NSpr
	Kublai Khan gx	NSpr
	Leda gx new	LBut
§	***limprichtii*** 🏆^{H2}	EBrs EFEx EPot LBut
	maculata	EFEx
	Marco Polo gx	LBut NSpr
	- 'Raymond' new	NSpr
	Marion Johnson gx	LBut
	Masaya gx	LBut
	Mawenzi gx	LBut
	Mazama gx	LBut
	Myojin gx	LBut
	Novarupta gx	LBut
	Orinoco gx	LBut
	Orizaba gx	LBut
	Paricutin gx	LBut

Pavlof gx	LBut
pinkepankii	see *P. grandiflora*
Piton gx	EPot LBut NSpr
§ ***pleionoides***	EPot LBut
- 'Blakeway-Phillips'	EPot
pogonioides misapplied	see *P. pleionoides*
pogonioides (Rolfe) Rolfe	see *P. bulbocodioides*
Quizapu gx 'Peregrine'	LBut
Rainier gx	LBut
Rakata gx	EPot
- 'Blackbird'	LBut
- 'Redwing'	LBut
- 'Shot Silk'	LBut NSpr
- 'Skylark'	LBut
San Salvador gx	LBut
Sangay gx	LBut
Santorini gx	LBut
saxicola **new**	LBut
scopulorum	EFEx
Shantung gx	CFir EPot LAma NSpr SIng
- 'Candyfloss'	NSpr
- 'Christine'	NSpr
- 'Ducat'	EPot LBut NSpr
- 'Gerry Mundey'	LBut NSpr
- 'Golden Jubilee'	NSpr
- 'Golden Plover'	LBut
- 'Mikki'	NSpr
- 'Muriel Harberd' ♀H2	NSpr
- 'Pixie'	NSpr
- R6.48	NSpr
- R6.7	NSpr
- 'Ridgeway'	LBut NSpr
- 'Silver Anniversary'	LBut
Shepherd's Warning gx 'Gillian Clare'	NSpr
- 'Mary Buchanan'	NSpr
Sorea gx	LBut
Soufrière gx	LBut NSpr
- 'Sunrise'	NSpr
speciosa Ames & Schltr.	see *P. pleionoides*
Starbotton gx	NSpr
Stromboli gx	NSpr
- 'Fireball'	EPot NSpr
- 'Robin'	LBut
Surtsey gx	EPot
Swaledale gx	NSpr
Taal gx 'Red-tailed Hawk' **new**	LBut
x ***taliensis***	LBut
Tarawera gx	LBut
Tolima gx	NSpr
- 'Moorhen'	LBut
Tongariro gx	CPBP EPot ERos NSpr SIng
- 'Jackdaw'	EPot NSpr
Versailles gx	EPot ERos NWCA
- 'Bucklebury' ♀H2	EPot LBut
- 'Heron'	LBut
Vesuvius gx	EBrs EPot NSpr WAbe
- 'Grey Wagtail'	LBut
- 'Leopard'	LBut NSpr
- 'Phoenix'	EPot LBut NSpr
- 'Tawny Owl'	LBut
Vicky gx	NSpr
Volcanello gx	EPot NSpr
- 'Honey Buzzard'	LBut
- 'Song Thrush'	LBut
'Wharfedale Pine Warbler'	LBut
yunnanensis misapplied	see *P. bulbocodioides* 'Yunnan'
yunnanensis (Rolfe) Rolfe	LBut
Zeus Weinstein gx	EPot LBut
- 'Desert Sands'	LBut

Pleiospilos (*Aizoaceae*)

bolusii ♀H1 **new**	EPem
compactus ♀H1 **new**	EPem
nelii ♀H1 **new**	EPem

Pleomele see *Dracaena*

Pleurospermum (*Apiaceae*)

HWJK 2329 from Nepal	WCru
aff. ***amabile*** BWJ 7886	WCru
benthamii B&SWJ 2988	WCru
brunonis	NChi
calcareum B&SWJ 8008	WCru

plum see *Prunus domestica*

Plumbago (*Plumbaginaceae*)

§ ***auriculata*** ♀H1-2	CBcs CCCN CHEx CRHN CSBt
	CTri CWSG EBak EBee ELan EPfP
	ERea EShb ISea LRHS MBri MLan
	NPal SOWG SPer SRms XPep
- var. ***alba*** ♀H1-2	CBcs CHEx CHal CRHN CSev EBak
	EBee EMil EPfP ERea EShb MLan
	SOWG XPep
- 'Crystal Waters'	CCCN CDoC ELan
- dark blue-flowered	CSpe MJnS XPep
- 'Escapade Blue' (Escapade Series)	EShb
caerulea **new**	CSpe
capensis	see *P. auriculata*
§ ***indica*** ♀H1	CCCN CHal EShb MJnS SOWG
- ***rosea***	see *P. indica*
larpentiae	see *Ceratostigma plumbaginoides*

Plumeria (*Apocynaceae*)

sp.	MJnS
rubra ♀H1	CCCN SOWG
- f. ***acutifolia***	SOWG

Pneumatopteris see *Cyclosorus*

Poa (*Poaceae*)

alpina	CBig NGdn NLar XIsg
- ***nodosa***	CBig
chaixii	CBig EPPr EPla GFor NLar NNor
	SLPl XIsg
cita	CBig GFor GMaP LRav WPnP
colensoi	CBrm CKno CRez EAlp EBee EPPr
	GKev MAvo WPnP
eminens from Magadan, Siberia	EPPr
x ***jemtlandica***	EPPr
labillardierei	CBrm CKno CWCL EBee ECha
	EGle EPPr EWsh GGar MAvo MSte
	SPer SPoG WDyG WMoo WPrP
	XPep
rodwayi	CBig
trivialis	CRWN
I 'Variegata'	SApp

Podalyria (*Papilionaceae*)

calyptrata	SPlb
sericea	SPlb

Podocarpus (*Podocarpaceae*)

acutifolius	CBcs CDoC ECou EPla GGar MBar
	STre
- (f)	ECou
- (m)	ECou
alpinus R. Br. ex Hook. f.	NHol
andinus	see *Prumnopitys andina*
'Autumn Shades' (m)	ECou
'Blaze' (f)	CBcs CDoC CRob ECho ECou
	LCon LLin NHol NLar SCoo SLim
	SPoG WEve
chilinus	see *P. salignus*
'Chocolate Box' (f)	ECou

	'County Park Fire'[PBR] (f)	CBcs CDoC CKen CRob CWSG ECho ECou EOrn EPfP LCon LLin MAsh MGos SCoo SLim SPoG SWvt WEve WFar WGor WSpi
	'County Park Treasure'	ECou
	cunninghamii	CBcs ECou WCwm
	- 'Kiwi' (f)	ECou
	- 'Roro' (m)	CBcs CDoC ECou LLin
	cunninghamii x ***nivalis*** (f)	ECou
	dacrydioides	see *Dacrycarpus dacrydioides*
	elongatus	CTrC IDee
	'Flame'	CDoC ECho ECou EPla NEgg SCoo WEve
	'Havering' (f)	CDoC ECou MGos
	henkelii	CTrC EShb GGar
	'Jill' (f)	ECou
	latifolius	ECou EShb IDee
	lawrencei	EHul GGar WThu
	- (f)	ECou MBar
	- 'Alpine Lass' (f)	ECou
	- 'Blue Gem' (f)	CDoC CRob ECho ECou EOrn EPla IArd IDee LCon LLin LRHS MAsh MBar MBri MGos NHol SCoo SLim SPoG WFar
	- 'Kiandra'	ECou
	- 'Red Tip'	CDoC CRob ECho LLin MAsh SCoo SLim STre
	'Macho' (m)	ECou
	macrophyllus	CHEx EOrn NLar SAPC SArc SMad STre WFar
	- (m)	ECou WFar
	- 'Aureus'	CBcs
	'Maori Prince' (m)	CDoC ECou EPla LLin
	nivalis	CBcs CDul CMac CTrC ECho ECou EOrn EPla GGar LLin MBar SCoo SRms
	- 'Arthur' (m)	ECou
	- 'Bronze'	CDoC EPla MGos WEve
	- 'Christmas Lights' (f)	CKen ECou
	- 'Clarence' (m)	ECou LLin
	- 'Cover Girl'	CRob
	- 'Green Queen' (f)	ECou
	- 'Hikurangi'	CDoC
	- 'Jack's Pass' (m)	ECho ECou SCoo
	- 'Kaweka' (m)	ECou
	- 'Kilworth Cream' (v)	CBcs CDoC CRob ECho ECou EPla LBuc LCon LLin MAsh MGos NHol NLar SCoo SLim SWvt WEve
	- 'Little Lady' (f)	ECou
	- 'Livingstone' (f)	ECou
	- 'Lodestone' (m)	ECou
	- 'Moffat' (f)	CBcs CDoC ECou LLin
	- 'Otari' (m)	ECho ECou LLin NLar WEve
	- 'Park Cover'	ECou
	- 'Princess' (f)	ECou
	- 'Ruapehu' (m)	CDoC ECou EPla
	- 'Trompenburg'	NLar
	nubigenus	CBcs
	'Orangeade' (f)	CBcs CDoC ECho LLin MGos NLar
	'Red Embers'	CDoC ECho NEgg SCoo
*	'Redtip'	ECho SLim
§	***salignus*** ♀H3	CBcs CBrd CDoC CDul CHEx CPLG CPle EPfP EPla IDee SAPC SArc SLim WFar WPic WSHC
	- (f)	ECou WFar
	- (m)	ECou
	spicatus	see *Prumnopitys taxifolia*
	'Spring Sunshine' (f)	CBcs CDoC ECou EPla LLin MGos NLar WEve
	totara	CBcs CTrC ECho ECou GGar LEdu STre WFar
	- 'Albany Gold'	CTrC
	- 'Aureus'	CBcs CDoC ECho ECou EPla MBar SCoo SHBN WEve WFar
	- 'Pendulus'	CDoC ECou
	'Young Rusty' (f)	CBcs CDoC ECou EPla LLin MAsh MGos WEve

Podophyllum (*Berberidaceae*)

	aurantiocaule	GGGa
§	***delavayi***	CBct CFir CHHB CLAP EBee EBla EBrs ECho GEdr MDun NLar WCot WCru WSpi
	difforme	CBct CLAP EBee GEdr MGol SKHP WCru
	emodi	see *P. hexandrum*
	- var. ***chinense***	see *P. hexandrum* 'Chinense'
§	***hexandrum***	CArn CBct COld CWCL EBla EBrs ECho EPot ERos GCrs GPoy ITer LAma MBri MRav MSal NBHF NBid NChi NEgg NMen NWCA SMad SPhx SPoG WAbe WBVN WCot WFar WPnP
	- BWJ 7908	WCru
	- SDR 2948	GKev
§	- 'Chinense'	CLAP EBee EBla EMan GBuc GEdr GKev IBlr LEdu SMad WCru
	- 'Chinese White'	WCot
	- 'Majus'	CFir CLAP EBee SMad WCot WHal
	'Kaleidoscope' (v)	NBhm SKHP
	peltatum	CArn CBct CLAP COld EBee EBla EBrs ECho GEdr GPoy LAma LEdu NMyG NSti SPhx WCru WFar WPGP WPnP
	pleianthum	CAby CBct CHHB CLAP EBee GEdr WCot WCru
	- B&SWJ 282 from Taiwan **new**	WCru
	- short	WCru
*	***tsayuensis*** **new**	CBct EBee
	veitchii	see *P. delavayi*
	versipelle	CLAP EBee SKHP WCru

Podranea (*Bignoniaceae*)

	brycei	CRHN EShb
§	***ricasoliana***	CHEx CRHN ERea EShb MJnS SOWG XPep
	- 'Comtesse Sarah'	XPep

Pogonarthria (*Poaceae*)

	squarrosa	CBig

Pogonatherum (*Poaceae*)

§	***paniceum***	MBri
	saccharoideum	see *P. paniceum*

Pogostemon (*Lamiaceae*)

	from An Veleniki Herb Farm, Pennsylvania	CArn
§	***cablin***	GPoy MSal
	patchouly	see *P. cablin*

Polemonium ✿ (*Polemoniaceae*)

	acutiflorum	see *P. caeruleum* subsp. *villosum*
	acutifolium var. ***nipponicum***	see *P. caeruleum* var. *nipponicum*
	ambervicsii	see *P. pauciflorum* subsp. *hinckleyi*
	'Apricot Beauty'	see *P. carneum* 'Apricot Delight'
N	***archibaldiae*** ♀H4	NBir SRms
§	***boreale***	EBee ECho NPol SWvt WFar WMoo
	- 'Heavenly Habit'	EBee LSou NPro NRnb NVic SHGN WWeb
§	***brandegeei*** Greene	EBee SHGN WPer
	- subsp. ***mellitum***	see *P. brandegeei* Greene
	Bressingham Purple = 'Polbress'	CBow EBee EBrs GBin MMHG WFar

	Name	Suppliers
	caeruleum misapplied, Himalayan	see *P. cashmerianum*
§	***caeruleum*** L.	More than 30 suppliers
	- 'Bambino Blue'	EBee LRHS NBre SWvt WPer
	- 'Blue Bell'	ELau
	- Brise d'Anjou = 'Blanjou'PBR (v)	More than 30 suppliers
	- subsp. ***caeruleum***	GKev LCro
	- - f. ***album***	More than 30 suppliers
I	- f. ***dissectum***	NPol
	- 'Golden Showers' (v)	NPro
	- var. ***grandiflorum***	see *P. caeruleum* subsp. *himalayanum*
§	- subsp. ***himalayanum***	WMoo WPer
	- 'Humile'	see *P.* 'Northern Lights'
	- 'Idylle'	EMan EMon NCot
§	- var. ***nipponicum***	EBee NPol WPer
	- 'Sky Blue'	NRnb
	- 'Snow and Sapphires' (v)	CBct EBee LAst LRHS MBNS MCCP MSte NPer NPri NTHB SPav SPoG SRkn STes WWeb
§	- subsp. ***villosum***	NPol
	- subsp. ***vulgare***	NPol
	californicum	NPol
	carneum	CTri CWan ECha EGle EMan GMaP LAst MCCP MNFA MNrw MTho MWgw NPol STes WAul WCAu WFar WMoo WPer
§	- 'Apricot Delight'	EBee EGle ERou GBri LAst LRHS MCCP MNrw NBir NDov NGdn NPol SGar SIde SPoG STes WBVN WFar WHer WPer WPnP WSpi WWeb
I	***cashmerianum***	EPPr GAbr LRHS WFar WHen WPtf
I	- ***album***	WBor
	chartaceum	CGra LTwo
	'Churchills'	CBre EBee WPGP WPrP WSHC
	'Dawn Flight'	WFar
	delicatum	see *P. pulcherrimum* Hook. subsp. *delicatum*
	'Eastbury Purple'	CElw MAvo
	'Elworthy Amethyst'	CElw EBee EMan MAvo NPol WPGP
	flavum	see *P. foliosissimum* A. Gray var. *flavum*
	foliosissimum misapplied	see *P. archibaldiae*
	foliosissimum A. Gray	EBee IGor MNrw WPer
	- var. ***albiflorum***	see *P. foliosissimum* A. Gray var. *alpinum*
§	- var. ***alpinum***	NBir NPol
	- 'Cottage Cream'	CBre CDes NPol
§	- var. ***flavum***	NPol
	- var. ***foliosissimum***	EWes NPol
	- 'White Spirit'	NPol
	'Glebe Cottage Lilac'	CCge CElw CHar EBee GCra NBir SBch WPGP
	grandiflorum	NPol
	'Hannah Billcliffe'	CDes CElw EBee ECtt EWes MBrN NChi NCot NPol WPGP
	'Heavenly Blue'	ECtt
§	'Hopleys'	EMan GBri MAvo NChi NCot NGdn WFar
	x ***jacobaea***	CDes EBee EMan WCot WPGP WTin
	'Katie Daley'	see *P.* 'Hopleys'
	'Lace Towers'	NSti
	'Lambrook Mauve' ♀H4	More than 30 suppliers
	'Mary Mottram'	NPol
	mellitum	see *P. brandegeei* Greene
	'North Tyne'	NChi NPol
§	'Northern Lights'	CDes CSev EBee EGle EMan EMon EPPr EWes GBri GMac LCro MBnl MNFA MNrw NCot NDov NPol NSti SBch SSvw STes WFar WMoo WPGP
	'Norwell Mauve'	MNrw
	occidentale subsp. ***occidentale***	NPol
	'Pam' (v)	CBow EBee NPol WCot WSPU
§	***pauciflorum***	CEnt CHFP CStu EBee ECtt EHrv EPfP EShb LAst LRHS MNFA MNrw MTho NBir NHol SHFr SPer WCAu WFar WMoo WPer WWeb
§	- subsp. ***hinckleyi***	GKev NChi NCot NPol SBch SGar
§	- subsp. ***pauciflorum***	LRHS NPol SGar SPav
	- silver-leaved	see *P. pauciflorum* subsp. *pauciflorum*
	- 'Sulphur Trumpets'	ECtt LSou SPav SWvt
	- subsp. ***typicum***	see *P. pauciflorum* subsp. *pauciflorum*
	'Pink Beauty'	CBre EBee ELan EPPr EPfP LRHS NBre NCot NPol
	pulchellum Salisb.	see *P. reptans*
	pulchellum Turcz.	see *P. caeruleum*
	pulcherrimum misapplied	see *P. boreale*
	- 'Tricolor'	see *P. boreale*
	pulcherrimum Hook.	NBro SPoG WPer WWeb
§	- subsp. ***delicatum***	MTho NPol
	- subsp. ***pulcherrimum***	LTwo NPol
§	***reptans***	CArn GBri GPoy MHer MSal NBro NPol WAul WFar WMoo WPer WPtf WWeb
	- 'Album'	see *P. reptans* 'Virginia White'
	- 'Blue Ice'	NPol
	- 'Blue Pearl'	CElw CMea EBee ELan EMan EPfP EShb LHop LRHS MBri MLLN MNrw NBro NCob NGdn NPol NPri SGar SPla WFar WHen WWeb
	- 'Firmament'	EBee WPGP
	- 'Pink Dawn'	EBee ELan EPfP MLLN MNFA MWgw NCob NGdn SPla STes
*	- 'Sky Blue'	NBro
	- 'Stairway to Heaven' (v)	More than 30 suppliers
§	- 'Virginia White'	CBre CDes CElw CMea CSev EBee LRHS MBnl NChi NPol WFar
	- 'White Pearl'	EShb NPri
	'Ribby'	NPol
	richardsonii misapplied	see *P.* 'Northern Lights'
	richardsonii Graham	see *P. boreale*
	'Sapphire'	CBre ELan EMan EMon MBrN NPol
	scopulinum	see *P. pulcherrimum* Hook. subsp. *delicatum*
	'Sonia's Bluebell'	CDes CElw EBee ECGP ECtt EMan EPPr EWes LPio MAvo MBnl MDKP MNrw MSte NCot NDov NPol NSti SBch WPGP
	'Theddingworth'	MAvo NPol WFar
	vanbruntiae	NPol
	viscosum	GBuc NPol SGar WHen
	- f. ***leucanthum***	NPol
	yezoense	CBre GBri MNrw NBre NPol WFar
	- var. ***hidakanum***	EShb NPol
	- 'Midnight Rain'	CSpe
	- 'Purple Rain'	CHar CSpe EBee ECtt EHrv EMan EPfP EShb EWes GBuc GMaP LCro LPio LSRN MBri MCCP MLLN NPol SPoG STes WFar WMoo

Polianthes (*Agavaceae*)

	Name	Suppliers
§	***geminiflora***	EBee EBrs
	nelsonii	CFir
	tuberosa ♀H1-2	CBcs CSpe CStu EBrs ECho IHer LRHS
	- 'The Pearl' (d)	CDes EBrs ECho LAma WHil WPGP

Poliomintha (*Lamiaceae*)

	Name	Suppliers
	bustamanta	NBir
	incana	EBee
	maderensis F&M 195 **new**	WPGP

Poliothyrsis (*Flacourtiaceae*)

sinensis $\mathrm{♀}^{H4}$	CAbP CTho EBee EPfP LAst LRHS MBri NLar WPGP

Polygala (*Polygalaceae*)

arillata new	CPLG
calcarea	ECho LTwo
- Bulley's form	EPot LRHS
- 'Lillet' ♀H4	ECho EPot EWes LHop LRHS LTwo NLAp NLar NMen NSla WFar WPat
- 'Susan's Blush'	NLAp
chamaebuxus ♀H4	CBcs ECho GCrs GKev LSou MDKP MGos NDlv NLar NSla SKHP SRms WBVN WSHC
I - ***alba***	LBee LRHS LSou NLar SChF WAbe
§ - var. ***grandiflora*** ♀H4	CBcs CFir ECho EPfP EPot GEdr GGar LBee MAsh MBar MDun MGos NLAp NMen NSla SBla SChF SIng SPoG WAbe WBVN WBod WFar WPat WSHC
- 'Kamniski'	ECho LBuc NLar
- 'Loibl'	EPot
- 'Purpurea'	see *P. chamaebuxus* var. *grandiflora*
- 'Rhodoptera'	see *P. chamaebuxus* var. *grandiflora*
§ x ***dalmaisiana*** ♀H1	CAbb CCCN CHEx CHll CRHN CSpe EBee MWea SGar WAbe WCFE
myrtifolia	CCCN CPLG EMil GFai MGos MPRe SGar SHFr SMrm SPlb WHil XPep
- 'Grandiflora'	see *P.* x *dalmaisiana*
'Rosengarten'	SBla
tenuifolia	CArn
vayredae	NLar
virgata	EBee ERea EShb WBod

Polygonatum ✿ (*Convallariaceae*)

ACE 1753	EPot
acuminatifolium	EBla
altelobatum	EBla
- B&SWJ 286	WCru
alternicirrhosum new	EBee
§ ***biflorum***	More than 30 suppliers
- dwarf	EBla EPla IBlr
canaliculatum	see *P. biflorum*
cathcartii	EBee
cirrhifolium	CDes CFir CLAP CMdw CPom EBee EBla ELan GBin WCot WCru WPGP
- red-flowered new	WCot
commutatum	see *P. biflorum*
'Corsley'	CPou
cryptanthum	EBee EBla EPot WCru
curvistylum	CAvo CBct CHFP CLAP CPom CStu EBee EBla ECha EGle EHrv EPPr GEdr IBlr NLar NRya SPhx WAbe WCru WFar
- CLD 761	GEdr
cyrtonema misapplied	see *Disporopsis pernyi*
cyrtonema Hua	CLAP EBee LEdu
- B&SWJ 271	WCru
* ***desoulavyi*** var. ***yezoense*** B&SWJ 764 new	WCru
falcatum misapplied	see *P. humile*
falcatum A. Gray	CLyd EBee EBla EGle EPot IBlr NOak WHer
- B&SWJ 1077	WCru
- silver-striped	EPot GEdr
- - B&SWJ 5101	WCru
- 'Variegatum'	see *P. odoratum* var. *pluriflorum* 'Variegatum'
'Falcon'	see *P. humile*
filipes	EBee WCru
franchetii new	CExc
fuscum	WCru
geminiflorum	CLAP EBla IBlr WCot WFar
- McB 2448	GEdr
giganteum	see *P. biflorum*
glaberrimum	CAvo EBla WCot
'Golden Gift'	SBla
§ ***graminifolium***	CBct CLAP CPom EBee EBla EBrs ECho EPot ERos GEdr MSte NMen SCnR WCot WCru
- G-W&P 803	IPot
§ ***hirtum***	CBct CLAP EBla EBrs ECho EMon EPla IBlr LEdu WCru WFar WTin
- BM 7012	EBee
- dwarf	WCot
hookeri	More than 30 suppliers
- McB 1413	GEdr
§ ***humile***	CBct CLAP EBee EBla EBrs ECho EHrv EMan EMon EPfP ERos GBri GGar IBal IBlr ITim LAst NMen SMac SMad WAul WCot WCru WFar WHil
§ x ***hybridum*** ♀H4	More than 30 suppliers
- 'Betberg'	CBct CLAP EBla ECha EHrv NBir SBla WCot
- 'Flore Pleno' (d)	EBla WHer
- 'Nanum'	CHid EBla
§ - 'Striatum' (v)	More than 30 suppliers
- 'Variegatum'	see *P.* x *hybridum* 'Striatum'
- 'Wakehurst'	EBla EHrv
- 'Weihenstephan' new	EBee
inflatum	EBee EBla ECho WCru
- B&SWJ 922	WCru
involucratum	EBee ECho WCru
- B&SWJ 4285	WCru
japonicum	see *P. odoratum*
kingianum	CExc EBee
- yellow-flowered B&SWJ 6562	WCru
'Langthorns Variegated' (v)	ELan
lasianthum	WCru
- B&SWJ 671	WCru
latifolium	see *P. hirtum*
leptophyllum	EBee
- KEKE 844	GEdr
multiflorum misapplied	see *P.* x *hybridum*
multiflorum L.	CBcs CDes CElw CSBt CWCL EBee EBrs ECha EPla EWsh GAbr LCro LRHS MAvo MRav NEgg NVic SAga SEND SMer SPlb SPoG SRms WBor WCAu WHer
- ***giganteum*** hort.	see *P. biflorum*
* ***nanum*** 'Variegatum' (v)	CBcs ECho
nodosum	EBee EBla WCru
obtusifolium	EBee EBla
§ ***odoratum*** ♀H4	CAby CAvo CBct CPom CSWP EBee EBla EBrs ECho EHrv ELau EPfP EPla GMaP IBlr MSal NBid NLar NRya WCru WFar WHil WPnP
§ - dwarf	ECho EMon IBlr LEdu
- 'Flore Pleno' (d) ♀H4	CDes CLAP EBee EBla EBrs ECha ECho EHrv EPla ERou LEdu SCnR SMHy WCot WHil WHoo WPGP WPnP WTin
- 'Grace Barker'	see *P.* x *hybridum* 'Striatum'
- var. ***maximowiczii*** new	WCru
- var. ***pluriflorum***	GBuc IBlr
§ - - 'Variegatum' (v) ♀H4	More than 30 suppliers
- 'Red Stem'	WCru
- 'Silver Wings' (v)	CLAP EBla ECha EHrv ERou NBir
officinale	see *P. odoratum*
oppositifolium	EBla WFar
- B&SWJ 2537	WCru
§ ***orientale***	CHid CLAP EBla EBrs ECho WCot

pluriflorum	see *P. graminifolium*
polyanthemum	see *P. orientale*
prattii	EBee EBla
- CLD 325	GEdr
pubescens	EBee WCru WThu
pumilum	see *P. odoratum* dwarf
punctatum	LEdu WFar
- B&SWJ 2395	CBct EBla WCru
roseum	CDes GEdr WHer WPGP
sewerzowii	EBla EPla
sibiricum	CAvo EBla GEdr IBlr WCot WCru
- DJHC 600	CDes
stenophyllum	EBla WCru
stewartianum	CLAP EBee EPPr IBlr
tonkinense HWJ 551	WCru
verticillatum	CAvo CBct CFwr CGHE CHid EBla EBrs ECha EPfP EPla IBlr LBBr LEdu MNrw MTho NMyG NWCA SMad WCot WCru WFar WPGP
- 'Himalayan Giant'	CHid EBee EBla ECho IPot
* - 'Rubrum'	CArn CBct CLAP EBla EGle EHrv EPPr EPla GEdr IBlr IPot LBBr LEdu LFur MAvo MSte MTho NBid NGby SPhx WCot WHil WPrP
- 'Serbian Dwarf'	CBct CHid EBee EBla ECho IPot
aff. ***verticillatum***	CSpe EMon
aff. ***wardii*** B&SWJ 6599 **new**	WCru
zanlanscianense	CBct EBee EBla WCru

Polygonum ✿ (*Polygonaceae*)

affine	see *Persicaria affinis*
- 'Darjeeling Red'	see *Persicaria affinis* 'Darjeeling Red'
- 'Donald Lowndes'	see *Persicaria affinis* 'Donald Lowndes'
- 'Superbum'	see *Persicaria affinis* 'Superba'
amplexicaule	see *Persicaria amplexicaulis*
aubertii	see *Fallopia baldschuanica*
aviculare	CArn
baldschuanicum	see *Fallopia baldschuanica*
bistorta	see *Persicaria bistorta*
- 'Superbum'	see *Persicaria bistorta* 'Superba'
capitatum	see *Persicaria capitata*
compactum	see *Fallopia japonica* var. *compacta*
equisetiforme misapplied	see *P. scoparium*
filiforme	see *Persicaria virginiana*
forrestii	EBee
- SDR 2578	GKev
longisetum	see *Persicaria longiseta*
molle	see *Persicaria mollis*
multiflorum	see *Fallopia multiflora*
odoratum	see *Persicaria odorata*
polystachyum	see *Persicaria wallichii*
runciforme	see *Persicaria runcinata*
§ ***scoparium***	CBcs CBrm EMan EPPr EPla SDry SDys SIng WDyG WFar WOld WTin
tinctorium	see *Persicaria tinctoria*
vacciniifolium	see *Persicaria vacciniifolia*
weyrichii	see *Persicaria weyrichii*

Polylepis (*Rosaceae*)

australis	CPle LEdu LRav MBri MGol SMad WCot WCru WPGP
pauta	WPGP

Polymnia (*Asteraceae*)

sonchifolia	EUnu LEdu
uvedalia	see *Smallanthus uvedalius*

Polypodium ✿ (*Polypodiaceae*)

aureum	see *Phlebodium aureum*
- 'Glaucum'	CSpe WCot
- 'Mandaianum' **new**	MPes
australe	see *P. cambricum*
californicum 'Sarah Lyman' **new**	SKHP
§ ***cambricum***	EFer WCot WFib WRic WTin
- 'Barrowii'	CBgR CLAP WAbe WFib
I - 'Cambricum' ♀H4	CBgR CLAP WAbe WRic
- 'Cristatum'	CLAP WFib
- (Cristatum Group) 'Grandiceps Forster'	CLAP
- - 'Grandiceps Fox' ♀H4	WFib
- 'Hornet'	GBin WFib
- 'Macrostachyon'	CLAP EFer GBin WFib
- 'Oakleyae'	SMHy
- 'Omnilacerum Oxford'	CLAP
- 'Prestonii'	WAbe WCot WFib
- Pulcherrimum Group	CLAP WAbe WRic
- - 'Pulchritudine'	CLAP WAbe
- 'Pulcherrimum Addison'	GBin WAbe WFib
- 'Richard Kayse'	CDes CLAP EBee WAbe WCot WFib WPGP
- Semilacerum Group	WRic
- - 'Carew Lane'	WFib
- - 'Robustum'	WFib
- 'Whilharris' ♀H4	CLAP CWsd WAbe
I x ***coughlinii*** bifid	WFib
formosanum **new**	WRic
glycyrrhiza	CLAP GPoy WFib
- bifid	see *P.* x *coughlinii* bifid
- 'Longicaudatum' ♀H4	CLAP EBee EMon WAbe WCot WFib WSPU
- 'Malahatense'	CLAP
- 'Malahatense' (sterile)	WAbe
interjectum	CBgR CLAP CWCL EBrs EFer MAsh MMoz MPes NVic WAbe WPnP WRic
- 'Cornubiense' ♀H4	CBgR CLAP EFer EMon GEdr MMoz NBid NBir NHol NVic WAbe WTin
- 'Glomeratum Mullins'	WFib
x ***mantoniae***	WFib WIvy
- 'Bifidograndiceps'	NBid WFib WRic
scouleri	CLAP NBro
vulgare	More than 30 suppliers
- 'Bifidocristatum'	see *P. vulgare* 'Bifidomultifidum'
§ - 'Bifidomultifidum'	CBgR CLAP CRez CWCL EMon GBin GEdr LLWP LRHS MAsh MCCP MGos MPes NHol NLar SPla WCot
* - 'Congestum Cristatum'	SRms
- 'Cornubiense Grandiceps'	SRms WIvy WRic
* - 'Cornubiense Multifidum'	EBee WCot
- 'Elegantissimum'	WFib
- 'Trichomanoides Backhouse'	CLAP WAbe WFib

Polypompholyx see *Utricularia*

Polyscias (*Araliaceae*)

'Elegans'	MBri
fruticosa	MBri
scutellaria 'Pennockii' (v)	MBri

Polystichum ✿ (*Dryopteridaceae*)

BWJ 8182 from China	WCru
acrostichoides	CFwr CLAP CMHG CRez EBee ECGP EPPr ERod GEdr GQui LRHS MBri MPes MWgw NLar NMyG WRic
aculeatum ♀H4	More than 30 suppliers
I - Densum Group	EFer
- Grandiceps Group	EFer
- 'Portia'	WFib
altum **new**	CExc
andersonii	CLAP CWCL NHol WRic

	bissectum new	CExc
	braunii	CBcs CBgR CMHG CPrp CWCL EGol EQua GBin GMaP LRHS MMoz MPes NHol NLar WFib WPnP WRic
	caryotideum	see *Cyrtomium caryotideum*
	deltodon	CExc
	dracomontanum new	WRic
	x ***dycei*** new	WRic
	falcatum	see *Cyrtomium falcatum*
	fortunei	see *Cyrtomium fortunei*
	imbricans	CLAP SArc
	interjectum new	MRav
	makinoi	CCCN CLAP CRez NHol WFib WRic
	munitum 🏆H4	More than 30 suppliers
	neolobatum	NVic WFib
	polyblepharum 🏆H4	More than 30 suppliers
	proliferum ambig.	WPtf
	proliferum (R. Br.) C. Presl	CLAP EAmu LAst WFib WRic
*	- ***plumosum***	CFwr NEgg
	rigens	CElw CFwr CLAP CPrp EBee EWsh LSou MAsh MPes NDlv NHol NLar SRms SRot WCru WFib WRic
	setiferum 🏆H4	More than 30 suppliers
§	- Acutilobum Group	CBcs CFwr CLAP CMHG CPrp CWCL ECha EPla GMaP LRHS MPes NHol SDix SMad SPer SRms STes WMoo WPGP WPnP WPrP
	- Congestum Group	CBgR CPrp GBin MMoz NCGa NHol SPer SRms WFib WRic
	- - 'Congestum'	CFwr CLAP CWCL EBee ELan ENot EPfP ERod LRHS MAsh MDun MPes MRav NBir NHol NMyG NSti SMac SPla SPoG WCot WGor WMoo WPrP
	- 'Cristatopinnulum'	CFwr CGHE CLAP EPla WPGP
	- Cristatum Group	CLAP EHrv SRms
	- Cruciatum Group	CLAP
	- - 'Cruciatum Kaye'	CLAP
	- Divisilobum Group	CBcs CElw CFee CLAP CMHG EFer ELan EMon ENot EWsh MGos MMoz NHol NVic SPla SRms STre WAbe WAul WFar WFib WHoo WIvy WPGP WRic WTin
	- - 'Dahlem'	CDoC CFwr CLAP EBee ECha EFer ELan EMon EWsh GMaP LRHS MDun MMoz MPes MSte NHol NMoo SPoG WAbe WBor WFib WMoo WPnP WRic
	- - 'Divisilobum Densum' 🏆H4	CBgR CLAP EHrv EPfP LRHS NBir NOrc
	- - 'Divisilobum Iveryanum' 🏆H4	CLAP NHol SRms WFib
	- - 'Divisilobum Laxum'	CLAP
	- - 'Herrenhausen'	More than 30 suppliers
	- - 'Mrs Goffey'	CGHE WFib
	- Foliosum Group	EFer
	- - 'Foliosum'	CLAP
	- 'Gracile'	MRav NBir
	- 'Grandiceps'	CGHE CLAP EFer ELan
	- Green Lace = 'Gracillimum'	GBin
	- 'Hamlet'	WFib
	- 'Helena'	WFib
	- 'Hirondelle'	SRms
	- Lineare Group	NEgg WFib WPat
	- Multilobum Group	CLAP SRms WFib
	- 'Othello'	WFib
	- Perserratum Group	NBid WFib
	- 'Plumo-Densum'	see *P. setiferum* 'Plumosomultilobum'
	- 'Plumosodensum'	see *P. setiferum* 'Plumosomultilobum'
	- Plumosodivisilobum Group	CLAP CMil ECha EGol LSou NBid SPla WAbe WFib
	- - 'Baldwinii'	CLAP WFib
	- - 'Bland'	WFib
I	- 'Plumosomultilobum'	More than 30 suppliers
	- Plumosum Group	CBgR CGHE CLAP CMHG CSpe EFer MPes NEgg NOrc SAPC SArc SRot
	- - dwarf	CSBt
*	- ***plumosum grande*** 'Moly'	CLAP SRms
	- 'Portmeirion' new	CLAP
	- Proliferum Group	see *P. setiferum* Acutilobum Group
*	- 'Proliferum Wollaston'	CBcs CFwr CPrp CWCL MMoz WWeb
	- 'Pulcherrimum Bevis' 🏆H4	CLAP CWsd GBin MRav NBid SHFr WCot WFib WPGP WPnP WRic
*	- 'Ramopinnatum'	CLAP
	- 'Revolvens Lowe'	CLAP
	- Rotundatum Group	CLAP
	- - 'Cristatum'	CLAP
	- - 'Rotundatum Ramosum'	CLAP
	- 'Smith's Cruciate'	CFwr CLAP GBin WFib
	- 'Wakeleyanum'	SRms
N	- 'Wollaston'	CFwr CLAP ETod GBin MAsh MPes MRav NEgg NHol NLar SMac WAbe
	silvaticum	EFer
	tsussimense 🏆H4	More than 30 suppliers
	vestitum	CLAP CTrC WRic

Polyxena (*Hyacinthaceae*)

	corymbosa	CStu
§	***ensifolia***	EBrs ECho ERos
	longituba	EDif
	odorata	CLyd CStu EBrs ECho
	pygmaea	see *P. ensifolia*

Pomaderris (*Rhamnaceae*)

	apetala	CPLG
	elliptica	CPLG ECou

pomegranate see *Punica granatum*

Poncirus (*Rutaceae*)

§	***trifoliata***	CAgr CArn CBcs CDoC CTri EBee ELan EPfP IMGH LRHS MAsh MBlu MJnS MRav NEgg NWea SMad SPer SPlb SPoG WBVN WFar WPGP WPat WSHC
	- 'Flying Dragon'	SMad

Ponerorchis (*Orchidaceae*)

	graminifolia	CBct LAma WWst

Pontederia (*Pontederiaceae*)

	cordata 🏆H4	CBen CDWL CHEx CWat EHon ELan EMFW EPfP ILad MCCP NPer SCoo SPlb SWat WFar WMAq WPnP
	- f. ***albiflora***	CDWL CWat EPfP MCCP NLar WMAq
	- 'Blue Spires'	CDWL
§	- var. ***lancifolia***	EMFW EPfP MCCP NPer SWat WTin
	- 'Pink Pons'	CDWL NLar
	dilatata	see *Monochoria hastata*
	lanceolata	see *P. cordata* var. *lancifolia*

Populus ✿ (*Salicaceae*)

	x ***acuminata***	WMou
	alba	CCVT CDoC CDul CLnd CSBt CTho CTri CWib ECrN EMac LBuc MBar NBee NWea SBLw SHBN SPer WMou WOrn
	- 'Bolleana'	see *P. alba* f. *pyramidalis*

	- 'Nivea'	SBLw
§	- f. ***pyramidalis***	CBcs SRms WMou
§	- 'Raket'	CCVT CLnd CTho ECrN ELan NWea SBLw SPer
	- 'Richardii'	CDul CLnd ECrN MAsh MBar SPer WCot WFar WMou
	- Rocket	see *P. alba* 'Raket'
	alba x ***grandidentata***	WMou
§	'Balsam Spire' (f) $\mathbb{Y}^{H4}$	CDoC CDul CLnd CTho EMac NWea WMou
§	***balsamifera***	CCVT CDoC CTho CTri ECrN EMac MGos NWea SBLw SHBN SPer SRms WCot WFar
	- 'Vita Sackville West'	MBlu
	x ***berolinensis***	CDoC
	x ***canadensis***	ECrN SBLw
§	- 'Aurea' $\mathbb{Y}^{H4}$	CDoC CDul CLnd CTho CWib EBee EMac LCro LRHS MGos MRav SPer WFar WMou
	- 'Eugenei' (m)	CTho
	- 'Robusta' (m)	CDoC CDul CLnd CTri EMil LBuc NWea WMou
	- 'Serotina' (m)	CCVT CDoC CDul ECrN WMou
	x ***candicans*** misapplied	see *P.* x *jackii*
	x ***canescens***	CDoC CLnd ECrN NWea SBLw WMou
	- 'De Moffart' (m)	SBLw
	- 'Tower'	WMou
	x ***generosa*** 'Beaupré'	WMou
§	x ***jackii*** (f)	NEgg
	- 'Aurora' (f/v)	CBcs CBrm CDul CLnd CSBt CTrG EBee ELan LBuc MBar MBri MGos MMuc MNHC MRav NBee NBlu NWea SBLw SHBN SPer SRms WFar WHar WJas
	lasiocarpa $\mathbb{Y}^{H4}$	CDoC CDul CEnd CGHE CMCN CPLG CSdC CTho EBee ELan EMil EPfP EPla IDee MBlu MRav SBLw SLPl WMou WPGP
*	- var. ***tibetica***	WMou
	maximowiczii	WMou
	nigra	CDul CLnd EMac EPfP NWea
	- (f)	ECrN SLPl
	- (m)	SLPl
	- subsp. ***betulifolia***	CCVT CDul CTho CWan NWea WMou
	- - (f)	ECrN WMou
	- - (m)	ECrN WMou
N	- 'Italica' (m) $\mathbb{Y}^{H4}$	CCVT CDoC CDul CLnd CSBt CTho CTri CWib ECrN ELan EMac LBuc MGos NBee NWea SBLw SHBN SPer SRms WOrn
	- 'Italica Aurea'	see *P. nigra* 'Lombardy Gold'
§	- 'Lombardy Gold' (m)	CEnd ECrN MBlu
	- 'Pyramidalis'	see *P. nigra* 'Italica'
	'Serotina Aurea'	see *P.* x *canadensis* 'Aurea'
	simonii 'Fastigiata'	WMou
	- 'Obtusata'	WMou
	szechuanica	WMou
	tacamahaca	see *P. balsamifera*
	'Tacatricho 32'	see *P.* 'Balsam Spire'
	tomentosa	WMou
	tremula $\mathbb{Y}^{H4}$	CCVT CDoC CDul CLnd CRWN CSBt CTho CTri CWib EBee ECrN ELan EMac LBuc LRHS NBee NWea SBLw SHBN SPer WHar WMou WOrn
§	- 'Erecta'	CDul CEnd CLnd CTho EBee IClo MBlu MBri SMad WFar WMou
	- 'Fastigiata'	see *P. tremula* 'Erecta'
	- 'Pendula' (m)	CEnd CLnd CTho EBee ECrN SBLw WCFE WMou
	trichocarpa	CDul CTho ECrN NWea SPer
	- 'Fritzi Pauley' (f)	CDul CTho WMou
	violascens	see *P. lasiocarpa* var. *tibetica*
	yunnanensis	CLnd WMou

Porophyllum (*Asteraceae*)

	coloratum	EUnu
	ruderale	EUnu MSal

Portulaca (*Portulacaceae*)

	'Firegold' **new**	SVil
	grandiflora	MBri
	- 'Fairytales Cinderella' (Fairytales Series) **new**	NPri
	oleracea	CArn MHer MNHC SIde WJek
	- var. ***aurea*** (hort.) G. Don	MNHC WJek

Portulacaria (*Portulacaceae*)

	afra 'Variegata' **new**	EShb

Potamogeton (*Potamogetonaceae*)

	crispus	CDWL EHon EMFW NSco WMAq
	natans	EMFW NSco

Potentilla ✿ (*Rosaceae*)

	alba	CPLG CTri EBee ECha ECho ELan GBuc GGar GMac MLHP MNFA MRav MWat NChi NSti SPer WAul WPer
	alchemilloides	SMer WPer
	alpicola	WPer
	ambigua	see *P. cuneata*
	andicola	EBee NBre
	anserina	CArn EGoo MHer WHer XPep
	- 'Golden Treasure' (v)	EBee EMar ITer MLLN NBre NEgg WHer
	anserinoides	EGoo EMan WDyG WMoo WPer
	arbuscula misapplied	see *P. fruticosa* 'Elizabeth'
	- 'Beesii'	see *P. fruticosa* 'Beesii'
	'Arc-en-ciel'	CFwr CHid CKno EBee EMar ERou GMac GSki LAst LBBr LSRN MBNS MBri MLHP NBPC NLar NPro SHar STes WBor WCAu WFar WMoo WPnP
	argentea	CRWN MBNS SPlb WFar WPer
	arguta	EBee NBre
	argyrophylla	see *P. atrosanguinea* var. *argyrophylla*
*	- ***insignis rubra***	NChi NRnb NWCA
	atrosanguinea	More than 30 suppliers
§	- var. ***argyrophylla***	CEnt COIW CSam EBee ECha ELan EPfP LHop LRHS MNFA MRav MWat MWgw NBir NBro NCGa SBri SRms WFar WHil WMoo WPer
	- - SS&W 7768	MSte
	- var. ***leucochroa***	see *P. atrosanguinea* var. *argyrophylla*
	aurea	EBee ECho ECtt EPfP GAbr MTho NBlu NEgg NLAp NMir NNor NWCA WBrk WPat
	- 'Aurantiaca'	EWes NLar SRot
§	- subsp. ***chrysocraspeda***	GCrs NMen
§	- 'Goldklumpen'	EBee ECtt MNFA MRav NPro
	- 'Plena' (d)	SRot
	'Blazeaway'	EBee ECGP EMan LRHS LSou MBNS MWgw NGdn NPro WCAu WFar
	brevifolia	NWCA
	calabra	EBee ECha EWes SHGN SMer WHer
§	***cinerea***	CTri ECho LBee
	collina	SBri
§	***crantzii***	CMea EBee GCrs MBar MSte SRms
	- 'Nana'	see *P. crantzii* 'Pygmaea'
§	- 'Pygmaea'	ECho ECtt EPfP NBir NMen
§	***cuneata*** $\mathbb{Y}^{H4}$	ECho GAbr MTho NWCA SIng WPer
	davurica 'Abbotswood'	see *P. fruticosa* 'Abbotswood'
	delavayi	MNrw

	detommasii	MHar WAbe WPer
	- MESE 400	EBee
	dickinsii	NMen
	'Emilie'	CSpe EBee EGle EMar ERou MBNS MBri NLar NPro NRnb SWvt WBor WFar WHal WHil
§	***erecta***	CArn CRWN CWan GPoy GWCH MSal
	eriocarpa	CLyd EBee ECho ECtt EPau GEdr MWat NLAp NMen SBri SPer WAbe WPat
	- var. ***tsarongensis*** CC 4627 **new**	EWld
	'Esta Ann'	EBee NCGa SRGP
	'Etna'	CEnt CHFP CHar CKno EBee ECtt ELan EWsh GMac LPio MLHP MNFA MNrw MWrn NBir NChi SBri WCAu WHen WHil WLin WMoo WPGP WPer
	'Everest'	see *P. fruticosa* 'Mount Everest'
	'Fireflame'	ECha NBre NLar WMoo
	fissa	EBee MBNS MNrw MSte NBir NBre SPhx
	'Flambeau' (d)	EBee EMan LHop MNFA MRav NBre NCob NGdn NLar NPro WCra
	'Flamenco'	CSam CTri ECtt ERou GMac MArl MBNS MBri MLHP MNrw MRav NBir NChi SAga WAbb WFar
	fragariiformis	see *P. megalantha*
	fruticosa	LBuc MGan NWea
§	- 'Abbotswood' ♀^{H4}	More than 30 suppliers
	- 'Abbotswood Silver' (v)	LAst MSwo SLim WFar WMoo
	- 'Alice'	WWeb
	- 'Annette'	CMac NPro WWeb
	- 'Apple Blossom'	CWib
	- var. ***arbuscula*** hort.	see *P. fruticosa* 'Elizabeth'
	- 'Argentea Nana'	see *P. fruticosa* 'Beesii'
	- 'Barnbarroch'	WWeb
§	- 'Beesii'	ELan EPfP ERas LRHS MBar SPla SPoG
	- 'Bewerley Surprise'	NBir WHCG WWeb
	- 'Cascade'	LHop
*	- 'Chelsea Star' ♀^{H4}	CMac MAsh MGos WWeb
	- 'Chilo' (v)	MGos NEgg WMoo WWeb
	- 'Clotted Cream'	MBar
	- var. ***dahurica*** W 1213	WPGP
	- - 'Farrer's White'	WFar
	- - 'Hersii'	see *P. fruticosa* 'Snowflake'
	- - 'Rhodocalyx'	CPle WFar
	- 'Dart's Cream'	LRHS MGan
	- 'Dart's Golddigger'	CTri SEND
	- 'Daydawn'	More than 30 suppliers
§	- 'Elizabeth'	CBcs CBrm CDoC CDul CSam CTri CWib EBee ELan EPfP ISea LAst LHop LRHS MBar MGos MRav NBlu NEgg NWea SCoo SHBN SPer SPoG SRms SWvt WBVN WCFE WFar WMoo
	- 'Farreri'	see *P. fruticosa* 'Gold Drop'
	- 'Floppy Disc'	ELan EPfP LRHS MGos NHol SHBN SPla
	- 'Frances, Lady Daresbury'	WWeb
	- 'Glenroy Pinkie'	CSam EPfP MRav NLar SCoo SLon WWeb
§	- 'Gold Drop'	CMac WTel
	- 'Gold Parade'	WWeb
	- 'Golden Dwarf'	MGos
	- 'Golden Spreader'	WWeb
	- 'Goldfinger'	CChe CDoC CSBt EBee ELan EPfP LHop LRHS MAsh MGos MRav MSwo MWat NEgg NHol SCoo SLim SMer SPer SPlb SPoG WAbe WTel WWeb
	- Goldkugel	see *P. fruticosa* 'Gold Drop'
	- 'Goldstar'	CDul ENot EQua IArd LRHS MBri MGos NHol SCoo SLon SPoG WFar WHCG WWeb
	- 'Goldteppich'	LBuc MBar NCGa SHBN
	- 'Goscote'	MGos
	- 'Grace Darling'	CAbP ELan EPfP EWes GGar MAsh NBir NEgg SPoG SWvt WBVN WHCG WMoo
	- 'Groneland' ♀^{H4}	EPfP MAsh WWeb
	- 'Haytor's Orange'	CWib
	- 'Honey'	WWeb
	- 'Hopleys Orange' ♀^{H4}	CChe CDoC CEnt CHar ENot EPfP EWes LHop LRHS MAsh MRav MWat NCGa NEgg NPri SCoo WBrE WFar WGor WMoo WWeb
	- 'Hopleys Pink'	WWeb
	- 'Hunter's Moon'	WWeb
	- 'Hurstbourne'	NPro
	- 'Jackman's Variety' ♀^{H4}	CSam CWib MAsh SPer SRms WRHF WWeb
	- 'Janet'	WWeb
	- 'Jolina'	WWeb
	- 'Katherine Dykes'	CChe CDoC CDul CSBt CTri CWib EBee EPfP LBMP LRHS LSRN MBar MRav NWea SCoo SLim SLon SPer SRms WBVN WFar WHar WMoo WTel WWeb
*	- 'King Cup' ♀^{H4}	MAsh WWeb
§	- 'Klondike'	CBcs CSBt EPfP MGan NWea
	- 'Knap Hill'	see *P. fruticosa* 'Knap Hill Buttercup'
§	- 'Knap Hill Buttercup'	WWeb
	- 'Kobold'	MBar
*	- 'Lemon and Lime'	MBlu NBir NPro WWeb
	- 'Limelight' ♀^{H4}	CSBt EBee ELan EPfP LRHS LSou MAsh MRav MSwo NHol NPri SPla SPoG WFar WHCG WWeb
	- 'Longacre Variety'	CMac CTri EQua MBar MSwo NWea SLPl WFar WTel
	- 'Lovely Pink'^{PBR}	see *P. fruticosa* 'Pink Beauty'
§	- 'Maanelys'	ELan EQua MGan MWat NHol NWea SPer SRms WFar WHCG WMoo
§	- 'Manchu'	CDoC CMac MBar MRav MWat SHBN SLPl SPer SRms WCFE
	- Mango Tango = 'Uman'^{PBR}	CDoC LBuc
§	- Marian Red Robin = 'Marrob'^{PBR} ♀^{H4}	CDoC CSBt CWib EBee ELan ENot EPfP LAst LCro LRHS MAsh MBri MRav MSwo MWat NCGa NWea SCoo SLim SLon SPer SPoG SWvt
	- 'Maybe'	WWeb
	- 'McKay's White'	WWeb
	- 'Medicine Wheel Mountain' ♀^{H4}	ELan EWes LRHS MAsh MGos MRav NHol NLar NPro SCoo SLim SPer WHCG WWeb
	- Moonlight	see *P. fruticosa* 'Maanelys'
§	- 'Mount Everest'	EQua NWea SLon SRms WBod WWeb
	- 'Nana Argentea'	see *P. fruticosa* 'Beesii'
	- 'New Dawn'	CDoC LRHS MBri NCGa SPer WFar WWeb
	- 'Orange Star'	WHCG WWeb
	- 'Orangeade'	LRHS MAsh NLar WWeb
	- 'Peaches and Cream'	WEas WWeb
*	- 'Peachy Proud'	NPro
§	- 'Pink Beauty'^{PBR} ♀^{H4}	CDoC CSBt EBee ELan ENot EPfP LRHS LSRN MAsh MRav NBlu NCGa NEgg NPri SCoo SPer SPoG SWvt WMoo WWeb
	- 'Pink Pearl'	WMoo
	- 'Pink Whisper'	NPro WWeb
	- 'Pretty Polly'	CSBt CWSG ELan EPfP LAst LRHS MAsh MBar MGos MSwo NBlu NHol SHBN SPla SSta WBor WFar WMoo WWeb

	- 'Primrose Beauty' ♀H4	CDoC CDul EBee ELan ENot EPfP LAst LRHS MBar MRav MSwo MWgw NCGa NHol SCoo SLim SMer SPer SPlb WBod WBrE WFar WMoo WWeb
§	- Princess = 'Blink'[PBR]	CBcs CDul CSBt CWSG ELan LRHS MAsh MBar MRav MSwo NEgg SCoo SLim SPer SReu SRms WFar WWeb
	- 'Red Ace'	More than 30 suppliers
	- Red Robin[PBR]	see *P. fruticosa* Marian Red Robin = 'Marrob'
	- var. ***rigida***	GKev
	- - CC 3685	WRos
	- 'Royal Flush'	MBar NHol
	- 'Snowbird'	EBee EPfP LRHS MGos NPro SLim WFar WWeb
§	- 'Snowflake'	CBcs WMoo
	- 'Sommerflor' ♀H4	EPfP EQua MRav NCGa
	- 'Sophie's Blush'	CChe MRav NHol NWea WHCG WSHC WWeb
	- 'Sunset'	CBcs CSBt CSam CWSG CWib EBee ELan EPfP LRHS MBar MGos MRav NBir NEgg NHol NWea SCoo SLim SPer SRms SSta WBVN WFar WMoo WWeb
	- 'Super Ace'	MGos
	- 'Tangerine'	More than 30 suppliers
	- 'Tilford Cream'	More than 30 suppliers
	- 'Tom Conway'	CMac NLar WHCG
	- var. ***veitchii***	CSBt SHBN
	- 'Vilmoriniana'	CTri ELan EPfP LRHS MAsh MLHP MRav MWea SLon SPer SPoG SSpi WAbe WCFE WHCG WSHC WSpi WTel WWeb
	- 'Wessex Silver'	CHar WHCG
	- 'Whirligig'	CMac WHCG
	- 'White Rain'	WWeb
	- 'Wickwar Beauty'	CWib
	- 'William Purdom'	WHCG
	- 'Wychbold White'	WWeb
	- 'Yellow Bird' ♀H4	LRHS MAsh MGos
	- 'Yellow Carpet'	WWeb
	- 'Yellow Giant'	WWeb
	'Gibson's Scarlet' ♀H4	More than 30 suppliers
	glandulosa	GAbr MNrw NBre NOak WBrk
	'Gloire de Nancy' (d)	CTca IGor LBMP LHop MRav NBir NChi WCot WPrP
	'Gold Clogs'	see *P. aurea* 'Goldklumpen'
	gracilis	EBee NEgg SBri
	'Harlow Cream'	NBid
	'Helen Jane'	GBuc LEdu LPio MHer NBir NGdn NLar NPro SAga STes WFar WMnd WPer
	heptaphylla	GSki NBre
	'Herzblut'	EBee EPfP GBuc MNrw NLar
	x ***hopwoodiana***	CFwr CSpe CTca EBee EGle ELan EPPr EPfP GMac LAst LHop LPio MNrw MRav NBPC NBir NCGa NDov NRnb SAga SPer SPhx WAbb WCAu WLin WMoo WPnP WPrP WPtf WWlt
*	x ***hybrida*** 'Jean Jabber'	EBee EWll GBuc MRav NLar NPro
	hyparctica	MDKP
	- ***nana***	LBee LRHS WPat
	'Jack Elliot'	NPro WWeb
	'Light My Fire'	LTwo MAvo MBNS NBPC NMoo
	'Mandshurica'	see *P. fruticosa* 'Manchu'
	'Maynard's'	NDov
§	***megalantha*** ♀H4	More than 30 suppliers
	- 'Gold Sovereign'	EBee ENot EPfP NPro SPoG
	'Melton'	EBee MNrw NBir NOak WHen
*	'Melton Fire'	CEnt CWan ECtt EShb LAst LEdu MNHC MWrn NBir SBri SGar WFar WMnd WMoo WPnP
	'Monarch's Velvet'	see *P. thurberi* 'Monarch's Velvet'
	'Monsieur Rouillard' (d)	CSam CTca EBee GCra IPot MCot MNrw MRav MWat NGdn WHal WHoo WLin WMnd
	'Mont d'Or'	MRav
	montana	WHer WPer
	nepalensis	CEnt EBee EPPr LAst MLHP NBro NChi NPro SBri SHFr WBrk WGwG
	- 'Flammenspiel'	WFar
	- 'Master Floris'	SAga WFar WHal
§	- 'Miss Willmott' ♀H4	More than 30 suppliers
	- 'Ron McBeath'	More than 30 suppliers
	- 'Roxana'	EBee ECGP ELan ERou GBuc GSki MBNS MRav NBro WAbb WFar WMoo WPer WRos
	- 'Shogran'	COIW EBee EWTr GAbr GBuc GMac LAst MWrn NCGa NGby NLar NPro NVic WHil WWeb
§	***neumanniana***	NBir NPri XPep
	- 'Goldrausch'	LEdu
§	- 'Nana'	ECho EPot LBee LRHS MHer NEgg NLAp NLar NMen NRya SPlb SRms WEas WFar WMoo WPat
	nevadensis	CLyd CTri ECho GEdr SRms WPer
	nitida	GEdr GKev NMen SRms WAbe
	- 'Alba'	ECho EPot NLAp NMen WAbe
	- 'Lissadell'	CPBP SBla
	- 'Rubra'	CFir ECho EDAr GCrs NBir NLAp NWCA SAga SBla SRms WAbe WFar WPat
	nivalis	ECho
*	'Olympic Mountains'	WPer
	ovina	WPer
	palustris	EBee NLar WMoo
	pamiroalaica	WLin
	parvifolia 'Klondike'	see *P. fruticosa* 'Klondike'
	pedata	LLWP
	pensylvanica	NEgg
	'Pink Orleans'	WWeb
	'Pink Panther'[PBR]	see *P. fruticosa* Princess = 'Blink'
	recta	COIW ELau EMan ERou EWin MNHC NPri WRos
	- 'Alba'	EGoo GMaP LAst NBre NEgg WPer
	- 'Citrina'	see *P. recta* var. *sulphurea*
	- 'Macrantha'	see *P. recta* 'Warrenii'
§	- var. ***sulphurea***	CEnt CMea CSam CSsd EBee EGoo GSki IGor MLHP MNrw NBir NBre SIng SPhx WCAu WFar WHal WHoo WLin WMnd WMoo WPer WPtf WTin
§	- 'Warrenii'	CSBt EBee EPla GMaP LAst LRHS MBNS MRav MWat NBir NEgg SIng SPer SRms WCAu WFar WHal WMoo WPer
	reptans	CRWN XPep
	'Roxanne' (d)	MHer
	rupestris	EBee ECha MLLN MNrw NDlv NEgg NSti SBri SGar WCAu WFar WHal WMoo WPer
	simplex	EBee NBre
	speciosa	EWes IGor WMoo
	sterilis	CHid WSFF
	'Sungold'	ECho WHCG
	tabernaemontani	see *P. neumanniana*
	ternata	see *P. aurea* subsp. *chrysocraspeda*
	thurberi	CAby CHFP EBee EGle GMac MMHG MNFA MNrw NBHF NLar NMoo SHGN SPhx WMoo
§	- 'Monarch's Velvet'	More than 30 suppliers
	- 'Pirate's Gold'	NPro
	tommasiniana	see *P. cinerea*
	x ***tonguei*** ♀H4	More than 30 suppliers
	tormentilla	see *P. erecta*
	'Twinkling Star'	EBee GMac NCGa

	uniflora	GCrs
	verna	see *P. neumanniana*
	– 'Pygmaea'	see *P. neumanniana* 'Nana'
	villosa	see *P. crantzii*
	'Volcan'	CMea CMil EBee EWTr EWes MBNS MBri NChi NDov NPro SAga SMHy SPhx WAbb WCra WFar WHal WPGP
	'White Queen'	EBee EWll MNrw NBre NCob SHar SPoG
	'William Rollison' ΨH4	More than 30 suppliers
	willmottiae	see *P. nepalensis* 'Miss Willmott'
	'Yellow Queen'	CBcs CTri EMil EPfP ERou GMaP GSki LHop MBNS MNrw MRav NHol SPer SWat WCAu WFar

Poterium see *Sanguisorba*

	sanguisorba	see *Sanguisorba minor*

Prasium (*Lamiaceae*)

	majus	XPep

Pratia (*Campanulaceae*)

§	***angulata***	CPLG
	– 'Jack's Pass'	ECho
	– 'Tim Rees'	EDAr
§	– 'Treadwellii'	EAlp ECha ECho EDAr EWin GEdr GGar GMac LRHS SPlb WHal WHen
	– 'Woodside'	ECho ECou EDAr NSfd
	angulata* x *pedunculata	GGar
	'Celestial Spice'	ECou EDAr NSfd
	irrigua	NSfd
§	***pedunculata***	CBrm CPLG CTca CTri ECha ECho ECou ECtt EDAr ELan GGar LBee LRHS MBar NChi NVic SBla SIng SPet SPlb SPoG SRms WFar WHen WHoo WMoo WPer WPtf
	– 'Blue Stars'	EDAr NSfd
	– 'County Park'	CEnt CSpe CTri EAlp ECha ECho ECou EDAr ELan EPfP GAbr GGar ITim MBar SBla SIng SPlb SPoG SRms WHoo WMoo WPat WPer
	– 'Kiandra'	ECou
	– 'Tom Stone'	MBNS
§	***perpusilla***	ECou EDAr
	– 'Fragrant Carpet'	ECou EDAr NSfd
	– 'Summer Meadows'	ECou

Prenanthes (*Asteraceae*)

§	***alba***	EBee

Preslia see *Mentha*

Primula ✿ (*Primulaceae*)

	CC 4070	CPLG
	Lismore 79-26	NHol
	acaulis	see *P. vulgaris*
	'Adrian Jones' (Au)	IPen ITim NHol WAbe
	'Alan Robb' (Pr/Prim/d)	CWCL EPfP NCGa NGHP NHol SPer SRGP WFar
	'Alexina' (*allionii* hybrid) (Au)	ITim MFie NHar
	algida (Al)	ECho GKev
	'Alice Collins' **new**	CGra
	allioni 'Hartside 12' (Au) **new**	IPen
§	***allionii*** (Au) ΨH2	IPen LRHS MFie NSum WAbe
	– HNG 12	ITim
	– Hartside 383/3	NHol
	– 'A.K. Wells' (Au)	ITim WAbe
	– 'Agnes' (Au)	ITim NMen
	– 'Aire Waves'	see *P.* x *loiseleurii* 'Aire Waves'
*	– 'Alexander' (Au)	CGra
	– 'Amy' (Au)	ITim
	– 'Andrew' (Au)	CGra
	– 'Anna Griffith' (Au)	IPen LRHS MFie NRya NWCA WAbe WLin
	– 'Anne' (Au)	IPen NDlv
	– 'Aphrodite' (Au)	NHar
	– 'Apple Blossom' (Au)	GAbr GKev
	– 'Archer' (Au)	IPen ITim NDlv NHol WLin
	– 'Ares' (Au)	NHar
	– 'Aries Violet' (Au)	NHar
	– 'Austen' (Au)	IPen ITim NDlv
	– 'Avalanche' (Au)	IPen ITim MFie WAbe
	– 'Bill Martin' (Au)	EPot IPen ITim
	– 'Blood Flake'	IPen ITim
	– 'Brilliant' (Au)	WAbe
	– 'Cherry' **new**	CGra
	– 'Chivalry' (Au)	CGra
	– 'Circes Flute' **new**	NHar
	– 'Crowsley Variety' (Au)	LRHS NMen NWCA WAbe
	– 'Crusader' (Au)	ITim WThu
	– 'Duncan' (Au)	ITim
§	– 'Edinburgh' (Au)	IPen ITim MFie NHol
	– 'Edrom' (Au)	IPen ITim
	– 'Elizabeth Baker' (Au)	IPen ITim MFie WAbe
	– 'Elizabeth Earle' (Au)	ITim WAbe
	– 'Elliott's Large'	see *P. allionii* 'Edinburgh'
	– 'Elliott's Variety'	see *P. allionii* 'Edinburgh'
	– 'Eureka' (Au)	CGra
	– 'Fanfare' (Au)	IPen LRHS NHar WGwG WLin
	– 'Frank Barker' (Au)	IPen NHol
	– 'Gavin Brown' (Au)	IPen ITim
	– GFS 1984 (Au)	CGra
	– 'Gilderdale Glow' (Au)	CGra NRya
	– 'Giuseppi's Form'	see *P. allionii* 'Mrs Dyas'
	– 'Grandiflora' (Au)	ITim
	– 'Hartside 12' x 'Appleblossom' **new**	CGra
	– 'Hartside 6' (Au) **new**	IPen NHar
	– 'Hemswell' (Au)	NHol
	– 'Hocker Edge' (Au)	MFie NHol
	– 'Huntsman' (Au)	MFie
	– Ingwersen's form (Au)	IPen
	– 'Io 2' **new**	NHar
	– 'Ions Amethyst' **new**	NHar
	– 'Jenny' (Au)	CGra WLin
	– 'Joe Elliott' (Au) **new**	IPen
	– 'Joseph Collins' (Au)	CGra
	– 'Julia' (Au)	CGra
	– K R W	see *P. allionii* 'Ken's Seedling'
§	– 'Kath Dryden' (Au)	GCrs GKev IPen
§	– 'Ken's Seedling' (Au)	IPen
	– 'Lacewing' (Au) **new**	CGra
	– 'Laura Louise' **new**	CGra
	– 'Little O' (Au)	WAbe
	– 'Lucy' **new**	NHar
	– 'Malcolm' (Au)	CGra
	– 'Margaret Earle' (Au)	WAbe
	– 'Marjorie Wooster' (Au)	IPen ITim MFie NWCA SBla WAbe
	– 'Martin' (Au)	IPen ITim
	– 'Mary Berry' (Au)	CGra IPen MFie WAbe
	– 'Mentors' (Au) **new**	CGra
	– 'Minuet' (Au)	WLin
	– 'Molly' (Au) **new**	IPen
§	– 'Mrs Dyas' (Au)	IPen ITim NHol WAbe
	– 'Neon' **new**	CGra
	– 'Neptunes Wave' (Au)	NHar
	– 'New Dawn' (Au)	NHar
I	– 'Norma' (Au)	WAbe
	– 'Peggy Wilson' (Au)	GKev NLar
	– 'Pennine Pink' (Au)	MFie
	– 'Perkie' (Au)	IPen
	– 'Picton's Variety' (Au)	NDlv
	– 'Pink Ice' (Au)	GCai GCrs ITim NHol
	– 'Pinkie' (Au)	CGra
	– 'Praecox' (Au)	CGra IPen
	– 'Raymond Wooster' (Au)	GKev LRHS NHol

- 'Robert' (Au)	CGra
- 'Scimitar' (Au)	CGra MFie NHol
- 'Snowflake' (Au)	CGra GKev IPen ITim LRHS MFie NWCA WAbe
- 'Stanton House' (Au)	NDlv
- 'Stephen' (Au)	ITim
- 'Tranquillity' (Au)	ITim MFie NHar NHol WAbe
- 'Travellers' (Au)	IPen
- 'William Earle' (Au)	GCrs GKev ITim LRHS MFie NDlv NHol NWCA WAbe
allionii x ***auricula*** 'Blairside Yellow' (Au)	CPBP CStu ECho IPen ITim NSum
allionii x ***auricula*** 'Old Red Dusty Miller' (Au)	CStu ECho GCrs MFie
allionii x ***clusiana*** (Au)	ECho
allionii x ***hirsuta*** (Au)	ITim MFie NHol NLAp SIng
allionii x 'Lismore Treasure' (Au)	CPBP NWCA
allionii x ***pedemontana***	see *P.* x *sendtneri*
allionii x ***pubescens*** (Au)	ECho
allionii x ***pubescens*** 'Harlow Car' (Au)	CLyd ITim
allionii x 'Snow Ruffles' (Au)	ITim
allionii x 'White Linda Pope' (Au)	IPen MFie NHar
alpicola (Si) 🏆H4	CFee CSWP CWCL EBee EPfP EShb GAbr GCrs GEdr GGar GKev IPen LRHS MFOX MFie NBHF NBid NBro NDlv NGdn NHol NLAp NPen NRnb NSum NWCA SPer WBVN WLin
- var. ***alba*** (Si)	CDWL CSWP EBee GBuc GEdr GGar GKev IPen MNrw NBid NLAp NPen SWat
§ - var. ***alpicola*** (Si)	CLAP CSWP EBee GBuc GCra GEdr GKev IPen MNrw
- hybrids (Si)	NEgg NRnb STes
- 'Kevock Sky' (Si)	EBee GKev
- var. ***luna***	see *P. alpicola* var. *alpicola*
- var. ***violacea*** (Si)	CAby CDWL CLAP CSWP EBee GCra GGar GKev IPen LRHS MFie MNrw NBid NPen SWat WGwG WPer
'Altaica'	see *P. elatior* subsp. *meyeri*
altaica grandiflora	see *P. elatior* subsp. *meyeri*
'Amanda Gabrielle' (Au)	CGra
'Amethyst' (Pr/Poly)	WSHC
amethystina (Am)	WAbe
- SDR 4745	GKev
amoena	see *P. elatior* subsp. *meyeri*
angustifolia (Pa)	WAbe
anisodora	see *P. wilsonii* var. *anisodora*
'Annemijne'	EMon
x ***arctotis***	see *P.* x *pubescens*
aurantiaca (Pf)	CFir EBee GBuc GCai GEdr GKev IPen SRms
aureata (Pe)	WAbe
auricula L. (Au) 🏆H4	EDAr IPen LRHS MFie MHer NBro NSla SPer SPet SPlb SPoG WAbe
- var. ***albocincta*** (Au)	EBee NWCA
- subsp. ***bauhinii*** (Au)	GKev
auricula ambig. (Au)	MFie WRHF
auricula misapplied '2nd Vic' (Au)	SPop WFar WHil
- A74 (Au)	NCob
- 'Abrigde' (Au/d)	WAln
- 'Achates' (Au/A)	WAln
- 'Admiral' (Au/A)	WAln
- 'Adrian' (Au/A)	GAbr IPen MAsh MFie NBro SPop WHil
- 'Adrienne Ruan' (Au/A)	WAln
- 'Aga Khan' (Au/A)	WAln
- 'Agamemnon' (Au/A)	MFie WAln

- 'Alamo' (Au/A)	MFie SPop
- 'Alan Ravenscroft' (Au/A)	MFie SPop WAln WFar
- 'Alansford' (Au/A)	WAln
- 'Albert Bailey' (Au/d)	GAbr GCai IPen ITim MFie SPop WAln
- 'Alexandra Georgina' (Au/A)	WAln
- 'Alf' (Au/A)	SPop WAln
- 'Alfred Charles' (Au/A)	WAln
- 'Alfred Niblett' (Au/S)	IPen WLin
- 'Alice Haysom' (Au/S)	CWCL ELan GCai IPen MAsh MFie SDnm SPav SPop WHil WLin
- 'Alicia' (Au/A)	MFie NHol SDnm SPop
- 'Alison Jane' (Au/A)	MFie
- 'Alison Telford' (Au/A)	WHil
- 'Alloway' (Au/d)	WAln
- 'Almand' (Au/d)	WAln
- alpine mixed (Au/A)	EPfP SRms
- 'Amber Light' (Au/S)	WAln
- 'Amicable' (Au/A)	MFie NHol SPop WHil
- 'Ancient Order' (Au/A)	WAln
- 'Ancient Society' (Au/A)	GAbr IPen SPop WHil
- 'Andrea Julie' (Au/A)	IPen ITim MFie SPop WHil WLin
- 'Andrew Hunter' (Au/A)	MFie SPop WAln
- 'Andy Cole' (Au/A)	WAln
- 'Angelo' (Au/A)	WAln
- 'Angie' (Au/d)	WAln
- 'Ann Taylor' (Au/A)	WAln
- 'Anne Hyatt' (Au/d)	GAbr MAsh WAln
- 'Anne Swithinbank' (Au/d)	WAln
- 'Antoc' (Au/S)	SPop
- 'Anwar Sadat' (Au/A)	GAbr MFie SPop WFar
- 'Applecross' (Au/A)	CWCL IPen ITim MFie SPop WHil WLin
- 'April Moon' (Au/S)	SPop WAln
- 'April Tiger' (Au/St)	WAln
- 'Arabian Night' (Au/A)	WAln
- 'Arapaho' (Au/A)	WAln
- 'Arctic Fox'	SPop WAln
- 'Argus' (Au/A)	GAbr MFie NBir NHol SPop WLin
- 'Arlene' (Au/A)	WAln
- 'Arthur Delbridge' (Au/A)	MFie WFar
- 'Arundell' (Au/S/St)	GAbr GCai IPen ITim MAsh MFie NHol SPop WFar WHil WLin
- 'Ashcliffe Gem' (Au/A)	WAln
- 'Ashcliffe Gold' (Au/A)	WAln
- 'Astolat' (Au/S)	CWCL IPen ITim MAsh NRya SDnm SPav SPop WHil WLin
- 'Athene' (Au/S)	WAln
- 'Audacity' (Au/d)	WAln
- 'Aurora' (Au/A)	EDAr MFie
- 'Austin' (Au/A)	IPen WAln
- 'Avon Citronella' (Au)	SPop
- 'Avril' (Au/A)	SPop WAln
- 'Avril Hunter' (Au/A)	IPen ITim MFie NHol SPop
- 'Aztec' (Au/d)	WAln
- 'Bacchante' (Au/d)	WAln
- 'Bacchus' (Au/A)	MFie
- 'Baggage' (Au)	SPop
- 'Balbithan' (Au/B)	GAbr
- 'Baltic Amber' (Au)	SPop
- 'Barbara Mason'	WAln
- 'Barbarella' (Au/S)	MAsh MFie SPop
- Barnhaven doubles (Au/d)	CSWP GAbr NSum
- 'Basilio' (Au/S)	WAln
- 'Basuto' (Au/A)	IPen MFie SPop WHil
- 'Beatrice' (Au/A)	CTri EShb GAbr GCai IPen ITim MFie NHol SPop WFar WHil WLin
- 'Beauty of Bath' (Au/S)	WAln
- 'Beckminster' (Au/A)	WAln
- 'Beechen Green' (Au/S)	GAbr GCai ITim MAsh SPop WLin WOFF
- 'Bellamy Pride' (Au/B)	GAbr MAsh SPop
- 'Belle Zana' (Au/S)	SPop WAln

– 'Bellezana'	IPen MAsh MFie
– 'Ben Lawers' (Au/S)	SPop WLin
– 'Ben Wyves' (Au/S)	NHol SPop
– 'Bendigo' (Au/S)	WAln
– 'Bewitched' (Au/A)	WAln
– 'Big Ben' (Au/S)	ECho
– 'Bilbao' (Au/A)	WAln
– 'Bilbo Baggins' (Au/A)	WAln
– 'Bill Bailey' (Au)	SPop
– 'Black Ice' (Au/S)	WAln
– 'Black Jack'[PBR] (Au/d)	CStu WAln
– 'Black Knight' (Au/d)	WAln
– 'Blackfield' (Au/S)	SPop
– 'Blackhill' (Au/S)	MFie
– 'Blackpool Rock' (Au/St)	WAln
– 'Blairside Yellow' (Au/B)	ECho EWes NLAp NSla
– 'Blakeney' (Au/d)	GCai MFie WAln
– 'Blossom' (Au/A)	GAbr MFie WFar
– 'Blue Bonnet' (Au/A/d)	WAln
– 'Blue Bonnet' (Au/A/d)	GAbr MFie SPop
– 'Blue Chips' (Au/S)	MFie WAln
– 'Blue Cliffs' (Au/S)	WAln
– 'Blue Denim' (Au/S)	WAln
– 'Blue Frills' (Au)	WAln
– 'Blue Heaven'	SPop WLin
– 'Blue Jean' (Au/S)	MFie SPop
– 'Blue Mist' (Au/B)	GAbr
– 'Blue Moon' (Au/S)	WAln
– 'Blue Nile' (Au/S)	SPop
– 'Blue Velvet' (Au/B)	GAbr IPen MFie NBro SPop
– 'Blue Yodeler' (Au/A) **new**	SPop
– 'Blush Baby' (Au/St) **new**	SPop WLin
– 'Bob Lancashire' (Au/S)	IPen ITim MFie NHol SPop WCot WHil
– 'Bokay' (Au/d)	WAln
– 'Bold Tartan' (Au/St)	WAln
– 'Bolero' (Au/A)	SPop
– 'Bollin Tiger' (Au/St)	WAln
– 'Bonafide' (Au/d)	WAln
– 'Bonanza' (Au/S)	WAln
– 'Bookham Firefly' (Au/A)	IPen MFie NHol NRya SPop WFar WHil WLin
– 'Boromir' (Au/A)	WAln
– 'Boy Blue' (Au/S)	WAln
– 'Bradford City' (Au/A)	SDnm SPav
– 'Branno' (Au/S)	WAln
– 'Brasso' (Au)	WAln
– 'Brazen Hussy' (Au/d)	WAln
– 'Brazil' (Au/S)	EBee GAbr IPen ITim LRHS MFie SPav SPop WHil
– 'Brazos River' (Au/A)	WAln
– 'Brenda's Choice' (Au/A)	IPen MFie WFar
– 'Brentford Bees' (Au/St)	WAln
– 'Bright Eyes' (Au/A)	IPen MFie
– 'Broad Gold' (Au/A)	SPop WAln
– 'Broadwell Gold' (Au/B)	GAbr NLar SPop
– 'Brompton' (Au/S)	WAln
– 'Brookfield' (Au/S)	IPen ITim MAsh MFie SPop
– 'Broughton' (Au/S)	MFie SPop
– 'Brown Ben' (Au)	MFie
– 'Brown Bess' (Au/A)	GAbr GCai IPen ITim MAsh MFie SPop WLin
– 'Brownie' (Au/B)	ITim NBir SDnm SPav WLin
– 'Buccaneer'	ECho WAln
– 'Bucks Green' (Au/S)	SPop
– 'Bunty' (Au/A)	MFie
– 'Butterwick' (Au/A)	GAbr GMaP IPen LRHS MBNS MFie SPav SPop WLin
– 'C.G. Haysom' (Au/S)	GAbr NRya SPop
– 'C.W. Needham' (Au/A)	CWCL IPen NLAp SPop
– 'Calypso' (Au/d)	WAln
– 'Cambodunum' (Au/A)	MFie SPop
– 'Camelot' (Au/d)	ECho ELan GCai MFie NBro NHol SPop WFar
– 'Cameo Beauty' (Au/d)	SPop
– 'Camilla' (Au/A)	WAln
– 'Candida' (Au/d)	SPop WAln
– 'Caramel' (Au/A)	WAln
– 'Carioca' (Au/A)	WAln
– 'Carole' (Au/A)	MFie WLin
– 'Catherine Redding' (Au/d)	WAln
– 'Catherine Wheel' (Au/St)	WAln
– 'Chaffinch' (Au/S)	GAbr SPop
– 'Chamois' (Au/B)	GAbr WHil WLin
– 'Channel' (Au/S)	WAln
– 'Chantilly Cream' (Au/d)	WAln
– 'Charles Bronson' (Au/d)	WAln
– 'Charles Rennie' (Au/B)	WAln
– 'Charlie's Aunt' (Au/A)	WAln
– 'Checkmate' (Au)	SPop WAln
– 'Chelsea Bridge' (Au/A)	IPen MFie SPop
– 'Cherry' (Au/S)	GAbr IPen ITim MFie
– 'Cherry Picker' (Au/A)	MFie SPop WFar
– 'Cheyenne' (Au/S)	GAbr MAsh MFie WLin
– 'Chiffon' (Au/S)	SPop WAln
– 'Chirichua' (Au/S)	WAln
– 'Chloris' (Au/S)	NBir WAln
– 'Chorister' (Au/S)	EBee ECho GAbr GCai IPen ITim MFie NBir NHol NPri WHil WLin
– 'Cicero' (Au/A)	WAln
– 'Cindy' (Au/A)	ECho
– 'Cinnamon' (Au/d)	MAsh MFie SPop WLin
– 'Ciribiribin' (Au/A)	WAln
– 'Clare' (Au/S)	MAsh MFie NRya SPop
– 'Clatter-Ha' (Au/d)	GCrs MAsh
– 'Claudia Taylor' (Au)	WLin
– 'Clouded Yellow' (Au/S)	SPop WAln
– 'Cloudy Bay' (Au)	WCot
– 'Cloverdale' (Au/d)	WAln
– 'Clunie' (Au/S)	IPen
– 'Clunie II' (Au/S)	IPen ITim WFar
– 'Cobden Meadows' (Au/A)	WAln
– 'Coffee' (Au/S)	CWCL MAsh MFie NRya WFar WLin WOFF
– 'Colbury' (Au/S)	SPop
– 'Colonel Champney' (Au/S)	ITim MFie SPop
– 'Comet' (Au/S)	IPen WHil
– 'Confederate' (Au/S)	WAln
– 'Connaught Court' (Au/A)	WAln
– 'Conservative' (Au/S)	GAbr WLin
– 'Consett' (Au/S)	MFie WHil
– 'Coppi' (Au/A)	IPen SPop WAln WLin
– 'Coral' (Au/S)	MFie WHil
– 'Coral Sea' (Au/S)	WAln
– 'Cornmeal' (Au/S)	ITim MFie WAln
– 'Corntime' (Au/S)	WAln
– 'Corporal Kate' (Au/St)	WAln
– 'Corrie Files' (Au/d)	WAln
– 'Cortez Silver' (Au/S)	WAln
– 'Cortina' (Au/S)	ECho GAbr GCai ITim NRya SDnm SPav SPop WFar WHil WLin
– 'County Park Red' (Au/B)	ECou
– 'Crackley Tagetes' (Au/d)	ECho
– 'Craig Vaughan' (Au/A)	MFie NHol WLin
– 'Cranbourne' (Au/A)	WAln
– 'Crecy' (Au/A)	WAln
– 'Crimson Glow' (Au/d)	NLAp SPop WAln WOFF
– 'Cuckoo Fair'	GAbr SPop
– 'Cuckoo Fare' (Au/S)	WAln
– 'Cuddles' (Au/A)	WAln
– 'Curry Blend' (Au/B)	GAbr
– 'Daftie Green' (Au/S)	GAbr IPen WHil
– 'Dales Red' (Au/B)	GAbr ITim MFie SDnm SPop WAln WHil WLin
– 'Dan Tiger' (Au/St)	ITim MFie WAln
– 'Daniel' (Au/A)	WAln
– 'Daphnis' (Au/S)	WAln

- 'Dark Eyes' (Au/d) NLAp SPop WAln WLin
- 'Dark Lady' (Au/A) WAln
- 'Dark Red' (Au/S) **new** IPen
- 'David Beckham' (Au/d) WAln
- 'Decaff' (Au/St) WAln
- 'Deckchair' (Au) SPop
- 'Dedham' (Au/d) WAln
- 'Delilah' (Au/d) GAbr ITim MFie SPop WLin
- 'Denise' (Au/S) WAln
- 'Denna Snuffer' (Au/d) GAbr NLAp
- 'Devon Cream' (Au/d) ECho ITim MFie SPop WFar
- 'Diamond' (Au/d) WAln
- 'Diane' (Au/A) MFie
- 'Digby' (Au/d) WAln
- 'Digit' (Au/d) WAln

* - 'Dill' (Au/A) WAln
- 'Dilly Dilly' (Au/A) SPop WAln
- 'Divint Dunch' (Au/A) IPen MFie SPop WFar
- 'Doctor Duthie' (Au/S) SPop WAln
- 'Doctor Jones' (Au/d) WAln
- 'Doctor Lennon's White' (Au/B) GAbr IPen MFie SPop
- 'Dolly Viney' (Au/d) WAln
- 'Donhead' (Au/A) MFie SPop WFar
- 'Donna Clancy' (Au/S) MFie SPop
- 'Dorado' (Au/d) WAln
- 'Doreen Stephens' (Au/A) WAln WFar
- 'Doris Jean' (Au/A) MFie
- 'Dorothy' (Au/S) WAln
- 'Doublet' (Au/d) ECho GAbr GCai IPen MFie NHol SPop WFar WHil WLin
- 'Doubloon' (Au/d) ECho
- 'Doublure' (Au/d) GAbr SPop
- 'Douglas Bader' (Au/A) MFie SPop
- 'Douglas Black' (Au/S) GAbr SPop WLin
- 'Douglas Blue' (Au/S) WAln
- 'Douglas Gold' (Au) WLin
- 'Douglas Green' (Au/S) IPen SPop
- 'Douglas Red' (Au/A) WLin
- 'Douglas White' (Au/S) MFie SPop
- 'Dovedale' (Au/S) WAln
- 'Doyen' (Au/d) ITim MAsh MFie WAln
- 'Drax' (Au/A) WAln
- 'Dubarii' (Au/A) WAln
- 'Duchess of Malfi' (Au/S) SPop
- 'Duchess of York' (Au) GBuc WCot

* - 'Dusky' (Au) WLin
- 'Dusky Girl' (Au/A) WAln
- 'Dusky Maiden' (Au/A) GCai MFie SPop WHil WLin
- 'Dusky Yellow' (Au/B) ECho
- 'Dusty Miller' (Au/B) ECho MRav NBir NHol
- 'Eastern Promise' (Au/A) GCai MFie SPop WFar
- 'Eddy Gordon' (Au/A) WAln
- 'Eden Carmine' (Au/B) MFie
- 'Eden David' (Au/B) MFie SPop WLin
- 'Edith Allen' (Au/A) WAln
- 'Edith Major' (Au/d) MFie
- 'Edward Sweeney' (Au/S) WAln
- 'Eli Jenkins' (Au) WAln
- 'Elizabeth Ann' (Au/A) GAbr IPen
- 'Ellen Thompson' (Au/A) GAbr MFie SPop WFar WLin
- 'Elsie May' (Au/A) ITim MAsh MFie SPop WLin
- 'Elsinore' (Au/S) MAsh
- 'Emberglow' (Au/d) WAln
- 'Embley' (Au/S) ITim SPop
- 'Emery Down' (Au/S) SPop WLin
- 'Emmett Smith' (Au/A) WAln
- 'Enigma' (Au/S) WAln
- 'Envy' (Au/S) NHol WAln
- 'Erica' (Au/A) IPen ITim MFie SPop WLin
- 'Erjon' (Au/S) MFie SPop WAln
- 'Error' (Au/S) WAln
- 'Ethel' (Au) WHil
- 'Etna' (Au/S) WAln
- 'Ettrick' (Au/S) WAln
- 'Eventide' (Au/S) EBee ITim SPop
- 'Everest Blue' (Au/S) GAbr MAsh SPop WOFF
- 'Excalibur' (Au/d) SPop WAln WLin
- (Exhibition Series) 'Exhibition Blau' (Au/B) MFie
- - 'Exhibition Gelb' (Au/B) MFie
- - 'Exhibition Rot' (Au/B) MFie
- 'Eyeopener' (Au/A) SPop WAln
- 'Fairy' (Au/A) WAln
- 'Fairy Moon' (Au/S) WAln
- 'Falaraki' (Au/A) SPop WAln
- 'Falstaff' (Au/d) WAln
- 'Fanciful' (Au/S) MFie WLin
- 'Fancy Free' (Au) SPop
- 'Fandancer' (Au/A) WAln
- 'Fanfare' (Au/S) MFie SPop WAln
- 'Fanny Meerbeck' (Au/S) GAbr GCai IPen MFie SPop WFar WLin
- 'Faro' (Au/S) MAsh WAln
- 'Favourite' (Au/S) GAbr IPen ITim MFie NHol SPop WFar WHil WLin
- 'Fen Tiger' (Au/St) WAln
- 'Fennay' (Au/S) WAln
- 'Ferrybridge' (Au/A) **new** IPen
- 'Fiddler's Green' (Au) GAbr SPop
- 'Figaro' (Au/S) GAbr MFie SPop WAln WLin
- 'Finchfield' (Au/A) IPen NHol
- 'Firecracker' (Au) WAln
- 'Firenze' (Au/A) MFie SPop
- 'Firsby' (Au/d) MAsh SPop WAln
- 'First Lady' (Au/A) WAln
- 'Fishtoft' (Au/d) WAln
- 'Fitzroy' (Au/d) **new** SPop
- 'Fleminghouse' (Au/S) MAsh SPop
- 'Florence Brown' (Au/S) ITim
- 'Forest Pines' (Au/S) WAln
- 'Fradley' (Au/A) WAln
- 'Frank Bailey' (Au/d) MAsh SPop WAln
- 'Frank Crosland' (Au/A) CStu ITim MFie WHil
- 'Frank Faulkner' (Au/A) WAln
- 'Frank Jenning' (Au/A) WAln
- 'Fred Booley' (Au/d) GAbr ITim MAsh NHol SPop WHil WLin
- 'Fred Livesley' (Au/A) WAln
- 'Fresco' (Au/A) SPop
- 'Friskney' (Au/d) WAln
- 'Frittenden Yellow' (Au/B) GAbr SPop WLin
- 'Fuller's Red' (Au/S) SPop WFar
- 'Funny Valentine' (Au/d) **new** SPop
- 'Fuzzy' (Au/St) WAln WLin
- 'G.L. Taylor' (Au/A) **new** IPen
- 'Gaia' (Au/d) SPop WAln
- 'Galatea' (Au/S) WAln
- 'Galen' (Au/A) MFie WFar
- 'Ganymede' (Au/d) WAln
- 'Gary Pallister' (Au/A) MAsh WAln
- 'Gavin Ward' (Au/S) WAln
- 'Gay Crusader' (Au/A) GAbr ITim MFie SPop
- 'Gazza' (Au/A) WAln
- 'Gee Cross' (Au/A) IPen SPop

§ - 'Geldersome Green' (Au/S) GCai MAsh MFie SPop WLin
- 'Generosity' (Au/A) SPop
- 'Geordie' (Au/A) WAln
- 'George Harrison' (Au/B) GAbr
- 'George Jennings' (Au/A) MFie WAln
- 'George Stephens' (Au/A) WAln
- 'Geronimo' (Au/S) MAsh MFie SPop WLin
- 'Girl Guide' (Au/S) WAln
- 'Gizabroon' (Au/S) CWCL GCai MFie SDnm SPav SPop WLin
- 'Glasnost' (Au/S) WAln

- 'Gleam' (Au/S)	CWCL EBee ECho EDAr GCai ITim LTwo MFie SPop WFar WHil WLin
- 'Glencoe' (Au/S)	ECho
- 'Gleneagles' (Au/S)	EShb GCai IPen SPop WAln
- 'Glenelg' (Au/S)	GAbr GCrs MAsh MFie SPop WHil WLin
- 'Glenna Goodwin' (Au/d)	WAln
- 'Gnome' (Au/B)	GAbr IPen NHol
- 'Gold Seam' (Au/A)	WAln
- 'Golden Boy' (Au/A)	WAln
- 'Golden Eye' (Au/S)	WAln
- 'Golden Fleece' (Au/S)	GAbr GCai MFie SPop
- 'Golden Glory' (Au/A)	WAln
- 'Golden Hill' (Au/S)	SPop
- 'Golden Hind' (Au/d)	NBro SPop WLin
- 'Golden Splendour' (Au/d)	IPen MAsh MFie NLAp SPop
- 'Golden Wedding' (Au/A)	IPen SPop WAln
- 'Goldwin' (Au/A)	WAln
- 'Gollum' (Au/A)	WAln
- 'Good Report' (Au/A)	MFie SPop WFar
- 'Grabley' (Au/S)	SPop WAln
- 'Grandad's Favourite' (Au/B)	SPop
- 'Green Finger' (Au/S)	SPop
- 'Green Frill' (Au)	ITim
- 'Green Goddess' (Au/St)	WAln
- 'Green Isle' (Au/S)	GAbr MAsh MFie NBir SPop WFar WLin
- 'Green Jacket' (Au/S)	IPen WLin
- 'Green Magic' (Au/S)	WAln
- 'Green Meadows' (Au/S)	SPop WAln
- 'Green Mustard' (Au/S) **new**	WLin
- 'Green Parrot' (Au/S)	SPop WHil
- 'Green Shank' (Au/S)	IPen SPop WLin
- 'Green Woodpecker' (Au/S) **new**	ITim
- 'Greenfield's Fancy' (Au)	CStu EBee ENot
- 'Greenfinger' (Au/S)	WAln
- 'Greenheart' (Au/S)	CWCL
- 'Greenpeace' (Au/S)	LRHS SPop WLin
- 'Greensleeves' (Au/S)	SPop
- 'Greenways' (Au/S)	WAln
- 'Greta' (Au/S)	EBee ECho GAbr IPen ITim NHol SPop WCot WFar WHil WLin
- 'Gretna Green' (Au/S)	MAsh SPop
- 'Grey Dawn' (Au/S)	WAln
- 'Grey Edge'	ECho
- 'Grey Friar' (Au/S)	WAln
- 'Grey Hawk' (Au/S)	MFie SPop
- 'Grey Lady' (Au/S)	WAln
- 'Grey Lag' (Au/S)	MFie
- 'Grey Monarch' (Au/S)	GCai ITim MAsh MFie SPop WLin
- 'Grey Owl' (Au/S)	MAsh WAln
- 'Grey Shrike' (Au/S)	WAln
- 'Grizedale' (Au/S)	WAln
- 'Grüner Veltliner' (Au/S) **new**	SPop
- 'Guildersome Green'	see *P. auricula* misapplied 'Geldersome Green'
- 'Guinea' (Au/S)	GAbr MFie SPop WLin
- 'Gwen' (Au/A)	MFie SPop WAln
- 'Gwen Baker' (Au/d)	SPop
- 'Gwen Gaulthiers' (Au/S)	WAln
- 'Gwenda' (Au/A)	SPop WAln WHil
- 'Gypsy Rose Lee' (Au/A)	WAln
- 'Habanera' (Au/A)	MFie SPop WFar
- 'Hadrian's Shooting Star' (Au/d)	WAln
- 'Haffner' (Au/S)	SPop WAln
- 'Hallmark' (Au/A)	WAln
- 'Hardley' (Au/S)	WAln
- 'Harmony' (Au/B)	MFie NBro NHol
- 'Harry Hotspur' (Au/A)	IPen MFie SPop WFar
- 'Harry 'O'' (Au/S)	SPop
- 'Harvest Glow' (Au/S)	SPop WHil
- 'Hawkwood' (Au/S)	CWCL IPen ITim MAsh SDnm SPav SPop WFar WHil
- 'Hawkwood Fancy' (Au/S)	MFie WLin
* - 'Hazel' (Au/A)	IPen MFie SPop
- 'Headdress' (Au/S)	CStu GAbr MFie SPop WHil
- 'Heady' (Au/A)	MFie SPop
- 'Heart of Gold' (Au/A)	MFie SPop WAln
- 'Hebers' (Au)	WAln
- 'Helen' (Au/S)	GAbr MFie SPop WHil
- 'Helen Barter' (Au/S)	MFie SPop
- 'Helen Ruane' (Au/d)	SPop WAln WLin
- 'Helena' (Au/S)	IPen ITim MAsh MFie WOFF
- 'Helena Dean' (Au/d)	MAsh WAln
- 'Hetty Woolf' (Au/S)	ECho GAbr ITim NHol
- 'Hew Dalrymple' (Au/S)	ITim SPop
- 'High Hopes' (Au)	WAln
- 'Hinton Admiral' (Au/S)	IPen SPop WAln WLin
- 'Hinton Fields' (Au/S)	CStu CWCL EBee EShb GAbr GCai IPen MAsh MFie SDnm SPav SPop WFar WHil WLin
- 'Hoghton Gem' (Au/d)	WAln
- 'Holyrood' (Au/S)	GAbr ITim SPop
- 'Honey' (Au/d)	NBro SPop WAln
- 'Honeymoon' (Au/S)	WAln
- 'Hopleys Coffee' (Au/d)	GAbr GCai SPop WAln
- 'Hurstwood Midnight' (Au)	MFie
* - 'Hyacinth' (Au/S)	LRHS
- 'Iago' (Au/S)	MAsh WAln
- 'Ian Greville' (Au/A)	IPen SPop WAln
- 'Ibis' (Au/S)	WAln
- 'Ice Maiden' (Au)	SPop WAln
- 'Idmiston' (Au/S)	ECho MAsh SPop WFar WLin
- 'Immaculate' (Au/A)	SPop WAln WHil
- 'Impassioned' (Au/A)	MFie SPop WAln WFar
- 'Impeccable' (Au/A)	WAln
- 'Imperturbable' (Au/A)	MFie WAln
- 'Indian Love Call' (Au/A)	IPen ITim MFie SPop WFar WHil
- 'Isabel' (Au/S)	WAln
- 'Isabella' (Au)	WAln
- 'Jack Dean' (Au/A)	MFie NHol SPop WAln WFar WHil
- 'James Arnot' (Au/S)	GAbr IPen MFie NRya SPop
- 'Jane' (Au/S)	WAln
- 'Jane Myers' (Au/d)	WAln
- 'Janet' (Au)	ECho GEdr
- 'Janie Hill' (Au/A)	MFie
- 'Jean Fielder' (Au/A)	SPop WAln
- 'Jean Jacques' (Au/A)	WAln
- 'Jeanne' (Au/A)	MFie
- 'Jeannie Telford' (Au/A)	MFie SPop
- 'Jenny' (Au/A)	EBee ECho GEdr IPen ITim MBNS MFie SPop WFar WHil
- 'Jersey Bounce' (Au/A)	WAln
- 'Jesmond' (Au/S)	WAln
- 'Jessie' (Au/d)	WAln
- 'Joan Elliott' (Au/A)	GAbr
- 'Joanne' (Au/A)	MFie
- 'Joe Perks' (Au/A)	IPen MFie SPop WAln WFar WHil
- 'Joel' (Au/S)	IPen MFie SPop WAln
- 'John Stewart' (Au/A)	MFie
- 'John Wayne' (Au/A)	MAsh MFie
- 'John Woolf' (Au/S)	ECho
- 'Jonathon' (Au/A)	WAln
- 'Joy' (Au/A)	CWCL ECho IPen LTwo MFie SPop WHil
- 'Joyce' (Au/A)	GAbr IPen MFie NBir SPop
- 'Julia' (Au/S)	WAln
- 'June' (Au/A)	MFie WAln
- 'Jungfrau' (Au/d)	WAln
- 'Jupiter' (Au/S)	WAln
- 'Jura' (Au/A)	WAln
- 'Just Steven' (Au/A)	WAln

- 'Karen Cordrey' (Au/S) EBee ECho GAbr GKev IPen ITim MAsh MFie NHol SDnm SPav SPop WFar WHil WLin
- 'Karen McDonald' (Au/A) SPop
- 'Kath Dryden' see *P. allionii* 'Kath Dryden'
- 'Kelso' (Au/A) MFie
- 'Ken Chilton' (Au/A) MFie WAln WFar WHil
- 'Kentucky Blues' (Au/d) SPop
- 'Kercup' (Au/A) MFie SPop
- 'Kevin Keegan' (Au/A) SPop WHil
- 'Key West' (Au/A) WAln
- 'Khachaturian' (Au/A) WAln
- 'Kim' (Au/A) IPen MFie
- 'Kingcup' (Au/A) MFie SPop
- 'Kingfisher' (Au/A) ITim SPop WHil
- 'Kiowa' (Au/S) ITim SPop
- 'Kirklands' (Au/d) ITim MFie SPop WHil
- 'Klondyke' (Au/A) WAln
- 'Kohinoor' (Au) MFie
- 'Königin der Nacht' (Au/St) WAln WHil
- 'Lady Daresbury' (Au/A) MFie SPop WFar
- 'Lady Diana' (Au/S) WAln
- 'Lady Emma Monson' (Au/S) ITim
- 'Lady of the Vale' (Au/A) WAln
- 'Lady Penelope' (Au/S) WAln
- 'Lady Zoë' (Au/S) MFie NHol SPop WAln
- 'Lambert's Gold' (Au) GAbr SPop
- 'Lamplugh' (Au/d) IPen WHil
- 'Lancelot' (Au/d) SPop WAln
- 'Landy' (Au/A) GCrs MFie SPop WHil
- 'Langley Park' (Au/A) EShb IPen MFie SPop WHil
- 'Lara' (Au/A) MFie WAln
- 'Laredo' (Au/A) WAln
- 'Larry' (Au/A) MFie SPop WAln WFar
- 'Lavender Beauty' (Au) **new** WLin
- 'Lavender Lady' (Au/B) SPav WLin
- 'Lavenham' (Au/S) WAln
- 'Laverock' (Au/S) NBir NBro NHol WHil
- 'Laverock Fancy' (Au/S) GCai IPen MFie NHol
- 'Lazy River' (Au/A) WAln
- 'Leather Jacket' (Au) GAbr
- 'Lechistan' (Au/S) ECho IPen ITim MAsh MFie SPop
- 'Lee' (Au/A) IPen WAln
- 'Lee Clark' (Au/A) WAln
- 'Lee Paul' (Au/A) CStu GAbr GCai IPen MAsh MFie NHol SPop WHil WLin
- 'Lee Sharpe' (Au/A) IPen SPop WAln
- 'Lemmy Getatem' (Au/d) SPop WLin
- 'Lemon Drop' (Au/S) ITim NBro SPop
- 'Lemon Sherbet' (Au/B) MFie
- 'Lepton Jubilee' (Au/S) WAln
- 'Leroy Brown' (Au/A) WAln
- 'Letty' (Au/S) WAln
- 'Leverton' (Au/d) WAln
- 'Lichfield' (Au/A/d) SPop WAln
- 'Light Hearted' (Au) ITim MFie
- 'Light Music' (Au/d) WAln
- 'Lila' (Au/S) WAln
- 'Lilac Domino' (Au/S) GAbr ITim MFie SPop WAln WHil WLin
- 'Lillian Hill' (Au/A) WAln
- 'Lima' (Au/d) WAln
- 'Limelight' (Au/A) SPop WAln
- 'Limelight' (Au/S) WAln
- 'Lincoln Fair' (Au) GAbr
- 'Lincoln Imp' (Au/d) SPop
- 'Lindsey Moreno' (Au/S) WAln
- 'Ling' (Au/A) MFie SPop
- 'Lintz' (Au) **new** WLin
- 'Lisa' (Au/A) ITim MFie SPop WFar WHil WLin
- 'Lisa Clara' (Au/S) EBee GCai IPen ITim MAsh MFie SPop WFar WLin
- 'Lisa's Smile' (Au/S) GCai ITim MFie
- 'Little Rosetta' (Au/d) ITim MFie WAln WHil
- 'Lord Saye and Sele' (Au/St) GAbr GCai IPen ITim MFie SPop WLin
- 'Lothlorien' (Au/A) WAln
- 'Louisa Woolhead' (Au/d) SPop
- 'Lovebird' (Au/S) GAbr ITim MAsh MFie SPop
- 'Lucky Strike' (Au) WAln
- 'Lucy Locket' (Au/B) CWCL NBir NHol WLin
- 'Ludlow' (Au/S) GAbr WAln
- 'Lupy Minstrel' (Au/S) WAln
- 'Lynn' (Au/A) WAln
- 'Lynn Cooper' (Au) WLin
- 'MacWatt's Blue' GAbr IGor SPop
- 'Maggie' (Au/S) GAbr WLin
- 'Maid Marion' (Au/d) MAsh
- 'Maizie' (Au/S) WAln
- 'Mandarin' (Au/A) MFie SPop WFar
- 'Mansell's Green' (Au/S) ITim WAln WHil
- 'Margaret' (Au/S) GAbr
- 'Margaret Dee' (Au/d) WAln
- 'Margaret Faulkner' (Au/A) GAbr GCai MFie WLin
- 'Margaret Irene' (Au/A) IPen SPop WAln WHil
- 'Margaret Martin' (Au/S) IPen SPop WAln WLin
- 'Margot Fonteyn' (Au/A) SPop WAln WHil
- 'Marie Crousse' (Au/d) CMea CPBP CSsd GMaP MFie NHol SPop WFar
- 'Marigold' (Au/d) WFar
- 'Marion Howard Spring' (Au/A) MFie WAln
- 'Marion Tiger' (Au/St) WAln
- 'Mark' (Au/A) IPen MAsh MFie NBro SPop WLin
- 'Marmion' (Au/S) IPen ITim MFie SPop WAln WFar WHil WLin
- 'Martha Livesley' (Au/A) WAln
- 'Martha's Choice' (Au/A) WAln
- 'Martin Luther King' (Au/S) CWCL
- 'Mary' (Au/d) GAbr SPop
- 'Mary Taylor' (Au/S) WAln
- 'Mary Zach' (Au/S) WHil
- 'Matthew Yates' (Au/d) CWCL EBee GAbr GCai IPen ITim MFie NHol NPri SDnm SPav SPop WCot WHil WLin
- 'Maureen Millward' (Au/A) IPen MFie SPop
- 'May' (Au/A) WAln
- 'Mazetta Stripe' (Au/S/St) GAbr ITim NLar SPop
- 'Meadowlark' (Au/A) ITim MFie WAln
- 'Mease Tiger' (Au/St) GAbr WAln
- 'Megan' (Au/d) WAln
- 'Mellifluous' (Au) MFie WAln
- 'Melody' (Au/S) IPen SPop
- 'Mere Green' (Au/S) WAln
- 'Merlin' (Au/A) EBee
- 'Merlin' (Au/S) WAln
- 'Merlin Stripe' (Au/St) ITim MFie SPop WHil
- 'Mermaid' (Au/d) GAbr
- 'Merridale' (Au/A) MFie
- 'Mersey Tiger' (Au/S) GAbr ITim MFie SPop
- 'Metha' (Au/A) MFie WAln
- 'Mexicano' (Au/A) WAln
- 'Michael' (Au/S) WAln
- 'Michael Watham' (Au/S) WAln
- 'Michael Wattam' (Au/S) WAln
- 'Mick' (Au/A) MAsh WAln
- 'Midnight' (Au/A) WAln
- 'Mikado' (Au/S) MAsh MFie SPop WOFF
- 'Milkmaid' (Au/A) WMAq
- 'Millicent' (Au/A) MFie WAln WFar
- 'Mink' (Au/A) MFie WFar WHil
- 'Minley' (Au/S) GCai MFie NBir NBro NHol SPop WHil WLin
- 'Mipsie Miranda' (Au/d) SPop

– 'Mirabella Bay' (Au/A)	WAln
– 'Mirandinha' (Au/A)	MFie WAln
– 'Miriam' (Au/A)	SPop WAln
– 'Mish Mish' (Au/d)	WHil
– 'Miss Bluey' (Au/d)	SPop WAln
– 'Miss Newman' (Au/A)	SPop WAln
– 'Miss Pinky'	SPop
– 'Mojave' (Au/S)	CWCL IPen MAsh MFie NHol NRya SPop WLin
– 'Mollie Langford' (Au/A)	MFie SPop WAln WHil
– 'Monet' (Au/S)	WAln
– 'Moneymoon' (Au/S)	MFie WHil
– 'Monk' (Au/S)	MFie WHil
– 'Monk's Eleigh' (Au/A)	WAln
– 'Moonglow' (Au/S)	MAsh MFie
– 'Moonlight' (Au/S)	GAbr WAln
– 'Moonriver' (Au/A)	ITim MFie NHol SPop WAln WFar WHil
– 'Moonshadow' (Au/d)	WAln
– 'Moonstone' (Au/d)	MFie
– 'Moselle' (Au/S)	WAln
– 'Mr A' (Au/S)	SPop WHil WLin
– 'Mrs L. Hearn' (Au/A)	MFie SPop
– 'Murray Lanes' (Au/A)	WAln
– 'My Fair Lady' (Au/A)	MFie WAln
– 'Myrtle Park' (Au/A)	WAln
– 'Nankenan' (Au/S)	MFie WAln
– 'Naughty' (Au/St) **new**	WLin
– 'Neat and Tidy' (Au/S)	ECho GAbr LRHS MAsh MFie NRya SPop WFar WLin
– 'Nefertiti' (Au/A)	IPen SPop WAln WHil
– 'Nessun Dorma' (Au)	MFie
– 'Nessundorma' (Au/A)	WAln
– 'Neville Telford' (Au/S)	IPen MAsh MFie WLin
– 'Nickity' (Au/A)	GAbr IPen MFie SPop WFar WLin
– 'Nicola Jane' (Au/A)	SPop WAln
– 'Nigel' (Au/d)	GAbr ITim
– 'Nightwink' (Au/S)	WAln
– 'Nina' (Au/A)	WAln
– 'Nita' (Au/d)	WAln
– 'Nocturne' (Au/S)	MAsh NBro NHol SPop WLin
– 'Noelle' (Au/S)	ITim
– 'Nona' (Au/d)	SPop
– 'Nonchalance' (Au/A)	MFie
– 'Norma' (Au/A)	MFie
– 'Notability' (Au/A)	WAln
– 'Notable' (Au/A)	WAln
– 'Nureyev' (Au/A)	WAln
– 'Nymph' (Au/d)	CStu MFie SPop
– 'Oakie' (Au/S)	WAln
– 'Oban' (Au/S)	ITim
– 'Oikos' (Au/B) **new**	SPop
– 'Ol' Blue Eyes' (Au/St)	WAln
– 'Old Clove Red' (Au/B)	GAbr WLin
– 'Old England' (Au/S)	MFie SPop
– 'Old Gold' (Au/S)	CWsd GAbr NHol WFar WLin
– 'Old Irish Blue' (Au/B)	ECho IGor ITim
– 'Old Irish Scented' (Au/B)	IGor IPen NBro WLin
– 'Old Mustard' (Au/B)	SMHy WLin
– 'Old Pink Dusty Miller' (Au/B)	GAbr
§ – 'Old Purple Dusty Miller' (Au/B)	GAbr
– 'Old Red Dusty Miller' (Au/B)	ECha LTwo NBir WHil
– 'Old Red Elvet' (Au/S)	SPop WAln
– 'Old Smokey' (Au/A)	MFie SPop WAln
– 'Old Suffolk Bronze' (Au/B)	GAbr
– 'Old Yellow Dusty Miller' (Au/B)	EWes GAbr GCai IPen MFie MSte NBro NHol NLAp NRya
– 'Olivia' (Au/d) **new**	SPop
– 'Olton' (Au/A)	IPen MFie
– 'Optimist' (Au/St) **new**	SPop
– 'Opus One' (Au/A)	WAln

– 'Orb' (Au/S)	GAbr IPen ITim MAsh MFie SPop WLin
– 'Ordvic' (Au/S)	WAln
– 'Orlando' (Au/S)	WAln
– 'Orwell Tiger' (Au/St)	SPop
– 'Osbourne Green' (Au/B)	GAbr GCai MAsh MFie SPop WHil
– 'Otto Dix' (Au/A)	WAln
– 'Overdale' (Au/A)	WAln
– 'Paddlin Madeleine' (Au/A)	WAln
– 'Pagoda Belle' (Au/A)	WAln
– 'Paleface' (Au/A)	IPen MFie WAln
– 'Pam Tiger' (Au/St)	WAln
– 'Panache' (Au/S)	WAln
– 'Papageno' (Au/St)	WAln
– 'Paphos' (Au/d)	SPop
– 'Paradise Yellow' (Au/B)	GEdr SPop
– 'Paragon' (Au/A)	WAln WHil
– 'Parchment' (Au/S) **new**	ITim
– 'Paris' (Au/S)	WAln
– 'Party Time' (Au/S)	IPen WAln
– 'Pat' (Au/S)	SPop
– 'Pat Barnard' (Au)	IPen
– 'Patience' (Au/S)	SPop WHil
– 'Patricia Barras' (Au/S)	WAln
– 'Pauline' (Au/A)	MFie
– 'Pauline Taylor' (Au/d)	WAln
– 'Pegasus' (Au/d)	SPop WAln
– 'Peggy' (Au/A)	WHil WLin
– 'Peggy's Lad' (Au/A)	WAln
– 'Pequod' (Au/A)	SPop WAln
– 'Peter Beardsley' (Au/A)	WAln
– 'Peter Hall' (Au/d)	WAln
– 'Phantom' (Au)	WAln
– 'Pharaoh' (Au/A)	EShb MFie SPop WAln WFar
– 'Phyllis Douglas' (Au/A)	IPen ITim MFie SPop
– 'Pierot' (Au/A)	IPen MFie SPop
– 'Piers Telford' (Au/A)	CWCL GAbr GCai IPen ITim MFie SBch SDnm SPav SPop WHil WLin
– 'Pink Fondant' (Au/d)	GAbr WAln
– 'Pink Lady' (Au/A)	MFie NBro SPop
– 'Pink Panther' (Au/S)	WAln
– 'Pinkie' (Au/A)	WAln WHil
– 'Pinstripe'	IPen SPop WHil
– 'Pioneer Stripe' (Au/S)	IPen WHil
– 'Pippin' (Au/A)	GAbr IPen MFie NBro SPop WFar WLin
– 'Pixie' (Au/A)	IPen WAln
– 'Playboy' (Au/A)	WAln
– 'Plush Royal' (Au/S)	WAln
– 'Polestar' (Au/A)	MFie SPop WFar WLin
– 'Pop's Blue' (Au/S/d)	SPop
– 'Portree' (Au/S)	GAbr
– 'Pot o' Gold' (Au/S)	EBee ECho IPen ITim MAsh MFie SPop WHil
– 'Prague' (Au/S)	GAbr IPen MFie NBir NHol SPop WLin
– 'Pretender' (Au/A)	SPop WAln
– 'Prince Bishop' (Au/S)	WAln
– 'Prince Charming' (Au/S)	IPen ITim MFie SPop WLin
– 'Prince Igor' (Au/A)	WAln
– 'Prince John' (Au/A)	CWCL ITim MFie NBro NHol SPop WHil WLin WOFF
– 'Prometheus' (Au/d)	MAsh NRya WAln
– 'Purple Dusty Miller'	see *P. auricula* 'Old Purple Dusty Miller'
– 'Purple Emperor' (Au/A)	MFie
– 'Purple Glow' (Au/d)	WAln WLin
– 'Purple Haze' **new**	WLin
– 'Purple Lovely' **new**	WLin
– 'Purple Prose' (Au/St) **new**	WLin
– 'Purple Sage' (Au/S)	GCai NHol
– 'Purple Velvet' (Au/S)	CWCL IPen NHol SPop
– 'Quatro' (Au/d)	SPop WAln

- 'Queen Alexandra' (Au/B) GAbr
- 'Queen Bee' (Au/S) GAbr MFie WFar WHil
- 'Queen of Sheba' (Au/S) WAln
- 'Queen's Bower' (Au/S) SPop
- 'Quintessence' (Au/A) MFie WAln
- 'Rab C. Nesbitt' (Au/A) WAln
- 'Rabley Heath' (Au/A) GCai MFie SPop
- 'Rachel' (Au/A) GAbr WAln
- 'Rajah' (Au/S) CWCL ECho GAbr IPen ITim MFie NHol SPop WFar WHil
- 'Raleigh Stripe' (Au/St) IPen WAln
- 'Ralenzano' (Au/A) WAln
- 'Rameses' (Au/A) IPen MFie WAln
- 'Rebecca Hyatt' (Au/d) WAln
- 'Red Admiral' (Au) WAln
- 'Red Arrows' (Au) WAln
- 'Red Embers' (Au/S) WAln
- 'Red Gauntlet' (Au/S) EDAr GAbr GCai IPen ITim MFie MRav MSte NHol SPop WFar WHil
- 'Red Mark' (Au/A) MFie
- 'Red Rum' (Au/S) GAbr MFie
- 'Red Wire' **new** WLin
- 'Redcar' (Au/A) GAbr WAln
- 'Redstart' (Au/S) IPen ITim
- 'Regency' (Au/A) WAln
- 'Remus' (Au/S) CWCL ECho ELan GAbr GCai IPen ITim LTwo MAsh MFie NHol SPop WHil
- 'Rene' (Au/A) GAbr IPen MFie
- 'Respectable' (Au/A) WAln
- 'Reverie' (Au/d) WAln
- 'Riatty' (Au/d) GAbr MFie WAln
- 'Richard Shaw' (Au/A) IPen MFie WLin
- 'Ring of Bells' (Au/S) WAln
- 'Rita' (Au/S) WAln
- 'Robert Lee' (Au/A) WAln
- 'Roberto' (Au/S) WAln
- 'Robin Hood' (Au/A) WAln
- 'Robinette' (Au/d) **new** SPop
- 'Rock Sand' (Au/S) ECho GCai ITim MFie WHil WLin
- 'Rodeo' (Au/A) GAbr IPen NLAp WPat
- 'Rolts' (Au/S) CWCL EBee ECho EShb GAbr IPen ITim MAsh MFie NBir NBro NHol SDnm SPav SPop WFar WHil WOFF
- 'Rondy' (Au/S) WAln
- 'Ronnie Johnson' (Au) WAln
- 'Rosalie' (Au) SPop
- 'Rosalie Edwards' (Au/S) MFie
- 'Rose Conjou' (Au/d) GAbr IPen WAln
- 'Rose Kaye' (Au/A) IPen SPop WAln
- 'Rosebud' (Au/S) GAbr
- 'Rosemary' (Au/S) ITim MFie WHil
- 'Rothesay Robin' (Au/A) WAln
- 'Rowena' (Au/A) GCai IPen MFie NBro SDnm SPav SPop WHil
- 'Roxborough' (Au/A) CWCL IPen WAln
- 'Roxburgh' (Au/A) MFie SPop
- 'Roy Keane' (Au/A) IPen MFie SPop
- 'Royal Mail' (Au/S) WAln
- 'Royal Marine' (Au/S) WAln
- 'Royal Purple' (Au/S) NBir
- 'Royal Velvet' (Au/S) GAbr IPen NHol WHil
- 'Ruby Hyde' (Au/B) GAbr
- 'Rusty Dusty' (Au) GAbr IGor
- 'Ryecroft' (Au/A) WAln
- 'Sabrina' (Au/A) WAln
- 'Saginaw' (Au/A) WAln
- 'Sailor Boy' (Au/S) MFie SPop
- 'Saint Boswells' (Au/S) GAbr ITim NRya SPop WAln
- 'Saint Quentin' (Au/S) WAln
- 'Salad' (Au/S) GAbr GCrs
- 'Sale Green' (Au/S) MFie
- 'Sally' (Au/A) WAln
- 'Sam Gamgee' (Au/A) WAln
- 'Sam Hunter' (Au/A) SPop WAln
- 'Samantha' (Au/A) WAln
- 'San Antonio' (Au/A) WAln
- 'Sandhills' (Au/A) MAsh MFie WAln
- 'Sandmartin' (Au/S) MFie
- 'Sandra' (Au/A) ECho ELan GAbr IPen MFie SPop WLin
- 'Sandra's Lass' (Au/A) WAln
- 'Sandwood Bay' (Au/A) EShb GAbr GCai LRHS MAsh MFie NBro NHol SPop WLin
- 'Sarah Gisby' (Au/d) **new** SPop
- 'Sarah Humphries' (Au/d) WAln
- 'Sarah Lodge' (Au/d) CWCL GAbr IPen MAsh MFie SPop WLin
- 'Scipio' (Au/S) WAln
- 'Scorcher' (Au/S) SPop WAln
- 'Sea Mist' (Au/d) WAln
- 'Serenity' (Au/S) MFie NHol WOFF
- 'Sergeant Wilson' (Au) WAln
- 'Shalford' (Au/d) MFie SPop WLin
- 'Sharman's Cross' (Au/S) MFie WAln
- 'Sharon Louise' (Au/S) MAsh WLin
- 'Sheila' (Au/S) ECho ITim MFie SPop WHil WLin
- 'Shere' (Au/S) MFie SPop WLin
- 'Shergold' (Au/A) MFie
- 'Sherwood' (Au/S) GCai IPen MAsh MFie SPop WHil WLin
- 'Shirley' (Au/S) WAln
- 'Shotley' (Au/A) ITim
- 'Showman' (Au/S) WAln
- 'Sibsey' (Au/d) MAsh SPop WAln
- 'Sidney' (Au/A) WAln
- 'Silas' (Au/B) SPav
- 'Silmaril' (Au) SPop WAln
- 'Silverway' (Au/S) ITim SPop WHil WLin
- 'Simply Red' (Au) WAln
- 'Sir John' (Au/A) MAsh MFie
- 'Sir John Hall' MFie
- 'Sir Robert' (Au/d) WAln
- 'Sirbol' (Au/A) IPen MFie SPop WFar
- 'Sirius' (Au/A) CWCL GAbr IPen ITim LRHS MFie NHol NRya SPop WHil WLin
- 'Skipper' (Au/d) SPop
- 'Skylark' (Au/A) GAbr IPen ITim SPop WAln WHil
- 'Slioch' (Au/S) ECho GAbr IPen ITim MFie NHol SPop
- 'Slip Anchor' (Au/A) WAln
- 'Smart Tar' (Au/S) WAln
- 'Snooty Fox' (Au/A) GAbr IPen MFie
- 'Snooty Fox II' (Au/A) SPop
- 'Snowy Owl' (Au/S) GAbr MFie SPop WLin
- 'Somersby' (Au/d) SPop WAln
- 'Soncy Face' (Au/A) MAsh WAln
- 'Sonny Boy' (Au/A) WAln
- 'Sonya' (Au/A) WLin
- 'Sophie' (Au/d) WAln
- 'South Barrow' (Au/d) GAbr SPop
- 'Sparky' (Au/A) WAln
- 'Spartan' (Au) WAln
- 'Spring Meadows' (Au/S) CWCL GAbr MAsh MFie NHol SPop WLin
- 'Springtime' (Au/A) SPop WAln
- 'Stant's Blue' (Au/S) EShb GCai IPen MFie NBro
- 'Star Wars' (Au/S) GAbr GWWP MFie NHol SPop WAln WLin
- 'Starburst' (Au/S) WAln
- 'Starling' (Au/B) GAbr SPop
- 'Stella Coop' (Au/d) WAln
- 'Stetson' (Au/A) WAln
- 'Stoke Poges' (Au/A) WAln
- 'Stoney Cross' (Au/S) SPop
- 'Stonnal' (Au/A) MFie SPop
- 'Stormin Norman' (Au/A) MFie WAln
- 'Stripey' (Au/d) IPen NHol WAln
- 'Stromboli' (Au/d) **new** SPop
- 'Stubb's Tartan' (Au/S) GWWP WLin

– 'Subliminal' (Au/A)	WAln
– 'Sue' (Au/A)	MFie WFar
– 'Sugar Plum Fairy' (Au/S)	GAbr WHil
– 'Sultan' (Au/A)	WAln
– 'Summer Sky' (Au/A)	SPop
– 'Summer Wine' (Au/A)	MFie
– 'Sumo' (Au/A)	GAbr MFie SPop WAln WHil WLin
– 'Sunflower' (Au/A/S)	EShb GAbr ITim MAsh MFie SPop WLin
– 'Super Para' (Au/S)	GAbr MFie SPop WLin
– 'Superb' (Au/S)	WAln
– 'Susan' (Au/A)	MFie
– 'Susannah' (Au/d)	CWCL GAbr GCai GMaP IPen LRHS MFie NHol NPri SDnm SPav SPop WFar
* – 'Sweet Chestnut' (Au/S)	WAln WLin
– 'Sweet Georgia Brown' (Au/A)	WAln
– 'Sweet Pastures' (Au/S)	ECho GAbr MFie NHol SPop
– 'Sword' (Au/d)	CStu ECho GAbr GCrs GWWP IPen ITim MAsh MFie NHol SPop WAln WFar WHil WLin WOFF
– 'Symphony' (Au/A)	ITim MFie SPop WFar WHil
– 'T.A. Hadfield' (Au/A)	MFie SPop WFar WHil
– 'Taffeta' (Au/S)	CWCL SDnm SPav WAln
– 'Tall Purple Dusty Miller' (Au/B)	SPop
– 'Tally-ho' (Au/A)	WAln
– 'Tamino' (Au/S)	WAln
– 'Tandem' (Au/St)	WAln
– 'Tarantella' (Au/A)	GAbr MFie SPop WLin
– 'Tawny Owl' (Au/B)	GAbr NBro
– 'Tay Tiger' (Au/St)	GAbr MFie SPop
– 'Teawell Pride' (Au/d)	ITim WHil
– 'Ted Gibbs' (Au/A)	ITim MFie WAln
– 'Ted Roberts' (Au/A)	EShb ITim MFie SPop WFar WLin
– 'Teem' (Au/S)	GAbr MAsh NRya SPop
– 'Temeraire' (Au/A)	MFie WAln
– 'Tenby Grey' (Au/S)	WLin
– 'Tender Trap' (Au/A)	WAln
– 'Terpo' (Au/A)	MFie WAln
– 'Tess' (Au/A)	WAln
– 'The Baron' (Au/S)	GCai IPen ITim MFie SPop WFar WHil WLin
– 'The Bishop' (Au/S)	IPen MFie SPop WHil
– 'The Cardinal' (Au/d)	WAln
– 'The Czar' (Au/A)	MFie
– 'The Egyptian' (Au/A)	IPen SPop WAln WHil
– 'The Hobbit' (Au/A)	WAln
– 'The Raven' (Au/S)	ITim MFie SPop WOFF
– 'The Sneep' (Au/A)	IPen SPop WHil
– 'The Snods' (Au/S)	EBee IPen MFie SPop
– 'The Wrekin' (Au/S)	WAln
– 'Thebes' (Au/A)	WAln
– 'Thetis' (Au/A)	MFie SPop WFar WLin
– 'Thirlmere' (Au/d)	WAln
– 'Three Way Stripe' (St)	WHil
– 'Thutmoses' (Au/A)	WAln
– 'Tie Lee' **new**	WLin
– 'Tiger Tim' (Au/St)	WAln
– 'Tinker' (Au/S)	WAln
– 'Tinkerbell' (Au/S)	MFie SPop WOFF
– 'Titania' (Au)	SPop
– 'Toddington Green' (Au/S)	WAln
– 'Toffee Crisp' (Au/A)	IPen WAln
* – 'Tomato' (Au)	WLin
– 'Tomboy' (Au/S)	IPen MFie SDnm SPop
– 'Toolyn' (Au/S)	WAln
– 'Tosca' (Au/S)	EBee GCai GCrs IPen ITim MAsh NRya SPop WFar WHil WLin
– 'Trish'	GAbr
– 'Trojan' (Au/S)	MAsh WLin
– 'Trouble' (Au/d)	CStu EBee GAbr GMaP IPen LRHS MBNS MFie NRya SPop WLin
– 'Troy Aykman' (Au/A)	WAln
– 'Trudy' (Au/S)	GAbr GCai IPen ITim MFie SPop WHil
– 'True Briton' (Au/S)	MFie SPop
– 'Trumpet Blue' (Au/S)	MFie SPop WFar
– 'Tumbledown' (Au/A)	MFie
– 'Tummel'	MFie SPop WAln WHil
– 'Tuthmoses'	MFie
– 'Twiggy' (Au/S)	GCai NRya SPop WAln
– 'Tye Lea' (Au/S)	WAln
– 'Typhoon' (Au/A)	MFie SPop
– 'Uncle Arthur' (Au/A)	WAln
– 'Unforgettable' (Au/A)	MFie WAln
– 'Upton Belle' (Au/S)	MAsh MFie SPop WAln
– 'Valerie' (Au/A)	IPen ITim SPop
– 'Valerie Clare'	WAln
– 'Vee Too' (Au/A)	GAbr MFie SPop
– 'Vega' (Au/A)	SPop WAln
– 'Vein' (Au/St)	WAln
– 'Velvet Moon' (Au/A)	MFie WAln WFar
– 'Venetian' (Au/A)	MFie SPop WAln WFar
– 'Venus' (Au/A)	WAln
– 'Vera Hill' (Au/A)	WAln
– 'Verdi' (Au/A)	WAln
– 'Victoria' (Au/S)	WAln
– 'Victoria de Wemyss' (Au/A)	MFie WLin
– 'Victoria Park' (Au/A)	WAln
– 'Virginia Belle' (Au/St)	WAln
– 'Vivian' (Au/S)	WAln
– 'Vulcan' (Au/A)	ECho MFie NBro SPop WLin
– 'Walter Lomas' (Au/S)	WAln
– 'Walton' (Au/A)	CWCL GAbr MFie SPop WFar WHil
– 'Walton Heath' (Au/d)	ECho IPen MAsh MFie SPop WLin
– 'Wanda's Moonlight' (Au/d)	WAln
– 'Watchett' (Au/S)	WAln
– 'Wayward' (Au/S)	WAln
– 'Wedding Day' (Au/S)	ITim MFie WAln
– 'Wentworth' (Au/A)	WAln
– 'Whistle Jacket' (Au/S)	SPop WAln
– 'White Ensign' (Au/S)	ECho GAbr IPen ITim MFie SPop WFar WHil WLin
– 'White Water' (Au/A)	MFie SPop WAln
– 'White Wings' (Au/S)	GCai ITim MFie SPop WLin
– 'Whitecap' (Au/S)	WAln
– 'Whoopee' (Au/A)	WAln
– 'Wichita Falls' (Au/A)	WAln
– 'Wilf Booth' (Au/A)	MFie SPop WAln WFar
– 'Wincha' (Au/S)	EShb GCai MFie SPop
– 'Windward Blue' (Au)	SBla
– 'Windways Mystery' (Au/B)	GAbr
– 'Windways Pisces' (Au/d)	WAln
– 'Winifrid' (Au/A)	EShb GAbr LRHS MFie NHol SPop WFar WHil
– 'Witchcraft' (Au)	SPop
– 'Woodmill' (Au/A)	MFie SPop WAln
– 'Wycliffe Midnight' (Au)	GAbr
– 'Wye Hen' (Au/St)	WAln
– 'Yellow Hammer' (Au/S)	WAln
– 'Yellow Isle' (Au/S)	WAln
– 'Yitzhak Rabin' (Au/A)	WAln WHil
– 'Yorkshire Grey' (Au/S)	IPen MFie NBro
– 'Zambia' (Au/d)	ECho GAbr ITim MFie SPop
– 'Zircon' (Au/S)	WAln
– 'Zodiac' (Au/S)	WAln
– 'Zoe' (Au/A)	WAln
– 'Zoe Ann' (Au/S)	WAln
– 'Zorro' (Au/St)	WAln WLin
auriculata (Or)	GKev SBla
'Barbara Barker' (Au)	GEdr NMen
'Barbara Midwinter' (Pr)	CDes GAbr SHar WAbe
Barnhaven Blues Group (Pr/Prim) $\mathbb{Y}^{H4}$	CSWP EBla GAbr

Barnhaven doubles (Pr/Prim/d)	CSWP
Barnhaven Gold-laced Group	see *P.* Gold-laced Group Barnhaven
Barnhaven hybrids	NSum
Barnhaven Traditional Group (Pr)	CSWP
'Beatrice Wooster' (Au)	CLyd IPen ITim LRHS MFie NDlv NLAp NWCA
'Bee' x 'Jo-Jo'	GCrs
'Beeches' Pink'	GAbr NHar
beesiana (Pf)	More than 30 suppliers
(Belarina Series) 'Belarina Butter Yellow' (Pr/Prim/d)	CHVG CWCL EPfP NLar SIng SVil
- 'Belarina Cream' (Pr/Prim/d)	CHVG CWCL SIng SVil
- 'Belarina Pink Ice' (Pr/Prim/d)	CWCL LHop SIng SVil
- 'Belarina Rosette Nectarine' (Pr/Prim/d)	CWCL LAst SIng SVil WHlf
'Belinda'	ITim
bellidifolia (Mu)	EBee GEdr IPen
§ - subsp. ***hyacinthina*** (Mu)	WAbe
aff. ***bellidifolia*** (Mu) SDR 3088	GKev
beluensis	see *P.* x *pubescens* 'Freedom'
Bergfrühling Julianas Group (Pr/Prim)	MFie
§ x ***berninae*** 'Windrush' (Au)	WAbe
'Bewerley White'	see *P.* x *pubescens* 'Bewerley White'
bhutanica	see *P. whitei* 'Sherriff's Variety'
'Big Red Giant' (Pr/Prim/d)	CWCL NGHP
bileckii	see *P.* x *forsteri* 'Bileckii'
'Blue Riband' (Pr/Prim)	CDes CWsd EBee WFar
'Blue Sapphire' (Pr/Prim/d)	CWsd GAbr LRHS MBNS MFie NCGa NGHP NWCA SPer
'Blutenkissen' (Pr/Prim)	GAbr
'Bon Accord Cerise' (Pr/Poly/d)	GAbr
'Bon Accord Lilac' (Pr/Poly/d) **new**	GAbr
'Bon Accord Purple' (Pr/Poly/d)	WFar
boothii (Pe)	NHar NSum
- EN 382	WThu
- ***alba*** (Pe)	GCrs LTwo NHar
- subsp. ***repens*** (Pe)	CEnt MNrw
'Boothman's Ruby'	see *P.* x *pubescens* 'Boothman's Variety'
§ ***bracteosa*** (Pe)	GCrs ITim
Bressingham (Pf)	WFar
brevicula x ***chionantha*** subsp. ***sinopurpurea*** (Cy)	NEgg
'Broadwell Milkmaid'	WAbe
'Broadwell Pink' (Au)	WAbe
'Broadwell Ruby' (Au)	WAbe
'Bronwyn' (Pr/Prim)	NBir WCot
'Broxbourne'	ITim NHol NLAp
'Buckland Wine' (Pr/Prim)	CElw
x ***bulleesiana*** (Pf)	CMMP EBee EMFW EPfP EWTr GKev LBMP LRHS NBro NChi NGdn NHol NLar NRnb SMrm SPer SPet SRms SWat WBrE WFar WHil WLin WMnd WMoo WPer
- Moerheim hybrids (Pf)	WFar
bulleyana (Pf) $\mathbb{Y}^{H4}$	More than 30 suppliers
- ACE 2484	WAbe
burmanica (Pf)	EBee GAbr GBuc GEdr GGar GKev IPen MDun MMuc NEgg SRms SWat WBVN WFar WMoo
'Butter's Bronze' (Pr/Prim)	WOut
'Butterscotch' (Pr/Prim)	CSWP
'Caerulea Plena' (Pr/Prim)	NBid
Candelabra hybrids (Pf)	CBre CHar COlW CWCL ECho EPot GAbr GGar ITim LSou MAvo MDun MNHC NBir NCob NGdn NRnb SPet SWal SWat WCra WRos
Candy Pinks Group (Pr/Prim)	CSWP
capitata (Ca)	CMMP CSWP CSpe EBee ECho EDAr GAbr GCrs GKev IPen MFie NLAp NWCA SPer SPoG WAbe WFar WGwG WWFP
- subsp. ***mooreana*** (Ca)	CFir EAlp GKev IPen NDlv NGdn NLAp NSum SPet SPlb SRot WBVN WHil WHrl WPtf
'Captain Blood' (Pr/Prim/d)	EPfP MFie MSte NWCA SIng WFar
Carnation Victorians Group (Pr/Poly)	MFie
carniolica (Au)	MFie
Casquet mixture (Pr/Prim)	CSWP
cernua (Mu)	GKev IPen
Chartreuse Group (Pr/Poly)	CSWP GWWP MFie
'Cherry' (Pr/Prim)	WHil
§ ***chionantha*** (Cy) $\mathbb{Y}^{H4}$	CLAP CWCL EBee EPfP GAbr GCra GCrs GGar GKev LRHS MDun MFie NBir NCob NEgg NGdn NLAp NMyG SPer SWat WAbe WFar WGwG WPtf
- subsp. ***chionantha*** (Cy)	EBee GKev IPen
§ - subsp. ***melanops*** (Cy)	EBee LRHS
§ - subsp. ***sinopurpurea*** (Cy)	CLAP CWCL EBee GGar GKev IPen ITim MDKP NCGa NLar NSum SBch SPer SWat WAbe WBVN WFar WHil WPer
- - SDR 2861	GKev
chungensis (Pf)	CBcs CLAP CWCL EBee EDAr GBuc GCra GEdr GGar GKev IPen ITim MLLN NDlv NEgg NGdn NRnb NSti SRms STes SWat SWvt WAbe WMoo WSpi
§ ***chungensis*** x ***pulverulenta*** (Pf)	CLAP GBuc GCai GEdr NEgg NLar NRnb SMrm WAbe WFar WMnd
x ***chunglenta***	see *P. chungensis* x *pulverulenta*
'Clarence Elliott' (Au)	CDes CGra CLyd CMea CPBP GCrs GKev IPen ITim MFie NHar SBla WAbe
clarkei (Or)	CLyd GEdr WAbe
clusiana (Au)	MFie WAbe
- 'Murray-Lyon' (Au)	GCrs NMen NSla
cockburniana (Pf) $\mathbb{Y}^{H4}$	EBee EBla EDAr GEdr GGar GKev GQui IPen MDKP MFie NEgg NGdn NSti SRms SWat WAbe WFar WHil
- SDR 1967	GKev
- hybrids (Pf)	SWat
- yellow-flowered (Pf)	EBee GEdr GKev IPen
concholoba (Mu)	GKev NLAp
'Corporal Baxter' (Pr/Prim/d)	CBgR EPfP MBNS NGHP NLar SPer SRGP
cortusoides (Co)	CLAP CMil CWsd EBee EDAr GAbr GCra GKev IPen LSou NLar NRnb SRms
- SDR 2831	GKev
Cowichan Amethyst Group (Pr/Poly)	CDes CSWP EBee
Cowichan Blue Group (Pr/Poly)	CSWP
Cowichan Garnet Group (Pr/Poly)	CDes CSWP GBuc MFie WPGP
Cowichan Red Group (Pr/Poly)	WFar
Cowichan Venetian Group (Pr/Poly)	CDes CSWP WFar

	Cowichan Yellow Group (Pr/Poly)	CDes WCot
	'Coy'	CGra WAbe WLin
	'Craven Gem' (Pr/Poly)	GBuc
	Crescendo Series (Pr/Poly)	GAbr WHil
	'Crimson Velvet' (Au)	GAbr IPen ITim MFie NLAp
	crispa	see *P. glomerata*
	cuneifolia (Cu)	GKev
	daonensis (Au)	GKev
	darialica (Al)	GKev LTwo
	'Dark Rosaleen' (Pr/Poly)	GAbr
	'David Valentine' (Pr)	GAbr GBuc WAbe
	'Dawn Ansell' (Pr/Prim/d)	CDes CHrt CWCL EBla ENot EPfP GAbr ITer LRHS MBNS MFie MSte NBir NDov NGHP NSti SIng SPer SRGP WCot WFar WHer
	Daybreak Group (Pr/Poly)	CSWP MFie
	deflexa (Mu)	GCrs GKev IPen LRHS
	- BWJ 7877	WCru
	denticulata (De) ℽH4	More than 30 suppliers
	- var. ***alba*** (De)	CBcs CSam CTri CWat EBee ECha ECho EPfP GAbr GCra GGar GKev LRHS MBri MFie MWgw NBid NCob NHol NLAp NOrc SPer SPoG WBor WBrE WCAu WHen WMoo WPer WWeb
	- blue-flowered (De)	ECho GAbr MWat NLar
	- 'Glenroy Crimson' (De)	CLAP EBee SRms SWvt
	- 'Karryann' (De/v)	CBow EBee EMon MBNS NEgg WCot
	- lilac-flowered (De)	ECho EHon MFie MWat NCob NLAp NPri WWeb
	- 'Prichard's Ruby' (De)	NCob
	- purple-flowered (De)	ECho WMoo
	- red-flowered (De)	ECho EPfP GGar MWgw NLAp NOrc WMoo
	- 'Robinson's Red' (De)	GBuc
	- 'Ronsdorf' (De)	LRHS
	- 'Rubin' (De)	CDWL CSam ECho EHon GAbr MAvo MBrN MBri MFie MLHP NChi NCob SPoG SRms WHen WHil WPer
	- 'Rubinball' (De)	EBee GCrs NHol
	- 'Snowball' (De)	WHen
	deorum (Au)	GKev
	x ***deschmannii***	see *P.* x *vochinensis*
	'Desert Sunset' (Pr/Poly)	CSWP MFie
	'Devon Cream' (Pr/Prim)	CWsd GBuc WFar
	'Dianne'	see *P.* x *forsteri* 'Dianne'
	'Discovering Stripes' (Pr/Poly)	WHil
	'Don Keefe' **new**	GBin LSou NLar WCot WCra
	'Dorothy' (Pr/Poly)	MRav
	'Double Lilac'	see *P. vulgaris* 'Lilacina Plena'
	dryadifolia (Dr)	GKev
	'Duckyls Red' (Pr/Prim)	GBuc WHal
	'Dusky Lady'	MBri WFar
	'Early Bird' (*allionii* hybrid) (Au)	IPen MFie
	'Easter Bonnet' (Pr/Prim)	LRHS NBid WCot
	edelbergii (Sp)	MMHG
	edgeworthii	see *P. nana*
§	***elatior*** (Pr) ℽH4	CBgR CRWN CSev EBee ECho ELau GCrs GKev LAst LRHS MHer MNrw MSal NChi NCob NEgg NLAp NMen NPri NVic SPer SPoG SRms SWvt WAbe WBrk WCot WFar WGwG WPtf
	- hose-in-hose (Pr/d)	NBid
	- hybrids (Pr)	GAbr
	- subsp. ***intricata*** (Pr)	GKev NWCA
I	- 'Jessica'	WHil
	- subsp. ***leucophylla*** (Pr)	EBee ECho SBch
§	- subsp. ***meyeri*** (Pr)	NEgg NLAp
I	- 'Mrs Statham's Oxslip' (Pr) **new**	CWsd
	- subsp. ***ruprechtii*** (Pr) **new**	GKev
	'Elizabeth Killelay'PBR (Pr/Poly/d)	CBct CBgR CElw CMea EBee EBla ELan ENot ERou GBuc GEdr GGar LDai LHop LSou MBri MFie NBir NCGa NChi NCot NEgg NLar NSti SPer SPoG WCot WFar WHrl
	'Ellen Page' (Au)	MFie
	'Ethel Barker' (Au)	CGra IPen ITim LRHS NDlv NHol NLAp SIng
	'Eugénie' (Pr/Prim/d)	CHid MBNS MDun NGHP NLar SRGP
	'Fairy Rose' (Au)	IPen ITim NHol WAbe
	farinosa (Al)	CEnt EBee EDAr IPen NEgg NGdn NLAp NRya NSum SPoG
	fasciculata (Ar)	GCai GEdr NWCA SBla
	- CLD 345	WAbe
	- SDR 3092	GKev
	'Fife Yellow' (Pr/Prim/d)	GBuc
	Firefly Group (Pr/Poly)	WCot
§	***firmipes*** (Si)	EWes GCrs IPen NSum
§	***flaccida*** (Mu)	GEdr GGGa GKev IPen NLAp WAbe
	Flamingo Group (Pr/Poly)	CSWP MFie
	x ***floerkeana*** (Au)	GCrs
	- f. ***biflora*** 'Alba' (Au)	SBla
	florida (Y)	NCob
	florindae (Si) ℽH4	More than 30 suppliers
	- bronze-flowered (Si)	GQui NBir SWat
I	- 'Butterscotch' (Si)	WHrl
	- hybrids (Si)	CDWL EHrv GAbr GEdr GGar GMaP ITim MFie NCob NEgg NHol WHil
	- Keillour hybrids (Si)	NChi NGdn WPtf
	- magenta-flowered (Si)	MDKP
	- orange-flowered (Si)	CSam GMac IPen ITim MDKP MNrw NRnb WCru WFar WMoo
	- peach (Si)	MDKP
	- 'Ray's Ruby' (Si)	CHar CLAP CWoW EBee GBuc GMac MDKP MFOX MNrw NBir NGdn SWat WMnd WRos WWFP
	- red-flowered (Si)	CDWL CDes GBin GBuc GGar GKev IPen MFie NBid NEgg NLar NRnb NSum WFar
	- terracotta-flowered (Si)	CSWP NGdn
	Footlight Parade Group (Pr/Prim)	CSWP
	forbesii (Mo) CC 4084	CPLG
	forrestii (Bu)	EBee EDAr IPen NPen WAbe
	- DJH 138	SPhx
§	x ***forsteri*** 'Bileckii' (Au)	CStu GCrs LRHS NBir NLAp NWCA SRms WAbe
	- 'Bileckii' white-flowered (Au)	GCrs
§	- 'Dianne' (Au)	EDAr GAbr GBuc GCrs NBro NHol NRya WAbe
	- 'Dianne' hybrids (Au)	MFie
	'Francisca' (Pr/Poly)	CElw CSpe EBee LSou MBNS NCot NGdn NSti WCot
	'Freckles' (Pr/Prim/d)	CWCL MBNS MDun SPer SWat
	'Freedom'	see *P.* x *pubescens* 'Freedom'
	frondosa (Al) ℽH4	CWCL ECho GCra IPen LRHS MDKP MFie NLAp NMen NWCA WAbe WBVN
	Fuchsia Victorians Group (Pr/Poly)	MFie
	gambeliana (Cf) **new**	GKev
	- AC 5467	GKev
	'Garnet' (*allionii* hybrid) (Au)	MFie WLin
	'Garryard Guinevere'	see *P.* 'Guinevere'
	gemmifera (Ar)	NLAp
	geraniifolia (Co)	GEdr

§	'Gigha' (Pr/Prim)	CSWP EBee GCrs
	'Gilded Ginger' **new**	GWWP
	glabra (G)	WAbe
	glaucescens (Au)	CLyd GCrs MFie NSum
§	***glomerata*** (Ca)	ECho GBuc IPen NLAp
	- CC 3843	GKev
	- CC 3924	GKev
	- GWJ 9213	WCru
	- GWJ 9280	WCru
	'Glowing Embers' (Pf)	GKev LRHS MFie NBir
	glutinosa All.	see *P. allionii*
	'Gold-laced Jack in the Green' Barnhaven **new**	GWWP
	Gold-laced Group (Pr/Poly)	CBre CMea CSWP CWCL EAlp EBee EDAr EPfP EShb ITer LSRN MHer NBPC NGdn NHol NPri NRya NSum NWCA SPer SPet WBor WFar WHer WHil WHlf WPtf WWeb WWlt
§	- Barnhaven (Pr/Poly)	CDes EBla GAbr ITer MFie NBir NCGa NEgg
	- Beeches strain (Pr/Poly) ♀H4	ITer NCob SSth
	- 'Dan-y-Banc Strain' **new**	SSth
	gracilipes (Pe)	CDes CLAP CWsd GCrs GGGa NLAp SRms WAbe
	- L&S 1166	WAbe
	- early-flowering (Pe)	WAbe
	- 'Major'	see *P. bracteosa*
	- 'Minor'	see *P. petiolaris*
	graminifolia	see *P. chionantha*
	Grand Canyon Group (Pr/Poly)	MFie
	grandis (Sr)	GKev IPen
	'Green Lace' (Pr/Poly)	NBhm WCot
	'Groenekan's Glorie' (Pr/Prim)	EWTr GAbr GEdr LRHS MRav NBir NSum WFar
§	'Guinevere' (Pr/Poly) ♀H4	CSam EBee EBrs EPfP GAbr GEdr GMaP LRHS MBri MFie NBid NBir NBro NDov NHol NSla NSti SPer SPlb WCot WEas WFar WHil WHoo WWeb
	'Hall Barn Blue'	CBgR EAlp GAbr GEdr NBPC NHar NHol NMyG
§	***halleri*** (Al)	EBee GKev IPen MDKP MFie NDlv NLAp NRnb NSum WAbe WLin
	- DJHC 0083	WCru
	- 'Longiflora'	see *P. halleri*
	Harbinger Group (Pr/Prim)	CSWP
	Harbour Lights mixture (Pr/Poly)	CSWP MFie
	Harlow Carr hybrids (Pf)	CSWP GCai GQui LRHS MLLN NDlv NEgg NSla SPoG WEas WMoo
	Harvest Yellows Group (Pr/Poly)	MFie WCot
	helodoxa	see *P. prolifera*
	'Hemswell Blush' (Au)	GCai ITim NLAp NLar
	'Hemswell Ember' (Au)	CPBP GCai GCrs NDlv NLAp NRya
	heucherifolia (Co)	IPen
	- BWJ 7740	WCru
	hidakana (R)	GEdr
	'High Point' (Au)	CGra
	hirsuta (Au)	GCrs GEdr IPen MFie
	- 'Lismore Snow' (Au)	NHar WAbe
	- red-flowered (Au)	NLAp
	hongshanensis (Cy)	GKev
	hose-in-hose (Pr/Poly/d)	CSWP ITer MNrw
	hose-in-hose, Barnhaven (Pr/Poly)	MFie
	'Hyacinthia' (Au)	CLyd IPen MFie NLar
	hyacinthina	see *P. bellidifolia* subsp. *hyacinthina*
	ianthina	see *P. prolifera*
	incana (Al)	EBee GKev NEgg
	Indian Reds Group (Pr/Poly)	CSWP MFie
	'Ingram's Blue' (Pr/Poly)	CBgR LRHS WPen
	Inshriach hybrids (Pf)	CMHG CSWP NSum WFar
	integrifolia (Au)	GBuc GEdr WAbe
	integrifolia x ***minima*** (Cu x Au)	CStu
	integrifolia x ***minima*** 'Kilchuimin' (Au)	CStu GCrs GEdr
§	'Inverewe' (Pf) ♀H4	GBin GCra GKev GQui NBir NBre NPen
	involucrata	see *P. munroi*
	ioessa (Si)	EWes GCra GQui NGdn WAbe
	- hybrids (Si)	NLAp
	'Iris Mainwaring' (Pr/Prim)	GAbr GCra GEdr NHol NWCA WCot
	irregularis (Pe)	WAbe
	Jack in the Green Group (Pr/Poly)	CDMG CSWP GWWP ITer MNrw MRav MWgw WBor WFar
	- Barnhaven (Pr/Poly)	EBla ITer MFie
	'Jackie Richards' (Au)	GCrs MFie WLin
	jaffreyana (Pu)	WAbe
	japonica (Pf)	CMHG CPLG CSam ECha GCrs GGar GQui IPen ITim LRHS MDun MNHC NBid NBro NChi NEgg NGdn NHol NRnb SWat WAbe WBrE WFar WHil WMoo WPer
	- 'Alba' (Pf)	CPrp CTri EBee ECho EHrv EPfP GGar IPen MAvo NBPC NBid NDlv NGdn NMyG NRnb WAbe WCAu WFar WHil
	- 'Apple Blossom' (Pf)	CFir CWCL EBee GBri GCai GKev IPen MBri NBHF NGdn NHol SWvt WHoo WPtf
*	- 'Carminea' (Pf)	CMil CWCL EBee GBuc GKev IPen NBro NGdn NLar NMyG WFar
	- 'Fuji' (Pf)	CSWP NBro
	- 'Fuji' hybrids (Pf)	NLar
	- hybrids (Pf)	GCra
	- 'Merve's Red' (Pf)	CAby CDes EBee WPGP
	- 'Miller's Crimson' (Pf) ♀H4	More than 30 suppliers
	- 'Oriental Sunrise' (Pf)	CMil CSWP GKev MFie NEgg
	- pale pink (Pf)	NSum
	- 'Peninsula Pink' (Pf) **new**	IPen
	- 'Pinkie' (Pf) **new**	IPen
	- 'Postford White' (Pf) ♀H4	More than 30 suppliers
	- red (Pf)	IPen WAbe
	- Redfield strain (Pf) **new**	IPen
	- 'Splendens' (Pf) **new**	IPen
	- 'Valley Red' (Pf)	GBuc GCai IPen
	jesoana (Co)	GGar LTwo WHil
	- B&SWJ 618	WCru
	'Joan Hughes' (*allionii* hybrid) (Au)	CLyd SBla WAbe WLin
	'Joanna'	ECou GCrs MHer WOut
	'Johanna' (Pu)	GAbr GBuc GEdr NGdn NHar NHol NSum NWCA WAbe
	'John Fielding' (Sr x Pr)	CBgR CElw GAbr GEdr MCot
	'Jo-Jo' (Au)	CLyd MFie WAbe WLin
	juliae (Pr)	ECho EDAr LRHS NBid NSum NWCA SPlb WAbe WCot
I	- 'Millicent' (Pr)	WCot
	- white-flowered (Pr)	NSum
	'Kate Haywood'	CLyd WLin
	'Ken Dearman' (Pr/Prim/d)	CWCL ENot EPfP MBNS MFie MSte NBir NGHP NWCA SIng SPer SRGP WFar
	kewensis (Sp) ♀H2	EShb GKev NLAp
	'Kinlough Beauty' (Pr/Poly)	EMon GAbr GEdr NRya NSti NWCA WEas WThu
§	***kisoana*** (Co)	CLAP CWsd GCai GKev IPen LTwo NLAp SBla WCru
	- var. ***alba*** (Co)	CLAP GGGa
	- var. ***shikokiana***	see *P. kisoana*

– 'Velvet' (Co) **new**	GEdr
'Lady Greer' (Pr/Poly) ♀H4	CBgR CSam CStu EBee EDAr EPfP GAbr GBuc GKev LLWP MFie MHer NBir NChi NGdn NHar NLAp NRya NSti NWCA SAga SIng SMac WFar WHer WOFF
latisecta (Co)	GEdr IPen
§ ***laurentiana*** (Al)	EBee NMen
'Lea Gardens' (*allionii* hybrid) (Au)	IPen ITim MFie NHol
'Lee Myers' (*allionii* hybrid) (Au)	IPen ITim MFie NDlv
leucophylla	see *P. elatior*
'Lilac Domino' (Au)	IPen
'Lilian Harvey' (Pr/Prim/d)	CElw CHrt EPfP NBir WRHF
'Lindum Serenade' (Au)	WThu
'Lingwood Beauty' (Pr/Prim)	CAby GAbr
'Lismore Jewel' (Au)	GCrs WAbe
'Lismore Sunshine' **new**	NHar
'Lismore Treasure' (Au)	MFie WAbe
'Lismore Yellow' (Au)	CGra NHar WAbe WLin
littoniana	see *P. vialii*
x ***loiseleurii*** 'Aire Mist' (Au)	CGra CLyd CPBP CStu GCai GCrs IPen ITer ITim MFie NHar NHol NLAp NMen NRya NSum SIng WAbe WHil WLin
§ – 'Aire Waves' (Au)	CLyd GCai ITim NHar NHol NLAp NMen WLin
– 'White Waves' (Au) **new**	IPen
longiflora	see *P. halleri*
longipes (Cy) **new**	GKev
luteola (Or)	ECho GGar GKev LTwo NEgg NGdn NLar NSum WFar WPer
macrocalyx	see *P. veris*
macrophylla (Cy)	EBee NEgg
– var. ***moorcroftiana*** (Cy) **new**	GKev
'MacWatt's Claret'	GAbr LLWP
'MacWatt's Cream'	CSWP EBee EBla EWTr GAbr GCra GCrs GEdr LHop LRHS NChi SIng WCot
magellanica (Al)	EBee GKev NGdn WAbe
malacoides (Mo)	MBri
mandarin red (Pf)	CSWP
marginata (Au) ♀H4	CPne ECho EPot GCrs GEdr IPen LFox LHop LRHS NDlv NHol NLAp NSum SBch SIng WAbe WFar
– from the Dolomites (Au)	NHol NLAp
– 'Adrian Evans' (Au)	ITim WLin
– ***alba*** (Au)	LRHS NBro NDlv NLAp
– 'Baldock's Mauve' (Au)	GCrs
– 'Baldock's Purple' (Au) **new**	IPen
– 'Barbara Clough' (Au)	CLyd GCrs GEdr IPen ITim SBla WFar
– 'Beamish' (Au) ♀H4	CLyd NBro NHol NRya
– 'Beatrice Lascaris' (Au)	CPBP GCrs MFie NRya WAbe
– 'Beverley Reid' (Au)	ITim NRya
– 'Boothman's Variety' (Au)	CTri ECho GCrs ITim NLAp
– 'Caerulea' (Au)	CLyd GKev ITim NLAp WAbe
– 'Casterino' (Au)	GCrs SBla
– 'Clear's Variety' (Au)	IPen ITim
– 'Correvon's Variety' (Au)	CLyd WAbe
– cut-leaved (Au)	ITim NHol
– 'Doctor Jenkins' (Au)	IPen ITim NHol NLar NRya
– 'Drake's Form' (Au)	GCrs IPen ITim NLAp NLar NRya SBla
– dwarf (Au)	LRHS MFie
– 'Earl L. Bolton'	see *P. marginata* 'El Bolton'
§ – 'El Bolton' (Au)	IPen ITim NHol WAbe
– 'Elizabeth Fry' (Au)	CLyd IPen LFox
– 'F.W. Millard' (Au)	NRya
– 'Grandiflora' (Au)	IPen NHol
– 'Highland Twilight' (Au)	IPen NSla WAbe
– 'Holden Clough' (Au)	IPen ITim NRya
– 'Holden Variety' (Au)	CStu NDlv NHol WAbe WLin
– 'Ivy Agee' (Au)	CLyd GCrs IPen ITim NLAp NRya
– 'Janet' (Au)	CLyd NLAp WLin
– 'Jenkins Variety' (Au)	CLyd ECho
– 'Kesselring's Variety' (Au)	CLyd CMMP CMea CStu ECho GCai GEdr IPen NDlv NLAp WAbe WFar WTin
– 'Laciniata' (Au)	IPen LRHS SBla
– lilac-flowered (Au)	IPen LFox
– 'Linda Pope' (Au) ♀H4	CLyd GCai GKev IPen ITim NBir NDlv NHar NHol NLAp NSla NSum WAbe
– 'Manfield'	WThu
– maritime form (Au)	IPen
– 'Millard's Variety' (Au)	CLyd IPen ITim
– 'Miss Fell' (Au) **new**	IPen
– 'Mrs Gatenby' (Au)	NWCA
– 'Nancy Lucy' (Au)	WAbe
– 'Napoleon' (Au)	GEdr IPen ITim NLAp
– 'Prichard's Variety' (Au) ♀H4	CLyd ECho ELan GEdr IPen ITim LFox MFie NCob NDlv NLAp NMyG NRya NWCA SBla WAbe WFar
– 'Rosea' (Au)	IPen
– 'Sheila Denby' (Au)	IPen ITim NLAp
– 'Snowhite' (Au)	NHar
– 'The President' (Au)	ITim
– violet-flowered (Au)	ECho
– 'Waithman's Variety' (Au)	GCrs IPen ITim NLAp NRya
– wild-collected (Au)	MFie
'Marianne Davey' (Pr/Prim/d)	MRav NBir
'Marie Crousse' (Pr/Prim/d)	CBgR CWCL ENot EPfP GAbr MBNS MDun MWgw NWCA SRGP WCot WFar WHal
Marine Blues Group (Pr/Poly)	CSWP MFie
'Maris Tabbard' (Au)	IPen MFie NLar SBla WAbe
'Marlene'	NBir
'Mars' (*allionii* hybrid) (Au)	NDlv NHol NRya WLin
'Marven' (Au)	CLyd GCai GEdr IPen WLin
'Mary Anne'	GAbr
Mauve Victorians Group (Pr/Poly)	CSWP MFie
maximowiczii (Cy)	GBuc GKev
megaseifolia (Pr)	GCrs GKev
melanops	see *P. chionantha* subsp. *melanops*
x ***meridiana*** (Au)	MFie NHol
§ – 'Miniera' (Au)	CLyd IPen ITim SIng WAbe WLin WThu
'Mexico'	MFie WCot
Midnight Group	CSWP GWWP MFie
'Miniera'	see *P.* x *meridiana* 'Miniera'
minima (Au)	NBro NLar NSla WAbe
– var. ***alba*** (Au)	CStu GCrs NRya
minima* x *wulfeniana	see *P.* x *vochinensis*
minor (Cy)	GCrs GKev
'Miss Indigo' (Pr/Prim/d)	CDes CHrt CWCL ENot EPfP GMaP MBNS MDun MFie MRav MSte NGHP NWCA SGar SPer WCAu WCot WFar
mistassinica f. ***leucantha*** (Al)	NEgg
– var. ***macropoda***	see *P. laurentiana*
miyabeana (Pf)	IPen
– B&SWJ 3407	WCru
modesta var. ***faurieae*** (Al)	GKev IPen MFie NWCA
– var. ***faurieae*** f. ***leucantha*** (Al) **new**	GKev
– 'Nemuro-koza-kura' (Al/v) **new**	CBow EMon
mollis (Co)	EBee GKev

	moupinensis	CLAP CStu EBee GGGa WAbe WCot
*	'Mrs Eagland'	GAbr
	'Mrs Frank Neave' (Pr/Prim)	IPen
	'Mrs McGillivray' (Pr/Prim)	GAbr
§	***munroi*** (Ar)	CDes EBee GEdr GKev IPen SWat WAbe
§	- subsp. ***yargongensis*** (Al)	GAbr GCrs GGar GKev IPen LRHS NLAp NPen SWat WAbe WFar
	- - SDR 3096	GKev
	muscarioides (Mu)	EBee GKev IPen
	Muted Victorians Group (Pr/Poly)	CSWP MFie
§	***nana*** (Pe)	IPen
	- 'Alba' (Pe)	WAbe
	New Pinks Group (Pr/Poly)	CSWP MFie
	'Nightingale'	ITim NHol
	nipponica (Su) **new**	GKev
	nivalis Pallas	see *P. chionantha*
§	***nivalis*** (Fed.) Halda subsp. ***xanthobasis*** (Cy)	EBee
	nutans Delavay ex Franch.	see *P. flaccida*
	nutans Georgi (Ar)	NEgg
	obconica (Ob)	LRHS MBri
	obtusifolia (Cy)	EBee GKev
	'Old Port' (Pr/Poly)	CBgR CElw EBee GKev LLWP NMen WCot
	Old Rose Victorians Group (Pr/Poly)	CSWP MFie
	'Olive Wyatt' (Pr/Prim/d)	NBir
	orbicularis (Cy)	GKev
	'Oriental Sunset'	MDKP
	Osiered Amber Group (Pr/Prim)	CSWP
	'Our Pat' (Pr/Poly/d)	GAbr
	Pagoda hybrids (Pf)	NEgg
	pale blue-flowered (Poly) **new**	SSth
	palinuri (Au)	IPen
	palmata (Co)	GCrs GEdr GGGa WAbe
	'Paris '90' (Pr/Poly)	CSWP ITer MFie
	parryi (Pa)	EBee GCrs GKev WFar
	'Peardrop' (Au)	GAbr IPen NHol
	pedemontana (Au)	GKev MSte WAbe
	- 'Alba' (Au)	CGra WPat
	'Perle von Bottrop' (Pr/Prim)	GAbr
	'Peter Klein' (Or)	GBuc GEdr LTwo NHol NLAp WAbe WTin
	petiolaris misapplied	see *P.* 'Redpoll'
§	***petiolaris*** (Pe)	GCra GCrs GGGa MDun NHar NSum NWCA WAbe
	- Sherriff's form	see *P.* 'Redpoll'
	'Petticoat'	NCGa NLar SPer
	'Pink Aire' (Au)	ITim MFie NMen NRya
	'Pink Fairy' (Au)	IPen ITim
	'Pink Ice' (*allionii* hybrid) (Au)	CGra CLyd CPBP GCrs GKev ITim MFie NHol NRya WLin
	pinnata **new**	GKev
	poissonii (Pf)	CDWL CTri EBee ELan GCra GEdr GGar GMac GQui IBal IPen MDun MFie MNrw NEgg NGby NGdn NHol NPen NRnb SWat WAbe WBVN WGwG WShi
	- ACE 1946	NWCA
	- ACE 2030	EPot
	- B&SWJ 7525	WCru
	- SDR 3201	GKev
	polyanthus (Pr/Poly)	WFar
	polyneura (Co)	EBee ECha EDAr GEdr GGar GKev IGor IPen MFie NBid NEgg NGdn NPen NSum SRms WCot
	'Port Wine' (Pr)	EBla GAbr

	prenantha (Pf)	EBee GKev LTwo WAbe
	'Prince Silverwings' (Pr/Poly/d)	WEas
§	***prolifera*** (Pf) Υ^{H4}	CDMG CMHG CPrp CWCL EBee ECha EHon GCra GEdr GGar GKev GMac GQui IPen MLLN MNrw NCGa NEgg NGdn NPen SPer SRms SWat WAbe WFar WGwG WMoo WPer WPtf
§	x ***pubescens*** (Au) Υ^{H4}	EAlp IPen LFox NEgg NGdn NLAp WPer
	- 'Apple Blossom' (Au)	CLyd IPen ITim MFie
	- 'Balfouriana' (Au)	LFox NHol
	x ***pubescens*** 'Beverley White' (Au) **new**	IPen
§	x ***pubescens*** 'Bewerley White' (Au)	CStu EBee ECho EPfP NDlv NLAp NMyG WHoo
	- 'Blue Wave' (Au)	IPen MFie
§	- 'Boothman's Variety' (Au)	CLyd CStu CTri EAlp ECho EDAr EPfP EWTr GKev IPen ITim LRHS MFie MSte NDlv NLAp NMyG NRnb WFar WHoo WTin
	- 'Carmen'	see *P.* x *pubescens* 'Boothman's Variety'
	- 'Christine' (Au)	CLyd CMea IPen ITim MFie NBir NDlv NLAp NSum WCot
	- 'Cream Viscosa' (Au)	MFie NDlv NLAp
	- 'Deep Mrs Wilson' (Au)	MFie
	- 'Faldonside' (Au)	CLyd IPen MFie NDlv NSum WHoo
§	- 'Freedom' (Au)	CLyd CTri ECho GAbr GKev IPen ITim LRHS MFie NBir NDlv NHol NLAp NLar SRms WEas WLin
	- 'Harlow Car' (Au)	CLyd CMea CPBP GMac GQui IPen ITim MFie NDlv NSum NWCA WFar WTin
	- 'Henry Hall' (Au)	CLyd EWes
	- 'Herbert Beresford' (Au)	GCrs
	- 'Joan Danger' (Au)	CLyd IPen ITim
	- 'Joan Gibbs' (Au)	CLyd ECho GCai IPen ITim MFie NLAp
	- 'Lilac Fairy' (Au)	IPen ITim NDlv NHol SIng
	- 'Mrs J.H. Wilson' (Au)	CGra CLyd GEdr MFie NDlv NHol NRya
	- 'Pat Barwick' (Au)	GCrs IPen ITim LFox NLAp WTin
	- 'Peggy' (Au)	MFie
	- 'Rufus' (Au)	CLyd CWCL ECho EWes GAbr GCrs IPen WCot WTin
	- 'S.E. Matthews' (Au)	NHol
	- 'Sid Skelton' (Au)	IPen
	- 'Snowcap' (Au)	CGra GCrs IPen
	- 'Sonya' (Au)	IPen ITim
	- 'The General' (Au)	CLyd CTri IPen ITim MFie SPop
	- 'Verity's Violet' (Au)	WOFF
§	- 'Wedgwood' (Au)	GCai IPen ITim
	- 'Winifred' (Au)	MFie SPop
	- yellow (Au) **new**	IPen
	pulchella (Pu)	GKev
	pulverulenta (Pf) Υ^{H4}	More than 30 suppliers
	- 'Bartley'	SWat
	- Bartley hybrids (Pf) Υ^{H4}	CDWL CDes CWCL GBuc LSou NBre
	- 'Bartley Pink' (Pf)	CHar GBuc
	'Quaker's Bonnet'	see *P. vulgaris* 'Lilacina Plena'
	'Rachel Kinnen' (Au)	IPen ITim MFie SIng WLin
	'Ramona' (Pr/Poly)	MFie
	'Ravenglass Vermilion'	see *P.* 'Inverewe'
	recubariensis (Au) **new**	GKev
	'Red Velvet' (Pr/Prim/d)	CWCL MDun MSte NGHP
§	'Redpoll' (Pe)	CDes CLAP WAbe
	- LS&H 19856	NHar
	reidii (So)	GCrs GEdr NSla
	- CC 4624	GKev
	- var. ***williamsii*** (So)	GGGa IPen
*	- - ***alba*** (So)	WAbe
	'Reverie' (Pr/Poly)	CSWP MFie

	'Rheniana' (Au)	IPen ITim SIng
	'Romeo' (Pr/Prim)	WCot
	'Rose O'Day' (Pr/Poly/d)	NBir
	rosea (Or) ♀^{H4}	CAby EBee ECho EDAr EMFW EPfP GEdr IPen LRHS MFie NBid NBir NLAp NRya NSti NVic WFar
	- 'Delight'	see *P. rosea* 'Micia Visser-de Geer'
	- 'Gigas' (Or)	CRez NHol
	- 'Grandiflora' (Or)	CPrp EAlp ECho EHon EPfP GGar GKev MRav MWat NDlv NEgg NWCA SIng SPoG SRms SWal SWat WFar WHil WPer
§	- 'Micia Visser-de Geer' (Or)	LRHS WTin
§	***rotundifolia*** (Cf)	GKev IPen
	'Rowallane Rose' (Pf)	GBuc IGor WWFP
I	'Rowena'	GCra GCrs WCot
	roxburghii	see *P. rotundifolia*
	'Roy Cope' (Pr/Prim/d)	CWCL EPfP GAbr MFie NBir NWCA SGar SRGP WFar
	'Roydon Ruby'	WCot
	rubra	see *P. firmipes*
	rusbyi (Pa)	EBee GKev NWCA WLin
	- subsp. ***ellisiae*** (Pe)	CGra IPen
	'Sapphire'	MFie
	saxatilis (Co)	GCrs MFie WFar
	scandinavica (Al)	GCrs GKev MFie
	x ***scapeosa*** (Pe)	GGGa
	scapigera (Pe)	GGGa
§	'Schneekissen' (Pr/Prim)	CBre GAbr GCra IPen MBri MHer NBir NBro NChi NGHP NMyG NPro WHil
	scotica (Al)	EBee EDAr GCrs GKev GMaP GPoy LFox NSla WAbe
	secundiflora (Pf)	CDWL CLAP CWCL EBee EDAr ELan GCra GCrs GEdr GGGa GGar GKev LRHS NChi NLAp SPlb SRms SWat WAbe WBVN WBrE WFar WGwG WMoo WPtf
	- B&SWJ 7547	WCru
§	x ***sendtneri*** (Au)	MFie
	x ***serrata***	see *P.* x *vochinensis*
	serratifolia (Pf)	GGGa
	sibthorpii	see *P. vulgaris* subsp. *sibthorpii*
	sieboldii (Co) ♀^{H4}	CEnt CGra ECho GCai GKev ITim LFox MLHP MNrw NEgg NMen NRya NWCA SMac SRms WAbe WFar
	- 'Bide-a-Wee Blue' (Co)	NBid
I	- 'Blue Lagoon' (Co)	EBrs MMHG
	- 'Blue Shades' (Co) **new**	IPen
	- blue-flowered (Co)	CLAP CWCL ECho GCrs GEdr NMen
	- 'Blush' (Co)	CLAP GEdr
	- 'Carefree' (Co)	CAby CLAP IPen LTwo NBro NLar NMen
	- 'Cherubim' (Co)	EBee GCra MMHG
	- 'Dancing Ladies' (Co)	CAby CLAP CMil CSWP IPen MFie NBro WFar
	- 'Duane's Choice' (Co)	CDes
	- 'Galaxy' (Co)	NBro NRya
	- 'Geisha Girl' (Co)	CFir CLAP MRav NLar WAbe WFar
	- f. ***lactiflora*** (Co)	CDes CLAP EBee GMac IPen NBro NDov NMen SMHy SRot WFar WPGP WTin
	- 'Lilac Sunbonnet' (Co)	EPfP LRHS LTwo NWCA WFar
	- 'Manakoora' (Co)	CLAP CSWP IPen MFie NBro NSum WFar
	- 'Mikado' (Co)	CLAP EBee GCra IPen MRav
	- 'Pago-Pago' (Co)	CAby CDes CLAP IPen MFie NBro WFar
	- 'Purple Back' (Co)	EBee
	- 'Seraphim' (Co)	CLAP EBee MMHG
	- 'Snowflake' (Co)	CAby CLAP MMHG NLar NSla WAbe

- 'Tah-ni' (Co)	NBro NSum
- 'Winter Dreams' (Co)	CLAP CSWP MFie NBid NBro NSum WFar
sikkimensis (Si) ♀^{H4}	CEnt CWCL ECho EDAr EPot GCrs GEdr GGGa GGar GKev IPen MNrw NGdn NPen NSum SPoG WBVN WFar WHil WPnP
- ACE 1422	GBuc
- B&SWJ 4808	WCru
- CC 3409	WRos
- CC 4944	MGol
- CC&McK 1022	GQui
- SDR 2560	GKev
- SDR 3233	GKev
- var. ***pseudosikkimensis*** (Si) **new**	IPen
- var. ***pudibunda*** (Si)	GEdr GKev
- 'Tilman Number 2' (Si)	CWCL GAbr SPer
aff. ***sikkimensis*** (Si)	ITim NEgg
- ACE 2176	GBuc
Silver-laced Group (Pr/Poly)	SWvt WCot WPtf
- 'Silver Lining' (Pr/Poly)	LRHS
'Silverwells' (Pf)	GEdr
sinopurpurea	see *P. chionantha* subsp. *sinopurpurea*
'Sir Bedivere' (Pr/Prim)	CDes GAbr GBuc NLar
smithiana	see *P. prolifera*
'Snow Carpet'	see *P.* 'Schneekissen'
'Snow Cushion'	see *P.* 'Schneekissen'
'Snow White' (Pr/Poly)	GEdr MRav
Snowcushion	see *P.* 'Schneekissen'
'Snowruffles'	ITim
sonchifolia (Pe)	CFir CLAP GGGa GKev MDun WCot
- SDR 2560	GKev
- from Tibet (Pe)	MDun
sorachiana	see *P. yuparensis*
'Sparkling Eyes' **new**	WCot
spectabilis (Au)	EBee GEdr GKev WLin
- SDR 2415	GKev
specuicola (Al)	GKev
Spice Shades Group (Pr/Poly)	CSWP GWWP ITer MFie WCot
stenocalyx (Pu)	GCrs WAbe
'Stradbrook Charm' (Au)	CPBP EPot NHol WFar WLin
'Stradbrook Dainty' (Au)	MFie WFar
'Stradbrook Dream' (Au)	ITim MFie NLAp WFar
'Stradbrook Gem' (Au)	WAbe WLin
'Stradbrook Lilac Lustre' (Au)	MFie
'Stradbrook Lucy' (Au)	IPen ITim NHol NLAp WAbe WFar WLin
'Stradbrook Mauve Magic' (Au)	MFie
Striped Victorians Group (Pr/Poly)	CSWP ITer MFie
stuartii (Cy) **new**	GKev
'Sue Jervis' (Pr/Prim/d)	CWCL NBir NCGa NGHP NLar NSti NSum SPer SRGP WGwG WHal
suffrutescens (Su)	WAbe
'Sunshine Susie' (Pr/Prim/d)	CHrt CWCL ENot EPfP MBNS MFie MRav MSte NCGa NGHP SIng SPer SRGP WCot
takedana (Bu)	EBee LTwo
'Tantallon' (Pe)	GGGa GGar GKev ITim
Tartan Reds Group (Pr/Prim)	CSWP
'Tawny Port' (Pr/Poly)	GAbr GBuc NBro SRms
'Tie Dye' (Pr/Prim)	CBgR CDes CElw ENot GBin GBri ITer LRHS NBhm NCot NLar WCot WFar WTMC
'Tipperary Purple' (Pr/Prim)	GAbr GEdr

	'Tomato Red' (Pr/Prim)	CBgR WCot
	'Tony' (Au)	CGra CPBP IPen WAbe WLin
	'Top Affair' (Au/d)	IPen WAln
	tosaensis var. ***brachycarpa*** (R)	GKev
	'Tournaig Pink' (Pf)	GGar
	'Val Horncastle' (Pr/Prim/d)	CWCL EPfP GAbr GMaP ITer LRHS MBNS MDKP MNrw MSte MWgw NCGa NGHP NLar NWCA SIng SPer SRGP WCot
	Valentine Victorians Group (Pr/Poly)	MFie
§	***veris*** (Pr) 𝕐H4	More than 30 suppliers
	- 'Catrillo' (Pr) **new**	LBuc
	- subsp. ***columnae*** (Pr)	EBee
	- feather-petalled (Pr)	WCot
	- hybrids (Pr)	NEgg SGar
	- 'Katy McSparron' (Pr/d)	CMea CSsd EBee GCra WCot
	- subsp. ***macrocalyx*** (Pr)	EBee NWCA
	- orange-flowered (Pr)	WMoo
	- red-flowered (Pr)	CMMP NBid NGdn SPer WMoo
	- 'Sunset Shades' (Pr)	ITer NChi NEgg NGHP NLar WPer
	vernalis	see *P. vulgaris*
	verticillata (Sp)	GKev IPen
§	***vialii*** (So) 𝕐H4	More than 30 suppliers
	Violet Victorians Group (Pr/Poly)	CSWP MFie
§	x ***vochinensis*** (Au)	CFee CStu NWCA
§	***vulgaris*** (Pr/Prim) 𝕐H4	More than 30 suppliers
	- var. ***alba*** (Pr/Prim)	NSla WAbe WBrk
	- 'Alba Plena' (Pr/Prim)	GBuc GGar IGor ITer NSti NSum
	- 'Alex Brenton' (Pr/d)	LHop
	- green-flowered	see *P. vulgaris* 'Viridis'
	- 'Greyshot'	NBir
§	- 'Lilacina Plena' (Pr/Prim/d)	CDes CWCL ENot EPfP MBNS MRav NCGa NCot NGHP NSum SPer WFar
§	- subsp. ***sibthorpii*** (Pr/Prim) 𝕐H4	CMHG CSam EBee ECho GAbr GBuc IPen ITim LFox LLWP LRHS MHer MLHP MRav MWgw NBro NChi NGHP NHol NMyG SRms WEas WHil WLin WOut
§	- 'Viridis' (Pr/Prim/d)	CDes
	waltonii (Si)	CMil EBee GBuc GCai GCrs GEdr GKev IPen MDKP MNrw
	- hybrids (Si)	NEgg
	'Wanda' (Pr/Prim) 𝕐H4	CBcs CStu CTri ECho ENot GAbr GCra LBMP LLWP LRHS NBid NSti NVic SRGP SRms WBrk WCFE WCot WEas WFar WHil WTin
	Wanda Group (Pr/Prim)	ECho NEgg
	'Wanda Hose-in-hose' (Pr/Prim/d)	EMon GAbr GCra MMHG NBir SSvw WCot WHer WHil
	'Wanda Jack in the Green' (Pr/Prim)	CBgR MLLN WCot WFar
	wardii	see *P. munroi*
	warshenewskiana (Or)	GEdr GGar GKev MNrw NCob NHol NLAp NMen NRya NWCA WAbe WFar WGwG WPat
	watsonii (Mu)	EBee GAbr GCrs GKev NLAp SWat
	- ACE 1402	IPen
	'Wedgwood'	see *P.* x *pubescens* 'Wedgwood'
	wessa var. ***hopeana*** (Si)	GCrs NSum
	'Wharfedale Ballerina' (Au)	ITim
	'Wharfedale Bluebell' (Au)	CLyd ITim NBir NRya
	'Wharfedale Buttercup' (Au)	ITim NHar
	'Wharfedale Butterfly' (Au)	ITim NHol
	'Wharfedale Crusader' (Au)	ITim
	'Wharfedale Gem' (*allionii* hybrid) (Au)	GCai ITim MFie NLAp NRya WAbe
	'Wharfedale Ling' (*allionii* hybrid) (Au)	CGra CPBP CStu GCai GCrs MFie NLAp NLar NRya
	'Wharfedale Sunshine' (Au)	GKev ITim MFie NLAp
	'Wharfedale Superb' (*allionii* hybrid) (Au)	ITim MFie NLAp
	'Wharfedale Village' (Au)	CLyd ITim NLAp WGwG WLin
	'White Linda Pope' (Au)	CLyd NMen
	'White Wanda' (Pr/Prim)	GAbr NCGa NDov WHil
	'White Waves' (*allionii* hybrid) (Au)	ITim
	whitei (Pe)	CWsd MDun
§	- 'Sherriff's Variety' (Pe)	CLAP GCrs SBla
	wigramiana (So)	WAbe
	'William Genders' (Pr/Poly)	GAbr
	wilsonii (Pf)	CDWL CTri GBuc GGar GKev GMac LDai NDlv NEgg NPen NRnb NWCA SWat WBVN WFar WGwG WHil WHoo WLin
§	- var. ***anisodora*** (Pf)	CLAP EBee GCrs GGar GKev GQui IPen MFie NEgg NGdn NLAp WPtf
	'Windrush'	see *P.* x *berninae* 'Windrush'
	'Winter White'	see *P.* 'Gigha'
	'Wisley Crimson'	see *P.* 'Wisley Red'
§	'Wisley Red' (Pr/Prim)	CElw
	wollastonii (So)	GKev
	wulfeniana (Au)	EDAr GCrs GEdr GKev WAbe
	- subsp. ***baumgarteniana*** (Au)	WLin
	xanthobasis	see *P. nivalis* (Fed.) Halda subsp. *xanthobasis*
	yargongensis	see *P. munroi* subsp. *yargongensis*
	yunnanensis (Y) **new**	GKev
§	***yuparensis*** (Al)	EBee GKev IPen NEgg NWCA
	zambalensis (Ar)	GCrs GKev IPen WAbe
	- SDR 1716	GKev

Prinsepia (Rosaceae)

	sinensis	CArn CBcs CFee CMCN MBlu NLar SLon WSHC
	utilis	CTrG

Pritzelago (Brassicaceae)

	alpina	GEdr NPro

Prostanthera (Lamiaceae)

	aspalathoides	ECou EWes SOWG
	'Badja Peak'	CTrC MAsh WAbe WBod
	baxteri	ECou
	chlorantha	SOWG
	cuneata 𝕐H4	More than 30 suppliers
	- 'Alpine Gold'	CMHG CWSG WFar
	- Kew form	CPLG WPGP
*	***digitiformis***	ECou SOWG
	incisa	CPLG SHDw SPla
	- 'Rosea'	EOHP SBod
	lasianthos	CBcs CDoC CHll ECou EShb EWes SHDw SOWG
	- 'Kallista Pink'	SOWG
	- var. ***subcoriacea***	CPLG CRHN
	magnifica	SOWG
	'Mauve Mantle'	ECou SOWG
	melissifolia	CArn CPLG CPrp ECre EShb LHop WSel
§	- var. ***parvifolia***	CBcs EBee ECre WAbe
	'Mint Delight' **new**	LBuc
	'Mint Royale' **new**	LBuc
	'Mint-Ice' **new**	LBuc
	nivea	ECou
	ovalifolia 𝕐H2	CTca ECou SOWG
I	- 'Variegata'	ECou SOWG
	'Poorinda Ballerina'	CDoC CPLG CWSG EBee ECou EShb LHop MDun MGos MNHC SOWG SPer SPoG WFar WLeb
	rotundifolia 𝕐H2	CBrm CDul CHEx CPrp CSBt CSev CTrG CTri CWSG EBee ECho EOHP ERea MNHC MWgw NGHP SEND SMad SOWG SPer WLeb
	- 'Chelsea Girl'	see *P. rotundifolia* 'Rosea'

§	– 'Rosea' 🏆H2	CDoC CPrp CSBt CTrC CTrG EBee ECou GGar SPoG
*	***scheelii***	SOWG
	scutellarioides 'Lavender Lady'	ECou
	sieberi misapplied	see *P. melissifolia* var. *parvifolia*
	walteri	CBrm CDoC ECou SKHP

Protea ✿ (*Proteaceae*)

	aurea	EShb SPlb
	burchellii	SPlb
	coronata	SPlb
	cynaroides	CBcs CCtw CHEx CTrC IDee LRHS SOWG SPlb
	dracomontana	SPlb
	effusa	SPlb
	eximia	CBcs EShb LRHS SPlb
	grandiceps	CCCN SPlb
	lacticolor	SPlb
	laurifolia	SPlb
	nana	SPlb
	neriifolia	CCCN EShb SPlb
	– 'Snowcrest'	CTrC
	obtusifolia	SPlb
	'Pink Ice'	CTrC
	repens	SPlb
	subvestita	CTrC SPlb
	susannae	SPlb
	venusta	CTrC

Prumnopitys (*Podocarpaceae*)

§	***andina***	WFar WThu
	elegans	see *P. andina*
§	***taxifolia***	CTrC ECou

Prunella (*Lamiaceae*)

§	***grandiflora***	CArn CHby CPrp ECha SMac SWat WFar WMoo WPGP
	– 'Alba'	CHFP CSBt EBee ECha EPfP GMaP MFOX MWgw NBid NGHP NGdn NLar SPer SPla WCAu WFar
	– 'Bella Deep Rose' new	SPad
	– 'Carminea'	EBee ECtt NGby SPer
	– light blue-flowered	NLar WMoo WOut
	– 'Little Red Riding Hood'	see *P. grandiflora* 'Rotkäppchen'
	– 'Loveliness' 🏆H4	CDoC EBee ECha ECtt GMaP MFOX MRav MWgw NBro NGdn NSti NVic SPer SPla SPlb SRGP WCAu WFar WTin
	– 'Pagoda'	CEnt CSpe NBre NLar
	– 'Pink Loveliness'	CPrp CSBt LRHS SRms WFar
	– 'Rosea'	CElw CSBt EBee EPfP WOut
§	– 'Rotkäppchen'	ECtt
	– 'Rubra'	EBee GAbr NGHP NLar SBch WMoo WPer
	– 'White Loveliness'	CElw CPrp LRHS WFar WPer
	hyssopifolia	XPep
	incisa	see *P. vulgaris*
*	'Inshriach Ruby'	GBin
	laciniata	CMCo EBee EPPr EShb WMoo
§	***vulgaris***	CArn CRWN GPoy MHer MNHC MSal NLan NMir NPri NSco SECG WHer
	– var. ***leucantha***	WHer
	– 'Voile'	LAst
	x ***webbiana***	see *P. grandiflora*
	– 'Gruss Aus Isernhagen' new	EBee

Prunus ✿ (*Rosaceae*)

	'Accolade' 🏆H4	CAbP CDul CEnd CLnd CSBt CTho CTri EBee ECrN ELan EPfP LAst LCro LPan LRHS MAsh MBri MRav NBea NWea SCrf SEND SHBN SLim SPer SPoG WFar WJas WOrn
§	'Amanogawa' 🏆H4	More than 30 suppliers
	americana	EMui
	amygdalus	see *P. dulcis*
	armeniaca 'Alfred' (F)	EMui ERea GTwe SDea SKee SPer
	– var. ***ansu*** 'Flore Pleno' (d)	NEgg
	– 'Blenheim' (F)	ERea
	– 'Bredase' (F)	CWib EMil SDea
	– 'Early Moorpark' (F)	CAgr CWib ECrN EPfP ERea GTwe LAst MBri SDea SGFT SLon WOrn
	– 'Farmingdale' (F)	ERea SDea
	– Flavorcot = 'Bayoto'PBR	CSut SGFT SPer
	– 'Garden Aprigold' (F)	EMui ENot NPri SPoG
	– 'Goldcot' (F)	CAgr ERea LRHS MCoo SDea SKee WOrn
	– 'Golden Glow' (F)	CAgr ECrN EMui ERea GTwe LRHS MCoo SKee
	– 'Goldrich' (F)	CAgr
	– 'Hargrand' (F)	CAgr
	– 'Harogem' (F)	CAgr
	– 'Hemskirke' (F)	ERea SKee
	– 'Hongaarse' (F)	SDea
	– 'Isabella' (F)	CAgr ECrN ERea LRHS MBri MCoo MGan MNHC SPoG
	– 'Moorpark' (F) 🏆H3	CEnd CSBt CTri CWib EMui ENot ERea GTwe LAst LBuc MGos SDea SHBN SKee SPer
	– 'New Large Early' (F)	EMui ERea GTwe SDea SEND SKee
	– 'Tomcot' (F)	CTho ECrN EMui LRHS MBri MCoo SFam SGFT SKee SPoG
	– 'Tross Orange' (F)	CWib SDea
	avium 🏆H4	CBcs CCVT CDul CLnd CRWN CSBt CTri CWib ECrN EMac EPfP LBuc MBar MGos MNHC MRav MSwo NBee NWea SFam SHBN SPer WHar WMoo WMou WOrn
	– 'Alfheim' (F) new	SKee
	– 'Amber Heart' (F)	SKee
	– 'August Heart' (F)	SKee
	– 'Belgian Rivers' (F) new	SKee
	– 'Bigarreau Gaucher' (F)	SHBN SKee
§	– 'Bigarreau Napoléon' (F)	GTwe SCrf SHBN SKee
	– 'Bigarreau Nomblot' (D) new	SKee
	– 'Birchenhayes'	see *P. avium* 'Early Birchenhayes'
	– 'Black Eagle' (F)	CTho
	– 'Black Heart' (F)	CWib
	– 'Black Tartarian' (F)	SKee
	– 'Black Varik' (F) new	SKee
	– 'Bottlers'	see *P. avium* 'Preserving'
	– 'Bradbourne Black' (F)	ECrN SCrf SKee
	– 'Bronnerkirsche' (F) new	SKee
	– 'Bullion' (F)	CEnd CTho
	– 'Burcombe' (F)	CEnd CTho
	– Celeste = 'Sumpaca'PBR (D)	CTri EMil EMui GTwe MBri MNHC SDea SFam SKee SPoG WOrn
	– 'Cherokee'	see *P. avium* 'Lapins'
	– 'Colney' (F) 🏆H4	GTwe SFam SKee WJas
	– 'Crown Morello' (F) new	CSut
	– 'Dun' (F)	CTho
§	– 'Early Birchenhayes' (F)	CEnd CTho
	– 'Early Rivers' (F)	CSBt CWib ECrN ENot GTwe SDea SHBN SKee
	– 'Elton Heart' (F)	CTho SKee
	– 'Emperor Francis' (F)	ECrN
	– 'Erianne' (F) new	SKee
	– 'Fice' (F)	CEnd CTho
	– 'Florence' (F)	SKee
	– 'Governor Wood' (F)	CWib GTwe SKee
	– 'Grandiflora'	see *P. avium* 'Plena'
	– 'Greenstem Black' (F)	CTho
	– 'Hannaford' (D/C)	CTho
	– 'Hertford' (F) 🏆H4	SFam SKee
	– 'Inga' (F)	SFam SKee
	– 'Kentish Red' (F)	CTho SKee

	– 'Knauff's Riesen' (F) **new**	SKee
	– 'Knauff's Schwarze' (F) **new**	SKee
§	– 'Lapins' (F)	CAgr CTho CTri ECrN EMui GTwe LAst LRHS SDea SFam SGFT SKee SPoG WHar WJas WOrn
	– 'May Duke'	see *P.* x *gondouinii* 'May Duke'
	– 'Merchant' (F) ♀H4	ECrN GTwe SKee
	– 'Mermat' (F)	SKee
	– 'Merpet' (F)	SKee
	– 'Merton Crane' (F)	SKee
	– 'Merton Favourite' (F)	SKee
	– 'Merton Glory' (F)	CSBt ECrN EMui ENot GTwe MGan MGos SCrf SFam SKee WOrn
	– 'Merton Late' (F)	SKee
	– 'Merton Marvel' (F)	SKee
	– 'Merton Premier' (F)	SKee
	– 'Mill's Seedling' (F) **new**	SKee
	– 'Moserkirsche' (F) **new**	SKee
	– 'Nabella' (F)	WJas
	– 'Napoléon'	see *P. avium* 'Bigarreau Napoléon'
	– 'Newstar' (F)	EMui
	– 'Noble' (F)	SKee
	– 'Noir Boccard' (F) **new**	SKee
	– 'Noir de Guben' (F)	ECrN GTwe SKee
	– 'Nutberry Black' (F)	SKee
	– 'Old Black Heart' (F)	SKee
	– 'Penny'	EMui SKee
§	– 'Plena' (d) ♀H4	CBcs CCVT CDul CLnd CSBt CTho CWSG EBee ECrN ELan EPfP LBuc LCro LRHS MGos MRav MSwo NBee NWea SCoo SCrf SPer WFar WHar WJas WOrn
§	– 'Preserving' (F)	CTho
	– 'Ronald's Heart' (F)	SKee
	– 'Roundel Heart' (F)	SKee
	– 'Schauenburger' (F) **new**	SKee
	– 'Small Black' (F)	CTho
	– 'Starkrimson' (F)	ECrN
	– 'Stella' (F) ♀H4	More than 30 suppliers
	– 'Stella Compact' (F)	CWib ECrN ENot LAst MBri SDea WHar
	– 'Summer Sun' (D) ♀H4	CSut CTho CTri EMil EMui GTwe LBuc LRHS MBri MCoo SCoo SDea SFam SGFT SKee SPoG
	– 'Summit' (F)	SHBN SKee
	– 'Sunburst' (F)	CAgr CCVT CEnd CTho CTri CWib ECrN EMil EMui GTwe LAst LBuc LRHS MBri SCoo SDea SFam SGFT SKee SPer SPoG WJas WOrn
	– 'Sweetheart' (F)	CAgr EMui ENot GTwe MBri SKee SPoG
	– 'Sylvia' (F)	SFam
	– 'Turkish Black' (F)	SKee
	– 'Upright' (F)	CTho
	– 'Ursula Rivers' (F) **new**	SKee
	– 'Van' (F)	ECrN ENot GTwe SKee
	– 'Vega' (F)	CAgr GTwe SFam SKee WJas
	– 'Vroege van Werder' (F) **new**	SKee
	– 'Waterloo' (F)	CTho SKee
	– 'Wellington A' (F) **new**	SKee
	– 'Werder's Early Black' (F) **new**	SKee
	– 'Werdersche Braune' (F) **new**	SKee
	– 'White Heart' (F)	CTho CWib ECrN SKee
	– 'Wildstar'	CEnd
	– 'Zweitfrühe' (F) **new**	SKee
	'Beni-yutaka'	CEnd CTho LBuc LRHS SCoo SLim
	besseyi	CAgr
	'Blaze'	see *P. cerasifera* 'Nigra'
	x ***blireana*** (d) ♀H4	CDoC CDul CEnd CTri ENot EPfP LAst LCro LRHS MBar MBri MDun MGos MRav MWat NLar NWea SBLw SCoo SPer SPoG WFar WHar
	– 'Moseri' (d)	SBLw
	'Blushing Bride'	see *P.* 'Shōgetsu'
	cerasifera	CAgr CDul CRWN CTri ECrN EMac LBuc NWea SEND SPer
	– 'Cherry Plum' (F)	CTri ECrN SDea SKee
	– 'Crimson Dwarf'	SCoo
	– 'First' (F)	CAgr
	– 'Golden Sphere' (F)	CAgr CTho EMui WOrn
	– 'Gypsy' (F)	CAgr CTho EMui
	– 'Hessei' (v)	CBow CEnd EBee LRHS MBlu MBri MDun MGos MRav SCoo SPoG
§	– Myrobalan Group (F)	ECrN EMui MRav SDea
	– – 'Magda Jensen' (C) **new**	CAgr
§	– 'Nigra' ♀H4	More than 30 suppliers
	– 'Pendula'	CTho ECrN
§	– 'Pissardii'	CWib ECrN LAst MAsh MBar MRav NBea NEgg NWea SCoo SFam SLim WFar WJas
*	– 'Princess'	CEnd CWSG EMui
	– 'Spring Glow'	CCVT CEnd EBee EPfP LRHS SCoo SLim SPoG WOrn
	– 'Woodii'	SBLw
	cerasus 'Montmorency' (F)	SKee
	– 'Morello' (C) ♀H4	More than 30 suppliers
	– 'Nabella' (F)	SKee
	– 'Rhexii' (d)	CLnd ECrN MAsh MGos SPer
	'Champagne Dream'	SCoo
	'Cheal's Weeping'	see *P.* 'Kiku-shidare-zakura'
	'Chocolate Ice'	MAsh MLan
§	'Chôshû-hizakura'	MGan
§	x ***cistena*** ♀H4	CBcs CCVT CDul CSBt CWSG EBee ELan ENot EPfP LAst MDun MGan MGos MWat NBlu SBLw SCoo SHBN SLim SPer SPla SPlb SPoG
	– 'Crimson Dwarf'	see *P.* x *cistena*
	'Collingwood Ingram'	MGos
	conradinae	see *P. hirtipes*
	davidiana	CTho SPlb
	domestica 'Allgroves Superb' (D)	ERea
	– 'Angelina Burdett' (D)	ERea GTwe SDea SKee
	– 'Anna Späth' (C/D)	SKee
	– 'Ariel' (C/D)	SDea SKee
	– 'Autumn Compote' (C)	SKee
	– 'Avalon' (D)	CAgr ECrN GTwe SDea SGFT SKee
	– 'Belgian Greengage' (F) **new**	SKee
	– 'Belgian Purple' (C)	SKee
	– 'Belle de Louvain' (C)	CDul CTho CTri ECrN EMil ERea GTwe SDea SKee
	– 'Birchenhayes' (F)	CEnd
	– 'Black Diamond'	see *P. salicina* 'Black Diamond'
	– 'Blaisdon Red' (C)	CTho
	– 'Blue Rock' (C/D) ♀H4	SKee
	– 'Blue Tit' (C/D) ♀H4	CAgr CTho EMui ERea GTwe LAst SDea SKee
§	– 'Bountiful' (C)	ERea
	– 'Brandy Gage' (C/D)	SKee
	– 'Brassai Szilvaja' (F) **new**	SKee
	– 'Bryanston Gage' (D)	CTho SKee
	– 'Burbank's Giant'	see *P. domestica* 'Giant Prune'
	– 'Burcombe'	CEnd
	– 'Bush' (C)	LAst
	– 'Cambridge Gage' (D) ♀H4	CAgr CCVT CDoC CDul CTri CWib ECrN EMui EPfP ERea GTwe LAst LRHS MBri MGan MWat SCoo SCrf SDea SFam SGFT SHBN SKee SPer SPoG WJas WOrn
	– 'Chrislin' (F)	CAgr CTho
	– 'Coe's Golden Drop' (D)	CCAT ECrN EMil EMui ERea GTwe LAst LRHS MGan MGos MRav SDea SFam SKee SPer

- 'Count Althann's Gage' (D)	ECrN GTwe SDea SFam SKee
- 'Cox's Emperor' (C)	SKee
- 'Crimson Drop' (D)	ERea SKee
- 'Cropper'	see *P. domestica* 'Laxton's Cropper'
- 'Curlew' (C)	SDea
- 'Czar' (C) ♀^{H4}	CAgr CCAT CCVT CDoC CDul CSBt CTri CWib ECrN EMui EPfP GBut GTwe LAst LBuc LRHS MGos NPri NWea SDea SFam SKee SPer SPoG WHar WOrn
- 'Denniston's Superb'	see *P. domestica* 'Imperial Gage'
- 'Diamond' (C)	SKee
- 'Dittisham Black' (C)	CAgr CTho
- 'Dittisham Ploughman' (C)	CTho SKee
- 'Drap d'Or d'Esperen' (D)	SKee
- 'Dunster Plum' (F)	CAgr CTho CTri CWib
- 'Early Laxton' (C/D) ♀^{H4}	ECrN ERea GTwe LAst SDea SFam SKee
- 'Early Prolific'	see *P. domestica* 'Rivers's Early Prolific'
- 'Early Rivers'	see *P. domestica* 'Rivers's Early Prolific'
- 'Early Transparent Gage' (C/D)	CCAT CSBt CTho ECrN EMil EMui ERea GTwe LAst LBuc MCoo SDea SFam SKee
- 'Early Victoria' (C/D)	SDea
- 'Edwards' (C/D) ♀^{H4}	CTri CWib ECrN EMil GTwe SDea SKee
- 'Excalibur' (D)	CAgr ECrN GTwe SDea SKee
§ - German Prune Group (C)	SKee
§ - 'Giant Prune' (C)	CCAT CWib ECrN GTwe SDea SKee
I - 'Godshill Big Sloe' (F)	SDea
- 'Godshill Blue' (C)	SDea
- 'Godshill Minigage' (F)	SDea
- 'Gold Dust'	ENot
- 'Golden Transparent' (D)	CTho GTwe MCoo SFam SKee
- 'Goldfinch' (D)	GTwe MCoo SKee
- Green Gage Group	see *P. domestica* Reine-Claude Group
- - 'Lindsey Gage' (F) **new**	SKee
- 'Grey Plum' (F)	CAgr CTho
- 'Grove's Late Victoria' (C/D)	SKee
- 'Guthrie's Late Green' (D)	SKee
- 'Hackman' (F) **new**	SKee
- 'Herman' (C/D)	CAgr ECrN EMil GTwe LAst LRHS MBri SDea SKee SPoG
- 'Heron' (F)	ECrN GTwe
- 'Impérial Epineuse' (D)	SKee
§ - 'Imperial Gage' (C/D) ♀^{H4}	CAgr CCAT CTho CTri CWib ECrN EMui ERea GTwe NLar SDea SFam SKee WOrn
- subsp. ***italica***	EMui
- 'Jan James' (F)	CEnd
- 'Jefferson' (D) ♀^{H4}	CAgr ECrN EMui ERea GTwe NLar SDea SFam SKee
* - 'Jubilaeum' (D)	CAgr EMui GTwe SKee
- 'Kea' (C)	CAgr CTho SKee
- 'Kirke's' (D)	CTho CTri ECrN ERea GTwe SDea SFam SKee WOrn
- 'Landkey Yellow' (F)	CAgr CTho
- 'Langley Gage'	CAgr ECrN SDea
- 'Late Muscatelle' (D)	ERea SKee
- 'Laxton's Bountiful'	see *P. domestica* 'Bountiful'
§ - 'Laxton's Cropper' (C)	CTri GTwe MCoo SKee
- 'Laxton's Delight' (D) ♀^{H4}	GTwe
- 'Laxton's Gage' (D)	SDea SKee
- 'Laxton's Supreme' (C/D)	SKee
- 'Madeleine Nomblot' (F) **new**	SKee
- 'Mallard' (D) ♀^{H4}	SKee
- 'Manaccan' (C)	CAgr CTho
- 'Marjorie's Seedling' (C) ♀^{H4}	CAgr CDoC CDul CSBt CTho CTri CWib ECrN EMui ERea GTwe LBuc LRHS MGan MLan MWat NPri SCoo SDea SEND SFam SGFT SKee SPer SPoG WHar WJas WOrn
- 'McLaughlin' (D)	SKee
- 'Merton Gage'	SKee
- 'Merton Gem' (C/D)	GTwe SKee
- 'Monarch' (C)	GTwe SKee
- 'Monsieur Jaune' (C/D) **new**	SKee
- 'Newark' (F) **new**	SKee
- 'Olympia' (C/D)	SKee
- 'Ontario' (C/D)	ECrN SKee
- 'Opal' (D) ♀^{H4}	CAgr CCAT CDoC CWSG CWib ECrN EMui ERea GBut GTwe LBuc MBri MGan MGos MLan MWat NWea SCrf SDea SEND SFam SGFT SKee SPoG WOrn
- 'Orleans' (C)	SKee
- 'Oullins Gage' (C/D) ♀^{H4}	CAgr CCAT CCVT CDoC CDul CSBt CTri CWib ECrN EMui ENot EPfP ERea GTwe LAst LBuc MBri MGan MRav SDea SFam SGFT SKee SPer SPoG WJas WOrn
- 'Pershore' (C) ♀^{H4}	CAgr CTho CWib ECrN ERea GTwe LAst MBri MNHC SDea SFam SKee WHar WOrn WSpi
- 'Pond's Seedling' (C)	CSBt SDea SKee
- 'President' (C/D)	GTwe SDea
- 'Priory Plum' (D)	SDea
- 'Purple Pershore' (C)	CAgr CTri CWib ECrN ERea GTwe SDea SFam SKee WOrn WSpi
- 'Quetsche d'Alsace'	see *P. domestica* German Prune Group
- 'Reeves' (C) ♀^{H4}	GTwe MCoo SFam SKee
- 'Reine-Claude Dorée'	see *P. domestica* Reine-Claude Group
§ - Reine-Claude Group (C/D)	ECrN EMui GTwe MGos SDea SFam SKee SPer
- - 'Old Green Gage'	see *P. domestica* (Reine-Claude Group) 'Reine-Claude Vraie'
- - 'Reine Claude de Brahy' (D)	SKee
- - 'Reine-Claude de Bavais' (D)	CTho CTri ERea GTwe SDea SFam SKee
- - 'Reine-Claude de Vars' (D)	SKee
- - 'Reine Claude Reforma' (F) **new**	SKee
- - 'Reine Claude' (RHS) (D) **new**	SLon
- - 'Reine-Claude Violette' (D)	ECrN ERea SKee
§ - - 'Reine-Claude Vraie' (C/D)	CWib ECrN EMui EPfP ERea LAst SLon SPoG WJas WOrn
§ - - 'Willingham Gage' (C/D)	ERea GTwe LRHS MLan
§ - 'Rivers's Early Prolific' (C)	CAgr CSBt CTho CTri ECrN ENot EPfP ERea GBut GTwe MCoo NWea SCoo SDea SHBN SKee WHar
- 'Royale de Vilvoorde' (D)	SKee
- 'Sanctus Hubertus' (D) ♀^{H4}	ECrN EPfP GTwe SDea SKee
- 'Seneca' (D) **new**	SGFT
- 'Severn Cross' (D)	GTwe SKee
- 'Stella'	CCVT CDul LAst NPri
- 'Stint' (C/D)	SKee
- 'Swan' (C)	ECrN GTwe
- 'Syston'	CTho MGos

- 'Thames Cross' (D)	SKee
- 'Transparent Gage' (D)	ECrN ERea
- 'Upright' (F)	CEnd
- 'Utility' (D)	SKee
- 'Valor' (C/D) ΨH4	ECrN
- 'Victoria' (C/D) ΨH4	More than 30 suppliers
- 'Violetta'PBR (C/D)	EMui GTwe SKee WBVN
- 'Wangenheimer Frühzwetsche' (F) **new**	SKee
- 'Warwickshire Drooper' (C)	CTho CWib ERea GTwe LAst SDea SFam SKee SPer WOrn
- 'Washington' (D)	SDea SKee
- 'White Magnum Bonum' (C)	SDea
- 'Willingham'	see *P. domestica* (Reine-Claude Group) 'Willingham Gage'
- 'Wyedale' (C)	GTwe
- 'Zimmers Frühzwetsche' (F) **new**	SKee
§ ***dulcis***	CDul CLnd CTri CWSG CWib ECrN EMui LAst LRHS MWat NBea NWea SBLw SCrf SDea SFam WBVN WOrn
- 'Ai' (F)	CAgr
- 'Ardechoise' (F)	CAgr
- 'Ferraduel' (F)	CAgr
- 'Ferragnes' (F)	CAgr
- 'Lauranne' (F)	CAgr
- 'Macrocarpa' (F)	ECrN
- 'Mandaline' (F)	CAgr
- 'Supernova' (F) **new**	CCCN
- 'Titan' (F)	ECrN
- 'Tuono' (F) **new**	CCCN
Easter Bonnet = 'Comet'PBR	ENot LBuc LRHS NPri SPoG
x ***eminens*** 'Umbraculifera'	SBLw
Fragrant Cloud = 'Shizuka'	CEnd CWSG CWib LRHS MAsh MBri SCoo SLim SPer SPoG WOrn
fruticosa 'Globosa'	LPan MAsh NHol
'Fugenzō'	CSBt
'Fuki'	MBri
glandulosa 'Alba Plena' (d)	CEnd CPLG CPle CSBt EBee ECrN LRHS NBea SBLw SHBN SPer SPlb SPoG SRms SWvt WBod WCFE
- 'Rosea Plena'	see *P. glandulosa* 'Sinensis'
§ - 'Sinensis' (d)	CEnd CPLG CPle CSBt EBee LRHS SBLw SHBN SPer SPoG SRms
§ x ***gondouinii*** 'May Duke' (F)	CTho SKee
- 'Schnee'	SBLw
'Gyoikō'	CEnd CTho
'Hally Jolivette'	CEnd ELan LRHS MAsh NWea SBLw
'Hanagasa'	EBee LRHS MAsh MBri NLar
'Hillieri'	ECrN MBar MGos
'Hillieri Spire'	see *P.* 'Spire'
'Hilling's Weeping'	EBee
§ ***hirtipes***	CLnd CTho
'Hisakura'	see *P.* 'Choshu-hizakura'
Hollywood	see *P.* 'Trailblazer'
'Horinji'	MBri SCoo
'Ichiyo' (d) ΨH4	CLnd ECrN EPfP LAst SCoo SCrf SPer
incisa	CTri NBea SPer WSpi
- 'Beniomi'	MRav
- 'February Pink'	CAbP CPMA MRav SBLw
- 'Fujima'	EBee LAst WSpi
- 'Kojo-no-mai'	More than 30 suppliers
- 'Mikinori'	NLar SCoo WFar WSpi
- 'Oshidori'	LRHS MBri MGos MRav NLar SLim SRms WFar
* - 'Otome'	WFar
- 'Paean'	NLar WSPU
- 'Pendula'	CPMA SCoo
- 'Praecox' ΨH4	CTho CWSG EPfP LRHS SCoo
- 'The Bride'	CDul CEnd CWSG LRHS MAsh MBri SCoo
§ - f. ***yamadae***	CBcs CEnd CPMA MAsh MBri NLar WSpi
insititia (F)	CRWN
- 'Black Bullace' (F)	EMui
§ - 'Bradley's King Damson' (C)	CWib ECrN GTwe SKee
- bullace (C)	SDea
- 'Dittisham Damson' (C)	CTho
- 'Farleigh Damson' (C) ΨH4	CAgr CWib ECrN ERea GBut GTwe LBuc SDea SEND SFam SGFT SKee SPer SPoG WJas
- 'Godshill Damson' (C)	SDea
- 'Golden Bullace'	see *P. insititia* 'White Bullace'
- 'King of Damsons'	see *P. insititia* 'Bradley's King Damson'
- 'Langley Bullace' (C)	CAgr CTho ECrN EMui ERea GTwe SGFT SKee
- 'Merryweather Damson' (C)	CAgr CCAT CCVT CDoC CDul CMac CSBt CTho CTri CWib ECrN EMui ERea GTwe LAst LBuc MBri MGan MGos NPri SCrf SDea SFam SGFT SKee SPoG WBVN WHar WJas WOrn
- 'Mirabelle de Nancy' (C)	CAgr CTho CTri GTwe LAst SDea SFam SGFT SKee
- 'Mirabelle de Nancy (Red)' (C)	SDea
§ - 'Prune Damson' (C) ΨH4	CDoC CTho CTri CWSG CWib ECrN EMui EPfP ERea GTwe LAst LBuc MBri NLar SDea SFam SKee SPer WHar WJas WOrn
- 'Shepherd's Bullace' (C)	CAgr CTho ERea SKee
- 'Shropshire Damson'	see *P. insititia* 'Prune Damson'
- 'Small Bullace' (C)	CAgr SKee
§ - 'White Bullace' (C)	CAgr ERea SKee
- 'Yellow Apricot' (C)	ERea SKee
'Jo-niōi'	CEnd CLnd CTho MBri SBLw
§ 'Kanzan' ΨH4	More than 30 suppliers
§ 'Kiku-shidare-zakura' ΨH4	More than 30 suppliers
Korean hill cherry	see *P. verecunda*
'Kulilensis Ruby' **new**	SLPl
kurilensis	see *P. nipponica* var. *kurilensis*
'Kursar' ΨH4	CDul CLnd CSBt CTho CTri EBee EMui EPfP LRHS MAsh MBri NWea SCoo SCrf SLim SPoG WOrn
laurocerasus ΨH4	CBcs CBrm CCVT CChe CDul CPMA CTrG CWSG EBee ECrN ELan EMac EPfP LAst MGos MRav NBea NEgg NWea SEND SPer SPoG SReu WFar WMoo WMou
- 'Aureovariegata'	see *P. laurocerasus* 'Taff's Golden Gleam'
- 'Camelliifolia'	CTri EPla EQua MBlu WCFE WHCG
§ - 'Castlewellan' (v)	CDoC CDul CPLG CTri CWib EPfP EPla LAst LHop MBar MGos MSwo NBea NEgg NPro SDix SLim SPer SPoG SSta WFar WHar WLeb WMoo
- 'Caucasica'	LPan MGos SMer
- 'Cherry Brandy'	MRav SLPl SPer
- Dart's Lowgreen	see *P. laurocerasus* Low 'n' Green = 'Interlo'
- Etna = 'Anbri'PBR	EBee ENot EPfP LBuc LRHS MBri MGos NPri SCoo
- 'Gajo' **new**	WBor
- 'Green Marble' (v)	CPMA CTri EBee
- 'Herbergii'	NLar
§ - 'Latifolia'	CHEx EPla EQua SLPl
§ - Low 'n' Green = 'Interlo'	MRav
- 'Magnoliifolia'	see *P. laurocerasus* 'Latifolia'
- 'Mano'	MGos NLar
- 'Marbled White'	see *P. laurocerasus* 'Castlewellan'
- 'Miky'	CPMA
- 'Mischeana'	SLPl

	- 'Mount Vernon'	LBuc MBar MBlu MGos
	- 'Novita'	EMil
	- 'Otinii'	CHEx
	- 'Otto Luyken' ♀H4	More than 30 suppliers
	- Renault Ace = 'Renlau'	MGos
	- 'Reynvaanii'	CPMA MBri
	- 'Rotundifolia'	More than 30 suppliers
	- 'Schipkaensis'	SLPl SPer
§	- 'Taff's Golden Gleam' (v)	CBow CPMA
	- 'Van Nes'	CPMA EBee EMil NLar
	- 'Variegata' misapplied	see *P. laurocerasus* 'Castlewellan'
	- 'Variegata' ambig. (v)	CPLG CWib EPla MBNS SRms
	- 'Zabeliana'	CDul CTri EBee ECrN ENot EPfP MBar MGos MSwo NHol NWea SHBN SPer SRms WFar WTel
	litigiosa	LRHS MBri NLar SCoo
	'Little Pink Perfection'	SCoo
	lusitanica ♀H4	More than 30 suppliers
	- subsp. ***azorica***	CDoC CPLG EQua MRav WFar WPGP
	- 'Myrtifolia'	CTri EBee ECrN EPfP EPla EQua LRHS MBri MLLN MRav SLon SWvt WCFE WGer WRHF
	- 'Variegata' (v)	CBcs CDul CSBt CTri CWib EBee ELan EPfP EPla LAst LHop LRHS MGos MLHP MRav MSwo NBlu NEgg NHol NSti SDix SHBN SLim SPer SPla SPoG SSta STop WFar
	maackii	CTho EPfP SBLw SEND SSpi
	- 'Amber Beauty'	CDoC CDul CEnd EBee EPfP MRav SBLw SCoo WFar
	'Mahogany Lustre'	see *P. serrula* 'Mahogany Lustre'
	'Matsumae-beni-murasaki'	MAsh SCoo
	'Matsumae-beni-tamanishiki'	MAsh
	'Matsumae-hana-gasa'	MBri
	'Mount Fuji'	see *P.* 'Shirotae'
	mume	CMCN CMen WNor
§	- 'Beni-chidori'	CEnd CWib EBee ECrN EPfP LBuc LRHS MBlu MBri MGos NBea NLar SCoo SHBN SLim SPoG WJas WOrn WPGP
	- 'Beni-shidori'	see *P. mume* 'Beni-chidori'
§	- 'Omoi-no-mama' (d)	CEnd CMen
	- 'Omoi-no-wac'	see *P. mume* 'Omoi-no-mama'
	- 'Pendula'	ECrN
	myrobalana	see *P. cerasifera* Myrobalan Group
§	***nipponica*** var. ***kurilensis***	MNHC
	- - 'Brilliant'	CBcs MAsh MBri MGos NLar SCrf WOrn
	- - 'Ruby'	CBcs CDul CEnd MBri MGos NBlu NEgg WFar
	'Okame' ♀H4	CChe CDul CLnd CSam CTho EBee ECrN ENot EPfP LAst LCro LRHS MAsh MBri MGos MRav NBlu NEgg NWea SCoo SCrf SLPl SLim SPer SPoG WBVN WFar WOrn WWeb
*	'Okame Harlequin' (v)	SLim SPoG
	'Okumiyako' misapplied	see *P.* 'Shōgetsu'
	padus	CCVT CDul CLnd CRWN CSBt CTri ECrN EMac LBuc MGos MSwo NBea NBee NBlu NWea SBLw WBVN WMou WOrn
	- 'Albertii'	CCVT CTho SCoo WJas
	- 'Colorata' ♀H4	CBcs CDoC CDul CEnd CSam CTho ECrN ELan EWTr LBuc MAsh MDun MGos NBee SBLw SCoo SHBN SPer WFar WJas
	- 'Grandiflora'	see *P. padus* 'Watereri'
	- 'Plena' (d)	CTho
	- 'Purple Queen'	CEnd CTho ECrN SCoo
§	- 'Watereri' ♀H4	CCVT CDoC CDul CEnd CLnd CMCN CTho CWib EBee ECrN ELan EPfP EWTr NWea SBLw SCoo SHBN SLim SPer WJas WOrn

	'Pandora' ♀H4	CLnd EBee ECrN EPfP LAst LCro LRHS MAsh MBri MGos MRav MSwo NBea NBee NWea SBLw SCoo SCrf SEND SHBN SPer SPoG WFar WOrn
	pendula	SCrf SGFT
	- var. ***ascendens*** 'Rosea'	EBee
§	- 'Pendula Rosea' ♀H4	CDoC CDul CEnd CSBt CTri CWib ENot EPfP LAst LPan MAsh SBLw SCrf SPoG WFar WJas WOrn
§	- 'Pendula Rubra' ♀H4	CDoC CEnd CLnd CSBt CWib EBee ECrN EPfP LAst LRHS MBri MGos MSwo SCoo SHBN SLim SPer SPoG WOrn WPat
§	- 'Stellata'	SPer
	persica 'Amsden June' (F)	CWib EMil ERea GTwe LRHS SDea SFam SKee
	- 'Bellegarde' (F)	ERea GTwe SDea SFam
	- 'Bonanza' (F)	EMui
	- 'Clara Meyer'	CTri
	- 'Dixi Red'	ERea LPan
	- 'Doctor Hogg' (F)	ERea SDea
	- 'Duke of York' (F) ♀H3	CTri ERea GTwe SDea SFam SKee WOrn
	- 'Dymond' (F)	ERea
	- 'Early Alexander' (F)	ERea
	- 'Flat China' (F)	ERea
	- 'Foliis Rubris' (F)	CDul WPGP
	- 'Francis' (F)	SKee
	- 'Garden Lady' (F)	ERea GTwe SKee SPoG
	- 'Hale's Early' (F)	EMil ERea GTwe LRHS SEND SFam SGFT SKee SPer SPoG WOrn
	- 'Hylands' (F)	SDea
	- 'Kestrel' (F)	ERea SKee
	- 'Melred'	MGos
	- 'Melred Weeping'	SBLw
	- 'Mesembrine'PBR (F) **new**	EMui
	- 'Natalia' (F)	SDea
	- var. ***nectarina*** Crimson Gold (F)	SDea
	- - 'Early Gem' (F)	ERea SDea
	- - 'Early Rivers' (F) ♀H3	ERea GTwe SDea SPer
	- - 'Elruge' (F)	ERea GTwe SDea SFam
	- - 'Fantasia' (F)	ENot ERea SDea
	- - 'Fire Gold' (F)	SDea
	- - 'Garden Beauty' (F/d)	EMui ENot NPri SPer SPoG
	- - 'Humboldt' (F)	ERea GTwe SDea SKee
	- - 'John Rivers' (F)	GTwe SDea SFam SGFT
	- - 'Lord Napier' (F) ♀H3	CAgr CDoC CSBt CTri CWSG CWib EMui EPfP ERea LAst LBuc LRHS MGan MGos SDea SFam SGFT SKee SPer SPoG WOrn
	- - 'Nectared' (F)	CWib ERea
	- - 'Nectarella' (F)	EMui ERea SGFT SKee
	- - 'Pineapple' (F)	CAgr CTri ERea GTwe LRHS MGan SDea SFam SGFT SKee
	- - 'Ruby Gold' (F)	SDea
	- - 'Terrace Ruby' (F)	CDul ENot NPri SPoG
	- 'Peregrine' (F) ♀H3	CAgr CDul CMac CSBt CTri CWSG CWib EMui ENot EPfP ERea GTwe LAst LBuc LRHS MBri MGan MGos MLan SDea SFam SGFT SHBN SKee SPer WJas
	- 'Pink Peachy' (F)	NLar
	- 'Purpurea'	EBee
	- 'Red Haven' (F)	CAgr CWib GTwe SDea SKee
	- 'Reliance' (F)	SDea
	- 'Robin Redbreast' (F)	SDea
	- 'Rochester' (F) ♀H3	CAgr CWSG CWib EMui ENot ERea GTwe LAst LRHS MBri SDea SFam SGFT SKee SPer SPoG WOrn
	- 'Royal George' (F)	GTwe SFam
	- 'Saturne' (F)	EMui ERea SPoG
	- 'Springtime' (F)	ERea SDea
	- 'Terrace Amber'	EMui ENot NPri SPer SPoG

- 'Terrace Diamond'	ENot NPri SPoG
- 'Terrace Garnet'	ENot NPri SPoG
- 'Terrace Pearl'	SPoG
- 'White Peachy' (F)	NLar
x ***persicoides*** 'Angélique' new	EMil
- 'Ingrid' (F)	MCoo SCoo
- 'Pollardii'	MAsh NWea WJas
- 'Robijn' (F)	CAgr ECrN LBuc
- 'Spring Glow'	CDoC MBri MWea NWea WJas
'Pink Perfection' ♀H4	CBcs CDul CLnd CSBt CWSG CWib EBee ECrN ENot EPfP LAst LRHS MBri MGos MWat NBee SCrf SHBN SPer WFar WJas WOrn
'Pink Shell' ♀H4	CLnd EBee ECrN EPfP MBri SFam SPur WOrn
pissardii	see *P. cerasifera* 'Pissardii'
'Pissardii Nigra'	see *P. cerasifera* 'Nigra'
* ***prostrata*** 'Anita Kistler'	ECho
* - var. ***discolor***	NLar WNor
pseudocerasus 'Cantabrigiensis'	ECrN
pumila var. ***depressa***	EMil MBar MBlu MMHG MRav NLar NPro
'Royal Burgundy' (d)	CCVT CDul CEnd CWSG EBee ECrN EMil ENot LRHS LSRN MAsh MBri MDun MGos MWat NBee SCoo SGFT SKee SLim SPer SPoG SPur WFar WGer WOrn
rufa	CPMA CTho EBee SSpi
salicina 'Beauty'	ERea
§ - 'Black Diamond' (F)	SDea
- 'Methley' (D)	ERea
- 'Satsuma' (F)	ERea
- 'Shiro' (D)	ERea
sargentii ♀H4	More than 30 suppliers
- 'Rancho'	CLnd SCoo SPoG WFar WOrn
x ***schmittii***	CLnd ECrN SCoo SPer WJas
'Sekiyama'	see *P.* 'Kanzan'
serotina	CDul NLar SBLw
§ ***serrula*** ♀H4	More than 30 suppliers
- Dorothy Clive form	EBee LRHS
§ - 'Mahogany Lustre'	CLnd WFar WPat
- var. ***tibetica***	see *P. serrula*
serrula x ***serrulata***	CBcs CTho
serrulata (d)	MGos
- 'Erecta'	see *P.* 'Amanogawa'
- 'Grandiflora'	see *P.* 'Ukon'
- 'Longipes'	see *P.* 'Shôgetsu'
- 'Miyako' misapplied	see *P.* 'Shôgetsu'
N - var. ***pubescens***	see *P. verecunda*
- 'Rosea'	see *P.* 'Kiku-shidare-zakura'
'Shidare-zakura'	see *P.* 'Kiku-shidare-zakura'
'Shimizu-zakura'	see *P.* 'Shôgetsu'
'Shirofugen' ♀H4	CBcs CDoC CDul CLnd CMCN CSBt CTho CWSG CWib EBee ECrN EMil ENot EPfP LBuc LCro LRHS MAsh MBri MRav MWat NBee NEgg SCrf SEND SGFT SPer SPoG WJas WOrn
§ 'Shirotae' ♀H4	More than 30 suppliers
§ 'Shôgetsu' ♀H4	CBcs CDul CEnd CLnd CSBt CTho CWSG EBee ECrN ELan ENot EPfP LAst LRHS MAsh MBri NBlu SCrf SFam SHBN SLim SPer SPoG
'Shosar'	CEnd CLnd CWib ECrN LAst LRHS SCoo SPer SPoG
'Snow Goose'	CDoC EBee LAst LRHS NEgg SCoo WFar
'Snow Showers'	CEnd CWSG EBee EMui LRHS MAsh MBri MWat NWea SPer WGer
spinosa	CCVT CDoC CDul CRWN CTri ECrN EMac EPfP LBuc LRHS MBar MBlu NWea SPer WFar WMou WNor XPep
- 'Plena' (d)	CEnd CTho MBlu
- 'Purpurea'	MAsh MBlu MBri NHol WHCG WMou WPat
§ 'Spire' ♀H4	CCVT CDoC CDul CLnd CMCN CSBt CTho CWib EBee ECrN EPfP LAst LBuc LRHS MAsh MGos MSwo NBlu NWea SCoo SHBN SPer WFar WJas WOrn
x ***subhirtella***	LAst WNor
- var. ***ascendens***	see *P. pendula* var. *ascendens*
- 'Autumnalis' ♀H4	More than 30 suppliers
- 'Autumnalis Rosea' ♀H4	More than 30 suppliers
- 'Fukubana'	CLnd EBee EPfP SBLw
- 'Pendula Plena Rosea' (d)	LAst LPan SBLw
- 'Pendula Rosea'	see *P. pendula* 'Pendula Rosea'
- 'Pendula Rubra'	see *P. pendula* 'Pendula Rubra'
N - 'Rosea'	CLnd MRav WBVN
- 'Stellata'	see *P. pendula* 'Stellata'
'Taihaku' ♀H4	More than 30 suppliers
'Taki-nioi'	ECrN
'Taoyame'	CLnd
tenella	CAgr CBcs ECrN ELan EWTr WCot
- 'Fire Hill'	CBcs CPMA CSBt CWib ECho ELan EPfP LRHS MGan MGos MRav MWea NHol SBLw SHBN SPer SSpi WBod WCot WJas WOrn WSpi
tibetica	see *P. serrula*
tomentosa	ECrN WBVN
§ 'Trailblazer' (C/D)	CEnd CLnd CSBt CTho ECrN EWTr LAst SBLw SPer WOrn
triloba	CBcs CSBt CWib ECrN ENot LBuc LRHS NBee NBlu NHol NPri NWea SBLw SHBN
- 'Multiplex' (d)	ECho ENot MGos MRav SPer SRms WJas WSPU
- Rosemund = 'Korros'	SCrf
§ 'Ukon' ♀H4	CBcs CDoC CDul CLnd CMCN CTho CTri EBee ECrN EPfP EWTr LPan LRHS MAsh MBar MBri MGos MRav NBee NWea SCrf SHBN SPer WFar WOrn
'Umineko'	CDoC CLnd CWib ECrN GQue LPan MGos SCoo SLPl SPer SPur
§ ***verecunda***	CLnd NWea WJas
- 'Autumn Glory'	CTho NBea
virginiana	CAgr
- 'Schubert'	CDul CLnd EBee ECrN SBLw SCoo WFar WJas WOrn WPat
'White Cloud'	CDul CTho
yamadae	see *P. incisa* f. *yamadae*
§ x ***yedoensis*** ♀H4	CCVT CDul CLnd CMCN CSBt CTho CTri CWSG EBee ECrN EPfP LAst NWea SBLw SLim SPer WJas WOrn
- 'Ivensii'	CBcs CDul CSBt CWib EBee LPan NBee NEgg NWea SCoo SHBN SPer
- 'Pendula'	see *P.* x *yedoensis* 'Shidare-yoshino'
- 'Perpendens'	see *P.* x *yedoensis* 'Shidare-yoshino'
§ - 'Shidare-yoshino'	CCVT CDul CEnd CLnd EBee ECrN EPfP LPan LRHS MBar MBri MGos MRav MSwo MWat NWea SBLw SLim SPoG WOrn
'Yoshino'	see *P.* x *yedoensis*
'Yoshino Pendula'	see *P.* x *yedoensis* 'Shidare-yoshino'

Pseuderanthemum (*Acanthaceae*)

laxiflorum new	CCCN
reticulatum orange-flowered new	CCCN

Pseudocydonia (*Rosaceae*)

§ ***sinensis*** — CAgr CBcs NLar

Pseudofumaria see *Corydalis*

alba — see *Corydalis ochroleuca*
lutea — see *Corydalis lutea*

Pseudogynoxys (*Asteraceae*)

chenopodioides — ELan ERea SOWG

Pseudolarix (*Pinaceae*)

§ ***amabilis*** 🏆H4 — CDoC CEnd CMCN CTho ECrN EHul EPfP LCon MBar MBlu MBri MPkF NWea SCoo SLim SPoG SSpi WNor WPGP
kaempferi — see *P. amabilis*

Pseudolithos (*Asclepiadaceae*)

caput-viperae new — LToo
dodsonianus new — LToo

Pseudomuscari see *Muscari*

azureum — see *Muscari azureum*

Pseudopanax (*Araliaceae*)

(Adiantifolius Group) 'Adiantifolius' — CBcs CDoC CHEx CTrC GQui
- 'Cyril Watson' 🏆H1 — CBcs CDoC CHEx EBee ELan
arboreus — CAbb CBcs CDoC CHEx CTrC ECou LEdu
chathamicus — CDoC CHEx SAPC SArc
crassifolius — CAbb CBcs CBrP CHEx CTrC EAmu EBee SAPC SArc SKHP WCot
- var. ***trifoliolatus*** — CHEx
davidii — SLon
discolor — ECou LEdu
ferox — CAbb CBcs CBrP EAmu IDee SAPC SArc SKHP SMad
laetus — CAbb CBcs CDoC CHEx CTrC ECou LEdu SAPC SArc
lessonii — CBcs CHEx ECou
- 'Gold Splash' (v) 🏆H1 — CBcs CDoC CHEx CTrC SEND
- 'Nigra' new — CTrC
- 'Rangitira' — CBcs
'Linearifolius' — CHEx CTrC LEdu
'Purpureus' 🏆H1 — CDoC CHEx CTrC
'Sabre' — CHEx
'Trident' — CDoC CHEx CTrC ECou LEdu

Pseudophegopteris (*Thelypteridaceae*)

levingei — EMon

Pseudophoenix (*Arecaceae*)

* ***nativo*** — MBri

Pseudosasa (*Poaceae*)

amabilis misapplied — see *Arundinaria gigantea*
§ ***amabilis*** (McClure) Keng f. — EPla LPal SDry WFar
§ ***japonica*** 🏆H4 — More than 30 suppliers
§ - 'Akebonosuji' (v) — CGHE EFul EPla MMoz MWht NMoo SDry WNor WPGP
I - var. ***pleioblastoides*** — EPla MWht SDry
- 'Tsutsumiana' — CHEx EBee ELon ENot EPla ERod MMoz MWht NLar NMoo SDry
- 'Variegata' — see *P. japonica* 'Akebonosuji'
orthotropa — see *Sinobambusa orthotropa*
owatarii — SDry
usawai — EPla
viridula — MWht NMoo

Pseudotsuga (*Pinaceae*)

§ ***menziesii*** 🏆H4 — CBcs CDoC CDul CLnd ECrN EMac EPfP LCon LLin LRHS LRav MBar MBlu MMuc NWea SPoG WFar WMou
- 'Bhiela Lhota' — CKen
- 'Blue Wonder' — CDoC CKen
- 'Densa' — CKen
- 'Fastigiata' — CKen
- 'Fletcheri' — CKen MBar
- var. ***glauca*** — LCon MBar
- 'Glauca Pendula' — LCon MBar MBlu MGos
I - 'Gotelli's Pendula' — CKen
- 'Graceful Grace' — CKen
- 'Idaho Gem' — CKen
- 'Julie' — CKen
- 'Knaphill' — NLar WEve
- 'Little Jamie' — CKen MBar
- 'Lohbrunner' — CKen
- 'McKenzie' — CKen
- 'Nana' — CKen
- Pendula Group — IDee
- 'Stairii' — CKen
taxifolia — see *P. menziesii*

Pseudowintera (*Winteraceae*)

§ ***colorata*** — CBcs CDoC CMac CPLG CWib EBee GGar IDee IMGH ISea LBuc MAsh NHol WCru WFar WFoF
- Elliot's form new — CWsd
- 'Mount Congreve' — IArd LBuc MBri NLar SSpi WGer

Psidium (*Myrtaceae*)

cattleyanum — see *P. littorale* var. *longipes*
guajava (F) — CCCN XBlo
littorale (F) — ERea
§ - var. ***longipes*** (F) — CCCN XBlo

Psilotum (*Psilotaceae*)

nudum — ECou

Psophocarpus (*Papilionaceae*)

tetragonolobus — CPLG

Psoralea (*Papilionaceae*)

bituminosa — WSHC XPep
glabra — SPlb
glandulosa — CArn CMdw EUnu LRav WSHC
oligophylla — SPlb
pinnata — CHEx CTrC CTrG IDee

Psychotria (*Rubiaceae*)

capensis — CPLG EShb
carthagenensis — MGol
viridis — MGol

Ptelea (*Rutaceae*)

trifoliata — CBcs CDul CLnd CMCN CTho CWib EBee ECrN EPfP IMGH MBlu SBLw SPer SRms WFar WHCG WNor WOrn WPGP
- 'Aurea' 🏆H4 — CAbP CBcs CEnd CLnd CMCN CPMA EBee ELan EPfP GBin LRHS MAsh MBlu MBri MGos SBLw SHBN SMad SPer SPoG SSpi WHCG WPat
- 'Fastigiata' — EPfP

Pteracanthus see *Strobilanthes*

Pteridophyllum (*Papaveraceae*)

racemosum — CWsd EFEx EPot GCrs GEdr WCru

Pteris (*Pteridaceae*)

from Yunnan — CLAP
angustipinna B&SWJ 6738 — WCru
argyraea — MBri

cretica ♀H1+3	CHEx MBri SAPC SArc
- var. ***albolineata*** ♀H1	GQui MBri SRms
- 'Cristata'	MBri
- 'Gautheri'	MBri
- 'Parkeri'	MBri
- 'Rivertoniana'	MBri
- 'Rowei'	MBri
- 'Wimsettii'	MBri
dentata	WRic
ensiformis	MBri
* - 'Arguta'	MBri
- 'Victoriae'	MBri
gallinopes	CLAP WAbe
nipponica new	WRic
tremula	CHEx GQui MBri SRms WRic
umbrosa	MBri WRic
vittata	SRms
wallichiana	CFir CGHE CHEx CLAP WPGP

Pterocarya (*Juglandaceae*)

fraxinifolia ♀H4	CBcs CDul CLnd CMCN CTrG ECrN EGFP EPfP MBlu SBLw
x ***rehderiana***	CTho MBlu WMou
rhoifolia	MBri
stenoptera	CBcs CDTJ CDul CLnd CMCN CTho EGFP
- 'Fern Leaf'	MBlu SMad WMou WPGP

Pteroceltis (*Ulmaceae*)

tatarinowii	CMCN

Pterocephalus (*Dipsacaceae*)

bretschneideri new	EBee
depressus	WPat
parnassi	see *P. perennis*
§ ***perennis***	CBrm CMea ECho LRHS MHer NBir NMen NRya NWCA SBla SRms WAbe WEas WHoo XPep
- subsp. ***perennis***	EGoo WHrl
pinardii	NWCA

Pterodiscus (*Pedaliaceae*)

ngamicus	LToo
speciosus	LToo

Pterostylis (*Orchidaceae*)

acuminata var. ***ingens***	EPot
coccinea	GCrs
curta	CStu ECho GCrs SCnR SKHP
obtusa	GCrs
revoluta	EPot

Pterostyrax (*Styracaceae*)

corymbosa	CMCN CPMA IArd IDee MBlu NLar SSpi WFar
hispida ♀H4	CAbP CBcs CDul CEnd CHEx CLnd CMCN CPMA CWib EBee EPfP EPla IArd IDee LAst LRHS MBlu MBri MGos MRav NLar SSpi SSta WBVN WFar WPGP
psilophylla	CMCN

Ptilostemon (*Asteraceae*)

afer	CMdw EGoo EHrv EMan MWea MWgw
§ ***diacantha***	CSam EBee LHop NBPC SRkn WSel WSpi
echinocephalus	EBee MDKP NBhm NBre

Ptilotrichum see *Alyssum*

spinosum 'Roseum'	see *Alyssum spinosum* 'Roseum'

Pueraria (*Papilionaceae*)

montana var. ***lobata***	CAgr CArn ELau MSal

Pulicaria (*Asteraceae*)

§ ***dysenterica***	CArn MHer MSal NMir SIde WSFF

Pulmonaria ✿ (*Boraginaceae*)

'Abbey Dore Pink'	WAbb
affinis 'Margaret'	NCob
angustifolia ♀H4	EBee EPfP GKev GMaP LRHS MDun MNHC MNrw MSal NOrc SRms WBVN WCru WEas WFar WTin
* - ***alba***	IFoB
- 'Azurea'	CElw EBee ELan EMon EPfP GMaP IBlr LAst LRHS MBNS MNHC MRav MWgw NBro NCGa NDov NEgg SBod SMer SPer SPla SRms WCAu WCFE WFar WMnd
- 'Blaues Meer'	CFir CSam EPfP GBuc MBNS MNFA WCru
- 'Munstead Blue'	CElw CLAP ECha EGle EHrv LCro LRHS MRav MTho MWgw NCob NHol NRya NSti SRms WCru
- 'Rubra'	see *P. rubra*
'Apple Frost'	CLAP MBnl NBhm NLar NSti WCra WLin
'Barfield Regalia'	CMHG EMon IGor NSti SDys WCru
'Benediction'	NSti SPhx
'Berries and Cream'	NSti
§ 'Beth's Blue'	EMon WCAu WCru
'Beth's Pink'	ECha GAbr WCru WFar
'Blauer Hügel'	CElw EMon NSti
'Blauhimmel'	EMon GCra
'Blue Buttons'	CBow CFir EBee ECtt EQua GQue NSti
'Blue Crown'	CElw CLAP CSev EBee EHrv EWes LRHS SAga WCAu WEas
'Blue Ensign'	More than 30 suppliers
'Blue Moon'	see *P. officinalis* 'Blue Mist'
'Blue Pearl'	NSti WCru
'Blueberry Muffin'	CSpe
'Bonnie'	SAga
'Botanic Hybrid'	WCru
'British Sterling'	EBee GBin
Cally hybrid	CElw CLAP EMon GBin NBre NSti WCru
'Cedric Morris'	CElw
'Chintz'	CLAP CSam EBee GBuc
'Cleeton Red'	NSti WCru
'Coral Springs'	MAvo NSti
'Corsage'	EBee ECtt
'Cotton Cool'	CElw CGHE CLAP CPrp EBee ECha ECtt EMon EShb GBuc MAvo MBNS MNFA NCGa NEgg NOrc NSti SPer WCAu WCru WMoo WPGP
'Crawshay Chance'	WCru
'De Vroomen's Pride' (v)	MSte WMnd
'Diana Clare'	More than 30 suppliers
'Elworthy Rubies'	CElw EPPr
'Emerald Isles'	NSti
'Esther'	GSki WCru
'Excalibur'	EBee EHrv ENot EPPr GBuc MNFA NLar
'Fiona'	CBct MAvo WCAu
'Glacier'	CElw CPrp CTca EBee EMon EPfP LRHS MSte NSti WCru
'Hazel Kaye's Red'	CElw NSti WCru
'Highdown'	see *P.* 'Lewis Palmer'
'Ice Ballet' (Classic Series)	EBee LRHS
'Joan's Red'	CElw WTin
§ 'Lewis Palmer' ♀H4	CMHG CMea CSam EBee ECtt EMar EPla EWTr GMaP GSki IBlr LRHS MNFA NBid NBir NHol SRGP WBrk WCFE WCot WCru WHoo WTin

	'Lime Close'	SAga
	'Linford Blue'	WCru
	'Little Star'	ECha EMon GBuc NBre NDov NSti SRGP WCru
	longifolia	CArn CFee CHar CPrp CSam EBee ECha ELan EPfP GAbr GSki LCro LLWP LRHS MNFA MSal NBir NGdn NOrc NSti SPer SPet WBrk WCru WEas WFar WSel
§	- 'Ankum'	CBct CElw CLAP CSam EGle EPfP EPla GBuc ITer LRHS MBrN MRav MSte NBir NSti SMrm WCot WLin WMoo WWlt
	- 'Ballyrogan Blue'	GBin IBlr
	- 'Bertram Anderson'	CBgR COlW CPrp CSsd CTca EBee ECtt GMaP LAst LCro LRHS MBnl MLLN NBir NCGa NVic SPer SRGP SWvt WBrk WCAu WCot WCru WFar WMnd
	- subsp. ***cevennensis***	CBgR CLAP CSam EBee ENot EPfP MBNS MBnl MBri MLLN MSte NCGa NSti WCAu WPtf
	- 'Coen Jansen'	see *P. longifolia* 'Ankum'
	- 'Coral Spring'	MBNS NBre SHGN WCAu
	- 'Dordogne'	CLAP GBuc MLLN MRav NBir NEgg NLar WCAu WCru
	- 'Howard Eggins'	EBee WSPU
	'Lovell Blue'	CElw NCot
	'Mado'	ECha
	'Majesté'	More than 30 suppliers
	'Margery Fish' ♀H4	CHar CLAP CSam EBee EPfP EPla LAst LRHS MBri MLLN MNFA NSti SPer WMnd WTel
	'Mary Mottram'	CElw ECtt ELan LAst MLLN MNFA NBir NPol NSti SAga SMrm WCru WMnd WMoo
	'Matese Blue'	CLAP
	'Mawson's Blue'	CLAP ECha EMon EWes LRHS MRav MWat MWea NBir NChi SWvt WBrk WCru WEas WMoo WRHF WSHC
	'May Bouquet'PBR	NRnb NSti
	'Melancholia'	IBlr
	'Merlin'	CLAP EMon LRHS NSti
	'Middleton Red'	CElw
§	'Milchstrasse'	CLAP
	Milky Way	see *P.* 'Milchstrasse'
	mollis	CLAP CSWP EBee ECGP EGoo EMon IBlr LRHS MNrw NSti SBch WCru
	- 'Royal Blue'	MRav
	- 'Samobor'	CLAP
	'Monksilver'	EMon GBin
	'Moonshine'PBR	NSti
	'Moonstone'	CElw CLAP CPom LAst WCru
	'Mountain Magic'PBR	CHVG ECtt EWll NSti SIde
	'Mournful Purple'	CElw EHrv SWat WCru
	'Mrs Kittle'	CBct CElw CMMP EBee EPPr GBri IFoB MFOX MLLN MNFA MRav NBir NSti SDys WBrk WCru WFar WLin WMnd
	'Netta Statham'	ECha NSti
	'Northern Lights'PBR	SHar
	'Nürnberg'	EMon
	obscura	WCru
	officinalis	CAgr CArn CHby EHon GPoy IFoB LLWP MDun MHer MLHP MWat NVic SIde WBrk WCru WFar
	- 'Alba'	ELan WBrk WCru
§	- 'Blue Mist'	CElw CLAP ECha ELan GBri GBuc GMaP NBir WAbb WBrk WCot WCru WHoo WMnd WMoo WTin
	- 'Bowles' Blue'	see *P. officinalis* 'Blue Mist'
	- Cambridge Blue Group	CPrp EBee ECGP EMon GMaP LAst LRHS MBNS MRav MWat NBir NLar WCAu WCot WCru WPtf
	- ***rubra***	see *P. rubra*
	- 'Stillingfleet Gran'	NSti
	- 'White Wings'	CElw CLAP EPla LRHS MBNS MRav NLar NPri NSti SIde SPoG WFar WMoo
	- 'Wuppertal' **new**	EBee
	'Oliver Wyatt's White'	CLAP EBee
	Opal = 'Ocupol'	More than 30 suppliers
	'Patrick Bates'	WCru
	'Pewter'	WCru
	'Polar Splash'	CBct EBee GBin SIde SPoG SRot WCra WFar
	'Raspberry Splash'PBR	CBct CLAP CPom EBee GKev LHop NEgg NLar NSti SHar SIde SPoG
	'Richard Nutt'	EMon
	'Roy Davidson'	CBgR CElw CLAP COlW CSam EBee ECha ECtt EHrv EMon EPPr LHop LRHS NBir NCGa NChi NSti SRGP SWvt WCot WCra WCru WFar WLin
§	***rubra*** ♀H4	CBcs CElw CPom CSWP ECha ELan EMar EShb GAbr LLWP NBid NCob NOrc NSti SRms WCAu WFar WTin
	- var. ***alba***	see *P. rubra* var. *albocorollata*
§	- var. ***albocorollata***	CBct CBgR CBre CElw CMHG EBee ECha EGle EHrv EMon GAbr LRHS MNFA MSte SHar WCru WFar WOut
	- 'Ann'	CBct CElw CLAP MBNS NMoo WCru WFar WTin
	- 'Barfield Pink'	EBee ELan LAst LRHS MLLN NBir NLar SHGN WBrk WRHF
	- 'Barfield Ruby'	EMon GBuc MAvo
	- 'Bowles' Red'	CPrp EBee ECtt EHrv EPfP IFoB LAst LRHS MRav MWat MWgw NBir NCGa NGdn SIde SPer STes WFar WMnd
	- 'David Ward' (v)	More than 30 suppliers
	- 'Prestbury Pink'	LRHS
	- 'Rachel Vernie' (v)	CLAP CPom CPou EBee MHar WBrk WCot
	- 'Redstart'	More than 30 suppliers
§	***saccharata***	ECha EHrv ELan GMaP NEgg SIde SPet SRms WCAu WCru WFar
	- 'Alba'	CElw ECha GBuc SRms
	- Argentea Group ♀H4	CSev CTri EBee ELan EPfP GMaP LAst LBMP LRHS MRav MTho NGdn SPer SPet WCAu WCot
	- blue-flowered	WCru
	- 'Brentor'	EBee WCru
	- 'Clent Skysilver'	EBee WSPU
	- 'Dora Bielefeld'	More than 30 suppliers
	- 'Frühlingshimmel'	CElw CSam EBee EBrs ECha ECtt MBNS MRav WCAu WFar
	- 'Glebe Cottage Blue'	CElw ECGP WCru
	- 'Jill Richardson'	ELan
	- 'Lady Lou's Pink'	WCru
	- 'Leopard'	CBct CElw CEnt CLAP CMea COlW CSam EBee ECtt EMil GBuc GMaP GSki LAst LRHS MLLN NBir NBre SApp SRGP WBrk WCot WCru WFar WHoo
	- 'Mrs Moon'	CSam CTri CWib EBee ECtt ENot EPfP GMaP LBMP LCro LRHS MBNS MHer NBlu NOrc NPri SMer SPer SRGP SWvt WHen WMnd
	- 'Old Rectory Silver'	CLAP NBir
	- 'Picta'	see *P. saccharata*
	- 'Pink Dawn'	CMHG LRHS WCru WMnd
	- pink-flowered	WCru
	- 'Reginald Kaye'	CElw ECha EWes MNrw SHBN
	- 'Silverado'PBR	EBee MBNS MWgw NOrc NSti
	- 'Stanhoe'	EBee EWes

- 'White Barn'	see *P.* 'Beth's Blue'
'Saint Ann's'	CBct CElw EMon NBre NSti WCru
'Samurai'	EBee MBNS MWgw NSti WPtf
'Silver Maid'	WCAu
'Silver Sabre'	IBlr
'Silver Shimmers'PBR	SHar
'Silver Surprise'	WCot
'Sissinghurst White' ♀H4	More than 30 suppliers
'Smoky Blue'	CLAP EBee ECtt EMon EPfP LBMP MRav MWgw NBPC NMoo SWat WCru WFar WMnd
'Spilled Milk'	NBre NLar
'Stillingfleet Meg'	CLAP CSam EBee ECGP LRHS MAvo MBNS MCot MLLN NCob NHol NSti SPla SRGP WCra
'Trevi Fountain'	CBct CLAP EBee ECha EShb GKev LHop NBre NEgg NSti SIde SPoG SRot WCot
'Vera May' ♀H4	NSti
'Victorian Brooch'PBR	CBct CLAP COIW EBee GAbr GKev GQue LRHS LSou MBri NEgg NLar NSti SIde SPoG WFar WPtf WSpi
'Weetwood Blue'	CBgR CBre CLAP EPfP EPla MNrw MSte WCru
'Wendy Perry'	CElw
'Wisley White'	CElw

Pulsatilla (*Ranunculaceae*)

alba	NWCA
albana	GKev LHop LRHS SBla
* - subsp. ***alpina***	GKev
- 'Lutea'	EBee GKev
alpina	ECho SRms WPat
§ - subsp. ***apiifolia*** ♀H4	EBee ELan GKev MFOX NRya
- subsp. ***sulphurea***	see *P. alpina* subsp. *apiifolia*
ambigua	LTwo
aurea	GKev
campanella	GAbr
caucasica	LRHS
cernua	EBee GBuc LHop LRHS
chinensis	EBee
dahurica	EBee
x ***gayeri***	EBee ECho EWld LTwo NBir
georgica	WLin
halleri ♀H4	EBee ECho GKev ITim
- subsp. ***slavica*** ♀H4	CLyd EBee EPot GCrs GKev LRHS NWCA
- subsp. ***taurica***	MSte
lutea	see *P. alpina* subsp. *apiifolia*
montana	EBee GBuc NMen SPlb
multifida	GBuc
occidentalis	EBee
§ ***patens***	LTwo NBHF
pratensis	GPoy SRms
- subsp. ***nigricans***	LHop LRHS
rubra	EBee ECho NEgg NGHP
turczaninovii	EBee GBuc
§ ***vernalis*** ♀H2	ECho EPot GBuc GCrs GKev ITim NSla NWCA WAbe WLin
§ ***vulgaris*** ♀H4	More than 30 suppliers
- 'Alba' ♀H4	More than 30 suppliers
- 'Barton's Pink'	EWes LHop LRHS SBla SIng
- 'Blaue Glocke'	CBgR CBrm EWll GEdr GSki MHer NLar SWvt WHil WWeb
- Czech fringed hybrids	WLin
- 'Eva Constance'	EPot LHop LRHS NBir SIng
- 'Gotlandica'	CLyd EBee
- subsp. ***grandis***	EPot NMen
- - 'Budapest Seedling'	GCrs
- - 'Papageno'	CBgR CBrm CPBP CSpe EBee ECho GMaP ITim LHop MAvo NHol NLar NWCA SMrm WFar WHil
- Heiler hybrids	EBee MWgw NChi NEgg NGdn WCra WHal
- 'Olga's Dream' **new**	EBee
- pale pink-flowered	ECha
- Red Clock	see *P. vulgaris* 'Röde Klokke'
§ - 'Röde Klokke'	CBgR EBee ENot GEdr GKev IBal ITim MAvo MWat NBPC NChi NHol NLar NPri SWvt WHil WSel WSpi WWeb
- ***rosea***	GAbr WBrE
- Rote Glocke	see *P. vulgaris* 'Röde Klokke'
- var. ***rubra***	More than 30 suppliers
- violet blue-flowered	ENot ITim
§ - 'Weisse Schwan'	ECho GEdr GMaP NMen
- White Swan	see *P. vulgaris* 'Weisse Schwan'
zimmermannii	NWCA

pummelo see *Citrus maxima*

Punica (*Lythraceae*)

granatum	CBcs CHEx CMen EPfP ERom LPan MGos MPRe SBLw SDnm SLim SOWG STre WBVN WSHC XPep
- 'André le Roi' (F) **new**	SLPl
- 'Chico'	CBcs XPep
- 'Fina Tendral'	ERea
- 'Fruits Violets'	XPep
- 'Legrelleae' (d)	SLPl XPep
- 'Maxima Rubra'	XPep
- 'Mollar de Elche'	XPep
- var. ***nana*** ♀H3	CArn CCCN CMen CPle EPfP EShb LPan MPRe MWya SMrm SPer SPoG SRms WPat
- f. ***plena*** (d)	CBcs MRav MWya WCFE
- - 'Flore Pleno Luteo' (d)	XPep
- 'Provence'	XPep
* - 'Striata'	SOWG

Purshia (*Rosaceae*)

aff. ***mexicana*** B&SWJ 9040	WCru

Puschkinia (*Hyacinthaceae*)

scilloides	EBrs ECho LRHS NBir
- 'Aragat's Gem' **new**	EBrs
§ - var. ***libanotica***	EBrs ECho EPfP EPot GAbr IHer LAma LHop LRHS SPer SPhx WHoo WShi
- - 'Alba'	EBrs ECho EPot LAma LRHS SPer SPhx

Puya (*Bromeliaceae*)

sp.	EBee
RCB/Arg L-3	WCot
RCB/Arg L-5	WCot
RCB/Arg S-2	WCot
alpestris	CBrP CCCN CHEx CTrC EShb LRHS SAPC SChr WCot
berteroana	CBct CCCN CDTJ EShb SPlb
castellanosii CDPR 3109	WPGP
chilensis	CAbb CBcs CBrd CCCN CDTJ CDoC CHEx CKob CTrC EBee LRHS SAPC SArc SChr SPlb
coerulea	CCCN CFir LEdu MGol SMad
§ - var. ***violacea***	EPyc
gilmartiniae	WCot
laxa	SChr
mirabilis	CAbb CHEx CKob CTrC EBee MFOX
venusta	CCCN SPlb
violacea	see *P. coerulea* var. *violacea*
weberbaueri	CHEx

Pycnanthemum (*Lamiaceae*)

pilosum	CArn EBee ELau EUnu MHer MSal NBre NLar NPri SBch SIde

tenuifolium	NBre

Pycnostachys (*Lamiaceae*)

reticulata	EShb
urticifolia	ECre EOHP EWes

Pygmea see *Chionohebe*

Pyracantha (*Rosaceae*)

Alexander Pendula = 'Renolex'	LHop MRav MSwo SRms WFar
angustifolia	WCFE
§ ***atalantioides***	CMac SPlb WCFE
§ - 'Aurea'	ERas
'Brilliant'	EPfP SCoo
'Buttercup'	EPla
§ ***coccinea*** 'Lalandei'	LAst SMer XPep
- 'Red Column'	CCVT CMac CWib EBee ECtt ELan EPfP EWTr LAst LBuc LHop LRHS MBar MGos MLHP MRav MSwo NBir NBlu NEgg NWea SCoo SLim SPoG SWvt WBod WFar WHar WWeb
- 'Red Cushion'	ENot LCro MGos MRav SPoG SRms
crenulata	WCFE
Dart's Red = 'Interrada'	CSBt LRHS SLim SPoG
'Fiery Cascade'	SPoG SRms
gibbsii	see *P. atalantioides*
- 'Flava'	see *P. atalantioides* 'Aurea'
'Gold Rush'	MAsh
'Golden Charmer' ♀H4	EBee ECtt ENot EPfP LRHS MAsh MGan MGos MRav MSwo MWgw NBlu NEgg NLar NWea SCoo SHBN SPer SPoG SRms SWvt WBod WFar WRHF
'Golden Dome'	LRHS
'Golden Glow'	LRHS
'Golden Sun'	see *P.* 'Soleil d'Or'
'Harlequin' (v)	SHBN WFar
'John Stedman'	see *P.* 'Stedman's'
'Knap Hill Lemon'	CChe MBlu
koidzumii 'Victory'	EBee MGos
'Mohave'	CBrm CChe CMac EBee ECrN ELan LRHS MAsh MBar MGan MNHC MWat NEgg NWea SCoo SHBN SLim SMer SPer SRms SWvt WBod
'Mohave Silver' (v)	CChe CWSG ELan LAst LRHS MAsh
'Monrovia'	see *P. coccinea* 'Lalandei'
'Mozart'	EBee WWeb
'Navaho'	EPfP MAsh SCoo SPoG
'Orange Charmer'	CBrm CTri EBee ELan ENot EPfP EWTr LHop MGan MGos MRav MWat NBlu NEgg NWea SHBN SMer SPer SPlb WBod WFar
'Orange Glow' ♀H4	More than 30 suppliers
'Renault d'Or'	SLPl
rogersiana ♀H4	EBee ECrN ENot EPfP MRav WFar WTel
- 'Flava' ♀H4	CSBt EBee ECrN EPfP LAst MAsh MBar MRav NWea SMer SPoG WTel
'Rosedale'	WSPU
Saphyr Jaune = 'Cadaune'PBR	CBcs CCVT CDoC CEnd CSBt CWSG EBee EMil ENot EPfP LBMP LCro MGos MRav NPri SBra SCoo SMer SPer SPoG WBod WWeb
Saphyr Orange = 'Cadange'PBR ♀H4	CBcs CCVT CDoC CEnd CSBt CWSG EBee EMil ENot EPfP EPla LCro LRHS MBri MGos MRav NCGa NPri SBra SCoo SMac SPer WWeb
Saphyr Panache = 'Cadvar' (v)	EBee SPoG
Saphyr Rouge = 'Cadrou'PBR ♀H4	CBcs CCVT CDoC CEnd CSBt CWSG EBee EMil ENot EPfP LCro LRHS MBri MGos MRav NCGa NPri SBra SCoo SPer SPoG WBod WFar WWeb
'Shawnee'	CSBt CWib ECot EPfP MSwo WWeb
§ 'Soleil d'Or'	More than 30 suppliers
'Sparkler' (v)	CMac EBee LAst LPan MGos WFar
§ 'Stedman's'	NLar
'Teton' ♀H4	CMac CWSG EBee ECrN ELan EPfP EPla LAst LHop LPan LRHS MAsh MBar MBri MSwo NBlu SMac SPoG SRms WFar WWeb
'Ventoux Red' **new**	SCoo
'Watereri'	NWea SLPl SPer WFar WSpi WTel
'Yellow Sun'	see *P.* 'Soleil d'Or'

Pyrenaria (*Theaceae*)

spectabilis	see *Tutcheria spectabilis*

Pyrethropsis see *Rhodanthemum*

hosmariense	see *Rhodanthemum hosmariense*

Pyrethrum see *Tanacetum*

Pyrola (*Ericaceae*)

calliantha **new**	EBee
forrestiana **new**	EBee
minor	NMen
picta	EBee
rotundifolia	WHer

Pyrostegia (*Bignoniaceae*)

venusta	CCCN SOWG

Pyrrocoma (*Asteraceae*)

clementis	EBee
§ ***lanceolata***	EBee

Pyrrosia (*Polypodiaceae*)

lingua	WRic

Pyrus ✿ (*Rosaceae*)

amygdaliformis	CTho
- var. ***cuneifolia***	CLnd
betulifolia	CMCN WJas
calleryana 'Bradford'	CLnd
- 'Chanticleer' ♀H4	More than 30 suppliers
- 'Chanticleer' variegated (v)	CLnd
communis (F)	CCVT CDul CTri EMac LBuc SBLw SKee SPer WMou
- 'Abbé Fétel' (D)	SKee
- 'Barnet' (Perry)	CTho
- 'Baronne de Mello' (D)	CTho SFam SKee
- 'Beech Hill' (F)	CDul CLnd EBee ECrN EMil EPfP SBLw SPer
- 'Belle Guérandaise' (D)	SKee
- 'Belle Julie' (D)	SKee
- 'Bergamotte Esperen' (D)	SKee
- 'Beth' (D) ♀H4	CAgr CDoC CSBt CTri CWib ECrN EMil EMui EPfP GTwe LAst LBuc MBri NPri SDea SFam SGFT SKee SPer WHar WOrn
- 'Beurré Alexandre Lucas' (D)	SKee
- 'Beurré Bedford' (D)	SKee
- 'Beurré Clairgeau' (C/D)	SKee
- 'Beurré d'Amanlis' (D)	SKee
- 'Beurré d'Avalon' (D)	SKee

	– 'Beurré de Naghin' (C/D)	SKee
	– 'Beurré Diel' (D)	SKee
	– 'Beurré Dumont' (D)	CAgr SFam
	– 'Beurré Giffard' (D)	CAgr
	– 'Beurré Hardy' (D) ♀H4	CAgr CCAT CDoC CDul CSBt CTho CTri CWib ECrN EMui ENot GTwe LAst LPan LRHS MBri MGan MWat SDea SFam SKee SPer WOrn
	– 'Beurré Mortillet' (D)	SKee
	– 'Beurré Rance' (F) **new**	SKee
	– 'Beurré Six' (D)	SKee
	– 'Beurré Superfin' (D)	ECrN GTwe MCoo SFam SKee
	– 'Bianchettone' (D)	SKee
	– 'Bishop's Thumb' (D)	SDea
	– 'Black Worcester' (C)	GTwe SDea SFam SKee WJas WOrn WSPU
	– 'Blakeney Red' (Perry)	CTho SDea
	– 'Blickling' (D)	SKee
	– 'Brandy' (Perry)	CTho SDea SKee
	– 'Bristol Cross' (D)	CAgr GTwe SKee
§	– 'Butirra Precoce Morettini' (D)	SDea
	– 'Catillac' (C) ♀H4	CAgr CTho GTwe SFam SKee
	– 'Chalk'	see *P. communis* 'Crawford'
	– 'Chaumontel' (D)	SKee
	– 'Clapp's Favourite' (D)	CTho ECrN GTwe SKee
	– 'Comte de Lamy' (D)	SKee
	– 'Concorde'[PBR] (D) ♀H4	More than 30 suppliers
	– 'Conference' (D) ♀H4	More than 30 suppliers
§	– 'Crawford' (D)	SKee
	– 'Deacon's Pear' (D)	SDea
	– 'Devoe' (D)	SDea
	– 'Docteur Jules Guyot' (D)	CAgr ECrN SDea SKee
	– 'Doyenné Blanc' (F)	SKee
	– 'Doyenné Boussoch' (D)	SKee
	– 'Doyenné d'Eté' (D)	ERea SFam
	– 'Doyenné du Comice' (D) ♀H4	More than 30 suppliers
	– 'Duchesse d'Angoulême' (D)	SKee
	– 'Durondeau' (D)	GTwe SDea SFam SKee
	– 'Emile d'Heyst' (D)	GTwe MCoo
	– 'Eva Baltet' (D)	SKee
	– 'Fertility' (D)	CLnd SKee
	– 'Fertility Improved'	see *P. communis* 'Improved Fertility'
	– 'Fondante d'Automne' (D)	CAgr CTho SKee
	– 'Forelle' (D)	SKee
	– 'Glou Morceau' (D)	CAgr CTho ECrN EMui GTwe MCoo MWat SDea SFam SKee
	– 'Glow Red Williams' (D)	SFam
	– 'Gorham' (D)	CAgr CTho ECrN GTwe MCoo SFam SKee
	– 'Gratiole de Jersey' (D)	CTho
	– 'Green Pear of Yair' (D)	SKee
	– 'Hacon's Imcomparable' (D)	SKee
	– 'Harrow Delight' (D)	SDea
	– 'Harvest Queen' (D/C)	SDea
	– 'Hessle' (D)	CAgr GTwe MCoo SDea SFam SKee
§	– 'Improved Fertility' (D)	CAgr CDoC GTwe SDea SKee SPoG
	– Invincible = 'Delwinor' (D/C)	CAgr CDul EMui LBuc LRHS MCoo SPoG
	– 'Jargonelle' (D)	CAgr CTho ECrN GTwe SDea SFam SKee
	– 'Joséphine de Malines' (D) ♀H4	CAgr GTwe SDea SFam SKee WOrn
	– 'Kieffer' (C)	CAgr
	– 'Laxton's Foremost' (D)	CAgr SKee
	– 'Laxton's Satisfaction' (D)	SFam

	– 'Le Lectier' (D)	SKee
	– 'Louise Bonne of Jersey' (D) ♀H4	CAgr CDoC CTri ECrN EMui GTwe LAst MGos SDea SFam SKee
	– 'Marguérite Marillat' (D)	SDea SKee
	– 'Marie-Louise' (D)	SKee
	– 'Max Red Bartlett'	MCoo
	– 'Merton Pride' (D)	CAgr CTho CTri ECrN GTwe MCoo MWat SDea SFam SKee
	– 'Merton Star' (D)	SKee
	– 'Moonglow' (D/C)	CAgr MCoo SDea
	– 'Morettini'	see *P. communis* 'Butirra Precoce Morettini'
	– 'Nouveau Poiteau' (C/D)	CAgr CTho ECrN GTwe SKee
	– 'Nye Russet Bartlett' (F) **new**	CAgr
	– 'Olivier de Serres' (D)	SKee
	– 'Onward' (D) ♀H4	CAgr CCAT CDul CLnd CTri CWib ECrN EMil EMui GTwe MBri NWea SDea SFam SKee WHar WOrn
	– 'Ovid' (D)	CAgr
§	– 'Packham's Triumph' (D)	CAgr CDoC CTri CWib ECrN GTwe LAst SDea SKee
	– 'Passe Crassane' (D)	SKee
	– 'Pear Apple' (D)	SDea
	– 'Pero Nobile'	SKee
	– 'Pitmaston Duchess' (C/D) ♀H4	ECrN GTwe MCoo SDea SKee
	– 'Précoce de Trévoux' (D)	SKee
	– 'Red Comice' (D/C)	GTwe SKee
	– 'Red Sensation Bartlett' (D/C)	EMui GTwe LBuc LRHS SKee
	– 'Robin' (C/D)	ERea SDea SKee
	– 'Roosevelt' (D)	SKee
	– 'Santa Claus' (D)	SDea SFam SKee
	– 'Seckel' (D)	SFam SKee
	– 'Sierra' (D)	CAgr
	– 'Soleil d'Automne' (F)	SKee
	– 'Souvenir du Congrès' (D)	CAgr
	– 'Swan's Egg' (D)	SKee
	– 'Terrace Pearl'	EMui ENot NPri SPoG
	– 'Thompson's' (D)	GTwe SFam SKee
	– 'Thorn' (Perry)	CTho
	– 'Triomphe de Vienne' (D)	SFam
	– 'Triumph'	see *P. communis* 'Packham's Triumph'
	– 'Uvedale's St Germain' (C)	SKee
	– 'Verbelu'	SKee
	– 'Vicar of Winkfield' (C/D)	GTwe SDea SKee
	– 'Williams' Bon Chrétien' (D/C) ♀H4	More than 30 suppliers
	– 'Williams Red' (D/C)	CSut EMui GTwe SKee
	– 'Winter Nelis' (D)	CAgr CTri CWib ECrN GTwe LRHS MBri SDea SFam SKee
	cordata	CDul CTho
	elaeagnifolia	CWSG
	– var. ***kotschyana***	CDul CEnd SLim WOrn
	– 'Silver Sails'	CLnd EMil LRHS MBlu MBri MGos NLar SCoo SPoG SPur
	nivalis	CDul CLnd CTho EBee ECrN EPfP MRav SBLw SCoo SPer
	– 'Catalia'	MBri NLar SCoo SPoG
	pashia	NLar
	– CC 3609	WRos
	pyraster	CDul
	pyrifolia 'Chojuro' (F)	ERea
	– 'Kumoi' (F)	SDea
	– 'Shinseiki' (F)	CLnd EMui ERea LRHS SDea SKee
	– 'Shinsui' (F)	SDea SKee
*	***salicifolia*** var. ***orientalis***	CTho
	– 'Pendula' ♀H4	More than 30 suppliers
	ussuriensis	CTho

Q

Qiongzhuea see *Chimonobambusa*

Quercus ✿ (*Fagaceae*)

	acerifolia	EPfP
§	***acuta***	CBcs
	acutissima	CBcs CDul CLnd CMCN EPfP MBlu MBri WNor
	aegilops	see *Q. ithaburensis* subsp. *macrolepis*
	agrifolia	CAgr CDul CMCN WPGP
	alba	CMCN CTho WPGP
	- f. ***elongata***	EPfP
	aliena	CDul CMCN
	- var. ***acutiserrata***	CMCN
	alnifolia	CDul
	austrina	CMCN
	x ***beadlei***	see *Q.* x *saulii*
	bicolor	CDul CMCN EPfP MBri WNor
	borealis	see *Q. rubra*
	x ***bushii***	CMCN EPfP MBlu MBri
	canariensis Υ^{H4}	CBcs CLnd CMCN CTho CTrG EPfP
	canariensis x ***faginea*** NJM 03.001	WPGP
	castaneifolia	CDul CMCN EPfP SBLw
	- 'Green Spire' Υ^{H4}	CDoC CMCN CTho EPfP IArd MBlu SMad SPer
	cerris	CBcs CCVT CDoC CDul CLnd CMCN EBee ECrN EMac EMil EPfP EWTr IArd LAst LPan MGos MLan NWea SBLw SEND SPer WMou
§	- 'Argenteovariegata' (v)	CDul CEnd CMCN CTho EBee ELan EMil EPfP IClo MAsh MBlu MGos SIFN SMad WOrn WPGP WPat
	- 'Variegata'	see *Q. cerris* 'Argenteovariegata'
	- 'Wodan'	CMCN EPfP MBlu
	chrysolepis	CMCN EPfP
	coccifera	CDul CGHE CMCN SKHP SSpi WPGP
	- subsp. ***calliprinos***	CMCN WPGP
	coccinea	CBcs CDul CLnd CMCN CTho CTri CWSG ECrN EPfP NBea NWea SBLw SLim SPer SPoG STre WNor
	- 'Splendens' Υ^{H4}	CDoC CDul CEnd CMCN CPMA CTho CTri ELan EPfP MAsh MBlu MBri NEgg SBLw SHBN SPer WOrn WPat
	dentata	CMCN EPfP
	- 'Carl Ferris Miller'	CBcs CMCN EPfP IDee MBlu MBri WPat
	- 'Pinnatifida'	CMCN EPfP IArd IClo IDee MBlu MBri SMad WPat
	douglasii	CMCN
	dumosa	CMCN WNor
	ellipsoidalis	CMCN WNor
	- 'Hemelrijk'	CDoC EPfP MBlu
	emoryi	CMCN
	engleriana new	CExc
	falcata	CDul CMCN EPfP
	- var. ***pagodifolia***	see *Q. pagoda*
	x ***fernaldii***	CMCN
	frainetto	CCVT CDoC CDul CLnd CMCN CTho EBee ECrN EPfP EWTr ISea LPan MLan NWea SBLw SEND SPer WMou WNor
	- 'Hungarian Crown' Υ^{H4}	CMCN EPfP MBlu SMad
	- 'Trotworth'	SMad
	- 'Trump'	CMCN MBlu
	gambelii	CMCN
	garryana	CMCN
	georgiana	CMCN EPfP
	gilva	CDul CMCN
	glandulifera	see *Q. serrata*
§	***glauca***	CMCN EPfP SAPC SArc WNor WPGP
	gravesii	EPfP
	grisea	CDul CMCN
	x ***hastingsii***	CMCN
	hemisphaerica	CDul CMCN EPfP
	x ***heterophylla***	CMCN EPfP
	x ***hickelii***	CMCN
	- 'Gieszelhorst'	MBlu
§	x ***hispanica***	CLnd WPic
	- 'Ambrozyana'	CDul CMCN EPfP SMad
	- 'Diversifolia'	CMCN EPfP MBlu
	- 'Fulhamensis'	CMCN MBlu SEND
§	- 'Lucombeana' Υ^{H4}	CBcs CDul CMCN CSBt CTho EPfP IArd IDee MBlu SPer
§	- 'Pseudoturneri'	CBcs CDul EBee EPfP LPan MBlu SIFN
	- 'Suberosa'	CTho
	- 'Waasland'	MBri
	- 'Wageningen'	CMCN EPfP MBri
	hypoleucoides	EPfP MBri
	ilex Υ^{H4}	More than 30 suppliers
	ilicifolia	CMCN WNor
	imbricaria	CDul CMCN MBlu
	incana Roxb.	see *Q. leucotrichophora*
	ithaburensis	EPfP
§	- subsp. ***macrolepis***	CMCN LEdu
	x ***jackiana***	EPfP
	kelloggii	CAgr CBcs CDul CMCN
	x ***kewensis***	CMCN
	laevigata	see *Q. acuta*
	laevis	CDul CMCN EPfP
§	***laurifolia***	CDul CMCN
§	***leucotrichophora***	CMCN WCFE
	liaotungensis	see *Q. wutaishanica*
	x ***libanerris*** 'Rotterdam'	CMCN
	libani	CDul CMCN EPfP
	lobata	CMCN LEdu
	x ***lucombeana***	see *Q.* x *hispanica*
	- 'William Lucombe'	see *Q.* x *hispanica* 'Lucombeana'
	x ***ludoviciana***	CMCN EPfP MBri
	lyrata	CMCN
	'Macon'	LPan
	macranthera	CLnd CMCN EPfP
	macrocarpa	CDul CLnd CMCN EPfP MBri SMad WNor
	macrolepis	see *Q. ithaburensis* subsp. *macrolepis*
	marilandica	CBcs CDul CEnd CMCN EPfP IDee WPGP
	'Mauri'	MBri
	mexicana	CMCN
	michauxii	CMCN
	mongolica subsp. ***crispula*** var. ***grosseserrata***	CMCN WPGP
	muehlenbergii	CMCN EPfP MBlu
	myrsinifolia	see *Q. glauca*
	myrtifolia	EPfP
	nigra	CDul CMCN WNor
	nuttallii	see *Q. texana*
	obtusa	see *Q. laurifolia*
§	***pagoda***	CMCN MBlu
	palustris Υ^{H4}	CCVT CDoC CDul CLnd CMCN CSam CTho ECrN EMac EPfP LPan MAsh MBlu MBri MLan NEgg NWea SBLw SPer STre WNor WOrn
*	- 'Compacta'	EPfP
	- 'Green Dwarf'	CMCN MBlu

	- 'Pendula'	CEnd CMCN
	- 'Swamp Pygmy'	CMCN EPfP MBlu
	pedunculata	see *Q. robur*
	pedunculiflora	see *Q. robur* subsp. *pedunculiflora*
§	***petraea*** ♀H4	CDoC CDul CLnd CSBt ECrN EMac EPfP IMGH LBuc MBlu NBee NLar NWea SBLw SPer WFar WMou
§	- 'Insecata'	CDoC CDul CEnd CMCN
	- 'Laciniata'	see *Q. petraea* 'Insecata'
§	- 'Purpurea'	CDul CLnd CMCN MBlu
	- 'Rubicunda'	see *Q. petraea* 'Purpurea'
§	***phellos***	CDul CLnd CMCN CTho ECrN EPfP MBlu SLPl SPoG WNor
	phillyreoides	CBcs CMCN EPfP IDee SLPl WNor
	polymorpha	CDul CMCN
	'Pondaim'	CMCN
	pontica	CDul CMCN EPfP MBlu NWea WPat
	prinoides	CMCN
	prinus Engelm.	see *Q. prinus* L.
§	***prinus*** L.	CMCN EPfP
	pubescens	CMCN EMac
	pumila Michx.	see *Q. prinus* L.
	pumila Walt.	see *Q. phellos*
	pyrenaica	CDul CMCN CTho MBri
	- 'Pendula'	CMCN EPfP
	rhysophylla	EPfP MBlu SKHP
§	***robur*** ♀H4	More than 30 suppliers
	- 'Argenteomarginata' (v)	CDul CMCN MBlu
	- 'Atropurpurea'	EBee MGos SIFN
*	- 'Compacta'	MBlu
	- 'Concordia'	CDoC CEnd CLnd CMCN EBee ELan EPfP LRHS MBlu NLar NWea SIFN
	- 'Contorta'	CMCN
	- 'Cristata'	CMCN
	- 'Cucullata'	CMCN
*	- ***dissecta***	CMCN
	- 'Facrist'	CDul
	- f. ***fastigiata***	CDoC CDul CLnd CTho EBee ECrN EPfP IMGH MBar MGos NBee NWea SBLw SCoo SLPl SLim SPer WFar WOrn
	- - 'Koster' ♀H4	CDoC CDul CMCN CTri EPfP LPan MBlu NWea SIFN SPoG
	- 'Fennesseyi'	CMCN
	- 'Filicifolia' misapplied	see *Q. robur* 'Pectinata'
	- 'Filicifolia'	see *Q.* x *rosacea* 'Filicifolia'
	- var. ***haas***	CDul
	- 'Hentzei'	CMCN
	- 'Irtha'	EPfP
§	- 'Pectinata'	EPfP MBlu
§	- subsp. ***pedunculiflora***	CMCN
	- 'Pendula'	CEnd CMCN MBlu MGos
	- 'Purpurascens'	CEnd CMCN MBlu
	- 'Raba'	CMCN
	- 'Salicifolia'	MBlu
	- Sherwood oak clone **new**	SMad
	- 'Strypemonde'	CMCN
	- f. ***variegata*** (v)	CPMA MGos
	- - 'Fürst Schwarzenburg' (v)	CMCN
	robur x ***turbinella***	CMCN
§	x ***rosacea*** 'Filicifolia'	CEnd CLnd NEgg NLar WPat
	rotundifolia NJM 03.009	WPGP
§	***rubra*** ♀H4	More than 30 suppliers
	- 'Aurea'	CEnd CMCN CPMA EBee EPfP MBlu SPer WPGP
	- 'Boltes Gold'	MBlu
	- 'Magic Fire'	EPfP MBlu MBri SMad
*	- 'Sunshine'	CMCN MBlu MBri
	rugosa	CDul CMCN
	sadleriana	CDul CMCN
	salicina	WPGP
§	x ***saulii***	CMCN
	x ***schochiana***	EPfP
§	***serrata***	CDoC CMCN MBri
	sessiliflora	see *Q. petraea*
	shumardii	CDul CMCN EPfP MBlu MBri WNor WPGP
	stellata	CMCN EPfP
	suber	CBcs CCVT CDoC CDul CLnd CMCN CTho ELan EPfP IArd ISea LEdu LPan MGos SAPC SArc SEND WCot WPGP
	- 'Cambridge'	EPfP
§	***texana***	CMCN EPfP
	- 'New Madrid' **new**	MBri
	trojana	CMCN
	turbinella	CMCN
	x ***turneri***	CDoC CLnd CMCN CTho EPfP MBri SBLw WMou WSpi
	- 'Pseudoturneri'	see *Q.* x *hispanica* 'Pseudoturneri'
	vacciniifolia	CMCN
	variabilis	CMCN EPfP
	velutina	CDul CLnd CMCN CPMA CTho EPfP IDee WPGP
	- 'Albertsii'	MBlu
	- 'Rubrifolia'	CMCN EPfP
	'Vilmoriana'	CMCN
	virginiana	CMCN
	'Warburgii'	EPfP
	wislizeni	CBcs CDul CMCN EGFP
§	***wutaishanica***	CDul CMCN

Quillaja (*Rosaceae*)

	saponaria	CCCN CPle CTrG

quince see *Cydonia oblonga*

Quisqualis (*Combretaceae*)

	indica	CCCN SOWG

R

Rabdosia (*Lamiaceae*)

	calycina	SPlb

Racosperma see *Acacia*

Ramonda (*Gesneriaceae*)

§	***myconi*** ♀H4	CLAP CPBP CStu ECho EWes GEdr ITim LSou LTwo NLAp NLar NMen NSla NWCA SBla SChF SIng SRms WAbe
	- var. ***alba***	CLAP ECho MTho WKif WThu
	- 'Jim's Shadow'	WAbe
	- 'Rosea'	CLAP SBla
	nathaliae ♀H4	CLAP CPBP NWCA WAbe WThu
	- 'Alba'	CLAP NSla SBla
	pyrenaica	see *R. myconi*
	serbica	ECho SBla WThu

Ranunculus ✿ (*Ranunculaceae*)

	abnormis	WAbe
	aconitifolius	CSpe EBee ECha GMaP NEgg NLar SHar SWat WHal WMnd WSpi
	- 'Flore Pleno' (d) ♀H4	CDes CFir CSpe EBee ECha ECho EHrv EPfP GAbr GBuc GMaP GMac IGor MBri MLHP MRav MWgw NBir NEgg SPhx WCot WFar WHer WHil WMoo WPnP
	acris	NBir NLan NPer
*	- 'Citrinus'	CElw CEnt ECtt EGle LRHS MCot MFOX MSte NCGa NRya SHar WHal WMoo

- 'Flore Pleno' (d) $\mathbb{Y}^{H4}$	CElw CFee CFir EBee ECha ECho EGle EHrv ELan EPPr EPfP GBuc GQue MRav MSte NBid NBro NCGa NDov NGdn NRya NSti SPoG SRms SSvw WCAu WHil WMoo WSpi
- 'Hedgehog'	EBee ECho EPPr LSou NDov WPrP
- 'Stevenii'	CFee EBee EPPr IGor SDix WHal WSHC
- 'Sulphureus'	CBre EBee ECha WEas WFar WHal
alpestris	ECho GEdr NMen NRya
amplexicaulis	EBee ERos GCrs GMaP NHar NMen SBla WAbe
aquatilis	EHon EMFW NSco SWat WPnP
x ***arendsii*** 'Moonlight'	SBla SRot
asiaticus	EBrs WCot
- var. ***albus***	SBla
- var. ***flavus***	SBla
bilobus	NMen
bulbosus	NMir NSco
§ - 'F.M. Burton'	EBee EGle EHrv NRya WCot WTMC
- ***farreri***	see *R. bulbosus* 'F.M. Burton'
- 'Speciosus Plenus'	see *R. constantinopolitanus* 'Plenus'
calandrinioides $\mathbb{Y}^{H2-3}$	ECho EWes NBir SBla WAbe WCot
- SF 137	WCot
§ ***constantinopolitanus*** 'Plenus' (d)	CElw EBee ECha GMac MBri MLLN MRav NBid NBro NRya WCot WEas WFar WMoo
cortusifolius	SWat WCru
crenatus	ECho GCrs GEdr NMen NRya WAbe
creticus	SPoG
ficaria	CArn CNat CTri MHer MSal NChi NMir NSco WFar WHer WShi
- 'Aglow in the Dark'	CHid
- var. ***albus***	CHid EMon ERos LEdu LRHS NRya SIng SPoG WOut
- anemone-centred	see *R. ficaria* 'Collarette'
- 'Ashen Primrose'	EBee
§ - var. ***aurantiacus***	CBgR CStu ECha EMon ERos LRHS MRav NLar NRya SIng SPhx SPoG SRms WAbe WFar WOut
- 'Bowles' Double'	see *R. ficaria* 'Double Bronze', 'Picton's Double'
- 'Brambling'	CBre CHid CLAP ECho EMon LRHS MRav SBch SBla SIng SSvw
- 'Brazen Child'	EBee MDKP
- 'Brazen Hussy'	More than 30 suppliers
- subsp. ***bulbilifer*** 'Chedglow'	MDKP
§ - subsp. ***chrysocephalus***	ECha EMon NRya SBch SIng WCot WFar
- 'Coffee Cream'	EBee
- 'Coker Cream'	ECha
§ - 'Collarette' (d)	CHid CStu EBee ECha ECho EMon ERos GBuc LRHS MAvo MTho NBir NMen NRya SBla SIng SMac SPoG WAbe WFar
- 'Coppernob'	CBre CElw CHid CWsd ECha ECho MAvo MDKP SBch SBla WCot WFar WOut WPnP
- 'Corinne Tremaine'	WHer
- 'Crawshay Cream'	CElw EBee
- 'Cupreus'	see *R. ficaria* var. *aurantiacus*
- 'Damerham' (d)	CHid EMon LRHS
- 'Deborah Jope'	ECha
- 'Diane Rowe'	EMon
§ - 'Double Bronze' (d)	CHid CStu ECho EMon ERos LEdu LRHS MDKP MTho NBir NLar NRya SIng
- double cream-flowered	see *R. ficaria* 'Double Mud'
- double, green-eyed (d)	CHid
§ - 'Double Mud' (d)	CBow CHid CLAP CSpe CStu EMon ERos EWsh GBuc LEdu LRHS MTho NRya SBla SIng SPoG WAbe WFar WHal WSHC
- double yellow	see *R. ficaria flore-pleno*
- 'Dusky Maiden'	EMon LRHS NLar SBch SIng WFar
- 'E.A. Bowles'	see *R. ficaria* 'Collarette'
- 'Elan' (d)	CDes EBee
- subsp. ***ficariiformis***	EBee EMon
§ - ***flore-pleno*** (d)	CBgR CFee CHid CStu CTri ECha ECho ELan EMar EMon EPPr ERos LRHS NRya NSti SBch SIng SRms WAbe WCot WFar
- 'Granby Cream'	EMon
- 'Green Petal'	CAby CHid CStu ECho EMon EPPr LEdu MDKP MHer MTho NBir NLar NRya SIng SPhx WHal WHer WOut
- 'Holly'	see *R. ficaria* 'Holly Green'
§ - 'Holly Green'	ECho
- 'Hyde Hall'	EMon LRHS NLar SBch SIng WFar
- 'Jake Perry'	CDes CHid EBee
- 'Jane's Dress'	CHid
- 'Ken Aslet Double' (d)	CDes CSpe EBee EMon LEdu LRHS WHal WOut
- 'Lambrook Black'	WHer
- 'Lemon Queen'	CHid
- 'Leo'	EMon MDKP
- subsp. ***major***	see *R. ficaria* subsp. *chrysocephalus*
- 'Mimsey' (d)	ECha
- 'Mobled Jade'	CHid EBee
- 'Mud'	MDKP
- 'Newton Abbot'	CBre
I - 'Nigrifolia'	EBee MDKP
- 'Old Master'	CBow EBee MAvo WCot
- 'Orange Sorbet'	ECha EMon LEdu NLar
§ - 'Picton's Double' (d)	CStu MTho NRya WAbe
- 'Primrose'	CHid EMon LRHS MTho NLar NRya SIng
- 'Primrose Brassy'	EMon
- 'Primrose Elf'	ECha
- 'Quantock Brown'	CBgR
- 'Quillet' (d)	EMon
- 'Ragamuffin' (d)	CDes EBee EMon
- 'Randall's White'	CSWP CStu EBee ECha MRav MTho SHar SPhx WFar WPtf WSHC
- 'Salmon's White'	CBre CFee ECho ELan EMar EPPr MRav NBir NCGa NLar NRya SIng SPhx WFar WHal WHer WHrl WPtf
- 'Sheldon Silver'	CHid
- 'Silver Collar'	EMon LEdu
- single cream-flowered	EMon
- 'Tortoiseshell'	CHid EBee MAvo MDKP WFar WPtf
- 'Winkworth'	EMon
- 'Wisley Double'	see *R. ficaria* 'Double Bronze'
- 'Wisley White'	NSti
- 'Witchampton'	CDes
- 'Yaffle'	CBre CHid EBee EMon LRHS MDKP MRav SIng
flammula	CBen CDWL EHon EMFW SWat WPnP
gouanii	NRya
gramineus $\mathbb{Y}^{H4}$	CMea CWCL CWsd EBee ECho EDAr EPot ERos EShb GBuc GCrs GMaP LBee LRHS MNrw MTho NMen NRya SMad SPhx SPoG SRms WCAu WFar WPer
- 'Pardal'	CWsd SCnR WFar
* ***guttatus***	NMen
illyricus	CDes EBee ECha EDAr NRya WHal
insignis	EBee
kamchaticus	see *Oxygraphis glacialis*
lanuginosus	EPPr

lingua	CFir COld EMFW MCCP NSco SPlb WSFF
- 'Grandiflorus'	CBen EHon NPer SWat WHal WMAq WPnP
lyallii	GGar SBla WAbe
macauleyi	GCrs
millefoliatus	EBee ECho ERos GBuc MTho NMen WPGP
montanus double (d)	EBee SBla WCot
- 'Molten Gold' ♀H4	CStu ECho ECtt GCrs GMaP MRav MTho NRya SBla WAbe
muelleri var. ***brevicaulis***	SBla
nivicola	NWCA
parnassiifolius	GCrs NMen SBla WAbe
platanifolius	SMHy SPhx
pyrenaeus	NMen
repens 'Buttered Popcorn'	CBow EBee NLar WMoo WSpi
- 'Cat's Eyes' (v)	CDes EBee EMan MAvo
- 'Gloria Spale'	CBre
- var. ***pleniflorus*** (d)	CBre EBee GGar WEas WFar
- 'Snowdrift' (v)	EMon WCot
- 'Timothy Clark' (d)	CBre EMon WSHC
rhomboideus	EBee
sceleratus	WHer
seguieri	WAbe
serbicus	EBee EPPr
speciosus 'Flore Pleno'	see *R. constantinopolitanus* 'Plenus'

Ranzania (*Berberidaceae*)

japonica	EBee WCru

Raoulia (*Asteraceae*)

australis misapplied	see *R. hookeri*
australis Hook.	EDAr GEdr GGar ITim MBar MWat NRya NWCA SIng WHoo
§ - Lutescens Group	ECha ECho EPot
haastii	ECho ECou
§ ***hookeri***	ECha ECho ECou EDAr GEdr ITim NWCA SIng SPlb SRms WAbe WFar WLin WPat
- var. ***apice-nigra***	EDAr WAbe
- var. ***laxa***	EPot EWes
x ***loganii***	see x *Leucoraoulia loganii*
lutescens	see *R. australis* Lutescens Group
monroi	EDAr
petriensis	ECho
x ***petrimia*** 'Margaret Pringle'	WAbe
subsericea	ECho ECou EWes NMen NWCA
tenuicaulis	ECha ECou SPlb

Raoulia x *Leucogenes* see x *Leucoraoulia*

raspberry see *Rubus idaeus*

Ratibida (*Asteraceae*)

columnifera	CMea CRWN EBee EBrs EMan EPfP LRHS LSou NBre SPav SPet
- 'Cheyenne Yellow'	EBrs SBra SPoG
- f. ***pulcherrima***	CMea CSpe EBee LHop LSou NBre SMad SPav SPet SPhx WCAu
- red	LRav SPav
- 'Red Midget'	EBrs SPav SPoG
pinnata	CAby CEnt CRWN CSam EBee LRHS LSRN MWgw NBre NSti SMad SPav SPet SPhx SPlb WCAu WHal WMnd
tagetes	EBee SPav

Ravenala (*Strelitziaceae*)

madagascariensis	EAmu LPal XBlo

Ravenea (*Arecaceae*)

rivularis	CCCN EAmu LPal

Rechsteineria see *Sinningia*

redcurrant see *Ribes rubrum* (R)

Regnellidium (*Marsileaceae*)

diphyllum new	LLWG

Rehderodendron (*Styracaceae*)

macrocarpum	CBcs CTrG

Rehmannia (*Scrophulariaceae*)

angulata misapplied	see *R. elata*
§ ***elata*** ♀H2	CPLG CSam CSev CSpe CWCL EBee ELan EPfP LAst LHop LLWP LPio LRHS MFOX MHer MLLN MNHC MWgw NOrc SGar SHGN SIng SPav WBor WCAu WFar WHil WPic WWlt
- 'White Dragon'	CSpe LPio
glutinosa ♀H3	CStu EBee

Reichardia (*Asteraceae*)

picroides	CAgr

Reineckea (*Convallariaceae*)

§ ***carnea***	CDes CFee CHid CPLG CPom CStu EBee ECha ELan EMar EPla ERos GEdr GGar LEdu LRHS MHar NSti SDys SPlb WCru WPGP WPtf WTin
- B&SWJ 4808	WCru
- SDR 330	GKev
- 'Variegata' (v)	WCot WCru

Reinwardtia (*Linaceae*)

elata	SMrm
§ ***indica***	CCCN CHll CPLG EShb SAdn
trigyna	see *R. indica*

Remusatia (*Araceae*)

hookeriana	CKob EAmu
pumila	CKob EAmu
vivipara	CKob

Reseda (*Resedaceae*)

alba	MHer
lutea	CBod MSal SECG SIde
luteola	CHby GPoy MHer MSal NSco SECG WHer

Restio (*Restionaceae*)

bifarius	CTrC
brunneus	CBig EBee WPGP
festuciformis	EAmu WPnP
quadratus	WNor WPGP
subverticillatus	see *Ischyrolepis subverticillata*
tetraphyllus	CAbb CBct CBig CBrm CFir CPen CTrC EBee GGar IDee LAst LHop MBNS NVic SMad WCot WDyG WPGP WPnP WPrP

Retama (*Papilionaceae*)

§ ***monosperma***	EShb XPep
raetam	XPep

Reynoutria see *Fallopia*

Rhamnella (*Rhamnaceae*)

franguloides new	CMCN

Rhamnus (*Rhamnaceae*)

alaternus	XPep
- var. ***angustifolia***	WFar WPGP
§ - 'Argenteovariegata' (v) ♀H4	More than 30 suppliers

- 'Variegata'	see *R. alaternus* 'Argenteovariegata'
californica	NLar
cathartica	CCVT CDul CLnd CTri ECrN EMac EPfP LBuc NLar NWea WMou WSFF WTel
frangula	see *Frangula alnus*
imeretina	CGHE WPGP
pallasii	NLar
pumila	NLar
purshiana	MSal
taquetii	NLar

Rhaphiolepis (*Rosaceae*)

x ***delacourii***	CMHG CMac CWSG CWib ELan EPfP LRHS MBri MWea SRms WBod WHCG WPic
- 'Coates' Crimson'	CDoC EBee ELan EMil EPfP IArd LHop MBri SBra SHBN SLon SOWG WPat WSHC
- Enchantress = 'Moness'	CMHG CSam EBee ELan EPfP LRHS SPoG
- 'Spring Song'	SLon
indica	ERom
- B&SWJ 8405	WCru
- 'Coppertone'	EMil LRHS SBra
- Springtime = 'Monme'	SPer XPep
umbellata Υ^{H2-3}	CBcs CBrm CHEx CPLG CSam CTri CWib EBee ELan EPfP IDee LAst LHop LRHS MBri MRav SBra SEND SLon SOWG WFar WHCG WSHC
- f. ***ovata***	CRez MWya
- - B&SWJ 4706	WCru

Rhaphithamnus (*Verbenaceae*)

cyanocarpus	see *R. spinosus*
§ ***spinosus***	EBee EPfP ERea GGar MBri WBod

Rhapidophyllum (*Arecaceae*)

hystrix	CBrP LPal NPal SAin WCot

Rhapis ✿ (*Arecaceae*)

§ ***excelsa*** Υ^{H1}	CBrP EAmu LPal NPal
multifida	LPal

Rhazya (*Apocynaceae*)

orientalis	see *Amsonia orientalis*

Rheum ✿ (*Polygonaceae*)

CC 4612	WCot
CC 4613	MGol WCot
CC 4768	CPLG MGol WCot
CC 4845	WCot
GWJ 9329 from Sikkim	WCru
§ 'Ace of Hearts'	CDWL CElw CHEx CHar CPrp EBee ECha EHrv ELan EMFW EPla GMaP LHop LRHS MBri MCCP MRav MWgw NBid NCGa NLar NSti SBod SPer SWat SWvt WCot WFar WMnd
'Ace of Spades'	see *R.* 'Ace of Hearts'
acuminatum	EBee GBin WPGP
- HWJCM 252	WCru
alexandrae	CFir EBee EWes GCra LPio NChi WCot
- BWJ 7670	WCru
- SDR 2924	GKev
altaicum	LEdu
'Andrew's Red'	GTwe
§ ***australe***	CArn CFir EBee LEdu LPio LRHS MGol MLLN NBro NLar WCot WFar WHoo WMnd
delavayi	EBee
- BWJ 7592	WCru
emodi	see *R. australe*
x ***hybridum*** 'Appleton's Forcing'	GTwe
- 'Baker's All Season'	GTwe
- 'Brandy Carr Scarlet'	NGHP
- 'Canada Red'	GTwe
- 'Cawood Delight'	GTwe LRHS NGHP
- 'Champagne'	CAgr EMil GTwe LCro WSpi
- 'Daw's Champion'	GTwe
- 'Early Cherry'	GTwe
- 'Fenton's Special'	CTri GTwe MCoo NGHP
- 'Glaskin's Perpetual'	CAgr CWib LBuc MAsh
- 'Goliath'	GTwe
- 'Greengage'	GTwe
- 'Hadspen Crimson'	CBct WCot
- 'Hammond's Early'	GTwe
- 'Harbinger'	GTwe
- 'Hawke's Champagne' Υ^{H4}	GTwe
- 'Holsteiner Blut'	EBee EBrs
- 'Livingstone'[PBR] (F)	ENot EPfP LRHS
- 'Mac Red' Υ^{H4}	GTwe
- 'Prince Albert'	GTwe NGHP
- 'Raspberry Red' **new**	ENot
- 'Red Champagne'	EBrs NGHP WSpi
- 'Red Prolific'	GTwe
- 'Reed's Early Superb' Υ^{H4}	GTwe
- 'Stein's Champagne' Υ^{H4}	GTwe
- 'Stockbridge Arrow'	CSut CTri GTwe NGHP
- 'Stockbridge Bingo'	GTwe
- 'Stockbridge Emerald'	GTwe
- 'Stockbridge Guardsman'	GTwe
- 'Strawberry'	EMil EMui GTwe MAsh NBir
- 'Strawberry Red'	LRHS
- 'Strawberry Surprise'	GTwe
- 'Sutton's Cherry Red'	GTwe
- 'The Sutton'	CWib GTwe
- 'Timperley Early' Υ^{H4}	CDoC CMac CTri CWib EMui ENot EPfP GTwe LRHS MAsh NBlu NGHP NPri SCoo SDea SKee SPer
- 'Tingley Cherry'	GTwe
- 'Valentine'	MAsh
- 'Victoria'	CAgr CTri CWib ELau ENot GTwe LBuc LRHS MAsh MCoo MHer MNHC NGHP
- 'Zwolle Seedling'	GTwe
kialense	CBct CDes NBid NSti WPGP WPnP
moorcroftianum	EBee GKev
nobile	EBee
- HWJK 2290	WCru
officinale	CArn CBct CHEx LRHS MBri SIde SWat
palmatum	CArn CBcs CDWL CWat EBee ECha ELan ELau EMFW EPfP GMaP LAst LRHS MNHC MRav MSal MWat NEgg NGdn SPer SWat WCAu WFar WWeb
- 'Atropurpureum'	see *R. palmatum* 'Atrosanguineum'
§ - 'Atrosanguineum' Υ^{H4}	CBct CMea EBee ECha ELan EPla EShb GBuc LBMP LRHS LRav MRav MWgw NBid NBro SPer SPlb SPoG SWat WCot WCru WMnd
- 'Bowles' Crimson'	CBct LBuc MBri
- 'Red Herald'	CBct LBuc SBla WCot
- ***rubrum***	EBee ENot LRHS MCCP NBir WFar
- 'Saville'	LBuc LRHS MBri MRav
- var. ***tanguticum***	CAgr CDWL CHar EBee ECha EMFW ENot EPfP EWTr LHop MCCP MDun NBPC NBid NCGa NEgg NGdn NSti SMad SMer SPer SPoG SRms SWat SWvt WFar WHoo WMnd WPnP
- - 'Rosa Auslese'	WHil

rhaponticum NLar
ribes EBee GBin WCot
subacaule NLar
tataricum EBee LEdu

Rhinanthus (*Scrophulariaceae*)

minor NSco

Rhodanthe (*Asteraceae*)

§ ***anthemoides*** ECou
§ - 'Paper Cascade'PBR LRHS

Rhodanthemum (*Asteraceae*)

from High Atlas, Morocco SIng
'African Eyes' EBee ECho ENot EPfP EWin GGar LRHS NBhm NPri SRot
§ ***atlanticum*** ECho EWes NSla
§ ***catananche*** CCCN CPBP ECho EWes LSou SRot XPep
§ - 'Tizi-n-Test' ECho LRHS SBla WKif
- 'Tizi-n-Tichka' CPBP ECho EWes LRHS NBir SBla WLin
§ ***gayanum*** CCCN EBee ECho EShb EWes LRHS WCot WHen XPep
- 'Flamingo' see *R. gayanum*
§ ***hosmariense*** ♀H4 CCCN CHrt CMHG EBee ECha ECho EDAr ELan EPfP EPot GGar GMaP LAst LHop LRHS NPri SBla SCoo SEND SPer SPoG SRms SRot WAbe WCot WEas WHoo WPat XPep

Rhodiola (*Crassulaceae*)

bupleuroides CLD 1196 EMon
crassipes see *R. wallichiana*
cretinii HWJK 2283 WCru
§ ***fastigiata*** EMon NMen NWCA
§ ***heterodonta*** ECha EGle ELan EMon MRav WCot
himalensis misapplied see *R.* 'Keston'
himalensis (D. Don) Fu CTri EMon
- HWJK 2258 WCru
§ ***ishidae*** CTri
§ 'Keston' CTri
§ ***kirilovii*** EMon
- var. ***rubra*** WFar
linearifolia EMon
§ ***pachyclados*** EAlp EBur ECho EDAr EPot GMaP LBee LRHS MBar MHer NBir NHol NRya SPlb SPoG SRot WAbe WEas WFar WHoo WPer
aff. ***purpureoviridis*** BWJ 7544 WCru
§ ***rosea*** More than 30 suppliers
semenovii EBee MHar NLar
sinuata HWJK 2318 WCru
- HWJK 2326 WCru
§ ***trollii*** CStu GCrs
§ ***wallichiana*** EMon GCrs MLHP NBid WCot WDyG
- GWJ 9263 WCru
- HWJK 2352 WCru

Rhodochiton (*Scrophulariaceae*)

§ ***atrosanguineus*** ♀H1-2 CArn CBcs CCCN CEnd CHEx CRHN CSpe ELan EPfP ERas EShb GGar GKev IDee ITim LRHS MAsh NEgg SGar SHFr SOWG SPer SPoG WBor WGwG
volubilis see *R. atrosanguineus*

Rhodocoma (*Restionaceae*)

arida CBct CCCN CCtw WPGP
capensis CAbb CBct CBig CCCN CCtw CFir CPen CSpe CTrC EAmu EBee IDee WPGP
fruticosa CTrC
gigantea CBig CCCN CCtw CFwr CPen CTrC EBee WNor WPGP
* ***ovida*** CBig

Rhododendron ✿ (*Ericaceae*)

SDR 1804 GKev
SDR 1883 GKev
'A. Gilbert' new SHea
'A.J. Ivens' see *R.* 'Arthur J. Ivens'
'Abegail' MGos SLdr
aberconwayi LMil SLdr SReu
- 'His Lordship' GGGa LHyd LMil NPen
acrophilum (V) Argent 2768 GGGa
'Actress' ISea WCwm
'Ada Brunieres' (K) CSdC
'Addy Wery' (EA) ♀H3-4 CDoC ECho MBar MGos SLdr SPoG
adenogynum CDoC GGGa LMil NPen SLdr
- Cox 6502 GGGa
§ - Adenophorum Group EMui
- - F 20444 SLdr
adenophorum see *R. adenogynum* Adenophorum Group
adenopodum GGGa SLdr
adenosum NHol
- R 18228 GGGa
'Admiral Piet Hein' SReu
'Adonis' (EA/d) CMac LMil LRHS MBar NEgg NLar SLdr
'Adriaan Koster' (M) SLdr
'Adriaan Koster' (hybrid) SHea
'Advance' (O) SLdr
aeruginosum see *R. campanulatum* subsp. *aeruginosum*
aganniphum GGGa ISea LMil NPen
§ - var. ***aganniphum*** Doshongense Group GGGa
- - - KR 4979 LMil
- - Glaucopeplum Group GGGa
- - Schizopeplum Group GGGa
- var. ***flavorufum*** GGGa MDun NPen
- - EGM 160 LMil
- pink-flowered, from Pe, Doshang La KR 3528 LMil
- 'Rusty' NPen
x ***agastum*** PW 98 LMil
'Ahren's Favourite' MAsh
'Aida' (R/d) CSBt SReu
'Aksel Olsen' CTri ECho GEdr LRHS MAsh MBar MDun
alabamense (A) new GKev
'Aladdin' (EA) CDoC ECho SLdr WBod WFar
Aladdin Group SReu
'Aladdin' (*auriculatum* hybrid) GGGa
Albatross Group IDee LMil SLdr SReu
'Albatross Townhill Pink' LMil
'Albert Schweitzer' ♀H4 CWri GGGa LMil MBar MDun SLdr SPoG WBod WFar
albrechtii (A) GGGa LMil SReu
- Whitney form (A) LMil
'Album Elegans' NPen
'Alena' GGGa LMil
'Alex Hill' CBcs
'Alexander' (EA) ♀H4 CDoC LMil LRHS MAsh MGos SHBN SReu
'Alfred' CWri LMil LRHS MAsh
'Alice' (EA) LHyd SLdr
'Alice' (hybrid) ♀H4 CSBt LHyd LMil SHea SLdr SReu
'Alice de Stuers' (M) SLdr
Alison Johnstone Group CBcs GGGa GGar MDun NPen SLdr SReu WPic
'Alix' LHyd

	'Aloha'	MBar NDlv SHBN
	Alpine Gem Group	GQui SLdr
	'Alpine Gem'	LHyd
	alutaceum var. ***alutaceum***	GGGa LMil
§	- - Globigerum Group	LMil
	- - - R 11100	GGGa
§	- var. ***iodes***	GGGa LMil NPen
§	- var. ***russotinctum***	GGGa MDun
	- - R 158	SLdr
§	- - Triplonaevium Group	CBcs
	- - - USDAPI 59442/ R10923	GGGa
	amagianum (A)	GGGa LMil
	Amaura Group	WCwm
	ambiguum	LMil NPen SLdr SReu WBod
I	- 'Crosswater'	LMil
	- dwarf new	CBcs
	- 'Golden Summit'	GGGa
	- 'Jane Banks'	LMil
	'Ambrosia' (EA)	CSBt
	'America'	CBcs MAsh MBar MDun SHea SLdr WFar
	amesiae	GGGa
	'Amity'	CWri ECho ISea LMil MAsh MBri MLea NPen SLdr WFar
§	'Amoenum' (EA/d)	CBcs CDoC CMac CSBt CTrG ECho LHyd LMil MBar MGos NPen SLdr SPer WBod WFar WPic
	'Amoenum Coccineum' (EA/d)	SReu WPat
	Amor Group	LHyd SHea
	'Anah Kruschke'	ENot LCro MAsh SLdr SPoG
	'Analin'	see *R.* 'Anuschka'
	'Anchorite' (EA)	LMil SLdr
*	'Andrae'	SReu
	'Angelo'	LHyd LMil WGer
	Angelo Group	CWri LHyd LMil SLdr SReu
	Anita Group	SHea
	'Ann Callingham' (K)	CSdC
	'Ann Cooper' (A)	LMil
	'Ann Lindsay'	NLar SReu
	'Anna Baldsiefen'	ECho ENot LMil MGos NLar SPoG SReu WBVN WBod
	'Anna H. Hall'	MAsh
	'Anna Rose Whitney'	CBcs CTri CWri GGGa LHyd LPan LRHS MAsh MBar MDun MGos NPen NPri SHBN WMoo
	'Annabella' (K) Ψ^{H4}	CSdC LMil MDun SLdr
	annae	GGGa LMil NPen
	aff. ***annae*** C&H 7185	LMil
	'Anne Frank' (EA)	MGos WBod WFar
	'Anne George'	LHyd
	'Anne Teese'	GGGa IDee LMil SLdr
	'Annegret Hansmann'	GGGa
	'Anneke' (A)	ENot LMil MBar MBri MDun NDlv SLdr SReu SSta WBod WFar
	anthopogon	LMil
	- from Marpha Meadow, Nepal	WAbe
	- 'Betty Graham'	GGGa
I	- 'Crosswater'	LMil
	- subsp. ***hypenanthum***	GCrs LMil MDun
	- - 'Annapurna'	GGGa WAbe
§	***anthosphaerum***	GGGa SLdr SReu
	'Antilope' (Vs)	CWri ECho LMil MDun MGos MLea NHol SLdr SPer SReu SSta WBVN
	'Antonio'	LMil
§	'Anuschka'	LMil LRHS MAsh
§	***anwheiense***	CWri LHyd LMil SHea
	aperantum F 27022	GGGa
	apodectum	see *R. dichroanthum* subsp. *apodectum*
	'Apotrophia'	SLdr

	'Apple Blossom' ambig.	CMac
	'Apple Blossom' Wezelenburg (M)	NHol SLdr
N	'Appleblossom' (EA)	see *R.* 'Ho-o'
	'Apricot Blaze' (A)	MDun NHol
	'Apricot Fantasy'	LMil
	'Apricot Surprise'	CTri LMil LRHS MAsh NPri
	'Apricot Top Garden'	SLdr
	'April Dawn'	GGGa
	'April Glow'	LHyd
	'April Showers' (A)	LMil
I	'Arabella'	MAsh
	'Arabesk' (EA)	MAsh MBri SLdr WFar
	araiophyllum BASEX 9698	GGGa
	- KR 4029	LMil
	arborescens (A)	GGGa LMil SLdr
	- pink-flowered (A)	LMil
	arboreum	CBcs CDoC CHEx CWri GGGa IDee LMil LRHS MDun NPen SLdr SReu WPic
	- B&SWJ 2244	WCru
	- 'Blood Red'	NPen SLdr
	- subsp. ***cinnamomeum***	CDoC GGGa LMil NPen SLdr SReu WGer
	- - var. ***album***	LHyd SLdr SReu
	- - var. ***cinnamomeum*** Campbelliae Group	NLar SLdr
	- - var. ***roseum***	GGGa
*	- - - ***crispum***	SLdr
	- - - 'Tony Schilling'	CDoC IDee LHyd LMil SLdr SReu WGer
	- subsp. ***delavayi***	GGGa LMil NPen SLdr
	- - C&H 7178	GGGa
	- - EGM 360	LMil
	- 'Heligan'	CWri SReu
	- mid-pink-flowered	CDoC SLdr
§	- subsp. ***nilagiricum***	GGGa SLdr
	- var. ***roseum***	SHea SLdr
§	- subsp. ***zeylanicum***	SLdr
	arboreum x ***grande*** new	SLdr
	'Arctic Fox' (EA)	GGGa
	'Arctic Regent' (K)	CSdC GQui SLdr
	'Arctic Tern'	see x *Ledodendron* 'Arctic Tern'
§	***argipeplum***	GGGa SLdr
	'Argosy' Ψ^{H4}	LMil SLdr SReu
	argyrophyllum	CWri NPen SLdr
	- subsp. ***argyrophyllum***	SLdr
	- - W/A 1210	SLdr
§	- subsp. ***hypoglaucum*** 'Heane Wood'	GGGa
	- subsp. ***nankingense***	GGGa LMil
	- - 'Chinese Silver' Ψ^{H4}	CDoC IDee LHyd LMil MDun NPen SReu WGer
§	***arizelum***	CDoC GGGa LMil LRHS MDun NPen SLdr
	- BASEX 9580	GGGa
	- R 25 GGGa	
	- subsp. ***arizelum*** Rubicosum Group	LMil MDun
	armitii (V) Woods 2518	GGGa
	'Arneson Gem' (M)	CDoC CSam GGGa ISea LMil LRHS MAsh NDlv NLar SLdr
	'Arneson Pink'	ISea NLar
	'Arpege' (Vs)	ECho LMil MBri MDun NLar SReu
	'Arthur Bedford'	CBcs CSBt SLdr SReu
§	'Arthur J. Ivens'	SLdr
	'Arthur Osborn'	GGGa SSpi
	'Arthur Stevens'	SLdr
	'Asa-gasumi' (EA)	LHyd SLdr
	'Ascot Brilliant'	SLdr
	asterochnoum	LMil
	- C&H 7051	GGGa
	- EGM 314	LMil
	Asteroid Group	SLdr

'Astrid'	LMil
atlanticum (A)	GGGa GKev LMil
- 'Seaboard' (A)	IDee LMil SLdr
atlanticum* x *canescens **new**	GKev
Augfast Group	ISea SLdr
'August Lamken'	MDun
augustinii	CBcs CTrG CWri GGGa ISea LHyd LMil MLea NLar NPen SLdr SPer SSpi SSta WBod
- subsp. ***augustinii*** C&H 7048	GGGa
§ - subsp. ***chasmanthum***	GGGa LMil MDun WBod
- - white-flowered C&Cu 9407	GGGa
- compact EGM 293	LMil
§ - Electra Group	CDoC GGGa GGar IDee LHyd LMil MDun SLdr SPer
- Exbury best form	LHyd LMil MDun SReu
§ - subsp. ***hardyi***	GGGa
- pale lilac-flowered	SLdr
- 'Picton Blue' **new**	WPic
§ - subsp. ***rubrum***	GGGa
* - 'Trewithen'	LMil
I - 'Werrington'	SLdr SReu
§ ***aureum***	GGGa LMil SLdr
auriculatum	GGGa IDee LHyd LMil MDun NLar NPen SLdr SReu SSpi SSta WBVN WGer
- PW 50	GGGa
- Reuthe's form	SReu
auriculatum* x *hemsleyanum	GGGa
auritum	GGGa NPen SLdr WPic
'Aurora' (K)	SLdr
'Aurore de Royghem'	SLdr
austrinum (A)	IDee LMil
- yellow-flowered (A)	LMil
'Autumn Gold'	SLdr
'Avalanche' 🏆H4	LMil SLdr SReu
Avocet Group	LMil SLdr
'Award'	LMil
'Aya-kammuri' (EA)	LHyd SLdr
Azamia Group	LHyd
Azor Group	LHyd SHea SReu
Azrie Group	SLdr
§ 'Azuma-kagami' (EA)	CDoC ISea LCro LHyd LMil SLdr WBod WFar
'Azurro'	GGGa LMil NLar
'Azurwolke'	LMil
'B. de Bruin'	SHea
'Babette'	see *R.* (Volker Group) 'Babette'
'Babuschka'	LMil
'Bad Eilsen'	MAsh
'Baden-Baden'	CDoC CTri ECho ENot GEdr LHyd MAsh MBar MDun MGos NEgg NHol NPen SHBN SLdr WBod WFar
'Bagshot Ruby'	SHea SLdr SReu
baileyi	GGGa NPen SLdr WAbe
bainbridgeanum	SLdr
'Balalaika'	NLar
balangense EN 3530	GGGa
balfourianum	GGGa LMil SLdr
'Balsaminiflorum'	see *R. indicum* 'Balsaminiflorum'
'Baltic Amber' (A)	GGGa
'Balzac' (K)	CSam ECho LHyd LMil MAsh MGos MLea NEgg SLdr SPer SPur WBVN
'Bambi'	LMil SLdr SReu
'Bandoola'	SReu
'Barbara Coates' (EA)	SLdr
barbatum	CDoC CHEx CWri GGGa GGar IDee LHyd LMil MDun NPen SLdr WPic
- B&SWJ 2237	WCru
'Barbecue' (K)	LMil
Barclayi Group	LHyd SLdr
'Bariton'	CDoC LMil
barkamense	LMil
'Barmstedt'	CWri MAsh
'Barnaby Sunset'	GGGa LMil LRHS MAsh
'Bashful' 🏆H4	CSBt ECho EMui EPfP MGos SLdr SReu
§ ***basilicum***	GGGa IDee LMil LRHS SLdr
- AC 616	NPen
- AC 3009	WCwm
x ***bathyphyllum*** Cox 6542	GGGa
bauhiniiflorum	see *R. triflorum* var. *bauhiniiflorum*
beanianum	GGGa
- KC 122	GGGa
- compact	see *R. piercei*
'Beatrice Keir'	LMil MDun SReu
Beau Brummel Group	CDoC LMil SHea
'Beaulieu Manor'	GQui
'Beauty of Littleworth'	LHyd SHea SReu
'Beefeater'	SLdr
'Beefeater' x ***yakushimanum***	SLdr
beesianum	GGGa LMil SLdr
- CN&W 1316	ISea
- JN 300	GGGa
- KR 4150	LMil
'Beethoven' (EA) 🏆H3-4	CTrG LHyd NPen SLdr SMer SReu WPic
'Belkanto'	MDun NBlu SPoG
'Belle Heller'	SLdr
'Ben Morrison' (EA)	SReu
'Bengal'	ECho GEdr LRHS MBar MDun NDlv NHol SReu
'Bengal Beauty' (EA)	GQui SLdr
'Bengal Fire' (EA)	CMac SLdr
§ 'Benifude' (EA)	LHyd
'Bergensiana' **new**	SReu
'Bergie Larson'	CBcs CDoC ECho LMil MAsh MDun MLea SLdr
bergii	see *R. augustinii* subsp. *rubrum*
'Berg's Yellow'	CWri ECho ISea LMil MAsh MDun MLea NPen WBVN WFar
'Bernard Shaw'	SReu
'Bernstein'	MAsh NBlu SPoG WFar
'Berryrose' (K) 🏆H4	CBcs CSBt CTri CWri ECho ENot EPfP LHyd LMil MBar MGos MLea NLar SLdr SPer WBVN WBod WFar
Berryrose Group	CDoC MDun
'Bert's Own'	SLdr
'Beryl Taylor'	GGGa
'Betty' (EA)	CTrG LHyd
'Betty Anne Voss' (EA)	ECho ENot LHyd LMil LRHS MGos NPri SCoo SLdr SReu
'Betty Wormald'	CSBt ECho LHyd LMil MBri MGos MLea NPen SHBN SHea SLdr SPer WBVN
bhutanense	LMil
- CH&M	GGGa
Bibiani Group	LMil SHea SLdr
'Big Punkin'	LMil
'Bijinsui' (EA)	LHyd
'Bijou de Ledeberg' (EA)	CMac
'Billy Budd'	SLdr
'Birthday Girl'	ECho ENot LMil MAsh MDun MLea SPoG
Biskra Group	GGGa LMil
'Blaauw's Pink' (EA) 🏆H3-4	CDoC CDul CMac CSBt CTrh ECho ENot EPfP GQui LCro LHyd LMil MBar MBri MGos NPen SLdr SPer SPlb SPoG SReu SRms WCwm WFar
'Black Hawk' (EA)	CBcs CTrG

'Black Knight' (A)	SLdr
'Black Magic'	CWri LMil MAsh
'Black Sport'	MLea
Blaue Donau	see *R.* 'Blue Danube'
'Blazecheck'	MGos SCoo
'Blewbury' 🏆H4	LHyd LMil MDun SLdr SReu SSta
'Blue Beard'	SLdr
'Blue Bell'	SHea
'Blue Boy'	ENot LMil
'Blue Chip'	LHyd SLdr
§ 'Blue Danube' (EA) 🏆H3-4	CDoC CDul CMac CSBt CTrG CTrh CTri ECho ENot EPfP LHyd LMil LRHS MAsh MBar MBri MDun MGos NBlu NPen NPri SLdr SPer SPoG SReu SSta WBod WFar WPic
Blue Diamond Group	CBcs CMHG CTrh ECho ENot EPfP LCro LRHS MAsh MBar MDun MGos NHol NPen SHBN SLdr SReu SRms
'Blue Diamond'	CSBt ECho LHyd MLea SPer SPoG WBod
'Blue Haze'	LHyd
'Blue Monday'	WBod
'Blue Peter' 🏆H4	CDoC CSBt CWri ECho ENot EPfP GGGa LCro LHyd LMil LRHS MAsh MBar MDun MGos MLea SBod SHBN SLdr SPer SReu SSta
'Blue Pool'	LMil MBar
Blue Ribbon Group	CMHG ISea SLdr
'Blue Silver'	ENot GGGa LMil LRHS MAsh NLar
'Blue Star'	ECho GGar LHyd MDun MLea NLAp NMen
'Blue Steel'	see *R. fastigiatum* 'Blue Steel'
Blue Tit Group	CBcs CSBt CTrG ECho ENot EPfP LHyd LRHS MAsh MBar MDun NEgg NHol NPen SHBN SLdr SReu SSta WBod
Bluebird Group	CSBt ECho MAsh MBar MDun MGos NHol NWCA SLdr SPer SPoG SRms
Bluestone Group	WBod
'Bluette'	ECho MDun MLea NDlv
'Blurettia'	CWri LMil MAsh NLar
'Blutopia'	LMil
'Bob Bovee'	NLar
'Bobbie'	SReu
'Bob's Blue'	MDun
'Boddaertianum'	LHyd SHea SLdr SReu
bodinieri	WBod
'Bodnant Yellow'	LMil
'Bonfire'	SHea SLdr SReu
boothii	GGGa
'Bo-peep'	GQui LMil SReu
Bo-peep Group	CBcs SLdr
'Boskoop Ostara'	CDoC LMil MGos
'Boule de Neige'	MDun
'Bouquet de Flore' (G) 🏆H4	CDoC CSdC EPfP LMil MBar SLdr SReu
Bow Bells Group	CSam CWri ISea LHyd MAsh MBar MDun MGos MLea SHBN
'Bow Bells' 🏆H4	ECho EPfP GEdr LMil LRHS NBlu NHol NLar NPri SHea SLdr WBod WFar
brachyanthum	GGGa
- subsp. ***hypolepidotum***	GGGa LMil
brachycarpum	GGGa SLdr
- subsp. ***brachycarpum*** Tigerstedtii Group	LMil
- 'Roseum Dwarf'	GGGa
brachysiphon	see *R. maddenii* subsp. *maddenii*
'Brambling'	GGGa
'Brazier' (EA)	CTrh LHyd NPen SLdr
'Brazil' (K)	CSBt
'Bremen'	ECho LMil
'Brianna' **new**	GGGa
Bric-à-brac Group	CBcs SLdr
'Bric-à-brac'	MDun WThu
'Bride's Bouquet' (EA/d)	SReu
'Bridesmaid' (O)	ENot EPfP SLdr
'Brigadoon'	MBri
'Bright Forecast' (K)	CWri ECho NLar SLdr
'Brigitte'	CDoC CWri GGGa LMil LRHS MAsh SLdr
'Brilliant' (EA)	MGos
'Brilliant' (hybrid)	MGos NHol WFar
'Brilliant Blue' (EA)	MAsh
'Brilliant Crimson' (EA)	SLdr
'Britannia'	CBcs CSBt CSam CWri ENot EPfP LHyd MAsh MBar SHBN SHea SPer SReu WFar
'Britannia' x ***griersonianum***	SLdr
'Brocade'	CSam LMil MDun NPen SHea SLdr
'Bronze Fire' (A)	NHol SLdr SReu WBod
'Brown Eyes'	ECho ISea MAsh MDun MLea SLdr WFar
'Bruce Brechtbill' 🏆H4	CDoC CWri ECho GGGa LMil MAsh MBri MDun MGos NHol NLar SLdr SReu SSta
'Bruce Hancock' (Ad)	ECho WBVN
§ 'Bruns Elfenbein'	NLar
§ 'Bruns Gloria'	LMil
'Bruns Schneewitchen'	SReu
'Buccaneer' (EA)	LHyd
'Bud Flanagan'	ENot MDun
'Buketta'	GGGa MDun
bullatum	see *R. edgeworthii*
'Bulstrode' (EA) **new**	SHea
bulu C&V 9503	GGGa
'Bungo-nishiki' (EA/d)	CMac
bureavii 🏆H4	CDoC GGGa IDee LHyd LMil MDun MGos NPen SLdr SReu SSta
- SEH 211	LMil
- SF 517	ISea
- 'Ardrishaig'	GGGa
* - ***cruentum***	LMil
I - 'Lem's Variety'	NLar
bureavii x Elizabeth Group	SReu
bureavii x ***yakushimanum***	NPen SReu
bureavioides	LMil NPen SReu
- Cox 5076	GGGa
'Burletta'	GGGa
burmanicum	GGGa LMil MDun WBod
'Burning Love'	NLar
'Butter Brickle'	ECho LMil MDun MLea WBVN WFar
'Butter Yellow'	ECho MDun WBod
'Butterball' **new**	GGGa
'Buttercup' (K)	MBar
'Butterfly'	MDun SHea SLdr
'Buttermint'	CDoC CWri ECho GQui MBri MDun MGos MLea SBod SHBN WBVN WFar
'Buttons and Bows' (K)	GGGa MBri
'Buzzard' (K)	CSdC LMil
'Byron' (A/d)	LMil SLdr
'Caerhays Lavender'	CBcs
caesium	SLdr
calendulaceum (A)	GKev LMil SReu
- red-flowered (A)	LMil
- yellow-flowered	IDee LMil
Calfort Group	SLdr
'Calico' (K)	CSdC
caliginis (V)	GGGa
callimorphum	GGGa LMil
- var. ***myiagrum*** F 21821a	SLdr
calophytum 🏆H4	CWri GGGa IDee LMil LRHS NPen SLdr

- EGM 343	LMil
- var. ***openshawianum*** C&H 7055	GGGa
calostrotum	CWri WAbe
- SF 357	ISea
- subsp. ***calostrotum***	GKev
- 'Gigha' ♀^{H4}	CDoC ECho GGGa LMil LRHS LTwo MAsh MDun MGos SLdr WAbe WGer
§ - subsp. ***keleticum*** ♀^{H4}	CDoC CTrG GEdr MBar MDun MGos WAbe
- - F 21756	SLdr
- - R 58	LMil
§ - - Radicans Group	GCrs GEdr MBar MDun MLea NHol WAbe WBod
- - - USDAPI 59182/ R11188	MLea
- subsp. ***riparium*** SF 95089	ISea
- - Calciphilum Group	GGGa MDun WThu
§ - - Nitens Group	CDoC GBin GGGa IDee MAsh NDlv NMen WAbe
§ - - Rock's form R178	GGGa
caloxanthum	see *R. campylocarpum* subsp. *caloxanthum*
'Calsap'	GGGa NLar
Calstocker Group	LMil
camelliiflorum	GGGa MDun
campanulatum	LMil MDun NPen SLdr SReu WAbe
- HWJCM 195	WCru
§ - subsp. ***aeruginosum***	GGGa LMil MDun NLar NPen SLdr SReu
- ***album***	SLdr
- subsp. ***campanulatum*** 'Roland Cooper'	NPen
- 'Knaphill'	NPen
§ 'Campfire' (EA)	SLdr WBod
Campirr Group	LHyd
campylocarpum	GGGa LHyd LMil MDun NPen SLdr SReu
- B&SWJ 2462	WCru
- from East Nepal	MDun
§ - subsp. ***caloxanthum***	GGGa LMil MDun SLdr
- - KR 6152	LMil
campylogynum ♀^{H4}	GCrs LMil MLea NMen SSpi WAbe
- SF 95181	ISea
- 'Album'	see *R.* 'Leucanthum'
- 'Bramble'	MDun
- Charopoeum Group	ECho GCrs GGGa MBar MDun WBod
- - 'Patricia'	ECho GCrs MDun WThu
- claret-flowered	ECho GGGa MDun
§ - Cremastum Group	CTrG GGGa LHyd
- - 'Bodnant Red'	GGGa LHyd MDun WBod
- Myrtilloides Group	CDoC ECho EPot GGGa GKev GQui IDee LHyd LMil MAsh MDun MGos NLAp NMen NPen SLdr SReu WAbe WBod
- - Farrer 1046	GGGa
- pink-flowered	MBar WAbe
- salmon pink-flowered	ECho GCrs GEdr MDun NLAp WBod
camtschaticum	GGGa LMil MBri WAbe
- from Hokkaido, Japan	GCrs NMen
- var. ***albiflorum***	GGGa NMen
- red-flowered	GGGa
canadense (A)	GGGa SLdr SReu
- f. ***albiflorum*** (A)	GGGa LMil
- dark-flowered (A)	LMil
- 'Deer Lake' (A)	SReu
'Canary'	SReu
canescens (A)	LMil
'Cannon's Double' (K/d) ♀^{H4}	CWri ECho GGGa ISea LHyd LMil MAsh MBri MDun MGos MLea NLar NPen SLdr SPer
'Canzonetta' (EA) ♀^{H4}	ECho GGGa LMil LRHS MAsh MGos
'Capistrano'	GGGa
capitatum	GGGa
'Caprice' (EA)	SReu
'Captain Jack'	GGGa SLdr
'Caractacus'	MBar WFar
'Carat' (A)	MBri SLdr SReu
cardiobasis	see *R. orbiculare* subsp. *cardiobasis*
Carita Group	SReu
'Carita Charm'	SLdr
'Carita Golden Dream'	LMil
'Carita Inchmery'	LHyd SLdr
'Carmen'	CWri ECho GCrs GEdr GGGa ISea LHyd LMil MAsh MBar MDun MGos MLea NHol NMen SHBN SLdr SReu SRms WBVN
carneum	GGGa LMil
'Carnival' (EA)	CBcs
'Caroline'	EMui
'Caroline Allbrook' ♀^{H4}	CDoC CWri ECho ENot EPfP GGGa LHyd LMil MAsh MBri MDun MGos MLea NDlv NHol NLar NPen SLdr SPoG WBVN
'Caroline de Zoete'	LHyd SHea
carolinianum	see *R. minus* var. *minus* Carolinianum Group
'Cary Ann'	CBcs CTri CWri LRHS MAsh SLdr SPoG SReu WFar
'Casablanca' (EA)	SLdr
'Cassata' **new**	LMil
'Cassley' (Vs)	LMil SLdr
'Castle of Mey'	SLdr
catacosmum	GGGa
§ 'Catalode'	GGGa
catawbiense	GGGa LHyd NPen SLdr
'Catawbiense Album'	CTri CWri GGGa MAsh WFar
'Catawbiense Boursault'	CWri SLdr WFar
'Catawbiense Grandiflorum'	LMil MAsh WFar
'Catherine Hopwood'	SLdr
§ ***caucasicum*** 'Cunningham's Sulphur'	MDun
'Caucasicum Pictum'	GGGa LHyd LMil MBar SLdr
Cavalier Group	MDun
'Cecile' (K) ♀^{H4}	CBcs CSam CWri ECho LHyd LMil MAsh MBar MBri MDun MGos NPen SBod SLdr SPer SReu WBVN
'Celestial' (EA)	CMac
'Centennial'	see *R.* 'Washington State Centennial'
cephalanthum	GGGa LMil
- subsp. ***cephalanthum*** SBEC 0751	WAbe
- - Crebreflorum Group	GGGa LMil WAbe
- - Nmaiense Group C&V 9513	GGGa
- subsp. ***platyphyllum***	GGGa LMil
cerasinum	GGGa ISea LMil NPen
- C&V 9504	GGGa
- KR 3460	LMil
- SF 95067	ISea
- 'Cherry Brandy'	LHyd NPen
'Cetewayo' ♀^{H4}	CWri LMil SReu
chaetomallum	see *R. haematodes* subsp. *chaetomallum*
chamaethomsonii	GGGa LMil
- CCH&H 8195	GGGa
- SF 95084	ISea
- var. ***chamaethauma*** KW 5847	LMil
- - KR 3506 from Pe, Doshang La	LMil

	chameunum	see *R. saluenense* subsp. *chameunum*
§	'Champagne' ♀H3-4	CSBt EPfP LHyd LMil LRHS MAsh MDun MLea SHea SLdr SReu
	championiae	GGGa
	'Chanel' (Vs)	MDun SReu SSta
	changii new	GGGa
	'Chanticleer' (EA)	CTrh SLdr SReu
	chapaense	see *R. maddenii* subsp. *crassum*
	'Chapeau'	LMil
	charitopes	GGGa LMil
	- subsp. ***charitopes*** F 25570	SReu
§	- subsp. ***tsangpoense***	GGGa GQui NHol WPic
	'Charlemagne' (G)	SLdr
*	'Charles Puddle'	WBod
	Charmaine Group	GGGa NHol SReu
	'Charme La'	GGGa
	chasmanthum	see *R. augustinii* subsp. *chasmanthum*
	'Cheer'	CWri MAsh MBar SLdr SReu WFar WMoo
	'Cheerful Giant' (K)	LMil MGos
	'Chelsea Reach' (K/d)	CSdC
	'Chelsea Seventy'	MAsh NLar NPen SLdr
	'Cherokee'	SLdr
	'Cherries and Cream'	LMil
	'Chetco' (K)	ENot LMil SLdr
	'Chevalier Félix de Sauvage' ♀H4	LMil SReu
	'Cheyenne'	SLdr
	'Chiffchaff'	LHyd NMen WAbe
	'Chikor'	CBcs CSBt CTrG ECho GEdr GGGa MAsh MBar MBri MDun MGos NHol NPen SLdr WBod WFar
	China Group	SReu
	'China A'	SLdr
	'Chinchilla' (EA)	GQui
	'Chink'	MBar MDun SLdr WThu
	'Chionoides'	GGGa NBlu SLdr WBod
	'Chipmunk' (EA/d)	LMil LRHS
	'Chippewa' (EA)	CTri GGGa LMil
	'Chocolate Ice' (K/d)	SLdr
	'Chopin' (EA)	WBod
	'Choremia' ♀H3	LHyd LMil SHea SLdr SReu WBod
	'Chris' (EA)	SLdr
	christi (V)	GGGa
	'Christina' (EA/d)	CMac NHol NLar SLdr SReu WBod
	'Christmas Cheer' (EA/d)	see *R.* 'Ima-shojo'
	'Christmas Cheer' (hybrid)	CBcs CMac CSBt CWri GGGa ISea LHyd LMil MGos MLea NBlu NLar NPen SHBN SLdr SPer SPoG SReu WPic
	'Chromatella'	LMil SLdr
	chrysanthum	see *R. aureum*
	chryseum	see *R. rupicola* var. *chryseum*
	chrysodoron	GGGa LMil
	ciliatum	CBcs CTrG GGGa LHyd SLdr
	ciliicalyx subsp. ***lyi***	see *R. lyi*
	Cilpinense Group	CBcs MAsh MBar MDun NPen SLdr SPer WFar
	'Cilpinense' ♀H3-4	CMac CSBt CWri ECho ENot EPfP GGGa LHyd LMil LRHS NPri SPoG SReu WBVN WBod WBrE WPic
	cinnabarinum	LMil MDun NPen SLdr
	- subsp. ***cinnabarinum***	MDun SLdr
	- - BL&M 234	LMil
	- - 'Aestivale'	LMil
	- - Blandfordiiflorum Group	GGGa LMil NPen SLdr
§	- - 'Conroy'	CDoC GGGa LMil MDun MLea SReu
	- - 'Nepal'	LHyd LMil
	- - Roylei Group	GGGa LHyd LMil MDun MLea SLdr WPic

	- - - 'Magnificum'	MDun
	- - - 'Vin Rosé'	LMil MDun
§	- subsp. ***tamaense***	GGGa
	- - KW 21021	GGGa
§	- subsp. ***xanthocodon***	IDee LMil MDun MLea NPen SLdr
§	- - Concatenans Group	GGGa LHyd LMil MDun MLea NPen SLdr WPic
	- - - C&V 9523	GGGa
	- - - KW 5874	LMil
	- - - 'Amber'	LMil MDun MLea
	- - - 'Copper'	SLdr
	- - 'Daffodilly'	LHyd
	- - Purpurellum Group	GGGa MDun NPen SLdr WBod
	Cinnkeys Group	GGGa MDun
	Cinzan Group	LMil SReu
	citriniflorum	LMil
	- R 108	GGGa LMil
	- Brodick form	LMil
	- var. ***citriniflorum***	LMil
	- var. ***horaeum***	SLdr
	- - F 21850*	GGGa
	- orange-flowered new	WGer
	'Citronella'	SLdr
	'Claret Bumble'	NPen
	'Claydian Variegated' (v)	GGGa
	clementinae	GGGa LMil MDun NPen SReu
	- F 25705	LMil
	- JN 729	GGGa
	'Cliff Garland'	GQui LMil
	'Coccineum Speciosum' (G) ♀H4	CSBt CSdC GGGa IDee LMil LRHS MBar
	coelicum F 25625	GGGa
	coeloneuron	GGGa LMil MDun
	- EGM 334	LMil
	'Colin Kenrick' (K/d)	SLdr
	collettianum H&W 8975	GGGa
	'Colonel Coen'	CDoC CWri ECho GGGa LMil MBri MGos MLea NPen SHBN WBVN
	Colonel Rogers Group	LHyd SLdr SReu
	(Comely Group) 'Golden Orfe'	SLdr
	complexum F 15392	GGGa
	'Comte de Gomer' (hybrid)	CBcs
	concatenans	see *R. cinnabarinum* subsp. *xanthocodon* Concatenans Group
	concinnum	CWri LHyd MDun MLea SLdr
	- Pseudoyanthinum Group	GGGa GQui LMil MDun SLdr SReu WPic
	'Concorde'	NBlu
	'Conroy'	see *R. cinnabarinum* subsp. *cinnabarinum* 'Conroy'
	'Constable'	LHyd
	'Contina'	GGGa
	cookeanum	see *R. sikangense* var. *sikangense* Cookeanum Group
	'Coral Mist'	CDoC GGGa LMil MDun
	'Coral Reef'	SLdr SReu
	'Coral Sea' (EA)	MDun SLdr SReu
	'Corany' (A)	SLdr
	coriaceum	GGGa LMil NPen SLdr WCwm
	- R 120	NPen
	'Corneille' (G/d) ♀H4	CSBt LMil SLdr SReu
	'Cornish Cracker'	SLdr
	Cornish Cross Group	LHyd SLdr SReu
	Cornish Early Red Group	see *R.* Smithii Group
	'Cornish Red'	see *R.* Smithii Group
	Cornubia Group	SLdr
	'Corona'	SHea
	'Coronation Day'	LMil SHea SLdr SReu
	'Coronation Lady' (K)	ENot
	coryanum	GGGa
	- KR 5775	LMil
	- KR 6315	LMil
	- 'Chelsea Chimes'	LMil NPen SLdr

'Cosmopolitan'	CWri ENot LCro LMil LRHS MAsh MBar MDun MGos SLdr SPoG SReu
Cote Group (A)	SLdr
'Cotton Candy'	LMil
'Countess of Athlone'	SLdr
'Countess of Derby'	MDun SHea SReu
'Countess of Haddington' ♀H2	CBcs ISea LMil MDun SLdr
'Countess of Stair'	WFar WPic
'County of York'	see *R.* 'Catalode'
cowanianum	GGGa
Cowslip Group	CSam CTri CWri LMil LRHS MAsh MBar MDun MGos MLea NPen NPri SHBN SLdr SReu
coxianum C&H 475B	GGGa
'Cranbourne'	LHyd SReu
'Crane' ♀H4	EPfP GGGa GQui LMil LRHS MAsh MDun NPri WGer
crassum	see *R. maddenii* subsp. *crassum*
'Cream Crest'	GQui MDun SHBN WFar
'Cream Glory'	LHyd
'Creamy Chiffon'	CWri GGGa MDun MGos MLea WBVN
§ 'Creeping Jenny'	ECho GGGa GGar LHyd MBar MDun SLdr WBod
cremastum	see *R. campylogynum* Cremastum Group
'Crest' ♀H3-4	GGGa LHyd LMil MAsh MDun MGos SHBN SLdr
'Crete'	LMil MDun SReu
'Crimson Pippin'	LMil
crinigerum	GGGa LHyd LMil MDun
- JN 756	GGGa
'Crinoline' (K)	SLdr SReu
'Croceum Tricolor' (G)	CSdC
Crossbill Group	CBcs
* ***crossium***	SReu
'Crosswater Belle'	LMil
'Crosswater Red' (K)	LMil
cubittii	see *R. veitchianum* Cubittii Group
cucullatum	see *R. roxieanum* var. *cucullatum*
cumberlandense (A)	GGGa IDee LMil
- 'Sunlight' (A)	LMil MBri
cuneatum	GGGa
'Cunningham's Blush'	GGGa SHBN
'Cunningham's Sulphur'	see *R. caucasicum* 'Cunningham's Sulphur'
'Cunningham's White'	CBcs CSBt CSam CTri CWri ELan ENot EPfP GGGa LCro LMil LRHS MAsh MBar MDun MGos NPen SLdr SPer SPoG SReu WBod WFar
'Cupcake'	see *R.* 'Delp's Cupcake'
'Cupreum Ardens' (G)	CSdC
'Curlew' ♀H4	CDoC CSBt ECho ENot EPfP GEdr GGGa ISea LMil LRHS MAsh MBar MBri MDun MGos NHol NMen NPen SHBN SLdr SPoG SReu SSpi WBVN WBod WFar
'Cutie'	CBcs
cyanocarpum	GGGa LMil
- Bu 294	GGGa
'Cynthia' ♀H4	CBcs CDoC CSBt CWri ECho EPfP GGGa LHyd LMil MBar MBri MDun MGos NPen SHBN SLdr SPer SReu SSta WBVN WBod
'Daimio' (EA)	LHyd
'Dairymaid'	SReu
dalhousieae	GGGa SLdr
§ - var. ***rhabdotum***	GGGa SLdr
Damaris Group	SLdr
'Damaris Logan'	see *R.* 'Logan Damaris'
'Damozel'	SHea SLdr
'Daphne Daffarn' **new**	SHea
'Daphne Millais'	SHea SLdr

'Dartmoor Blush'	SReu
'Dartmoor Pixie'	SReu
'Dartmoor Rose'	SReu
dasycladum	see *R. selense* subsp. *dasycladum*
dasypetalum	ECho MBar MDun NDlv
dauricum	SLdr
- 'Arctic Pearl'	GGGa SLdr
- 'Midwinter' ♀H4	GGGa LHyd SLdr
* 'Dauricum Splendens'	WBod
'David' ♀H4	LHyd SHea SLdr SReu
davidii	GGGa LMil SLdr
- AC 4100	LMil
- EN 4213	GGGa
davidsonianum ♀H3-4	GGGa LHyd LMil SLdr SSpi WPic
- EGM 351	LMil
- Bodnant form	LMil MDun
- 'Caerhays Blotched'	SLdr
- 'Caerhays Pink'	GGGa SLdr
- 'Ruth Lyons'	LMil
'Daviesii' (G) ♀H4	CBcs CDoC CSBt CSam CSdC CTri CWri ECho ENot EPfP GGGa GQui IDee LHyd LMil LRHS MAsh MBri MDun MLea SBod SLdr SPer SPoG SReu SSpi WBVN WBrE WCFE WFar
'Dawn's Delight'	SLdr
* 'Day Dawn'	SReu
'Day Dream'	SHea SReu
'Daybreak' (K)	GQui
N 'Daybreak' (EA/d)	see *R.* 'Kirin'
'Dear Grandad' (EA)	CTri LMil LRHS NPri SCoo
'Dearest' (EA)	LRHS NPri
N 'Debutante'	ENot NHol WBod
decorum ♀H4	CDoC GGGa GKev IDee LHyd LMil MDun NPen SLdr SReu WGer WPic
- Bu 286	NHol
- C&H 7023	GGGa
- 'Cox's Uranium Green'	SReu
§ - subsp. ***diaprepes***	LMil
- - 'Gargantua'	LMil SReu
- late-flowering	LMil
- pink-flowered	SLdr
decorum x ***yakushimanum***	SLdr SReu
degronianum	GGGa
§ - subsp. ***degronianum***	LMil SLdr
- - 'Gerald Loder'	LHyd
§ - subsp. ***heptamerum***	GGGa MDun
- - 'Ho Emma'	LMil MDun
§ - - var. ***kyomaruense***	LMil
- - 'Oki Island'	LMil
- 'Metternianum'	see *R. degronianum* subsp. *heptamerum* var. *kyomaruense*
- 'Rae's Delight'	LMil
dekatanum	GGGa
deleiense	see *R. tephropeplum*
'Delicatissimum' (O)	CBcs CWri ECho GGGa GQui MAsh MLea NLar SBod SLdr SPer WBVN
§ 'Delp's Cupcake'	NLar
'Delta'	NBlu
dendricola	SLdr
- KW 20981	GGGa
dendrocharis	GGGa
- CC&H 4012	GGGa
- Cox 5016	GGGa NHol WAbe
- 'Glendoick Gem'	GGGa
* 'Denny's Rose' (A)	LMil MDun SReu
'Denny's Scarlet'	MDun SReu
'Denny's White'	LMil MDun NHol SLdr SReu WBod
denudatum C&H 70102	GGGa
- C&H 7118	GGGa
- EGM 294	LMil
- SEH 334	LMil

	desquamatum	see *R. rubiginosum* Desquamatum Group
	x ***detonsum*** F 13784	SLdr
	'Devisiperbile' (EA)	SLdr
	'Diadem' (V)	MAsh
	(Diamant Group) 'Diamant Enzianblau' (EA)	LMil
	- 'Diamant Purpur'	see *R.* Diamant Group purple
	- 'Diamant Rot'	see *R.* Diamant Group red
	- lilac-flowered (EA)	ECho LMil MLea
	- pink-flowered (EA)	ECho GCrs LMil MDun MGos MLea SLdr SReu
§	- purple-flowered (EA)	ECho GCrs LMil MDun MGos MLea NEgg SLdr WBod
§	- red-flowered (EA)	ECho GCrs LMil MDun MLea SLdr WBod
	- rosy red-flowered (EA)	ECho
	- salmon pink-flowered (EA)	LMil
	- white-flowered (EA)	ECho GCrs MDun MLea SLdr
	'Diana Pearson'	LHyd
	diaprepes	see *R. decorum* subsp. *diaprepes*
	dichroanthum	GGGa LHyd LMil MDun SLdr SReu
	- CCH&H 8198	GGGa
§	- subsp. ***apodectum***	GGGa LMil
	- subsp. ***dichroanthum***	LMil
	- - SBEC 545	GGGa
§	- subsp. ***scyphocalyx***	GGGa LMil SLdr
	- - F 24546	GGGa
	- - Farrer 1024	GGGa
	- subsp. ***scyphocalyx*** x 'Tally Ho'	SLdr
	- subsp. ***septentroniale***	GGGa
	- - JN 575	GGGa
	didymum	see *R. sanguineum* subsp. *didymum*
	'Dietrich'	WFar
	dignabile C&V 9569	GGGa
	- KR 5385	LMil
	dilatatum	LMil
	- 'Satsumense'	NPen
	dimitrum	MDun
	'Diny Dee'	MGos
	'Diorama' (Vs)	SReu SSta
	'Directeur Charles Baumann'	SLdr
§	'Directeur Moerlands' (M)	SLdr
	discolor	see *R. fortunei* subsp. *discolor*
	'Doc'	CBcs ENot EPfP MAsh MBar MDun MGos NBlu NDlv SLdr SReu WFar
	'Doctor A. Blok'	SLdr
	'Doctor Ernst Schäle'	GGGa
	'Doctor H.C. Dresselhuys'	LMil MBar SHBN
	'Doctor Herman Sleumer' (V)	GGGa
	'Doctor M. Oosthoek' (M) ♀H4	CSBt SLdr SReu
	'Doctor Stocker'	NPen
	'Doctor V.H. Rutgers'	MBar MDun WFar
	'Don Giovanni'	NLar
	'Don Quixote' (K)	CSdC MAsh
	'Doncaster'	ENot MBar MGos SHBN SPer WFar
	'Dopey' ♀H4	CBcs CDoC CSBt CWri ECho EMui ENot EPfP GGGa GGar LHyd LMil LRHS MAsh MBar MBri MDun MGos MLea NDlv NHol NPen SHBN SLdr SPoG SReu WBVN
	'Dora Amateis' ♀H4	CBcs ECho ENot GGGa LMil LRHS MAsh MBar MGos NHol NPen NPri SLdr SPer SReu WPic
	Dormouse Group	CBcs CDoC ECho GGGa LMil MAsh SLdr SReu WBVN
	'Dorothea'	SLdr
	'Dorset Sandy' (EA)	LMil
	'Dörte Reich'	GGGa
	doshongense	see *R. aganniphum* var. *aganniphum* Doshongense Group
	'Double Beauty' (EA/d)	SReu SSta
	'Double Damask' (K/d) ♀H4	SLdr
	'Double Date' (d)	CDoC SLdr
	double yellow	SLdr
	'Douglas McEwan'	MDun SLdr
	'Dracula' (K)	GGGa
	Dragonfly Group	SReu
	Dragonfly Group x ***serotinum***	SLdr
	'Drake's Mountain'	ECho MBar MDun MLea
	'Drapa' (EA)	GGGa
	'Dreamland' ♀H4	CBcs CDoC CSBt CWri ECho ENot LMil LRHS MAsh MDun MGos MLea NLar NPen SLdr SReu WBod WFar
	'Driven Snow' (EA)	SLdr
	drumonium	see *R. telmateium*
	'Drury Lane' (K)	GQui LMil
	dryophyllum misapplied	see *R. phaeochrysum* var. *levistratum*
	'Duchess of Teck'	SReu
	'Dusky Dawn'	SLdr
	'Dusky Orange'	MDun SReu
	'Dusty'	MDun
	'Dusty Miller'	ECho ENot LHyd LRHS MAsh MBar MDun MGos NDlv NLar NPen SHBN SLdr WBod
	'Earl of Athlone'	SHea SReu
	'Earl of Donoughmore'	MDun SReu SSta
	'Early Beni' (EA)	LHyd
	'Ebony Pearl'	CBcs CWri ECho GBin GGGa ISea MGos WBVN
	eclecteum	LMil MDun SLdr
	- Cox 6054	GGGa
	- 'Rowallane Yellow'	SLdr
§	***edgeworthii*** ♀H2-3	GGGa ISea SLdr WAbe
	- KC 0106	GGGa
	edgeworthii x ***leucaspis***	CBcs
	'Edith Bosley'	GGGa
	'Edith Mackworth Praed'	SReu
	Edmondii Group	LHyd
	'Edna Bee' (EA)	LMil
	'Effner'	LMil LRHS
	'Egret' ♀H4	CDoC ECho GEdr GGGa GGar LMil MAsh MBar MDun MGos MLea NLar SLdr WAbe WThu
	'Ehrengold'	LMil SPoG
	'Eider'	GGGa MAsh SLdr SReu
	'Eileen'	LMil SReu
	'El Camino'	ECho ISea LMil NPen SHBN SLdr
	'El Greco'	SLdr
	Eldorado Group	GQui
	'Eleanor' (EA)	WBod
	Electra Group	see *R. augustinii* Electra Group
	elegantulum	GGGa LMil MDun NPen
	'Elfenbein'	see *R.* 'Bruns Elfenbein'
	'Elfin Gold'	SReu
	'Elisabeth Hobbie' ♀H4	ECho GEdr GGGa LMil MAsh MBar MDun WMoo
	Elizabeth Group	CBcs CDoC GGGa LHyd LMil LRHS MAsh MBar SBod SHBN SLdr SPer SReu WFar
N	'Elizabeth' (EA)	CSBt EPfP MGos NWCA SLdr
	'Elizabeth'	CTri ECho MGos NHol NPri WBod
	'Elizabeth de Rothschild'	MDun SLdr
	'Elizabeth Jenny'	see *R.* 'Creeping Jenny'
	'Elizabeth Lockhart'	ECho GEdr GGGa GQui MBar MDun MGos WBod
	'Elizabeth of Glamis'	GGGa
	'Elizabeth Red Foliage'	CDoC CTri GGGa LHyd LMil LRHS MAsh MDun SPer SReu

	'Elizabeth' x ***yakushimanum***	GGGa
	elliottii	GGGa SReu
	Elsae Group	SLdr SReu
	'Else Frye'	GGGa
	'Elsie Lee' (EA/d) ♀$^{H3-4}$	CTrh ECho GGGa LMil MAsh SLdr
	'Elsie Pratt' (A)	MBar NHol
	'Elsie Straver'	MDun NHol SHBN SLdr SReu
	'Elsie Watson'	GGGa LMil
	'Elspeth'	LHyd
	'Emasculum'	LMil SLdr SReu
	Emerald Isle Group	SReu
	'Emma Williams'	CBcs
	'Endsleigh Pink'	LMil
	'English Roseum'	SLdr
	'Erato'	GGGa
	eriocarpum 'Jitsugetsuse' (EA)	LHyd
	eriogynum	see *R. facetum*
	eritimum	see *R. anthosphaerum*
	'Ernest Inman'	LHyd LMil SLdr
	erosum	GGGa SLdr
N	'Esmeralda'	CMac CTrG
	Ethel Group	SLdr
	'Etna' (EA)	SLdr
	'Etta Burrows'	CWri GGGa MDun
	'Euan Cox'	GGGa NMen
	euchroum	NPen
	eudoxum	GGGa NPen
	'Eunice Updike' (EA)	LHyd
	'Europa'	SReu
	eurysiphon	NPen
	- Arduaine form	GGGa
	'Evening Fragrance' (A)	SReu
	'Everbloom' (EA)	SLdr
	'Everest' (EA)	ENot LHyd LMil MAsh NLar SLdr SPoG WBod
	'Everestianum'	GGGa MBar SHea SLdr
	'Everitt Hershey' (A)	SLdr
§	'Everlasting'	SReu
	Everred = '851C'	GGGa
	'Evita' (EA)	GGGa
	exasperatum KC 0116	GGGa
	- KC 0126	GGGa
	- KW 8250	GGGa
	'Exbury Calstocker'	LMil
	'Exbury Naomi'	LHyd LMil SLdr
	'Exbury White' (K)	GQui
	'Excalibur'	GGGa
	excellens	LMil WCwm
	- AC 146	GGGa
	- SF 92074	ISea
	- SF 92079	ISea
	- SF 92303	ISea
	eximium	see *R. falconeri* subsp. ***eximium***
	'Exquisitum' (O) ♀^{H4}	CDoC CWri ECho EPfP GGGa LMil MBri MLea NLar SLdr WBVN
	exquisitum	see *R. oreotrephes* Exquisitum Group
	faberi	GGGa LMil SLdr
	- subsp. ***prattii***	see *R. prattii*
	'Fabia' ♀^{H3}	CDoC CMac GGGa LHyd LMil MAsh MDun SHea
	Fabia Group	MDun NPen SLdr
	'Fabia Roman Pottery'	MDun
§	'Fabia Tangerine'	MDun MLea SReu WBod
	'Fabia Waterer'	CDoC LMil SLdr
§	***facetum***	GGGa LMil MDun
	- AC 3049	LMil
	'Faggetter's Favourite' ♀^{H4}	LMil MDun SHea SReu SSta
	Fairy Light Group	LMil SLdr
	'Falcon'	see *R.* (Hawk Group) 'Hawk Falcon'
	falconeri ♀$^{H3-4}$	CHEx GGGa IDee ISea LMil LRHS MDun NPen SLdr SPer WGer
	- from East Nepal	MDun
§	- subsp. ***eximium***	GGGa LMil MDun
	'Fanal' (K)	MBri
	'Fanny'	see *R.* 'Pucella'
	'Fantastica' ♀^{H4}	CDoC ELan EPfP GGGa LHyd LMil LRHS MAsh MBri MDun NLar NPen SReu WBod
	fargesii	see *R. oreodoxa* var. *fargesii*
	'Fashion'	CTrG SLdr
	fastigiatum	ECho GCrs GEdr ISea LMil MBar MLea NLAp NPen
	- C&H 7159	GGGa
	- SBEC 804/4869	GGGa MDun WThu
§	- 'Blue Steel' ♀^{H4}	CBcs CDoC CTri CWri LMil MAsh MDun MGos SPlb SPoG SReu WPat
	'Fastuosum Flore Pleno' (d) ♀^{H4}	CBcs CSBt CWri ENot EPfP GBin GGGa LHyd LMil MBar MDun MGos MLea NPen SLdr SPer SPoG SReu SSta WFar
	faucium	GGGa LMil
	- KR 3465 from Pe, Doshang La	LMil
	- KR 3771	LMil
	- KR 5024	GGGa
	- KR 5040	LMil
	- KR 6229	LMil
	'Favorite' (EA)	LHyd NPen SLdr
	'Fedora' (EA)	CBcs SLdr
	'Fénelon' (G)	SLdr
	'Fernanda Sarmento' (A)	SReu
	ferrugineum	GGGa LHyd LMil MBar MGos WBod
*	- ***compactum***	ECho
	- 'Plenum' (d)	MDun
	'Feuerwerk' (K)	NEgg SLdr
	FH134	SLdr
	fictolacteum	see *R. rex* subsp. *fictolacteum*
	Fire Bird Group	SHea SLdr
	'Fire Rim'	GGGa
	'Fireball' (K) ♀^{H4}	CBcs CDoC CSam CTri CWri ECho ENot GGGa LHyd LMil MAsh MBri MLea NDlv SBod SLdr SPer WMoo
	'Fireball' (hybrid)	SLdr
	Firedrake Group	SReu
	'Firefly' (K)	ENot
	'Firefly' (EA)	see *R.* 'Hexe'
	'Fireglow'	CSBt CSdC SLdr WFar
	'Firelight' (hybrid)	LMil
	'Fireman Jeff'	SLdr
	'Firetail' **new**	SHea
	'Flaming Bronze'	SReu
	'Flaming Gold' **new**	GGGa
	Flamingo Group	SLdr
§	***flammeum*** (A)	GKev LMil
	'Flanagan's Daughter'	LMil LRHS
	'Flautando' **new**	LMil
	Flava Group	see *R.* Volker Group
	flavidum	CBcs GGGa SLdr
	- Cox 6143	GGGa
	- 'Album'	SLdr WBod WThu
	fletcherianum	LHyd
	- 'Yellow Bunting'	GGGa
	fleuryi KR 3286	GGGa
§	***flinckii***	GGGa LHyd LMil MDun WCwm
	- CH&M 3080	GGGa
	floccigerum	GGGa LMil SLdr
	'Floradora' (M)	SReu
	'Floriade' x ***yakushimanum***	SLdr
	floribundum	LMil NPen SLdr WCwm
	- EGM 294	LMil
	- 'Swinhoe'	SLdr
	'Florida' (EA/d) ♀$^{H3-4}$	CMac LMil MAsh SLdr SReu WBod WFar WMoo
	'Flower Arranger' (EA)	LMil LRHS NPri SCoo

formosanum	GGGa
formosum	CBcs GGGa GQui SLdr
§ - var. ***formosum*** Iteaphyllum Group	GGGa WBod
- - 'Khasia'	GGGa
- var. ***inaequale*** C&H 301	GGGa
forrestii	GGGa NPen
- KR 6113	LMil
- subsp. ***forrestii***	LMil
- - Repens Group	GGGa GKev LMil SLdr
- - - 'Seinghku'	GGGa
- Tumescens Group	GGGa
- - C&V 9517	GGGa
'Fortune' **new**	LHyd
Fortune Group	SLdr
fortunei	GGGa LHyd LMil LRHS MDun SLdr SReu
§ - subsp. ***discolor*** 𝕐H4	GGGa LMil MDun NPen SLdr WGer
- - PW 34	GGGa
§ - - Houlstonii Group	LMil SLdr
- - - 'John R. Elcock'	CDoC LMil
- subsp. ***discolor*** x 'Lodauric Iceberg'	SLdr
- 'Foxy'	SLdr
- 'Lu-Shan'	MDun
- 'Mrs Butler'	see *R. fortunei* 'Sir Charles Butler'
§ - 'Sir Charles Butler'	CDoC LMil MDun SLdr
'Fox Hunter'	SLdr
fragariiflorum	ISea
- C&V 9519	GGGa
- LS&E 15828	GGGa
'Fragrans'	SLdr
'Fragrant Star' (A)	GGGa SLdr
'Fragrantissimum' 𝕐H2-3	CBcs CDoC CTrG CWri GGGa GGar ISea LHyd LMil MDun MRav NLar NPen SKHP SLdr WBod WPic
'Francesca'	GGGa
Francis Hanger (Reuthe's) Group	SLdr SReu
'Frank Baum'	SReu
'Frank Galsworthy' 𝕐H4	LMil NLar SReu
'Frans van der Bom' (M)	MBri SLdr
'Fraseri' (M)	SLdr
'Fred Hamilton'	CWri
'Fred Nutbeam' (EA)	LMil
'Fred Peste'	CDoC ECho LMil MAsh MBri MDun MGos MLea NPen SReu
'Fred Wynniatt'	LHyd SLdr
'Fred Wynniatt Stanway'	see *R.* 'Stanway'
'Frere Organ' (G)	SLdr
'Freya' (R/d)	LMil SLdr
'Fridoline' (EA)	GGGa
'Frieda' (EA)	SLdr
'Frigata' (A)	SLdr
'Frilled Petticoats'	SReu
'Frilly Lemon' (K/d)	CDoC MDun NLar SLdr
'Frosted Orange' (EA)	LMil MAsh SLdr
'Frosthexe'	GGGa WAbe
'Frühlingstraum'	LHyd
'Fulbrook'	LMil
fulgens	GGGa LMil MDun NPen
fulvum 𝕐H4	CDoC GGGa IDee LHyd LMil MDun NPen SLdr SReu SSta
- AC 3083	LMil
- subsp. ***fulvoides***	LMil
- - Cox 6532	GGGa
§ 'Fumiko' (EA)	CSBt ECho ENot LMil LRHS MAsh MBar MDun MLea WFar
'Furnivall's Daughter' 𝕐H4	CSBt CWri ECho EPfP GGGa LHyd LMil MBar MDun MGos NLar NPen SHea SLdr SPer SReu SSta WFar
'Fusilier'	SHea SReu
'Gabriella' **new**	MAsh
'Gabrielle Hill' (EA)	CDoC ENot MAsh MGos SLdr
'Gaiety' (EA)	LMil SReu
'Galactic'	SLdr
galactinum	LMil MDun
- EN 3537	GGGa
'Galathea' (EA)	CDoC
'Gandy Dancer'	CWri MBri MDun SLdr
'Garden State Glow' (EA/d)	SLdr
'Garibaldi' **new**	SHea
'Gartendirektor Glocker'	CWri ECho GGGa MAsh MDun NPen SLdr
'Gartendirektor Rieger' 𝕐H4	CWri GGGa LMil MAsh MDun SHea SReu
'Gauche' (A)	GQui SLdr
'Gaugin'	GQui
Gaul Group	SLdr
'Gay Lady'	SLdr
'Geisha' (EA)	MBar
'Geisha Lilac'	see *R.* 'Hanako'
'Geisha Orange'	see *R.* 'Satschiko'
'Geisha Pink'	see *R.* 'Momoko'
'Geisha Purple'	see *R.* 'Fumiko'
'Geisha Red'	see *R.* 'Kazuko'
'Geisha White'	see *R.* 'Hisako'
'Gena Mae' (A/d)	GGGa SLdr
'General Eisenhower'	CSBt SHea SReu
'General Eric Harrison'	SLdr
'General Practitioner'	NPen SLdr
'General Sir John du Cane'	SHea
'General Wavell' (EA)	CMac SLdr
'Gene's Favourite'	SReu
genestierianum CC&H 8080	GGGa
'Genoveva'	LMil
'Geoffroy Millais'	LMil
'Georg Arends' (Ad)	LRHS NPri SLdr
'George Haslam'	SLdr
'George Hyde' (EA)	ENot LMil LRHS MGos SCoo
'George Reynolds' (K)	ECho LHyd LMil MLea SLdr
'George's Delight'	GGGa MAsh MLea WMoo
'Georgette'	LHyd SLdr
§ x ***geraldii***	SLdr
'Germania'	CDoC LMil LRHS MAsh MBar SPoG SReu WBod
Gertrud Schäle Group	CTri ECho GEdr MBar MDun SHea SReu
Gibraltar Group	CTri
'Gibraltar' (K) 𝕐H4	CBcs CDoC CSBt CTri CWri ENot EPfP GGGa LMil MAsh MBar MBri MDun MGos MLea NBlu NPri SBod SLdr SPer SReu SSta WBod WFar WMoo
giganteum	see *R. protistum* var. *giganteum*
'Gilbert Mullie' (EA)	LMil MAsh MBri NBlu
I 'Gill's Arboreum'	SLdr
'Gill's Crimson'	SHea SLdr SReu
'Ginger' (K)	CSBt LMil SLdr
'Ginny Gee' 𝕐H4	CDoC CSBt CWri ECho ENot EPfP GCrs GEdr GGGa GGar LHyd LMil LRHS MAsh MBar MBri MDun MGos MLea NHol NMen NPen SLdr SPoG SReu SSta WBod WFar
'Gipsy King' **new**	SHea SLdr
§ 'Girard's Hot Shot' (EA)	CTrh ECho ENot GQui LRHS MAsh MGos SLdr SReu WBVN WFar
'Girard's Hot Shot' variegated (EA/v)	GGGa MAsh
'Glacier' (EA)	MGos SLdr
glanduliferum C&H 7131	GGGa
- EGM 347	LMil
- PW 044 from Miao Miao Shan	LMil
glaucophyllum	GGGa LMil MDun NPen SLdr WAbe WBod
- B&SWJ 2638	WCru
- var. ***album***	GGGa

- Borde Hill form	LMil
'Glendoick Butterscotch'	GGGa
'Glendoick Dream' (EA)	GGGa
'Glendoick Ermine' (EA)	GGGa
'Glendoick Frolic'	GGGa
'Glendoick Garnet' (EA)	GGGa
'Glendoick Glacier'	GGGa
'Glendoick Goblin' (EA)	GGGa
'Glendoick Gold'	GGGa
'Glendoick Honeydew'	GGGa
'Glendoick Mystique'	GGGa
'Glendoick Petticoats'	GGGa
'Glendoick Ruby'	GGGa
'Glendoick Silver' **new**	GGGa
'Glendoick Vanilla'	GGGa
'Glendoick Velvet'	GGGa
'Gletschernacht'	CWri LMil
glischrum	GGGa NPen
- subsp. ***glischroides***	GGGa LMil
- subsp. ***glischrum***	GGGa
§ - subsp. ***rude***	GGGa NPen
- - C&V 9524	GGGa
globigerum	see *R. alutaceum* var. *alutaceum* Globigerum Group
glomerulatum	see *R. yungningense* Glomerulatum Group
'Gloria'	see *R.* 'Bruns Gloria'
'Gloria Mundi' (G)	SHea
'Gloriana'	WBod
'Glory of Littleworth' (Ad)	LMil WPic
'Glowing Embers' (K)	CDoC CSam CTri CWri ECho ENot LMil LRHS MAsh MBri MDun MLea NHol NPri SLdr SPur SReu WBVN WCwm
Goblin Group	SLdr
'Gog' (K)	CSBt
'Gold Mohur'	SLdr SReu
'Gold Tee'	LHyd
§ 'Goldbukett'	GGGa LHyd LMil NLar
'Golden Bee'	GGGa NHol
'Golden Belle'	CWri MAsh
Golden Bouquet	see *R.* 'Goldbukett'
'Golden Clipper'	LHyd
'Golden Coach'	CDoC CWri ECho MDun MGos MLea SLdr SPer WBVN
'Golden Eagle' (K)	CDoC ECho LHyd LMil LRHS MAsh MDun MGos NEgg SLdr WBVN
'Golden Flare' (K)	CBcs CDoC CSam CWri ECho MAsh MBri MLea SLdr WBrE WMoo
'Golden Fleece'	SReu
'Golden Gate'	CDoC ECho LMil MDun SReu
'Golden Horn' (K)	GQui
'Golden Lights' (A)	CDoC CWri ECho LMil MBri MDun MGos SBod SLdr WBVN
'Golden Orfe'	LHyd
Golden Oriole Group	NHol
§ - 'Talavera'	SSpi
'Golden Princess'	LMil MDun NHol
'Golden Ruby'	MGos SPer
'Golden Splendour'	LMil
'Golden Sunlight'	see *R.* 'Directeur Moerlands'
'Golden Sunset' (K)	CSdC ECho ENot LHyd LMil MAsh MBar MBri MDun MLea NEgg NHol NLar SLdr SPur
'Golden Torch' 𝕐^{H4}	CAbP CBcs CMHG CSBt CWri ECho ENot EPfP GGar LHyd LMil LRHS MAsh MBri MDun MGos MLea NDlv NPen SHBN SLdr SPer SPoG SReu SSta WBVN WBod
'Golden Wedding'	CBcs CDoC CSBt CWri ECho ENot ISea LHyd LMil MAsh MDun MGos MLea NLar SLdr WBVN
'Golden Wit'	ECho MAsh MDun
'Goldfinger'	MDun MGos
'Goldflamme'	SLdr
'Goldflimmer' (v)	CDoC EMil ENot GGGa LMil LRHS MAsh MGos MLan MLea NBlu NPri SLdr SPoG SReu WFar
'Goldfort'	SReu
'Goldika'	LMil
'Goldkrone' 𝕐^{H4}	CDoC CWri ECho ENot EPfP GGGa LHyd LMil LRHS MAsh MDun MGos MLea NLar SLdr SPer SPoG SReu
Goldschatz = 'Goldprinz'	GGGa LMil
'Goldstrike'	LMil SLdr
'Goldsworth Crimson'	LHyd
'Goldsworth Orange'	CSBt CWri GGGa MAsh MGos SBod SLdr SReu
'Goldsworth Pink'	SReu
'Goldsworth Yellow'	CSBt MGos SReu
'Golfer'	CWri GGGa LMil MLea
'Gomer Waterer' 𝕐^{H4}	CDoC CSBt CSam CWri ECho ENot EPfP GGGa ISea LHyd LMil LRHS MBar MBri MDun MGos MLea NBlu NPen SBod SLdr SPer SPoG SReu SSta WBVN WBod WFar
gongshanense **new**	GGGa
'Gordon Jones'	GGGa
'Govenianum' (Ad)	SLdr
'Grace Seabrook'	CDoC CSam CTri CWri ECho ENot GGGa LHyd MDun MGos NPri SLdr SPer SReu WBVN
gracilentum (V)	GGGa
'Graciosum' (O)	SReu
'Graf Lennart'	LMil
'Graham Thomas'	LMil SReu
'Grand Slam'	CDoC ECho LMil MDun MLea NPen WBVN
grande	GGGa LMil NPen SLdr
- KC 0105	GGGa
- pink-flowered	NPen
'Grandeur Triomphante' (G)	CSdC SReu
gratum	see *R. basilicum*
'Graziella'	GGGa LMil
'Greensleeves'	CDoC LMil LRHS
'Greenway' (EA)	CBcs SLdr
'Grenadier' **new**	SHea
'Greta' (EA)	LHyd
'Gretzel'	NLar SReu
griersonianum	GGGa LHyd LMil MDun WGer WPic
griersonianum x ***yakushimanum***	SLdr
griffithianum	CWri GGGa SLdr
'Gristede' 𝕐^{H4}	CDoC ECho LMil LRHS MAsh MDun NHol SLdr SReu WBVN
groenlandicum	see *Ledum groenlandicum*
'Grosclaude'	CMac SHea
'Grouse' x ***keiskei*** var. ***ozawae*** 'Yaku Fairy'	ECho
'Grumpy'	CBcs CBrm CDoC CSBt CWri ECho EMui ENot GGGa LHyd LMil LRHS MAsh MBar MGos NDlv NPen SHBN SLdr SReu WBod
'Guelder Rose'	SLdr
'Gumpo' (EA)	CBcs CMac SLdr WBod
'Gumpo Pink' (EA)	SLdr
'Gumpo White' (EA)	ENot LCro LRHS MAsh MGos
'Gundula' **new**	LMil
'Gwenda' (EA)	CTri LHyd SLdr
'Gwillt-king'	WCwm
'H.H. Hume' (EA)	SLdr
habrotrichum	GGGa LMil
'Hachmann's Anastasia' **new**	LMil
'Hachmann's Brasilia'	LMil LRHS MAsh SReu
'Hachmann's Charmant'	GGGa LMil

	'Hachmann's Constanze'	LMil
	'Hachmann's Diadem'	LMil LRHS
	'Hachmann's Eskimo'	LMil LRHS MAsh
	'Hachmann's Feuerschein'	LMil NBlu NLar
	'Hachmann's Kabarett'	LMil MDun
	'Hachmann's Marianne' **new**	LMil
	'Hachmann's Marlis' ♀H4	ENot LHyd LMil MAsh SReu
§	'Hachmann's Polaris' ♀H4	ENot LHyd LMil MBri MDun WBod
	'Hachmann's Porzellan'	EMil LMil NLar
§	'Hachmann's Rokoko' (EA)	ECho GGGa LMil
	haematodes	GGGa LHyd LMil MDun NPen SRms
	- CLD 1283	LMil
	- 'Blood Red'	SLdr
§	- subsp. ***chaetomallum***	GGGa LMil SLdr
	- - JN 493	GGGa
	- subsp. ***haemotodes***	LMil
	- - SBEC 585	GGGa
	'Haida Gold'	SLdr SReu
	'Halfdan Lem'	CBcs CDoC CDul ECho GGGa ISea LHyd MAsh MBri MDun MGos MLea NPen SHBN SLdr SPer SReu SSta WBVN
	'Hallelujah'	MAsh
	'Halopeanum'	SHea SLdr
	'Hamlet' (M)	LMil
	'Hana-asobi' (EA)	LHyd SLdr WBod
§	'Hanako' (EA)	ECho LMil LRHS MBar MDun MGos MLea NDlv WBod
	hanceanum	SLdr
	- 'Canton Consul'	GGGa LHyd
	- Nanum Group	GGGa
	'Hansel'	CDoC ECho GQui LMil MAsh MDun NLar WFar
	haofui Guiz 75	GGGa
	Happy Group	ECho SHBN
	'Hardijzer Beauty' (Ad)	SLdr
	hardyi	see *R. augustinii* subsp. *hardyi*
	'Harkwood Premiere'	GGGa
	'Harkwood Red' (EA)	LHyd SLdr
	Harmony Group	SLdr
	'Harry Tagg'	CTrG SLdr WAbe
	'Harumiji' (EA)	SLdr
	'Harvest Moon' (K)	MDun SCoo SLdr SReu
	'Harvest Moon' (hybrid)	MBar SReu
	'Hatsugiri' (EA)	CMac ENot LHyd LMil MBar SLdr SReu
	(Hawk Group) 'Hawk Buzzard'	SLdr
§	- 'Hawk Falcon'	SReu
	'Heather Macleod' (EA)	LHyd SLdr
	heatheriae	LMil
	- KR 6150	GGGa
	- KR 6158	GGGa
	- KR 6176	LMil
	- SF 99068	ISea
	heftii	NPen SLdr
	'Helen Close' (EA)	CTrh SLdr
	'Helen Curtis' (EA)	SReu
	'Helen Martin'	NLar
	'Helena Pratt' (Vs)	LMil
	'Helene Schiffner' ♀H4	GGGa LMil SReu
	heliolepis	GGGa LMil WPic
	- SF 489	ISea
	- SF 516	ISea
	- var. ***fumidum***	see *R. heliolepis* var. *heliolepis*
§	- var. ***heliolepis***	LMil
	- - CN&W 1038	ISea
	hemidartum	see *R. pocophorum* var. *hemidartum*
	hemitrichotum	WThu
	hemsleyanum	GGGa LMil MDun NPen SLdr
	heptamerum	see *R. degronianum* subsp. *heptamerum*

	'Herbert' (EA)	CMac
	'Heureuse Surprise' (G)	SLdr
§	'Hexe' (EA)	WBod
	'High Summer'	CDoC LMil WGer
	'Hilda Margaret'	SReu
	'Hilda Niblett' (EA)	ENot MGos
	'Hille' PBR	LMil
	'Hinamayo'	see *R.* 'Hinomayo'
	'Hino-crimson' (EA) ♀H3-4	CBcs CDoC CMac CSBt CTrG CTrh CTri ENot LMil LRHS MAsh MBar MBri MGos NHol SLdr SPer SReu SSta WFar
	'Hinode-giri' (EA)	CBcs CMac CSBt LHyd MAsh SLdr SReu WBod WFar WPic
	'Hinode-no-taka' (EA)	LHyd
N	'Hinomayo' (EA) ♀H3-4	CMac CSBt CTrG CTri EPfP GQui LHyd LMil MAsh MBar NPen SLdr SReu SSta WBod WPic
	'Hino-scarlet'	see *R.* 'Campfire'
	'Hino-tsukasa' (EA)	SLdr
	hippophaeoides	CDoC LMil MDun NMen NPen SLdr WAbe WFar
	- F 22197a	SLdr
	- Yu 13845	GGGa LMil MDun
	- 'Bei-ma-shan'	see *R. hippophaeoides* 'Haba Shan'
	- 'Glendoick Iceberg'	GGGa
§	- 'Haba Shan' ♀H4	ECho GGGa LMil MDun
	hirsutum	GGGa LHyd LMil SReu WBod
	- f. ***albiflorum***	GGGa SReu
	- 'Flore Pleno' (d)	ECho GCrs GEdr GGGa GKev MBar MDun MLea
	hirtipes	GGGa LMil
	- C&V 9546	GGGa
	- KR 5059	LMil
	- KR 5219	LMil
§	'Hisako' (EA)	ECho MDun NDlv
	hodgsonii	CDoC GGGa IDee LHyd LMil MDun NHol SLdr SReu
	- B&SWJ 2656	WCru
	- TSS 42A	SLdr
	- TSS 9	SLdr
	'Holden'	WFar
	'Hollandia' (hybrid)	SHBN
	'Homebush' (K/d) ♀H4	CBcs CDoC CTri CWri ECho ENot EPfP GGGa LCro LHyd LMil LRHS MAsh MBar MBri MDun MGos MLea SLdr SPer SPoG SSta WBVN
	'Honey Butter' **new**	LMil
	'Honeysuckle' (K)	MBar NHol SLdr SReu WBod
	hongkongense	GGGa
§	'Ho-o' (EA)	CBcs NEgg NLar SLdr
	hookeri	CTrG LHyd LMil SReu
	- Tigh-na-Rudha form	GGGa
	'Hope Findlay'	LHyd
	'Hoppy'	CBcs CDoC CSBt CWri ENot GWCH LMil LRHS MAsh MDun MGos MLea NBlu NPen SLdr SPoG WBVN
	'Horizon Lakeside'	GGGa
	'Horizon Monarch' ♀H3-4	CDoC CWri GGGa LHyd LMil LRHS MDun WBod
	horlickianum	GGGa
	'Hortulanus H. Witte' (M)	CSBt SLdr SReu WFar
	'Hot Shot'	see *R.* 'Girard's Hot Shot'
	'Hot Shot Variegated' (EA/V)	CDoC
	'Hotei' ♀H4	CBcs CDoC CSBt CWri ECho EPfP GEdr GGGa LHyd LMil LRHS MAsh MBar MDun MGos NPen NPri SHBN SReu WBVN WBod WFar
	Hotspur Group (K)	LHyd
	'Hotspur' (K)	CSBt CSam CWri ECho GBin ISea MGos NLar SLdr SPer WBVN
	'Hotspur Red' (K) ♀H4	CDoC CDul LMil MAsh SReu
	'Hotspur Yellow' (K)	SReu

houlstonii	see *R. fortunei* subsp. *discolor* Houlstonii Group
huanum	LMil
- C&H 7073	GGGa
- EGM 316	LMil
'Hugh Koster'	CSBt MGos SLdr
'Hullaballoo'	LMil
'Humboldt'	LMil WFar
Humming Bird Group	CMHG ECho GEdr GGGa ISea LHyd MBar MDun MLea NHol SHBN SLdr SRms WBod
hunnewellianum	NPen
'Hussar'	CWri
'Hyde and Seek'	GQui
'Hydie' (EA/d)	ENot LMil LRHS MGos SCoo SPoG
'Hydon Amethyst'	LHyd
'Hydon Ben'	LHyd
'Hydon Comet'	LHyd
'Hydon Dawn' ♀H4	CDoC CWri ECho GGGa LHyd LMil MAsh MDun MGos MLea NDlv NLar NPen SHea SPer SReu SSta
'Hydon Glow'	LHyd
'Hydon Gold'	LHyd
'Hydon Haley'	LHyd
'Hydon Hunter' ♀H4	ECho LHyd LMil MLea NDlv NPen SHea SLdr SReu SSta
'Hydon Juliet'	LHyd
'Hydon Mist'	LHyd
'Hydon Pearl'	LHyd
'Hydon Pink'	SHea
'Hydon Rodney'	LHyd
'Hydon Salmon'	LHyd
'Hydon Velvet'	LHyd LMil SReu
hylaeum	NPen
- BASEX 9659	GGGa
Hyperion Group	LMil SReu SSta WFar
hyperythrum	GGGa LHyd LMil MDun SLdr
- ETOT 196	MDun
hypoglaucum 'Heane Wood'	see *R. argyrophyllum* subsp. *hypoglaucum* 'Heane Wood'
'Ice Cube'	ECho MBri MDun NLar WFar
'Ice Maiden'	SReu
'Iceberg'	see *R.* 'Lodauric Iceberg'
'Idealist'	CWri LMil SReu
'Idealist' x 'Victory'	SLdr
'Ightham Gold'	SReu
'Ightham Peach'	SReu
'Ightham Purple'	SReu
'Ightham Yellow'	MDun SHea SLdr SReu
'Igneum Novum' (G)	SReu
'Il Tasso' (R/d)	SLdr
§ 'Ilam Melford Lemon' (A)	LMil
§ 'Ilam Ming' (A)	LMil
'Ilam Violet'	LHyd LMil
'Imago' (K/d)	CSdC SLdr
§ 'Ima-shojo' (EA/d)	CSBt LHyd LMil LRHS MAsh SLdr
impeditum	CBcs CDoC CSBt CWib ECho ENot GGGa GKev GQui LHyd LRHS MAsh MBar MDun MGos MLea NLAp NMen NPen SLdr SPer SPoG SReu SSta WBVN WBrE WFar
- F 29268	GGGa
- 'Blue Steel'	see *R. fastigiatum* 'Blue Steel'
- 'Indigo'	MDun WAbe
- 'Pygmaeum'	GEdr WAbe WThu
- Reuthe's form	SReu
- 'Williams'	SLdr
imperator	see *R. uniflorum* var. *imperator*
'Impi'	NPen SReu
Impi Group	MDun NLar
'Inamorata'	SLdr
indicum (EA)	WBVN
§ - 'Balsaminiflorum' (EA/d)	CMac SLdr
§ - 'Macranthum' (EA)	LHyd SLdr WBod

x ***inopinum***	GGGa
insigne ♀H4	CDoC GGGa IDee LMil MDun NPen WGer
- Reuthe's form	SReu
insigne x ***yakushimanum***	SReu
x ***intermedium*** white	GGGa
Intrepid Group	SReu
intricatum	GGGa WAbe
Intrifast Group	GGGa LHyd NMen
iodes	see *R. alutaceum* var. *iodes*
'Irene Koster' (O) ♀H4	CSBt CWri ECho ENot EPfP GGGa LHyd LMil MAsh MBri MDun MLea NLar SLdr WBrE WCFE
'Irish Mist' **new**	GGGa
'Irohayama' (EA) ♀H3-4	CMac ECho GQui LHyd LMil MLea SLdr
irroratum	LMil SLdr
- subsp. ***irroratum*** C&H 7100	GGGa
* - subsp. ***kontumense*** var. ***ningyuenense*** EGM 339	LMil SLdr
- 'Langbianense' KR 3295	LMil
- 'Polka Dot'	GGGa LHyd LMil SLdr
'Isabel Pierce'	CWri LMil
Isabella Group	MAsh SLdr WFar
'Isabella Mangles'	LHyd
'Isola Bella'	GGGa
'Issho-no-haru' (EA) **new**	WBod
iteaphyllum	see *R. formosum* var. *formosum* Iteaphyllum Group
'Ivette' (EA)	CMac LHyd
Iviza Group	SReu
'Izayoi' (EA)	WBod
'J.C. Williams'	CBcs
'J.G. Millais'	SLdr
'J.J. de Vink' **new**	SHea
'J.M. de Montague'	see *R.* 'The Hon. Jean Marie de Montague'
'J.R.R. Tolkien'	SLdr
'Jabberwocky'	LHyd
'Jack Skilton'	LHyd SLdr
'Jacksonii'	ISea MBar SHea SLdr SReu
Jalisco Group	SLdr
'Jalisco Elect'	CDoC LMil SLdr SPer
'Jalisco Emblem' **new**	SLdr
'Jalisco Goshawk'	SLdr
'Jalisco Janet'	SHea SLdr
'James Barto'	LHyd SLdr
'James Burchett' ♀H4	CDoC LMil SLdr SReu
'James Gable' (EA)	MAsh SLdr
'Jan Bee'	SLdr
'Jan Dekens'	SReu
'Jan Steen' (M)	SLdr
'Jane Abbott' (A)	GGGa
'Janet Blair'	CDoC CWri MDun SLdr WBVN
'Janet Ward'	LHyd SReu
'Janine Alexandre Debray'	SLdr
japonicum (A. Gray) Valcken	see *R. molle* subsp. *japonicum*
japonicum Schneider var. ***japonicum***	see *R. degronianum* subsp. *heptamerum*
- var. ***pentamerum***	see *R. degronianum* subsp. *degronianum*
'Jason'	SLdr
javanicum (V)	GGGa
'Jazz Band' (V)	GGGa
'Jean Marie Montague'	see *R.* 'The Hon. Jean Marie de Montague'
'Jeff Hill' (EA)	ECho NLar SReu WBVN WCwm
'Jenny'	see *R.* 'Creeping Jenny'
'Jeremy Davies'	SReu
'Jervis Bay'	SReu
'Jingle Bells'	GGGa NLar
'Joan Paton' (A)	SLdr

	'Jock'	SLdr
	Jock Group	CBcs CMHG
	'Jock Brydon' (O)	GGGa LMil SLdr
	'Jock Coutts' (K)	CSdC
	'Johann Sebastian Bach' (EA)	WBod
	'Johann Strauss' (EA)	WBod
	'Johanna' (EA) ♀^{H4}	CBcs CDoC CTri GGGa LMil LRHS MAsh MBar MMHG NHol SLdr SMer SPer SReu WBod
	'John Barr Stevenson'	LHyd
	'John Cairns' (EA)	CMac LHyd MBar SLdr WBod WPic
	'John Walter'	MBar SLdr
	'John Waterer'	CSBt WFar
	'Johnny Bender'	SLdr
	johnstoneanum	CBcs GGGa LMil NPen SLdr WBod
	- KW 7732	SLdr
	- 'Double Diamond' (d)	LMil
	'Jolie Madame' (Vs)	CSam CWri ECho LMil LRHS MAsh MBri NLar SLdr SPur SReu
	'Jonathan Shaw'	GGGa
	'Josefa Blue'	GGGa
	'Joseph Baumann' (G)	CSdC SLdr
	'Joseph Hill' (EA)	ECho MAsh NHol SReu WPat
	'Josephine Klinger' (G)	CSdC SReu
	'Jubilant'	SHea
	'Jubilee'	SLdr
	Jubilee Queen Group	SLdr
	'June Fire' (A)	MDun SReu
	'Jungfrau'	CWri
	kaempferi (EA)	CBcs GGGa LHyd LMil SLdr
	- 'Damio'	see *R. kaempferi* 'Mikado'
	- 'Firefly'	see *R.* 'Hexe'
§	- 'Mikado' (EA)	LMil SReu
	- orange (EA)	CMac
	'Kakiemon' (EA)	LHyd
	'Kalinka'	EMil ENot LHyd LMil LRHS MAsh MDun NHol SPoG
	'Kantilene'	ENot
	'Kaponga'	MGos
	'Karen Triplett'	LMil
	'Karin'	MDun SHBN SLdr
	'Karin Seleger'	GGGa
	'Kasane-kagaribi' (EA)	LHyd
	kasoense HECC 10009 **new**	GGGa
	- HECC 10040	GGGa
	'Kate Waterer' ♀^{H4}	CWri MBar MDun MGos MLan SReu WFar
N	'Kathleen' (A)	SLdr
	'Kathleen' van Nes (EA)	LHyd
	'Katisha' (EA)	LHyd SLdr
	'Katy Watson'	SReu
	kawakamii (V)	GGGa
§	'Kazuko' (EA)	ECho ENot EPfP LCro LMil LRHS MAsh MBar MDun MGos MLea NDlv WBod WFar
	'Keija'	SReu
	keiskei	LHyd
	- compact	GKev SLdr
	- var. ***ozawae*** 'Yaku Fairy' ♀^{H4}	GGGa ITim LMil MDun WAbe
	keleticum	see *R. calostrotum* subsp. *keleticum*
	'Ken Janeck'	GGGa MDun NLar
§	***kendrickii***	GGGa MDun
	- MH 62	GGGa
	'Kentucky Colonel'	SLdr
	'Kentucky Minstrel' (K)	SLdr
	'Kermesinum' (EA)	CTri LMil MBar MGos SLdr SPlb SReu WPat
I	'Kermesinum Album' (EA)	LMil MBar MGos SLdr SReu
I	'Kermesinum Rosé' (EA)	CSBt ECho GGGa LMil MAsh MBar MDun MGos MLea NBlu SLdr SReu WCwm

	kesangiae	MDun SLdr
	- AC 110	NPen
	- CH&M 3058	GGGa
	- CH&M 3099	GGGa
	Kewense Group	LHyd
	keysii	GGGa LHyd LMil MDun SLdr
	- EGM 064	LMil
	- KC 0112	GGGa
	- KC 0115	GGGa
	'Kilimanjaro'	GGGa LHyd LMil SReu
	'Kimberly'	GGGa
	'Kimbeth'	GGGa
	'Kimigayo' (EA)	LHyd
	'King George' Loder	see *R.* 'Loderi King George'
	'King George' van Nes	SReu
	'King of Shrubs'	NLar
	kingianum	see *R. arboreum* subsp. *zeylanicum*
	'Kings Ride'	LHyd
	'Kingston'	MDun
§	'Kirin' (EA/d)	CBcs CMac CSBt LHyd SLdr WBod WPat
	'Kirishima' (EA)	SRms
	'Kiritsubo' (EA)	LHyd
	'Kitty Cole'	SLdr
	kiusianum (EA) ♀^{H4}	GGGa LHyd LMil SReu SRms
	- 'Album' (EA)	LHyd LMil SReu WAbe
	- 'Hillier's Pink' (EA)	LMil
	'Kiwi Majic'	LMil MBri MDun
	'Klondyke' (K) ♀^{H4}	CBcs CSBt CTri ENot EPfP GGGa LCro LMil LRHS MAsh MBri MDun MGos SLdr SReu
	'Kluis Sensation' ♀^{H4}	CSBt LHyd MDun NHol NPen SHBN SLdr SReu
	'Kluis Triumph'	SLdr SReu
	'Knap Hill Apricot' (K)	LMil
	'Knap Hill Red' (K)	CDoC LMil WMoo
	'Knap Hill White' (K)	CSdC
	'Kobold' (EA)	SLdr
	'Koche-ne-mo' **new**	WBod
	'Koichiro Wada'	see *R. yakushimanum* 'Koichiro Wada'
	'Kokardia'	EMil LMil
	kongboense	GGGa
	- C&V 9540	GGGa
	'Königstein' (EA)	LMil
§	'Koningin Emma' (M)	LMil MBri NLar SLdr
§	'Koningin Wilhelmina' (M)	SLdr WBod
	konori var. ***phaeopeplum*** (V)	GGGa
	'Koromo-shikibu' (EA) **new**	GGGa
	'Koromo-shikibu White' (EA) **new**	GGGa
	'Koster's Brilliant Red' (M)	CSBt ENot EPfP LMil MBri MGos SReu
	kotschyi	see *R. myrtifolium*
	'Kralingen'	NLar
	'Kupferberg'	GGGa
§	'Kure-no-yuki' (EA/d)	CSBt CTrG EPfP LHyd LMil MAsh SLdr
	'Lackblatt'	see *R.* (Volker Group) 'Lackblatt'
	lacteum	LMil MDun SLdr
	- CN&W 936	LMil
	- KR 2760	GGGa
	- SBEC 345	GGGa
	'Lady Adam Gordon'	SLdr
	'Lady Alice Fitzwilliam' ♀$^{H2-3}$	CBcs CEnd CMHG CTrG GGGa IDee ISea LHyd LMil WGer
	'Lady Armstrong'	CSBt
	Lady Bessborough Group	SLdr
	'Lady Bowes Lyon'	LHyd SLdr
	Lady Chamberlain Group	GGGa NPen SLdr
	'Lady Chamberlain Salmon Trout'	see *R.* 'Salmon Trout'

'Lady Clementine Mitford' ♀H4	CDoC CSBt CWri ECho ENot EPfP GGGa GQui LHyd LMil MAsh MBri MDun MGos MLea NLar SHBN SLdr SPer SPoG SReu
'Lady Decies'	SReu
'Lady Digby'	CWri
'Lady Eleanor Cathcart'	SLdr
'Lady Longman'	LHyd SHea
'Lady Louise' (EA)	SLdr
'Lady Primrose'	SReu
'Lady Robin' (EA)	SLdr
'Lady Romsey'	LMil NPen SLdr
'Lady Rosebery' (K)	CSdC MDun
Lady Rosebery Group	MLea
Ladybird Group	SReu
laetum (V)	GGGa
Lamellen Group	LHyd SLdr
'Lampion'	GGGa
'Lamplighter'	SHea SLdr SReu
lanatoides	LMil
- C&C 7548	GGGa
- C&C 7574	GGGa
- C&C 7577	GGGa
- KR 6385	LMil
lanatum	GGGa LMil
- dwarf, cream-flowered	GGGa
- Flinckii Group	see *R. flinckii*
lanatum* x *yakushimanum	GGGa
'Langworth'	CWri ECho GQui ISea LMil MAsh MDun MGos MLea NPen SLdr SReu WCwm
lanigerum	LMil MDun NPen SReu WGer
- C&V 9530	GGGa
- KW 8251	GGGa
lapponicum Confertissimum Group	GGGa
- Parvifolium Group from Siberia	GGGa WAbe
'Lapwing' (K)	SLdr
'Laramie' **new**	GGGa
'Lascaux'	SReu
'Late Inverue' (EA)	MAsh
'Late Love' (EA)	CDoC MGos
late pink, from Inverewe	WBVN WMoo
* ***laterifolium***	GGGa
§ ***latoucheae*** (EA) PW 86	GGGa
laudandum var. ***temoense***	GGGa LMil
Laura Aberconway Group	SLdr WBod
'Laura Morland' (EA)	LHyd
'Lava Flow'	LHyd
'Lavender Girl' ♀H4	GGGa LHyd LMil NLar NPen SHea SLdr SReu SSta
'Lavender Lady' (EA)	CTrG
'Lavender Queen'	CWri ENot
'Lavendula'	GGGa
'Le Progrès'	LMil MAsh SReu
'Lea Rainbow'	MLea
'Ledifolium'	see *R.* x *mucronatum*
'Ledifolium Album'	see *R.* x *mucronatum*
'Lee's Dark Purple'	CDoC CSBt CWri LMil MBar MDun WFar
'Lee's Scarlet'	LMil LRHS
'Lem'	SReu
'Lemon Dream'	LMil
* 'Lemon Drop' (A)	GGGa
'Lemonora' (M)	LRHS MAsh MBri SLdr
'Lem's 45'	CWri MDun SLdr
'Lem's Cameo' ♀H3	GGGa LHyd LMil MDun SReu SSta
'Lem's Monarch' ♀H4	CBcs CDoC CDul CWri ECho GGGa LHyd LMil MBri MDun MGos MLea SReu SSta
'Lem's Tangerine'	CDoC LMil WGer

'Lemur' (EA)	ECho GEdr GGGa LMil MAsh MDun MLea NHol NLar SReu WBod WPat
'Leny' (EA)	NHol
'Leo' (EA)	GQui LHyd SLdr
'Leo' (hybrid)	EPfP
'Leonardslee Giles'	SLdr
'Leonardslee Primrose'	SLdr
Leonore Group	SReu
lepidostylum	CBcs CDoC CWri GGGa LHyd LMil MBar MDun NHol SLdr SReu WFar
lepidotum	GGGa LMil MDun WAbe
- Elaeagnoides Group	GGGa
- yellow-flowered McB 110	WThu
§ ***leptocarpum***	GGGa
leptothrium	CBcs GGGa
Letty Edwards Group	CSBt SLdr SReu
§ 'Leucanthum'	GGGa WThu
leucaspis	GGGa LHyd MDun SLdr SReu
'Leuchtfeuer' (EA) **new**	LMil
'Leverett Richards'	SReu
levinei	GGGa
'Lewis Monarch'	GQui
'Libretto' **new**	LMil NLar
'Lila Pedigo'	CWri ECho MAsh MBri MDun MLea NPen SPer WBVN WFar
'Lilac Time' (EA)	MBar SLdr
'Lilacinum' (EA)	WPic
liliiflorum Guiz 163	GGGa
'Lilliput' (EA)	MAsh
'Lilofee'	LMil
'Lily Marleen' (EA)	CTri LRHS SCoo SReu
'Linda' ♀H4	CBcs CDoC CSam CTri ECho GGGa LMil LRHS MAsh MBar MDun MGos NBlu SLdr
'Linda Lee'	SLdr
lindleyi	GQui LHyd
- L&S	GGGa
- 'Dame Edith Sitwell'	LMil
'Linearifolium'	see *R. stenopetalum* 'Linearifolium'
Lionel's Triumph Group	LMil SLdr
'Little Beauty' (EA)	SLdr
'Little Ben'	ECho GEdr MBar MDun
'Loch Awe'	GGGa
'Loch Earn'	GGGa
'Loch Laggan' **new**	GGGa
'Loch Leven'	GGGa
'Loch Lomond'	GGGa
'Loch Morar' **new**	GGGa
'Loch o' the Lowes'	ECho GGGa LMil MAsh MBri MDun MGos MLea WFar
'Loch Rannoch'	CDoC ECho GGGa ISea LMil MGos WBVN WFar
'Loch Tummel'	GGGa
lochiae (V)	GGGa
'Lochinch Spinbur'	GQui
x ***lochmium***	GGGa
Lodauric Group	SLdr SReu
§ 'Lodauric Iceberg' ♀H3-4	CDoC LMil SLdr SReu
'Lodbrit'	SReu
Loderi Group	SLdr
'Loderi Fairy Queen'	SLdr
'Loderi Fairyland'	LHyd
'Loderi Game Chick' ♀H3-4	LHyd MDun MLea SLdr SReu
'Loderi Georgette'	SLdr
'Loderi Helen'	SLdr
§ 'Loderi King George' ♀H3-4	CBcs CDoC CDul CWri ECho GGGa IDee ISea LHyd LMil MAsh MDun MGos MLea NPen SLdr SPer SReu SSta WBVN WBod
'Loderi Patience'	SLdr
'Loderi Pink Coral'	LMil SLdr
'Loderi Pink Diamond' ♀H3-4	CWri LMil MDun SLdr

	'Loderi Pink Topaz' 𝕐$^{H3-4}$	LHyd SLdr
	'Loderi Pretty Polly'	CWri SLdr
	'Loderi Princess Marina'	SLdr
	'Loderi Sir Edmund'	LHyd SLdr
	'Loderi Sir Joseph Hooker'	LHyd SLdr
	'Loderi Titan'	SLdr SReu
	'Loderi Venus' 𝕐$^{H3-4}$	CDoC CWri GGGa LHyd MDun MLea SLdr SReu SSta WBVN
	'Loderi White Diamond'	LHyd SLdr
	'Loder's White' 𝕐$^{H3-4}$	CWri GGGa LHyd LMil MDun SHea SLdr SReu SSta
§	'Logan Damaris'	LHyd SLdr SReu
	longesquamatum	GGGa LMil NPen SLdr
	longipes	LMil SLdr
	- EGM 336	LMil
	- var. ***chienianum***	LMil
	- var. ***longipes*** C&H 7072	GGGa
	- - C&H 7113	GGGa
	longistylum	GGGa
	'Looking Glass'	MDun
	'Lord Roberts' 𝕐^{H4}	CBcs CTri CWri ECho ENot EPfP GGGa LCro LMil MAsh MBar MGos MLea NEgg NPen SHBN SLdr SPer SReu WBVN WBod WFar WMoo
	'Lord Swaythling'	LHyd SLdr
	'Loreley' **new**	NLar
	'Lori Eichelser'	ECho GEdr MDun
	'Lorna' (EA)	GQui LMil WBod
	'Louis Aimée van Houtte' (G)	SLdr
	'Louis Hellebuyck' (G)	SLdr
	'Louis Pasteur'	SReu
	'Louisa' (EA)	MAsh
	'Louisa Hill' (EA)	ENot MGos
	'Louise' (EA)	SLdr
	'Louise Dowdle' (EA)	LMil SLdr
	'Love Poem' **new**	GGGa
	'Lovely William'	CMac LMil NPen SLdr
	lowndesii	WAbe
	luciferum CER 9935	GGGa
	'Lucy Lou'	GGGa
	ludlowii	GGGa
	ludwigianum	GGGa
	'Lugano' **new**	NLar
	'Lullaby' (EA)	SLdr
	'Lumina' **new**	NLar
	'Lunar Queen'	LHyd SLdr
	Luscombei Group	LHyd SLdr
	luteiflorum	LMil NPen
	- KW 21556	GGGa
	lutescens	CBcs ISea LMil MDun NPen SHea SLdr SLon SReu SSta WAbe
	- C&H 7124	GGGa
	- 'Bagshot Sands' 𝕐$^{H3-4}$	GGGa LHyd LMil
	luteum (A) 𝕐^{H4}	More than 30 suppliers
	- 'Golden Comet' (A)	GGGa
§	***lyi*** KR 2962	GGGa
	maccabeanum 𝕐$^{H3-4}$	CBcs CDoC CWri GGGa IClo IDee LHyd LMil LRHS MBri MDun NPen SLdr SPer SReu SSpi SSta WFar WHer
	- SEH 27	GGGa
	- SEH 52	GGGa
	- deep cream-flowered	SLdr
	- Embley form	SLdr
	- Reuthe's form	SReu
	- Tower Court form	SLdr
	maccabeanum x ***sinogrande***	SReu
	macgregoriae (V) Woods 2646	GGGa
	macranthum	see *R. indicum* 'Macranthum'
	'Macranthum Roseum' (EA)	MMHG SReu
	macrophyllum	GGGa
	macrosmithii	see *R. argipeplum*
	'Macrostemon'	see *R.* (Obtusum Group) 'Macrostemon'
	maculiferum	GGGa SLdr
	- subsp. ***anwheiense***	see *R. anwheiense*
	'Madame Galle'	NBlu
	'Madame Knutz' (A)	SLdr
	'Madame Masson'	CDoC CTri CWri ECho GGGa GWCH ISea LMil LRHS MAsh MBri MDun MGos MLea NBlu NPen NPri SHBN SLdr SPer SPoG SReu SSta WBVN WBod WFar
	'Madame van Hecke' (EA)	CTri LMil LRHS MAsh MBri SLdr SReu WFar
	maddenii	IDee LMil SLdr WPic
§	- subsp. ***crassum***	CBcs GGGa LMil SKHP SLdr WPic
§	- subsp. ***maddenii*** KR 2978	LMil
§	- - Polyandrum Group	CBcs GQui ISea SLdr
	'Madeline's Yellow'	SLdr
	'Mademoiselle Masson'	ENot WFar
	'Magic Flute' (EA)	ENot LRHS MGos SPoG WBod
I	'Magic Flute' (V)	LMil NPri SCoo
	'Magnificum' (O)	SLdr
	magnificum	SReu
	'Maharani'	GGGa NPri
	'Maja' (G)	SLdr
§	***makinoi*** 𝕐^{H4}	CDoC GGGa LHyd LMil MDun NLar NMen SLdr SReu SSta
	- 'Fuju-kaku-no-matsu'	MGos NLar
	'Malahat'	NPen
	mallotum	GGGa IDee LHyd LMil MDun NPen SLdr SReu
	- BASEX 9672	GGGa
	- Farrer 815	GGGa
	'Malvaticum' (EA)	WBod
	Mandalay Group	LHyd SHea
	'Mandarin Lights' (A)	LMil LRHS MAsh MBri
	maoerense	GGGa
	'Marcel Ménard'	LMil NBlu NLar SReu WBod WFar
	'Marchioness of Lansdowne'	CSBt SHea
	'Marcia'	SLdr
	'Mardi Gras'	GGGa LMil
	Margaret Dunn Group	CWri
	'Margaret Falmouth'	SReu
	'Margaret George' (EA)	LHyd
	'Maria Derby' (EA)	ENot
	'Maria Elena' (EA/d)	LMil
	'Maricee'	GGGa
	'Marie Curie'	LMil SReu
	'Marie Verschaffelt' (G)	SLdr
	'Marietta'	LHyd
	'Marilee' (EA)	CDoC ECho LRHS MAsh MGos NLar SLdr
	Mariloo Group	SLdr
	'Marinus Koster'	MDun SLdr
	'Marion Street' 𝕐^{H4}	LHyd LMil SLdr SReu
	'Mark Turner'	SReu
	'Markeeta's Flame'	MDun
	'Markeeta's Prize' 𝕐^{H4}	CDoC CWri ECho EPfP GGGa LMil LRHS MAsh MBri MDun MGos MLea SBod SHea SLdr SPoG SReu WBVN
	'Marley Hedges'	CDoC GGGa LMil
	'Marlies' (A)	SLdr
	'Marmot' (EA)	ECho MBar MDun MLea NLar WBod
	'Mars'	GGGa SLdr SReu
	'Martha Hitchcock' (EA)	SRms
	'Martha Isaacson' (Ad) 𝕐^{H4}	MGos SReu WCwm
	'Martine' (Ad)	MGos
	martinianum	LMil SLdr
	aff. ***martinianum*** KW 21557	GGGa

	'Maruschka' (EA)	LMil
	'Mary Drennen'	LMil
	'Mary Fleming'	MAsh MDun SLdr
	'Mary Helen' (EA)	LHyd LMil LRHS MAsh NPri SCoo SReu WBod WPat
	'Mary Meredith' (EA)	LHyd
	'Mary Poppins' (K)	CTri ENot LCro LMil LRHS MAsh SCoo SPoG
	'Maryke'	CDoC LMil
	'Master of Elphinstone' (EA)	SLdr
	Matador Group	SLdr SReu
	'Matador'	LHyd LMil SHea WBod
	maximum	GGGa
	- SDR 2205	GKev
§	'Maxwellii' (EA)	CMac SLdr
	'May Day' ♀$^{H3-4}$	CDoC CMac MAsh NLar SHea WBod
	May Day Group	CBcs CWri ISea MDun MGos NPen SHBN SLdr
	'May Glow'	MGos
	May Morn Group	SReu
	'Mayor Johnstone'	CTri MAsh NPri
	meddianum	GGGa
	- var. ***atrokermesinum*** KW 2100a	GGGa
	Medea Group	SLdr
	Medusa Group	GGGa SHea SLdr SReu
	megacalyx	CBcs GGGa ISea
	'Megan' (EA)	ECho GGGa MAsh NLar
	megaphyllum	see *R. basilicum*
	megeratum	GGGa SLdr SReu
	- 'Bodnant'	WAbe
	mekongense	GGGa
	- KR 5044	LMil
	- var. ***mekongense***	SReu
	- - Viridescens Group	see *R. viridescens*
§	- var. ***melinanthum***	SReu
	- var. ***rubrolineatum***	LMil
	'Melford Lemon'	see *R.* 'Ilam Melford Lemon'
	'Melidioso'	LMil
	'Melina' (EA/d)	GGGa LMil
	melinanthum	see *R. mekongense* var. *melinanthum*
	mengtszense	NPen
	'Merganser' ♀^{H4}	ECho GCrs GEdr GGGa GKev LMil MDun MLea NDlv NHol SReu WAbe WBod
	'Merlin' (EA)	SLdr
	Metis Group	WBod
	metternichii	see *R. degronianum* subsp. *heptamerum*
	- var. ***pentamerum***	see *R. degronianum* subsp. *degronianum*
	'Mi Amor'	LMil
	'Miami' (A)	SLdr
	'Michael Hill' (EA)	CDoC LHyd MAsh
	'Michael Waterer'	MDun NPen SLdr
	'Michael's Pride'	CBcs GQui
	micranthum	GGGa MDun SLdr
	microgynum	LMil
	- F 14242	GGGa
	microleucum	see *R. orthocladum* var. *microleucum*
	micromeres	see *R. leptocarpum*
	'Midnight Mystique'	GGGa LMil
	'Midsummer'	CWri SHea SLdr
	'Mikado' (EA)	see *R. kaempferi* 'Mikado'
	'Mikado' (hybrid)	SLdr
	'Milton' (R)	LMil SLdr
	mimetes	LMil
§	- var. ***simulans*** F 20428	GGGa
	'Mimi' (EA)	CMac LHyd
	'Mimra'	SLdr
	'Mina van Houtte' (G)	SLdr
	'Mindy's Love'	LMil
	'Ming'	see *R.* 'Ilam Ming'
	'Minterne Cinnkeys'	MDun
	minus	GQui
	- SDR 2228	GKev
	- var. ***minus***	SLdr
§	- - Carolinianum Group	LMil
	- - - 'Epoch'	LMil
§	- - Punctatum Group	MBar
	'Miss Muffet' (EA)	SLdr
	'Moerheim' ♀^{H4}	CBcs CWri ECho EMil ENot LRHS MAsh MBar MGos NHol SReu WBVN
§	'Moerheim's Pink'	CDoC LHyd LMil MDun NHol SLdr
	'Moffat'	SReu
	'Moidart' (Vs)	LMil
	'Moira Salmon' (EA)	LHyd
§	***molle*** subsp. ***japonicum*** (A)	GGGa LMil SLdr
	- - JR 871	GGGa
	- subsp. ***molle*** (A)	LMil
	- - C&H 7181	GGGa
	mollicomum F 30940	SLdr
	'Mollie Coker'	CWri SLdr
	Mollis orange-flowered (M)	MBar SRms
	Mollis pink-flowered (M)	GGGa MBar NBlu SRms
	Mollis red-flowered (M)	MBar NBlu SRms
	Mollis salmon-flowered (M)	GGGa GQui
	Mollis yellow-flowered (M)	GQui MBar NBlu SRms
	'Molly Ann'	ECho GGGa MDun MGos NPen SLdr SReu
	'Molten Gold' (v)	LMil LRHS MAsh
§	'Momoko' (EA) **new**	LRHS
	monanthum CCH&H 8133	GGGa
	monosematum	see *R. pachytrichum* var. *monosematum*
	montiganum AC 2060	LMil
	montroseanum	CDoC ISea LMil MDun SLdr WCru
*	- 'Baravalla'	GGGa
	- white-flowered **new**	SLdr
	'Moon Maiden' (EA)	ECho GQui NLar SLdr
	Moonshine Group	SLdr
	'Moonshine'	SReu
	'Moonshine Bright'	LHyd MDun
	Moonstone Group	CWri ECho MBar MDun MLea SLdr WBod
	- pink-tipped	GEdr
	'Moonwax'	CWri SLdr
§	'Morgenrot'	EMui GGGa LMil MAsh MGos NBlu SReu WFar
	morii	GGGa LHyd LMil MDun
	'Morning Cloud' ♀^{H4}	CAbP ECho EPfP LHyd LMil LRHS MAsh MBar MLea NDlv NHol SReu
	'Morning Magic'	CWri LHyd SLdr
	Morning Red	see *R.* 'Morgenrot'
	'Moser's Maroon'	CDoC CWri ENot MAsh MGos MLea NLar NPen SLdr SPoG WBVN
	'Motet' (K/d)	CSdC SLdr
	'Mother of Pearl'	SHea SLdr SReu
	'Mother's Day' (EA) ♀^{H4}	More than 30 suppliers
	Moulten Gold = 'Blattgold'	GGGa
	'Mount Everest'	CDoC GGGa LHyd LMil SReu SSta
	'Mount Rainier' (K)	SLdr SReu
	'Mount Saint Helens'	GGGa LMil SLdr
	'Mount Seven Star'	see *R. nakaharae* 'Mount Seven Star'
	'Mountain Star'	SLdr
	moupinense	CBcs GGGa IDee LHyd LMil SLdr SReu
	'Möwe' (K) **new**	LMil
	'Mozart' (EA)	WBod
	'Mrs A.C. Kenrick'	SHea SLdr
	'Mrs A.T. de la Mare' ♀^{H4}	CSBt GGGa LHyd LMil MDun NHol SHea SLdr SReu SSta

'Mrs Betty Robertson'	CDoC ECho GWCH LMil MAsh MBri MDun MGos MLea SLdr SReu
'Mrs C.B. van Nes'	SReu
Mrs C. Whitner Group	SLdr
'Mrs C. Whitner' x 'Tally Ho'	SLdr
'Mrs Charles E. Pearson' ΨH4	CSBt ENot LHyd LMil NPen SHBN SHea SLdr SReu
'Mrs Davies Evans' ΨH4	CWri LHyd MBar SReu SSta
'Mrs Dick Thompson'	SReu
'Mrs Donald Graham'	SReu
'Mrs E.C. Stirling'	LHyd SRms
'Mrs Emil Hager' (EA)	LHyd SLdr
'Mrs Furnivall' ΨH4	CBcs CWri ECho EPfP GGGa LHyd LMil LRHS MAsh MDun MGos MLea SHea SLdr SReu
'Mrs G.W. Leak'	CDoC CSBt CSam CWri EPfP GGGa ISea LHyd LMil MDun MLea SHBN SHea SLdr SReu
'Mrs Henry Agnew'	SLdr
'Mrs J.C. Williams' ΨH4	LMil
'Mrs J.G. Millais'	LMil MDun SHea
'Mrs James Horlick'	CWri
'Mrs John Kelk'	LMil
'Mrs Kingsmill'	SLdr
'Mrs Lionel de Rothschild' ΨH4	MDun SReu
'Mrs P.D. Williams'	SReu
'Mrs Peter Koster' (M)	SLdr WFar
'Mrs R.S. Holford' ΨH4	SHea SLdr
'Mrs T.H. Lowinsky' ΨH4	CDoC CSBt ECho EPfP GGGa LMil MAsh MDun MGos MLea NPen SHea SLdr SPer SReu SSta WBVN
'Mrs W.C. Slocock'	MDun SLdr
§ x ***mucronatum*** (EA)	CBcs LHyd SRms WBod WPic
mucronulatum	CBcs GGGa NPen WBod
- pink-flowered	WPGP
- var. ***chejuense***	see *R. mucronulatum* var. *taquetii*
- 'Cornell Pink' ΨH4	GGGa LHyd WFar
§ - var. ***taquetii***	GGGa
'Multiflorum'	SReu
'Muncaster Mist'	LHyd
§ ***myrtifolium***	LMil
'Nabucco' (A) new	LMil
nakaharae (EA)	NPen SLdr SReu
§ - 'Mariko' (EA)	GGGa LHyd MBar NHol NLAp SLdr WPat
§ - 'Mount Seven Star' (EA) ΨH4	ECho GGGa LHyd LMil MAsh MGos NHol NLAp SLdr WAbe WBVN WPat
§ - orange-flowered (EA)	ECho LMil LRHS MAsh MGos NPri SHBN SReu
- pink-flowered (EA)	ECho LMil MAsh MGos NPri SLdr SPer SReu SSta
- red-flowered (EA)	ECho MGos
'Nakahari Orange'	see *R. nakaharae* orange-flowered
'Nakahari-mariko'	see *R. nakaharae* 'Mariko'
'Nancy Buchanan' (K)	SLdr
'Nancy Evans' ΨH3-4	CDoC CSBt CWri ECho EPfP GGGa LHyd LMil LRHS MAsh MBri MDun MLea NPri SLdr SReu SSpi WFar WGer
'Nancy of Robinhill' (EA)	ENot SReu
'Nancy Waterer' (G) ΨH4	ENot EPfP LMil NLar SReu
'Nanki Poo' (EA)	LHyd SLdr
Naomi Group	CWri LHyd NPen SHea SLdr
'Naomi' (EA)	GQui NPen SHBN SLdr WPic
'Naomi Astarte'	MDun SLdr
'Naomi Hope'	SLdr
'Naomi Nautilus'	LMil
'Naomi Stella Maris'	LHyd
'Narcissiflorum' (G/d) ΨH4	CDoC CSBt CTri ENot EPfP IDee LHyd LMil NLar SPoG
'Naselle'	GGGa LMil SReu
'Nassau' (EA/d)	MAsh
neriiflorum	GGGa LMil MDun NPen SReu

- Bu 287	GGGa
- subsp. ***neriiflorum*** L&S 1352	GGGa
§ - subsp. ***phaedropum***	MDun
- - CCH&H 8125	GGGa
- - KR 5593	LMil
nervulosum Sleumer (V)	GGGa
'Nestor'	SReu
'Netty Koster'	SLdr
'New Comet'	LHyd SLdr
'New Moon'	SReu
'Newcomb's Sweetheart'	LMil MDun
'Niagara' (EA) ΨH3-4	CTrh ENot EPfP LHyd LMil MGos NMen SLdr SPoG WBod
'Nichola' (EA)	SReu
'Nico' (EA)	CMac LRHS WBod WPat
'Nicoletta'	ENot LMil
'Night Sky'	CDoC ECho GGGa LHyd LMil LRHS MAsh MDun MGos MLea NLar NPen SLdr WBVN
'Nightingale'	LMil SReu
nigroglandulosum	GGGa
nilagiricum	see *R. arboreum* subsp. *nilagiricum*
'Nimbus'	LMil SLdr
Nimrod Group	SLdr
'Nippon'	SLdr
nipponicum	SReu
'Nishiki' (EA)	CMac
nitens	see *R. calostrotum* subsp. *riparium* Nitens Group
nitidulum var. ***omeiense***	NPen
- - KR 185	GGGa
nivale subsp. ***boreale***	WPic
- - Ramosissimum Group	GGGa
§ - - Stictophyllum Group	GGGa WAbe
niveum ΨH4	CDoC GGGa IDee LMil LRHS MDun NPen SLdr SReu WGer
- B&SWJ 2675	WCru
- 'Nepal'	LHyd
nobleanum	see *R.* Nobleanum Group
§ Nobleanum Group	GGGa LHyd LMil NPen SLdr SSta
'Nobleanum Album'	GGGa LHyd LMil SReu SSta
'Nobleanum Coccineum'	ISea SLdr SReu
'Nobleanum Lamellen'	SLdr
'Nobleanum Venustum'	CSBt IDee LHyd LMil SReu SSta WBod
'Nofretete'	GGGa
'Nora'	WPic
'Nordlicht' (EA)	SLdr
N 'Norma' (R/d) ΨH4	LMil SReu
Norman Shaw Group	LHyd
'Northern Hi-Lights' (A)	LMil LRHS MAsh SLdr
'Northern Star'	LHyd
'Northern Starburst'	LMil
'Nova Zembla'	CDoC CTri ECho EPfP GGGa ISea LMil LRHS MAsh MBar MGos NPri SHBN SLdr SPer SPoG SReu SSta WBVN WBod
nudiflorum	see *R. periclymenoides*
nudipes	LMil
nuttallii	GGGa LMil SLdr
'Oban'	ECho ITim LMil MDun NLAp NMen WAbe
obtusum f. ***amoenum***	see *R.* 'Amoenum'
Obtusum Group (EA)	LHyd SLdr
§ - 'Macrostemon' (EA)	WBod
occidentale (A) ΨH4	GGGa IDee LMil MDun SLdr SSpi
- 'Crescent City Double' SM 28-2	GGGa
ochraceum	LMil
- C&H 7052	GGGa
- EGM 312	LMil
'Odee Wright'	CDoC CTri CWri GGGa LRHS MAsh MDun MLea NLar NPri SLdr SReu

	'Odoratum' (Ad)	MLea
	'Oh! Kitty' **new**	WCwm
	'Oi-no-mezame' (EA)	LHyd SLdr
	'Old Copper'	CWri SLdr
	'Old Gold' (K)	ECho MLea SLdr SReu
	'Old Port' ♀H4	CWri LHyd LMil SHBN
	oldhamii (EA)	CPLG
	- B&SWJ 3742	WCru
	- ETOT 601	GGGa
	'Olga' ♀H4	LHyd LMil SHea SLdr SReu SSta
	'Olga Niblett' (EA)	ENot LMil LRHS MGos SReu
	oligocarpum	GGGa
	- Guiz 148*	GGGa
	'Olin O. Dobbs'	SReu
	'Olive'	LHyd LMil
	'Olympic Flame' (EA) **new**	LMil
	Olympic Lady Group	MLea SLdr
	Omar Group	MBar
§	'One Thousand Butterflies'	GGGa MDun SLdr
N	'Ophelia'	SLdr
	'Oporto'	SLdr
	'Orange Beauty' (EA) ♀H3-4	CBcs CDoC CMac CSBt CTrh ECho GGGa LHyd LMil MAsh MBar MGos NPen SLdr SReu WBVN WFar
	'Orange King' (EA)	ENot LMil MGos SPoG
	'Orange Scout'	SLdr WMoo
	'Orange Sunset'	MDun
	'Orangengold'	MDun
	orbiculare ♀H3-4	GGGa LMil MDun NPen SLdr
	- C&K 230	GGGa
§	- subsp. ***cardiobasis***	LMil MDun SLdr
	- Sandling Park form	SReu
	'Orchid Lights'	LRHS MAsh
	'Oregon' (EA)	SLdr
	oreodoxa	LMil
§	- var. ***fargesii*** ♀H4	GGGa LHyd LMil SLdr
	- var. ***oreodoxa***	LMil
	- - EN 4212	GGGa
	- var. ***shensiense***	GGGa
	oreotrephes	CBcs LHyd LMil MDun MLea NPen SHea SLdr SReu WBod
	- 'Bluecalyptus'	GGGa
§	- Exquisitum Group	CBcs SLdr SReu
	- 'Pentland'	GGGa LMil
	- Timeteum Group	SReu
	Orestes Group	SLdr
	orthocladum	LMil
§	- var. ***microleucum***	GGGa
	- var. ***orthocladum*** F 20488	GGGa
	- - JN 819	GGGa
	'Oryx' (O)	CSdC
	'Osaraku Seedling' (EA)	EPfP
	'Osmar' ♀H4	CBcs GGGa MGos NPen SReu
	'Ostara'	MDun MGos
	'Ostergold'	LMil LRHS
	'Oudijk's Sensation'	CBcs CWri ECho GQui MAsh MDun MGos NBlu SLdr WBVN
	ovatum	CBcs
	- CN&W 548	ISea
	'Oxydol' (K)	MBri SLdr
§	***pachypodum***	GGGa
	- KR 4053	LMil
	pachysanthum ♀H4	CDoC IDee LHyd LMil MDun NPen SLdr SReu SSpi
	- RV 72/001	GGGa SLdr
	- 'Crosswater'	LMil MDun
	pachysanthum x ***yakushimanum***	GGGa SReu
	pachytrichum	GGGa SLdr
	- W 1435	SLdr
§	- var. ***monosematum***	SLdr SReu
	- - CN&W 953	LMil
	- var. ***pachytrichum*** 'Sesame'	LMil
	'Palestrina' (EA) ♀H3-4	CBcs CMac CSBt CTrh ECho EPfP LHyd LMil MAsh MGos NHol NPen SLdr SMer SPer SReu SSta WBod WCwm WFar WMoo
	'Pallas' (G)	SReu
	'Pamela Miles' (EA)	LHyd
	'Pamela Robinson'	LHyd
	'Pamela-Louise'	LHyd
	'Pancake'	CMac
	'Panda' (EA) ♀H4	CDoC CSBt CTri ECho EPfP GGGa LHyd LMil LRHS MBar MBri MDun MLea NDlv NLar NPri SPoG SReu WBod
	'Papaya Punch'	CDoC LMil MDun
	'Paprika Spiced'	CDoC CWri ECho ISea LMil MAsh MBri MDun MGos MLea NLar SBod WBVN WFar
	'Paradise Pink' (EA)	LMil
	paradoxum	GGGa
	'Paris'	LHyd
	'Parkfeuer' (A)	LMil LRHS SLdr
	parmulatum	LMil MDun WBod
	- C&C 7538	GGGa
	- 'Ocelot'	GGGa LHyd MDun
	- pink-flowered	GGGa
	parryae	GGGa
	'Party Pink'	CWri
	'Patty Bee' ♀H4	More than 30 suppliers
	patulum	see *R. pemakoense* Patulum Group
	'Peace'	GGGa WAbe WBod
	'Peach Blossom'	see *R.* 'Saotome'
	'Peach Lady'	SLdr
	'Peep-bo' (EA)	LHyd SLdr
	'Peeping Tom'	CDoC MDun SReu
	pemakoense	CDoC CSBt CTrG GGGa IDee MBar MDun NHol NPen SLdr SReu WAbe
§	- Patulum Group	ECho MBar SLdr
	'Pemakofairy'	WAbe
	pendulum LS&T 6660	GGGa
	Penelope Group	SReu
	'Penheale Blue' ♀H4	CBrm CDoC CTrh CWri GGGa LMil MAsh MDun NLar
	'Penjerrick Cream'	SLdr
	'Penjerrick Pink'	LHyd
	'Pennsylvannia' (A) **new**	GGGa
	'Penny' **new**	SReu
	pentaphyllum (A)	LMil
	'Peppina'	GGGa
	'Percy Wiseman' ♀H4	More than 30 suppliers
	'Perfect Lady'	LMil
§	***periclymenoides*** (A)	GGGa GKev LMil SLdr
	'Persil' (K) ♀H4	CBcs CSBt CWri ECho ENot EPfP GGGa LCro LHyd LMil LRHS MAsh MBar MBri MDun MGos MLea NBlu SCoo SLdr SPer SReu WBVN WBod WBrE
	'Peter Bee'	GGGa
	'Peter Berg'	MGos
	'Peter John Mezitt'	see *R.* (PJM Group) 'Peter John Mezitt'
	'Peter Koster' (M) **new**	SHea WFar
	'Peter Koster' (hybrid)	CWri SHBN SLdr WFar
	petrocharis Guiz 120	GGGa
	'Petrouchka' (K)	MDun
	'Pfauenauge' **new**	LMil
	phaedropum	see *R. neriiflorum* subsp. *phaedropum*
	phaeochrysum	GGGa LMil NPen SLdr
	- var. ***agglutinatum***	GGGa
§	- var. ***levistratum***	SLdr SReu
	- - AC 1757	WCwm
	'Phalarope'	ECho GEdr GGGa MBar SLdr SReu WBod
	'Phoebe' (R/d)	SLdr SReu

	'Phyllis Korn'	CDoC CDul CWri LHyd MBri MDun NLar SLdr
	'Piccolo' (K/d)	CSdC
§	***piercei***	LMil MDun NPen
	- KW 11040	GGGa
	Pilgrim Group	LMil
	pingianum	LMil SLdr
	- EGM 304	LMil
	- KR 184	GGGa
	'Pink and Sweet' (A)	LMil
	'Pink Bride'	SLdr
	'Pink Cameo'	CWri
	'Pink Cherub' ♀H4	CDoC ECho EMui ENot MAsh MBar MBri MDun NBlu SLdr SReu
	'Pink Delight'	GQui NLar
I	'Pink Delight' (A)	ECho MAsh MGos MLea SLdr
	'Pink Drift'	CSBt ECho LMil LRHS MBar MDun MGos NHol SHBN SLdr SPer WBod
	'Pink Gin'	LMil MDun
	'Pink Glory'	SLdr
	'Pink Lady' ambig. (A)	SReu
	'Pink Leopard'	LMil MLea SLdr
	'Pink Mimosa' (Vs)	SLdr
	'Pink Pancake' (EA) ♀H4	ECho EPfP GQui LMil LRHS MAsh MGos NLar SLdr SSpi WGer
	'Pink Pearl' (EA)	see *R.* 'Azuma-kagami'
	'Pink Pearl' (hybrid)	CBcs CSBt CTri CWri ECho ENot EPfP GGGa LMil LRHS MAsh MBar MBri MDun MGos NPen NPri SLdr SPer SPoG SReu SSta WBVN WBod WFar
	'Pink Pebble' ♀H3-4	ECho LHyd MAsh MDun MLea WBod
	'Pink Perfection'	MBar MGos NPen SHea SLdr SReu WFar
	'Pink Photo'	SLdr
	'Pink Polar Bear'	LMil
N	'Pink Ruffles'	SLdr WBod
	'Pink Sensation'	MDun
	'Pintail'	GGGa IDee LMil WAbe
	'Pipit'	GGGa WAbe
	'Pippa' (EA)	CMac CTrG
	PJM Group	MDun
§	- 'Peter John Mezitt' ♀H4	LHyd MAsh SLdr
	'PJM Elite'	LHyd NLar
	planetum	LMil
	platypodum **new**	GGGa
	'Plover' **new**	GGGa
	pocophorum	GGGa NPen SLdr
	- 'Cecil Nice'	LHyd
§	- var. ***hemidartum***	GGGa NPen
	- var. ***pocophorum***	SLdr
	'Point Defiance'	CWri ECho GGGa ISea LMil MBri MDun NLar NPen SLdr SPer
	'Polar Bear' (EA)	MBar MDun SLdr
	'Polar Bear' ♀H3-4	CBcs CDoC CSam IDee LHyd LMil MGos MLan SReu WBVN
	Polar Bear Group	CWri ECho GGGa LMil MLea NPen SLdr
	'Polaris'	see *R.* 'Hachmann's Polaris'
	'Polaris' (EA)	SReu
	'Polarnacht' **new**	LMil
§	***poluninii***	GGGa
	polyandrum	see *R. maddenii* subsp. *maddenii* Polyandrum Group
	polycladum	LMil
§	- Scintillans Group	ECho LHyd MBar MDun MLea NHol SLdr WPic
	- - 'Policy' ♀H4	GGGa SReu
	polylepis	GGGa LMil NPen
	- C&K 284	GGGa
	ponticum	CBcs CDul CSBt CTri IDee MBar MGos NScw SPer SReu WBod WFar
	- AC&H 205	GGGa

	- 'Foliis Purpureis'	SReu
§	- 'Silver Edge' (v)	CSBt LMil LRHS SLdr
	- 'Variegatum' (v)	CBcs CTri EPfP GGGa LRHS MAsh MBar MDun MGos MLea NBlu NPen NPri SPer SPoG SReu SRms SSta WBod WFar
	'Pooh-Bah' (EA)	LHyd
	'Pook'	LHyd
	'Popocatapetl'	SReu
	'Potlatch'	GGGa
	poukhanense	see *R. yedoense* var. *poukhanense*
	'Praecox' ♀H4	CBcs CDoC CDul CSBt ECho ENot EPfP GGGa ISea LHyd LMil LRHS MAsh MBar MDun MGos NBlu NHol NPri SHBN SLdr SPer SPoG SReu SSta WBod WFar WPic
	praestans	GGGa LMil MDun SLdr
	praevernum	GGGa LMil
§	***prattii***	SLdr
	- 'Perry Wood'	LMil
	'Prawn'	SReu
	Prelude Group	SLdr
	preptum	GGGa SLdr
	'President Roosevelt' (v)	CSBt EPfP LMil LRHS MAsh MDun MGos MLea NPri SHBN SPer SPoG SReu WBod WFar
	'Pretty Woman'	LMil
	'Pride of Leonardslee'	SLdr
	'Pridenjoy'	LMil
	'Prima Donna'	ENot LMil
	primuliflorum	GGGa WAbe
	- 'Doker-La'	LMil WAbe
	- white-flowered	WAbe
	'Prince Camille de Rohan'	LMil SHea
	'Prince Henri de Pays Bas' (G)	CSdC SLdr
	'Princess Alice'	CBcs LHyd WAbe WBod WPic
	'Princess Anne' ♀H4	CDoC CMHG CSam ECho EPfP GGGa LHyd LMil MAsh MBar MDun MGos MLea NPen SHBN SLdr SPer SReu SSta WBod WMoo
	'Princess Galadriel'	SLdr
	'Princess Ida' (EA)	LHyd
	'Princess Juliana'	ECho ISea LMil MLea WBod WMoo
	'Princess Margaret of Windsor' (K)	GQui LMil
	'Princess Margaret Toth'	CSdC
	principis	LMil SLdr
	- C&V 9547	GGGa
	- KR 3844 from Pasum Tzo	LMil
	- SF 95085	ISea
	- 'Lost Horizon'	CDoC LMil MDun
§	- Vellereum Group	SLdr
	- - SF 99093	ISea
§	***prinophyllum*** (A)	IDee LMil
	'Prins Bernhard' (EA)	MAsh SLdr
	'Prinses Juliana' (EA)	SLdr SReu WFar
	'Professor Hugo de Vries' ♀H4	SHea SLdr SReu
	'Professor J.H. Zaayer'	MGos
	pronum	GGGa
	- R.B. Cooke form	GGGa
	- Towercourt form	GGGa
	'Prostigiatum'	SLdr
	prostratum	see *R. saluenense* subsp. *chameunum* Prostratum Group
	proteoides	GGGa
*	- 'Ascreavie'	GGGa
	proteoides x ***tsariense***	GGGa
	proteoides x ***yakushimanum***	GGGa
	protistum	SLdr
	- KR 1986	GGGa
§	- var. ***giganteum***	SReu
	pruniflorum	GGGa

prunifolium (A)	GGGa LMil SLdr
przewalskii	GGGa
- subsp. ***dabanshanense***	GGGa
pseudochrysanthum ♀H4	CDoC CStu GGGa LHyd LMil NLar NPen SLdr SReu SSta
- dwarf	WAbe
pseudociliipes	GGGa
Psyche Group	see *R.* Wega Group
'Psyche' (EA)	MDun
'Ptarmigan' ♀H3-4	CBcs CDoC ECho EPfP GEdr GGGa IDee LHyd LMil MAsh MBar MGos MLea NEgg NHol NLAp NMen NPen SLdr SReu SSta WBVN WFar
pubicostatum	LMil
- AC 2051	LMil
- CN&W 906	ISea
§ 'Pucella' (G) ♀H4	CWri NLar SLdr SReu
pudorosum L&S 2752	GGGa
'Pulchrum Maxwellii'	see *R.* 'Maxwellii'
pumilum	GGGa LTwo MDun NMen WAbe
'Puncta'	GGGa SLdr
punctatum	see *R. minus* var. *minus* Punctatum Group
purdomii	GGGa
'Purple Diamond'	see *R.* Diamant Group purple
'Purple Gem'	ENot
purple Glenn Dale (EA)	SLdr
'Purple Heart'	ENot LMil SPoG
'Purple Lace'	CDoC
'Purple Queen' (EA/d)	MAsh
'Purple Splendor' (EA)	CMac SLdr SPoG
'Purple Splendour' ♀H4	CBcs CDoC CSBt CWri ECho ENot EPfP IDee ISea LHyd LMil MAsh MBar MBri MDun MGos MLea NEgg SHBN SPer SReu SSta WBVN WBod WFar WMoo
'Purple Triumph' (EA) ♀H3	LMil LRHS SLdr SReu SSta
'Purpurkissen' (EA)	LMil
'Purpurtraum' (EA) ♀H4	GGGa LMil
'Quail'	GGGa
Quaver Group	SRms
'Queen Alice'	MDun
'Queen Elizabeth II' ♀H4	LHyd
Queen Emma	see *R.* 'Koningin Emma'
'Queen Mary'	MBar MDun SHea
'Queen Mother'	see *R.* 'The Queen Mother'
'Queen of England' (G)	CSdC
'Queen of Hearts'	LHyd LMil SHea SLdr SReu
'Queen Souriya'	SLdr SReu
Queen Wilhelmina	see *R.* 'Koningin Wilhelmina'
'Queenswood Centenary'	LMil
'Quentin Metsys' (R)	LMil SLdr
quinquefolium (A)	GGGa LMil NPen SLdr
racemosum ♀H4	LMil MBar MDun NPen SLdr SSpi WAbe
- ACE 1367	WAbe
- SSNY 47	GGGa
- 'Glendoick'	GGGa
- 'Rock Rose' ♀H3-4	CWri GGGa LHyd LMil
racemosum* x *tephropeplum	MBar
'Racil'	MBar MDun MGos
'Racine' (G)	SLdr
'Racoon' (EA) ♀H4	GGGa
'Radiant' (M)	SLdr
radicans	see *R. calostrotum* subsp. *keleticum* Radicans Group
'Rainbow'	SLdr
'Ramapo' ♀H4	ECho ENot GGGa GKev LMil LRHS MAsh MBar MDun MGos NHol NMen NPri SReu WBVN WBod
ramsdenianum	GGGa LMil SLdr
- KR 5619	LMil
- KR 6033	LMil

'Raphael de Smet' (G/d)	SReu
'Rashomon' (EA)	LHyd SHea SLdr SReu
'Raspberry Ripple'	SReu
'Rasputin'	CDoC LMil
'Raymond Burfield'	SLdr
'Razorbill' ♀H4	CDoC ECho GGGa LHyd LMil MGos WBod
recurvoides	GGGa LHyd LMil MDun NPen SLdr SReu WBod
- Keillour form	GGGa
'Red Arrow'	LHyd
'Red Carpet'	LMil SLdr
'Red Dawn' new	LRHS
'Red Delicious'	CWri ECho GGGa LMil WBVN
'Red Diamond'	see *R.* Diamant Group red
'Red Fountain' (EA)	ECho ENot MAsh MGos SLdr WPat
'Red Glow'	LHyd
'Red Glow' x ***yakushimanum***	SLdr
'Red Jack'	CDoC LMil SReu WBod
'Red Panda' (EA) new	GGGa
'Red Pimpernel' (EA)	SLdr
'Red Sunset' (EA/d)	SLdr
'Red Wood'	GGGa
'Redpoll'	LHyd
'Redwing' (EA)	CDoC MAsh SLdr
'Reich's Charmant'	GGGa
'Rendezvous' ♀H4	LMil SLdr SReu
'Rennie' (A)	ECho MGos
'Renoir' ♀H4	CSBt LHyd LMil SLdr SReu
'Replique' (Vs)	SLdr
reticulatum (A)	CBcs GGGa LMil NPen SLdr SReu
* - ***leucanthum*** (A)	GGGa
- 'Sea King' (A)	LHyd
retusum (V)	GGGa
'Reuthe's Purple'	LHyd NHol SReu WAbe
'Rêve d'Amour' (Vs)	MBri MDun SLdr SReu SSta
Review Order Group	WPic
'Rex' (EA)	ENot MAsh SLdr WFar
rex	CDoC GGGa IDee LMil LRHS MDun SLdr
- EGM 295	LMil
- subsp. ***arizelum***	see *R. arizelum*
§ - subsp. ***fictolacteum*** ♀H3-4	CDoC CWri GGGa LMil MDun SLdr SReu
- - SF 649	ISea
- - Miniforme Group	LMil MDun
- subsp. ***gratum***	CDoC LMil
- - AC 3009 from Zibenshan	LMil
- yellow-flowered AC 901	MDun
- - AC 2079	LMil
rex* x *yakushimanum	SReu
rhabdotum	see *R. dalhousieae* var. *rhabdotum*
rigidum	WAbe
* - ***album***	LMil
'Ring of Fire'	CDoC CWri ECho LMil MAsh MDun MGos MLea NEgg SLdr WBVN
'Ripe Corn'	SLdr SReu
ripense (EA)	LHyd
'Riplet'	ECho MDun NDlv NLar WBod
'Ripples' (EA)	CTrh
ririei	GGGa LHyd LMil SLdr SReu WCwm
- AC 2036	LMil
'Robert Croux'	SLdr
'Robert Keir'	SLdr
'Robert Korn'	LMil MDun
'Robert Seleger'	GGGa LMil LRHS MAsh SReu
'Robert Whelan' (A)	MDun NHol NLar SReu
'Robin Hill Frosty' (EA)	SLdr
'Robinette'	CBcs CWri ECho LMil MAsh MBri SLdr

	'Rocket'	CDoC CTri ECho ENot MAsh MDun MGos MLea NBlu SLdr WBVN
	'Rokoko'	see *R.* 'Hachmann's Rokoko'
	Romany Chai Group	LHyd
	'Romany Chal'	SHea
	'Romy'	WPic
	'Rosa Mundi'	CSBt ENot
	'Rosata' (Vs) ♀^{H4}	MBri MDun SReu SSta
	'Rose Bud'	CBcs CSBt CTri MDun
	'Rose de Flandre' (G)	SLdr
	'Rose Elf'	ECho MDun NDlv NLAp WThu
	'Rose Glow' (A)	MDun SReu
	'Rose Gown'	SReu
	'Rose Greeley' (EA)	CDoC CTrh ECho GQui NLar SLdr SReu WBod WFar
	'Rose Haze' (A)	MDun SReu
	'Rose Torch' (A)	MDun SReu
	roseatum F 17227	GGGa
	'Rosebud' (EA/d) ♀$^{H3-4}$	CBcs CMac CTrh ECho LHyd MBar MGos NHol NPen SLdr SMer SReu WBod
	'Rosemary Hyde' (EA)	SCoo SLdr
	roseotinctum	see *R. sanguineum* subsp. *sanguineum* var. *didymoides* Roseotinctum Group
	roseum	see *R. prinophyllum*
	'Roseum Elegans'	ECho MAsh MBar NBlu NPri WFar
	'Rosiflorum'	see *R. indicum* 'Balsaminiflorum'
	'Rosy Dream'	CAbP CWri ECho MAsh MDun NPen
	'Rosy Fire' (A)	NHol SReu
	'Rosy Lea'	MLea
	'Rosy Lights' (A)	CTri LMil MBri NPri
	'Rothenburg'	CSam LHyd MDun SLdr
	rothschildii	CDoC GGGa LMil
	- AC 1868 from Dapo Shan	LMil
	- C&Cu 9312	GGGa
	'Rouge' **new**	SHea
	rousei (V)	GGGa
	roxieanum	LHyd LMil NPen SReu
§	- var. ***cucullatum***	MDun
	- - CN&W 695	LMil
	- - SBEC 350	GGGa
	- var. ***oreonastes*** ♀^{H4}	CDoC GGGa LHyd LMil MDun NPen SSta
	- - USDAPI 59222/R11312	GGGa
	- - Nymans form	SReu
	- var. ***parvum***	GGGa
	- var. ***recurvum***	LMil
	'Royal Blood'	LHyd SLdr
	'Royal Command' (K)	CWri LMil MBar MDun NEgg SLdr
	Royal Flush Group	CBcs
	'Royal Lodge' (K)	SLdr
	'Royal Mail' **new**	SHea
	'Royal Ruby' (K)	CWri ECho MAsh MBri MGos MLea SLdr
	'Roza Stevenson'	LHyd NPen SLdr
	'Rubicon'	CDoC CWri ECho GQui MAsh MDun SLdr WCwm
	rubiginosum	CBcs GGGa LHyd LMil NPen
§	- Desquamatum Group	CBcs LHyd SLdr
	- pink-flowered	LMil
	- white-flowered	LMil
	rubineiflorum	GGGa
	'Rubinetta' (EA)	LMil WFar
	'Ruby F. Bowman'	CBcs SReu
	'Ruby Hart'	GGGa MAsh MDun NHol SReu
	rude	see *R. glischrum* subsp. *rude*
	'Ruffles and Frills'	ECho MDun
	rufum	CDoC GGGa SLdr
	rupicola	LMil NMen SLdr
§	- var. ***chryseum***	GGGa LHyd
	- var. ***muliense*** Yu 14042	GGGa

	russatum ♀^{H4}	EPfP GGGa LMil MDun NPen SLdr SPer SPoG WAbe WFar
	- blue-black-flowered	LMil
	- 'Purple Pillow'	CSBt
	russotinctum	see *R. alutaceum* var. *russotinctum*
	'Sacko'	CWri ECho GGGa LMil LTwo MAsh MDun NHol NLar WBVN
	'Saffrano'	NLar
	'Saffron Queen'	CBcs CTrG ISea LMil SLdr WBod WPic
	'Sahara' (K)	CSdC LMil SLdr
	'Saint Breward'	CTrG GGGa GQui LHyd MDun MLea SLdr WBod
	'Saint Kew'	SLdr
	'Saint Merryn' ♀^{H4}	CDoC CTrG ECho GEdr GGGa LHyd MDun NLAp NLar SLdr WBod
	'Saint Michael'	SReu
	'Saint Minver'	LHyd SLdr
	'Saint Tudy'	EPfP LHyd MDun SLdr WAbe
	'Sakata Red' (EA)	WBod
	'Salmon Bedspread'	SReu
	'Salmon Queen' (M)	WFar
	'Salmon Sander' (EA)	SLdr
§	'Salmon Trout'	LMil
	'Salmon's Leap' (EA/v)	CSBt ENot GQui LHyd LMil LRHS MAsh NPri SHBN SLdr SReu WAbe WFar
	saluenense	GGGa LHyd LMil NPen SLdr
	- JN 260	GGGa
§	- subsp. ***chameunum***	GGGa LMil SLdr
	- - ACE 2143	WAbe
§	- - Prostratum Group	GGGa WAbe
	'Sammetglut'	CWri SReu
	'Samuel Taylor Coleridge' (M)	NLar
	'Sanderling'	GGGa
	'Sang de Gentbrugge' (G)	CSdC SReu
	sanguineum	GGGa LMil MDun NPen SLdr
§	- subsp. ***didymum***	GGGa MDun
§	- subsp. ***sanguineum*** var. ***didymoides*** Roseotinctum Group USDAPI 59038/R10903	GGGa
	- - var. ***haemaleum***	CWri GGGa LMil
	- - var. ***sanguineum*** F 25521	LMil
	'Santa Maria'	ECho MAsh SLdr SReu SSta
§	'Saotome' (EA)	LHyd SLdr
	'Sapphire'	CSBt CTrG ECho GEdr MAsh MBar MDun NDlv SLdr SRms
	'Sappho'	CBcs CDul CSBt CWri ECho EPfP GBin GGGa ISea LHyd LMil MAsh MBar MBri MDun MGos MLea NPen SHBN SLdr SPer SReu SSta WBVN WFar WGer
	'Sapporo'	GGGa LMil
	'Sarah Boscawen'	SReu
	sargentianum	GGGa LMil NMen WAbe
	- 'Whitebait'	GGGa WAbe
	'Sarita Loder'	LHyd
	'Sarled' ♀^{H4}	GGGa LMil NMen WThu
	Sarled Group	SRms WAbe
	'Sarsen' (K)	CSdC
	'Satan' (K) ♀^{H4}	CSBt SKHP SReu
§	'Satschiko' ♀^{H4} (EA)	CBcs CSBt CTrh ECho EPfP GGGa LMil LRHS MAsh MBar MDun MGos MLea NDlv NPri SLdr SMer WBod
	'Satsop Surprise'	GGGa
	'Satsuki' (EA)	ECho
	'Saturne' (G)	SLdr
	'Saturnus' (M)	LRHS MAsh
	scabrifolium	CTrG

§ - var. ***spiciferum***	GGGa SLdr WAbe
- - SF 502	ISea
'Scandinavia'	LHyd SHea
'Scarlet Wonder' $\mathbb{Y}^{H4}$	CBcs CDoC CMHG CSBt CTrh CWri ECho ENot EPfP GGGa IDee ISea LMil LRHS MAsh MBar MBri MDun MGos NBlu NHol NPen NPri SLdr SPoG SReu WBod WFar WMoo
schistocalyx F 17637	NPen
'Schlaraffia'	NLar
schlippenbachii (A)	CBcs CTrG GGGa LMil NPen SLdr SSpi WPic
- 'Sid's Royal Pink' (A)	LMil MDun
'Schneegold' (K) **new**	ENot
'Schneekrone'	GGGa LMil MAsh MDun NBlu
'Schneeperle' (EA)	LMil
'Schneewolke'	LMil
'Schubert' (EA)	MBar WBod
scintillans	see *R. polycladum* Scintillans Group
'Scintillation'	CWri GGGa LMil MAsh MBar MDun MLea NPen SHBN SLdr
scopulorum	SLdr
- C&C 7571	GGGa
- KR 5770	LMil
- KW 6354	GGGa
'Scotian Bells'	GGGa
scottianum	see *R. pachypodum*
'Scout' (EA)	SLdr
scyphocalyx	see *R. dichroanthum* subsp. *scyphocalyx*
Seagull Group	SLdr
searsiae	LMil SLdr
'Seaview Sunset' **new**	GGGa
'Seb'	SLdr
'Second Honeymoon'	CBcs CDoC CWri ECho LMil MAsh MLea NLar NPen SReu WFar
seinghkuense	LMil
- CCH&H 8106	GGGa
- KW 9254	GGGa
selense	GGGa
§ - subsp. ***dasycladum***	NPen
- subsp. ***jucundum***	GGGa MDun
- - SF 660	ISea
semnoides	GGGa LMil SLdr
'Senator Henry Jackson'	GGGa MLea
'Sennocke'	LHyd
'September Song'	CBcs CDoC CWri ECho GGGa LHyd LMil MAsh MBri MDun MGos MLea NHol NLar SLdr WBVN WFar WPic
'Serendipity'	GGGa
serotinum	LHyd LMil SLdr SReu
- C&H 7189	GGGa
- KR 4653	LMil
- SEH 242	LMil
serpyllifolium (A)	CBcs GGGa SLdr
'Sesostris' (G)	CSdC
'Sesterianum'	CMHG SLdr
Seta Group	CBcs SLdr SReu
'Seta'	LHyd SHea WBod WPic WThu
setosum	GGGa LMil MDun WAbe
'Seven Stars'	CSBt
'Shamrock'	CDoC ECho ENot EPfP GEdr ISea LRHS MAsh MBar MDun MGos MLea NLAp SLdr SReu WBod WFar
'Sheila' (EA)	CSBt LRHS NPri
shepherdii	see *R. kendrickii*
sherriffii	GGGa LMil MDun NPen
'Shiko' (EA)	MAsh
'Shiko Lavender' (A)	ENot LMil MAsh SPoG
Shilsonii Group	LHyd SLdr SReu
'Shi-no-noe' (EA)	SLdr
'Shin-seikai' (EA/d)	SLdr
'Shintoki-no-hagasane' (EA)	LHyd WBod
Shot Silk Group	SLdr
'Shrimp Girl'	ENot LHyd MAsh MDun NPen SLdr SReu
shweliense	SReu
sichotense	GGGa
sidereum	GGGa LMil SLdr
- AC 3056	WCwm
siderophyllum	LMil SLdr
sikangense	NPen SLdr
- EGM 108	LMil
- var. ***exquisitum***	GGGa ISea MDun
- - EGM 349 from Wumenshan	LMil
- var. ***sikangense***	LMil
§ - - Cookeanum Group	LHyd SLdr
§ 'Silberwolke'	ENot LMil MAsh SReu
'Silver Anniversary'	MGos
Silver Cloud	see *R.* 'Silberwolke'
'Silver Edge'	see *R. ponticum* 'Silver Edge'
'Silver Fountain' (EA)	LMil
'Silver Glow' (EA)	CMac
'Silver Jubilee'	CBcs LHyd LMil
'Silver Moon' (EA)	SLdr
'Silver Queen' (A)	ECho EMil MGos
'Silver Sixpence'	CBcs ECho ENot EPfP ISea LRHS MAsh MBar MBri MDun MGos NPen SHBN SLdr SPoG SReu
'Silver Skies'	LMil
'Silver Slipper' (K) $\mathbb{Y}^{H4}$	ECho ENot LHyd LMil MAsh MBar MBri MDun MLea NHol NLar SLdr SReu SSta WFar
'Silver Thimbles' (V)	GGGa
'Silverwood' (K)	LMil
'Silvester' (EA)	MBri SLdr
'Simona'	SReu
simsii (EA)	CMac LMil SLdr
simulans	see *R. mimetes* var. *simulans*
sinofalconeri	IDee LMil LRHS SLdr
- C&H 7183	GGGa
- SEH 229	LMil
sinogrande $\mathbb{Y}^{H3}$	CBcs CDoC CHEx GGGa IClo IDee LHyd LMil LRHS MBri MDun SLdr SPer WFar WGer
- KR 4027	LMil
- SF 350	ISea
'Sir Charles Lemon' $\mathbb{Y}^{H3-4}$	CDoC CWri ECho LHyd LMil MAsh MBri MDun MGos MLea NLar NPen SKHP SLdr SPer SReu
'Sir Robert' (EA)	LRHS
'Sir William Lawrence' (EA)	SReu
'Skookum'	ECho MBri MDun MGos WBVN
'Skookumchuck'	MBri
'Sleeping Beauty'	WAbe
'Sleepy'	CBcs ECho MAsh MGos NDlv NPen
smirnowii	GGGa LMil NPen SHea SReu
smithii	see *R. argipeplum*
§ Smithii Group	CWri SReu
smithii Argipeplum Group	see *R. argipeplum*
'Sneezy'	CBcs CSBt CWri ECho ENot EPfP GGGa LHyd LRHS MAsh MBar MBri MGos NHol NPen SLdr WBod WFar
'Snipe'	CBcs CDoC CTri ECho ENot GEdr LHyd LMil LRHS MAsh MBar MDun MGos NHol NPri SLdr SPoG SReu WBod
'Snow' (EA)	CSBt MBar SLdr
'Snow Crown' (*lindleyi* hybrid)	ECho
'Snow Hill' (EA)	GQui LHyd LMil LRHS
'Snow Lady'	CBcs ECho ENot EPfP GEdr GGar GQui MAsh MBar MDun MGos NLAp SLdr SPer SPoG SReu WBVN

'Snow Queen'	LMil
Snow Queen Group	LMil SReu
Snow White Group	LMil
'Snowbird' (A)	LMil MAsh MLea NLar
'Snowflake' (EA/d)	see *R.* 'Kure-no-yuki'
'Snowstorm'	ECho
'Soho' (EA)	CSdC GQui
'Soir de Paris' (Vs)	ECho GGGa LHyd LMil MAsh MBar MBri MDun MLea NHol NLar NPen SBod SLdr SReu SSta WBVN WBod WFar
'Soldier Sam'	SReu
'Solidarity'	ECho MAsh MBri MDun MGos MLea WBVN
'Solway' (Vs)	CSdC LMil
'Son de Paris' (A)	GQui
'Sonata'	CWri GGGa MDun SReu WBod
'Songbird'	CDoC ECho LHyd LMil MAsh MBar MDun SLdr SReu WBod
sororium (V) KR 3080	GGGa
- KR 3085	LMil
Souldis Group	MDun SLdr
souliei	CDoC LMil MDun SLdr
- deep pink-flowered	GGGa
- white-flowered	GGGa
'Southern Cross'	MLea SLdr
'Souvenir de D.A. Koster'	SLdr
'Souvenir de Doctor S. Endtz' ♀H4	CDoC CSBt MBar NPen SHea SLdr
'Souvenir du Président Carnot' (G/d)	SLdr
'Souvenir of Anthony Waterer' ♀H4	MDun SHea SReu
'Souvenir of W.C. Slocock'	SHBN SLdr SReu
'Sparkler' (Vs)	GGGa
speciosum	see *R. flammeum*
'Spek's Brilliant' (M)	ENot
'Spek's Orange' (M) ♀H4	MGos
sperabile var. ***weihsiense***	GGGa LMil SLdr
sperabiloides	GGGa
sphaeranthum	see *R. trichostomum*
sphaeroblastum	GGGa SLdr
- var. ***wumengense***	CDoC MDun
- - CN&W 1051	LMil
- - CN&W 962	LMil
- - CN&W 968	GGGa
- - EGM 350	LMil
- - EGM 359	LMil
spiciferum	see *R. scabrifolium* var. *spiciferum*
spilotum	GGGa LMil SLdr
'Spinner's Glory' **new**	MAsh
spinuliferum	GGGa
- SF 247	ISea
'Spitfire'	MDun NHol SReu
'Splendens' (G)	CSdC
'Spring Beauty' (EA)	CMac SLdr SReu
'Spring Magic'	NPen SLdr
'Spring Pearl'	see *R.* 'Moerheim's Pink'
'Spring Rose'	SLdr
'Spring Sunshine'	LMil
'Springbok'	LHyd
'Squirrel' (EA) ♀H4	CDoC ECho GEdr GGGa LHyd LMil MAsh MDun MGos MLea NDlv NHol NLar NPen SLdr SReu WBod WGer
'Squirrel' tall (EA)	SLdr
Stadt Essen Group	LMil SLdr
'Stadt Westerstede' **new**	LMil
stamineum	GGGa LMil NPen
- SF 417	ISea
'Standishii'	SLdr
'Stanley Rivlin'	LHyd
§ 'Stanway'	SLdr
'Starbright Champagne'	LMil
'Starcross'	LHyd
'Starfish'	SReu
§ ***stenopetalum*** 'Linearifolium' (A)	CMac LHyd LMil SLdr WAbe
stenophyllum	see *R. makinoi*
stewartianum	GGGa LMil MDun SLdr
- SF 370	ISea
'Stewartstonian' (EA)	CMac ENot LHyd MBar NBlu NHol SPoG SReu SSta WBod WFar WPic
stictophyllum	see *R. nivale* subsp. *boreale* Stictophyllum Group
'Stoat' (EA)	GQui MDun
'Stopham Girl' (A)	LMil
'Stopham Lad' (A)	LMil
'Stranraer'	MDun
'Strategist'	SHea SLdr
'Strawberry Cream'	GGGa
'Strawberry Ice' (K) ♀H4	CBcs CDoC CSBt CWri ECho EPfP GGGa ISea LMil LRHS MAsh MBar MBri MDun MGos MLea MMHG NLar SLdr SPer SReu WMoo
strigillosum	GGGa LMil MDun NPen SLdr
- C&H 7035	GGGa
- EGM 305	LMil
- EGM 338	LMil
- Reuthe's form	SReu
'Suave'	WBod
subansiriense C&H 418	GGGa
suberosum	see *R. yunnanense* Suberosum Group
succothii	MDun SLdr
- EGM 086	LMil
- LS&H 21295	SLdr
'Suede'	MDun
'Sugared Almond' (K)	LMil
'Sui-yohi' (EA)	LHyd
sulfureum SBEC 249	GGGa
'Sulphamer'	SLdr
'Summer Blaze' (A)	SReu
'Summer Flame'	SReu
'Summer Fragrance' (O) ♀H4	LMil MDun NHol SReu SSta
'Sun Chariot' (K)	CBcs CSam ECho LMil MAsh MLea MMHG NEgg SLdr SReu
'Sun of Austerlitz' **new**	SHea
'Sunbeam' (EA)	see *R.* 'Benifude'
'Sunbeam' (hybrid)	SReu
'Sunny' (V)	GGGa
(Sunrise Group) 'Sunrise'	NPen SLdr
'Sunset Pink' (K)	SLdr
'Sunspray'	NPen
'Sunte Nectarine' (K) ♀H4	ECho GQui LHyd LMil MBri MDun MLea SLdr
superbum (V)	GGGa
'Superbum' (O)	SLdr
'Surprise' (EA)	CDoC CTrh CTri EPfP SLdr
'Surrey Heath'	CBcs CDoC CWri ECho ENot EPfP LMil LRHS MAsh MBar MDun MGos NDlv NPen NPri SLdr WBod
'Susan' ♀H4	CDoC CSBt CWri GGGa LHyd LMil MDun SLdr SPer SPoG SReu
'Susannah Hill' (EA)	CBcs CDoC ENot MAsh MGos SLdr
'Sussex Bonfire'	SLdr
sutchuenense	CDoC GGGa IDee LMil LRHS MDun SLdr WCwm WGer
- var. ***geraldii***	see *R.* x *geraldii*
'Swamp Beauty'	CWri ECho GGar LMil MAsh MDun MLea NLar WBVN WGer
'Swansong' (EA)	CMac
'Sweet Simplicity'	CSBt CWri SHea
'Sweet Sue'	SLdr SReu
'Swift'	CDoC ECho GGGa GQui LMil LTwo MAsh NHol NPri SReu WBVN WGer
'Sword of State' (K)	CWri
'Sylphides' (K)	MDun

'Sylvester'	CTri LRHS MGos NMen NPri SReu
'T.S. Black' (EA)	SLdr
taggianum 'Cliff Hanger'	LMil
'Taka-no-tsukasa' (EA)	SLdr
'Takasago' (EA/d)	CBcs LHyd
'Talavera'	see *R.* (Golden Oriole Group) 'Talavera'
taliense	GGGa LHyd LMil MDun
- KR 4056 from Cangshan	LMil
'Tally Ho'	SHea SLdr
Tally Ho Group	SLdr
tamaense	see *R. cinnabarinum* subsp. *tamaense*
'Tama-no-utena' (EA)	LHyd SLdr
'Tamarindos'	LMil
'Tanager' (EA)	CTrh SLdr
'Tangerine'	see *R.* 'Fabia Tangerine'
tapetiforme	GGGa
'Tarantella'	LMil NBlu NEgg
tashiroi (EA)	SLdr
tatsienense	GGGa
'Taurus' ♀H4	CDoC CWri ECho GGGa LMil LRHS MAsh MDun MGos MLea NPen SLdr WBVN
taxifolium (v)	GGGa
'Tay' (K)	SLdr
'Teal'	ECho GEdr MBar MDun MGos MLea NHol
'Teddy Bear'	CWri GGGa GGar LMil MDun MLea SLdr
§ ***telmateium***	SLdr
temenium	MDun
- var. ***dealbatum***	LMil
- var. ***gilvum*** 'Cruachan'	GGGa LMil
- - R 22272	LMil
'Temple Belle'	CWri ECho MDun WBod
Temple Belle Group	CSam LHyd MLea NDlv SLdr
'Tender Heart' (K)	SLdr
§ ***tephropeplum***	GGGa MDun
- USDAPQ 3914/R18408	GGGa
- Deleiense Group	see *R. tephropeplum*
'Tequila Sunrise'	LHyd LMil
'Terra-cotta'	CDoC LMil
'Terra-cotta Beauty' (EA)	CTrG WPat
'Tessa'	CBcs ECho MAsh
Tessa Group	ECho LMil MGos
'Tessa Bianca'	GGGa
'Tessa Roza' (EA) ♀H4	GGGa GQui NBlu
thayerianum	GGGa
'The Dowager'	SLdr
'The Freak'	SLdr
§ 'The Hon. Jean Marie de Montague' ♀H4	CAbP CDoC CSam CWri ECho EPfP LMil MAsh MBri MDun MGos MLea NPen SHea SLdr SReu WBVN
'The Master' ♀H4	LHyd LMil SLdr SReu
§ 'The Queen Mother'	LHyd
thomsonii	GGGa IDee LHyd LMil MDun NHol SLdr SReu
- B&SWJ 2638	WCru
- subsp. ***lopsangianum***	GGGa
- subsp. ***thomsonii*** L&S 2847	GGGa
'Thor'	GGGa MDun SReu
'Thousand Butterflies'	see *R.* 'One Thousand Butterflies'
'Thunderstorm'	LHyd SReu
thymifolium	GGGa
'Tibet' ♀H3-4	GQui LMil MBar MDun SHBN SLdr
'Tidbit' ♀H4	CDoC GGGa LMil MGos MLea NPen SLdr
'Timothy James'	ENot MAsh
'Tinkerbird'	GGGa
'Tinsmith' (K)	SLdr
'Tit Willow' (EA)	LHyd LMil LRHS NPri SCoo SLdr
'Titian Beauty'	CBcs CDoC CSBt CWri ECho ENot EPfP GGGa ISea LHyd LMil LRHS MAsh MBri MDun MGos NBlu NDlv NPen NPri SBod SLdr SPer WBVN WBrE WFar
'Titipu' (EA)	LHyd SLdr
'Titness Delight'	SLdr
'Tolkien'	SReu
'Tom Hyde' (EA)	LMil
'Top Banana'	MDun SLdr
'Topsvoort Pearl'	SReu
'Toreador' (EA)	CTrG SLdr
'Torero'	GGGa LMil
'Tornado' **new**	MAsh
'Torridon' (Vs)	LMil
'Tortoiseshell Champagne'	see *R.* 'Champagne'
'Tortoiseshell Orange' ♀H3-4	CDoC CSBt EMil LHyd LMil MDun NBlu SHBN SHea SLdr SPoG SReu SSta
'Tortoiseshell Salome'	SHea SLdr SReu
'Tortoiseshell Scarlet'	MDun SReu
'Tortoiseshell Wonder' ♀H3-4	EPfP LMil LRHS MAsh NPri SHea SLdr SReu
'Totally Awesome' (K)	MBri SLdr
'Toucan' (K)	CSBt MDun SLdr
'Tower Beauty' (A)	LHyd
'Tower Dainty' (A)	LHyd
'Tower Daring' (A)	LHyd SLdr
'Tower Dexter' (A)	LHyd
'Tower Dragon' (A)	LHyd LMil SLdr
'Trail Blazer'	GGGa
traillianum	GGGa LMil NPen SLdr
- SDR 2599	GKev
Treasure Group	LHyd SLdr
'Treecreeper'	GGGa
'Tregedna Red'	SReu
'Trelawny'	SLdr
'Trewithen Orange'	MBar MDun SHBN SLdr
trichanthum	GGGa LMil WBVN
- 'Honey Wood'	LMil SLdr
- white-flowered	LMil
§ ***trichostomum***	GGGa SSpi WAbe WBod
- Ledoides Group	LMil MLea SReu
- - 'Collingwood Ingram' (EA) ♀H4	LMil SLdr
triflorum	GGGa ISea LMil MDun
- C&V 9573	GGGa
- SF 95149	ISea
§ - var. ***bauhiniiflorum***	CBcs GGGa NPen SLdr
'Trilby'	SReu
trilectorum	GGGa
'Trill' (EA)	SLdr
'Trinidad'	MDun
triplonaevium	see *R. alutaceum* var. *russotinctum* Triplonaevium Group
'Troll' (EA)	SLdr
'Tromba'	LMil
'Trude Webster'	GGGa SReu
tsangpoense	see *R. charitopes* subsp. *tsangpoense*
tsariense	GGGa LMil NPen
- Poluninii Group	see *R. poluninii*
- var. ***trimoense***	CDoC GGGa LMil MDun NPen
- - KW 8288	LMil
- 'Yum Yum'	GGGa SLdr
tsariense x ***yakushimanum***	GGGa
§ ***tsusiophyllum***	GGGa
'Tsuta-momiji' (EA)	LHyd SLdr
'Tuffet'	SLdr SReu
'Tunis' (K)	ECho
'Turacao'	GGGa
'Twilight Pink'	SLdr
'Twilight Sky' (A)	SLdr
'Ukamuse' (EA/d)	LHyd SLdr
'Umpqua Queen' (K)	MBri

	ungernii	GGGa LMil SLdr WGer
§	***uniflorum*** var. ***imperator***	LMil
	- - KW 6884	GGGa
	'Unique' (G)	ECho EPfP ISea LRHS MGos NEgg NHol SLdr SPer
	'Unique' (*campylocarpum* hybrid) ♀H4	CBcs CDoC CSam GGGa LHyd MAsh MBri MDun NPen SHBN SLdr SReu SSta WMoo
	'Unique Marmalade'	CDoC ECho LMil MAsh MBri NPen SLdr WBVN
	uvariifolium	GGGa SLdr
	- Cox 6519	GGGa
	- KR 4158 from Zhongdian, Napa Hai	LMil
	- var. ***griseum***	IDee LMil SLdr
	- - C&C 7506	GGGa
	- - KR 3423	LMil
	- - KR 3428	LMil
	- - KR 3774	LMil
	- - KR 3782	LMil
	- 'Reginald Childs'	LMil SLdr
	- 'Yangtze Bend'	GGGa
	vaccinioides (V) CCH&H 8051	GGGa
	'Valentine' (EA)	GGGa
	valentinianum	CBcs GGGa NPen SLdr
	- F 24347	NPen
	- var. ***oblongilobatum*** C&H 7186	LMil
	'Van'	LMil
	'Van Houttei Flore Pleno'	SLdr
	'Van Nes Sensation'	LMil
	'Van Weerden Poelman'	NLar
	Vanessa Group	LMil SReu
	'Vanessa Pastel' ♀H3-4	CDoC CMac GGGa LHyd LMil MDun SReu WBod
	vaseyi (A) ♀H3-4	GGGa GKev LMil SLdr
	- 'White Find'	GGGa
	- white-flowered (A)	LMil
	'Vayo' (A)	SLdr
	veitchianum	GGGa
§	- Cubittii Group	GGGa SLdr
	- - 'Ashcombe'	LHyd
	- KNE Cox 9001	GGGa
	'Veldtstar'	LHyd
	vellereum	see *R. principis* Vellereum Group
	'Velvet Gown' (EA)	ENot
	venator	GGGa MDun
	'Venetian Chimes'	ECho ENot ISea MDun NLar NPen SLdr SReu
	vernicosum	GGGa LMil NPen
	- JN 180	GGGa
	- SF 415	ISea
	'Veryan Bay'	CBcs
	vialii (A)	GGGa
	'Victoria Hallett'	SLdr SReu
	'Vida Brown' (EA/d)	CMac SLdr SReu WPat WThu
	'Viennese Waltz'	GGGa
	'Viking' (EA)	LHyd
	'Viking Silver'	GGGa
	'Vincent van Gogh'	LMil NPen
	'Vinecourt Duke' (R/d)	CWri ECho LRHS MAsh MDun MLea NLar SLdr WBVN
	'Vinecourt Troubador' (K/d)	CDoC CWri ECho MAsh MDun SBod WBVN
	'Vineland Dream' (K/d)	CWri ECho MAsh SLdr
	'Vineland Fragrance'	MDun SLdr
	'Vintage Rosé' ♀H4	ENot LMil MLea SLdr SPoG SReu
	'Violet Longhurst' (EA)	LHyd
	'Violetta' (EA)	NMen SLdr
	Virginia Richards Group	CDoC CWri LRHS MGos SLdr SReu
§	***viridescens***	NPen
	- 'Doshong La'	GGGa LMil
	viscidifolium	GGGa
	'Viscosepalum' (G)	CSdC
	viscosum (A) ♀H4	GGGa GQui IDee LHyd LMil MDun MLea SLdr SPer SReu SSpi WBVN WBrE WMoo WPic
	- SDR 2312	GKev
	- 'Grey Leaf' (Vs)	LMil
	- var. ***montanum*** (A)	ENot IBlr
	- f. ***rhodanthum*** (A)	LMil
	- 'Roseum' (Vs)	LMil
	'Viscount Powerscourt'	ENot SLdr
	'Viscy' ♀H4	CDoC CDul CWri ECho EPfP GGGa GQui LHyd LMil MBri MDun MGos MLea NLar NPen WBVN WBod
§	Volker Group	CWri ECho LMil LRHS MAsh MBar MDun SReu SSta WFar
§	- 'Babette'	ENot LMil
§	- 'Lackblatt'	CDoC LMil MBri MLea SLdr
	'Vulcan' ♀H4	CDoC EPfP GGGa LMil MLea SHBN
	'Vulcan' x ***yakushimanum***	SReu
	'Vuyk's Rosyred' (EA) ♀H4	CBcs CDoC CMac CSBt CTri ENot GQui LHyd LMil LRHS MAsh MBar MGos NHol SLdr SPer SPoG SReu WBod WFar
	'Vuyk's Scarlet' (EA) ♀H4	CBcs CBrm CDoC CDul CMac CSBt CTrh CTri EPfP GGGa GQui LHyd LMil LRHS MAsh MBar MDun MGos NBlu NHol NPen NPri SLdr SPer SPlb SReu SSta WBod WFar WMoo
	'W.E. Gumbleton' (M)	SReu
	'W.F.H.' ♀H4	CWri LMil MDun SLdr WGer
	wadanum var. ***leucanthum***	LMil
	wallichii	GGGa LHyd MDun SLdr
	- DM 21	LMil
	Walloper Group	SReu
	'Wallowa Red' (K)	ECho GBin MLea SLdr
	'Wally Miller'	ECho MAsh MBri MDun SReu WBVN WFar
	aff. ***walongense*** C&H 373	GGGa
	wardii	CDoC GGGa IDee ISea LHyd LMil MDun NPen SHea SLdr
	- KR 3684	LMil
	- KR 4913	LMil
	- KR 5268	LMil
	- L&S	SReu
	- var. ***puralbum***	GGGa NPen
	- var. ***wardii***	LMil
	- - Litiense Group	SLdr
	- - CN&W 1079	ISea
§	'Washington State Centennial' (A)	GGGa MBri
	wasonii	CDoC GGGa LHyd LMil NPen
	- f. ***rhododactylum*** KW 1876	GGGa
	- var. ***wenchuanense*** C 5046	GGGa
	'Waterfall'	SLdr
	watsonii	GGGa
	- Cox 5075	GGGa
	wattii new	GGGa
	'Waxbill'	GGGa
	websterianum	SLdr
	- Cox 5123	GGGa
	'Wee Bee' ♀H4	CDoC ECho GCrs GEdr GGGa GGar LMil LTwo MAsh MDun MLea NDlv NHol NLar SLdr SPoG SReu WAbe WBod
§	Wega Group	LHyd
	'Wendy'	MAsh
	'Western Lights' (A)	LMil LRHS MAsh
	'Westminster' (O)	LMil

	'Weston's Pink Diamond' (d)	GGGa LMil
	'Weybridge'	SLdr
	weyrichii (A)	GGGa LMil
	'Wheatear'	GGGa
	'Whidbey Island'	LMil
	'Whisperingrose'	ECho LMil MDun NDlv
	'White Bird' **new**	ISea
	'White Frills' (EA)	SLdr
	White Glory Group	SLdr
	'White Gold'	GGGa MDun
	'White Grandeur' (EA)	CTrh
	'White Jade' (EA)	SLdr
	'White Lady' (EA)	LMil MBar SLdr
	'White Lights' (A) ♀H4	EPfP LMil LRHS MAsh MBri NPri SLdr
	'White Perfume'	MDun SReu
	'White Rosebud' (EA)	SReu WFar
	'White Swan' (K)	MGos WCwm
	'White Swan' (hybrid)	SReu
	'White Wings'	GQui LHyd SLdr
	'Whitethroat' (K/d) ♀H4	CSdC CWri ECho EPfP GQui ISea LMil MAsh MDun MLea MMHG SLdr SPer WBVN
	'Whitney's Dwarf Red'	SLdr
	'Wigeon'	GGGa LMil NHol
	wightii	GGGa MDun NPen SLdr
	'Wild Affair'	MDun
	'Wilgen's Ruby'	CDoC CSBt LMil MBar MGos NBlu NHol NPen SHBN SHea SLdr SPoG WBod WFar
	'Willbrit'	CBcs CDoC CWri ECho LHyd MAsh MGos SLdr WBVN WBrE
	'William III' (G)	SLdr
	williamsianum ♀H4	CBcs CDoC CTrG CWri ECho GBin GEdr LHyd LMil LRHS MAsh MBar MDun MLea SLdr SReu SRms SSpi WBod WFar
	- Caerhays form	LMil MDun
	- 'Special'	GGGa
	'Willy' (EA)	SLdr
	wilsoniae	see *R. latoucheae*
	Wilsonii Group	CTrG
	wiltonii ♀H4	GGGa LHyd LMil MDun SLdr
	- CC&H 3906	GGGa
	'Windlesham Scarlet'	LHyd SLdr
	'Windsor Lad'	SReu
	'Windsor Sunbeam' (K)	CWri
	Wine and Roses = 'Pinkros' **new**	GGGa
	'Winsome' (hybrid) ♀H3	CBcs CDoC GGGa LHyd NPri SHea SReu
	Winsome Group	CWri LRHS MAsh MBar MDun NPen SLdr SSta
	'Winston Churchill' (M)	MBar NHol SReu
	'Wishmoor'	SLdr SReu
	'Wisley Blush'	CDoC LMil LRHS MAsh
	'Witch Doctor'	ECho LMil MDun
	'Witchery'	GGGa
	'Wombat' (EA) ♀H4	CTri EPfP GGGa LHyd LMil LRHS MGos NHol NLar NPri SLdr SReu
	wongii	GGGa GQui SLdr
	'Woodcock'	SHea WBod
	'Wren'	CDoC ECho GCrs GEdr GGGa LMil MAsh MBar MDun MLea NLAp SReu WBVN WBod
	'Wryneck' (K)	CSdC LHyd SLdr SReu
	'Wye' (K)	SLdr
	xanthocodon	see *R. cinnabarinum* subsp. *xanthocodon*
	xanthostephanum	WAbe
	- CCH&H 8070	GGGa
	- KR 3095	LMil
	- KR 4462	LMil
	'Yaku Angel'	MDun

	'Yaku Incense'	ECho MAsh MBri MDun MLea NPen
	'Yaku Prince'	ECho MAsh MBri MDun MGos SLdr WFar
	yakushimanum	CBcs CDoC CMHG CSam CWri ECho ENot EPfP GGGa GKev IDee ISea LHyd LMil MAsh MBar MBri MDun MGos MLea NHol NPen SLdr SPer SReu SSta WFar WGer
	- 'Berg'	MDun
	- 'Edelweiss'	ENot
	- Exbury form	SReu
	- Exbury form x ***roxieanum*** var. ***oreonastes***	SReu
	- FCC form	see *R. yakushimanum* 'Koichiro Wada'
§	- 'Koichiro Wada' ♀H4	EPfP GGGa GGar LHyd LMil LRHS MAsh MDun MGos NHol SLdr SPoG SReu WGer
	- subsp. ***makinoi***	see *R. makinoi*
	- 'Snow Mountain'	SReu
	'Yamato-no-hikari' **new**	WBod
*	'Yaya'	SLdr
	'Yaye' (EA)	CDoC
	'Yaye-hiryu' (EA)	LHyd
§	***yedoense*** var. ***poukhanense***	SLdr SReu
	'Yellow Cloud' (K)	ECho LMil MDun
	'Yellow Hammer' ♀H4	CBcs CTrG ECho EMil EPfP ISea LHyd LMil MDun WBod WBrE WFar
	Yellow Hammer Group	CWri GGGa MBar MGos NPen SHBN SLdr SPer SReu SSta
	'Yellow Rolls Royce'	MDun
	'Yol'	SLdr
I	'Yolanta'	WAbe
	'Youthful Sin'	ISea
	yuefengense	GGGa
	yungningense	MDun
§	- Glomerulatum Group	SLdr
	yunnanense	CDoC GGGa ISea LHyd LMil MDun NPen SLdr SSpi
	- AC 751	MDun
	- C&H 7145	GGGa
	- KGB 551	SReu
	- KGB 559	SReu
	- SF 379	ISea
	- SF 400	ISea
	- SF 96102	ISea
	- 'Openwood' ♀H3-4	GGGa LMil LRHS
	- pink-flowered	GGGa
	- 'Red Throat'	SLdr
	- red-blotched	LMil
§	- Suberosum Group	SLdr
	- white-flowered	GGGa LMil
	zaleucum	LMil MDun
	- AC 685	MDun
	- F 15688	GGGa
	- KR 2687	GGGa
	- KR 3979	LMil
	- SF 347	ISea
	- SF 578	ISea
	'Zanna' **new**	SHea
	Zelia Plumecocq Group	SReu
	zeylanicum	see *R. arboreum* subsp. *zeylanicum*
	'Zuiderzee'	NPen
	Zuiderzee Group	SLdr

Rhodohypoxis (*Hypoxidaceae*)

	'Albrighton'	CWsd ECho ERos EWes GEdr IBal ITim LAma NHol NMen SAga SBla SIng WAbe WPat
	'Andromeda'	EWes

'Appleblossom' CPen CTca EBrs ECho EPot ERos EWes IBal LBee MSte NLar NMen SCnR SIng WAbe WFar
baurii ♀H4 CElw CMea CPBP CTca ECho GCrs GEdr IBal ITim LRHS MTho NMen NSla SAga SPoG SRms WAbe WFar
- 'Alba' CMea ECho IBal ITim NMen
- var. ***baurii*** EWes LBee SIng
- 'Bridal Bouquet' (d) EWes WFar
- 'Coconut Ice' EPot EWes IBal
- var. ***confecta*** CPen CWsd ECho EWes ITim SBla SIng
- 'Daphne Mary' EWes
- 'David Scott' EWes
- 'Dulcie' CPen EBrs ECho EWes GEdr ITim SCnR WAbe WFar
- 'Goliath' **new** EWes
- 'Lily Jean' (d) CFwr CStu EBrs ECho EPfP EWes GEdr IBal ITim LRHS NCGa NLar SIng
- 'Mars' EWes
- 'Pearl' ECho ITim NLar
- 'Perle' ECho ERos EWes GEdr NHol SCnR WAbe
- 'Pictus' ECho IBal ITim
- 'Pink Pearl' EPot EWes IBal NHol
- pink-flowered CWsd EBrs ITim NLAp WCru
- var. ***platypetala*** CFwr CStu EBrs ECho ENot EPfP EPot EWes GEdr IBal ITim LRHS NHol NMen WAbe
- - Burtt 6981 EWes
- var. ***platypetala*** × ***milloides*** IBal LTwo NHol WAbe
- 'Rebecca' ECho EWes
- 'Red King' EWes IBal
- red-flowered EBrs ECho NLAp SPlb
- 'Susan Garnett-Botfield' CWsd ECho EPot EWes GEdr IBal NMen WAbe WFar
- 'The Bride' **new** EWes
- white-flowered CWsd EBrs ECho EPot NLAp NMen WCru
'Betsy Carmine' CPen GEdr IBal
'Bright Eyes' (d) EWes
'Burgundy' SIng
'Candy Stripe' ECho EWes GEdr SIng
'Carina' EWes
'Confusion' EWes WAbe WFar
'Dainty Dee' (d) EWes
'Dawn' CPen CTca CWsd EBrs ECho EPot EWes GEdr IBal LAma NLar NMen SBla SIng WAbe
deflexa CGra CLyd CPen CWsd ECho EWes GCrs GEdr IBal ITim MSte NHol SBla SCnR SIng WAbe WFar
'Donald Mann' ECho EWes NMen
double, red-flowered (d) CStu
'Douglas' CPen CTca EBrs ECho ENot EPfP EPot EWes GEdr IBal ITim LAma NHol NMen SBla SIng WAbe WFar WSPU
'Dusky' EBrs EWes GEdr
'E.A. Bowles' CPen ECho EWes IBal ITim NMen WAbe WFar
'Ellicks' IBal
'Emily Peel' EBrs ECho EWes WAbe
'Eva-Kate' ECho ERos EWes ITim LAma SBla SIng WAbe WFar WPat
'Fred Broome' CTca CWsd EBrs ECho EWes GEdr LAma NHol NMen SBla SIng WAbe WFar WPat
'Garnett' ECho EDAr EWes IBal NMen SBla WAbe
'Great Scot' ECho ERos EWes GEdr IBal ITim WFar
'Harlequin' ECho EPot EWes GEdr IBal ITim LAma NHol NMen SIng WAbe WFar
'Hebron Farm Biscuit' see *Hypoxis parvula* var. *albiflora* 'Hebron Farm Biscuit'
'Hebron Farm Cerise' see × *Rhodoxis* 'Hebron Farm Cerise'
'Hebron Farm Pink' see × *Rhodoxis hybrida* 'Hebron Farm Pink'
§ 'Helen' ECho EWes GEdr IBal SBla SIng WAbe WFar
'Hinky Pinky' CFwr GEdr
'Holden Rose' ECho NHol
hybrids CWCL ELan
'Jupiter' **new** GEdr
'Kiwi Joy' (d) CStu EWes WFar
'Knockdolian Red' NHol
'Margaret Rose' CTca CWsd ECho EWes IBal ITim NMen WAbe WFar
'Midori' EWes GEdr
milloides CTca CWsd EBrs ECho EPot EWes GEdr GGar IBal ITim LBee NHol NLAp NMen NWCA SBla SIng WAbe WFar
- 'Claret' CEnt CSam CStu CWsd ECho EWes IBal ITim LTwo SAga SBla SIng WAbe WFar WPat
- 'Damask' CStu CWsd EWes SAga SBla
- 'Drakensberg Snow' EWes
- giant ECho
'Monty' ECho EWes GEdr SIng WAbe
'Mystery' EWes NHol WAbe
'Naomi' EWes
'New Look' EBrs ECho ERos EWes GEdr IBal LTwo NMen SIng WAbe WFar
'Pearl White' ECho IBal
'Picta' (v) ECho EPot EWes GEdr IBal LAma LBee NHol SBla WAbe
'Pink Ice' GEdr IBal
'Pinkeen' CWsd ECho EPot EWes GEdr IBal ITim LTwo SIng WAbe WFar
'Pinkie' IBal
'Pintado' CWsd EWes SBla
'Rosie Lee' EWes
'Ruth' EBrs ECho EWes IBal LAma MSte NHol SBla WAbe WFar
'Shell Pink' EWes IBal ITim WAbe
'Snow' EWes
'Snow White' EWes
'Starlett' EWes
'Starry Eyes' (d) CStu ECho EWes
'Stella' EBrs ECho EPot ERos EWes GEdr IBal MSte NHol NMen SBla SIng WAbe
'Tetra Pink' ECho EWes IBal NHol SIng WAbe
'Tetra Red' CFwr CTca EBrs ECho EWes IBal NHol NMen SIng WAbe WFar
'Tetra Rose' GEdr
'Tetra White' see *R.* 'Helen'
thodiana CStu CWsd ECho ERos EWes GEdr IBal NMen SBla SCnR SIng WAbe WFar
'Twinkle Star Mixed' **new** LBuc
'Two Tone' EWes
'Venetia' CMea ECho IBal NHol WAbe
'Westacre Picotee' EWes
'White Prince' IBal
'Wild Cherry Blossom' CFwr ECho EWes SIng

Rhodohypoxis × *Hypoxis* see × *Rhodoxis*

R. baurii × ***H. parvula*** see × *Rhodoxis hybrida*

Rhodophiala (*Amaryllidaceae*)

WAL 7443 **new** WCot
WAL 9561 WCot

§ ***advena***	EPot WCot
bagnoldii F&W 8695	WCot
§ ***bifida***	SCnR WCot
chilensis	WCot
elwesii	WCot
fulgens	WCot
'Harry Hay' **new**	WCot
late-flowering WAL 9586 **new**	WCot
mendocina BC&W 5028	CStu
pratensis	EBee
rhodolirion	WCot

Rhodora see *Rhododendron*

Rhodothamnus (*Ericaceae*)

chamaecistus	GCrs WAbe

Rhodotypos (*Rosaceae*)

kerrioides	see *R. scandens*
§ ***scandens***	CPLG CPle CTri EBee EMil EPfP EWTr IMGH MBri MMHG MWea NLar SLon SSpi WCru WPat WSHC WSPU

x *Rhodoxis* (*Hypoxidaceae*)

'Aurora'	EWes
'Bloodstone'	EWes
'Hebron Farm Biscuit'	see *Hypoxis parvula* var. *albiflora* 'Hebron Farm Biscuit'
§ 'Hebron Farm Cerise'	ERos EWes GEdr NMen
'Hebron Farm Rose' **new**	LTwo
§ ***hybrida***	CPen CPne EBrs ECho EWes IBal ITim NMen SIng WAbe
- 'Aya San'	EWes SIng
§ - 'Hebron Farm Pink'	CWsd ECho ERos EWes GEdr IBal NMen SBla SCnR SIng WAbe WFar
- 'Hebron Farm Red Eye'	EWes GEdr SBla SCnR SIng WAbe WFar
'Little Pink Pet'	EWes

Rhoeo see *Tradescantia*

spathacea 'Variegata'	see *Tradescantia spathacea* 'Vittata'

Rhopalostylis (*Arecaceae*)

baueri	CBrP LPal
sapida	CBrP CKob CTrC LPal
- 'Chatham Island'	CBrP

rhubarb see *Rheum* x *hybridum*

Rhus (*Anacardiaceae*)

ambigua	EPfP
- B&SWJ 3656	WCru
§ ***aromatica***	CAgr CArn ELan EPfP NEgg NLar
chinensis	CDoC CMCN EPfP NLar
copallina	ELan EPfP LRHS
coriaria	CArn EPfP NLar
cotinus	see *Cotinus coggygria*
glabra	CAgr CArn CBcs CDoC EPfP MGos SPer
- 'Laciniata' misapplied	see *R.* x *pulvinata* Autumn Lace Group
- 'Laciniata' Carrière	NLar
glauca	EShb
N ***hirta***	see *R. typhina*
incisa	SPlb
integrifolia	CArn LRav
magalismontana	EShb
potaninii	EBee EPfP LRHS MAsh SPoG
§ x ***pulvinata*** Autumn Lace Group	CDoC EBee EPfP MGos SDix SHBN WPat
- - 'Red Autumn Lace' Υ^{H4}	LRHS MBlu MBri MRav SPer
punjabensis	CBcs
§ ***radicans***	CArn COld GPoy
succedanea	CDTJ
toxicodendron	see *R. radicans*
trichocarpa	EPfP SSpi
trilobata	see *R. aromatica*
N ***typhina*** Υ^{H4}	CBcs CDoC CDul CHEx CLnd CTrG CTri EBee ECrN ELan ENot EPfP LRHS MAsh MBar MGos MRav NBea NBlu NWea SHBN SPer SPoG SSta WBrE WFar WTel
§ - 'Dissecta' Υ^{H4}	CBcs CDoC CDul CLnd CSBt EBee ECrN ELan ENot EPfP LPan MAsh MBar MBri MGan MGos MRav MWat NBea NBlu NEgg SEND SPer SPoG WFar WOrn WTel
- 'Laciniata' hort.	see *R. typhina* 'Dissecta'
- Tiger Eyes = 'Bailtiger'	EBee ELan ENot EPfP LBuc LRHS MAsh MBri MGos NSti SCoo SPoG
§ ***verniciflua***	CLnd EGFP NLar SSpi

Rhynchelytrum see *Melinis*

Rhynchospora (*Cyperaceae*)

colorata	CStu NOak NPer SHom WHal
latifolia	CKno WCot

Ribes ✿ (*Grossulariaceae*)

alpinum	CPLG EMac MRav MWht NSti NWea SPer SRms WGwG
- 'Aureum'	WCot
- 'Schmidt'	EBee MBar
americanum 'Variegatum' (v)	ELan EPla MRav NHol SPer WPat
aureum hort.	see *R. odoratum*
* - 'Roxby Red'	MCoo
'Ben Hope'^{PBR} (B)	CAgr EMui MAsh
'Black Velvet' (D)	CAgr MCoo MGan
§ x ***culverwellii*** jostaberry (F)	CAgr CWib EMui GTwe LBuc LEdu MAsh SDea SPoG
divaricatum	CAgr LEdu
- 'Worcesterberry'	see *R.* 'Worcesterberry'
gayanum	CBcs CPMA NLar
x ***gordonianum***	CDoC CPLG CPMA EBee ELan EPfP EWTr GBin IDee ISea LAst LHop LRHS MAsh MBri MRav NHol NVic SAga SEND SLim SLon SPer SPla SPoG SSpi WCot WFar WHCG
himalense GWJ 9331	WCru
jostaberry	see *R.* x *culverwellii* jostaberry
latifolium	CPLG
laurifolium	CBcs CPLG EBee ELan EQua EWTr MBri MRav NLar SPer WFar WHCG WSHC WSpi
- (f)	CMac EPfP
- (m)	CHar CMac EPfP WPat
- 'Mrs Amy Doncaster'	EPla WCot
- Rosemoor form	CSam EPfP SKHP SPoG SSpi WCot WHCG WPGP
menziesii	CHll EWes WCot
nigrum	SEND
- 'Baldwin' (B)	CDoC CTri CWSG EPfP LRHS NLar SDea SKee SPoG
- 'Barchatnaja' (B)	CAgr
- 'Ben Alder'^{PBR} (B)	CAgr CWib LRHS MAsh SDea
- 'Ben Connan'^{PBR} (B) Υ^{H4}	CAgr CWib EMui EPfP ERea GTwe LRHS MAsh MBri MGos NLar SCoo SDea SKee SPer SPoG
- 'Ben Gairn'^{PBR} (B)	CAgr
- 'Ben Lomond'^{PBR} (B) Υ^{H4}	CAgr CSBt CTri CWib EMui ENot GTwe LAst LBuc LRHS MAsh MGos MRav SDea SGFT SKee SPer
- 'Ben More' (B)	CAgr CSBt CWib MBri SDea
- 'Ben Nevis' (B)	CAgr CSBt CTri CWib GTwe SDea SKee

- 'Ben Sarek'PBR (B) ♀H4	CAgr CDoC CSBt CSut CTri CWSG CWib EMui ENot GTwe LBuc LRHS MAsh MGos MNHC MRav NLar SDea SGFT SKee SPer SPoG WOrn
- 'Ben Tirran'PBR (B)	CAgr CDoC CWib ERea LBuc LRHS MAsh MBri MGos NLar SKee SPoG WOrn
- 'Black Reward' (B)	CAgr MCoo
- 'Boskoop Giant' (B)	CAgr CTri GTwe MGan SPer
* - 'Byelorussian Sweet' (B)	CAgr
- 'Consort' (B)	CAgr
- 'Daniel's September' (B)	GTwe
* - 'Hystawneznaya' (B)	CAgr
- 'Jet' (B)	CAgr ENot GTwe
* - 'Kosmicheskaya' (B)	CAgr
- 'Laxton's Giant' (B)	GTwe
- 'Mendip Cross' (B)	GTwe
- 'Pilot Alexander Mamkin' (B)	CAgr
- 'Seabrook's' (B)	CAgr MGan
- 'Titania' (B)	EMui LRHS SGFT
- 'Tsema' (B)	MCoo
- 'Wellington XXX' (B)	CAgr CSBt CTri GTwe LBuc MGan NBlu SPer
- 'Westwick Choice' (B)	GTwe
§ ***odoratum***	More than 30 suppliers
- 'Crandall'	CAgr LEdu
praecox	CBcs SEND
'Redwing' (R) **new**	LRHS
rubrum 'Blanka' (W)	CSut
- 'Cascade' (R)	CAgr
- 'Cherry' (R)	CAgr MCoo
- 'Fay's New Prolific' (R)	GTwe
- 'Hollande Rose' (P)	GTwe
- 'Jonkheer van Tets' (R) ♀H4	CAgr CSBt CWSG CWib EMil EMui EPfP GTwe IArd LRHS MAsh MCoo NLar SDea SGFT SKee SPer
- 'Junifer' (R)	CAgr EMui GTwe LRHS SGFT SKee
- 'Laxton's Number One' (R)	CAgr CTri EMui ENot GTwe MAsh MGan MRav SDea SPer
- 'Laxton's Perfection' (R)	MCoo
- 'October Currant' (P)	GTwe
- 'Raby Castle' (R)	GTwe
- 'Red Lake' (R) ♀H4	CAgr CTri CWSG CWib EPfP ERea GTwe LBuc LCro LRHS MGan MGos MNHC NBlu NLar SDea SKee SPer SPoG WOrn
- 'Redpoll' (R)	LRHS SKee
- 'Redstart' (R)	CAgr CSBt CTri CWib GTwe LBuc MAsh MBri NLar SDea SKee SPoG
- 'Rondom' (R)	CAgr SDea
- 'Rosetta' (R) **new**	MCoo
- 'Rovada' (R)	CAgr CSut CWib EMil EMui ERea GTwe LRHS MAsh SGFT SKee
- 'Stanza' (R) ♀H4	CAgr EMil GTwe MCoo SDea
- 'Transparent' (W)	GTwe
§ - 'Versailles Blanche' (W)	CAgr CMac CSBt CTri CWib EMui ENot EPfP GTwe LBuc MAsh MBri MGan MGos SDea SGFT SKee SPer SPoG WOrn
- 'White Dutch' (W)	MCoo
- 'White Grape' (W) ♀H4	GTwe
- 'White Pearl' (W)	MCoo SDea
- White Versailles	see *R. rubrum* 'Versailles Blanche'
- 'Wilson's Long Bunch' (R)	GTwe
sanguineum	CDul EMac MBar NEgg WBVN WFar WMoo
I - 'Atrorubens Select'	MBri
- 'Brocklebankii'	CAbP CMac CPLG EBee ELan EPfP EPla LRHS MAsh MGos MRav SHBN SLim SPer SPla WEas WPen WSHC
- 'Elkington's White'	SLon
- 'King Edward VII'	More than 30 suppliers
- 'Koja'	EBee GBin LBuc LRHS LSRN MAsh MBri MGos NPri SPoG WPat
- 'Lombartsii'	MRav
- 'Poky's Pink'	CMac EWTr GSki MBri MGos MRav WOVN
- 'Pulborough Scarlet' ♀H4	More than 30 suppliers
- 'Red Pimpernel'	CDoC CSBt EBee LSRN MBNS NCGa SCoo SWvt WFar
- 'Splendens'	EBee
- 'Taff's Kim' (v)	EPla LRHS MAsh SLon SPoG
- 'Tydeman's White'	CChe CPLG CSBt ELan EPfP MBar NLar NPri SDnm SGar SSpi WPat
- var. ***variegata***	CMac WFar
- White Icicle = 'Ubric' ♀H4	More than 30 suppliers
speciosum ♀H3	More than 30 suppliers
trilobum	LEdu
uva-crispa 'Achilles' (D)	GTwe
- 'Admiral Beattie' (F)	GTwe
- 'Annelii'	CAgr SDea
- 'Bedford Red' (C/D)	GTwe
- 'Bedford Yellow' (C/D)	GTwe
- 'Beech Tree Nestling' (D)	GTwe
- 'Blucher' (D)	GTwe
- 'Bright Venus' (D)	GTwe
- 'Broom Girl' (D)	GTwe
- 'Captivator' (C)	GTwe SDea
- 'Careless' (D) ♀H4	CMac CSBt EMui ENot GTwe LRHS MAsh MGan MGos SDea SKee SPer SPoG
- 'Catherine'	SDea
- 'Cook's Eagle' (C)	GTwe
- 'Cousen's Seedling' (D)	GTwe
- 'Criterion' (D)	GTwe
- 'Crown Bob' (C/D)	GTwe MGan
- 'Dan's Mistake' (D)	GTwe
- 'Drill' (D)	GTwe
- 'Early Sulphur' (D)	GTwe SDea
- 'Firbob' (D)	GTwe
- 'Forester' (D)	GTwe
- 'Freedom' (C)	GTwe
- 'Gipsy Queen' (D)	GTwe
- 'Glenton Green' (D)	GTwe
- 'Golden Ball' (D)	SDea
- 'Golden Drop' (D)	GTwe
- 'Green Gem' (C/D)	GTwe
- 'Green Ocean' (D)	GTwe
- 'Greenfinch' (C) ♀H4	CAgr EMui GTwe SDea
- 'Gretna Green' (F)	GTwe
- 'Guido' (F)	GTwe
- 'Gunner' (C/D)	GTwe
- 'Heart of Oak' (F)	GTwe
- 'Hebburn Prolific' (D)	GTwe
- 'Hedgehog' (D)	GTwe
- 'Hero of the Nile' (D)	GTwe
- 'High Sheriff' (D)	GTwe
- 'Hinnonmäki' (F)	CAgr
- 'Hinnonmäki Gul' (D)	CAgr ENot SDea SGFT
- 'Hinnonmäki Röd' (C/D)	CAgr EMil ENot GTwe MBri MCoo SDea SGFT SPoG
- 'Howard's Lancer' (C/D)	GTwe SDea
- 'Invicta' (C) ♀H4	CAgr CDoC CMac CSBt CSut CTri CWSG EMui ENot EPfP LBuc LCro LRHS MAsh MBri MGan MGos MNHC MRav SCoo SDea SKee SPer SPoG WBVN WOrn
- 'Ironmonger' (D)	GTwe
- 'Jubilee' (C/D)	LBuc MGos
- 'Keen's Seedling' (D)	GTwe
- 'Keepsake' (C/D)	GTwe SDea WBVN
- 'King of Trumps' (F)	GTwe
- 'Lancashire Lad' (C/D)	GTwe
- 'Langley Gage' (D)	GTwe MCoo
- 'Laxton's Amber' (D)	GTwe

- 'Leveller' (D) ♀H4	CMac CSBt CSut CTri EMui ENot GTwe LAst LBuc LRHS MAsh MCoo MGan MGos SDea SGFT SKee SPer
- 'London' (C/D)	GTwe
- 'Lord Derby' (C/D)	GTwe
- 'Martlet' (F)	CAgr GTwe LBuc MAsh MCoo
- 'May Duke' (C/D)	SDea
- 'Mitre' (D)	GTwe
- 'Pax'PBR (D)	CAgr CDoC CSBt CSut EMil EMui EPfP GTwe LBuc LRHS MAsh MBri SDea SKee SPoG WOrn
- 'Peru' (D)	GTwe
- 'Pitmaston Green Gage' (D)	GTwe
- 'Plunder'	GTwe
- 'Prince Charles' (F)	GTwe
- 'Queen of Trumps' (D)	GTwe
- var. ***reclinatum*** 'Aston Red'	see *R. uva-crispa* 'Warrington'
- 'Red Champagne'	GTwe
- 'Remarka' (C/D) **new**	EMui
- 'Rifleman' (D)	GTwe
- 'Rokula'PBR (C/D)	CDoC EMui GTwe SDea SGFT SKee
- 'Rosebery' (D)	GTwe
- 'Scotch Red Rough' (D)	GTwe
- 'Scottish Chieftan' (D)	GTwe
- 'Snow' (F)	EPfP SCoo
- 'Snowdrop' (D)	GTwe
- 'Spinefree' (C)	GTwe
- 'Surprise' (D)	GTwe
- 'Telegraph' (F)	GTwe
- 'Tom Joiner' (F)	GTwe
- 'Victoria' (C/D)	GTwe
§ - 'Warrington'	GTwe
- 'Whinham's Industry' (C/D) ♀H4	CMac CSBt CTri EMil EMui ENot GTwe LAst LBuc LRHS MAsh MBri MGos MRav SDea SPer SPoG WBVN
- 'White Lion' (C/D)	GTwe
- 'White Transparent' (C)	GTwe
- 'Whitesmith' (C/D)	CTri GTwe MCoo MGan NBlu SDea
- 'Woodpecker' (D)	GTwe
- 'Yellow Champagne' (D)	GTwe
viburnifolium	CSam LEdu NLar
§ 'Worcesterberry' (C)	EMui MGos SDea SPer

Richea (*Epacridaceae*)

dracophylla	GGar SAPC

Ricinocarpos (*Euphorbiaceae*)

pinifolius	ECou

Ricinus (*Euphorbiaceae*)

communis	CDTJ
- 'Carmencita' ♀H3	LRav SGar
- 'Carmencita Pink'	CDTJ
- 'Carmencita Red'	CDTJ
- 'Gibsonii'	CDTJ
- 'Impala'	CDTJ CSpe
- 'Raven' **new**	LRav
- 'Zanzibariensis'	CDTJ EShb

Riocreuxia (*Asclepiadaceae*)

torulosa	CPLG SPlb

Robinia (*Papilionaceae*)

x ***ambigua***	SSpi
§ ***boyntonii***	LSRN SLon
§ ***hispida***	CDul CEnd CLnd CWib ECrN ELan EPfP EWTr MAsh MBlu SBLw SHBN SPer SPoG SSpi WJas WOrn WSPU
- 'Macrophylla'	CEnd
- 'Rosea' misapplied	see *R. boyntonii*, *R. hispida*
- 'Rosea' ambig.	CBcs EBee LPan SBLw
kelseyi	CDul EBee EWes SPer WSpi
x ***margaretta*** Casque Rouge	see *R.* x *margaretta* 'Pink Cascade'
§ - 'Pink Cascade'	CCVT CDoC CDul CEnd CLnd EBee ECrN EPfP EWTr LAst LPan LRHS MAsh MBlu MBri MGos SBLw SBod SCoo SCrf SHBN SLim SLon SPer WFoF WPGP
neomexicana	CLnd
pseudoacacia	CCVT CDul CLnd EBee ECrN ELan EMac EPfP EWTr LBuc LPan LRav MCoo SBLw SPlb WBVN WFar WNor
- 'Bessoniana'	EBee ECrN LAst SBLw SCoo
- 'Fastigiata'	see *R. pseudoacacia* 'Pyramidalis'
- 'Frisia' ♀H4	More than 30 suppliers
- 'Inermis' hort.	see *R. pseudoacacia* 'Umbraculifera'
§ - 'Lace Lady'PBR	CWSG EBee ELan ENot EPfP LPan LRHS MAsh MBri MGos MRav NLar SCoo SLim SPoG
- 'Myrtifolia'	SBLw
§ - 'Pyramidalis'	EBee SBLw
- 'Rozynskiana'	CDul MAsh
- 'Tortuosa'	CDul CEnd EBee ECrN ELan EMil LAst LPan LRHS MBlu MGos SBLw SPer WPGP
- 'Twisty Baby'PBR	see *R. pseudoacacia* 'Lace Lady'
§ - 'Umbraculifera'	CDul CLnd ECrN EMac EMil LPan MBri MGos SBLw SCoo
- 'Unifoliola'	SBLw
x ***slavinii*** 'Hillieri' ♀H4	CDoC CDul CEnd CLnd EBee ECrN ELan EPfP EWTr LRHS LSRN MAsh MBlu MBri MGos SCrf SPer SPoG WOrn WPGP WSpi

Rochea see *Crassula*

Rodgersia ✿ (*Saxifragaceae*)

ACE 2303	GBuc
CLD 1329	NHol
CLD 1432	NHol
from Tibet **new**	CWsd
aesculifolia ♀H4	More than 30 suppliers
- green bud	IBlr
- var. ***henrici***	CBct CLAP NBro NMyG SWat WMoo WTin
- - hybrid	EBee EWTr GBuc ITim NHol NLar WAul WHil
- pink-flowered	SSpi
- 'Red Dawn'	IBlr
aff. ***aesculifolia*** petaloid	IBlr
'Blickfang'	IBlr
Cally strain **new**	EDAr
'Die Anmutige'	CLAP
'Die Schöne'	CLAP EBee GBin NLar
'Die Stolze' **new**	GBin
'Elfenbeinturm'	IBlr
'Fireworks'	CFir CLAP EBee ELan GBin MSte SPer WFar WPnP
'Herkules'	CBct EBee ECtt EGle GBin GMaP LSou MBNS NBhm NLar SSpi WCot WGwG
'Ideal'	WCot
'Irish Bronze' ♀H4	CLAP EBee GBin LRHS SSpi WCAu WFar WMoo WPnP
'Koriata'	IBlr
'Kupfermond'	IBlr
'La Blanche' **new**	EBee WCot WGwG
'Maigrün'	IBlr

nepalensis	CLAP IBlr MDun
'Panache'	IBlr
'Parasol'	CBct CLAP CWsd GBin GBuc IBlr NHol SSpi WPGP WPnP
pinnata	More than 30 suppliers
- B&SWJ 7741A	WCru
- L 1670	CLAP SSpi
- SDR 3301	GKev
- 'Alba'	EBee IBlr MLLN NHol WMAq WPnP
- 'Buckland Beauty'	CWsd IBlr SBla SSpi
- 'Cally Salmon'	EGle EWes IBlr
- 'Chocolate Wing'	CLAP CSpe EBee EPfP GBin GQue MAvo MBNS NBPN NBhm NLar NMRc NMoo SPoG
- 'Crûg Cardinal'	WCru
- 'Elegans'	CBct CDes EBee ELan EMFW ENot EPfP EPla GMaP IBlr LCro LRHS MRav NEgg NHol NMyG NOrc SMad SPer SWvt WAul WCot WHil WPnP
- 'Jade Dragon Mountain'	IBlr
- 'Maurice Mason'	CLAP EGle IBlr SDix SMHy
- 'Mont Blanc'	IBlr
- Mount Stewart form	IBlr
- 'Perthshire Bronze'	IBlr
- pink-flowered **new**	WCru
- 'Rosea'	IBlr
- 'Superba' ♀H4	More than 30 suppliers
- white-flowered	GAbr WCru
pinnata* x *sambucifolia	IBlr
podophylla ♀H4	More than 30 suppliers
- 'Braunlaub'	CLAP EBee NBPN NBro WFar WMoo WPnP
- 'Bronceblad'	EBee IBlr
- Donard form	GBin IBlr MBri WPGP
- 'Rotlaub'	CDes CLAP EBee EGle IBlr LRHS WCot WMoo WPGP
- 'Smaragd'	CDes CLAP EBee EGle GBin IBlr LRHS NLar
purdomii hort.	CDes CLAP EBee LRHS WCot WPGP
'Reinecke Fuchs'	IBlr
'Rosenzipfel'	IBlr
sambucifolia	CBcs CDWL CLAP EBee EMFW GKev GSki ITim LEdu NEgg NLar NSti SMac SPer WCAu WFar WMoo WPnP WTin
- B&SWJ 7899	WCru
- dwarf pink-flowered	IBlr
- dwarf white-flowered	IBlr
- 'Mountain Select'	WCot WFar
- white-flowered	ITim
tabularis	see *Astilboides tabularis*

Rohdea (*Convallariaceae*)

japonica	CHEx EBee WCot WPGP
- B&SWJ 4853	WCru
- 'Godaishu' (v)	WCot
- 'Gunjaku' (v)	EMon WCot
- 'Lance Leaf'	EPla
- long-leaved	WCot WFar
- 'Miyakonojo' (v)	EBee WCot
- 'Talbot Manor' (v)	CBct EBee EBla EPla WCot
- 'Tama-jishi' (v)	WCot
- 'Tuneshige Rokujo' (v)	WCot
watanabei	EBee
- B&SWJ 1911	WCru

Romanzoffia (*Hydrophyllaceae*)

californica	EBee
§ ***sitchensis***	CTri EBee MAvo
suksdorfii E. Greene	see *R. sitchensis*
tracyi	CDes CLAP EBee GGar GKev NRya WBor WPrP
unalaschcensis	CLAP EBee GKev NWCA SRms WBVN WPer WPtf

Romneya (*Papaveraceae*)

coulteri ♀H4	More than 30 suppliers
§ - var. ***trichocalyx***	CBct CFir CGHE CPLG EBee SKHP WPGP
§ - 'White Cloud' ♀H4	CBct CPLG EBee ELan SKHP SMad SSpi WPGP WSpi
x ***hybrida***	see *R. coulteri* 'White Cloud'
trichocalyx	see *R. coulteri* var. *trichocalyx*

Romulea (*Iridaceae*)

amoena 'Nieuwoudtville'	ECho
atrandra	CStu
autumnalis	CStu ECho
barkerae 'Paternoster'	ECho
battandieri	EBrs ECho
bulbocodium	ECho WAbe
- var. ***clusiana***	EBrs ECho
- var. ***crocea*** **new**	EBrs
* - 'Knightshayes'	SCnR
camerooniana	CPLG CStu
campanuloides	EDif WAbe
columnae	EBrs ECho
dichotoma	ECho
engleri	CStu
eximea **new**	WCot
gigantea	CStu
kamisensis	ECho
leipoldtii	ECho
linaresii	GKev
longituba	see *R. macowanii*
* ***luteoflora*** var. ***sanguinea***	EBee GCrs NMen
§ ***macowanii***	EBrs
- var. ***alticola***	WAbe
- var. ***macowanii***	CStu
namaquensis	ECho
nivalis	EBrs ECho
obscura var. ***blanda***	ECho
- var. ***obscura***	ECho
- var. ***subtestacea***	ECho
ramiflora	CPBP CPLG EBrs ECho
requienii	NMen
rosea	CPBP WCot
saldanhensis	CStu
tempskyana	CPBP EBrs
tortuosa	CPLG

Rondeletia (*Rubiaceae*)

amoena	SOWG

Rorippa (*Brassicaceae*)

nasturtium-aquaticum	EMFW WMAq

Rosa ✿ (*Rosaceae*)

ACE 241	CFee
A Shropshire Lad = 'Ausled'PBR (S)	LRHS LStr MAus MJon NEgg NSRo SWCr
Abbeyfield Gold (F) **new**	ENot
Abbeyfield Rose = 'Cocbrose'PBR (HT) ♀H4	ENot GCoc GGre MGan MRav SPer
§ 'Abbotswood' (*canina* hybrid)	MAus
Abigaile = 'Tanelaigib'PBR (F)	MJon
Abraham Darby = 'Auscot'PBR (S)	CGro EBee EPfP ESty LAst LCro LRHS LStr MAsh MAus MJon MRav MWgw NEgg SPer SPoG SSea SWCr WAct WHCG
Absent Friends = 'Dicemblem' (F) **new**	IDic
'Adam Messerich' (Bb)	EBee MAus SLon SWCr WHCG
'Adélaïde d'Orléans' (Ra) ♀H4	CRHN EBee LRHS MAus MRav NSRo SFam SPer SWCr WAct WHCG

Admirable = 'Searodney' (Min)	MJon
'Admiral Rodney' (HT)	MGan MJon
Adriana = 'Frydesire' (HT)	MBri
Agatha Christie = 'Kormeita'[PBR] (ClF)	ENot MRav SWCr
'Aglaia' (Ra)	MAus WHCG
'Agnes' (Ru) 🏆[H4]	ECnt EPfP GCoc IArd LRHS MAus MGan MRav NLar SPer SSea SWCr WAct WHCG WOVN
'Agnès Schilliger' **new**	MRav
'Aimée Vibert' (Ra)	CSam EBee MAus MRav NLar SPer SWCr WAct WHCG
'Alain Blanchard' (G)	MAus MGan SWCr WHCG
Alan Titchmarsh = 'Ausjive' **new**	LRHS LStr MAsh MAus SCoo SPer SWCr
§ x ***alba*** 'Alba Maxima' (A)	CBgR GCoc GGre LRHS MAus MGan MRav NEgg NLar SFam SPer SSea SWCr WAct WHCG
§ - 'Alba Semiplena' (A) 🏆[H4]	LRHS MAus MGan SPer SWCr WAct WHCG
- Celestial	see *R.* 'Céleste'
- 'Maxima'	see *R.* x *alba* 'Alba Maxima'
Alba Meidiland = 'Meiflopan'[PBR] (S/GC)	WOVN
'Albéric Barbier' (Ra) 🏆[H4]	CRHN CSBt CSam CWSG EBee ECnt ELan ENot EPfP LCro LRHS LStr MAus MBri MGan MJon MRav NBir NPri NWea SMad SPer SSea SWCr WAct WHCG
'Albertine' (Ra) 🏆[H4]	More than 30 suppliers
'Alchymist' (S/Cl)	CPou EBee ENot EPfP LRHS MAsh MAus MGan MRav NLar SPer SWCr WAct WHCG
Alec's Red = 'Cored' (HT)	CBcs CGro CSBt CTri CWSG ENot GCoc GGre LAst LCro LRHS LStr MAsh MAus MGan MJon MRav NPri SPer SPoG SWCr
Alexander = 'Harlex' (HT) 🏆[H4]	CGro CSBt ENot GCoc LGod LStr MAus MGan MJon MRav SPer SSea SWCr
'Alexander von Humboldt' (Cl)	MGan
'Alexandre Girault' (Ra)	CRHN EBee LRHS MAus NLar SPer SWCr WHCG
'Alfred de Dalmas' misapplied	see *R.* 'Mousseline'
'Alfresco'[PBR] (ClHT)	CSBt LGod MBri MJon SSea SWCr
'Alida Lovett' (Ra)	MAus
Alison = 'Coclibee'[PBR] (F)	GCoc
§ 'Alister Stella Gray' (N)	EBee LRHS MAus MCot MGan NEgg SPer SSea SWCr WAct WHCG
'Allen Chandler' (ClHT)	MAus
'Allgold' (F)	CBcs CGro MGan
Alnwick Castle = 'Ausgrab'[PBR] (S)	MAus MBri SCoo SWCr
'Aloha' (ClHT) 🏆[H4]	CBcs CGro CTri EBee EPfP ESty LAst LCro LRHS LStr MAsh MAus MBri MGan MJon MRav NLar SPer SPoG SSea SWCr WAct
alpina	see *R. pendulina*
'Alpine Sunset' (HT)	CTri ESty GGre LWoR MAsh MRav SPer SPoG SWCr
altaica misapplied	see *R. spinosissima* 'Grandiflora'
altaica Willd.	see *R. spinosissima*
Altissimo = 'Delmur' (Cl)	EBee MAus MGan SPer SSea SWCr WAct
'Amadis' (Bs)	MAus WHCG
Amanda = 'Beesian' (F)	ESty MBri
'Amazing Grace' (HT)	GGre SWCr
Amber Abundance = 'Harfizz'[PBR] (S)	ESty MRav
Amber Cover = 'Poulbambe'[PBR] (GC)	ECnt SWCr
Amber Nectar = 'Mehamber'[PBR] (F)	MAsh MJon SWCr
Amber Queen = 'Harroony'[PBR] (F) 🏆[H4]	CGro CSBt CTri EPfP ESty GCoc GGre IArd LGod LStr LWoR MAsh MAus MBri MGan MJon MRav NPri SPer SPoG SWCr
Amber Star = 'Manstar' (Min)	MJon
Amber Sunset = 'Manamsun' (Min)	MJon
Ambridge Rose = 'Auswonder' (S)	LRHS MAus MJon NEgg SPer
'Amélia'	see *R.* 'Celsiana'
Amelia = 'Poulen011'[PBR] (S)	ECnt MAsh SWCr
'American Pillar' (Ra)	CGro CRHN CSBt CSam CTri CWSG EBee ECnt ELan ENot LCro LRHS LStr MAsh MAus MGan MRav SPer SSea SWCr WHCG WKif
'Amy Robsart' (RH)	MAus MGan
'Anaïs Ségalas' (G)	MAus
§ 'Andersonii' (*canina* hybrid)	ISea MAus WAct
'Andrea' (ClMin)	MJon
§ 'Anemone' (Cl)	MAus
anemoniflora	see *R.* x ***beanii***
anemonoides	see *R.* 'Anemone'
- 'Ramona'	see *R.* 'Ramona'
'Angel Gates'	WAct
Angela Rippon = 'Ocaru' (Min)	CSBt MJon SPer
'Angela's Choice' (F)	MGan
Anisley Dickson = 'Dickimono'[PBR] (F) 🏆[H4]	IDic LGod MGan SPer
'Ann Aberconway' (F)	WBod
Ann = 'Ausfete'[PBR]	LRHS MAus
Anna Ford = 'Harpiccolo' (Min/Patio) 🏆[H4]	CWSG LStr MAus MGan SPer SWCr
Anna Livia = 'Kormetter'[PBR] (F) 🏆[H4]	ECnt ENot GGre MGan MJon
Anne Boleyn = 'Ausecret'[PBR] (S)	LRHS MAsh MAus NEgg SCoo SWCr
'Anne Cocker' (F)	GCoc
'Anne Dakin' (ClHT)	MAus
Anne Harkness = 'Harkaramel' (F)	MAus MGan SPer
'Anne of Geierstein' (RH)	MAus MGan
Annick = 'Fryfrenzy'[PBR] (F)	MBri
Antique '89 = 'Kordalen'[PBR] (ClF)	ENot MJon WGer
Aperitif = 'Macwaira'[PBR] (HT)	EBee ECnt ESty GCoc MJon
apothecary's rose	see *R. gallica* var. *officinalis*
'Apple Blossom' (Ra)	MGan SSea SWCr WHCG
Apricot Ice = 'Diceyti'[PBR] (Poly/F)	IDic
'Apricot Nectar' (F)	MAus MGan SPer
'Apricot Silk' (HT)	CBcs CTri LAst MAus MGan MRav SPer SWCr
Apricot Summer = 'Korpapiro' (Patio)	MBri
Apricot Sunblaze = 'Savamark' (Min)	CSBt
'Aquarius' **new**	LWoR
'Archiduc Joseph' misapplied	see *R.* 'Général Schablikine'
'Archusa' **new**	SLon
Ards Beauty = 'Dicjoy' (F)	SPer
'Arethusa' (Ch)	EBee SPla
'Aries' **new**	LWoR
'Arizona Sunset' (Min)	MJon
§ ***arkansana*** var. ***suffulta***	WHCG
Armada = 'Haruseful' (S)	SSea
'Arrillaga' (HP)	MAus

	'Arthur Bell' (F) Υ^{H4}	CGro CSBt CWSG ENot EPfP ESty GGre IArd LAst LCro LRHS LStr LWoR MAsh MAus MGan MRav NPri SPer SPoG SSea SWCr
	'Arthur de Sansal' (DPo)	MAus WHCG
	arvensis	CCVT CRWN LBuc MAus NHaw NWea WAct
	'Assemblage des Beautés' (G)	MAus
	'Astra Desmond' (Ra)	WTin
	Audrey Wilcox = 'Frywilrey' (HT)	CSBt
	'Auguste Gervais' (Ra)	LRHS MAus SPer WHCG
	Austrian copper rose	see *R. foetida* 'Bicolor'
	Austrian yellow	see *R. foetida*
	'Ausvariety'^{PBR}	see *R.* Kathryn Morley = 'Ausclub'
	'Autumn Delight' (HM)	MAus WHCG
	Autumn Fire	see *R.* 'Herbstfeuer'
	'Autumn Sunlight' (ClF)	MGan SPer SWCr
	'Autumn Sunset' (S)	MJon
	'Autumnalis'	see *R.* 'Princesse de Nassau'
	'Aviateur Blériot' (Ra)	MAus
	'Avignon' (F)	ECnt
	Avon = 'Poulmulti'^{PBR} (GC) Υ^{H4}	EBee ECnt ELan GCoc LGod MJon MRav NPri SPer SWCr WHCG
	Awakening = 'Probuzení' (Cl)	EBee MGan NLar SWCr WHCG WOVN
	'Ayrshire Splendens'	see *R.* 'Splendens'
	Baby Baccara = 'Meipaede' **new**	SWCr
	'Baby Bio' (F/Patio)	CBcs SWCr
	'Baby Darling' (Min)	MGan SWCr
	'Baby Faurax' (Poly)	MAus
	Baby Gold Star (Min)	see *R.* 'Estrellita de Oro'
	Baby Love = 'Scrivluv'^{PBR} (yellow) (Min/Patio) Υ^{H4}	CTri LGod MAus
	Baby Masquerade = 'Tanba' (Min)	MGan MJon MRav SPer SWCr
	Babyface = 'Rawril'^{PBR} (Min)	ESty
	'Ballerina' (HM/Poly) Υ^{H4}	CBcs CGro CSBt EBee ECnt ELan ENot EPfP ESty EWTr GCoc GGre LAst LGod LRHS LStr MAsh MAus MBri MGan MJon MRav MWgw NEgg SPer SSea SWCr WAct WHCG WKif
	Ballindalloch Castle = 'Cocneel'^{PBR} (F)	GCoc
	'Baltimore Belle' (Ra)	CRHN MAus WAct WHCG
	banksiae (Ra)	CPou GQui SRms
	- SF 96051	ISea
	- 'Alba Plena'	see *R. banksiae* var. *banksiae*
§	- var. ***banksiae*** (Ra/d)	CPou CSBt CTri EBee ELan EPfP ERea IClo LCro LPan LStr MAus SBra WGer XPep
	- 'Lutea' (Ra/d) Υ^{H3}	More than 30 suppliers
	- 'Lutescens' (Ra)	XPep
	- var. ***normalis*** (Ra)	CSBt LRHS MAus NSti SLon SWCr WCot WHer WOut XPep
I	- 'Rosea'	NLar
	'Bantry Bay' (ClHT)	CSBt EBee ELan ENot LStr MGan NBlu SPer SPla SSea SWCr
	Barbara Austin = 'Austop'^{PBR} (S)	LRHS MAus
	Barkarole = 'Tanelorak'^{PBR} (HT)	CSBt ESty LStr SWCr
	'Baron de Wassenaer' (CeMo)	MGan
	'Baron Girod de l'Ain' (HP)	EBee ELon ESty MAsh MAus MCot MGan MRav NEgg NHaw NLar SPla SWCr WAct WGer WHCG
	'Baroness Rothschild' (HP)	see *R.* 'Baronne Adolph de Rothschild'
	'Baroness Rothschild' (HT)	see *R.* Baronne Edmond de Rothschild = 'Meigriso'
§	'Baronne Adolph de Rothschild' (HP)	EBee MGan MRav
§	Baronne Edmond de Rothschild = 'Meigriso' (HT)	MAus MGan WAct
	Baronne Edmond de Rothschild, Climbing = 'Meigrisosar' (Cl/HT)	CSBt
	'Baronne Prévost' (HP)	MAus SFam WAct WHCG
	Baroque Floorshow = 'Harbaroque'^{PBR} (S)	MRav
§	x ***beanii*** (Ra)	EPla SMad
	'Beau Narcisse' (G)	MAus
	'Beauté' (HT)	MGan
	Beautiful Britain = 'Dicfire'^{PBR} (F)	CWSG IDic LStr MGan MRav SLon SWCr
	Beautiful Sunrise = 'Bostimebide'^{PBR} (Cl/Patio)	MAsh MBri MJon SWCr
	Behold = 'Savahold' (Min)	MJon
	'Bel Ange' (HT)	MGan SWCr
	bella	LRHS
§	Bella = 'Pouljill'^{PBR} (S)	CPou EPfP
	'Belle Amour' (AxD)	MAus WAct WHCG
	'Belle Blonde' (HT)	MGan SPer
	'Belle de Crécy' (G) Υ^{H4}	CPou CSam EBee LRHS LStr MAsh MAus NPri SFam SPer SPoG SWCr WAct WHCG
	'Belle des Jardins' misapplied	see *R.* x *centifolia* 'Unique Panachée'
	Belle Epoque = 'Fryyaboo'^{PBR} (HT)	GCoc LStr MGan MJon SWCr
	'Belle Isis' (G)	MAus MRav SPer
	'Belle Portugaise' (ClT)	MAus
§	'Belvedere' (Ra)	MAus MBri MGan WHCG
	'Bengal Beauty' (Ch)	WGwG WTMC
	Benita = 'Dicquarrel' (HT)	IDic
	Benjamin Britten = 'Ausencart'^{PBR} (S)	CSBt EPfP LRHS MAus MJon NEgg SWCr
§	'Bennett's Seedling' (Ra)	SSea
	Benson and Hedges Gold = 'Macgem' (HT)	CWSG
	Benson and Hedges Special = 'Macshana'^{PBR} (Min)	ENot ESty GGre MJon
	Berkshire = 'Korpinka'^{PBR} (GC) Υ^{H4}	ENot LStr MGan SSea SWCr
	Best of Friends = 'Pouldunk'^{PBR} (HT)	EBee ECnt SWCr
	Best Wishes = 'Chessnut'^{PBR} (Cl/v)	SPoG SWCr
	Bettina = 'Mepal' (HT)	MGan
	Betty Boop = 'Wekplapic'^{PBR} (F)	MJon SWCr
	Betty Driver = 'Gandri'^{PBR} (F)	MGan SPer
	Betty Harkness = 'Harette'^{PBR} (F)	GCoc LStr
	'Betty Prior' (F)	GCoc MGan
§	Bewitched = 'Poulbella'^{PBR} (F)	ECnt EPfP SWCr
	Bianco = 'Cocblanco'^{PBR} (Patio/Min)	GCoc MAus MRav
	'Big Chief' (HT)	MJon
	Big Purple = 'Stebigpu'^{PBR} (HT)	ECnt ESty MJon SWCr
	Birthday Boy = 'Tan97607' (HT) **new**	ESty SWCr
	Birthday Girl = 'Meilasso'^{PBR} (F)	ESty LAst MJon MRav SLon SSea SWCr
	Birthday Wishes = 'Guesdelay' (HT)	CTri LRHS MAsh SWCr
	Bishop Elphinstone = 'Cocjolly' (F)	GCoc

'Bishop of Bradford' (Cl) new	ECnt
Black Baccara = 'Meidebenne'PBR new	ESty MBri SWCr
'Black Beauty' (HT)	MAus MJon
'Black Ice' (F)	CGro MGan SWCr
'Black Jack' (Ce)	see *R.* 'Tour de Malakoff'
Black Jade = 'Benblack' (Min/Patio)	MJon
'Blairii Number Two' (ClBb) ♀H4	LRHS MAus MRav NEgg NLar SFam SPer SWCr WAct WHCG
'Blanche de Vibert' (DPo)	EBee MAus
'Blanche Double de Coubert' (Ru) ♀H4	CDul CSam CTri EBee ECnt ELan EPfP GCoc LBuc LCro LSRN LStr MAus MGan MJon MWgw SFam SPer SPoG SSea SWCr WAct WEas WHCG WOVN
'Blanche Moreau' (CeMo)	EBee MAus MGan NHaw NLar SLon SPer WAct
'Blanchefleur' (CexG)	EBee MAus MRav
'Blessings' (HT) ♀H4	CBcs CGro CSBt ENot GGre LAst LCro LStr MAsh MAus MGan MJon MRav NBlu SPer SWCr
'Bleu Magenta' (Ra) ♀H4	EBee EWTr IArd MAus MRav NLar SWCr WAct WHCG WKif
'Bloomfield Abundance' (Poly)	CPou MAus MGan MRav SPer SWCr WAct WHCG WHer
'Blossomtime' (Cl)	SMad SPer
'Blue Diamond' (HT)	SWCr
Blue Moon = 'Tannacht' (HT)	CGro CTri ELan EPfP GCoc GGre LAst MGan MJon MRav NPri SPer SPoG SSea SWCr
Blue Peter = 'Ruiblun'PBR (Min)	ESty MJon
'Blush Damask' (D)	WHCG
'Blush Hip' (A)	MAus
'Blush Noisette'	see *R.* 'Noisette Carnée'
'Blush Rambler' (Ra)	CSBt EBee MAus MGan SPer SPla SSea SWCr WAct WHCG
'Blushing Lucy' (Ra)	MTPN SMrm WAct WHCG
Blythe Spirit = 'Auschool'PBR (S)	LCro LStr MAus MBNS NEgg SWCr
'Bobbie James' (Ra) ♀H4	CPLG EBee EPfP LRHS LStr MAus MBri MGan MJon MRav NEgg NLar NSRo SPer SSea SWCr WAct WBVN WHCG
'Bobby Charlton' (HT)	SSea
Bonica = 'Meidomonac'PBR (GC) ♀H4	More than 30 suppliers
Bonita = 'Poulen009'PBR (S)	ECnt LRHS MAsh SWCr
'Bonn' (HM/S)	CBcs
'Bonnie Scotland' (HT)	MGan SWCr
Boogie-Woogie = 'Poulyc006'PBR (Cl)	ECnt LRHS MAsh SPoG SWCr
'Botzaris' (D)	SFam
'Boule de Neige' (Bb)	CBcs CBgR CGro EBee ECnt ELan ENot EPfP GCoc LCro LRHS LStr MAus MGan MRav SFam SPer SPla WAct WHCG WOVN
'Bouquet d'Or' (N)	EBee MAus SWCr
'Bouquet Tout Fait' misapplied	see *R.* 'Nastarana'
'Bouquet Tout Fait' (N)	WHCG
'Bourbon Queen' (Bb)	MAus SWCr WHCG
Bow Bells = 'Ausbells' (S)	MAus
Bowled Over = 'Tandolgnil'PBR (F)	ESty SWCr
Boy O Boy = 'Dicuniform' (GC)	IDic
Boys' Brigade = 'Cocdinkum' (Patio)	GCoc
§ ***bracteata***	CHll CRHN EWes GQui MAus WHCG
Brass RingPBR	see *R.* Peek-a-boo
Brave Heart = 'Horbondsmile' (F)	GGre MAus MBri MRav SPoG SWCr
Breath of Life = 'Harquanne'PBR (ClHT)	CGro CSBt CTri CWSG ELan EPfP GGre LCro LGod LStr MAus MGan MJon MRav SPer SPoG SSea SWCr
Breathtaking = 'Hargalore'PBR (HT)	ESty SWCr
Bredon = 'Ausbred' (S)	MAus
§ 'Brenda Colvin' (Ra)	ISea MAus
Bride = 'Fryyearn'PBR (HT)	ESty GCoc LStr MRav SPoG
Bridge of Sighs = 'Harglowing'PBR (Cl)	EBee ECnt ESty LStr MBri MJon SPoG SWCr
Bright Day = 'Chewvermillion'PBR (Min/Cl)	MAsh SWCr
Bright Fire = 'Peaxi'PBR (Cl)	MBri SSea
Bright Smile = 'Dicdance' (F/Patio)	IDic MAus MGan MRav SPer SSea
Brilliant Pink Iceberg = 'Probril' (F)	EBee ECnt LStr SWCr
'Brindis' (ClF)	MGan SWCr
Britannia = 'Frycalm'PBR (HT)	ECnt ESty LRHS MAsh MJon SWCr
Broadlands = 'Tanmirsch'PBR (GC)	LGod MGan NLar SLon SWCr
Brother Cadfael = 'Ausglobe'PBR (S)	EBee LRHS LStr MAus MBri NLar SCoo SPer SSea SWCr
Brown Velvet = 'Maccultra'PBR (F)	ESty MJon SWCr
'Brownie' (F)	GGre
§ ***brunonii*** (Ra)	CPLG EWes MAus WCot
- CC 4515	GKev
- CC 4891	EWld
- 'Betty Sherriff' (Ra)	GGar
§ - 'La Mortola' (Ra)	EBee MAus MRav SPer SWCr
Brush-strokes = 'Guescolour' (F)	ESty
Buck's Fizz = 'Poulgav'PBR (F)	MGan
'Buff Beauty' (HM) ♀H4	CSBt CSam CWSG EBee ECnt ELan ENot EPfP EWTr GCoc LCro LRHS LStr MAsh MAus MGan MJon MRav MWgw NEgg NPri SFam SMad SPer SSea SWCr WAct WHCG WOVN XPep
'Bullata'	see *R.* x *centifolia* 'Bullata'
§ 'Burgundiaca' (G)	MAus SSea WAct
Burgundian rose	see *R.* 'Burgundiaca'
Burgundy Ice = 'Prose' (F)	ESty MGan SWCr
'Burma Star' (F)	MGan
burnet, double pink	see *R. spinosissima* double pink
burnet, double white	see *R. spinosissima* double white
Bush Baby = 'Peanob'PBR (Min)	LGod LStr SPer SWCr
Buttercup = 'Ausband'PBR (S)	LRHS MAus SWCr
'Butterscotch Dream' (Patio)	GGre
Buxom Beauty = 'Korbilant'PBR (HT)	EBee ECnt ENot ESty GCoc LRHS MAsh MJon NPri SCoo SWCr
'C.F. Meyer'	see *R.* 'Conrad Ferdinand Meyer'
'Café' (F)	SWCr
californica (S)	MAus
- 'Plena'	see *R. nutkana* 'Plena'
'Callisto' (HM)	MAus WHCG
CalypsoPBR	see *Rosa* Concert
'Camayeux' (G)	CPou EBee ECnt MAus NLar SPer SWCr WAct WHCG
Cambridgeshire = 'Korhaugen'PBR (GC)	LGod LStr MAus NPri SPer SSea SWCr
'Camélia Rose' (Ch)	WHCG
'Cameo' (Poly)	MAus MGan
Camille Pisarro = 'Destricol' (F)	LCro MRav SPoG

'Canary Bird'	see *R. xanthina* 'Canary Bird'
'Cancer' **new**	LWoR
Candle in the Wind = 'Mackincat' (S)	MJon
'Candy Stripe' (HT)	NBlu
canina (S)	CArn CCVT CDul CGro CLnd CRWN CTri EMac EPfP LBuc MAus MRav NPri NWea WMou WOut XPep
- 'Abbotswood'	see *R.* 'Abbotswood'
- 'Andersonii'	see *R.* 'Andersonii'
'Cantabrigiensis' (S) Υ^{H4}	CSam EBee MAus SFam SPer SSea SWCr WAct WFar WHCG
Canterbury = 'Ausbury' (S)	MAus
'Capitaine Basroger' (CeMo)	MAus
'Capitaine John Ingram' (CeMo) Υ^{H4}	MAus SLon SPer SSea WHCG
I 'Capricorn' **new**	LWoR
'Captain Christy' (ClHT)	see *R.* 'Climbing Captain Christy'
Caramella = 'Korkinteral'^{PBR}	ENot
'Cardinal de Richelieu' (G) Υ^{H4}	CPou CSam CTri EBee ELon EPfP GCoc LAst LCro LRHS LStr MAsh MAus MGan MRav NEgg SFam SPer SPoG SWCr WAct WHCG
Cardinal Hume = 'Harregale' (S)	MGan SPer SWCr
Carefree Days = 'Meirivouri' (Patio)	ENot GGre LRHS MAsh SWCr
Carefree Wonder = 'Meipitac' (S)	LAst
Caribbean Dawn = 'Korfeining'^{PBR} (Patio)	ENot
'Caring' (Patio)	SWCr
Caring for You = 'Coclust'^{PBR} (HT)	GCoc SWCr
'Carmenetta' (S)	MAus NHaw WAct
'Carol' (Gn)	see *R.* 'Carol Amling'
§ 'Carol Amling' (Gn)	MJon
carolina	LHop NHaw SLPl WHCG
'Caroline Testout'	see *R.* 'Madame Caroline Testout'
Cascade = 'Poulskab'^{PBR} (Min/Cl)	EBee ECnt
§ Casino = 'Macca' (ClHT)	CTri GCoc GGre MAsh MGan MJon MRav SPer SPoG SWCr
'Castle Apricot'^{PBR}	see *R.* Lazy Days
'Castle Cream'	see *R.* Perfect Day
'Castle Fuchsia Pink'^{PBR}	see *R.* Bewitched = 'Poulbella'
Castle of Mey = 'Coclucid' (F)	GCoc
'Castle Red'^{PBR}	see *R.* Krönberg
'Castle Shrimp Pink'^{PBR}	see *R.* Fascination = 'Poulmax'
'Castle Yellow'^{PBR}	see *R.* Summer Gold
'Catherine Mermet' (T)	MAus
§ 'Cécile Brünner' (Poly) Υ^{H4}	CTri EBee ECnt ELan ENot GCoc LStr MAus MCot MGan NLar SPer SPla SSea SWCr WAct WHCG
'Cécile Brünner, White'	see *R.* 'White Cécile Brünner'
Celebration 2000 = 'Horcoffitup'^{PBR} (S)	MAus
§ 'Céleste' (A) Υ^{H4}	GCoc LGod LRHS LStr MRav SFam SPer SSea SWCr WAct WHCG WOVN
'Célina' (CeMo)	MGan
'Céline Forestier' (N) Υ^{H3}	CPou MAus MRav SFam SLon SPer SWCr WHCG
§ 'Celsiana' (D)	CSam LRHS MAus NEgg SFam SPer SSea SWCr WAct WHCG
Centenaire de Lourdes = 'Delge' (F)	SWCr
Centenary = 'Koreledas'^{PBR} (F) Υ^{H4}	ENot SPer
§ x ***centifolia*** (Ce)	LRHS MAus MRav SSea SWCr WAct WHCG
§ - 'Bullata' (Ce)	MAus
§ - 'Cristata' (Ce) Υ^{H4}	CSam ECnt EPfP LStr SFam SPer SSea SWCr WAct WHCG
§ - 'De Meaux' (Ce)	MAus MRav NLar SPer SPla SSea WAct WHCG
§ - 'Muscosa' (CeMo)	GCoc LStr MAus MGan MRav MWgw NEgg SFam SPoG SSea WAct
- 'Muscosa Alba'	SSea
- 'Parvifolia'	see *R.* 'Burgundiaca'
§ - 'Shailer's White Moss' (CeMo)	EWTr LRHS MAus MGan SFam SSea WHCG
- 'Spong' (Ce)	EBee MAus
§ - 'Unique' (Ce)	MAus SSea
§ - 'Unique Panachée' (Ce)	MAus MGan
'Centifolia Variegata'	see *R.* x *centifolia* 'Unique Panachée'
Centre Stage = 'Chewcreepy'^{PBR} (S/GC)	MJon
Century Sunset = 'Tansaras'^{PBR} (HT)	MBri
'Cerise Bouquet' (S) Υ^{H4}	LRHS MAus MGan MRav SPer SWCr WAct WHCG WKif
Champagne Cocktail = 'Horflash'^{PBR} (F) Υ^{H4}	GGre LWoR SPer SWCr
'Champagne Dream' (Patio)	LRHS LWoR MAsh SWCr
Champagne Moments = 'Korvanaber'^{PBR} (F)	CGro CSBt EBee ECnt ELan ENot ESty GCoc GGre LGod LRHS LStr MAsh MBri MJon MRav SPer SPoG SWCr
'Champneys' Pink Cluster' (China hybrid)	MAus SFam
Chandos Beauty = 'Harmisty' **new**	ECnt ESty GCoc
'Chanelle' (F)	MGan SPer SWCr
Chantal Merieux = 'Masmaric' **new**	MRav
Chapeau de Napoléon	see *R.* x *centifolia* 'Cristata'
'Chaplin's Pink Climber' (Cl)	MGan SWCr
Charity = 'Auschar' (S)	MAus
Charles Austin = 'Ausles' (S)	MAus MRav WAct WHCG
Charles Darwin = 'Auspeet'^{PBR} (S)	MAus SCoo SPer SWCr
Charles de Gaulle	see *R.* Katherine Mansfield = 'Meilanein'
'Charles de Mills' (G) Υ^{H4}	CSam EBee ECnt ELan ELon EPfP LCro LRHS LStr MAus MRav NEgg NSRo SFam SPer SSea SWCr WAct WHCG
Charles Notcutt = 'Korhassi' (S)	ENot
Charles Rennie Mackintosh = 'Ausren'^{PBR} (S)	CSBt LRHS LStr MAus NEgg SWCr
Charlie's Rose = 'Tanellepa' (HT)	ESty MBri SWCr
Charlotte = 'Auspoly'^{PBR} (S) Υ^{H4}	EPfP ESty LRHS LStr MAus MBri MJon SCoo SPer SSea SWCr
Charmant = 'Korpeligo'^{PBR}	ENot
Charmian = 'Ausmian' (S)	MAus
Charming Cover = 'Poulharmu'^{PBR} (GC/S)	SWCr
Chartreuse de Parme = 'Delviola' (S)	LCro MRav SWCr
'Château de Clos-Vougeot' (HT)	IArd
Chatsworth = 'Tanotax'^{PBR} (Patio/F)	MRav SPer SSea SWCr
Chaucer = 'Auscer' (S)	MAus
§ Cheek to Cheek = 'Poulslas'^{PBR} (Min/Cl)	MAsh SWCr
Cheerful Charlie = 'Cocquimmer' (F)	GCoc MBri MRav SWCr
Chelsea Belle = 'Talchelsea' (Min)	MJon

Cherry Brandy '85 = 'Tanryrandy'PBR (HT)	CSBt MGan
Cheshire = 'Fryelise'PBR (HT)	GCoc MJon SWCr
Cheshire = 'Korkonopi' PBR (County Rose Series) (S)	ENot MAus MBri
'Cheshire Life' (HT)	MAus MGan MJon NPri SWCr
Chester Cathedral = 'Franshine' (HT)	MJon
'Chevy Chase' (Ra)	WAct
Chianti = 'Auswine' (S)	MAus MGan NLar WAct WHCG
Chicago Peace = 'Johnago' (HT)	MGan SLon SWCr
Child of AchievementPBR	see *R.* Bella = 'Pouljill'
Childhood Memories = 'Ferho' (HM/Cl)	SPla
Chilterns = 'Kortemma'PBR (GC)	SWCr
'Chinatown' (F/S) ♀H4	CBcs CGro CSBt ENot EPfP GGre LStr MAsh MAus MGan MJon MRav NBlu SPer SPoG SWCr
chinensis misapplied	see *R.* x *odorata*
- 'Mutabilis'	see *R.* x *odorata* 'Mutabilis'
- 'Old Blush'	see *R.* x *odorata* 'Pallida'
Chivalry = 'Macpow' (HT)	SWCr
Chloe = 'Poulen003'PBR (S)	CPou ECnt SLon SWCr
'Chloris' (A)	CPou
Chris = 'Kirsan'PBR (Cl)	EBee ECnt ESty MGan MJon SWCr WGor
Christian Dior = 'Meilie' (HT)	SWCr
'Christine Gandy' (F)	MGan
Christopher = 'Cocopher' (HT)	GCoc
Christopher Columbus = 'Meinronsse' (HT)	IArd
Christopher Marlowe = 'Ausjump'PBR (S)	MAus SCoo SWCr
Cider Cup = 'Dicladida'PBR (Min/Patio) ♀H4	CTri EPfP ESty GGre IDic LStr MAus SWCr
Cinderella (Cl) <u>**new**</u>	ENot
'Cinderella' (Min)	CSBt MGan SWCr
Citron-Fraise = 'Delcifra' (S)	SWCr
City Lights = 'Poulgan'PBR (Patio)	CSBt
'City of Cardiff' (HT)	MGan
'City of Leeds' (F)	CWSG GGre LWoR MAsh MGan
City of London = 'Harukfore'PBR (F)	CSBt LStr MJon SPer SWCr
'City of Portsmouth' (F)	CBcs
Clair Matin = 'Meimont' (ClS)	MAus SPer SWCr WAct
'Claire Jacquier' (N)	EBee MAus SFam SPer SWCr WHCG
Claire Rayner = 'Macpandem' (F/Patio)	MJon
Claire Rose = 'Auslight'PBR (S)SPoG	CGro LRHS MAus MJon MRav SPer
Clarinda = 'Cocsummery'PBR (F)	GCoc SWCr
Claude Monet = 'Jacdesa' (HT)	MRav SPoG SWCr
Cleo = 'Beebop' (HT)	MJon
Cleopatra = 'Korverpea'PBR (HT)	ENot
'Cliff Richard' (F)	ESty
'Climbing Alec's Red' (ClHT)	SWCr
'Climbing Allgold' (ClF)	SLon SWCr
'Climbing Arthur Bell' (ClF) ♀H4	CSBt CTri ESty GGre LAst LGod LWoR MAsh SPer SPoG SSea SWCr
'Climbing Ballerina' (Ra)	CSBt MGan SWCr
'Climbing Blue Moon' (ClHT)	LAst MGan SWCr

§ 'Climbing Captain Christy' (ClHT)	MAus
'Climbing Cécile Brünner' (ClPoly) ♀H4	CSBt CTri EBee ECnt EPfP LRHS LStr MAsh MAus MCot MGan MRav MWgw SPer SPoG SSea SWCr WAct WHCG
'Climbing Château de Clos-Vougeot' (ClHT)	MAus
'Climbing Christine' (ClHT)	MAus
§ 'Climbing Columbia' (ClHT)	ERea SPer WHCG
'Climbing Crimson Glory' (ClHT)	CPou MAus MGan SWCr WAct
§ 'Climbing Devoniensis' (ClT)	CPou
'Climbing Ena Harkness' (ClHT)	CBcs CTri GCoc GGre LRHS MAsh MAus MBNS MGan MRav SEND SPer SPla SPoG SWCr
'Climbing Etoile de Hollande' (ClHT) ♀H4	CSBt CSam CTri CWSG EPfP GCoc GGre LCro LRHS LStr MAsh MAus MGan MJon MRav MWgw SFam SMad SPer SSea SWCr
Climbing Fragrant Cloud = 'Colfragrasar' (ClHT)	CBcs ELan MGan
Climbing Gold Bunny = 'Meigro-Nurisar' (ClF)	MJon
'Climbing Iceberg' (ClF) ♀H4	CGro CSBt EBee ELan ENot EPfP ESty GGre IArd LCro LRHS LStr LWoR MAsh MAus MGan MJon MRav SPer SPla SSea SWCr WAct WHCG
'Climbing Jazz'PBR	see *R.* That's Jazz = 'Poulnorm'
'Climbing Josephine Bruce' (ClHT)	LRHS MGan
'Climbing la France' (ClHT)	MAus MRav
§ 'Climbing Lady Hillingdon' (ClT) ♀H3	ECGP EPfP LRHS MAus MGan MRav MWgw NEgg NLar SFam SPer SPoG SSea SWCr WAct WHCG
'Climbing Lady Sylvia' (ClHT)	CSBt EBee EPfP LRHS MAus MGan SPer SWCr
'Climbing Little White Pet'	see *R.* 'Félicité Perpétue'
'Climbing Madame Abel Chatenay' (ClHT)	MAus
'Climbing Madame Butterfly' (ClHT)	LRHS MAus MGan NLar SPer SWCr
'Climbing Madame Caroline Testout' (ClHT)	CPou CTri EBee MAsh MAus NPri SPer SWCr
§ 'Climbing Madame Edouard Herriot' (ClHT)	MAus SWCr
'Climbing Madame Henri Guillot' (ClHT)	MAus
'Climbing Maman Cochet' (ClT)	MAus
'Climbing Masquerade' (ClF)	MAus MGan MJon MRav SPer SSea SWCr
§ 'Climbing Mevrouw G.A. van Rossem' (ClHT)	MAus
'Climbing Mrs Aaron Ward' (ClHT)	MAus
'Climbing Mrs G.A. van Rossem'	see *R.* 'Climbing Mevrouw G.A. van Rossem'
'Climbing Mrs Herbert Stevens' (ClHT)	EBee LRHS MAus MRav SPer SWCr WHCG
'Climbing Mrs Sam McGredy' (ClHT) ♀H4	CSBt CSam MAus MGan SWCr
'Climbing Niphetos' (ClT)	MAus SWCr
'Climbing Ophelia' (ClHT)	CPou MAus SPer
Climbing Orange Sunblaze = 'Meiji Katarsar'PBR (ClMin)	SPer
'Climbing Pascali' (ClHT)	MGan
§ 'Climbing Paul Lédé' (ClT)	EBee EWTr LRHS MAus NEgg SWCr

	'Climbing Peace' (ClHT)	CSBt
	'Climbing Picture' (ClHT)	MAus
§	'Climbing Pompon de Paris' (ClMinCh)	CTri LHop LRHS MAus MGan MRav SLPl SPer WHCG
	'Climbing Ruby Wedding'	SPoG
	'Climbing Shot Silk' (ClHT) ΨH4	CSBt EBee MGan SPer SWCr
§	'Climbing Souvenir de la Malmaison' (ClBb)	CPou EBee MAus SPer SWCr WAct WHCG
	'Climbing Sterling Silver' (ClHT)	MGan
	Climbing Super Star = 'Tangostar' (ClHT)	MAus
	'Climbing Sutter's Gold' (ClHT)	MGan
	'Climbing The Queen Elizabeth' (ClF)	SWCr
	'Climbing Trumpeter' (ClF)	MAsh
	'Climbing White Cloud'PBR	see *R.* White Cloud = 'Korstacha'
	Clodagh McGredy = 'Macswanle'PBR (F)	ESty MJon
	Cloud Nine = 'Fryextra' (HT)	EBee ECnt ESty GCoc LGod SWCr
	Cocktail = 'Meimick' (S)	MGan
	'Coconut Ice' (F) **new**	SWCr
	Colchester Beauty = 'Cansend' (F)	ECnt
	Colchester Castle = 'Poulcs008'PBR	ECnt
	Colibri = 'Meimal' (Min)	SPer
§	'Colonel Fabvier'	MAus XPep
	colonial white	see *R.* 'Sombreuil'
	'Columbian'	see *R.* 'Climbing Columbia'
	'Commandant Beaurepaire' (Bb)	EBee LRHS MAus SWCr
	common moss	see *R.* x *centifolia* 'Muscosa'
	Commonwealth Glory = 'Harclue'PBR (HT)	ESty SWCr
	'Compassion' (ClHT) ΨH4	More than 30 suppliers
	'Compassionate' (F) **new**	MRav
	'Complicata' (G) ΨH4	CAbP CTri ECGP EPfP LRHS LStr MAus MGan MRav SFam SPer SSea SWCr WAct WHCG WOVN
N	'Comte de Chambord' misapplied	see *R.* 'Madame Knorr'
	Comtes de Champagne = 'Ausufo'PBR (S)	LRHS MAus SCoo
	'Comtesse Cécile de Chabrillant' (HP)	MAus
	'Comtesse de Lacépède' misapplied	see *R.* 'Du Maître d'Ecole'
§	'Comtesse de Murinais' (DMo)	MAus SFam
	Comtesse de Ségur = 'Deltendre' (S)	MRav
§	'Comtesse du Caÿla' (Ch)	MAus SSea
§	Concert = 'Poulclimb'PBR (Cl)	ECnt MBri SWCr
	'Conditorum' (G)	SFam WAct
	Congratulations = 'Korlift' (HT)	CSBt EBee ECnt ENot GCoc IArd LCro LStr MAus MGan MJon MRav NPri SPer SPoG SSea SWCr
	Connie = 'Boselftay'PBR (F)	ESty GGre SWCr
§	'Conrad Ferdinand Meyer' (Ru)	CSBt MAus MGan NHaw SPer
	Conservation = 'Cocdimple'PBR (Min/Patio)	GCoc GGre LAst MBri SWCr
	Constance Finn = 'Hareden'PBR (F)	MRav SPoG SWCr
	'Constance Spry' ΨH4	EBee ECnt ELan ENot EPfP LCro LRHS LStr MAsh MAus MBri MGan MJon MRav NEgg NPri SFam SPer SWCr WAct WGer WHCG
§	'Cooperi' (Ra)	CAbP CWib EWTr MAus SPer SSea SWCr WAct WHCG WKif WPGP
	Cooper's Burmese	see *R.* 'Cooperi'
	'Copenhagen' (ClHT)	MAus
	Copper Pot = 'Dicpe' (F)	MGan SPer
	'Coral Cluster' (Poly)	MAus MGan
	Coral Reef = 'Cocdarlee'PBR (Min/Patio)	GGre LWoR SWCr
	'Coral Satin' (Cl)	MGan
	Cordelia = 'Ausbottle'PBR (S)	LRHS MAus MBri
	'Cornelia' (HM) ΨH4	CBcs CSBt CSam CTri EBee ENot EPfP EWTr GCoc IArd LAst LCro LRHS LStr MAsh MAus MGan MJon MRav SFam SPer SSea SWCr WAct WHCG WOVN
	Coronation Street = 'Wekswetrup' (F) **new**	MJon
	'Coronet' (F)	WHCG
	Corvedale = 'Ausnetting'PBR (S)	MAus
	cottage maid	see *R.* x *centifolia* 'Unique Panachée'
	Cottage Rose = 'Ausglisten'PBR (S)	CGro MAus MRav NEgg SWCr
	Countess of Wessex = 'Beacream' **new**	MBri SWCr
	'Coupe d'Hébé' (Bb)	MAus
§	Courage = 'Poulduf'PBR (HT)	ECnt
	Courvoisier = 'Macsee'	CSBt
	'Cramoisi Picotée' (G)	MAus
	'Cramoisi Supérieur' (Ch)	MAus WHCG
	Crathes Castle = 'Cocathes'	GCoc
	Crazy for You = 'Wekroalt'PBR (F)	ESty LGod MAsh MJon SSea SWCr
	Cream Abundance = 'Harflax'PBR (F)	ESty LStr SWCr
	'Cream Patio' (Patio) **new**	LWoR
	'Cream Silk' **new**	LWoR
	'Crème Anglaise'PBR (Cl)	EBee ECnt MGan
	'Creme Brulee'PBR (Cl)	MGan
	Crème de la Crème = 'Gancre'PBR (Cl)	CGro CSBt EBee ECnt ESty GCoc MBri MGan MJon MRav SSea SWCr WAct
	'Crépuscule' (N)	EBee SWCr WHCG
	Cressida = 'Auscress' (S)	MAus
	crested moss	see *R.* x *centifolia* 'Cristata'
	Cricri = 'Meicri' (Min)	MAus MGan
	Crimson Cascade = 'Fryclimbdown'PBR (Cl)	CSam ESty LRHS MAsh MAus MBri MGan MRav SPoG SSea SWCr WHCG
	crimson damask	see *R. gallica* var. *officinalis*
	'Crimson Descant' (Cl)	ECnt
	'Crimson Globe' (Mo)	MGan
	'Crimson Glory' (HT)	EBee MGan SWCr
	'Crimson Shower' (Ra) ΨH4	CSam LRHS MAsh MAus MGan MJon MRav NEgg NSRo SPer SWCr WAct WGer WHCG WHer
	'Cristata'	see *R.* x *centifolia* 'Cristata'
	Crocus Rose = 'Ausquest'PBR (S)	EPfP LCro LRHS MAus MBri MRav NEgg SWCr
	Crown Princess Margareta = 'Auswinter'PBR (S)	EBee ECnt LCro LRHS MAus MBri MJon NEgg SCoo SPer SWCr
	cuisse de nymphe	see *R.* 'Great Maiden's Blush'
	'Cupid' (ClHT)	MAus SPer SWCr
I	'Cutie' (Patio) **new**	SWCr
	Cymbeline = 'Auslean' (S)	SPer
	Dacapo = 'Poulcy012' (Cl/Patio)	ECnt
	'D'Aguesseau' (G)	EBee MAus

	'Daily Mail'	see *R.* 'Climbing Madame Edouard Herriot'
	'Dainty Bess' (HT)	MAus SSea
	'Dainty Maid' (F)	MAus
	x ***damascena*** var. ***bifera***	see *R.* x *damascena* var. *semperflorens*
§	- var. ***semperflorens*** (D)	CBgR MAus MRav NLar SSea SWCr WAct WHCG
N	- 'Trigintipetala' misapplied	see *R.* 'Professeur Emile Perrot'
§	- var. ***versicolor*** (D)	MGan SFam SPer SSea SWCr WAct
	'Dame de Coeur' (HT)	NBlu SWCr
	Dame Wendy = 'Canson' (F)	MAus MGan
	Dames de Chenonceau = 'Delpabra' (S)	MRav SWCr
	'Danaë' (HM)	CSam EBee MAus SWCr WHCG
	Dancing Pink = 'Hendan' (F)	MJon
	'Dancing Queen' (Cl)	ECnt GCoc
	Danny Boy = 'Dicxcon'PBR (Patio)	IDic MJon WGor
	Danse des Sylphes = 'Malcair' (Cl)	SWCr
	'Danse du Feu' (Cl)	CBcs CGro CSBt CTri CWSG EBee ELan GGre LCro LGod LRHS LStr MAsh MAus MGan MJon MRav NPri SPer SPoG SWCr WBVN
	'Daphne Gandy' (F)	MGan
	Dapple Dawn = 'Ausapple' (S)	MAus SPer
	Darling Flame = 'Meilucca' (Min)	MRav
	'Dart's Defender'	SLPl
	David Whitfield = 'Gana'PBR (F)	MGan SWCr
	davidii	MAus
	Dawn Chorus = 'Dicquasar'PBR (HT) ♀H4	CGro CSBt CWSG ECnt ENot EPfP ESty GCoc IDic LGod LRHS LStr MAsh MAus MBri MGan MRav SPer SPoG SSea SWCr
	'Daybreak' (HM)	CTri MAus WAct WHCG
	Dazzling Delight = 'Cocuseful'PBR (F)	GCoc
	'De Meaux'	see *R.* x *centifolia* 'De Meaux'
	'De Meaux, White'	see *R.* 'White de Meaux'
§	'De Rescht' (DPo) ♀H4	CBgR CPou CTri EBee ECnt EPfP LCro LRHS MAsh MAus MGan MJon MRav MWgw SPer SPla SPoG SSea SWCr WAct WGer WHCG
	'Dearest' (F)	CBcs CSBt MGan MRav SLon SPer SWCr
	'Debbie Thomas' (HT)	MJon
	Deb's Delight = 'Legsweet'PBR (F)	MJon
	'Debutante' (Ra)	CSam EBee LRHS MAus SWCr WHCG
	'Deep Secret' (HT) ♀H4	CGro CTri CWSG EBee ECnt EPfP ESty GCoc GGre LRHS LStr MAsh MGan MJon MRav SPer SPoG SSea SWCr
	'Delambre' (DPo)	MAus
	'Delicata' (Ru)	MAus
	Della Balfour = 'Harblend'PBR (Cl)	SWCr
	'Dentelle de Malines' (S)	LRHS MAus WAct
	Desert Island = 'Dicfizz'PBR (F)	GCoc IDic SWCr
	'Designer Sunset' **new**	LWoR
§	'Desprez à Fleurs Jaunes' (N)	EBee IArd LRHS MAus MRav NEgg NLar SFam SPer SWCr WHCG
	'Devon Maid' (Cl)	SWCr
	'Devoniensis' (ClT)	see *R.* 'Climbing Devoniensis'
	Devotion = 'Interfluco'PBR (HT)	IDic
	Diamond Border = 'Pouldiram'PBR (S)	ECnt
	'Diamond Jubilee' (HT)	MGan NBlu SWCr
	Diamond = 'Korgazell'PBR (Patio)	ENot ESty GCoc LStr MJon
	'Diamond Wishes' (HT)	LRHS MAsh SWCr
	Dick's Delight = 'Dicwhistle'PBR (GC)	ESty IDic MJon SWCr
	Die Welt = 'Diekor' (HT)	MBri MJon
	'Directeur Alphand' (HP)	WHCG
	Dixieland Linda = 'Beadix' (ClHT)	SSea
	Dizzy Heights = 'Fryblissful'PBR (Cl)	EBee ECnt ESty GCoc MAsh MGan SWCr
	'Docteur Grill' (T)	MAus
	Doctor Dick = 'Cocbaden' (HT)	MBri
	Doctor Goldberg = 'Gandol' (HT)	MGan
	Doctor Jackson = 'Ausdoctor' (S)	MAus
	Doctor Jo = 'Fryatlanta'PBR (F)	SWCr
	'Doctor John Snow' (HT)	MGan
	Doctor McAlpine = 'Peafirst' (F/Patio)	MBri
	'Doctor W. Van Fleet' (Ra/Cl)	MAus
	'Don Juan' (Cl)	MGan SWCr
	'Doris Tysterman' (HT)	CGro CTri GGre LStr MAus MGan SPer SWCr
	Dorothy = 'Cocrocket'PBR (F)	GCoc MRav
	'Dorothy Perkins' (Ra)	CGro CSBt CTri GCoc GGre LRHS MAus MGan MJon MRav NPer SPer SSea SWCr WHCG
	'Dorothy Wheatcroft' (F)	MGan
	'Dortmund' (ClHScB) ♀H4	CPLG EBee LGod LRHS MAus MGan NHaw SPer SWCr WAct WHCG
	Double Delight = 'Andeli' (HT)SPer	CGro ESty GCoc GGre MGan MJon
	'Dream Girl' (Cl)	MAus SFam
	Dream Lover = 'Peayetti'PBR (Patio)	ESty MJon SWCr
	'Dreaming Spires' (Cl)	CSBt ENot SPer SSea
	Drummer Boy = 'Harvacity'PBR (F/Patio)	GGre LWoR MGan SWCr
§	'Du Maître d'Ecole' (G)	MAus MRav WHCG WHer
	Dublin Bay = 'Macdub' (Cl) ♀H4	CSBt CTri EBee ECnt ELan ENot EPfP ESty GGre IArd LAst LGod LRHS LStr MAsh MBri MGan MJon MRav SPer SPoG SSea SWCr WAct WGer
	'Duc de Guiche' (G) ♀H4	CSam MAus SFam SLon SPer SWCr WAct WHCG WHer
	'Duchess of Cornwall' **new**	SWCr
	'Duchess of Portland'	see *R.* 'Portlandica'
	Duchess of YorkPBR	see *R.* Sunseeker = 'Dicracer'
	'Duchesse d'Angoulême' (G)	MAus SFam
	'Duchesse de Buccleugh' (G)	MAus MRav WAct
§	'Duchesse de Montebello' (G) ♀H4	MAus NLar SFam SPer WAct WHCG
	'Duchesse de Verneuil' (CeMo)	MAus SFam
	'Duke of Edinburgh' (HP)	MAus
	'Duke of Wellington' (HP)	SWCr WHCG
	'Duke of Windsor' (HT)	MGan SPer SWCr
	'Dundee Rambler' (Ra)	MAus
§	'Duplex' (S)	LRHS MAus MRav WAct WHCG
	'Dupontii' (S)	MAus MGan NLar SFam SPer WAct WOVN XPep
	'Dupuy Jamain' (HP)	WHCG

	'Dusky Maiden' (F)	EBee MAus SWCr WHCG
	Dusty Springfield = 'Horluvdust' (F)	MGan SWCr
	'Dutch Gold' (HT)	CWSG MAus MGan SPer SSea SWCr
	'E.H. Morse'	see *R.* 'Ernest H. Morse'
	'Easlea's Golden Rambler' (Ra) 🏆H4	CSBt EBee LRHS MAus MRav SLon SWCr WAct WHCG
	Easy Cover = 'Pouleas'PBR (GC)	SWCr
	Easy Going = 'Harflow'PBR (F)	GGre IArd MRav SWCr
	'Eblouissant' (Poly)	MGan
	ecae	MAus
	'Eddie's Jewel' (*moyesii* hybrid)	MAus MGan SWCr
	'Eden Rose' (HT)	MGan
	Eden Rose '88 = 'Meiviolin'PBR (ClHT)	MJon SPer SWCr
	Edith Holden = 'Chewlegacy'PBR (F)	MBri
	'Edward Hyams'	MAus
	eglanteria	see *R. rubiginosa*
	Eglantyne = 'Ausmak'PBR (S) 🏆H4	CSBt EPfP ESty GCoc LCro LRHS LStr MAus MBri MJon MRav SPer SPoG SSea SWCr
	'Eleanor' (Patio) **new**	SLon
	Eleanor = 'Poulberin'PBR (S)	ECnt SWCr
	'Elegance' (ClHT)	MAus
§	***elegantula*** 'Persetosa' (S)	MAus NLar SPer SWCr WAct WHCG
	Elfe = 'Tanelfe' (HT)	NHaw
§	Elina = 'Dicjana'PBR (HT) 🏆H4	CSBt EBee ECnt ENot GGre IDic LGod LStr MAus MGan MJon MRav NBlu SPer SPoG SWCr
	Elizabeth = 'Coctail'PBR (F)	GCoc
	'Elizabeth Harkness' (HT)	CWSG MAus MGan SPer SWCr
	Elizabeth of Glamis = 'Macel' (F)	CGro CTri CWSG GCoc MGan SPer SWCr
	'Elizabeth Stuart' **new**	MRav
	Elle = 'Meibderos'PBR (HT)	ESty SWCr
	Ellen = 'Auscup' (S)	MAus
	'Ellen Poulsen' (Poly)	MGan
	'Ellen Willmott' (HT)	EBee MAus MCot SWCr
	'Elmshorn' (S)	CBcs MGan WHCG
	'Else Poulsen' (Poly)	WHCG
	Emanuel = 'Ausuel' (S)	MAus
	'Emilien Guillot' **new**	MRav
	'Emily Gray' (Ra)	CGro CSBt CTri EBee ECnt ENot GGre LCro LRHS LStr MAsh MAus MGan MRav NPri SPer SSea SWCr WAct WHCG
	'Emma Wright' (HT)	MAus
	'Emotion' (F)	SWCr
	'Empereur du Maroc' (HP)	EBee EWTr MAus MRav WHCG
	Empress Michiko = 'Dicnifty'PBR (HT)	ESty IDic
	'Ena Harkness' (HT)	CTri ELan GGre LRHS MGan SWCr
§	England's Rose = 'Ausrace'PBR (S)	MAus
	English Elegance = 'Ausleaf' (S)	MAus
	English Garden = 'Ausbuff'PBR (S)	CGro EBee ENot EPfP LRHS LStr MAus MRav SPer SWCr
	'English Miss' (F) 🏆H4	CSBt CTri EBee ECnt ENot EPfP ESty LAst LStr MAsh MAus MGan MJon MRav SPer SPoG SWCr
	'Erfurt' (HM)	MAus MGan SPer SWCr WHCG
§	'Erinnerung an Brod' (S)	WHCG
§	'Ernest H. Morse' (HT)	CSBt CTri CWSG GCoc GGre LAst MGan MJon MRav SPer SSea SWCr
	'Ernest May' (HT)	SSea
	Escapade = 'Harpade' (F) 🏆H4	MAus SWCr
	Especially for You = 'Fryworthy'PBR (HT)	CSBt CTri ESty GCoc LGod LRHS LStr MAsh NPri SCoo SPoG SSea
	Essex = 'Poulnoz'PBR (GC)	MRav SPer SWCr
§	'Estrellita de Oro' (Min)	SPer
	'Etain' (Ra)	EBee ECnt
§	'Etendard'	MGan MRav SPer SPla SWCr WAct
	Eternal Flame = 'Korassenet'PBR (F)	ENot ESty SWCr
	Eternally Yours = 'Macspeego'PBR (HT)	ECnt MJon
	'Ethel' (Ra)	CPou EBee SWCr
	'Etoile de Hollande' (HT)	CSBt EBee ELan ENot LRHS NEgg NLar NPri SLon
	'Eugénie Guinoisseau' (Mo)	WHCG
	Euphoria = 'Intereup'PBR (GC/S)	GCoc IDic SWCr
	Euphrates = 'Harunique' (*persica* hybrid)	MAus WAct
	'Europeana' (F)	MGan
	'Evangeline' (Ra)	MAus
	Evelyn = 'Aussaucer'PBR (S) 🏆H4	CSBt EBee EPfP ESty GCoc LRHS LStr MAsh MAus MGan MJon MRav NEgg SPer SPla SWCr
§	Evelyn Fison = 'Macev' (F)	CSBt CTri ELan MAus MGan MRav SPer SWCr
	Evening Light = 'Chewpechette'PBR (ClMin)	MAsh
	Evening Light = 'Tarde Gris' (Min/Cl)	ESty MBri
	'Excelsa' (Ra)	CSBt CTri EPfP IArd LGod MAsh MGan MRav NWea SWCr
	Eye Paint = 'Maceye' (F)	MAus SMrm
	'Eyecatcher' (F)	EBee ECnt
	Eyeopener = 'Interop'PBR (S/GC)	CGro SWCr
	'F.E. Lester'	see *R.* 'Francis E. Lester'
§	'F.J. Grootendorst' (Ru)	EBee LRHS MAus MGan SSea WAct
	Fab = 'Bosconpea'PBR (F)	GGre SWCr
	'Fabvier'	see *R.* 'Colonel Fabvier'
	Fairest Cape = 'Kortifhar' (F) **new**	ENot
	Fairhope = 'Talfairhope' (Min)	MJon
	Fairy Prince = 'Harnougette' (GC)	ESty
	Fairy Queen = 'Sperien' (Poly/GC)	IDic MAsh SWCr
	'Fairy Rose'	see *R.* 'The Fairy'
	Fairyland = 'Harlayalong' (Poly)	MGan
	Faithful = 'Haressay'PBR (F)	GGre SWCr
	Falstaff = 'Ausverse'PBR (S)	CSBt ECnt EPfP LCro LRHS LStr MAus MBNS MJon MRav NEgg NSRo SPoG SWCr
	'Fantin-Latour' (*centifolia* hybrid) 🏆H4	CTri EBee ECnt ELan EPfP GCoc LAst LCro LGod LRHS LStr MAsh MAus MGan MRav NEgg SFam SMad SPer SSea SWCr WAct WHCG WKif
	farreri var. ***persetosa***	see *R. elegantula* 'Persetosa'
	Fascination = 'Jacoyel' (HT)	LStr MBri SCoo
§	Fascination = 'Poulmax'PBR (F) 🏆H4	CSBt ECnt ENot EPfP GCoc LRHS MAsh MGan MRav SPer SPoG SWCr
	fedtschenkoana misapplied	MAus SPer WAct WHCG
	fedtschenkoana Regel	SLPl
	Fée des Neiges	see *R.* Iceberg = 'Korbin'
	'Felicia' (HM) 🏆H4	CSBt CSam CTri EBee ECnt ELan ENot EPfP GCoc LCro LGod LRHS LStr MAsh MAus MGan MJon MRav SFam SPer SWCr WAct WHCG WKif WOVN

Name	Suppliers
'Félicité Parmentier' (AxD) ♀H4	EBee LRHS MAus MGan MRav NEgg NLar SFam SPer SWCr WAct WHCG
§ 'Félicité Perpétue' (Ra) ♀H4	CBcs CSBt EBee ELan ENot EPfP GCoc GGre ISea LRHS LStr LWoR MAus MBri MGan MRav NEgg NSRo SFam SPer SPoG SSea SWCr WAct WHCG XPep
Felicity Kendal = 'Lanken' (HT)	MJon
'Fellemberg' (ClCh)	MAus WHCG XPep
Fellowship = 'Harwelcome'^{PBR} (F) ♀H4	ECnt ENot ESty GCoc GGre LGod LStr MAus MGan MJon MRav SCoo SPoG SSea SWCr
'Femina' (HT)	MGan
'Ferdinand Pichard' (Bb) ♀H4	CBgR CPou CSBt EBee ECnt EPfP ESty LAst LCro LRHS MAus MBri MGan MJon MRav MWgw NEgg SPer SPoG SSea SWCr WAct WFoF WGer WHCG WKif WOVN
Ferdy = 'Keitoli'^{PBR} (GC)	MRav SPer SWCr
Fergie = 'Ganfer'^{PBR} (F/Patio)	MGan SWCr
ferruginea	see *R. glauca* Pourr.
Festival = 'Kordialo'^{PBR} (Patio)	ENot ESty LStr MRav SPer SPoG SWCr
Fiery Hit = 'Poulfiry'^{PBR} (Min)	ECnt MAsh
Fiery Sunblaze = 'Meineyta'^{PBR} (Min)	SWCr
Fiesta = 'Macfirinlin' (Patio)	MBri MJon
filipes 'Brenda Colvin'	see *R.* 'Brenda Colvin'
§ - 'Kiftsgate' (Ra) ♀H4	More than 30 suppliers
§ 'Fimbriata' (Ru)	CPou EWTr MAus NLar SPer SSea SWCr WAct
Financial Times Centenary = 'Ausfin' (S)	MAus
Fiona = 'Meibeluxen'^{PBR} (S/GC)	GGre SWCr
'First Love' (HT)	MGan SWCr
'Fisher and Holmes' (HP)	MAus WAct WHCG
Fisherman's Friend = 'Auschild'^{PBR} (S)	MAus SPer
Flashdance = 'Poulyc004'^{PBR} (ClMin)	ECnt SWCr
Flirt = 'Korkopapp'^{PBR}	ENot
'Flora McIvor' (RH)	MAus MGan
'Flore' (Ra)	CRHN MAus SFam
'Florence Mary Morse' (S)	SDix
Florence Nightingale = 'Ganflor'^{PBR} (F)	MGan SWCr
'Flower Carpet Coral'^{PBR} (GC)	CGro GCoc LRHS MAsh SCoo SWCr
Flower Carpet Gold = 'Noalesa'^{PBR} (GC) **new**	LRHS MAsh
Flower Carpet Pink^{PBR}	see *R.* Pink Flower Carpet
Flower Carpet Red Velvet = 'Noare'^{PBR} (GC)	CGro ELan GCoc LStr MAsh MGan SCoo SPer
§ Flower Carpet Sunshine = 'Noason'^{PBR} (GC)	CGro CTri ELan EPfP GCoc LRHS LStr MAsh MBri SCoo SWCr
Flower Carpet Velvet (GC/S)	EPfP LRHS SWCr
Flower Carpet White = 'Noaschnee'^{PBR} (GC) ♀H4	CGro CTri ELan EPfP GCoc LRHS LStr MAsh MBri MGan SCoo SPer SPoG SWCr
Flower Power = 'Frycassia'^{PBR} (Patio)	CSBt ECnt ENot ESty GCoc GGre LStr MAsh MAus MBri MJon MRav SPoG SWCr
§ ***foetida*** (S)	EBee MAus NHaw
§ - 'Bicolor' (S)	LRHS MAus NHaw NLar SPer WAct
§ - 'Persiana' (S)	MAus MGan NHaw
foliolosa	SLPl WHCG

Name	Suppliers
Fond Memories = 'Kirfelix'^{PBR} (Patio)	ESty GCoc LStr MJon SWCr
For You With Love = 'Fryjangle' (Patio) **new**	MGan
Forever Royal = 'Franmite' (F)	ESty
Forever Young = 'Jacimgol'^{PBR} (F)	IDic
forrestiana	MAus WHCG
x ***fortuneana*** (Ra)	WFar
Fortune's double yellow	see *R.* x *odorata* 'Pseudindica'
'Fountain' (HT/S)	MAus MGan SPer SWCr
Fragrant Cloud = 'Tanellis' (HT)	CGro CTri CWSG EBee ECnt ENot EPfP ESty GCoc GGre LAst LRHS LStr LWoR MAsh MAus MBri MGan MJon MRav SPer SPoG SSea SWCr
'Fragrant Delight' (F) ♀H4	CSBt ELan GCoc GGre LAst LStr MAus MGan MJon MRav SPer SPoG SWCr
Fragrant Dream = 'Dicodour'^{PBR} (HT)	CGro ESty IDic LStr MGan MRav SWCr
Fragrant Memories = 'Korpastato'^{PBR} (HT/S)	ENot ESty GCoc LRHS MAsh NPri SCoo SPoG SWCr
Frances Perry = 'Bosrexcity'^{PBR} (F)	SWCr
'Francesca' (HM)	CPou LRHS MAus MGan SFam SPer SWCr WAct WHCG
Francine Austin = 'Ausram'^{PBR} (S/GC)	LRHS MAus MJon NEgg SPer SWCr WAct
§ 'Francis E. Lester' (HM/Ra) ♀H4	CRHN CSam EBee LCro LRHS MAus MBri MJon NLar NSRo SPer SSea SWCr WAct WHCG
x ***francofurtana*** misapplied	see *R.* 'Impératrice Joséphine'
- 'Empress Josephine'	see *R.* 'Impératrice Joséphine'
'François Juranville' (Ra) ♀H4	CPou CRHN CSBt EBee LAst LRHS LStr MAus MBri MGan MRav NLar SPer SWCr WAct
'Frau Dagmar Hartopp'	see *R.* 'Fru Dagmar Hastrup'
§ 'Frau Karl Druschki' (HP)	MAus WAct
'Fred Loads' (F/S) ♀H4	MAus MCot MGan MRav
Freddie Mercury = 'Batmercury' (HT)	MJon
Free as Air = 'Mehbronze' (Patio)	MBri
Freedom = 'Dicjem'^{PBR} (HT) ♀H4	CGro CTri ECnt ENot GCoc GGre IDic LGod LStr MAus MGan MRav NPri SPer SWCr
'Frensham' (F)	CBcs LStr MGan SSea SWCr
Fresh Pink (Min/Poly)	MGan
Friend for Life = 'Cocnanne'^{PBR} (F) ♀H4	GCoc GGre LWoR MJon MRav SWCr
'Friendship' (Patio)	GGre
'Fritz Nobis' (S) ♀H4	CAbP LRHS LStr MAus MGan MRav NLar SPer SWCr WAct WKif
Frothy = 'Macfrothy'^{PBR} (Patio)	ECnt MJon
§ 'Fru Dagmar Hastrup' (Ru) ♀H4	CDul CSBt EBee ECnt ELan EPfP GCoc LBuc LCro LRHS LStr MAus MGan MJon MWgw SPer SPoG SWCr WAct WHCG WOVN
'Frühlingsanfang' (PiH)	CTri MAus SWCr WAct
'Frühlingsduft' (PiH)	SMad SWCr WAct
'Frühlingsgold' (PiH) ♀H4	CBcs ELan EPfP GCoc LRHS LStr MAus MCot MGan MRav NLar NWea SPer SWCr WAct WHCG WKif WOVN
'Frühlingsmorgen' (PiH)	GCoc LStr MAus MGan MRav NPri SPer SSea SWCr WHCG WOVN
Fulton Mackay = 'Cocdana'^{PBR} (HT)	GCoc GGre MGan
Fyvie Castle = 'Cocbamber' (HT)	GCoc
'Gail Borden' (HT)	MGan SWCr
§ ***gallica*** (G)	WAct

	Name	Suppliers
§	- var. ***officinalis*** (G) Ψ^{H4}	CAbP CBgR CSam CTri GCoc GPoy LRHS MAsh MAus MGan MJon MRav SFam SPer SSea SWCr WAct WHCG
	- 'Velutiniflora' (G)	SSea
§	- 'Versicolor' (G) Ψ^{H4}	More than 30 suppliers
	Galway Bay = 'Macba' (ClHT)	EBee GGre LRHS LWoR MAsh MGan MRav SPer SWCr
§	Garden News = 'Poulrim'^{PBR} (HT)	EBee ECnt MAsh SWCr
	'Gardenia' (Ra)	CPou EBee MAus SWCr WHCG
	'Gardiner's Pink' (Ra)	MCot WHCG
	'Garnette Carol'	see *R.* 'Carol Amling'
	'Garnette Pink'	see *R.* 'Carol Amling'
	'Gaujard'	see *R.* Rose Gaujard = 'Gaumo'
	'Gelbe Dagmar Hastrup'^{PBR}	see *R.* Yellow Dagmar Hastrup = 'Moryelrug'
I	'Gemini' **new**	LWoR
	'Général Jacqueminot' (HP)	MAus
	'Général Kléber' (CeMo)	MAus MRav SFam SSea WAct WHCG
§	'Général Schablikine' (T)	EBee MAus SWCr
	'Genesis' (Patio) **new**	ECnt
N	***gentiliana*** misapplied	see *R.* 'Polyantha Grandiflora'
N	***gentiliana*** H. Lév. & Variot	see *R. multiflora* var. *cathayensis*
	Gentle Hermione = 'Ausrumba' **new**	MAsh MAus SWCr
	Gentle Touch = 'Diclulu'^{PBR} (Min/Patio)	CSBt CWSG IDic LAst MRav SPer SPla SWCr
	Geoff Hamilton = 'Ausham'^{PBR} (S)	CSBt ESty LRHS LStr MAsh MAus MBNS NEgg SCoo SPer SWCr
	'Georg Arends' (HP)	MAus
	'George Dickson' (HT)	MAus
	'Georges Vibert' (G)	EBee EWTr MAus SLon WHCG
	Geraldine = 'Peahaze' (F)	SWCr
	'Geranium' (*moyesii* hybrid) Ψ^{H4}	CBcs CDul CSam EBee ELan ENot EPfP GCoc IArd LCro LGod LRHS LStr MAsh MAus MBri MGan MJon MRav NBlu NEgg NPri NScw SEND SPer SSea SWCr WAct WHCG WOVN
	Gerbe d'Or	see *R.* Casino = 'Macca'
	'Gerbe Rose' (Ra)	MAus
	Gertrude Jekyll = 'Ausbord'^{PBR} (S) Ψ^{H4}	More than 30 suppliers
	'Ghislaine de Féligonde' (Ra/S)	CPou EBee EWTr LStr MGan NLar SPer SPoG SSea SWCr WHCG WPen
	Ghita = 'Poulren013' (S)	ECnt
	gigantea	ISea
	- 'Cooperi'	see *R.* 'Cooperi'
	Giggles = 'Kingig' (Min)	MJon
	Ginger Syllabub = 'Harjolina'^{PBR} (Cl)	ESty GCoc GGre MBri MRav SWCr
	Gingernut = 'Coccrazy'^{PBR} (Patio)	SWCr
	Gipsy Boy	see *R.* 'Zigeunerknabe'
	Glad Tidings = 'Tantide'^{PBR} (F)	CSBt CWSG LAst MBri MGan MRav SPer SWCr
	Glamis Castle = 'Auslevel'^{PBR} (S)	CBcs CTri ESty LCro LRHS LStr MAus MBri NEgg SCoo SPer SWCr
	glauca ambig.	EMac
§	***glauca*** Pourr. (S) Ψ^{H4}	More than 30 suppliers
	'Glenfiddich' (F)	CGro CSBt CTri CWSG GCoc GGre LStr LWoR MAus MBri MRav NPri NWea SPer SWCr
	'Glenn Dale' (Cl)	EBee
	Glenshane = 'Dicvood'^{PBR} (GC/S)	IDic MRav
	Global Beauty = 'Tan 94448' (HT)	SWCr
	'Gloire de Bruxelles' (HP)	MRav
	'Gloire de Dijon' (ClT)	More than 30 suppliers
	'Gloire de Ducher' (HP)	MAus MGan WAct WHCG
	'Gloire de France' (G)	MAus MRav WHer
	'Gloire de Guilan' (D)	MAus WAct
	'Gloire des Mousseuses' (CeMo)	EBee SFam WHCG
	'Gloire du Midi' (Poly)	MAus
	'Gloire Lyonnaise' (HP)	EBee SLon WHCG
	Gloriana = 'Chewpope'^{PBR} (ClMin)	CGro ESty LRHS MAsh MAus MBri MJon MRav SCoo SPer SPoG SSea SWCr
	Glorious = 'Interictira'^{PBR} (HT)	ESty IDic MBri MJon SWCr
	'Glowing Abundance' (F) **new**	SWCr
	Glowing Amber = 'Manglow' (Min)	ESty MJon
	'Glowing Pink' **new**	LWoR
	Gold Crown	see *R.* 'Goldkrone'
	Gold Symphonie =	MAsh
	'Goldbusch' (RH)	MGan WAct
	'Golden Anniversary' (Patio)	LStr MAsh SPer SWCr
	'Golden Anniversary' (HT)	LCro
	Golden Beauty = 'Korberbeni'^{PBR} (F)	ENot ESty
	Golden Beryl = 'Manberyl' (Min)	MJon
	Golden Celebration = 'Ausgold'^{PBR} (S) Ψ^{H4}	CSBt CWSG EBee ECnt EPfP ESty GCoc LAst LGod LRHS LStr MAsh MAus MBri MJon MRav NPri SPer SPoG SWCr WGer
	'Golden Chersonese' (S)	MAus
	Golden Future = 'Horanymoll'^{PBR} (Cl)	GGre LWoR MJon SWCr
*	Golden Gate = 'Korgolgat' (Cl)	ENot ESty LStr MBri
	Golden Jewel = 'Tanledolg'^{PBR} (F/Patio)	ENot ESty MAsh MBri SPoG SWCr
	Golden Jubilee = 'Cocagold' (HT)	CTri GCoc GGre MRav SWCr
	Golden Kiss = 'Dicalways'^{PBR} (HT)	GCoc IDic SWCr
	Golden Memories = 'Korholesea'^{PBR} (F)	CGro CSBt EBee ENot ESty GCoc GGre LGod LRHS LStr MAsh MBri MJon MRav NPri SCoo SSea SWCr
	Golden Oldie = 'Fryescape'^{PBR} (HT)	GCoc
§	Golden Penny = 'Rugul' (Min)	MGan
	'Golden Rambler'	see *R.* 'Alister Stella Gray'
	'Golden Salmon' (Poly)	MGan
	'Golden Showers' (Cl) Ψ^{H4}	More than 30 suppliers
	'Golden Slippers' (F)	CBcs
	'Golden Sunblaze'	see *R.* 'Rise 'n' Shine'
	Golden Symphonie = 'Meitoleil' (Min/Patio)	ENot SWCr
	Golden Tribute = 'Horannfree' (F)	MGan
	Golden Trust = 'Hardish'^{PBR} (Patio)	GGre LStr
	Golden Wedding = 'Arokris'^{PBR} (F/HT)	CGro CSBt CTri CWSG EBee ECnt ELan ENot EPfP ESty GCoc GGre IArd LCro LGod LRHS LStr MAsh MAus MGan MJon MRav NPri NWea SPer SPoG SSea SWCr
	'Golden Wedding Celebration'	CGro ESty GGre LWoR
	'Golden Wings' (S) Ψ^{H4}	CTri ELan EPfP GCoc LRHS LStr MAsh MAus MGan MJon MRav SEND SPer SSea SWCr WAct WHCG
	'Goldfinch' (Ra)	EBee ELan EPfP LRHS LStr MAus MBri MRav NEgg NLar NSRo SPer SPoG SWCr WAct WHCG

§	'Goldkrone' (HT)	SWCr
	Goldstar = 'Candide' (HT)	ECnt MGan
	Good as Gold = 'Chewsunbeam'PBR (ClMin)	CSBt ECnt ESty LStr MBri MJon NPri SPer SWCr WGer
	Good Life = 'Cococircus'PBR (HT)	GCoc GGre SCoo SPoG SWCr
	Good Luck = 'Burspec' (F/Patio)	GCoc
	Good News 95 = 'Chespink'PBR	SWCr
	Gordon Snell = 'Dicwriter' (F)	IDic
	Gordon's College = 'Cocjabby'PBR (F) ♀H4	ESty GCoc LWoR MJon
	Grace = 'Auskeppy'PBR (S)	CSBt EBee EPfP MAus MBri MJon NEgg SWCr
	Gracious Queen = 'Bedqueen' (HT)	GCoc MBri SWCr
	'Graciously Pink' **new**	LWoR
	Graham Thomas = 'Ausmas'PBR (S) ♀H4	CGro CSBt EBee ECnt ENot EPfP ESty GCoc LAst LCro LGod LRHS LStr MAsh MAus MGan MJon MRav MWgw NEgg NPri SMad SPer SPla SSea SWCr WAct WHCG WKif WOVN
	'Grandad' **new**	LWoR
	Grande Amore = 'Korcoluma' (HT)	ENot GCoc
	'Grandma' (F) **new**	LWoR
	Grand-mère Jenny = 'Grem' (HT)	MGan
	'Grandpa Dickson' (HT)	CSBt CWSG GGre LAst LBMP LGod LWoR MAsh MAus MGan MJon MRav NPri SPer SWCr WBVN
	Granny's Favourite (F)	GGre LWoR SWCr
	Great Expectations = 'Jacdal' (F)	EBee ENot SPoG
	Great Expectations = 'Lanican' (HT)	CBcs
	Great Expectations = 'Mackalves'PBR (F)	CSBt ECnt EPfP ESty GCoc IArd LGod LRHS LStr MAsh MJon MRav SCoo SPer SWCr
§	'Great Maiden's Blush' (A)	GCoc MRav NLar SFam WAct
	'Great News' (F)	MAus
	Greenall's Glory = 'Kirmac'PBR (F/Patio)	MAus MJon MRav
	'Greenmantle' (RH)	MAus
	Greensleeves = 'Harlenten' (F)	SPer
	Greetings = 'Jacdreco'PBR (F)	IDic MAsh MRav SWCr
	Grenadine = 'Poulgrena'PBR (HT)	EBee ECnt
	Grimaldi = 'Delstror' (F)	LCro SWCr
	'Grootendorst'	see *R.* 'F.J. Grootendorst'
	'Grootendorst Supreme' (Ru)	MAus SPer
N	'Gros Choux de Hollande' (Bb)	WHCG
	Grouse 2000 = 'Korteilhab'PBR (GC)	ENot
	Grouse = 'Korimro'PBR (S/GC) ♀H4	GCoc LRHS MAus NLar SPer SWCr WAct WOVN
	'Gruss an Aachen' (Poly)	EPfP LStr MAus MCot MGan NLar SPer SWCr WAct WHCG
	'Gruss an Teplitz' (China hybrid)	MAus SPer WHCG
	'Guinée' (ClHT)	CSBt EBee ECnt ELan ELon ENot EPfP ESty EWTr LAst LCro LRHS LStr MAsh MAus MGan MRav MWgw NPri SPer SPla SPoG SSea SWCr WHCG
	Guletta	see *R.* Golden Penny = 'Rugul'

	'Gustav Grünerwald' (HT)	MAus
	Guy Savoy = 'Delstrimen'PBR (F)	MRav SWCr
	Gwen Mayor = 'Cocover'PBR (HT)	GCoc
	Gwent = 'Poulurt'PBR (GC)	CSBt ELan GCoc LSRN LStr SPer SSea SWCr WAct WOVN
§	***gymnocarpa*** var. ***willmottiae***	MGan SPer SSea WAct WHCG
	Gypsy Boy	see *R.* 'Zigeunerknabe'
	'Hakuun' (F/Patio) ♀H4	MAus MGan SWCr
	Hallé = 'Fryelectric'PBR (HT)	EBee
	'Hamburger Phönix' (Ra)	CGro MGan SPer WAct
	Hampshire = 'Korhamp'PBR (GC)	MAus MGan
	Hand in Hand = 'Haraztec'PBR (Patio/Min)	GGre MAsh SPoG SWCr
	Handel = 'Macha' (Cl) ♀H4	CGro CSBt CTri CWSG ELan ENot EPfP ESty GGre LAst LCro LRHS LStr LWoR MAsh MBri MGan MJon MRav SPer SPoG SSea SWCr WBVN
	Hanky Panky = 'Wektorcent'PBR	ESty GCoc MBri MJon SWCr
	Hannah Gordon = 'Korweiso'PBR (F)	EBee ECnt ENot MGan SSea SWCr
	'Hanne' (HT)	NBlu
	'Hansa' (Ru)	EBee GCoc LBuc MAus MGan SPer SWCr WHCG WOVN
	Happy Anniversary = 'Bedfranc'PBR	ESty MJon NPri SWCr
	Happy Anniversary = 'Delpre' (F)	CGro CTri GGre LCro LRHS LStr LWoR MAsh MRav SPoG SSea
	'Happy Birthday' (Min/Patio)	CGro CWSG ENot ESty GGre LCro LStr LWoR SPoG SWCr
	Happy Child = 'Auscomp'PBR (S)	CWSG LRHS MAus MJon SPer
	Happy Retirement = 'Tantoras'PBR (F)	ESty GCoc LRHS LStr MAsh MGan MRav NPri SCoo SPoG SSea SWCr
	'Happy Thought' (Min)	CWSG
	Happy Times = 'Bedone'PBR (Patio/Min)	ENot GGre LRHS LWoR MAsh SPoG SWCr
§	x ***harisonii*** 'Harison's Yellow' (PiH)	MAus
§	– 'Williams' Double Yellow' (PiH)	GCoc MAus MGan WAct
	Harlow Carr = 'Aushouse'	LRHS MAsh MAus SCoo SWCr
	'Harry Edland' (F)	GGre LWoR SSea SWCr
	'Harry Wheatcroft' (HT)	CBcs CGro MAus MGan SPer SWCr
	Harvest Fayre = 'Dicnorth'PBR (F)	CGro CTri GGre IDic MGan SPer
	'Headleyensis'	MAus WHCG
	Heart of Gold = 'Coctarlotte'PBR (HT)	ECnt GCoc MRav
	Heartbeat '97 = 'Cocorona'PBR (F)	GCoc GGre SWCr
	Heartbreaker = 'Weksibyl' (Min)	MJon
	Heather Austin = 'Auscook'PBR (S)	LRHS MAus
	'Heather Muir' (*sericea* hybrid) (S)	MAus
	'Heaven Scent' (F)	MJon
	Heavenly Rosalind = 'Ausmash'PBR (S)	LRHS MAus
§	'Hebe's Lip' (DSwB)	MAus MGan WAct
	'Helen Knight' (*ecae* hybrid) (S)	MAsh MAus SSea WHCG
	Helena = 'Poulna'PBR (S)	LRHS MAsh SPoG SWCr
	helenae	CTri EBee MAus MGan NLar SPer SWCr
	– hybrid	WHCG
	'Helhein'PBR	see *R.* Super Sparkle = 'Helfels'
	hemisphaerica (S)	MAus WAct

§	'Henri Martin' (CeMo)	MAus MGan NLar SLon SPer SWCr WAct WHCG
	Henri Matisse = 'Delstrobla' (HT)	LCro MRav SPoG SWCr
	'Henry Nevard' (HP)	MAus
	Her Majesty = 'Dicxotic'[PBR] (F)	IDic
§	'Herbstfeuer' (RH)	MAus SPer
	Heritage = 'Ausblush'[PBR] (S)	CGro EBee ELan ENot EPfP GCoc LCro LGod LRHS LStr MAus MRav NEgg SPer SPla SPoG SWCr WHCG WOVN
	'Hermosa' (Ch)	CBgR EBee LAst LRHS MAus MRav SPla SWCr WAct WHCG XPep
	Hero = 'Aushero' (S)	MAus
	Hertfordshire = 'Kortenay'[PBR] (GC) 🏆H4	ELan ENot MAus MRav NPri SPer SWCr
	'Hidcote Gold' (S)	MAus
	Hide and Seek = 'Diczodiac'[PBR] (F)	IDic
	High Flier = 'Fryfandango' (Cl)	MBri
	High Hopes = 'Haryup'[PBR] (Cl) 🏆H4	CSBt EBee ECnt GGre LRHS LStr MAsh MAus MGan MJon SPer SPla SSea SWCr WHCG
	'Highdownensis' (*moyesii* hybrid) (S)	ELan MAus SPer
	Highfield = 'Harcomp' (Cl)	CSBt MAus SPer SPoG SWCr
	Hilda Murrell = 'Ausmurr' (S)	MAus
	'Hillieri' (S)	MAus
	'Hippolyte' (G)	MAus
	holy rose	see *R.* x *richardii*
	Home of Time = 'Cocquamber'[PBR] (HT)	GCoc
	Home Sweet Home = 'Mailoeur' (Cl/G)	SSea
	'Homère' (T)	MAus
	Honey Bunch = 'Cocglen'[PBR] (F)	GCoc LCro LStr MRav SPer SWCr
	Honeymoon	see *R.* 'Honigmond'
	Honeywood = 'Fryfixit'[PBR] (F)	GCoc
§	'Honigmond' (F)	CWSG SWCr
	'Honorine de Brabant' (Bb)	CPou EBee MAus SPer SPla SWCr WHCG WKif
	Hospitality = 'Horcoff'[PBR] (F)	ESty
	Hot Chocolate = 'Wekpaltez' (F)	ECnt EPfP ESty GCoc LGod LRHS LStr MAsh MBri MGan MJon MRav SCoo SPoG SWCr
	Hot Stuff = 'Maclarayspo' (Min)	MBri MJon SWCr
	Hot Tamale = 'Jacpoy' (Min)	MJon
	House Beautiful = 'Harbingo'[PBR] (Patio)	GGre MRav
	'Hugh Dickson' (HP)	MAus SWCr
	hugonis	see *R. xanthina* f. *hugonis*
	- 'Plenissima'	see *R. xanthina* f. *hugonis*
	'Hula Girl' (Min)	LGod
	Humanity = 'Harcross'[PBR] (F)	MRav
	'Hunter' (Ru)	WAct
	Hyde Hall = 'Ausbosky'	LRHS MAus SCoo SWCr
	I Love You = 'Geelove' (HT)	SLon
	Ice Cream = 'Korzuri'[PBR] (HT) 🏆H4	CWSG ENot ESty LCro LStr MAus MGan MJon MRav SPoG SSea SWCr
§	Iceberg = 'Korbin' (F) 🏆H4	CBcs CGro CSBt CTri CWSG EBee ECnt ENot EPfP ESty GCoc GGre LAst LBMP LCro LGod LRHS LStr MAsh MAus MGan MJon MRav NBlu SPer SPoG SSea SWCr WAct WBVN

	'Iced Ginger' (F)	CGro MGan SPer SWCr
§	'Impératrice Joséphine' 🏆H4	CSam EBee LRHS MAus MRav NEgg SFam SWCr WAct WHCG
	In the Pink = 'Peaverity' (F)	SWCr
	Incognito = 'Briincog' (Min)	MJon
	Indian Summer = 'Peaperfume'[PBR] (HT) 🏆H4	CGro CSBt CWSG ESty GCoc GGre LAst LGod LWoR MBri MRav SPoG SWCr
	'Indica Major'	XPep
	'Indigo' (DPo)	CPou EWTr MAus WHCG
	Ingrid Bergman = 'Poulman'[PBR] (HT) 🏆H4	CTri EBee ECnt ENot GCoc GGre LStr MAus MBri MGan MJon MRav SWCr
	Innocence = 'Cocoray'[PBR] (Patio)	GCoc
	Innocencia = 'Korenbon' (GC) **new**	ENot
	Intense Cover = 'Poultw001'[PBR] (GC/S)	SWCr
	Intrigue = 'Korlech'[PBR] (F)	CSBt ENot LStr MJon SSea SWCr
	Invincible = 'Runatru'[PBR] (F)	EBee MGan SWCr
	'Ipsilanté' (G)	MAus WAct WHCG
	'Irène Watts' (Ch)	CPou EBee ECre EPfP EWTr MAus SPla SSea SWCr WAct WHCG
	'Iris' (HT) **new**	GCoc
	Irish Eyes = 'Dicwitness'[PBR] (F)	CWSG ECnt EPfP ESty IArd IDic LGod LRHS LStr MAsh MBri MGan MJon MRav NPri SCoo SPer SWCr
	Irish Hope = 'Harexclaim'[PBR] (F)	SWCr
	Irish Wonder	see *R.* Evelyn Fison = 'Macev'
	Irresistible = 'Tinresist' (Min/Patio)	MJon
	Isabella = 'Poulisab'[PBR] (S)	CPou CTri ECnt EPfP LRHS MAsh SPoG SWCr
	Isis[PBR] (HT)	see *R.* Silver Anniversary = 'Poulari'
	Isobel Derby = 'Horethel' (HT)	SWCr
	'Ispahan' (D) 🏆H4	CFee EPfP LRHS MAus MCot NEgg NLar NSRo SFam SLPl SPer SWCr WAct WHCG
	Jack's Wish = 'Kirsil' (HT)	MJon
§	x ***jacksonii*** 'Max Graf' (GC/Ru)	LRHS MAus MGan MRav WAct WFar
	- Red Max Graf[PBR]	see *R.* Rote Max Graf = 'Kormax'
§	- White Max Graf = 'Korgram'[PBR] (GC/Ru)	MRav WAct
	Jacobite rose	see *R.* x *alba* 'Alba Maxima'
	'Jacpico'[PBR]	see *R.* 'Pristine'
	Jacqueline du Pré = 'Harwanna'[PBR] (S) 🏆H4	CSBt EBee ECnt EPfP ESty GCoc LRHS MAus MCot MGan MJon MRav SPer SWCr WAct WHCG
	Jacquenetta = 'Ausjac' (S)	MAus
N	'Jacques Cartier' hort.	see *R.* 'Marchesa Boccella'
	James Galway = 'Auscrystal'[PBR] (S)	CSBt CWSG LGod LRHS LStr MAus MBri MJon NEgg SCoo SWCr
	'James Mason' (G)	CSam MAus
	'James Mitchell' (CeMo)	MAus WHCG
	'James Veitch' (DPoMo)	MAus WHCG
	Jane Asher = 'Peapet' (Min/Patio)	SWCr
	Janet = 'Auspishus'[PBR] (S)	CSBt LRHS MAus SWCr
	'Janet's Pride' (RH)	MAus
§	'Japonica' (CeMo)	MAus
§	Jardins de Bagatelle = 'Meimafris' (HT)	MJon MRav SPoG
	Jasmina = 'Korcentex' (Cl) **new**	ENot
	'Jaune Desprez'	see *R.* 'Desprez à Fleurs Jaunes'
	Jayne Austin = 'Ausbreak'[PBR] (S)	CSBt CWSG MAus SPer SWCr
	Jazz[PBR] (Cl)	see *R.* That's Jazz

	Name	Suppliers
	'Jean Armour' (F)	GGre
	Jean = 'Cocupland'[PBR] (Patio)	GCoc
	Jean Kenneally = 'Tineally' (Min)	MJon
	'Jean Mermoz' (Poly)	MAus
	'Jeanie Deans' (RH)	MAus
	'Jeanne de Montfort' (CeMo)	MAus
	'Jenny Duval' misapplied	see *R.* 'Président de Sèze'
	'Jenny Wren' (F)	MAus
	'Jenny's Dream' (HT)	LGod
	Jenny's Rose = 'Cansit' (F)	EBee ECnt MGan SWCr
	'Jens Munk' (Ru)	NHaw WAct
	Jillian McGredy = 'Macarnhe' (F)	MJon
	Jill's Rose = 'Ganjil'[PBR] (F)	MGan SWCr
	'Jimmy Greaves' (HT)	MGan
	'Joanne' (HT)	MJon
	'Jocelyn' (F)	SWCr
	Joëlle Marouani = 'Masjoma' **new**	MRav
	'John Cabot' (S)	SSea
	John Clare = 'Auscent'[PBR] (S)	LRHS MAus SWCr
	John Gibb = 'Coczorose' (F) **new**	GCoc
	'John Hopper' (HP)	MAus SWCr
	'Josephine Bruce' (HT)	CBcs CSBt LGod LRHS MGan SWCr
	'Joseph's Coat' (S/Cl)	IArd LGod LStr MGan SSea SWCr
	'Journey's End' (HT)	MGan SWCr
	'Jubilee Celebration' (F)	EPfP
	Jubilee Celebration = 'Aushunter'[PBR] (S)	CSBt EPfP LRHS MAus SWCr
	Jude the Obscure = 'Ausjo'[PBR] (S)	ESty LCro LRHS MAus MBri MJon NEgg SWCr
	'Judy Fischer' (Min)	LGod
	'Julia's Rose' (HT)	CGro LStr MAus MGan MJon SPer SSea SWCr
	jundzillii	CFee
	'Juno' (Ce)	MAus WHCG
	'Just for You' (F)	GGre SWCr
	'Just Jenny' (Min)	MJon
	'Just Joey' (HT) Y[H4]	CGro CSBt CWSG EBee ECnt ELan ENot EPfP GCoc GGre IArd LAst LCro LGod LRHS LStr LWoR MAsh MAus MBri MGan MJon MRav NPri SPer SPoG SSea SWCr
	Just Married **new**	SWCr
	'Kanegem' (HT)	NBlu
	'Katharina Zeimet' (Poly)	CPou CTri MAus MGan NLar WAct WHCG
§	Katherine Mansfield = 'Meilanein' (HT)	CSBt
	'Kathleen Ferrier' (F)	MGan
	'Kathleen Harrop' (Bb)	EBee LRHS LStr MAus NLar SFam SPer SSea SWCr WAct WHCG
	Kathleen's Rose = 'Kirkitt' (F)	MJon
	Kathryn McGredy = 'Macauclad' (HT)	ESty MJon
§	Kathryn Morley = 'Ausclub'[PBR] (F)	LRHS MAus
	'Katie' (ClF)	MGan SWCr
N	'Kazanlik' misapplied	see *R.* 'Professeur Emile Perrot'
	Keep Smiling = 'Fryflorida' (HT)	ESty GCoc LStr MAsh MBri SWCr
	Keepsake = 'Kormalda' (HT)	MGan MJon
§	Kent = 'Poulcov'[PBR] (S/GC) Y[H4]	ECnt ELan ENot EPfP ESty GCoc LCro LStr MGan MJon MRav NPri SPer SPla SPoG SWCr WAct WHCG
	'Kew Rambler' (Ra)	CRHN CSam EBee MAus MRav SEND SFam SPer WHCG
	'Kiese' (*canina* hybrid)	NHaw
	'Kiftsgate'	see *R. filipes* 'Kiftsgate'
	'Kilworth Gold' (HT)	MGan
	Kind Regards = 'Peatiger' (F)	LAst
	King's Macc = 'Frydisco'[PBR] (HT)	ESty LGod MAus MBri SWCr
	'King's Ransom' (HT)	CBcs CSBt MGan MRav SPer SSea SWCr
	Knirps = 'Korverlandus'[PBR] (S) **new**	ENot
	Knock Out = 'Dadler' (F)	MAsh SWCr
§	'Königin von Dänemark' (A) Y[H4]	CSam EBee ECnt EPfP GCoc LCro LRHS MAsh MAus MCot MRav NEgg NSRo SPer SSea SWCr WAct WHCG
	'Kordes' Robusta'	see *R.* Robusta = 'Korgosa'
	Korona = 'Kornita' (F)	MGan SPer
	'Korresia' (F)	CSBt CTri ECnt ENot EPfP ESty GCoc GGre LAst LGod LStr MAsh MAus MBri MGan MJon MRav SPer SPoG SWCr
	Kristin = 'Benmagic' (Min)	MJon
§	Krönberg = 'Poultry'[PBR] (F)	EPfP
	'Kronprinzessin Viktoria' (Bb)	EBee MAus WHCG
	L.D. Braithwaite = 'Auscrim'[PBR] (S) Y[H4]	CGro ELan EPfP ESty GCoc LAst LCro LGod LRHS LStr MAsh MAus MGan MJon MRav NEgg NLar NPri SPer SWCr WAct WHCG
	'La Belle Distinguée' (RH)	MAus WHCG
	'La Belle Sultane'	see *R.* 'Violacea'
	'La France' (HT)	MAus
	'La Mortola'	see *R. brunonii* 'La Mortola'
	'La Perle' (Ra)	CRHN MAus
	'La Reine Victoria'	see *R.* 'Reine Victoria'
	'La Rubanée'	see *R.* x *centifolia* 'Unique Panachée'
	La Sévillana = 'Meigekanu'[PBR] (F/GC)	EBee SPer SWCr WAct WOVN
	'La Ville de Bruxelles' (D) Y[H4]	LRHS MAus SFam SLon SPer WAct WHCG
	'Lady Curzon' (Ru)	MAus
	Lady Emma Hamilton = 'Ausbrother' **new**	LRHS MAsh MAus SCoo SWCr
	'Lady Gay' (Ra)	EBee SWCr WHCG WOVN
	'Lady Godiva' (Ra)	MAus
	'Lady Hillingdon' (T)	MAus
	'Lady Hillingdon' (ClT)	see *R.* 'Climbing Lady Hillingdon'
	'Lady Iliffe' (HT)	MGan SWCr
	Lady in Red = 'Sealady' (Min)	MJon
	'Lady Love '95' (Patio)	ENot
	Lady MacRobert = 'Coclent' (F)	GCoc
	Lady Penelope = 'Chewdor'[PBR] (ClHT)	CSBt MAsh MJon SSea SWCr
§	'Lady Penzance' (RH) Y[H4]	CBcs MAus MGan SPer SWCr WAct
	Lady Rachel = 'Candoodle' (F)	EBee ECnt
	Lady Rose = 'Korlady' (HT)	MAsh SWCr
	'Lady Sylvia' (HT)	CSBt LRHS MAus MGan NEgg SPer SWCr
	'Lady Waterlow' (ClHT)	EBee MAus NLar SPer SWCr WHCG
	laevigata (Ra)	CArn MAus NLar XPep
	- 'Anemonoides'	see *R.* 'Anemone'
	Laguna = 'Koradigel' (Cl) **new**	ENot
	L'Aimant = 'Harzola'[PBR] (F) Y[H4]	CSBt ESty GCoc LGod LStr MAus MGan MRav SWCr
	'Lamarque' (N)	CPou EBee MAus SWCr
§	Lancashire = 'Korstesgli'[PBR] (GC) Y[H4]	ECnt ENot ESty GCoc LGod LSRN LStr MAus MGan MRav SSea

Laura Anne = 'Cocclarion' (HT)	GCoc
Laura Ashley = 'Chewharla' (GC/ClMin)	MAus
Laura Ford = 'Chewarvel'PBR (ClMin) ♀H4	CGro CSBt CTri ENot ESty GGre LCro LRHS LStr MAsh MAus MJon MRav NPri SPer SPoG SSea SWCr
'Laure Davoust' (Ra)	CPou EBee
'Lavender Jewel' (Min)	MAus
'Lavender Lassie' (HM) ♀H4	CSam MAus MGan SPer SSea SWCr WHCG
'Lavender Pinocchio' (F)	MAus
LaviniaPBR	see *R.* Lawinia = 'Tanklewi'
§ Lawinia = 'Tanklewi'PBR (ClHT) ♀H4	CSBt EPfP LStr MAsh MRav NPri SPer SSea SWCr
'Lawrence Johnston' (Cl)	LRHS MAus SPer SWCr
§ Lazy Days = 'Poulkalm'PBR (F)	EBee ECnt EPfP
'Le Rêve' (Cl)	MAus SWCr
'Le Vésuve' (Ch)	MAus
Leander = 'Auslea' (S)	MAus
Leaping Salmon = 'Peamight'PBR (ClHT)	CGro CSBt EBee ELan ESty EWTr GCoc LAst LGod LStr MAus MGan MRav SPer SPoG SSea SWCr
'Leda' (D)	LAst MAus NLar SFam SPer SSea SWCr WAct
'Lemon Couture' (Patio) **new**	LWoR
'Lemon Pillar'	see *R.* 'Paul's Lemon Pillar'
'Leo' **new**	LWoR
Léonardo de Vinci = 'Meideauri'PBR (F)	CSBt
'Léontine Gervais' (Ra)	CAbP CRHN LRHS MAus MRav NLar SWCr WAct
'Leo's Eye'	EPfP
Leslie's Dream = 'Dicjoon' (HT)	IDic
'Leverkusen' (Cl) ♀H4	EBee LRHS MAus MCot MGan MJon MRav NEgg SPer SPla SWCr WAct WHCG
'Ley's Perpetual' (ClT)	EBee SWCr
x ***lheritieriana*** (Bs)	SWCr
'Libra' **new**	LWoR
Lichtkönigin Lucia = 'Korlillub' (S)	SSea
Life Begins at 40! = 'Horhohoho' (F)	GGre LWoR SWCr
'Lilac Dream' (F)	GGre SWCr
Lilac Rose = 'Auslilac' (S)	MAus
Lilian Austin = 'Ausli' (S)	MAus
Lilian Baylis = 'Hardeluxe'PBR (F)	GGre
Liliana = 'Poulsyng'PBR (S)	ECnt LRHS MAsh SPla SWCr
Lilli Marlene = 'Korlima' (F)	CSBt CWSG GCoc GGre MGan SLon SPer SWCr
Lincoln Cathedral = 'Glanlin'PBR (HT)	MJon SPer
'Lionheart' (HT)	GGre LWoR SPoG SWCr
Lisa = 'Kirdisco' (F)	MJon
Little Bo-peep = 'Poullen'PBR (Min/Patio) ♀H4	MJon
'Little Buckaroo' (Min)	LGod SPer SWCr
'Little Flirt' (Min)	MAus MGan SWCr
'Little Gem' (DPMo)	MAus MGan
Little Jackie = 'Savor' (Min)	MJon
Little Muff = 'Horluisbond' (Min)	MJon
Little Rambler = 'Chewramb'PBR (MinRa) ♀H4	CSBt ECnt ENot LRHS LStr MAsh MAus MBri MGan MJon SCoo SPer SSea SWCr WGer
'Little White Pet'	see *R.* 'White Pet'
Little Woman = 'Diclittle'PBR (Patio)	IDic LStr
'Little Wonder' (HT) **new**	SWCr
Lochinvar = 'Ausbilda'PBR (S)	MAus
Lolita = 'Litakor' (HT)	MBri
'Long John Silver' (Cl)	MAus SSea
longicuspis misapplied	see *R. mulliganii*
longicuspis Bertoloni (Ra)	SPla
- AC 2097	GGar
§ - var. ***sinowilsonii*** (Ra)	GGar MAus
aff. ***longicuspis*** AC 1808	GGar
Lord Byron = 'Meitosier' (ClHT)	LStr NBlu SSea SWCr
'Lord Penzance' (RH)	CGro MGan MRav SPer WAct
Lorna = 'Cocringer' (F)	GCoc
'L'Ouche' misapplied	see *R.* 'Louise Odier'
'Louis Gimard' (CeMo)	MAus SPer WAct
'Louis XIV' (Ch)	WHCG
Louisa Stone = 'Harbadge' (S)	GGre
§ 'Louise Odier' (Bb)	CBgR EBee ECnt EPfP IArd LRHS LStr MAus MGan MJon MRav SFam SPer SPla SSea SWCr WAct WHCG WKif WOVN
Love (F)	MBri
Love & Peace = 'Baipeace'PBR (HT)	ELan ESty MBri SWCr
Love Knot = 'Chewglorious'PBR (ClMin)	CSBt ECnt ESty MAsh MBri MJon MRav SCoo SWCr WGor
Lovely Bride **new**	MAsh SWCr
Lovely Fairy = 'Spevu'PBR (Poly/GC)	IDic WAct
Lovely Lady = 'Dicjubell'PBR (HT) ♀H4	CSBt ECnt ESty IDic LStr MGan MJon MRav SSea SWCr
Lovely Meidiland = 'Meiratcan'PBR (Patio)	ENot SWCr
'Lovers' Meeting' (HT)	GGre MGan MRav SPer SSea SWCr
Loving Memory = 'Korgund'PBR (HT)	CGro CSBt CWSG ECnt ENot ESty GCoc GGre IArd LCro LStr MBri MGan MJon MRav NPri SPer SPoG SWCr
Lucetta = 'Ausemi' (S)	MAus SPer
luciae var. ***onoei***	CLyd
'Lucy Ashton' (RH)	MAus
Lucy = 'Kirlis' (F)	MJon
Ludlow CastlePBR	see *R.* England's Rose
'Lykkefund' (Ra)	MAus WHCG
'Mabel Morrison' (HP)	MAus
Macartney rose	see *R. bracteata*
Macmillan Nurse = 'Beamac' (S)	ESty
'Macrantha' (Gallica hybrid)	LRHS MAus WAct
macrophylla	MAus
- B&SWJ 2603	WCru
§ - 'Master Hugh' ♀H4	MAus
'Macyou'PBR	see *R.* Regensberg = 'Macyoumis'
'Madame Abel Chatenay' (HT)	MAus
'Madame Alfred Carrière' (N) ♀H4	More than 30 suppliers
'Madame Alice Garnier' (Ra)	CPou EBee SPer SWCr
'Madame Bravy' (T)	MAus
'Madame Butterfly' (HT)	MAus MGan SFam SSea SWCr
§ 'Madame Caroline Testout' (HT)	LRHS MGan MRav SFam SPoG
'Madame de Sancy de Parabère' (Bs)	IArd MAus SFam SWCr WHCG
'Madame Delaroche-Lambert' (DPMo)	CPou EBee MAus WAct WHCG
'Madame Driout' (ClT)	WHCG
'Madame Ernest Calvat' (Bb)	CPou EBee MAus SWCr
'Madame Eugène Résal' misapplied	see *R.* 'Comtesse du Caÿla'

Madame Figaro = 'Delrona' (S)	LCro MRav
'Madame Georges Bruant' (Ru)	MAus
§ 'Madame Grégoire Staechelin' (ClHT) ♀H4	CWSG EBee ECnt ELan ENot EPfP LAst LCro LRHS LStr MAus MBri MGan MJon MRav NEgg SFam SMad SPer SPoG SWCr WAct WHCG
'Madame Hardy' (ClD) ♀H4	CBgR CPou CSBt ECnt EPfP GCoc LGod LRHS LStr MAsh MAus MGan MJon MRav NEgg NLar SFam SPer SSea SWCr WAct WHCG WOVN
'Madame Isaac Pereire' (ClBb) ♀H4	CSBt CTri EBee ECnt ENot EPfP ESty GCoc LRHS LStr MAsh MAus MBri MGan MJon MRav NEgg SFam SMad SPer SPoG SSea SWCr WAct WHCG
'Madame Jules Gravereaux' (ClT)	MAus
'Madame Jules Thibaud' (Poly)	MAus
§ 'Madame Knorr' (DPo) ♀H4	CBgR CPou EBee EPfP LRHS MAsh MRav MWgw SPer SSea WAct WHCG WOVN
'Madame Laurette Messimy' (Ch)	EBee MAus WHCG
'Madame Lauriol de Barny' (Bb)	MAus MGan MRav NLar SFam SWCr WHCG
'Madame Legras de Saint Germain' (AxN)	CPou EBee MAus SFam SPer SWCr WAct WHCG
'Madame Louis Laperrière' (HT)	MAus
'Madame Louis Lévêque' (DPMo)	NLar WAct WHCG
'Madame Pierre Oger' (Bb)	EBee ECnt LCro LRHS LStr MAus MGan MRav SPer SWCr WAct
'Madame Plantier' (AxN)	CPou LRHS MAus MRav NHaw NLar SPer SWCr WHCG WOVN
'Madame Scipion Cochet' (T)	WHCG
'Madame Zöetmans' (D)	MAus
'Madeleine Selzer' (Ra)	ECGP MGan
'Madge' (HM)	SDix
Madrigal = 'Harextra'PBR (S/F)	ESty GGre LWoR SWCr
'Magenta' (S/HT)	MAus SPer
Magic Carpet = 'Jaclover'PBR (S/GC) ♀H4	CWSG ECnt ELan GCoc IDic MAus MGan MRav NPri SSea SWCr
Magic Hit = 'Poulhi004'PBR (Min)	LRHS
'Magnifica' (RH)	MAus MGan
'Maid of Kent'PBR (Cl)	CSBt MGan MJon SBra SCoo SPer SWCr
'Maiden's Blush' (A) ♀H4	CTri ELan GGre LRHS MAsh MAus MGan SFam SPer SSea SWCr WHCG
'Maiden's Blush, Great'	see *R.* 'Great Maiden's Blush'
'Maigold' (ClPiH) ♀H4	CBcs CGro CSam CTri CWSG EBee ECnt ELan ENot EPfP GCoc GGre LCro LGod LRHS LStr MAsh MAus MGan MJon MRav NEgg SMad SPer SWCr WAct WHCG
Majestic = 'Poulpm001'PBR (HT)	EBee
Make a Wish = 'Mehpat'PBR (Min/Patio)	ESty LStr
Maltese rose	see *R.* 'Cécile Brünner'
Malvern Hills = 'Auscanary'PBR (Ra)	CSBt LRHS MAsh MAus MBri MGan MJon SSea SWCr WAct
Mandarin = 'Korcelin'PBR (Min)	ENot ESty LStr MJon MRav
'Manning's Blush' (RH)	MAus SSea WAct

Manou Meilland = 'Meitulimon' (HT)	SSea
'Manx Queen' (F)	SWCr
Many Happy Returns = 'Harwanted'PBR (S/F) ♀H4	CGro CSBt CWSG EBee ECnt ELan ENot EPfP GCoc LCro LGod LRHS LStr MAsh MGan MJon MRav SPer SPoG SSea SWCr
'Marbrée' (DPo)	MAus
'Märchenland' (F/S)	MAus
§ 'Marchesa Boccella' (DPo) ♀H4	CPou CSam CTri EBee ENot EPfP LRHS MAsh MAus MGan NPri SPer SPla SPoG SSea SWCr WAct WHCG
'Marcie Gandy' (HT)	MGan
'Maréchal Davoust' (CeMo)	MAus SFam WAct
'Maréchal Niel' (N)	ERea EShb MAus SPer SWCr WHCG
'Margaret' (HT)	MGan SWCr
Margaret Merril = 'Harkuly' (F/HT) ♀H4	CGro CSBt CTri CWSG EBee ECnt ELan ENot EPfP ESty GCoc GGre IArd LBMP LCro LGod LRHS LStr MAsh MAus MBri MGan MJon MRav SPer SPoG SSea SWCr
Margaret's World = 'Kirbill' (F)	MJon
'Margo Koster' (Poly)	MAus
'Marguerite Hilling' (S) ♀H4	CAbP CTri EBee EPfP GCoc MAus MGan MRav SPer SSea SWCr WAct WHCG WOVN
Maria McGredy = 'Macturangu'PBR (HT)	MJon
x ***mariae-graebnerae***	MAus SLPl WHCG
'Marie Louise' (D)	MAus SFam WAct WHCG
'Marie Pavič' (Poly)	MAus WHCG
'Marie van Houtte' (T)	MAus
'Marie-Jeanne' (Poly)	MAus
Marilyn Monroe = 'Weksunspat' (HT) **new**	MJon
Marinette = 'Auscam'PBR (S)	MAus
Marjorie Fair = 'Harhero' (Poly/S) ♀H4	ESty MAsh MAus MGan MRav SWCr
Marjorie Marshall = 'Hardenier'PBR	MRav
'Marlena' (F/Patio)	GCoc MAus
Marry Me = 'Dicwonder'PBR (Patio) ♀H4	ESty IDic
'Martha' (Bb)	MAus
'Martian Glow' (F/S)	MGan
'Martin Frobisher' (Ru)	MAus SSea
'Mary' (Poly)	LStr
Mary Magdalene = 'Ausjolly'PBR (S)	LRHS LStr MAus NEgg SWCr
'Mary Manners' (Ru)	SPer
Mary Rose = 'Ausmary'PBR (S) ♀H4	CGro CSBt CWSG EBee ELan ENot EPfP ESty GCoc LCro LGod LRHS LStr MAus MBri MGan MJon MRav NPri SPer SSea SWCr WKif
'Mary Wallace' (Cl)	MAus
Mary Webb = 'Auswebb' (S)	MAus
Marylin = 'Meiguitan' **new**	CWGr
'Masquerade' (F)	CBcs CGro CWSG ELan ENot MGan MRav SPer SSea SWCr
'Master Hugh'	see *R. macrophylla* 'Master Hugh'
Matangi = 'Macman' (F) ♀H4	MGan SWCr
Matawhero MagicPBR	see *R.* Simply the Best
'Max Graf'	see *R.* x *jacksonii* 'Max Graf'
'Maxima'	see *R.* x *alba* 'Alba Maxima'
'May Queen' (Ra)	CPou EBee LRHS MAsh MAus MGan MRav NLar SFam SPer SWCr WHCG
Mayor of Casterbridge = 'Ausbrid'PBR (S)	LRHS MAus

'McCartney Rose'PBR	see *R.* The McCartney Rose = 'Meizeli'
'Meg' (ClHT)	EBee LRHS MAus MGan SPer SSea SWCr WAct WHCG
'Meg Merrilies' (RH)	MAus MGan NLar SSea WAct
'Megiddo' (F)	MGan SWCr
Mellow Yellow = 'Wekosomit' (HT)	GCoc
Melody Maker = 'Dicqueen'PBR (F)	CWSG IDic
Memento = 'Dicbar' (F) ♀H4	MGan SWCr
'Memoriam' (HT)	MGan SWCr
Memory Lane = 'Peavoodoo'PBR (F)	SWCr
'Mermaid' (Cl) ♀H3-4	CBcs CBrm CGro CSBt CTri CWSG EBee ECnt ELon ENot EPfP LHop LRHS LStr MAus MGan MJon SBra SMad SPer SPla SSea SWCr WAct WHCG XPep
§ Message = 'Meban' (HT)	SWCr
'Meteor' (F/Patio)	MGan
§ 'Mevrouw Nathalie Nypels' (Poly) ♀H4	EBee LRHS LStr MAus MRav SPer SWCr WHCG WKif WOVN
Michael Crawford = 'Poulvue'PBR (HT)	ECnt
'Michèle Meilland' (HT)	MAus
Michelle Chetcuti = 'Kirchief' (HT) **new**	MJon
x ***micrugosa***	MAus
- 'Alba'	MAus
Midsummer Night's Dream = 'Rawroyal'	SWCr
'Millennium Rose 2000'PBR	see *R.* Rose 2000
'Mills and Boon' (F)	MGan
'Minnehaha' (Ra)	LGod MAus SSea
Minnie Pearl = 'Savahowdy' (Min)	MJon
mirifica stellata	see *R. stellata* var. *mirifica*
Mischief = 'Macmi' (HT)	ELan GGre MGan SPer SWCr
Miss Alice = 'Ausjake'PBR (S)	LRHS MAus NSRo
Miss Dior = 'Harencens'PBR (S)	MRav
'Miss Edith Cavell' (Poly)	MAus
Miss Flippins = 'Tuckflip' (Min)	MJon
Missing You = 'Horcakebread' (F)	MGan
§ 'Mister Lincoln' (HT)	ESty LGod MGan SPer SSea SWCr
Mistress Quickly = 'Ausky'PBR (S)	LRHS MAus NEgg
Misty Hit = 'Poulhi011'PBR (Patio)	ECnt
§ 'Moersdag' (Poly/F)	GGre LStr MJon NPri SPoG SWCr
'Mojave' (HT)	MGan
'Moje Hammarberg' (Ru)	MJon WAct
Molineux = 'Ausmol'PBR (S) ♀H4	CSBt CTri ECnt EPfP GCoc LRHS MAsh MAus MBri NEgg NPri SSea SWCr
'Monique' (HT)	MGan SWCr
Moonbeam = 'Ausbeam' (S)	MAus
'Moonlight' (HM)	CTri ELan LRHS MAus MGan MRav SPer SWCr WAct WHCG
'Morgengruss' (Cl)	MGan SWCr
Moriah = 'Ganhol'PBR (HT)	MGan
'Morlettii' (Bs)	MRav SWCr WHCG
'Morning Jewel' (ClF) ♀H4	GCoc MGan SPer SWCr
Morning Mist = 'Ausfire' (S)	LRHS MAus
Mortimer Sackler = 'Ausorts'PBR (S)	LCro LRHS MAus MBri MJon SCoo SWCr
moschata (Ra)	MAus MRav SSea SWCr WAct WHCG
- 'Autumnalis'	see *R.* 'Princesse de Nassau'

- var. ***nepalensis***	see *R. brunonii*
Mother's Day	see *R.* 'Moersdag'
Mother's Joy = 'Horsiltrop' (F)	GGre LWoR SWCr
Mountain Snow = 'Aussnow' (Ra)	LRHS MAus NSRo SWCr
Mountbatten = 'Harmantelle'PBR (F) ♀H4	CBcs CGro CWSG ELan EPfP GGre LBMP LGod LRHS LStr LWoR MAsh MAus MGan MJon MRav NPri SPer SPoG SSea SWCr
§ 'Mousseline' (DPoMo)	CPou EBee MAus MCot MRav NLar SSea SWCr WAct WHCG
'Mousseuse du Japon'	see *R.* 'Japonica'
moyesii (S)	CTri ELan GCra ISea MAus MGan NWea SMad SPer WAct WOVN
- 'Evesbatch' (S)	WAct
'Mozart' (HM)	WHCG
'Mr Bluebird' (MinCh)	MAus MGan SWCr
'Mr Lincoln'	see *R.* 'Mister Lincoln'
'Mrs Anthony Waterer' (Ru)	MAus SPer SWCr WAct WHCG
Mrs Doreen Pike = 'Ausdor'PBR (Ru)	MAus
'Mrs Eveline Gandy' (HT)	MGan
'Mrs Honey Dyson' (Ra)	WHCG
'Mrs John Laing' (HP)	EBee EPfP LRHS MAus MRav SLon SWCr
'Mrs Oakley Fisher' (HT)	EBee EWTr MAus MBri MCot SDix SPer SWCr WAct WCot
'Mrs Paul' (Bb)	MAus
'Mrs Sam McGredy' (HT)	CSBt MAus MGan SSea
'Mullard Jubilee' (HT)	MGan NBlu SWCr
§ ***mulliganii*** (Ra) ♀H4	EBee EPfP MAus SWCr WAct WHCG
multibracteata (S)	MAus WHCG
multiflora (Ra)	LBuc MAus NHaw NWea WAct
§ - var. ***cathayensis*** (Ra)	MAus WBor WHCG XPep
§ - 'Grevillei' (Ra)	CPou EBee MAus SPer SWCr
- 'Platyphylla'	see *R. multiflora* 'Grevillei'
MummyPBR	see *R.* Newly Wed = 'Dicwhynot'
mundi	see *R. gallica* 'Versicolor'
- 'Versicolor'	see *R. gallica* 'Versicolor'
'Mutabilis'	see *R.* x *odorata* 'Mutabilis'
'My Choice' (HT)	MGan SWCr
My Everything = 'Coccastle' **new**	GCoc
My Love = 'Cogamo' (HT)	GGre MJon
My Mum = 'Webmorrow'PBR	ESty SWCr
My Valentine = 'Mormyval' (Min)	ESty
Myriam = 'Cocgrand' (HT)	GCoc
Mystique = 'Kirmyst' (F)	MJon
Nahéma = 'Deléri' (Cl)	LCro MRav
'Nan of Painswick'	WAct
Nancy Renaissance = 'Poulninga'PBR **new**	CSam
'Narrow Water' (Ra)	CPou EBee SWCr WAct WHCG
§ 'Nastarana' (N)	EBee
'Nathalie Nypels'	see *R.* 'Mevrouw Nathalie Nypels'
'National Trust' (HT)	ENot GGre IArd MAsh MGan MJon SPer SWCr
'Nestor' (G)	MAus
'Nevada' (S) ♀H4	CSBt CTri EBee ECnt ELan ENot EPfP GCoc IArd LAst LGod LStr MAus MGan MRav NWea SPer SSea SWCr WAct WHCG WOVN
New Age = 'Wekbipuhit'PBR (F)	ESty GCoc MBri MJon SWCr
'New Arrival' (Patio/Min)	GCoc GGre MGan SWCr
§ 'New Dawn' (Cl) ♀H4	More than 30 suppliers
'New Look' (F)	MGan SWCr
New Zealand = 'Macgenev'PBR (HT)	MJon SWCr
§ Newly Wed = 'Dicwhynot'PBR (Patio)	IDic LStr MJon SSea

News = 'Legnews' (F)	MAus MGan
Nice Day = 'Chewsea'PBR (ClMin) ♀H4	CGro CSBt CWSG ENot EPfP ESty GGre LGod LRHS LStr MAsh MJon MRav SPer SPoG SSea SWCr
'Nice 'n' Easy' (Patio)	GGre SWCr
'Nicola' (F)	MGan SWCr
Nigel Hawthorne = 'Harquibbler' (S)	WAct
Night Light = 'Poullight'PBR (Cl)	EBee ECnt MBri MGan MRav SWCr
Night Sky = 'Dicetch'PBR (F)	IDic SSea
Nina = 'Mehnina'PBR (S)	SWCr
Nina Nadine = 'Kirhand' (F)	MJon
'Nina Weibull' (F)	SWCr
nitida	EMac MAus MGan NHaw NWea SPer SSea SWCr WAct WHCG WHer WOVN
Noble Antony = 'Ausway'PBR (S)	LRHS LStr MAus MJon SWCr
§ 'Noisette Carnée' (N)	CSam EBee EPfP EWTr GCra LRHS LStr MAsh MAus MBNS MGan MJon MRav NLar NSRo SLPl SPer SSea SWCr WAct
Norfolk = 'Poulfolk'PBR (GC)	SPer SPla SWCr
'Norma Major' (HT)	MJon
Northamptonshire = 'Mattdor'PBR (GC)	MGan
'Northern Lights' (HT)	GCoc
'Norwich Pink' (Cl)	MAus
'Norwich Salmon' (Cl)	MAus
'Norwich Union' (F)	MBri
Nostalgia = 'Savarita' (Min)	ESty MAsh MGan
Nostalgie = 'Taneiglat'PBR (HT)	ECnt GGre LStr MBri MJon MRav SPoG SSea SWCr
'Nottingham Millennium' (F)	MGan
'Nova Zembla' (Ru)	MAus
'Nozomi' (ClMin/GC) ♀H4	CGro CLyd CTri ELan ESty GCoc GGre MAus MGan MJon MRav MWgw NWCA SMad SPer SPoG SSea SWCr WAct WHCG WOVN
'Nuits de Young' (CeMo) ♀H4	GCoc MAus SFam SSea SWCr WAct WHCG
'Nur Mahal' (HM)	MAus SWCr WHCG
nutkana (S)	MAus
§ - 'Plena' (S) ♀H4	EPfP MAus MGan NLar SFam SWCr WAct WGer WHCG
'Nymphenburg' (HM)	MAus SPer SWCr
'Nyveldt's White' (Ru)	MAus
Octavia Hill = 'Harzeal'PBR (F/S)	CSBt MRav NPri SPer SPoG SWCr
§ x ***odorata***	XPep
- 'Fortune's Double Yellow'	see *R.* x *odorata* 'Pseudindica'
§ - 'Mutabilis' (Ch) ♀H3-4	CRHN EBee ECre ENot EPfP EWTr GCoc LCro LRHS MAus MGan MRav SMad SMrm SPer SSea SWCr WAct WCFE WCot WHCG WOVN XPep
§ - 'Pallida' (Ch)	CBgR EBee EPfP GCoc MAus MCot MRav SPer SPla WAct WHCG
§ - 'Pseudindica' (ClCh)	MAus
§ - Sanguinea Group (Ch)	WHCG XPep
- - 'Bengal Crimson' (Ch)	LRHS WCot
§ - 'Viridiflora' (Ch)	EBee MAus SMad SPer SSea SWCr WHCG
Odyssey = 'Franski'PBR (F)	ESty
'Oeillet Flamand'	see *R.* 'Oeillet Parfait'
'Oeillet Panaché' (Mo)	WAct
§ 'Oeillet Parfait' (G)	MAus
officinalis	see *R. gallica* var. *officinalis*
'Oklahoma' (HT)	MGan NBlu SWCr
old blush China	see *R.* x *odorata* 'Pallida'
old cabbage	see *R.* x *centifolia*
Old John = 'Dicwillynilly'PBR (F)	IDic
old pink moss rose	see *R.* x *centifolia* 'Muscosa'
Old Port = 'Mackati'PBR (F)	IArd MJon SWCr
old red moss	see *R.* 'Henri Martin'
old velvet moss	see *R.* 'William Lobb'
old yellow Scotch (PiH)	see *R.* x *harisonii* 'Williams' Double Yellow'
Olympic Palace = 'Poulymp'PBR (F)	ECnt
'Omar Khayyám' (D)	MAus MRav
omeiensis	see *R. sericea* subsp. *omeiensis*
Open Arms = 'Chewpixcel'PBR (ClMin) ♀H4	ENot ESty MAus MBri MJon SPer SSea SWCr WGer
'Ophelia' (HT)	EBee MAus MGan NEgg SWCr
'Orange Sensation' (F)	CTri CWSG MAus MGan SLon
§ Orange Sunblaze = 'Meijikatar'PBR (Min)	CSBt MGan SPer
Orangeade (F)	MGan
Oranges and Lemons = 'Macoranlem'PBR (S/F)	CGro ECnt ELan ENot ESty GCoc LGod LStr MAsh MAus MGan MJon SPoG SSea SWCr
'Orient Express' (HT)	CWSG
Othello = 'Auslo'PBR (S)	MAus SPer WAct
'Our Dream' (Patio) **new**	MAsh
Our George = 'Kirrush' (Patio)	MJon
Our Jubilee = 'Coccages' (HT)	ESty SLon
Our Love = 'Andour' (HT)	CWSG
Our Molly = 'Dicreason'PBR (GC/S)	IDic MGan MJon SWCr
Oxfordshire = 'Korfullwind'PBR (GC) ♀H4	ENot LStr MRav SSea SWCr
Paddy McGredy = 'Macpa' (F)	MGan
Paddy Stephens = 'Macclack'PBR (HT)	MGan MJon SWCr
Painted Moon = 'Dicpaint' (HT)	ESty
Panache = 'Poultop'PBR (Patio)	ECnt LStr MAsh
'Papa Gontier' (T)	MAus
Papa Meilland = 'Meisar' (HT)	CGro CSBt MAus MGan MJon SPer SWCr
Paper Anniversary (Patio)	LWoR SWCr
Papi Delbard = 'Delaby' (Cl)	MRav
'Parade' (Cl) ♀H4	MAus MRav WHCG
'Paradise' (Patio)	GGre SPoG SWCr
Paradise = 'Weizeip' (HT)	MGan
'Parkdirektor Riggers' (Cl)	CSam EBee LStr MAus MBri MGan NLar SPer SWCr WHCG
'Parkjuwel' (CeMo)	MGan
Parson's pink China	see *R.* x *odorata* 'Pallida'
Partridge = 'Korweirim'PBR (GC)	MAus MGan SPer SWCr WAct WOVN
'Party Girl' (Min)	MJon
parvifolia	see *R.* 'Burgundiaca'
Pas de Deux = 'Poulhult'PBR (Cl)	EBee LRHS MAsh SWCr
Pascali = 'Lenip' (HT)	CTri EPfP GCoc GGre MAus MGan MJon MRav NBlu SPer SSea SWCr
Pat Austin = 'Ausmum'PBR (S) ♀H4	CSBt EBee ECnt ESty LRHS LStr MAus MBNS MBri MRav NEgg NLar SPoG SWCr
Pathfinder = 'Chewpobey' (GC)	MJon
Patricia = 'Korpatri' (F)	SWCr
'Paul Crampel' (Poly)	MAus MGan NBir WAct
'Paul Lédé' (ClT)	see *R.* 'Climbing Paul Lédé'

Paul McCartney^{PBR} (HT)	see *R.* The McCartney Rose = 'Meizeli'
'Paul Neyron' (HP)	EWTr MAus SPer WHCG
'Paul Ricault' (CexHP)	MAus
Paul Shirville = 'Harqueterwife'^{PBR} (HT) ♀^{H4}	ELan ESty MAus MGan MRav SPer SWCr
'Paul Transon' (Ra) ♀^{H4}	CPou CRHN EBee LRHS MAus NEgg SPer SWCr WHer
§ 'Paulii' (Ru)	CArn MAus WAct WOVN
'Paulii Alba'	see *R.* 'Paulii'
'Paulii Rosea' (Ru/Cl)	MAus WAct
'Paul's Himalayan Musk' (Ra) ♀$^{H3-4}$	More than 30 suppliers
§ 'Paul's Lemon Pillar' (ClHT)	EBee LRHS MAus SPer SSea SWCr
'Paul's Perpetual White' (Ra)	WHCG
'Paul's Scarlet Climber' (Cl/Ra)	CGro CSBt ELan ENot EPfP GGre LAst LCro LGod LStr LWoR MAsh MAus MGan MJon MRav NBlu NEgg NPri SPer SWCr WBVN
'Pax' (HM)	CPou MAus SWCr WAct WHCG WKif
Peace = 'Madame A. Meilland' (HT) ♀^{H4}	CGro CSBt ECnt ELan ENot EPfP ESty GCoc GGre LCro LGod LRHS LStr LWoR MAsh MAus MBri MGan MJon MRav NBlu SPer SPoG SSea SWCr
'Peace Maker' (F)	CSBt
Peacekeeper = 'Harbella'^{PBR} (F)	CSBt GGre MRav SWCr
Peach Blossom = 'Ausblossom' (S)	MAus
Peach Surprise = 'Poulrise'^{PBR} (HT)	EBee
§ Pearl Abundance = 'Harfrisky'^{PBR} (F)	ESty SWCr
§ Pearl Anniversary = 'Whitston'^{PBR} (Min/Patio)	CSBt ESty GCoc GGre LCro LStr LWoR MRav SLon SWCr
Pearl Drift = 'Leggab' (S)	MAus MJon SPer SWCr WHCG
Peaudouce^{PBR}	see *R.* Elina = 'Dicjana'
§ Peek-a-boo = 'Dicgrow'^{PBR} (Min/Patio)	IDic MGan MRav SPer
Peer Gynt = 'Korol' (HT)	GGre MGan NBlu SWCr
Pegasus = 'Ausmoon'^{PBR} (S)	LRHS LStr MAus NEgg SSea SWCr
§ ***pendulina***	LBuc MAus NHaw WHCG
- 'Nana'	NHol
'Penelope' (HM) ♀^{H4}	CSBt CSam CTri EBee ECnt ELan ENot EPfP EWTr GCoc LCro LRHS LStr MAsh MAus MBri MGan MJon MRav SFam SPer SSea SWCr WAct WHCG WKif WOVN XPep
Penny Lane = 'Hardwell'^{PBR} (Cl) ♀^{H4}	CSBt ECnt ENot EPfP ESty GCoc GGre LAst LBMP LGod LRHS LStr LWoR MAsh MAus MBri MGan MJon MRav MWgw NPri SCoo SPer SSea SWCr
Pensioner's Voice = 'Fryrelax'^{PBR} (F)	MGan SWCr
x ***penzanceana***	see *R.* 'Lady Penzance'
Peppermint Ice = 'Bosgreen' (F)	SWCr
Perception = 'Harzippee'^{PBR} (HT)	SWCr
Perdita = 'Ausperd' (S)	ESty LRHS MAus MJon MRav SPer
Perennial Blue = 'Mehblue'	EBee ECnt ESty SWCr
Perestroika = 'Korhitom'^{PBR} (F/Min)	ENot
§ Perfect Day = 'Poulrem' (F)	EBee ECnt
Perfecta = 'Koralu' (HT)	MGan
'Perle des Jardins' (T)	MAus
§ 'Perle d'Or' (Poly) ♀^{H4}	ECGP ECnt ENot EPfP MAus MGan SMad SPer SWCr WAct WHCG
Perpetually Yours = 'Harfable'^{PBR} (Cl)	CGro GGre LStr MRav SCoo SPoG SWCr
Persian yellow	see *R. foetida* 'Persiana'
Peter Pan = 'Chewpan'^{PBR} (Min)	ENot MAsh MAus MJon SWCr
Peter Pan = 'Sunpete' (Patio)	LRHS NPri SPoG
'Petite de Hollande' (Ce)	MAus NLar WAct WHCG
'Petite Lisette' (CexD)	MAus NLar
Phab Gold = 'Frybountiful'^{PBR} (F)	ESty GCoc MAsh
Pheasant = 'Kordapt'^{PBR} (GC)	GCoc MAus MGan MJon SPer SWCr WAct WHCG WOVN
Phillipa = 'Poulheart'^{PBR} (S)	ECnt SWCr
Phoebe (Ru)	see *R.* 'Fimbriata' (Ru)
'Phyllis Bide' (Ra) ♀^{H4}	CAbP EBee EPfP IArd LRHS LStr MAus MGan MJon NLar NSRo SPer SSea SWCr WAct WHCG WKif
Picasso = 'Macpic' (F)	MGan SWCr
Piccadilly = 'Macar' (HT)	CGro CSBt CTri ENot GGre MGan MJon MRav SPer SSea SWCr
Piccolo = 'Tanolokip'^{PBR} (F/Patio)	CGro ESty LStr MBri MJon MRav SWCr
'Picture' (HT)	MGan SPer
Pigalle '84 = 'Meicloux' (F)	SWCr
'Pilgrim'^{PBR}	see *R.* The Pilgrim
Pimpernelle = 'Deldog' (S)	SWCr
pimpinellifolia	see *R. spinosissima*
- 'Altaica'	see *R. spinosissima* 'Grandiflora'
- double yellow	see *R.* x *harisonii* 'Williams' Double Yellow'
- 'Harisonii'	see *R.* x *harisonii* 'Harison's Yellow'
Pink Abundance = 'Harfrothy'^{PBR} (F)	ESty LStr
Pink Bells = 'Poulbells'^{PBR} (GC)	GCoc MAus SPer
'Pink Bouquet' (Ra)	CRHN
'Pink Favorite' (HT)	CSBt MGan SPer SWCr
Pink Fizz = 'Poulycool'	ECnt LRHS SWCr
§ Pink Flower Carpet = 'Noatraum'^{PBR} (GC) ♀^{H4}	CGro CSBt CTri ELan EPfP GCoc LRHS LStr MAsh MAus MBri MGan SCoo SPer SPoG SWCr
'Pink Garnette'	see *R.* 'Carol Amling'
'Pink Grootendorst' (Ru) ♀^{H4}	EBee EPfP LRHS MAus MGan NLar SPer SSea SWCr WAct WHCG
§ Pink Hit = 'Poultipe'^{PBR} (Min/Patio)	ECnt
Pink La Sevillana = 'Meigeroka'^{PBR} (F/GC)	SWCr
pink moss	see *R.* x *centifolia* 'Muscosa'
'Pink Parfait' (F)	MAus MGan SPer SWCr
'Pink Patio'^{PBR} (Patio)	GGre
Pink Peace = 'Meibil' (HT)	GGre MRav SLon SPoG SWCr
'Pink Perpétué' (Cl)	CBcs CGro CSBt CTri ECnt ELan ENot EPfP GCoc GGre LAst LRHS LStr MAsh MAus MBri MGan MJon MRav SPer SSea SWCr WAct
'Pink Prosperity' (HM)	MAus
'Pink Showers' (ClHT)	WAct
Pink Skyliner = 'Franwekpink'^{PBR} (ClS)	MJon
Pink Surprise = 'Lenbrac' (Ru)	MAus
'Pink Tiara' **new**	LWoR
Pirouette = 'Poulyc003'^{PBR} (Cl)	ECnt LRHS MAsh SWCr
'Pisces' **new**	LWoR
'Playboy' (F) **new**	GCoc
Playtime = 'Morplati' (F)	MAus
Pleine de Grâce = 'Lengra' (S)	LRHS MAus

Poetry in Motion = 'Harelan'PBR (HT)	GGre LWoR MJon SWCr
Polar Star = 'Tanlarpost'PBR (HT)	CSBt EBee ECnt GGre LCro LGod LStr MAsh MGan MRav SPer SPoG SWCr
x ***polliniana***	SLPl
'Polly' (HT)	MGan
§ 'Polyantha Grandiflora' (Ra) **new**	LRHS
pomifera	see *R. villosa* L.
- 'Duplex'	see *R.* 'Duplex'
'Pompon Blanc Parfait' (A)	MAus
'Pompon de Bourgogne'	see *R.* 'Burgundiaca'
'Pompon de Paris' (ClMinCh)	see *R.* 'Climbing Pompon de Paris'
'Pompon Panaché' (G)	MAus
Portland rose	see *R.* 'Portlandica'
§ 'Portlandica'	CGro CTri LRHS MAsh MAus SPer WAct WHCG
Portmeirion = 'Ausguard'PBR (S)	MAsh MAus SCoo SWCr
Pot o' Gold = 'Dicdivine' (HT)	SPer
'Poulink'PBR	see *R.* Pink Hit = 'Poultipe'
Pour Toi = 'Para Ti' (Min)	MAus MGan MJon NPri SWCr
prairie rose	see *R. setigera*
Precious Moments = 'Lyopr'	GGre SWCr
'Precious Platinum' (HT)	LGod MJon SPer SWCr
Preservation = 'Bosiljurika'PBR (S/F)	GGre SWCr
§ 'Président de Sèze' (G) 🏆H4	MAus NLar SFam SPer SWCr WAct WHCG
Pretty in Pink = 'Dicumpteen'PBR (GC)	ECnt IDic MJon SWCr
Pretty Jessica = 'Ausjess' (S)	CGro LRHS MAus MJon MRav SPer
Pretty Lady = 'Scrivo'PBR (F) 🏆H4	LStr MAus MJon SSea SWCr
Pretty Polly = 'Meitonje'PBR (Min) 🏆H4	CGro ENot EPfP ESty GGre LAst LRHS LStr MAsh MBri MGan MRav SPoG SWCr
Pride of England = 'Harencore'PBR (HT)	GCoc LWoR MJon SWCr
Pride of Scotland = 'Macwhitba' (HT)	GCoc MJon
'Prima Ballerina' (HT)	CGro CSBt CTri CWSG ENot GCoc GGre LAst LRHS LStr MAsh MGan MJon SPer SSea SWCr
primula (S) 🏆H3-4	EWTr MAus MGan MJon NLar SSea SWCr WAct WHCG
'Prince Camille de Rohan' (HP)	MAus WHCG
'Prince Charles' (Bb)	MAus SWCr WHCG WKif
Prince Palace = 'Poulzin'PBR (F)	ECnt
Prince Regent = 'Genpen' (S)	SSea
Princess Alexandra = 'Pouldra'PBR (S)	CSam CTri ECnt EPfP LRHS MAsh SWCr
Princess Alice = 'Hartanna' (F)	MGan SWCr
Princess Nobuko = 'Coclistine'PBR (HT)	GCoc
'Princess of Wales' (HP)	EPfP
Princess of Wales = 'Hardinkum'PBR (F) 🏆H4	CGro CSBt ENot EPfP GGre LRHS LStr MAsh MBri MGan MRav NPri SCoo SPer SWCr
Princess Royal = 'Dicroyal'PBR (HT)	GCoc IDic
§ 'Princesse de Nassau' (Ra)	MAus WAct WHCG
'Princesse Louise' (Ra)	CRHN MAus SFam
'Princesse Marie' misapplied	see *R.* 'Belvedere'
§ 'Pristine' (HT)	IDic MAus SPer
§ 'Professeur Emile Perrot' (D)	SWCr WAct
'Prolifera de Redouté' misapplied	see *R.* 'Duchesse de Montebello'
'Prosperity' (HM) 🏆H4	CBcs CSam CTri EBee EPfP GCoc LRHS MAus MGan MJon MRav SPer SWCr WAct WHCG WOVN
Prospero = 'Auspero' (S)	MAus MBri NLar
Pur Caprice = 'Deljavert' (S)	SWCr
'Pure Abundance' (F) **new**	SWCr
Pure Bliss = 'Dictator'PBR (HT)	EBee ECnt ESty GCoc IDic MGan SWCr
'Purezza' (Ra)	NLar
'Purity' (Cl)	EBee
'Purple Beauty' (HT)	MGan
Purple Skyliner = 'Franwekpurp'PBR (ClS)	ESty MJon
Purple Tiger = 'Jacpurr'PBR (F)	ESty IDic SSea SWCr
'Purpurtraum' (Ru)	WHCG
Quaker Star = 'Dicperhaps' (F)	IDic
quatre saisons	see *R.* x *damascena* var. *semperflorens*
'Quatre Saisons Blanche Mousseuse' (DMo)	WAct
Queen Elizabeth	see *R.* 'The Queen Elizabeth'
Queen Margarethe = 'Poulskov'PBR (F)	ECnt
Queen Mother = 'Korquemu'PBR (Patio) 🏆H4	CSBt ELan ENot EPfP GCoc LCro LGod LStr MAus MGan MRav NPri SPer SPoG SWCr
Queen of Denmark	see *R.* 'Königin von Dänemark'
Queen of Sweden = 'Austiger'	ECnt LRHS MAsh MAus SWCr
Queen's Palace = 'Poulelap'PBR (F)	ECnt
'Rachel' ambig.	GCoc
Rachel = 'Tangust'PBR (HT)	ESty MJon MRav SPoG SWCr
Racy Lady = 'Dicwaffle'PBR (HT)	IDic MJon
Radio Times = 'Aussal'PBR (S)	ESty MAus
Rainbow Magic = 'Dicxplosion'PBR (Patio)	ESty IDic
'Ralph Tizzard' (F)	SSea
'Rambling Rector' (Ra) 🏆H4	More than 30 suppliers
Rambling Rosie = 'Horjasper' (Ra) **new**	ECnt MJon
§ 'Ramona' (Ra)	MAus SWCr
'Raspberry Royale' **new**	LWoR
'Raubritter' ('Macrantha' hybrid)	CAbP ECGP LRHS MAsh MAus SPer SSea SWCr WAct WHCG
Ray of Hope = 'Cocnilly'PBR (F)	GCoc LGod SWCr
Ray of Sunshine = 'Cocclare'PBR (Patio)	GCoc
Raymond Blanc = 'Delnado' **new**	SWCr
'Raymond Chenault' (Cl)	CGro MGan SWCr
Rebecca (Patio)	ESty
'Rebecca Claire' (HT)	SWCr
Reconciliation = 'Hartillery'PBR (HT)	ESty SWCr
Red AbundancePBR	see *R.* Songs of Praise = 'Harkimono'
Red Bells = 'Poulred'PBR (Min/GC)	MAus SPer WOVN
Red Blanket = 'Intercell' (S/GC)	GCoc MAus SPer WAct WOVN
Red Caviar = 'Poulfl001'PBR (HT) **new**	ECnt

Red Coat = 'Auscoat' (F)	MAus
Red Devil = 'Dicam' (HT)	GGre MAsh MGan MJon MRav SCoo SPoG SWCr
Red Eden Rose = 'Meidrason'PBR (Cl)	ESty SSea SWCr
'Red Facade' (Cl) **new**	MAsh
Red Finesse = 'Korvillade'PBR	ENot
'Red Grootendorst'	see *R.* 'F.J. Grootendorst'
'Red Hot' (Patio) **new**	MJon
'Red Max Graf'PBR	see *R.* Rote Max Graf = 'Kormax'
red moss	see *R.* 'Henri Martin'
Red New Dawn	see *R.* 'Etendard'
Red Rascal = 'Jacbed'PBR (S/Patio)	CSBt IDic
'Red Romance' **new**	LWoR
red rose of Lancaster	see *R. gallica* var. *officinalis*
Red Trail = 'Interim' (S/GC)	ESty
'Red Wing' (S)	MAus
Redouté = 'Auspale'PBR (S)	LRHS MAus SPer SWCr
§ Regensberg = 'Macyoumis'PBR (F/Patio)	MAus MBri MGan MJon MRav SPer SWCr
'Reine des Centifeuilles' (Ce)	SFam
'Reine des Violettes' (HP)	CGro CPou EPfP IArd LCro LRHS LStr MAsh MAus MCot MGan MRav SPer SPoG SWCr WAct WHCG
§ 'Reine Victoria' (Bb)	EBee EPfP LRHS LStr MAus MGan MRav SPer SPla SWCr WAct
Remember Me = 'Cocdestin'PBR (HT) ♀H4	CGro CWSG ECnt ENot ESty GCoc GGre IArd LCro LGod LStr MAus MBri MGan MJon MRav NPri SPer SPoG SWCr
Remembrance = 'Harxampton'PBR (F) ♀H4	CGro CTri ESty LGod LRHS LStr LWoR MAsh MGan MJon MRav NPri SPer SPoG SWCr
Renaissance = 'Harzart'PBR (HT)	CSBt ESty GCoc LStr SWCr
'René André' (Ra)	CPou CRHN MAus SWCr
'René d'Anjou' (CeMo)	MAus
'Rescht'	see *R.* 'De Rescht'
Rest in Peace = 'Bedswap' (Patio/F)	GGre LWoR SWCr
'Rêve d'Or' (N)	CSam MAus SLon SPer SWCr
'Réveil Dijonnais' (ClHT)	MAus
Rhapsody in Blue = 'Frantasia'PBR (S)	CGro CSBt CTri EBee ECnt ELan ENot EPfP ESty GGre LCro LGod LRHS LStr MAsh MAus MBri MGan MJon MRav NPri SCoo SPer SPoG SSea SWCr
§ x ***richardii***	MAus MGan MRav WAct WHCG
'Rick Stein' (HT) **new**	SWCr
§ 'Rise 'n' Shine' (Min)	LGod
'Rival de Paestum' (T)	MAus
'River Gardens'	NPer
Rob Roy = 'Cocrob' (F)	GCoc MGan SPer SWCr
Robbie Burns = 'Ausburn' (PiH)	MAus WAct
'Robert Burns' (HT)	GGre
'Robert le Diable' (Ce)	CPou MAus NLar SPer SWCr WAct WHCG
'Robin Hood' (HM)	EBee
§ Robusta = 'Korgosa' (Ru)	EBee ECnt MAus MGan SSea
Rockabye Baby = 'Dicdwarf' (Patio)	GCoc IDic SWCr
'Roger Lambelin' (HP)	MAus
Romance = 'Tanezamor'PBR (S)	MRav
Romantic Palace = 'Poulmanti'PBR (F)	ECnt
'Rosa Mundi'	see *R. gallica* 'Versicolor'
Rosabell = 'Cocceleste'PBR (F/Patio)	ESty GCoc
Rosalie Coral = 'Chewallop'PBR (ClMin)	ESty
Rosarium Uetersen = 'Kortersen' (ClHT)	MJon
§ Rose 2000 = 'Cocquetrum'PBR (F)	SWCr
§ 'Rose d'Amour' (S) ♀H4	CFee MAus
'Rose de Meaux'	see *R.* x *centifolia* 'De Meaux'
'Rose de Meaux White'	see *R.* 'White de Meaux'
'Rose de Rescht'	see *R.* 'De Rescht'
'Rose du Maître d'Ecole'	see *R.* 'Du Maître d'Ecole'
'Rose du Roi' (HP/DPo)	MAus WAct WHCG
'Rose du Roi à Fleurs Pourpres' (HP)	MAus
§ Rose Gaujard = 'Gaumo' (HT)	GGre LGod MAsh MGan NBlu SPoG SWCr
Rose of Picardy = 'Ausfudge'	LRHS MAus SWCr
'Rose of Yunnan'	WAct
Rose Pearl = 'Korterschi'PBR (S)	ENot MGan
Rose-Marie = 'Ausome' (S)	MAus SWCr
'Rose-Marie Viaud' (Ra)	CFee CPou CSam EBee MAus SWCr WHCG
'Rosemary Gandy' (F)	MGan
Rosemary Harkness = 'Harrowbond'PBR (HT)	ESty LStr MRav SPer
'Rosemary Rose' (F)	SPer
Rosemoor = 'Austough'	CSBt LRHS MAus SWCr
Rosendal = 'Pouldahle'PBR (F)	EBee ECnt
Rosenprofessor SieberPBR	see *R.* The Halcyon Days Rose = 'Korparesni'
'Roseraie de l'Haÿ' (Ru) ♀H4	More than 30 suppliers
Rosy Cushion = 'Interall' (S/GC) ♀H4	CSam LRHS MAus MCot MGan SPer SWCr WAct WHCG WOVN
Rosy Future = 'Harwaderox'PBR (F/Patio)	CSBt SWCr
'Rosy Mantle' (Cl)	CBcs CSBt MGan SPer SWCr
§ Rotary Sunrise = 'Fryglitzy' (HT)	MBri
§ Rote Max Graf = 'Kormax'PBR (GC/Ru)	MRav WAct
'Roundelay' (HT)	MAus
roxburghii (S)	CArn LEdu MBri MGan SWCr WAct WHCG
- var. ***hirtula*** (S)	CPLG
- f. ***normalis*** (S)	CFee
- 'Plena'	see *R. roxburghii* f. *roxburghii*
§ - f. ***roxburghii*** (d/S)	MAus
'Royal Albert Hall' (HT)	GCoc
Royal Celebration = 'Wekbiphitsou' (F)	MJon
Royal Copenhagen = 'Poulht001'PBR (HT)	ECnt
'Royal Gold' (ClHT)	LAst MBri MGan SLon SWCr
'Royal Occasion' (F)	SPer SWCr
Royal Parks = 'Harlyric' (HT)	GCoc
Royal William = 'Korzaun'PBR (HT) ♀H4	CSBt ECnt ELan ENot ESty GGre LBMP LCro LGod LRHS LStr MAsh MAus MBri MGan MJon MRav NBlu NPri SLon SPer SPoG SWCr
§ ***rubiginosa***	CArn CCVT CDul CGro CRWN EMac EPfP GPoy ILis LBuc MAus MHer MJon MRav NWea SFam SPer SWCr WAct WMou
rubra	see *R. gallica*
rubrifolia	see *R. glauca* Pourr.
'Rubrotincta'	see *R.* 'Hebe's Lip'
rubus (Ra)	MAus
- SF 96062	ISea
- ***velutescens***	WAct

Ruby Anniversary = 'Harbonny'PBR (Patio)	CGro CSBt CWSG ESty GGre LCro LStr MAsh MRav SCoo SSea SWCr
Ruby Celebration = 'Peawinner'PBR (F)	CWSG ESty MJon SWCr
'Ruby Pendant' (Min)	MJon
'Ruby Wedding' (HT)	More than 30 suppliers
'Ruby Wedding Anniversary' (F)	GGre
rugosa (Ru)	CDul CLnd CTri EBee EMac EPfP LBuc MAus MBri MHer MRav NBlu NWea SPlb SWCr WBVN
- 'Alba' (Ru) ♀H4	CBcs CCVT CDul CTri EBee ECnt ELan EMac EPfP GBin LAst LBuc LCro LRHS LStr MAus MGan MJon MRav NWea SPer SPoG SSea SWCr WAct WHen WOVN
- 'Rubra' (Ru) ♀H4	CBcs CCVT CTri CWib EBee EPfP LAst LBuc LCro LStr MGan SPer SPoG WAct WHen
- Sakhalin form	MCCP
- 'Scabrosa'	see *R.* 'Scabrosa'
'Rugspin' (Ru)	WAct
'Rumba' (F)	NBlu SWCr
Rush = 'Lenmobri' (S)	MAus
Rushing Stream = 'Austream' (GC)	MAus NSRo
'Ruskin' (HPxRu)	MAus
'Russelliana' (Ra)	EBee MAus SFam SWCr WAct WHCG
Rutland = 'Poulshine'PBR (Min/GC)	MWgw SWCr
Safe Haven = 'Jacreraz'PBR (F)	ECnt ESty IDic MGan
'Sagittarius' **new**	LWoR
Saint Alban = 'Auschesnut'PBR (S)	CSBt MAus SWCr
Saint Boniface = 'Kormatt' (F/Patio)	CSBt
'Saint Catherine' (Ra)	CFee
Saint Cecilia = 'Ausmit'PBR (S)	LRHS MAus SWCr
Saint Dunstan's Rose = 'Kirshru' (S)	MJon
Saint Edmunds Rose	EBee
Saint Ethelburga = 'Beabimbo' (S)	MBri
Saint John = 'Harbilbo'PBR (F)	CSBt MRav
Saint John's rose	see *R.* x *richardii*
Saint Mark's rose	see *R.* 'Rose d'Amour'
'Saint Nicholas' (D)	CAbP MAus
Saint Swithun = 'Auswith'PBR (S)	EBee ECnt LCro LRHS MAus MJon SSea SWCr
'Salet' (DPMo)	MAus WHCG
'Sally Holmes' (S) ♀H4	ECnt GCoc MAus MGan MJon MRav MWgw SPer SSea SWCr WAct WHCG
Sally's Rose = 'Canrem' (HT)	EBee ECnt SWCr
Salmo = 'Poulnoev'PBR (Patio)	MBri
SalsaPBR	see *R.* Cheek to Cheek
Samaritan = 'Harverag'PBR (HT)	CSBt ESty MRav SWCr
sancta	see *R.* x *richardii*
'Sander's White Rambler' (Ra) ♀H4	CRHN CSam CTri EBee EPfP LRHS LStr MAus MGan MJon MRav NEgg NPri SMad SPer SSea SWCr WAct WHCG
Sandra = 'Carsandra' **new**	SLon
Sandra = 'Poulen055'PBR (Renaissance Series)	LRHS MAsh SWCr
'Sanguinea'	see *R.* x *odorata* Sanguinea Group
Sarah (HT)	see *R.* Jardins de Bagatelle
'Sarah van Fleet' (Ru)	CTri EBee EPfP GCoc IArd LRHS LStr MAus MGan MRav NLar SFam SMad SPer SPla SWCr WAct WOVN
Sarah, Duchess of YorkPBR	see *R.* Sunseeker = 'Dicracer'
Savoy Hotel = 'Harvintage'PBR (HT) ♀H4	CGro CSBt ECnt GGre LGod LStr MAus MGan MRav SPer SWCr
§ 'Scabrosa' (Ru) ♀H4	ECnt GCoc LAst LRHS MAsh MAus MGan MJon SPer SPoG SSea SWCr WAct WHCG WOVN
Scarborough Fair = 'Ausoran' (S)	MAsh MAus SWCr
Scarlet Fire	see *R.* 'Scharlachglut'
Scarlet Glow	see *R.* 'Scharlachglut'
Scarlet Hit = 'Poulmo'PBR (F)	ECnt MAsh
Scarlet Patio = 'Kortingle'PBR (Patio)	ENot ESty LRHS MAsh SPoG
Scarlet Queen Elizabeth = 'Dicel' (F)	CBcs GGre LWoR MRav
'Scented Abundance' **new**	SWCr
'Scented Air' (F)	MGan SPer
Scented Carpet = 'Chewground'PBR (GC) **new**	ECnt MBri SWCr
Scented Memory = 'Poulht002'PBR (HT)	ECnt
Scentimental = 'Wekplapep'PBR (F)	ESty MAsh MBri SCoo SSea SWCr
Scent-sation = 'Fryromeo'PBR (HT)	CWSG ESty GCoc LGod LRHS MAsh MBri MGan MRav NPri SCoo SPoG SWCr
Scepter'd Isle = 'Ausland'PBR (S) ♀H4	CSBt EBee ECnt LRHS LStr MAus NPri SCoo SPer SWCr
§ 'Scharlachglut' (ClS) ♀H4	CPou LRHS MAus MGan MRav SPer SWCr WAct WHCG WOVN
* ***schmidtiana***	CFee
'Schneelicht' (Ru)	MAus
Schneewittchen	see *R.* Iceberg = 'Korbin'
§ 'Schneezwerg' (Ru) ♀H4	CGro GCoc MAus MGan MJon MRav SPer SPla SSea SWCr WAct WHCG WOVN
'Schoolgirl' (Cl)	CBcs CGro CSBt CTri EBee ELan ENot EPfP GGre LAst LRHS LStr LWoR MAsh MBri MGan MJon MRav SPer SPoG SWCr
'Scintillation' (S/GC)	MAus
'Scorpio' **new**	LWoR
Scotch pink (PiH)	WAct
Scotch rose	see *R. spinosissima*
Scotch yellow (PiH)	see *R.* x *harisonii* 'Williams' Double Yellow'
'Seagull' (Ra) ♀H4	CGro CTri CWSG EBee ECnt EPfP ESty LAst LGod LRHS LStr MAsh MGan MJon MRav NPri NWea SLon SMad SPer SPla SPoG SSea SWCr WHCG WHer
'Seale Peach' (Patio)	SSea
'Sealing Wax' (*moyesii* hybrid)	MBri WAct
Selfridges = 'Korpriwa' (HT)	MJon
'Semiplena'	see *R.* x *alba* 'Alba Semiplena'
sempervirens (Ra)	XPep
sericea (S)	CFee GBin MAus WHCG
- CC 3306	WRos
- var. ***morrisonensis*** B&SWJ 7139	WCru
§ - subsp. ***omeiensis*** BWJ 7550	WCru
- - f. ***pteracantha*** (S)	CBcs EBee ELan EPfP EWTr GGar MAus MGan MRav NWea SMad SPer SPoG SSea WAct WOVN
- - - 'Atrosanguinea' (S)	CArn

§ ***setigera***	MAus
setipoda	MAus WAct WFar WHCG
seven sisters rose	see *R. multiflora* 'Grevillei'
Seventh Heaven = 'Fryfantasy' (HT)	GCoc MBri SWCr
Sexy Rexy = 'Macrexy'PBR (F) ♀H4	CGro CSBt EPfP ESty GCoc GGre LAst LBMP LRHS LStr MAsh MAus MBri MGan MJon MRav SPer SPoG SWCr
'Shailer's White Moss'	see *R.* x *centifolia* 'Shailer's White Moss'
Sharifa Asma = 'Ausreef'PBR (S)	CSBt EBee ELan ENot EWTr LCro LRHS LStr MAus MBNS MRav NEgg SPer SWCr WAct
Sheila's Perfume = 'Harsherry'PBR (HT/F)	CGro ECnt ESty GCoc GGre LStr LWoR MGan MJon MRav SPer SSea SWCr
'Sherbert Fizz' new	LWoR
Shine On = 'Dictalent'PBR (Patio) ♀H4	CSBt ECnt ESty IDic MAsh MBri MRav SPoG SWCr
Shining Light = 'Cocshimmer'PBR (Patio)	GCoc GGre LWoR MBri SCoo SWCr
Shocking Blue = 'Korblue'PBR (F)	CSBt EBee ECnt ENot MGan MJon SPer SWCr
Shona = 'Dicdrum' (F)	IDic
'Shot Silk' (HT)	CSBt MGan SWCr
Shrimp Hit = 'Poulshrimp'PBR (Patio)	ECnt
'Shropshire Lass' (S)	LRHS MAus SPer
§ Silver Anniversary = 'Poulari'PBR (HT) ♀H4	CGro CSBt CTri EBee ECnt ELan ENot GCoc GGre LAst LCro LGod LRHS LStr MAsh MAus MBri MGan MJon MRav NPri SCoo SPer SPoG SWCr
Silver Ghost = 'Kormifari' (S)	ENot
'Silver Jubilee' (HT) ♀H4	CBcs CGro CSBt ECnt ENot EPfP ESty GCoc GGre IArd LBMP LGod LRHS LStr LWoR MAsh MAus MGan MJon MRav SPer SPoG SWCr
'Silver Lining' (HT)	SWCr
'Silver Moon' (Cl)	CRHN
'Silver Wedding' (HT)	CWSG ELan GCoc IArd LAst MAus MRav NBir NWea SPer SWCr
'Silver Wedding Celebration' (F)	CTri ESty GGre LWoR SWCr
Silver Wishes = 'Poulhipe'	LRHS MAsh SWCr
Simba = 'Korbelma'PBR (HT)	ENot MGan
'Simplex Multiflora' new	CWib
Simply Heaven = 'Diczombie'PBR (HT)	ESty GCoc IDic SWCr
§ Simply the Best = 'Macamster'PBR (HT)	CGro CSBt ECnt ELan ENot ESty GCoc GGre LGod LRHS LStr MAsh MAus MJon MRav SCoo SPer SPoG SWCr
§ Singin' in the Rain = 'Macivy' (F)	MJon SWCr
sinowilsonii	see *R. longicuspis* var. *sinowilsonii*
'Sir Cedric Morris' (Ra)	EBee SSea WAct
Sir Clough = 'Ausclough' (S)	MAus
Sir Edward Elgar = 'Ausprima'PBR (S)	LStr MAus
'Sir Galahad' new	MRav SPoG
'Sir Joseph Paxton' (Bb)	CAbP MAus
Sir Walter Raleigh = 'Ausspry' (S)	MAus MRav
Smarty = 'Intersmart' (S/GC)	CAbP MAus SPer WAct
'Smooth Angel' (HT)	MGan
Smooth Lady = 'Hadlady' (HT)	LGod MGan
Smooth Melody = 'Hadmelody' (F)	LAst
Smooth Prince = 'Hadprince' (HT)	LAst LGod
'Smooth Velvet' (HT)	LAst SPer
Snow Carpet = 'Maccarpe' (Min/GC)	ELan MAus MJon
'Snow Dwarf'	see *R.* 'Schneezwerg'
Snow Goose = 'Auspom'PBR (Cl/S)	CSBt LRHS MAus MBri NSRo SWCr
Snow Hit = 'Poulsnows'PBR (Min/Patio)	ECnt LRHS NPri SWCr
'Snow Queen'	see *R.* 'Frau Karl Druschki'
Snow Sunblaze = 'Meigovin' (Min)	CSBt MRav SPer SPoG
Snowball = 'Macangeli' (Min/GC)	MJon
Snowcap = 'Harfleet'PBR (Patio)	ESty GGre SPoG SSea
'Snowdon' (Ru)	LRHS MAsh MAus
'Snowdrift' (Ra)	WHCG
'Snowflake' (Ra)	WHCG
'Soldier Boy' (Cl)	WHCG
Solitaire = 'Macyefre'PBR (HT)	MJon
Solo Mio = 'Poulen002'PBR (S)	CSam CTri ECnt LRHS MAsh SPla SWCr
§ 'Sombreuil' (ClT)	EBee EPfP IArd LRHS MAsh MAus MRav NEgg NLar SFam SPer SPla SSea SWCr WAct WHCG
Something Special = 'Macwyo'PBR (HT)	ECnt ESty GCoc MJon SWCr
§ Songs of Praise = 'Harkimono'PBR (F)	ESty
Sonia	see *R.* Sweet Promise = 'Meihelvet'
'Sophie's Perpetual' (ClCh)	CPou ENot LRHS MAus MGan SPer SWCr WAct WHCG XPep
Sophy's Rose = 'Auslot'PBR (S)	ESty LRHS LStr MAus MBri MJon NEgg SWCr
soulieana (Ra/S) ♀H3-4	MAus WAct WKif
'Soupert et Notting' (DPoMo)	LRHS MAus MRav SPer WAct
'Southampton' (F) ♀H4	ENot GGre LStr MAsh MAus MRav SPer SSea SWCr
'Souvenir d'Alphonse Lavallée' (ClHP)	WHCG
'Souvenir de Brod'	see *R.* 'Erinnerung an Brod'
'Souvenir de Claudius Denoyel' (ClHT)	EBee MAus MGan SPer WAct
'Souvenir de Jeanne Balandreau' (HP)	WHCG
'Souvenir de la Malmaison' (ClBb)	see *R.* 'Climbing Souvenir de la Malmaison'
'Souvenir de la Malmaison' (Bb)	EBee GCoc MAus MGan MRav NLar SPer SWCr WAct
Souvenir de Louis Amade = 'Delalac' (S)	CGro MRav SWCr
'Souvenir de Madame Léonie Viennot' (ClT)	CPou MAus MRav
Souvenir de Marcel Proust = 'Delpapy' (S)	SWCr
'Souvenir de Saint Anne's' (Bb)	EBee MAus SWCr WAct WHCG
'Souvenir di Castagneto' (HP)	MRav
'Souvenir du Docteur Jamain' (ClHP)	CPou EBee ELan ESty LStr MAus MRav SFam SMrm SPer SPoG SSea SWCr WAct WHCG WKif
Spangles = 'Ganspa'PBR (F)	MGan SWCr
'Spanish Beauty'	see *R.* 'Madame Grégoire Staechelin'
Sparkling Scarlet = 'Meihati' (ClF)	ELan GGre MAsh MGan

Sparkling Yellow = 'Poulgode'PBR (GC/S) — ECnt SWCr
Special Anniversary = 'Whastiloc' (HT) — CGro ESty GGre LRHS MAsh MBri NPri SCoo SPoG SWCr
Special Child = 'Tanaripsa' — SWCr
Special Friend = 'Kirspec'PBR (Patio) — GCoc LStr MJon
'Special Lady' **new** — SWCr
Special Occasion = 'Fryyoung'PBR (HT) — ENot ESty GCoc MRav SWCr
'Spectabilis' (Ra) — ELan WHCG
Spek's Centennial (F) — see *R.* Singin' in the Rain = 'Macivy' (F)
SpellboundPBR — see *R.* Garden News = 'Poulrim'
Spice of Life = 'Diccheeky'PBR (F/Patio) — GCoc IDic
§ ***spinosissima*** — CDul EBee EMac LBuc LRHS MAus MGan NHaw NWea SPer SSea WAct WHCG WOVN
- 'Andrewsii' ♀H4 — MAus MRav WAct
§ - double pink — WBor WOut
§ - double white — CNat ECha GCoc IGor MAus
- 'Dunwich Rose' — WAct EBee EPfP LRHS MAus MGan MJon NEgg SPer SWCr WAct WHCG
- 'Falkland' — ECha GCra MAus
- 'Glory of Edzell' — MAus
§ - 'Grandiflora' — MAus
- 'Marbled Pink' — MAus
- 'Mary, Queen of Scots' — MAus MGan SRms WAct
- 'Mrs Colville' — MAus
- 'Ormiston Roy' — MAus
- 'Robbie' — WAct
- 'Single Cherry' — MAus SSea
- 'Variegata' (v) — CArn
- 'William III' — EWes GCra MAus SLPl
Spirit of Freedom = 'Ausbite'PBR (S) — LRHS MAsh MAus NEgg SWCr
§ 'Splendens' (Ra) — EBee SLPl SWCr WAct
St. Helena = 'Canlish' (F) — EBee ECnt
St Tiggywinkle = 'Korbasren'PBR (GC) — ENot
'Stanwell Perpetual' (PiH) — CBgR CSam EBee EPfP GCoc LStr MRav NLar SEND SPer SSea SWCr WAct WHCG WOVN
'Star of Waltham' (HP) — WHCG
'Star Performer'PBR (ClPatio) — CSBt EBee ECnt ESty MAsh MBri MJon SWCr
Stardust = 'Peavandyke'PBR (Patio/F) — ESty LWoR MJon SWCr
Starina = 'Megabi' (Min) — MGan
Starlight Express = 'Trobstar'PBR (Cl) — MAsh MBri SCoo SPer SPoG SWCr
Starry Eyed = 'Horcoexist' (Patio) — MGan SWCr
'Stars 'n' Stripes' (Min) — LGod MAus
Stella (HT) — MGan SWCr
stellata — MAus
§ - var. ***mirifica*** — EBee MAus MGan SSea SWCr
'Sterling Silver' (HT) — MGan SPoG SWCr
Sting = 'Meimater'PBR — SWCr
Strawberries and Cream = 'Geestraw' (Min/Patio) — ELan ESty
Strawberry Fayre = 'Arowillip'PBR (Min/Patio) — ESty MRav SPoG
§ Sue Hipkin = 'Harzazz'PBR (HT) — ESty MRav SPoG SWCr
Suffolk = 'Kormixal'PBR (S/GC) — CBrm CGro CSBt ELan ENot GCoc LStr MAus MGan MRav SPer SSea SWCr WAct
suffulta — see *R. arkansana* var. *suffulta*
Sugar and Spice = 'Peaallure'PBR (Patio) — MBri SPoG
Sugar Baby = 'Tanabagus'PBR (Patio) — ESty MAsh SPoG SWCr
Sugar 'n' Spice = 'Tinspice' (Min) — MRav
Suma = 'Harsuma' (GC) — ESty MJon WAct
Summer Breeze = 'Korelasting'PBR (Cl) — ENot MBri
Summer Dream = 'Frymaxicot'PBR (F) — CSBt
Summer Fever = 'Tan99106' (Patio) **new** — ESty SWCr
Summer Fragrance = 'Tanfudermos'PBR (HT) — CSBt ESty GCoc SWCr
§ Summer Gold = 'Poulreb'PBR (F) — ECnt EPfP SWCr
'Summer Holiday' (HT) — SPer SWCr
'Summer Magic' (Patio) — GGre
Summer Memories = 'Koruteli' (F) — ENot
Summer Palace = 'Poulcape'PBR (F/Patio) — ECnt
Summer Snow = 'Weopop' (Patio) — MJon
Summer Song = 'Austango' **new** — LRHS MAsh MAus SWCr
Summer Wine = 'Korizont'PBR (Cl) ♀H4 — CSBt EBee ECnt ENot ESty LRHS MAsh MGan MJon SCoo SPer SSea SWCr
Summertime = 'Chewlarmoll' (Patio/Cl) — CGro CSBt EBee ECnt ELan ENot ESty GCoc LGod LRHS LStr MBri MGan MJon MRav NPri SCoo SPer SPoG SWCr
Sun Hit = 'Poulsun'PBR (Patio) — CSBt ECnt MAsh MRav SWCr
'Sunblaze'PBR — see *R.* Orange Sunblaze = 'Meijikatar'
Sunblest = 'Landora' (HT) — ENot GGre LRHS MAsh MRav SPoG SWCr
Sunrise = 'Kormarter'PBR (Cl) — ENot ESty MBri SWCr WGer
§ Sunseeker = 'Dicracer'PBR (F/Patio) — ENot EPfP ESty GGre IDic LRHS MAsh MRav SPoG SWCr
Sunset BoulevardPBR — see *R.* Sunset Boulevard = 'Harbabble'
§ Sunset Boulevard = 'Harbabble'PBR (F) ♀H4 — CSBt EBee ECnt ENot LGod LStr MAsh MAus MBri MGan MRav SCoo SPer SSea SWCr
Sunset CelebrationPBR — see *R.* Warm Wishes = 'Fryxotic'
'Sunshine' (Poly) — MGan SPer
'Sunsilk' (F) — SWCr
Sunsplash = 'Cocweaver'PBR (F) — GCoc GGre MRav SPoG SWCr
Super Dorothy = 'Heldoro' (Ra) — MAus MJon SWCr
Super Elfin = 'Helkleger'PBR (Ra) ♀H4 — ECnt LStr MGan MJon MRav SPer SSea SWCr
Super Excelsa = 'Helexa' (Ra) — ESty GGre LStr MAsh MAus MGan MJon SPoG SSea SWCr
Super Fairy = 'Helsufair'PBR (Ra) — EBee ECnt LStr MAus MGan MJon MRav SPer SSea SWCr
§ Super Sparkle = 'Helfels'PBR (Ra) — ECnt LStr SSea SWCr
§ Super Star = 'Tanorstar' (HT) — CTri GGre LStr MGan MJon MRav SPoG SWCr
'Surpasse Tout' (G) — MAus WHCG
§ 'Surpassing Beauty of Woolverstone' (ClHP) — WHCG
Surprise = 'Presur'PBR **new** — SWCr
Surrey = 'Korlanum'PBR (GC) ♀H4 — CSBt ECnt ELan ENot ESty EWTr LCro LGod LStr MAus MGan MRav NLar NPri SPer SPla SSea SWCr WAct
Susan = 'Poulsue' (S) — EBee ECnt SBra SWCr

	Name	Suppliers
	Sussex = 'Poulave'[PBR] (GC)	CSBt GCoc LStr MGan MRav NPri SPer SWCr
	'Sutter's Gold' (HT)	MAus MGan
	Swan = 'Auswhite' (S)	MAus
	Swan Lake = 'Macmed' (Cl)	EBee ECnt ELan ENot EPfP ESty GGre LGod LStr MGan MRav NPri SPer SWCr
	Swany = 'Meiburenac' (Min/GC) 𝕐[H4]	CGro ESty LSRN MAus MGan SPer SWCr WHCG
	Sweet Cover = 'Poulweeto'[PBR]	SWCr
	Sweet Dream = 'Fryminicot'[PBR] (Patio) 𝕐[H4]	CGro CSBt CTri ECnt ELan ENot EPfP ESty GCoc GGre LCro LGod LRHS LStr MAsh MAus MBri MGan MJon MRav NPri SPer SPla SPoG SSea SWCr
	'Sweet Fairy' (Min)	CSBt
	Sweet Juliet = 'Ausleap'[PBR] (S)	CAbP CSBt CWSG ESty LGod LRHS MAus MJon NEgg NPri NSRo SPer SWCr
*	'Sweet Lemon Dream' (Patio)	CTri
	Sweet Magic = 'Dicmagic'[PBR] (Min/Patio) 𝕐[H4]	CGro CSBt CTri ENot EPfP GGre IDic LCro LRHS LStr MAsh MBri MGan MJon MRav NPri SPla SPoG SWCr
	Sweet Memories = 'Whamemo' (Patio)	CTri ECnt ENot EPfP ESty GCoc GGre LGod LRHS LStr MAsh MJon MRav NPri SCoo SPer SPla SPoG SWCr WGer
§	Sweet Promise = 'Meihelvet' (GC)	MGan
	'Sweet Remembrance' (HT)	LStr MJon
	'Sweet Repose' (F)	MGan SWCr
	'Sweet Revelation'[PBR]	see *R.* Sue Hipkin = 'Harzazz'
	Sweet Symphonie = 'Meibarke'[PBR] (Patio)	SWCr
	'Sweet Velvet' (F)	MGan
	'Sweet Wonder' (Patio)	ENot EPfP GGre LWoR MAsh SPoG SWCr
N	Sweetheart = 'Cocapeer' (HT)	GCoc MBri
	'Sweetie' (Patio) **new**	SWCr
	sweginzowii	MAus
	'Sydonie' (HP)	WHCG
	'Sympathie' (ClHT)	MGan SPer SSea SWCr
	Tall Story = 'Dickooky'[PBR] (F) 𝕐[H4]	IDic MJon SWCr WHCG WOVN
	Tamora = 'Austamora' (S)	MAus
	Tango = 'Macfirwal' (F)	MJon
	Tango = 'Poulyc005'[PBR] (Patio/Cl)	ECnt SWCr
	Tapis Jaune	see *R.* Golden Penny = 'Rugul'
	Tatoo = 'Poulyc002'[PBR] (Patio/Cl)	ECnt SWCr
	Tatton = 'Fryentice'[PBR] (F)	ESty MAus MBri MJon SWCr
I	'Taurus' **new**	LWoR
	Tawny Tiger = 'Frygolly' (F)	ESty SWCr
	Tear Drop = 'Dicomo'[PBR] (Min/Patio)	IDic LStr MGan SWCr
	Teasing Georgia = 'Ausbaker'[PBR] (S)	EBee ECnt EPfP ESty LCro LRHS MAus MBri MJon NEgg SCoo SWCr
	'Telstar' (F)	MGan
	Temptress = 'Korramal' (Cl)	ENot MAsh MJon
	Tenacious = 'Macblackpo'[PBR] (F) **new**	LStr
	'Tenerife' (HT)	GGre
	Tequila Sunrise = 'Dicobey'[PBR] (HT) 𝕐[H4]	CGro CTri ECnt ELan EPfP ESty GGre IDic LRHS LStr MAsh MAus MBri MGan MJon MRav SMrm SPer SSea SWCr

	Name	Suppliers
§	Terracotta = 'Meicobuis'[PBR] (HT)	ESty SWCr
	Tess of the D'Urbervilles = 'Ausmove'[PBR] (S)	LCro LRHS LStr MAus MBri NEgg SCoo SWCr
	'Tessa' (F)	MGan SWCr
	Thank You = 'Chesdeep'[PBR] (Patio)	ESty GCoc GGre LStr SPoG SWCr
§	That's Jazz = 'Poulnorm'[PBR] (ClF)	EBee ECnt LRHS MAsh MJon SWCr
	The Alexandra Rose = 'Ausday'[PBR] (S)	LRHS MAus
	The Attenborough Rose = 'Dicelope'[PBR] (F)	IDic SWCr
	'The Bishop' (CexG)	MAus
	The Compass Rose = 'Korwisco'[PBR] (S)	ENot SPer
	The Compassionate Friends = 'Harzodiac'[PBR] (F)	LWoR SWCr
	The Countryman = 'Ausman'[PBR] (S)	LRHS MAus SWCr
	The Dark Lady = 'Ausbloom'[PBR] (S)	LCro LRHS MAsh MAus NEgg SPer SWCr
	'The Doctor' (HT)	MGan SSea SWCr
	The Dove = 'Tanamola'[PBR] (F)	MGan
	'The Ednaston Rose' (Cl)	WHCG
§	'The Fairy' (Poly) 𝕐[H4]	CSBt CTri EBee ECnt ELan ENot EPfP GGre LAst LGod LStr MAsh MAus MGan MJon MRav SMad SPer SPla SSea SWCr WAct WCFE WHCG WOVN
	'The Garland' (Ra) 𝕐[H4]	CRHN EBee LRHS MAus SFam SPer WHCG XPep
	The Generous Gardener = 'Ausdrawn'[PBR] (S)	LCro LRHS MAus NEgg NSRo SCoo SWCr
	The Gold Award Rose = 'Poulac008'[PBR]	ECnt
§	The Halcyon Days Rose = 'Korparesni'[PBR] (F)	ENot
	The Herbalist = 'Aussemi' (S)	LRHS MAus SSea
	The Ingenious Mr Fairchild = 'Austijus'[PBR] (S)	LCro MAus SCoo SWCr
	The Jubilee Rose = 'Poulbrido'[PBR] (F)	EBee ECnt SCoo
	'The Lister Rose' (F) **new**	MGan
	The Maidstone Rose = 'Kordauerpa'[PBR]	SCoo
	'The Margaret Coppola Rose'[PBR]	see *R.* White Gold = 'Cocquiriam'
	The Mayflower = 'Austilly'[PBR] (S)	CSBt LRHS MAus MBri MJon NSRo SSea SWCr
§	The McCartney Rose = 'Meizeli'[PBR] (HT)	GGre LStr MJon SPer SWCr
	'The New Dawn'	see *R.* 'New Dawn'
	The Nun = 'Ausnun' (S)	MAus
	The Painter = 'Mactemaik'[PBR] (F)	LStr MJon SSea
§	The Pilgrim = 'Auswalker'[PBR] (S)	CSBt CSam ENot EPfP ESty EWTr LRHS LStr MAsh MAus MBri MJon NEgg SPer SPla SWCr WHCG
	The Prince = 'Ausvelvet'[PBR] (S)	LRHS LStr MAsh MAus MBNS NEgg SPer SPoG SSea SWCr
	The Prince's Trust = 'Harholding'[PBR] (Cl)	LStr MBri MJon SWCr
	'The Prioress' (S)	MAus
§	'The Queen Elizabeth' (F)	CBcs CGro CSBt CTri CWSG ECnt ENot GCoc GGre LCro LGod LStr LWoR MAsh MBri MGan MJon MRav NBlu SEND SPer SPoG SSea SWCr
	The Reeve = 'Ausreeve' (S)	MAus
	The Rotarian	see *R.* Rotary Sunrise

	Name	Suppliers
I	'The Rugby Rose' (HT)	MGan SWCr
	The Scotsman = 'Poulscots'PBR (HT)	EBee ECnt GCoc
	The Shepherdess = 'Austwist' **new**	MAus
	The Soham RosePBR	see *R.* Pearl Abundance
	The Soroptimist Rose = 'Benstar' (Patio)	MJon
	The Squire = 'Ausquire' (S)	MAus
	The Times Rose = 'Korpeahn'PBR (F) 🏆H4	EBee ECnt ENot LGod LStr MAus MGan MJon MRav SPer SWCr
	'Thelma' (Ra)	MAus
	'Thérèse Bugnet' (Ru)	MAus NHaw
	Thinking of You = 'Frydandy'PBR (HT)	ESty GCoc LGod LRHS LStr MAsh MGan SWCr
	'Thisbe' (HM)	MAus WAct WHCG XPep
	Thomas Barton = 'Meihirvin' (HT)	ESty LStr
	'Thoresbyana'	see *R.* 'Bennett's Seedling'
	'Thoughts of You' (Patio)	SWCr
	'Thoughts of You' (HT)	GGre
	'Threave' (B) **new**	SWCr WHCG
	Three Cheers = 'Dicdomino'PBR (F)	IDic
	threepenny bit rose	see *R. elegantula* 'Persetosa'
	Tickled Pink = 'Fryhunky' (F) **new**	ECnt ENot ESty
	Tigris = 'Harprier' (*persica* hybrid) (S)	WAct
	Times Past = 'Harhilt'PBR (Cl)	ESty GCoc LStr MGan MJon MRav SPoG SWCr
	'Tina Turner' (HT)	MJon
	Tintinara = 'Dicuptight'PBR (HT)	ECnt IDic MGan
	Tip Top = 'Tanope' (F/Patio)	CBcs MGan SPer
	'Tipo Ideale'	see *R.* x *odorata* 'Mutabilis'
	Titanic = 'Macdako'PBR (F)	MBri MJon SWCr
	'Toby Tristam' (Ra)	CRHN
	Together Forever = 'Dicecho' (F) **new**	GCoc IDic
	'Tom Foster' (HT)	MJon
	'Tom Marshall' **new**	WHCG
	Too Hot to Handle = 'Macloupri'PBR (S/Cl)	MJon SSea
	Top Marks = 'Fryministar'PBR (Min/Patio)	CGro CSBt CTri EPfP GCoc LGod LStr MBri MGan MJon MRav NPri SCoo SPer SWCr
	Topaz JewelPBR	see *R.* Yellow Dagmar Hastrup = 'Moryelrug'
	Topkapi Palace = 'Poulthe'PBR (F)	ECnt
	Toprose = 'Cocgold'PBR (F)	GCoc GGre MAsh
	'Topsi' (F/Patio)	SPer
	'Touch of Glamour' **new**	LWoR
§	'Tour de Malakoff' (Ce)	CPou CSBt LRHS MAus MRav SFam SPer SWCr WAct WHCG
	Tournament of Roses = 'Jacient' (HT)	MJon
	Tower Bridge = 'Haravis' (HT)	ESty GGre
	'Trade Winds' (HT)	MGan SWCr
	Tradescant = 'Ausdir'PBR (S)	LRHS MAus
	TraditionPBR	see *R.* Tradition '95 = 'Korkeltin'
§	Tradition '95 = 'Korkeltin'PBR (Cl) 🏆H4	ENot SWCr
	'Treasure Trove' (Ra)	CRHN LRHS MAus MGan MJon SWCr WAct
	Trevor Griffiths = 'Ausold'PBR (S)	MAus
	'Tricolore de Flandre' (G)	MAus
	'Trier' (Ra)	CPou EBee MAus SWCr WHCG
	'Trigintipetala' misapplied	see *R.* 'Professeur Emile Perrot'
	'Triomphe de l'Exposition' (HP)	MAus
	'Triomphe du Luxembourg' (T)	MAus
	triphylla	see *R.* x *beanii*
	Troika = 'Poumidor' (HT) 🏆H4	CSBt ELan ENot GGre LRHS LStr MAsh MAus MGan MRav NBlu SPer SPoG SWCr
	Troilus = 'Ausoil' (S)	MAus
	'Tropicana'	see *R.* Super Star = 'Tanorstar'
	Trumpeter = 'Mactru' (F) 🏆H4	CSBt EBee ECnt ENot GGre IArd LRHS LStr LWoR MAsh MAus MGan MJon MRav SPer SPoG SSea SWCr
	'Tuscany' (G)	GCoc MAus WAct WHCG
	'Tuscany Superb' (G) 🏆H4	CBgR CPou CSam EBee ENot EPfP ISea LAst LCro LRHS MAsh MAus MGan MRav SPer SSea SWCr WAct WHCG WKif
	Twenty-one Again! = 'Meinimo'PBR (HT)	SWCr
	Twice in a Blue Moon = 'Tan96138' (HT)	ECnt ESty LGod LRHS MAsh MJon MRav SCoo SPoG SWCr
	Twist = 'Poulstri'PBR (Patio/Cl)	CGro ECnt ESty MAsh SWCr
	Tynwald = 'Mattwyt'PBR (HT)	ENot LStr MJon
	'Ulrich Brünner Fils' (HP)	MAus
	Uncle Walter = 'Macon' (HT)	SWCr
	UNICEF = 'Cocjojo'PBR (F)	GCoc
	'Unique Blanche'	see *R.* x *centifolia* 'Unique'
	Valencia = 'Koreklia'PBR (HT) 🏆H4	CSBt ECnt ENot ESty MAus
	Valentine Heart = 'Dicogle'PBR (F) 🏆H4	CSBt ESty IArd IDic LRHS MAsh MAus MBri MRav SPoG SWCr
	Valiant Heart = 'Poulberg' (F)	EBee ECnt
	'Vanity' (HM)	MAus
	'Variegata di Bologna' (Bb)	EPfP LRHS MAus MRav SSea SWCr WAct
	Variety Club = 'Haredge'PBR (Patio)	LGod
	'Veilchenblau' (Ra) 🏆H4	CRHN CSBt EBee ECnt ELan EPfP LAst LCro LGod LRHS LStr MAus MGan MRav NEgg NPri SPer SPoG SSea SWCr WAct WHCG WKif
	Velvet Fragrance = 'Fryperdee'PBR (HT)	CSBt ECnt ESty GCoc GGre LRHS LStr MAsh MAus MBri MGan MJon MRav SPoG SWCr
	'Venusta Pendula' (Ra)	MAus
	'Verschuren' (HT/v)	MJon
	versicolor	see *R. gallica* 'Versicolor'
	Versigny = 'Masversi' **new**	MRav
	'Vick's Caprice' (HP)	MAus
	'Vicomtesse Pierre du Fou' (ClHT)	MAus
	'Victor Madeley' (F) **new**	MGan
	'Victoriana' (F)	SSea
	Vidal Sassoon = 'Macjuliat'PBR (HT)	MGan MJon SWCr
	'Village Maid'	see *R.* x *centifolia* 'Unique Panachée'
§	***villosa*** L.	CArn MAus WAct
	- 'Duplex'	see *R.* 'Duplex'
§	'Violacea' (G)	EBee LRHS MAus WAct WHCG
	'Violette' (Ra)	CPou CRHN EBee MAus SWCr WAct WHCG
	virginiana 🏆H4	CFee MAus MGan MSte NHaw NWea SPer WAct WHCG WHen
	- 'Harvest Song'	NHaw
	- 'Plena'	see *R.* 'Rose d'Amour'
	'Virgo' (HT)	NBlu
I	'Virgo' **new**	LWoR
	'Viridiflora'	see *R.* x *odorata* 'Viridiflora'
	Waltz = 'Poulkrid'PBR (Patio/Cl)	ECnt LRHS

	Wandering Minstrel = 'Harquince' (F)	SWCr
	wardii var. ***culta***	MAus
	Warm Welcome = 'Chewizz'^{PBR} (ClMin) $\mathbb{Y}^{H4}$	CGro ECnt ENot EPfP ESty GGre LCro LGod LRHS LStr MAsh MAus MBri MGan MJon MRav MWgw NEgg SMad SPer SPoG SSea SWCr
§	Warm Wishes = 'Fryxotic'^{PBR} (HT) $\mathbb{Y}^{H4}$	CSBt EBee ECnt ENot ESty GCoc GGre LGod LRHS LStr MAus MBri MGan MJon MRav NBlu NPri SPoG SWCr
	'Warrior' (F)	MGan SPer
	Warwick Castle = 'Auslian'^{PBR} (S)	MAus SPer
	Warwickshire = 'Korkandel'^{PBR} (GC)	SPer SWCr
	webbiana	MAus SPer WHCG
	Wedding Celebration = 'Poulht006' (HT) **new**	ECnt
	'Wedding Day' (Ra)	More than 30 suppliers
	Wee Cracker = 'Cocmarris'^{PBR} (Patio)	ESty GCoc GGre LGod
	Wee Jock = 'Cocabest'^{PBR} (F/Patio)	GCoc GGre LWoR SPoG SWCr
	'Weetwood' (Ra)	CRHN SPer
	'Weisse aus Sparrieshoop' (S)	MGan
	Weisse Wolcke^{PBR}	see *R.* White Cloud = 'Korstacha'
	Welcome Home = 'Koraubala'^{PBR} (F)	ENot
	'Well Done' (Patio)	GGre SPoG SWCr
	Well-Being = 'Harjangle'^{PBR} (S)	ESty MJon SWCr
	'Wendy Cussons' (HT)	CBcs CGro CTri CWSG GCoc MGan MJon MRav SPer SSea SWCr
	Wenlock = 'Auswen' (S)	MAus SPer
	'West Country Millennium' (F)	MGan
	Westerland = 'Korwest' (F/S) $\mathbb{Y}^{H4}$	MGan MJon SPoG SWCr
	Where the Heart Is = 'Cocoplan'^{PBR} (HT)	GCoc
	'Whisky Gill' (HT)	MGan
	Whisky Mac = 'Tanky' (HT)	CBcs CGro CSBt CTri CWSG ELan GCoc GGre MGan MJon MRav NPri SPer
	'White Bath'	see *R.* x *centifolia* 'Shailer's White Moss'
	White Bells = 'Poulwhite'^{PBR} (Min/GC)	MRav SPer
§	'White Cécile Brünner' (Poly)	MAus WHCG
	'White Christmas' (HT)	MGan SWCr
§	White Cloud = 'Korstacha'^{PBR} (S/ClHT) $\mathbb{Y}^{H4}$	CSBt EBee ECnt ENot ESty LGod LRHS MAsh MJon SPoG SWCr WHCG
	White Cloud = 'Savacloud' (Min)	MBri
	'White Cockade' (Cl)	EBee GCoc MGan SPer SWCr
	White Cover^{PBR}	see *R.* Kent
§	'White de Meaux' (Ce)	MAus
	White Diamond = 'Interamon'^{PBR} (S)	ECnt IDic
§	White Gold = 'Cocquiriam'^{PBR} (F)	GCoc GGre LWoR MRav SPoG SWCr
	'White Grootendorst' (Ru)	MAus SSea WAct
	White Knight (HT)	see *R.* Message = 'Meban'
	White Knight = 'Poullaps' (ClHT/S)	SWCr
	'White Lace' **new**	LWoR
	White Max Graf^{PBR}	see *R.* x *jacksonii* White Max Graf = 'Korgram'
	white moss	see *R.* 'Comtesse de Murinais', *R.* x *centifolia* 'Shailer's White Moss'
§	'White Pet' (Poly) $\mathbb{Y}^{H4}$	CSBt EBee ECnt EPfP EWTr GCoc LGod LStr MAus MBri MGan MJon MRav NEgg SEND SPer SPla SWCr WAct WKif
	white Provence	see *R.* x *centifolia* 'Unique'
	'White Queen Elizabeth' (F)	SWCr
	white rose of York	see *R.* x *alba* 'Alba Semiplena'
	White Skyliner = 'Franwekwhit'^{PBR} (ClS)	MJon
	'White Tausendschön' (Ra)	MAus
	'White Wings' (HT)	MAus MGan SPer SWCr WAct WHCG WKif
N	***wichurana*** (Ra)	MAus MGan SWCr WHCG XPep
	- 'Variegata' (Ra/v)	CBow CSWP
*	- 'Variegata Nana' (Ra/v)	MRav SMad
	'Wickwar' (Ra)	CSWP EPla MSte SWCr WAct WHCG
	Wife of Bath = 'Ausbath' (S)	MAus
	Wild Edric = 'Aushedge' (Ru) **new**	LRHS MAsh MAus SCoo SWCr
	Wildeve = 'Ausbonny'^{PBR} (S)	LCro LRHS MAus MBri NSRo SWCr
	Wildfire = 'Fryessex' (Patio)	ECnt ESty LRHS MAsh MAus MBri SWCr
	'Wilhelm' (HM)	MAus MRav SPer WHCG
	'Will Scarlet' (HM)	MAus
	'William Allen Richardson' (N)	MAus WHCG
	'William Cobbett' (F)	SSea
§	'William Lobb' (CeMo) $\mathbb{Y}^{H4}$	CBgR CPou CRHN CSBt EPfP EWTr LCro LRHS LStr MAus MGan MRav MWgw NEgg SPer SSea SWCr WAct WHCG WKif
	William Morris = 'Auswill'^{PBR} (S)	CSBt EBee LCro LRHS MAsh MAus MJon NEgg SWCr
	William Shakespeare 2000 = 'Ausromeo'^{PBR} (S)	CSBt ECnt EPfP ESty LCro LGod MAus MBNS MBri SCoo SWCr
	William Shakespeare = 'Ausroyal'^{PBR} (S)	LRHS MBNS NEgg NSRo SPer
	'William Tyndale' (Ra)	MJon WHCG WOVN
	'Williams' Double Yellow'	see *R.* x *harisonii* 'Williams' Double Yellow'
	willmottiae	see *R. gymnocarpa* var. *willmottiae*
	Wilton = 'Eurosa'	SWCr
	Wiltshire = 'Kormuse'^{PBR} (S/GC) $\mathbb{Y}^{H4}$	CSBt ECnt ENot ESty LSRN LStr MJon MRav NPri SSea SWCr
	Winchester Cathedral = 'Auscat'^{PBR} (S)	CGro CSBt EBee ECnt EPfP ESty LCro LGod LRHS LStr MAsh MAus MBri MJon MRav NEgg NPri NSRo SPer SWCr
	Windflower = 'Auscross' (S)	LRHS MAus
	Windrush = 'Ausrush' (S)	MAus MJon WAct WHCG
	Wine and Dine = 'Dicuncle'^{PBR} (GC)	IDic
	Winter Magic = 'Foumagic' (Min)	MJon
	x ***wintoniensis***	WAct WHCG
	Wise Portia = 'Ausport' (S)	MAus
	Wishing = 'Dickerfuffle'^{PBR} (F/Patio)	IDic MAus MGan SWCr
	Wisley = 'Ausintense' (S)	CSBt LRHS MAsh MAus SCoo SWCr
	With All My Love = 'Coczodiac' (HT) **new**	GCoc
	With Love = 'Andwit' (HT)	GGre SWCr
	With Thanks = 'Fransmoov'^{PBR} (HT)	ESty SWCr
	'Woburn Abbey' (F)	CWSG SSea
	'Wolley-Dod'	see *R.* 'Duplex'
	Woman o'th' North = 'Kirlon' (F/Patio)	MJon

	Wonderful News = 'Jonone'PBR (Patio)	ESty GCoc MJon
	Wonderful = 'Poulpmt005' (HT) **new**	ECnt
§	***woodsii***	MAus WHCG
	- var. ***fendleri***	see *R. woodsii*
	'Woolverstone Church Rose'	see *R.* 'Surpassing Beauty of Woolverstone'
	Worcestershire = 'Korlalon'PBR (GC)	CSBt ENot GCoc MAus MGan MMHG MRav SPer SWCr WAct
	World Peace (F)	SPoG
	World Peace 2000 = 'Peayellow' (HT)	SWCr
§	***xanthina*** 'Canary Bird' (S) ♀H4	More than 30 suppliers
§	- f. ***hugonis*** ♀H4	EWTr MAus MGan NHaw SPer WAct
	- f. ***spontanea***	CArn
	X-rated = 'Tinx' (Min)	MJon
	Yellow Button = 'Auslow' (S)	WAct
	'Yellow Cécile Brünner'	see *R.* 'Perle d'Or'
	Yellow Charles Austin = 'Ausyel' (S)	MAus
§	Yellow Dagmar Hastrup = 'Moryelrug'PBR (Ru)	EBee MGan MJon SPer SPla SWCr WAct WOVN
	'Yellow Doll' (Min)	MAus SWCr
	'Yellow Dream' (Patio)	GGre LWoR SPoG
	Yellow Floorshow = 'Harfully'PBR (GC) **new**	MRav
	Yellow Flower CarpetPBR	see *R.* Flower Carpet Sunshine
	'Yellow Patio' (Min/Patio)	LRHS LStr MAsh SPoG SSea SWCr
	yellow Scotch	see *R.* x *harisonii* 'Williams' Double Yellow' (PiH)
	Yellow Sunblaze = 'Meitrisical' (Min)	CSBt
	'Yesterday' (Poly/F/S) ♀H4	EBee MAsh MAus MGan SWCr
	York and Lancaster	see *R.* x *damascena* var. *versicolor*
	Yorkshire = 'Korbarkeit'PBR (GC)	ENot GCoc LGod LStr MRav SSea
	'Yorkshire Lady' (HT)	MJon
	'Yvonne Rabier' (Poly) ♀H4	LStr MAus MGan MRav SPer SWCr WAct WHCG WKif
	Zambra = 'Meicurbos' (F)	CBcs
	'Zéphirine Drouhin' (Bb)	More than 30 suppliers
§	'Zigeunerknabe' (S)	EBee ECnt ELan MAus MCot MGan MRav NLar SPer SPoG SWCr WAct WHCG
	Zorba = 'Poulyc008' (Patio/Cl)	ECnt MAsh
	'Zweibrücken' (Cl)	MGan

Roscoea ✿ (*Zingiberaceae*)

	ACE 2539	GEdr
	alpina	CBct CLAP CPLG CPrp EBee EBrs ECho EHrv EPot ERos GBuc GCrs GEdr GKev GSki ITim MTho NGdn NLAp NMen NWCA SRms WCru WLin
	- CC 3667	GEdr GKev WRos
	- pink-flowered	IBlr ITer LFur
	- purple-flowered **new**	IBlr
	- short **new**	WCru
§	***auriculata***	More than 30 suppliers
	- early-flowering	IBlr WCru
	- 'Floriade'	CLAP GBuc GMac IBlr WSHC
	- late-flowering	WCru
	- 'Special'	CLAP
	auriculata x ***australis*** **new**	IBlr
	australis	CFir GBuc GEdr MNrw WCru
	- pink-flowered KW 22124 **new**	IBlr
	- purple-flowered KW 22124 **new**	IBlr
	'Ballyrogan Lavender' **new**	IBlr
	'Beesiana'	CAvo CBct CDWL CFir CFwr CHEx CLAP CMea EBee EBrs ECho ECtt EMar ERos GBuc GEdr GSki IBlr LAma MRav MTho NBPC NBid NHar NHol NMyG SPhx WCru WFar
	'Beesiana' dark-flowered	ERos IBlr
	'Beesiana' pale-flowered	ECho ERos LEdu WCru
	'Beesiana' white-flowered	CBct CDes CFwr CLAP EBee EBrs EHrv ELon EPfP EPot GEdr GSki IBlr MBNS MMHG NBir NGdn NMyG SPhx WPGP
	blanda	EPot NLAp
	brandisii	CBct EBrs ECho
	cautleyoides ♀H4	More than 30 suppliers
I	- 'Alba'	NGdn NLAp WCot
	- Blackthorn strain	SBla
	- var. ***cautleyoides***	CDWL EBee
	- - red-flowered	CFir
	- - white-flowered	CFir
	- 'Early Purple'	CDes CLAP ECho GSki WPGP
	- hybrid	ECho GSki MLLN
	- 'Jeffrey Thomas'	CBct CFwr CLAP CSam EBee EBrs ECho EPot GBuc GEdr GSki IBlr MLHP NBhm NMyG WCot
	- 'Kew Beauty' ♀H4	CDes CFir CLAP CWsd EBee GSki MTho SRms WCot WPGP
	- 'Kew Beauty' seedlings	EGle
	- late, lavender-flowered **new**	IBlr
	- late, yellow-flowered **new**	IBlr
	- 'Paars' **new**	NBhm
	- plum-flowered **new**	IBlr
	- 'Purple Giant'	CLAP WCot
	- purple-flowered	CWsd GBuc IBlr NHar
	- 'Reinier'	CLAP GBuc WCot
	- 'Washfield Purple' **new**	IBlr
	cautleyoides x ***humeana***	CLAP IBlr
	cautleyoides x ***scillifolia*** dark-flowered **new**	IBlr
	forrestii	IBlr
	'Gestreept'	CLAP
	'Himalaya'	CLAP
	humeana ♀H4	CBct CFee CLAP CSam EBee EBrs ECho ERos GBin GCrs GEdr GMac LAma LRHS SBla WCFE WCot WThu
	- ACE 2539	IBlr
	- CC 1820	IBlr
	- Forrest's form	IBlr
	- lavender-flowered	IBlr
	- 'Long Acre Sunrise' **new**	CLAP
	- f. ***lutea***	CLAP IBlr
	- pink-flowered **new**	IBlr
	- 'Purple Streaker'	CBct CDes CLAP EBee WPGP
	- 'Rosemoor Plum'	CLAP GEdr
	- 'Snowy Owl'	CLAP WCot
	- f. ***tyria***	IBlr
	- - 'Inkling' **new**	WWst
	'Monique'	CDes CLAP IBlr WPGP
	procera misapplied	see *R. auriculata*
	procera Wall.	see *R. purpurea*
§	***purpurea***	More than 30 suppliers
	- CC 3628	WCot
	- HWJK 2400	WCru
	- KW 13755	IBlr
	- MECC 2	IBlr
	- MECC 10	IBlr
	- 'Brown Peacock'	CDes CLAP IBlr SBla WCot WPGP
	- var. ***gigantea***	CLAP IBlr
	- - CC 1757	MNrw
	- lilac-flowered	CDWL GSki
	- 'Nico'	CBct CLAP ELan WCot
	- 'Niedrig'	EBee

	– pale-flowered	EBla
	– 'Peacock'	CLAP IBlr WFar
	– 'Peacock Eye'	CLAP IBlr WCot
	– var. ***procera***	see *R. purpurea*
	– 'Red Gurkha'	SBla
	– Rosemoor form	WWst
	– short	CLAP IBlr
	– tall	CLAP NLAp WPGP
	– 'Wisley Amethyst'	CLAP CPrp IBlr SBla
	schneideriana	IBlr MLul NLAp WThu
	– SDR 3213	GKev
	scillifolia	CDes CFir CPBP EBrs ECho ERos GBuc GEdr GSki ITim LAma LFur LHop LRHS MTho NBir NGdn NMen SBla SIng WCru WLin WPrP
	– dark-flowered	CPom CStu EBee EHrv IBlr WCru WPGP WThu
	– pink-flowered	CBct ECho EHrv EPot ERos GEdr IBlr IFoB NMen NMyG WAbe WCot WPrP
	tibetica	CFir CFwr CLAP EBee GEdr GKev IBlr ITim NLAp WCru WThu
	– ACE 2538	IBlr
	tumjensis	CLAP EBee EWes IBlr
	'Vincent'	WCot
	wardii	IBlr
	'Yeti'	CLAP

rosemary see *Rosmarinus officinalis*

Rosmarinus ✿ (*Lamiaceae*)

	corsicus 'Prostratus'	see *R. officinalis* Prostratus Group
§	***eriocalyx***	XPep
	lavandulaceus misapplied	see *R. officinalis* Prostratus Group
	lavandulaceus Noë	see *R. eriocalyx*
	officinalis	More than 30 suppliers
	– var. ***albiflorus***	CArn CPrp CSev ELau EOHP EPfP GPoy LRHS MBar MHer MNHC SDow SHDw SLim SPer SPlb STre WGwG XPep
	– – 'Lady in White'	CSBt EBee ELan EMil EPfP LAst LRHS NGHP SDow SPer WGwG WJek
	– 'Alderney'	MHer SDow
	– var. ***angustissimus***	XPep
§	– – 'Benenden Blue' ♀H4	CBcs CBgR CSBt CSev CWan CWib EAro EBee EGoo ELau EOHP EShb GPoy LHop LRHS MNHC MWgw SDix SMer SPer SPlb STre WGwG WSpi
	– – 'Corsican Blue'	CArn EBee ELan EPfP GPoy MHer MNHC NGHP SDow SHDw SIde SLon SMer WBrE WPer XPep
	– – 'Corsicus Prostratus'	ELau
	– arching	MNHC
*	– 'Argenteovariegatus' **new**	WPGP
	– 'Aureovariegatus'	see *R. officinalis* 'Aureus'
§	– 'Aureus' (v)	CBow CTca NBlu SDry WEas WJek
	– 'Baie d'Audierne'	EMil XPep
	– 'Baie de Douarnenez'	XPep
	– 'Barbecue'PBR	ELau EWin MHer MNHC NGHP SIde
	– 'Barcelona'	XPep
	– 'Blue Lagoon'	EBee ELau EOHP EWin MHer MNHC NGHP SIde WGwG WJek
	– 'Blue Rain'	CBod EAro LAst MHer NGHP SIde
	– 'Boule'	CArn CPrp EWin MHer SDow WGwG WJek XPep
	– 'Bowles'	ELau
	– 'Cap Béar'	XPep
	– 'Capercaillie'	SDow
	– 'Cisampo'	XPep
	– 'Collingwood Ingram'	see *R. officinalis* var. *angustissimus* 'Benenden Blue'
	– 'Columbian'	MNHC
	– 'Cottage White' **new**	WGwG
	– dwarf, blue-flowered	ELau
	– 'Eve'	XPep
	– 'Farinole'	CArn CPrp ELau MNHC XPep
	– 'Fastigiatus'	see *R. officinalis* 'Miss Jessopp's Upright'
	– 'Fota Blue'	CArn CBgR CBod CBow CPrp CSev CWib EAro ELau IArd MHer MNHC NGHP SAga SDow SHDw SIde WFar WGwG WJek
	– 'Foxtail'	EWin
	– 'Frimley Blue'	see *R. officinalis* 'Primley Blue'
	– 'Genges Gold' (v) **new**	SPoG
	– 'Golden Rain'	see *R. officinalis* 'Joyce DeBaggio'
	– 'Gorizia'	SDow WGwG XPep
	– 'Green Ginger'	CBod CPrp CSpe EOHP EPfP EUnu EWin GBin LHop LRHS MAsh MHer MRav NGHP NPer SDow SPoG WGwG WMnd
	– 'Guilded'	see *R. officinalis* 'Aureus'
	– 'Haifa'	CBod EBee ELau EWin GGar MNHC NGHP SIde
	– 'Henfield Blue'	SHDw
	– 'Iden Blue'	SIde
	– 'Iden Blue Boy'	SIde
	– 'Iden Pillar'	SIde
§	– 'Joyce DeBaggio' (v)	LSou MHer SDow WGwG
	– 'Ken Taylor'	SPhx
	– 'Lady in Blue'	WGwG
	– ***lavandulaceus***	see *R. officinalis* Prostratus Group
	– 'Lérida'	XPep
	– 'Lilies Blue'	GPoy
	– 'Lockwood Variety'	see *R. officinalis* (Prostratus Group) 'Lockwood de Forest'
	– 'Loupian'	XPep
	– 'Majorca Pink'	CBgR CChe CSBt CTca CWan EGoo ELau ENot GGar LCro MAsh MHer MNHC SDow SIde SLon SPer SRms WGwG XPep
	– 'Maltese White'	WCot
	– 'Marenca'	ELau MNHC XPep
	– 'Marinka'	CWan
	– 'Mason's Finest'	SDow
	– 'McConnell's Blue' ♀H4	CArn CBgR CDoC CPrp EBee ELan ELau EShb GAbr LHop LRHS MAsh MGos MNHC SDow SDry SHDw SPla WFar WGwG WHoo WPGP
	– 'Minerve'	XPep
§	– 'Miss Jessopp's Upright' ♀H4	More than 30 suppliers
	– 'Montagnette'	XPep
	– 'Mrs Harding'	CBod MHer
	– 'Pointe du Raz'	CAbP EBee ELan EMil EPfP SChF SPoG WSpi
§	– 'Primley Blue'	CArn CMea CPrp CSam CSev CWSG EBee ECtt ELau LRHS MHer MNHC MRav NGHP SIde SMer WFar WPer WSpi
§	– Prostratus Group	More than 30 suppliers
	– – 'Capri'	CAbP CSBt LRHS MBrN MHer NGHP SMer SPoG
	– – 'Deben Blue'	ENot
	– – 'Gethsemane'	SIde
	– – 'Jackman's Prostrate'	CBcs ECtt
§	– – 'Lockwood de Forest'	LSou WGwG
	– 'Punta di Canelle'	XPep
	– f. ***pyramidalis***	see *R. officinalis* 'Miss Jessopp's Upright'
	– ***repens***	see *R. officinalis* Prostratus Group
	– 'Rex'	ELau
	– 'Roman Beauty'	CBcs LAst LSRN SPoG WSpi
	– 'Rosemarey'	XPep
	– 'Roseus'	CArn CEnt CPrp CSBt CWib EBee ELan ELau EMil EOHP EPfP GPoy LHop LRHS MHer MNHC SDow

	SLim SPoG WAbe WGwG WHer WMnd WPer WWeb
- 'Russell's Blue'	WFar
- 'Saint Florent'	XPep
- 'Salem'	MHer
- 'Santa Barbara Blue'	XPep
- 'Sea Level'	CBod ELau MHer WGwG
- 'Severn Sea' ♀^{H4}	More than 30 suppliers
- 'Shimmering Stars' **new**	SDow
- 'Silver Sparkler'	WPat
- Silver Spires = 'Wolros'	LRav MNHC WFar
- 'Sissinghurst Blue' ♀^{H4}	CArn CBcs CDul CSev CWan EBee ECha ELan ELau EMil EPfP LRHS MHer MLHP MNHC MRav NGHP SDow SIde SLim SMer SPer SPlb SRms WGwG WSel XPep
- 'Sissinghurst White'	WGwG
- 'South Downs Blue'	SHDw
- 'Spanish Snow' **new**	WGwG
- 'Sudbury Blue'	EAro EBee ELau EMil EPfP EWin MHer MNHC NGHP SDow SHDw WEas WFar WJek XPep
- 'Trusty'	CWan LRHS XPep
- 'Tuscan Blue'	CDoC CPLG CSWP CSev EBee ECGP ECha ECot ELan ELau LFol LRHS MHer MNHC MSwo MWgw NGHP SDow SDry SIde SMer SPoG SRms WFar WGwG WJek WPGP WSpi XPep
- 'Ulysse'	XPep
- 'Variegatus'	see *R. officinalis* 'Aureus'
- 'Vicomte de Noailles'	ERea XPep
repens	see *R. officinalis* Prostratus Group

Rostrinucula (*Lamiaceae*)

dependens	EMan EWes NLar WSHC
sinensis	CPLG

Rosularia ✿ (*Crassulaceae*)

from Sandras Dag	CWil LBee LRHS
alba	see *R. sedoides* var. *alba*
alpestris from Rhotang Pass	WThu
§ ***chrysantha***	EBur EDAr LRHS NMen SFgr SPlb
- number 1	CWil
crassipes	see *Rhodiola wallichiana*
§ ***muratdaghensis***	EBur
pallida ambig.	SFgr
pallida A. Berger	see *R. chrysantha*
platyphylla misapplied	see *R. muratdaghensis*
sedoides	CWil LRHS MBar SIng
§ - var. ***alba***	ECho EDAr EPot GGar NLAp WFar WTin
sempervivum	CWil ECho EWes NMen
§ - subsp. ***glaucophylla***	CWil WAbe
spatulata hort.	see *R. sempervivum* subsp. *glaucophylla*

Rothmannia (*Rubiaceae*)

capensis	EShb SOWG
§ ***globosa***	ERea

Rubia (*Rubiaceae*)

peregrina	CArn GPoy MSal
tinctorum	CArn CBod CHby EOHP EUnu GPoy GWCH MSal SWat

Rubus ✿ (*Rosaceae*)

RCB/Eq C-1	WCot
alceifolius Poir.	CFee SDys SMac
arcticus	EBee EPPr GGar MCCP NLAp NLar SHar SRms SRot WCru WPat
x ***barkeri***	ECou
§ 'Benenden' ♀^{H4}	More than 30 suppliers
'Betty Ashburner'	CAgr CBcs CDoC EBee ECrN EPfP GQui LAst LBuc MGos MRav MWgw NHol SLPl SPer WBVN WMoo WTin
biflorus ♀^{H4}	EBee EMon EPfP EWes LEdu MBlu SMac WPGP
'Black Butte'	CSut EMil LRHS SDea
'Boatsberry'	SDea
'Boysenberry, Thornless' (F)	EMil EMui GTwe LBuc LRHS MGan SDea SPer
calophyllus	CDul WPGP
calycinoides Hayata	see *R. rolfei*
chamaemorus	GPoy
cissoides	WCot
cockburnianus (F)	CArn CBcs CTri EBee ELan EPfP EWTr IFoB LBuc LRHS MBlu MRav MSwo NHol NSti NWea SPer SPlb SRms WEas WFar WSpi
- 'Goldenvale' ♀^{H4}	More than 30 suppliers
crataegifolius	CWan MRav SMac WPat
deliciosus **new**	WFar
§ ***discolor*** (F)	NWea
'Emerald Spreader'	SBod
flagelliflorus	MBar
fockeanus misapplied	see *R. rolfei*
formosensis B&SWJ 1798	WCru
N ***fruticosus*** agg.	WSFF
- 'Adrienne' (F)	CAgr EMui
- 'Ashton Cross' (F)	CDoC GTwe LBuc
- 'Bedford Giant' (F)	CSBt ECrN ENot GTwe LBuc MAsh MGan MGos SPoG
- 'Black Satin' (F)	CAgr LRHS NLar SDea
- 'Chester' (F)	EMil SKee
- 'Fantasia'^{PBR} (F) ♀^{H4}	EMui
- 'Godshill Goliath' (F)	SDea
- 'Helen'	CAgr CSut EMil EMui SDea
- Himalayan berry	see *R. discolor*
- 'Himalayan Giant' (F)	ENot GTwe MGan MRav NEgg NLar SDea SPer
- 'John Innes' (F)	MCoo
- 'Kotata' **new**	EMil MRav
- 'Loch Ness'^{PBR} (F) ♀^{H4}	CAgr CSBt CWib EMil EMui ENot ERea GTwe IArd LBuc LRHS MAsh MCoo NEgg SCoo SDea SKee SPer
- 'Merton Thornless' (F)	CSBt CWib ERea GTwe MAsh MGan MGos
- 'No Thorn' (F)	SDea
- 'Oregon Thornless' (F)	CAgr CCVT CDoC CSBt CWib ECrN EMui ENot EPfP GTwe LCro LRHS MAsh MBri MRav NEgg NLar SCoo SDea SPer SPoG SRms WOrn
- 'Parsley Leaved' (F)	SDea
* - 'Sylvan' (F)	EMil MCoo MGos SPer
- 'Thornfree' (F)	CAgr CDoC CTri NLar SDea
- 'Variegatus' (v)	MBlu SMad WCot
- 'Veronique' (F)	EMui
- 'Waldo'	CAgr CSBt CWib ECrN EMui LBuc MAsh MGos SDea
'Golden Showers'	CWib
hakonensis B&SWJ 5555	WCru
henryi	EPla MRav NLar NSti SLon SMac SPoG WCot WFar
- var. ***bambusarum***	CMCN EBee EMan EPfP EPla MCCP MRav NVic WCru
hupehensis	SLPl
ichangensis	EPla LEdu
idaeus 'All Gold'	CSut
- 'Aureus' (F)	ECha ELan EPla EWes MRav NBid NBre SDry SMac WCot WFar WMoo WRHF
- 'Autumn Bliss'^{PBR} (F) ♀^{H4}	CAgr CSBt CTri CWSG CWib ECrN EMui ENot EPfP ERea GTwe LBuc LCro LRHS MAsh MBri MGan MGos MNHC MRav NEgg SCoo SDea SKee SPer SPoG WOrn

- 'Fallgold' (F)	CAgr CWib ECrN EMil EMui EPfP ERea LRHS MAsh MCoo SKee SPer SPoG WOrn
- 'Galante'PBR (F)	EMui
- 'Glen Ample'PBR (F) ♀H4	CAgr CSBt CSut CTri CWSG CWib ECrN EMui EPfP GTwe LBuc LRHS MAsh MBri MCoo SCoo SDea SKee SPer SPoG WOrn
- 'Glen Clova' (F)	CAgr CSBt CTri CWib ECrN ENot GTwe LCro LRHS MAsh MGan MNHC MRav NBlu NEgg SKee SPer SPoG WOrn
- 'Glen Lyon'PBR (F)	CWib EMui GTwe LBuc MAsh MBri SCoo
- 'Glen Magna'PBR (F)	CSBt CSut CWSG CWib EMil EMui GTwe LBuc LRHS MAsh MBri MRav SCoo SDea SKee SPoG
- 'Glen Moy'PBR (F) ♀H4	CAgr CSBt CTri CWib ECrN EMil EMui EPfP GTwe MAsh MGos SCoo SDea SKee
- 'Glen Prosen'PBR (F) ♀H4	CAgr CSBt CWib ECrN EMui GTwe LCro MAsh MBri SCoo SDea SKee SPer
- 'Glen Rosa' (F)	GTwe
- 'Glen Shee' (F)	GTwe
- 'Heritage' (F)	CWib ENot MAsh SCoo
- Himbo Top = 'Rafzaqu'PBR (F) **new**	EMil
- 'Joan J'PBR (F)	CSut EMil
- 'Joan Squire'PBR (F)	SKee
- 'Julia' (F)	CAgr GTwe LCro MCoo
- 'Leo'PBR (F) ♀H4	CAgr CSBt CTri CWib EMui ERea GTwe MAsh MGos NEgg SCoo SKee SPer
- 'Malling Admiral' (F) ♀H4	CTri CWib EMui ENot GTwe MAsh SCoo SKee SPer
- 'Malling Delight' (F)	CSBt CWib MAsh SCoo
- 'Malling Jewel' (F) ♀H4	CSBt CWib EMui ENot ERea GTwe LBuc MAsh MGan NEgg SDea SKee SPer
- 'Malling Promise' (F)	CWib ERea
- 'Octavia'PBR (F)	EMui MAsh
- 'Polka'PBR (F)	ECrN SKee
- 'Redsetter' (F)	EMui
- 'Summer Gold' (F)	GTwe
- 'Tiny Tim' (F) **new**	SGFT
- 'Tulameen' (F)	CAgr CWib EMil EMui LBuc LRHS MAsh MBri SCoo SKee SPoG
- 'Zeva Herbsternte' (F)	CWib MAsh
illecebrosus (F)	ITer
irenaeus	EBla
Japanese wineberry	see *R. phoenicolasius*
'Kenneth Ashburner'	CDoC NLar SLPl WFar WTin
'King's Acre Berry' (F)	EMui
laciniatus	EPla
leucodermis NNS 00-663	EPPr
lineatus	CDoC CMCo CPLG EPfP EWTr EWes LRHS MCot NSti SDix SDry SMad WCru WPGP WPat
- HWJ 892 from Vietnam	WCru
- HWJK 2045 from Nepal	WCru
- from Nepal	GCra
x ***loganobaccus*** 'Brandywine'	SDea
- 'Ly 59' (F) ♀H4	ECrN EMui EPfP GTwe MRav NEgg SDea SKee SRms
- 'Ly 654' (F) ♀H4	ERea GTwe LBuc MBri MGos SDea SPer
- thornless (F)	CAgr CTri CWSG CWib ECot ERea GTwe MAsh MGan SDea SPoG
'Margaret Gordon'	MRav
microphyllus 'Variegatus' (v)	MRav WPat
§ ***nepalensis***	CAgr CDoC CEnd GCra LEdu
nutans	see *R. nepalensis*
odoratus	CPLG CPom ELan EPPr EPfP EWTr LEdu MRav NPal SPer WBor WCot WFar WHCG WTin
parviflorus	CArn
- double (d)	EPPr WCru
- 'Sunshine Spreader'	WPat
parvus	ECou
pectinellus var. ***trilobus***	CFee EWld LEdu NLar SMac
- - B&SWJ 1669B	GSki WCru
peltatus	CGHE NLar WPGP
pentalobus	see *R. rolfei*
§ ***phoenicolasius***	CAgr EMui EPfP GTwe LEdu LHop MBlu MCoo MGan MRav NSti SDea SPer WAbb WHCG
§ ***rolfei***	CTri EPPr MBar NMyG SMac WFar
- B&SWJ 3546 from Taiwan	WCru
- B&SWJ 3878 from the Philippines	WCru
- 'Emerald Carpet'	CAgr NLar SBod
rosifolius	CSpe
- 'Coronarius' (d)	CFee CHar CSpe ECrN ELan GAbr LSou MRav NPro WCot WFar WHil
sanctus	CNat
setchuenensis	CMCN CSWP EWes
'Silvan' (F) ♀H4	EMui ENot GTwe
spectabilis	CBcs CSev CWib ELan EPPr EPla EWTr LEdu MRav WFar WSHC WWFP
- 'Flore Pleno'	see *R. spectabilis* 'Olympic Double'
§ - 'Olympic Double' (d)	More than 30 suppliers
splendidissimus B&SWJ 2361	WCru
squarrosus	ECou
'Sunberry' (F)	GTwe SDea
swinhoei B&SWJ 1735	WCru
taiwanicola	EBla EDAr GEdr
- B&SWJ 317	GBin NPro WCru WPrP
Tayberry Group (F) ♀H4	CTri ECrN EMui ENot GTwe MAsh MGan MGos NLar SPer SRms
- 'Buckingham' (F)	CSut EMil EMui GTwe LBuc MAsh
- 'Medana Tayberry' (F)	CAgr EMui EPfP ERea LRHS SDea SKee SPoG
§ ***thibetanus*** ♀H4	More than 30 suppliers
- 'Silver Fern'	see *R. thibetanus*
tricolor	CAgr CBcs CDul CSBt CTri CWib EBee ECrN EPfP GBri MMuc MRav MSwo NEgg NHol SDix SHBN SLon SMac SPer WHCG
- 'Dart's Evergreen'	SLPl
- 'Ness'	SLPl
tridel 'Benenden'	see *R.* 'Benenden'
trilobus B&SWJ 9096	WCru
'Tummelberry' (F)	EMil GTwe
ulmifolius 'Bellidiflorus' (d)	MBlu MRav MSwo NSti SDix SMac SPer WAbb WEas WHrl
ursinus	LEdu
'Veitchberry' (F)	GTwe
xanthocarpus	NLar
'Youngberry' (F)	SDea

Rudbeckia ✿ (*Asteraceae*)

Autumn Sun	see *R. laciniata* 'Herbstsonne'
californica	CSam EBee WPer
- var. ***intermedia*** 'Anthony Brooks' **new**	WCot
deamii	see *R. fulgida* var. *deamii*
echinacea purpurea	see *Echinacea purpurea*
fulgida	NNor
§ - var. ***deamii*** ♀H4	More than 30 suppliers
- var. ***fulgida***	EBee NRnb SMad
§ - var. ***speciosa*** ♀H4	CKno CMMP CPLG CSam EBee ECha ECtt ELan EPfP ERou GAbr LAst MHar NBPC SBch SMac SPlb

	SRms WEas WFar WMoo WPer WPtf WTel WTin
- var. ***sullivantii*** 'Goldsturm' ♀H4	More than 30 suppliers
- - 'Pot of Gold' **new**	EBee ERou
- Viette's Little Suzy = 'Blovi'	EBee LRHS
gloriosa	see *R. hirta*
'Golden Jubilee'	LRHS WWeb
§ ***hirta***	CHar CHrt NBir
- 'Autumn Colours' (mixed) **new**	CMea
- 'Chim Chiminee'	LBMP
- 'Goldilocks'	GWCH
- 'Indian Summer' ♀H3	SPav
- 'Irish Eyes'	LRav SPav
- 'Marmalade'	LBMP NEgg NGBl
- 'Prairie Sun'	LBMP NGBl
- var. ***pulcherrima***	EBee MGol SMHy
- 'Sonora'	WHal
- 'Toto' ♀H3	LBMP SPav SWvt
- 'Toto Gold'	LBMP
- 'Toto Lemon' **new**	WHil
- 'Toto Rustic'	LBMP
July Gold	see *R. laciniata* 'Juligold'
laciniata	CElw CHFP CKno EBee EBrs ELan EMon EPPr EPfP GQue LEdu MDKP MWrn NLar NOrc NRnb NSti SMHy SPhx WCot WMoo WOld
- 'Golden Glow'	see *R. laciniata* 'Hortensia'
- 'Goldquelle' (d) ♀H4	More than 30 suppliers
§ - 'Herbstsonne' ♀H4	More than 30 suppliers
§ - 'Hortensia' (d)	EBee EMon GQue MLLN WOld
§ - 'Juligold'	CPrp EBee IPot LBMP LRHS MAvo MBNS MGol NBre NEgg NGdn SMrm SPla SPoG WCAu WFar
- 'Starcadia Razzle Dazzle' **new**	WCot
maxima	CDes CKno CSpe EBee ECha EDAr GMac IFoB LCro LEdu LRHS MAvo MBri MCCP MNFA NCGa NEgg NLar NPri NSti SDix SMad SMrm SPlb WCot WFar
missouriensis	EBee NBre
mollis	EBee NBre
newmannii	see *R. fulgida* var. *speciosa*
nitida	EBee EShb WSpi
occidentalis	MLLN NBre NRnb NVic WFar WPer
- 'Black Beauty'PBR	CHFP EBee EHrv EPfP MBNS MMHG NBPN NBhm NBro NMoo NSti WMnd WSpi
- 'Green Wizard'	More than 30 suppliers
* ***paniculata***	EBee NBre SPhx WCot
purpurea	see *Echinacea purpurea*
speciosa	see *R. fulgida* var. *speciosa*
subtomentosa	CPLG CSam EBee EMon EWes MAvo MDKP MNFA NBre NSti SMHy WCAu WOld
- 'Loofahsa Wheaten Gold' **new**	WCot
'Takao'	CWCL EBee LSou MAvo MBNS MDKP MLLN MWea NLar SPoG WBor WWFP
triloba	CEnt CHFP CMea CSam EBee EPPr EPfP EShb MNrw NGdn NRnb SAga SMad WCAu WFar WMoo WPGP WTin

rue see *Ruta graveolens*

Ruellia (*Acanthaceae*)

amoena	see *R. graecizans*
§ ***graecizans***	ECre
humilis	EBee EShb NLar WBVN WHil
macrantha	CCCN EShb MJnS
makoyana ♀H1	CHal CSev EShb MBri
'Mr Foster'	CHal
tweediana	MJnS

Rumex (*Polygonaceae*)

acetosa	CArn CHby CSev CWan ELau GPoy GWCH LRHS MHer MNHC NBir NGHP NPri NSco SEND SIde WHer WSFF WSel
- 'Abundance'	ELau
- subsp. ***acetosa*** 'Saucy' (v)	WCot
- 'De Belleville'	CPrp
- 'Profusion'	GPoy
- subsp. ***vinealis***	EBee WCot
acetosella	CArn MNHC MSal NMir WSFF WSel
alpinus	EBee LEdu SPhx WCot
flexuosus	EBee EShb EUnu MDKP NLar WJek
hydrolapathum	CArn CHEx EMFW SPlb WSFF
obtusifolius 'Golden My Foot'	CNat
patientia	CArn
sanguineus	CTri EMan EPfP EShb EUnu EWin LBMP NCob NLar SWal WBrk WFar WMAq WWeb
- var. ***sanguineus***	CArn CBgR CElw CSev EBee ELan EPla IFoB LRHS MHer MNrw MTho NBro NHol WHer WPer WSel
'Schavel'	CAgr LEdu WOut
scutatus	CAgr CArn CHby CPrp CSev ELau EUnu GPoy MHer MNHC SIde SPlb WHer WJek WOut
- 'Silver Shield'	CBod ELau EMar SIde WJek
venosus	MSal

Rumohra (*Davalliaceae*)

adiantiformis ♀H1	CCCN LRHS MPes SEND WFib WRic
- RCB/Arg D-2	WCot

Ruschia (*Aizoaceae*)

uncinata	SChr

Ruscus ✿ (*Ruscaceae*)

aculeatus	CArn CBcs CDul CRWN ELan ENot EPfP GPoy IDee LEdu MGos MRav NWea SAPC SArc SCoo SPer SPlb SPoG SRms SSta WHer WPGP WRHF
- (f)	WFar WMou
- (m)	WCFE WMou
- hermaphrodite	EPfP EPla EWes MBri SMad WGer WPGP WPat WThu
- var. ***angustifolius*** Boiss.	EPla
- - (f)	EPla
- 'Christmas Berry'	ELan EPfP MBri NLar
- 'John Redmond'PBR **new**	WSpi
* - 'Wheeler's Variety' (f/m)	CPMA MRav
hypoglossum	SEND WPGP WRHF WSpi
'John Redmond'	CHid CSpe EBee EWes LRHS MAsh MWea NHol SCoo SPoG WCot
x ***microglossum*** (f)	CDul
racemosus	see *Danae racemosa*

Russelia (*Scrophulariaceae*)

§ ***equisetiformis*** ♀H1	CHll EShb MJnS SOWG XPep
- 'Lemon Falls' **new**	SOWG
- yellow-flowered	EShb
juncea	see *R. equisetiformis*

Ruta (*Rutaceae*)

chalepensis	CArn XPep
corsica	CArn
graveolens	CArn CDul CPLG CWan EPfP EWin GPoy GWCH MNHC NPri SECG SIde WJek WPer XPep
- 'Jackman's Blue'	CBcs CPrp CSev CTri EBee ECrN ELan EOHP EPfP GMaP GPoy LAst MGos MHer MRav MSwo MWgw SLim SMer SPer SRms WEas WMnd WSpi WTel
- 'Variegata' (v)	CBow CWan ELan EOHP MNHC NPer SPer WJek WPat WRHF

x *Ruttyruspolia* (*Acanthaceae*)

'Phyllis van Heerden'	GFai SOWG

Rytidosperma (*Poaceae*)

* ***strictum***	CBig

S

Sabal (*Arecaceae*)

§ ***bermudana***	EAmu LPal
domingensis	EAmu
etonia	LPal
§ ***mexicana***	EAmu
minor	CBrP CDTJ CHEx CPHo EAmu ETod LPal MPRe NPal SAin
palmetto	CArn CDoC EAmu LPal WNor
princeps	see *S. bermudana*
rosei	LPal
texana	see *S. mexicana*
uresana	LPal
yapa new	SAin

Saccharum (*Poaceae*)

arundinaceum	EPPr
§ ***baldwinii***	CBig GFor
brevibarbe var. ***contortum***	CBig EBee XIsg
officinarum	MJnS
- var. ***violaceum*** new	MJnS
ravennae	CBig CBod CPLG EBee GFor LRav MSte SApp SMad SPlb WFar XIsg
strictum (Ell.) Ell. ex Nutt.	see *S. baldwinii*

sage see *Salvia officinalis*

sage, annual clary see *Salvia viridis*

sage, biennial clary see *Salvia sclarea*

sage, pineapple see *Salvia elegans*

Sageretia (*Rhamnaceae*)

§ ***thea***	STre
theezans	see *S. thea*

Sagina (*Caryophyllaceae*)

boydii	ECho EWes
subulata	ECho EDAr LAst MFOX
§ - var. ***glabrata*** 'Aurea'	CMea CTri EAlp ECha ECho ECtt EDAr MBNS SIng SPoG SRms WEas WFar WPer

Sagittaria (*Alismataceae*)

japonica	see *S. sagittifolia*
latifolia	COld NPer SMad
* ***leucopetala*** 'Flore Pleno' (d)	NLar NPer
§ ***sagittifolia***	CBen CDWL CWat EHon EMFW EPfP NSco SWat WFar WMAq WPnP
- 'Flore Pleno' (d)	CBen CDWL CWat EMFW SWat WMAq WPnP
- var. ***leucopetala***	WMAq

Saintpaulia (*Gesneriaceae*)

'Bangle Blue'	WDib
'Beatrice Trail'	WDib
'Betty Stoehr' new	WDib
'Blue Dragon'	WDib
'Bob Serbin' (d)	WDib
'Bohemian Sunset'	WDib
'Buffalo Hunt'	WDib
'Centenary'	WDib
'Cherries 'n' Cream'	WDib
'Chiffon Fiesta'	WDib
'Chiffon Mist' (d)	WDib
'Chiffon Moonmoth'	WDib
'Chiffon Stardust'	WDib
'Chiffon Vesper'	WDib
'Coroloir'	WDib
'Delft' (d)	WDib
'Electric Dreams'	WDib
'Golden Glow' (d)	WDib
'Halo' (Ultra Violet Series)	WDib
'Halo's Aglitter'	WDib
'Irish Flirt' (d)	WDib
'Lemon Drop' (d)	WDib
'Lemon Whip' (d)	WDib
'Love Spots'	WDib
'Lucky Lee Ann' (d)	WDib
'Marching Band'	WDib
'Mermaid' (d)	WDib
'Midget Lillian' (v)	WDib
'Midnight Flame'	WDib
'Midnight Waltz'	WDib
'Nubian Winter'	WDib
'Otoe'	WDib
'Powder Keg' (d)	WDib
'Powwow' (d/v)	WDib
'Ramblin' Magic' (d)	WDib
'Rapid Transit' (d)	WDib
'Rob's Bamboozle'	WDib
'Rob's Cloudy Skies' (d) new	WDib
'Rob's Dandy Lion'	WDib
'Rob's Denim Demon'	WDib
'Rob's Dust Storm' (d)	WDib
'Rob's Firebrand'	WDib
'Rob's Gundaroo' (d)	WDib
'Rob's Heat Wave' (d)	WDib
'Rob's Hopscotch'	WDib
'Rob's Ice Ripples' (d)	WDib
'Rob's June Bug' new	WDib
'Rob's Loose Goose'	WDib
'Rob's Love Bite' new	WDib
'Rob's Macho Devil'	WDib
'Rob's Mad Cat' (d)	WDib
'Rob's Red Bug' (d/r) new	WDib
'Rob's Rinky Dink' (d)	WDib
'Rob's Sarsparilla' (d)	WDib
'Rob's Seduction'	WDib
'Rob's Shadow Magic' (d)	WDib
'Rob's Smarty Pants' new	WDib
'Rob's Sticky Wicket'	WDib
'Rob's Toorooka' (d)	WDib
'Rob's Twinkle Pink'	WDib
shumensis	WDib
'Sky Bandit' (d)	WDib
'Sky Bells' (v) new	WDib
'The Madam'	WDib
§ 'Tippy Toe' (d)	WDib
'Tippy Toes'	see *S.* 'Tippy Toe'

Salix ✿ (*Salicaceae*)

	Name	Suppliers
	acutifolia	EBee ELan EQua SPla
	- 'Blue Streak' (m) 🏆^{H4}	CDul CEnd CWiW CWon EPfP EPla EWes MAsh MBlu MRav NBir SMHy SWat WFar
	- 'Lady Aldenham No 2'	EPla
	- 'Pendulifolia' (m)	MAsh SBLw WPat
	aegyptiaca	CDoC CLnd ECrN MBlu NWea WMou
	alaxensis	WWll
	alba	CCVT CDul CLnd CWiW ECrN EMac LBuc NWea SBLw WMou WOrn
	- f. ***argentea***	see *S. alba* var. *sericea*
	- 'Aurea'	CLnd CTho CWon MRav WIvy WMou
	- 'Belders' (m)	SBLw
	- var. ***caerulea***	CDul CLnd CWon NWea WMou
	- - 'Wantage Hall' (f)	CWiW
	- 'Cardinalis' (f)	CWiW CWon GQue SWat WWll
	- 'Chermesina' hort.	see *S. alba* var. *vitellina* 'Britzensis'
	- 'Dart's Snake'	CBgR CTho ELan ENot EPfP EPla MAsh MBrN MRav NScw SCoo
	- 'Hutchinson's Yellow'	CDoC CTho CWon ECrN EQua MGos NWea SCoo SLim
	- 'Liempde' (m)	MRav SBLw
	- 'Raesfeld' (m)	CWiW CWon
	- 'Saint Oedendrode'	CWon
§	- var. ***sericea*** 🏆^{H4}	CBcs CDoC CLnd CTho CWon ECrN EPfP MBlu MRav NWea SBLw SHBN SPer WGer WIvy WMou
	- 'Splendens'	see *S. alba* var. *sericea*
	- 'Tristis' misapplied	see *S.* x *sepulcralis* var. *chrysocoma*
§	- 'Tristis' ambig.	CCVT CLnd CTri ELan LRHS MBri MGos MSwo NLar NWea SBLw SLim SRms SWat WFar WHar
	- 'Tristis' Gaud.	MMuc
	- var. ***vitellina*** 🏆^{H4}	CDul CTri CWon EMac EPfP GQue LBuc LPan MBNS MBrN NWea SLon SWat WIvy WJas WMoo WWll
§	- - 'Britzensis' (m) 🏆^{H4}	More than 30 suppliers
	- 'Vitellina Pendula'	see *S. alba* 'Tristis' ambig.
	- 'Vitellina Tristis'	see *S. alba* 'Tristis' ambig.
§	- var. ***vitellina*** 'Yelverton'	SWat WWll
§	***alpina***	ECho NBir
	'Americana'	CWiW WWll
	amplexicaulis 'Pescara' (m)	CWiW WWll
	amygdaloides	CWiW
	'Aokautere'	see *S.* x *sepulcralis* 'Aokautere'
	apennina 'Cisa Pass'	CWon
	apoda	CWon
	- (m)	ECho EWes WPer
§	***arbuscula***	CWon ECho NWCA
	arctica var. ***petraea***	NLAp WPat
	arenaria	see *S. repens* var. *argentea*
	aurita	NLar NWea
	babylonica	CEnd CTrG CWon LPan SBLw SHBN WMou
	- 'Annularis'	see *S. babylonica* 'Crispa'
	- 'Bijdorp' new	MBri
§	- 'Crispa'	CDul CWon ELan EPla LHop MBri MTPN NPro SMad SPla WFar
§	- 'Lavalleei' (m)	WWll
	- 'Pan Chih-kang'	CWiW
	- var. ***pekinensis*** 'Snake'	CWon WWll
§	- - 'Tortuosa' 🏆^{H4}	More than 30 suppliers
*	- 'Tortuosa Aurea'	LPan MCCP SWvt
	x ***balfourii***	CWon
	bebbiana	CWon WWll
	bicolor (m)	WWll
	'Blackskin' (f)	CWiW
	x ***blanda***	CWon
	bockii	LRHS LTwo MBar WFar
§	'Bowles' Hybrid'	MRav WMou
	'Boydii' (f) 🏆^{H4}	CFee CWon ECho EPfP EPot GAbr GCrs ITim MAsh MDun MGos NBir NHol NLAp NMen NRya NSla SBla SIng SPoG SRms WAbe WFar WPat
§	'Boyd's Pendulous' (m)	CLyd CWib MBar
	breviserrata	CLyd NWCA
	burjatica	CWon
	caesia	EMac NWCA WIvy WWll
	x ***calliantha***	WWll
	x ***calodendron*** (f) new	WWll
	candida	CWon WWll
	cantabrica	CWon WWll
	caprea	CBcs CCVT CDul CLnd CTri CWon ECrN EMac EPfP LBuc NWea SBLw SPer WMou WSFF
	- 'Black Stem'	CDul
	- 'Curlilocks'	LAst MBar MSwo NEgg
§	- 'Kilmarnock' (m)	More than 30 suppliers
	- var. ***pendula*** (m)	see *S. caprea* 'Kilmarnock' (m)
	- 'Silberglanz'	WWll
	x ***capreola***	CWon
	cashmiriana	CLyd GEdr WPat
	caspica	WWll
*	- ***rubra nana***	SWat
	x ***cernua***	NWCA
	chaenomeloides	EBrs
	'Chrysocoma'	see *S.* x *sepulcralis* var. *chrysocoma*
	cinerea	CBcs CDoC CWon ECrN EMac LBuc NWea SBLw
	- 'Tricolor' (v)	CArn NPro
	- 'Variegata' (v)	WBod
	cordata	ECrN SLPl WWll
	x ***cottetii***	IArd MBar
	daphnoides	CCVT CDoC CDul CLnd EBee EMac EPfP MBrN MGos MSwo NWea SBLw SPer SPla SRms STre SWat WFar WJas WMou WSFF
	- 'Aglaia' (m)	CBcs CWon ECrN MGos WIvy
	- 'Continental Purple'	CWon WWll
	- 'Meikle' (f)	CWiW SWat
	- 'Netta Statham' (m)	CWiW
	- 'Ovaro Udine' (m)	CWiW
	- 'Oxford Violet' (m)	CWon ECrN NWea WIvy WWll
	- 'Sinker'	WIvy
	- 'Stewartstown'	CWiW
	x ***dasyclados***	CWon
	- 'Grandis'	NWea
	discolor new	WWll
§	x ***doniana*** 'Kumeti'	CWiW
	'E.A. Bowles'	see *S.* 'Bowles' Hybrid'
	x ***ehrhartiana***	CNat CWon
§	***elaeagnos***	CCVT CDoC CLnd CTho CTri ECrN EPfP MBlu MBrN MRav SLon SWat WFar WMou
§	- subsp. ***angustifolia*** 🏆^{H4}	CDul EBee ELan EMil GQue LRav MAsh MBar MRav MSwo NLar NWea SRms STre WIvy WWll
	'Elegantissima'	see *S.* x *pendulina* var. *elegantissima*
	x ***erdingeri***	EPla
	eriocephala 'American Mackay' (m)	CWiW
	- 'Green USA'	CWon
	- 'Kerksii' (m)	CWiW CWon
	- 'Mawdesley' (m)	CWiW
	- 'Russelliana' (f)	CWiW
§	'Erythroflexuosa'	CBcs CBgR CDoC CEnd EBee ELan ENot EPfP EPla LAst LBMP LHop LRHS MAsh MBar MGos MRav MWya NBlu NScw NWea SLim

		SPer SPla SPoG SWat WFar WHer WPat WWll
	exigua	CBcs CDul CLnd CTho ECrN ELan EPfP EWes LBuc LRHS MBar MBlu MBrN MBri MCoo MGos MLHP MSwo NBir NCGa NWea SCoo SDry SLPl SLim SMad SMrm SPer WMou WPat
	fargesii	CDoC CEnd CFee EBee ELan EPfP LEdu LHop LRHS MAsh MBlu MDun MGos MRav NBid NHol SDix SMad SPoG SSpi WCru WFar WPGP WPat
§	x ***finnmarchica***	CWon GEdr NWCA
	formosa	see *S. arbuscula*
	fragilis	CCVT CDul CLnd ECrN EMac MRav NWea SBLw WMou
	- var. ***bullata***	WWll
	- 'Legomey'	WIvy
	x ***friesiana***	CWon
	x ***fruticosa*** 'McElroy' (f)	CWiW
§	***fruticulosa***	CTri GBin GKev NWCA SBla WPat
	'Fuiri-koriyanagi'	see *S. integra* 'Hakuro-nishiki'
	furcata	see *S. fruticulosa*
	geyeriana	WWll
	glauca	CNat
	glaucophylloides	CWon
	glaucosericea	EPla
	'Golden Curls'	see *S.* 'Erythroflexuosa'
	gracilistyla	CTho CWon ECrN NWea SCoo SLPl WMou
§	- 'Melanostachys' (m)	More than 30 suppliers
	x ***greyi***	EPla NPro
	hastata (f)	SWat
	- 'Wehrhahnii' (m) ♀H4	CBcs CWib CWon EBee ECho ELan EPfP GCra LEdu LRHS MAsh MBNS MBar MRav MSwo NBir NEgg NWea SHBN SPer SWat WFar WPat WPer
	helvetica ♀H4	CBcs CBgR EBee ECho ELan EPfP GAbr LRav MBar MBlu MBri MRav MWgw NBir NEgg NLAp NWCA NWea SHBN SPer WFar WPat
	herbacea	ECho GEdr NMen
	hibernica	see *S. phylicifolia*
I	***himalayas***	CWon
	x ***hirtei*** 'Rosewarne'	CWon
	hookeriana	CLnd CTho CWon EBee ELan EPla MBlu MBrN MRav SLPl SSpi WCFE WIvy WMou WPGP WTin WWll
	x ***hungarica***	CWon
	incana	see *S. elaeagnos*
	integra new	WWll
	- 'Albomaculata'	see *S. integra* 'Hakuro-nishiki'
	- 'Flamingo' PBR	SPoG
§	- 'Hakuro-nishiki' (v)	More than 30 suppliers
	- 'Pendula' (f)	CEnd MAsh MBri
	irrorata	CDul CLnd CTho CWon EBee ECrN MBlu MRav MSwo SWat WWll
	'Jacquinii'	see *S. alpina*
	japonica misapplied	see *S. babylonica* 'Lavalleei'
	kinuyanagi (m)	CWon ELan EPla WIvy
§	***koriyanagi***	CWiW CWon
	'Kumeti'	see *S.* x *doniana* 'Kumeti'
	'Kuro-me'	see *S. gracilistyla* 'Melanostachys'
	lanata ♀H4	CBcs CMea CWon EBee ECho ECrN ELan EPfP EPot GGar GKev LRHS MAsh MGos MRav MWgw NBid NBir NBlu NEgg NHol NLAp NMen NWea SHBN SPer SSta SWat WAbe WFar
	- 'Drake's Hybrid'	NMen
	- 'Mrs Mac' (m)	CWon
	lapponum	GEdr NWea SRms

	lasiolepis	WWll
	x ***laurina*** (f)	CWon
§	***lindleyana***	NBir
	lucida	CWon ECrN
	mackenzieana	CWon
	'Maerd Brno' (f)	MBlu
	magnifica ♀H4	CDul CEnd CGHE CLnd CMCN CTho EBee ELan EMil EPfP EPla IDee LEdu MSte NPen SDry SMad SPoG SSpi SWat WFar WMou WPGP WSpi
	'Mark Postill' (f)	CBgR CDoC CWon EBee EMil GBin LRHS MBNS SPla SPoG SPur WPen
	matsudana 'Tortuosa'	see *S. babylonica* var. *pekinensis* 'Tortuosa'
	- 'Tortuosa Aureopendula'	see *S.* 'Erythroflexuosa'
	'Melanostachys'	see *S. gracilistyla* 'Melanostachys'
	x ***meyeriana***	WIvy
	- 'Daza'	WWll
	- 'Lumley' (f)	CWiW
	miyabeana	WWll
	x ***mollissima*** var. ***hippophaifolia***	WWll
	- var. ***hippophaifolia*** 'Jefferies' (m)	CWiW
	- - 'Notts Spaniard' (m)	CWiW
	- - 'Stinchcombe'	WIvy
	- - 'Trustworthy' (m)	CWiW
	- var. ***undulata*** 'Kottenheider Weide' (f)	CWiW
	moupinensis	CWon EPfP MBri NLar
	- EDHCH 97.319	WPGP
§	***myrsinifolia***	EBee EPla MBlu NSti WWll
	- subsp. ***alpicola***	CWon
	myrsinites var. ***jacquiniana***	see *S. alpina*
	myrtilloides	CLyd
	- 'Pink Tassels' (m)	CWon ECho GEdr NWCA SIng
	myrtilloides x ***repens***	see *S.* x *finnmarchica*
	nakamurana var. ***yezoalpina***	CEnd CFee CWon EMil EPot EWes GAbr GEdr MRav NHar NPro NWCA WAbe WFar WIvy WPat
	nepalensis	see *S. lindleyana*
	nigricans	see *S. myrsinifolia*
	nivalis	see *S. reticulata* subsp. *nivalis*
	x ***ovata***	CLyd GKev NMen
§	x ***pendulina*** var. ***elegantissima***	CTho ECrN SWat
	pentandra	CDul CLnd ECrN LRav NWea WFar WMou
	- 'Patent Lumley'	CWiW
	'Philip's Fancy'	NWCA
§	***phylicifolia***	ECrN WMou
	- 'Malham' (m)	CWiW
	polaris	CLyd
	pseudopentandra	WWll
§	***purpurea***	CCVT CDul EMac NWea SRms WGwG WMou
	- 'Brittany Blue'	WWll
	- 'Brittany Green' (f)	CWiW WWll
	- 'Carl Jensen'	WWll
	- 'Continental Reeks'	CWiW WIvy
	- 'Dark Dicks' (f)	CWiW WIvy WWll
	- 'Dicky Meadows' (m)	CWiW WIvy WWll
*	- 'Elegantissima'	WWll
	- 'Goldstones'	CWiW WIvy WWll
	- f. ***gracilis***	see *S. purpurea* 'Nana'
	- 'Green Dicks'	CWiW WIvy
	- 'Helix'	see *S. purpurea*
	- 'Howki' (m)	CWon WMou
	- 'Irette' (m)	CWiW WWll
	- 'Jagiellonka' (f)	CWiW WIvy
	- var. ***japonica***	see *S. koriyanagi*
	- subsp. ***lambertiana***	CWiW WIvy

	- 'Lancashire Dicks' (m)	CWiW
	- 'Leicestershire Dicks' (m)	CWiW
	- 'Light Dicks'	CWiW
	- 'Lincolnshire Dutch' (f)	CWiW
§	- 'Nana'	EBee EMac EPfP MMuc NLar SLPl SLon SPer SPur STre WFar WMoo
	- 'Nancy Saunders' (f)	CTho CWiW EPPr EPla GBuc MBNS MBlu MBrN MBri MRav MSte NPro NSti SCoo SMHy WCot WIvy WPen WWll
I	- 'Nicholsonii Purpurascens'	CWon WWll
	- 'Norbury'	WWll
	- 'Pendula' 🏆^{H4}	CCVT CEnd CWib CWon EBee ECrN EMil LAst LRHS MAsh MBar MBri MGos MRav MSwo NWea SPer SPoG
	- 'Procumbens'	WWll
	- 'Read' (f)	CWiW
	- 'Reeks' (f)	CWiW
	- 'Richartii' (f)	CWiW CWon
	- 'Uralensis' (f)	CWiW
	- 'Whipcord'	WWll
	pyrenaica	CLyd EWes NWCA
	pyrenaica* x *retusa	ECho
	pyrifolia	CWon WWll
	rehderiana	CWon
	repens	ECho ECrN EMac LRav MBar NWea SRms STre SWat WGwG
§	- var. ***argentea***	CWon EPfP EQua EWes MBar MRav NWCA NWea SPer STre WFar
	- 'Armando'^{PBR}	MGos
	- 'Iona' (m)	CLyd MBar
	- ***pendula***	see *S.* 'Boyd's Pendulous' (m)
	- 'Voorthuizen' (f)	CWib ECho LAst MBar MGos WGer
	reticulata 🏆^{H4}	ECho EPot GCrs NBir NLAp NMen NRya NSla WAbe
§	- subsp. ***nivalis***	NWCA
	retusa	CTri ECho NBir NLAp
	retusa* x *serpyllifolia	EPot NWCA
	rosmarinifolia misapplied	see *S. elaeagnos* subsp. *angustifolia*
§	x ***rubens*** var. ***basfordiana***	WWll
	- 'Basfordiana' (m)	CDoC CDul CLnd CTho CWiW EPla EWes MBNS MRav NEgg NWea SWat WMou
	- 'Bouton Aigu'	CWiW
	- 'Farndon'	CWiW
	- 'Flanders Red' (f)	CWiW
	- 'Fransgeel Rood' (m)	CWiW
	- 'Glaucescens' (m)	CWiW
	- 'Golden Willow'	CWiW CWon
	- 'Hutchinson's Brown'	CWon
	- 'Jaune de Falaise'	CWiW
	- 'Jaune Hâtive'	CWiW
	- 'Laurina'	CWiW
	- 'Natural Red' (f)	CWiW CWon
	- 'Parsons'	CWiW
	- 'Rouge Ardennais'	CWiW
	- 'Rouge Folle'	CWiW
	- 'Russet' (f)	CWiW
	x ***rubra***	CWiW
	- 'Abbey's Harrison' (f)	CWiW
	- 'Continental Osier' (f)	CWiW CWon
	- 'Eugenei' (m)	CDul ECrN EPla GQui MBlu SWat WIvy WMou
	- 'Fidkin' (f)	CWiW
	- 'Harrison's' (f)	CWiW
	- 'Harrison's Seedling A' (f)	CWiW
	- 'Mawdesley'	CWiW
	- 'Mawdesley Seedling A' (f)	CWiW
	- 'Pyramidalis'	CWiW
	sachalinensis 'Kioryo'	CWon WWll
	x ***sanguinea***	see *S.* x *rubens* var. *basfordiana*
	Scarlet Curls = 'Scarcuzam'	WPat
	schwerinii	WWll
	x ***sepulcralis***	NWea
§	- 'Aokautere'	CWiW
	- 'Caradoc'	CWiW NScw WWll
§	- var. ***chrysocoma***	CDoC CDul CSBt CWib EBee ECrN ENot EPfP LAst LBuc LPan LRHS MBar MGos MWat NBea NBee NBlu NEgg SBLw SCoo SHBN SLim SPer SPoG SWat WOrn
	x ***sericans***	CWon
	serpyllifolia	CLyd CTri NMen WPat
	serpyllum	see *S. fruticulosa*
	sessilifolia	WWll
	'Setsuka'	see *S. udensis* 'Sekka'
	x ***simulatrix***	CLyd CWon EPot MBar NWCA
	sitchensis	WWll
	x ***smithiana***	NWea
	x ***stipularis*** (f)	CWon NWea
	'Stuartii'	GAbr MBar NMen NWCA SRms
	subfragilis	WWll
	subopposita	CDul EBee ELan EWes MBNS MBar NPro SLon STre WGwG
	'Tora'^{PBR} (f)	LRav
	triandra	CWon WMou WWll
	- 'Belge'	WWll
	- 'Black German' (m)	CWiW
	- 'Black Hollander' (m)	CWiW WIvy
	- 'Black Maul'	CWiW WWll
	- 'Faux Plant de Tourraine'	WWll
	- 'Grisette de Falaise'	CWiW
	- 'Grisette Droda' (f)	CWiW
	- 'Grisette Noire'	WWll
	- var. ***hoffmanniana***	WWll
	- 'Long Bud'	CWiW
	- 'Noir de Challans'	CWiW WWll
	- 'Noir de Touraine'	CWiW
	- 'Noir de Villaines' (m)	CWiW CWon WIvy WWll
	- 'Rouge d'Orléans'	ECrN
	- 'Sarda d'Anjou'	CWiW
	- 'Semperflorens' (m)	CNat WWll
	- 'Whissander'	CWiW WIvy
	x ***tsugaluensis*** 'Ginme' (f)	SLPl WPat WWll
	udensis	WWll
§	- 'Sekka' (m)	CTho CWon EBee ECtt ELan LRav NBir NWea STre SWat WFar WIvy WMou WWll
	'Ulbrichtweide'	WWll
	uva-ursi	CLyd
	viminalis	CCVT CDul CWon ECrN EMac LBuc NWea WMou
	- 'Black Satin'	WWll
	- 'Brown Merrin'	WIvy
	- 'Green Gotz'	CWiW WIvy
	- 'Mulattin'	CWon WWll
	- 'Reader's Red' (m)	WIvy WWll
	- 'Riefenweide'	WIvy
	- 'Romanin'	CWon
	- 'Stone Osier'	WWll
	- 'Yellow Osier'	CWon WIvy
	vitellina 'Pendula'	see *S. alba* 'Tristis' ambig.
	waldsteiniana	MBar NWCA
	x ***wimmeriana***	SRms
	'Yelverton'	see *S. alba* var. *vitellina* 'Yelverton'

Salpiglossis (*Solanaceae*)

sinuata new	CSpe

Salsola (*Chenopodiaceae*)

soda	CArn EUnu

Salvia ✿ (*Lamiaceae*)

ACE 2172	SPin
CD&R 1162	SPin
CD&R 1458	SPin

CD&R 1495	SHGN SPin
CD&R 3071	SPin
DJH 93 T	SPin
PC&H 226	SPin
acetabulosa	see *S. multicaulis*
aerea	CPom
aethiopis	CPle EAro EWes SDnm SPav SPhx SPin WOut XPep
§ ***africana***	CPle GGar SPin WDyG WOut XPep
africana-caerulea	see *S. africana*
africana-lutea	see *S. aurea*
agnes	SPin
albimaculata	SBla SPin
algeriensis	CSpe SBch SPin
'Allen Chickering'	XPep
amarissima	CPle SPin
'Amber'	SPin
ambigens	see *S. guaranitica* 'Blue Enigma'
ampelophylla B&SWJ 10751 new	WCru
§ ***amplexicaulis***	EAro EPPr LSou MGol MWea NLar SBch SPin WPer XPep
angustifolia Cav.	see *S. reptans*
angustifolia Mich.	see *S. azurea*
'Anthony Parker'	CPle MAJR SAga SDys SPin
apiana	CArn EAro EOHP EPyc EUnu MDKP MGol MHer MSal SGar SPin XPep
argentea ♀H3	More than 30 suppliers
arizonica	CBgR CPle CPom EAro MHom MLLN MSte SDys SPin XPep
atrocyanea	CPle CSpe EPyc LPio MLLN SDys SGar SPin WHal WKif WWlt
§ ***aurea***	CHal CHll CPle CSev CSpe EKen EPyc EShb LHop LPio MGol MSte SGar SPin WFar WPer XPep
- 'Kirstenbosch'	CPle CSev EAro EBee ECtt EMan EWin MLLN NCGa SDys SPin WGwG WHer WKif WOut WPer WRos
aurita	SPin
- var. ***galpinii***	SPin
austriaca	CPle SHFr SPin
§ ***azurea***	CPle CRWN EUnu MSte SAga SBod SMrm SPhx SPin XPep
- var. ***grandiflora***	LRav SPin
bacheriana	see *S. buchananii*
§ ***barrelieri***	CPle SHFr SPin XPep
'Bee's Bliss'	XPep
'Belhaven'	WDyG WHil WOut
bertolonii	see *S. pratensis* Bertolonii Group
bicolor Des.	see *S. barrelieri*
'Black Knight'	SPin
blancoana	CArn CMea CPle ECha ELau MHer MLLN MSte SAga SBch SDys SPin
blepharophylla	CPle CSpe EAro EBee ECtt EShb LAst LHop LPio MHar MHer MSte NCGa NGHP SAga SBch SDnm SPav SPin SRkn SRot WHil
- 'Diablo'	ECtt SDys SKHP SPin
- 'Painted Lady'	CPle SDys SPin WOut WWlt
'Blue Chiquita'	SDys SPin
'Blue Sky'	SDys
'Blue Vein'	NPri
brandegeei	SPin
broussonetii	SPin
§ ***buchananii*** ♀H1+3	CHal CHll CPle CPom CSWP CSam CSpe EAro EBee ECtt EPfP EShb GQui LHop LPio MHar MHer MHom MLLN SAga SGar SPav SPin SPoG SRkn SWal WFar
bulleyana misapplied	see *S. flava* var. *megalantha*
bulleyana Diels	CBgR CHFP CSev EDAr EWes GKev LEdu MDKP MGol MHer MLLN MWgw NLar SDnm SHFr SPav WCru WFar
cacaliifolia ♀H1+3	CBgR CDMG CPLG CPle CRHN CSpe CWCL ECtt EPyc MHer MLLN MNrw MSte NGHP SBch SDnm SGar SHFr SPer SPin SRkn WFar WOut WPic WSHC WWlt
cadmica	SPin
caerulea misapplied	see *S. guaranitica* 'Black and Blue'
caerulea L.	see *S. africana*
caespitosa	NMen SBla SPin
campanulata	CPom EWld MGol SPhx SPin
- CC 4038	ITer
- CC 4193	MGol
- CC&McK 1071	CFir
- GWJ 9294	WCru
canariensis	CPle EAro EShb IGor MLLN SHFr SPin XPep
- f. ***candidissima***	WOut XPep
candelabrum ♀H3-4	CAbP CArn CMea CPle CSpe ECtt MHer MLLN MSte SBch SHFr SPav SPhx SPin WEas WKif WSHC WWlt XPep
candidissima	SPin
canescens	EAro XPep
cardinalis	see *S. fulgens*
carduacea	SPin
cedrosensis	SDys
§ ***chamaedryoides***	CBgR CPle CSev CWGN EPyc MHom NGHP SBla SDnm SDys SGar SPhx SPin WSHC XPep
- var. ***isochroma***	EAro SDys SPin
- 'Marine Blue'	SDys SPin
- silver-leaved	CBgR MSte SAga SPhx SPin WOut XPep
aff. ***chamaedryoides*** B&SWJ 9032 from Guatemala	SPin WCru
chamaedryoides x ***microphylla***	EAro XPep
chamelaeagnea	GFai LHop SDys SHar SPin WOut WPrP XPep
chapalensis	SAga SPin
chiapensis	CPle CSpe MAJR MLLN SDys SPin
chinensis	see *S. japonica*
'Christine Yeo'	CDes CPLG CPle CSpe EBee ECtt EPPr EPyc GGar MDKP MSte NGHP SBch SDys SGar SMeo SPav SPin WDyG WHil WMnd WPGP WPtf WSHC
cleistogama misapplied	see *S. glutinosa*
clevelandii	CPle EAro EWes MGol MHer SPav SPin WJek XPep
- 'Winnifred Gilman'	EAro SBHP SDys
clinopodioides	SPin
coahuilensis ambig.	LSou NDov SAga SGar SHFr SMeo SMrm SPin WSHC
coahuilensis Fernald	EAro EBee MGol
coccinea	MHer SHFr SPin
- 'Brenthurst'	SDys SPin
- (Nymph Series) 'Coral Nymph'	ECtt LDai LRHS SDnm SDys SMrm SPav SPin SWal SWat
- - 'Lady in Red' ♀H3	ECtt SDys SPav SWat
columbariae	SPin
concolor misapplied	see *S. guaranitica*
concolor Lamb.	CDes CPle EWld MGol MHom SPin WDyG WPGP WSHC
confertiflora	CDMG CDes CHEx CHVG CPle CPom CSam CSpe EBee ECtt ELan EShb GCra MHar MHer MHom MLLN MSte NGHP SAga SDys SGar SPin SWal WDyG WFar WPGP WPic WWlt
corrugata	CBcs CDes CFee CPle CPne CPrp CSam CSpe EBee EShb GBri IDee

		LHop MHer MLLN SDys SPhx SPin SRkn WPGP WPic WWlt
	'Crème Caramel'	SDys
	cyanescens	CPBP CPle EPot EWld SPin XPep
*	***cyanosa***	EBee
	daghestanica	SDys SPin
	darcyi misapplied	see *S. roemeriana*
	darcyi J. Compton	CDTJ CHll CPle CPom CSpe EBee EPyc EWes LPio MSte SAga SDys SHFr SKHP SPhx SPin WEas WHil WSHC XPep
	'Darky'	SPin
	davidsonii	SPin
	dentata	EUnu SDys SPin XPep
	desoleana	EAro XPep
	digitaloides BWJ 7777	SPin WCru
	discolor ♀H1	CFir CPle CPne CSev CSpe EBee ECtt ELan EOHP ERea EShb GQui LDai LPio MHer MLLN MTho NGHP SDys SEND SGar SPav SPet SPin SRkn SWal WFar WHlf WWlt
*	- ***nigra***	CArn CMdw
	disermas	CPle EUnu SDys SPin SPlb WOut XPep
	disjuncta	SPin
	divinorum	EOHP EWin GPoy MGol MSal NGHP
	dolichantha	CDMG CHFP CSpe EAro EDAr EPyc EShb EWsh MAvo MDKP MFOX MGol MWea MWrn SBch SBod SGar SPin WHil WSHC
	dolomitica	SPav SPin XPep
	dombeyi	CHll CPle CPne EAro EWld SDys SPin
	dominica	SPin XPep
	dorisiana	CFee CPle CPne CSpe EAro ELan EOHP EUnu MLLN SDys SPhx SPin
	dorrii	SPin
	eigii	SPin
	elegans	CPle CSev CTca ELau EWes GCra MHom MNHC MSte WFar
	- 'Honey Melon'	EOHP EUnu SDys
§	- 'Scarlet Pineapple'	More than 30 suppliers
	- 'Sonoran Red'	EAro SDys
	- 'Tangerine'	CArn CPrp CWan ELau EOHP LAst LFol LSou MGol MHer NGHP SBch SDnm SPet SPin SWal WGwG
	evansiana	CPom
	- BWJ 8013	SPin WCru
	fallax	MHar SPin
	farinacea	SPin
	- 'Rhea'	LRHS
	- 'Strata'	LRHS SDys
	- 'Victoria' ♀H3	ELau SDys WGwG
§	***flava*** var. ***megalantha***	CBod CDes CPle EBla ELan LEdu LRHS LSRN NChi NGdn SPin WFar WPer
	- - BWJ 7974	WCru
	forreri	CBgR CDes EAro EBee EPyc SAga SBHP SDys SPin WPGP WSPU
	- 'Karen Dyson' **new**	SDys
§	***forsskaolii***	More than 30 suppliers
	'Frieda Dixon'	EOHP LSou WMnd
§	***fruticosa***	CArn CPle EAro EBee ELau LRHS SIde SPin XPep
§	***fulgens*** ♀H3	CPle ILis MHom NGHP SAga SBHP SBch SGar SHFr SPin SRkn WFar WWeb WWlt
	gesneriiflora	CPle ECtt EWld MGol MSte SDys SPin WOut
	- 'Tequila'	MAJR SPin
	gilliesii	SPin XPep
	glechomifolia	SPin
§	***glutinosa***	CArn CBgR CHFP CPLG CPle CSpe EAro EBee ECtt EPPr EPyc LDai MGol MNrw NBro SPav SPin SWal WCAu WGwG WOut WPer
	gracilis	SPin
	grahamii	see *S. microphylla* var. *microphylla*
	greggii	CDMG EBee ECtt EWes GKev MHer MSte NGHP SBod WKif WPer XPep
	- CD&R 1148	EAro LSou MCot SDys WSPU
	- 'Alba'	CBgR CHal CPle EBee LPio NGHP SAga SDys XPep
	- 'Belize' **new**	EAro
	- 'Blush Pink'	see *S. microphylla* 'Pink Blush'
	- 'Caramba' (v)	CBgR CBow EAro EPyc EShb EWin MLLN NGHP SAga SDnm SHGN SPav SPoG WCra
	- 'Devon Cream'	see *S. greggii* 'Sungold'
	- 'Furman's Red'	XPep
	- 'Magenta'	MDKP WHil
*	- (Navajo Series) 'Navajo Cream'	EAro EPyc WFar
*	- - 'Navajo Dark Purple'	CSpe EAro EPyc LSou SAga WFar
	- - Navajo Pink = 'Rfd-s019' **new**	SGar
*	- - 'Navajo Purple' **new**	CMdw
	- - Navajo Rose = 'Rfd-s018'	WFar
	- - Navajo Salmon Red = 'Rfd-s016'	EPyc WFar
*	- - 'Navajo White'	EPyc WFar
	- 'Peach' misapplied	see *S.* x *jamensis* 'Pat Vlasto'
	- 'Peach'	CBgR CDes CHar CPle CSpe CWGN EBee ELau EPfP LHop LRHS MHer MLLN MSte NGHP SAga SDnm SGar SPav SPin SWal WMnd WPGP WWeb
	- 'Sierra San Antonio'	see *S.* x *jamensis* 'Sierra San Antonio'
	- 'Sparkler' (v)	CPle SBch
	- 'Stormy Pink'	CDes CHll CMdw CPle CSpe EBee EPyc WIvy WPGP WSHC
§	- 'Sungold'	CDes CPle EAro EBee ECtt EPfP LHop LRHS MLLN NGHP SAga SBch SDys SHGN SPin WMnd WWeb
	- variegated (v)	XPep
	- yellow-flowered	LRHS XPep
	greggii x ***lycioides***	see *S. greggii* x *serpyllifolia*
§	***greggii*** x ***serpyllifolia***	CAbP CBgR CPle CSpe EPyc SDys SGar SPin WPGP WWlt XPep
§	***guaranitica***	CBcs CBgR CEnt CHEx CPle CPne ECtt EShb GCra SAga SDnm SDys SPav SPer SPin SRkn WKif WPGP WWlt
	- 'Argentine Skies'	CPle ECtt EPPr EPyc EWin MAvo MSte SAga SDys SMrm SPin WDyG WPGP WWlt
§	- 'Black and Blue'	CBgR CPle CPne CRHN CSWP CSev EBee ECtt EPPr LPio MAvo MSte NGHP SAga SBch SDnm SGar SPav SPhx SPin WHil WPGP WPer WPrP WSHC
§	- 'Blue Enigma' ♀H3-4	More than 30 suppliers
	- 'Indigo Blue'	ECtt EPfP MLLN NEgg SPin WWlt
	- 'Purple Emperor' **new**	MGol
	- 'Purple Splendor'	CPne EShb
	- purple-flowered	CSam
	haematodes	see *S. pratensis* Haematodes Group
	haenkei	SPin
	- 'Prawn Chorus' **new**	CSpe
	heldreichiana	SPin
	henryi	SPin
	hians	CPom EAro EBee EWin GCra LAst MDKP MLLN MNrw SDnm SGar SPav SPin SRms WPer

- CC 1787	MGol SPin
hirtella	SPin
hispanica misapplied	see *S. lavandulifolia*
hispanica L.	CSam SPin
holwayi	SPin
horminum	see *S. viridis* var. *comata*
huberi	SPin
hypargeia	SPin
indica	SPin WOut XPep
'Indigo Spires'	CHll CHrt CPle CSpe CWGN EBee ECtt EPPr EShb LPio MEHN MHar MHom MLLN SBch SDys SMrm SPhx SPin WDyG WOut WPen WSHC WWlt
interrupta	CPle EWes SHFr SPin WKif WPen XPep
involucrata ♀H3	CFir CPLG CPom CSev GCra GQui MCot MHar MHom NBro SBch SDys SPin WSHC
- B&SWJ 8995	WCru
- 'Bethellii' ♀H3-4	CArn CDes CPle CPne CSev CWCL EBee ECtt ELan EShb GBri GSki LPio LRHS MHer MLLN SAga SDix SDnm SGar SHFr SMrm SPav SPin WKif WPer WSHC WWeb WWlt
- 'Boutin' ♀H3	CPle GBri MAJR MHom MLLN SDys
§ - 'Hadspen'	CHll CRHN CSam CSpe MSte SPin WKif
- 'Joan'	CPle
- 'Mrs Pope'	see *S. involucrata* 'Hadspen'
* - var. ***puberula***	CPle SDys SPin
iodantha	CPle CSpe SAga SDys SPin
iodochroa B&SWJ 10252 new	WCru
x ***jamensis***	SDys XPep
- 'Cherry Queen'	CPle CSpe EAro EBee EPyc SDys SPin WFar WHil
- 'Dark Dancer'	CPle SDys WHil WWlt
- 'Desert Blaze' (v)	CAbP CBgR CBow CDes EAro EBee ECtt MHar NCGa SDys SPin WHer WHil WPGP WSPU WWeb
- 'Dyson's Orangy Pink'	CAby
- 'Fuego'	CPle
- 'James Compton'	EAro MHom MSte SDys SGar
- 'La Luna'	CEnt CPle CPom CPrp CSam CTri CWGN EAro ECtt EPfP EShb GGar LHop LPio MHar MHer MHom MSte SDys SGar SHGN SPin WFar WMnd WPGP WSHC
- 'La Siesta'	EAro EBee SDys WWeb
- 'La Tarde'	CAby CEnt CTri MSte SBch SDys
- 'Lemon Sorbet'	SDys
- 'Los Lirios' ♀H3-4	CBgR CPle CSpe CTri EAro EPyc MSte SAga SDys SMrm SPin WSPU
- 'Maraschino'	CAbP EAro EBee EPfP EWin LPio LRHS MCot SDys SMrm SPin WMnd
* - 'Mauve'	SDys
- 'Moonlight Over Ashwood' (v)	CPle EAro ENot EPyc SBHP SDys SPin
- 'Moonlight Serenade'	CAby CPle EAro EBee EPyc EWin MWea NSti SAga SBch SDys SHGN WHil WHoo WSPU WWeb
§ - 'Pat Vlasto'	CSpe EAro EBee EPyc MHom MWea NGHP SDys SMrm SPin
- 'Pleasant Pink'	CPle CSev EBee SDys SPin
- 'Raspberry Royale' ♀H3-4	CDes CHar CPle CPom CSev CWGN EAro EBee ECtt ELan EPfP ERou LHop LRHS MHer MLLN MSte NCGa NGHP SDnm SGar SMrm SPav SPin SWat WHoo WMnd WSHC
- 'Red Velvet'	CPle ECtt MHom WEas WSHC
- 'San Isidro Moon'	WHil
- 'Señorita Leah'	SDys
§ - 'Sierra San Antonio'	CPle CSev CSpe EAro ECtt MWea SAga SBHP SDys SMrm
§ - 'Trebah'	CDes CPle CPom CSpe ECre EPyc LSou MHom MSte SDys SGar SPav SPin SRot WHil WIvy WPGP
- 'Trenance'	CAby CPle ECre EPyc LRHS LSou MHom MSte SDys SGar SPav SPin SRot
- white-flowered	SPin
§ ***japonica***	CArn CPle SPin
judaica	SPin XPep
jurisicii	CArn CFir CPle CWib EAro EBee EPyc EShb MGol MWgw SGar SPav SPhx SPin WJek
- pink-flowered	CSpe SPin
karwinskyi	SPin
- B&SWJ 9081	WCru
keerlii	SPin
koyamae	SPin
lanceolata	EAro SPin XPep
lanigera	SPin
§ ***lavandulifolia***	More than 30 suppliers
lavanduloides B&SWJ 9053	WCru
lemmonii	see *S. microphylla* var. *wislizeni*
leptophylla	see *S. reptans*
leucantha ♀H1	More than 30 suppliers
- 'Eder' (v)	MAJR SDys SPin
- 'Purple Velvet'	CPle EBee MAJR MHar MHom MSte NGHP SDys SPin WWlt
- 'San Marcos Lavender'	SPin
- 'Santa Barbara'	SDys
leucophylla	XPep
- NNS 01-375	SPin
littae	SPin
longispicata	SPin
longistyla	SPin
lycioides misapplied	see *S. greggii* x *serpyllifolia*
lycioides A. Gray	CAbP CHll CPle LPio NDov SDys SPhx SPin SRkn WDyG XPep
lyrata	CBgR CPle EOHP EUnu MDKP MGol MSal SGar SHFr SPin
- 'Burgundy Bliss'	see *S. lyrata* 'Purple Knockout'
§ - 'Purple Knockout'	CBcs CBod CBow CKno EAro EBee EMan EMil EPPr EPyc EShb GSki LAst LHop MBri NGHP SBod SGar SHGN SPav SPhx SPin SWal WWeb
- 'Purple Vulcano'	see *S. lyrata* 'Purple Knockout'
macellaria misapplied	see *S. microphylla*
macellaria Epling	CSam
madrensis	MAJR SPin
- 'Dunham'	SDys
melissodora	SDys SPin
mellifera	CArn CPle SPin XPep
merjamie	EBee SPin XPep
- 'Mint-sauce'	CSev EAro ELan SHFr WFar WHer WPer
mexicana	CPle CSam MWea SBch SPin
- T&K 550	CArn
- var. ***minor***	CPle MAJR
- 'Tula'	SDys
meyeri	CPle MAJR SPin
§ ***microphylla***	CArn CHrt CMHG CPle CPom CPrp CWan EAro ELau EOHP EWes GGar LFol LHop MHer NSti SBri SHFr SPet WCru WHCG WPer XPep
- CD&R 1141	SPin
- 'Cerro Potosí'	CBgR CMdw CPle CPom CSev CSpe EBee ELon MLLN MSte SAga SDys SGar SHFr SMrm SPin WDyG WHil WPen WWlt

- 'Dieciocho de Marzo' SDys
- 'Hot Lips' CPle EWes LBuc LRHS MBri NGHP SDys SPin WOut
- 'Huntington' EOHP
- hybrid, purple-flowered CPom
- 'Kew Red' ♀$^{H3-4}$ CFir CHVG CPle CSpe CWGN EBee MNrw MWea SBch SPin WHoo WPen WWeb
- 'La Trinidad' SDys

§ - var. ***microphylla*** CFee CHal CPle CRHN CSev CSpe CTri CWib EBee ECtt ELan EPfP MHer MNHC NGHP SDry SGar SHFr SMrm SOWG SPav SPin SRkn WCFE WCru WFar WHil WPer WSHC XPep

- - 'La Foux' CPle ECtt LSou MWea SBch SDys SMeo SMrm SPhx WSPU
- - 'Newby Hall' ♀$^{H3-4}$ CAby CBrm CPle EBee ECtt EPyc EWes MSte MWea NGHP SPhx WPGP
- var. ***neurepia*** see *S. microphylla* var. *microphylla*
- 'Orange Door' SDys
- 'Oregon Peach' LRHS
- 'Oxford' SDys SPin

§ - 'Pink Blush' ♀$^{H3-4}$ CPle EAro EBee ECtt ELan EPfP GBri IDee LRHS MHer MHom MLLN MSte NGHP SMrm SPin WHil WKif WPGP WSHC

- 'Pleasant View' ♀$^{H3-4}$ CPle EPyc EWin
- 'Rosy Cheeks' **new** WOut

§ - 'Ruth Stungo' (v) ECre

- 'San Carlos Festival' CDes CSev EAro EBee ECtt EPyc EWin NGHP SBch SDys SPin WHil WPGP WWlt
- 'Trelawny Rose Pink' see *S.* 'Trelawney'
- 'Trelissick Creamy Yellow' see *S.* 'Trelissick'
- 'Trewithen Cerise' see *S.* 'Trewithen'
- 'Variegata' splashed see *S. microphylla* 'Ruth Stungo'
- 'Wild Watermelon' CPle EAro EPyc SDys WWeb

§ - var. ***wislizeni*** CPle SDys SPin WHil WPer

miltiorhiza CArn EUnu MGol MSal SPin

miniata CPle CSev MAJR SBHP SDys SPin WOut

misella CMdw CSpe SPin

mohavensis SPin

'Monrovia' EWin

moorcroftiana MGol SDnm SPin

'Mrs Beard' XPep

muelleri misapplied see *S. greggii* x *serpyllifolia*

muelleri Epling EAro EPyc WBor

muirii SHar SPin

'Mulberry Wine' CDes CHll CMdw CPle CSev CSpe EAro EBee ECtt EPyc EWes EWin GBri MAJR MHom SAga SDys SPin WKif WPGP WWeb

§ ***multicaulis*** ♀^{H4} CPle ECha EMan EPyc GBri MSte SHFr SPin WEas WSHC

munzii CFir XPep

* ***murrayi*** CAbP SPin

namaensis CSpe EAro SDys SPin XPep

nana B&SWJ 10272 **new** WCru

napifolia EBee EWsh GSki MGol NBHF SAga SBod SDnm SPav SPhx SPin WGwG WPer

'Nazareth' EAro

nemorosa SHFr SPin SRms XPep

- 'Amethyst' ♀^{H4} CPle CPrp EBee EGle EPPr EPfP LAst LRHS MBri MLLN MRav MSte NCGa NDov NMoo NPri SDys SHBN SMHy SMer SPhx WCAu WCot WKif WWlt
- 'Blue Mound' ENot
- 'Caradonna' More than 30 suppliers
- East Friesland see *S. nemorosa* 'Ostfriesland'
- 'Lubecca' ♀^{H4} CPrp EBee EBrs ECGP ECtt EGle EHrv EPfP EPla EShb LHop LRHS MBri MLLN MWgw NCGa NDov NLar SPer WCAu WFar WMnd
- Marcus = 'Haeumanarc'[PBR] CKno CPrp CSpe EBee EBrs ECtt EGle ELan EMan ENot EPfP EPyc LAst LHop LRHS LSRN MBNS MBri MLLN NLar SDys SMer SPla SPoG WCot WFar
- 'Midsummer' EWld MGol

§ - 'Ostfriesland' ♀^{H4} More than 30 suppliers

- 'Phoenix Pink' SPhx
- 'Plumosa' see *S. nemorosa* 'Pusztaflamme'
- 'Porzellan' ♀^{H4} ECtt

§ - 'Pusztaflamme' ♀^{H4} CPrp CWGN EBee ECha ECtt EMan EPfP MMHG NOrc NSti WCAu

- 'Rose Queen' CBgR ECtt ENot EPPr GSki LAst MCot MWat NBir NDlv SDys SPer SPla SWat WFar
- 'Rosenwein' CSam EBee GBuc LBMP LDai MAvo MDKP MNrw NBPC NGdn SMrm SPhx SPoG
- 'Royal Distinction' EBee ECtt EMan ERou LSou
- 'Schwellenburg' EBee EGle EMan EPfP ERou LBuc LHop LSou MAvo MBNS NBPC NMoo SMrm SPoG WCot
- 'Sensation Rose' **new** EBrs
- 'Snow Mound' **new** ENot

§ - subsp. ***tesquicola*** EBee ECGP ECha EGle EPyc NGdn NLar SMrm SPhx WOut

- 'Wesuwe' EBee ELon NDov NGby

neurepia see *S. microphylla* var. *microphylla*

nilotica CArn EAro EBee MGol SHFr SPin WLin XPep

nipponica CPle

- B&SWJ 5829 SPin WCru
- 'Fuji Snow' (v) CBow EMan EPyc EWes LSou MLLN

nubicola CBgR CPLG CPle EBee EPPr EWld GKev GPoy LDai MGol SPin WOut XPep

- CC 4607 MGol

officinalis CArn CHal CHby CHrt CPrp EBee ELau GAbr GMaP GPoy LCro LRHS LSRN MBar MBri MGos MNHC MSwo MWat NGHP NPri SHBN SPlb SWal WBrk WGwG WPer WTel WTin XPep

- 'Alba' see *S. officinalis* 'Albiflora'

§ - 'Albiflora' CBod ECtt EGoo EOHP MSte NGHP SBch SPin WJek WPer XPep

I - 'Albiflora Nana' LRav

N - 'Aurea' ambig. CWib ECho GPoy MBar NPri

- 'Berggarten' CArn CPrp EBee ECha ELau EMan EPfP EUnu LHop LPio MBri MHer MRav SDix SPhx SPin WCFE WHer WMnd XPep
- 'Blackcurrant' CHal EUnu LSou

§ - broad-leaved CSWP CWan ELau MHer SWat WJek

- 'Crispa' EOHP SPin XPep
- 'Extrakta' EUnu
- 'Grandiflora' EAro
- 'Grete Stolze' EBee
- 'Growers Friend' EWin
- 'Herrenhausen' MSte

§ - 'Icterina' (v) ♀^{H4} More than 30 suppliers

- 'Kew Gold' ELau MRav WJek
- ***latifolia*** see *S. officinalis* broad-leaved
- 'Minor' EGoo
- narrow-leaved see *S. lavandulifolia*
- 'Nazareth'[PBR] EBee EWin

* - 'Pink Splash' (v) CBow

	- ***prostrata***	see *S. lavandulifolia*
	- 'Purpurascens' ΨH4	More than 30 suppliers
	- 'Purpurascens Variegata' (v)	WEas
	- 'Rosea'	EOHP
	- Tomentosa Group	CArn
	- 'Tricolor' (v)	More than 30 suppliers
	- 'Variegata'	see *S. officinalis* 'Icterina'
	- variegated (v)	ECho
	omeiana	EWld
	- BWJ 8062	WCru
	- 'Crûg Thundercloud' **new**	WCru
	oppositiflora misapplied	see *S. tubiflora*
	oppositiflora ambig.	CBgR CPle SDys SPin WOut
	pachyphylla	SPin XPep
	pachystachya	SPin
	palaestina	XPep
	pale blue, B&SWJ 8985 from Guatemala	WCru
§	***patens*** ΨH3	More than 30 suppliers
	- 'Alba' misapplied	see *S. patens* 'White Trophy'
	- 'Blue Angel'	EAro EBee EWes
	- 'Cambridge Blue' ΨH3	More than 30 suppliers
	- 'Chilcombe'	CBgR CPle CSam CSpe EBee ECtt EPyc ERou EShb EWin LSou MHar MLLN MSte SAga SDys SHFr SPin SWal WHil WOut WWlt
	- 'Guanajuato'	CBcs CPle CPom CSam CSpe EBee EShb EUnu EWes GMaP LAst LPio MHar MHer MSte MWrn SDnm SDys SMad SPin SRkn SRot WSHC
	- 'Guanajuato Lavender'	LPio
	- 'Oxford Blue'	see *S. patens*
	- 'Royal Blue'	see *S. patens*
§	- 'White Trophy'	CPle EBee ELan ERou EShb LHop LRHS MHer MSte NGHP NPri SDnm SDys SGar SPer SPin SWal WFar WWeb
	pauciserrata	SPin
	penstemonoides	SDys SPin XPep
	'Peru Blue'	SDys
	phlomoides	MGol
	pinguifolia	SPin
	'Pink Ice'	CPom
	pisidica	SPin
	plectranthoides	SPin
	pogonochila	CPom
	polystachya	CPle EBee SPin
	pratensis	CArn CBgR CPle CWib EBee ELan MNHC MSal MWgw NChi SECG SGar SPin SWat WOut WPer XPep
	- 'Albiflora'	CDes SWat
§	- Bertolonii Group	EPyc
§	- Haematodes Group ΨH4	CBgR CPle EBee ECha ELan EPyc LDai MGol MNrw NLar SBch SDnm SPav SPin SRms SWat WPer XPep
	- 'Indigo' ΨH4	CDes CPrp EBee ECGP ECtt EPPr EPfP LRHS MCot MRav MWgw NDov NLar SPhx SPin WMnd WPGP
	- 'Lapis Lazuli'	CDes EAro EBee EMon EPyc EWes LCro MWea NBre SPhx SPin WKif
	- 'Pink Delight' PBR	EBee ERou MSte
	- 'Rose Rhapsody' **new**	EDAr LDai
	- 'Rosea'	CBgR EBee ECha LRHS SPhx SPin
	- 'Swan Lake'	CBod NBHF NChi NHol SPhx WPer
	- 'White Swan'	SPlb WOut
	prostrata	EOHP
	prunelloides	SPin
	przewalskii	CDes CHFP CPle CPom GSki MCCP MGol MSal MWgw NEgg SBch SDnm SGar SHFr SPhx SPin WBVN WLin WPer

	- ACE 1157	EBee
	- BWJ 7920	SPin WCru
	- DJH 210524	EPPr
	'Purple Majesty'	CHll CPle CPne CSev CSpe EBee EPPr LHop LPio MLLN MSte NCGa SAga SDys SMrm SPhx SPin SRkn WKif WWeb WWlt
	'Purple Queen'	CPle MBri
	purpurea	LAst LSRN SPin
	recognita	CPle NBHF SPin WKif WSHC XPep
	reflexa	SPin
	regeliana misapplied	see *S. virgata* Jacq.
	regeliana Trautv.	EBee MGol MLLN NBir SPin
	regla	CPle SDys SPin WHil WOut XPep
	- 'Jame'	SPin
	- 'Mount Emory'	SPin
	repens	CDMG CPle EAro EBee EPyc IGor LSou SDys SPin WLin WOut
	- var. ***repens***	SGar XPep
§	***reptans***	CPle CSam CWCL LHop SPin WDyG WHil WPer XPep
	- from Mexico	SDys
	- from Western Texas	SDys
	ringens	EAro NBHF SBHP SDys SPin XPep
	riparia misapplied	see *S. rypara*
	roborowskii	SPin
§	***roemeriana*** ΨH3	CPle CSpe EPyc MHom NWCA SDnm SDys SPin WPGP XPep
	rubescens	MCot SDys SPin
	rubiginosa	SDys SPin
	runcinata	EAro SPhx SPin XPep
	rutilans	see *S. elegans* 'Scarlet Pineapple'
§	***rypara***	CPle CPom EAro SDys SPin
	sagittata	SDys SPin WWlt
*	***sauntia***	SPin
	scabiosifolia	SPin
	scabra	CFir CPle EBee MGol MSte SDys SPin WOut XPep
	sclarea	CArn CHby CWan ECtt ELau GPoy LRHS MHer MNHC NChi NGHP NGdn SECG SIde SPin WPer WSel XPep
	- var. ***sclarea***	CKno EBee EBla ECtt
	- var. ***turkestanica*** hort.	More than 30 suppliers
§	- - 'Vatican White'	CBcs EAro EBee EBrs EMar LDai LHop MBri NCGa NChi NGdn SBch SDnm SPav SPhx WMnd WPer WSHC WWeb
	- white-bracted	CBod CWib NDlv NGHP NLar SBod SPin SWvt XPep
*	***scordifolia***	SPin
	scutellarioides	SPin WOut
	semiatrata misapplied	see *S. chamaedryoides*
	semiatrata ambig.	CMdw
	semiatrata Zucc.	CDes CPle CPom CSpe EBee LSou SAga SDys SPin SRkn
	serpyllifolia	SDys SPin WOut
	sessei	SPin
	'Shirley's Creeper'	XPep
	'Silas Dyson'	SBch SDys
	'Silke's Dream'	CPle EAro EBee ECtt EPyc SBHP SDys SPin WWlt
	sinaloensis	CBgR CPle EBee EMan EPyc EShb LSou SBch SDys SPin WFar
	somalensis	CPle SDys SHar SPin WPen XPep
	sonomensis	XPep
	spathacea ΨH3-4	CDes CPle EMan EShb MDKP SDys SPhx SPin XPep
	splendens	SPin
	- 'Dancing Flame' (v)	EBee EWin
	- 'Peach'	SPin
§	- 'Van-Houttei' ΨH3	CPle CSpe ECre EPyc MLLN SDys SPin WWlt
	sprucei	SPin
	squalens	SPin

§	***staminea***	MGol SDys SHFr SPhx SPin XPep
	stenophylla	CPle EAro MGol SPin WOut WPer
	stepposa	SPin XPep
	x ***superba*** ♀H4	CPrp CSBt EBee ECtt ELan EPfP EShb LAst LEdu LRHS MBri MHer MWat MWgw NEgg SDix SHBN SPer SRms SSvw WHoo
	- 'Adrian'	ECtt LRHS
	- 'Dear Anja'	EGle LHop NDov SPhx
	- 'Forncett Dawn'	EBee
	- 'Merleau'	EBee EPyc
	- 'Merleau Rose'	NBlu
*	- 'Rosea'	NEgg
	- 'Rubin' ♀H4	EBee ECtt NBre NDov SMrm
I	- 'Superba'	CSev ECha ECtt EHrv MRav SPhx SRkn WCAu
	x ***sylvestris***	LAst SPin WOut XPep
	- 'Blauhügel' ♀H4	CPrp EBee ECha ECtt ELan EPfP EShb LRHS MArl MLLN MSte MWgw NDov NPri SBch SMrm SPhx WCAu WPer WPtf
§	- 'Blaukönigin'	EBee EPfP ERou GMaP IBal LCro LRHS MNHC MWat NDlv NEgg NLar NMir NVic SPet SPhx SPlb SPoG SWal SWvt WBrk WFar WHil WPer WWeb
	- Blue Queen	see *S.* x *sylvestris* 'Blaukönigin'
	- 'Lye End'	ECtt ERou MRav NCGa NDov
§	- 'Mainacht' ♀H4	More than 30 suppliers
	- May Night	see *S.* x *sylvestris* 'Mainacht'
	- 'Negrito'	EBee EGle EWll NDov
	- 'Rhapsody in Blue'[PBR]	EAro EBee EMil ERou LBuc LRHS NDov NLar WCot
	- 'Rose Queen'	EBee ECha ECtt ELan EPfP ERou EShb GMaP IBal LCro LHop LRHS MSte MWgw NDov NOrc SCoo SHBN SPer SPet SPhx SPoG SWal SWvt WPer WWeb
	- 'Rügen'	EBee EGle EPyc IBal MBri
	- 'Schneehügel'	EBee ECha EGle ELan ELon EPPr EPfP GMaP LAst LBMP LRHS MBNS MBri MWgw NBre NCob NMoo NPri NPro SPer WCAu WMnd
	- 'Tänzerin' ♀H4	EBee ELon EPyc NDov SDys WCot
	- 'Viola Klose'	CPrp CWGN EBee EBrs ECha EGle EShb LCro LHop LRHS LSRN MBri MCot NCGa NLar SMrm WCAu
	tachiei hort.	see *S. forsskaolii*
	'Tammy'	SPin
	taraxacifolia	SDys SPin WOut
	tesquicola	see *S. nemorosa* subsp. *tesquicola*
	tiliifolia	CArn EAro EUnu MGol SHFr SPav SPin SRms
	tingitana	SDys SPin WOut
	tomentosa	CPle EUnu MGol SPin
	transcaucasica	see *S. staminea*
	transsylvanica	CArn CBgR CPle EPPr LDai LRHS MGol MWgw SDnm SPav SPhx SPin STes SWat WCAu WMnd WPer XPep
	- 'Blue Spire'	CPrp EBee ECtt MBri MCot MWrn SPav SPur
	'Trebah Lilac White'	see *S.* x *jamensis* 'Trebah'
§	'Trelawney'	EPyc LRHS MHar MSte SDys SPav SPin SRot
§	'Trelissick'	ECre EPyc LAst LHop LRHS MHom MSte SDys SPav SPin SRot WWlt
§	'Trewithen'	CPom ECre EPyc LAst LRHS MSte SPav SPin SRot
	trijuga	SPin
	triloba	see *S. fruticosa*
	tubifera	SPin
§	***tubiflora*** ♀H1+3	CSpe EPyc SPin
	uliginosa ♀H3-4	More than 30 suppliers
	- 'African Skies'	CChe MNrw SPin WDyG
	urica	CSpe MAJR SDys SPav SPin
	- short	CMdw CSpe SDys
	'Valerie' **new**	SDys
	'Van-Houttei'	see *S. splendens* 'Van-Houttei'
	'Vatican City'	see *S. sclarea* 'Vatican White'
	verbenaca	CArn MHer MSal NMir NSco SPin WOut WPer XPep
	verticillata	CArn EBee ECha EGoo EHrv LEdu LRHS MGol MWgw NSti SDys SEND SPin WCAu WPer XPep
§	- 'Alba'	CAbP CBgR CHFP CPle EBee ECtt EPPr EPfP ERou EShb LRHS MRav NGdn NSti SMer SPer SPin WCAu WPer XPep
	- subsp. ***amasiaca***	SGar
	- 'Purple Rain'	More than 30 suppliers
	- 'Smouldering Torches'	NDov SPhx
	- 'White Rain'	see *S. verticillata* 'Alba'
	villicaulis	see *S. amplexicaulis*
	villosa	SPin
§	***virgata*** Jacq.	CPle EBee SGar SPin WOut
	viridis	EWsh MGol MNHC SPhx SPin WPer
§	- var. ***comata***	CArn GSki NGHP SIde WJek
	- var. ***viridis***	SBod WHrl
	viscosa Jacq.	CPle MGol SPin WOut XPep
	wagneriana	MHar SPin
	'Waverly'	CDes CHll CPle CSpe EBee EWld MAJR MSte SDys WWlt
	xalapensis	SPin
	yunnanensis	EBee
	- BWJ 7874	WCru
	aff. ***yunnanensis***	SPin

Salvinia (*Salviniaceae*)

	auriculata	WDyG

Sambucus ✿ (*Caprifoliaceae*)

	adnata	EBee WFar
	- B&SWJ 2252	WCru
	caerulea	see *S. nigra* subsp. *caerulea*
	callicarpa	NLar
	chinensis B&SWJ 6542	WCru
	coraensis	see *S. williamsii* subsp. *coreana*
	ebulus	EBee LEdu NLar NSti SMad WDyG
	- DJHC 0107	WCru
	formosana	LEdu
	- B&SWJ 1543	WCru
§	***javanica*** B&SWJ 4047	WCru
	kamtschatica	WBVN
	miquelii	NLar SPoG
	nigra	CArn CBcs CCVT CDul CRWN EMac GPoy GWCH MHer NWea SIde WFar WMou XPep
	- 'Albomarginata'	see *S. nigra* 'Marginata'
	- 'Albovariegata' (v)	CDoC EBee LSou WMoo
*	- 'Ardwall'	CAgr
N	- 'Aurea' ♀H4	CBcs CDul CLnd CSBt CWan ECrN ELan EMac EPfP MBar MRav NWea SPer WFar WMoo WSHC
	- 'Aureomarginata' (v)	CBcs CBgR EBee ECrN ELan ENot EPfP ISea MRav NLar NPen NSti SHBN WCFE WFar
	- 'Bradet'	CAgr
	- 'Cae Rhos Lligwy'	CAgr WHer
	- subsp. ***canadensis*** 'Aurea'	CWib MBar MBlu NWea WHar
	- - 'Goldfinch'	LRHS NHol
	- - 'John's'	CAgr
	- - 'Maxima'	EPfP EWes SMad WCot
	- - 'York' (F)	CAgr
§	- subsp. ***caerulea***	CAgr EPfP SMad WSpi
	- 'Donau' **new**	CAgr
§	- 'Eva'[PBR]	More than 30 suppliers
	- 'Frances' (v)	EPPr WCot

	- 'Franzi' **new**	CAgr
	- 'Fructu Luteo'	NLar
§	- 'Gerda'^{PBR} ΨH4	More than 30 suppliers
	- 'Godshill' (F)	CAgr SDea
	- 'Haschberg' **new**	CAgr
	- 'Heterophylla'	see *S. nigra* 'Linearis'
	- 'Ina'	CAgr
	- 'Körsör' (F) **new**	NLar
	- f. ***laciniata*** ΨH4	CBgR CDul CPLG EBee ELan EPPr EPfP EPla MBlu MLLN MRav NBea NEgg NGHP NSti NWea SDix SLon SPer WCFE WCot WFar WPGP
§	- 'Linearis'	CPMA ELan EPla MRav NLar
	- 'Long Tooth'	CDul CNat
	- 'Madonna' (v)	CBgR EBee EPla LRHS LSou MGos MLLN MRav NLar SPer SPla WCot
§	- 'Marginata' (v)	CBcs CDul CPLG CWan CWib GAbr ISea MBar MHer MLLN MRav SDix SLon SPer SPoG WBod WCot WFar WHar
	- 'Marion Bull' (v)	CDul CNat
I	- 'Marmorata' **new**	NLar
I	- 'Monstrosa'	NLar SMad
	- 'Nana'	EMon
	- 'Plaque' (v)	CNat
	- 'Plena' (d)	EPla WCot
	- f. ***porphyrophylla*** 'Black Beauty'^{PBR}	see *S. nigra* 'Gerda'
	- - 'Black Lace'^{PBR}	see *S. nigra* 'Eva'
§	- - 'Guincho Purple'	CBcs CDoC CDul CTri CWib EBee ECrN ELan EPPr EPfP EWTr GAbr ISea MBar MBlu MCCP MDun MHer MRav NHol WCot WFar WMoo
	- - 'Purple Pete'	CDul CNat
	- - 'Thundercloud'	CMHG EWes LBMP MAsh MBri NChi NLar NPro WCot WFar WPat
	- 'Pulverulenta' (v)	CBgR CBow CDoC EPfP EPla LHop MLLN MRav NLar SPer WCot WFar
	- 'Purpurea'	see *S. nigra* f. *porphyrophylla* 'Guincho Purple'
	- 'Pyramidalis'	CPMA EPla MBlu NLar SMad
	- 'Sambu' (F)	CAgr
	- 'Samdal' (F)	CAgr
	- 'Samidan' (F)	CAgr
	- 'Samnor' (F)	CAgr
	- 'Sampo' (F)	CAgr
	- 'Samyl' (F)	CAgr
*	- 'Tenuifolia'	MRav
	- 'Urban Lace' **new**	CAgr
	- 'Variegata'	see *S. nigra* 'Marginata'
	- f. ***viridis***	CAgr CBgR CNat EMon
	racemosa	EPfP GWCH NWea
	- 'Aurea'	NEgg
	- 'Chedglow'	CNat
	- 'Crûg Lace'	WCru WSHC
	- 'Goldenlocks'	CRez EWes LRHS MGos MSwo NLar SPer
	- 'Plumosa Aurea'	More than 30 suppliers
	- 'Sutherland Gold' ΨH4	More than 30 suppliers
	- 'Tenuifolia'	CPMA CSWP ELan EPfP LRHS NLar WPGP
	tigranii	NLar
	wightiana	see *S. javanica*
§	***williamsii*** subsp. ***coreana***	CMCN WFar

Samolus (*Primulaceae*)

	repens	CPBP ECou

Sanchezia (*Acanthaceae*)

	nobilis misapplied	see *S. speciosa*
§	***speciosa***	CHal

Sandersonia (*Colchicaceae*)

	aurantiaca	CKob CPne EBrs ECho EPot LAma LRHS

Sanguinaria (*Papaveraceae*)

	canadensis	More than 30 suppliers
	- f. ***multiplex*** (d)	CDes CLAP EBrs ECho EMan EMon EPot ERos GEdr ITer LRHS
	- - 'Paint Creek Double' (d)	SBla
	- - 'Plena' (d) ΨH4	CAvo CBct CLyd CMea CWCL EBee ECho GCra GCrs LAma NCGa NDov NMen NRya SIng SPer SPoG WAbe WBVN WEas WFar WHil WLin WPGP WTin

Sanguisorba (*Rosaceae*)

	DJHC 535 from Korea	SMHy
§	***albiflora***	CCVN CDes CFwr CKno EBee EBla EGle ELan EMon EPPr ERou GBuc LCro MRav NDov NGdn NLar NPro WCAu WFar WPGP
	armena	EBee EBla EPPr EWes MNrw NDov SSvw WTin
	benthamiana	CHEx EBla
	'Blacksmiths Burgundy' **new**	EBla
	canadensis	CDes CKno EBee EBla ECha EMar EPPr GMaP GPoy GSki MSte MWgw NDov NVic SAga SPhx SWat WAul WCAu WCot WFar WMoo WOld WTin
*	***caucasica***	CAby EBee EWes LEdu NBre NDov SMeo SPhx
	'Chocolate Tip'	IPot NBro NDov
	hakusanensis	CDes CHar CKno EBee EBla EPPr LEdu MNrw NBir NBre NBro NChi NDov NPro SMeo WCot WFar WPGP WTin
	- B&SWJ 8709	WCru
	'John Coke'	NLar
	'Korean Snow' **new**	NDov SPhx
	magnifica	CDes CFir EWes LEdu WPGP
	- ***alba***	see *S. albiflora*
	'Major Roma' **new**	GBin
	menziesii	More than 30 suppliers
§	***minor***	CArn CHby CPrp EBee EBla ELau EUnu GAbr GPoy MBar MDun MHer MNHC NBro NGHP NMir NPri SIde SPlb WBrk WGwG WHer WMoo
	- subsp. ***muricata***	GWCH
	obtusa	More than 30 suppliers
	- var. ***albiflora***	see *S. albiflora*
	officinalis	CArn CKno CSam CWan EBee EBla EDAr EGle EHrv EPfP LEdu MHer NEgg NMir NPro SPer SPhx SWat WCAu WFar WMoo
	- CDC 262	NDov
	- CDC 282	SPhx
	- 'Arnhem'	CKno CMdw EBee EBla EGle EPPr LEdu NDov SMHy SPhx WCot WTin
	- 'False Tanna'	CWib WFar
	- 'Lemon Splash' (v)	CBow WCot
	- 'Martin's Mulberry'	EBee EWes
	- 'Pink Tanna'	CFwr CKno EBee EBla EGle EMan EMar EMon EPPr LEdu MAvo MBri MDKP MSte NBhm NBid NBre NBro NDov NGHP NSti SMHy SPhx SPoG WCot WMoo WTin
	- 'Red Thunder'	EBee IPot LCro NDov NLar
	- 'Shiro-fukurin' (v)	EMon WCot
	parviflora	see *S. tenuifolia* var. *parviflora*
	pimpinella	see *S. minor*

'Pink Brushes'	EBla NDov NLar SPhx
riishirensis new	EBee
sitchensis	see *S. stipulata*
§ ***stipulata***	EBee EGle MNrw NDov NGby
'Tanna'	More than 30 suppliers
'Tanna' seedling	EPPr
tenuifolia	CAby CBrm CEnt EBla EGle LRHS MCot MGol NDov NLar NPro SPhx WMoo
- 'Alba'	CDes CKno EBee EBla EGle EWes GBuc MDun MSte NDov NPro SAga SMHy SMad SPhx WCot WFar WOld
- - CDC	NDov
§ - var. ***parviflora***	EBee LEdu MNrw NCob NLar SMHy WPGP
- - white-flowered	EBla WTin
- 'Pink Elephant'	CDes CFwr CKno EBee EBla ECtt GBin LEdu NLar SMad WPGP WTin
- 'Purpurea'	CDes CKno EBee EBla EPPr LEdu NLar WFar WPGP
- 'Stand Up Comedian'	EBee IPot NLar
- 'White Elephant' new	EBla
'Touch of Green' new	EBla

Sanicula (*Apiaceae*)

coerulescens	NBhm WCot
europaea	EBee GPoy NSco WHer WTin

Sansevieria (*Dracaenaceae*)

trifasciata 'Golden Hahnii' (v) ♀^{H1}	MBri
- var. ***laurentii*** (v) ♀^{H1}	MBri

Santolina (*Asteraceae*)

benthamiana	EAro XPep
§ ***chamaecyparissus*** ♀^{H4}	More than 30 suppliers
- var. ***corsica***	see *S. chamaecyparissus* var. *nana*
- 'Double Lemon' (d)	CBgR EBee EPfP EWin SPla WCot WSpi
- 'Lambrook Silver'	CDoC CHar EBee EGoo EPfP LRHS MAsh SCoo SLim SPla SPoG
- 'Lemon Queen'	CArn CDoC EBee EGoo ELau EPfP LRHS MAsh MGos MHer MNHC MSwo NBir NPri SIde SPla SWat WFar WGwG WPer WSpi XPep
§ - var. ***nana*** ♀^{H4}	CPrp EBee ECha ECho ENot EPfP LRHS MAsh MBar MDun MHer MRav MSwo SPoG SRms SWat WLeb WPer XPep
- - 'Weston'	ECho
- 'Pretty Carol'	CAbP EBee ELan EMil EPfP GGar LRHS MAsh MBri NGHP SIde SMeo SPla WFar WWeb XPep
- 'Small-Ness'	CDoC EBee ECho EGoo ELan EPfP EWes GEdr LRHS MAsh MHer MSte NLAp SBla SIng SPer STre SWvt WAbe WCot WFar WPat
- subsp. ***squarrosa***	XPep
elegans	WAbe
incana	see *S. chamaecyparissus*
* ***lindavica***	XPep
'Oldfield Hybrid'	EWin WCot XPep
pectinata	see *S. rosmarinifolia* subsp. *canescens*
pinnata	CArn CSev CTri MHer WPer
§ - subsp. ***neapolitana*** ♀^{H4}	CArn CSBt CSev CWib EBee ECha ECho ECrN ELan EPfP MBri MNHC NCob NPri SDix SIde WEas WHCG WMnd WSel WTin XPep
- - cream	see *S. pinnata* subsp. *neapolitana* 'Edward Bowles'
§ - - 'Edward Bowles'	More than 30 suppliers
- - 'Sulphurea'	CArn CMea EBee ECGP ECrN EGoo EPfP EWin LRHS MAsh NCob NGHP SAga SPer SPhx WKif WPer XPep
rosmarinifolia	CArn CDoC CDul CWan EBee ECrN ELau EWTr GWCH MNHC MRav NGHP SLon SPlb SRms WSel XPep
I - 'Caerulea'	XPep
§ - subsp. ***canescens***	EPfP EWin MBri WPer
§ - subsp. ***rosmarinifolia***	CPrp CSev ECha ECrN EGoo ELan ENot EPfP LRHS MBri MHer MNHC MRav MSwo MWgw SDix SIde SPer SPoG SWvt WBrE WFar WGwG WHoo WLin WTel
- - 'Primrose Gem' ♀^{H4}	CBcs CDoC CEnt CPrp CSBt CSam CTri EBee ECha ECho ECrN ELau EMil ENor EPfP LHop LRHS MAsh MSwo MWat NCob NPri SBod SPer SPla SWvt WPer WSpi XPep
- - white-flowered	SSvw
tomentosa	see *S. pinnata* subsp. *neapolitana*
virens	see *S. rosmarinifolia* subsp. *rosmarinifolia*
viridis	see *S. rosmarinifolia* subsp. *rosmarinifolia*

Sanvitalia (*Asteraceae*)

sp.	LAst
'Aztekengold'	EWin LAst
'Cuzco Compact'	WGor
'Little Sun'	LRHS SPet
procumbens 'Aztec Gold'	NBlu
'Sunbini'PBR	CSpe NPri SVil WGor

Sapindus (*Sapindaceae*)

mukorossi	CBcs

Saponaria (*Caryophyllaceae*)

x ***boissieri***	GKev
'Bressingham' ♀^{H4}	CPBP EAlp ECho ECtt EDAr EPfP LBee LRHS NLAp NMen SBla SBod SIng SPoG WAbe WPat
caespitosa	ECho EWes WAbe
x ***lempergii*** 'Max Frei'	CAbP CSam EBee ELon EMan EPPr GBuc LRHS LSou MRav MSte NCob NDov SAga SBla SDix SHar SPhx WCot WOVN WOld WSHC XPep
lutea	GKev
ocymoides ♀^{H4}	More than 30 suppliers
- 'Alba'	ECha ECho GAbr WFar
- 'Rubra Compacta' ♀^{H4}	LRHS WAbe
- 'Snow Tip'	EBee ECho EPfP NGdn NLar SBch
- 'Splendens'	ECho XPep
officinalis	CArn CBre CHby CHrt CPbn CWan ELau EUnu GKev GPoy LEdu MHer MLHP MSal NGHP NPri SECG SIde SPlb WBrk WFar WHer WMoo WPer
- 'Alba Plena' (d)	CBre EBee EBrs ECha NLar NSti SHar WFar WHer WPer WPtf WTin
- 'Betty Arnold' (d)	CDes EBee ECtt EWes GMac WCot WFar WTin
§ - 'Dazzler' (v)	EMan EPPr EUnu NBir WHer
- 'Rosea Plena' (d)	More than 30 suppliers
- 'Rubra Plena' (d)	CBre EBee ELan EWes MLHP NBre NGHP NSti SHar WHer WTin
- 'Variegata'	see *S. officinalis* 'Dazzler'
x ***olivana*** ♀^{H4}	CPBP EAlp ECho GAbr MTho NLAp NMen SBla WAbe WPat
pamphylica	MNrw
persica new	GKev
pumila	GKev NGdn SPlb
'Rosenteppich'	SBla WLin WPat
zawadskii	see *Silene zawadskii*

Saposhnikovia (*Apiaceae*)

	divaricata	CArn MSal

Sarcocapnos (*Papaveraceae*)

	enneaphylla	GKev LSRN

Sarcococca ✿ (*Buxaceae*)

	confusa ♀H4	More than 30 suppliers
	hookeriana ♀H4	CTrG ECot EPfP GSki IFoB LAst LSRN MDun NPri WFar WPGP
	- B&SWJ 2585	WCru
	- HWJK 2393	WCru
	- Sch 1160	CGHE
	- Sch 2396	EPla
	- var. ***digyna*** ♀H4	More than 30 suppliers
	- - 'Purple Stem'	CHar CTri EPfP EPla ERas MGos MRav NBPN NLar SCoo SPoG WCru
I	- - 'Schillingii'	MAsh SPoG
	- var. ***hookeriana***	CPMA
	- - GWJ 9369	WCru
	- var. ***humilis***	More than 30 suppliers
	orientalis	CAbP CMCN CPMA ELan EPfP EPla LBuc LRHS MAsh MGos SKHP SLon SPla SPoG SSpi WFar WPGP WSpi
	'Roy Lancaster'	see *S. ruscifolia* 'Dragon Gate'
	ruscifolia	CBcs CBgR CDul CMCN CPMA CSBt EBee ECrN ELan ENot EPfP EPla LRHS MAsh MGos MRav NPri SLim SLon SMac SPer SPoG SRms SSpi WCru WFar
	- var. ***chinensis*** ♀H4	CPMA CSam EPfP EPla SLon WCru WFar WGwG WPGP
	- - L 713	EPla
§	- 'Dragon Gate'	CDoC CGHE CPMA ELan EPfP EPla LRHS LTwo MAsh SKHP SPoG SReu SSta WCot WPGP WPat
	saligna	CBcs CPMA EPfP NLar SLon WCru
	vagans B&SWJ 7285	WCru
	wallichii	CGHE SKHP WPGP
	- B&SWJ 2291	WCru
	- GWJ 9427	WCru

Sarcopoterium (*Rosaceae*)

	spinosum	XPep

Sarcostemma (*Asclepiadaceae*)

	viminale	EShb

Sarmienta (*Gesneriaceae*)

	repens ♀H2	CGHE SKHP WAbe WCru WPGP

Sarothamnus see *Cytisus*

Sarracenia ✿ (*Sarraceniaceae*)

	alata	CFwr CSWC MCCP SHmp WSSs
	- 'Black Tube'	WSSs
	- heavily-veined	SHmp WSSs
	- pubescent	CSWC WSSs
	- 'Red Lid'	CSWC WSSs
	- wavy lid	SHmp WSSs
	- white-flowered	WSSs
	alata* x *flava var. ***maxima***	CSWC
	x ***areolata***	CSWC WSSs
	x ***catesbyi*** ♀H1	CSWC SHmp WSSs
	'Dixie Lace'	CSWC
	x ***excellens*** ♀H1	CSWC WSSs
	x ***exornata***	CSWC
	flava ♀H1	CFwr CSWC MCCP WSSs
	- all green giant	see *S. flava* var. *maxima*
	- var. ***atropurpurea***	WSSs
	- 'Burgundy'	MYeo WSSs
	- var. ***cuprea***	WSSs
	- var. ***flava***	WSSs
§	- var. ***maxima***	CSWC WNor WSSs
	- var. ***ornata***	CSWC SHmp WSSs
	- var. ***rubricorpora***	SHmp WSSs
	- var. ***rugelii***	MYeo SHmp WSSs
	- veinless	CSWC
	x ***harperi***	CSWC
	'Juthatip Soper' **new**	SHmp WSSs
	'Ladies in Waiting'	CSWC
	leucophylla ♀H1	CFwr CSWC SHmp WSSs
	- green	WSSs
	- pubescent	WSSs
	- 'Schnell's Ghost'	WSSs
	leucophylla* x *oreophila	CSWC
	'Lynda Butt'	SHmp WSSs
	x ***miniata***	SHmp
	minor	CSWC SHmp WSSs
§	- 'Okee Giant'	CHew CSWC MYeo WSSs
	- 'Okefenokee Giant'	see *S. minor* 'Okee Giant'
	minor* x *oreophila	CSWC
	x ***mitchelliana*** ♀H1	CFwr WSSs
	x ***moorei***	WSSs
	- 'Brook's Hybrid'	CHew CSWC WSSs
	oreophila	CSWC MYeo SHmp WSSs
	oreophila* x *purpurea subsp. ***venosa***	CSWC
	x ***popei***	CSWC
	psittacina	CSWC SHmp WSSs
*	- f. ***heterophylla***	CSWC MYeo
	purpurea	NWCA
	- subsp. ***purpurea***	CFwr CSWC MCCP SHmp WSSs
	- - f. ***heterophylla***	CSWC MYeo WSSs
	- subsp. ***venosa***	CSWC SHmp WSSs
	- - var. ***burkii***	CSWC WSSs
	x ***readii***	SHmp WSSs
	- 'Farnhamii'	CSWC
	x ***rehderi***	SHmp
	rubra	CSWC WSSs
	- subsp. ***alabamensis***	CSWC SHmp WSSs
	- subsp. ***gulfensis***	CSWC SHmp WSSs
*	- - f. ***heterophylla***	CSWC WSSs
	- subsp. ***jonesii***	CSWC WSSs
*	- - f. ***heterophylla***	CSWC WSSs
	- subsp. ***rubra***	CSWC WSSs
	- subsp. ***wherryi***	CSWC WSSs
	- - giant	WSSs
	- - yellow-flowered	CSWC WSSs

Saruma (*Aristolochiaceae*)

	henryi	CAby CDes CExc CHHB CLAP CMdw CPom EBee LFur LSou SBla WCot WCru WPGP WSHC

Sasa ✿ (*Poaceae*)

	chrysantha misapplied	see *Pleioblastus chino*
	disticha 'Mirrezuzume'	see *Pleioblastus pygmaeus* 'Mirrezuzume'
	glabra f. ***albostriata***	see *Sasaella masamuneana* 'Albostriata'
	kagamiana	NLar
	kurilensis	CMCo EBee EPla EWTr LPal MWht NMoo SDry WFar XIsg
§	- 'Shima-shimofuri' (v)	EPPr EPfP EPla ERod MMoz MWht SDry
	- 'Shimofuri'	see *S. kurilensis* 'Shima-shimofuri'
	- short	EPla
	megalophylla 'Nobilis'	see *S. senanensis* f. *nobilis*
	nana	see *S. veitchii* f. *minor*
	nipponica	SDry
	- 'Aureostriata'	SDry
	oshidensis	EPla
§	***palmata***	CAbb CBcs CDul COld CTrG CWib EBee LCro MCCP MMuc SEND WFar WHer WPnP

- f. ***nebulosa***	CBcs CBct CDoC CFir CHEx EBee EFul EHul ENBC ENot EPfP EPla EWes MBrN MMoz MWht NMoo SAPC SArc SDry WDyG WFar WMoo WPnP
- 'Warley Place' (v)	SDry
quelpaertensis	EPla MWht SDry
senanensis	SDry
§ - f. ***nobilis***	SDry
tessellata	see *Indocalamus tessellatus*
tsuboiana	CBcs CDoC EBee ENBC EPla GQui LPal MMoz MNHC MWht NGdn NLar SDry WDyG WFar WMoo
§ ***veitchii***	CAbb CBcs CKno CPLG CTrC CTrG EBee ECha ENBC ENot EPfP EPla LEdu MMoz MPRe MWgw NMoo SDry SPer SPla WBor WFar WMoo
§ - f. ***minor***	MCCP MMoz WMoo

Sasaella (*Poaceae*)

bitchuensis hort.	SDry
glabra	see *S. masamuneana*
§ ***masamuneana***	CDul ENBC EPla
§ - 'Albostriata' (v)	CDoC CMCo CWib EBee ENBC EPPr EPla ERod GAbr LEdu LPal MBar MCCP MMoz MWgw MWht NGdn NMoo SDry WDyG WFar WMoo WPGP
- f. ***aureostriata*** (v)	EPla MMoz NPal SDry
§ ***ramosa***	CHEx CTca EPla LEdu MCCP MMoz MWht NMoo SDry

Sassafras (*Lauraceae*)

albidum	CArn CBcs CCCN CMCN CTho EBee EPfP LEdu LRHS MBri SKHP SSpi WPGP
tzumu	CGHE EBee WPGP

satsuma see *Citrus unshiu*

Satureja ✿ (*Lamiaceae*)

amani	XPep
coerulea ♀H4	CWan ECho EWes NBir NLAp
douglasii	CArn EOHP SHDw WJek
- 'Indian Mint'PBR	MHer MNHC NGHP
hortensis	CBod GPoy ILis MHer MLan MNHC SIde WJek WSel
- 'Selektion'	LLWP
montana	CArn CHby CPrp CWan ECho ELau EUnu GPoy ILis LLWP MBri MHer MNHC NMen SDix SHGN SIde SRms WHer WPer XPep
* - ***citriodora***	GPoy MHer WJek XPep
§ - subsp. ***illyrica***	GEdr WJek WPer
- 'Purple Mountain'	GPoy LLWP MHer
- ***subspicata***	see *S. montana* subsp. *illyrica*
parnassica	LLWP WPer
repanda	see *S. spicigera*
§ ***spicigera***	CArn CBod CPBP CPrp ECho ELau EPot GEdr LEdu LFol LLWP MHer NBir NMen SHGN SIde WJek WSel
thymbra	CArn EOHP SHDw XPep
§ ***viminea***	EOHP

Saurauia (*Actinidiaceae*)

subspinosa	CHEx

Sauromatum (*Araceae*)

guttatum	see *S. venosum*
§ ***venosum***	CHEx CKob CMea EAmu EBee EBrs ECho EShb ITer LAma LEdu LFur LRHS WCot WCru WPGP WRos

Saururus (*Saururaceae*)

cernuus	CBen CDWL CHEx CWat EHon ELan EMFW EPfP SRms SWat WMAq WPnP

Saussurea (*Asteraceae*)

albescens	EBee EMan WCot
obvallata HWJK 2272	WCru
uniflora GWJ 9269	WCru

savory, summer see *Satureja hortensis*

savory, winter see *Satureja montana*

Saxegothaea (*Podocarpaceae*)

conspicua	CDoC ECou IDee WCwm

Saxifraga ✿ (*Saxifragaceae*)

McB 1377	CLyd
McB 1397 from Nepal	CLyd
SEP 22	CLyd
SEP 45	CLyd
'Ada' (x *petraschii*) (7)	NMen
'Aemula' (x *borisii*) (7)	NMen
§ 'Afrodite' (*sempervivum*) (7)	CLyd
aizoides (9)	ECho GKev
- var. ***atrorubens*** (9)	ECho
aizoon	see *S. paniculata*
'Aladdin' (x *borisii*) (7)	NMen
'Alan Hayhurst' (8)	SBla WAbe WFar
'Alan Martin' (x *boydilacina*) (7)	CLyd ECho EPot MHer NMen
'Alba' (x *apiculata*) (7)	ECho EDAr EPot LFox LRHS MHer NLAp NMen NRya SBla SPlb WAbe WPat
'Alba' (x *arco-valleyi*)	see *S.* 'Ophelia'
'Alba' (*oppositifolia*) (7)	CLyd ECho ELan EWes ITim NDlv NLAp NWCA WAbe
'Albert Einstein' (x *apiculata*) (7)	NMen
'Albertii' (*callosa*)	see *S.* 'Albida'
§ 'Albida' (*callosa*) (8)	ECho WAbe
'Aldebaran' (x *borisii*) (7)	NMen
'Aldo Bacci' (Milford Group) (7)	NMen
'Alfons Mucha' (7)	CLyd EPot NMen WAbe
'Allendale Acclaim' (x *lismorensis*) (7)	NDlv NMen
'Allendale Accord' (*diapensioides* x *lilacina*) (7)	NDlv NMen
'Allendale Allure' (7)	NMen
'Allendale Amber' (7)	NMen
'Allendale Andante' (x *arco-valleyi*) (7)	CLyd NMen
'Allendale Angel' (x *kepleri*) (7)	CLyd NMen
'Allendale Argonaut' (7)	CLyd NDlv NMen WAbe
'Allendale Ballad' (7)	NMen
'Allendale Ballet' (7)	CLyd NMen
'Allendale Bamby' (x *lismorensis*) (7)	NMen
'Allendale Banshee' (7)	CLyd NMen
'Allendale Beau' (x *lismorensis*) (7)	NMen
'Allendale Beauty' (7)	CLyd NMen
'Allendale Betty' (x *lismorensis*) (7)	CLyd NMen
'Allendale Billows' (7)	NMen
'Allendale Blossom' (x *limorensis*) (7)	CLyd NMen
'Allendale Bonny' (7)	EPot GCrs NMen WAbe

'Allendale Boon' (x *izari*) (7)	NMen
'Allendale Bounty' (7)	CLyd NMen
'Allendale Bravo' (x *lismorensis*) (7)	CLyd NMen WAbe
'Allendale Cabal' (7)	CLyd NMen
'Allendale Celt' (x *novacastelensis*) (7)	CLyd NMen
'Allendale Charm'	see *S.* (Swing Group) 'Allendale Charm'
'Allendale Chick' (7)	EPot GCrs NMen
'Allendale Comet' (7)	GCrs NMen
'Allendale Dance' (7)	NMen
'Allendale Divine' (7) **new**	WAbe
'Allendale Dream' (7)	EPot NMen
'Allendale Duo' (7)	NMen
'Allendale Elegance' (7)	CLyd NMen
'Allendale Elf' (7)	CLyd NMen
'Allendale Elite' (7)	CLyd NMen
'Allendale Enchantment' (7)	NMen
'Allendale Envoy' (7)	EPot NMen
'Allendale Epic' (7)	NMen
'Allendale Fairy' (7)	NMen
'Allendale Fame' (7)	NMen
'Allendale Frost' (7)	NMen
'Allendale Garnet' (7)	CLyd NDlv NMen
'Allendale Ghost' (7)	NMen
'Allendale Goblin' (7)	NMen NWCA WAbe
'Allendale Grace' (7)	CLyd NMen WAbe
'Allendale Gremlin' (7)	NMen
'Allendale Harvest' (7)	NMen
'Allendale Hobbit' (7)	EPot NMen
'Allendale Host' (7)	NMen
'Allendale Ina' (7) **new**	NMen
'Allendale Joy' (x *wendelacina*) (7)	NMen
'Allendale Pearl' (x *novacastelensis*) (7)	CLyd NMen
'Allendale Ruby' (7)	CLyd NMen
'Allendale Snow' (x *rayei*) (7)	NMen
'Alpenglow' (7)	NMen
alpigena (7)	CLyd WAbe
'Amitie' (x *gloriana*) (7)	CFee NMen
andersonii (7)	CLyd GCrs NDlv NMen NRya
'Andrea Cesalpino' (Renaissance Group) (7) **new**	WAbe
x ***andrewsii*** (8x11)	MTho
angustifolia Haw.	see *S. hypnoides*
'Anna' (x *fontanae*) (7)	NMen
'Anne Beddall' (x *goringiana*) (7)	CLyd NMen WAbe
'Antonio Vivaldi' (7)	NMen WAbe
'Aphrodite' (*sempervivum*)	see *S.* 'Afrodite'
x ***apiculata*** *sensu stricto* hort.	see *S.* 'Gregor Mendel'
'Apple Blossom' (15)	ECtt NPro NRya SPoG WGor WHoo
'Arabella' (x *edithae*) (7) **new**	ECho
'Archdale' (*paniculata*) (8)	EAlp
'Archfield White' (*callosa*) (8)	CStu
§ 'Arco' (x *arco-valleyi*) (7)	NMen
x ***arco-valleyi*** *sensu stricto* hort.	see *S.* 'Arco'
x ***arendsii*** pink-flowered (15)	NBlu
- purple-flowered (15)	NBlu NNor
§ 'Aretiastrum' (x *boydii*) (7)	CLyd LFox NDlv NMen
aretioides (7)	NMen
'Ariel' (x *hornibrookii*) (7)	CLyd LFox NMen
'Arthur' (x *anglica*) (7)	NMen
'Assimilis' (x *petraschii*) (7)	CLyd NMen WAbe
'August Hayek' (x *leyboldii*) (7)	NMen
'Aurea Maculata' (*cuneifolia*)	see *S.* 'Aureopunctata'
§ 'Aureopunctata' (x *urbium*) (11/v)	CTri ECha ECho EMan GAbr GBuc MHer MRav MWgw NHol SPer SPlb SPoG SRms WMoo WPtf
'Autumn Tribute' (*fortunei*) (5)	CLAP WAbe WFar
'Balcana' (*paniculata*) (8)	EPot WAbe
'Baldensis'	see *S. paniculata* var. *minutifolia*
'Ballawley Guardsman' (15)	LFox SIng
'Balkan' (*marginata*) (7)	CLyd
'Barford' (*poluanglica*) (7) **new**	WAbe
§ 'Beatrix Stanley' (x *anglica*) (7)	CLyd LFox MHer NDlv NHol NLAp NMen NRya WGor
'Becky Foster' (x *borisii*) (7)	NMen
'Bellisant' (x *hornibrookii*) (7)	CLyd NMen
'Benimizu'	IPot
'Berenika' (x *bertolonii*) (7)	NMen
'Beryl' (x *anglica*) (7)	NMen
'Bettina' (x *paulinae*) (7)	NMen
x ***biasolettoi*** *sensu stricto* hort	see *S.* 'Phoenix'
x ***bilekii*** (7)	CLyd ECho NMen
'Birch Baby' (15)	SIng
'Birch Yellow'	see *S.* 'Pseudoborisii'
'Black Beauty' (15)	CWCL MHer NHol SIng
'Black Ruby' (*fortunei*) (5)	More than 30 suppliers
'Blackberry and Apple Pie' (*fortunei*) (5)	CBct CBod CElw CLAP EBee ECtt GEdr IBal MBrN MLHP MNrw MSte NBro NEgg NHol NMen NPri SWvt WAul WBor WCot WFar WWeb
'Blaník' (x *borisii*) (7)	CLyd NMen
'Blanka' (x *borisii*) (7)	NMen
(Blues Group) 'Louis Armstrong' (7)	CPBP EPot WAbe
'Bob Hawkins' (15/v)	CLyd EAlp EDAr LFox NHol
§ 'Bodensee' (x *hofmannii*) (7)	NDlv WPat
'Bohdalec' (x *megaseiflora*) (7)	NMen
'Bohemia' (7)	CLyd CStu ECho EPot ITim NMen NSla SBla WAbe
x ***borisii*** *sensu stricto* hort.	see *S.* 'Sofia'
'Bornmuelleri' (7)	NMen
'Boston Spa' (x *elisabethae*) (7)	CLyd ECho LRHS MHer NDlv NLAp NMen SPlb WPat
'Brailes' (x *poluanglica*) (7)	CLyd ITim NMen
'Bridget' (x *edithae*) (7)	CLyd CMea ECho LFox LRHS NDlv NMen SIng WAbe
'Brno' (x *elisabethae*) (7)	EPot NMen
bronchialis (10)	CLyd
'Brookside' (*burseriana*) (7)	EPot NMen
brunoniana	see *S. brunonis*
§ ***brunonis*** (1)	LFox WCru
- CC&McK 108	NWCA
bryoides (10)	CLyd ECho GCrs NRya NWCA
'Buckland' (*fortunei*) **new**	CWsd
x ***burnatii*** (8)	CLyd LFox LRHS NDlv NMen NPro WGor
burseriana (7)	ECho NLAp WAbe WGor
'Buster' (x *hardingii*) (7)	NMen
'Buttercup' (x *kayei*) (7)	CLyd NLAp NMen NWCA WHoo
x ***byam-groundsii*** (7)	CLyd
caesia misapplied (x *fritschiana*)	see *S.* 'Krain'
caesia L. (8)	SRms
§ ***callosa*** (8) ♀H4	ECho EDAr GEdr MDKP MHer MLHP MWat NHol NLAp SBla WEas WFar WPat WTin

- subsp. ***callosa*** (8)	ECho
§ - - var. ***australis*** (8)	EPot GCrs NBro NHol NMen WAbe
- var. ***lantoscana***	see *S. callosa* subsp. *callosa* var. *australis*
- ***lingulata***	see *S. callosa*
- 'Wartosque'	EPot
callosa* x *cochlearis	see *S.* Silver Farreri Group
'Cambridge Seedling' (7)	NDlv NMen
'Camyra' (7)	WAbe
§ 'Canis-dalmatica' (x *gaudinii*) (8) ♀H4	CLyd CSsd ECho ECtt EGoo EPot GGar LRHS NDlv NHol NMen NWCA WGor WPer
§ 'Carmen' (x *elisabethae*) (7)	NDlv NLAp NMen WAbe
§ 'Carniolica' (*paniculata*) (8)	CLyd EPot LFox MBar NBro NHol NMen NWCA SBla
'Carniolica' (x *pectinata*) (8)	WAbe
carolinica	see *S.* 'Carniolica' (*paniculata*)
'Castor' (x *bilekii*) (7)	NMen
'Caterhamensis' (*cotyledon*) (8)	NHar
'Cathy Reed' (x *polulacina*) (7)	NMen
caucasica (7)	ECho
cebennensis (15) ♀H2	CLyd EPot LFox NMen NRya
- dwarf (15)	WAbe
cespitosa (15)	WAbe
'Chambers' Pink Pride'	see *S.* 'Miss Chambers'
'Charlecote' (x *poluanglica*) (7)	CLyd CStu ITim
'Charles Chaplin' (7)	CLyd CPBP ECho NHar NMen WAbe
'Cheap Confections' (*fortunei*) (4)	CBct CBod CElw CHEx CLAP CMMP CSpe EBee ECtt EWll GAbr GEdr LTwo MSte NEgg NHol NMen SPla WBor WCot WFar WHil WOld WPGP
§ ***cherlerioides*** (10)	ECtt NEgg NRya NVic WFar
'Cherry Pie' (*fortunei*) (5)	CBct CLAP GAbr LHop LTwo MNrw NBir NCGa NEgg NHar NMyG WCot WGwG
'Cherrytrees' (x *boydii*) (7)	NMen WAbe
'Chetwynd' (*marginata*) (7)	CLyd NMen WAbe
'Chez Nous' (x *gloriana*) (7/v)	CLyd NMen
'Chodov' (7)	NMen
'Christine' (x *anglica*) (7)	CLyd ECho LFox NDlv NHol NLAp NMen
cinerea (7)	GCrs NMen WAbe
'Cio-Cio-San' (Vanessa Group) (7)	NMen
'Citronella' (7)	ECho WAbe
'Claire Felstead' (*cinerea* x *poluniniana*) (7)	GCrs NMen
'Clare' (x *anglica*) (7)	NMen
'Clare Island' (15)	SIng
§ 'Clarence Elliott' (*umbrosa*) (11) ♀H4	CLyd CMea CTri EAlp EBee ECho EWes GKev MDKP MHar MHer NHol NRya NVic WFar WHoo WPat
'Claudia' (x *borisii*) (7)	NMen
'Cleo' (x *boydii*) (7)	NMen
§ x ***clibranii*** hort. (15)	SIng
'Cloth of Gold' (*exarata* subsp. *moschata*) (15)	CLyd CWCL EAlp ECha ECho ECtt EDAr ELan GMaP LAst LRHS MBar MHer NHol NMen NRya SIng SPer SPlb SPoG SRms WAbe WBVN WFar
cochlearis (8)	CTri GEdr LBee LRHS MWat NBro NDlv NMen WAbe WPer
'Cockscomb' (*paniculata*) (8)	EAlp ECho EPot NHol NMen NRya WAbe
columnaris (7)	NMen WAbe
columnaris* x *dinnikii	NMen NSla

'Combrook' (x *poluanglica*) (7)	CLyd NMen
'Coningsby Queen' (x *hornibrookii*) (7) **new**	NMen
continentalis (15)	NWCA
'Conwy Snow' (*fortunei*) (5)	CLAP WAbe WFar
'Conwy Star' (*fortunei*) (5)	CLAP WAbe WFar
'Coolock Gem' (7)	CLyd NMen
'Coolock Kate'	CLyd CStu NMen WAbe
'Cordata' (*burseriana*) (7)	NMen
'Corona' (x *boydii*) (7)	LFox NMen
'Correnie Claret' (15)	EWes
'Correvoniana' (*paniculata*) (8) **new**	EDAr WFar
'Corrie Fee' (*oppositifolia*) (7)	GCrs
cortusifolia (5)	CLAP EBee ECho
- B&SWJ 5879	WCru
- var. ***fortunei***	see *S. fortunei*
- var. ***stolonifera*** (5)	ECho
- - B&SWJ 6205	WCru
'Cotton Crochet' (*fortunei*) (5/d)	CBct EBee EMan GEdr GSki LAst MBNS MLLN NMyG WCot WFar WOld
cotyledon (8)	ECho GCrs NHol WEas WPer
§ 'Cranbourne' (x *anglica*) (7) ♀H4	CLyd CMea CStu ECho EPot GCrs ITim LFox LRHS NHol NLAp NMen SBla WPat
'Cream' (*paniculata*) (8)	ECho
'Cream Seedling' (x *elisabethae*) (7)	ECho NDlv NLAp NMen
'Crenata' (*burseriana*) (7)	CLyd EPot GCrs LFox LRHS NDlv NMen WAbe WHoo
'Crimscote-Love' (*poluanglica*) (7) **new**	WAbe
'Crimson Rose' (*paniculata*)	see *S.* 'Rosea' (*paniculata*)
§ ***crustata*** (8)	EAlp ECho MDKP NMen SIng WThu
- var. ***vochinensis***	see *S. crustata*
'Crystal Pink' (*fortunei*) (5/v)	CBct CMil EBee EHrv GAbr GEdr GKev LAst LHop MNrw NBro NHar NMen NMyG WBor WCot WFar WGwG WOld
'Crystalie' (x *biasolettoi*) (7)	EPot LRHS NDlv NMen NRya WPat
'Cultrata' (*paniculata*) (8)	NBro
'Cumulus' (*iranica* hybrid) (7) ♀H4	CLyd EDAr GCrs GKev NMen SBla WAbe
§ ***cuneifolia*** (11)	ECho GGar LBee LRHS MHer MWat NDlv NSti NWCA WFar WPer WRos
- var. ***capillipes***	see *S. cuneifolia* subsp. *cuneifolia*
§ - subsp. ***cuneifolia*** (11)	ECtt
* - var. ***subintegra*** (11)	ECho
'Cuscutiformis' (*stolonifera*) (5)	CAby CElw CHid CPLG EBee EBla EWld SBch SBla SIng SRms WAbe WCru WPGP
cymbalaria (2)	EBur SIng
'Cyril Mortimor Pritchard' (x *hardingii*) (7)	CLyd
dahurica	see *S. cuneifolia*
'Dainty Dame' (x *arco-valleyi*) (7)	CLyd GCrs LFox NDlv NMen
'Dana' (x *megaseiflora*) (7)	CLyd NHol NMen
'Dartington Double' (15/d)	EWes NHol WFar
'Dartington Double White' (15/d)	NHol
'David' (7)	EPot NMen WAbe
'Dawn Frost' (7)	CLyd EAlp EPot NDlv NLAp NMen SBla WAbe
'Delia' (x *hornibrookii*) (7)	CLyd EPot NMen
§ 'Denisa' (x *pseudokotschyi*) (7)	NMen

	Name	Suppliers
	densa	see *S. cherlerioides*
	'Densa' (*hypnoides*) (15) **new**	EAlp
	'Dentata' (x *geum*)	see *S.* 'Dentata' (x *polita*)
§	'Dentata' (x *polita*) (11)	CMea CSpe ECha ECho GGar NVic WMoo
	'Dentata' (x *urbium*)	see *S.* 'Dentata' (x *polita*)
	desoulavyi (7)	GCrs NMen
	diapensioides (7)	CLyd WAbe
	dinnikii	NMen WAbe
	'Dobruska' (x *irvingii*) (7)	NMen
	'Doctor Clay' (*paniculata*) (8)	EPot GKev NHar NMen NRya WAbe
	'Doctor Ramsey' (8)	EWes GEdr LBee LRHS NBro NDlv NHol NLar NMen WAbe WGor WPnn
	'Don Giovanni' (7)	WAbe
	'Donald Mann' (15)	EWes
	'Dorothy Milne' (7)	NMen
	aff. ***doyalana*** (7)	NDlv
	'Drakula' (*ferdinandi-coburgi*) (7)	CLyd LRHS NDlv NMen SIng
	'Dubarry' (15)	EWes NRya WPnn
	'Dulcimer' (x *petraschii*) (7)	NMen
	'Duncan Lowe' (*andersonii*) (7) Υ^{H4}	CLyd GCrs
	'Dwight Ripley' (7)	LFox
	'Edgar Irmscher' (7)	CLyd LFox NDlv NMen NWCA
	'Edith' (x *edithae*) (7)	ECho LRHS SIng
	'Edward Elgar' (x *megaseiflora*) (7)	NHol NMen
	x ***elegantissima***	see *S.* x *clibranii* hort.
	'Elf' (7)	see *S.* 'Beatrix Stanley'
	'Elf' (15)	ECtt EPfP LRHS NHol NMen SIng SPoG SRms WGor
	'Eliot Hodgkin' (x *millstreamiana*) (7)	LFox NMen
	x ***elisabethae*** Sünd. (7) **new**	EDAr
	- *sensu stricto* hort.	see *S.* 'Carmen'
	'Elizabeth Sinclair' (x *elisabethae*) (7)	CLyd EAlp EPot GKev ITim NMen
	'Ellie Brinckerhoff' (x *hornibrookii*) (7)	NMen
	x ***engleri*** (8)	CLyd
§	'Ernst Heinrich' (x *heinrichii*) (7)	CLyd NMen
	'Esther' (x *burnatii*) (8)	CMea EPot GCrs GEdr GKev LRHS NHol NMen NWCA SBla SMer WAbe WPnn
§	'Eulenspiegel' (x *geuderi*) (7)	CLyd EPot NHol NMen
	'Eva Hanzliková' (x *izari*) (7)	CLyd NMen WAbe
	exarata (15)	LFox NMen WAbe
	fair maids of France	see *S.* 'Flore Pleno'
	'Fairy' (*exarata* subsp. *moschata*) (15)	ECtt ELan EPot
	'Faldonside' (x *boydii*) (7) Υ^{H4}	CLyd GCrs LFox NDlv NLAp NMen NRya WAbe WHoo WPat
	'Falstaff' (*burseriana*) (7)	CLyd LFox NDlv NHol NRya WAbe
	x ***farreri*** (15)	GEdr
§	'Faust' (x *borisii*) (7)	NMen WAbe
	'Favorit' (x *bilekii*) (7)	NMen
§	***federici-augusti*** (7)	GCrs
§	- subsp. ***grisebachii*** (7) Υ^{H2-3}	CLyd ECho NSla WAbe
	'Ferdinand' (x *hofmannii*) (7)	NMen
	ferdinandi-coburgi (7) Υ^{H4}	CLyd ECtt EPot LFox LRHS NDlv NRya NWCA WAbe WBrE
	- var. ***pravislavii***	see *S. ferdinandi-coburgi* var. *rhodopea*
	- var. ***radoslavoffii***	see *S. ferdinandi-coburgi* var. *rhodopea*
§	- var. ***rhodopea*** (7)	CLyd EPot GCrs LRHS NDlv NMen SBla SIng
	'Findling' (15)	EPot NHol NMen SPoG WAbe
	'Firebrand' (7)	NMen WAbe WLin
	'Five Color' (*fortunei*)	see *S.* 'Go-nishiki'
§	***flagellaris*** (1)	NMen WAbe
	'Flavescens' misapplied	see *S.* 'Lutea' (*paniculata*)
	x ***fleischeri*** (7)	NMen
§	'Flore Pleno' (*granulata*) (15/d)	CFir EBee EWes LFox MAvo NBir SIng WCot WFar
	'Florissa' (*oppositifolia*) (7)	CLyd
	'Flowers of Sulphur'	see *S.* 'Schwefelblüte'
	'Flush' (x *petraschii*) (7) **new**	WAbe
§	***fortunei*** (5) Υ^{H4}	CHEx CLAP ECho EWTr GMaP NBir NLAp SRms WAbe WCru WMoo
	- B&SWJ 6346	WCru
	- f. ***alpina*** (5)	CLAP
	- - from Hokkaido (5)	CLAP WCru
	- var. ***koraiensis*** B&SWJ 8688 (5)	WCru
	- var. ***obtusocuneata*** (5)	CLAP EBee ECho LTwo NMen WAbe
	- f. ***partita***	CLAP WCru
	- var. ***pilosissima*** (5) B&SWJ 8557	WCru
	- pink-flowered (5)	CLAP WAbe WFar WTMC
	- var. ***suwoensis*** (5)	CLAP
	'Foster's Gold' (x *elisabethae*) (7)	CLyd NMen WAbe
	'Four Winds' (15)	EWes SIng SPer
	'Francesco Redi' (7)	NMen WAbe
	'Francis Cade' (8)	CStu GAbr WAbe
	'Frank Sinatra' (x *poluanglica*) (7)	CLyd NMen
	'Franz Liszt' (7)	WAbe
	'Franzii' (x *paulinae*) (7)	NMen
	'Freckles' **new**	GKev
	frederici-augusti	see *S. federici-augusti*
	'Frederik Chopin' (7)	WAbe
	'Friar Tuck' (x *boydii*) (7)	NMen WAbe
	'Friesei' (x *salmonica*) (7)	CLyd EPot NMen
	x ***fritschiana***	GEdr NMen
	'Frosty' (8)	EPot
	'Fumiko' (*fortunei*) (5)	CLAP WAbe WCru
	'Funkii' (x *petraschii*) (7)	NMen
	'Gaertneri' (*mariae-theresiae*) (7)	NMen
	'Gaiety' (15)	EAlp SPoG WFar
	'Galaxie' (x *megaseiflora*) (7)	CLyd EPot LFox NDlv NMen
	'Ganymede' (*burseriana*) (7)	NMen WAbe
	'Gaydon-Love' (x *poluanglica*) (7) **new**	WAbe
	'Gelber Findling' (7)	EPot WAbe
	'Gem' (x *irvingii*) (7)	CLyd NDlv NMen WAbe
	'General Joffre' (15)	see *S.* 'Maréchal Joffre'
	'Geoff Wilson' (x *biasolettoi*)	NMen
	georgei (7)	CLyd GCrs NDlv NMen WAbe
	georgei x 'Winifred'	CLyd
	'Gertie Pritchard' (x *megaseiflora*)	see *S.* 'Mrs Gertie Prichard'
	x ***geuderi*** *sensu stricto* hort.	see *S.* 'Eulenspiegel'
§	x ***geum*** (11)	CHid MLHP MRav SIng WFar WMoo
	- Dixter form (11)	ECha SMHy
	'Gleborg' (15)	EAlp EWes SPoG
	'Gloria' (*burseriana*) (7) Υ^{H4}	CLyd LFox LRHS NMen NSla SBla SIng WPat
	'Gloriana'	see *S.* 'Godiva'
	'Gloriosa' (x *gloriana*) (7)	see *S.* 'Godiva'

§ 'Godiva' (x *gloriana*) (7)	CLyd NMen WAbe
'Goeblii' (7)	NDlv
'Gold Dust' (x *eudoxiana*) (7)	CLyd CStu ECho GCrs LFox NLAp NMen NRya
'Golden Falls' (15/v)	EAlp EWes LAst NEgg NHol SPlb SPoG
Golden Prague (x *pragensis*)	see *S.* 'Zlatá Praha'
§ 'Go-nishiki' (*fortunei*) (5)	EBee LTwo
'Goring White' (7)	NMen WAbe
'Gothenburg' (7)	CLyd EPot NMen WAbe
'Grace' (x *arendsii*) (15/v)	see *S.* 'Seaspray'
'Grace Farwell' (x *anglica*) (7)	ECho EPot GCrs MBar NDlv NHol NMen NRya NWCA SBla WAbe WHoo
granulata (15)	CRWN ECho EDAr NSco WAbe WFar
'Gratoides' (x *grata*) (7)	NMen
§ 'Gregor Mendel' (x *apiculata*) (7) ♀H4	CLyd CMea CSam CStu ECho EPot LRHS NDlv NHol NLAp NMen SBla SRms WAbe WFar WHoo
grisebachii	see *S. federici-augusti* subsp. *grisebachii*
- subsp. ***montenegrina***	see *S. federici-augusti*
'Haagii' (x *eudoxiana*) (7)	CStu CTri ECho ELan NDlv NLAp NMen
'Harbinger' (7)	CLyd WAbe WGor WLin
'Hare Knoll Beauty' (8)	ECho GCrs ITim NHar NLAp NMen NRya WAbe
'Harlow Car' (7)	CLyd LFox NMen NSla
'Harry Marshall' (x *irvingii*) (7)	CLyd NDlv NHol NMen
'Hartside Pink' (*umbrosa*) (11)	CLyd
'Hartswood White' (15)	MWat
'Harvest Moon' (*stolonifera*) (5)	CBow CHEx EMan NCGa
'Hedwig' (x *malbyana*) (7)	NMen
x ***heinreichii*** *sensu stricto* hort.	see *S.* 'Ernst Heinrich'
'Hi-Ace' (15/v)	CLyd ECtt EDAr LFox MHer NLAp SBla SPlb SPoG
'Highdownensis' (8)	NDlv
'Hime' (*stolonifera*) (5)	WCru
'Hindhead Seedling' (x *boydii*) (7)	CLyd LRHS NDlv NMen SIng WAbe
hirsuta (11)	EBla EWld GGar WCru
'Hirsuta' (x *geum*)	see *S.* x *geum*
'Hirtella' (*paniculata*) (8)	EAlp EPot
'His Majesty' (x *irvingii*) (7)	LFox NMen WAbe
'Hocker Edge' (x *arco-valleyi*) (7)	CLyd ITim LFox NDlv NMen WAbe
'Holden Seedling' (15)	ECtt EWes
'Honington' (x *poluanglica*) (7)	ITim
x ***hornibrookii*** (7)	WPat
hostii (8)	CLyd ECho EDAr LBee LRHS NHol NLAp WTin
- subsp. ***hostii*** (8)	GEdr
- - var. ***altissima*** (8)	STre
- subsp. ***rhaetica*** (8)	GBin NBro NDlv NMen WAbe
'Hradcany'	NMen
'Hsitou Silver' (*stolonifera*) (5)	CFee EBee EPPr MDKP WCru
'Hunscote' (x *poluanglica*) (7)	NMen
hybrid JB 11	NMen
§ ***hypnoides*** (15)	WAbe
hypostoma (7)	CLyd
'Icicle' (x *elisabethae*) (7)	NMen
'Ignaz Dörfler' (x *doerfleri*) (7)	NMen WAbe
imparilis	CLAP EHrv WCru
'Ingeborg' (15)	ECha SIng
iranica (7)	CLyd CStu ITim NMen NSla
'Irene Bacci' (x *baccii*) (7)	CLyd NMen
'Iris Prichard' (x *hardingii*) (7)	CLyd EPot ITim WAbe
x ***irvingii*** (7)	ECho NDlv
- *sensu stricto* hort.	see *S.* 'Walter Irving'
'Isobel Young' (7)	WAbe
'Ivana' (x *caroliquarti*) (7)	CPBP NMen WAbe
jacquemontiana (1)	WAbe
'James' (7) **new**	NSla
'James Bremner' (15)	GMaP SIng
'Jan Neruda' (x *megaseiflora*) (7)	NMen
'Jan Palach' (x *krausii*) (7)	CMea EPot NMen
'Jason' (x *elisabethae*) (7)	NMen
'Jenkinsiae' (x *irvingii*) (7) ♀H4	CFee CLyd CStu ECho EDAr EPot GMaP LRHS NDlv NLAp NMen NRya NWCA SMer WAbe WPat
'Joachim Barrande' (x *siluris*) (7) **new**	WAbe
§ 'Johann Kellerer' (x *kellereri*) (7)	CFee EPot LFox NDlv SBla WAbe
'John Tomlinson' (*burseriana*) (7)	CLyd NMen
'Jorg' (x biasolettoi)	EPot
'Josef Čapek' (x *megaseiflora*) (7)	CLyd EPot NMen
'Josef Mánes' (x *borisii*) (7)	NMen
'Joy'	see *S.* 'Kaspar Maria Sternberg'
'Joy Bishop' (7)	SBla
'Judith Shackleton' (x *abingdonensis*) (7)	CLyd CStu EPot GCrs NDlv NMen WAbe
'Juliet'	see *S.* 'Riverslea'
§ ***juniperifolia*** (7)	CMea ECho EDAr GCrs LRHS MHer NDlv NLAp NWCA SMer SRms
'Jupiter' (x *megaseiflora*) (7)	CLyd NDlv NLAp NMen WAbe
'Kampa' (7)	CLyd NMen
§ ***karadzicensis*** (7)	NMen
'Karasin' (7)	CLyd NMen
'Karel Čapek' (x *megaseiflora*) (7)	CLyd EPot GCrs NDlv NRya NSla WAbe
'Karel Stivín' (x *editbae*) (7)	CLyd GCrs NMen
'Karlstejn' (x *borisii*) (7)	NDlv WAbe
§ 'Kaspar Maria Sternberg' (x *petraschii*) (7)	CLyd GCrs LFox NMen WPat
'Kath Dryden' (x *anglica*) (7)	ECho GKev ITim WAbe
'Kathleen Pinsent' (8) ♀H4	CLyd ECho NDlv NWCA WAbe
'Kathleen' (x *polulacina*) (7)	CLyd NLAp WAbe
'Katrin' (x borisii) (7)	WAbe
x ***kellereri*** *sensu stricto* hort.	see *S.* 'Johann Kellerer'
'Kew Gem' (x *petraschii*) (7)	ECho NMen
'Kewensis' (x *kellereri*) (7)	NDlv NMen WAbe
'Kineton' (x *poluanglica*) (7)	NMen
'King Lear' (x *bursiculata*) (7)	CLyd EPot LFox LRHS NMen SBla
'Kingscote White' (15)	SIng
'Kinki Purple' (*stolonifera*) (5)	EBee EHrv EPPr EWld GGar WCru
'Klondike' (x *boydii*) (7)	WAbe
'Knapton Pink' (15)	EDAr EPfP NPro NRya SIng WAbe WFar
'Knapton White' (15)	SIng
'Knebworth' (8)	ECho
'Koigokora' (*fortunei*) **new**	WOld
§ 'Kolbiana' (x *paulinae*) (7)	CLyd
'Kon Tiki' (7) **new**	WAbe
'Kosumosu' (*fortunei*) **new**	WOld
§ 'Krain' (x *fritschiana*) (8)	ECho EPot

'Krákatit' (x *megaseiflora*) (7) NMen
'Krasava' (x *megaseiflora*) (7) CLyd EPot ITim NMen
'Kyrillii' (x *borisii*) (7) CLyd NMen
'Labe' (x *arco-valleyi*) (7) CLyd EPot NMen SBla WAbe
'Ladislav Celakovsky' (7) NMen WAbe
'Lady Beatrix Stanley' see *S.* 'Beatrix Stanley'
'Lagraveana' (*paniculata*) (8) 🏆H4 ECtt EDAr EPot NDlv NRya WGor
x ***landaueri*** *sensu stricto* hort. see *S.* 'Leonore'
'Lantoscana Superba' (*callosa*) EPot
'Latonica' (*callosa*) (8) EPot
'Lemon Hybrid' (x *boydii*) (7) NMen
'Lemon Spires' (7) NMen
'Lenka' (x *byam-groundsii*) (7) NMen NSla WAbe
'Leo Gordon Godseff' (x *elisabethae*) (7) CStu LRHS NDlv NMen
§ 'Leonore' (x *landaueri*) (7) LRHS WAbe
'Letchworth Gem' (x *urbium*) (11) ECho NWCA
'Lidice' (7) CLyd NDlv NMen SBla WHoo
'Lilac Time' (x *youngiana*) (7) NMen WAbe
lilacina (7) CLyd CStu NMen WAbe WPat
'Limelight' (*callosa* subsp. *callosa* var. *australis*) (8) WAbe
'Lindau' (7) NMen
lingulata see *S. callosa*
'Lismore Carmine' (x *lismorensis*) (7) CLyd GCrs NDlv NMen NWCA
'Lismore Cherry' (7) CLyd
'Lismore Gem' (x *lismorensis*) (7) ECho GCrs ITim NMen
'Lismore Mist' (x *lismorensis*) (7) CLyd CPBP NMen
'Lismore Pink' (x *lismorensis*) (7) CLyd EPot GCrs NDlv NMen NWCA
* 'Little Piggy' (*epiphylla*) (5) WCru
'Lohengrin' (x *hoerhammeri*) (7) EPot NMen
'Lohmuelleri' (x *biasolettoi*) (7) GKev
'Long Acre Pink' (*fortunei*) new CLAP
longifolia (8) ECho GKev NSla WGor
Love Me see *S.* 'Miluj Mne'
'Ludmila Šubrová' (x *bertolonii*) (7) CLyd NMen
'Lusanna' (x *irvingii*) (7) CLyd
'Lutea' (*aizoon*) see *S.* 'Lutea' (*paniculata*)
'Lutea' (*diapensioides*) see *S.* 'Wilhelm Tell', 'Primulina'
'Lutea' (*marginata*) see *S.* 'Faust'
§ 'Lutea' (*paniculata*) (8) 🏆H4 ECho EDAr EPot GEdr GMaP NBro NDlv NHol
§ 'Luteola' (x *boydii*) (7) 🏆H4 NDlv
'Lužníce' (x *poluluteopurpurea*) (7) NMen
macedonica see *S. juniperifolia*
maderensis (15) new GKev
'Magdalena' (x *thomasiana*) (7) NMen
'Major' (*cochlearis*) (8) 🏆H4 LRHS WGor
'Major Lutea' see *S.* 'Luteola'
'Maly Trpaslik' (7) new WAbe
§ 'Maréchal Joffre' (15) GAbr GMaP LAst NEgg NPri
'Margaret Webster' (*trifurcata*) (15/v) MAvo
'Margarete' (x *borisii*) (7) CLyd NMen
marginata (7) CLyd LFox WAbe
- var. ***balcanica*** see *S. marginata* var. *rocheliana*
- var. ***boryi*** (7) CLyd EPot NMen
- var. ***coriophylla*** (7) EPot NMen NWCA WAbe
- var. ***karadzicensis*** see *S. karadzicensis*
§ - var. ***rocheliana*** (7) CLyd EPot NDlv NMen SAga
'Maria Callas' (x *poluanglica*) (7) CLyd WGor
'Maria Luisa' (x *salmonica*) (7) GCrs LFox NDlv NMen NWCA WAbe
'Marianna' (x *borisii*) (7) CLyd CMea CStu NDlv NMen NRya
'Marie Louise' CFee
'Maroon Beauty' (*stolonifera*) (5) EBee ECtt EMan EMar MDKP NBre WCot
'Mars' (x *elisabethae*) (7) NMen
'Marshal Joffre' (15) see *S.* 'Maréchal Joffre'
§ 'Martha' (x *semmleri*) (7) CLyd NMen
'Mary Golds' see *S.* (Spring Group) 'Mary Golds'
matta-florida (7) NMen
'May Queen' (7) NMen
x ***megaseiflora*** *sensu stricto* hort. see *S.* 'Robin Hood'
'Melrose' (x *salmonica*) (7) NMen
mertensiana (6) CLyd GEdr NBir WCru
'Meteor' (7) CStu NDlv NRya
micranthidifolia (4) CLAP EBee WPGP
'Mikuláš Koperník' (x *zenittensis*) (7) new WAbe
'Millstream' (8) NWCA
'Millstream Cream' (x *elisabethae*) (7) CLyd ECho ITim NMen
§ 'Miluj Mne' (x *poluanglica*) (7) CStu ECho LFox MHer NDlv NMen WAbe
'Minnehaha' (x *elisabethae*) (7) WAbe
'Minor' (*cochlearis*) (8) 🏆H4 EPot LFox LRHS NHol NMen NWCA SIng WGor WPat
§ 'Miss Chambers' (x *urbium*) (11) EMan WCot WMoo WPen WSHC
'Mona Lisa' (x *borisii*) (7) CLyd NMen WAbe WPat
'Monarch' (8) 🏆H4 GCrs WAbe
'Moonlight' see *S.* 'Sulphurea'
'Morava' (7) NMen
'Mossy Pink' NBlu
'Mossy Triumph' GMaP NEgg
'Mother of Pearl' (x *irvingii*) (7) CLyd ECho NDlv NLAp NMen WAbe
'Mother Queen' (x *irvingii*) (7) CLyd NLAp NMen WPat
'Mount Nachi' (*fortunei*) (5) CBct CDes CLyd CWCL CWsd EBee EBrs EPfP EWes GAbr GEdr GMaP IBal LFur LRHS MLHP MSte MWgw NBhm NBro NMen NMyG SPla SPoG WAbe WCot WFar WPGP WPer WSpi
§ 'Mrs Gertie Prichard' (x *megaseiflora*) (7) LFox NMen WAbe
'Mrs Helen Terry' (x *salmonica*) (7) CLyd EPot NDlv NMen
'Mrs Leng' (x *elisabethae*) (7) MDKP NMen
'Multipunctata' (*paniculata*) (8) CStu
mutata (9) CLyd GKev
'Myra' (x *anglica*) (7) CLyd ECho LFox NHol NMen NWCA WHoo WPat
'Myra Cambria' (x *anglica*) (7) NDlv NHol NMen WAbe
'Myriad' (7) CLyd NMen
'Nancye' (x *goringiana*) (7) CLyd EPot ITim NDlv NMen WAbe
§ ***nelsoniana*** (4) NHol
'Nimbus' (*iranica*) (7) CLyd NMen WAbe
'Niobe' (x *pulvilacina*) (7) CLyd NMen

	'Notata' (*paniculata*) (8)	NLAp
	'Nottingham Gold' (x *boydii*) (7)	CLyd EAlp EPot GCrs NMen
	'Obristii' (x *salmonica*) (7)	GCrs NDlv NMen NRya
§	***obtusa*** (7)	EPot MHer NMen
	'Ochroleuca' (x *elisabethae*) (7)	NMen WAbe
	'Odysseus' (*sancta*) (7)	NMen
	'Olymp' (*scardica*) (7)	NMen
	'Opalescent' (7)	CLyd LFox NMen
§	'Ophelia' (x *arco-valleyi*) (7)	NMen
	oppositifolia (7)	ECho MBNS MHer NLAp NSla SPlb SPoG SRms WAbe
	- 'Iceland' (7)	WAbe
	- subsp. ***oppositifolia*** var. ***latina*** (7)	CLyd ECho GCrs NLAp
	'Oriole' (x *boydii*) (7)	NMen
	'Orjen' (*paniculata* var. *orientalis*) (8)	GEdr
	'Ottone Rosai' (7)	NMen
	'Oxhill' (7)	ITim NMen
§	***paniculata*** (8)	ECho EDAr EPot GGar GKev GMaP LRHS MDKP MHer MWat NDlv NLAp NSla SPlb SRms WAbe WFar WHoo
§	- subsp. ***cartilaginea*** (8)	NHol SBla WAbe
	- subsp. ***kolenatiana***	see *S. paniculata* subsp. *cartilaginea*
§	- var. ***minutifolia***	CLyd CPBP CTri ECho LFox LRHS MBar NBro NDlv NHol NLAp NMen NRya NWCA SBla SPlb WAbe
	paradoxa (15)	EPot GEdr LRHS SBla WGor
	'Parcevalis' (x *finnisiae*) (7 x 9)	CLyd WAbe
	'Parsee' (x *margoxiana*) (7)	CStu NDlv NMen
	'Paula' (x *paulinae*) (7)	NMen
	'Peach Blossom' (7)	CLyd EPot GCrs NDlv NMen NRya
	'Peach Melba' (7)	CLyd CStu EAlp EPot NMen WAbe WLin
	'Peachy Head' new	NMen
	'Pearl Rose' (x *anglica*) (7)	LFox
	'Pearly Gates' (x *irvingii*) (7)	CLyd NDlv NMen
	'Pearly Gold' (15)	CMea NRya
	'Pearly King' (15)	GMaP MHer WAbe WFar
	x ***pectinata*** Schott, Nyman & Kotschy	see *S.* 'Krain'
*	***pedemontana*** from Mount Kasbak (15)	CLyd
	'Penelope' (x *boydilacina*) (7)	CLyd CMea CStu ECho EPot GCrs NMen WAbe WHoo WPat
	pensylvanica (4)	GCra
	'Perikles' (7)	NMen
	'Peter Burrow' (x *poluanglica*) (7) ♀H4	CLyd CPBP ECho NMen WAbe
	'Peter Pan' (15)	EAlp EDAr EPfP EPot GMaP LFox MHer NHol NMen NPro NRya SIng SPoG WFar WPnn
	'Petra' (7)	CLyd EPot NMen WAbe
	x ***petraschii*** (7)	CLyd
§	'Phoenix' (x *biasolettoi*) (7)	LRHS WAbe WThu
	'Pilatus' (x *boydii*) (7)	NMen
	'Pink Cloud' (*fortunei*) (5)	CLAP WAbe
	'Pink Haze' (*fortunei*) (5)	CLAP WAbe
	'Pink Mist' (*fortunei*) (5)	CLAP WAbe
	'Pink Pagoda' (*nipponica*) (5)	CLAP GEdr WCot WCru
	'Pink Pearl' (7)	CMea GCrs NMen
	'Pirina' (7) new	WAbe
	'Pixie' (15)	CTri ECtt NHol NMen SIng SPoG SRms
	'Pixie Alba'	see *S.* 'White Pixie'
	'Plena' (*granulata*)	see *S.* 'Flore Pleno'
	'Pollux' (x *boydii*) (7)	EPot ITim NMen
	poluanglica 'Loxley' (7)	GEdr
	poluniniana (7)	CLyd GCrs LFox WAbe
	poluniniana x 'Winifred'	CLyd ECho EPot
	'Pompadour' (15)	NPro
	'Popelka' (*marginata*) (7)	CLyd NMen
	porophylla (7)	GCrs GKev NMen
	- var. ***thessalica***	see *S. sempervivum* f. *stenophylla*
	aff. ***porophylla*** (7)	NWCA
	'Precious Piggy' (*epiphylla*)	WCru
	'Primrose Bee' (x *apiculata*) (7)	EPot ITim
	'Primrose Dame' (x *elisabethae*) (7)	ECho ITim MDKP NMen WAbe
	'Primulaize' (9 x 11)	CLyd EWin MHer NMen
	'Primulaize Salmon' (9 x 11)	MWgw NDlv NHol WHoo WPer
§	'Primulina' (x *malbyana*) (7)	LFox NMen
	'Primuloides' (*umbrosa*) (11) ♀H4	ECho EDAr LFox NMen NPri SPoG SRms SWvt WEas WFar
	'Prince Hal' (*burseriana*) (7)	CLyd EAlp ECho EDAr EPot LRHS NDlv NMen
	'Princess' (*burseriana*) (7)	CLyd EDAr LRHS NMen
	'Probynii' (*cochlearis*) (8)	EPot MWat NDlv NMen WAbe
	'Prometheus' (x *prossenii*) (7)	CLyd
	'Prospero' (x *petraschii*) (7)	NMen
	x ***prossenii*** *sensu stricto* hort.	see *S.* 'Regina'
§	'Pseudoborisii' (x *borisii*) (7)	EPot
	'Pseudofranzii' (x *paulinae*) (7)	NWCA
	x ***pseudokotschyi*** *sensu stricto* hort.	see *S.* 'Denisa'
	'Pseudopungens' (x *apiculata*) (7)	EPot
	'Pseudoscardica' (x *wehrhahnii*) (7)	NMen
	'Pseudovaldensis' (*cochlearis*) (8)	NHar WAbe
	pubescens (15)	WAbe
	- subsp. ***iratiana*** (15)	NLAp
	punctata Sternbo. (4)	see *S. nelsoniana*
	'Pungens' (x *apiculata*) (7)	NDlv NMen
	'Purple Piggy' (*epiphylla*) (5)	CFee CLAP EBee WCru
	'Purpurea' (*fortunei*)	see *S.* 'Rubrifolia'
§	'Pygmalion' (x *webrii*) (7)	CLyd WAbe WGor
	'Pyramidalis' (*cotyledon*) (8)	EPfP SRms
	'Pyrenaica' (*oppositifolia*) (7)	ECho NMen
	'Quarry Wood' (x *anglica*) (7)	CLyd NHol NMen
	'Radway' (x *poluanglica*) (7) new	WAbe
	'Rainsley Seedling' (8)	EPot GKev NBro NMen
	ramulosa (7)	NMen
	'Red Poll' (x *poluanglica*) (7)	CLyd CPBP EPot GCrs ITim NDlv NMen NRya NWCA SBla WAbe
	'Regent' new	WAbe
§	'Regina' (x *prossenii*) (7)	CLyd GCrs MHer NMen
	retusa (7)	CLyd NMen NSla WAbe
§	'Riverslea' (x *hornibrookii*) (7)	LFox LRHS NMen WAbe
§	'Robin Hood' (x *megaseiflora*) (7)	CFee CLyd CPBP EPot LFox NMen SBla WAbe WHoo WPat
	'Rokujō' (*fortunei*) (5)	CLAP EBee NLar NPro WFar WTMC
	'Romeo' (x *hornibrookii*) (7)	CLyd NMen
	rosacea (15) new	EDAr
	'Rosea' (*cortusifolia*) (5)	CLAP CWsd
§	'Rosea' (*paniculata*) (8) ♀H4	GMaP LBMP LBee NBro NDlv NHol NSla SBla SRms WFar

	'Rosea' (x *stuartii*) (7)	NDlv NMen
	'Rosemarie' (x *anglica*) (7)	CLyd ECho NMen
	'Rosenzwerg' (15)	WFar
	'Rosina Sündermann' (x *rosinae*) (7)	EPot NDlv NMen
	rotundifolia (12)	CLyd EBee MDKP
	- subsp. ***chrysospleniifolia*** var. ***rhodopea*** (12)	WCru
	'Roy Clutterbuck' (7)	NMen
	'Rubella' (x *irvingii*) (7)	CLyd
	'Rubra' (*aizoon*)	see *S.* 'Rosea' (*paniculata*)
§	'Rubrifolia' (*fortunei*) (5)	CLAP CSpe EBee ECha ECtt EMan GAbr GEdr IBal LAst MWgw NEgg NMen NMyG SAga SMad SPoG SWvt WAbe WBor WCot WCru WFar WGer WTMC
*	'Ruby Red'	NPro
	'Ruby Wedding' (*cortusifolia*) (5)	WCru
	rufescens (5)	EHrv GEdr
	- BWJ 7510	WCru
	- BWJ 7684	WCru
	'Rusalka' (x *borisii*) (7)	CLyd GCrs NMen
	'Russell Vincent Prichard' (x *irvingii*) (7)	NMen
	'Ruth Draper' (*oppositifolia*) (7)	WAbe WFar
	'Ruth McConnell' (15)	CMea
	'Sabrina' (x *fallsvillagensis*) (7)	CLyd
	'Saint John's' (8)	EBur ECho GEdr WAbe
	'Saint Kilda' (*oppositifolia*) (7)	GCrs ITim
	x ***salmonica*** sensu stricto hort.	see *S.* 'Salomonii'
§	'Salomonii' (x *salmonica*) (7)	CLyd NDlv NMen SRms
	'Samo' (x *bertolonii*) (7)	CLyd NMen
	sancta (7)	CLyd ECho LFox LRHS NMen SRms WAbe
	- subsp. ***pseudosancta*** (7)	see *S. juniperifolia*
	- - var. ***macedonica***	see *S. juniperifolia*
	'Sandpiper' (7)	NMen
	'Sanguinea Superba' (x *arendsii*) (15) ♀H4	SIng
	'Sara Sinclair' (x *arco-valleyi*) (7)	CMea
	'Šárka' (7)	NMen
	sarmentosa	see *S. stolonifera*
	'Sartorii'	see *S.* 'Pygmalion'
	'Saturn' (x *megaseiflora*) (7)	NMen WAbe
	'Sázava' (x *poluluteopurpurea*) (7)	CLyd NMen WAbe
	scardica (7)	NBro NMen
	- var. ***dalmatica***	see *S. obtusa*
	- f. ***erythrantha*** (7)	CLyd
	- subsp. ***korabensis*** (7)	GCrs
§	'Schelleri' (x *petraschii*) (7)	NMen
§	'Schwefelblüte' (15)	GMaP NPri NWCA SPoG WPat
	scleropoda (7)	EPot NMen
§	'Seaspray' (x *arendsii*) (15/v)	EWes
	'Seissera' (*burseriana*) (7)	NMen
	'Semafor' (x *megaseiflora*) (7)	NMen
	x ***semmleri*** sensu stricto hort.	see *S.* 'Martha'
	sempervivum (7)	CLyd LFox NGdn NMen NSla NWCA WLin WTin
§	- f. ***stenophylla*** (7)	ECho MHer
	sendaica (5)	CLAP EBee WCru
	- B&SWJ 7448	GEdr
§	'Silver Cushion' (15/v)	CMea CTri EDAr ELan GGar LAst LRHS MBar NBlu NPri NPro SMer SPer SPlb SPoG WAbe WFar
	'Silver Edge' (x *arco-valleyi*) (7)	NMen WAbe
§	(Silver Farreri Group) 'Snowflake' (8) ♀H4	NDlv WAbe
	'Silver Maid' (x *engleri*)	NMen
	'Silver Mound'	see *S.* 'Silver Cushion'
	'Silver Velvet' (*fortunei*)	CLAP NMyG WCot
	'Sir Douglas Haig' (15)	SIng
	'Snowcap' (*pubescens*) (15)	NDlv NWCA
	'Snowdon' (*burseriana*) (7)	NMen
	'Snowflake'	see *S.* (Silver Farreri Group) 'Snowflake'
§	'Sofia' (x *borisii*) (7)	EPot LFox NMen WFar
	'Sorrento' (*marginata*) (7)	NMen
	Southside Seedling Group ♀H4	CLyd EAlp ECho EDAr EPfP GAbr GCrs GEdr GGar GKev GMaP LHop LRHS MAvo MBar MLHP NBro NHol NMen NRya NWCA SIng SPet SPoG SRms WHoo WLin WPat WTin
	- 'Slack's Ruby Southside' ♀H4	MDKP NLAp NSla WAbe WFar
	- 'Southside Star' ♀H4	WAbe WFar
	'Spartakus' (x *apiculata*) (7)	NDlv
	spathularis (11)	CEnt EBee MHar WCot WEas
	'Speciosa' (*burseriana*) (7)	NDlv
	'Splendens' (*oppositifolia*) (7) ♀H4	ECho EPfP LFox NDlv NHol NLAp SBla SRms WAbe WPat
*	'Spotted Dog'	GEdr NHar
	'Sprite' (15)	LRHS SPoG
	spruneri (7)	NMen
	- var. ***deorum*** (7)	NMen
	'Stansfieldii' (*rosacea*) (15)	EAlp LRHS NMen SPlb WFar
§	'Stella' (x *stormonthii*) (7)	SBla
	stenophylla subsp. ***stenophylla***	see *S. flagellaris*
	stolitzkae (7)	NMen NWCA WAbe
§	***stolonifera*** (5) ♀H2	CArn CCVN CEnt CHEx CHal CSpe ECho EWTr GBin LDai MHar NBro SDix SIng SWvt WEas WFar WMoo WPnn
	'Stormonth's Variety'	see *S.* 'Stella'
	stribrnyi (7)	NMen
	- JCA 861-400	NWCA
	'Sturmiana' (*paniculata*) (8)	NMen SRms
	'Suendermannii' (x *kellereri*) (7)	NDlv SIng
	'Suendermannii Major' (x *kellereri*) (7)	CLyd LRHS NRya
	'Sugar Plum Fairy' (*fortunei*) (5)	CBcs CBct EBee EHrv EMil GSki LFur MBNS NBro NCGa SPer WCot WGwG WTMC WWlt
§	'Sulphurea' (x *boydii*) (7)	CStu LFox LRHS NMen SIng WAbe WHoo WPat
	'Sunset' (*anglica*) (7)	WThu
	'Superba' (*callosa* subsp. *callosa* var. *australis*) (8) ♀H4	GCrs
	'Swan' (x *fallsvillagensis*) (7)	NMen
§	(Swing Group) 'Allendale Charm' (7)	CLyd CPBP NMen WAbe
§	- 'Mary Golds' (7)	CLyd EDAr WGor
	'Sylva' (x *elisabethae*) (7)	NMen
	'Symons-Jeunei' (8)	WAbe
	'Tábor' (x *schottii*) (7)	NMen
	'Tamayura' (*fortunei*) (5)	LSou MBNS NCGa
	'Theoden' (*oppositifolia*) (7) ♀H4	CLyd ECho EWes GCrs NLAp NWCA SBla WAbe
	'Theresia' (x *mariae-theresiae*) (7)	NDlv NMen

	'Thorpei' (7)	NMen
	'Timmy Foster' (x *irvingii*) (7)	CLyd NHol NMen
	tombeanensis (7)	CLyd NMen
	'Tricolor' (*stolonifera*) (5) ♀H2	CBow EBak WFar
	trifurcata (15)	GGar
	'Triumph' (x *arendsii*) (15)	ECtt NEgg NPri SBla WBVN
	'Tully' (x *elisabethae*) (7)	NLAp WGor WPat
	'Tumbling Waters' (8) ♀H4	EAlp ECho EPot GAbr LHop LRHS NHol NMen NSla SIng WAbe WGor WPat
§	'Tvůj Den' (x *poluanglica*) (7)	ECho NDlv NMen WAbe
§	'Tvůj Píseň' (x *poluanglica*) (7)	CLyd ECho NDlv NMen
§	'Tvůj Polibek' (x *poluanglica*) (7)	ECho MDKP NDlv NMen SBla WAbe
§	'Tvůj Přítel' (x *poluanglica*) (7)	ECho NDlv
§	'Tvůj Úsměv' (x *poluanglica*) (7)	CLyd ECho NDlv NMen
§	'Tvůj Úspěch' (x *poluanglica*) (7)	CLyd ECho GCrs NDlv NMen SBla WAbe
	'Tycho Brahe' (x *doerfleri*) (7)	CLyd NDlv NMen WAbe
	'Tysoe' (7)	CLyd ITim NMen
	umbrosa (11)	CBrm CTri EBee ECho EDAr LRHS MRav SPer SPlb SRms SWvt WCAu WFar WHen WMoo
	- 'Aurea'	see *S.* 'Aureopunctata'
	'Unique'	see *S.* 'Bodensee'
	x ***urbium*** (11) ♀H4	CHEx CTri EBee ECho ELan EPfP LAst LEdu MWgw NSti SIng SRms WBrk WFar WPer
	- 'Elliott's Variety'	see *S.* 'Clarence Elliott'
	'Vaccariana' (*oppositifolia*) (7)	ECho NHol
	'Václav Hollar' (x *gusmusii*) (7)	NMen
	'Vahlii' (x *smithii*) (7)	NMen
	'Valborg'	see *S.* 'Cranbourne'
	'Valentine'	see *S.* 'Cranbourne'
	'Valerie Finnis'	see *S.* 'Aretiastrum'
	'Valerie Keevil' (x *anglica*) (7) **new**	NMen
I	'Variegata' (*cuneifolia*) (11/v)	ECho ECtt EPfP GGar MBar NBlu NEgg NHol NVic SHFr SPet SPlb SPoG WFar WMoo WPer WTel
	'Variegata' (*umbrosa*)	see *S.* 'Aureopunctata'
I	'Variegata' (x *urbium*) (11/v)	EBee ECho EPfP GGar LAst NLar NSti NVic SRms WEas WFar
	vayredana (15)	GCrs NWCA WAbe
	veitchiana (5)	EBee EDAr GEdr NBro
	'Vesna' (x *borisii*) (7)	CLyd NMen
	'Vincent van Gogh' (x *borisii*) (7)	CLyd NMen
	'Vladana' (x *megaseiflora*) (7)	CLyd EPot NMen SIng
	'Vlasta' (7)	CLyd NMen
	'Vltava' (7)	CLyd NMen
	'Volgeri' (x *hofmannii*) (7)	CLyd NMen
	'Vreny' (8)	GKev
	'Wada' (*fortunei*) (5)	CAbP CBct CDes CHar CLAP CSam EBee ECtt GEdr GKev LAst LFur LRHS MBri MDun MSte NBir NMyG NPri SPer WBor WCot WFar WOld WPGP WTMC WWeb
	'Wallacei' (15)	NMen
	'Walpole's Variety' (8)	CBrm WAbe WPer
	'Walter Ingwersen' (*umbrosa*) (11)	SIng SRms
§	'Walter Irving' (x *irvingii*) (7)	CLyd EPot NHol NMen WAbe
	'Walton' (7)	WAbe
	'Weisser Zwerg' (15)	WAbe
	'Wellesbourne' (x *abingdonensis*) (7)	CLyd ITim
	'Welsh Dragon' (15)	WAbe
	'Welsh Red' (15)	WAbe WFar
	'Welsh Rose' (15)	WAbe
	wendelboi (7)	CLyd LFox NMen
	'Wendrush' (x *wendelacina*) (7)	CLyd NMen WAbe
	'Wendy' (x *wendelacina*) (7)	NMen WAbe
	'Wetterhorn' (*oppositifolia*) (7)	CLyd
	'Wheatley Gem' (7) **new**	NMen
	'Wheatley Lion' (x *borisii*) (7)	NMen
	'Wheatley Rose' (7)	CLyd ITim LRHS
	'White Cap' (x *boydii*) (7)	NMen
	'White Imp' (7)	NMen
§	'White Pixie' (15)	CLyd EAlp ECtt EDAr EPfP GMaP LFox MHer NPri NPro NRya SBla SIng SPer SPlb SPoG SRms WFar
	'White Star' (x *petraschii*)	see *S.* 'Schelleri'
	'Whitehill' (8) ♀H4	CLyd CMea EAlp ECho ELan GEdr GMaP ITim LBee LFox LRHS MDKP NBro NHol NMen SPet WFar WHoo WPat WPer WTin
§	'Wilhelm Tell' (x *malbyana*) (7)	NMen
	'William Boyd' (x *boydii*) (7)	NSla WAbe
	'Winifred' (*anglica*) (7)	CLyd ECho EPot GCrs LFox NLAp NMen WAbe
	'Winifred Bevington' (8 x 11) ♀H4	CLyd EAlp ECho EDAr EPot GKev LRHS MMuc NBro NDlv NHol NLAp NMen NPri NRya SAga WAbe WFar WHoo WPer WPnn
	'Winston Churchill' (15)	CTri EPfP LRHS NHol NPri SIng
I	'Winston Churchill Variegata' (v) **new**	EAlp
	'Winton' (x *paulinae*) (7)	CLyd NMen WAbe
	'Wisley' (*federici-augusti* subsp. *grisebachii*) (7) ♀H2-3	NLAp NMen WPat
	'Wisley Primrose'	see *S.* 'Kolbiana'
	'Yellow Rock' (7)	NDlv NMen NRya
	Your Day	see *S.* 'Tvůj Den'
	Your Friend	see *S.* 'Tvůj Přítel'
	Your Good Fortune	see *S.* 'Tvůj Úspěch'
	Your Kiss	see *S.* 'Tvůj Polibek'
	Your Smile	see *S.* 'Tvůj Úsměv'
	Your Song	see *S.* 'Tvůj Píseň'
	Your Success	see *S.* 'Tvůj Úspěch'
	'Yuinagi' (*fortunei*) **new**	WOld
	x ***zimmeteri*** (8 x 11)	CLyd ECho NMen
§	'Zlatá Praha' (x *pragensis*) (7)	CLyd EPot NDlv NMen NRya WAbe
	'Zlín' (x *leyboldii*) (7)	NMen

Scabiosa (Dipsacaceae)

	africana	CElw EWes LSou
	'Agnes Whitfield'	EWin
	alpina L.	see *Cephalaria alpina*
	argentea	EBee EWes LEdu SMHy WPGP
	atropurpurea	CEnt EGoo LEdu SPav
	- 'Ace of Spades'	CSpe CWCL EBee LCro LRHS MBri MDun SMad SPav SPoG WCot WPGP WSpi
§	- 'Chile Black'	More than 30 suppliers
§	- 'Chilli Pepper'PBR	CWCL EBee EMan ENot EPfP LHop NLar NPri SAga SPoG SRGP WSpi
§	- 'Chilli Red'	SAga
§	- 'Chilli Sauce'PBR	CBcs CHar CWCL EMan ENot EPfP LCro LHop NLar NPri

	- dark-flowered	SPav
§	- subsp. ***maritima***	EBee
	- 'Nona'	LTwo
	- 'Peter Ray'	CElw ECtt SPav WWlt
	- 'Salmon Queen'	NBre
	banatica	see *S. columbaria*
	'Blue Diamonds'	CKno EBee IBal MBri WHil WSpi
	'Burgundy Bonnets'	LRHS
§	'Butterfly Blue'	EBee ECtt EPfP LCro LFur LRHS LSRN MBri MWgw NLar NMoo NRnb SCoo SHBN SMrm SPer SPla SPoG SWvt WAul WCAu WCot WFar WGwG
	caucasica	CEnt EBee EPfP LAst LEdu MGol NBlu SPhx WFar WHoo
	- var. ***alba***	CBcs CKno EHrv EPfP WFar WHal WHoo
	- 'Blausiegel'	CSam EBee LAst LBMP MWgw NBre NCGa NGdn SPet SPla SPoG
	- 'Clive Greaves' ♀H4	CHar CTri EBee ECha EHrv ELan EPfP ERou LCro LHop LRHS MBri MRav MWat NCob SPer SPet SPla SRms SWvt WAul WEas WFar WMnd WWeb
	- 'Deep Waters' new	CSpe
	- 'Fama'	CMdw CSpe CWCL CWib EBee EKen EMan EShb LCro LHop MBNS MWrn NBir NLar SPhx SPlb SPoG SRms WFar WHil WPtf
	- 'Goldingensis'	CWCL EBee GWCH MHer NBre NGdn NPri WBVN WPer
	- House's hybrids	CSBt NGdn SRms
	- 'Isaac House'	EBee NEgg NLar
	- 'Kompliment'	ENot NBre NChi NEgg NLar WHoo
	- 'Lavender Blue'	NBPC WFar WGwG
	- 'Miss Willmott' ♀H4	CMMP CSam EBee ECha ELan EPfP ERou LAst LBMP LHop LRHS MBri MHer MLHP MRav MWat MWgw NCGa NCob SPer SPet SPla SPoG SWvt WAul WCAu WFar WMnd
	- 'Moerheim Blue'	EBee ERou NGby
	- 'Nachtfalter'	EBee
	- Perfecta Series	CSpe CWib EBee LAst LRHS MMHG NGdn NLar SMrm SWat
	- - 'Perfecta Alba'	CEnt COIW CSpe CWib EBee EMan GMaP GMac LAst MWat NChi NLar NOrc NPri NRnb SHGN SMrm SPer STes SWat WHil WPtf
	- - 'Perfecta Lilac Blue'	CWib GMaP GMac NRnb STes
	- 'Stäfa'	CKno CMMP EBee ECha ERou EShb LRHS MBri MRav NCGa NLar SPla WAul WFar WMnd
	'Chile Black'	see *S. atropurpurea* 'Chile Black'
	'Chile Pepper'PBR	see *S. atropurpurea* 'Chilli Pepper'
	'Chile Red'	see *S. atropurpurea* 'Chilli Red'
	'Chile Sauce'PBR	see *S. atropurpurea* 'Chilli Sauce'
	'Chile Spice'	CHar WHlf
	cinerea	SPhx
§	***columbaria***	CBgR EBee ECGP MLLN NBre NLan NMir NSco NWCA SECG SMrm WHer WJek WSFF
	- 'Flower Power'	EBee
	- 'Misty Butterflies'	CBrm CSam EDAr ENot EShb GBri GSki NBHF NGdn NLar NMoo NVic SPad SVil
	- 'Nana'	CBrm CMdw EBee EGoo EShb GEdr GSki IBal NBir NCGa NGdn NLar NMen NPri SBch WCFE WGwG WHil
§	- subsp. ***ochroleuca***	CKno CSpe ECha EDAr EGoo EHrv EShb GMac GSki LEdu LLWP LRHS MBri MLLN MWrn NBir NChi NDov NEgg NLar NPri SMad SPhx SRms WCAu WFar WHoo WPGP WTin
	- - MESE 344	EBee
	- 'Pincushion Pink'	NBHF NGdn NPri WHil
	cretica	XPep
	drakensbergensis	CDMG EBee EKen EMan EWes LSou MTPN SPav STes WHrl WLin
	farinosa	CDes EBee ECtt LEdu LSou MHar SGar WFar WPer
	gigantea	see *Cephalaria gigantea*
	graminifolia	ECho EGoo GBuc LRHS MDKP NBir NMen NRnb NWCA SBch SRms
	- ***rosea***	EWes
	'Grand Stone' new	EBee ERou
	'Helen Dillon'	CBgR CFir EBee ECtt EMan EWes EWin LSou
	hymnettia	XPep
	'Irish Perpetual Flowering'	EMan NDov WCot
	japonica	MGol NEgg WPer
	- var. ***acutiloba***	NDov
	- var. ***alpina***	CEnt CPrp EBee GAbr GBuc GSki IBal MGol MLLN NGdn NHol SHGN SPet WAbe WHoo WTin
	lucida	EBee ECho ECtt EPfP EShb LRHS MRav NLAp NPri SBla WCAu WPGP WPer
	maritima	see *S. atropurpurea* subsp. *maritima*
	'Midnight'	CMea CSpe
	'Miss Havisham'	EBee ECtt EMan EWes LEdu LSou WPGP
	montana Mill.	see *Knautia arvensis*
	montana (Bieb.) DC.	see *Knautia tatarica*
	ochroleuca	see *S. columbaria* subsp. *ochroleuca*
	parnassi	see *Pterocephalus perennis*
	'Peggotty'	EBee ECtt EWin
	'Perpetual Flowering'	see *S.* 'Butterfly Blue'
	Pink Buttons = 'Walminipink'	CFir CKno EBee LRHS NEgg SPla
	'Pink Mist'PBR	EBee EPfP EWll LRHS MBri NBir NEgg NLar SCoo SHBN SPer SPoG SRms WCAu
	pterocephala	see *Pterocephalus perennis*
	'Rosie's Pink'	ECtt EMan SMrm
	rumelica	see *Knautia macedonica*
	'Satchmo'	see *S. atropurpurea* 'Chile Black'
	silenifolia	EBee
	succisa	see *Succisa pratensis*
	tatarica	see *Cephalaria gigantea*
	tenuis	CSpe LPio NDov SHar SPhx
	triandra	EBee LEdu LHop
	ucranica	EShb XPep

Scadoxus ✿ (*Amaryllidaceae*)

	multiflorus	EBrs LAma LRHS MBri WCot
§	- subsp. ***katherinae*** ♀H1	ECho ERea

Scaevola (*Goodeniaceae*)

	aemula 'Blue Fan'PBR	see *S. aemula* 'Blue Wonder'
§	- 'Blue Wonder'PBR	LAst LSou NPer SWvt
	- 'New Wonder'	LAst
	- 'Petite'	CHal
	- 'Zig Zag'PBR	CCCN LAst LSou NPri
	Blauer Facher = 'Saphira'PBR	CCCN EWin NBlu
	crassifolia	SPlb
	'Diamond'	LAst LSou
	'Mini Blue' new	CCCN
	'My Blue'	SVil
	saligna Blue Ice = 'Danscaice'PBR	LAst
	- Blue Yonder = 'Scabushy'	LSou SVil

Scandix (*Apiaceae*)

	pecten-veneris	MSal SECG

Sceletium (*Aizoaceae*)

	tortuosum	MGol

Schefflera (*Araliaceae*)

	actinophylla 🏆H1	SRms
	alpina B&SWJ 8247 new	WCru
	arboricola 🏆H1	CHEx SEND XBlo
	- B&SWJ 7040	WCru
	- 'Compacta'	MBri
	- 'Gold Capella' 🏆H1	LRHS MBri SEND XBlo
	- 'Trinetta'	MBri
	brevipedicellata HWJ 870 new	WCru
	chapana HWJ 982 new	WCru
	delavayi	CExc CHEx
	digitata	CHEx
§	***elegantissima*** 🏆H1	EShb SEND
	- 'Castor' new	EShb
I	- 'Castor Variegata' (v) new	EShb
	gracilis HWJ 622	WCru
	hoi var. ***fantsipanensis*** B&SWJ 8228	WCru
	impressa	CHEx
	- GWJ 9375	WCru
	kornasii HWJ 918 new	WCru
	microphylla B&SWJ 3872	WCru
	taiwaniana	CHEx
	- B&SWJ 7096	WCru

Schima (*Theaceae*)

	argentea	see *S. wallichii* subsp. *noronhae* var. *superba*
§	***wallichii*** subsp. ***noronhae*** var. ***superba***	CCCN CPLG EPfP
	- subsp. ***wallichii*** var. ***khasiana***	ISea
*	***yunnanensis***	GGGa

Schinus (*Anacardiaceae*)

	molle	IDee XPep
	polygamus	CBcs

Schisandra (*Schisandraceae*)

	TH	CHEx
	arisanensis B&SWJ 3050	WCru
	aff. ***bicolor*** BWJ 8151	WCru
	chinensis	CAgr CArn CBcs EBee EBrs GPoy LEdu MSwo WBVN WNor
	- B&SWJ 4204	WCru
	grandiflora	CDoC EBee ECot ELan EPfP LRHS MBlu NLar SCoo
	- B&SWJ 2245	WCru
	grandiflora x ***rubriflora***	WCru
	henryi subsp. ***yunnanensis*** B&SWJ 6546	WCru
	aff. ***neglecta*** BWJ 7739	WCru
	nigra B&SWJ 5897	WCru
	propinqua var. ***sinensis***	CSPN LEdu MBlu NLar WSHC
	- - BWJ 8148	WCru
	rubriflora	CBrm CHEx CSPN CTri CWSG EBee EPfP LRHS MAsh MBlu MGos NSti SHBN SPer SSpi WSpi
	- (f)	CBcs ELan EMil MGos SBra WSHC
	- (m)	NHol
	- BWJ 7898	WCru
	sphenanthera	EBee ELan EMil EPfP IMGH LRHS NLar WSHC
	verrucosa HWJ 664	WCru

Schizachyrium (*Poaceae*)

§	***scoparium***	CBig CBrm CKno CSpe EBee EPPr EPau GFor GSki LRHS LRav NSti WDyG WWeb XIsg
	- 'The Blues'	CBig

Schizanthus (*Solanaceae*)

	lacteus new	CSpe
	porrigens	CSpe

Schizocentron see *Heterocentron*

Schizocodon see *Shortia*

Schizopetalon (*Brassicaceae*)

	walkeri	CSpe

Schizophragma (*Hydrangeaceae*)

	corylifolium	CBcs NLar
	hydrangeoides	CBcs CDoC EBee ELan EPfP LCro LRHS MBlu MGos NPal SBra SHBN SLim SLon SPoG SSpi SSta SWvt
	- B&SWJ 5954	WCru
	- B&SWJ 6119 from Yakushima, Japan	WCru
	- B&SWJ 8505 from Korea	WCru
	- from Korea	MBri
	- 'Brookside Littleleaf'	see *Hydrangea anomala* subsp. *petiolaris* var. *cordifolia* 'Brookside Littleleaf'
	- 'Iwa Garami'	CBcs MBri NLar
	- 'Moonlight'	More than 30 suppliers
*	- f. ***quelpartensis*** B&SWJ 1160	WCru
	- 'Roseum' 🏆H4	CAbP CBrm CDoC CMHG CMil CSBt CSPN EBee ELan EPfP EWes IArd LAst LRHS MBlu MBri MDun MGos NCGa NEgg NPal NPri SLim SPer SPoG SSpi SWvt WCru WFar WPGP
	integrifolium 🏆H4	CBcs EBee ELan EPfP LRHS NEgg NLar SDix SHBN SSpi WPGP WSHC
	- var. ***fauriei***	CBcs NLar WSHC
	- - B&SWJ 1701	WCru
	aff. ***megalocarpum*** BWJ 8150	WCru

Schizostachyum (*Poaceae*)

§	***funghomii***	EPla MMoz SDry WPGP

Schizostylis ✿ (*Iridaceae*)

§	***coccinea***	More than 30 suppliers
	- f. ***alba***	More than 30 suppliers
	- 'Anne'	WHoo
	- 'Ballyrogan Giant'	CFir CKno CTca EBee ECho GBuc IBlr MAvo NCot WPGP WSHC
	- 'Big Moma' new	NCot
	- 'Cardinal'	WFar
	- 'Caroline' new	NCot
	- 'Cindy Towe'	EBee EGle GBuc
	- 'Countesse de Vere'	EBee NCot
	- deep pink-streaked new	WOut
	- 'Elburton Glow'	NCot WFar WHoo
	- 'Fenland Daybreak'	More than 30 suppliers
	- 'Gigantea'	see *S. coccinea* 'Major'
	- 'Good White'	EBee EGle MAvo
	- 'Grandiflora'	see *S. coccinea* 'Major'
	- 'Hilary Gould'	EBee EPPr GBuc MAvo NCGa NCot SChr WFar WHal
	- 'Hint of Pink'	MAvo MDKP WOut
	- 'Jack Frost'	EBee GMac MAvo WMoo
	- 'Jennifer' 🏆H4	More than 30 suppliers

- 'Maiden's Blush'	ECGP ECtt EGle EHrv GBuc LRHS MAvo MCot MDKP MSte NCot NLar SPet WFar WMnd
§ - 'Major' ♀H4	More than 30 suppliers
* - 'Marietta'	GBin MAvo
- 'Mollie Gould'	CStu CTca EBee EGle EHrv EKen ELon EMar EShb GMac LAst LBMP MAvo MBNS MMHG NBre NCGa NCot NHol NLar SCoo SRGP WFar WOut WPrP WTin
- 'Mrs Hegarty'	More than 30 suppliers
- 'November Cheer'	CTca ECot IBlr LRHS MAvo MSte NBir NCot NLar WFar
- 'Oregon Sunset'	EBee GBuc
- 'Pallida'	CAby CMil CPom CSam ECha EHrv ELan GBuc MLHP MRav MWea NBir NCot NLar WFar
- 'Pink Marg' **new**	NCot
- 'Professor Barnard'	CCCN CFee CHar CSpe CTca ECho ELon EShb GAbr IBlr LAst MAvo MBNS MSte NBir NCot SApp SPla WFar WHil WMoo WOld WPnn
- 'Red Dragon'	EBee GBuc GMac MAvo NCot WFar WHoo
- 'Salmon Charm'	EBrs GBin GBuc LRHS MAvo WFar
- 'Salome' **new**	NCot
- 'Silver Pink'	IBlr
- 'Snow Maiden'	CAbP CBgR CElw ECtt GBuc GMac IBal LRHS MAvo MBNS SPav
- 'Strawberry'	NCot SPav
- 'Strawberry Fair'	SMrm
§ - 'Sunrise' ♀H4	More than 30 suppliers
- 'Sunset'	see *S. coccinea* 'Sunrise'
- 'Tambara'	CMHG CMdw CPou CSam EBee EHrv GAbr GBuc MAvo MWea NCot NLar SApp WFar
- 'Vera' **new**	NCot
- 'Viscountess Byng'	CAby CTca CTri EBee ECho EGle ELon EPau ERou GAbr IBlr IGor LAst MAvo NCot NLar SPav SPer WFar WPer
- 'Wilfred H. Bryant'	CBcs CKno CPen ECtt EKen IBal LBMP MAvo MBnl MDKP NCGa NCot NHol NPri NSti SCoo SPoG SRot STes WHil WOld
- 'Zeal Salmon'	CAby CFee CFir CPou ECha GAbr LHop MAvo NBir NCot NHol SApp SMHy WFar WMoo
* ***rosea*** **new**	CChe EBrs

Schoenoplectus (*Cyperaceae*)

§ ***lacustris***	EMFW GFor XIsg
§ - subsp. ***tabernaemontani***	XIsg
- - 'Albescens' (v)	CBen CDWL CKno CWat EBee EMFW SWat WDyG WHal WPrP
- - 'Zebrinus' (v)	CBen CDWL CKno CWat EAlp EHon ELan EMFW EPfP NScw SPlb SWat WDyG WFar WHal WMAq WPnP WPrP
pungens	GFor XIsg

Schoenus (*Cyperaceae*)

pauciflorus	CBgR CWCL EBee ECou EMan EPPr EWes LLWG MAvo NBro NOak WDyG WMoo WPGP WPrP

Schotia (*Caesalpiniaceae*)

afra	CKob
brachypetala	CKob

Schrebera (*Oleaceae*)

alata	CKob

Sciadopitys (*Sciadopityaceae*)

verticillata ♀H4	CBcs CDoC CDul CKen CTho EHul IDee LBee LCon LLin LPan LRHS MAsh MBar MBlu MBri MDun MGos SCoo SLim SPoG SWvt WEve WFar WNor WOrn
- 'Firework'	CKen
- 'Globe'	CKen
- 'Gold Star'	CKen
- 'Goldammer'	NLar
- 'Golden Pendula'	WEve
- 'Golden Rush'	CKen ECho LCon LLin MAsh MGos NLar WEve
- 'Goldmahne'	CKen
- 'Grüne Kugel'	CKen ECho NLar SLim
- 'Jeddeloh Compact'	CKen
- 'Kugelblitz'	WEve
- 'Kupferschirm'	CKen ECho NLar
- 'Mecki'	CKen ECho LCon LLin WEve
- 'Megaschirm'	CKen
- 'Ossorio Gold'	CKen ECho WEve
- 'Picola'	CKen ECho NLar
- 'Pygmy'	CKen
- 'Richie's Cushion'	CKen ECho NLar WEve
- 'Shorty'	CKen
- 'Speerspitze'	CKen
- 'Starburst'	CKen
- 'Sternschnuppe'	CDoC CKen ECho LCon LLin MBri NLar SLim WEve

Scilla (*Hyacinthaceae*)

adlamii	see *Ledebouria socialis*
x ***allenii***	see x *Chionoscilla allenii*
amethystina	see *S. litardierei*
amoena	EBrs ECho WCot
aristidis	EBrs
- from Algeria	ECho
autumnalis	CAvo CDes CPom CStu CTca EBrs ECho EPot ERos LAma WCot WShi
- from Crete	ECho
- subsp. ***fallax***	EBrs ECho
* - ***rosea*** **new**	EPot
bifolia ♀H4	CAvo CFFs CPom CStu EBrs ECho EPot LAma LLWP LRHS SPhx WCot WRHF WShi
- 'Alba'	EBrs ECho LRHS SPhx
- 'Norman Stevens'	SCnR
- 'Rosea'	EBrs ECho EPot LAma LLWP LRHS
bithynica ♀H4	WShi
campanulata	see *Hyacinthoides hispanica*
chinensis	see *S. scilloides*
cilicica	CStu ERos
greilhuberi	CStu EBrs ECho ERos WAbe WCot WWst
hohenackeri	ERos WThu
- BSBE 811	WCot
hughii **new**	EBrs ECho
hyacinthoides	EBrs ECho ERos WBVN
ingridiae	ECho ERos WWst
italica	see *Hyacinthoides italica*
japonica	see *S. scilloides*
latifolia from Morocco	ECho
libanotica	see *Puschkinia scilloides* var. *libanotica*
liliohyacinthus	CAvo EBrs IBlr MMHG SSvw WShi WWst
- 'Alba'	ERos
lingulata	CStu ECho ERos WCot
- var. ***ciliolata***	EBrs ECho EPot ERos
§ ***litardierei*** ♀H4	CAvo CFFs CHHB CPom CStu EBrs ECho EPPr EPot ERos LAma LRHS MBri NMen SPhx WShi
- ***hoogiana***	ERos
- 'Orjen' **new**	EBrs ECho

	messeniaca	CPom
	- MS 38 from Greece	WCot
	mischtschenkoana ♀H4	CAvo CFFs ECho EPot LAma LRHS MBri SPer WBVN
	- 'Armenia' **new**	EBrs
§	- 'Tubergeniana' ♀H4	CBgR CMea EBrs ECho GKev SPhx WCot
	- 'Zwanenburg'	ECho
	monophyllos	ECho
	- var. ***tingitana***	ERos
	morrisii	ERos
	natalensis	see *Merwilla plumbea*
	non-scripta	see *Hyacinthoides non-scripta*
	numidica	EBrs ECho
	nutans	see *Hyacinthoides non-scripta*
	obtusifolia	EBrs ECho
	persica ♀H4	CPom EBrs ECho ERos WCot
	- JCA 0.876.501	WCot
	peruviana	More than 30 suppliers
	- S&L 285	WCot
	- SB&L 20/1	WCot
	- 'Alba'	CBcs CFwr CSWP CSpe CStu ECho LPio MTho SMrm WCot
	- 'Grand Bleu'	CFwr
	- var. ***ifniensis***	WCot
	- var. ***venusta*** S&L 311/2	WCot
	pratensis	see *S. litardierei*
	puschkinioides	ECho
	ramburei	EBrs ECho
	reverchonii	EBrs ECho ERos WWst
	rosenii	EBrs ECho
§	***scilloides***	EBrs ECho ERos SCnR SRot WCot
	siberica ♀H4	CAvo CFFs CTca EBrs ECho EPfP IHer LAma LRHS NBlu SBch SPer WShi
	- 'Alba'	EBrs ECho EPfP EPot LAma LHop LRHS SBch WShi
	- subsp. ***armena***	ECho
	- 'Spring Beauty'	CMdw CMea EBrs ECho EPot LAma LHop LRHS MBri SPhx SRms
	- var. ***taurica***	ECho ERos
	'Tubergeniana'	see *S. mischtschenkoana* 'Tubergeniana'
	verna	CDes EBrs ECho ERos WHer WShi WThu
	vicentina	see *Hyacinthoides vicentina*
	violacea	see *Ledebouria socialis*

Scindapsus (*Araceae*)

	aureus	see *Epipremnum aureum*
	pictus (v)	LRHS MBri

Scirpoides (*Cyperaceae*)

§	***holoschoenus***	CBig CRWN EBee GFor XIsg

Scirpus (*Cyperaceae*)

	cernuus	see *Isolepis cernua*
	holoschoenus	see *Scirpoides holoschoenus*
	lacustris	see *Schoenoplectus lacustris*
	- 'Spiralis'	see *Juncus effusus* f. *spiralis*
	maritimus	see *Bolboschoenus maritimus*
	sylvaticus	XIsg
	tabernaemontani	see *Schoenoplectus lacustris* subsp. *tabernaemontani*

Scleranthus (*Illecebraceae*)

	biflorus	CTrC CWil ECho EDAr EWes NDlv NWCA SPlb WPer
	perennis	ECho
	uniflorus	CLyd CTrC ECho EShb GAbr NHol NWCA SMad SPlb WPrP

Sclerochiton (*Acanthaceae*)

	harveyanus	EShb

Scoliopus (*Trilliaceae*)

	bigelowii	CStu SCnR WFar WHal
	hallii	EBee EBrs GCrs GEdr NMen SCnR WCot WCru WWst

Scolopendrium see *Asplenium*

Scopolia (*Solanaceae*)

	anomala	CArn CPLG
	carniolica	CArn CFir COld CWCL EBee EGle ELan EMon GPoy GWWP IBlr LEdu MBlu MPhe MSal MSte NChi NLar NSti SPhx SPlb WCru WPGP
	- from Poland **new**	LEdu
§	- var. ***brevifolia***	EHrv EPPr GBin SDys WHil WTin
	- - WM 9811	MPhe
	- subsp. ***hladnikiana***	see *S. carniolica* var. *brevifolia*
	- 'Zwanenburg'	CHFP EBrs EHrv EPPr EWes SPhx WCot
	lurida	see *Anisodus luridus*
	physaloides	MSal
	sinensis	see *Atropanthe sinensis*
	stramoniifolia	CElw

Scorzonera (*Asteraceae*)

	suberosa subsp. ***cariensis***	EBee

Scrophularia (*Scrophulariaceae*)

	aquatica	see *S. auriculata*
§	***auriculata***	ELau EPfP MHer MSal NMir NPer WHer
§	- 'Variegata' (v)	CArn CBcs EBee ECha ECtt ELan ENot EPfP ERou LRHS MBri MDun MHer MWgw NBid NEgg NSti SDnm SPer SPoG SRms WFar
	buergeriana	MSal
	- 'Lemon and Lime' misapplied	see *Teucrium viscidum* 'Lemon and Lime'
	californica	EBee
	calliantha	MDKP
	fargesii **new**	CExc
	grandiflora	NBre WFar WTMC
	marilandica	EBee
	nodosa	CArn CRWN EBee ELau GPoy MSal NMir NSco WHer WSel
	- *tracheliodes*	CNat
	- *variegata*	see *S. auriculata* 'Variegata'
	scopolii	EBee

Scutellaria ✿ (*Lamiaceae*)

	albida	EBee EWin
§	***alpina***	CPBP EBee ECho EMan GCrs GEdr LAst LBee LRHS SBla SPlb SRms SRot WGor WPer
	- 'Arcobaleno'	CEnt SPet
	- 'Greencourt'	WPat
	- 'Moonbeam'	GEdr SHGN
	altissima	CArn CDMG CHFP CPLG EBee ECha ELan EMan EMar GBuc MSal NBro NCGa SBod SPlb WPer WPtf
	'Amazing Grace'	EWes
	baicalensis	CArn CHFP EBee GPoy IBlr MSal SBHP SBla WPer WPtf
	barbata	MSal
	canescens	see *S. incana*
	columnae	EBee
	diffusa	ECtt WPer
	formosana 'China Blue'	EPfP
	galericulata	GPoy GWCH MHer MNHC MSal NVic WHer
	hastata	see *S. hastifolia*
§	***hastifolia***	CTri ECho ECot ECtt NSti WPer
§	***incana***	CBct CHFP CPom CSam EBee ECGP EHrv ELan EMon LHop

	LRHS MWea NDov NSti SMrm SPhx WCot WOut WTMC
indica	WCFE WPat
- var. ***japonica***	see *S. indica* var. *parvifolia*
§ - var. ***parvifolia***	CPBP CStu EBee EBur ECho EMan EWes GEdr LRHS SBla SRot
- - 'Alba'	CPBP ECho LRHS LTwo SBla
lateriflora	CArn CBod EBee ELau EOHP GPoy MGol MSal NCGa SPhx WHer WJek WPer WSel
maekawae	WPGP
- B&SWJ 557a	WCru
novae-zelandiae	ECou LRHS
orientalis	CMdw ECtt GEdr LRHS SBch SBla WLin WPat
- subsp. ***bicolor***	ECtt NWCA
- 'Eastern Sun'	EBee
- subsp. ***pectinata***	ITim
- subsp. ***pinnatifida***	GEdr NWCA SPhx
pontica	CEnt CPBP GEdr MAvo SBch WFoF
prostrata	EMan LTwo WPat
scordiifolia	CEnt CLyd CMea CMil CSam EBee ECha ECho EDAr GEdr GMaP NRya NWCA SBHP SBla SRms WFar WHal WHoo WTin
- 'Seoul Sapphire'	EWes GCrs LSou WBVN WPtf
suffrutescens	XPep
- 'Texas Rose'	CSpe EMon LRHS MAsh MWea SIng SRot
supina	see *S. alpina*
tournefortii	ECtt LLWP
* ***zhongdianensis***	CEnt WPtf

seakale see *Crambe maritima*

Sebaea (*Gentianaceae*)

thomasii	GCrs WAbe

Securigera see *Coronilla*

Sedastrum see *Sedum*

Sedum ✿ (*Crassulaceae*)

B&SWJ 737	EGoo
NS 622	NWCA
'Abbeydore'	CDes EBee EGle EGoo EMan EMon EWsh NGby WAbb WPGP WWeb
acre	CTri ECho ECot GPoy LAst LEdu MBar MHer MNHC NBlu SPlb XPep
- 'Aureum'	ECho EDAr EPfP LAst MBar NBlu NLar NPri SPer SPoG WFar WPat
- 'Elegans'	ECtt
- 'Golden Queen' **new**	EAlp
§ - var. ***majus***	CChe
- 'Minus'	ECho EDAr
- 'Oktoberfest' **new**	EAlp
adolphi	EPfP
§ 'African Pearl'	CBcs CElw EBee EGle EPfP GBin IPot NBPN NCGa NDov NLar
'African Sunset'	see *S.* 'African Pearl'
§ ***aizoon***	EAro ECho LAst NBre SIde SPlb WBVN WFar
- 'Aurantiacum'	see *S. aizoon* 'Euphorbioides'
§ - 'Euphorbioides'	EBee ECha ECtt EGoo ELan LDai LRHS MBNS MHer MRav MWgw NLar SAga SGar SPer SPlb WFar WTin
albescens	see *S. rupestre* f. *purpureum*
alboroseum	see *S. erythrostictum*
§ ***album***	CHal EAlp MBNS NBro WPer
- 'Coral Carpet'	CBrm EAlp ECho EDAr EPfP EPot GAbr MBar MRav MWat NPri NRya SPoG WCot WFar XPep
§ - subsp. ***teretifolium*** 'Murale'	CTri MBar STre
altissimum	see *S. sediforme*
altum	EMon NBre WCot WFar WMoo
amplexicaule	see *S. tenuifolium*
anacampseros	EGoo NHol WPer
- B&SWJ 723	WCru
anglicum	SChr
athoum	see *S. album*
atlanticum	see *S. dasyphyllum* subsp. *dasyphyllum* var. *mesatlanticum*
Autumn Charm = 'Lajos' **new**	EBee
'Autumn Fire' **new**	EBee
Autumn Joy	see *S.* 'Herbstfreude'
'Bertram Anderson' ♀H4	More than 30 suppliers
beyrichianum misapplied	see *S. glaucophyllum*
bithynicum 'Aureum'	see *S. hispanicum* var. *minus* 'Aureum'
'Black Emperor'	EBee
brevifolium	GGar
caeruleum	EGle SIng
'Carl'	CDes CKno CPrp EBee EBrs ECha EGle EGoo EMon EPfP EShb GMaP LHop LRHS MNFA MRav MSte MWgw NBro NCGa NOrc NSti SAga SRGP WCot WHil WHoo WMnd WMoo WWeb
caucasicum	WAbb WCot WEas
cauticola ♀H4	CLyd COlW CSpe ECho EDAr EMan GEdr MBrN MHer MRav NBre SMrm SPoG SRms SRot WAbe
- from Lida	ECho
- 'Coca-Cola'	CBct CCVN EAlp EPPr EWin LAst NPri WFar
- 'Lidakense'	CHEx CMea CStu ECho ECtt EGle EMan EPfP LRHS MBar MBri MLHP NSla SBch SBla SIng SPer SRot WFar
- 'Purpurine'	ECho
- 'Robustum'	EWll
'Chocolate' **new**	EBee
'Citrus Twist'	EBee LBMP LRHS LSou MBNS NBPC NBhm NMRc NPro
compressum	EDAr SEND
confusum	SChr SEND WFar
crassipes	see *Rhodiola wallichiana*
crassularia	see *Crassula setulosa* 'Milfordiae'
'Crazy Ruffles'	WCot
cryptomerioides B&SWJ 054	WCru
cyaneum Rudolph	EPot WAbe
dasyphyllum	ECha ECho EDAr MBar MHer MWat NRya SIng SRms XPep
- subsp. ***dasyphyllum*** var. ***glanduliferum***	CHal
§ - - var. ***mesatlanticum***	NBir
- ***mucronatis***	see *S. dasyphyllum* subsp. *dasyphyllum* var. *mesatlanticum*
divergens	XPep
douglasii	see *S. stenopetalum* 'Douglasii'
drymarioides	NBre
'Dudley Field'	MHer SBch
'Eleanor Fisher'	see *S. telephium* subsp. *ruprechtii*
ellacombeanum	see *S. kamtschaticum* var. *ellacombeanum*
§ ***erythrostictum***	MTho WAbb
- 'Frosty Morn' (v)	More than 30 suppliers
§ - 'Mediovariegatum' (v)	CChe COlW EBee EGle EGoo ELan EMon EPfP ERou EShb LRHS MHer MNrw MRav NEgg SHBN SWvt WBrE WFar WHil WMnd WMoo WPer
'Evening Cloud'	EBee
ewersii	CHEx EBee ECho ECtt EDAr GMaP LRHS NBro NLar SPlb WAbe
- var. ***homophyllum*** 'Rosenteppich'	LBuc LRHS MAsh MBrN SWvt WWeb

	fabaria	EMan EWsh WAbb WCot WFar
	fastigiatum	see *Rhodiola fastigiata*
	floriferum	see *S. kamtschaticum*
	forsterianum subsp. ***elegans***	SPlb
	frutescens	STre
	furfuraceum	NMen WAbe
	Garnet Brocade = 'Garbro'	CCVN EBee SVil
§	***glaucophyllum***	WPer
	'Gold Mound'	CStu EPfP LAst MGos NLar SVil
	'Great Expectations'	EGle LRHS MRav
*	'Green Expectations'	EBee EGle EShb MSte MWat NBre
	gypsicola	EBee WPer
	'Harvest Moon'	EBur
§	'Herbstfreude' ♀H4	More than 30 suppliers
	heterodontum	see *Rhodiola heterodonta*
	hidakanum	CAby CLyd ECtt EPot GGar GMaP NBro NHol NMen WHoo WPat WTin
	himalense misapplied	see *Rhodiola* 'Keston'
	hispanicum	EAlp ECho EDAr NBre SPlb
	- ***glaucum***	see *S. hispanicum* var. *minus*
§	- var. ***minus***	ECho ECtt MBNS MBar NPri SIng SPlb
§	- - 'Aureum'	ECha ECho EDAr MBar NHol
	- 'Pewter'	ECho
	humifusum	EBur EPot NWCA SIng
§	***hybridum***	WEas
	- 'Czar's Gold' **new**	EAlp
	ishidae	see *Rhodiola ishidae*
	'Jaws'	CKno EBee EGle LSou SPoG WCot
	'Joyce Henderson'	COlW EBee ECtt EGle EMan GQue LHop MRav NCGa NCob NEgg NLar SPer SRGP WBrk WCot WEas WMoo WTin
§	***kamtschaticum*** ♀H4	EAlp ECho MBar WFar
§	- var. ***ellacombeanum*** ♀H4	EDAr EGoo NMen WCot
	- - B&SWJ 8853	WCru
§	- var. ***floriferum*** 'Weihenstephaner Gold'	CEnt CTri ECho ECtt EDAr EGoo EPfP GAbr GEdr GGar GMaP LRHS MBar MHer MRav MWat NBir NMen NPri NVic SIng SPlb SPoG SRms WFar WPat XPep
	- var. ***kamtschaticum*** 'Variegatum' (v) ♀H4	CBrm CLyd CMea EBee ECho ECtt EDAr EPPr EPfP LAst LBMP LBee MHer MWat SBla SIng SPoG SRms SRot SWvt WEas
	'Karfunkelstein'	GBin SPhx
	kirilovii	see *Rhodiola kirilovii*
	lanceolatum	WPer
	'Lemon Bells' **new**	GBin
	lineare	CHEx LAst
	'Little Gem'	see x *Cremnosedum* 'Little Gem'
	x ***luteoviride*** **new**	EAlp
§	***lydium***	CTri ECho MBar MHer SFgr SPlb
	- 'Aureum'	see *S. hispanicum* var. *minus* 'Aureum'
	- 'Bronze Queen'	see *S. lydium*
	'Lynda Windsor'PBR	CBct CBow CHVG CWCL EBee ECtt EGle EHrv EPfP LAst LHop MBNS NBPC NBPN NBhm NLar NMoo SPoG
	makinoi 'Ogon'	CStu EBee
I	'Marchant's Best Red'	SMHy
	maweanum	see *S. acre* var. *majus*
	maximowiczii	see *S. aizoon*
	middendorffianum	CLyd ECho EDAr EGoo EPPr MBrN MHer MWat NMen SRms SRot WHoo
	'Moonglow'	ECtt NMen
	moranense	CHal
	morganianum ♀H1	CHal EBak EShb

	murale	see *S. album* subsp. *teretifolium* 'Murale'
N	***nevii*** hort.	EGle SPlb
	nicaeense	see *S. sediforme*
	obcordatum	NMen
§	***obtusatum***	EAlp ECtt EDAr GGar GKev NBro NSla STre WFar
	ochroleucum	XPep
	oppositifolium	see *S. spurium* var. *album*
	oreganum	ECha ECho EDAr EWin GAbr GMaP MBar MHer MWat NMen SPlb SRms SRot STre WPer
	- 'Procumbens'	see *S. oreganum* subsp. *tenue*
§	- subsp. ***tenue***	LEdu NHol NRya WPat
§	***oregonense***	EBur NMen
	oryzifolium 'Minor'	EAlp EBur
	oxypetalum	STre
	pachyclados	see *Rhodiola pachyclados*
	pachyphyllum	EPfP
	palmeri	CHEx CSpe EMan LSou MRav NBir SChr SSvw XPep
	'Picolette' **new**	EBee MBNS NBPN
	pilosum	NMen NWCA
	'Pink Chablis'PBR (v)	EBee MLLN NBPC NBhm WCot
§	***pluricaule***	CStu ECho SPlb SRms
	populifolium	EBee ECha MHer SDry STre WPer
	'Postman's Pride' **new**	LBuc
	praealtum	GGar SChr STre WCot
§	'Purple Emperor'	More than 30 suppliers
	'Red Cauli'	CKno EBee EGle IPot MBNS MBri SMHy SPhx
	'Red Rum'	LRHS SMeo
	reflexum L.	see *S. rupestre* L.
	reptans	ECho
	rhodiola	see *Rhodiola rosea*
	'Ringmore Ruby'	MHar WCot
	rosea	see *Rhodiola rosea*
	rubroglaucum misapplied	see *S. oregonense*
	rubroglaucum Praeger	see *S. obtusatum*
	x ***rubrotinctum***	CHEx CHal SChr XPep
	- 'Aurora'	SChr
	'Ruby Glow' ♀H4	More than 30 suppliers
	'Ruby Port'	CSpe
§	***rupestre*** L.	EAlp ECho GGar MBNS MBar NBlu SPlb WFar WHer XPep
	- 'Angelina'	EBee ENot EPPr EWes EWin MAsh MAvo NBir NPro WCot
	- 'Monstrosum Cristatum'	ITer NBir SMad
§	- f. ***purpureum***	NRya
	ruprechtii	see *S. telephium* subsp. *ruprechtii*
	sarcocaule hort.	see *Crassula sarcocaulis*
	sarmentosum	ECho
§	***sediforme***	CArn EDAr XPep
	- ***nicaeense***	see *S. sediforme*
	selskianum	EBee EWin GGar NBre
	sempervivoides	ECho
	sexangulare	ECho EDAr GAbr GGar MBar MHer NRya SEND SPlb SRms WFar WPer XPep
	sibiricum	see *S. hybridum*
	sieboldii	EBee ECho
	- 'Mediovariegatum' (v) ♀H2-3	CHEx COlW EAlp ECho EMan LAst MHer SPlb WFar WPer
	'Silver Moon'	EBur NHol
	spathulifolium	CTri ECha ECho EPot MDKP WEas
	- 'Aureum'	EBur ECho ECtt NRya WAbe
	- 'Cape Blanco' ♀H4	More than 30 suppliers
	- 'Purpureum' ♀H4	More than 30 suppliers
	spectabile ♀H4	CArn CChe CHEx CHrt CPrp CTri EBee ELan EPfP GMaP LRHS MHer MRav NGdn SGar SHFr SPlb SRms WBVN WBor WBrk WCAu WFar WSFF WTel WTin XPep
	- 'Abendrot'	EMon
	- 'Album'	CHEx

- 'Brilliant' ♀^{H4} More than 30 suppliers
- 'Carmen' EBee NEgg WMoo
- 'Iceberg' More than 30 suppliers
- 'Indian Chief' CMMP COlW CPrp CTca EBee ECtt EGle GCra GMaP LAst LRHS MBrN MRav MSte SPoG WFar WMnd WMoo
- 'Lisa' EMon MTPN NLar
- 'Meteor' EBee MBNS MLLN MSte MWat NLar WAbe WCAu WPer
* - 'Mini' ELan MRav
- 'Neon' EBee LRHS
- 'Pink Fairy' WHil
- 'Red Coully' **new** NPro
- 'Rosenteller' EBee EGle EMon NBre
- September Glow see *S. spectabile* 'Septemberglut'
§ - 'Septemberglut' EBee EGoo EMan EMon NBre NSti WCot
- 'Stardust' CKno COlW CPrp CTri EBee EBrs EGle EMil EPfP ERou GMaP LCro LRHS MBNS MHer MRav NCGa NOrc SPer SPet SPoG WCAu WFar WGor WWeb
- 'Steve Ward' EBee EWes
- 'Variegatum' see *S. erythrostictum* 'Mediovariegatum'

spinosum see *Orostachys spinosa*

spurium CHEx ECho EGoo MBNS NHol NPro SEND SGar SRms STre

§ - var. ***album*** EGoo NRya
* - 'Atropurpureum' ECha WMoo
- 'Coccineum' EAlp ECho MBar MNHC NBlu WBVN WRHF
- Dragon's Blood see *S. spurium* 'Schorbuser Blut'
- 'Erdblut' LRHS NMen
- 'Fuldaglut' CHal CTri EBee ECho EDAr EWin GBuc GMaP MBNS NRya SIng SMrm SPer WFar WMoo WPer
- 'Green Mantle' EBee ECha ECho EPfP EWin MWgw SMer
- Purple Carpet see *S. spurium* 'Purpurteppich'
- 'Purpureum' EGoo SRms
§ - 'Purpurteppich' ECho LRHS MRav NBPN NBro NHol NLar SRms
- 'Roseum' EWll SRms
- 'Ruby Mantle' EWll SBch WBVN
§ - 'Schorbuser Blut' ♀^{H4} CMea EBee ECho ECtt EPau EPfP EPot MBNS MLHP MWat NBir NRya NVic SPlb SRms WEas WFar WHoo WPat WTin WWeb
- 'Summer Glory' EAlp NLar
- 'Tricolor' see *S. spurium* 'Variegatum'
I - 'Variegatum' (v) CBrm CHEx CTri EAlp EBee ECha ECho EDAr EGoo GGar LAst LBMP MBar MHer MLHP MNHC MRav NPri NRya SBod SIng SPlb SPoG WEas WFar WMoo WPat
- 'Voodoo' CBrm CChe EAlp EWTr EWes GWWP

stenopetalum SPlb

§ - 'Douglasii' SRms

'Stewed Rhubarb Mountain' CPrp EBee ECtt EGle EMan LBMP LCro LDai LHop MBNS MRav MSte MWgw NBro NDov WCot WFar WMoo WPGP

stoloniferum ECho
- 'Variegatum' WWeb

'Strawberries and Cream' More than 30 suppliers

'Sunset Cloud' CHEx CMHG CSam EBee ECtt EGle EWes LRHS NBre NCob

takesimense B&SWJ 8518 WCru

tatarinowii EDAr

telephium CAgr CArn CMea MBNS NBir SRms
- 'Arthur Branch' EPPr GBuc MNrw MSte MTho
- 'Black Jack' **new** ENot IPot LBuc NDov SPoG WCot
- 'Bon Bon' EBee EGle MBNS NBPN
- var. ***borderei*** CElw EGle EMan EMon LHop LRHS SBch SPhx
- 'El Cid' EBee EGle EWes
- 'Emperor's Waves' **new** EDAr NGdn
* - 'Hester' WSpi
- 'Jennifer' WCot
- 'Leonore Zuuntz' EBee NBre
- 'Matrona' More than 30 suppliers
- subsp. ***maximum*** 'Atropurpureum' ♀^{H4} CMea COlW EBee EGle ELan EPfP MRav SWvt WCot WEas
- - 'Bressingham Purple' EBrs
- - 'Gooseberry Fool' CAby COlW EBee ECGP ECtt EGle EGoo EMon ERou GMaP LCro MBri NSti SBch SPhx WCot WFar WWeb
- 'Mohrchen' CPrp EBee EGle EHrv GMaP LRHS MHar MLLN MRav NGdn NLar SMrm SPla SPoG WCAu WFar WMnd WMoo
- 'Munstead Red' More than 30 suppliers
§ - subsp. ***ruprechtii*** CBgR COlW CPrp EBee ECha ECtt EGle EGoo EMon EPPr EPfP GMaP LHop LRHS MNFA MRav MWgw NCGa NSti SBla SMeo SPer SPet SPhx WBVN WEas WFar WMoo WPer
- - 'Hab Gray' CBgR COlW CSpe EBee ECtt EGle EWes GBin GQue LAst MSte NLar WCot WGwG
- 'Samuel Oliphant' (v) WCot
- subsp. ***telephium*** 'Lynda et Rodney' CKno EGle EGoo EMon EWes MSte WCot
- - var. ***purpureum*** GCra
- 'Variegatum' (v) LRHS MDKP WHal

§ ***tenuifolium*** EBur
- subsp. ***tenuifolium*** EBur

ternatum SBch

trollii see *Rhodiola trollii*

urvillei Sartorianum Group **new** MHer

ussuriense EBee ECha EMon WOut

'Vera Jameson' ♀^{H4} CChe CKno CMea CPrp EBee ECha EGle EPfP GGar LRHS LSRN MBrN MRav MWat MWgw NHol NSti SBch SHBN SPer SPla WEas WFar WMoo WSpi

viviparum B&SWJ 8662 WCru

* 'Wallaceum' **new** EAlp

'Washfield Purple' see *S.* 'Purple Emperor'

'Weihenstephaner Gold' see *S. kamtschaticum* var. *floriferum* 'Weihenstephaner Gold'

weinbergii see *Graptopetalum paraguayense*

'Xenox' **new** EBee EPfP MBNS

yezoense see *S. pluricaule*

Seemannia see *Gloxinia*

Selaginella ✿ (*Selaginellaceae*)

apoda MBri

braunii CLAP SKHP WCot

helvetica CKob CStu

kraussiana ♀^{H1} CHal CKob CLAP EDAr GGar LRHS MBri NRya WRic
- 'Aurea' CCCN CHal CLAP SMad WRic
- 'Brownii' ♀^{H1} CCCN CLAP LRHS
- 'Gold Tips' CCCN CLAP LRHS

lepidophylla EBrs

martensii ♀^{H1} **new** CKob

moellendorfii WRic

sanguinolenta CKob CStu SIng

uncinata ♀^{H1} CExc CLAP WRic

Selago (*Scrophulariaceae*)

myrtifolia GFai

Selinum (*Apiaceae*)

carvifolium EBee LDai NLar WBor
tenuifolium see *S. wallichianum*
§ ***wallichianum*** CDes CWsd EBrs ECGP EDAr EGoo EWTr GBuc GCra ITer MWat NBid NCGa SMHy SMad SMeo SPer SPhx WCot WHal WPGP WPrP
- EMAK 886 EBee GPoy NSti SDix
- HWJK 2224 WCru
- HWJK 2347 WCru

Selliera (*Goodeniaceae*)

radicans ECou EDAr GGar
- 'Lake Ellerman' NHol

Semele (*Ruscaceae*)

androgyna CHEx CRHN EShb

Semiaquilegia (*Ranunculaceae*)

§ ***adoxoides*** CPom SHar WCot
- B&SWJ 1190 WCru
'Early Dwarf' EDif NLar
§ ***ecalcarata*** CHFP CPom CSpe EBee ECho GGar LDai MAvo NLar SBch SRms SSvw WCot WCru WFar WHal WPGP WPer WWFP
* - f. ***bicolor*** CPom WCru
simulatrix see *S. ecalcarata*

Semiarundinaria (*Poaceae*)

from Korea EPla
§ ***fastuosa*** ♀H4 CAbb CBig CDoC CEnt CHEx EAmu EBee EFul ENBC EPfP EPla ERod LPal MBri MMoz MWht NMoo NVic SAPC SArc SDix SDry SPlb
- var. ***viridis*** CEnt EPla ERod LPJP MWht SDry WCru
kagamiana CDoC CMCo EBee ENBC EPla MMoz MMuc MWht NMoo SDry SEND
makinoi CGHE EPla MWht WPGP
nitida see *Fargesia nitida*
§ ***okuboi*** ENBC EPla ERod LPal MMoz MWht
villosa see *S. okuboi*
yamadorii EPla ERod MMoz MWht SDry
- 'Brimscombe' EPla SDry
yashadake EPla ERod SDry
- 'Gimmei' **new** EPla
- f. ***kimmei*** CAbb CDoC CDul ENBC EPla ERod LCro MAsh MGos MMoz MPRe MWht NMoo SBLw SDry SEND WDyG WFar WMoo WPGP

Semnanthe see *Erepsia*

Sempervivella see *Rosularia*

Sempervivum ✿ (*Crassulaceae*)

from Andorra NHol
from Sierra Nova NDlv
'Abba' CMea WHal WPer
acuminatum see *S. tectorum* var. *glaucum*
'Adelaar' CWil NMen
'Adelmoed' CWil SFgr
'Adeltruid' NHol
'Adlerhorst' NHol
'Aglow' MHom NMen
'Aladdin' CWil NMen SRms
'Albernelli' NHol SFgr
'Aldo Moro' CWil ECha EDAr GAbr LBee LRHS MHom NMen SFgr WIvy
allionii see *Jovibarba allionii*
'Alluring' GAbr
'Alpha' CTca EBee LBee LRHS NHol NMen SFgr SIng SRms STre WHal WPer WTin
altum CWil MHom NMen SIng
'Amanda' CWil ECha NMen SIng SRms WHoo WPer WTin
'Ambergreen' NMen
andreanum see *S. tectorum* subsp. *alpinum*
'Apache' NMen
'Apollo' NHol SFgr
'Apple Blossom' CMea ECha NMen
arachnoideum ♀H4 More than 30 suppliers
- from Gorges du Valais EPem
- 'Ararat' SDys
- var. ***bryoides*** CWil MBrN NMen WAbe WIvy WPer
- 'Clärchen' NHol NMen NSla SFgr
- cristate CWil
* - ***densum*** MBrN NRya WAbe WFar
- subsp. ***doellianum*** see *S. arachnoideum* subsp. *tomentosum* var. *glabrescens*
- form No 1 ECho
- 'Laggeri' see *S. arachnoideum* L. subsp. *tomentosum* (C.B. Lehm. & Schnittsp.) Schinz & Thell.
- 'Peña Prieta' NHol
- red NMen
- 'Rubrum' CHEx CTca EDAr GGar GMaP LRHS NEgg
- subsp. ***tomentosum*** misapplied see *S.* x *barbulatum* 'Hookeri'
§ - subsp. ***tomentosum*** (C.B. Lehm. & Schnittsp.) Schinz & Thell. ♀H4 CHEx CHal CWil EPot GKev MHer NHol NMen NPer SFgr SRms WAbe WBrE WPer
- - GDJ 92.04 CWil
§ - - var. ***glabrescens*** NMen SDys WPat
- - 'Minus' NHol NMen SIng
§ - - 'Stansfieldii' GAbr NMen SDys SIng STre WHal
§ - 'White Christmas' CTca CWil
arachnoideum x ***calcareum*** CWil NHol NMen WIvy WTin
arachnoideum x ***montanum*** see *S.* x *barbulatum*
arachnoideum x ***nevadense*** CWil SDys
arachnoideum x ***pumilum*** GAbr
arachnoideum x ***pittonii*** CWil NHol NMen WAbe
arenarium see *Jovibarba arenaria*
armenum NMen
'Arondina' CWil
'Aross' CMea GAbr NMen
'Artist' CWil NMen
arvernense see *S. tectorum*
'Ashes of Roses' CTca EGoo EPot GKev ITim MHom NMen WAbe WGor WPer
'Asteroid' CWil NMen
'Astrid' CWil
atlanticum MHom NDlv NMen NSla SRot
- from Atlas Mountains, Morocco CWil
- from Oukaïmeden, Morocco CWil GAbr NHol NMen WTin
- 'Edward Balls' CWil EPem SDys SFgr
'Atlantis' NHol
'Atropurpureum' CHEx CWil EDAr GKev MBrN NMen SRms WGor WIvy WPer
'Aureum' see *Greenovia aurea*
'Averil' CWil

	balcanicum	CWil EDAr NMen WIvy
	ballsii	NMen
	- from Kambeecho, Greece	MHom
	- from Smólikas, Greece	CWil MHom NMen
	- from Tschumba Petzi, Greece	CWil MHom SDys
	'Banderi'	CWil
	'Banyan'	MTPN
	'Barbarosa'	CWil
§	x ***barbulatum***	NMen SDys WPer
§	- 'Hookeri'	CTri CWil GKev NLar NMen SFgr SIng WAbe WPer
	'Bascour Zilver'	CMea CWil ECha LBee SFgr WHal
	'Beaute'	CWil
	'Bedivere'	CPBP CWil GKev LBee NMen SRms
	'Bedivere Crested'	CWil
	'Bedley Hi'	MHom
	'Bella Donna'	MHom NHol NMen WPer
	'Bella Meade'	CWil GKev NMen SFgr SRms WPer
	'Bellotts Pourpre'	CWil NHol
	'Benny Hill'	CWil
	'Bernstein'	CWil MHer SFgr WHal
	'Beta'	MHom NHol NMen WAbe WPer WTin
	'Bethany'	CWil NHol NMen WHal
	'Bicolor'	EPfP
	'Big Mal'	NHol
	'Big Slipper'	EPem NHol
	'Binstead'	NHol
	'Birchmaier'	NMen SFgr
	'Black Beauty'	EPot
	'Black Claret'	NHol
	'Black Knight'	CStu CTca LBee LRHS MHer SBla SRms WHal
	'Black Mini'	CTca CWil GAbr GKev MDKP NBir NMen SRms WAbe
	'Black Mountain'	CHEx CWil GKev LBee SIng
	'Black Prince'	CTca ECha SPer
	'Black Velvet'	WIvy WPer
	'Bladon'	WPer
	'Blood Sucker'	WGor
	'Blood Tip'	CHEx CHal CWil EBee ECha GAbr GCra GKev LBee LRHS MHer NHol NMen NRya SBch SPoG SRms WFar WGor WHal
	'Blue Boy'	CTca CWil ECha GAbr GKev LBee LRHS MSte NHol NMen SFgr SRms WHoo WLin WPer
	'Blue Moon'	NMen
	'Blue Time'	CTca CWil SFgr WTin
	'Blush'	CTca EDAr
	'Boissieri'	see *S. tectorum* subsp. *tectorum* 'Boissieri'
	'Booth's Red'	CHEx NMen WGor
	'Boreale'	see *Jovibarba hirta* subsp. *borealis*
	borisii	see *S. ciliosum* var. *borisii*
	borissovae	CWil MHom NMen SDys
	'Boromir'	CWil
	'Boule de Neige'	NMen
	'Bowles's Variety'	WPer
	'Britta'	SDys
	'Brock'	CWil ECha MHer MHom NHol WPer
	'Bronco'	CTca CWil EBee ECho LBee MHom NMen SRms WFar
	'Bronze Pastel'	CTca CWil ECha MHom NMen NSla SFgr SRms SRot WTin
	'Bronze Tower'	NHol
	'Brown Owl'	CWil ECho NHol SRms WFar
	'Brownii'	CTca GAbr NMen SBla WPer WTin
	'Brunette'	ECho GAbr
	'Burgundy'	ECha
	'Burnatii'	CWil NMen

	'Burning Desire'	CTca WGor
	'Butterbur'	CWil
	'Café'	CWil EGoo NHol NMen SFgr SIng SRms WIvy WPer
	x ***calcaratum***	SIng SRms
	calcareum	CMea CSam CTca CWil EPot GKev LRHS NBro NEgg NMen SPlb SRms SRot WBVN WFar WHoo WLin WPer
	- from Alps, France	CWil
	- from Calde la Vanoise, France	CWil NMen
	- from Ceüze, France	CWil WIvy
	- from Col Bayard, France	CWil GAbr NMen
	- from Colle St Michel, France	CWil NMen SFgr
	- from Cleizé, France	see *S. calcareum* 'Limelight'
	- from Gorges supérieures du Cians, France	CWil NMen
	- from Guillaumes, Mont Ventoux, France	CWil NMen SFgr SRot WHoo
	- from Mont Ventoux, France	CWil
	- from Queyras, France	CWil NMen
	- from Route d'Annôt, France	CWil NMen
	- from Triora, Italy	CWil NHol NMen
	- 'Benz'	SDys
	- 'Cristatum'	CStu
	- 'Extra'	CHEx CWil GAbr SFgr SRot
	- from Petite Ceüse, France	SRot
	- - GDJ 92.15	CWil
	- - GDJ 92.16	CWil
	- 'Greenii'	CTca CWil EPem GKev LRHS NDlv NHol NMen SPlb
§	- 'Grigg's Surprise'	CWil MHer NMen
§	- 'Limelight'	CMea CTca CWil NHol NMen WHal WIvy WTin
	- 'Monstrosum'	see *S. calcareum* 'Grigg's Surprise'
	- 'Mrs Giuseppi'	CTca CWil EBee ECho ETod GAbr GKev LBee LRHS MSte NMen SBla SFgr SRms STre WAbe WFar WPer
	- 'Pink Pearl'	CWil NMen SDys SFgr WIvy WTin
	- 'Sir William Lawrence'	CMea CPBP CWil ECho EDAr EPem NMen SFgr WAbe WHal WHoo WIvy WPer WThu WTin
	'Caldera'	NHol
*	***callosum barnesii***	GAbr
*	***calopticum*** x ***nevadense***	WTin
	'Cameo'	see *Jovibarba heuffelii* var. *glabra* 'Cameo'
	'Canada Kate'	CWil NHol WPer
	'Candy Floss'	CTca CWil NMen WGor
	cantabricum	CWil EDAr GKev NMen SIng
	- from Cuevas del Sil, Spain	CWil
	- from Navafria, Spain	CWil NHol SIng WTin
	- from Peña Prieta, Spain	NMen
	- from Riaño, Spain	CWil GAbr
	- from San Glorio, Spain	CWil GAbr NMen
	- from Santander, Spain	NHol
	- from Ticeros	EPem NMen
	- from Tizneros, Spain	CWil
	- from Valvarnera, Spain	NMen
	- subsp. ***cantabricum*** from Leitariegos, Spain	CWil GAbr MHom NMen
	- - from Peña de Llesba, Spain GDJ 93.13	CWil
	- - from Pico del Lobo, Spain	CWil
	- subsp. ***guadarramense***	see *S. vicentei* subsp. *paui*
	- - from Pico del Lobo, Spain, No 1	SRot
	- - - No 2	EPem

- - from Valvanera, Spain, No 1	CWil NMen
- subsp. ***urbionense***	CWil SIng
- - from El Gatón	CWil
- - from Picos de Urbión, Spain	CWil NMen
- - from Sierra de la Demanda GDJ 94.09	CWil
- - - GDJ 94.10	CWil
- - from Sierra de Pineda GDJ 95.01	CWil
- - from Sierra de Urbión GDJ 94.12	CWil
cantabricum x ***montanum*** subsp. ***stiriacum***	WEas WTin
cantabricum x ***giuseppii*** from Picos de Europa GDJ 93.10	CWil
cantabricum x ***montanum*** subsp. ***stiriacum*** 'Lloyd Praeger'	CWil
'Canth'	NHol
'Cappachino' **new**	CTca
'Carmen'	CHal GAbr SFgr
'Carneum'	NHol
'Carnival'	CHal NMen WPer
caucasicum	CWil MHom NMen
'Cavo Doro'	CTca CWil SFgr
charadzeae	CWil LBee LRHS NHol
'Cherry Frost'	ECho NDlv NMen SFgr
'Cherry Glow'	see *Jovibarba heuffelii* 'Cherry Glow'
'Chilli Pepper' **new**	CTca
'Chocolate'	NHol WPer
§ x ***christii***	NHol NMen
'Christmas Time'	CTca NHol SFgr
ciliosum ♀^{H4}	CMea CPBP CWil ECho NMen NRya
- from Alí Butús, Bulgaria	SDys
§ - var. ***borisii***	CWil EPfP GKev NDlv NMen NRya WAbe WHal
- var. ***galicicum*** from Mali Hat, Albania	NMen WPer
ciliosum x ***ciliosum*** var. ***borisii***	CHal CTri NMen
ciliosum x ***grandiflorum***	CWil NMen
ciliosum x ***marmoreum***	NMen
ciliosum x ***tectorum***	WTin
'Cindy'	SRms
'Circlet'	CWil NMen
* ***cistaceum***	WEas
'Clara Noyes'	SMer WFar WPer WRHF
'Clare'	EPem MHer
'Cleveland Morgan'	ECha LRHS MHom NBro NMen
'Climax'	CTca EBee ECho MHom NMen SMer WFar
'Clivette' **new**	CTca
'Cobweb Capers'	MHom
'Cobweb Centres'	NMen
'Collage'	NHol
'Collecteur Anchisi'	NHol SDys SFgr
'Commander Hay' ♀^{H4}	CHEx COlW CTca CWil EBee EDAr EPfP ETod EWes GCra GKev MBNS MHom MWgw NMen NPer SBch SRGP SRms STre WEas WHal WIvy WPer
'Comte de Congae'	NMen
'Congo'	NMen SFgr
'Conran'	NHol
'Cornstone'	ECha NHol
'Corona'	CWil GKev NHol SFgr SRms WPer
'Corsair'	CWil ECha EDAr GKev MBrN NMen SFgr WGor WIvy WPer WTin

'Crimson King' **new**	SFgr
'Crimson Velvet'	CHEx EDAr GKev LBee LRHS NHol SFgr WPer
'Crimson Webb' **new**	SIng
§ 'Crispyn'	CTca CWil EPot GKev LBee MHer MHom NHol NMen SFgr SIng WEas WPer
'Croton'	WPer
'Cupream'	CWil NDlv SRms WPer
'Czakor'	NHol
'Dakota'	CWil NHol NMen
'Dallas'	CWil NHol NMen SRms
'Damask'	CWil LBee NMen WPer
'Darjeeling'	CWil
'Dark Beauty'	CMea CWil ECha GKev NMen WAbe WGor WHal WPer
'Dark Cloud'	CWil LBee LRHS WHoo WIvy WPer
'Dark Point'	CWil MHom NMen SFgr SIng
'Darkie'	CWil SFgr WPer
davisii	ECha
'Deebra'	CWil
'Deep Fire'	CWil NHol NMen SRms WAbe WIvy WTin
x ***degenianum***	GAbr NMen SFgr WPer
'Delta'	NMen WHoo WTin
densum	see *S. tectorum*
'Devon Glow' **new**	CTca
'Devon Jewel'	CTca WGor
'Diane'	CWil SFgr
'Director Jacobs'	CWil EDAr GAbr NHol NMen SFgr WEas WPer WTin
'Doctor Roberts'	NHol
dolomiticum	NMen
dolomiticum x ***montanum***	CWil GKev NBro NMen SFgr WTin
'Donarrose'	NHol
'Downland Queen'	CWil NHol
'Duke of Windsor'	NMen SFgr
'Dyke'	CTri CWil GAbr NHol NMen SFgr WHal
dzhavachischvilii	NMen
'Edge of Night'	CWil NHol SRms
* ***edisseri*** **new**	EPem
'Eefje'	CWil
'El Toro'	ECha MHom
'Elgar'	WIvy WPer
'Elizabeth'	WPer
'Elvis'	CWil NMen SFgr
'Emerald Giant'	CWil NHol SRms WPer WTin
'Emerson's Giant'	CWil NMen
'Emmchen'	CWil
'Engle's'	CTca CTri EBee ECha EWin GKev LRHS NMen SRms WHal WPer
'Engle's 13-2'	NBro NHol NMen
'Engle's Rubrum'	CPBP EPot GAbr GKev LBee NHol NMen
erythraeum	MHom NHol NMen WAbe WFar WHal
- from Pirin, Bulgaria	NMen
- from Rila, Bulgaria	NMen
'Excalibur'	NMen WIvy
'Exhibita'	CWil SDys SRms
'Exorna'	CWil ECha MHom NMen SFgr SIng WEas WIvy WPer
'Fabienne'	CWil
'Fair Lady'	CWil GKev MHom NMen
'Fame'	NHol
'Fat Jack'	CWil
x ***fauconnettii***	CWil EDAr NHol NMen SFgr
- 'Thompsonii'	CWil NHol NMen SIng
'Feldmaier'	WFar
'Festival'	NMen
'Fiesta'	WHal
fimbriatum	see *S.* x *barbulatum*
'Fire Glint'	CWil NHol SRms WIvy

'Firebird'	NMen SFgr
'Flaming Heart'	CTca CWil EDAr MBrN NMen WGor WPer
'Flamingo'	ECha NMen
'Flanders Passion'	CTca ECha EPot ITim LBee LRHS NMen SRms WPer
'Flasher'	WEas WPer
'Flavipiluns'	WFar
'Forden'	CHEx SFgr WGor
'Ford's Amiability'	SDys
'Ford's Shadows'	SDys
'Ford's Spring'	CWil NHol NMen WIvy WPer
'Freeland'	WPer
'Frigidum'	NDlv
'Frolic'	SIng
'Fronika'	CWil
'Frost and Flame'	NHol
'Frosty'	CWil SFgr SRms
'Fuego'	CWil MHom SFgr
x ***funckii***	CHEx CWil EDAr MBrN NHol NMen SDys SIng WPer WTin
– var. ***aqualiense***	CWil
'Galahad'	GAbr
'Gallivarda'	CWil
'Gambol'	NHol
'Gamma'	CHEx CWil LBee LRHS NHol NMen SDys SIng SRms WEas WTin
'Garnet'	ECho WIvy WPer
'Gay Jester'	CTca CTri CWil SFgr SIng WHoo WTin
'Gazelle'	WIvy WPer
'Genevione'	CWil
'Georgette'	CWil ECha NMen WPer
'Ginnie's Delight'	CWil NMen
'Gipsy'	CWil
giuseppii	LBee MHer NHol NMen SIng WPer WRHF
– GDJ 93.04 from Cumbre de Cebolleda	CWil
– GDJ 93.17 from Coriscao, Spain	CWil
– from Peña Espigüete, Spain	CWil GAbr NMen SDys
– from Peña Prieta, Spain	CWil NMen
– from Vega de Liordes-W	CWil
'Gizmo'	CWil
'Glaucum'	see *S. tectorum* var. *glaucum*
'Gloriosum'	GAbr SFgr WPer
'Glowing Embers'	CWil GKev MHom NMen WHal WPer
'Godaert' **new**	CTca
'Graceum'	CWil
'Granada'	NMen
'Granat'	CWil MHer NMen SRms WIvy WPer
'Granby'	CWil ECho LBee NMen SDys
grandiflorum	CWil GKev NMen SIng WBrE WPer
– from Valpine	NMen
– 'Fasciatum'	CWil NMen
grandiflorum x ***montanum***	see *S.* x *christii*
'Grape Idol'	CWil
'Grapetone'	MHom NMen SDys WHal
'Graupurpur'	CWil
'Gray Dawn'	MHom
'Green Apple'	CWil GAbr MHom NMen SDys
'Green Dragon'	CWil
'Green Gables'	WPer
'Green Giant'	MTPN
'Greenwich Time'	NMen
'Grey Ghost'	NMen WIvy WPer
'Grey Green'	CWil NHol
'Grey Lady'	CWil
'Grey Owl'	GMaP LRHS
'Grey Velvet'	CWil

'Greyfriars'	CMea CTca EPot EWll LBee LRHS NMen SFgr WGor WOut WPer
'Greyolla'	CWil WPer
'Gruaud Larose'	NHol
'Gulle Dame'	CTca CWil SFgr
'Halemaumau'	CWil
'Hall's Hybrid'	CTca CWil GAbr NBro SIng SRms STre
'Happy'	CWil NMen SFgr SRms WGor WIvy WPer WThu
'Hart'	CTca CWil NHol SRms WTin
'Haubyi' **new**	CTca
'Havana'	NMen
'Hayling'	EDAr LRHS NHol NMen SIng SRms WPer
'Heavenly Joy'	NHol
'Heigham Red'	CTca CWil GKev LBee LRHS NHol NMen WPer
'Heliotroop'	SDys SRot
helveticum	see *S. montanum*
'Herkules' **new**	CTca
'Hester'	CHEx CTca CWil EBee ECho GAbr MBrN NBro NMen SRms WFar
'Hey-hey'	CTca EDAr EPot LBee LRHS MBrN NMen SIng SPlb SRms WPer
'Hidde'	CWil SFgr WIvy WPer
'Hidde's Roosje'	NMen
'Hirsutum'	see *Jovibarba allionii*
hirtum	see *Jovibarba hirta*
'Hookeri'	see *S.* x *barbulatum* 'Hookeri'
'Hopi'	CWil NHol SRms
'Hortulanus Smit'	NMen
'Hurricane'	CWil WIvy WPer
'Icicle'	CHEx CMea CTca LRHS NBro NHol NMen SRms WAbe WGor
imbricatum	see *S.* x *barbulatum*
'Imperial'	CWil MHom
'Infinity' **new**	CTca
ingwersenii	MHom SIng
ingwersenii x ***pumilum***	CWil EPem
'Iophon'	LBee
'Irazu'	CWil GAbr NMen SDys SFgr SRms WPer
'Isaac Dyson'	SDys SRot
ispartae	CWil
italicum	MHom NMen
'Itchen'	NMen
'Iwo'	CHEx NMen SFgr WIvy
'Jack Frost'	CWil EPem NBro NMen SFgr
'Jacquette'	CWil
'Jamie's Pride' **new**	WGor
'Jelly Bean'	CWil NMen SFgr
'Jet Stream'	CTca CWil GKev NMen SDys WGor
'Jewel Case'	CTca CWil LRHS NMen SRms
'John T.'	WEas
'Jolly Green Giant'	MHom
'Jo's Spark'	NSla
'Jubilee'	CMea CTca CWil ECho EDAr ELan EPem EPot MHer NHol NMen SRms STre WGor WPer
'Jubilee Tricolor'	NHol NMen SFgr WAbe
'Julia' **new**	SIng
'Jungle Fires'	CTca CWil EPot ITim NHol SDys SRms WHoo
'Jungle Shadows'	EDAr
'Jupiter'	GKev
'Jurato'	NHol
'Just Peachy' **new**	CTca
'Justine's Choice'	CWil SRms
'Kalinda'	MHom NMen
'Kansas Gorge' **new**	CTca
'Kappa'	CTri NBro NHol NMen SDys SRot WPer
'Katmai'	CWil NHol

	'Kelly Jo'	CWil EBee EWin EWll ITim NBro NMen SIng WTin
	'Kermit'	MHom NMen
	'Kerneri'	NHol
	'Kibo'	WIvy
	'Kimble'	WPer
	kindingeri	CWil MHom NMen NWCA
	'King George'	CHal CTri CWil ECha GKev ITim LBee LRHS NMen SFgr SRms STre WGor WHal WHoo WPer WTin
	'Kip'	CMea ECha NMen WGor WIvy WPer
	'Kismet'	NMen
	'Koko Flanel'	CWil SFgr
	'Korspel Glory 4'	CWil
	'Korspelsegietje'	CWil
	kosaninii	NHol NMen SFgr WPer WTin
	- from Koprivnik	NMen SDys WAbe
*	- from Visitor	CWil
	- 'Hepworth'	NHol
	'Kramers Purpur'	NMen
	'Kramers Spinrad'	CHEx CMea CTca CWil ECha GAbr LBee LEdu LRHS NMen SDys SFgr SIng STre WEas WHoo WIvy WTin
	'Lady Kelly'	CMea GKev NMen WIvy
	'Launcelot'	ECha WPer
	'Lavender and Old Lace'	CHEx CWil GAbr LRHS NMen SFgr WPer
	'Laysan'	CWil NHol
	Le Clair's hybrid No 4	NMen
	'Lennik's Glory'	see *S.* 'Crispyn'
	'Leocadia's Nephew'	NMen
	'Leon Smits'	CWil
	'Lilac Time'	CWil GAbr LRHS MHer NMen SFgr SRms WHal WIvy WPer
	'Limbo'	CWil
	'Linaria'	MTPN
	'Lipari'	EBee ECha EPot GKev MWgw NMen SIng SRms
	'Lipstick'	NMen
	'Lively Bug'	CTca CWil LBee LRHS SDys SIng WGor WPer
	'Lloyd Praeger'	see *S. montanum* subsp. *stiriacum* 'Lloyd Praeger'
	'Lonzo'	CWil SRms
	'Lynne's Choice'	CWil GAbr SFgr SIng WHal WIvy
	macedonicum	EDAr NDlv NMen WTin
	- from Ljuboten	CWil NMen
	'Madeleine'	CWil
	'Magic Spell'	CWil NMen
	'Magical'	CWil
	'Magnificum'	CWil NMen WGor
	'Mahogany'	CHEx CTca CTri CWil ECho EDAr GKev LBee LRHS NBlu NHol NMen NWCA SBla SFgr SRms SWal WEas WGor WHal WIvy
	'Maigret'	CWil WPer
	'Majestic'	CWil LBee NMen
	'Major White'	CHEx
	'Malby's Hybrid'	see *S.* 'Reginald Malby'
	'Marella'	WPer
	'Maria Laach'	CWil SIng
	'Marijntje'	CWil NHol NMen
	'Marjorie Newton'	CWil
§	***marmoreum***	CTca ECho EPot GKev LBee LRHS NMen SRms STre WHal WPer
	- from Kanzan Gorge	EPot NHol NMen
	- from Monte Tirone	CWil SDys
	- from Okol	NMen
	- var. ***angustissimum*** **new**	CTca
	- 'Brunneifolium'	CWil EGoo GAbr LBee LRHS NHol NMen SIng WIvy WPer
	- subsp. ***marmoreum*** var. ***dinaricum***	CWil MHer NMen
	- 'Ornatum'	SRms
	'Mate'	NMen
	'Maubi'	CHEx CWil
	'Mauvine'	NHol
	'Medallion'	SFgr
	'Meisse'	ECho
	'Melanie'	CWil MBrN NMen WIvy
	'Mercury'	CTca CWil GAbr LRHS NBro NHol NMen SRms
	'Midas'	CTca CWil ECha SFgr
	'Mila'	CWil
	'Mini Frost'	CWil NMen WPer
	'Mint Choc Chip' **new**	CTca
	'Missouri Rose'	NHol
	'Mixed Spice'	CWil
	'Moerkerk's Merit'	CWil NHol NMen
	'Mondstein'	CWil GKev SFgr SRms WIvy
	'Montage'	CWil
§	***montanum***	LEdu LRHS NMen WPer
	- from Arbizion	CWil
	- from Windachtal	CWil NMen
	- subsp. ***burnatii***	CWil MHom SIng WIvy
	- subsp. ***carpaticum***	CWil
	- - 'Cmiral's Yellow'	EPot NMen SFgr WAbe WIvy
*	- Fragell form	SChr SFgr
	- from Monte Tonale, Italy	CWil
	- subsp. ***montanum***	CWil
	- 'Rubrum'	see *S.* 'Red Mountain'
	- subsp. ***stiriacum***	CTca CWil NMen SFgr SIng
§	- - 'Lloyd Praeger'	CWil GKev LBee LRHS NMen SDys SFgr WIvy
	montanum* x *tectorum var. ***boutignyanum*** GDJ 94.15	CWil
	'Moondrops'	CWil
	'More Honey'	CWil NMen SFgr SRms
	'Morning Glow'	CMea WGor WHal
	'Mount Hood'	LRHS SIng SRms WHal
	'Mulberry Wine'	CWil EBee LBee LRHS NHol
	'Mystic'	CWil MBrN NMen WPer
	'Neon'	CWil
	nevadense	CWil EPot NMen SFgr SRms
	- from Puerto de San Francisco	CWil
	- from Calar de Santa Barbara, Spain GDJ 96A-07	CWil
	- var. ***hirtellum***	CWil NMen
	'Nico' CWil SRms	
	'Night Raven'	CMea SIng WIvy
	'Nigrum'	see *S. tectorum* 'Nigrum'
	'Niobe'	SFgr WHal
	'Noir'	CWil EDAr NBPN NBro NMen WAbe
	'Norbert'	CWil EDAr SRms WIvy
	'Nouveau Pastel'	CMea CWil NMen WHal
	'Novak'	CWil
	'Octet'	CWil EPem NMen
	octopodes	NBir SIde
	- var. ***apetalum***	CWil GAbr GKev NMen SIng SRms WIvy
	'Oddity'	CPBP CWil ECha MBrN MHer NMen WCot WHal WPer
	'Ohio Burgundy'	ECha LRHS NDlv NMen WPer WTin
	'Olivette'	ECha NMen WPer WTin
	'Omega'	WPer
	'Opitz'	WPer
	'Ornatum'	EPot MHer NMen WAbe WEas WHal WIvy
	ossetiense	CWil GKev NMen
	'Othello'	CHEx CHal CTri EBee EPfP EWin GAbr GCra GKev MBNS NBPN NBir STre WCot WTin
	'Pacific Feather Power'	NMen

'Pacific Purple Shadows'	CWil
'Packardian'	CWil GKev NHol NMen SFgr WIvy
'Painted Lady'	CWil
'Palissander'	CTca EDAr GAbr GKev NMen SFgr
'Pam Wain'	MHom NMen
'Panola Fire'	WFar
'Paricutin'	SDys
'Passionata'	CWil SFgr
'Pastel'	CTca CWil NMen
patens	see *Jovibarba heuffelii*
'Patrician'	CWil LBee LRHS SRms
'Pekinese'	CTca CWil EDAr EPot GKev ITim LBee LRHS MSte NBro NHol NMen SIng SRms WCot WEas WGor WPer
'Penny Jo' **new**	CTca
'Peterson's Ornatum'	SDys
'Petsy'	CWil SRms
'Pilatus'	EBee ECha EWes GKev LBMP MBNS MWgw SRms WFar
'Pink Astrid'	CWil
'Pink Cloud'	CWil EPem NMen SBla SRms
'Pink Flamingoes'	SRot
'Pink Lemonade'	CWil MHom
'Pink Mist'	WPer
'Pink Puff'	CWil MHom NMen SRms
'Pink Stirling' **new**	CTca
'Pipit' **new**	GKev
'Pippin'	CMea CWil GAbr SRms WPer
'Piran'	CWil
pittonii	CHal CMea CWil EPot NMen WHal
'Pixie'	CWil GKev NDlv NMen SFgr WIvy
'Plum Frosting'	WGor
'Plum Mist'	NHol
'Plumb Rose'	CWil NMen WIvy
'Pluto'	CWil LBee NHol
'Polaris'	CWil MHom
x ***pomelii***	WAul
'Ponderosa'	CWil
'Pottsii'	CWil
'Proud Zelda'	GAbr NMen
'Pruhonice'	CWil SRms WFar
'Pseudo-ornatum'	EPfP LBee LRHS SRms
'Pumaros'	NMen SDys
pumilum	CWil LRHS MBar NMen
- from Adyl Su No 1	CWil
- from Armchi	SDys
- from El'brus No 1	CWil
- from Techensis	CWil NMen
pumilum x ***ingwersenii*** from Spain	NMen
'Purdy'	MHom WAbe
'Purdy's 50-6'	CWil GAbr
'Purple Beauty'	EPot GKev
'Purple King'	MHom SDys
'Purple Queen'	CWil SIng
'Pygmalion'	CWil SIng
'Queen Amalia'	see *S. reginae-amaliae*
'Quintessence'	CWil NHol SFgr SRms
'Racy'	CWil
'Ramses'	SDys
'Raspberry Ice'	CMea GKev ITim LBee NBro NHol NMen SIng WPer
'Rauer Kulm'	CWil
* 'Rauheit'	WFar
'Rauhreif'	WFar
'Red Ace'	CWil ECha EPem NBro NMen SFgr SRms WFar
'Red Beam'	CWil
'Red Chief' **new**	GKev
'Red Chips'	MHom
'Red Delta'	CWil NBir NMen SFgr
'Red Devil'	CWil EBee ECha NHol NMen WHoo WLin WTin
'Red Lion'	CWil SFgr
'Red Lynn'	CWil
§ 'Red Mountain'	CHal CWil EPem LBee LRHS NWCA SRms
'Red Pink'	CWil
'Red Robin'	EBee LRHS SIng
'Red Rum'	SIng WPer
'Red Shadows'	LBee WPer WTin
'Red Spider'	CWil MHom NBro NMen
'Red Wings'	ECha NMen SRms
'Regal'	NMen
'Reggy'	CTca CWil WGor
'Regina'	NMen
reginae	see *S. reginae-amaliae*
§ ***reginae-amaliae***	CWil EPot NHol NMen WLin
- from Kambeecho, Greece, No 2	NMen SDys
- from Mavri Petri	CWil SDys
- from Sarpun, Turkey	CWil NMen SDys WTin
- from Vardusa, Serbia	CWil SDys
§ 'Reginald Malby'	CTri ECho LRHS NMen SFgr SRms WIvy
* ***regis-fernandii***	ECho
'Reinhard'	CBrm CMea CTca CWil ECha EDAr EPem EPot LRHS MBrN MHer NMen SIng SRms WCot WFar WHal WHoo WIvy WLin WPer
'Remus'	CTca CWil ECha NMen SDys SFgr SRms WGor
'Rex'	NMen
'Rhöne'	CWil LBee
* ***richardii***	MBar
'Risque'	CWil LBee WPer
'Rita Jane'	CTca CWil ECha MHom NMen SFgr SIng WTin
'Robin'	ITim LBee LRHS NBro NHol SRms WTin
'Ronny'	CWil
'Rose Splendour'	NHol
x ***roseum*** 'Fimbriatum'	CWil GAbr LBee LRHS NDlv NHol SFgr WEas
'Rosie'	CMea CPBP CTca CWil EPot ITim LBee LRHS NHol NMen SIng SPoG SRms WHal WHoo WLin WPer WTin
'Rotkopf'	CTca CWil NHol NMen SFgr SRms
'Rotmantel'	SDys WTin
'Rotsandsteinriese'	SIng
'Rotund'	CWil
'Rouge'	NMen
'Royal Opera'	CWil EDAr GKev NMen
'Royal Ruby'	CTca ECha GAbr LBee LRHS MBrN NMen SRms WIvy
'Rubellum'	CWil
'Rubellum Mahogany' **new**	SFgr
'Rubin'	CMea CTri EBee ECha EGoo EPPr EPfP GGar GKev MSte NBir NEgg NMen NWCA SPoG SRms WAbe WEas WPer
'Rubrum Ash'	CWil EPem GAbr NMen WAbe WTin
'Rubrum Ornatum'	MHom
'Rubrum Ray'	CWil SRms
* 'Ruby Glow'	EDAr GKev
'Russian River'	CTca WHoo WTin
'Rusty'	CWil SFgr
ruthenicum	EDAr LRHS MHom
'Safara'	CWil
'Saffron'	NMen
'Saga'	EPem MHom
'Sarah'	NMen
'Sarotte'	CWil
'Sassy Frass'	CTca NMen
'Saturn'	NMen
schlehanii	see *S. marmoreum*
'Seminole'	CWil
'Sha-Na'	CWil

	'Sharon's Pencil'	CWil
	'Sheila'	GAbr
	'Shirley Moore'	CWil WTin
	'Shirley's Joy'	CHal NMen WTin
	'Sideshow'	CWil
	'Silbering' **new**	EBee
	'Silberkarneol' misapplied	see *S.* 'Silver Jubilee'
	'Silberspitz'	CWil MHer MHom NBro NMen WPer
	'Silver Cup'	CWil WIvy
§	'Silver Jubilee'	CTca CWil ECha EDAr GAbr NBro NDlv SPlb SRms WGor
	'Silver Queen'	CWil SFgr
	'Silver Shadow'	CTca WGor
	'Silver Thaw'	CWil ECha EPem NMen
	'Silverine'	CWil
	'Silvertone'	CWil
	'Simonkaianum'	see *Jovibarba hirta*
	'Sioux'	CPBP CTca CWil GAbr LBee LRHS MBrN NMen SIng WFar WHal WIvy WOut WPer WTin
	'Skrocki's Bronze'	GAbr WPer
	'Slabber's Seedling'	CTca CWil
	'Small Wonder'	CWil
	'Smaragd'	CWil ECha LBee WFar
	'Smokey Jet'	SFgr
	'Snowberger'	CMea CTca CWil EPem EPot GKev LRHS NMen SFgr SIng SRms WHal WPer
	soboliferum	see *Jovibarba sobolifera*
	'Soothsayer'	CTca CWil NMen
	'Sopa'	CWil NMen
	sosnowskyi	CWil NMen
	'Spanish Dancer'	NMen
	'Sparkler' **new**	CTca
	'Spherette'	CTca CWil MBrN NMen WAbe WPer
	'Spider's Lair'	SIng
	'Spinnelli'	WTin
	'Spring Mist'	CMea CTca CWil GAbr MBrN SFgr SPoG SRms WGor WPer WTin
	'Sprite'	CWil NMen SDys WIvy WTin
	stansfieldii	see *S. arachnoideum* subsp. *tomentosum* 'Stansfieldii'
	'Starion'	CWil
	'Starshine'	MHer NHol NMen
	'State Fair'	CTca CWil NHol NMen WIvy WPer
*	***stoloniferum***	GAbr
	'Strider'	CWil GAbr WTin
	'Stuffed Olive'	CWil SDys SRot
	'Sun Waves'	CWil NHol SDys SFgr
	'Sunray Magic'	WGor
	'Super Dome'	CWil
	'Syston Flame'	CWil NMen
	'Tarantula' **new**	CTca
	'Tarita'	CWil
§	***tectorum*** ♀H4	CArn CHby CSam CTca CTri CWil EBee ECho EDAr ELan EPfP GKev GPoy LBee LRHS MBar MHer MNHC NMen SIde SIng SPlb STre WFar WJek
	- from Eporn	CWil NMen
	- from Fonderaise **new**	CTca
§	- var. ***alpinum***	CWil LRHS MHom NBro NHol NMen SIng
	- - from Sierra del Cadi, Spain	NHol
	- var. ***andreanum***	CWil
	- 'Atropurpureum'	ECho ELan NHol NMen WTin
	- 'Atrorubens'	NHol
	- 'Atroviolaceum'	EDAr NHol NLar NMen WFar WIvy WTin
*	- 'Aureum' **new**	SFgr
	- var. ***boutignyanum*** from Route de Tuixèn GDJ 94.04	CWil
	- - from Sant Joan de Caselles GDJ 94.02	CWil
	- - - GDJ 94.03	CWil
	- var. ***calcareum***	ECho
	- subsp. ***cantalicum***	SRms
§	- var. ***glaucum***	NDlv
§	- 'Nigrum'	LBee LRHS MHer NBro NHol NMen SDys SRms WGor WTin
	- 'Red Flush'	CTca CWil EDAr GKev MBrN NMen SDys SFgr SPoG WFar
	- 'Royanum'	GAbr
*	- subsp. ***sanguineum***	EDAr
	- 'Sunset'	CWil EDAr NMen SDys SFgr SIng WHal
§	- subsp. ***tectorum*** 'Boissieri'	CWil NMen SRms WIvy
	- - 'Triste'	CHEx CWil EBee LBee LRHS NMen SRms WAbe WFar
	- 'Violaceum'	MHom SRms STre WGor
	tectorum* x *zeleborii	WTin
	'Tederheid'	EBee LBMP MBNS MWgw
	'Telfan'	NMen
	'Tenburg'	CTca
	'Terracotta Baby'	CTca CWil SFgr
	'Thayne'	NMen
	'The Platters'	CWil
	'The Rocket'	CWil
	thompsonianum	CWil GKev NDlv NHol NMen SFgr SIng
	'Thunder'	CWil
	'Tiffany'	NHol WPer
	'Tiger Bay'	NHol
	'Tina'	WPer
	'Tip Top'	CTca CWil SFgr
	'Titania'	CWil EPem NBro NMen WHal WTin
	'Topaz'	CWil ECha LBee LRHS NMen SBla SFgr SRms
	'Tordeur's Memory'	CWil LBee LRHS NMen
	'Toy Enamel' **new**	CTca
	'Trail Walker'	CWil GKev LBee LRHS SRms
	transcaucasicum	CWil
	'Tree Beard'	CWil
	triste	CTca
	'Tristesse'	CWil GAbr NMen SFgr WGor
	'Truva'	CWil NMen SFgr
	'Tumpty'	WGor
	'Twilight Blues'	CWil SFgr
	'Undine'	CWil SFgr
	x ***vaccarii***	CWil NMen
	'Vanbaelen'	CWil GAbr NMen SDys
	'Vanessa'	CWil
*	***verschaffii***	EPem
	x ***versicolor***	NHol
	'Veuchelen'	CWil
	vicentei	CTca MHom NDlv NMen WTin
	- from Gaton	LBee LRHS NMen WFar
§	- subsp. ***paui***	NSla
	'Video'	CWil MHom NMen SFgr
	'Virgil'	CTca CWil GAbr MBrN NMen SDys SIng WAbe WGor WPer WTin
	'Virginus'	CWil GAbr
	'Warners Pink'	MDKP
	webbianum	see *S. arachnoideum* subsp. *tomentosum* (C.B. Lehm. & Schnittsp.) Schinz & Thell.
	'Webby Flame'	CWil
	'Webby Ola'	NMen
	'Wega'	NMen
	'Weirdo'	CTca CWil
	'Wendy'	NMen
	'Westerlin'	CTca CWil ECha GKev NMen
	'White Christmas'	see *S. arachnoideum* 'White Christmas'
	'White Eyes'	NMen

'Whitening'	GAbr NMen
'Wollcott's Variety'	CTca CWil EBee ECho EPem EWin LRHS MDKP NBir NMen SFgr WPer WTin
wulfenii	CWil NMen
* ***- roseum***	EDAr
'Xaviera'	CWil
zeleborii	CHal SDys WHal
'Zenith'	CWil EPem GAbr SFgr SRms
'Zenobia'	MHom
'Zenocrate'	WHal
'Zepherin'	CWil
'Zilver Moon'	CWil NMen
'Zilver Suzanna'	CWil
'Zircon'	NMen
'Zone'	CHEx NMen
'Zorba'	NMen
'Zulu'	ECha SFgr

Senecio (*Asteraceae*)

B&SWJ 9115 from Guatemala	WCru
B&SWJ 10361 from Guatemala	WCru
B&SWJ 10703 from Colombia new	WCru
HWJK 2118 from Nepal	WCru
§ ***articulatus***	CHal EShb
aureus	see *Packera aurea*
bicolor subsp. ***cineraria***	see *S. cineraria*
bidwillii	see *Brachyglottis bidwillii*
buchananii	see *Brachyglottis buchananii*
candicans	see *S. cineraria*
canescens B&SWJ 10720 new	WCru
chrysanthemoides	see *Euryops chrysanthemoides*
§ ***cineraria***	NBlu XPep
- 'Ramparts'	EBee
- 'Silver Dust' ♀^{H3}	EPfP LRHS
- 'White Diamond'	ECha SBch
* ***coccinilifera***	SBch
compactus	see *Brachyglottis compacta*
crassissimus	EShb
doria	LRHS WCot WFar WHrl
fistulosus	LEdu
formosus B&SWJ 10700 new	WCru
glastifolius	ERea
'Goldplate'	NLar
'Gregynog Gold'	see *Ligularia* 'Gregynog Gold'
greyi misapplied	see *Brachyglottis* (Dunedin Group) 'Sunshine'
greyi Hook.	see *Brachyglottis greyi* (Hook. f.) B. Nord.
heritieri DC.	see *Pericallis lanata* (L'Hér.) B. Nord.
hoffmannii	EShb
integrifolius subsp. ***capitatus***	EBee
kleiniiformis	EShb
laxifolius hort.	see *Brachyglottis* (Dunedin Group) 'Sunshine'
leucophyllus	WAbe
leucostachys	see *S. viravira*
macroglossus	CHll EShb
- 'Variegatus' (v) ♀^{H1}	CHal ERea EShb LAst
maritimus	see *S. cineraria*
monroi	see *Brachyglottis monroi*
niveoaureus B&SWJ 714 new	WCru
petasitis	CHEx
polyodon	CCCN CSpe EBla EShb GBin GBri MNrw NCGa NDov NLar WPGP
- S&SH 29	CFir EBee SAga
- subsp. ***subglaber***	EMan EMon EWes LBBr
przewalskii	see *Ligularia przewalskii*
pulcher	CDTJ CDes CFwr CGHE CSam EBee GBri LEdu LSou MNrw MTho SMrm WCot WPGP
reinholdii	see *Brachyglottis rotundifolia*
rowleyanus	EBak EShb
scandens	CCCN CMac CPLG ERea EShb MNrw WCwm WPGP
scaposus	WCot
seminiveus	EBee
§ ***serpens***	CHal CStu EShb
§ ***smithii***	CHid ELan EMan NBid WCot WCru WFar
spedenii	see *Brachyglottis spedenii*
squalidus	WHer
'Sunshine'	see *Brachyglottis* (Dunedin Group) 'Sunshine'
talinoides subsp. ***cylindricus*** 'Himalaya' new	EShb
tamoides 'Variegatus' (v)	ERea
tanguticus	see *Sinacalia tangutica*
§ ***viravira*** ♀$^{H3-4}$	EBee EGoo EPfP ERea EShb EWin MWgw SMad SMrm SPer WEas WSHC XPep

Senna (*Caesalpiniaceae*)

alata B&SWJ 9772	WCru
alexandrina	CCCN EShb WPGP
artemisioides ♀^{H1}	SOWG XPep
§ ***corymbosa***	CBcs CCCN CHEx CRHN CSpe CTri ERea LRHS LRav SOWG XPep
didymobotrya	SOWG
x ***floribunda***	XPep
hebecarpa	EMan
§ ***marilandica***	CArn EBee ELan ELau EShb EWes WCot
§ ***obtusifolia***	MSal
retusa	CHEx
septemtrionalis	CCCN WPGP

Sequoia (*Cupressaceae*)

sempervirens ♀^{H4}	CBcs CDoC CDul CLnd CMCN CTho CTrG ECrN EHul EPfP ERom ISea LCon LLin MBar MLan SBLw SLon SPoG WEve WMou WNor
- 'Adpressa'	CDoC CDul CMac CRob CSli CTho EHul EOrn EPla IDee LCon LLin MAsh MBar MGos NHol NWea SCoo SLim SPoG WEve WFar
- 'Cantab'	CDul SLim
- 'Prostrata'	CDoC CSli EOrn LLin MAsh MBar SLim WFar

Sequoiadendron (*Cupressaceae*)

giganteum ♀^{H4}	More than 30 suppliers
- 'Bajojeka'	NLar
- 'Barabits Requiem'	IArd IDee MBlu NLar SLim SMad
- 'Blauer Eichzwerg'	NLar SLim
- 'Blue Iceberg'	CKen
- 'Bultinck Yellow'	NLar SMad
- 'Cannibal'	MBri
- 'Conrad Appel' new	NLar
- 'French Beauty'	NLar
- 'Glaucum'	CDoC CTho EMil LCon LPan MAsh MBlu MBri NLar SLim SMad SPoG WEve
- 'Greenpeace'	NLar
- 'Hazel Smith'	SMad
- 'Little Stan'	CKen NLar
- 'Pendulum'	CBcs CDoC CKen EMil ERod LCon LLin LPan MBlu MGos NLar SLim SMad SWvt WEve
- 'Peve Bonsai'	NLar
- 'Philip Curtis'	NLar

- 'Powdered Blue' NLar
* - 'Type Wittbold Muller' new NLar
- 'Variegatum' (v) LLin MAsh MGos
- 'Von Martin' NLar

Serapias (Orchidaceae)

lingua SBla SCnR WHil
parviflora WHer

Serenoa (Arecaceae)

repens CBrP EAmu LPal SAin

Seriphidium (Asteraceae)

caerulescens var. **gallicum** EEls XPep
§ **canum** EEls MHer
§ **ferganense** EEls
§ **fragrans** EEls
§ **maritimum** CArn EWTr GGar ILis MHer NSti XPep
- var. **maritimum** EEls
§ **nutans** EBee EEls MRav MWgw
§ **tridentatum** CArn EBee
- subsp. **tridentatum** EEls
- subsp. **wyomingense** EEls
tripartitum var. **rupicola** EEls
§ **vallesiacum** ♀H4 EBee ECGP EEls MWgw WEas XPep
vaseyanaum EEls

Serissa (Rubiaceae)

japonica 'Pink Mystic' new EMil
- **rosea** STre
- 'Variegata' (v) STre

Serratula (Asteraceae)

coronata EBee
§ **seoanei** CMea CPom CStu CWsd EBee ECha EDAr EMan EMon LHop MHer SAga SBch SDix SIng SPhx SRms WCot WEas WFar WMoo WPGP WPat WPrP WTMC WTin
shawii see *S. seoanei*
tinctoria CArn EBee MSal NLar NMir
- subsp. **macrocephala** EBee LRHS SHGN
wolffii EBee

Serruria (Proteaceae)

florida SPlb

Sesamum (Pedaliaceae)

indicum CArn

Sesbania (Papilionaceae)

punicea CCCN CSpe SOWG XPep

Seseli (Apiaceae)

elatum CSpe LPio
- subsp. **osseum** EBee LPio
globiferum LPio SPhx
gummiferum CAby CArn CSpe EBee EMan EWin LPio MCCP MNFA SDix SKHP SPhx
hippomarathrum LPio SMHy SPhx WCot WHoo WHrl WPGP
libanotis CSpe EBee LEdu LPio MLLN NDov NLar SAga SBch SPhx
montanum CDes CSpe EBee WPGP
rigidum EBee

Sesleria (Poaceae)

autumnalis EBee EMon LCro LEdu SPhx
caerulea CAby CSam EAlp EBee ELan GFor LEdu MBar MLLN MMoz NLar WPtf XIsg XPep
- 'Malvern Mop' CBrm EBee WHrl WPGP
* **candida** EPPr
glauca CRez MNHC NLar NOak NPro WPer
heufleriana CElw EBee EPPr EPla GFor NLar SLPl SPlb XIsg
insularis CSWP EMon EPPr EShb
'Morning Dew' EBee
nitida CBig CKno EBee EMon GFor LEdu MMoz SApp SPhx SWal WPGP XIsg
sadleriana CBig EBee EPPr EWes GFor XIsg

Setaria (Poaceae)

RCB/Arg BB-2 WCot
macrostachya ♀H3 CKno GFor LLWP MAvo SBch SPhx
palmifolia CHEx CHll CKno CKob EPPr SDix WCot WDyG WPrP
- BWJ 8132 WCru
pumila new XIsg
viridis CHrt CSpe NChi NSti WCot WTin

Setcreasea see *Tradescantia*

shaddock see *Citrus maxima*

Sharon fruit see *Diospyros kaki*

Shepherdia (Elaeagnaceae)

argentea CAgr CBcs CPle NLar

Sherardia (Rubiaceae)

arvensis MSal

Shibataea (Poaceae)

kumasaca CAbb CBcs CBig CBrm CDoC CHEx EBee ENBC EPfP EPla ERod IBal LEdu LPal MBrN MCCP MMoz MWht NMoo NVic SDry SLPl WNor WPGP
- 'Aureostriata' EPla SDry
lancifolia CMCo EPla SDry

Shortia (Diapensiaceae)

galacifolia IBlr
- var. **brevistyla** IBlr
soldanelloides IBlr
- var. **ilicifolia** IBlr
- var. **magna** IBlr
uniflora IBlr
- var. **kantoensis** GGar
- var. **orbicularis** 'Grandiflora' CMac CWsd GCrs IBlr

Sibbaldia (Rosaceae)

procumbens EBee

Sibbaldiopsis (Rosaceae)

tridentata 'Lemon Mac' MAsh SIng SMac
- 'Nuuk' CStu GSki LRHS MAsh MBar NHol SMac

Sibthorpia (Scrophulariaceae)

europaea CGHE CHEx CPLG

Sida (Malvaceae)

acuta MGol
hermaphrodita EBee EMan WCot

Sidalcea (Malvaceae)

'Brilliant' CBcs CElw EBee EPfP LAst LCro LRHS MBnl MDKP MNrw NBPC

	NMRc NRnb NSti SPer SRkn WFar WMoo WWFP
candida	CBgR CSam EBee ECtt ELan EPfP GGar GMaP LAst LEdu LHop LRHS MBNS MRav MSte MWgw NCGa NEgg NGdn NRnb NSti SPer SPla SPoG WCAu WCot WFar WSpi
- 'Bianca'	CMea EBee EHrv ERou EShb MFOX MSte NLar NPri WFar WHal WMoo WPer
'Candy Girl' new	ERou MBnl
'Crimson King'	WFar
'Croftway Red'	CBgR CFir CTca EBee ELan EMan EPfP GCra GGar LRHS MAvo MRav MWgw NBro NCob NEgg NGdn NHol NRnb SAga SPet SPoG SWvt WAul WCAu WFar WMoo
cusickii	WOut
'Elsie Heugh' ♀H4	More than 30 suppliers
* ***grandiflora***	EBee
hendersonii	EBee
hickmanii subsp. ***anomala***	EBee
hirtipes	EBee
'Little Princess'PBR	CElw CFir EBee EKen ENot ERou EWes GBri LBuc MBNS MBri NDov NLar SPoG
'Loveliness'	CMMP CTca EBee ECtt ELan EMan EShb LHop LSou MAvo MRav NBro NChi NCob NGdn NHol NLar SAga SRGP
malviflora	MGol NBre NSti SEND SRms WBVN
- 'Alba'	WFar
- 'Crimson Beauty' new	EBee
'Mary Martin'	SMrm
'Monarch'	MDKP WFar
'Moorland Rose Coronet'	WMoo
'Mr Lindbergh'	EBee EPfP ERou LRHS MAvo NHol SAga WFar
'Mrs Borrodaile'	CBgR CMMP EBee ECtt EMan GBuc GMac LAst LRHS MBNS MBnl MBri MRav MWgw NBro NCob NEgg NGdn NHol NPro WCAu WFar WMoo WSpi
'Mrs Galloway'	WFar
'Mrs T. Alderson'	WFar WMoo
'My Love'	ECha NDov SMrm
neomexicana	EMan
'Oberon'	EBee GBuc WFar
oregana	NBid NGdn
- subsp. ***spicata***	WFar WMoo
'Party Girl'	More than 30 suppliers
'Präriebrand'	LSou SAga SMrm
'Purpetta'	CBrm EBee MDKP MFOX NGBl NLar NPro NRnb STes WPer
'Reverend Page Roberts'	MRav WCot WFar
'Rosaly'	CEnt CMdw CMea EBee GAbr IFoB LBMP MWrn NLar WGor WHal WLin WPer
'Rosanna'	CBrm EBee GAbr GMaP LRHS MDKP NLar SPhx WHal WPer WWeb
'Rose Bud'	CElw
'Rose Queen'	CKno EBee ECha LHop LRHS MAvo MBNS MCot MFOX MRav NBro NCob NHol SPer SRms WCAu WFar
'Rosy Gem'	ECtt LCro LRHS MBNS NBre WFar
Stark's hybrids	LRHS SRms
'Sussex Beauty'	CMCo CSam EBee EMan LRHS MArl MAvo MBri MLLN MRav MSte NCiC NDov NEgg NGdn WAul WFar WMoo WWeb
'Sweet Joy'	SMrm
'The Duchess'	WFar
'William Smith' ♀H4	CSam EBee ECha ECtt EPfP EWes LRHS MBri MLLN MRav NChi NCiC NCob NGdn NOrc SGar SPer SPla SRGP WBVN WCAu WFar
'Wine Red'	CFir CKno EBee EMan ERou EShb IPot MAvo MBnl MDKP MSte NCob NGdn SWvt WCAu WCra WFar WSpi

Sideritis (*Lamiaceae*)

cypria	EMan XPep
scordioides	EBee XPep
syriaca	CArn EMan EOHP SGar

Sieversia (*Rosaceae*)

pentapetala	see *Geum pentapetalum*
§ ***reptans***	GBin NCob

Silaum (*Apiaceae*)

silaus	NMir

Silene (*Caryophyllaceae*)

acaulis	ECho EDAr MTho NLAp NLar NMen SBla SRms WAbe
§ - subsp. ***acaulis***	ECho SPlb SRms
- 'Alba'	CMea ECho EWes NLan NMen WAbe WPat
- 'Blush'	NMen WAbe
- subsp. ***elongata***	see *S. acaulis* subsp. *acaulis*
- 'Frances'	GCrs GMaP NHar NLAp NMen NRya NSla WAbe
- 'Francis Copeland'	ECho NMen
- 'Helen's Double' (d)	ECho
* - ***minima***	EPot
- 'Mount Snowdon'	ECho EDAr ELan EPfP EWes GMaP LBee NEgg NLar NMen NRya NWCA SPlb SPoG SRms WPat
- 'Pedunculata'	see *S. acaulis* subsp. *acaulis*
alba	see *S. latifolia*
alpestris	EBee EPfP MBar MHer MTho SRms SRot WMoo
- 'Flore Pleno' (d) ♀H4	EWes LBee NSla WPat
araratica	WAbe
x ***arkwrightii***	see *Lychnis* x *arkwrightii*
armeria	WHer
- 'Electra'	CSpe
asterias	GBuc GCra IGor MNrw NBid NBre NSti WPer
- MESE 429	GBin
atropurpurea	see *Lychnis viscaria* subsp. *atropurpurea*
bellidioides	WPGP
californica	NWCA SKHP
caroliniana	CHrt
chungtienensis	GKev
§ ***compacta***	NLar WKif
§ ***davidii*** new	GKev
§ ***dioica***	CArn CHrt CRWN EGoo EPfP MHer NLan NLar NMir NVic SECG SGar SWat WHen WMoo WRos WSFF WShi
- 'Clifford Moor' (v)	ECtt NSti SCoo
- 'Compacta'	see *S. dioica* 'Minikin'
§ - 'Flore Pleno' (d)	GCra GMac LBBr MRav MTho NBid NBro NGdn SMrm WEas WFar WHoo WPer WTin
§ - 'Graham's Delight' (v)	WMoo
- 'Inane'	EPPr LBBr MAvo SBch SHar
- f. ***lactea***	MHer
- lilac-flowered new	WCot
§ - 'Minikin'	ECha EMon LBBr MAvo WTin
- 'Pembrokeshire Pastel' (v)	MAvo
- 'Richmond' (d)	EBee GBuc NBre SBch SHar

- 'Rosea Plena' (d) CBre EMan MTho NCob WPer
- 'Rubra Plena' see *S. dioica* 'Flore Pleno'
- 'Thelma Kay' (d/v) CDes CFee CMil CSev ECtt EWes GBuc MDun NBid NBre NLar WMoo WPGP WWFP
- 'Underdine' EBee EWes
- 'Valley High' (v) new SPoG
- 'Variegata' see *S. dioica* 'Graham's Delight'

elisabethae NEgg
§ ***fimbriata*** CFir CSpe EBee EHrv ELan EPyc EShb GMaP LEdu MMHG MNFA MRav NChi NSti SAga SBri SMrm SPhx WAbb WCot WKif WMoo WPGP WPen WPtf WRHF WSHC WTin
- 'Marianne' MNrw

gracilicaulis GKev
hookeri WLin
- Ingramii Group CGra CPBP

'Ice Clips' WPtf
inflata see *S. vulgaris*
italica NCGa WCot
kantzeensis see *S. davidii*
keiskei var. ***akaisialpina*** new ITim
- var. ***minor*** EWes LRHS MTho

laciniata 'Jack Flash' LDai MGol MHar WHil WHrl
* - ***major*** new WLin
§ ***latifolia*** CArn NMir NSco WHen
- subsp. ***alba*** GWCH SECG

maritima see *S. uniflora*
maroccana CRWN
moorcroftiana GKev
multifida see *S. fimbriata*
nigrescens GKev NWCA
- HWJK 2287 WCru

nutans SRms WHer WSFF
orientalis see *S. compacta*
parishii var. ***latifolia*** NNS 03-556 NWCA
petersonii NWCA
pusilla CHal EDAr NLar
regia LRav MNrw NBre SKHP WPGP
'Rolley's Favourite' new EBee
rubra see *S. dioica*
saxifraga XPep
schafta ♀H4 CChe CHal CHrt CTca CTri EAlp ECha ECho ECtt EPfP GKev LRHS NBid NBlu NCob NPri NWCA SHGN SRms WAbe WFar WHoo WPer WWlt
- 'Abbotswood' see *Lychnis* x *walkeri* 'Abbotswood Rose'
- 'Robusta' LRHS SBla WAbe
- 'Shell Pink' ECha EPot EWes LBee LRHS LSou NCob NDov NLar NWCA WHoo

sieboldii see *Lychnis coronata* var. *sieboldii*
* ***tenuis*** GBuc
- ACE 2429 GBuc

thessalonica CEnt
§ ***uniflora*** CHrt ECho ECtt EMar EPfP GGar GKev MWat NBid NBlu NBro SBch SPlb SRms SWal WFar WHen WHer WMoo
- 'Alba Plena' see *S. uniflora* 'Robin Whitebreast'
I - 'Compacta' CEnt ECho EDAr EPPr NDlv SHGN WMoo WPtf
§ - 'Druett's Variegated' (v) More than 30 suppliers
- 'Flore Pleno' see *S. uniflora* 'Robin Whitebreast'
- pink-flowered LBee
§ - 'Robin Whitebreast' (d) CHar EBee ECha ECho ECtt EPfP MBar MNHC MTho MWat NBid NBro NOak NPri SRms SRot WMoo WPer
- 'Rosea' EBee ECtt EPfP GGar GKev LRHS MRav SPlb SRot WFar WOut WPer
- 'Silver Lining' (v) GBuc
- 'Variegata' see *S. uniflora* 'Druett's Variegated'
- Weisskehlchen see *S. uniflora* 'Robin Whitebreast'
- 'White Bells' CTri ECtt EPfP WHoo WKif WSHC

virginica CDes SKHP
§ ***vulgaris*** CRWN LEdu MHer NLan NMir NSco SECG
- SDR 1761 GKev
- subsp. ***maritima*** see *S. uniflora*

wallichiana see *S. vulgaris*
'Wisley Pink' CHal ECtt
yunnanensis SPhx WSHC
§ ***zawadskii*** GBuc MDKP SWal WTin

Silphium (*Asteraceae*)

integrifolium EBee NBre NDov SAga SMad WCot WOld
laciniatum CArn CWCL NBre NDov SMad SMrm SPhx WCot
perfoliatum ♀H4 CArn COld EBee ELon GPoy NBre NDov NLar NRnb SMrm SPhx WCot WFar WOld
terebinthinaceum EBee NDov SMad SPhx WCot

Silybum (*Asteraceae*)

marianum CArn CSpe EBee ELan EPfP GAbr GPoy MNHC MSal MWgw NGHP SECG SIde SPav WFar WHer
- 'Adriana' EGoo EUnu SPav

Simmondsia (*Simmondsiaceae*)

chinensis CArn EOHP MSal

Sinacalia (*Asteraceae*)

§ ***tangutica*** CPLG CSam CSpe ECha EPPr GGar MAvo MBNS MFOX NBid NBro NDov SDix WAbb WCru WFar

Sinarundinaria (*Poaceae*)

anceps see *Yushania anceps*
jaunsarensis see *Yushania anceps*
maling see *Yushania maling*
murielae see *Fargesia murielae*
nitida see *Fargesia nitida*

Sinningia (*Gesneriaceae*)

'Blue Wonder' MBri
* ***caerulea*** WDib
canescens ♀H1 ERea WDib
§ ***cardinalis*** CHal CSpe EBak WDib
- 'Innocent' WDib

§ x ***cardosa*** MBri
'Diego Rose' MBri
'Duchess of York' CSut
'Duke of York' CSut
'Kaiser Wilhelm' MBri
nivalis WDib
speciosa 'Etoile de Feu' MBri
- 'Kaiser Friedrich' MBri
- 'Mont Blanc' MBri
- 'Violacea' MBri

Sinobambusa (*Poaceae*)

§ ***intermedia*** EBee EPla
* ***orthotropa*** EPla WPGP
rubroligula EPla NMoo WPGP
tootsik EPla SDry
§ - 'Albostriata' (v) EBee EPla LPJP SDry
- 'Variegata' see *S. tootsik* 'Albostriata'

x *Sinocalycalycanthus* (*Calycanthaceae*)

raulstonii 'Hartlage Wine' CPMA EPfP

Sinocalycanthus (*Calycanthaceae*)

chinensis CBcs CMCN CPMA CPle ELan EPfP EWTr IDee IMGH MBlu MBri NLar SPoG SSpi WBVN WFar WPGP

Sinofranchetia (*Lardizabalaceae*)

sp. CBcs WCru

Sinojackia (*Styracaceae*)

rehderiana CBcs CPle
xylocarpa CBcs EPfP MBlu MBri NLar SSpi WFar

Sinowilsonia (*Hamamelidaceae*)

henryi CBcs NLar

Siphocampylus (*Campanulaceae*)

foliosus EBee
- CDPR 3240 WPGP

Siphocranion (*Labiatae*)

§ **macranthum** CDes CPom EBee EMan EWes MHar WPGP

Sisymbrium (*Brassicaceae*)

§ **luteum** WHil

Sisyrinchium ✿ (*Iridaceae*)

x **anceps** see *S. angustifolium*
§ **angustifolium** CMHG EAlp EBur ECha ECho MBNS MBar MNFA MSal NBir NLAp NLar SChF SPlb SRms WPer
- **album** ECho NLar
§ **arenarium** CMea CPBP EBur EPot
atlanticum NBro WPer
bellum hort. see *S. idahoense* var. *bellum*
bellum dwarf EBee
bermudianum see *S. angustifolium*
- 'Album' see *S. graminoides* 'Album'
'Biscutella' CBod CKno CLyd CPrp CSsd CTca CTri EBee EBur ECho ECtt EPfP GMaP ITer LEdu LHop NEgg NMen NRya SIng SPla SPlb SPoG SWal SWvt WFar WHal WHoo WKif
'Blue Ice' CBrm CMea CPBP CWCL EAlp EBee EBur EDAr MAvo NHol WAbe WHoo WMoo WPat WPer
boreale see *S. californicum*
brachypus see *S. californicum* Brachypus Group
'Californian Skies' More than 30 suppliers
§ **californicum** CBen EBur ECho EHon EMFW EPfP MBar NBid NBro WFar WMAq WPer
§ - Brachypus Group EAlp EBee ECho ECtt EDAr EPfP EPot MBNS MWgw NBir NLAp NLar NPri NVic SGar SPlb SPoG SWal SWat SWvt WMoo
* **capsicum** CPLG
§ **chilense** ERos
coeleste EBur
coeruleum see *Gelasine coerulea*
commutatum ECho GBuc MNrw SGar
convolutum LRHS NDov
- B&SWJ 9117 WCru
cuspidatum see *S. arenarium*
demissum CLyd EBur
depauperatum CLyd EBur EDAr MNrw WHer WPer
'Devon Blue' ECho
'Devon Skies' CHid CMCo CMHG CRez CTca CWCL EBur ECho MDKP MWea NMen SBch SIng SWvt WAbe WFar
douglasii see *Olsynium douglasii*
'Dragon's Eye' CElw CFis CMea CPBP EBur EWes MAvo MBrN SIng SMHy SRot SSvw WKif WPer WRHF
'E.K. Balls' More than 30 suppliers
elmeri EBur
'Emmeline' EBur
filifolium see *Olsynium filifolium*
graminoides EBur EDAr IFoB NBro WPer
§ - 'Album' EBur GGar LRHS NBro WPer
grandiflorum see *Olsynium douglasii*
'Hemswell Sky' CLyd EBur ECho EPot NRya
'Iceberg' EAro EBur ECha EDAr EMan EShb MWgw SBch WKif
idahoense ECha ECho EDAr GEdr GKev LRHS LSou MHer NRya SPlb SRms
- 'Album' see *S. idahoense* var. *macounii* 'Album'
§ - var. **bellum** EBee EBur ECho EPfP GGar LRHS MBNS NEgg NPri NWCA SGar SPet SRms WHen WMoo WPat WPer XPep
- - pale-flowered CKno SMHy
- - 'Rocky Point' CElw CLyd CMCo CSpe EAro EBee EBur EWes MAvo NLAp SPoG SRot WFar WHoo WPat
- var. **macounii** WFar
§ - - 'Album' ♀H4 CMea CSsd EAlp EBur ECho EDAr EMFW ERos GAbr LRHS MTho MWat NHol NLAp SAga SPet WAbe WFar WPat WPer
iridifolium see *S. micranthum*
junceum see *Olsynium junceum*
littorale CPLG EBur NLar WPer
macrocarpon ♀H2-3 CFee CLyd CPBP CSsd EBur ECho EPot ERos LRHS MDKP NMen SWal WPer
'Marie' EBur
'Marion' CMea CPBP MAvo MBrN NLar SBch SBla SMHy SPet SRot SSvw WPer
'May Snow' see *S. idahoense* var. *macounii* 'Album'
'Miami' EBur
§ **micranthum** EBur ECho WRos
montanum ECho ERos
'Mrs Spivey' EBee EBur ECho ECtt MBar MHer NBir
'North Star' see *S.* 'Pole Star'
nudicaule x **montanum** CFee EBur ECho GAbr MNrw NLAp NRya SRot WPer
palmifolium CDes CSpe CSsd EBee MAvo MDKP MHer MLLN MWea SGar WCot
- JCA 2.880.010 SKHP WPGP
patagonicum CPLG EBur EDAr ERos GBuc WPer
§ 'Pole Star' CFee CLyd CSpe EBur ECho LRHS LSou NHol WPer
'Quaint and Queer' CPLG CSpe CWCL EBee EBur ECha ECho ECtt EMar EPot ERou EShb MBrN MLHP MNFA MTho MWgw NBir NBro NChi NOak SHBN SWvt WLin WMnd WMoo WPer WSHC
'Raspberry' CMea EBur WAbe
'Sapphire' CHar NPri STes WFar
scabrum see *S. chilense*
'Sisland Blue' EBur EWes
§ **striatum** More than 30 suppliers
§ - 'Aunt May' (v) More than 30 suppliers
- 'Variegatum' see *S. striatum* 'Aunt May'

Sium (*Apiaceae*)

sisarum ELau EUnu GPoy MHer MSal

Skimmia ✿ (*Rutaceae*)

	anquetilia	CMac MBar
	arborescens GWJ 9374	WCru
	- subsp. ***nitida*** B&SWJ 8239	WCru
	arisanensis B&SWJ 7114	WCru
	x ***confusa***	WFar
	- 'Kew Green' (m) ♀H4	More than 30 suppliers
	japonica	CDul CMHG CMac CWib GQui MAsh MGan MGos NScw SReu SSta WFar WHCG
	- (f)	CMac CTrG CTri ELan EPfP SRms
	- B&SWJ 5053	WCru
	- 'Alba'	see *S. japonica* 'Wakehurst White'
	- 'Bowles' Dwarf Female' (f)	CMHG EPla MBar MBri MGos MRav MWht NHol SLim SLon
	- 'Bowles' Dwarf Male' (m)	CMHG EPla MAsh MBar NHol SLim
	- 'Bronze Knight' (m)	CMac EQua MBar MBri MRav NHol SLim WFar
	- 'Cecilia Brown' (f)	WFar
	- 'Chameleon'	LAst
*	- 'Claries Repens'	EPla
	- 'Dad's Red Dragon' **new**	NHol
	- 'Emanuella' **new**	ENot
	- 'Emerald King' (m)	MAsh MBar MBri WFar
N	- 'Foremanii'	see *S. japonica* 'Veitchii'
§	- 'Fragrans' (m) ♀H4	CDoC CMac CSBt CSam CTri CWib EBee ECrN ENot EPfP LCro LRHS MBar MBri MGos MRav MWgw NCGa NHol NPri SHBN SLim SPer SPoG SWvt WBod WFar WGob WGwG
	- 'Fragrant Cloud'	see *S. japonica* 'Fragrans'
	- 'Fragrantissima' (m)	WBod WFar
	- 'Fructu Albo'	see *S. japonica* 'Wakehurst White'
	- 'Godrie's Dwarf' (m)	CWSG EBee EMil EPfP WFar
	- 'Highgrove Redbud' (f)	MBar MGos WBod
	- var. ***intermedia*** f. ***repens***	WFar
	- - B&SWJ 5560	WCru
	- 'Keessen' (f)	WFar
	- 'Kew White' (f)	CAbP CDoC CWib EBee ECrN EPfP EQua IArd LRHS MAsh MGos MLan NHol SHBN SLon SPer SRms SWvt WCFE WFar WHCG
	- Luwian = 'Wanto'PBR	EBee NHol WFar
	- 'Marlot' (m)	EBee EPfP NLar SPoG
	- 'Nymans' (f) ♀H4	CDoC CEnd CSam EBee ELan EPfP LCro LRHS MAsh MBar MBri MRav MWht NDlv SHBN SLim SMer SPer SPla SPoG SReu SRms SSpi SSta WFar WGob
	- 'Oblata'	SMer
	- 'Obovata' (f)	EPla
	- Obsession = 'Obsbolwi'PBR **new**	ENot
	- 'Pigmy' (f)	CPLG
	- 'Red Dragon'	CMac
	- 'Red Princess' (f)	EPla LAst MAsh WFar
*	- 'Red Riding Hood'	NHol SLon
	- 'Redruth' (f)	CBcs CDoC CMac CSBt CSam EBee EQua LAst LHop LRHS MAsh MBar MGos MWat MWht NHol SSta WFar
§	- subsp. ***reevesiana***	More than 30 suppliers
	- - B&SWJ 3763	WCru
	- - 'Chilan Choice'	EPfP LRHS MAsh SLim SPla SPoG SSta
	- - 'Fata Morgana' (m)	MGos
	- - var. ***reevesiana***	LCro
	- - - B&SWJ 3544	WCru
	- - 'Robert Fortune'	MBar
§	- Rogersii Group	CMac CTri MBar
	- - 'Dunwood'	MBar
	- - 'George Gardner'	EMil MBar
	- - 'Helen Goodall' (f)	MBar
	- - 'Nana Mascula' (m)	CTri MGos
	- - 'Rockyfield Green'	MBar
	- - 'Snow Dwarf' (m)	MBar WFar
	- 'Rubella' (m) ♀H4	More than 30 suppliers
	- 'Rubinetta' (m)	CChe EPfP IArd LSRN MAsh MBar MGos NCGa NHol SLim WFar
	- 'Ruby Dome' (m)	MAsh MBar NHol WFar
	- 'Ruby King' (m)	CDoC CSBt ECrN EQua IArd LSRN MAsh MBar NHol NLar
	- 'Scarlet Dwarf' (f)	MBar NHol
	- 'Scarlet Queen' (f)	CWib
	- 'Stoneham Red'	EPla
	- 'Tansley Gem' (f)	EPfP LRHS MAsh MBar MBri MWht SPoG SSta WFar
	- 'Thelma King'	WFar
§	- 'Veitchii' (f)	CBcs CDul CMac CSBt CTri CWSG EBee ELan EPfP IArd IMGH LRHS MAsh MBar MGos MRav MSwo NHol SEND SHBN SLim SMer SPer SPoG SWvt WTel
§	- 'Wakehurst White' (f)	CMHG CMac CPle CSBt CTri EPfP MAsh MBar MRav NLar SLim SLon SReu SSpi WBod WFar
	- 'White Gerpa'	MGos
	- 'Winifred Crook' (f)	EPla LBuc MBar MBri WFar
	- 'Winnie's Dwarf'	MGos
	- 'Wisley Female' (f)	CTri ECtt EPla NHol WFar
	laureola	CDoC CPLG CSam EBee ECot MRav NHol SRms WFar WSHC
	- GWJ 9364	WCru
	- 'Borde Hill' (f)	NPri
	- subsp. ***multinervia*** B&SWJ 8259	WCru
*	***mica***	ISea
	'Olympic Flame'	CWSG ENot MGos SHBN WFar
	reevesiana	see *S. japonica* subsp. *reevesiana*
	rogersii	see *S. japonica* Rogersii Group

Smallanthus (*Asteraceae*)

§	***uvedalius***	MSal

Smilacina see *Maianthemum*

Smilax (*Smilacaceae*)

	B&SWJ 6628 from Thailand	WCru
	from Thailand	LEdu
	asparagoides 'Nanus'	see *Asparagus asparagoides* 'Myrtifolius'
	aspera	EPla EShb LEdu WCru WPGP
	china B&SWJ 4427	WCru
	discotis	CBcs SEND
	glaucophylla B&SWJ 2971	WCru
	nipponica B&SWJ 4331	WCru
	rotundifolia	LEdu
	sieboldii	LEdu MRav
	- B&SWJ 744	WCru

Smithiantha (*Gesneriaceae*)

	'Extra Sassy' **new**	EABi
	'Little One'	WDib
	'Multiflora'	WDib
I	'Temple Bells' **new**	EABi

Smyrnium (*Apiaceae*)

	olusatrum	CArn CSev CSpe MHer MNHC MSal SIde SWat WHer
	perfoliatum	CHid CSpe EBee EHrv ELan EMar EWes MBNS MNFA NChi SDix WCot WEas WFar WHal WSHC

	rotundifolium	WCot

Socratea (*Arecaceae*)

	montana	LPal

Solandra (*Solanaceae*)

	grandiflora misapplied	see *S. maxima*
	hartwegii	see *S. maxima*
§	***maxima***	CCCN ERea EShb MJnS

Solanum (*Solanaceae*)

	aculeatissimum	EUnu
	aethiopicum 'Black Stem' new	EUnu
	atropurpureum	CSpe
	aviculare G.Forst.	EUnu XPep
	bonariense	XPep
	caripense new	EUnu
	conchifolium hort.	see *S. linearifolium*
	crispum	SGar
	- 'Autumnale'	see *S. crispum* 'Glasnevin'
	- 'Elizabeth Jane Dunn' (v)	WCot
§	- 'Glasnevin' ♀H3	More than 30 suppliers
	- 'Variegatum' (v)	WGwG
	dulcamara	CArn GPoy
	- 'Hullavington' (v)	CNat
	- 'Lucia' (v) new	CNat
	- 'Variegatum' (v)	CMac CWan EBee ECrN EPfP EWin LRHS MAsh MBNS NSti SPoG WFar WSHC
	giganteum	EUnu
	hispidum	CHEx
	jasminoides	see *S. laxum*
	laciniatum	CArn CCCN CDTJ CHEx CPLG CSev CSpe EShb EWes GGar LHop SAPC SArc SGar SHFr SNew SPav WKif WWlt
§	***laxum***	EBee EShb LRHS MNHC MSwo NSti SMad SPer SPet SPoG SRms SWvt WFar WSHC XPep
	- 'Album' ♀H3	More than 30 suppliers
	- 'Album Variegatum' (v)	CWib ELan LRHS MBNS NBlu NSti SBra WSHC
*	- 'Aureovariegatum' (v)	CBcs CSBt EBee EPfP EShb EWin MGos NEgg SCoo SLim SPer SPla SPlb SPoG WWeb
§	***linearifolium***	WPGP WSPU
	macrocarpon new	EUnu
	mammosum new	CDTJ
	muricatum (F)	CCCN EShb EUnu EWin
	nigrum 'Chichelite' new	EUnu
	- 'Hei-tien-tsai' new	EUnu
	opacum new	EUnu
	pseudocapsicum	EUnu MBri
	- 'Ballon'	MBri
	- variegated (v)	EShb WCot
	quitoense (F)	CDTJ CHEx EUnu
§	***rantonnetii***	CCCN CHll CSpe ELan ERea EShb IDee MCot SOWG XPep
	- 'Royal Robe'	CBcs CRHN CTri
*	- 'Variegatum' (v)	CSpe ERea EShb
	salicifolium	EShb EWin
	seaforthianum	EShb SOWG
§	***sessiliflorum*** (F)	EUnu MJnS
	sinaicum 'Burbankii'	EUnu
	sisymbriifolium	EUnu WWlt
*	***spontaneum***	EUnu
	aff. ***stenophyllum*** B&SWJ 10744 new	WCru
	surattense new	EUnu
	tomentosum	EUnu
	topiro	see *S. sessiliflorum*
	wendlandii	CHll

Soldanella (*Primulaceae*)

	alpina	EBee ECho GCra GCrs GKev LBMP MTho MWea NMen SBla SIng SRms WAbe WBVN WLin
I	- 'Alba'	ECho WAbe
	carpatica	ECho GKev LTwo NHol WAbe
	- 'Alba'	ECho MDKP NSla SBla WAbe
	carpatica* x *pusilla	CPBP ECho NRya NSla SBla
	carpatica* x *villosa	ECho MDKP
	cyanaster	EBee ECho GEdr NRya SBla WAbe
	dimoniei	CFee ECho GKev ITim NMen NSla NWCA SBla WAbe
§	***hungarica***	CLyd ECho ITim MTho WAbe WFar
	minima	CLyd ECho GCrs NDlv NMen NRya NSla NWCA SBla WAbe
	- 'Alba'	WAbe
	minima* x *pusilla new	NHol
	montana	CLAP CLyd ECho EDAr GCrs LTwo MTho NLar NMen SIng
	- subsp. ***hungarica***	see *S. hungarica*
	pindicola	EBee ECho EMan EWes NDlv NMen NWCA WAbe WFar
	pusilla	EBee GKev ITim NSla
*	- ***alba***	ECho
	'Sudden Spring' new	WAbe
	villosa	CBgR CDes CLAP EBee ECho GCrs GGar GKev LEdu LRHS MDun MTho NHol NRya NSla SBch SBla WAbe WFar WSHC

Soleirolia (*Urticaceae*)

	soleirolii	CHEx CHal CKob CTri LRHS MBri MCCP SHFr SIng SPer STre WDyG WHer XPep
	- 'Argentea'	see *S. soleirolii* 'Variegata'
§	- 'Aurea'	CHal CKob CTri EDAr EWin SIng STre
	- 'Golden Queen'	see *S. soleirolii* 'Aurea'
	- 'Silver Queen'	see *S. soleirolii* 'Variegata'
§	- 'Variegata' (v)	CHal CKob WHer

Solenomelus (*Iridaceae*)

	chilensis	see *S. pedunculatus*
§	***pedunculatus***	CFee WPGP
	sisyrinchium	CPBP ERos

Solenopsis (*Campanulaceae*)

	axillaris	see *Isotoma axillaris*

Solenostemon ✿ (*Lamiaceae*)

	'Alice Horn'	NHor
	'Angel of the North'	NHor
	'Anne Boleyn' (v)	CHal
	'Autumn'	NHor
	'Autumn Gold'	CHal NHor
	'Autumn Rainbow'	WDib
	'Beauty' (v)	CHal NHor WDib
	'Beauty of Lyons'	CHal NHor
	'Beckwith's Gem'	CHal NHor
	'Billy Elliot'	NHor
	'Bizarre Croton' (v)	CHal NHor
	'Black Dragon'	CHal NHor
	'Black Heart'	NHor WDib
	'Black Prince'	CHal NHor WDib
	'Blackheart'	NHor
	'Brightness' (v)	NHor
	'Brilliant' (v)	NHor WDib
	'Bronze Gloriosus' (v)	NHor
	'Buttercup'	CHal NHor WDib
	'Buttermilk' (v) ♀H1	CHal NHor
	'Carnival' (v)	CHal NHor WDib
	'Carousel' (v)	NHor
	'Castle Eden'	NHor
	'Catherine Cookson'	NHor

'Chamaeleon' (v)	NHor WDib
'City of Durham' (v)	NHor
'City of Liverpool'	CHal NHor
'City of Middlesborough'	NHor
'City of Newcastle'	NHor
'City of Sunderland'	NHor
'Combat' (v)	CHal NHor SVil WDib
'Copper Sprite'	CHal
'Coppersmith'	NHor
'Crimson Ruffles' (v) ♀H1	CHal NHor WDib
'Crimson Velvet'	CHal NHor
'Crinkly Bottom'	NHor
'Crown of Bohemia'	NHor
'Dairy Maid' (v)	CHal NHor
'Dazzler' (v)	CHal NHor
'Display'	CHal NHor WDib
'Dolly' (v)	NHor
'Dracula'	CHal NHor
'Durham Gala'	NHor
'Ella's Fire'	NHor
'Emerald Forest'	NHor
'Etna' (v)	CHal NHor
'Fire Fingers'	NHor SVil
'Firebrand' (v) ♀H1	CHal NHor
'Firedance' (v)	NHor
'Firefly'	CHal NHor
'Flamenco Dancer'	NHor
'Flamestitch'	CSpe
'Freckles' (v)	CHal NHor WDib
'Funfair' (v)	CHal NHor
'Gertrude Jekyll'	NHor
'Gloriosus'	CHal NHor
'Glory of Luxembourg' (v) ♀H1	CHal NHor
'Goldie' (v)	CHal NHor
'Grace Darling'	NHor
'Green Mars' (v)	NHor
'Hanna Hauxwell'	NHor
'Hannay Harding'	NHor
'Harvest Time' (v)	NHor
'Holly' (v)	NHor
'Inky Fingers' (v)	CHal NHor WDib
'Jean' (v)	NHor
'Joseph's Coat' (v)	NHor
'Juliet Quartermain'	CHal NHor WDib
'Jupiter'	CHal NHor
'Kate Adie'	NHor
'Kentish Fire' (v)	CHal NHor
'Kiwi Fern' (v)	CHal NHor WDib
'Klondike'	CHal NHor
Kong Series	LRHS
- 'Kong Rose'	NPri
'Laing's Croton' (v)	CHal NHor WDib
'Lemon Dash'	NHor
'Lemondrop'	CHal NHor
'Leopard' (v)	NHor
'Lindisfarne' **new**	NHor
'Lord Falmouth' ♀H1	CHal NHor WDib
'Luminous'	NHor
'Mardigras' **new**	NHor
'Masquerade' **new**	NHor
'Melody' (v)	CHal NHor WDib
'Midas'	CHal NHor
'Midnight'	NHor
'Mission Gem' (v)	CHal NBlu NHor SVil
'Molten Lava' (v)	NHor
'Mrs Pilkington' (v)	NHor
'Muriel Pedley' (v)	CHal NHor
'Nettie' (v)	NHor
'Ottoman'	CHal NHor
'Paisley Shawl' (v) ♀H1	CHal NHor WDib
'Palisandra'	CSpe
pentheri	CHal NHor
'Percy Roots'	NHor
'Peter Wonder' (v)	CHal NBlu NHor SVil WDib
'Phantom'	NHor
'Pheasant's Eye' (v)	NHor
'Picturatus' (v) ♀H1	CHal NHor WDib
'Pineapple Beauty' (v) ♀H1	CHal NHor WDib
'Pineapplette' ♀H1	CHal NHor WDib
'Pink Devil' (v)	NHor
'Pink Shawl'	NHor
'Primrose Cloud' (v)	NHor
'Primrose Spire' (v)	NHor
'Purple Oak'	CHal NHor
'Raspberry Ripple'	CHal
'Red Angel' **new**	WDib
'Red Croton' (v)	NHor WDib
'Red Mars'	NHor WDib
'Red Nettie' (v)	CHal NHor WDib
'Red Paisley Shawl' (v)	NHor
'Red Rosie'	CHal NHor WDib
'Red Stinger'	CHal
'Red Velvet'	CHal NHor
'Rose Blush' (v)	CHal NHor WDib
'Rosie'	NHor
'Roy Pedley'	CHal NHor WDib
'Royal Scot' (v) ♀H1	CHal NHor WDib
'Salmon Plumes' (v)	CHal NHor
'Saturn'	NHor
'Scarlet Poncho'	NHor
'Scarlet Ribbons'	CHal NHor SVil
'Speckles' (v)	CHal NHor
'Spire' (v)	NHor
'Strawberry Jam'	CHal NHor
'Sunbeam' (v)	NHor
'The Durham Angel'	NHor
'Theresa Horn' **new**	NHor
thyrsoideus	see *Plectranthus thyrsoideus*
'Timotei'	NHor
'Tom Cooke'	NHor
'Treales' (v)	CHal NHor WDib
'Vesuvius'	CHal NHor
'Volcano'	NHor
'Walter Turner' (v) ♀H1	CHal NHor SVil WDib
'White Gem' (v)	CHal NHor
'White Pheasant' (v)	CHal NHor
'Winsome' (v)	CHal NHor WDib
'Winter Sun' (v)	CHal NHor
'Wisley Flame'	NHor WDib
'Wisley Tapestry' (v) ♀H1	CHal LAst NHor SVil WDib
'Yellow Croton' (v)	NHor

Solidago (*Asteraceae*)

	Babygold	see *S.* 'Goldkind'
	brachystachys	see *S. cutleri*
	caesia	EBee ECha EMon ERou EShb EWes MFOX MSte NBir WFar WMoo WOld WTin
	canadensis	CTri ELan NBre SEND SPlb WFar WHer
	- var. ***scabra***	WOld WTin
	'Cloth of Gold'	CBcs EBee ECho LRHS NPro SWvt WMnd WOld
§	'Crown of Rays'	CPrp EBee ECtt ERou LRHS MRav MWgw WFar WMnd
§	***cutleri***	EBee ECho ELan EWsh MBar MTho MWat NLar SBla SPlb SRms WFar WPer WTin
I	- ***nana***	ECho EWes WBor
	'Dzintra'	EBee
	'Early Bird'	WFar
§	***flexicaulis***	GMaP
	- 'Variegata' (v)	CWan EBee ELan EMan EMar EMon EPfP GMaP LRHS MHar NLar NSti WFar WHer WOld WPer
	'Gardone' ♀H4	WFar
	gigantea	EMon WFar WPer
	glomerata	EMon EShb NBre NLar NNor WPer
	Golden Baby	see *S.* 'Goldkind'

§ 'Golden Dwarf'	LRHS MBri
'Golden Fleece'	see *S. sphacelata* 'Golden Fleece'
'Golden Thumb'	see *S.* 'Queenie'
'Golden Wings'	CBre ERou
'Goldenmosa' ♀H4	CAby CSBt EMan EPfP ERou EWes GMaP LRHS MRav MWat SPer SPoG WCot WFar WOld
'Goldilocks'	NPri SRms
§ 'Goldkind'	CHrt CMMP CSBt CTri CWib EBee ECho ECtt EPfP ERou EShb GAbr MNHC NEgg NNor NOrc SPet SPoG SWal SWvt WBrk WFar WMoo WWeb
Goldzwerg	see *S.* 'Golden Dwarf'
graminifolia	see *Euthamia gymnospermoides*
'Harvest Gold'	CElw ERou
hispida	EMon
hybrida	see x *Solidaster luteus*
latifolia	see *S. flexicaulis*
'Laurin'	EMil EPfP NLar WTin
'Ledsham'	EBee LEdu LRHS MCot NBre WMnd
'Lemore'	see x *Solidaster luteus* 'Lemore'
'Linner Gold'	NBre
odora	MSal
ohioensis	EBee
* 'Peter Pan'	ERou LHop WFar
§ 'Queenie'	EBee ECha ECho MHer MLHP NBre NPro NVic SRms
rigida	NBre WCot WPer
- JLS 88002WI	EMon
roanensis	NBre
rugosa	ECha MWgw NBre WCot
- subsp. ***aspera***	EMon
- 'Fireworks'	CBgR CBre CMHG CPrp CSam EBee EBrs ECtt EMan EPPr ERou GQue MAvo MBNS MHar MNFA MSte NBPC NDov WCot WFar WHil WHoo WOld WTin
sciaphila	EBee NBre
sempervirens	WCot WFar
simplex subsp. ***simplex*** var. ***nana***	NWCA WLin WPer
'Sonnenschein'	NBre
speciosa	EUnu NBre WPer
spectabilis var. ***confinis***	EBee
§ ***sphacelata*** 'Golden Fleece'	EBee LHop LRHS NBre WHoo WMnd
spiraeifolia	EBee NBre
Strahlenkrone	see *S.* 'Crown of Rays'
'Summer Sunshine'	ERou
Sweety = 'Barseven' PBR	MBri
'Tom Thumb'	MRav SRms WEas
uliginosa	EShb NBre
ulmifolia	EBee NBre
virgaurea	CArn CSam EBee GPoy GWCH MHer MNHC NBre NLar NSco WHer WPer WSel
- subsp. ***alpestris*** var. ***minutissima***	CLyd CStu NBre WPat
- var. ***cambrica***	see *S. virgaurea* subsp. *minuta*
§ - subsp. ***minuta***	CSam GBin
§ - 'Variegata' (v)	NPro
vulgaris 'Variegata'	see *S. virgaurea* 'Variegata'
'Yellowstone' new	EBee

x *Solidaster* (*Asteraceae*)

hybridus	see x *S. luteus*
§ ***luteus***	CBgR EBee GBri MBri MHar SRms WEas WFar WHil
§ - 'Lemore' ♀H4	CHrt CMea CPrp EBee ELan ENot EPfP ERou EWsh GMac LRHS MWat MWgw NCGa NPri NSti NVic SPer WCot WFar
'Super'	CAby WCot WFar

Sollya (*Pittosporaceae*)

fusiformis	see *S. heterophylla*
§ ***heterophylla*** ♀H1	More than 30 suppliers
- 'Alba'	CBcs CCCN EBee ELan EPfP LBuc LRHS SPoG SWvt
- mauve-flowered	ECou
- 'Pink Charmer'	EBee ELan ERea LRHS SPer SPoG WSHC
- pink-flowered	CCCN CSPN EPfP LBMP SPad SWvt

Sonchus (*Asteraceae*)

fruticosus	CHEx
giganteus	CHll
palustris	EMon
pinnatus new	SPlb

Sophora (*Papilionaceae*)

§ ***davidii***	CGHE CPle CWib EBee EPfP MBlu MGos MWea SKHP SOWG WPGP WSHC
flavescens	NLar
japonica ♀H4	CAbP CBcs CDul CLnd CWib EBee EPfP EWTr LBuc MGos MNHC SBLw SHBN SPlb WBod WNor WOrn
- 'Pendula'	CBcs ELan EMil LRHS MBlu MGos NPal SBLw
- Princeton Upright = 'Fleright' new	EMil
§ 'Little Baby'	CWib EBee EPfP LAst LBuc MCCP MGos MWea SHFr SPoG SWvt WPGP WPat
macrocarpa	GQui WBod
microphylla	CBcs CHEx CPle CTri EBee ECou EPfP LHop SEND WBVN WHer WPGP
- 'Dragon's Gold'	CBcs EBee ECou ELan EPfP LBuc LRHS MAsh SPoG SSta
- 'Early Gold'	GQui
- var. ***fulvida***	ECou
- var. ***longicarinata***	ECou
mollis	CPLG
- CC 4540	MGol
molloyi new	ECou
prostrata misapplied	see *S.* 'Little Baby'
prostrata ambig.	CGHE
prostrata Buch.	ECou
- Pukaki form	ECou
Sun King = 'Hilsop' PBR ♀H4	CCVT EBee ELan EMui ENot EPfP EWes LCro LRHS LSRN MBlu MGos MLan NLar SCoo SLon SPoG WGer
tetraptera ♀H3	CAbP CBcs CDul CMac EBee ECou EPfP GQui ISea MLan SEND SPer SRms WBVN WPGP WPic
- 'Grandiflora'	CBrm
viciifolia	see *S. davidii*

Sorbaria (*Rosaceae*)

SF 95205	ISea
aitchisonii	see *S. tomentosa* var. *angustifolia*
arborea	see *S. kirilowii*
aff. ***assurgens*** BWJ 8185	WCru
§ ***kirilowii***	CPLG MRav NLar SLon WDyG WOut
- AC 3433	NPen
lindleyana	see *S. tomentosa*
rhoifolia	EPfP
sorbifolia	CAbP CBcs CMCo EBee ECrN EMil EWTr LRHS MBar MDun MLHP NPro SEND SPer SPoG WCot WFar WHil
- 'Sem' PBR	CBgR CHid ELan EPfP GBin LBuc LRHS MAsh MGos NLar NPal NPri SJoo WBor WMoo

- var. ***stellipila***	SLPl
- - B&SWJ 776	WCru
§ ***tomentosa***	CAbP SHBN WCot WHCG
§ - var. ***angustifolia*** ♀H4	CBcs CDul CTri CWan EBee ELan EPfP IMGH MRav NHol NPro SEND SLon SPer SPoG WCru WEas WFar WHer WSpi
* - 'Anthony Waterer'	MLan

x *Sorbocrataegus* (*Rosaceae*)

'Ivan's Belle'	see x *Crataegosorbus miczurinii* 'Ivan's Belle'

Sorbopyrus (*Rosaceae*)

auricularis	CTho

Sorbus ✿ (*Rosaceae*)

Harry Smith 12732	LRHS MDun
alnifolia	CLnd CMCN CTho EBee EPfP MBlu MBri SLPl
americana	CLnd NWea
- 'Belmonte'	SBLw
- ***erecta***	see *S. decora* (Sarg.) C.K. Schneid.
amurensis	see *S. aucuparia*
anglica	CDul CNat
'Apricot'	CEnd
'Apricot Lady'	MAsh MGos
'Apricot Queen'	CLnd EBee ECrN EMil EWTr LAst MDun NEgg SBLw
aria	CCVT CDul CLnd CSBt CTri ECrN EMac EPfP LBuc MBar MGan MGos NBee NEgg NPen NWea WMou WOrn
- 'Aurea'	CLnd MBlu MGos WFar
- 'Chrysophylla'	CDul CSBt EBee ECrN IMGH MBri MGos NWea SLim SPer
- 'Decaisneana'	see *S. aria* 'Majestica'
- 'Lutescens' ♀H4	More than 30 suppliers
- 'Magnifica'	CDoC CDul CTho ECrN ELan LPan NEgg SBLw SCoo WJas
§ - 'Majestica' ♀H4	CCVT CDoC CDul CLnd CTho EBee ECrN LPan NWea SBLw SCoo SPer SPoG WJas WOrn
- 'Mitchellii'	see *S. thibetica* 'John Mitchell'
- 'Orange Parade'	SBLw
arnoldiana 'Golden Wonder'	see *S.* 'Lombarts Golden Wonder'
aronioides misapplied	see *S. caloneura*
arranensis	CDul CNat
§ ***aucuparia***	More than 30 suppliers
- B&SWJ 8665	WCru
- 'Aspleniifolia'	CBcs CCVT CDul CLnd CMCN CSBt CWSG EBee ECrN LAst LPan LRHS MBri MDun MGos NWea SBLw SLim SPer SPoG WFar WJas WOrn
I - 'Aurea'	SBLw SKHP
§ - 'Beissneri'	CDul CLnd EPfP GBin MBri MGos NLar SCoo SLon
- Cardinal Royal = 'Michred'	CCVT CDoC ECrN GQui LRHS NEgg SCoo WJas
- 'Crème Lace'	CDul SCoo
- 'Dirkenii'	CDul CWSG MAsh MDun SPoG WJas
§ - var. ***edulis*** (F)	CDul CLnd CTho ECrN LBuc LPan MGos SBLw SCoo
- - 'Rossica' misapplied	see *S. aucuparia* var. *edulis* 'Rossica Major'
§ - - 'Rossica Major'	CDul ECrN GQui SBLw SCoo WFar
§ - 'Fastigiata'	CEnd CLnd CSBt CTri ECrN EPfP LAst MGos NBee SBLw WFar
- 'Hilling's Spire'	CTho MLan
- 'Pendula'	EBee SBLw
- var. ***rossica*** Koehne	see *S. aucuparia* var. *edulis*
- 'Rossica Major'	see *S. aucuparia* var. *edulis* 'Rossica Major'
- 'Scarlet King'	see *S.* x *thuringiaca* 'Scarlet King'
- 'Sheerwater Seedling' ♀H4	CCVT CDoC CDul CLnd CMCN EBee ECrN ELan EPfP LAst LRHS MGos MLan MRav MSwo NBlu NEgg SLim SPer SSta WFar WOrn
- 'Wettra'	SBLw
- 'Winterdown'	CNat
- var. ***xanthocarpa*** ♀H4	CLnd ECrN EPfP SBLw
Autumn Spire = 'Flanrock'	CDoC CWSG LRHS MAsh MBri MGos MLan SCoo
'Bellona'	WPat
'Burka'	see *Aronia* x *Sorbus* 'Burka'
§ ***caloneura***	EPfP SSpi WPGP
'Carpet of Gold'	CLnd
cashmiriana misapplied, pink-fruited	see *S. rosea*
cashmiriana Hedl. ♀H4	More than 30 suppliers
chamaemespilus	WPat
'Chamois Glow'	WJas
'Chinese Lace'	More than 30 suppliers
§ ***commixta***	CBcs CEnd CLnd CMCN CTho EBee ECrN EPfP EPla LAst LCro LRHS MAsh MBar MBlu MBri MGos MLan MRav MSwo NBea SBLw SLim SPer WJas WOrn
- 'Embley' ♀H4	CBcs CCVT CDul CMCN CSBt CSam CTho CTri ECrN ELan ENot EPfP EWTr GQue LCro MBar MDun MGos MRav NWea SLim SPoG SSta WOrn
- var. ***rufoferruginea***	GQui
- - B&SWJ 6078	WCru
conradinae	see *S. esserteauana*
'Copper Kettle'	MAsh MBri SCoo
'Coral Beauty'	CDul CLnd
'Covert Gold'	CEnd CLnd
croceocarpa	CDul CNat
cuspidata	see *S. vestita*
§ ***decora*** (Sarg.) C.K. Schneid.	NBlu SBLw
* - 'Grootendorst'	CDul
- var. ***nana***	see *S. aucuparia* 'Fastigiata'
devoniensis	CDul CNat CTho
- 'Devon Beauty'	CAgr
discolor misapplied	see *S. commixta*
discolor (Maxim.) Maxim.	CLnd CMCN EBee MBlu NWea SEND WJas
domestica	CDul CMCN EPfP
- 'Rosie' **new**	CAgr
'Eastern Promise'	CSam CWSG EBee ECrN LCro LRHS MAsh MBlu MBri MDun MLan MWat NLar NWea SCoo SLim SPoG WJas WOrn
eminens	CDul CNat
§ ***esserteauana***	CTho EPfP
'Fastigiata'	see *S. aucuparia* 'Fastigiata', *S.* x *thuringiaca* 'Fastigiata'
folgneri	CEnd
- 'Emiel'	EPfP MBlu MBri
- 'Lemon Drop'	CDul CEnd CLnd CWSG EPfP MAsh MBlu MDun MLan NLar SCoo SMad SSpi
§ ***foliolosa***	EPfP NWea SCoo WKif
- 'Lowndes'	CLnd
forrestii	CLnd EPfP NBea NLar SLPl
I ***fruticosa*** McAllister	CEnd CLnd EBee EPfP GKev NWea SSta WJas
- 'Koehneana'	see *S. koehneana* C.K. Schneid.
'Ghose'	CEnd CLnd MBlu SCoo SSpi
'Glendoick Gleam' **new**	GGGa
'Glendoick Glory' **new**	GGGa
'Glendoick Ivory' **new**	GGGa

	'Glendoick Pearl' **new**	GGGa
	'Glendoick Ruby' **new**	GGGa
	'Glendoick Spire' **new**	GGGa
	'Glendoick White Baby' **new**	GGGa
	glomerulata **new**	LTwo
	'Golden Wonder'	see *S.* 'Lombarts Golden Wonder'
*	***gorrodini***	CLnd
§	***graeca***	CMCN SEND
	harrowiana	WPat
	'Harvest Moon'	GQui
	hedlundii	GBin MGos NLar WOrn WPGP
	hemsleyi	CDul CLnd MBri MDun WPGP
	- 'John Bond' **new**	MBri
	x ***hostii***	MRav SPer
	hupehensis C.K. Schneid. ♀^{H4}	CBcs CDul CEnd CLnd CMCN CTho CTri EBee ECrN EPfP GKev LAst LRHS MBar MRav NBee NEgg NWea SBLw SHBN SLPl SPer WCru WFar WHar WJas WNor WOrn WPat
	- 'November Pink'	see *S. hupehensis* 'Pink Pagoda'
§	- var. ***obtusa*** ♀^{H4}	CCVT CDoC CDul CLnd CMCN EPfP EWTr MDun SSpi
§	- 'Pink Pagoda'	CDoC CDul CLnd CWSG CWib EBee ECrN EMui EPfP GKev IArd IMGH LRHS LSRN MAsh MBlu MDun MGos MRav MWat NWea SCoo SLim SLon SPoG
	- 'Rosea'	see *S. hupehensis* var. *obtusa*
	x ***hybrida*** misapplied	see *S.* x *thuringiaca*
	hybrida L.	ECrN
	- 'Gibbsii' ♀^{H4}	CDoC CLnd EBee ELan EPfP MAsh MBri MLan SPur
	insignis	CDoC EPfP WPat
	intermedia	CCVT CDul CLnd CSBt CTho CTri CWib ECrN MGos NBee NBlu NWea SBLw WMou
	- 'Brouwers'	ELan LPan SBLw
	'Joseph Rock'	More than 30 suppliers
§	x ***kewensis***	CDul CLnd NWea SPer SPlb
	'Kirsten Pink'	CDul CLnd CWib EBee ECrN MDun MMuc SPer WFar
	koehneana hort.	see *S. fruticosa* McAllister
§	***koehneana*** C.K. Schneid. ♀^{H4}	CBcs CLnd CMCN ECrN EWTr GCrs GGGa GKev GQui IDee MDun NBlu NMen NWea SCoo WPat WTin
	aff. ***koehneana*** ambig.	WCwm
	- Harry Smith 12799	GQui
	lanata misapplied	see *S. vestita*
	lancastriensis	CDul CNat
	latifolia	CLnd ECrN NWea SBLw
	'Leonard Messel'	MAsh MBri NBea SCoo
	'Leonard Springer'	ECrN EPfP GQui SSta
	leptophylla	CDul CNat
	leyana	WMou
§	'Lombarts Golden Wonder'	CBcs CDoC CDul CLnd MAsh MBlu NWea SBLw WJas
	'Maidenblush'	SBLw
	matsumurana misapplied	see *S. commixta*
	megalocarpa	CDoC CPMA EPfP SSpi WCwm WNor WPGP WPat
	microphylla GWJ 9252	WCru
	'Molly Sanderson'	SSta
	monbeigii (Card.) Yü	CLnd
	moravica 'Laciniata'	see *S. aucuparia* 'Beissneri'
§	***munda***	CMCN GBin SCoo
	'Peachi-Ness'	CLnd
	'Pearly King'	CSam CTho MAsh NBea WJas
§	'Pink Pearl'	CDul MDun
	'Pink-Ness'	EBee MDun SCoo SLim SPoG
	pluripinnata	see *S. scalaris* Koehne
	pohuashanensis misapplied	see *S.* x *kewensis*
	porrigentiformis	CDul CNat
	poteriifolia	GCrs GGGa WPat
	prattii misapplied	see *S. munda*
	prattii Hand.-Mazz.	see *S. forrestii*
	prattii Koehne	CLnd GKev WCwm
	- var. ***subarachnoidea***	see *S. munda*
*	***pseudobalsomnensis*** **new**	CBcs
	pseudovilmorinii	GBin MBri
	- MF 93044	SSpi
	randaiensis misapplied	see *S. commixta*
	randaiensis (Hayata) Koidz.	GQui SPlb
	- B&SWJ 3202	NHol SSpi WCru
	'Red Tip'	CDul CLnd MBar
	reducta ♀^{H4}	CBcs CEnd CMCN CSWP EBee EPfP GBin GCrs GKev GQui ISea LRHS MBlu NBlu NHar NHol NWea SCoo SPer SPoG SSpi WFar WNor
	reflexipetala misapplied	see *S. commixta*
	rehderiana misapplied	see *S. aucuparia*
	rehderiana Koehne	CLnd WNor
	rosea	EMui LRHS
	- 'Rosiness'	CLnd MAsh MBri MDun MLan SCoo SLim
	'Rowancroft Coral Pink'	EBee MBar MGos
	rufopilosa	WPat
	'Salmon Queen'	CLnd
	sargentiana ♀^{H4}	CCVT CDul CEnd CLnd CMCN CTho CTri EBee ECrN ELan EPfP IMGH LAst LCro LRHS MBlu MBri MGos MRav MSwo NWea SLim SMad SPer SSpi WJas WOrn
§	***scalaris*** Koehne	CBcs CCVT CEnd CTho CTri EBee EPfP LRHS MBlu MBri MGos SCoo SPer SPoG SSpi WJas WOrn
	scalaris ambig.	EMil MGos
	'Schouten'	ECrN SBLw
	scopulina misapplied	see *S. aucuparia* 'Fastigiata'
	setschwanensis	CMCN GGGa
	'Sunshine'	CCVT CDoC CDul MAsh MGos NBlu WJas
	thibetica	WPGP
§	- 'John Mitchell' ♀^{H4}	CAgr CDul CEnd CLnd CMCN CWib ECrN EPfP GQui LRHS MAsh MBlu MBri MGos MRav MWya NBea NLar NWea SLim SPer WFar WJas WOrn
	aff. ***thibetica*** BWJ 7757a	WCru
	thomsonii GWJ 9363 **new**	WCru
§	x ***thuringiaca***	NBea WMou
§	- 'Fastigiata'	CBcs CDul CLnd CSBt EPfP LPan MAsh MGos NBee SBLw SCoo WJas
§	- 'Scarlet King'	EBee
	torminalis	CCVT CDul CLnd CTho CTri EBee ECrN EMac EPfP LRHS MAsh MBri MRav MWya NWea SBLw SCoo SPer WFar WHar WMou WOrn WSpi
	umbellata	CMCN
	- var. ***cretica***	see *S. graeca*
	ursina	see *S. foliolosa*
	x ***vagensis***	CLnd WMou
	verrucosa var. ***subulata*** HWJ 579	WCru
§	***vestita***	CLnd CMCN CTho MBlu
	vexans	CDul CNat GBin
	vilmorinii ♀^{H4}	More than 30 suppliers
	- 'Robusta'	see *S.* 'Pink Pearl'
	aff. ***vilmorinii***	LAst
	wardii	CBcs CLnd CTho EPfP MBlu
	'White Swan'	NBlu

'White Wax'	CDul CWSG EPfP GQue LAst MAsh MGos SBLw SPer WPat
'Wilfrid Fox'	CLnd SHBN SLPl
wilmottiana	CDul
wilsoniana	CLnd GQui
'Wisley Gold'	CWSG LRHS MGos NLar SCoo SLim WHCr

Sorghastrum (*Poaceae*)

avenaceum	see *S. nutans*
§ ***nutans***	CBig CKno CRWN ECha GFor LEdu LRav SMad XIsg
- 'Indian Steel'	CBig CPen CSam EBee EPPr EWin GFor MSte

Sorghum (*Poaceae*)

halepense	MSte
nigrum	WCot

sorrel, common see *Rumex acetosa*

sorrel, French see *Rumex scutatus*

Souliea see *Actaea*

soursop see *Annona muricata*

Sparaxis (*Iridaceae*)

bulbifera	ECho
'Colour Mill'	WHil
elegans	EPot
- 'Coccinea'	WCot
grandiflora subsp. ***grandiflora***	CGrW ECho WCot
hybrids	LAma
parviflora	ECho
tricolor	EBrs ECho WHil
variegata subsp. ***metelerkampiae*** (v)	CDes
villosa	ECho

Sparganium (*Sparganiaceae*)

§ ***erectum***	EHon EMFW NPer NSco SWat WFar WMAq WSFF XIsg
ramosum	see *S. erectum*

Sparrmannia (*Tiliaceae*)

africana ♀H1	CBcs CHEx CHll CKob CPLG CPle CTrG EAmu ERea EShb MBri SDnm SPav
- 'Variegata' (v)	ERea
palmata	see *S. ricinocarpa*
§ ***ricinocarpa***	CKob

Spathipappus see *Tanacetum*

Spartina (*Poaceae*)

patens	EPPr
pectinata	CHEx GFor NNor WFar XIsg
- 'Aureomarginata' (v)	More than 30 suppliers

Spartium (*Papilionaceae*)

junceum ♀H4	More than 30 suppliers
- 'Brockhill Compact'	EMil LRHS SBra SPoG

Spartocytisus see *Cytisus*

Spathantheum (*Araceae*)

orbignyanum	EBee ITer LFur WCot

Spathiphyllum (*Araceae*)

'Viscount'	MBri
wallisii	CHal LRHS MBri

spearmint see *Mentha spicata*

Speirantha (*Convallariaceae*)

§ ***convallarioides***	CDes CGHE CLAP CPom CStu EBee ECho EHrv ELon ERos LEdu WCot WCru WPGP
gardenii	see *S. convallarioides*

Spergularia (*Caryophyllaceae*)

purpurea	ECho
rupicola	ECho SECG

Sphacele see *Lepechinia*

Sphaeralcea (*Malvaceae*)

ambigua	ELan XPep
'Childerley'	CMdw CSpe EBee LHop SAga
coccinea	LPio SPlb
fendleri	CBcs CHll CSam
- subsp. ***venusta***	CPom XPep
'Hopleys Lavender'	EBee EMan EPPr EWin LHop NLar SAga SWvt
'Hyde Hall'	EBee EPPr EWin WBor
incana	LPio SAga
malviflora	CDTJ WPer
miniata	CHll ELan SAga WCot
munroana	CDMG CPom CSev EBee ECGP ELan EWin LHop XPep
- 'Dixieland Pink'	EBee
- 'Manor Nursery' (v)	EMan EWes LHop MDKP
- pale pink-flowered	ECtt EMan EWin
* - 'Shell Pink'	CSpe ECGP
'Newleaze Coral'	CChe CSpe EBee EMan EPPr LAst LHop LPio NLar SAga SPoG SWvt
'Newleaze Pink'	LHop LPio SAga
obtusiloba	CSpe
parvifolia	EBee
remota	CPLG EMan SPlb
rivularis	EMan
umbellata	see *Phymosia umbellata*

Sphaeromeria (*Asteraceae*)

§ ***capitata***	NWCA

Spigelia (*Loganiaceae*)

marilandica	CDes
- 'Wisley Jester'	LBuc LCro LRHS MBri SCoo SKHP

Spilanthes (*Asteraceae*)

acmella misapplied	see *Acmella oleracea*
oleracea	see *Acmella oleracea*

Spiraea ✿ (*Rosaceae*)

'Abigail'	CDoC
albiflora	see *S. japonica* var. *albiflora*
arborea	see *Sorbaria kirilowii*
arcuata	EMac
§ 'Arguta' ♀H4	More than 30 suppliers
x ***arguta*** 'Bridal Wreath'	see *S.* 'Arguta'
bella	SLon WTin
betulifolia	CDul MRav NHol SMac WHCG
- var. ***aemiliana***	CWSG EBee ECtt LBMP MAsh MGos SLPl WFar
x ***billardii*** misapplied	see *S.* x *pseudosalicifolia*
- 'Triumphans'	see *S.* x *pseudosalicifolia* 'Triumphans'
x ***bumalda***	see *S. japonica* 'Bumalda'
- 'Wulfenii'	see *S. japonica* 'Walluf'
callosa 'Alba'	see *S. japonica* var. *albiflora*
canescens	CPLG GKev
- AC 1354	NPen
- CC 4545	MGol
§ ***cantoniensis*** 'Flore Pleno' (d)	SLon
- 'Lanceata'	see *S. cantoniensis* 'Flore Pleno'

x ***cinerea*** 'Grefsheim' ŸH4	CDoC CSBt EBee ECtt ENot MBri MMuc NEgg SLim SPer WCFE WFar
crispifolia	see *S. japonica* 'Bullata'
douglasii	CMac MBar
formosana	WCru
- B&SWJ 1597	CPLG
§ x ***foxii***	SLPl
fritschiana	CMac SLPl SLon
hayatana	SLon
- RWJ 10014	WCru
hendersonii	see *Petrophytum hendersonii*
japonica	SBod SMer WFar
§ - var. ***albiflora***	CBcs CEnd CMac CSBt CTri CWib ELan EPfP LRHS MBar MGos MRav MSwo MWat NEgg NHol NPri SEND SHBN SLim SPer SPla SRms SWvt WFar WHCG WMoo WSpi WWeb
- 'Allgold'	CBcs
- 'Alpina'	see *S. japonica* 'Nana'
- 'Alpine Gold'	GBin NPro WWeb
- 'Anthony Waterer' (v)	More than 30 suppliers
- 'Barkby Gold'	MGos
- 'Blenheim'	SRms
§ - 'Bullata'	CFee CMac EPfP GEdr MBar NWCA SPer SRms WAbe
§ - 'Bumalda'	MGol WFar
- 'Candlelight' ŸH4	CAbP CBcs CSBt CWSG EBee EPfP LAst LRHS MAsh MBri MGos NEgg NHol NPri SCoo SHBN SLim SPer SPla SPoG SWvt WMoo
- 'Crispa'	CRez EPfP LRHS MBar NPro WBod WFar WLeb WMoo WWeb
- 'Dart's Red' ŸH4	NPri WFar
- 'Firelight'	CAbP CBcs CSBt EBee ECrN ELan ENot EPfP LHop LRHS MAsh MBri MGos MSwo NHol NPri SCoo SLim SPer SPla SPoG SSta SWvt WBrE WFar
§ - 'Genpei'	CChe CMac NBlu SPer
- 'Glenroy Gold'	SLon WHen
- 'Gold Mound'	CChe CMac CPLG CWSG CWib EBee ECrN ELan ENot EPfP LBMP LRHS MAsh MBar MGos MRav MSwo MWgw NHol NPri SCoo SHFr SPer SPlb SRms WFar WHar WWeb
- Golden Princess = 'Lisp'PBR ŸH4	CMac CTri CWSG EPfP LAst LBuc LRHS MAsh MBar MGos NHol NPri SCoo SMer SReu SRms SSta WCFE WFar WWeb
- 'Goldflame'	More than 30 suppliers
- 'Little Princess'	CBcs CBrm CMac CWSG CWib EBee ECrN EMil ENot LCro LRHS MAsh MBar MRav MSwo NEgg NHol NPri SCoo SLim SPer SRGP SRms SSta SWvt WBVN WFar WHar
- 'Macrophylla'	CEnt
- Magic Carpet = 'Walbuma'PBR (v) ŸH4	EBrs LBuc LRHS MAsh NLar SCoo SPoG
- 'Magnifica'	WHCG WPat
§ - 'Nana' ŸH4	CMac CSBt ECho MBar MRav SRms WEas WPer
- 'Nyewoods'	see *S. japonica* 'Nana'
- 'Shiburi'	see *S. japonica* var. *albiflora*
- 'Shirobana' misapplied	see *S. japonica* 'Genpei'
- 'Shirobana'	see *S. japonica* var. *albiflora*
- 'Snow Cap'	CWib
§ - 'Walluf'	CMac CPLG CTri CWib WHCG
- 'White Cloud'	ELan
- 'White Gold'PBR	CAbP CSBt EBee ELan EPfP LAst LBuc LRHS MAsh MBri MMHG NPro SCoo SPer SPoG SWvt WMoo WOVN
'Margaritae'	SPer SWvt
micrantha	CPLG
nipponica	CBcs MBar
- 'Halward's Silver'	LBuc MGos MRav NHol NPro SLPl
- 'June Bride'	NBlu
§ - 'Snowmound' ŸH4	More than 30 suppliers
- var. ***tosaensis*** misapplied	see *S. nipponica* 'Snowmound'
- var. ***tosaensis*** (Yatabe) Makino	LHop SReu
palmata 'Elegans'	see *Filipendula purpurea* 'Elegans'
§ ***prunifolia*** (d)	CDul CMac ECrN ELan MBlu MRav SLon SPer SPoG WBod WPat WTel
- 'Plena'	see *S. prunifolia*
§ x ***pseudosalicifolia*** 'Triumphans'	SHFr
salicifolia	WFar
stevenii	SPer
'Summersnow'	SLPl
'Superba'	see *S.* x *foxii*
thunbergii ŸH4	CDul CSBt CTri CWib EBee ENot EPfP MRav NWea SCoo SLim SMer SRms WGwG WHCG
- 'Mellow Yellow'	see *S. thunbergii* 'Ogon'
- 'Mount Fuji'	CAbP CMac CWib GSki MGos MRav NPro WFar
§ - 'Ōgon'	WFar WPen
ulmaria	see *Filipendula ulmaria*
x ***vanhouttei***	CBcs CSBt CTri EBee EPfP MBar MRav MSwo NEgg SHBN SLim SPer SPla SRms WFar WTel
- 'Gold Fountain'	GBin NHol SPoG WFar
- 'Pink Ice' (v)	CAbP CBcs CDoC CMHG CPMA CWib EPfP LAst LBMP LHop LRHS MAsh MGos NHol SHBN SPer SPlb SPoG SWvt WFar WTel
veitchii	MRav
venusta 'Magnifica'	see *Filipendula rubra* 'Venusta'

Spiranthes (*Orchidaceae*)

cernua var. ***odorata***	LSou
- - 'Chadd's Ford'	More than 30 suppliers
spiralis	WHer

Spirodela (*Lemnaceae*)

§ ***polyrhiza***	EMFW

Spodiopogon (*Poaceae*)

sibiricus	CBig CBrm CKno EBee EMon EPPr GFor LEdu MSte SMad XIsg

Sporobolus (*Poaceae*)

airoides	CBig CBrm EBee EPPr GFor MWea
cryptandrus	EBee
heterolepis	CBig EBee EShb NDov SMad XIsg
'Heterolepis Cloud' **new**	GBin
wrightii	EBee WSPU

Spraguea (*Portulacaceae*)

'Powder Puff'	LRHS

Sprekelia (*Amaryllidaceae*)

formosissima	CSpe CStu EBrs ECho LAma LRHS SPav

Staberoha (*Restionaceae*)

aemula	CBig
remota	CBig

Stachys ✿ (*Lamiaceae*)

B&SWJ 10427 from Guatemala **new**	WCru
aethiopica 'Danielle'	see *S. thunbergii* 'Danielle'
§ ***affinis***	CAgr CArn CFir ELau GPoy LEdu
albens	EBla

	albotomentosa	EBee EBla EMan EShb GBri LHop LSou MBNS MDKP SPhx WCot
	alpina	CNat EBee
	bacanica	EBee
	- MESE	WPGP
	balansae	NSti
	betonica	see *S. officinalis*
§	***byzantina***	More than 30 suppliers
§	- 'Big Ears'	CAby CBow EBee ECha ENot EPfP EWTr GMaP LAst LCro LHop MBri MRav MWat NDov SBch SEND SMrm SPhx SPoG WBor WCAu WCFE WCot WFar WHoo WMnd WMoo
§	- 'Cotton Boll'	COIW EBee ECha MHar SBch SPer WCot WFar
	- 'Countess Helen von Stein'	see *S. byzantina* 'Big Ears'
	- gold-leaved	see *S. byzantina* 'Primrose Heron'
	- large-leaved	see *S. byzantina* 'Big Ears'
	- 'Limelight'	WCot
§	- 'Primrose Heron'	EBee ECha ECot EMan GKev LRHS MRav MWgw NLar NOrc SMer SPoG SWvt WFar WOut
	- 'Sheila McQueen'	see *S. byzantina* 'Cotton Boll'
	- 'Silken Fleece' **new**	EDAr
	- 'Silver Carpet'	CBcs COIW EBee ECha EPfP EWTr GMaP LAst LCro LRHS LSRN MRav MWat MWgw NBlu NBro NOrc NSti SPer SPla SRms SWvt WCAu WCot WFar WHoo WMnd WMoo WWeb
§	- 'Striped Phantom' (v)	CBow EBla EMan WCAu WEas
	- 'Variegata'	see *S. byzantina* 'Striped Phantom'
	candida	WAbe
	chamissonis var. ***cooleyae***	EBee
	chrysantha	SPhx
	citrina	CMea EBee EBla LRHS SBla SPhx
	coccinea	CHFP CPom EBee ECtt EHrv EShb LRHS MHer SBch SDnm SHFr SPav SRkn SWal WCot WFar WMoo WRos
	- B&SWJ 10418	WCru
	- 'Burning Embers'	LAst
	corsica	WPGP
	cretica	WWlt XPep
	- subsp. ***salviifolia***	XPep
	densiflora	see *S. monieri*
§	***discolor***	CMea EBee GBri MDKP MLLN NChi NLar SPhx WCot WOut WPer
	germanica	CPom NBre
	- subsp. ***bithynica***	EBee
	glutinosa	MDKP XPep
	grandiflora	see *S. macrantha*
	heraclea	XPep
	'Hidalgo'	CSpe SAga
	iva	SPhx
	lanata	see *S. byzantina*
	lavandulifolia	WLin
§	***macrantha***	CArn CHar CKno COIW CTri EBee ECha EWsh GGar LAst LRHS MLHP MWgw NChi NOak NOrc NSti SGar SMrm SPhx SPla SRms STes WCot WEas WFar WHil WLin WTin WWlt
*	- 'Alba'	ECha WMoo
	- 'Hummelo'	see *S. officinalis* 'Hummelo'
*	- 'Nivea'	CSam EHrv ELan MMHG WPat
	- 'Robusta' ♀H4	CDes ELan NBro NGdn WCAu WCot WRHF
	- 'Rosea'	CElw CMHG ELan GMaP LLWP MArl MAvo MLHP SPlb WCFE WEas WPer
	- 'Superba'	CSpe EBee EBla ECtt EPfP GCra GMaP IBal LAst LBMP LRHS MBri MDun MMHG MRav NEgg SMrm SPer SWvt WBor WCot WFar WMnd WMoo
	- 'Violacea'	MBrN NChi WCot WPGP
	mexicana misapplied	see *S. thunbergii*
	monieri misapplied	see *S. officinalis*
	monieri ambig.	CAbP CMMP EBee EGle EShb LBMP LRHS MAvo NLar SWal WPer
§	***monieri*** (Gouan) P.W. Ball	CEnt GBin LBMP MAvo WOut
*	- 'Rosea'	NBre NLar WOut
	- 'Saharan Pink'	see *S. officinalis* 'Saharan Pink'
	nivea	see *S. discolor*
	obliqua	NBre
§	***officinalis***	CArn CBgR CEnt CPrp CRWN CSev CWan EBee EUnu GPoy LEdu MHer MNHC MSal NEgg NLan NMir NPri WGwG WHer
	- SDR 3554	GKev
	- 'Alba'	CArn CBgR CPrp EBee NBro STes WCAu WFar WHer WOut WTin
§	- 'Hummelo'	EBee ECtt EGle ELon EMon EPPr EPfP GAbr GQue LHop LSou MDKP NBPC NDov NLar SAga SPhx WCAu WFar WWeb
	- mauve-flowered	WTin
	- 'Minor' **new**	GBin
	- 'Powder Puff'	EBee
	- 'Rosea'	CMea NBro STes WCot WFar WSHC WTin
	- 'Rosea Superba'	CBgR EBee ECha MDKP NBre SIng WCAu WCot WFar WMoo
§	- 'Saharan Pink'	CBgR EBee EPfP EWll LSou MHer SSvw WMoo WOut
	- 'Spitzenberg' **new**	EMon
	- 'Wisley White'	EBee WCot
	olympica	see *S. byzantina*
	ossetica	CDes EBee
	palustris	NLan NMir NSco WFar WOut
	'Pinkie'	WWeb
	plumosa	XPep
	recta	CEnt NBHF SPhx
	saxicola	MDKP
	scardica MESE 362	MDKP
	setifera	EBee EBla NBre
	spicata	see *S. macrantha*
	swainsonii	XPep
	sylvatica	CArn NLan NMir NSco SECG WHer
	- 'Huskers' (v)	ITer LSou NBre
	thirkei	SBch XPep
§	***thunbergii***	CDes CHFP CSpe EShb LLWP MBrN MDKP MSte SAga SMeo SPhx SSvw WOut WPGP WPrP
§	- 'Danielle'	CBow EAro EBee ECtt LAst MGol MHer NBre SPoG SRkn WMoo WOVN
	tuberifera	see *S. affinis*

Stachyurus (*Stachyuraceae*)

chinensis	CBcs CMCN CPMA CTri CWib IArd IDee IMGH LRHS MGos NLar SMad SPoG
- 'Celina'	CPMA EMil MBlu MBri MGos NLar
- 'Goldbeater'	NLar
- 'Joy Forever' (v)	CBcs CDul CEnd CMCN EMil EPfP IArd IClo LTwo MBlu MBri MGos MWea NLar SPoG SSpi SSta SWvt WCot
himalaicus	NLar
- HWJCM 009	WCru
- HWJK 2035	WCru
leucotrichus	CPMA
'Magpie' (v)	CPMA ENot EPfP MGos NLar SAga WCru

praecox ♀H4	More than 30 suppliers
- B&SWJ 8898	WCru
- var. ***matsuzakii***	CPMA NBhm
- - B&SWJ 2817	WCru
- - 'Scherzo' (v)	WCru
* - 'Rubriflorus'	CPMA ELan EPfP LRHS MBri NLar WFar
salicifolius	CGHE CMCN CPMA IDee MBri NLar WPGP
* ***sigeyosii*** B&SWJ 6915	WCru
aff. ***szechuanensis*** BWJ 8153	WCru
yunnanensis	WSHC

Staehelina (*Asteraceae*)

dubia	XPep

Stapelia (*Asclepiadaceae*)

grandiflora	EShb
variegata	see *Orbea variegata*

Staphylea (*Staphyleaceae*)

bolanderi	CBcs NLar
bumalda	CBcs CPMA EPfP NLar
colchica	CBcs CDul ELan EPfP EWTr MGos NPal SMad SPer WSHC
holocarpa	CBcs CPMA EPfP LHop MRav WBVN WFar
- 'Innocence'	CBcs NLar
N - var. ***rosea***	CPMA EPfP MBri SMad
N - 'Rosea'	CBcs CMCN CPMA MBlu NLar SKHP SSpi
pinnata	CAgr CBcs CEnd CPMA EBee EPfP LEdu NPen WHCr WNor WPat
trifolia	CAgr CBcs

Statice see *Limonium*

Stauntonia (*Lardizabalaceae*)

hexaphylla	CBcs CDoC CHEx CSam CTri EBee ELon EPfP LRHS MAsh MBri MDun SAdn SBra SPoG SReu SRkn SSpi SSta WBrE WCot WSHC
obovatifoliola B&SWJ 3685 new	WCru
purpurea	NLar
- B&SWJ 3690	WCru

Stegnogramma (*Thelypteridaceae*)

pozoi	EFer

Stellaria (*Caryophyllaceae*)

holostea	CArn CRWN NMir NSco WShi

Stellera (*Thymelaeaceae*)

chamaejasme new	CExc
- var. ***chrysantha*** new	GKev

Stemmacantha (*Asteraceae*)

carthamoides	MSal
§ ***centaureoides***	EBee ECGP ECha EGle GBin GQue NBid NBre SAga SMeo SPhx WCAu WCot WSpi
§ ***rhapontica***	NBre

Stenanthium (*Melanthiaceae*)

occidentale	EBee WCot
robustum	WPGP

Stenocarpus (*Proteaceae*)

sinuatus	EShb

Stenochlaena (*Blechnaceae*)

palustris	MBri

Stenomesson (*Amaryllidaceae*)

§ ***miniatum***	CStu WCot
pearcei	WCot
variegatum	WCot

Stenotaphrum (*Poaceae*)

secundatum	EShb XPep
- 'Variegatum' (v) ♀H1	CHal EShb MAvo WDyG

Stephanandra (*Rosaceae*)

chinensis	SLon
incisa	CBcs CPLG GKev WHCG
§ - 'Crispa'	CDoC CDul CPle CTri EBee ECrN ELan EMil EPfP EWTr LAst LHop MBar MBlu MRav MWgw NEgg NHol SHBN SPer SPla SPoG WCFE WFar WHCG WMoo WTel
- 'Dart's Horizon'	SLPl
- 'Prostrata'	see *S. incisa* 'Crispa'
tanakae	CBcs CDoC CDul CPLG CPle CTri EBee ELan EPfP EWTr IMGH LAst MBar MBlu MRav NEgg SHBN SLPl SLon SPer SPla WFar WHCG

Stephania (*Menispermaceae*)

japonica B&SWJ 2396	WCru

Stephanotis (*Asclepiadaceae*)

floribunda ♀H1	CBcs CCCN EBak LRHS MBri NBlu SOWG

Sterculia (*Sterculiaceae*)

rupestris	see *Brachychiton rupestris*

Sternbergia (*Amaryllidaceae*)

'Autumn Gold'	EBee EBrs ECho EPot GKev LAma
candida	EBrs ECho
§ ***clusiana***	EBrs ECho WWst
colchiciflora	EBrs WWst
fischeriana	EBrs
greuteriana	EBrs ECho WWst
lutea	CAvo CHHB CPBP CStu EBrs ECho EPot EWes LAma LRHS NWCA SDix WEas WTin
- Angustifolia Group	CDes CMea EBee EBrs ECho EMon WCot WWst
macrantha	see *S. clusiana*
sicula	CHHB CStu EBrs ECho EPot WCot WWst XPep
- var. ***graeca***	EBrs ECho WWst
- - from Crete	ECho
- 'John Marr'	WThu

Stevia (*Asteraceae*)

rebaudiana	CArn EBee EOHP EUnu EWin GPoy MSal WCot

Stewartia ✿ (*Theaceae*)

gemmata	see *S. sinensis*
'Korean Splendor'	see *S. pseudocamellia* Koreana Group
koreana	see *S. pseudocamellia* Koreana Group
malacodendron ♀H4	EPfP LRHS
monadelpha	CMen EPfP SSpi WNor
ovata	CMen SSpi
N - var. ***grandiflora***	LRHS
pseudocamellia ♀H4	More than 30 suppliers
§ - Koreana Group ♀H4	CBcs CDul CEnd CMCN CTho ECrN EPfP LRHS MBri MDun NLar SSpi WFar WNor WPGP
pteropetiolata	WPGP
rostrata	CBcs CPMA IDee MBlu MBri NLar SSpi WFar WNor

serrata	CMen IDee NBhm SSpi
§ ***sinensis*** 🏆^{H4}	CBcs CPMA EPfP IDee LPan MBlu NLar SSpi SSta WNor

strawberry see *Fragaria*

Stigmaphyllon (*Malpighiaceae*)

ciliatum	CCCN
littorale new	CCCN

Stipa (*Poaceae*)

arundinacea	see *Anemanthele lessoniana*
barbata	CBig CDes CKno CSpe EBee ECha EGle EPPr EWes GFor LRHS MAvo MNHC SApp SMHy SPer WCot WPGP WRos XIsg XPep
- 'Silver Feather'	CBig EWsh LRav SLim
* ***boysterica***	CFee
brachytricha	see *Calamagrostis brachytricha*
§ ***calamagrostis***	More than 30 suppliers
- 'Lemperg'	EPPr
capillata	CKno CWsd EBee EGle EPPr MNHC NCGa SMad SWal WOVN WPGP WPnP XIsg XPep
- 'Brautschleier'	CHrt CWib NBre SWal WPtf
* - 'Lace Veil'	CBig LRav
chrysophylla F&W 9321	WPGP
columbiana	MLLN
comata	LRav
elegantissima	CKno CSam GFor
extremiorientalis	CBig CKno ECha EPPr GFor GSki LAst SLPl SMad XIsg
* ***gerardi***	SApp
gigantea 🏆^{H4}	More than 30 suppliers
- 'Gold Fontaene'	CBig CDes CFir CKno EBee ECha EPPr EWes MAvo MMoz MNrw NDov SBch SPhx WCot WPGP WPrP
- 'Pixie'	ELon EWsh SApp SPhx
grandis	CBig CKno ECha EPPr GBin GFor WHal WMoo WPer XIsg
ichu new	CKno
lasiagrostis	see *S. calamagrostis*
lessingiana	CHrt CPLG CSam EBee EHul GBin NLar WPGP XIsg
offneri	EBee EPPr EWes
pekinense new	EBee
pennata	CBcs CBig CKno GBin GFor LRav MNHC NCGa XIsg
pulcherrima	CBow LBMP LRHS MAvo MBNS XIsg XPep
- 'Windfeder'	CFir LBMP SLPl SMad SMrm WPnP
ramosissima	CKno
robusta	EBee EPPr LRav XPep
splendens misapplied	see *S. calamagrostis*
splendens Trin.	CBig WFoF
stenophylla	see *S. tirsa*
stipoides	GGar
tenacissima	EBee ECha EHul GFor GSki NCob WMoo XPep
tenuifolia misapplied	see *S. tenuissima*
tenuifolia Steud.	CHar CMea CMil EBee EHul EPfP LRHS MBri MRav NBir NBro NHol NSti NVic SIng SPer WCAu WHal WMoo XPep
§ ***tenuissima***	More than 30 suppliers
§ ***tirsa***	GBin NDov
turkestanica	EBee GBin NDov SWat WHal
ucrainica	CAby CBig GAbr GFor XIsg
verticillata	CKno CRez

Stokesia (*Asteraceae*)

cyanea	see *S. laevis*
§ ***laevis***	CPrp EBee ECGP ECha EGle EPfP GAbr LAst LRHS NBro NLar SMer SMrm SPet SPlb WBrE WCAu WFar WMoo WPer WWeb
- 'Alba'	CMMP COIW CPrp CTca EBee ECha EGle EHrv ELan EMan EPfP ERou LAst LRHS MRav SPer SPhx STes WCAu
- 'Blue Star'	More than 30 suppliers
- 'Klaus Jelitto'	CFwr EBee ERou MBri SHar
- 'Mary Gregory'	More than 30 suppliers
- mixed	CPou MLan
- 'Omega Skyrocket'	CBgR CMHG CPou EBee ELon ERou LRHS MBri MLLN NHol SMrm SPoG WBor WCAu WCot WFar
- 'Peach Melba'	EBee ECtt NCGa WMoo
- 'Purple Parasols'	More than 30 suppliers
- 'Silver Moon'	CMHG EBee ECtt EGle EMan EMar EMil EPfP ERou EShb GMac LAst MTPN NBir NEgg NHol SAga WBor WCot WFar WTMC
- 'Träumerei'	EBee EGle EMar LAst LRHS NHol SPet WMnd WMoo

Stranvaesia see *Photinia*

Stranvinia see *Photinia*

Stratiotes (*Hydrocharitaceae*)

aloides	CDWL CWat EHon EMFW NPer NSco SWat WMAq WPnP

Strelitzia (*Strelitziaceae*)

alba	CCCN EAmu
juncea	ERea XBlo
nicolai	CAbb CHEx CKob EAmu ITer LPal LPan MJnS NPer XBlo
reginae 🏆^{H1}	CAbb CBcs CKob ELan ERea EShb LPal LPan LRHS MJnS NPal NPer NScw SAPC SArc SChr SEND SPlb SRms XBlo
- var. ***citrina***	ERea
- 'Kirstenbosch Gold'	XBlo

Streptocarpella see *Streptocarpus*

Streptocarpus ✿ (*Gesneriaceae*)

'Albatross' 🏆^{H1}	SBrm SDnm SPav WDib
'Alice'	SBrm WDib
'Amanda' Dibley 🏆^{H1}	WDib
'Amanda' PBR Fleischle (Marleen Series)	WDib
'Anne'	CSpe SBrm WDib
'Athena'	CSpe SBrm WDib
baudertii	WDib
'Beryl'	WDib
'Bethan' 🏆^{H1}	SAga SBrm WDib
'Black Gardenia'	WDib
'Black Panther'	SAga WDib
'Blue Gem'	WDib
'Blue Heaven'	SBrm WDib
'Blue Moon'	CHal WDib
'Blue Nymph'	WDib
§ 'Blue Upstart'	SBrm
'Blushing Bride' (d)	SAga SDnm SPav WDib
* 'Boysenberry Delight'	WDib
'Branwen'	SAga SBrm SDnm SPav WDib
'Brimstone'	SBrm
'Bristol's Black Bird'	SBrm WDib
'Bristol's Ice Castle'	SBrm WDib
'Bristol's Very Best'	WDib
'Buttons'	SBrm
caeruleus	WDib
'Caitlin'	WDib
candidus	WDib
'Carol'	WDib

	'Carys' ♀H1	WDib
	'Catania' (Marleen Series)	WDib
	'Catrin' ♀H1	SBrm WDib
	caulescens	CHal WDib
*	- 'Compactus'	CHal
	- var. ***pallescens***	EOHP WDib
	'Charlotte'	SBrm WDib
	'Chorus Line' ♀H1	SDnm SPav WDib
	'Clare'	WDib
	'Clouds'	CSpe
	'Concord Blue'	WDib
	'Constant Nymph'	SBrm WDib
	'Coral Flair'	WDib
	'Crystal Beauty' PBR	WDib
	'Crystal Blush' PBR	WDib
	'Crystal Charm' PBR	WDib
	'Crystal Dawn' PBR	WDib
	'Crystal Ice' PBR ♀H1	WDib
	'Crystal Snow' PBR	WDib
	'Crystal Wonder' PBR	WDib
	cyaneus	WDib
	- subsp. ***polackii***	WDib
	'Cynthia' ♀H1	SBrm WDib
	'Daphne' ♀H1	SAga WDib
	'Demeter'	SBrm
	'Diana'	SBrm WDib
	dunnii	SGar WDib
	'Eira'	WDib
	'Elegance'	SBrm
	'Ella'	SBrm
	'Elsi'	SBrm SDnm SPav WDib
	'Emily'	SBrm WDib
	'Emma'	SBrm WDib
	'Falling Stars' ♀H1	CSpe ERea SAga SBrm WDib
	'Festival Wales'	SBrm WDib
	'Fiona'	SBrm WDib
	floribundus hort.	WDib
	gardenii	WDib
	glandulosissimus ♀H1	CHal EOHP WDib
	'Gloria' ♀H1	CSpe SAga SBrm WDib
	'Good Hope'	ERea
	'Gower Midnight'	SBrm
	'Grape Slush'	WDib
	'Gwen'	SBrm WDib
	'Hannah Ellis'	SBrm
	'Happy Snappy' ♀H1	SBrm SDnm SPav WDib
	'Heidi' ♀H1	SDnm SPav WDib
	'Helen' ♀H1	SBrm WDib
	'Huge White'	CSpe SAga
	'Ida'	SBrm
	'Inky Fingers'	SBrm
	'Izzy'	SBrm
	'Jaco's Gem'	WDib
	'Jane Elizabeth'	SBrm
	'Jennifer' ♀H1	SBrm SDnm SPav WDib
	'Joanna'	SBrm WDib
	johannis	WDib
	'Josie'	SBrm
	'Julie'	WDib
	'Karen'	SBrm SDnm SPav WDib
	kentaniensis	WDib
	'Kim' ♀H1	CSpe EShb SBrm SDnm SPav WDib
	kirkii	WDib
	'Largesse'	SBrm
	'Laura' ♀H1	SAga SBrm WDib
	'Lemon Ice'	SBrm
	'Little Gem'	CSpe
	'Louise'	SBrm WDib
	'Lynette'	SBrm
	'Lynne'	SBrm WDib
	'Maassen's White' ♀H1	ERea SBrm WDib
	'Mandy'	SDnm SPav WDib
	'Margaret'	WDib
	'Marie'	WDib
	'Mary'	SBrm
	'Megan'	SBrm WDib
	'Melanie' Dibley ♀H1	SBrm WDib
I	'Melanie' (Marleen Series)	WDib
	meyeri	WDib
	'Midnight Flame'	ERea EShb SAga WDib
	'Mini Nymph'	CSpe WDib
	'Misty Pink' **new**	SBrm
	modestus	WDib
	'Molly'	SBrm
	'Moonlight'	SBrm WDib
	'Neptune'	SBrm WDib
	'Nerys' PBR	SBrm WDib
	'Nia'	CSpe WDib
	'Nicola'	SBrm WDib
	'Olga'	WDib
	'Olwen'	WDib
	'Pale Rider'	SBrm
	'Party Doll'	SBrm WDib
	'Passion Pink'	SBrm WDib
	'Patricia'	SBrm
	'Paula' ♀H1	SBrm WDib
	pentherianus	WDib
	'Pink Fondant'	CSpe
	'Pink Souffle'	SBrm SDnm SPav WDib
	'Plum Crazy'	SBrm
	polyanthus subsp. ***dracomontanus***	WDib
	primulifolius	WDib
	- subsp. ***formosus***	WDib
	'Princesse' (Marleen Series)	WDib
	prolixus	WDib
*	'Purple Passion'	SBrm
	rexii	WDib
	'Rhiannon'	CSpe SAga SBrm SDnm SPav WDib
	'Rosebud'	SAga SBrm WDib
	'Rosemary' (d)	SPav WDib
	'Ruby' ♀H1	EShb SBrm WDib
	'Ruby Anniversary'	SBrm
	'Ruffled Lilac'	CSpe
	'Ruffles'	SBrm
	'Sally'	SBrm WDib
	'Sandra'	SBrm SDnm SPav WDib
	'Sarah'	SBrm SPav WDib
	saxorum ♀H1	CCCN CHal EMan EOHP EShb EWin LSou MBri SRms WDib WFar
	- compact	CCCN EOHP WDib
	'Sian'	SBrm SDnm SPav WDib
	silvaticus	WDib
	'Snow White' ♀H1	CSpe SDnm SPav WDib
	'Something Special'	SAga SBrm SDnm WDib
	'Sophie'	WDib
	'Southshore'	SBrm WDib
	'Stacey'	SBrm
	'Stella' ♀H1	SBrm WDib
	'Stephanie'	CSpe WDib
	stomandrus	WDib
	'Stormy' **new**	SBrm
	'Strawberry Fondant'	SBrm
	'Sugar Almond'	CSpe SBrm
	'Susan' ♀H1	SAga WDib
	'Swaybelle'	SBrm
	'Tanga'	SBrm
	'Tatan Blue' **new**	SBrm
	'Terracotta'	SAga SBrm
	'Texas Hot Chili'	SBrm WDib
	thompsonii	WDib
	'Tina' ♀H1	SAga SBrm SDnm SPav WDib
	'Tracey'	SBrm WDib
	'Turbulent Tide'	SBrm
	'Upstart'	see *S.* 'Blue Upstart'
	variabilis	WDib
	'Velvet Underground'	SBrm
	'Vera'	SBrm
	'Violet Lace'	CSpe
	wendlandii	WDib

'Wendy'	SBrm SPav WDib
'White Wings'	SBrm
'Wiesmoor Red'	SAga WDib
'Winifred'	SBrm WDib

Streptopus (*Convallariaceae*)

amplexifolius	EBee EBrs ECho GBuc NMen WCot WCru
- M&PS 98/022	GCrs
obtusatus	EBee
roseus	EBee GCrs
simplex	EBee

Streptosolen (*Solanaceae*)

jamesonii ♀H1	CHal CHll CPle CSev CSpe EBak ELan ERea EShb SAga
- 'Fire Gold'	ERea

Strobilanthes (*Acanthaceae*)

CC 4071	CPLG
CC 4573	CPLG MGol
anisophylla	ERou EShb WSpi
atropurpurea misapplied	see *S. attenuata*
atropurpurea Nees	see *S. wallichii*
§ ***attenuata***	ECha ECtt ELan EMar EPfP EWll EWsh GCra GKev LHop LLWP LRHS MHar MRav NCGa NSti SGar SPhx WBVN WCAu WCot WCru WFar WMoo WPer WPic WWlt
- dwarf **new**	WTMC
- subsp. ***nepalensis***	CHll CLAP EBee EMar MGol WPrP WRHF
- 'Out of the Ocean'	WOut
- 'Pieter' **new**	EMon
dyeriana ♀H1	CHal CSpe EBak EBee ECtt ELan EMan EShb GBri LSou SGar WCot WGwG
- 'Persian Shield' **new**	WHlf
flexicaulis	CDes EBee WPGP WPrP
- B&SWJ 354	WCru
- clone 2	LSou
nutans	CDes CLAP CPLG CPom CPou CSpe EBee LSou WHil WPrP
rankanensis	CDes CLAP EBee SDys SKHP WHil WPrP
- B&SWJ 1771	WCru
'Silver Star'	EShb
violacea	CPrp CStu WPer
§ ***wallichii***	CDes CLAP CPLG EBee EPPr EWes EWld LRHS LSou NSti WCru WFar WPrP WSHC

Stromanthe (*Marantaceae*)

amabilis	see *Ctenanthe amabilis*
sanguinea	CHal MBri
- 'Triostar'PBR (v)	XBlo
'Stripestar'	MBri

Strongylodon (*Papilionaceae*)

macrobotrys	SOWG

Strophanthus (*Apocynaceae*)

speciosus	CCCN CHll EShb

Stuartia see *Stewartia*

Stylidium (*Stylidiaceae*)

affine	SPlb
graminifolium	GGar SPlb
- 'Little Sapphire'	EBee
- 'Tiny Trina'	EBee LRHS

Stylophorum (*Papaveraceae*)

diphyllum	CFwr CPBP CPou EBee ECha EGle EMar EWld GBri GEdr MAvo MRav MSal NMen SBch WCru WFar WPnP
lasiocarpum	CPLG CPom CSpe EMar EWes EWld LFur MGol NBid SGar WCru WPrP WRos

Styphelia (*Epacridaceae*)

colensoi	see *Leucopogon colensoi*

Styrax (*Styracaceae*)

from Yunnan **new**	CExc
americanus	CBcs NLar
confusus	CMCN
faberi	CExc
formosanus	CGHE CTho EBee
- var. ***formosanus***	EPfP WPGP
- - B&SWJ 3803	WCru
- var. ***hayatiana*** B&SWJ 6823	WCru
hemsleyanus ♀H4	CAbP CBcs CEnd CTho ECrN EPfP IDee IMGH LRHS MBlu MDun NLar SPer SSpi WBor WFar WNor WPGP
japonicus ♀H4	More than 30 suppliers
- B&SWJ 4405	WCru
§ - Benibana Group ♀H4	SReu SSta
- - 'Pink Chimes'	CAbP CBcs CMCN CPLG CPMA EBee ELan EPfP IDee LRHS MAsh MBlu MBri NLar SCoo SKHP SPer SSpi SSta
- 'Carillon'	CPMA
- 'Fargesii'	CBcs CDoC CDul CPMA CTho ECrN EPfP IDee IMGH LRHS MBri MDun SCoo SSpi WFar
- 'Purple Dress'	NLar
- 'Roseus'	see *S. japonicus* Benibana Group
- 'Sohuksan'	WPGP
obassia ♀H4	CArn CBcs CDul CMCN CPne CTho EPfP IClo IDee IMGH LRHS MBlu MBri MDun MWya NLar SSpi WNor
- B&SWJ 6023	WCru
odoratissimus	CExc WPGP

Suaeda (*Chenopodiaceae*)

vera	XPep

Succisa (*Dipsacaceae*)

§ ***pratensis***	CArn EBee MHer NDov NLan NLar NMen NSco NWCA SBch SMHy SPhx WHer WPrP WSFF WTin
- ***alba***	EWes MDKP SBch
- 'Buttermilk'	SKHP
- dwarf	NGby NRya
- 'Peddar's Pink'	EBee EWes SPhx
- purple-flowered **new**	CSpe

Succisella (*Dipsacaceae*)

inflexa	SPhx
- 'Frosted Pearls' **new**	EDAr

sunberry see *Rubus* 'Sunberry'

Sutera (*Scrophulariaceae*)

Abunda Blue Improved = 'Balabimblu' (Abunda Series)	NPri
Breeze Plum = 'Balbreplum' **new**	LSou
Cabana Trailing White	WGor
Candy Floss = 'Yasflos'	LAst
(Copia Series) Copia Dark Pink = 'Dancop19' **new**	NPri

- Copia Golden Leaves **new**	LSou NPri
- Copia Gulliver White = 'Dangul14' **new**	LSou
- Copia Pink Touch	LAst
cordata 'Blizzard'	LAst LSou WGor
- Blue Showers = 'Bacoble'PBR	LAst
- 'Bridal Showers'	NPri
- Lavender Showers = 'Sunlav'PBR	NPri
- pale pink-flowered	LAst
- 'Pink Domino'	ECtt EWin LAst SPet
§ - 'Snowflake'	ECtt EWin LAst MLan NBlu NPer SCoo SPet SPoG
- 'Typhoon White P.'	LAst
'Giant Cloud'	EWin LAst
microphylla **new**	CPBP
neglecta	SPlb WPGP
Olympic Gold = 'Prosutv' (v)	ECtt EWin LAst NBlu SCoo SPoG
Sea Mist = 'Yagemil'PBR	NPri
Suteranova Pink = 'Mogoto'PBR (Suteranova Series)	LAst

Sutherlandia (*Papilionaceae*)

frutescens	CArn CBod CSpe GGar SPlb XPep
- 'Prostrata'	EMan MBri WPat

sweet cicely see *Myrrhis odorata*

Swainsona (*Papilionaceae*)

galegifolia	CHll
- 'Albiflora'	CSpe SOWG WWlt

Syagrus (*Arecaceae*)

§ ***romanzoffiana***	CBrP EAmu LPJP LPal
weddeliana	see *Lytocaryum weddellianum*

x *Sycoparrotia* (*Hamamelidaceae*)

semidecidua	CBcs CPMA MBlu NLar SLPl WPGP

Sycopsis (*Hamamelidaceae*)

sinensis	CAbP CMCN CWib EMil EPfP LRHS MBlu NLar SDnm SSpi WBod WFar WPGP WSHC

Symphoricarpos (*Caprifoliaceae*)

albus	CDul ECrN EMac MSwo NWea SPoG
- 'Constance Spry'	SRms
§ - var. ***laevigatus***	EPfP LBuc MBar
§ - 'Taff's White' (v)	WMoo
- 'Variegatus'	see *S. albus* 'Taff's White'
x ***chenaultii*** 'Hancock'	CMac CSBt EBee ECrN ELan EMac EPfP MBar MGos MRav MSwo NPro SLim SPer WFar
x ***doorenbosii*** 'Magic Berry'	MBar MRav NWea
- 'Mother of Pearl'	ELan EMac EPfP MBar MGos MRav NBlu NWea SPer SPoG
- 'White Hedge'	CSBt ELan LBuc MRav NWea SPer SPlb SPoG
orbiculatus	IMGH SLon
- 'Albovariegatus'	see *S. orbiculatus* 'Taff's Silver Edge'
- 'Argenteovariegatus'	see *S. orbiculatus* 'Taff's Silver Edge'
- 'Bowles' Golden Variegated'	see *S. orbiculatus* 'Foliis Variegatis'
§ - 'Foliis Variegatis' (v)	CChe CTri EBee ECrN ELan EPfP MGos MRav NPro NSti SPer WEas WFar WHCG WSHC
§ - 'Taff's Silver Edge' (v)	MBar NSti
- 'Variegatus'	see *S. orbiculatus* 'Foliis Variegatis'
rivularis	see *S. albus* var. *laevigatus*

Symphyandra (*Campanulaceae*)

asiatica	see *Hanabusaya asiatica*
ossetica	see *Campanula ossetica*
pendula alba	see *Campanula pendula*

Symphyotrichum see *Aster*

Symphytum (*Boraginaceae*)

asperum	ECha ELan EMon MRav MSal NLar WMoo WTMC
* ***azureum***	EBee ELan MSte NLar WCAu WFar WMnd WTMC
'Belsay'	GBuc WHil
'Belsay Gold'	SDix
caucasicum ♀H4	CElw CMHG EBee ECha GPoy LEdu LRHS MBri MHar SBch SIde SSvw WHer WHil WMoo WWlt
- 'Eminence'	EGoo
- 'Norwich Sky'	CKno CPLG EBee
- pale blue-flowered	SSvw
cordatum	EMon EPPr
'Denford Variegated' (v)	ITer NBid
§ 'Goldsmith' (v)	More than 30 suppliers
grandiflorum	CArn CTri CWan EBee GKev GPoy LEdu STes WGwG
* - 'Sky-blue-pink'	EBee NCot
'Hidcote Blue'	CBct CBre CPrp CTri EBee ECha ECtt EPfP EPla ILis LBMP LCro LRHS MSte MWgw NBro NEgg NGHP NHol SLPl SPoG WCAu WCru WMnd WMoo WTMC
§ 'Hidcote Pink'	CBct CPom CPrp EBee ECha EPla EWsh LBMP LCro LRHS MSte MWgw NBir NEgg NSti SBch SLPl SPer SPoG WCAu WFar WMnd WMoo WPnP WTMC
ibericum	CArn CSam EBee ECha EHrv ELau EPfP EPla GMaP GPoy LCro LRHS MWgw NBlu NSti SGar SRms WBor WCAu WMoo WTMC
- 'All Gold'	CArn ECha ECtt ELau EWsh GSki WCAu WMoo WTMC
- 'Blaueglocken'	CSev ECha WMoo WPrP
- dwarf	CPrp NPri WMoo
- 'Gold in Spring'	EGoo NLar WFar
- 'Jubilee'	see *S.* 'Goldsmith'
- 'Lilacinum'	WHer
- 'Variegatum'	see *S.* 'Goldsmith'
- 'Wisley Blue'	CBcs EPfP NLar WFar WMnd WMoo
'Lambrook Sunrise'	CFis CLAP EBee EPPr LAst LHop LRHS MBri MHar NBro SPla WCot WMoo WTMC
'Langthorns Pink'	CPom ELan GBri GBuc
'Mereworth'	see *S.* x *uplandicum* 'Mereworth'
officinale	CArn COld CSev CWan EBee GPoy MHer MNHC MNrw MSal NBlu NGHP NMir NPer NSco NSti SIde SRms WBrk WHer
- 'Boraston White'	MHer
- var. ***ochroleucum***	WHer WTMC
orientale	CPom EMon
peregrinum	see *S.* x *uplandicum*
'Roseum'	see *S.* 'Hidcote Pink'
'Rubrum'	CDes CEnt CPom CPrp EBee ECot EHrv ELan ELau EPPr EPfP EWes GSki LAst LEdu LRHS MHer NEgg NGHP NOrc SBch WCAu WCot WFar WGwG WPGP WTMC
tuberosum	CArn CBre CElw CEnt COld CPom CSam EPPr GPoy LEdu MHer MSte NHol NSti WBor WFar WHer WTMC

§ x ***uplandicum*** CSev CTri ELan ELau GCra GPoy GWCH MHer MSal SIde WJek
- 'Axminster Gold' (v) CBct CDes CEnt CLAP CMea EMan IBlr ITer LHop SBch SPhx WPGP
- 'Bocking 14' CAgr CBod CEnt CHby CPbn CPrp EOHP GAbr SIde
- 'Droitwich' (v) WCot
§ - 'Mereworth' (v) CBct SMad
- 'Moorland Heather' MAvo WMoo
- 'Variegatum' (v) 🏆H4 CLAP EBee ECha ECtt ELan EPfP EWes GMaP GPoy ITer LBMP MTho MWgw NBir NGHP NGdn NSti SDix SMeo WCAu WCot WFar WHil WMoo WSpi WTMC

Symplocarpus (*Araceae*)

foetidus ECho ITer WCot

Symplocos (*Symplocaceae*)

paniculata see *S. sawafutagi*
§ ***sawafutagi*** CBcs EPla MBri NLar WPGP

Syncarpha (*Asteraceae*)

argyropsis new GFai
eximia SPlb

Syneilesis (*Asteraceae*)

aconitifolia CDes CFwr CLAP EBee GEdr MLul WCot WPGP
- B&SWJ 879 WCru
palmata CLAP EBee GEdr LEdu WCot
- B&SWJ 1003 WCru
subglabrata CLAP LEdu
- B&SWJ 298 WCru

Syngonium (*Araceae*)

'Maya Red' MBri
podophyllum 🏆H1 XBlo
- 'Emerald Gem' CHal
- 'Silver Knight' MBri
- 'Variegatum' (v) MBri
'White Butterfly' CHal MBri

Synnotia see *Sparaxis*

Synthyris (*Scrophulariaceae*)

missurica CDes CLAP EBrs GBuc SKHP
- var. ***stellata*** CLAP EBee EHrv EWsh LEdu NGby SBla WFar WHal WPGP
pinnatifida GBuc NWCA
reniformis CLAP GBuc WPGP

Syringa ✿ (*Oleaceae*)

afghanica misapplied see *S. protolaciniata*
'Alexander's Pink' new WGob
x ***chinensis*** ECrN WFar WGob WSpi
- 'Saugeana' IDee NLar SPer
'Correlata' (graft-chimaera) SLon
emodi WHCG
- 'Aurea' IArd IClo IDee MGos NLar
- 'Aureovariegata' see *S. emodi* 'Elegantissima'
§ - 'Elegantissima' (v) CBcs CDoC CEnd EMil EPfP LRHS MAsh MDun NEgg SKHP SSpi
'Hagny' WGob
x ***hyacinthiflora*** 'Clarke's Giant' IArd IDee
- 'Esther Staley' 🏆H4 ECrN ENot EPfP MRav NPri SBLw
Josée = 'Morjos 060F' EMil EPfP EQua MAsh SPoG SWvt WFar WGob WPat WWeb
x ***josiflexa*** CPLG
- 'Agnes Smith' NLar WGob
- 'Anna Amhoff' GBin NLar
- 'Bellicent' 🏆H4 CEnd CLnd EBee ELan ENot EPfP ISea LAst MBar MRav NEgg NLar NPri NSti SHBN SPer SPlb SPoG SRms SSpi SWvt WGob WHCG WPat WPen WSpi WTel
- 'James MacFarlane' EBee LBuc NLar WGob
- 'Lynette' EPla NPro
- 'Redwine' EBee MGos NBlu NLar
§ - 'Royalty' EBee NLar WGob
josikaea CSBt EBee MBar NLar SPer WGob WHCG WSpi
'Kim' MRav NLar WWeb
komarowii NLar
- L 490 GGGa
§ - subsp. ***reflexa*** CDul EPfP MBar MGos WFar WGob
§ x ***laciniata*** Mill. CPMA EBee EPfP LRHS MGos MRav MWea NLar SCoo SEND SPer SSpi WGor WHCG WKif WPGP WRHF
§ ***meyeri*** 'Palibin' 🏆H4 More than 30 suppliers
microphylla see *S. pubescens* subsp. *microphylla*
'Minuet' MGos NBlu NLar WGob
'Miss Canada' MBri NLar WGob
palibiniana see *S. meyeri* 'Palibin'
patula misapplied see *S. meyeri* 'Palibin'
patula (Palibin) Nakai see *S. pubescens* subsp. *patula*
pekinensis see *S. reticulata* subsp. *pekinensis*
x ***persica*** 🏆H4 CPLG CPMA CSam CTri EPfP EWTr MGos MRav NLar NPal SLon SPer WTel XPep
- 'Alba' 🏆H4 CPMA EBee GQui MRav WFar WHCG WPat
- var. ***laciniata*** see *S.* x *laciniata* Mill.
pinnatifolia IArd IDee MBri MWea NLar WHCG
x ***prestoniae*** 'Audrey' WGob
- 'Coral' WFar
- 'Desdemona' SSta
- 'Donald Wyman' MBri WGob
- 'Elinor' 🏆H4 CLnd CMHG ENot EPfP MRav NSti SPer
- 'Hiawatha' MGos
- 'Isabella' MGos SCoo
- 'Nocturne' MGos WFar WGob
- 'Royalty' see *S.* x *josiflexa* 'Royalty'
§ ***protolaciniata*** CPle LBMP MAsh MGos SKHP WFar
- 'Kabul' EPfP NLar
§ ***pubescens*** subsp. ***microphylla*** CBrm CFwr EWTr LCro
§ - subsp. ***microphylla*** 'Superba' 🏆H4 More than 30 suppliers
§ - subsp. ***patula*** CMac ECho EPfP MRav NEgg NHol NWea SEND SLon SPla SPoG WFar
- - 'Miss Kim' 🏆H4 CDoC CSBt CWSG EBee ELan ENot IArd LAst LRHS LSRN MAsh MBri MGos MRav MSwo NBlu NEgg SCoo SHBN SLim SPoG SSta WFar WGob WHCG WPat
'Red Pixie' LBuc LCro LRHS MBri MGos SCoo
reflexa see *S. komarowii* subsp. *reflexa*
reticulata 'City of Toronto' EBee
- 'Ivory Silk' CWSG EPfP MAsh NLar
§ - subsp. ***pekinensis*** CMCN IDee WBVN
- - 'Pendula' IArd IClo IDee
- - 'Yellow Fragrance' new MBri
x ***swegiflexa*** CDul CPLG NLar
sweginzowii EWTr LBuc MBri NLar SPer WFar WSpi
- 'Superba' LAst WMoo
tomentella MBri NWea SRms
velutina see *S. pubescens* subsp. *patula*
villosa MBri SPlb WBVN WGob
vulgaris CLnd ECrN EMac LBuc MBar NWea XPep

	- 'Agincourt Beauty'	MBri
	- var. ***alba***	MBar
	- 'Albert F. Holden'	WGob
§	- 'Andenken an Ludwig Späth' 𝕐H4	More than 30 suppliers
	- 'Aurea'	EPla EQua MRav NPro WFar
	- Beauty of Moscow	see *S. vulgaris* 'Krasavitsa Moskvy'
	- 'Belle de Nancy' (d)	CDul CWib EBee ELan LAst MRav SBLw SEND SHBN SWvt
	- Burgundy Queen = 'Lecburg'	WGob
	- 'Charles Joly' (d) 𝕐H4	More than 30 suppliers
	- 'Comtesse d'Harcourt' new	EMil EQua
	- 'Congo'	MRav NMoo SEND SPer WGob
	- 'Edward J. Gardner' (d)	ECrN SCoo SPer WGob
	- 'Firmament' 𝕐H4	EBee ELan EPfP MRav NEgg SCoo SEND SHBN SPer WGob WSpi
	- 'G. J. Baardse'	SBLw
	- 'Gaby' new	EMil
	- 'Général Pershing' (d)	SBLw
	- 'Katherine Havemeyer' (d) 𝕐H4	More than 30 suppliers
§	- 'Krasavitsa Moskvy' (d)	EWes MBri
	- 'La Tour d'Auvergne'	SBLw
	- 'Madame Antoine Buchner' (d)	ENot
	- 'Madame Florent Stepman'	CMac
	- 'Madame Lemoine' (d) 𝕐H4	More than 30 suppliers
	- 'Masséna'	MRav WSPU
	- 'Maud Notcutt'	SPer
	- 'Michel Buchner' (d)	CBcs CDul CWib EBee ELan ENot LAst MBar MGan MRav NBlu NPri SBLw SCoo SLim SPer WBVN WGob
	- 'Miss Ellen Willmott' (d)	MBri MRav SBLw
	- 'Mont Blanc'	SBLw
	- 'Mrs Edward Harding' (d) 𝕐H4	EBee ECrN ENot EPfP EQua LAst LBuc MGos MRav NPri NWea SCoo SPer SRGP WGob
	- 'Nadezhda' (d) new	WGob
	- 'Olivier de Serres' (d)	MBri SBLw
	- 'P.P. Konchalovskii' new	EMil
	- 'Paul Deschanel' (d)	EBee
	- 'Président Fallières' (d)	EBee WSPU
	- 'Président Grévy' (d)	CDoC CLnd CMac LAst NEgg SBLw SPer
	- 'President Lincoln'	SBLw
	- 'Primrose'	CBcs CDoC CDul CMac CSBt CWib EBee ECrN ELan ENot EPfP GBin IArd LAst LRHS MBri MGos MRav NEgg NPen NPri SCoo SEND SPer SPoG SSta WFar WGob WSpi
	- 'Prince Wolkonsky' (d)	EBee EMil EQua WFar WGob
	- 'Princesse Sturdza' new	EMil
	- 'Ruhm von Horstenstein' new	EBee
	- 'Sensation'	CBcs CDoC CSBt CWSG EBee ECrN ENot EPfP IArd IMGH LAst LBuc LRHS LSRN MAsh MGos MRav MSwo NEgg NPri NWea SCoo SEND SHBN SLim SPer SPoG SSta WGob WSpi
	- 'Souvenir d'Alice Harding' (d)	LRHS
	- 'Souvenir de Louis Spaeth'	see *S. vulgaris* 'Andenken an Ludwig Späth'
	- variegated (v)	EWes MGos
	- variegated double (d/v)	WCot
	- 'Vestale' 𝕐H4	MRav
	- 'Viviand-Morel' (d)	WGob
	- 'Znamya Lenina'	MBri
	wolfii	CArn WBVN
	yunnanensis	CPLG GGGa LTwo WBod WSpi
	- 'Prophecy'	WGob
	- 'Rosea'	WGob

Syzygium (*Myrtaceae*)

australe	EShb
jambos	EShb
paniculatum	EShb IDee

T

Tabernaemontana (*Apocynaceae*)

	coronaria	see *T. divaricata*
§	***divaricata***	CCCN SOWG

Tacca (*Taccaceae*)

chantrieri	CCCN EAmu EBrs ECho
integrifolia	EAmu EBrs ECho

Tacitus see *Graptopetalum*

Tagetes (*Asteraceae*)

lemmonii	SHDw SMad XPep
'Lemon Gem' new	EUnu
lucida	CArn CBod EOHP MSal NBlu NTHB WJek
patula	EUnu
tenuifolia	CArn

Taiwania (*Cupressaceae*)

cryptomerioides new	CDul

Talbotia (*Velloziaceae*)

§	***elegans***	CSpe WFar

Talinum (*Portulacaceae*)

calycinum	EAlp EWin
'Kingwood Gold'	CBow
okanoganense	CCCN EAlp
paniculatum new	CCCN

tamarillo see *Cyphomandra betacea*

tamarind see *Tamarindus indica*

Tamarindus (*Caesalpiniaceae*)

indica (F)	SPlb

Tamarix (*Tamaricaceae*)

	africana	EBee EMil
	gallica	CSBt NWea SAPC SArc WSHC XPep
§	***parviflora***	EBee EMil LRHS MGos
	pentandra	see *T. ramosissima*
§	***ramosissima***	CTri ECrN ELan EPfP MBar MBrN MSwo SEND SLim SRms SSta WSHC
	- 'Pink Cascade'	CBcs CSBt EBee EMil ENot EPfP LCro LPan LRHS MBri MGos MRav NBlu SPer SPoG SWvt WBod XPep
	- 'Rosea'	CBcs MGan SLon
§	- 'Rubra' 𝕐H4	CChe CDoC CWSG EBee EMil EPfP LRHS MAsh MBlu MGos NLar SLon SPer
	- 'Summer Glow'	see *T. ramosissima* 'Rubra'
	tetrandra 𝕐H4	More than 30 suppliers
	- 'Africance'	ERom
	- var. ***purpurea***	see *T. parviflora*

Tamus (*Dioscoreaceae*)

communis	CArn MSal

Tanacetum ✿ (*Asteraceae*)

§	***argenteum***	ECho MRav SIde
	- subsp. ***canum***	ECho EWes LRHS
§	***balsamita***	CArn CCge CHrt COld CPrp EAro EBee ELan ELau GPoy LEdu MBri MHer MNHC MSal NTHB SHGN SWal WJek WPer WSel WTin XPep
§	- subsp. ***balsamita***	CBod CWan GPoy MSal SIde
§	- subsp. ***balsamitoides***	CBod CHby CPrp ELau GWCH MHer WJek
	- var. ***tanacetoides***	see *T. balsamita* subsp. *balsamita*
	- ***tomentosum***	see *T. balsamita* subsp. *balsamitoides*
	capitatum	see *Sphaeromeria capitata*
§	***cinerariifolium***	CArn CBod CPrp CWan GPoy MNHC WPer XPep
§	***coccineum***	GPoy MSal NBPC SGar SPoG SRms WFar
	- 'Alfred' **new**	EBee
	- 'Aphrodite' (d)	CPrp EBee ECtt LRHS MBNS NEgg WCAu WHil
	- 'Beauty of Stapleford'	CPrp EBee LRHS NEgg NOrc WCAu WHil
	- 'Bees' Pink Delight'	EBee LRHS MBNS NEgg SPoG
	- 'Brenda'	EBee EPfP LHop LRHS MBNS MRav MWat NEgg
	- 'Duro'	CEnt CFir GBuc WHrl
	- 'Eileen May Robinson' ♀H4	CBcs EBee ECot ENot EPfP EShb LHop LRHS LSRN MWgw NBre NEgg NGdn SHar WCAu WCra
	- 'Evenglow'	EBee ECtt EPfP LRHS NEgg WCAu
	- 'H.M. Pike'	EBee LRHS MBNS
	- 'James Kelway' ♀H4	CPrp EBee ECot ECtt ELan EPfP EShb GGar LRHS MRav MWat MWgw NBir NEgg NGdn SPoG SRms WCAu WCra WHil
	- 'King Size'	SGar WFar
	- 'Madeleine' (d)	CPrp EBee LBMP MWgw SRGP
	- Robinson's giant-flowered	SRms WMoo
	- 'Robinson's Pink'	CMdw CPrp EBee ELan ENot EPfP GMaP LAst LRHS MWgw NBre SRGP SRms WHil
	- 'Robinson's Red'	CSBt GMaP LAst MBNS NPri NVic SPur SRms SWvt WBVN WCot
	- 'Robinson's Rose'	MBNS WCot
*	- ***rubrum***	GWCH
	- 'Salmon Beauty'	ITim
	- 'Scarlet Glow'	EBee LRHS MBNS
	- 'Snow Cloud'	EBee ELan LRHS MBNS MWgw NBre SPoG WCAu
	- 'Vanessa'	CPrp EBee MBNS NEgg
§	***corymbosum***	EBee GMac
	densum	ECho EPot WCFE
	- subsp. ***amani***	EBee ECha ECho GMaP LRHS MHer NWCA SEND SPoG SRms XPep
	'H.M. Pike' **new**	NOrc
§	***haradjanii***	CMea ECho ECtt ELan SBch SBla WHer
	herderi	see *Hippolytia herderi*
	macrophyllum misapplied	see *Achillea grandifolia* Friv.
§	***macrophyllum*** (Waldst. & Kit.) Sch.Bip.	CTca ECtt EMon EPPr SPhx WCot WPer
	niveum	CArn EAro ECha MSal WCot
	- 'Jackpot'	CWib EAro EBee EDAr EWes LRHS MBNS MBri SHar SSvw
§	***parthenium***	CArn CBod CHby CPbn CWan ELau GPoy MHer MNHC NPer SIde SRms WHer
	- 'Aureum'	CEnt CHid CPbn CPrp ECha ELan ELau EWes EWin GPoy MBri MHer MNHC MWgw NGHP SIng SPer SPlb SRms WCot WEas WFar WHer WMoo WPer
	- double white-flowered (d)	CSWP EUnu MNHC NPer SEND SRms
	- 'Golden Ball'	MNHC
	- 'Golden Moss'	NVic
	- 'Malmesbury'	CNat
	- 'Plenum' (d)	EHrv SBch SIng
§	- 'Rowallane' (d)	EBee ELan ERou GBuc GMac MBri WCot
	- 'Sissinghurst White'	see *T. parthenium* 'Rowallane'
	- 'Snowball' (d)	EUnu
	- 'White Bonnet' (d)	WEas
	poteriifolium	EBee EBrs
§	***ptarmiciflorum*** ♀H3-4	MNHC
	- 'Silver Feather'	WJek
	vulgare	CArn CHby CSev ECtt ELau GPoy MHar MHer MNHC MSal NSco SIde WMoo WSFF
	- var. ***crispum***	CBod CHby CPrp CWan EBee ELau GPoy MHer SIde SMad WFar WJek WSel
	- 'Isla Gold' (v)	CBow CElw EBee EPPr EWes GMaP LHop MHar MRav NBid NBre NSti WCot WFar WMoo
	- 'Silver Lace' (v)	CBow EBee GBri ITer NBid NGHP WFar WHer WMoo WOut

Tanakaea (*Saxifragaceae*)

radicans	EBee WCru

tangelo see *Citrus* x *tangelo*

tangerine see *Citrus reticulata*

tangor see *Citrus* x *nobilis Tangor Group*

Tapiscia (*Staphyleaceae*)

sinensis	CExc

Taraxacum (*Asteraceae*)

albidum	CNat WCot
- DJH 452	CHid
coreanum	CNat
faeroense	WCot
officinale agg.	CArn
- variegated agg. (v)	WCot
pseudoroseum	CNat
rubrifolium	CSpe WHrl

Tarchonanthus (*Asteraceae*)

camphoratus	CTrC

tarragon see *Artemisia dracunculus*

Tasmannia see *Drimys*

Taxodium (*Cupressaceae*)

	ascendens 'Nutans'	see *T. distichum* var. *imbricatum* 'Nutans'
	distichum ♀H4	More than 30 suppliers
	- 'Cascade Falls'PBR	CDul LCon MBlu MBri MGos NLar SLim
	- 'Hursley Park'	SLim
	- var. ***imbricatum***	CGHE CMCN EPfP WPGP
§	- - 'Nutans' ♀H4	CBcs CEnd CTho EMil LCon LPan LRHS MAsh MBlu SCoo SLim SMad
	- 'Little Twister' **new**	NLar
	- 'Minaret'	MBlu
	- 'Peve Minaret'	CDoC CMen LCon LRHS MAsh NLar SLim
	- 'Peve Yellow'	NLar
	- 'Schloss Herten'	SLim
	- 'Secrest'	CBcs LRHS MAsh MBlu MBri SLim
	- Shawnee Brave = 'Mickelson'	MBlu NLar
	mucronatum	CDoC

– F&M 198	WPGP

Taxus ✿ (*Taxaceae*)

baccata ♀H4	More than 30 suppliers
– 'Adpressa' (f)	ECho NEgg
– 'Adpressa Aurea' (v)	CKen ECho EPla SCoo
– 'Adpressa Variegata' (m/v) ♀H4	CDoC ECho EHul
– 'Aldenham Gold'	CKen ECho
– 'Amersfoort'	CDoC EOrn LCon NLar SCoo SLim SPoG
– 'Argentea Minor'	see *T. baccata* 'Dwarf White'
– Aurea Group	NHol SRms
I – 'Aurea Pendula'	ECho EOrn
I – 'Aureomarginata' (v)	CBcs CBow CSBt ECho EOrn MAsh NEgg SWvt
– 'Autumn Shades'	CBcs ECho LLin
– 'Bridget's Gold' **new**	CKen
– 'Cavendishii' (f)	ECho
– 'Compacta'	EOrn EPla
– 'Corleys Coppertip'	CBgR CKen CRob ECho EHul LCon MAsh MBar NEgg NHol NLar SCoo SLim WEve WFar
– 'Cristata'	CKen NLar
– 'David'	IArd MBri NLar SCoo SPoG WEve
– 'Dovastoniana' (f) ♀H4	CMac ECho MBar NLar NWea SCoo WMou
– 'Dovastonii Aurea' (m/v) ♀H4	CMac ECho EHul EOrn EPfP EPla LCon MAsh MBar MBlu MBri MGos NEgg NLar NPri NWea SCoo SLim WCFE WFar
– 'Drinkstone Gold' (v)	ECho EHul
§ – 'Dwarf White' (v)	ECho EOrn EPla SCoo WGor
– 'Elegantissima' (f/v)	CTho ECho EHul EPfP SCoo SPoG WEve WFar
– 'Erecta' (f)	ECho EHul SHBN
§ – 'Fastigiata' (f) ♀H4	More than 30 suppliers
– Fastigiata Aurea Group	CLnd CWib ECho EHul EPfP GKev IArd LBuc LLin MAsh MGan MGos NGHP NHol NPri SRms STre WBrE WEve WFar WHar
– 'Fastigiata Aureomarginata' (m/v) ♀H4	CDoC CMac CRob CTri ECho EHul EOrn EPfP IMGH ISea LAst LBee LCon LRHS MBar MBri MGos NBlu NWea SAga SCoo SLim SLon SPer SPoG SWvt WCFE WEve WOrn
– 'Fastigiata Robusta' (f)	CDoC CRob ECho EPfP EPla LCon LLin MBar MBri NHol SCoo SLim SPoG WEve WFar WGer
– 'Goud Elsje'	CKen NLar
– 'Gracilis Pendula'	ECho
– 'Grayswood Hill'	ECho
– 'Green Column'	CKen ECho
– 'Green Diamond'	CKen NLar
– 'Hibernica'	see *T. baccata* 'Fastigiata'
– 'Icicle'	CBcs ECho EPla LCon LLin MAsh MGos NLar WEve
– 'Itsy Bitsy'	CKen
– 'Ivory Tower'	CBcs CDoC CKen ECho ELan LBee LCon LLin LRHS MAsh MGos NLar SLim SPoG WEve WFar WGor
– 'Klitzeklein'	CKen
– 'Laurie'	SCoo
– 'Melfard'	CDoC EHul
– 'Nana'	ECho
– 'Nutans'	CDoC CKen CRob CSBt ECho EHul EOrn IMGH LLin MBar SCoo
– 'Overeynderi'	EHul
– 'Pendula'	ECho MRav
– 'Prostrata'	CMac WFar
– 'Pygmaea'	CKen
– 'Repandens' (f) ♀H4	EHul IArd LCon MBar SHBN WCFE WFar
I – 'Repens Aurea' (v) ♀H4	CDoC CKen CRob ECho ECrN EHul EOrn EPfP LCon LLin LRHS MAsh MBar MGos NEgg SCoo WFar
– 'Semperaurea' (m) ♀H4	CAgr CBcs CDoC CMac ECho EHul EOrn LBuc LCon LRHS MAsh MBar MGan MGos NEgg NHol NWea SCoo SLim SPla SPoG WCFE WFar
– 'Silver Spire' (v)	CKen MDKP
– 'Standishii' (f) ♀H4	More than 30 suppliers
– 'Stove Pipe'	CKen
– 'Summergold' (v)	CRob ECho EHul ELan EPfP LCon LRHS MAsh MBar MBri MGos MRav NBir NBlu NEgg NHol NLar SCoo SLim WEve WFar
– 'Washingtonii' (v)	IArd MBar SHBN
– 'White Icicle'	ECho EOrn MGos WGor
brevifolia	EPla
cuspidata	CMen ECho LLin
– 'Aurescens' (v)	CKen EPla SRms
– var. ***nana***	EHul EOrn LCon MBar
– 'Robusta'	EHul
– 'Straight Hedge'	CDoC ECho EHul IMGH LRHS SLim
x ***media*** 'Brownii'	EHul LBuc
– 'Hicksii' (f) ♀H4	CDul ECho EHul IMGH LBuc LRHS MBar MGan MGos NBlu NWea SCoo SLim WFar
– 'Hillii'	MBar MBri SCoo
– 'Lodi'	LBee LRHS
– 'Strait Hedge' (f) **new**	CAgr

Tayberry see *Rubus* Tayberry Group

Tecoma (*Bignoniaceae*)

x ***alata***	SOWG
capensis ♀H1	CHEx CSev LRHS SOWG
– 'Aurea'	CSev EShb SOWG
– 'Coccinea'	EShb
– 'Lutea'	EShb LRHS
cochabambensis RCB/Arg L-8 **new**	WCot
garrocha	EShb
'Orange Glow'	SOWG
ricasoliana	see *Podranea ricasoliana*
stans	SOWG

Tecomanthe (*Bignoniaceae*)

speciosa	CHEx ECou SOWG

Tecomaria see *Tecoma*

Tecophilaea (*Tecophilaeaceae*)

cyanocrocus ♀H2	CAvo EBrs ECho EPot GCrs IHer LAma LRHS NMin SBla WCot
– 'Leichtlinii' ♀H2	EBrs ECho EPot IHer LAma LRHS NMin SCnR
– 'Purpurea'	see *T. cyanocrocus* 'Violacea'
– Storm Cloud Group	GCrs
§ – 'Violacea'	CAvo EBrs ECho GCrs IHer LRHS NMin
violiflora	EBrs ECho LAma

Tectaria (*Dryopteridaceae*)

gemmifera	GQui

Telanthophora (*Asteraceae*)

grandifolia	CHEx SAPC SArc

Telekia (*Asteraceae*)

§ ***speciosa***	CHar CHrt COIW CSam EBee ELan EPfP EWsh GAbr ITim MCCP MWrn NBro NChi SDix SLPl SPlb WCFE WFar WHer WHoo WMoo WPer WPnP

Telesonix see *Boykinia*

Teline see *Genista*

Tellima (*Saxifragaceae*)

grandiflora	More than 30 suppliers
- 'Bob's Choice' **new**	WCot
- 'Delphine' (v)	CBow EBee EMan EPPr SAga WCot
- 'Forest Frost'	CBct CBow CFis EBee EMan GCai LAst LHop MDun NBre NGdn NLar NSti WCot WMoo WOut
- Odorata Group	CBre ECha EGoo MRav NSti WCot WHen WMoo
- 'Perky'	ECho
- 'Purpurea'	see *T. grandiflora* Rubra Group
- 'Purpurteppich'	EBee EBrs ECha ECho EGoo EHrv EMan EPPr GAbr LBBr LRHS MRav NDov NGdn WCot WMnd WMoo WOut WTMC
§ - Rubra Group	More than 30 suppliers
- 'Silver Select'	EPPr

Telopea (*Proteaceae*)

'Dawn Fire' **new**	CTrC
speciosissima	CCCN CTrC SOWG SPlb
- 'Red Embers'	CTrC
truncata	WCru

Templetonia (*Papilionaceae*)

retusa	ECou

Temu see *Blepharocalyx*

Tephroseris (*Asteraceae*)

integrifolia	WHer

Tephrosia (*Papilionaceae*)

vogelii	CArn

Tetracentron (*Tetracentraceae*)

sinense	EPfP IArd LRHS NLar WPGP

Tetradenia (*Lamiaceae*)

riparia	EOHP

Tetradium (*Rutaceae*)

§ ***daniellii***	CBcs CBrd CMCN EPfP IArd IDee NLar SSpi WPGP WPat
* - ***henryi***	NLar
§ - Hupehense Group	CMCN CPle MBri NPen WOrn
- 'Moonlight'	MBri NLar
glabrifolium	EBee WPGP
- B&SWJ 3541	WCru
ruticarpum	WPGP
- B&SWJ 6882	WCru
* ***velutinum***	NLar

Tetragonia (*Tetragoniaceae*)

tetragonoides	CArn

Tetragonolobus see *Lotus*

Tetraneuris (*Asteraceae*)

§ ***grandiflora***	GAbr
§ ***scaposa***	EPot LRHS

Tetrapanax (*Araliaceae*)

§ ***papyrifer*** ♀H2-3	CBrP CDTJ CHEx SAPC SArc SDix XBlo
- B&SWJ 7135	WCru
- 'Empress'	WCru
- 'Rex'	CDTJ CGHE CHEx CPLG EAmu EGFP WCru WPGP

Tetrapathaea see *Passiflora*

Tetrastigma (*Vitaceae*)

obtectum	ECre EWes MTPN
voinierianum ♀H1	EShb MBri SAPC SArc WCot

Tetratheca (*Tremandraceae*)

ciliata var. ***alba***	SOWG
thymifolia	ECou
- pink-flowered	SOWG

Teucrium (*Lamiaceae*)

* ***ackermannii***	CLyd ECho LBee LRHS NMen SBla SMac WAbe WEas WHoo WPat WTin XPep
arduinoi	XPep
aroanium	CLyd ECho EPot LBee LRHS NMen NWCA SBla
asiaticum	EGoo XPep
bicolor	CPle
botrys	MHer MSal
brevifolium	XPep
canadense	MSal
chamaedrys misapplied	see *T.* x *lucidrys*
chamaedrys L.	CHal CPom CPrp CSam CWan CWib ECho EGoo GAbr LAst LEdu LRHS LSRN MSwo NGHP NWCA SLim SRms STre WBrk WJek WSel WTin WWeb XPep
- 'Nanum'	ECho
- 'Rose'	WMoo
- 'Rose Carpet'	EGoo
- 'Summer Sunshine' **new**	LBuc LRHS MAsh
- 'Variegatum' (v)	EMan WPer
aff. ***chamaedrys***	MNHC
cossonii	XPep
§ ***creticum***	ECho WLin
divaricatum	XPep
- NS 614	NWCA
dunense	EAro XPep
flavum	CArn EDAr EGoo NBre SGar SHFr WJek WOut XPep
- subsp. ***grandiflorum***	XPep
fruticans	More than 30 suppliers
- 'Azureum' ♀H3	CBcs CMMP COIW CWSG EBee EPfP EWin LAst LRHS LSou SBra SMad SPer SRkn WEas XPep
- 'Compactum'	CChe CDoC COIW EBee ELon ENot EWin LAst LSou MCCP SLon SPer SPla
- 'Drysdale'	CDoC
gnaphalodes	XPep
hircanicum	More than 30 suppliers
- 'Paradise Delight'	ECtt MAvo NBid NOrc NPro SPoG WCra
- 'Purple Tails'	CPrp CSpe CWib LSou NBir NCob SPoG WHal
laciniatum	XPep
lamiifolium	EBee
§ x ***lucidrys***	CArn CMea CPom CSev CSpe CWan EBee ECha ECho EGoo ELan ELau EPfP GPoy LAst LRHS MHer MRav MWat MWgw NGHP SGar SHFr SIde SPer SPoG WCFE WEas WHoo XPep
lucidum	XPep
marum	CArn CTri MSal NGHP NMen SBla SHGN WJek XPep
- 'Feuilles Vertes'	XPep
'Massif Central'	LRHS
massiliense misapplied	see *T.* x *lucidrys*
massiliense L.	EAro EBee XPep
microphyllum	XPep
micropodioides	XPep

montanum	EGoo EShb SHGN XPep
nivale **new**	EBee
orientale	XPep
polium	CArn CPLG ECho MWat NLAp WJek WPat XPep
- subsp. ***aureum***	NWCA SBla XPep
- subsp. ***capitatum***	XPep
pyrenaicum	CMea CPBP CPom EBee ECho EMan EPot EWes GCrs GEdr MHer MSte NWCA SBch SBla WPat
rosmarinifolium	see *T. creticum*
scordium	CNat
scorodonia	CArn COld CRWN CSev EGoo ELau GPoy MHer MNHC MSal NMir WHer WJek WSel XPep
- 'Binsted Gold'	EBee EGoo EMan EMon EPPr LDai LSou MHar WOut
- 'Crispum'	CWan ELau EUnu MHar MHer MLLN MMuc MWgw NBro NCob SBch SPer WBrE WGwG WHoo WJek WKif WMnd WMoo WPer WSel
- 'Crispum Marginatum' (v)	COlW EBee ECha EGoo EHrv EPPr EPfP IBlr ILis LHop LRHS MNrw MRav NHol NSti WCra WEas WFar WTin WWeb
- 'Spring Morn'	EBee
- 'Winterdown' (v)	CBow CRez EBee EGoo EMan EPPr NPro SAga SBch WLin WWeb
subspinosum	CMea ECho LBee LRHS NLAp NMen WHoo WPat XPep
§ ***viscidum*** 'Lemon and Lime' (v)	EBee ECtt EMan LHop LSou MHar NSti SDnm
webbianum	ECho
'Winterdown'	GBri WDyG

Thalia (*Marantaceae*)

dealbata	CBen CDWL CHEx CMdw EAmu EMFW LLWG NLar SDix WMAq
geniculata	CDWL

Thalictrum (*Ranunculaceae*)

CC 3691	ITer
CC 4575	CPLG MGol
CC 4576	CPLG GKev MGol WCot
CC 4577	CPLG MGol WCot
from Afghanistan	see *T. isopyroides*
actaeifolium	CLAP CWib
- B&SWJ 4664	WCru
- var. ***brevistylum***	EBee LSou
- - B&SWJ 8819	WCru
- - 'Twinkling Star' **new**	MBnl NCob WCot
acutifolium **new**	EBee
adiantifolium	see *T. minus* 'Adiantifolium'
alpinum	EPPr SBch
angustifolium	see *T. lucidum*
aquilegiifolium	More than 30 suppliers
- var. ***album***	CMea CMil COlW EBee ECha EGle ELan EPfP ERou GCra LAst LHop MNFA MSte MWgw NBid NChi SPhx SPla WCAu WMnd WPer WSHC WSpi
- dwarf	CMea
* - 'Hybridum'	WFar WMoo WPer
- 'Purple Cloud'	see *T. aquilegiifolium* 'Thundercloud'
- 'Purpureum'	CPom CSev NLar SPla WCAu WHoo
- 'Sparkler'	GCai
§ - 'Thundercloud' ♀H4	CBct CCVN CFir CKno CTca CWan EBee ECtt EGle ENot EPfP ERou LFur LHop LRHS MBri MDKP MSte NBPC NCot NLar NRnb NSti SMer WBrE WCot WCra WHlf WSpi WWeb
baicalense	CPom EBee
'Black Stockings'	CAby CKno
'Braveheart'	NRnb
chelidonii	CWsd GMaP MGol MHar
- GWJ 9349	WCru
- HWJK 2216	WCru
clavatum	CDes CLAP EBee WPGP
contortum	EBee SDys
coreanum	see *T. ichangense*
cultratum	CDes CHid CWCL NCGa NSti WPGP
- HWJCM 367	EBee NLar WCru
dasycarpum	EBee MLLN NLar WPnP
§ ***delavayi*** ♀H4	More than 30 suppliers
- BWJ 7903	WCru
- DJHC 473	CDes WCru
- var. ***acuminatum*** BWJ 7535	WCru
- - BWJ 7971	WCru
- 'Album'	CHFP CLAP CSpe CWCL CWsd EBee EBrs ECha EGle ENot EPPr GMac GQue LFur LPio LRHS NBPC NCGa NCob NLar NMRc NPri SMad SPhx SPoG WCot WGwG WMoo WPrP
- 'Ankum'	EBee
- var. ***decorum***	CFwr CLAP CWCL EPPr GBin GEdr GMac LPio NCGa NCob SBla SPhx WCot WCru WSHC
- - CD&R 2135	CAby
- 'Hewitt's Double' (d) ♀H4	More than 30 suppliers
- var. ***mucronatum***	WCru
- purple-stemmed BWJ 7748	WCru
diffusiflorum	CDes CEnt CLAP GBri GBuc GEdr SBla WCru WSHC
dioicum	EBee WPnP
dipterocarpum misapplied	see *T. delavayi*
dipterocarpum Franch.	EBee WMnd
- ACE 4.878.280	CMil
elegans HWJK 2271	WCru
'Elin'	CDes CElw CFir CKno CLAP CSam CSpe EBee EGle EPPr ERou EWes GBuc GMac IPot LFur LHop MBri MLLN MNFA NBir NCGa NCob NCot NDov NEgg SMHy SPoG WKif WPGP
fendleri	GBin GBuc
filamentosum B&SWJ 777	WCru
- var. ***yakusimense*** B&SWJ 6094	WCru
finetii	CLAP
aff. ***finetii***	CLAP
flavum	CHar CPLG EBee ECtt EHon GBin NBro SPhx SWat WBrE WShi
- 'Chollerton'	see *T. isopyroides*
§ - subsp. ***glaucum*** ♀H4	More than 30 suppliers
- - 'True Blue'	LRHS MSte
- 'Illuminator'	CDes CKno CPar CTri EBee EGle ELon EPPr EPfP ERou GBri LPio LRHS MArl MHer MRav NEgg SMad SPlb SPoG WCAu WCot WFar WPnP WPrP
flexuosum	see *T. minus* subsp. *minus*
foetidum	NBre
- BWJ 7558	WCru
foliolosum B&SWJ 2705	WCru
- HWJK 2181	WCru
- S&SH 382	GBri
grandidentatum **new**	EBee
grandiflorum	NCob
honanense	EBee WCot
§ ***ichangense***	EBee GBri
* - var. ***minus***	WCru

§	***isopyroides***	CFir CPBP CPom CSev EBee EMar EPla GBin GBuc LAst LPio LRHS MRav MWgw NChi NGdn NMen WCot WDyG WSpi WTin
	javanicum	LEdu
	- B&SWJ 9506	WCru
	- var. ***puberulum***	GMac
	- - B&SWJ 6770	WCru
	johnstonii B&SWJ 9127	WCru
	kiusianum	More than 30 suppliers
	- Kew form	SBla WSHC
	koreanum	see *T. ichangense*
§	***lucidum***	CAby CKno CPou EBee ELan EShb LPio MLLN MRav NBre NDov NLar NSti SGar SHar SMHy SPhx WCot WFar WPrP
	minus	CMHG EBee ECGP ELan EMon GBuc LPio MLLN NBre SEND
§	- 'Adiantifolium'	EBee MLLN MRav MWgw NBre NCob NGdn NLar SHar SRms WFar WPer
	- var. ***hypoleucum*** B&SWJ 8634	WCru
	- subsp. ***kemense***	EBee
§	- subsp. ***minus***	NBre
§	- subsp. ***olympicum***	WPer
	- subsp. ***saxatile***	see *T. minus* subsp. *olympicum*
	- var. ***sipellatum*** B&SWJ 5051	WCru
	morisonii	NBid
	occidentale JLS 86255	MNrw
	omeiense	CDes EBee WPGP
	- BWJ 8049	WCru
	orientale	EWes SBla
	osmundifolium	EBee
	platycarpum B&SWJ 2261 **new**	WCru
	polygamum	see *T. pubescens*
	przewalskii	WCru
§	***pubescens***	CAby ECha GBin GBri GMaP MSal NBre NDov SHar WPrP
	punctatum	CLAP LPio NEgg WCot
	- B&SWJ 1272	WCru
	reniforme	CExc CFir EBee GBuc MHar WCot
	- B&SWJ 2610	WCru
	- HWJK 2152	WCru
	reticulatum	WCru
	rochebruneanum	More than 30 suppliers
	sachalinense	CDes EBee MCCP NCGa WPGP
	- AER 0279	EKen
	- RBS 0279	EKen EPPr ITer MGol MHar WCot
	shensiense **new**	EBee GEdr
	simplex	MLLN
	- var. ***brevipes*** B&SWJ 4794	WCru
	speciosissimum	see *T. flavum* subsp. *glaucum*
	sphaerostachyum	GMac LRHS MBri SMrm WHal
	squarrosum	EBee LRHS
	tenuisubulatum BWJ 7929	WCru
	tuberosum	CDes CElw CMea CWsd EBee EPot GBuc MLLN NDov NLAp SBla WPGP WPat
	uchiyamae	CFwr CPom EBee EGle GBin GBri LBMP WCot WSPU
	virgatum B&SWJ 2964	WCru
	yunnanense **new**	WCru

Thamnocalamus (*Poaceae*)

	aristatus	CGHE EPfP EPla WDyG WPGP
	crassinodus	EPla SDry
	- dwarf	EPla
	- 'Gosainkund'	EPla
	- 'Kew Beauty'	CAbb CDoC CGHE CPen EFul EPfP EPla ERod MBrN MBri MMoz MWht NPal SDry WCot WDyG WPGP
	- 'Lang Tang'	CGHE EFul EPla ERod MMoz WPGP
	- 'Merlyn'	CDoC CPen EPfP EPla ERod MMoz MWht SDry WPGP
	- 'Pitt White'	MBri
	falcatus	see *Drepanostachyum falcatum*
	falconeri	see *Himalayacalamus falconeri*
	funghomii	see *Schizostachyum funghomii*
	khasianus	see *Drepanostachyum khasianum*
	maling	see *Yushania maling*
	spathaceus misapplied	see *Fargesia murielae*
§	***spathiflorus***	CEnt EFul EPla SDry
	- subsp. ***nepalensis***	EPla MMoz WPGP
§	***tessellatus***	EFul ENBC EPla MMoz SDry WDyG

Thamnochortus (*Restionaceae*)

	bachmannii	CBcs CTrC
	cinereus	CBct CBig CCtw CTrC EAmu WPGP
	insignis	CBcs CBig CCtw CHEx CTrC SPlb WNor WPrP
	lucens	CTrC
	rigidus	CCCN CTrC
	spicigerus	CBig CTrC

Thapsia (*Apiaceae*)

	decipiens	see *Melanoselinum decipiens*
	garganica	CArn

Thea see *Camellia*

Thelypteris (*Thelypteridaceae*)

	kunthii	WRic
	limbosperma	see *Oreopteris limbosperma*
	nevadensis NNS 00-725	WCot
	palustris	CRWN EBee EMon EWsh MAsh MPes NHol NVic SRms WFib WPnP WRic
	phegopteris	see *Phegopteris connectilis*

Themeda (*Poaceae*)

	japonica	EPPr
	triandra	SMad

Thermopsis (*Papilionaceae*)

	caroliniana	see *T. villosa*
	fabacea	see *T. lupinoides*
	lanceolata	CTri EBee ECGP EDAr ELon ENot EPfP GBin LRHS MBri MEHN MLLN MNFA MWgw NBPC NCGa NPri NSti SAga SPhx SPoG WAul WCAu WFar WHrl WPer
§	***lupinoides***	ECha EHrv EWTr MFOX MGol NBre NEgg WFar WPer
	- RBS 0280	ITer
	macrophylla	EBee
	- 'Agnina'	WCot
	mollis	CPLG NBid
	montana	see *T. rhombifolia* var. *montana*
§	***rhombifolia*** var. ***montana***	CRez CWCL EBee EDAr ELan EPfP GGar GMaP LBMP LHop MNrw MSte MWgw NBre NCGa NEgg NLar NOrc NPol NSti SBod SPer WAbb WBVN WMoo WPer
§	***villosa***	CPom CWCL MGol MLLN MNFA MRav MSte MWrn NBre NDov NGdn WCot WHoo WPGP

Therorhodion see *Rhododendron*

Thevetia (*Apocynaceae*)

	neriifolia	CCCN
	peruviana	LRHS MSal

Thladiantha (*Cucurbitaceae*)

	dubia	SDix

Thlaspi (*Brassicaceae*)

	alpinum	EPot
	bellidifolium	NBir
	biebersteinii	see *Pachyphragma macrophyllum*
	fendleri	MNrw
	montanum	WBVN

Thrinax (*Arecaceae*)

	campestris	SAin
	radiata	EAmu

Thryptomene (*Myrtaceae*)

	baeckeacea **new**	CCCN
	saxicola	ECou
	- 'F.C. Payne'	CBcs

Thuja ✿ (*Cupressaceae*)

	'Extra Gold'	see *T. plicata* 'Irish Gold'
	'Gnome'	IBal
	'Green Giant' **new**	SLim
§	***koraiensis***	IDee LCon LRHS MBar SCoo SPoG WCwm WThu
	occidentalis	EMac NWea
	- 'Amber Glow'	CBrm CDoC CKen CRob ECho GBin LCon LLin LRHS MAsh MGos NHol NLar SCoo SLim SPoG WBor WEve
	- Aurea Group	ECho MBar
	- 'Aureospicata'	ECho EHul
	- 'Bateman Broom'	CKen
	- 'Beaufort' (v)	CKen ECho EHul MBar
	- 'Brabant'	CBrm CDul ECho LPan NLar SCoo SLim
	- 'Brobecks Tower'	CKen NLar SLim
	- 'Caespitosa'	CFee CKen ECho LLin NEgg NHol NLar SCoo SPoG WEve WGor
	- 'Cloth of Gold'	ECho
	- 'Cristata Aurea'	CKen
	- 'Cuprea'	ECho
	- 'Danica' ΥH4	CMac CRob ECho EHul EOrn LCon LLin MAsh MBar NEgg NWea SCoo SLim SMer SPoG SRms WCFE WEve WFar
	- 'Degroot's Spire' **new**	CKen SLim
	- 'Dicksonii'	EHul
	- 'Douglasii Aurea' (v)	CKen
	- 'Ellwangeriana Aurea'	MGos
	- Emerald	see *T. occidentalis* 'Smaragd'
	- 'Ericoides'	CDoC CTri ECho EHul LRHS MBar MGos SRms
	- 'Europa Gold'	CBrm CDoC ECho EHul LBee MBar MGos NHol NLar SLim
	- 'Fastigiata'	ECho MBar
	- 'Filiformis'	CKen ECho EPla
	- 'Globosa'	CMac ECho MBar WRHF
I	- 'Globosa Compacta Nana'	ECho
I	- 'Globosa Variegata' (v)	CKen MBar
	- 'Gold Drop'	CKen
	- 'Golden Globe'	CDoC ECho EHul EOrn LLin LPan MBar MGos NEgg NHol SCoo SLim SPla SPoG WRHF
	- 'Golden Minaret'	EHul
	- 'Golden Tuffet'	LCon MGos SCoo SLim
	- 'Hetz Midget'	CKen ECho EHul IMGH LLin MBar NEgg NHol NLar SCoo SLim SMer SPlb WFar
	- 'Holmstrup' ΥH4	CDoC CMac CRob CSBt CTri CWib ECho EHul EOrn LLin LRHS MAsh MBar NBlu SCoo SLim SPoG SRms WEve WFar WTel
	- 'Holmstrup's Yellow'	ECho EHul LCon NHol SLim SPoG WBVN
	- 'Hoveyi'	CMac CTri EHul WEve
	- 'Linesville'	CKen
	- 'Little Champion'	EHul NLar
	- 'Little Gem'	ECho EHul MGos NHol NLar SRms
	- 'Lutea Nana' ΥH4	CMac ECho EHul EOrn MBar NDlv WCFE WRHF
	- 'Marrisen's Sulphur'	EHul LRHS NLar SCoo SLim SPla
	- 'Meineke's Zwerg' (v)	CKen NLar
	- 'Miky'	CKen
	- 'Mr Bowling Ball'	SCoo SLim
	- 'Ohlendorffii'	CDoC CKen ECho EHul EOrn LLin MBar NHol
	- 'Orientalis Semperaurescens'	see *Platycladus orientalis* 'Semperaurea'
	- 'Perk Vlaanderen' (v) **new**	EMon
I	- 'Pumila Sudworth'	NHol
I	- 'Pygmaea'	CKen ECho MBar SLon
	- 'Pyramidalis Aurea'	MGos NHol WEve
	- 'Pyramidalis Compacta'	EHul WGor
	- 'Recurva Nana'	EHul MBar NHol
	- 'Rheingold' ΥH4	More than 30 suppliers
	- 'Robusta'	ECho
§	- 'Smaragd' ΥH4	More than 30 suppliers
*	- 'Smaragd Variegated' (v)	CKen
	- 'Smokey' **new**	CKen
	- 'Southport'	CKen WEve
	- 'Spaethii'	EHul EOrn
	- 'Spiralis'	ECho EHul IMGH MBar NLar WCFE
§	- 'Stolwijk' (v)	ECho EHul EOrn LLin MBar MGos SCoo
	- 'Sunkist'	CKen CMac CRob CSBt CSli CTri CWib ECho EHul EOrn LPan MAsh MBar MGos NEgg NHol SCoo SLim SMer SPla SPoG WEve WFar
	- 'Suzie'	LLin
	- 'Teddy'	CDoC CFee CRob ECho LBee LCon LLin LRHS MAsh NHol NLar SCoo SLim SPoG WFar
	- 'Tiny Tim'	CDoC CMac CRob CSBt CWib ECho EHul IMGH LCon LLin MBar MGos NHol SCoo WEve WFar WGor
	- 'Trompenburg'	CRob ECho EHul EOrn MAsh NLar SCoo
	- 'Wansdyke Silver' (v)	CMac ECho EHul EOrn LRHS MBar SCoo SLim SPoG WRHF
	- 'Wareana'	CMac
	- 'Wareana Aurea'	see *T. occidentalis* 'Wareana Lutescens'
§	- 'Wareana Lutescens'	CWib EHul EOrn MBar MGos NHol
	- 'Woodwardii'	ECho EHul MBar SMer
	- 'Yellow Ribbon'	CKen CSBt ECho EHul LCon LRHS MBar NLar SCoo SLim SMer SPla SPoG WEve WFar
	orientalis	see *Platycladus orientalis*
	- 'Miller's Gold'	see *Platycladus orientalis* 'Aurea Nana'
	plicata	CCVT CChe CDul CMac EHul EMac EPfP MBar MGos NBlu NWea SLim SPer SPoG WMou
	- 'Atrovirens' ΥH4	CDul CTri ECho ECrN ENot LBee LBuc LCon LLin LPan LRHS MAsh MBar MBri MGos SBLw SCoo SLim SMer SPoG SRms WEve WHar
*	- 'Atrovirens Aurea'	SLim WEve

- 'Aurea' $\mathbb{Y}^{H4}$	ECho EHul LBee LRHS MAsh SLim SRms
- 'Barabits'	ECho
- 'Brooks Gold'	CKen
- 'Can-can' (v)	CRob ECho NLar SCoo
I - 'Cole's Variety'	CWib ECho MBar MGos SLim
- 'Collyer's Gold'	CTri ECho EHul LLin NHol NLar SRms WEve
- 'Copper Kettle'	CKen ECho EHul LCon MAsh MBar NDlv NEgg NLar SCoo SLim WEve WGor WRHF
- 'Cuprea'	CKen ECho EHul MBar
- 'Doone Valley'	CKen CSli ECho EHul EOrn MBar NDlv
- 'Fastigiata' $\mathbb{Y}^{H4}$	CDul CMac LRHS
- 'Gelderland'	CTho ECho EHul NBlu NLar SCoo SLim WEve WFar
- 'Gracilis Aurea'	ECho EHul
- 'Grüne Kugel'	CDoC
- 'Hillieri'	CDul MBar
§ - 'Irish Gold' (v) $\mathbb{Y}^{H4}$	CAbP CDul CMac LCon LLin LRHS
- 'Rogersii'	CDoC CKen CMac CTri ECho EHul EOrn EPfP LCon LLin MAsh MBar MGos NHol SCoo SPoG SRms WFar WTel
- 'Stolwijk's Gold'	see *T. occidentalis* 'Stolwijk'
- 'Stoneham Gold' $\mathbb{Y}^{H4}$	CDoC CMac ECho EHul EOrn LBee LCon MAsh MBar MGos NHol SLim SMer SPer SPoG SRms WCFE WEve WTel
- 'Sunshine'	CKen
- 'Whipcord'	LCon LRHS SCoo SLim
* - 'Windsor Gold'	ECho EHul
- 'Winter Pink' (v)	CKen NLar
- 'Zebrina' (v)	CBcs CBrm CDoC CDul CMac CSBt CSli CTri CWib ECho EHul ELan EOrn EPfP LCon LLin LRHS MAsh MBar MGos NEgg NWea SCoo SLim SPer SPoG SWvt WEve WFar WHar

Thujopsis (*Cupressaceae*)

dolabrata $\mathbb{Y}^{H4}$	CBcs CDul CTrG EHul LRHS MBar NEgg NLar NWea SHBN WBrE WFar WPGP
- 'Aurea' (v)	CDoC CKen EHul EOrn LCon LLin LRHS MBar MGos NLar SCoo SHBN SLim WEve
- 'Laetevirens'	see *T. dolabrata* 'Nana'
- 'Melbourne Gold' **new**	NLar
§ - 'Nana'	CDoC CKen CMac EHul EOrn LCon LLin MBar NLar SCoo SLim SRms STre WEve WFar
- 'Variegata' (v)	CDoC CDul CFee EHul EOrn LCon LLin LRHS MBar NLar SCoo SHFr SLim SPoG WEve WFar
koraiensis (Nakai) hort.	see *Thuja koraiensis*

Thunbergia (*Acanthaceae*)

alata LBMP MBri	
- 'African Sunset'	CSpe EShb WHil
battiscombeii	CCCN EShb MJnS SOWG
coccinea	EShb MJnS
erecta	CCCN ELan ERea SOWG
fragrans	ERea EShb WHil
grandiflora $\mathbb{Y}^{H1}$	CCCN CHll CTrG ELan EPfP ERea EShb MJnS SOWG
- 'Alba'	CCCN CHll EShb WHil
gregorii $\mathbb{Y}^{H1+3}$	CCCN CHll CSpe ERea EShb SOWG
mysorensis $\mathbb{Y}^{H1}$	CCCN ERea MJnS SOWG
natalensis	CCCN ERea EShb

Thymbra (*Lamiaceae*)

spicata	XPep

thyme, caraway see *Thymus herba-barona*

thyme, garden see *Thymus vulgaris*

thyme, lemon see *Thymus citriodorus*

thyme, wild see *Thymus serpyllum*

Thymus ✿ (*Lamiaceae*)

from Albania **new**	CArn
from Turkey	ECho EWes LLWP SHDw
§ 'Alan Bloom'	LLWP
'Anderson's Gold'	see *T. pulegioides* 'Bertram Anderson'
azoricus	see *T. caespititius*
'Caborn Lilac Gem'	LLWP SHDw
'Caborn Pink Carpet' **new**	LLWP
'Caborn Rosanne'	LLWP
§ ***caespititius***	CArn ECho ELau EUnu GKev GMaP GPoy MHer NMen NRya SPlb SRot WPer
caespitosus	CTri LLWP
camphoratus	CArn CBod ELau EPot EUnu EWes MHer MNHC NGHP NMen SHDw WJek XPep
- 'A Touch of Frost'	SHDw
- 'Derry'	CSpe
capitatus	CArn XPep
carnosus misapplied	see *T. vulgaris* 'Erectus'
carnosus Boiss.	STre XPep
'Carol Ann' (v)	ECho ELau EWes LLWP MBNS MNHC
'Caroline'	SHDw
'Carshalton'	CWan
cephalotos	WAbe
ciliatus	LLWP WPer XPep
cilicicus misapplied	see *T. caespititius*
cilicicus ambig.	MNHC NMen SBla WAbe
cilicicus Boiss. & Bail.	EWes
citriodorus	CArn CHby CHrt CWan ECho EDAr ELau GAbr GPoy LLWP MBrN MHer MNHC MWat NGHP NNor SWal WBrE WGwG WHen WJek WPer XPep
- 'Archer's Gold'	see *T. pulegioides* 'Archer's Gold'
- 'Aureus'	see *T. pulegioides* 'Aureus'
- 'Bertram Anderson'	see *T. pulegioides* 'Bertram Anderson'
§ - 'Golden King' (v)	CEnt ECha ECho EDAr ELan LHop LLWP LRHS MBar MBri MHer NGHP NSti WHoo WPer WSel
- 'Golden Lemon' misapplied	see *T. pulegioides* 'Aureus'
- 'Golden Lemon' (v)	CArn GPoy LLWP WJek
- 'Golden Queen' (v)	ECho EDAr GKev MHer MWat NBlu NGHP NPri SHDw SPer SPet SRms WFar
- 'Lemon Supreme'	LLWP
- 'Lime'	LLWP
- ***repandus***	see *T.* 'Rosemary's Lemon Carpet'
- 'Silver King' (v)	ECho LLWP
- 'Silver Posie'	see *T. vulgaris* 'Silver Posie'
- 'Silver Queen' (v) $\mathbb{Y}^{H4}$	CBcs CSam ECha ECho EDAr ELan EPfP GGar GKev GMaP LRHS MBar MHer MNHC MWgw NBlu NGHP SPlb WFar
- 'Variegatus' misapplied	see *T. citriodorus* 'Golden King'
* - 'Variegatus' (v)	LHop LSRN MBri MNHC NGHP
- 'Villa Nova' (v)	see *T. citriodorus* 'Golden King'
'Coccineus'	see *T.* Coccineus Group
'Coccineus Major'	CMea CWan ECho EDAr LRHS MHer MNHC SIde WJek XPep
N Coccineus Group $\mathbb{Y}^{H4}$	CArn CPrp CTri ECha ECho ECtt ELan ELau GMaP LCro LLWP LRHS

		MBar MBri MHer MNHC NCGa NGHP NPri SBla SIng SPer SRms SRot WAbe WHen WHoo WPat
§	- 'Atropurpureus' misapplied	LLWP SHDw
	- 'Bethany'	LLWP SGar
	- 'Kurt'	LLWP SHDw
§	- 'Purple Beauty'	LLWP MHer NGHP
§	- 'Purpurteppich'	LLWP
§	- 'Red Elf'	ECho SHDw WJek
	comosus	SHDw WEas WPer
	'Cow Green'	LLWP SHDw
	'Creeping Lemon'	ELau EUnu LLWP MHer SHDw WGwG WJek
	'Dark Eyes'	SHDw
	'Dartmoor'	LLWP SHDw SIng
	'Desboro'	LLWP MBNS MHer
	doerfleri	CLyd ECha LLWP WSel XPep
	- 'Bressingham'	CArn CMea CPrp CTri CWan ECho ECtt EDAr ELau LBee LCro LLWP LRHS MHer MNHC NGHP SBla SPlb SRms SWal WFar WPat WPer WTel
	'Doone Valley' (v)	More than 30 suppliers
	drucei	see *T. polytrichus* subsp. *britannicus*
	'E.B.Anderson'	see *T. pulegioides* 'Bertram Anderson'
	'Eastgrove Pink'	LLWP SHDw
	'Elf'	NWCA
	'Emma's Pink'	LLWP
	erectus	see *T. vulgaris* 'Erectus'
*	***ericoides***	EPot
	'Fragrantissimus'	CArn CEnt CHrt CMea ELau EUnu GPoy GWCH LLWP MHer MNHC MWat NGHP SIde SPlb WAbe WFar WHen WJek WPer
	'Gibson's Cave'	LLWP
	'Glenridding'	LLWP
	'Gowbarrow'	LLWP
	'Gratian'	LLWP SHDw
	'Hans Stam'	LLWP
§	'Hartington Silver' (v)	More than 30 suppliers
	herba-barona	CArn CHrt CMea CPrp CTri CWan ECha EDAr ELau EUnu GPoy LEdu LLWP MHer MNHC MWat NGHP NHol NRya SIde SRms WGwG WPer XPep
	- 'Bob Flowerdew'	LLWP
	- ***citrata***	see *T. herba-barona* 'Lemon-scented'
§	- 'Lemon-scented'	ECha ELau GPoy LLWP MHer SHDw SIde
	'Highdown'	ECtt SHDw
	'Highdown Adus'	SHDw
	'Highdown Lemon'	SHDw
	'Highdown Red'	SHDw
	'Highdown Stretham'	SHDw
	'Highland Cream'	see *T.* 'Hartington Silver'
	hirsutus	NBir XPep
	integer	SBla
	'Lake District'	LLWP
I	'Lantanii'	LLWP SHDw
	lanuginosus misapplied	see *T. pseudolanuginosus*
	'Lavender Sea'	ELau EOHP EWes LLWP
	'Lemon Caraway'	see *T. herba-barona* 'Lemon-scented'
	'Lemon Sorbet'	SHDw
*	'Lemon Variegated' (v)	EDAr ELau EPfP SPer
	leucotrichus	WPat XPep
	'Lilac Time'	EWes LLWP MHer NTHB SHDw SIde SPlb WGwG WJek
	longicaulis	CArn CLyd ECha ELau EWin LLWP MBNS MHer WJek XPep
	'Low Force'	LLWP
	marschallianus	see *T. pannonicus*
	mastichina	CArn SBla WGwG XPep
	- 'Didi'	MHer
	membranaceus	CPBP WAbe
	micans	see *T. caespititius*
	minus	see *Calamintha nepeta*
	montanus Waldst. & Kit.	see *T. pulegioides*
	'Mountain Select'	LLWP SHDw
	neiceffii	CLyd ECha ELau LLWP NWCA XPep
	'New Hall'	SHDw
*	***nummularius***	ELau
	'Orange Balsam'	LLWP
	'Orange Spice'	LLWP SHDw
	pallasianus	ELau SHDw
§	***pannonicus***	LLWP MHer WPer
	parnassicus	XPep
	'Peter Davis'	CArn CPBP LHop MBNS MHer MNHC NBir NCGa NGHP SBla SIde WAbe WJek
	'Pink Ripple'	CBod CMea EAlp EDAr ELau EWes LLWP MHer SBch SHDw SIde SIng WGwG WHal WHoo WJek
	polytrichus misapplied	see *T. praecox*
	polytrichus A. Kern. ex Borbás	XPep
§	- subsp. ***britannicus***	ECho GPoy LLWP LSou NSti SHDw SPlb WAbe WJek WPer
	- - 'Minor'	ECho EPot LLWP WPer
§	- - 'Thomas's White' ♀H4	CTri ECho LLWP
	- - 'Timothy's White' **new**	CEnt
	'Porlock'	CMea CPrp CTri CWan ECho ELau EPfP GMaP GPoy LCro LLWP MHer MNHC NChi NGHP NRya SIde SRms WGwG WHoo WJek WPer
§	***praecox***	CPbn LLWP MHer NLan NSco
	- subsp. ***arcticus***	see *T. polytrichus* subsp. *britannicus*
	- - 'Albus'	see *T. polytrichus* subsp. *britannicus* 'Thomas's White'
	'Provence'	LLWP
§	***pseudolanuginosus***	More than 30 suppliers
	- 'Hall's Variety'	ELau
§	***pulegioides***	CArn CBod CHby CHrt ELau GGar GPoy LLWP MBri MHer MNHC NPri SHDw SIde WGwG WJek WPer
§	- 'Archer's Gold'	CTri EAlp ECho ECtt EDAr ELau EPfP GAbr GKev LAst LBee LHop LLWP LRHS LSRN MBri MHer NBir NBlu NGHP NPri NSti SIde SMer SRms STre WFar WJek WPat WPer
§	- 'Aureus' ♀H4	GMaP LCro LLWP LRHS MBar MBri NBlu NWCA SBla SGar SPer SPla WFar WHoo
§	- 'Bertram Anderson' ♀H4	More than 30 suppliers
	- 'Foxley' (v)	CBod CBow CWan EAlp ECho ELau EPfP EUnu LLWP LSou MHer MNHC NGHP NHol NPro NTHB SHDw SIde SPlb WJek WRHF
	- 'Golden Dwarf'	LLWP
§	- 'Goldentime'	LLWP LRHS NGHP WSel
	- 'Sir John Lawes'	LLWP MHer SHDw
	- 'Sundon Hills'	LLWP
	- 'Tabor'	EUnu GMaP MNHC NGHP NTHB SHDw WJek WOut
	'Rasta' (v)	CStu EAlp LLWP SIng
	'Redstart'	ECha ELau EOHP LBee LLWP LRHS MHer SBch SHDw SIde
	richardii subsp. ***nitidus*** misapplied	see *T. vulgaris* 'Suditin'
	- - 'Compactus Albus'	see *T. vulgaris* 'Snow White'
	'Rosa Ceeping'	SHDw
	'Rosalicht'	LLWP

	'Rosalind'	SHDw
	'Rosedrift'	LLWP SHDw
§	'Rosemary's Lemon Carpet'	LLWP
	rotundifolius misapplied	see *T. vulgaris* 'Elsbeth'
	'Ruby Glow'	CEnt CHrt ELau EWes MHer MNHC SHDw WFar
	serpyllum misapplied	see *T. polytrichus* A. Kern. ex Borbás
	serpyllum ambig.	CArn ELau MBri NGHP SIde SPet SPlb SRms WJek WPer
	serpyllum L.	EAro LCro LLWP WBVN XPep
	- var. ***albus***	CPrp ECha ECho ELau GPoy LAst LLWP MNHC NGHP NHol NPri SBla SIde SPer SRms WHoo WRHF XPep
	- 'Albus Variegatus'	see *T.* 'Hartington Silver'
N	- 'Annie Hall'	CWan ECho EDAr ELau EPfP EPot GAbr GGar LAst LLWP LRHS MHer NGHP NPri SBch SIde SPer STre WCFE WGwG WPer
	- 'Atropurpureus'	see *T.* (Coccineus Group) 'Atropurpureus' misapplied
	- 'August Moon' **new**	LLWP
	- ***coccineus*** 'Minor' misapplied	see *T.* Coccineus Group
	- - 'Minor' Bloom	see *T.* 'Alan Bloom'
	- 'Conwy Rose'	LLWP WAbe
N	- 'East Lodge'	LLWP MNHC
	- 'Elfin'	CArn CLyd ECho EDAr EWes LBee MBri SBla SHDw SIng SPlb WAbe XPep
N	- 'Fulney Red'	EWes
	- 'Goldstream' (v)	CBrm CLyd CMea ECho ELau EPfP LHop LLWP LRHS MBar MBri MHer NGHP NRya NSti SPlb SRms WGwG WPer
	- subsp. ***lanuginosus***	see *T. pseudolanuginosus*
	- 'Lemon Curd'	CBrm CWan ELau EUnu LLWP MHer MNHC NGHP NHol NSti SHDw SIde SMer SPlb WFar WGwG WJek WSel XPep
§	- 'Minimalist'	CArn CBrm CLyd CMea ECha ELau LLWP MBri MHer MLHP MNHC NGHP NHol NRya NSti SIde SPet SPlb SRot WBVN WHoo WPat WPer WSel
	- 'Minimus'	see *T. serpyllum* 'Minimalist'
§	- 'Minor'	CEnt CPrp CTri ECho ECtt GWCH LLWP NMen NSla SBla SHDw WAbe WGwG WLin XPep
N	- 'Minor Albus'	ECho
	- 'Minus'	see *T. serpyllum* 'Minor'
	- 'Petite'	EPot EWes LLWP
N	- 'Pink Chintz' 🏆^{H4}	CBrm CHar CLyd CMea CPrp ECha ECho ECtt EDAr ELau EPfP EPot GBuc GPoy LLWP LRHS MBar MBri MHer MNHC NBlu NGHP NPri NRya SBla SIng SPer SPlb WHoo WPer
	- 'Posh Pinky'	EDAr EPot NMen
	- subsp. ***pulchellus***	LLWP
	- 'Purple Beauty'	see *T.* (Coccineus Group) 'Purple Beauty'
	- 'Purpurteppich'	see *T.* (Coccineus Group) 'Purpurteppich'
	- 'Pygmaeus'	LLWP
	- 'Rainbow Falls' (v)	CBod EPfP EWin LLWP MHer MNHC NGHP NHol SHDw SIde WGwG
	- 'Red Elf'	see *T.* (Coccineus Group) 'Red Elf'
	- 'Red Glow'	EPot
	- 'Roger's Snowdrift'	LLWP
N	- 'Roseus'	SIde
N	- 'Russetings'	CBrm CLyd CPrp EAlp ECtt ELau EPfP EPot LLWP MBar MHer MNHC NEgg NGHP NHol SIde SIng SPer SRms WFar WHoo
N	- 'September'	LLWP MHer
	- 'Snowcarpet'	LLWP
N	- 'Snowdrift'	CArn CBrm CMea CWan ECho ECtt EDAr ELau EPfP EPot GKev LEdu MBar MHer MNHC NHol NMen NRya NSti SBch SIde SPlb WCFE WFar WGwG WJek WLin WPat WPer
N	- 'Splendens'	LLWP
	- subsp. ***tanaensis***	CArn
	- 'Variegatus'	see *T.* 'Hartington Silver'
	- 'Vey'	ECho EWes GMaP LLWP MHer NTHB SHDw SIng
	sibthorpii	CArn
N	'Silver Posie'	see *T. vulgaris* 'Silver Posie'
	'Snowdonia Idris'	LLWP
	'Snowdonia Ifor'	LLWP
	'Snowdonia Imperial Beauty'	LLWP
	'Snowdonia Iorwerth'	LLWP
	'Snowdonia Isolde'	LLWP
	'Snowdonia Istyn'	LLWP
	'Snowdonia Lass'	LLWP SHDw
	'Snowdonia Pedr'	LLWP
	'Snowdonia Pink Gem'	LLWP
	'Snowdonia Pryderi'	LLWP
	'Snowdonia Pwyll'	LLWP
	'Snowdonia Rosie'	LLWP
	'Snowdonia Rowena'	LLWP
	'Snowman'	SHDw
	'Swaledale'	LLWP
*	***valesiacus***	LLWP SHDw
§	***villosus***	ECho
	vulgaris	CArn CHby CPbn CSam CSev CTri ECha ELau GPoy LAst LLWP MBar MBri MHer MLHP MNHC MWat NBlu NGHP NHol NVic SDix SECG SPer SPlb SWal WGwG WJek WPer XPep
	- ***albus***	ECho WHen
	- 'Aureus' hort.	see *T. pulegioides* 'Goldentime'
	- 'Boule'	LLWP XPep
*	- 'Compactus'	GPoy LLWP MNHC
	- 'Deutsche Auslese' **new**	LLWP
	- 'Diamantis'	LLWP
	- 'Dorcas White'	LLWP MHer WPer
§	- 'Elsbeth'	ECho ELau LLWP SHDw XPep
	- 'English Winter'	SIde
§	- 'Erectus'	CArn CLyd CStu MHer WPer
	- French	ELau LLWP MHer SHDw SPlb
	- French, summer	SIde
	- 'Golden Pins'	MHer MNHC
	- 'Haute Vallée de l'Aude'	XPep
	- 'Lemon Queen'	ECho ELau
	- 'Lucy'	CPrp EUnu LLWP MHer MNHC
	- 'Pinewood'	EAlp LLWP MHer SIde
	- 'Saint Chinian Blanc'	XPep
	- 'Saint Chinian Rose'	XPep
	- 'Silver Pearl' (v)	ECho
§	- 'Silver Posie'	More than 30 suppliers
§	- 'Snow White'	ELau EWes LLWP SHDw
	- 'Suditin'	STre
	'Widecombe' (v)	LLWP MHer SHDw
	zygis	CArn XPep

Tiarella (*Saxifragaceae*)

	'Black Velvet'^{PBR}	GCai MLLN NCGa NLar SJoo SPer
	'Bronze Baby'	NEgg
	'Butterfly Wings'	EBee NRnb
	collina	see *T. wherryi*
	cordifolia 🏆^{H4}	More than 30 suppliers
	- 'Glossy'	CBct EBee GBuc WPGP
	- 'Greenmarsh' **new**	WBrk

- 'Oakleaf' CLAP EBee NBre NBro NEgg NSti WCAu
- 'Rosalie' see x *Heucherella alba* 'Rosalie'
- 'Running Tapestry' CLAP WBrk WMoo
- 'Slick Rock' ECha EPPr
'Crow Feather'PBR **new** EBee
'Cygnet'PBR CBct CLAP EBee EMan EPPr EShb GCai LHop MLLN NCGa NEgg SHar SIng SJoo SPer SPoG SRot STes WFar
'Dark Star' ECtt NBre
'Dunvegan' EBee MLLN NRnb WFar WMoo WWeb
'Elizabeth Oliver' CLAP EBee
'Freckles' MRav
'Hidden Carpet' **new** CHid
'Inkblot' EBee ELan MLLN NBro NRnb SJoo WCAu WFar WMoo WSpi
'Iron Butterfly'PBR CBct CChe CCol CLAP CWCL EBee ECGP EMar EPfP GBin GMaP LAst LSRN MLLN MRav MSte NBro NCGa NEgg NPri SHar SPer SRot STes WFar WPGP WSpi
'Jeepers Creepers'PBR GCai NCob SHar
* 'Laciniate Runner' CLAP
'Martha Oliver' CLAP EBee GBuc NBre SBch WPGP WTin
'Mint Chocolate'PBR CLAP CWCL EBee ECtt EHrv ELan EMil EPfP GMaP GSki MBri MLLN MRav MSte MWgw NCob NGdn NLar SMer SPer SPla SWvt WAul WCra WFar WPGP
Morning Star = 'Tntia042' EBee EWll LAst SJoo SRot
'Neon Lights'PBR CBow CHar EKen EWes NBPC NBro NCGa NCob NGdn SJoo SPoG SWvt
§ 'Ninja'PBR CHid CWCL EBee ECha ECtt EHrv ELan GMaP GSki LAst LFur LRHS MDun MLLN MRav MWgw NBir NEgg NGdn NLar NSti SMer SPer SRot SWvt WFar WHoo
'Petite Pink Bouquet' GSki NGdn
'Pink Bouquet' CAbP CBow CLAP EBee ECtt EHrv ENor GSki LBMP LRHS MBNS MBri MLLN MWgw NEgg NHol SPla WBVN WFar WGor WMoo WPnP
'Pink Brushes' EBee NRnb
'Pink Skyrocket'PBR EBee GCai NCob SHar SJoo
'Pinwheel' EBrs ECha LRHS MRav NBre WTMC
'Pirate's Patch' GCai LTwo SJoo
polyphylla CBow CSsd ELan GAbr GBin MGol MLLN NBre NLar SMac SWal WFar WMoo
- 'Baoxing Pink' **new** WCru
- 'Filigran' EBee MWrn NHol NLar
- 'Moorgrün' EPPr WFar
- pink-flowered CLAP EHrv
- - BWJ 8088 WCru
'Running Tiger' EBee NRnb
'Sea Foam' **new** SJoo WSpi
'Skeleton Key' EBee
'Skid's Variegated' (v) CBct CBow EBee ECtt EMan LAst LSou MBNS MWgw NSti SJoo SWvt WCot
'Skyrocket' EKen
'Spanish Cross'PBR **new** SJoo
'Spring Symphony'PBR CLAP CWCL EBee EShb GBin GCai LSou MBri NBir NCGa NEgg NLar NPer SHar SIng SPoG WFar WSpi
Starburst = 'Tntia041' SJoo
'Starfish' MLLN NBPC NBre NCob WPrP
'Tiger Stripe' EBee ECha EMan ENot EPfP LRHS MRav NBro NEgg NRnb SPer SPur WFar WMoo WPnP WSpi
trifoliata MRav NBre WFar
unifoliata CMCo EBee MSal
'Viking Ship'PBR see x *Heucherella* 'Viking Ship'
§ ***wherryi*** ♀H4 CBrm CHrt CWCL EBee ECtt EHrv ELan EMar EPfP GMaP LAst NBir NBlu NBro NGdn NOrc NPri SPer SPla SPlb SWvt WFar WMoo WPer WPnP
- 'Bronze Beauty' CBct CLAP EBee EPPr GBuc LAst LBBr MRav NDov NPro SAga SPla SWat WAbe WBrk WFar WMoo WPGP WSpi
- 'Green Velvet' ECha
- 'Heronswood Mist' (v) CAbP CBct CBow CFir EBee GEdr GQue LFur LSou MLLN MWgw NBro SPer SWvt WCot
- 'Montrose' NBre WPGP

Tibouchina (*Melastomataceae*)

grandifolia CRHN WBod
granulosa SOWG
graveolens ERea
'Jules' CBcs LSou SOWG
* ***laxa*** 'Skylab' LSou SOWG
organensis CBcs CHll SJoo SOWG WPGP
paratropica CPle CRHN WSHC
semidecandra hort. see *T. urvilleana*
§ ***urvilleana*** ♀H1 CBcs CCCN CDoC CHEx CHrt CKno CRHN CSBt CSpe CTri EAmu EBak ECre ELan EPfP ERea EShb ISea NCGa SAPC SArc SBLw SDnm SOWG SPer SRkn SRms WCot WGwG
- 'Edwardsii' EMan LSou MLan SAdn SMrm
- 'Jazzie' LSou
- 'Rich Blue Sun' CSpe
- variegated (v) CCCN EShb LSou WCot

Tigridia ✿ (*Iridaceae*)

B&SWJ 10393 from Guatemala **new** WCru
lutea ECho
pavonia CAby CHHB CPLG CTca EBrs ECho EDif EShb EWll IGor LAma MBri
- B&SWJ 10244 from Mexico **new** WCru
- 'Alba' **new** EBrs EDif
- 'Alba Grandiflora' **new** ERCP
- 'Aurea' CFwr
- 'Canariensis' **new** EBrs
- 'Lilacea' CFwr EBee EBrs ECho ERCP
- 'Speciosa' CFwr

Tilia ✿ (*Tiliaceae*)

americana CLnd CMCN NWea SCoo
- 'Dentata' CDul
- 'Nova' CDoC SBLw
amurensis CMCN
argentea see *T. tomentosa*
begoniifolia see *T. dasystyla*
chenmoui MBlu MBri WPGP
chinensis CMCN
chingiana CDul CMCN MBlu SLon
cordata ♀H4 CBcs CCVT CDul CLnd CSBt CTri EBee ECrN ELan EMac EPfP IMGH LBuc LCro MSwo NBee NWea SBLw SCoo SHBN SPer WMou WOrn
§ - 'Böhlje' CDul LPan SBLw SLPl WMoo
- 'Dainty Leaf' CDul
- 'Erecta' see *T. cordata* 'Böhlje'
- 'Greenspire' ♀H4 CCVT CDoC CDul CLnd CWib EBee ECrN LPan LRHS NBee SBLw WOrn
- 'Len Parvin' WPGP
- 'Lico' CMen WMou

- 'Monto'	CMen
- 'Plymtree Gold'	CDul
- 'Swedish Upright'	CDul CLnd CTho
- 'Winter Orange'	CDul CEnd EBee ECrN LAst LRHS MBlu MBri SCoo
§ ***dasystyla***	CMCN
x ***euchlora*** ♀H4	CBcs CCVT CDul CLnd CMCN EBee ECrN EPfP LAst LPan NBee NWea SBLw SPer SSta WFar WOrn
§ x ***europaea***	CBcs CDul CLnd CRWN ELan EWTr NWea SBLw WMou
- 'Pallida'	CDul CLnd CTho NWea SBLw WMou
- 'Wratislaviensis' ♀H4	CDoC CDul CLnd EPfP LRHS MAsh MBlu NWea SMad
x ***flavescens*** 'Glenleven'	CDul SBLw
§ 'Harold Hillier'	MBlu
henryana	CDoC CDul CEnd CLnd CMCN CTho CWib EBee ECrN EMil EPfP ERod IArd IDee MBlu MBri SIFN WPGP
- var. ***subglabra***	WMou
§ ***heterophylla***	CMCN CTho WPGP
- var. ***michauxii***	CLnd
'Hillieri'	see *T.* 'Harold Hillier'
insularis	CMCN MBlu WMou
japonica	CDul CMCN WMou WPGP
kiusiana	CMCN MBri WPGP
mandshurica	CMCN
maximowicziana	WPGP
mexicana	WPGP
miqueliana	CMCN
'Moltkei'	CLnd CMCN WPGP
mongolica	CDoC CDul CLnd CMCN CTho EBee EPfP SCoo WPGP
monticola	see *T. heterophylla*
oliveri	CDul CMCN MBlu NWea WPGP
paucicostata	CMCN
'Petiolaris' ♀H4	CCVT CDoC CDul CEnd CLnd CMCN EBee ECrN ELan EPfP LRHS MBlu MBri MSwo NBee NWea SBLw SHBN SPer SSta
platyphyllos	CCVT CDul CLnd CMCN CSBt CTri EBee ECrN EMac EMil EPfP LBuc NBee NWea SBLw SCoo SPer WMou
- 'Aurea'	CDul CLnd CTho ECrN MBlu
- 'Corallina'	see *T. platyphyllos* 'Rubra'
- 'Dakvorm'	SBLw
- 'Delft'	SBLw
- 'Erecta'	see *T. platyphyllos* 'Fastigiata'
§ - 'Fastigiata'	CDul CTho ECrN SBLw SLPl
- 'Laciniata'	CDul CEnd CMCN CTho EBee
* - 'Pendula'	CTho
§ - 'Rubra' ♀H4	CDoC CLnd CTho ECrN EPfP LBuc MGos NWea SBLw WFar
- 'Tortuosa'	CDoC
§ ***tomentosa***	CDul CLnd CMCN CTho ECrN ELan EMil IMGH NWea SBLw SCoo SEND WMou
- 'Brabant' ♀H4	CDoC EPfP EWTr IMGH SBLw
tuan	CMCN
x ***vulgaris***	see *T.* x *europaea*

Tillaea see *Crassula*

Tillandsia (*Bromeliaceae*)

aeranthos	SChr
argentea ♀H1	MBri
cyanea ♀H1	LRHS MBri
usneoides	CHal SHmp

Tinantia (*Commelinaceae*)

pringlei	CDes EBee SKHP WPGP
- AIM 77	WCot

Titanopsis (*Aizoaceae*)

calcarea ♀H1	CCCN EPfP EShb

Tithonia (*Asteraceae*)

rotundifolia 'Torch'	SMrm

Todea (*Osmundaceae*)

barbara	WRic

Tofieldia (*Melanthiaceae*)

coccinea new	GEdr
pusilla	ERos

Tolmiea (*Saxifragaceae*)

menziesii	ECha MBNS MBri MCot MWgw NHol SPer SWal WBrE
- 'Goldsplash'	see *T. menziesii* 'Taff's Gold'
- 'Maculata'	see *T. menziesii* 'Taff's Gold'
§ - 'Taff's Gold' (v) ♀H4	CWan EBee EMar EOHP EShb GAbr GMaP GQue MHer NBid NGdn NVic SPlb WEas WHoo WTin
- 'Variegata'	see *T. menziesii* 'Taff's Gold'

Tolpis (*Asteraceae*)

barbata	CSpe

Tonestus (*Asteraceae*)

§ ***lyallii***	WPer

Toona (*Meliaceae*)

§ ***sinensis***	CDul CEnd CGHE CLnd CMCN CPle CTho CWib ELan EPfP WBVN WFar WPGP
- 'Flamingo' (v)	CBcs CWSG EBee EPfP IDee LRHS MAsh NLar SMad SSta WCot

Torenia (*Scrophulariaceae*)

(Moon Series) Pink Moon = 'Dantopkmn'	LAst
- Purple Moon = 'Dantopur'PBR	LAst SVil
- Violet Moon	WHlf
- White Moon = 'Dantorwhite'PBR	LAst SVil
Summer Wave Series	CCCN LSou SCoo
- 'Summer Wave Violet'PBR	LSou

Torilis (*Apiaceae*)

japonica new	CBre

Torreya (*Taxaceae*)

grandis	CBcs EGFP

Townsendia (*Asteraceae*)

§ ***alpigena*** var. ***alpigena***	CGra CPBP
condensata	CPBP
exscapa	GKev ITim WLin
formosa	CSam ECho NBir
hookeri	CGra NWCA WLin
incana	CPBP
leptotes	CPBP
montana	see *T. alpigena* var. *alpigena*
parryi	ITim
§ ***rothrockii***	CGra CPBP NMen
spathulata	CPBP
wilcoxiana misapplied	see *T. rothrockii*

Toxicodendron (*Anacardiaceae*)

vernicifluum	see *Rhus verniciflua*

Trachelium (*Campanulaceae*)

§ ***asperuloides***	CPBP WAbe

caeruleum ♀H1	SGar WBrE
- 'Black Knight' new	CSpe
- 'Purple Umbrella'	CPLG EMan NBre
- 'White Umbrella'	EMan
jacquinii subsp. ***rumelianum***	CPBP NWCA WPat

Trachelospermum ✿ (*Apocynaceae*)

from Nanking, China	EShb
§ ***asiaticum*** ♀H2-3	More than 30 suppliers
- B&SWJ 4814	WCru
* - 'Aureum'	ERea
- 'Golden Memories'	CWGN EMil EPfP LRHS MAsh MGos SBra SPoG SSpi SSta
- 'Goshiki' (v)	CBow EShb GQui MGos SSpi
- var. ***intermedium***	NPal WPGP
- - B&SWJ 8733	WCru
- 'Kulu Chiriman' new	WCot
- 'Nagaba' (v)	SKHP
- 'Theta'	SKHP SSpi
'Chameleon'	NPal
jasminoides ♀H3-4	More than 30 suppliers
- B&SWJ 5117	WCru
- 'Big White Star' new	SPoG
§ - 'Japonicum'	CSPN IArd LRHS SBra SLon SPla WSHC
- 'Major'	CSPN CTrG EBee SPoG SSpi
- 'Tricolor' (v)	CBcs IArd SWvt
- 'Variegatum' (v) ♀H3-4	More than 30 suppliers
- 'Waterwheel'	CWGN SBra SKHP SPoG SSpi WPGP WSHC
- 'Wilsonii'	CDul CMac CSPN CSam EBee ELan EMil EPfP EPla EShb LHop LRHS MCCP SAPC SArc SBod SLim SPer SPoG SWvt WCru WHar WPGP WPat XPep
majus misapplied	see *T. jasminoides* 'Japonicum'
majus Nakai	see *T. asiaticum*

Trachycarpus (*Arecaceae*)

from Manipur	MJnS
§ ***fortunei*** ♀H3-4	More than 30 suppliers
latisectus	CBrP CKob EAmu LPJP LPal NPal SAin
martianus	CKob CTrC EAmu LPJP LPal SChr
nanus	CKob LPal
oreophilus	LPal
princeps from Meeldijk new	CKob
I 'Takaghii'	SAin
takil	CBrP CKob EAmu LPJP LPal MJnS NPal
wagnerianus	CBrP CDTJ CGHE CHid CPHo CTrC EAmu EBee EPla ETod LPJP LPal MJnS NPal SAin SChr SDry WPGP

Trachymene (*Apiaceae*)

coerulea	CSpe

Trachystemon (*Boraginaceae*)

orientalis	CBre CHEx CHid CPLG CSev EBee ECha EGol ELan EPfP LCro MAvo MHar MRav NBid SDnm WBor WCAu WCru WDyG WFar WHer WMoo WPnP

Tradescantia ✿ (*Commelinaceae*)

albiflora	see *T. fluminensis*
x ***andersoniana*** W. Ludwig & Rohw.	see *T.* Andersoniana Group
§ Andersoniana Group	CWib MSal SPet WPer WWeb
- 'Baby Doll'	WLin
- 'Bilberry Ice'	More than 30 suppliers
- 'Blanca'	MWrn
- 'Blue and Gold'	CBcs CBct CFwr COIW EBee ECtt EMon ENot EPPr EPfP GBuc LAst LBMP LHop LRHS MRav NEgg NPri NSti SPla SPoG WCAu WCot WHil
- 'Blue Stone'	CMdw CMea CSBt ECha ECtt ERou MAvo MBNS MRav NCGa NPri SRms WFar WHoo WTin
- 'Blushing Bride'	GSki
- 'Bridal Veil'	CHII
- 'Caerulea Plena'	see *T. virginiana* 'Caerulea Plena'
- Carmine Glow	see *T.* (Andersoniana Group) 'Karminglut'
- 'Charlotte'	EBee ECGP ECha EMFW GSki LRHS MWgw NBre NBro NEgg NGdn SBch SRGP WCAu WMnd WTMC
- 'Chedglow'	LHop
- 'Concord Grape'	More than 30 suppliers
- 'Danielle'	EGle EPfP GMac NGdn NRnb WTMC
- 'Domaine de Courson'	EBee
- 'In the Navy'	EBee ERou LDai MEHN NBre NLar WCot
- 'Innocence'	More than 30 suppliers
- 'Iris Prichard'	CPrp CTca EBee ELan EPfP ERou GCra GMaP LAst LHop LRHS NBre NCGa NLar SRGP WFar
- 'Isis' ♀H4	CBcs CHar CPrp CTri EBee ECGP ECtt ELan EPfP GCra LRHS MRav MWgw NBir NCGa NGdn NOrc SPer SPla WMnd WTin
- 'J.C. Weguelin' ♀H4	EBee EGle EMil EPfP EWTr LBMP NBir NBre SRms WCAu WMnd
§ - 'Karminglut'	EBee ECtt ELan EPfP ERou GMaP LAst MNrw NBir NGdn NOrc NVic WCAu WHil WHoo
- 'Leonora'	COIW ENot EPfP ERou NLar
- 'Little Doll'	CWCL ECtt ERou GBri GSki LAst MDKP MHar MLLN MNFA NBro NCGa NPri NRnb WCot WFar WTMC
- 'Little White Doll'	CPrp CWCL EBee ECtt ERou GMac GSki LAst MBNS MDKP MNFA MSte NBre SPoG WFar
- 'Mariella'	EBee EGle GMac
- 'Mrs Loewer'	EMon
- 'Navajo Princess'	EBee
- 'Osprey' ♀H4	More than 30 suppliers
- 'Pauline'	CHar EBee ECtt EPla ERou GSki LAst LRHS MNrw MRav NBir NLar SPoG WFar WHil WHoo WTel WTin
- 'Perinne's Pink'	CWCL EBee EPfP MBri NBPC NDov NLar NSti
- 'Pink Chablis' PBR	CWCL EBee ERou NBro NLar NMoo
- 'Purewell Giant'	CTri EBee ECot EMil ERou LCro LHop NBro NEgg NLar WGor WKif WMnd
- 'Purple Dome'	CHar CSsd EBee ECtt EMFW EPla GMaP LAst LRHS MHar MRav MWgw NBir NBro NCGa NGdn SPla SPoG STes WCAu WMnd WTin
- 'Red Grape'	COIW EBee ECtt ERou GSki LRHS MBNS NCGa NPro NSti WBor WCAu
- 'Rosi'	EBee
- 'Rubra'	CPrp CSBt EBee EPfP ERou GSki MWgw NOrc NPri SBod SRms
- 'Satin Doll' PBR	COIW EBee ECtt EMan SPoG
- 'Sweet Kate'	CBct CHar CWCL EBrs ERou LFur MBNS MCCP NBro SAga SMer SRGP WBor
- 'Sylvana'	EBee EGle GMac SApp WCAu
- 'Valour'	CWat EBee LRHS WFar

	- 'Zwanenburg Blue'	EBee ECha ECtt EHrv ELan ERou GMac LBMP LRHS MLHP MWgw NCGa NRnb SPlb WMnd WTel
	'Angel Eyes'	GSki MDKP
	'Baerbel'	GSki
	blossfeldiana	see *T. cerinthoides*
	canaliculata	see *T. ohiensis*
§	***cerinthoides***	CHal
§	***fluminensis***	SChr
	- 'Albovittata'	CHal
§	- 'Aurea' 🏆H1	CHal MBri
	- 'Laekenensis' (v)	CHal MBri
	- 'Maiden's Blush' (v)	CHal CSpe EShb EWin SGar SRms WFoF
	- 'Quicksilver' (v) 🏆H1	CHal MBri
	- 'Tricolor Minima' 🏆H1	CHal
	- 'Variegata'	see *T. fluminensis* 'Aurea'
	multiflora	see *Tripogandra multiflora*
	navicularis	see *Callisia navicularis*
§	***ohiensis***	CFee EBee
	pallida 🏆H2-3	CHal
§	- 'Purpurea' 🏆H2-3	EShb
	pendula	see *T. zebrina*
	'Purple Sabre'	CBcs EBee ERou LAst SDys
	purpurea	see *T. pallida* 'Purpurea'
	sillamontana 🏆H1	CHal EOHP MBri
	spathacea	CHal EShb
§	- 'Vittata' 🏆H1	CHal EShb
	tricolor	see *T. zebrina*
	virginiana	MWrn SGar
	- 'Alba'	WPer
*	- 'Brevicaulis'	EBee ECha EPla ERos GBuc NBre NBro
§	- 'Caerulea Plena' (d)	CHFP CHar CMHG EBee ELan EMan EPfP EPla ERou GSki LRHS MRav NCGa SRms WCra WFar WTin
	- 'Rubra'	ECGP MLHP SPlb
§	***zebrina*** 🏆H1	CHal
	- ***discolor***	CHal
	- ***pendula***	see *T. zebrina*
	- 'Purpusii' 🏆H1	CHal SRms
	- 'Quadricolor' (v) 🏆H1	CHal

Tragopogon (*Asteraceae*)

	crocifolius	CSpe EBee WCot
	porrifolius	ILis SECG WGwG
	pratensis	CArn NMir

Trapa (*Trapaceae*)

	natans	WFar

Trautvetteria (*Ranunculaceae*)

	carolinensis var. ***japonica***	CLAP GEdr WCru
	- var. ***occidentalis***	GEdr WCru

Trevesia (*Araliaceae*)

	palmata	CKob

Triadica (*Euphorbiaceae*)

	sebifera **new**	SKHP

Trichopetalum (*Anthericaceae*)

§	***plumosum***	ECho

Tricuspidaria see *Crinodendron*

Tricyrtis ✿ (*Convallariaceae*)

	B&SWJ 3229 from Taiwan **new**	WCru
	'Adbane'	CBct CChe CLAP ELan EPPr EWes GBuc GKev LRHS MAvo MMHG NLar WCot WFar WGwG
	affinis	CLAP GAbr GBin GBuc GGar NLar
	- B&SWJ 2804	WCru
	- B&SWJ 5640	WCru
	- B&SWJ 5847	WCru
	- B&SWJ 6182	WCru
	- 'Early Bird' **new**	WCru
	- 'Variegata'	see *T.* 'Variegata'
	'Amanagowa'	CLAP
	bakeri	see *T. latifolia*
	'Blue Wonder'	IBal LCro MBNS NGdn NPro SPet
	dilatata	see *T. macropoda*
	'Empress'	CBct CHFP COIW CPLG CSam EBee EBla ELon EMan EPfP ERou EWes GCai IBal LEdu LSou MAvo MBNS MBnl MCCP NBPC NCob NEgg SPet SPoG WFar WSel
	flava	EBee WCru
	formosana 🏆H4	More than 30 suppliers
	- B&SWJ 306	CLAP EBla MNrw WCot WFar WRos
	- B&SWJ 3073	WCru
	- B&SWJ 355	WCru WFar
	- B&SWJ 3616	WCru
	- B&SWJ 3712	WCru WFar
	- B&SWJ 6705	CLAP WCru WPrP
	- B&SWJ 6741	WCru
	- B&SWJ 6970	WCru
	- B&SWJ 7071	WFar
	- 'Blushing Toad' **new**	WCru
	- dark	GAbr LBMP NCGa WFar
	- 'Dark Beauty'	CDes CEnt CLAP CPom CWCL EBee EHrv EMan EMar ERou GBuc GSki IBal LCro MAvo MBnl MBri MCCP MHer MPop NBPC NPro SMad SPur WBVN WFar WPGP WWFP
	- 'Gilt Edge' (v)	More than 30 suppliers
	- f. ***glandosa***	WFar
	- - B&SWJ 7084	WCru
	- var. ***grandiflora*** B&SWJ 6905	WCru WFar
	- 'Lodge Farm'	EBla
	- pale	CBct WFar
	- 'Purple Beauty'	CBct CTca EBee MDKP MSte
	- 'Samurai' (v)	CLAP CMil CWCL EBee EMan EPPr ERou EWes NCGa NMoo WCot WFar
	- 'Shelley's'	CBct CLAP CPLG NBro WFar WPrP
	- 'Small Wonder'	WCru
§	- Stolonifera Group	CBcs CMHG CMMP CMea EBee ECha EHrv ELan EMar EPfP LEdu LHop LRHS MWgw NEgg NGdn NHol SDix SPoG WFar WMnd WWeb
	- - B&SWJ 7046	WCru WFar
	- 'Taroko Toad'	WCru
	- 'Tiny Toad'	WCru WFar
	- 'Variegata' (v)	CBct LEdu MMHG NBir NLar WBor WCru WFar
	'Harlequin'	LEdu MAvo NLar WFar
§	***hirta***	More than 30 suppliers
	- B&SWJ 2827	WCru
	- 'Alba'	CSam EHrv SBch WFar WThu
*	- 'Albomarginata' (v)	CPrp EBee EMar EPPr EPfP EShb LBMP MCCP NCGa NHol NLar NSti SBch SPoG SWvt WFar WPGP
	- 'Golden Gleam'	WCot WFar
	- hybrids	CMMP
	- 'Kinkazan'	EBee
	- 'Makinoi Gold'	WFar
	- var. ***masamunei***	WCru
	- 'Matsukaze'	CLAP CPom MAvo WFar
	- 'Miyazaki'	CBct CFir CLAP EGle EMan GBuc LSou MHer MNrw NCGa NLar SMac SMrm WFar

- 'Taiwan Atrianne'	CSam EMar GAbr LDai LRHS MAvo MBri MDKP NCob NHol
- 'Variegata' (v)	CBct CTca CTri EMan EWes GBuc GKev LHop NLar WCot WCru WFar WHrl WPrP
N Hototogisu	CBct CLAP CMea CPom EBee EBla EGle ELan EMar GAbr GMac GSki LHop LRHS MAvo MCCP MTho NBir NCGa NEgg NHol SDnm SPav WFar WHil WMnd WSpi
ishiiana	CDes CLAP CWsd EBee EBla WCot WCru WFar WPGP
- var. ***surugensis***	EBla LEdu WCru WFar
japonica	see *T. hirta*
'Kohaku'	CBct CLAP CPom CWsd EBee EBla ELan EPPr EWes NPro SPav WCot WCru WFar WPGP
lasiocarpa	CBct CLAP GQue LEdu MAvo NMyG WFar
- B&SWJ 3635	CLAP CMil EBla WCru WFar
- B&SWJ 6861	WCru
- B&SWJ 7013	WCru WPrP
- B&SWJ 7014	WCru
- B&SWJ 7103	WCru
§ ***latifolia***	CBct CTca CWsd EBee ELan EPPr GAbr GGar GMaP GSki MNrw NGdn NLar SPoG WBVN WBor WCru WFar
- from Japan	WFar
'Lemon Lime' (v)	CBct CWsd ECha EMan LSou MDKP NPro SPav
'Lightning Strike' (v)	CBct EBee ECha ECtt EWes GBuc GSki LFur LSou MBri MDKP NBPC NCob NMyG SPoG WCot WFar
'Lilac Towers'	CBct EBrs ELan WCru WFar
macrantha	CMil GAbr GGar WCru
§ - subsp. ***macranthopsis***	CBct CLAP CWsd EBla EPot GBuc GEdr MDKP WCot WCru WFar
- - 'Juro' (d) **new**	WCru
macranthopsis	see *T. macrantha* subsp. *macranthopsis*
N ***macropoda***	CBct CFwr CSam EBee EBla ELan EMan EPfP GAbr GBuc GMaP IBal ITim LEdu MAvo MCCP NCGa NGdn NWCA SMac SMad WFar WMnd
- B&SWJ 1271	CBct EBla WCru
- B&SWJ 2804 from Japan **new**	WCru
- B&SWJ 5013	WCru
- B&SWJ 5556	WCru
- B&SWJ 5847	WCru
- B&SWJ 6209	WCru
- B&SWJ 8700	WCru
- B&SWJ 8829	WCru
- from Yungi Temple, China	CLAP EBla EPPr MDKP WCot WFar
- 'Tricolor' **new**	WCot
- variegated (v)	CBow
maculata	CPLG WFar
- HWJCM 470	WCru
- HWJK 2010	WCru
- HWJK 2411	WCru
'Moonlight Treasure' **new**	EBee
nana	CLAP WCru
- 'Karasuba' **new**	EBee
- 'Raven's Back'	WCru
'Niitaka' **new**	EBee
ohsumiensis	CBct CDes CLAP CPom CWsd EBee EBla ECha EMan GBuc GEdr LEdu MDKP MTho SBch WCru WFar WPGP
perfoliata	CLAP CWsd LEdu WCru WFar
- variegated (v) **new**	WCru
'Raspberry Mousse'	CHFP CWCL EBee EHrv EKen EMar IPot LFur MBNS MPop NBPN NMoo NSti
setouchiensis	WCru
'Shimone'	CHid CLAP CPLG CStu EBee ECha ELan GBuc SMac WFar WKif
'Sinonome' **new**	GBin
stolonifera	see *T. formosana* Stolonifera Group
suzukii RWJ 10111	WCru
'Tojen'	More than 30 suppliers
'Tresahor White'	CBct WFar
§ 'Variegata' (*affinis* hybrid) (v)	WFar
'Washfields'	CBct WFar WPGP
'White Towers'	More than 30 suppliers
'White Towers' spotted	WBrE

Tridens (*Poaceae*)

flavus **new**	XIsg

Trifolium (*Papilionaceae*)

angustifolium	CArn
badium	GBri
incarnatum	CSpe MHer
ochroleucon	CElw CFwr CHFP EBee EDAr EHrv GBri GMaP MCCP MNFA MWgw MWrn NCGa NSti SBch SEND SPhx SSvw SWal WCot WFar WMoo
pannonicum	CBgR CFir CMea EBee EHrv EMon MLLN MSte NBre NCot WFar WPGP WSHC WTin
pratense	MHer NSco SECG WSFF
- 'Dolly North'	see *T. pratense* 'Susan Smith'
- 'Ice Cool'	see *T. repens* 'Green Ice'
- 'Nina'	EBee EMan EWin
§ - 'Susan Smith' (v)	CCCN EBee ECGP EWes EWin LRHS MNrw NGHP SIng WFar
repens	COld EHrv NSco WCAu WSFF
- 'Douglas Dawson'	LDai
- 'Dragon's Blood'	EBee MBNS NEgg NPro SIng SVil
- 'Gold Net'	see *T. pratense* 'Susan Smith'
- 'Good Luck'	MTho
§ - 'Green Ice'	CBre EBee EMan EWin LRHS MTho MWgw NBir NCob NSti WDyG WFar WHal WPtf
- 'Harlequin' (v)	EBee EWin GGar MAvo MHer MTho WCot WFar WOut WPer WPtf
- 'Pentaphyllum'	see *T. repens* 'Quinquefolium'
- 'Purpurascens'	CArn CBre CEnt ECGP EPfP GGar GMac ILis LRHS MBNS MHer MWgw NSti SPoG WHen WKif
§ - 'Purpurascens Quadrifolium'	CMea CSpe CStu CWCL CWan EBee ECha ECho EPau EWes EWin LBMP NBid NEgg NGHP NMir NPer NPri SIng SPer SPlb WFar WPtf
- 'Quadrifolium'	EDAr
§ - 'Quinquefolium'	EBee
- 'Saint Patrick' **new**	CNat
- 'Tetraphyllum Purpureum'	see *T. repens* 'Purpurascens Quadrifolium'
- 'Wheatfen'	CBow CBre EBee EMan EWin NDov NGHP NPer WCot
- 'William'	CBow CBre EBee EGoo EMan EWin LCro LEdu SPur WCot
rubens	More than 30 suppliers
- 'Peach Pink'	CFwr CSpe EBee EMan EMon EShb LHop LSou MHar MLLN MMHG NCob SPhx WCot
- 'Red Feathers'	ECGP EWin LFur MWea

Triglochin (*Juncaginaceae*)

maritimum	CRWN
palustre	CRWN

Trigonella (*Papilionaceae*)

foenum-graecum	CArn MSal SIde

Trillidium see *Trillium*

Trillium ✿ (*Trilliaceae*)

albidum	CAby CLAP EBee EBrs ECho EPot GBuc GCrs GMaP NMen SKHP SSpi WCru WHal
angustipetalum	CLAP EBrs SKHP WWst
- hybrid	SKHP
apetalon	GEdr LAma WCru
camschatcense	CHHB CLAP EBee EBrs GBuc GCrs GEdr LAma WCru
- from China	WWst
- from Japan	WWst
§ ***catesbyi***	CLAP EBee EBrs ECho EHrv EPot ERCP GEdr GGar GKev IBal ITer LAma NHol NMyG WCru WWst
cernuum	CLAP CWsd ECho GCra IBal NMyG WCru WShi
chloropetalum	EBee ITer SBla SSpi WCru WFar WKif WLin WPGP
- var. ***chloropetalum*** x ***parviflorum*** new	SKHP
§ - var. ***giganteum*** ♀H4	CLAP GBuc GEdr NMen SKHP SSpi WCru WWst
- var. ***rubrum***	see *T. chloropetalum* var. *giganteum*
- white-flowered	CLAP ECha IBal
cuneatum	CBcs CBct CFwr CLAP EBee EBrs ECho EHrv ELan EPot GBin GBuc GEdr GGar GMaP IBal ITer LAma LRHS MTho NHol NMen NMyG SBod SSpi WCru WFar WWst
- red-flowered	GCrs
decipiens	WWst
decumbens	SKHP WWst
erectum ♀H4	More than 30 suppliers
- f. ***albiflorum***	CFir CLAP CWsd EBee EBrs ECha ECho GBuc GEdr GGar ITer LAma NHol NMyG SSpi WCru
- 'Beige'	CLAP GSki IBal
erectum x ***flexipes***	CAby CLAP EBee ECho EHrv GBuc GEdr GGar GKev NMen SKHP SSpi WWst
- f. ***luteum***	CBct CLAP EPfP SSpi WCru
- purple-flowered	IBal
- red-flowered	IBal
flexipes	CLAP CWsd EBee EBrs ECho EHrv EPot GCrs GEdr GKev IBal LAma NMen WCru
- erect new	NMen
foetidissimum new	SKHP WWst
govanianum	WCru
grandiflorum ♀H4	More than 30 suppliers
- dwarf	NHar
- 'Flore Pleno' (d)	CLAP CWsd ECha ECho GBuc MTho SBla SCnR SPhx WWst
- 'Kath's Dwarf' new	GEdr
- 'Quicksilver' new	SKHP
- f. ***roseum***	CLAP EBrs WWst
- 'Snowbunting' (d)	EBrs EWes GBin GCrs MMHG WThu
kurabayashii	CAby CBct CFir CFwr CLAP CPLG EBee EBrs ECho GBuc GCrs SKHP SSpi WAbe WCot WPGP WWst
lancifolium	SKHP WWst
ludovicianum	SKHP WWst
§ ***luteum*** ♀H4	More than 30 suppliers
maculatum	WWst
nivale	EBee WWst
ovatum	CLAP CWCL EPot GBuc GCrs GGar NMen WHal
- from Oregon	CLAP
- f. ***hibbersonii***	CStu EPot GBuc GCra GCrs NMen
- 'Roy Elliott'	EPot
parviflorum	CLAP ECho GEdr NMen SKHP SSpi WWst
pusillum	CLAP EBee ECho ELan EPot GEdr GGar GKev IBal NHol SKHP SSpi
* - var. ***alabamicum*** new	SKHP
- var. ***ozarkanum*** new	SKHP
- var. ***pusillum***	GCrs SBla
- var. ***virginianum***	CLAP EBrs LAma WCru
recurvatum	CBcs CLAP EBee EBrs ECho EHrv EPot GAbr GEdr GGar GKev GSki IBal ITer LAma NHol NMen NMyG SKHP WCru WFar WPnP
reliquum new	WWst
rivale ♀H3	CElw CLAP CStu EBee ECho EHrv EPot GBuc GCrs ITim NMen SBla SKHP WAbe WFar WWst
- pink-flowered	CWsd EPot GEdr NMen
- 'Purple Heart'	CLAP EPot GCrs GEdr SKHP
rugelii	CAby CLAP EBee EBrs ECho EHrv EPot EWes GBuc GCrs GMaP LAma NMen SKHP SSpi WCru WWst
- Askival hybrids	CLAP EBee EBrs ECho GBuc NMen SKHP SSpi WWst
rugelii x ***vaseyi***	EBee EHrv EWes NMen SKHP SSpi WWst
sessile	CFwr CLAP CMea EBee EBrs ECho ENot EPot EWTr GBuc GKev GSki IBal LAma MAvo NBir NCGa NMen NMyG SGar SKHP WCAu WCru WFar WKif WPnP WSHC WShi
- 'Rubrum'	see *T. chloropetalum* var. *giganteum*
simile	CLAP CWsd EBee EBrs ECho EPot GCrs SKHP SSpi WWst
smallii	WCru WWst
stamineum	CLAP EBee ECho GEdr GGar IBal NMyG SKHP
stylosum	see *T. catesbyi*
sulcatum	CLAP EBee EBrs ECho EHrv GBuc GCrs GEdr GGar GMaP IBal NMen SKHP SSpi WCru WFar
texanum new	SKHP
tschonoskii	CHHB CLAP EBee EBrs ECho GBuc GEdr LAma WCru WWst
- var. ***himalaicum***	WCru
underwoodii	SKHP WWst
undulatum	CLAP EBee ECho EPot GEdr GGar IBal LAma NHol NMen NMyG WCru
vaseyi	CLAP EBee EBrs ECha ECho EHrv EWes GBuc GCrs GEdr GGar ITer LAma NMen SSpi WCru
- prostrate new	WWst
viride	CLAP EPot IBal NGby WCru WFar WPnP
viridescens	CLAP EBee EBrs ECho GEdr LAma NMyG WFar WWst

Trinia (*Apiaceae*)

glauca	EBee

Triosteum (*Caprifoliaceae*)

himalayanum	CLAP GKev
- BWJ 7907	WCru
pinnatifidum	CLAP

Tripetaleia (*Ericaceae*)

§ ***bracteata***	NLar

Tripleurospermum (*Asteraceae*)

§ ***maritimum***	XPep

Tripogandra (*Commelinaceae*)

§ ***multiflora***	CHal

Tripsacum (*Poaceae*)

dactyloides	EPPr

Tripterospermum (*Gentianaceae*)

* aff. ***chevalieri*** B&SWJ 8359	WCru
cordifolium B&SWJ 081	WCru
fasciculatum B&SWJ 7197	WCru
aff. ***hirticalyx*** B&SWJ 8264	WCru
japonicum	EBee LTwo WBor
- B&SWJ 1168	WCru
lanceolatum B&SWJ 085	WCru
taiwanense B&SWJ 1205	WCru

Tripterygium (*Celastraceae*)

regelii	CBcs NLar WPGP
- B&SWJ 5453	WCru
wilfordii	WCru

Trisetum (*Poaceae*)

flavescens	CBig GFor NBre XIsg

Tristagma (*Alliaceae*)

WAL 9450	WCot
* ***nivale*** f. ***nivale*** F&W 9612	WCot

Triteleia (*Alliaceae*)

bridgesii	WCot
californica	see *Brodiaea californica*
§ 'Corrina'	CAvo CFFs EBee EBrs ECho EPot LBBr MNrw SMeo WHil
grandiflora	ECho WCot
hendersonii NNS 00-738	WCot
hyacinthina	EBee EBrs ECho ERos WCot
ixioides	ECho ERos
- var. ***scabra***	WCot
- 'Splendens'	EBee EBrs ECho
- 'Starlight'	CAvo CBgR CFFs CMea CSpe CSsd CTri EBee EBrs ECho EPot ERCP MWgw SBch SPer WCot WHil
§ ***laxa***	ECho GCrs WBVN WCot
- 'Allure'	EBee EBrs ECho IPot LRHS
§ - 'Koningin Fabiola'	CMea CPrp CTri EBee EBrs ECho EMan EPot IPot LAma LBBr LHop LRHS MBri MWgw NBir SBch SMeo SPer WBrE WCot WLin
- Queen Fabiola	see *T. laxa* 'Koningin Fabiola'
lilacina NNS 00-745	WCot
§ ***peduncularis***	CHFP EBee EBrs ECho WCot
- NNS 95-499	WCot
x ***tubergenii***	EBee EBrs ECho
uniflora	see *Ipheion uniflorum*

Trithrinax (*Arecaceae*)

acanthocoma	CBrP EAmu LPJP LPal
campestris	CBrP EAmu ETod LPal

Tritoma see *Kniphofia*

Tritonia (*Iridaceae*)

crocata ♀$^{H2-3}$	CPou EBrs
- 'Baby Doll'	CDes EBee EBrs WHil WPGP
- 'Bridal Veil'	EBee EBrs EPot
- 'Pink Sensation'	CDes EBee EBrs ECho EPot WCot WHil WPGP
- 'Plymouth Pastel' **new**	CDes
- 'Prince of Orange'	CPou WPGP
- 'Princess Beatrix'	CDes WCot WPGP
- 'Serendipity'	CDes CTca EBee EBrs
- 'Tangerine' **new**	CPBP CTca EBrs
§ ***disticha*** subsp. ***rubrolucens***	More than 30 suppliers
hyalina **new**	EBee
laxifolia	CPne CTca EBee EBrs ECho EPot
lineata	CDes CPou EBee EBrs ECho WPGP WPrP
- 'Parvifolia' **new**	EBee
pallida	SPlb
rosea	see *T. disticha* subsp. *rubrolucens*

Trochetiopsis (*Sterculiaceae*)

§ ***ebenus***	WPGP
melanoxylon misapplied	see *T. ebenus*
melanoxylon (Sol. ex Sims) Marais	EShb

Trochocarpa (*Epacridaceae*)

clarkei **new**	WThu
thymifolia red-flowered **new**	WThu
- white-flowered	WAbe

Trochodendron (*Trochodendraceae*)

aralioides	CBcs CDoC CHEx CTho CWib EBee ECrN EPfP IMGH LRHS MBri MGos SAPC SArc SLPl SLon SMad SPer SReu SSpi SSta WPGP
- B&SWJ 6727 from Taiwan	WCru

Trollius (*Ranunculaceae*)

ACE 1187	GEdr
acaulis	EBee ECho EGle EWes GAbr MTho WFar WPat
altaicus **new**	EBee
asiaticus	EBee ECho GBuc
aff. ***buddae*** BWJ 7958	WCru
§ ***chinensis***	EBee ECha NChi SRms SWat
- 'Golden Queen' ♀^{H4}	More than 30 suppliers
x ***cultorum*** 'Alabaster'	CBgR CDes CFir CLAP CMea CSam EBee ERou GBuc LCro LLWG MRav NLar NRnb SBla SMad SMeo WCFE WCot WFar WPGP WPnP WTin
- 'Baudirektor Linne'	MRav NGdn WFar
- Bressingham hybrids	WFar
- 'Byrne's Giant'	WFar WPnP
- 'Canary Bird'	ELan EMil EPfP GBri NGdn SRms WSpi
- 'Cheddar'	CElw MBri MCCP MRav NBro NGdn NLar NPro SMHy WFar WSpi
- 'Commander-in-chief'	CDes EBee WFar WPGP WPnP
- 'Earliest of All'	CDWL CSam EBee EGle EKen LRHS MBri MSte NGby NGdn SPer SRms WFar WSHC
- 'Etna'	CDWL EBee EGle ERou WFar WPnP
§ - 'Feuertroll'	CDWL EBee ECha LLWG MBNS MRav NCob NGby NPro WFar
- Fireglobe	see *T.* x *cultorum* 'Feuertroll'
- 'Glory of Leiden'	EBee
- 'Golden Cup'	ECot NBir NGdn
- 'Golden Monarch'	WFar
- 'Goldquelle' ♀^{H4}	EHon
- 'Goliath'	EWes NCob SMad WFar
- 'Helios'	CSam ECha
- 'Lemon Queen'	CDWL CWat EBee EHrv ENot EPfP ERou GMaP LBMP LRHS MBri MNFA MRav NBPC NBlu NRnb SPoG SWat WCAu WFar WSpi
- 'Meteor'	WFar
- 'Orange Crest'	EBee EGle MBri WFar WHal
- 'Orange Globe'	GAbr LBMP NBPC NCob NGby SMrm WFar WWeb
- 'Orange Glow'	SMad

	- 'Orange Princess' ♀H4	CDWL CWat EBee EPfP ERou GMaP LBMP LCro LRHS MCCP MSte NBro NLar NPri SPer SRms
	- 'Orange Queen'	SWvt
	- 'Prichard's Giant'	CDWL CMHG CRez EBee EGle ELan EMar GBri LAst MBNS NBro NGby NRnb WCAu WFar WSpi
§	- 'Superbus' ♀H4	CDes CPSs ECho EGle ELan EPfP GMaP LAst MBNS MBri NGdn NRnb SPer WBrE WFar WMoo
	- 'T. Smith'	EGle GMac NBro NGby WCot WFar
*	- 'Taleggio'	EMon SPhx
	- 'Yellow Beauty'	SMer WFar
	dschungaricus	EBee
	europaeus	More than 30 suppliers
	- 'Superbus'	see *T.* x *cultorum* 'Superbus'
	hondoensis	GBin NLar NPro
	iruticus	EBee GKev
	laxus	EWes
	- 'Albiflorus'	NWCA
	ledebourii misapplied	see *T. chinensis*
	pumilus	EBee ECha ECho ELan GBri GCrs GKev GMaP LRHS MHer NWCA SPer WFar WPer WWeb
	- ACE 1818	EPot GBuc WCot
	- 'Wargrave'	EPot
	ranunculoides new	EBee
	stenopetalus	CDes EBee ECha EWes MBri MNrw MRav NMyG NRnb SHar WFar
	vaginatus new	WLin
	yunnanensis	EBee GBuc GKev LRHS NBid NGby WFar WPnP
	- CD&R 2097	WCru
	- f. ***eupetalus*** BWJ 7614	WCru

Tropaeolum ✿ (*Tropaeolaceae*)

	azureum	CCCN EBee
	beuthii	EBee
	- F&W 8990	WCot
	brachyceras	CCCN EBee WCot
	ciliatum ♀H1	CCCN CFir CGHE CMea CPLG CSam CStu EBee EBrs ECho ELan EPot MPRe MTho NBid NSti WCot WCru WFar WHer WNor WPGP
	hookerianum subsp. ***austropurpureum***	EBee ERos
	- subsp. ***hookerianum***	WCot
	- - F&W 9467	WPGP
	incisum	CCCN EBee WCot
	kingii F&W 8676	WCot
	lepidum	WCot
	majus	MNHC WSel
	- Alaska Series (v) ♀H3	CPrp SBch SIde WJek WSel
	- 'Banana Split'	LAst
	- 'Crimson Beauty'	CSpe
§	- 'Darjeeling Double' (d) ♀H4	EShb EWin WCru
	- 'Darjeeling Gold'	see *T. majus* 'Darjeeling Double'
	- 'Empress of India'	CPrp WEas WJek
	- 'Hermine Grashoff' (d) ♀H2-3	CSWP CSpe EWin LRHS NPer
	- 'Margaret Long' (d)	CSpe EWin
	- 'Melba Yellow'	LSou
	- 'Peach Melba'	LSou
*	- 'Peaches and Cream'	CPrp WJek
	- 'Red Wonder'	CCCN CSWP CSpe EPfP EWin LAst LSou SMrm
	- Tom Thumb mixed	MNHC WJek
	pentaphyllum	CSpe CWsd EBee ECho ELan EWes GCrs LFur LTwo MTho WBor WCot
	peregrinum	CSpe
	polyphyllum	CCCN CDes CWsd EBee ECha EPfP GBuc GCrs SBla SCnR SKHP SMHy WAbe WCot WPGP
	sessilifolium	EBee
	speciosum ♀H4	More than 30 suppliers
	sylvestre	EWld NVic WCru
	tricolor ♀H1	CAvo CCCN EBee EBrs ECho ELan EPot EWld MAsh MTho WBor
	tuberosum	CEnd EBee EBrs ECho GPoy IHer LRHS MAsh WBrE WPrP
	- var. ***lineamaculatum*** 'Ken Aslet' ♀H3	CPLG CPrp CRHN CSpe EBee EBrs ECha ECho ELan EPfP EPot ERos EUnu EWin GAbr GGar IHer LAma LRHS MPRe MTho NGHP SPoG WCru WFar WHil WPGP WPtf
	- var. ***piliferum*** 'Sidney'	IBlr WCru

Tsuga (*Pinaceae*)

	canadensis	EHul LCon LPan MBar NBlu NWea WMou
	- 'Abbott's Dwarf'	CKen EOrn LCon MGos
§	- 'Abbott's Pygmy'	CKen
	- 'Albospica' (v)	EOrn WFar WGor
	- 'Arnold Gold Weeper'	CKen
	- 'Aurea' (v)	LCon MBar NLar WEve
	- 'Bacon Cristate'	CKen
	- 'Baldwin Dwarf Pyramid'	MBar
	- 'Beehive'	ECho WGor
	- 'Bennett'	EHul LCon MBar
	- 'Betty Rose' (v)	CKen
	- 'Brandley'	CKen
§	- 'Branklyn'	CKen
	- 'Cappy's Choice'	CKen
	- 'Cinnamonea'	CKen
	- 'Coffin'	CKen
	- 'Cole's Prostrate'	CKen EOrn LCon LLin MAsh MBar NHol NLar
	- 'Coryhill'	CDHC ECho MAsh SCoo
	- 'Creamey' (v)	CKen
	- 'Curley'	CKen
	- 'Curtis Ideal'	CKen
	- 'Essex'	NLar
*	- 'Everitt's Dense Leaf'	CKen
	- 'Everitt's Golden'	CKen
	- 'Fantana'	CDoC CRob ECho EHul LBee LCon LLin LRHS MAsh MBar NHol NLar SCoo SLim
	- 'Gentsch White' (v)	LCon LLin MGos NLar
	- 'Golden Splendor'	LLin
	- 'Horsford'	CKen NLar
	- 'Horstmann' No 1	CKen
	- 'Hussii'	CKen LCon NLar
	- 'Jacqueline Verkade'	CKen NLar
	- 'Jeddeloh' ♀H4	CDoC CRob ECho EHul EOrn IMGH LCon LLin LRHS MAsh MBar MBri MGos NHol SCoo SLim SPoG WEve
	- 'Jervis'	CDoC CKen LCon MAsh NHol NLar
	- 'Julianne'	CKen
	- 'Kingsville Spreader'	CKen
	- 'Little Joe'	CKen
	- 'Little Snow'	CKen
I	- 'Lutea'	CKen
	- 'Many Cones'	CKen
	- 'Minima'	CKen
	- 'Minuta'	CDoC CKen ECho EHul EOrn LBee LCon LLin MBar MGos NLar SCoo SLon SPoG WGor
	- 'Nana'	EHul
	- 'Palomino'	CKen MAsh MBar
	- 'Pendula' ♀H4	CDoC CKen ECho EHul EOrn EPfP LCon LRHS MAsh MBar SLim SPoG WEve WFar
	- 'Pincushion'	CKen

	- 'Popeleski' **new**	NLar
	- 'Prostrata'	see *T. canadensis* 'Branklyn'
	- 'Pygmaea'	see *T. canadensis* 'Abbott's Pygmy'
	- 'Rugg's Washington Dwarf'	CKen SCoo
	- 'Snowflake'	CKen LCon
	- 'Stewart's Gem'	CKen
	- 'Verkade Petite'	CKen
	- 'Verkade Recurved'	CKen LCon MBar NLar
	- 'Von Helms' Dwarf'	CKen
	- 'Warnham'	CKen ECho EOrn LBee MAsh SCoo
	caroliniana 'La Bar Weeping'	CKen NLar
	diversifolia 'Gotelli'	CKen
	heterophylla 🏆H4	CDoC CDul CLnd EPfP LBuc LCon LRHS MBar NWea SHBN SMad SPer SPoG STre WEve WFar
	- 'Iron Springs'	CKen EOrn
	- 'Laursen's Column'	CKen
	- 'Thorsens Weeping'	CKen NLar
	menziesii (Mirb.) hort.	see *Pseudotsuga menziesii*
	mertensiana	LCon NWea
	- 'Blue Star'	CKen NLar
	- 'Elizabeth'	CDoC CKen
	- 'Glauca'	CKen NLar
I	- 'Glauca Nana'	CKen
I	- 'Horstmann' **new**	CKen
	- 'Quartz Mountain'	CKen
	sieboldii 'Baldwin'	CKen
	- 'Green Ball' **new**	CKen NLar
	- 'Honeywell Estate'	CKen
	- 'Nana'	CKen

Tsusiophyllum (*Ericaceae*)

tanakae	see *Rhododendron tsusiophyllum*

Tuberaria (*Cistaceae*)

lignosa	CStu EMan MWrn WAbe

Tulbaghia ✿ (*Alliaceae*)

acutiloba	CAvo CPen ERos WPrP
alliacea	CAvo CFee EBla ECho ERos EShb NHoy WCot
alliacea* x *violacea	ECho
capensis	CFee CPou LPio MHom
cepacea	CStu ERos NBir WHil WSPU
cepacea* x *natalensis	ERos
cernua hybrid	NHoy WPrP
cernua* x *violacea **new**	WPrP
coddii	CAvo CFee EBla MHom WCot WPrP
cominsii	CPLG CStu EDif ERea SBch SCnR
cominsii* x *violacea	CPLG CTca EBee ERos MHom WPrP
'Cosmic'	WPrP
dregeana	ERos WCot
'Fairy Star'	CDes ERos EShb WCot WOut WPGP WPrP
fragrans	see *T. simmleri*
- 'Alba' **new**	EBrs
galpinii	CPen ERos NWCA WPrP
'Hazel'	WPrP
'John May's Special'	CDes CKno EBee EMan EShb MSte WCot WPGP WPrP
leucantha	CAvo CStu EBee EBla ERos NHoy NWCA SBla WCot WPrP
- H&B 11996	CDes
- from Sentinel Park, South Africa **new**	WPrP
ludwigiana	ERea
maritima	see *T. violacea* var. *maritima*
Marwood seedling	MTPN
montana	CDes EBee WPGP WPrP
natalensis	CPou EBee ECho

	- B&V 421	CDes
	- CD&R 84	WPrP
	- pink-flowered	ECho ERos MHom WCot WPrP
	natalensis* x *violacea **new**	NWCA
§	***simmleri***	CPou EBee EBla EBrs ECho EHrv EPot EPyc ERos EShb EWes GSki LAma LPio NHoy NWCA WCot
	- pink-flowered	CDes CPen CTca
	- white-flowered	CPen CPou CTca EMan EPot
	verdoorniae	ERos EShb WCot
	violacea	More than 30 suppliers
*	- 'Alba'	EBla ERos GSki LPio NHoy NLAp WFar WHoo WTin
§	- var. ***maritima***	CDes EBee EDif ERea ERos EShb MHom NHoy WCot
I	- 'Fine Form'	SMHy
*	- ***grandiflora***	CAvo
	- 'John Rider'	NWCA WPer
*	- var. ***maritima***	EBee NHoy NWCA WPrP
	- var. ***obtusa*** **new**	WPrP
	- 'Pallida'	CAvo CDes CMdw CPne CPou CTca EBee ECho LEdu LPio NHoy NWCA WPGP WPrP
	- 'Pearl'	CPou WPrP
	- var. ***robustior***	CPou CTca EBee EBla EWes NHoy WPrP
§	- 'Silver Lace' (v)	More than 30 suppliers
	- 'Variegata'	see *T. violacea* 'Silver Lace'
	- var. ***violacea*** **new**	WPrP

Tulipa ✿ (*Liliaceae*)

'Abba' (2)	LRHS
'Absalon' (9) **new**	LAma
'Abu Hassan' (3)	CAvo CFFs EBrs LAma MBri SPhx
acuminata (15)	CBgR CHHB CTca EBrs ECho ERCP IHer LAma LCro LEdu LRHS NMin SMeo SPhx
'Ad Rem' (4)	MBri
'Addis' (14) 🏆H4	LAma
'African Queen' (3)	LAma
agenensis	EBrs
aitchisonii	see *T. clusiana*
'Aladdin' (6)	LAma LRHS
'Aladdin's Record' (6)	EBrs
albertii (15)	EBrs ECho LAma NMin WWst
'Alfred Cortot' (12) 🏆H4	LAma
'Ali Baba' (14) 🏆H4	LRHS
'Allegretto' (11)	MBri
altaica (15) 🏆H4	EBrs EPot LAma
amabilis	see *T. hoogiana*
'American Eagle' **new**	ERCP
'Ancilla' (12) 🏆H4	LAma
'Angélique' (11) 🏆H4	CAvo CFFs CMea CTca EBrs EPfP ERCP LAma LCro LRHS NBir SMeo SPer
'Annie Schilder' (3) **new**	LRHS
'Apeldoorn' (4)	EBrs LAma MBri SPer
'Apeldoorn's Elite' (4) 🏆H4	LAma MBri
'Apricot Beauty' (1) 🏆H4	CTca EBrs EPfP LAma LRHS MBri NBir SPer
'Apricot Jewel'	see *T. linifolia* (Batalinii Group) 'Apricot Jewel'
'Apricot Parrot' (10) 🏆H4	CAvo CFFs EPfP LAma MBri SPer
'Arabian Mystery' (3)	CAvo CFFs EBrs LAma NBir NHol
armena var. ***lycica***	WWst
'Artist' (8) 🏆H4	EBrs LAma MNFA MWgw NBir
'Attila' (3)	EBrs LAma
aucheriana (15) 🏆H4	CHHB EBrs ECho EPot ERos LAma LTwo NMin
australis (15)	ECho
aximensis (15)	EBrs ECho LRHS
'Bacchus' **new**	LAma
bakeri	see *T. saxatilis* Bakeri Group
'Ballade' (6) 🏆H4	CAvo CFFs EBrs ERCP LAma MSte

	'Ballerina' (6) ♀H4	CAvo CFFs CMea CTca EBrs ERCP LAma LRHS MBri MMHG MWgw SMeo SPer SPhx
	'Banja Luka' (4)	EBrs SPer
	batalinii	see *T. linifolia* Batalinii Group
	'Beauty of Apeldoorn' (4)	LAma MBri
	Beauty Queen (1)	EBrs
	'Bellflower' (7)	LAma
	biebersteiniana (15)	EBrs
§	***biflora*** (15)	CGrW CTca EBrs EPot LAma LRHS LTwo SPhx
	bifloriformis (15)	CHHB EBrs LRHS SPhx
I	- 'Maxima' **new**	EBrs NMin
	- 'Starlight' **new**	EBrs
	'Big Chief' (4) ♀H4	LAma
	'Big Smile' **new**	LRHS
	'Bird of Paradise' (10)	EBrs
	'Black Hero'	CAvo CFFs EBrs ERCP LAma LRHS NBPN SMeo SPer
	'Black Horse'	LAma
	'Black Jewel' **new**	ERCP
	'Black Parrot' (10) ♀H4	CAvo CFFs CHid EBrs EPfP ERCP LAma LRHS MBri MMHG MSte NBPN SMeo SPer SPhx
	'Black Stallion' **new**	LAma
	'Blenda' (3)	EBrs
	'Bleu Aimable' (5)	CAvo CFFs EBrs LAma
	'Blue Diamond' (11)	CAvo CFFs ERCP LRHS SPer
	'Blue Heron' (7) ♀H4	EBrs ERCP LAma
	'Blue Parrot' (10)	CAvo CFFs EBrs ERCP LAma LRHS MSte
	'Blue Ribbon' (3)	CAvo CFFs
	'Blueberry Ripple' **new**	LRHS
	'Boutade'	NPer
	'Bridesmaid' (5) **new**	LAma
	'Burgundy' (6)	EBrs ERCP LAma SMeo
	'Burgundy Lace' (7)	EBrs LAma
	'Café Noir' **new**	ERCP
	'Calibra' (7) **new**	LRHS
	'Calypso' (14) ♀H4	EBrs
	'Candela' (13) ♀H4	LAma LRHS
	'Candy Club' (5)	EBrs LAma LRHS SPer
	'Cantata' (13)	LAma
	'Cape Cod' (14)	EPfP LAma LRHS
	'Carnaval de Nice' (11/v) ♀H4	CAvo CFFs CTca EBrs ERCP LAma LRHS MBri
	'Carrousel' (7)	EBrs
	'Casablanca' (11) **new**	CMea EBrs
	'Cassini' (3)	LAma
§	***celsiana*** (15)	EBrs ECho LAma LRHS WWst
	'China Pink' (6) ♀H4	CAvo CFFs CMea CTca EBrs EPfP ERCP LAma MBri MWgw SMeo
	'China Town' (8) ♀H4	EBrs LAma LRHS MBri
	'Christmas Marvel' (1)	EBrs LAma
	chrysantha Boiss. ex Baker	see *T. montana*
	'Claudia' (6) **new**	ERCP SPer
	'Cloud Nine' (5)	LAma
§	***clusiana*** (15)	CHFP CHHB EBrs ERCP IHer LAma NMin
	- var. ***chrysantha*** (15) ♀H4	CAvo CFFs CGrW CHHB CMea EBrs ECho LAma LRHS SPhx WHoo
	- - 'Tubergen's Gem' (15)	EBrs EPot LAma LRHS MBri
	- 'Cynthia' (15) ♀H4	CHFP CHHB CSWP CTca EBrs ECGP EPot LAma LRHS MSte NMin SMeo SPhx
	- 'Sheila' (15) **new**	EBrs NMin SPhx
	'Colour Spectacle' PBR (5)	LSou SPer
	'Columbine' (5) **new**	LAma
	'Compostella' (14) **new**	LRHS
	'Concerto' (13)	EBrs MBri NPer
	'Corona' (12)	EBrs
	'Couleur Cardinal' (3)	EBrs LAma
	'Creme Upstar' (11) **new**	LRHS
	cretica (15)	EBrs ECho NMin WWst
	'Curly Sue' (7) **new**	ERCP
	'Czaar Peter' ♀H4	CAvo CFFs LRHS MBri NPer
	'Dancing Show' (8)	CAvo CFFs LAma
	dasystemon (15)	EBrs EPot LAma LTwo SBch
	dasystemonoides (15) **new**	EBrs
	'Davenport' (7) **new**	LRHS
	'Daydream' (4) ♀H4	EPfP SPer
	'Daylight' (12)	EBrs
	'Deirdre' (8) **new**	LRHS
	didieri	see *T. passeriniana*
	'Doll's Minuet' (8)	LAma SPer
	'Don Quichotte' (3) ♀H4	LRHS MBri
	'Donna Bella' (14) ♀H4	EPfP
	'Dordogne' **new**	LRHS
	'Douglas Bader' (5)	CAvo CFFs
	'Dreamboat' (14)	MBri
	'Dreaming Maid' (3)	LAma
	'Dreamland' (5) ♀H4	MBri
	'Duc van Tol' (1) **new**	IHer
	'Duc van Tol Rose'	LAma
	'Duc van Tol Salmon'	LAma
	'Dynasty' (3) **new**	LRHS SPer
	'Early Harvest' (12) ♀H4	CAvo CFFs
	'Easter Surprise' (14) ♀H4	MBri
	eichleri	see *T. undulatifolia*
	'Electra' (5)	LAma MBri
	'Elegant Lady' (6)	CAvo CFFs EBrs LAma LRHS SPer
	'Esperanto' (8/v) ♀H4	LAma
	'Estella Rijnveld' (10)	EBrs LAma LRHS MBri MSte NBir
	'Esther' (5)	ERCP
	'Eternal Flame' (2) **new**	LAma
	'Exotic Emperor'	LAma
	'Eye Catcher' (8)	LRHS
	'Fancy Frills' (7) ♀H4	EBrs LAma LRHS
	'Fantasy' (10) ♀H4	LAma LRHS
	'Fashion' (12)	EPfP
	'Fats Domino' (3) **new**	EBrs
	ferganica (15)	EBrs ECho EPot LAma NMin
	'Finola' (11) **new**	ERCP
	'Fire Queen' (3) ♀H4	EBrs LAma
	'First Impression' (14) **new**	LRHS
	'Flair' (1)	LAma
	'Flaming Parrot' (10)	CAvo CFFs EBrs LAma LRHS MBri
	'Flaming Purissima' (13)	CAvo CFFs
*	'Flowerdale'	CFFs CMea EBrs
	'Fontainebleau' (3) **new**	LRHS
	'Freeman' (11) **new**	LRHS
	'Fritz Kreisler' (12)	LAma
	'Frosta' (7) **new**	ERCP
	'Fulgens' (6)	EBrs
	'Gabriella' (3) **new**	LRHS
	'Garden Party' (3) ♀H4	LAma
	'Gavota' (3)	CAvo CFFs EBrs EPfP ERCP LAma LRHS SPer
	'Generaal de Wet' (1)	EBrs IHer LAma MBri
	'Georgette' (5)	LAma LRHS LSou MBri
	'Gerbrand Kieft' (11) ♀H4	EBrs ERCP
	'Giuseppe Verdi' (12)	LAma MBri
	'Glück' (12) ♀H4	LRHS
	'Golden Apeldoorn' (4)	LAma MBri
	'Golden Artist' (8)	EBrs LAma LRHS MWgw
	'Golden Emperor' (13)	EBrs EPfP LAma SPer
	'Golden Melody' (3)	EBrs LAma LRHS
	'Golden Nizza' (11) **new**	LRHS
	'Golden Oxford' (4)	LAma
	'Golden Parade' (4)	LAma
	'Goudstuk' (12)	LAma
	'Green Wave' (10)	EPfP ERCP LAma SPer
	greigii (14)	CBgR
	grengiolensis (15)	EBrs ECho LAma LRHS WWst
	'Groenland' (8)	CAvo CFFs ERCP LAma LRHS MBri SPer
	'Gudoshnik' (4)	LAma

'Guus Papendrecht' (3) new	LRHS
'H. D. Genscher'	EBrs
hageri (15)	EBrs LAma LRHS MBri
- 'Splendens' (15)	EBrs LAma WBor
'Hamilton' (7) 🏆H4	LAma MBNS
'Happy Family' (3)	LAma LRHS
'Happy Generation' (3)	LAma LRHS MBri
'Happy Hour' (7) new	ERCP
'Havran'	CAvo CFFs LAma
'Heart's Delight' (12)	EBrs LAma MBri
'Helmar' (3) new	CAvo
'Hermitage' (3)	LAma
heweri new	EBrs NMin
'Hit Parade' (13)	LAma
'Hocus Pocus' (5)	SPer
'Hollandia' (3) new	LRHS
'Hollywood' (8)	LAma
§ ***hoogiana*** (15)	EBrs
§ ***humilis*** (15)	CGrW LAma LRHS MBri SBch SPhx
- 'Eastern Star' (15)	CSam CTca EBrs ECho GCrs GKev LAma LRHS MBri
§ - 'Lilliput' (15)	CMea EBrs ECho EPot GKev LRHS NMin
- 'Magenta Queen' (15) new	EBrs
- 'Odalisque' (15)	EBrs EPot GKev LAma LRHS
- 'Pegasus' (15) new	EBrs
- 'Persian Pearl' (15)	CHHB EBrs ECho EPfP EPot ERCP GCrs LAma LRHS MBri NMin SBch SPer WBor
- 'Pink Charm' new	EBrs
- var. ***pulchella*** Albocaerulea Oculata Group (15)	CHFP CHHB CMea CPou CTca EBrs EPot ERCP GCrs LAma LRHS LTwo MSte NMin WWst
- 'Rosea'	EBrs LRHS NMin
§ - Violacea Group (15)	CMea CPBP CPrp ECho LAma MBri WBor
- - black base (15)	EBrs EPot GKev LRHS MBri NMin
- - yellow base (15)	EBrs EPot LAma LRHS
- 'Zephyr' (15) new	NMin
'Humming Bird' (8)	LAma
'Ile de France' (5)	LAma SPer
iliensis (15)	EBrs ECho EPot NMin WWst
ingens (15)	EBrs ECho LAma WWst
'Insulinde'	LAma
'Inzell' (3)	EBrs EPfP LAma
'Ivory Floradale' (4) 🏆H4	EBrs LAma
'Jackpot' new	ERCP
'Jeantine' (12) 🏆H4	EPfP
'Jewel of Spring' (4) 🏆H4	LAma
'Joffre' (1)	MBri
'Johann Strauss' (12)	CTca LAma LRHS MBri
'Juan' (13) 🏆H4	LRHS MBri
julia (15)	NMin
'Karel Doorman' (10)	LAma
kaufmanniana (12)	CAvo CBgR CFFs EBrs ECho EPot
- 'Ugam'	LRHS
§ 'Kees Nelis' (3)	LRHS MBri
'Keizerskroon' (1) 🏆H4	IHer LAma
kolpakowskiana (15) 🏆H4	EBrs EPfP ITim LAma LRHS MBri NWCA SBch
kurdica (15)	CPBP EBrs ECho LAma LRHS WWst
- purple-flowered	WWst
- red-flowered	WWst
'La Courtine' new	LRHS
'Lac van Rijn' (1) new	IHer
* 'Lady Diana' (14)	MBri
'Lady Jane' (15)	CAvo CFFs CHFP CHHB EBrs SPer SPhx
'Lambada' (7) 🏆H4 new	LRHS
lanata (15)	EBrs
'Latvian Gold' (15) new	EBrs

'Leen van der Mark' (3)	LAma MBri
'Libretto Parrot' (10)	LAma
'Lilac Perfection' (11)	CTca EBrs ERCP MBri
'Lilac Wonder'	see *T. saxatilis* (Bakeri Group) 'Lilac Wonder'
'Lilliput'	see *T. humilis* 'Lilliput'
'Lilyrosa' (6) new	EBrs
linifolia (15) 🏆H4	CAvo CFFs CHHB CPBP EBrs ECho EPfP EPot GKev ITim LAma LRHS MBri NWCA SBch
§ - Batalinii Group (15) 🏆H4	CHHB EBrs ECho LAma MBri
§ - - 'Apricot Jewel' (15)	CGrW EBrs ECho EPot GKev MSte
- - 'Bright Gem' (15) 🏆H4	CAvo CFFs CTca EBrs ECho EPot GKev LAma LRHS MBri SBch SPhx WHoo
- - 'Bronze Charm' (15)	CAvo CFFs CMea EBrs EPot LAma MBri MSte SPhx
- - 'Honky Tonk' (15) new	CMea EBrs
- - 'Red Gem' (15)	EBrs GKev LAma SPhx
- - 'Red Hunter' (15) 🏆H4	ENot SPer
- - 'Red Jewel' (15)	MSte
- - 'Yellow Jewel' (15)	EBrs LAma SPhx
§ - Maximowiczii Group	EBrs ECho EPot LAma NWCA SMeo SPhx
'Lipgloss' (3) new	SPer
'Little Beauty' (15) 🏆H4	CMea CSam EBrs ECho EGoo LAma LRHS MBri SBch WBor WHoo
'Little Princess'	CAvo CSam EBrs ECho EPfP LAma LRHS
'Lovely Surprise' (14)	EBrs
'Lucifer' (5)	ERCP
'Lucky Strike' (3)	MBri
'Mabel' (9) new	LAma
§ 'Madame Lefeber' (13)	EBrs LRHS MBri
'Magier' (5)	MBri
'Maja' (7)	MBri
'March of Time' (14)	MBri
'Mariette' (6)	LAma LRHS MBri
'Marilyn' (6)	CAvo CFFs CMea EBrs LAma LRHS
marjolletii (15)	CAvo CBgR CFFs EBrs ERos LAma SPhx
'Mary Ann' (14)	EBrs LAma
'Mascotte' new	ERCP
'Maureen' (5) 🏆H4	EBrs LAma LRHS
mauritiana 'Cindy' (15) new	EBrs
maximowiczii	see *T. linifolia* Maximowiczii Group
'Maytime' (6)	CAvo CFFs LAma LRHS MBri MWgw SPer
'Maywonder' (11) 🏆H4	MBri
'Menton' (5)	EBrs LAma LRHS
'Mickey Mouse' (1)	MBri
'Miss Holland' (3)	MBri
'Modern Style' (5) new	ERCP
'Mona Lisa' (6)	CMea EBrs LAma LRHS
'Monsella' (2)	EBrs
§ ***montana*** (15)	CTca EBrs ECho EPot LAma LRHS NBid SMeo SPhx
- yellow-flowered new	EBrs
'Monte Carlo' (2) 🏆H4	ENot LAma LRHS MBri
'Montreux'	LAma
'Moonshine' (6)	LRHS MWgw
'Mount Tacoma' (11)	CAvo CFFs EBrs EPfP ERCP LAma LRHS MBri SPer
'Mr Van der Hoef' (2)	LAma MBri
'Mrs John T. Scheepers' (5) 🏆H4	LAma
'Negrita' (3)	ERCP LAma LRHS MBri SPer
neustruevae (15)	EBrs ECho EPot NMin SPhx WRos
'New Dawn' new	SPer
'New Design' (3/v)	EBrs ERCP LAma MBri SPer
'New Look' (7)	EBrs
'Ollioules' (4) 🏆H4	EBrs LRHS SPer

'Orange Bouquet' (3) ♀H4	ENot LAma LRHS MBri
'Orange Breeze' (13) **new**	LRHS
'Orange Elite' (14)	LRHS MBri
'Orange Emperor' (13) ♀H4	CAvo CFFs LAma LRHS MBri SPer
'Orange Favourite' (10)	CAvo CFFs LAma LRHS
'Orange Princess' (11) ♀H4	CTca ERCP LRHS
'Orange Triumph' (11)	MBri
'Oranje Nassau' (2) ♀H4	LAma MBri
'Oratorio' (14) ♀H4	LRHS MBri
orphanidea (15)	CGrW EBrs ECho LAma LRHS NMin SCnR
- 'Flava' (15)	CHHB EBrs ECGP EPot ERCP LAma SPhx
§ - Whittallii Group (15) ♀H4	CAvo CFFs CHFP CHHB EBrs ECho ERCP LAma LRHS NMin SMeo SPhx
ostrowskiana (15)	EBrs ECho LAma NMin
'Oxford' (4) ♀H4	LAma LRHS
'Oxford's Elite' (4)	LAma
'Page Polka' (3)	EBrs LRHS MBri
'Pandour' (14)	MBri
'Papillon' (9) **new**	LAma
'Parade' (4) ♀H4	MBri
§ ***passeriniana*** (15)	EBrs LRHS
'Passionale' (3)	EPfP LRHS
'Paul Scherer' **new**	ERCP
'Peach Blossom' (2)	CMea EBrs LAma LRHS MBri SPer
'Peaches and Cream'	SPer
'Perestroyka' (5)	MBri
persica	see *T. celsiana*
'Philippe de Comines' (5)	ERCP LAma
'Picture' (5) ♀H4	EBrs ERCP LAma
'Pieter de Leur'	EPfP LAma MBri SPer
'Pimpernel' (8/v)	LAma LRHS
'Pink Impression' (4) ♀H4	EBrs LAma MBri SPer
'Pink Star' (11) **new**	ERCP
'Pinocchio' (14)	LRHS MBri
'Plaisir' (14) ♀H4	CAvo CFFs LAma MBri
planifolia (15) **new**	LRHS
platystigma (15)	EBrs ECho LAma NMin
polychroma	see *T. biflora*
praestans (15)	EBrs ECho EPfP LAma SPer
- 'Fusilier' (15) ♀H4	CMea EBrs EPfP EPot LAma LRHS MBri NBir SBch
- 'Unicum' (15/v)	CMea EBrs ERCP LAma MBri
- 'Van Tubergen's Variety' (15)	EBrs LAma
- 'Zwanenburg Variety' (15) **new**	EBrs
'Princeps' (13)	LAma MBri
'Princesse Charmante' (14) ♀H4	EBrs MBri
'Prinses Irene' (3) ♀H4	CAvo CMea CTca EBrs EPfP ERCP LAma LRHS MBri NBir SPer
'Professor Röntgen' (10)	LAma
pulchella humilis	see *T. humilis*
§ 'Purissima' (13) ♀H4	CAvo CFFs CPrp EBrs LAma LRHS MBri SPhx
'Purple Prince' (5)	EPfP
'Queen of Night' (5)	CAvo CFFs CMea CTca EBrs EPfP ERCP LAma LCro LRHS LSou MBri MWgw NBPN NHol SBch SPer SPhx WRos
'Queen of Sheba' (6) ♀H4	CAvo CFFs CMea LAma
'Recreado' (5)	EBrs
'Red Bouquet' (3) **new**	LRHS
'Red Emperor'	see *T.* 'Madame Lefeber'
'Red Georgette' (5) ♀H4	LAma LSou MBri NBir
'Red Impression'PBR (4) ♀H4 **new**	LRHS
'Red Paradise' (1) ♀H4 **new**	LRHS
'Red Riding Hood' (14) ♀H4	CAvo CFFs CMea EBrs ENot EPfP LAma LRHS MBri NBir SPer
'Red Shine' (6) ♀H4	LAma LRHS MBri
'Red Springgreen' (8)	LAma
Rembrandt mix	MBri
'Renown Unique' (11)	ERCP LAma
rhodopea	see *T. urumoffii*
'Ringo'	see *T.* 'Kees Nelis'
'Robassa' (13) **new**	EBrs
'Rockery Master' (14)	EBrs
'Rococo' (10)	ERCP LRHS MBri
'Royal Virgin' (3) **new**	CAvo
'Salmon Impression'PBR (4) **new**	SPer
'Sapporro' (6)	LAma
saracenica **new**	EBrs
saxatilis (15)	CHHB EBrs ECho EPfP LAma MBri NWCA SMeo
§ - Bakeri Group (15)	CPou EBrs ECho
§ - - 'Lilac Wonder' (15) ♀H4	CAvo CFFs CSam EBrs ECho EPot ERCP GGar GKev IHer LAma LRHS MBri MWgw SBch SMeo WBor
'Scarlet Baby' (12)	EPfP LRHS MBri
'Schoonoord' (2)	LAma MBri
schrenkii (15)	EBrs EPot IHer LAma NMin WWst
'Shakespeare' (12)	EBrs LAma
'Shirley' (3)	CAvo CFFs CTca EBrs EPfP ERCP LAma LRHS MBri
'Showwinner' (12) ♀H4	CAvo CFFs EBrs LAma MBri SPer
'Silverstream' (4)	LAma
'Snow Parrot' (10)	CAvo CFFs
sogdiana (15)	EBrs LAma NMin WWst
'Sonnet' **new**	ERCP
'Sorbet' (5) ♀H4	EBrs LAma LRHS
sosnowskyi (15)	EBrs ECho
sprengeri (15) ♀H4	CAvo CLAP ECGP ECha ERas GMaP LAma SCnR WBVN WHal WIvy
- Trotter's form (15)	WCot
'Spring Green' (8) ♀H4	CAvo CFFs EBrs EPfP ERCP LAma LCro LRHS MBri MNFA MSte MWgw SBch SMeo SPer SPhx
stapfii	EBrs NMin WWst
'Stockholm' (2) ♀H4	LAma
'Stresa' (12) ♀H4	CAvo CFFs EBrs LAma LRHS
subpraestans (15)	EBrs ECho EPot LAma
'Sunwing' **new**	LSou
'Super Parrot'	LAma
'Swan Wings' (7)	EBrs ERCP LAma LRHS SPer
'Sweet Desire' **new**	EBrs
'Sweet Harmony' (5) ♀H4	LAma MBri
'Sweetheart' (13)	EBrs LRHS MBri SPer
sylvestris (15)	CMea CTca EBrs ERCP LAma LRHS MBri NMin SPer SPhx WCot WHer WShi
'Synaeda King' (6) ♀H4 **new**	LRHS
systola **new**	WWst
tarda (15) ♀H4	CAvo CFFs EBla EBrs ECho EPfP EPot GGar LAma LSou MBri MWgw SBch SPhx WRos
- 'Kazakhstan' **new**	EBrs
'Temple of Beauty' (5) ♀H4	EBrs
tetraphylla (15)	EBrs
'Texas Flame' (10)	EBrs LAma LRHS MBri
'Texas Gold' (10)	CFFs EBrs LAma
'The First' (12)	CAvo CFFs EBrs
'The Lizard' (9) **new**	LAma
'Tinka' (15)	CSam EBrs LSou SPhx
'Top Lips' **new**	LRHS
'Toronto' (14) ♀H4	LAma LRHS LSou MBri
'Toulon' (13) ♀H4	MBri
'Très Chic' (6) **new**	CTca EBrs
'Trinket' (14) ♀H4	LAma
'Triumphator' (2)	CAvo

tschimganica (15) EBrs LAma LRHS WWst
tubergeniana (15) EBrs
- 'Keukenhof' (15) EBrs
turkestanica (15) ♀H4 CAvo CBgR CFFs CSWP CTca EBrs ECho EPfP EPot EWTr LAma MBri MWgw NSla SBch SPhx WHoo
'Turkish Delight' NPer
'Typhoon' (3) new EBrs
'Uncle Tom' (11) EPfP ERCP LAma MBri NBPN SPer
§ ***undulatifolia*** (15) CBgR EBrs ECho LAma
- 'Clare Benedict' (15) new EBrs
- 'Excelsa' (15) new EBrs
'Union Jack' (5) ♀H4 LAma
'United States' (14) EBrs NPer
'Up Stripe' (11) new ERCP
'Upstar' (11) new EBrs
urumiensis (15) ♀H4 CAvo CFFs EBrs ECho EPot LAma MBri SBch SPhx WHoo
§ ***urumoffii*** (15) ECho LAma
'Valentine' (3) ♀H4 LRHS
'Valery Gergiev' (7) new ERCP
'Verona' (2) EBrs LRHS
violacea see *T. humilis* Violacea Group
'Viridiflora' (8) EBrs
vvedenskyi (15) EBrs EPot LAma SPhx
- 'Tangerine Beauty' (15) ♀H4 EBrs ECho LRHS MBri
'Washington' (3) new EBrs LRHS
'Weber's Parrot' (10) MBri
'Weisse Berliner' (3) EBrs EPfP LAma LRHS
'West Point' (6) ♀H4 CAvo CFFs CMea EBrs ERCP LAma LEdu MBri SPhx
'White Dream' (3) EBrs LAma MBri
'White Elegance' (6) MWgw SPer
'White Emperor' see *T.* 'Purissima'
'White Parrot' (10) CAvo CFFs EBrs LAma LRHS MSte SPhx
'White Triumphator' (6) ♀H4 CAvo CFFs CMea EBrs ERCP LAma LCro LRHS NBir SMeo SPhx
whittallii see *T. orphanidea* Whittallii Group
'Willemsoord' (2) LAma MBri
wilsoniana see *T. montana*
'Wirosa' (11) ♀H4 new LRHS
'World's Favourite' (4) CAvo LRHS SPer
'Yellow Dawn' (14) LRHS
'Yellow Emperor' (5) MBri
'Yellow Flight' (3) LAma LRHS
'Yellow Pompenette'PBR new ERCP
'Yellow Purissima' (13) ♀H4 EPfP LRHS
'Yokohama' (3) EBrs LAma LRHS
'Zampa' (14) ♀H4 MBri
'Zombie' (13) LAma
'Zomerschoon' (5) EBrs LAma
'Zurel' (3) EBrs ERCP LAma

tummelberry see *Rubus* 'Tummelberry'

Tunica see *Petrorhagia*

Tupistra (*Convallariaceae*)
aurantiaca GEdr WCot
- B&SWJ 2267 WCru WPrP
chinensis 'Eco China Ruffles' WCot
grandistigma EBee
nutans CKob
wattii B&SWJ 8297 new WCru

Turbina (*Convolvulaceae*)
corymbosa MGol

Turnera (*Turneraceae*)
ulmifolia MSal

Turraea (*Meliaceae*)
obtusifolia EShb

Tussilago (*Asteraceae*)
farfara CArn CNat ELau GPoy GWCH MHer MSal NMir NSco WHer WSFF

Tutcheria (*Theaceae*)
§ ***spectabilis*** CExc EPfP

Tweedia (*Asclepiadaceae*)
§ ***caerulea*** ♀H2 CBcs CDTJ CSpe EMan SAga SBch SHFr SKHP SPer SWal WCot
- pink-flowered SPad

Tylecodon (*Crassulaceae*)
paniculatus EPem LToo

Typha (*Typhaceae*)
angustifolia CBen CKno CWat EHon EMFW GAbr GFor MMuc NPer NSco SPlb SWat WFar WPnP XIsg
gracilis CBen EMFW LLWG XIsg
latifolia CBen CWat EHon EMFW GFor NLan NPer NSco SWat WDyG WFar WHer WMAq WPnP
- 'Variegata' (v) CBen CDWL CKno CWat ELan EMFW LLWG NScw WCot WMAq
§ ***laxmannii*** CBen CDWL CStu EMFW GFor NLan WPnP
minima CBen CDWL CFwr CSsd CStu CWat EHon ELan EMFW EPfP NPer SCoo SMad SWat WFar WMAq WPnP WRos
stenophylla see *T. laxmannii*

Typhonium (*Araceae*)
alpinum new EBee
diversifolium new EBee
giganteum SKHP WCot
kunmingense new EBee
trifoliatum yunnanense new EBee

Typhonodorum (*Araceae*)
lindleyanum XBlo

U

ugli see *Citrus* x *tangelo* 'Ugli'

Ugni (*Myrtaceae*)
§ ***molinae*** CBcs CDul CFir CPLG CSBt CTrC EBee ELon GGar IDee LEdu MCCP MHer SAdn SHFr SLPl SOWG SWvt WFar WJek WMoo WPic WSHC XPep
- 'Flambeau' CAgr EMil LEdu MGos NLar SKHP SWvt

Ulex (*Papilionaceae*)
europaeus CArn CCVT CDoC CDul CRWN ECrN ELan EPfP GPoy GWCH LBuc MCoo MGos NWea SCoo SPoG WHar WMou
§ - 'Flore Pleno' (d) ♀H4 CBcs CDoC CDul CSBt EBee EMon ENot EPfP EPla GAbr GGar IArd MBlu MGos NEgg NLar NWea SHBN SPer SPoG WFar
- 'Prostratus' MBar
gallii 'Mizen Head' GGGa GGar GSki MBlu SLon

§	***minor***	EPla
	nanus	see *U. minor*

Ulmus ✿ (*Ulmaceae*)

	alata new	EGFP
	americana 'Princeton'	CKno
	'Dodoens'	IArd MGos SBLw SCoo
§	***glabra***	CDul CRWN ECrN EMac NWea SBLw SCoo
	- 'Camperdownii'	CDoC CTho EBee ECrN ELan NBee NEgg SBLw
	- 'Exoniensis'	CTho SBLw
	- 'Gittisham'	CTho
	- 'Horizontalis'	see *U. glabra* 'Pendula'
	- 'Lutescens'	CDoC CEnd CTho CTri LRHS SBLw SCoo SLim
§	- 'Pendula'	CDul EMil SBLw
	x ***hollandica*** 'Commelin'	SBLw
	- 'Dampieri'	SBLw
§	- 'Dampieri Aurea'	CDul CEnd EBee ECrN ELan EPfP LBuc LRHS MAsh MBar MBlu MGos MRav NBlu SBLw SHBN SPer WOrn WPat
	- 'Groeneveld'	SBLw
	- 'Jacqueline Hillier'	CBgR CDul ECho ELan EPfP EPla IMGH LAst MAsh MBar MGos NBlu SBLw SLon STre WAbe WCFE WFar WPat
	- 'Lobel'	CDul MGos SBLw
	- 'Wredei'	see *U. x hollandica* 'Dampieri Aurea'
	laevis	CDul ECrN
	Lutèce = 'Nanguen' new	CDoC
	minor	EMac NEgg SBLw
	- 'Dampieri Aurea'	see *U. x hollandica* 'Dampieri Aurea'
	- subsp. ***sarniensis***	SBLw
	- 'Silvery Gem' (v)	IClo LRHS
	- 'Variegata' (v)	EBee MAsh SCoo SLon WPat
	montana	see *U. glabra*
	parvifolia	CMCN CMen ECrN NWea STre WNor WPGP
	- 'Frosty' (v)	ECho
	- 'Geisha' (v)	ECho ELan MAsh MGos MRav WBod WPat
§	- 'Hokkaido'	CMen LTwo NLAp SBla WAbe WPat WThu
	- 'Pygmaea'	see *U. parvifolia* 'Hokkaido'
	- 'Yatsubusa'	CLyd ECho EWes LTwo MAsh MRav NLar SIng STre WPat
	'Plantijn'	SBLw
	procera	CTho ECrN LBuc MGos SMad WSFF
	- 'Argenteovariegata' (v)	CDul MGos SMad
	pumila	EBee NWea WNor
	rubra	CArn EGFP MSal
	'Sapporo Autumn Gold'PBR	CDoC LBuc
	x ***vegeta***	SBLw

Umbellularia (*Lauraceae*)

californica	CArn CPne EPfP SAPC SArc SSpi WSHC

Umbilicus (*Crassulaceae*)

rupestris	CArn CHrt CRWN NWCA SChr SECG WHer WShi

Uncinia (*Cyperaceae*)

	from Chile	EWes
*	***cyparissias*** from Chile	NBir
	egmontiana	EBee EBla EKen EMan EPPr EPau EPfP EShb EWsh GFor GSki GWWP MNrw NLar SHGN WCot WFoF WHrl WLeb WMnd WPtf
	lechleriana	GBin
N	***rubra***	More than 30 suppliers
	uncinata	CBcs CMMP ECha EMan GSki LHop MFOX NCob NHol SDix
*	- ***rubra***	CFir CHar CKno COIW CTri CWCL ECot EHrv GSki LAst LRHS MMHG MNrw MWgw NCGa NCob NGdn SLim SMer SWvt WGwG WPGP WWeb

Uniola (*Poaceae*)

latifolia	see *Chasmanthium latifolium*
paniculata	SApp

Urceolina (*Amaryllidaceae*)

miniata	see *Stenomesson miniatum*
peruviana	see *Stenomesson miniatum*

Urechites see *Pentalinon*

Urginea (*Hyacinthaceae*)

fugax	EBee
maritima	CArn CMdw CPou EBee EBrs ECho ERCP ERea LAma LRHS MNrw MSal
ollivieri	EBrs ECho

Urospermum (*Asteraceae*)

dalechampii	CSam ECha LLWP

Ursinia (*Asteraceae*)

alpina	CPBP
montana	NWCA
nana	WFar

Urtica (*Urticaceae*)

dioica 'Chedglow 2' (v)	CNat
- 'Dog Trap Lane'	CNat
- 'Good as Gold'	CNat
- subsp. ***gracilis*** var. ***procera***	CNat
galeopsifolia	CNat

Utricularia (*Lentibulariaceae*)

	alpina	CSWC
	australis	EFEx
	biloba	CHew
	bisquamata	CSWC SHmp
	blancheti	CSWC
	calycifida	CSWC SHmp
	dichotoma	CSWC EFEx
	exoleta R. Brown	see *U. gibba*
§	***gibba***	EFEx
	heterosepala	CHew
	intermedia	EFEx
	lateriflora	CHew EFEx
	livida	CSWC EFEx
	longifolia	CSWC SHmp
	macrorhiza	CSWC
	menziesii	EFEx
	microcalyx new	CHew SHmp
	monanthos	CHew CSWC EFEx
	nephrophylla	CHew SHmp
	novae-zelandiae	CHew CSWC
	ochroleuca	EFEx
	paulineae	CHew
	praelonga	CSWC SHmp
	pubescens	CHew CSWC SHmp
	reniformis	CSWC EFEx SHmp
	- ***nana***	EFEx
	sandersonii	CSWC SHmp
	- blue-flowered	CSWC
	simplex new	CHew
	subulata	EFEx
	tricolor	CHew CSWC SHmp
	uniflora	CHew

vulgaris	CDWL CSWC EFEx
welwitschii new	CHew

Uvularia (*Convallariaceae*)

§ ***caroliniana***	EBee ECho
disporum	ECho
grandiflora ♀H4	More than 30 suppliers
- dwarf	ECho IBlr
- golden-leaved new	WWst
- var. ***pallida***	CAvo CBct CLAP CPom CStu CWsd EBee ECha ECho EGle EHrv EPot GBri GBuc GEdr IBlr LEdu MRav NCGa SMHy SPhx WAbe WCru WFar WPGP WPnP
grandiflora x ***perfoliata***	ECho IBlr
- 'Susie Lewis'	WCru
perfoliata	CBct CDes CLAP CWsd EBee ECha ECho EDAr EGle EPfP GBri GCrs GGar IBlr LAma LEdu MRav NChi SIng WAbe WBrE WCru WPGP WPnP
pudica	see *U. caroliniana*
sessilifolia	CBct CLAP EBee ECho EPPr GEdr IBlr LAma LEdu NLar NMen SSvw WCru

V

Vaccaria (*Caryophyllaceae*)

§ ***hispanica***	MSal
segetalis	see *V. hispanica*

Vaccinium ✿ (*Ericaceae*)

arctostaphylos	NLar SReu SWvt
'Berkeley' (F)	CAgr CWib ECrN GTwe LBuc LRHS MBlu SDea SPoG
'Bluejay' (F)	ECrN LRHS MAsh SCoo
'Blueray' (F)	CWib SCoo
'Chippewa' (F) new	MCoo
'Cinderella'	CDBb
corymbosum (F) ♀H4	CBcs EPfP MBar MGos MNHC SCoo SReu SSta WBVN
- 'Blauweiss-goldtraube' (F)	CWSG CWib ERea LSRN MBlu MGos SDea SPoG WBVN WFar
- 'Bluecrop' (F)	CAgr CDBb CMac CTrh CTri CWib ECrN EMil EMui ENot EPfP ERea GTwe LBuc LCro LRHS LSRN MAsh MBlu MBri MGos NLar SCoo SDea SGFT SKee SPer SPoG SWvt WFar
- 'Bluegold' (F)	CDBb EMil LRHS MAsh MGos SCoo
- 'Bluetta' (F)	CAgr CDBb CTri CWib EMui GTwe LRHS MBri SCoo WFar WHlf
- 'Brigitta' (F)	CDBb EMil GTwe
- 'Chandler' (F)	CAgr CDBb CMac ECrN EMil LRHS SPoG
- 'Concord' (F)	SCoo
- 'Coville' (F)	EMui
- 'Darrow' (F)	CAgr CTrh GTwe LBuc LRHS SPoG
- 'Elliott' (F)	ECrN
- 'Grover' (F)	LRHS
- 'Hardyblue' (F)	CDBb
- 'Herbert' (F)	CDBb CMac CTrh EMil EMui GTwe LBuc MGos SCoo
- 'Ivanhoe' (F)	SCoo
- 'Jersey' (F)	ENot EPfP LRHS MAsh MCoo SCoo SDea
- 'Legacy' (F)	CDBb
- 'Nelson' (F)	LBuc SCoo
- 'Northblue' (F)	CDBb
- 'Nui' (F)	CDBb ECrN
- 'Pioneer' (F)	MBar
- 'Polaris' (F)	LRHS SPoG
- 'Stanley'	ELan LRHS MAsh
- 'Toro' (F)	CDBb CTrh ECrN EMil GTwe LBuc LRHS MAsh MGos
- 'Weymouth' (F)	SDea
crassifolium subsp. ***sempervirens*** 'Well's Delight' (F)	LRHS MAsh
cylindraceum ♀H4	EPfP NLar WBod WFar WPat
- 'Tinkerbell'	ITim WAbe
delavayi	ECho LRHS MAsh MBar NMen SReu SSta WAbe WFar WThu
'Duke' (F) ♀H4	CDBb CTrh ECrN ELan EMil EPfP LRHS MAsh MGos SGFT SKee
dunalianum var. ***caudatifolium*** B&SWJ 1716	WCru
'Earliblue' (F)	CAgr EMil EMui LRHS MGos SDea WFar
floribundum	CDoC CMHG ECho GGar IDee LRHS MAsh NLar SPoG SSpi WPGP WPic
glaucoalbum ♀H3-4	CAbP CDoC CWsd EPfP GGGa IDee LRHS MAsh MBar MRav SMad SPoG SSpi WBod
* ***grandiflorum***	ECho
griffithianum	CDBb SReu SSta
'Groover'	LSRN
macrocarpon (F)	CDBb ECho ELan EMil EMui GTwe LRHS MAsh MBar MBri NWCA SDea SPoG SRms
- 'Centennial' (F)	CDBb
- 'Centerville' (F)	CDBb
- 'CN' (F)	CAgr MGos
- 'Early Black' (F)	LBuc MGos
- 'Franklin' (F)	CAgr CDBb GCrs
- 'Hamilton'	CStu GCrs GEdr LTwo NLAp NMen WPat WThu
- 'Howes' (F)	CDBb
- 'McFarlin' (F)	EMui
- 'Olson's Honkers' (F)	CAgr
- 'Pilgrim' (F)	CDBb MAsh
- 'Red Star' (F) new	MCCP
'Misty' (F)	CAgr MCoo SPoG
mortinia	NMen
moupinense	CDoC CPLG ECho LRHS MAsh NMen
- 'Variegatum' (v)	LTwo
myrsinites	ECho
myrtillus	CDBb GPoy MBar WSFF
'Nimo Pink'	MBar
'Northland' (F)	CWib GTwe MAsh SCoo SDea SPoG
nummularia	ECho GEdr NHar NLar NMen SSpi WAbe WThu
ovatum	CDBb CMHG IDee LRHS MBar SSta
- 'Thundercloud'	CAbP LRHS MAsh
§ ***oxycoccos*** (F)	CArn GPoy MGos WHlf
'Ozarkblue'	CDBb
padifolium	WCwm WPGP
pallidum	IBlr
palustre	see *V. oxycoccos*
'Patriot' (F)	CAgr CDBb CTrh CWib GTwe LBuc LRHS MGos SCoo SPoG
praestans	NHol WThu
- RBS 0285	CStu
retusum	WBod WPic
sikkimense	GGGa
'Spartan' ♀H4	CDBb EMil GTwe LBuc LRHS SCoo
'Sunrise' (F)	GTwe LRHS
'Sunshine Blue' (F)	CAgr CDBb EMui ENot LRHS SGFT SKee
'Tophat' (F)	EMui

vitis-idaea	ECho EPfP EWTr EWes GGar GPoy MBar MGos MNHC SPoG SRot WFar
- RBS 0287	CStu
- 'Autumn Beauty'	NLar
- 'Compactum'	EWes LSou
- Koralle Group ♀^{H4}	CAgr EPfP MBar MBri NHol SPer WPat
- subsp. ***minus***	GCrs MAsh NLar NMen WAbe
- - 'Betsy Sinclair'	CStu
- 'Red Pearl'	CAgr CDBb CSBt EPfP LRHS MAsh MGos MSwo
* - 'Variegatum' (v)	EWes NLAp WPat
wrightii var. ***formosanum***	ECho

Valeriana (*Valerianaceae*)

'Alba'	see *Centranthus ruber* 'Albus'
alliariifolia	EBee EMon NBro WCot
arizonica	CStu MSte
'Coccinea'	see *Centranthus ruber*
coreana	CFee WMoo
dioica	SECG
hardwickii	EBee
jatamansii	CArn GPoy
montana	NBro NRya SRms SWat WMoo
officinalis	CArn CBod CHby CHrt CRWN CSev EBee ECha EHrv ELau GPoy ILis MHer MLHP MNHC NBro NLar NPri SAga SIde SPhx SRms SWat WCAu WHer WMoo WPer WShi
- subsp. ***sambucifolia***	CFee CPom EPPr NDov SHar WCAu WHil WOut
phu 'Aurea'	More than 30 suppliers
pyrenaica	ECha EHrv EPPr MMHG SPhx WCot WHil WMoo
saxatilis	NLar NRya
supina	NWCA
wallrothii	WCot

Valerianella (*Valerianaceae*)

§ ***locusta***	CArn GPoy
olitoria	see *V. locusta*

Vallea (*Elaeocarpaceae*)

stipularis	CDoC
- var. ***pyrifolia***	CPle

Vallota see *Cyrtanthus*

Vancouveria (*Berberidaceae*)

chrysantha	CDes CLAP CPom EBee ECha EMan ERos GBuc MNrw MRav NLar NRya NWCA WCru WMoo
hexandra	CBct CDes CGHE CLAP CPom CSpe EBee EHrv EPfP ERos GBuc LEdu NRya NSti NWCA WCot WCru WPGP
planipetala	CLAP WCru
I - 'Bellevue Strain'	WCot

Vania see *Thlaspi*

veitchberry see *Rubus* 'Veitchberry'

Vellozia (*Velloziaceae*)

elegans	see *Talbotia elegans*

Veltheimia (*Hyacinthaceae*)

§ ***bracteata*** ♀^{H1}	CAbb CHal CHll CPou CPrp EBak EBrs ECho IBlr LToo NPal WCot
§ ***capensis*** ♀^{H1}	CSev
viridifolia misapplied	see *V. capensis*
viridifolia Jacq.	see *V. bracteata*

x *Venidioarctotis* see *Arctotis*

Venidium see *Arctotis*

Veratrum ✿ (*Melanthiaceae*)

album	CPne EBee EBrs ECha ECho GBuc GPoy LEdu LRHS MRav NEgg SBla SMad WBrE WCot WCru WFar WSHC
- var. ***flavum***	CAby IPot SPhx WCru
- var. ***oxysepalum***	WCru
californicum	CBct CHid EBee IBlr MNrw WBor WCot WSHC
- compact **new**	MNrw
dolichopetalum B&SWJ 4195	WCru
formosanum	CDes MNrw
- B&SWJ 1575	WCru
grandiflorum B&SWJ 4416	WCru
maackii **new**	CWsd
- var. ***maackii***	WSHC
- - B&SWJ 5831	WCru
mengtzeanum	CBct WCot
nigrum ♀^{H4}	CBct CDes CFir CPne CPom EBee ECha EHrv GBuc GMaP IPot MDun MNrw NBhm NBir NChi NCob NEgg NLar SBla SMad SPer SPhx SPlb SPoG WCot WCru WFar WHil WPnP
- B&SWJ 4450	WCru
schindleri B&SWJ 4068	WCru
stamineum	WCru
viride	CHid ECha EWes IBlr WBor

Verbascum ✿ (*Scrophulariaceae*)

adzharicum	WHoo
Allestree hybrids	EHrv
'Annie May'	CDes EBee EBla EMan EPfP EShb LPio LRHS LSRN NCob NOrc SPhx SPur WCra
'Apricot Sunset'	CDes EBee EMan LRHS NCob SMeo SPhx WCra WPGP
'Arctic Summer'	see *V. bombyciferum* 'Polarsommer'
arcturus	SPhx WPer
'Aurora'	MAvo SJoh SMeo SPhx
'Aztec Gold'	CDes EBee MAvo SJoh SPhx WPGP
* ***bakerianum***	EBla ECtt
'Banana Custard'	EBee ECtt ENot EWin LSou MBNS NGBl SPet SPoG
'Bill Bishop'	ECho NHar
blattaria	EHrv NBir NRnb SPav SWat WFar WHer WPer
- f. ***albiflorum***	CSpe EBee EMar ERou LCro LHop LLWP MNFA NChi NDov NSti SBch SGar SPhx SPlb WHer WMoo WPer WRHF WTin
- 'Pink White Blush'	LSou
- pink-flowered	SPav STes
- yellow-flowered	NRnb SPav SWat
'Blushing Bride'	CMea EBee LSou NBhm WCot
§ ***bombyciferum***	CBre CSev ECha GMaP MFOX NGdn NSti SRms WCot XPep
- BSSS 232	WCru
* - 'Arctic Snow'	SPav
§ - 'Polarsommer'	CHrt CSpe EBee ENot EPfP ERou EWTr LRHS MBri NBir NBlu NVic SPav SPer SPet SPoG SRms SWal SWat WWeb
- 'Silver Lining'	NLar NPer SDnm SPav
'Brookside'	MSte SPhx
'Broussa'	see *V. bombyciferum*
'Buttercup'	EBee SPoG

'Caribbean Crush'	EBee ECtt ELan EMan EPfP EShb LAst LSou MBNS MBri NCGa NEgg NLar NMoo NPri SPav SPhx WGor
(Caribbean Crush Group) 'Mango'	ENot
chaixii	CSam ECha ECtt EHrv EUnu GAbr GBuc MMHG NBir NEgg SBla WFar WMoo WPer
- 'Album' Y^{H4}	More than 30 suppliers
- 'Helene Bowles'	CHar
- 'Sixteen Candles'	MWat NBHF NChi WHal WPtf
chaixii x 'Wendy's Choice'	MDKP
'Charles Harper'	MSte SMeo SPhx
'Charlotte'	MAvo
'Cherokee'	MAvo SPhx
'Cherry Helen'PBR	CHFP EBee EPfP ERou LAst LCro LRHS MBNS MBri MWgw NBPC NLar NMoo NRnb SMrm SPer SPoG SRGP WHlf WHoo WOVN WSpi WWeb
'Claire'	MAvo SJoh SPhx
'Clementine'	MAvo SJoh SPhx
(Cotswold Group) 'Cotswold Beauty' Y^{H4}	CPar CSam EBee EBla ECtt EPfP ERou GMac LAst LRHS MRav MWat MWgw NDov NGdn SPer SPhx SPla WCAu WMnd WPGP
- 'Cotswold Queen'	CBcs CMMP COlW CWCL EBee EBla ECtt ELan EPfP ERou LCro LRHS MRav MWat NCGa NGdn NPri SPer SPhx SWvt WCAu WMnd WSpi WWeb
- 'Gainsborough' Y^{H4}	More than 30 suppliers
- 'Mont Blanc'	EBla ECot EHrv GMaP LAst LCro LPio LRHS MCot MRav MSte SPer SWat WSpi
- 'Pink Domino' Y^{H4}	More than 30 suppliers
- 'Royal Highland'	COlW CPrp EBee ECot ECtt EHrv ELan EPfP ERou LPio LRHS NGdn NLar SDnm SPav SWvt WFar WMnd WWeb
- 'White Domino'	EBee ERou LRHS MBNS NGby SMrm SPer SPla WCAu WHlf
'Cotswold King'	see *V. creticum*
§ ***creticum***	CSpe ERou MDKP NEgg SBch SDnm SPav SPla WCot WPGP WPer
'Daisy Alice'	LPio MAvo MSte SPhx
§ ***densiflorum***	CArn EBee ERou MBri SPer SPhx WFar WPer
'Dijon'	EBee ECtt EWes
dumulosum Y^{H2-3}	EPot NWCA WAbe
'Dusky Maiden'	NWCA
'Ebenezer Howard'	LPio
'Eleanor's Blush' <u>**new**</u>	EBrs
'Elektra' <u>**new**</u>	MAvo
'Ellenbank Jewel'	GMac
epixanthinum	LSou MCCP MDKP NCGa NLar NRnb SPhx
'Flower of Scotland' <u>**new**</u>	MBNS
'Gold Nugget' <u>**new**</u>	MMHG
'Golden Wings' Y^{H2-3}	ECtt ITim NMen WAbe
Harptree smokey hybrids	CHar
'Helen Johnson'	More than 30 suppliers
'Hiawatha'	SJoh SMeo SPhx
'High Noon'	SJoh SPhx
x ***hybridum*** 'Copper Rose'	CWan ENot EPfP MBri MHer NRnb WPer WRHF
- 'Snow Maiden'	CWan EBee ECtt EWTr MHer NRnb SDnm
- 'Wega'	EBee NLar
'Hyde Hall Sunrise'	ENot LBuc LRHS
'Innocence'	CDes MDKP
'Jackie'	More than 30 suppliers
'Jackie in Pink'	EKen ERou EWes LBuc MBNS NBPC NMoo
'Jackie in Yellow' <u>**new**</u>	ERou
'Jolly Eyes'	EBee MBri NCGa NRnb WHil
'June Johnson'	EBee SHar SRGP
'Kalypso'	MAvo SJoh SPhx
'Klondike'	MAvo SJoh SPhx
'Kynaston'	EBee EBla IPot MAvo NCGa NGdn SHar
'Letitia' Y^{H3}	CBcs CMea EBee ECho ECtt ELan EPot EWes LAst LRHS MTho NMen NPri NWCA SIng SPav SPoG SRot SWvt WAbe WKif
longifolium	LRHS WFar
- var. ***pannosum***	see *V. olympicum*
* ***luridifolium***	EBee SPhx WPGP
lychnitis	CArn SMeo SPhx WHer WKif
'Megan's Mauve'	EBee EBla ECot EWll NEgg SPer SWvt WSpi
'Monster'	SPhx WPGP
'Moonshadow'	MAvo SJoh SPhx
'Mystery Blonde'	SJoh SPhx
nigrum	CArn EBee ECtt EPfP EUnu GAbr MBNS NChi NGHP NLar SEND WBrE WFar WMnd WMoo WPer
- var. ***album***	ERCP LEdu NChi NGHP NLar WMoo
'Nimrod'	SJoh
'Norfolk Dawn'	CDes EBee EBla EMan EPfP EShb LAst MAvo MSte MWgw NCob NGdn SMeo SPhx WCra WPGP
§ ***olympicum***	CHrt CKno CSam CWCL EBee ECtt EGoo ELan ENot EPfP EUnu MBNS MWat SDix SEND SPoG WBrE WCAu WCot WFar WPer XPep
oreophilum	EBee
'Pandora' <u>**new**</u>	EBrs
'Patricia'	CDes EBee EBla EKen MSte NCGa NCob SPhx WPGP
'Petra'	CDes EBee SPhx WPGP
phlomoides	SPhx
phoeniceum	CArn CEnt ELan EPfP LRHS MNHC MWgw NBlu NBro NEgg SBri SGar SPet SPlb SWal WBrE WEas WHen WMoo WPer
* - 'Album'	CSpe WBrE
- 'Flush of Pink'	ECtt
- 'Flush of White'	CMea EBee ECtt EPPr ERou GMac LAst LRHS MNFA MWat NChi SDnm SPav SSvw STes WGor WHen WHil WMoo WRHF
- hybrids	CSpe CTri ECtt EGoo GMaP LBMP NChi NEgg NGdn NVic SRms SWat WFar WGor WPer
- 'Rosetta'	EPPr EShb GBri MWat SPad
- 'Violetta'	More than 30 suppliers
'Phoenix'	CDes EBee SJoh SPhx WPGP
'Pink Glow'	LRHS
'Pink Ice'	EPPr MDKP MHar
'Pink Kisses'	EBee ENor LBuc LCro LRHS
'Pink Petticoats'	ENot LBuc LRHS SPoG
'Plum Smokey'	CMea EBee WCot
'Primrose Cottage'	MBri SPhx
'Primrose Path'	CBct EBee LRHS SRot
'Purple Prince'	ECtt
pyramidatum	SPhx
'Raspberry Ripple'	EBee ELan EMan EMar LAst LBMP MPop NCGa NDov NMoo SPav SPer SPet SPoG
rorippifolium	EBee NCGa NRnb SPhx
'Rosie' <u>**new**</u>	EBrs
'Southern Charm'	CChe EBee ECtt EGoo ERou EWll GMaP LBMP LRHS MBri MCCP NChi NGHP SPav SPoG STes WFar WHil WPtf
* 'Spica'	LCro NLar SPhx WSpi

spicatum	WFar
'Sugar Plum'	EBee WCot
'Summer Sorbet'	ELan EMan EPfP SPer SPoG WWlt
thapsiforme	see *V. densiflorum*
thapsus	CBgR COld CSev GPoy GWCH MHer MNHC NMir NRnb NSco SECG WSel
'Tilney Moonbeam'	ECtt EMar
'Tilney Sundown'	EMar
'Tropic Blush' new	MAvo
'Tropic Dawn' new	MAvo
'Tropic Mystery' new	MAvo
'Tropic Rose' new	MAvo
'Tropic Spice' new	MAvo
'Tropic Sun' new	MAvo
'Twilight'	EBrs
undulatum	CArn
'Valerie Grace'	MSte SPhx
'Virginia'	SJoh SPhx
wiedemannianum	EBee

Verbena (*Verbenaceae*)

'Adonis Light Blue' (G)	LRHS
'Aphrodite'	LAst
'Apple Blossom' (G)	LRHS
(Aztec Series) Aztec Cherry Red = 'Balazcherd'^{PBR} (G) new	NPri
- Aztec Coral = 'Balazcoral' (G) new	NPri
- Aztec Magic Plum = 'Balazplum'^{PBR} (G)	NPri
- Aztec Magic Silver = 'Balazsilma'^{PBR} (G)	LSou NPri SCoo
- Aztec Pearl (G)	SCoo
- Aztec Red = 'Balazred' (G)	SCoo
(Babylon Series) Babylon Dark Blue with Eye = 'Darkeyena'^{PBR}	WGor
- Babylon Red = 'Oxena'^{PBR}	NBlu
'Betty Lee'	ECtt
'Blue Cascade' (G)	LAst
'Blue Prince' (G)	CSpe MAsh
§ ***bonariensis*** Υ^{H3-4}	More than 30 suppliers
'Boon' (G)	ECtt LSou
'Booty' (G)	ECtt LSou
'Boughton House' (G)	MSte
'Bright Eye' (Escapade Series) new	LSou
canadensis 'Perfecta' (G)	CSpe
'Candy Carousel' (G)	SPet
'Carousel' (G)	LAst SPoG
chamaedrifolia	see *V. peruviana*
§ 'Claret' (G)	CAby CElw CSam CSpe EBee ECtt EMan EPfP EShb EWin GBri LRHS LSRN LSou MWea SAga SCoo SMHy SMeo SMrm SPhx SPoG
'Corsage Peach'	LAst LSou
'Corsage Red'	LAst
corymbosa	CBrm CEnt CHll CMMP CPLG CWCL EBee ECha EPPr GSki LHop MDKP NLar SAga SBod SPer WHil WPer WPtf
- 'Gravetye'	CHrt GBuc NChi NCob WFar
'Diamond Butterfly' (G)	EWin SAga
'Diamond Carouselle' (G)	EWin
'Diamond Merci' (G)	EShb SAga WHoo
'Edith Eddleman' (G)	EBee ECtt EPfP EWin MNrw
Flamenco Dark Red = 'Wesverdark'^{PBR}	LSou
* 'Foxhunter' (G)	ECtt
'Hammerstein Pink'	EBee EPfP
hastata	CHar EBee ECot ECtt LHop LRHS MAvo MNrw NCob NDov NEgg NRnb NSti SAga SGar SMeo SMrm SPhx SPla SPlb SPoG SWat SWvt WFar WMnd WMoo WPer WSHC
- 'Alba'	CEnt CHar EBee EMon EPyc GBuc GSki LDai MDKP MLLN MRav NDov NRnb SPoG WMoo WPer
- 'Pink Spires' new	SPad
- 'Rosea'	CArn CElw CHar CKno CMea EBee ELan EMon GBuc GSki LCro LHop MAvo MDKP MLHP MLLN MRav MWgw NBPC NCob NDov NRnb SPhx SPoG SWat WCAu WHoo WMoo WSHC
'Hidcote Purple' (G)	MSte
'Homestead Purple' (G)	CChe CSam CSev EBee ECtt EMan ENor EPfP EShb GSki LAst LDai LSRN MWgw NRnb SAga SMrm SPer SPoG SWvt
'Huntsman' (G)	GBuc
'Imagination' (G)	LRHS
'Jenny's Wine'	see *V.* 'Claret'
'La France' (G)	CAby CSam EBee ECha ECtt EPfP EShb EWTr EWin LSou SAga SDix SMHy SMeo SMrm SPhx WHoo WMnd
(Lanai Series) Lanai Burgundy = 'Lan Burg'^{PBR} (G)	ECtt LAst
- Lanai Lavender Star = 'Lan Lav Star' (G)	ECtt LAst
- Lanai Peach = 'Lan Peachy'^{PBR} (G)	ECtt LAst LSou
lasiostachys	EBee
litoralis	EBee LHop
'Lois' Ruby'	see *V.* 'Claret'
macdougalii	EGoo LRav MDKP MWgw NEgg NRnb SPhx
officinalis	CArn CRWN CWan GPoy MGol MHer MNHC MSal SIde WHer WJek WPer WSel XPep
patagonica	see *V. bonariensis*
'Peaches and Cream' (G) Υ^{H3}	LRHS LSou NPri
§ ***peruviana*** (G)	EBee EPfP EShb EWin LBMP LRHS SAga SDix SIng SRms
'Pink Bouquet'	see *V.* 'Silver Anne'
'Pink Cascade'	EShb
'Pink Parfait' (G)	CHal EMan EPfP EWin LAst LHop SAga SPet SPoG
'Pink Pearl' (G)	ECtt
'Pink Stars'	NPri
'Raspberry Crush' (G)	LRHS
'Red Cascade'	SPet
§ ***rigida*** Υ^{H3}	CFir CHar CHll CKno COlW CWCL EBee ECha ECtt ENot EPfP EShb LCro LDai LRHS LSRN MRav NBir NDov NGdn NSti SMrm SPla SPoG SRms SWvt WFar WWeb XPep
- 'Lilac Haze' new	LBuc LRHS NSti
- 'Lilacina'	XPep
- 'Polaris'	CHar EBee ECGP ELon EMan EShb LHop LRHS LSou MRav NDov SHar SMHy SMrm SPer SPhx WRos
Sandy Series (G) Υ^{H3} new	WFar
§ 'Silver Anne' (G) Υ^{H3}	CHal CHrt CSam EBee ECtt EMan EWin LDai LSou SDix SMer WHen
§ 'Sissinghurst' (G) Υ^{H2-3}	CSam ECtt EMan EWin MAsh NPri SAga SIng SMrm SPoG SRms WHen
'Sissinghurst Pink'	LAst
* 'Snow Flurry'	CFir
(Splash Series) 'Splash Rose'	LAst

- 'Splash Violet'	LAst
stricta	EBee MDKP NLar
(Superbena Series)	LSou
Superbena Burgundy = 'Usbenal5'	
- Superbena Bushy Merlot = 'Usbena5117'	NPri
- Superbena Ruby Red = 'Usbena5122'	LSou NPri
- Superbena Violet Blue = 'Usbenas10'	NPri
(Tapien Series) Tapien Pink = 'Sunver' PBR (G)	LAst NBlu
- Tapien Salmon = 'Sunmaref Tp-sap' (G)	LAst LSou WGor
- Tapien Sky Blue (G)	LAst LSou
- Tapien Violet = 'Sunvop' PBR (G)	LAst LSou NBlu
- Tapien White = 'Suntapipurew' PBR (G)	LAst
(Temari Series) Temari Blue = 'Sunmariribu' PBR (G)	LAst NBlu
- Temari Burgundy = 'Sunmariwaba' (G)	LAst WGor
- Temari Coral Pink = 'Sunmariripi' PBR (G)	LAst
- Temari Neon Red = 'Sunmarineopi' (G)	LAst
- Temari Scarlet = 'Sunmarisu' PBR (G)	LAst NBlu
- Temari Vanilla = 'Sunmarivani' (G)	LAst
- Temari Violet = 'Sunmariba' PBR (G)	WGor
- Temari White = 'Sunmaririho' PBR (G)	LAst
'Tenerife'	see *V.* 'Sissinghurst'
tenuisecta (G)	LRav MWea SPhx WPer XPep
Tukana Scarlet = 'Scarlena' PBR (Tukana Series)	WGor
venosa	see *V. rigida*
'White Sissinghurst' (G)	LAst

Verbesina (*Asteraceae*)

alternifolia	CArn MGol
- 'Goldstrahl'	EPPr NDov WPer
encelioides	CPLG
helianthoides	CPLG EWll LSou MGol MHar WGwG WHil

Vernonia (*Asteraceae*)

crinita	CAby ECha EWes LCro MGol NLar SMad SMer WBor
- 'Betty Blindeman' new	EBee
- 'Mammuth'	EBee EWes LHop NCob NDov SPhx WCot
fasciculata	EMan EShb EWes LRHS MNFA NLar WCot
gigantea	MGol NLar SBHP WHrl
missurica	EBee
noveboracensis	EBee MGol MWea NLar WPer
- 'Albiflora'	EWes WPer

Veronica (*Scrophulariaceae*)

amethystina	see *V. spuria* L.
anagallis-aquatica	NSco
'Anna' PBR	NDov
armena	ECho EWes MDKP MHer MSte MWat NMen NWCA SBla SRot WFar
§ ***austriaca***	GSki MLLN NBre NChi WFar WMoo
- var. ***dubia***	see *V. prostrata*
- 'Ionian Skies'	CMea CPBP CTri EBee ECha ECtt EGoo EPPr EWes GBuc LBee LRHS MNrw NCGa NDov SBla SEND SGar SPer WFar WKif WPat WPer WSHC
- 'Jacqueline'	NBre
§ - subsp. ***teucrium***	CArn CSam CTri EBee ECho EPot GSki MFOX NDlv NEgg SRms WBrk WFar WPer
- - 'Crater Lake Blue' ♀H4	EBee ECtt ELan ENot ERou EShb LAst LCro LHop LRHS MAvo MRav MWgw NBid NBre NCGa NVic SMrm SPhx SPla SPlb SRms WCot WEas WFar WMnd WPer
- - 'Kapitän'	ECha GBuc MNrw NPro WFar WPer
- - 'Knallblau'	EBee EMil MBri NCGa NGby SSvw WFar
- - 'Royal Blue' ♀H4	EBee ECot EPfP EShb EWin GBuc GMaP GSki LAst LCro LRHS MNFA NSti SPer SRms WFar WMnd WWeb
- subsp. ***vahlii*** MESE 124	EBee
'Baby Doll'	ERou IBal MBNS MBri NBhm NLar
bachofenii	WTin
beccabunga	CArn CBen CWat EHon ELan EMFW EPfP GPoy NMir NPer NSco SWat WFar WHer WMAq WPnP WSFF
'Bergen's Blue'	EBee EPfP GMac NLar SHGN SHar
Blue Bouquet	see *V. longifolia* 'Blaubündel'
'Blue Indigo'	CHar EBee ELan IBal NBre NCGa SPer
'Blue Spire'	SWat WPer
bombycina	ECho SBla
- subsp. ***bolkardaghensis***	NMen SBla
bonarota	see *Paederota bonarota*
caespitosa	CPBP
- subsp. ***caespitosa***	CLyd NMen WAbe
candida	see *V. spicata* subsp. *incana*
x ***cantiana*** 'Kentish Pink'	GBuc MHer SPla WDyG WFar WMoo WPer WSpi
caucasica	WCru
chamaedrys	ECho NMir XPep
§ - 'Miffy Brute' (v)	EBee NBir NPro
- 'Pam' (v)	CBow ECtt EMan EPPr LSou
- 'Variegata'	see *V. chamaedrys* 'Miffy Brute'
cinerea ♀H4	CLyd GMaP MLHP WEas WHoo WSHC
dabneyi	CDes EBee WPGP WSPU
'Dark Martje'	GBin WCot
'Darwin's Blue' PBR	CMHG GAbr MBNS NLar NMoo NOrc SPur WCot WHrl
'Ellen Mae'	EBee ECtt EWes WCAu WMnd
'Eveline' PBR	EBee ECtt EPfP ERou LSou MBNS MBnl NLar WCot
exaltata	EBee GBuc MSte NChi NDov WCot WPer WSpi
'Fairytale' new	CSpe ERou IPot MAvo MBnl
'Fantasy'	NDov
filiformis	GWCH
- 'Fairyland' (v)	EMan EWes MBNS WFar
formosa	see *Parahebe formosa*
§ ***fruticans***	ECho NMen
fruticulosa	NEgg NWCA
gentianoides ♀H4	More than 30 suppliers
- 'Alba'	CMea LAst NBid NBre NChi NGby NSti
- 'Barbara Sherwood'	EBee EKen GBin GMac MLLN NBre
- 'Blue Streak'	EWll GSki NDlv WRHF
- 'Lilacina'	EBee
- 'Nana'	CAby CEnt EBee EPfP
- 'Pallida'	EBee EMan EPfP GAbr LRHS MBrN MRav NMoo NPri SPlb WBor WFar

	- 'Robusta'	CHrt EBee ECGP EHrv GMac GSki LHop LRHS NCGa NCob WMnd
	- 'Tissington White'	CChe CHar EBee EBla EGle EWTr GMaP GMac LAst LHop LRHS MLHP MLLN NBir NCob NPri SHar SPhx SPoG SWat WAbb WCAu WFar WLin WWeb
	- 'Variegata' (v)	More than 30 suppliers
	gigantea	MGol
	grandis	CDMG CEnt EBee EPPr GAbr MAvo MDKP MGol NChi NLar SHGN SWal WBrk WHoo WHrl WMoo
	x ***guthrieana***	CAbP ELan MBNS NMen SRms SRot WFar WPer
	hendersonii	see *V. subsessilis hendersonii*
	'Heraud'	WCAu
	incana	see *V. spicata* subsp. *incana*
	'Inspiration'	MLLN NBre NDov
	kellereri	see *V. spicata*
	kiusiana	CHFP CMHG EBee EKen NBPC NLar WHrl
*	- var. ***maxima***	MGol WBVN
	liwanensis	ECho NMen XPep
	- Mac&W 5936	EPot MDKP
	longifolia	CHFP CHar CMea CSBt ECha ELan EPfP EShb GCra GSki GWCH MLHP NEgg NSti NVic SHGN WEas WFar WMoo
	- 'Alba'	EBee ELan EPfP NGby NLar STes WCAu WMoo
§	- 'Blaubündel'	CMdw EBee ERou NDlv NGdn
	- 'Blauer Sommer'	EBee MCot MWgw NGdn SPer SPur
§	- 'Blauriesin'	CTri EBee ECGP ECtt EMil EPfP ERou GMaP MBri NBre SPer SSvw WFar WSpi
	- Blue Giantess	see *V. longifolia* 'Blauriesin'
	- 'Blue John'	EBee NBre WCAu
	- 'Fascination'	NGdn NPro SMrm
	- 'Foerster's Blue'	see *V. longifolia* 'Blauriesin'
	- 'Joseph's Coat' (v)	CBow EBee EGle NBre
	- 'Lila Karina'	WPer
	- 'Lilac Fantasy'	CMMP EBee LAst NSti WCAu
	- 'Oxford Blue'	EBee WHoo WRHF
	- pink-flowered	EShb EWTr
	- 'Rose Tone'	ECha EGoo ERou GSki MFOX MGol MWea NEgg NLar WHal WHrl WMoo
	- 'Rosea'	ERou MGol WBrE WPer
	- 'Schneeriesin'	CHar CPrp EBee ECha EHrv GMaP LRHS MBri MRav NBir NLar SPer SPur
	lyallii	see *Parahebe lyallii*
	montana 'Corinne Tremaine' (v)	CBow EBee EMan EMar EWin LSou MHar NBir NCGa NLar SRms WHer
	- golden-variegated (v)	EWin
	nipponica	WPer
	nummularia	WPer
	officinalis	CArn
	oltensis	CLyd CPBP ECho EDAr EPot EWes LTwo MHer NMen SBla WLin WPat
	orchidea	EBee SRms
	orientalis subsp. ***orientalis***	EPot NMen
	ornata	EBee EGoo EMan MGol WPer
	'Pacific Ocean'	EBee
	pectinata	ECtt
	- 'Rosea'	ECho ECtt EWes WPer XPep
	peduncularis	LRHS WEas
I	- 'Alba'	WPer
§	- 'Georgia Blue'	More than 30 suppliers
	- 'Oxford Blue'	see *V. peduncularis* 'Georgia Blue'
	perfoliata	see *Parahebe perfoliata*
	petraea 'Madame Mercier'	EWin SRot
	'Pink Damask'	CHar CSpe CWCL EBee ECtt ELan EPfP ERou GMaP LRHS MBri MWat NCob NDov NLar NSti SMrm WEas WFar WHoo WMnd WTin WWlt
	pinnata 'Blue Eyes'	LBee LHop
	- 'Blue Feathers'	CBrm CEnt SMad SSvw
	porphyriana	EPPr SMad WHoo
	prenja	see *V. austriaca*
	'Prince of Wales Feathers'	NCGa
§	***prostrata*** ♀H4	CEnt CLyd CMea CSam CTri ECho ECtt EPfP EWTr LAst LBee LRHS MLHP NHol SHFr SRms WEas WFar WHoo WLin WMoo
	- 'Alba'	MLHP MWat WFar WHoo
	- 'Aztec Gold'PBR	NBro NLar NPro
§	- 'Blauspiegel'	CPBP SBla
	- Blue Mirror	see *V. prostrata* 'Blauspiegel'
	- 'Blue Sheen'	ECho ECtt GEdr MBNS NBir SIng WAbe WFar WMoo WPer
	- 'Lilac Time'	NBir NLar SIng SRms
	- 'Loddon Blue'	ECho LRHS NVic SBla SRms WPer
	- 'Miss Willmott'	see *V. prostrata* 'Warley Blue'
	- 'Mrs Holt'	CLyd ECho ECtt GEdr LRHS NBir NMen SBla SIng SRGP SRms WAbe WBrk WCru WFar
	- 'Nana'	ECho ECtt EPot EWes MWat NMen WAbe
	- 'Nestor'	CBrm CTri EGoo LIMB NDlv WMoo
	- 'Rosea'	ECho MWat WLin WPer
	- 'Spode Blue' ♀H4	CHar CMea COIW ECho ECtt GAbr GMaP LAst LHop LRHS NWCA SBla SIng SPoG SRms WBVN WFar WLin WMoo
	- 'Trehane'	CEnt COIW EBee ECho ECtt EDAr LAst LBee LHop LRHS MHer MWat NOak NPri NRya SPlb SPoG SRms SRot SWat WBVN WFar WMoo
§	- 'Warley Blue'	ECho
*	***pseudolysimachion***	MHer WMoo
	'Purpleicious'	EBee LRHS MAvo MBnl MBri SPoG
	repens	ECho NBlu NNor NPro SPlb WGwG WPer
	'Rosalinde'	GBuc WPer
	'Royal Pink'	CMMP LAst NCGa NLar STes
	rupestris	see *V. prostrata*
	saturejoides	CPBP SRms WPer
	saxatilis	see *V. fruticans*
	schmidtiana	EShb GSki WPer
	- 'Nana'	CPBP GKev
	selleri	see *V. wormskjoldii*
	'Shirley Blue' ♀H4	CPrp CWib EBee ELan EPfP LCro MBNS MHer MWat NCGa SMer SPoG SRGP SRms WCFE WHen WPer WTel
§	***spicata***	CEnt ELan EPfP LCro LEdu LRHS MBNS MDun NBid NBlu SECG SRms WBrk WCAu WFar WMoo WPer
	- 'Alba'	CHFP EBee EMil MBNS MRav MWat NGby NLar WPer WTin
	- 'Barcarolle'	EBee ELan EPfP MLLN NGby
§	- 'Blaufuchs'	CSam ECtt WTel
	- 'Blue Bouquet'	IBal NBre NLar WWeb
	- Blue Fox	see *V. spicata* 'Blaufuchs'
§	- 'Erika'	ECha ECtt EPfP GBuc IPot LCro MLLN NBir NBre SAga
§	- 'Glory'PBR	CGrW CSpe EBee ECtt ELan ENot EPfP GBri LBuc LCro LSou MSte NBre NCGa NMoo SPer STes WBrE WCot
	- 'Heidekind'	More than 30 suppliers
	- 'High Five'	IBal MBnl NBhm SPoG
	- subsp. ***hybrida***	WCot WHer

§ - 'Icicle'	CDes CMMP EBee MBrN MSte NBre WHlf WRHF
§ - subsp. ***incana***	CMea EBee ECho ELan EPfP ERou EShb GSki LBMP SBla SPlb SRms SWat WCFE WFar WMoo WPer WTin WWeb XPep
- - 'Nana'	ECha MLHP NBir SRms
- - 'Saraband'	WPer
- - 'Silbersee'	CBrm CHFP MLHP WLin
- - 'Silver Carpet'	EBee EMan LAst LBMP LRHS LSou MNFA MRav NBre NSti SPer SPla WMnd
- 'Nana Blauteppich'	CBrm NBre NLar NVic WWeb
- 'Noah Williams' (v)	ECtt EGle EMan GBuc MBNS MFOX NPro
- 'Pink Goblin'	NBre WPer
- 'Pink Panther'	ERou MBnl NBhm
- Red Fox	see *V. spicata* 'Rotfuchs'
- 'Romiley Purple'	EBee ERou MLLN MRav MSte NBre SPer WFar WSpi
- 'Rosalind'	NLar
- ***rosea***	see *V. spicata* 'Erika'
- 'Rosenrot'	ECho
§ - 'Rotfuchs'	COIW CPrp EBee ECtt ELan ERou LCro MBri MRav NBPC NBir NEgg NMoo NOrc NPri SPoG SRms WBVN WCot WFar WHlf WPer WSHC WTel
- 'Royal Candles'PBR	see *V. spicata* 'Glory'
- 'Sightseeing'	CWib ERou MGol NBir NBre SPet SRms SWal WFar
- 'Twilight'	MBnl MBri
- ***variegata*** (v)	MLLN NBir
§ ***spuria*** L.	WPer
stelleri	see *V. wormskjoldii*
subsessilis	WPer
- 'Blaue Pyramide'	EBee NBre WPtf
* - ***hendersonii***	NBre NGby
'Sunny Border Blue'	EBee EMan EMar EPfP GBuc MBNS NBre NDov NLar WCot WFar WRHF
telephiifolia	ECho ECtt EMan EWes MDKP NMen NWCA WAbe
teucrium	see *V. austriaca* subsp. *teucrium*
thessalica	ECho
thymoides subsp. ***pseudocinerea***	NWCA
virginica	see *Veronicastrum virginicum*
'Waterperry Blue'	LRHS WFar WPer
wherryi	WPer
'White Icicle'	see *V. spicata* 'Icicle'
'White Jolanda'	CBgR EBee EPfP ERou MBnl NLar NPro NSti SPer SPoG
whitleyi	MMuc
§ ***wormskjoldii***	EBee ECho EDAr MAvo MBrN NCGa NEgg NLar NMen NWCA SBla SPoG SRms WFar WLin WPer
- 'Alba'	MLHP WPer

Veronicastrum (*Scrophulariaceae*)

japonicum	SGar
latifolium	LPio WSHC
- BWJ 8158	WCru
sibiricum	ECha EMar EShb LEdu MGol NBid NBre NHol SBla WCot WMoo
- BWJ 6352	WCru
- var. ***yezoense*** RBS 0290	MGol NPro WBVN
villosulum	CSpe EBee EWes MWgw NBid NBro NLar WCot WCru WSHC
§ ***virginicum***	CArn CEnt CKno CTca EBee ECha ECtt EHrv EPyc LBMP MGol MLHP NBir SRms WGwG WMoo WPer
- 'Alboroseum'	WTin
- 'Album'	More than 30 suppliers
- 'Apollo'	CBre EBee ECtt EGle EMan EPfP ERou GAbr GMaP LAst LHop LPio MBri MLLN NBro NCGa NLar NOrc NSti SPhx WAul WCAu WHrl WTMC
- 'Diane'	EBee EGle GMaP LCro NBre NDov
- 'Erica'	EBee GBin GQue MBNS NBPC NChi NDov NMoo NSti SPoG
- 'Fascination'	More than 30 suppliers
- var. ***incarnatum***	see *V. virginicum* f. *roseum*
- 'Lavendelturm'	CAby CSam EBee ECha EGle EMil ERou GMaP GQue IPot LCro MBri MCot MLLN NCGa NDov NLar NSti SMad SPer SPhx WAul WCot WSpi WTMC
- 'Pointed Finger'	GMaP GMac LCro LEdu NBre SMrm WWlt
§ - f. ***roseum***	EBee ECha ELan GMaP LCro MRav MWgw NBro NDov SMHy SPhx SPoG WFar WKif WMoo WSHC
- - 'Pink Glow'	CHar CKno COIW CTca EBee EBrs ECtt ELan EMan EMil EPfP GAbr LCro LHop MBnl MRav NCGa NDov NGdn NSti SAga SMrm SPer SPhx SPla STes WCAu WFar WMnd WSpi
- 'Spring Dew'	CBre EBee ECtt EGle EMan ERou GMac LCro MLLN MWgw NBid NBro NLar NPro SPhx WMnd
- 'Temptation'	EBee EGle EMan ERou GBin GMaP LCro MLLN NBPC NBre NBro NLar NPro SMHy SPhx WCAu
'White Jolan'	CFir

Verschaffeltia (*Arecaceae*)

splendida	XBlo

Verticordia (*Myrtaceae*)

chrysantha	SOWG
longistylis	SOWG
minutiflora	SOWG
plumosa purple-flowered	SOWG

Vestia (*Solanaceae*)

§ ***foetida*** ♀H1	CBcs CHll CPom CSpe CWib EBee ELan EMan EPfP EShb MNrw NLar SDnm SGar SHFr SOWG WHil WKif WPGP WPer WSHC
lycioides	see *V. foetida*

Vetiveria (*Poaceae*)

zizanioides	MSal

Viburnum ✿ (*Caprifoliaceae*)

acerifolium	CPle WBod WFar WHCG WPat
alnifolium	see *V. lantanoides*
annamensis B&SWJ 8302 **new**	WCru
atrocyaneum	CGHE CPLG CPle EBee NLar WFar WHCG WPGP WPat
- B&SWJ 7272	WCru
awabuki	CHEx EPfP MBlu MGos NLar WPGP
- B&SWJ 3397	WCru
- B&SWJ 6913	WCru
- B&SWJ 8404	WCru
§ - 'Emerald Lustre'	CDoC CHEx WPat
betulifolium	CAbP CBcs CMCN CPLG CPMA EBee EPfP EPla EQua NHol NLar SLon WBod WHCG WPat
- B&SWJ 1619	WCru
- 'Hohuanshan'	WCru
bitchiuense	CPMA CPle ELan WPat
x ***bodnantense***	CMac CTri CWSG EBee MAsh MDun MRav NPen NPri SAga WHar WTel
- 'Charles Lamont' ♀H4	More than 30 suppliers

- 'Dawn' ♀H4	More than 30 suppliers
- 'Deben' ♀H4	CDoC CMac EBee ENot EPfP EQua MRav MWya SPer WBod WFar
bracteatum	NLar
buddlejifolium	CMac EPfP EWes LHop SPoG WCru WFar WHCG WPGP
x ***burkwoodii***	More than 30 suppliers
- 'Anika'	NLar
- 'Anne Russell' ♀H4	CAbP CBcs CMac CPMA CTri EBee ECrN ELan ENot EPfP EWes IArd LRHS MAsh MGos MRav MSwo NHol NSti SHBN SLon SPer SPla SPlb SSta SWvt WBrE WFar
- 'Chenaultii'	EPfP WCru
- 'Compact Beauty'	CPMA EPfP WPat
- 'Conoy'	CPMA WPat
- 'Fulbrook' ♀H4	CAbP CMHG EPfP LRHS MAsh MGos WBod WFar WPat
- 'Mohawk'	CAbP CDoC CEnd CPMA EBee ELan EMil EPfP IDee LRHS MAsh MBri NLar SCoo SPla SPoG SWvt WFar WPGP WPat WSpi
- 'Park Farm Hybrid' ♀H4	CAbP CDoC CMac CPLG CPMA CPSs CSam CTri CWSG CWib EBee ECrN ELan ENot EPfP LAst LRHS MAsh MRav MSwo NBea NLar NSti SLPl SPer SRms WBod WFar WPat WSpi
x ***carlcephalum*** ♀H4	More than 30 suppliers
- 'Cayuga'	MAsh NLar WPat
* - 'Variegatum' (v)	CPMA
carlesii	CBcs CMac CTri CWib EBee ENot EPfP LAst LRHS MBlu MGan MRav MSwo NPri SBLw SCoo SLim SMer SPer SReu WTel
- B&SWJ 8838	WCru
- 'Aurora' ♀H4	More than 30 suppliers
- 'Charis'	CMac CPLG CPMA CSBt LRHS NLar WBod
- 'Compactum'	CPMA MAsh
- 'Diana'	CEnd CMHG CMac CPMA EBee EPfP LRHS MAsh MRav MWya NLar SPer WCFE WPGP WPat
- 'Marlou'	CPMA NLar WPat
cassinoides	EPfP GBin WFar WPat
- 'Sear Charm' **new**	WPat
'Chesapeake'	CDoC CPMA EWes SEND
chingii	CGHE CPMA EBee SLon WCru WPGP
cinnamomifolium ♀H3	CAbP CBcs CHEx CMac CPLG EBee EPfP LRHS MAsh SAPC SArc SLon SPoG SSpi WBod WFar WHCG WPGP WSHC
cotinifolium	CPLG GKev NLar WCot
- CC 4541	MGol
cylindricum	CGHE CMCN CPle EPfP LHop SKHP SSpi WCru WPGP
- B&SWJ 6479 from Thailand	WCru
- B&SWJ 7239	WCru
- B&SWJ 9719	WCru
- BWJ 7778 from China	WCru
- HWJCM 434 from Nepal	WCru
dasyanthum	EPfP NLar
davidii ♀H4	More than 30 suppliers
- (f)	CBcs CDoC CSBt ELan EPfP MAsh MDun MGos SHBN SPer SPla SPoG SReu SRms SSta WPat
- (m)	CBcs CDoC CSBt CWSG ELan EPfP MAsh MDun MGos MRav SPer SPla SPoG SReu SRms SSta WPat
- 'Angustifolium'	EBee EMil
dentatum	CPLG EPfP
- 'Moon Glo'	NLar
- 'White and Blue' **new**	NLar

dilatatum	CPne
- B&SWJ 4456	WCru
- 'Asian Beauty' **new**	MBri
- 'Erie'	EBee EPfP
- 'Iroquois'	EPfP
- 'Michael Dodge'	MBri NLar
- 'Sealing Wax' **new**	NLar
erosum B&SWJ 3585	WCru
erubescens	CAbP CPMA IDee WFar
- B&SWJ 8281	WCru
- var. ***gracilipes***	CPMA EPfP WPat
'Eskimo'	CAbP CBcs CMac CWSG EBee ECrN ENot EPfP LAst LRHS LSRN MAsh MBNS MBlu MGos MRav NBlu NMoo SLim SPoG SWvt WFar WHCG
§ ***farreri*** ♀H4	More than 30 suppliers
- 'Album'	see *V. farreri* 'Candidissimum'
§ - 'Candidissimum'	CDul CMac EBee ELan EPfP IArd LHop LRHS MRav NLar SPer SPoG SSpi WBod WPat
- 'December Dwarf'	CPMA
- 'Farrer's Pink'	CAbP CPMA NHol WBod
- 'Fioretta'	NLar
- 'Nanum'	CMac CPMA EBee EPfP LRHS MAsh MBar MBrN MRav MWat NHol NLar WFar WHCG WPat
foetens	see *V. grandiflorum* f. *foetens*
foetidum var. ***rectangulatum*** B&SWJ 3637	WCru
fragrans Bunge	see *V. farreri*
'Fragrant Cloud'	ECrN
furcatum ♀H4	CPLG EPfP IArd MBri NLar SSpi WPat
- B&SWJ 5939	WCru
x ***globosum*** 'Jermyns Globe'	CAbP CDoC CEnd CMHG EBee EMil MBar MGos MRav MSte MWya SLon SPoG WCru WFar WHCG WPGP
grandiflorum	CPMA CSBt EPfP NLar
- HWJK 2163	WCru
§ - f. ***foetens***	EPfP WBod
harryanum	CMHG CPle EBee EPfP MBNS NLar SOWG WCru WFar
henryi	CAbP CPMA ECrN EPfP NLar WPat
x ***hillieri***	GBin WFar WHCG WKif
- 'Winton' ♀H4	CAbP CDoC CEnd CPMA CWib EBee EPfP EPla IClo LHop LRHS LSRN MBri MGos NHol NPal SLim SLon SOWG SPoG SSpi WBod WCru WFar WPGP
'Huron'	MGos NEgg WPat
ichangense	CPMA NLar
japonicum	CHEx CMac CPLG CPle EPfP SHBN SLon
- B&SWJ 5968	WCru
x ***juddii*** ♀H4	More than 30 suppliers
koreanum	WBod
- B&SWJ 4231	WCru
lantana	CCVT CDul CLnd CRWN CTri CWib ECrN EMac GWCH LBuc NWea SPer SPoG WFar WMou
- 'Aureum'	EBee ECtt MAsh MBlu NLar
- 'Candy' **new**	NLar
- var. ***discolor*** **new**	NLar
- 'Mohican'	NLar
- 'Variefolium' (v)	CPMA
§ ***lantanoides***	EPfP SSpi
lentago	CAbP CPle NLar
lobophyllum	EPfP NLar
luzonicum B&SWJ 3930	WCru
* - var. ***floribundum*** B&SWJ 8281	WCru

	- var. ***oblongum*** B&SWJ 3549	WCru
	macrocephalum	CPMA SLon
	- f. ***keteleeri***	CEnd CPMA
	mariesii	see *V. plicatum* f. *tomentosum* 'Mariesii'
	mongolicum	NLar
	nervosum B&SWJ 2251a	WCru
	nudum	EBee EPfP IClo NLar
	- 'Pink Beauty'	CGHE CPMA CWSG EBee EMil LRHS NLar WFar WPGP
	- 'Winterthur'	NLar
	odoratissimum misapplied	CBcs EBee EPfP IArd SHBN SSpi WSHC
	odoratissimum Ker Gawl.	CHEx CPLG CSam EMil MWea SMad XPep
	- RWJ 10046	WCru
	- 'Emerald Lustre'	see *V. awabuki* 'Emerald Lustre'
	'Oneida'	NLar WPat
	opulus	More than 30 suppliers
	- var. ***americanum*** 'Bailey's Compact'	WPat
	- - 'Hans' new	NLar
	- - 'Phillips'	CAgr
	- - 'Wentworth'	CAgr
	- 'Apricot'	NLar
	- 'Aureum'	CChe CHar CMHG CMac CSam CTri CWib EBee ECtt ELan EPfP LBMP LRHS MAsh MGos MRav NEgg NHol NMyG SHBN SPer SPoG SSta WFar WHCG WMoo WPat
	- 'Compactum' ♀H4	More than 30 suppliers
*	- 'Harvest Gold'	EBee SCoo SLim
	- 'Nanum'	CAbP CBcs CPle EBee ELan EPfP EPla EShb MBar MRav NHol NLar NMen NPro WHCG WPat
	- 'Notcutt's Variety' ♀H4	EBee ENot EPfP MBlu MGos SHBN SRms WPat
	- 'Park Harvest'	CDul LRHS MAsh NLar NSti SLPl WPat
§	- 'Roseum' ♀H4	More than 30 suppliers
	- 'Sterile'	see *V. opulus* 'Roseum'
*	- 'Sterile Compactum'	IMGH SWvt
	- 'Sunshine' new	MBri
N	- 'Xanthocarpum' ♀H4	More than 30 suppliers
	parvifolium	NLar
N	***plicatum***	CTri CWib IArd MBar
	- 'Janny'	MBlu
	- 'Mary Milton'	NLar
	- 'Nanum'	see *V. plicatum* f. *tomentosum* 'Nanum Semperflorens'
	- 'Pink Sensation'	CPMA
	- 'Popcorn'	CAbP CPMA EBee EMil LRHS MAsh MBri MRav SPoG SReu SSta WHCG WPat
	- 'Rosace'	MBlu MBri NLar SSpi
	- 'Roseum'	CPle
	- 'Shoshoni' new	NLar
	- f. ***tomentosum***	EWTr
	- - 'Cascade'	EWTr NEgg NLar SHBN SSpi
	- - 'Dart's Red Robin'	ECtt NLar WPat
	- - 'Grandiflorum'	CAbP CDoC CPle EPfP LRHS MBar MBri SPer WHCG WMoo
	- - 'Lanarth'	CBcs CDoC CDul CMac CPLG CSBt CTri CWSG CWib EBee ECrN ECtt EMil ENot EPfP LHop LRHS MBlu MGos MRav NSti SPer SPla SPoG SWal SWvt WBod WFar WHCG
§	- - 'Mariesii' ♀H4	More than 30 suppliers
	- - 'Molly Schroeder'	MBri NLar
§	- - 'Nanum Semperflorens'	CDoC CMac CWSG ECtt IArd MBlu MGos NBlu NHol SLPl SPer SPoG WFar WHCG WPat
	- - 'Pink Beauty' ♀H4	More than 30 suppliers
	- - 'Rotundifolium'	IClo MRav NLar SHBN WPat
	- - 'Rowallane'	EPfP MBri WPat
	- - 'Shasta'	CMCN EPfP MBri NLar WFar WSpi
	- - 'Summer Snowflake'	CDoC CEnd CWGN CWSG EBee ECrN ENot EPfP LRHS MSwo NEgg NHol NPri SHBN SPer SPoG WFar WHCG
	- 'Watanabe'	see *V. plicatum* f. *tomentosum* 'Nanum Semperflorens'
	'Pragense' ♀H4	CAbP CBcs CDul CMCN EBee EPfP EQua MBar MGos NBlu NHol SLon SPer WBod WFar WHCG WPat
	propinquum	CAbP NLar WFar
	- B&SWJ 4009	WCru
	prunifolium	NLar
	- 'Mrs Henry's Large' new	NLar
	punctatum B&SWJ 9532	WCru
*	'Regenteum' new	CWib
	x ***rhytidophylloides***	WFar
	- 'Alleghany'	EBee NLar
	- Dart's Duke = 'Interduke'	SLPl
	- 'Willowwood'	EBee LRHS NLar SMad SPer SPoG WPat
	rhytidophyllum	CBcs CDul CHEx CMac CSBt CTri EBee ECrN ENot EPfP ISea LHop LPan MBar MDun MGos MRav MSwo NBlu NEgg SBLw SCoo SHBN SMer SPer SReu SRms WCFE WFar WMoo
	- 'Roseum'	CPLG SLPl SWvt
	- 'Variegatum' (v)	CPMA NLar
	'Royal Guard'	NLar WPat
	sargentii	EPfP GBin
	- f. ***flavum***	NLar
	- 'Onondaga' ♀H4	More than 30 suppliers
	- 'Susquehanna'	EPfP
	semperflorens	see *V. plicatum* f. *tomentosum* 'Nanum Semperflorens'
§	***setigerum***	EPfP IArd IDee NLar SLPl
	- 'Aurantiacum'	EPfP NLar
	sieboldii B&SWJ 2837	WCru
	- 'Seneca'	CPLG EPfP NLar
	taiwanianum B&SWJ 3009	WCru
	theiferum	see *V. setigerum*
	tinoides B&SWJ 10757 new	WCru
	tinus	More than 30 suppliers
	- 'Bewley's Variegated' (v)	CBcs CDoC EBee ECrN ENot EQua MGos MRav SPer
I	- 'Compactum'	SWvt
	- 'Eve Price' ♀H4	More than 30 suppliers
	- 'French White' ♀H4	CDoC CDul CMac CWSG EBee ECrN EPfP EPla LCro LRHS MGos MRav SCoo SLim SPoG STop SWvt WFar
	- 'Gwenllian' ♀H4	More than 30 suppliers
	- 'Israel'	SPer SPla WFar
	- 'Lucidum'	CBcs CPMA CSam NLar SHBN WFar
	- 'Lucidum Variegatum' (v)	CMac CPMA SDry SLim
*	- 'Macrophyllum'	SPoG SWvt WFar WWeb XPep
	- 'Pink Prelude'	MWya WSpi
	- 'Purpureum'	CDul CSBt EBee ECrN EPfP EPla LRHS MAsh MGos MRav MSwo NBlu NEgg NHol NPri SCoo SHBN SLPl SLim SPer SPoG WFar WGwG WMoo WPat WWeb
	- Spirit = 'Anvi'PBR	EBee MBri MGos NLar SPoG WRHF
	- 'Spring Bouquet'	MAsh MGos MWya NLar
	- 'Variegatum' (v)	More than 30 suppliers
	- 'Villa Noailles'	XPep

tomentosum	see *V. plicatum*
urceolatum B&SWJ 6988	WCru
utile	EPfP NLar WFar WHCG
wrightii	EPfP MRav NLar WHCG WPat
- B&SWJ 8780	WCru
- 'Hessei'	EPfP
- var. ***stipellatum*** B&SWJ 5844	WCru

Vicia (*Papilionaceae*)

cracca	GWCH NLan NMir NSco WSFF
sativa new	SECG
sepium	NSco
sylvatica	CBgR CPom EWes
unijuga	CPom

Vigna (*Papilionaceae*)

§ ***caracalla***	CCCN MJnS

Villaresia see *Citronella*

Villarsia (*Menyanthaceae*)

bennettii	see *Nymphoides peltata* 'Bennettii'

Vinca (*Apocynaceae*)

difformis ♀H3-4	CBgR CHar COlW CTri CWan EBee ECha EMan LLWP LRHS MGos NCGa SBri SDix SDry WHer WPic
* - 'Alba'	CPom SBch
- subsp. ***difformis***	CHid EMon
- Greystone form	CHid EPPr EPfP LHop MBNS NHol NLar SEND WCAu WGwG WPnP WRHF
- 'Jenny Pym'	CBgR CHid COlW CPom CTca EBee EPPr EWes LHop LRHS MSte SBch SMad SPoG WFar WWeb
- 'Oxford'	WBrE
- 'Ruby Baker'	EBee LRHS NChi WHrl WSPU
- 'Snowmound'	CWan EBee LRHS MRav SPoG
'Hidcote Purple'	see *V. major* var. *oxyloba*
major	CBcs CDul CSBt CWib EBee ELan ENot EPfP GPoy LBuc LCro LRHS MGan MGos MSwo NCGa NPri NWea SHBN SPer SPoG SRms WFar WGwG WMoo XPep
- 'Alba'	CPLG CWib GBuc WEas
- 'Caucasian Blue'	WPGP
- 'Elegantissima'	see *V. major* 'Variegata'
§ - subsp. ***hirsuta*** (Boiss.) Stearn	EMon MWgw WBod
- var. ***hirsuta*** hort.	see *V. major* var. *oxyloba*
- 'Honeydew' (v)	EMon
- 'Jason Hill'	EMon
§ - 'Maculata' (v)	CBcs CDoC COlW CSBt EBee EMon LRHS MBar MLHP MSwo NBPC NEgg NHol SDry SLim SPer SPoG WMoo WWeb
§ - var. ***oxyloba***	CBgR CFis COld CPLG CTri EBee ECha ECtt ELan EMon EPla GSki LHop MRav SLPl SLim SMac SRms WFar WHen WHer WPic WSel
- var. ***pubescens***	see *V. major* subsp. *hirsuta* (Boiss.) Stearn
- 'Reticulata' (v)	ELan EMon
- 'Surrey Marble'	see *V. major* 'Maculata'
§ - 'Variegata' (v) ♀H4	More than 30 suppliers
- Westwood form	CFee
- 'Wojo's Jem' (v)	EBee ENot EWes LBuc LRHS MBri MGos SPoG
minor	CBgR CDoC CDul ELan ENot EPfP GAbr GPoy LCro MAsh MBar MGos MNHC NBlu NPri NWea SHFr SPoG WBrE WFar XPep
- f. ***alba*** ♀H4	CBcs CDoC EBee ECha EGoo ENot EPfP LBMP LRHS MAsh MBar MGos MWgw NBlu NPri SHBN SMac SPer STre WCot WFar WPtf
- - 'Gertrude Jekyll' ♀H4	CBgR CBrm CDoC CSBt EBee ELan ENot EPfP ILis LCro LRHS LSRN MAsh MBri MGos MRav MWat NCGa NHol NPri SBod SCoo SEND SLim SPer SPla SPoG WBor WMoo
- 'Alba Aureovariegata'	see *V. minor* 'Alba Variegata'
§ - 'Alba Variegata' (v)	CBgR CPLG EPla GAbr GGar MBar MGos NChi NGHP NHol NPri NPro SPer SRms STre WEas WFar WTel
§ - 'Argenteovariegata' (v) ♀H4	More than 30 suppliers
§ - 'Atropurpurea' ♀H4	More than 30 suppliers
- 'Aurea'	SPla WFar
§ - 'Aureovariegata' (v)	CBcs CPLG EBee GAbr LRHS MBar MGos MRav NBlu NCGa NHol NPri SPer SPlb WFar WHen WTel
- 'Azurea'	CHid
§ - 'Azurea Flore Pleno' (d) ♀H4	More than 30 suppliers
* - 'Blue and Gold'	EGoo EMon
- 'Blue Drift'	EWes MBNS MSwo WSpi
- 'Blue Moon'	ECtt SPer SPla
- 'Bowles' Blue'	see *V. minor* 'La Grave'
- 'Bowles' Variety'	see *V. minor* 'La Grave'
- 'Burgundy'	CFee MWgw SRms
- 'Caerulea Plena'	see *V. minor* 'Azurea Flore Pleno'
- 'Dartington Star'	see *V. major* var. *oxyloba*
- 'Double Burgundy'	see *V. minor* 'Multiplex'
- Green Carpet	see *V. minor* 'Grüner Teppich'
§ - 'Grüner Teppich'	EMon WFar
- 'Illumination' (v)	More than 30 suppliers
§ - 'La Grave' ♀H4	More than 30 suppliers
- 'Maculata' (v)	ELan
- 'Marie'	MGos
- 'Marion Cran'	GSki
§ - 'Multiplex' (d)	CBgR EBee ECtt EMan EPPr EPla MAsh MBar NChi NHol NPri SRms WCFE WHrl WSel
- 'Persian Carpet' (v)	EMon
- 'Purpurea'	see *V. minor* 'Atropurpurea'
- 'Ralph Shugert'	EBee EPPr EWes LRHS NLar SPoG
- 'Rubra'	see *V. minor* 'Atropurpurea'
- 'Sabinka'	CHid EGoo EMon EPPr EPla
- 'Silver Service' (d/v)	CFee CHid CWan EBee EMan EMon GBuc MRav NHol WCot WHoo
- 'Variegata'	see *V. minor* 'Argenteovariegata'
- 'Variegata Aurea'	see *V. minor* 'Aureovariegata'
- 'White Gold'	EBee NHol NPri NPro
sardoa	EBee EMon EPPr EWes

Vincetoxicum (*Asclepiadaceae*)

forrestii	CPLG
§ ***hirundinaria***	EBee EPPr GPoy LEdu
nigrum	EDAr MGol NChi WCot WTin
officinale	see *V. hirundinaria*
scandens	CRHN

Viola ✿ (*Violaceae*)

B&SWJ 8301 from Vietnam	WCru
'Ada Jackson' (ExVa)	WOFF
'Admiral Avellan'	see *V.* 'Amiral Avellan'
'Admiration' (Va)	WBou WOFF
adunca	NWCA
- var. ***minor***	see *V. labradorica*
'Agnes Cochrane' (ExVa)	WOFF
§ ***alba***	EWes NMen
'Alethia' (Va)	GMac WOFF
'Alex Blackwood' (SP)	WOFF
'Alexander Rayfield' (Va)	WOFF

	'Alice' (Vt)	CDev CGro
	'Alice Kate'	CAby WBou WOFF
	'Alice Witter' (Vt)	CBre CDev CGro EBee ECha MFOX NChi
	'Alice Wood' (ExVa)	WOFF
*	'Alison' (Va)	GMaP WBou WOFF
	'Amelia' (Va)	WBou
§	'Amiral Avellan' (Vt)	CDev CGro
	'Ann' (SP)	WOFF
	'Annette Hays Wallace' (FP)	WOFF
	'Annette Ross' (Va)	WOFF
I	'Annie' (Vt)	CBre CGro
	'Annie Roberts' (FP)	WOFF
	'Arabella' (Va)	WBou
	'Ardross Gem' (Va)	CAby CCge EBee ECho ECtt GAbr GMac NChi WBou WEas WPer
	arenaria	see *V. rupestris*
	'Arkwright's Ruby' (Va)	SRms
	'Ashvale Blue' (PVt)	CGro
	'Aspasia' (Va) ♀H4	CAby GMac NCob WBou WOFF
	'Avril' (Va)	NCob
	'Avril Lawson' (Va)	SHar WBou WOFF
	'Baby Blue'	CDev
	'Baby Franjo'	NVic
	'Baby Lucia' (Va)	NVic SBch SRms
	'Barbara' (Va)	WBou WOFF
	'Barnsdale Gem'	MBNS
	'Baroness de Rothschild' misapplied	see *V.* 'Baronne Alice de Rothschild'
	'Baroness de Rothschild' ambig. (Vt)	CGro WHer
§	'Baronne Alice de Rothschild' (Vt)	CCge CDev GMaP SHar
	'Beatrice' (Vtta)	WBou WOFF
	'Becky Groves' (Vt)	CGro
	'Beechy's Double White' (d) **new**	CGro
*	***bella***	WEas
	'Bella' (C)	EBee
§	'Belmont Blue' (C)	CCge CEnt CSam CSpe EAlp EBee ECtt EWes GCra GMaP GMac LCro LHop MHer MRav MWat MWgw NBir NCGa NChi NDov SAga SBla SPer SRkn SRms WBou WSHC WSpi
	'Bernard Cox' (FP)	WOFF
§	***bertolonii***	WBou
	'Beshlie' (Va) ♀H4	ECtt GMac MBNS WBou WEas WOFF WTin
*	***betonicifolia albescens***	EBee
	- var. ***oblongosagittata***	EBee
	'Betty' (Va)	WOFF
	'Betty Dale' (ExVa)	WOFF
	biflora	CMHG MTho NChi
	'Bishop's Belle' (FP)	WOFF
	'Black Bun'	WPGP
	'Blackfaulds Gem' (SP)	WOFF
	'Blue Butterfly' (C)	GMac
	'Blue Moon' (C)	WBou WTin
	'Blue Moonlight' (C)	CAby CElw EBee GBuc GMac LRHS NChi
	'Boughton Blue'	see *V.* 'Belmont Blue'
	'Bournemouth Gem' (Vt)	CBre CDev CGro
§	'Bowles' Black' (T)	CArn CSWP CSpe EBee EPfP LBMP LEdu LRHS NBro NGHP NVic SBla SPla SRGP SRms WEas
	'Boy Blue' (Vtta)	ECtt WOFF
	'Bruneau' (dVt)	WCot
*	'Bryony' (Vtta)	WBou WOFF
	'Bullion' (Va)	EBee WBou WOFF
	'Burncoose Yellow'	WBou
	'Buttercup' (Vtta)	COIW EBee ECtt EWin GMaP GMac NCob NEgg SPoG WBou WOFF
	'Butterpat' (C)	GMac

	'Buxton Blue' (Va)	GBuc WOFF
	calcarata	GKev
	canadensis	NWCA
	'Candy'	CDev
	canina	NBro NMir
*	- ***alba***	CBre
	'Catalina' **new**	CGro
*	'Catforth Gold'	NCob
	'Catforth Suzanne'	NCob
	'Catherine Williams' (ExVa)	WOFF
	'Cat's Whiskers'	CElw EBee
	cazorlensis	SBla
	chaerophylloides var. ***chaerophylloides***	CGro
§	- var. ***sieboldiana***	CPMA
	'Chandler's Glory' (Va)	WOFF
	'Chantal' (Vtta)	WOFF
	'Chantreyland' (Va)	NBir
	'Charles William Groves' (Vt)	CGro
	'Charlotte'	CAby WBou WOFF
	'Christmas' (Vt)	CGro
	'Cinders' (Vtta)	GMac
	'Citron' (Va)	NCob
	'Cleeway Crimson' (FP)	WOFF
	'Clementina' (Va) ♀H4	MRav WBou
	'Cleo' (Va)	EBee GMac WBou WOFF
	'Clive Groves' (Vt)	CBre CGro CHid
	'Coeur d'Alsace' (Vt)	CBre CDev EBee MCot NLar WCot WEas WHal WOFF
	'Collette'	WOFF
	'Colombine' (Vt)	CGro NSti
	'Columbine' (Va)	CDev CElw EBee ECtt EPfP GMaP GMac LAst LCro LRHS MHer NBir NEgg NPri SIng SMrm SPer SPoG WBou WCot WEas WFar
	'Comte de Chambord' (dVt)	SHar WFar
	'Connigar'	CSam
	'Connor Glendinning' (ExVa)	WOFF
§	'Conte di Brazza' (dPVt)	CDev CGro EHrv EShb GMac SHar WHer WOFF
	'Cordelia' (Va)	EBee SBla WFar
	'Cornetto'	MHer
	cornuta ♀H4	CAby CElw CMea ECho GGar GKev MLHP MWat NBir NBro NChi NCob SBch SRms WBou WFar WHen WHoo WRos
	- Alba Group ♀H4	More than 30 suppliers
§	- 'Alba Minor'	CAby CEnt CSsd ECho EPfP EShb EWes GBuc GMac IGor MBNS MWat NBro NChi SHGN WFar
	- blue-flowered	ECho MHer MLHP NCob SHGN WMoo
	- 'Cleopatra' (C)	CAby GMac
	- 'Clouded Yellow'	GMac
	- 'Gypsy Moth' (C)	CAby GMac
	- 'Icy But Spicy'	EBee EHrv WBou
	- Lilacina Group (C)	ECha MRav MSte NChi SWat WFar WMnd WPtf
	- 'Maiden's Blush'	EMan GMac NChi
	- 'Minor' ♀H4	CAby GMac NBro SBla WBou
	- 'Minor Alba'	see *V. cornuta* 'Alba Minor'
	- 'Netta Statham' **new**	WBou
	- 'Pale Apollo' (C)	GMac
*	- 'Paris White'	EBee EPfP
	- 'Purple Gem'	GMac
	- Purpurea Group	CMea ECha GBuc NCob WMnd
	- 'Spider'	CRez GMac
	- 'Victoria's Blush' (C)	CAby CCge CSpe EBee ECtt GBuc GMaP GMac MHer MSte NBir NChi NDov SPoG SSvw WBou
	- 'Violacea'	GMac
	- 'Yellow King'	EHrv

	corsica	CEnt CSpe NChi SHGN WOFF XPep
	'Cox's Moseley' (ExVa)	WOFF
	'Crepuscle' (Vt)	CGro
§	***cucullata*** ♀H4	ECho SRms WFar WPrP
§	- 'Alba' (Vt)	ECho LLWP NBir NChi NSti SRms WEas
	- ***rosea***	EWes
*	- 'Striata Alba'	MWgw NBre NBro
	'Czar'	see *V.* 'The Czar'
§	'Czar Bleu' (Vt)	CDev
	'Daisy Smith' (Va)	GMac NChi WBou WOFF
	'Dancing Geisha' (Vt)	EBee EHrv EPfP MBNS WAul
	'David Rhodes' (FP)	WOFF
	'David Wheldon' (Va)	WOFF
	'Davina' (Va)	WOFF
	'Dawn' (Vtta)	EBee ECtt EWin GMaP LSou NPri SPer SRGP WBou WOFF
	declinata	EBee
	'Delicia' (Vtta)	NChi WBou
	'Delmonden' (Va)	SBla
	delphinantha	SBla WAbe
	'Delphine' (Va)	MSte NChi
	'Des Charentes' (Vt)	CGro
	'Desdemona' (Va)	CAby GMac WBou
	'Desmonda' (Va)	WOFF
	'Devon Cream' (Va)	GMac WBou
	'Diana Groves' (Vt)	CGro
	diffusa	EBee
	dissecta	WCot WPer
	- var. ***sieboldiana***	see *V. chaerophylloides* var. *sieboldiana*
	'Donau' (Vt)	CBre CDev CGro
	'Doreen' (Vt)	CGro
	'Double White' (dVt)	CGro NWCA
	douglasii	CGro
	dubyana	GAbr GBuc NChi
	'Duchesse de Parme' (dPVt)	CDev EShb GMac NWCA SHar SRms WOFF
	'D'Udine' (dPVt)	CDev CGro GMac WOFF
	'Dusk'	WBou
	'E.A. Bowles'	see *V.* 'Bowles' Black'
	'Eastgrove Blue Scented' (C)	GMaP GMac NCob WBou WCot WEas WPtf WWFP
	'Eastgrove Elizabeth Booth'	WEas WSHC
	'Eastgrove Ice Blue' (C)	WBou WEas
	'Eastgrove Twinkle' (C)	NCob WEas
	eizanensis	MTho
	'Elaine Quin'	NPri SPer SPoG SRGP WBou
§	***elatior***	CEnt CSWP EBee EBla EMon EPPr EShb EWTr GBri GBuc LRHS MNrw NChi WLin WPer WPtf WSHC
	'Elizabeth' (Va)	ECtt NCGa WBou WOFF
	'Elizabeth Bailes' (Vt)	CGro
	'Elizabeth Lee'	CGro
	'Elizabeth McCallum' (FP)	WOFF
	'Elliot Adam' (Va)	WBou WOFF
	'Elsie Coombs' (Vt)	CDev
	'Emma' (Va)	CAby
	'Emperor Blue Vein'	LSou
	'Emperor Magenta Red'	LSou
	'Emperor White'	LSou
	erecta	see *V. elatior*
	'Eris' (Va)	NChi WBou
	'Etain' (Va)	CCge CHVG COIW EBee ECho ECtt ELan EWes GBuc GMaP LRHS MSte NCGa NCob NDov NEgg NPri SPhx SPoG WBou WEas WOFF
	'Evelyn Jackson' (Va)	WOFF
	'Fabiola' (Vtta)	GMac NBir
	'Famecheck Apricot'	EFam NChi
*	'Fantasy'	WBou
	'Farewell' (ExVa)	WOFF
	'Feline' (PVt) **new**	CGro
	'Fiona' (Va)	CAby EBee GMaP GMac MSte NChi NCob WBou WOFF
	'Fiona Lawrenson' (Va)	WOFF
	flettii	NChi
	'Florence' (Va)	CAby NChi WBou
	'Foxbrook Cream' (C)	EMan GBuc GMac WBou
	'Francesca' (Va)	WOFF
	'Freckles'	see *V. sororia* 'Freckles'
	'Frederica' (Vt)	CDev
	'George Carter' (FP)	WOFF
	'George Hughes' (FP)	WOFF
	'George Lee' (Vt)	CGro
	glabella	WOFF
	'Gladys Findlay' (Va)	GMac WBou WOFF
	'Gladys Hughes' (FP)	WOFF
*	'Glenda'	WBou WOFF
	'Glenholme'	CAby GMac SMeo
	'Gloire de Verdun' (PVt)	CGro NWCA
	'Gloriole' (Vt)	CGro
	'Governor Herrick' (Vt)	CCge CDev CGro
§	***gracilis***	NBir WFar
	- 'Lutea'	CSam
	- 'Major'	WBou
	'Granddad's Violet' (Vt)	CGro
	grayi **new**	NChi
	'Green Goddess'PBR	EBee EWin LAst MBNS MWea NCGa NEgg NPri WFar
	'Green Jade' (v)	MBNS NBir
	'Grey Owl' (Va)	LRHS WBou WEas WOFF WPGP
	'Grovemount Blue' (C)	CMea
§	***grypoceras*** var. ***exilis***	EMan GBri NGdn NSum
	- var. ***exilis*** 'Sylettas'	CBow CStu GBin LSou MHer MMuc NBPC SAga
	- f. ***variegata*** (v)	NBir
	'Gustav Wermig' (C)	NDov WBou
	'H.H. Hodge' (ExVa)	WOFF
	'Hansa' (C)	GBin NChi
	'Haslemere'	see *V.* 'Nellie Britton'
*	'Heaselands'	SMHy
§	***hederacea***	CDev CMHG CStu EBee ECho ECou GMaP GQui NBro SAga SRms WFar WOFF
	- blue-flowered	CFee SIng
	- 'Putty Road' (Vt)	CGro
	'Helen' (Va)	ECtt
§	'Helen Mount' (T)	MNHC
	'Helen W. Cochrane' (ExVa)	WOFF
	'Helena' (Va)	WBou
	'Hespera' (Va)	WOFF
	heterophylla subsp. ***epirota***	see *V. bertolonii*
*	'Hetty Gatenby'	WBou WOFF
	hirsutula	EBla EHrv EMon
I	- 'Alba'	EBla
I	- 'Purpurea'	EBla
	'Hudsons Blue'	CElw WEas
	'Hugh Campbell' (ExVa)	WOFF
	'Huntercombe Purple' (Va) ♀H4	LHop MWat NBir SBch SBla SRms WBou WHal WKif WOFF
	'I.G. Sherwood' (FP)	WOFF
	'Iden Gem' (Va)	WBou WOFF
	'Inverurie Beauty' (Va) ♀H4	GMaP GMac NChi NDov WBou WOFF
	'Irene Hastings' (ExVa)	WOFF
	'Irish Elegance'	see *V.* 'Sulfurea'
	'Irish Molly' (Va)	More than 30 suppliers
	'Isabel' **new**	WBou
	'Ivory Queen' (Va)	CAby EBee GMac MRav MWgw WBou WOFF
	'Jack Frost' (FP)	WOFF
	'Jack Sampson' (Vt)	CDev CGro
	'Jackanapes' (Va) ♀H4	EBee ECho ECtt ELan EPfP LRHS NEgg NPri SIng SPer SPoG SRms WBou WFar WOFF

	'Jacqueline Snocken' (ExVa)	WOFF
	'James Pilling' (Va)	WOFF
	'Janet' (Va)	EBee ECtt EWin NCGa NPri SRGP WOFF
	japonica	GGar
	'Jeannie Bellew' (Va)	EBee ECtt NCob SPer SPoG SRms WBou WFar WSpi
	'Jennifer Andrews' (Va)	WBou WOFF
	'Jersey Gem' (Va)	WOFF
	'Jessica' (Va)	WOFF
	'Jessie' (SP)	WOFF
	'Jessie East'	WEas
	'Jessie Taylor' (FP)	WOFF
	'Jimmy's Dark' (ExVa)	WOFF
	'Joanna' (Va)	WBou
	'John Powell' (FP)	WOFF
*	'John Raddenbury' (Vt)	CDev GMaP SHar
	'John Rodger' (SP)	WOFF
	'Johnny Jump Up'	see *V.* 'Helen Mount'
	jooi	CEnt CPBP EBee ECho EWTr GCrs GKev MWea NBir NChi NMen SBla SRms WOFF WPat
	'Josephine' (Vt)	CGro
	'Josie' (Va)	WOFF
	'Joyce Gray' (Va)	WBou
	'Judy Goring' (Va)	GMac
	'Julia' (Va)	WBou
	'Julian' (Va)	CAby EBee GMac SBla SRms WBou WOFF
	'Juno' (Va)	GMac WOFF
	'Jupiter' (Va)	EBee WOFF
	'Kathleen Hoyle' (ExVa)	WOFF
	keiskei	NEgg
	- white-flowered	EBee
	'Kim'	CDev
	'Kitten'	GMac MSte NChi NDov WBou
I	'Kitty'	CCge
§	'Königin Charlotte' (Vt)	CCge CDev CGro EPfP GMac MHer MWgw NChi NWCA WCot WHil WMoo WOFF
	koreana	see *V. grypoceras* var. *exilis*
	'La France' (Vt)	CGro SBla
N	***labradorica*** misapplied	see *V. riviniana* Purpurea Group
§	***labradorica*** ambig.	CHar ECho EMil EWTr LRHS MRav NPri SHFr SMer WCra WFar
N	- ***purpurea*** misapplied	see *V. riviniana* Purpurea Group
	lactiflora	EBee
	'Lady Hume Campbell' (PVt)	CBre CGro NWCA WHer
	'Lady Jane' (Vt)	CGro
	'Lady Saville'	see *V.* 'Sissinghurst'
	'Lady Tennyson' (Va)	WOFF
	'Laura' (C)	GBuc NCob
	'Laura Cawthorne'	EBee
	'Lavender Lady' (Vt)	CBre CGro
	'Lavinia' (Va)	CAby LRHS WBou
	'Lees Peachy Pink' (Vt)	CGro
	'Lemon Sorbet'	GBuc
	'Lesley Keay' (ExVa)	WOFF
	'Letitia' (Va)	EBee GMaP NDov NEgg SRms WBou WFar
	'Lianne' (Vt)	CDes CDev CGro
	'Lilac Rose' (Va)	NDov WBou
	'Lindsay'	WBou
	'Lisa Tanner' (Va) new	WOFF
	'Lise Lazare' (Vt)	CGro
	'Little David' (Vtta) ♀H4	CAby CSam CTri GMac SRms WBou WPGP
	'Lord Plunket' (Va)	WBou WOFF
	'Lorna Cawthorne' (C)	CAby MSte WBou
	'Lorna Moakes' (Va)	SAga
	'Louisa' (Va)	GMac WBou
	'Love Duet'	NBir
§	***lutea***	NChi WBou

	- subsp. ***elegans***	see *V. lutea*
	'Luxonne' (Vt)	CBre CGro
	'Lydia' (Va)	WOFF
	'Lydia Groves' (Vt)	CGro
	'Lydia's Legacy' (Vt)	CGro
	'Madame Armandine Pagès' (Vt)	CBre
	'Maggie Mott' (Va) ♀H4	EBee ECha ECho ECtt GAbr GBuc GMac LHop LRHS MBri NChi NDov NPri SBla SPer SRGP WBou WFar WKif WOFF WSpi WWFP
	'Magic'	CAby EBee GBuc GMaP GMac WBou WOFF
	'Magnifico'	LRHS
	mandshurica	NWCA
	- f. ***albiflora***	EBee
	- 'Fuji Dawn' (v)	CBow EBee EMan ITer MFOX WCot WPtf
	- f. ***hasegawae***	EPPr
	- 'Ikedaeana'	EBee
	'Margaret' (Va)	WBou
	'Marie Rose' (Vt)	CGro
	'Marie-Louise' (dPVt)	CDes CDev CGro EBee EShb GMaP SHar
I	'Mars'	ECtt ENot GBin LSRN LSou MWgw NCGa WBor WFar
	'Mars' (Va)	EBee ECtt MCCP NEgg SBch SHGN SPoG WSpi
	'Martin' (Va) ♀H4	CAby COIW EBee ECha ECtt EWin GMaP GMac LHop MHer NDov SPer SRGP SSvw WBou WFar WOFF
	'Mary Mouse'	WBou
	'Mauve Haze' (Va)	GMac MSte WBou
	'Mauve Radiance' (Va)	GMac NVic WBou WOFF
	'May Mott' (Va)	GMaP GMac WBou
	'Mayfly' (Va)	MSte WBou
	'Melinda' (Vtta)	NDov WBou
	'Melting Moments' (Va)	LAst SIng
	'Mercury' (Va)	WBou
	'Milkmaid' (Va)	CAby NBir WLin
	'Mina Walker' (ExVa)	WOFF
	minor pale purple-flowered	EBee
	'Miss Brookes' (Va)	WBou WOFF
	'Misty Guy' (Vtta)	NChi NDov WBou
	'Molly Sanderson' (Va) ♀H4	More than 30 suppliers
	'Mona' (Va)	LAst
	'Moonlight' (Va) ♀H4	CAby ECha ECho ELan GMac LHop MHer SBla WBou WOFF
	'Moonraker'	GMaP NBir
	'Morwenna' (Va)	CAby WBou
	'Moseley Ideal' (ExVa)	WOFF
	'Mrs C.M. Snocken' (FP)	WOFF
	'Mrs Chichester' (Va)	WOFF
	'Mrs Cotterell'	EBee GBuc
	'Mrs David Lloyd George' (dVt)	CDev CGro
	'Mrs G. Robb' (ExVa)	WOFF
	'Mrs Lancaster' (Va)	CAby EBee EWin GMaP GMac LHop MBNS NBir NChi NPri SPoG SRGP SRms WBou
	'Mrs M.B. Wallace' (ExVa)	WOFF
	'Mrs R. Barton' (Vt)	CGro SHar
	'Myfawnny' (Va)	CAby EBee ECho ECtt ELan EWes GMac LRHS NChi SPoG SRms WBou WFar WSpi
	'Neapolitan'	see *V.* 'Pallida Plena'
§	'Nellie Britton' (Va) ♀H4	ECho ECtt GMac SRms
	'Netta Statham'	see *V.* 'Belmont Blue'
	'Nora'	CAby WBou WOFF
	'Norah Church' (Vt)	CDev CGro SBla SHar SSvw
	'Norah Leigh' (Va)	EOHP WBou
	obliqua	see *V. cucullata*

odorata (Vt) CArn CBcs CBod CDev CGro CPrp CRWN CSWP EBee EGoo EPfP GMac GPoy LCro LRHS MRav MWat NCGa NCob NPri SECG SIde SPer SRms STes
- 'Alba' (Vt) CBre CDev CGro CPom CSWP EBee ECho ELan EPfP EShb EWTr ILis LAst MHer NCob NPri SBla SRms WMoo
- 'Alba Plena' (dVt) EHrv NChi SBla WHer
- 'Albiflora' **new** CEnt
- apricot-flowered see *V.* 'Sulfurea'
- blue, double-flowered (d) LHop
- var. ***dumetorum*** see *V. alba*
- 'Katy' CPom SBla
- 'King of Violets' (dVt) SHar WCot WFar
- pink-flowered see *V. odorata* Rosea Group
- 'Princeana' **new** CGro
- 'Red Devil' WCot WFar
§ - Rosea Group (Vt) CDes CEnt CGro CPom EBee GMac MRav SIde WCot WOFF
- 'Weimar' **new** GBin
'Opéra' (Vt) CGro
'Orange' (Vt) CGro
'Orchid Pink' (Vt) CGro GMaP SHar
§ 'Pallida Plena' (dPVt) CBre CDev CGro
palmata NPro
'Palmer's White' (Va) WBou WOFF
palustris CRWN WHer WSFF WShi
'Pamela Zambra' (Vt) CDev GMaP SHar WPrP
'Pam's Fancy' (ExVa) WOFF
papilionacea see *V. sororia*
* 'Paradise Blue' (Vt) CGro
'Parme de Toulouse' (dPVt) CBre CDev CGro WOFF
'Pasha' (Va) GMac
'Pat Creasy' (Va) CAby GMac WBou WOFF
'Pat Kavanagh' (C) GAbr GMac NChi NDov WBou
'Patience' WBou
pedata EBee EPot MWrn SKHP WAbe WHil WPer
- 'Bicolor' WAbe
pedatifida CElw EBee MBNS MTho
'Peggy Brookes' (FP) WOFF
'Penelope' (SP) WOFF
pensylvanica see *V. pubescens* var. *eriocarpa*
'Peppered-palms' EHrv
'Perle Rose' (Vt) CDev CGro EHrv EShb SBla SHar
x ***permixta*** **new** EMon
'Petra' (Vtta) GMac
'Phyl Dove' (Vt) CGro
'Pickering Blue' (Va) WBou WOFF
pilosa B&SWJ 7204 WCru
'Primrose Dame' (Va) WBou
'Primrose Pixie' (Va) WBou
'Prince Henry' (T) MNHC
'Prince John' (T) MNHC
'Princess Mab' (Vtta) WBou WOFF
'Princess of Prussia' (Vt) CBre CDev CGro WHer
'Princess of Wales' see *V.* 'Princesse de Galles'
§ 'Princesse de Galles' (Vt) CGro CTri NSti WHal
'Pritchard's Russian' (Vt) CGro
§ ***pubescens*** var. ***eriocarpa*** SRms
'Purity' (Vtta) GMac WOFF
'Purple Wings' (Va) WBou
'Putty' ECou WCru
Queen Charlotte see *V.* 'Königin Charlotte'
'Queen Victoria' see *V.* 'Victoria Regina'
'R.N. Denby' (ExVa) WOFF
'Raven' GMac NChi SPhx WBou
'Rawson's White' (Vt) CDev CGro
'Rebecca' (Vtta) CAby CCge CSam CSpe EBee ECho ECtt ELan EPfP GMaP GMac LAst MBNS MHer NBir NCGa NChi NCob NEgg NPri SPer SPoG SRGP SRms WBou WEas WFar WOFF
'Red Charm' (Vt) EBee MWgw
'Red Giant' (Vt) CGro CPrp EBla EHrv MRav
'Red Lion' (Vt) CDev CGro
'Red Queen' (Vt) CGro NSti
reichei CRWN
'Reine des Blanches' (dVt) WCot
reniforme see *V. hederacea*
'Richard's Yellow' (Va) NCob
riviniana CArn CGro CRWN GWCH MHer NSco SEND WHer WJek WSFF WShi
- 'Ed's Variegated' (v) CBow EBee EMan EPPr WCot
§ - Purpurea Group More than 30 suppliers
- white-flowered EWes
'Rodney Davey' (Vt/v) EBee EMan LSou NBir
'Rodney Fuller' (FP) WOFF
'Rodney Marsh' NBir
'Rosanna' (Vt) NCob
'Roscastle Black' CMea EBee ECtt GMaP GMac LRHS MBNS MCot NDov SMrm WBou WCot WOFF WPGP WSpi
'Rosine' (Vt) CGro WOFF
'Royal Elk' (Vt) CDev CGro
'Royal Robe' (Vt) CGro
'Rubra' (Vt) WPer WPtf
§ ***rupestris*** CTri ECho EWTr
* - ***rosea*** CEnt CPom CSsd EBee EDAr EPfP EShb EWTr GAbr LLWP MHer MWgw NWCA SBch STre WEas WOut
* 'Ruth Elkins' (Va) WOFF
'Saint Helena' (Vt) CDev CGro
'Sarah Binnie' (ExVa) WOFF
schariensis EWes
selkirkii ITer NBro NWCA
- 'Variegata' (v) GBuc NBir
sempervirens SKHP
septentrionalis see *V. sororia*
'Serena' (Va) WBou
'Sherbet Dip' WBou
'Shirobana' NBir WCru
'Sidborough Poppet' CStu EWes
§ 'Sissinghurst' (Va) MHer NBir
'Sisters' (Vt) CGro
'Smugglers' Moon' MSte WBou
'Sophie' (Vtta) WBou
§ ***sororia*** EBee ECha ECho EMan EPPr GSki LRHS MFOX MLHP MNrw MWgw NBir NBro WBrE WPen WPtf
* - 'Albiflora' ♀H4 CBre CGro CHid CMMP CSWP CWCL EBee EBrs ECho EMil EPfP GGar GSki LRHS MBNS MWgw NWCA WCAu WCFE WFar WJek WPer
§ - 'Freckles' More than 30 suppliers
- 'Freckles' dark EBee ECho LHop NWCA
- 'Priceana' CBre CCge CDes CDev CElw CMMP EBee ECGP ECha EPyc EWTr NBir NCGa NChi WCot WPGP WSpi
- 'Red Sister' **new** MHer
- 'Speckles' (v) CBow CDev CGro EBla EMon
* 'Spencer's Cottage' WBou
'Steyning' (Va) WBou
stojanowii CEnt CSpe ECho SBla
striata WRos
'Sue's Choice' (FP) WOFF
§ 'Sulfurea' (Vt) CDev CEnt CPBP CPMA CSWP ECho EShb GMaP MHar MMHG NCGa NRya NWCA WCot WEas WFar WOFF WPer
'Susie' (Va) WBou
'Swanley White' see *V.* 'Conte di Brazza'

	'Sybil' (SP)	WBou
	'Sylvia Hart'	MTho
	'Talitha' (Va)	WOFF
	'Tanith' (Vt)	EBee
§	'The Czar' (Vt)	CBre CCge CGro ILis NChi
	'Tiger Eyes' (Va)	EBee ITer LAst MBNS MWea NCGa NEgg
	'Tinpenny Purple'	WCot
	'Titania' (Va)	CGro
	'Tom' (SP)	WOFF
	'Tom Tit' (Va)	WBou
	'Tony Venison' (C/v)	EBee EMan EWin LSou MBNS MTho NEgg SPoG WBou WFar WHer WSpi
	tricolor	CPrp ECho GPoy GWCH MHer MNHC NGHP NPri NSco SBch SIde WHer WJek WSel
	- 'Sawyer's Blue'	WPer
	'Valentine'	LRHS
	'Vanessa' (Va)	GMac
	velutina	see *V. gracilis*
	verecunda	CLAP
	- B&SWJ 604a	WCru
§	- var. ***yakusimana***	CStu
	'Victoria'	see *V.* 'Czar Bleu'
	'Victoria Cawthorne' (C)	CAby CElw EBee EMan GBuc GMaP GMac MHer MSte MWat NDov SBla SHGN WBou WEas
§	'Victoria Regina' (Vt)	CBre CDev
	'Virginia' (Va)	WBou
	'Vita' (Va)	GBuc GMac MBNS NDov SBla SRms WBou
	'Wasp' (Va)	CAby GMac
	'Wendy' (SP)	WOFF
	'White Ladies'	see *V. cucullata* 'Alba'
	'White Pearl' (Va)	SPhx WBou
	'White Perfection' (C)	CWib LRHS MBNS
	'White Swan' (Va)	NChi WOFF
	'William' (Va)	NDov
	'William Fife' (ExVa)	WOFF
	'William Snocken' (FP)	WOFF
	'Winifred Jones' (Va)	WBou WOFF
	'Winifred Warden' (Va)	MBNS WSpi
	'Winona Cawthorne' (C)	CAby EBee GMac NChi NDov
	'Wisley White'	EBee EWes WFar
	'Woodlands Cream' (Va)	GMac MHer NCob WBou WOFF
	'Woodlands Lilac' (Va)	WBou WOFF
	'Woodlands White' (Va)	WOFF
	yakusimana	see *V. verecunda* var. *yakusimana*
	'Zoe' (Vtta)	EBee ECtt EWin NCGa NPri SPer SRGP WBou WFar

Viscaria (*Caryophyllaceae*)

	vulgaris	see *Lychnis viscaria*

Vitaliana (*Primulaceae*)

§	***primuliflora***	ECho GCrs NLAp NMen NRya NSla
	- subsp. ***praetutiana***	NHol NMen NWCA SBla WFar WLin WPat
	- subsp. ***tridentata***	NMen

Vitex (*Verbenaceae*)

	agnus-castus	CAgr CArn CBcs CDul COld EBee ELau EOHP EShb EUnu GPoy LEdu LRHS MCCP MHer SLon SPer WFar WHer WSHC XPep
	- 'Alba'	CWib EBee EPfP XPep
	- var. ***latifolia***	CWib EBee ELan EPfP LRHS LSRN NLar SPoG WPGP XPep
I	- 'Rosea'	NLar XPep
	- 'Silver Spire'	ELan LRHS SPoG WPGP
	incisa	see *V. negundo* var. *heterophylla*
	lucens	CHEx
	negundo	CArn EOHP
§	- var. ***heterophylla***	EWes
	trifolia 'Variegata' **new**	EShb

Vitis ✿ (*Vitaceae*)

	'Abundante' (F)	WSuV
	'Alden' (O/B)	WSuV
	'Amandin' (G/W)	WSuV
	amurensis	EBee EPfP LRHS MBri MGol NLar
	- B&SWJ 4138	WCru
	'Atlantis' (O/W) **new**	WSuV
	'Aurore' (W)	WSuV
	'Baco Noir' (O/B)	GTwe SDea WSuV
	'Bianca' (O/W)	MCoo WSuV
	Black Hamburgh	see *V. vinifera* 'Schiava Grossa'
*	'Black Strawberry' (B)	WSuV
§	'Boskoop Glory' (O/B) ♀H4	CMac EMil LAst LBuc MCoo NBlu NPal SCoo SDea WSuV
	'Brant' (O/B) ♀H4	More than 30 suppliers
	'Brilliant' (B)	WSuV
	'Buffalo' (B)	WSuV
	'Canadice' (O/R/S)	SDea WSuV
	'Cascade'	see *V.* Seibel 13053
	Castel 19637 (B)	WSuV
	'Chambourcin' (B)	WSuV
	coignetiae ♀H4	More than 30 suppliers
	- B&SWJ 4550 from Korea	WCru
	- B&SWJ 4744	WCru
	- Claret Cloak = 'Frovit'^{PBR}	CBcs CWCL EBee ELan EPfP LRHS LSRN MAsh MRav NLar SBra SCoo SPer SPoG SSpi WPGP WPat WSpi
	- var. ***glabrescens*** B&SWJ 8537 **new**	WCru
	- 'Purple Cloak'	CHEx
I	- Sunningdale form **new**	WSpi
	'Dalkauer' (W)	WSuV
I	'Diamond' (B)	WSuV
	'Dutch Black' (O/B)	WSuV
	'Edwards No 1' (O/W)	WSuV
	'Eger Csillaga' (O/W)	WSuV
	'Einset' (B/S)	WSuV
	ficifolia	see *V. thunbergii*
	flexuosa B&SWJ 5568	WCru
	- var. ***choii*** B&SWJ 4101	WCru
§	'Fragola' (O/R)	CAgr CMac CTri EBee ECha EMil EPfP EPla ERea GTwe LRHS MAsh MRav SDea SPer SPoG SRms WSuV
	'Gagarin Blue' (O/B)	CAgr EMui GTwe SDea WSuV
	'Glenora' (F/B/S)	ERea WSuV
	'Hecker' (O/W)	WSuV
	henryana	see *Parthenocissus henryana*
	'Himrod' (O/W/S)	ERea GTwe SDea SGFT WSuV
	'Horizon' (O/W) **new**	WSuV
	inconstans	see *Parthenocissus tricuspidata*
	'Interlaken' (O/W/S)	ERea WSuV
	'Kempsey Black' (O/B)	WSuV
	'Kozmapalme Muscatoly' (O/W)	WSuV
	'Kuibishevski' (O/R)	WSuV
	labrusca 'Concord' (O/B)	ERea
	Landot 244 (O/B)	WSuV
	'Léon Millot' (O/G/B)	CAgr CSBt EMui ERea LRHS LSRN SDea WSuV
	'Maréchal Foch' (O/B)	WSuV
	'Maréchal Joffre' (O/B)	GTwe WSuV
	'Mars' (O/B/S) **new**	WSuV
	'Muscat Bleu' (O/B)	CCCN EMui WSuV
	'Nero'^{PBR} **new**	CAgr SGFT
	'New York Muscat' (O/B) ♀H4	ERea WSuV
	'New York Seedless' (O/W/S) **new**	WSuV
	'Niagara' (O/W) **new**	WSuV
	Oberlin 595 (O/B)	WSuV
	'Orion' (O/W)	EMui WSuV
	'Paletina' (O/W)	WSuV

	parsley-leaved	see *V. vinifera* 'Ciotat'
	parvifolia	WPat
	'Perdin' (O/W)	WSuV
	'Phönix' (O/W)	CAgr EMil EMui GTwe MBri MGos SGFT SKee SLim WSuV
	piasezkii	WCru
	- B&SWJ 5236	WCru
*	'Pink Strawberry' (O)	WSuV
	'Pirovano 14' (O/B)	GTwe SDea WSuV
§	'Plantet' (O/B)	WSuV
*	'Poloske Muscat' (W)	GTwe WSuV
	pseudoreticulata	WPGP
	purpurea 'Spetchley Park' (O/B)	WSuV
	quinquefolia	see *Parthenocissus quinquefolia*
	'Ramdas' (O/W) **new**	WSuV
	Ravat 51 (O/W)	WSuV
	'Rayon d'Or' (O/W)	WSuV
	'Regent'PBR	CAgr CWSG EMui GTwe MBri MCoo MGos NLar SGFT SKee SLim SPoG WOrn WSuV
	'Reliance' (O/R/S)	ERea WSuV
	'Rembrant' (R)	NPal WSuV
	'Riederother Monschrebe' (O/B) **new**	WSuV
	riparia	NLar WCru
	'Rondo' (O/B)	EMui
	- EM 6494-5	WSuV
	'Saturn' (O/R/S) **new**	WSuV
	'Schuyler' (O/B)	WSuV
	Seibel (F)	GTwe SDea SPoG
	Seibel 5279	see *V.* 'Aurore'
	Seibel 5409 (W)	WSuV
	Seibel 5455	see *V.* 'Plantet'
	Seibel 7053	WSuV
	Seibel 9549	WSuV
§	Seibel 13053 (O/B)	LRHS MAsh SDea WSuV
	Seibel 138315 (R)	WSuV
	'Seneca' (W)	WSuV
	'Serena' (O/W)	WSuV
§	'Seyval Blanc' (O/W)	CAgr GTwe SDea WSuV
	Seyve Villard ambig.	NPer
	Seyve Villard 12.375	see *V.* 'Villard Blanc'
	Seyve Villard 20.473 (F)	LRHS MAsh NPer WSuV
	Seyve Villard 5276	see *V.* 'Seyval Blanc'
	'Suffolk Seedless' (B/S)	WSuV
	'Tereshkova' (O/B)	CAgr ERea SDea WSuV
	'Thornton' (O/S)	WSuV
§	***thunbergii*** B&SWJ 4702	WCru
	'Triomphe d'Alsace' (O/B)	CAgr CSBt EMui LRHS NPer SDea SGFT WSuV
	'Trollinger'	see *V. vinifera* 'Schiava Grossa'
	'Vanessa' (O/R/S)	SDea WSuV
§	'Villard Blanc' (O/W)	WSuV
	vinifera	LCro MGos STrG
	- EM 323158B	WSuV
	- 'Abouriou' (O/B)	WSuV
	- 'Acolon' (O/B) **new**	WSuV
	- 'Adelheidtraube' (O/W)	WSuV
	- 'Albalonga' (W)	WSuV
§	- 'Alicante' (G/B)	ERea GTwe NPal SDea WSuV
	- 'Apiifolia'	see *V. vinifera* 'Ciotat'
	- 'Appley Towers' (G/B)	ERea
	- 'Augusta Louise' (O/W)	WSuV
	- 'Auxerrois' (O/W)	WSuV
	- 'Bacchus' (O/W)	SDea WSuV
	- 'Baresana' (G/W)	NPal WSuV
	- 'Beauty' **new**	CAgr
	- 'Black Alicante'	see *V. vinifera* 'Alicante'
	- 'Black Corinth' (G/B/S)	ERea
	- 'Black Frontignan' (G/O/B)	ERea WSuV
	- Black Hamburgh	see *V. vinifera* 'Schiava Grossa'
	- 'Black Monukka' (G/B/S)	ERea WSuV
	- 'Black Prince' (G/B)	WSuV
	- 'Blauburger' (O/B)	WCru
	- 'Blue Portuguese'	see *V. vinifera* 'Portugieser'
§	- 'Bouvier' (W)	WSuV
	- 'Bouviertraube'	see *V. vinifera* 'Bouvier'
	- 'Buckland Sweetwater' (G/W)	ERea GTwe MGos SDea WSuV
	- 'Cabernet Sauvignon' (O/B)	LCro LRHS MAsh MGos SDea WSuV
	- 'Canon Hall Muscat' (G/W)	ERea
	- 'Cardinal' (O/R)	EMil ERea WSuV
	- 'Chardonnay' (O/W)	CCCN EMui LCro LRHS MAsh NPer SDea WSuV
§	- 'Chasselas' (G/O/W)	ERea LRHS MAsh SDea WSuV
	- 'Chasselas de Fontainebleau' (F)	CCCN EMil
	- 'Chasselas de Tramontaner' (F)	EMil
	- 'Chasselas d'Or'	see *V. vinifera* 'Chasselas'
	- 'Chasselas Rosé' (G/R)	ERea WSuV
	- 'Chasselas Rose Royal' (O/R)	CCCN
	- 'Chasselas Vibert' (G/W)	ERea WSuV
	- 'Chenin Blanc' (O/W)	WSuV
§	- 'Ciotat' (F)	EPla ERea SDea WSuV
	- 'Cot Précoce de Tours' (O/B) **new**	WSuV
	- 'Crimson Seedless' (R/S)	ERea WSuV
	- 'Csabyongye' (O/W)	WSuV
	- 'Dattier de Beyrouth' (G/W)	WSuV
	- 'Dattier Saint Vallier' (O/W)	WSuV
	- 'Dolcetto' (O/B)	WSuV
	- 'Dornfelder' (O/R)	CCCN CSut SGFT SPoG WSuV
	- 'Dunkelfelder' (O/R)	WSuV
	- 'Early Van der Laan' (F)	NBlu
	- 'Ehrenfelser' (O/W)	WSuV
	- 'Elbling' (O/W)	WSuV
	- 'Excelsior' (W)	WSuV
	- 'Faber' (O/W)	WSuV
	- 'Fiesta' (W/S)	WSuV
	- 'Findling' (W)	WSuV
	- 'Flame'	CAgr EMui
	- 'Flame Red' (O/D)	CCCN SGFT
	- 'Flame Seedless' (G/O/R/S)	EMui SPoG WSuV
	- 'Forta' (O/W)	WSuV
	- 'Foster's Seedling' (G/W)	ERea GTwe SDea SPoG WSuV
	- 'Frühburgunder' (O/B)	WSuV
	- 'Gamay Hâtif' (O/B)	ERea
	- 'Gamay Hâtif des Vosges'	WSuV
	- 'Gamay Noir' (O/B)	WSuV
	- Gamay Teinturier Group (O/B)	WSuV
	- 'Gewürztraminer' (O/R)	LRHS MAsh SDea WSuV
	- 'Glory of Boskoop'	see *V.* 'Boskoop Glory'
	- 'Golden Chasselas'	see *V. vinifera* 'Chasselas'
	- 'Goldriesling' (O/W)	WSuV
	- 'Gros Colmar' (G/B)	ERea WSuV
	- 'Grüner Veltliner' (O/W)	WSuV
	- 'Gutenborner' (O/W)	WSuV
	- 'Helfensteiner' (O/R)	WSuV
	- 'Huxelrebe' (O/W)	WSuV
	- 'Incana' (O/B)	EBee EPfP EPla MRav WCFE WCot WSHC
	- 'Juliaumsrebe' (O/W)	WSuV
	- 'Kanzler' (O/W)	WSuV
	- 'Kerner' (O/W)	WSuV
	- 'Kernling' (F)	WSuV
	- 'King's Ruby' (F/S)	ERea WSuV
	- 'Lady Downe's Seedling' (G/B)	ERea
	- 'Lady Hastings' (G/B)	ERea
	- 'Lady Hutt' (G/W)	ERea

	– 'Lakemont' (O/W/S)	CAgr EMil ERea GTwe LRHS SGFT SKee SPoG WSuV
	– 'Lival' (O/B)	WSuV
	– 'Madeleine Angevine' (O/W)	CAgr CDul EMui ERea GTwe LRHS LSRN MAsh MGos NPer SDea WSuV
	– 'Madeleine Celine' (B)	WSuV
	– 'Madeleine Royale' (G/W)	ERea WSuV
	– 'Madeleine Silvaner' (O/W)	CSBt EMui ERea GTwe LRHS MAsh MGos NPer SDea SPer WBVN WSuV
	– 'Madresfield Court' (G/B)	ERea GTwe WSuV
	– 'Merlot' (G/B)	SDea WSuV
§	– 'Meunier' (B)	WSuV
	– 'Mireille' (F)	GTwe SDea WSuV
	– 'Morio Muscat' (O/W)	WSuV
	– 'Mrs Pince's Black Muscat' (G/B)	ERea
§	– 'Müller-Thurgau' (O/W)	EMui ERea GTwe LRHS LSRN MAsh MGos SDea SGFT SPer WSuV
	– 'Muscat Blanc à Petits Grains' (O/W)	SWvt WSuV
	– 'Muscat Champion' (G/R)	ERea
	– 'Muscat de Lierval' (O/B)	WSuV
	– 'Muscat de Saumur' (O/W)	WSuV
	– 'Muscat Hamburg' (G/B)	EMil EMui ERea LRHS LSRN MAsh MGos SDea SWvt WSuV
	– 'Muscat of Alexandria' (G/W)	CBcs CCCN CMac EMui MRav NPal SDea SPer SPoG
	– 'Muscat of Hungary' (G/W)	ERea
	– 'Muscat Ottonel' (O/W)	WSuV
	– 'Muscat Saint Laurent' (W)	WSuV
	– 'Nebbiolo' (O/B) **new**	WSuV
	– 'No 69' (W)	WSuV
	– 'Noir Hâtif de Marseille' (O/B)	WSuV
	– 'Olive Blanche' (O/W) **new**	WSuV
	– 'Oliver Irsay' (O/W)	ERea WSuV
	– 'Optima' (O/W)	WSuV
	– 'Ora' (O/W/S)	WSuV
	– 'Ortega' (O/W)	CCCN WSuV
	– 'Perle' (O/W)	WSuV
	– 'Perle de Czaba' (G/O/W)	EMil ERea WSuV
	– 'Perlette' (O/W/S)	CCCN CSut EMui ERea LRHS MAsh WSuV
	– 'Petit Rouge' (R)	WSuV
	– 'Pinot Blanc' (O/W)	CCCN LRHS MAsh WSuV
	– 'Pinot Gris' (O/B)	SDea WSuV
	– 'Pinot Noir' (O/B)	CCCN LCro LRHS NPal WSuV
§	– 'Portugieser' (O/B)	WSuV
	– 'Précoce de Bousquet' (O/W)	WSuV
	– 'Précoce de Malingre' (O/W)	ERea SDea
	– 'Prima' (O/B)	WSuV
	– 'Primavis Frontignan' (G/W)	WSuV
	– 'Purpurea' (O/B) ♀H4	More than 30 suppliers
	– 'Queen of Esther' (B)	GTwe MBri SKee SLim SPoG WSuV
	– 'Regner' (O/W)	WSuV
	– 'Reichensteiner' (O/G/W)	SDea WSuV
	– 'Reine Olga' (O/R)	ERea
	– 'Riesling' (O/W)	CCCN LRHS MAsh WSuV
	– Riesling-Silvaner	see *V. vinifera* 'Müller-Thurgau'
	– 'Rish Baba'	ERea
	– 'Royal Muscadine' (G/O/W)	WSuV
	– 'Saint Laurent' (G/O/W)	ERea WSuV
	– 'Sauvignon Blanc' (O/W)	CCCN WSuV
	– 'Scheurebe' (O/W)	WSuV
§	– 'Schiava Grossa' (G/B/D)	More than 30 suppliers
	– 'Schönburger' (O/W)	SDea WSuV
	– 'Schwarzriesling'	see *V. vinifera* 'Meunier'
	– 'Sémillon'	LRHS MAsh
	– 'Septimer' (O/W)	WSuV
	– 'Shiraz' (B)	WSuV
	– 'Siegerrebe' (O/W/D)	CAgr EMui ERea GTwe LRHS MAsh SDea SGFT WSuV
	– 'Silvaner' (O/W)	EMui WSuV
	– 'Spetchley Red'	WCru WPGP WPat WSPU WSpi
	– strawberry grape	see *V.* 'Fragola'
	– 'Suffolk Red' (G/R/S)	ERea
§	– 'Sultana' (W/S)	CAgr CCCN EMil EMui ERea GTwe SDea SGFT WSuV
	– Teinturier Group (F)	ERea
	– 'Theresa'	MBri SPoG WOrn WSuV
	– 'Thompson Seedless'	see *V. vinifera* 'Sultana'
	– 'Trebbiano' (G/W)	ERea
*	– 'Triomphe' (O/B)	EMui
	– 'Triomphrebe' (W)	WSuV
	– 'Vitalis Gold'	MGos
	– 'Vitalis Ruby'	MGos
	– 'Wrotham Pinot' (O/B)	SDea WSuV
	– 'Würzer' (O/W)	WSuV
	– 'Zweigeltrebe' (O/B)	WSuV
*	'White Strawberry' (O/W)	WSuV
	'Zalagyöngye' (W)	WSuV

Vriesea (*Bromeliaceae*)

	carinata	MBri
	hieroglyphica	MBri
	x ***poelmanii***	MBri
	x ***polonia***	MBri
	saundersii ♀H1	MBri
	splendens ♀H1	MBri XBlo
	'Vulkana'	MBri

W

Wachendorfia (*Haemodoraceae*)

	brachyandra	GGar
	thyrsiflora	CAbb CAby CDes CFir CHEx CMCo CPLG CPen CPne EBee IGor LEdu WFar WPGP WPic WPrP

Wahlenbergia (*Campanulaceae*)

	sp.	ECou
	akaroa **new**	EDAr
	albomarginata	ECho ECou EDAr GKev LRHS NWCA
	– 'Blue Mist'	ECho ECou
	ceracea	GKev NLAp
	congesta	ECho EDAr LRHS NSfd
	gloriosa	ECho ECou GCrs LRHS NLAp WAbe WFar
	pumilio	see *Edraianthus pumilio*
§	***saxicola***	ECho EMan NSfd NWCA
	serpyllifolia	see *Edraianthus serpyllifolius*
	stricta	ECou
	tasmanica	see *W. saxicola*
	undulata	CSpe

Waldsteinia (*Rosaceae*)

	fragarioides	WPer
	geoides	EBee EMan EPPr EPfP LAst NBre NLar NPro SPer
	ternata	More than 30 suppliers
§	– 'Mozaick' (v)	EBee EWes NBid NBir NBre NPro
	– 'Variegata'	see *W. ternata* 'Mozaick'

Wallichia (*Arecaceae*)

	densiflora	LPal

disticha	LPal

walnut, black see *Juglans nigra*

walnut, common see *Juglans regia*

Wasabia (*Brassicaceae*)

wasabi	CArn GPoy LEdu

Washingtonia (*Arecaceae*)

filifera ♀H1	CAbb CCCN CDoC CPHo EAmu EShb ETod LPal MBri NMyG SAPC SAin SArc SEND SPlb
robusta	CTrC EAmu LPal NPal SAin SChr SPlb

Watsonia (*Iridaceae*)

aletroides	CCtw CDes CPen CTca EBee EBrs ECho LPio NCGa SKHP WCot WPGP
angusta	CDes CGHE CPen CPne CPrp EBee IBlr WPGP
- JCA 3.950.409	WCot
ardernei	see *W. borbonica* subsp. *ardernei* 'Arderne's White'
beatricis	see *W. pillansii*
I 'Best Red'	LPio WCot
§ ***borbonica***	CAbb CCtw CPne CPou CPrp EShb GGar NCot WCot
- subsp. ***ardernei*** misapplied	see *W. borbonica* subsp. *ardernei* 'Arderne's White'
- subsp. ***ardernei*** (Sander) Goldblatt	EShb
§ - - 'Arderne's White'	CBre CDes CFul CGHE CPen CPne CPrp CTca CWsd EBee EBrs ECho ERos EShb GGar IBlr LPio MSte SBla WPGP WPic
- subsp. ***borbonica***	CDes CWsd EBee IBlr WPGP
brevifolia	see *W. laccata*
coccinea Baker	see *W. spectabilis*
coccinea	CDes CPBP WCot WPGP
densiflora	CPou EBee EShb IBlr IDee MSte WCot
distans	EBee
'Flame'	NCGa
fourcadei	CAby CPLG CPne EBee EShb WPGP
fulgens	CPne LEdu MSte
galpinii	CFir EBee IBlr NCot WPGP
- pink-flowered	CPrp
gladioloides	CPLG WPGP
§ ***humilis***	CDes CPBP CPou WPGP
knysnana	CDes CPou EBee EShb IBlr WCot WPGP
§ ***laccata***	CFir CPBP CPne CPou EBee EShb GGar WCot WPGP
lepida	CPou EBee IBlr SKHP
x ***longifolia***	CAbb WCot
marginata	CDes CPou GGar SKHP WCot WPGP
- 'Star Spike'	WCot
meriania	CPen CPou EBee GGar GSki IBlr NCGa WCot WHil
- var. ***bulbillifera***	CAby CGHE CPrp CTca EBee EBrs ECho GAbr GCra GGar GMac IBlr LPio WPGP
* 'Mount Congreve'	CTca
§ ***pillansii***	CCtw CGHE CHEx CPen CPne CPou CPrp CTca CTrC EBee ERos EShb GSki IBlr LRHS WFar WMnd
- pink-flowered	CDes CPen CPrp EBee
- red-flowered **new**	GBin
- salmon-flowered	CPen
pyramidata	see *W. borbonica*
roseoalba	see *W. humilis*
schlechteri	WPGP
§ ***spectabilis***	CPne WFar WPGP
'Stanford Scarlet'	CDes CPne CPou CPrp CWsd ELon IBlr SBla SChr SHom WPGP WSHC
stenosiphon	IBlr
strubeniae	IBlr
tabularis	CAbb CCtw CDTJ IBlr WCot
transvaalensis	EBee
'Tresco Dwarf Pink'	CAby CDes CPrp CSam IBlr LEdu WCot WPGP
Tresco hybrids	CAbb CHll CPen CPne CSsd WCFE
vanderspuyae	CCtw CPne CPou CPrp GGar IBlr NCot WCot WPGP
'White Dazzler'	SApp
wilmaniae	CPne CPou CPrp EBee IBlr WPGP
- JCA 3.955200	SKHP
- 'Ice Angel' **new**	SKHP

Wattakaka see *Dregea*

Weigela ✿ (*Caprifoliaceae*)

CC 1231	CPLG
'Abel Carrière'	CMac CTri EBee ECtt EPfP EWes NWea SEND WCFE WFar WSpi WTel
'Anne Marie'	MGos
'Avalanche' Lemoine	see *W. praecox* 'Avalanche'
'Avalanche' misapplied	see *W.* 'Candida'
'Boskoop Glory'	GQui SPer
§ Briant Rubidor = 'Olympiade' (v)	CDoC CSBt CWSG EBee ECtt ENot EPfP LRHS MAsh MBNS MBar MGos MRav NEgg NVic SEND SLim SPer SPlb SPoG WBod WFar WWeb
'Bristol Ruby'	CBrm CDul CPLG CWib EBee ECrN ELan EPfP LRHS MBar MGan MGos MHer MLHP MRav MSwo NPri NWea SGar SHBN SLon SMer SPer SPlb SRms WBVN WBrE WFar WMoo WTel
§ 'Candida'	CTri ELan EMil EWes GSki MBar MRav NBlu NHol NLar SMer SPer WSpi WTel
'Cappuccino'	SPoG
Carnaval = 'Courtalor'PBR	CBcs CWib EBee EMil EQua LRHS NHol SPoG
'Conquête'	SLon
coraeensis	CHll IArd MBlu MMHG MWgw WPat
- 'Alba'	SPer
decora	GQui
'Eva Rathke'	CTri NLar NWea SCoo
'Evita'	MBar MGos WFar
Feline = 'Courtamon'	MBri
florida	CDul EPfP MBar MGos SMer SPad WGwG
- B&SWJ 8439	WCru
- f. ***alba***	CBcs WFar
* - 'Albovariegata' (v)	CPLG LAst WBVN
- 'Bicolor'	CMac ELan
- 'Bristol Snowflake'	EBee EPfP LSou MBar MHer MSwo NEgg NHol NLar SLon SPoG WBod
- 'Foliis Purpureis' ♀H4	More than 30 suppliers
- Minor Black = 'Verweig 3' **new**	MBri
- Monet = 'Verweig' (v)	EMil ENot LBuc LRHS MAsh MBri MGos MPkF NLar SLim SPoG WCot
- Moulin Rouge = 'Brigela'PBR	CBcs CDoC ENot EPfP LBuc LRHS MAsh MBri MGos SPoG
- 'Pink Princess'	LRHS MSwo WWeb
- 'Samabor'	WFar
- 'Sunny Princess'	EQua NHol
- 'Suzanne' (v)	MGos NPro
- 'Tango'	CPMA ECtt LRHS MAsh MWya NHol NPro WWeb

	'Florida Variegata' (v) ♀H4	More than 30 suppliers
	florida 'Versicolor'	CMHG CMac CPLG CWib GQui SLon SMrm WFar WGor
	- Wine and Roses = 'Alexandra'	CAbP CBcs CDoC EBee ELan EMil ENot EPfP LAst LBuc LRHS LSRN MAsh MBri MGos MRav MWat NLar NPri SMac SPoG SWvt WLeb WWeb
	'Gold Rush'	NHol NLar
	'Golden Candy'	NPro
	'Gustave Malet'	CMCN GQui
	hortensis	CPLG
	- 'Nivea'	MBri
	japonica	CPle
	- 'Dart's Colourdream'	EBee ECtt EWes LAst LSou MRav NHol SCoo SLim SMer
	'Jean's Gold'	ELan MGos MRav NCGa
	'Kosteriana Variegata' (v)	EWTr LRHS MAsh SLon WFar
	lonicera	WHil
	'Looymansii Aurea'	CMHG CPLG CTri EBee ELan EPfP LAst MRav NHol SLon SPer WBod WFar WHar WPen
	Lucifer = 'Courtared'PBR	CBcs CDoC NHol
	maximowiczii	CPLG CPle EBee GQui GSki
§	***middendorffiana***	More than 30 suppliers
	'Minuet'	EBee EPfP GSki MBar MGos MRav MSwo NPro SLPl WWeb
	'Mont Blanc'	MMHG
	Nain Rouge = 'Courtanin'PBR	CBcs EBee GGar LRHS MBri NHol
	'Nana Variegata' (v)	CPLG EPfP LRHS MBar MBri NBlu SLPl WGwG
	Naomi Campbell = 'Bokrashine'PBR	CBow GBin GGar MGos MWea SCoo WFar WMoo
	'Newport Red'	EBee ENot MBNS MRav MWat NWea SMer WFar
	'Pink Poppet'	CAbP CSBt EKen EMil LAst LBMP LBuc LRHS LSRN LSou MAsh NPro SCoo SPoG SWvt
§	***praecox*** 'Avalanche'	ECtt MRav SGar
	'Praecox Variegata' (v) ♀H4	CChe CTri EBee ELan EPfP LAst LRHS MAsh MRav SMac SPer SPla SPoG SReu SRms WCFE WFar WHCG
	'Red Prince' ♀H4	EBee ELan GWCH LAst LRHS MGos MSwo NBlu NCGa NEgg NHol SPoG WBod
	'Red Trumpet'	SLon
	Rubidor	see *W.* Briant Rubidor = 'Olympiade'
	Rubigold	see *W.* Briant Rubidor = 'Olympiade'
	'Ruby Queen'PBR	EPfP
	'Rumba'	MMHG MRav NPro
	sessilifolia	see *Diervilla sessilifolia*
	'Snowflake'	CChe CDul EBee ECtt EWTr NPri NPro SRms WFar
	subsessilis B&SWJ 1056	WCru
	'Victoria'	CDoC CDul CWib EBee ECtt ELan EPfP LAst LBMP LRHS MAsh MGos MSwo NEgg NHol SCoo SPer SPla SPoG WBrE WGor WHar WMoo
	'Wessex Gold' (v)	WHCG

Weinmannia (*Cunoniaceae*)

	racemosa 'Kamahi'	CTrC
	trichosperma	GBin IDee SAPC SArc

Weldenia (*Commelinaceae*)

	candida	EBla ECho IBlr LTwo NMen SIng WAbe

Westringia (*Lamiaceae*)

	angustifolia	ECou
	brevifolia	ECou
	- var. ***raleighii***	ECou
§	***fruticosa*** ♀H1	CArn CBcs CPLG ECou EShb WJek XPep
	- 'Smokie'	ECou
	- 'Variegata' (v)	GQui LHop MNHC WJek
	- 'Wynyabbie Gem'	LHop
	longifolia	ECou
	rosmariniformis	see *W. fruticosa*
	'Smokie'	SOWG

Wettinia (*Arecaceae*)

	maynensis	LPal

whitecurrant see *Ribes rubrum* (W)

Widdringtonia (*Cupressaceae*)

	cedarbergensis	CPne GGar
	cupressoides	see *W. nodiflora*
§	***nodiflora***	GGar
	schwarzii	CBcs GGar

Wigandia (*Hydrophyllaceae*)

	caracasana	CHII CKob

Wikstroemia (*Thymelaeaceae*)

	gemmata	SCoo SSta
	kudoi	WCru

Willdenowia (*Restionaceae*)

	incurvata	CBig

wineberry see *Rubus phoenicolasius*

Wisteria ✿ (*Papilionaceae*)

§	***brachybotrys***	CMCN SLau SLim
§	- Murasaki-kapitan	CEnd CTri SIFN WSpi
	- 'Okayama'	SIFN
	- 'Pink Chiffon'	LRHS
	- 'Shiro-beni'	LRHS MGos
§	- 'Shiro-kapitan'	CEnd CSPN CTri CWGN EBee EPfP LPan LRHS MAsh MBri MDun MGos MRav NHol SBra SCoo SHBN SIFN SLau SLim SLon SPer WPGP
*	- 'White Silk'	CBcs CEnd LRHS MAsh MGos NCGa
§	'Burford'	CEnd CSPN CWGN EMui ERas LRHS MAsh MBri MDun MGan MWat NHol SCoo SLau SLim SPoG WHar WPGP WSpi
	'Caroline'	CBcs CDoC CEnd CMen CSBt CSPN CSam CWGN EBee EPfP ERas LRHS MAsh MBlu MGos NBea SBLw SHBN SLau SPer SPur SSpi WPGP WSHC
	floribunda	CBcs CRHN CWib ELan ENot EPfP LCro LRHS SBLw SBra SHBN WFar WNor
§	- 'Alba' ♀H4	More than 30 suppliers
	- 'Black Dragon'	see *W. floribunda* 'Yae-kokuryû' (d)
	- 'Burford'	see *W.* 'Burford'
	- 'Cannington'	SLim
*	- 'Cascade'	CPMA MGos NCGa WSpi
§	- 'Domino'	CBcs CEnd CTri EBee EPfP LHop LPan LRHS MAsh MBar MGan MGos MRav NHol SBLw SBra SCoo SLau SLim SPer SSta WFar
	- 'Fragrantissima'	see *W. sinensis* 'Jako'
	- 'Geisha'	CBcs CEnd MLan SBLw SIFN
	- 'Hagoromo Nishiki' (V)	MGos
*	- 'Harlequin'	CBcs CSPN EBee LRHS MGos NLar SPoG WFar
	- 'Hocker Edge' **new**	SLau
	- 'Hon-beni'	see *W. floribunda* 'Rosea'
	- 'Honey Bee Pink'	see *W. floribunda* 'Rosea'
	- 'Honko'	see *W. floribunda* 'Rosea'

	– 'Issai'	LRHS
	– 'Issai Perfect'	LPan LRHS LSRN NLar SCoo SPoG
	– 'Jakohn-fuji'	see *W. sinensis* 'Jako'
§	– 'Kuchi-beni'	CBcs CEnd CSBt CSPN EBee ELan LCro LHop LRHS MAsh MGos NCGa NHol NLar SCoo SLau SLim SPer SPoG
	– 'Lawrence'	CEnd CSPN LRHS MBri NLar SIFN SLau
	– 'Lipstick'	see *W. floribunda* 'Kuchi-beni'
	– 'Longissima'	see *W. floribunda* 'Multijuga'
	– 'Longissima Alba'	see *W. floribunda* 'Alba'
	– 'Macrobotrys'	see *W. floribunda* 'Multijuga'
	– 'Magenta'	CBcs LRHS
§	– 'Multijuga' ♀H4	More than 30 suppliers
	– Murasaki-naga	see *W. floribunda* 'Purple Patches'
	– 'Nana Richin's Purple'	CEnd LRHS SLau
	– 'Peaches and Cream'	see *W. floribunda* 'Kuchi-beni'
	– 'Pink Ice'	see *W. floribunda* 'Rosea'
§	– 'Purple Patches'	LRHS MGos NPri SLim
	– Reindeer	see *W. sinensis* 'Jako'
§	– 'Rosea' ♀H4	More than 30 suppliers
	– 'Royal Purple'	LRHS MBri NLar SLau SPoG WFar WGor
	– 'Russelliana'	CBcs EBee SLim
	– 'Shiro-naga'	see *W. floribunda* 'Alba'
	– 'Shiro-nagi'	see *W. floribunda* 'Alba'
	– 'Shiro-noda'	see *W. floribunda* 'Alba'
	– 'Snow Showers'	see *W. floribunda* 'Alba'
N	– 'Violacea Plena' (d)	CBcs CDoC ENot EPfP EQua LPan LRHS MGos NBlu NPri SHBN SPer SPur SWvt WFar
N	– 'Yae-kokuryū' (d)	CEnd CSBt CSPN CTri CWGN EBee ECrN ELan ENot EPfP LCro LRHS MBri MGos NHol SBra SCoo SHBN SIFN SLau SLim SMad SPer SReu SSpi SSta SWvt WFar WGor
	x ***formosa***	MGan SLau SLim
	– 'Black Dragon'	see *W. floribunda* 'Yae-kokuryū'
	– 'Domino'	see *W. floribunda* 'Domino'
	– 'Issai' Wada *pro parte*	see *W. floribunda* 'Domino'
	– 'Kokuryū'	see *W. floribunda* 'Yae-kokuryū'
	– 'Yae-kokuryū'	see *W. floribunda* 'Yae-kokuryū'
	frutescens	EBee SBLw WFar WNor
	– 'Alba'	see *W. frutescens* 'Nivea'
	– 'Amethyst Falls'PBR	CEnd CWGN LRHS SCoo SIFN
	– 'Magnifica'	see *W. macrostachya* 'Magnifica'
§	– 'Nivea'	SIFN
	Kapitan-fuji	see *W. brachybotrys*
	'Lavender Lace'	CBcs CDul CEnd EBee EPfP LRHS MAsh NCGa NLar SLau SPoG WFar
	macrostachya 'Bayou Two o'Clock'	SIFN
	– 'Clara Mack'	SIFN
§	– 'Magnifica'	LRHS WSpi
	– 'Pondside Blue'	SIFN
	multijuga 'Alba'	see *W. floribunda* 'Alba'
	'Showa-beni'	CEnd CWGN EBee LHop LRHS MAsh MGos SCoo SIFN SLau SLim SPoG WPGP
	sinensis ♀H4	More than 30 suppliers
	– 'Alba' ♀H4	CBcs CDoC CDul CMen CWib EBee ECrN ELan EPfP LAst LBuc LCro LRHS LSRN MBar MGan MGos MNHC MWat NBlu NScw SBra SEND SLau SLim SPer SPla SPoG WFar WOrn
	– 'Amethyst'	CBcs CEnd CSBt CSPN EBee EPfP LRHS MBri MDun MGos MLan MRav NSti SBLw SBra SIFN SLau SPla SPoG SReu
	– 'Blue Sapphire'	CBcs CMen CSPN EBee LRHS SBra SLau SPur
	– 'Consequa'	see *W. sinensis* 'Prolific'
	– 'Cooke's Special'	SIFN
§	– 'Jako'	CEnd MAsh MGos SIFN
	– 'Oosthoek's Variety'	see *W. sinensis* 'Prolific'
	– 'Prematura'	see *W. floribunda* 'Domino'
	– 'Prematura Alba'	see *W. brachybotrys* 'Shiro-kapitan'
§	– 'Prolific'	CDul CSBt CSam CTri CWib EBee ELan EMac EPfP LBuc LRHS MAsh MBri MDun MGos MLan MRav NBlu NHol SBLw SBra SCoo SPer SPla SSpi SWvt WFar WOrn WPGP WPat
	– 'Rosea'	LSRN MGos MLan MNHC SPur SWvt WSpi
	– 'Shiro-capital'	see *W. brachybotrys* 'Shiro-kapitan'
	'Tiverton'	CBcs EBee
	venusta	see *W. brachybotrys* 'Shiro-kapitan'
	– var. ***violacea*** misapplied	see *W. brachybotrys* Murasaki-kapitan
	villosa	WNor

Withania (*Solanaceae*)

somnifera	CArn EUnu GPoy MSal

Wittsteinia (*Alseuosmiaceae*)

vacciniacea	WCru

Wodyetia (*Arecaceae*)

bifurcata	EAmu LPal

Woodsia (*Woodsiaceae*)

obtusa	CLAP CWCL EBee EFer GMaP LAst LRHS NLar NMyG SRot WRic
polystichoides ♀H4	GQui SRms

Woodwardia (*Blechnaceae*)

from Emei Shan, China	CLAP
areolata	SKHP
fimbriata	CBod CCCN CFwr CHid CLAP CWCL EBee ERod EShb LRHS MAvo MGos MPes MWgw NBPC NHol NMyG NWCA SPer WBor WFib WMoo WPGP WPnP WRic
orientalis	WCot WFib
– var. ***formosana***	CLAP
– – B&SWJ 6865	WCru
radicans ♀H3	CAbb CHEx CHid CLAP CPLG EWes EWld GQui ISea SAPC SArc WFib WPic WRic
unigemmata	CHEx CLAP EFer EWes EWld SAPC SArc WAbe WFib WHal WPnP WRic
virginica	CLAP EFer

Worcesterberry see *Ribes* 'Worcesterberry'

Wulfenia (*Scrophulariaceae*)

amherstiana	GCrs
carinthiaca	EBee ECho GAbr GEdr GKev NBir NHol NLar WPer
x ***schwarzii***	CDes EBee

Wurmbea (*Colchicaceae*)

recurva	CStu

X

Xanthium (*Asteraceae*)

sibiricum	CArn

Xanthoceras (*Sapindaceae*)

sorbifolium ♀H3-4	CAgr CArn CBcs CLnd CMCN CWib EBee ECrN ELan EPfP IDee LEdu MBlu MBri NHol SCoo SSpi WFar WNor WPat WSpi XPep

Xanthocyparis see *Chamaecyparis*

Xanthorhiza (*Ranunculaceae*)

simplicissima	CBcs CGHE CPLG EPfP LEdu MBri NLar SDys SPer SSpi WPGP

Xanthorrhoea (*Xanthorrhoeaceae*)

australis	EShb SPlb
glauca new	CCCN

Xanthosoma (*Araceae*)

lindenii	see *Caladium lindenii*
sagittifolium	CKob EAmu
violaceum	CDTJ CDWL CKob EAmu

Xerochrysum (*Asteraceae*)

§ ***bracteatum*** 'Coco'	CMHG CSpe EMan MAJR WWlt
§ - 'Dargan Hill Monarch'	CHll CMHG CSev CSpe MAJR SRms WWlt
- Sundaze White = 'Redbrawhi'PBR (Sundaze Series)	SPoG
- 'Wollerton'	WWlt

Xeronema (*Phormiaceae*)

callistemon	CTrC

Xerophyllum (*Melanthiaceae*)

tenax	CFir EWes GBin GGar NMen

Xylorhiza see *Machaeranthera*

Xyris (*Xyridaceae*)

torta	WPGP

Y

youngberry see *Rubus* 'Youngberry'

Ypsilandra (*Melanthiaceae*)

cavaleriei	CExc EBee GEdr
thibetica	CDes CExc CGHE EBee EBla GEdr LAma WCot WCru WPGP WSHC

Yucca ✿ (*Agavaceae*)

SDR 3701 new	GKev
aloifolia	CCCN CDoC CHEx LRHS MGos MPRe SAPC SArc SChr SEND SNew SPlb
§ - f. ***marginata*** (v)	LPal MPRe SAPC SArc
- 'Purpurea'	MAga SPlb
- 'Tricolor' (v)	MPRe
- 'Variegata'	see *Y. aloifolia* f. *marginata*
angustifolia	see *Y. glauca*
angustissima NNS 99-509	WCot
arizonica	CBrP
baccata	CCCN CTrC LEdu XPep
- NNS 99-510	WCot
brevifolia	CHEx
carnerosana	CTrC EAmu
§ ***elata***	CCCN CTrC ETod SChr
§ ***elephantipes*** 🏆H1	EAmu ETod LRHS MBri SEND
- 'Jewel' (v)	EAmu SEND
faxoniana	MAga
faxoniana × ***glauca***	MAga
filamentosa 🏆H4	More than 30 suppliers
- 'Bright Edge' (v) 🏆H3	More than 30 suppliers
- 'Color Guard' (v)	CDul CTrC LAst MBri NLar WCot WFar
- 'Garland's Gold' (v)	CBcs CBrm CCCN CDoC GQui LRHS MAsh MGos WCot WFar
- 'Variegata' (v) 🏆H3	CBcs EPfP LRHS MGos SRms WFar WGer
flaccida	CBcs MGos NEgg SDix SEND SPoG
- 'Golden Sword' (v) 🏆H3	More than 30 suppliers
- 'Ivory' 🏆H3-4	CBcs CDoC CEnd CHar EBee ECtt ELan ENot EPfP GAbr LEdu LRHS LSRN MBlu MBri MGos MRav SMad SPer SRms SSta STre WLeb WMoo WPic WWeb
× ***floribunda***	SAPC SArc
§ ***glauca***	CAbb CBrP EPfP LEdu LRHS MBri MPRe NPal SAPC SPoG XPep
* - var. ***radiosa***	CTrC
gloriosa 🏆H4	CBcs CDoC CDul CHEx CTri EPfP EPla EWTr LRHS LRav MGos MPRe NPal NScw SAPC SArc SEND SHBN SPer SPoG SWvt WBrE WBrk
- 'Aureovariegata'	see *Y. gloriosa* 'Variegata'
- 'Moon Frost'	WCot
§ - 'Variegata' (v) 🏆H4	More than 30 suppliers
guatemalensis	see *Y. elephantipes*
linearis	EAmu
'Nobilis'	CHEx SDix
radiosa	see *Y. elata*
recurvifolia 🏆H4	CHEx EAmu EPfP MGos NPal SAPC SArc
- 'Variegata' (v)	WCot
rigida	CBrP
rostrata	CAbb CBrP CCCN CTrC EAmu EShb ETod LPal MPRe SAPC SArc SChr XPep
schidigera	WCot
- NNS 03-597	WCot
schottii	CAbb CBrP CTrC MAga
thompsoniana	CTrC EAmu
torreyi	CTrC SChr XPep
treculeana	EAmu MAga
'Vittorio Emanuele II'	SMad
whipplei	CAbb CBrP CCCN CDoC EBee ELan LEdu LRHS MAga MPRe NPal SAPC SSpi WBrE WPGP XPep
- SDR 3710	GKev
- subsp. ***caespitosa***	WCot
- subsp. ***intermedia***	WCot
- subsp. ***parishii***	WCot
- subsp. ***percursa***	WCot

Yushania (*Poaceae*)

§ ***anceps***	CBcs CDoC CEnt CHEx CPLG EBee EFul ENBC EPfP EPla GBin LCro MBar MGos MMoz MWht NVic SAPC SArc SDry WFar WMoo WPGP XIsg
- 'Pitt White'	CGHE EPla MWht SDry WPGP
- 'Pitt White Rejuvenated'	EPla ERod WPGP
brevipaniculata	EPla
chungii	EPla WPGP
maculata	EPla ERod MMoz MWht SDry
§ ***maling***	EPfP EPla ERod MMoz SDry
Yunnan 5 new	WPGP

Z

Zaluzianskya (*Scrophulariaceae*)

sp.	NMen
JCA 15665	WAbe
capensis	CHrt LPio WGwG
'Katherine'	SIng SRot
microsiphon new	SPlb
'Orange Eye'	CPBP CStu EPot LHop NPro NSla SBla WAbe

	ovata	CBcs CPBP EPot GBri LHop LPio MAvo MTho NSla NWCA SAga SBla SIng SPoG
	pulvinata	SPlb WAbe
	'Semonkong'	CMdw EMan LPio LSou MNrw MSte WHil

Zamia (*Zamiaceae*)

	floridana	LPal
	furfuracea	CBrP CKob LPal
	muricata	LPal
	skinneri	LPal

Zamioculcas (*Araceae*)

	zamiifolia	CCCN

Zantedeschia (*Araceae*)

§	***aethiopica*** ♀H3	More than 30 suppliers
	- B&SWJ 3959	WCru
	- 'Apple Court Babe'	CElw CStu MAvo MNrw WDyG WPic
	- 'Caerwent'	CPen
	- 'Childsiana'	EBee SApp
I	- 'Childsiana Lisa' **new**	EBrs
	- 'Crowborough' ♀H3	More than 30 suppliers
	- 'Gigantea'	CHEx
	- 'Glow'	CBct EBee ITer LAst LFur LSou MAvo MNrw NCGa NGdn WCot WGwG
	- 'Green Goddess' ♀H3	More than 30 suppliers
	- 'Little Gem'	SAga SMad WFar
*	- 'Marshmallow'	EBee EBla ELan EShb LRHS NCGa
	- 'Mr Martin'	CAbb CBct CCCN CDes CHid EBee ELon EWll GAbr LFur MNrw NCGa SMad SPoG SWvt WCot WPGP
	- 'Pershore Fantasia' (v)	CBct EBee EBla ITer MAvo MNrw WCot WFar WSPU
	- pink-flowered	CHEx
	- 'Tiny Tim'	SChr
	- 'Whipped Cream'	MDKP MNrw
	- 'White Gnome'	CDes WCot WFar WPGP
	- 'White Mischief'	EBee
	- 'White Sail'	CBct EBee EBla EMar LRHS MNrw MRav NGdn SPoG
	albomaculata	CHHB CPLG CWib EBrs EPfP LAma MNrw SGar SPlb
	'Anneke'	CStu CWib EBrs ECho EPfP SPer WBrE WFar
	'Apricot Glow'	CHll
	'Best Gold'	see *Z.* 'Florex Gold'
	black-flowered	CSut
	'Black Crusader'[PBR] **new**	NBPN
	'Black Eyed Beauty'	CWib EBrs LAma WPnP
	'Black Magic'	EBrs ECho EPfP SPer WFar
	'Black Pearl'	LAma
	'Black Star'	see *Z.* 'Edge of Night'
	'Cameo'	EBrs ECho LAma MNrw WFar
	'Captain Corona'[PBR] **new**	ENot
	'Captain Eskimo'[PBR] **new**	ENot
	'Captain Tendens'[PBR] **new**	ENot
	'Carmine Red'	MNrw WBrE
	'Celeste'	EBrs
	'Crystal Blush'	CWib ENot LAma
§	'Edge of Night' **new**	ENot
	elliottiana ♀H1	CFir CHEx CHal CPou CStu CTri EBrs EPfP GQui LAma MNrw
	- 'Cream' **new**	SWal
	'Flame'	EBrs
§	'Florex Gold'	ENot
	'Galaxy'	EBrs ENot
	'Harvest Moon'	EBrs LAma
	'Kiwi Blush'	CAbP CBcs CBen CBgR CCCN CDWL CDes CFir CHEx CSpe EBee EBla ELan EMan EPfP ERou EWll IBal ITer LCro LRHS MAvo MCCP NGdn NPal SApp SPla SPoG WFar WGwG
	'Lime Lady'	CBct ECha
	'Majestic Red'	EBrs
	'Mango'	CWib EBrs EWll LAma MNrw WCot WPnP
	'Pink Mist'	CBct CHHB EBee EBrs EMar ERCP EShb LAma WHil WPnP
	'Pink Persuasion'	CWib EBrs ENot LAma MNrw WFar WPnP
	rehmannii ♀H1	CPou CStu EBrs ENot EPfP GQui LAma MNrw NLar SGar SRms WSPU
	'Schwarzwalder'[PBR]	EBrs
	'Sensation'	EBrs
	'Silver Lining'	LAma
	'Solfatare'	EBrs ECho MNrw WPnP
	'Sunshine'	EWll
	'Treasure'	EBrs
	'White Pixie'	EBee EMan ENot EPfP LSou NPal SAga SPoG

Zanthorhiza see *Xanthorhiza*

Zanthoxylum (*Rutaceae*)

	acanthopodium B&SWJ 7237	WCru
	ailanthoides	EPfP
	- B&SWJ 8535	WCru
	americanum	CAgr ELan LEdu
	armatum	CAgr
	bungeanum HWJK 2131	WCru
	oxyphyllum	WPGP
	piasezkii	CBcs
	piperitum	CAgr GPoy WPGP
	- B&SWJ 8593	WCru
	schinifolium	CAgr LEdu
	- B&SWJ 1245	WCru
	simulans	CArn CBcs CLnd CPLG EBee LEdu MBlu NLar WPGP

Zauschneria (*Onagraceae*)

	arizonica	see *Z. californica* subsp. *latifolia*
§	***californica***	CHll CSam CTri ECho EDAr EPfP MBrN NMen SGar SLon SWat WBod WHrl
	- 'Albiflora'	WAbe
§	- subsp. ***cana***	ECha MHar SWat XPep
	- - 'Sir Cedric Morris'	EPfP LRHS MAsh
	- 'Catalina'	XPep
§	- 'Dublin' ♀H3	More than 30 suppliers
	- 'Ed Carman'	EBee ECtt EMan LSou
§	- subsp. ***garrettii***	ECho NWCA SDys SWat XPep
	- 'Glasnevin'	see *Z. californica* 'Dublin'
§	- subsp. ***latifolia***	XPep
	- - 'Sally Walker'	EWes
§	- subsp. ***mexicana***	CWib EPot MHer SRms
	- 'Olbrich Silver'	EBee ECha ECtt EMan EShb EWes LHop NMen NWCA WAbe WFar WHoo WPat
	- 'Schieffelin's Choice'	XPep
	- 'Sierra Salmon'	WAbe WPat XPep
	- 'Solidarity Pink'	EBee MTho NMen NWCA WAbe WPat XPep
	- 'Western Hills' ♀H4	CFir CLyd CSpe CTri EBee ECha ECho ECtt EDAr LHop LSou MRav NWCA SAga SBch SBla SIng SPhx WAbe WHoo WPat XPep
	cana villosa	see *Z. californica* subsp. *mexicana*
I	'Pumilio'	NMen WAbe
§	***septentrionalis***	SBla WAbe

Zebrina see *Tradescantia*

Zelkova ✿ (*Ulmaceae*)

carpinifolia	CDoC CDul CMCN CMen CTho LRHS SBLw WNor
'Kiwi Sunset'	EBee ENot
schneideriana	CMen EGFP
serrata ♀H4	CBcs CDul CLnd CMCN CMen CTho EBee ECrN ELan EPfP IArd ISea MBar MBri NBea NHol NWea SBLw SPer STre WFar WHCr WNor WOrn
- B&SWJ 8491 from Korea	WCru
- 'Goblin'	CLnd WPat
- 'Green Vase'	LPan LRHS
- 'Urban Ruby' **new**	MGos
- 'Variegata' (v)	CPMA MBlu MGos
- 'Yatsubusa'	STre
sinica	CLnd CMCN CMen WNor

Zenobia (*Ericaceae*)

pulverulenta	More than 30 suppliers
- 'Blue Sky'	CAbP CDul CMCN EBee EPfP MAsh MBlu MBri NLar SSpi SSta WPGP
- 'Misty Blue' **new**	GGGa LRHS
- 'Raspberry Ripple'	MBlu MBri NLar SSta
- 'Viridis'	NLar

Zephyranthes ✿ (*Amaryllidaceae*)

atamasca	CStu ERos SKHP
candida	CAvo CFFs CSpe CStu EBee EBrs ECho EMan EMon EPot ERos EShb ITim LAma LRHS SDix WHil
citrina	CGrW EBee EBrs ECho EPot ERos LAma WCot
drummondii	CStu EBee ECho WCot
flavissima	EBrs ECho WCot WPGP WPrP
grandiflora ♀H2-3	ECho
'Grandjax'	WCot
'La Buffa Rose'	CStu SKHP WCot
lindleyana	WCot
mexicana	ERos
minima	CStu ECho LTwo
robusta	see *Habranthus robustus*
rosea	CGrW EBee EBrs EPot
verecunda	CStu SIng

Zieria (*Rutaceae*)

cytisoides	ECou

Zigadenus (*Melanthiaceae*)

elegans	EBee ECha EDAr ERos GAbr LRHS SMad WTin
fremontii	EBee EBla WLin
nuttallii	EBee EBrs ECho EMan ERos LHop MDKP SPhx WCot
venenosus	EBee
virescens **new**	EBrs

Zingiber (*Zingiberaceae*)

chrysanthum	CKob
clarkei	CKob
malaysianum	CKob
mioga	CKob GPoy LEdu MSal WDyG WPGP
- 'Dancing Crane' (v)	CKob EBee
officinale	CKob MSal
purpureum	CKob
rubens	CKob
'Yellow Delight'	CKob
zerumbet	CKob
- 'Darceyi' (v)	CKob

Zinnia (*Asteraceae*)

'Red Spider'	CSpe

Zizania (*Poaceae*)

caducifolia	see *Z. latifolia*
§ ***latifolia***	SNin

Zizia (*Apiaceae*)

aptera	EBee SPhx WPGP
aurea	EBee WSHC WTin

Ziziphus (*Rhamnaceae*)

§ ***jujuba*** (F)	CAgr CBcs
- 'Lang' (F)	ERea
- 'Li' (F)	LPan
- var. ***spinosa***	CArn
sativa	see *Z. jujuba*

Zoysia (*Poaceae*)

matrella	XPep
tenuifolia	XPep

BIBLIOGRAPHY

This is by no means exhaustive but lists some of the more useful works used in the preparation of the *RHS Plant Finder*. The websites of raisers of new plants (not listed here) are also an invaluable source of information.

GENERAL

African Botany Supplementary Vol. No. 13. Kirstenbosch, South Africa: National Botanic Gardens.

Allan, H.H., et al. 2000. *Flora of New Zealand.* Wellington. (5 vols).

Ball Colegrave. *Plants and Seed Catalogue 2005/6.* 2004. West Adderbury, Oxon: Ball Colegrave.

Bean, W.J. 1988. *Trees and Shrubs Hardy in the British Isles.* (8th ed. edited by Sir George Taylor & D.L. Clarke & Supp. ed. D.L. Clarke). London: John Murray.

Beckett, K. (ed.). 1994. *Alpine Garden Society Encyclopaedia of Alpines.* Pershore, Worcs: Alpine Garden Society

Boufford, D.E., et al. (eds). 2003. *Flora of Taiwan Checklist.* A checklist of the vascular plants of Taiwan. Taipei, Taiwan: NTU. http://tai2.ntu.edu.tw/fot/v6/v6checklist.pdf

Bramwell, D. & Bramwell, Z.I. 2001. *Wild Flowers of the Canary Islands.* (2nd ed.). Madrid: Editorial Rueda, S.L

Brickell, C. (ed.). 2003. *The Royal Horticultural Society A-Z Encyclopedia of Garden Plants.* (2nd ed.) London: Dorling Kindersley.

Brickell, C.D. et al (eds.). 2004. *International Code of Nomenclature for Cultivated Plants* (7th ed.). ISHS.

Brummitt, R.K. & Powell, C.E. (eds). 1992. *Authors of Plant Names.* Kew: Royal Botanic Gardens.

Brummitt, R.K. (comp.). 1992. *Vascular Plant Families and Genera.* Kew: Royal Botanic Gardens.

Castroviejo, S., Laínz, M., López González, G., Montserrat, P., Muñoz Garmendia, F., Paiva, J. & Villar, L. (eds). *Flora Iberica.* 1987-2001. (Vols 1-8, 14). Madrid: Real Jardín Botánico, C.S.I.C.

Cave, Y. & Paddison, V. 1999. *The Gardener's Encyclopaedia of New Zealand Native Plants.* Auckland: Godwit.

Cooke, I. 1998. *The Plantfinder's Guide to Tender Perennials.* Newton Abbot, Devon: David & Charles.

Cronquist, A., Holmgren, A.H., Holmgren, N.H., Reveal, J.L. & Holmgren, P.H. et al. (eds). *Intermountain Flora: Vascular Plants of the Intermountain West, USA.* (1986-97). (Vols 1, 3-6). New York: New York Botanical Garden.

Davis, P.H., Mill, R.R. & Tan, K. (eds). 1965-88. *Flora of Turkey and the East Aegean Islands* (Vols 1-10). Edinburgh University Press.

Forrest, M. (comp.) & Nelson, E.C. (ed.). 1985. *Trees and Shrubs Cultivated in Ireland.* Dublin: Boethius Press for An Taisce.

Goldblatt, P. & Manning, J. 2000. *Cape Plants. A Conspectus of the Cape Flora of South Africa.* South Africa / USA: National Botanical Institute of South Africa / Missouri Botanical Garden.

Graf, A.B. 1963. *Exotica 3. Pictorial Cyclopedia of Exotic Plants.* (3rd ed.). New Jersey, USA: Roehrs.

Graf, A.B. 1986. *Tropica.* Color Cyclopedia of Exotic Plants and Trees. (3rd ed.). New Jersey, USA: Roehrs.

Greuter, W., et al. (eds). 2000. *International Code of Botanical Nomenclature (Saint Louis Code).* Königstein, Germany: Koeltz Scientific Books.

Greuter, W., Brummitt, R.K., Farr, E., Kilian, N., Kirk, P.M. & Silva, P.C. (comps). 1993. *NCU-3. Names in Current Use for Extant Plant Genera.* Königstein, Germany: Koeltz Scientific Books. www.bgbm.fu-berlin.de/iapt/ncu/genera/NCUGQuery.htm

Grierson, A.J.C., Long, D.G. & Noltie, H.J. et al. (eds). 2001. *Flora of Bhutan.* Edinburgh: Royal Botanic Garden.

Güner, A., Özhatay, N., Ekîm, T., Baser, K.H.C. & Hedge, I.C. 2000. *Flora of Turkey and the East Aegean Islands.* Supplement 2. Vol. 11. Edinburgh: Edinburgh University Press.

Harkness, M.G. 1993. *The Bernard E. Harkness Seedlist Handbook.* (2nd ed.). London: Batsford.

Hickman, J.C. (ed.). 1993. *The Jepson Manual. Higher Plants of California.* Berkeley & Los Angeles: University of California Press.

Hillier, J. & Coombes, A. (eds). 2002. *The Hillier Manual of Trees & Shrubs.* (7th ed.). Newton Abbot, Devon: David & Charles.

Hirose, Y. & Yokoi, M. 1998. *Variegated Plants in Colour.* Iwakuni, Japan: Varie Nine.

Hirose, Y. & Yokoi, M.. 2001. *Variegated Plants in Colour.* Vol. 2. Iwakuni, Japan: Varie Nine.

Hoffman, M. (ed.). 2005. *List of Woody Plants. International Standard ENA 2005-2010.* Netherlands: Applied Plant Research.

Huxley, A., Griffiths, M. & Levy, M. (eds). 1992. *The New RHS Dictionary of Gardening.* London: Macmillan.

Jelitto, L. & Schacht, W. 1990. *Hardy Herbaceous Perennials.* Portland, Oregon: Timber Press. (2 vols).

Krüssmann, G. & Epp, M.E. (trans.). 1986. *Manual of Cultivated Broad-leaved Trees and Shrubs.* London: Batsford (3 vols).

Leslie, A.C. (trans.). *New Cultivars of Herbaceous Perennial Plants 1985-1990.* Hardy Plant Society.

Lloyd, C. 2000. *Great Dixter Nurseries: Clematis and General Plant List 2000.*

Mabberley, D.J. 1997. *The Plant-Book. A Portable Dictionary of the Vascular Plants.* (2nd ed.). Cambridge: Cambridge University Press.

McGregor, R.L., Barkley, T.M., Brooks, R.E. & Schofield, E.K. et al. (eds). 1987. *Flora of the Great Plains.* Lawrence, Kansas: University Press of Kansas.

Metcalf, L.J. 1987. *The Cultivation of New Zealand Trees and Shrubs.* Auckland: Reed Methuen.

Munz, P. 1973. *A Californian Flora and Supplement.* London: University of California Press.

Nelson, E.C. 2000. *A Heritage of Beauty: The Garden Plants of Ireland: An Illustrated Encyclopaedia.* Dublin: Irish Garden Plant Society.

Ohwi, J. 1965. *Flora of Japan.* Washington DC: Smithsonian Institution.

Phillips, R. & Rix, M. 1989. *Shrubs.* London: Pan

Phillips, R. & Rix, M. 1993. *Perennials.* London: Pan (2 vols).

Phillips, R. & Rix, M. 1997. *Conservatory and Indoor Plants.* London: Macmillan. (2 vols).

Platt, K. (comp.). 2002. *The Seed Search.* (5th ed.). Sheffield: Karen Platt

Polunin, O. & Stainton, A.. 1984. *Flowers of the Himalaya.* Oxford: Oxford University Press.

Press, J.R. & Short, M.J. (eds). 1994. *Flora of Madeira.* London: Natural History Museum/HMSO.

Rehder, A. 1940. *Manual of Cultivated Trees and Shrubs Hardy in North America.* (2nd ed.). New York: Macmillan.

Stace, C. 1997. *New Flora of the British Isles.* (2nd ed.). Cambridge: Cambridge University Press.

Stainton, A. 1988. *Flowers of the Himalaya. A Supplement.* Oxford University Press.

Stearn, W.T. 1992. *Botanical Latin.* (4th ed.). Newton Abbot, Devon: David & Charles.

Stearn, W.T. 1996. *Stearn's Dictionary of Plant Names for Gardeners.* London: Cassell

Thomas, G.S. 1990. *Perennial Garden Plants. A Modern Florilegium.* (3rd ed.). London: Dent.

Thomas, G.S. 1992. *Ornamental Shrubs, Climbers & Bamboos.* London: John Murray

Trehane, P. (comp.). 1989. *Index Hortensis. Volume 1: Perennials.* Wimborne: Quarterjack

Tutin, T.G., et al. (ed.). 1993. *Flora Europaea. Volume 1. Psilotaceae to Platanaceae.* (2nd ed.). Cambridge University Press.

Tutin, T.G., et al. 1964. *Flora Europaea.* Cambridge University Press. Vols 1-5.

Walter, K.S. & Gillett, H.J. (eds). 1998. *1997 IUCN Red List of Threatened Plants.* Gland, Switzerland and Cambridge, UK: IUCN.

Walters, S.M. & Cullen, J. et al. (eds). 2000. *The European Garden Flora.* Cambridge: Cambridge University Press. (6 vols).

Willis, J.C. & Airy-Shaw, H.K. (eds). 1973. *A Dictionary of the Flowering Plants and Ferns.* (8th ed.). Cambridge University Press.

GENERAL PERIODICALS

Dendroflora

New, Rare and Unusual Plants.

The Hardy Plant Society. *The Hardy Plant.*

The Hardy Plant Society. *The Sport.*

Internationale Stauden-Union. *ISU Yearbook.*

Royal Horticultural Society. *The Garden.*

Royal Horticultural Society. *The Plantsman.*

Royal Horticultural Society. *The New Plantsman.*

GENERAL WEBSITES

Annotated Checklist of the Flowering Plants of Nepal. www.efloras.org/flora_page.aspx?flora_id-110

Australian Cultivar Registration Authority. Jan 2006. www.anbg.gov.au/acra

Australian Plant Breeders Rights – Database Search. Jan 2006. pbr.ipaustralia.optus.com.au/

Australian Plant Names Index. Australian National Botanic Gardens (comp.). Jan 2006. www.anbg.gov.au/anbg/names.html

Canadian Ornamental Plant Foundation. Jan 2006. www.copf.org/plants_list.asp

Canadian Plant Breeders' Rights Office: Canadian Food Inspection Agency. Jan 2006. www.inspection.gc.ca/english/plaveg/pbrpov/pbrpove_html

Catálogo de las Plantas Vasculares de la República Argentina. Jan 2006. www.darwin.edu.ar/Publicaciones/CatalogoVascll/CatalogoVascll.asp

DEFRA Plant Varieties and Seeds Gazette. Dec 2004. www.defra.gov.uk/planth/pvs.gaz.htm

Fischer France. www.pelfi.fr

Flora Mesoamericana Internet Version (W3FM). Apr 2003 Missouri Botanical Garden. www.mobot.org/mobot/fm/

Flora of Chile. www.efloras.org/flora_page.aspx?flora_id=60

Flora of China Checklist. Jan 2005. http://flora.huh.harvard.edu/china

Flora of North America Website. Jan 2006. Morin, N.R., et al. http://hua.huh.harvard.edu/fna/index.html

GRIN (Germplasm Resources Information Network) Taxonomy. Dec 2005. www.ars-grin.gov/cgi-bin/npgs/html/index.pl

Index Synonymique de la Flore de France. Oct 1999. www.inra.fr/flore-france/consult.html

International Plant Names Index. Jan 2006. www.ipni.org

IOPI Provisional Global Plant Checklist. Jan 2006. www.bgbm.fu-berlin.de/iopi/gpc/query.asp

Manual de plantas de Costa Rica. Apr 2001. www.mobot.org/manual.plantas/lista.html

Plants Database. Jan 2006. USDA, NRCS. http://plants.usda.gov

Synonymized Checklist of the Vascular Flora of the United States, Puerto Rico and the Virgin Isles. BIOTA of North America Program. www.csdl.tamu.edu/FLORA/b98/check98.htm. Jan 2006

US Patent Full-Text Database. US Patent and Trademark Office, (comp.). Jan 2006. www.uspto.gov/patft/index.html

VAST TROPICOS. Jan 2006. Missouri Botanical Garden. http://mobot.mobot.org/W3T/Search/vast.html

World Checklist of Monocots (2004). The Board of Trustees of the Royal Botanic Gardens, Kew. www.kew.org/monocotChecklist/default.jsp

Genera and other Plant Groupings

Acacia

Simmons, M.H. 1987. *Acacias of Australia.* (2nd ed.). Melbourne: Nelson.

Acer

Harris, J.G.S. 2000. *The Gardener's Guide to Growing Maples.* Newton Abbot, Devon: David & Charles.

Van Gelderen, C.J. & Van Gelderen, D.M. 1999. *Maples for Gardens.* A Color Encyclopedia. Portland, Oregon: Timber Press.

Vertrees, J.D. 2001. *Japanese Maples.* Momiji and Kaede. (3rd ed.). Portland, Oregon: Timber Press.

Actaea

Compton, J. 1992. *Cimicifuga* L. *Ranunculaceae. The Plantsman* 14(2):99-115.

Compton, J. 1992. *Cimicifuga.* A Bane of a Name for a Fine Plant. *The Garden* (RHS) 117(11):504-506.

Compton, J.A. & Culham, A. 2000. The Name is the Game. *The Garden* (RHS) 125(1):48-52.

Compton, J.A., Culham, A. & Jury, S.L. 1998. Reclassification of *Actaea* to include *Cimicifuga* and *Souliea* (*Ranunculaceae*). *Taxon* 47:593-634.

Adiantum

Goudey, C.J. 1985. *Maidenhair Ferns in Cultivation.* Melbourne: Lothian.

Agapanthus

Snoeijer, Wim 2004. *Agapanthus. A Revision of the Genus.* Portland, Oregon: Timber Press.

Agavaceae

Irish, M. & Irish, G. 2000. *Agaves, Yuccas and Related Plants.* A Gardener's Guide. Portland, Oregon: Timber Press.

Aizoaceae

Burgoyne, P. et al. 1998. *Mesembs of the World. Illustrated Guide to a Remarkable Succulent Group.* South Africa: Briza Publications.

Allium

Davies, D. 1992. *Alliums. The Ornamental Onions.* London: Batsford

Gregory, M., et al. 1998. *Nomenclator Alliorum.* Kew: Royal Botanic Gardens.

Mathew, B. 1996. *A Review of Allium Section Allium.* Kew: Royal Botanic Gardens.

Androsace

Smith, G. & Lowe, D. 1997. *The Genus Androsace.* Pershore, Worcs: Alpine Garden Society.

***Anemone*, Japanese**

McKendrick, M. 1990. Autumn Flowering Anemones. *The Plantsman* 12(3):140-151.

McKendrick, M. 1998. Japanese Anemones. *The Garden* (RHS) 123(9):628-633.

Anthemis

Leslie, A. 1997. Focus on Plants: *Anthemis tinctoria. The Garden* (RHS) 122(8):552-555.

Apiaceae

Pimenov, M.G. & Leonov, M.V. 1993. *The Genera of the Umbelliferae.* Kew: Royal Botanic Gardens.

Aquilegia

Munz, P.A. 1946. *Aquilegia:* the Cultivated and Wild Columbines. *Gentes Herb.* 7(1):1-150.

***Arecaceae* (*Palmae*, palms)**

Jones, D.L. 1995. *Palms Throughout the World.* Chatswood, NSW: Reed Books.

Uhl, N.W. & Dransfield, J. 1987. *Genera Palmarum.* A Classification of Palms Based on the Work of Harold E. Moore Jr. Lawrence, Kansas: Allen Press.

Argyranthemum

Cheek, R. 1993. La Belle Marguerite. *The Garden* (RHS) 118(8):350-355.

Humphries, C.J. 1976. A Revision of the Macaronesian Genus *Argyranthemum. Bull. Brit. Mus. (Nat. Hist.) Bot.* 5(4):145-240.

Arisaema

Gusman, G. & Gusman, L. 2002. *The Genus Arisaema: A Monograph for Botanists and Nature Lovers.* Ruggell, Leichtenstein: A.R. Gantner Verlag Kommanditgesellschaft.

Pradhan, U.C. 1997. *Himalayan Cobra Lilies* (Arisaema). Their Botany and Culture. (2nd ed.). Kalimpong, West Bengal, India: Primulaceae Books.

Arum

Bown, D. 2000. *Plants of the Arum Family.* (2nd ed.). Portland, Oregon: Timber Press.

Boyce, P. 1993. *The Genus Arum.* London: HMSO.

Asclepiadaceae

Eggli, U. (ed.). 2002. *Illustrated Handbook of Succulent Plants: Asclepiadaceae.* Heidelberg, Germany: Springer-Verlag.

Aster

Picton, P. 1999. *The Gardener's Guide to Growing Asters.* Newton Abbot: David & Charles.

Asteraceae

Bremer, K. et al. 1994. *Asteraceae: Cladistics and Classification.* Portland, Oregon: Timber Press.

Cubey, J. & Grant, M. 2004. *Perennial Yellow Daisies: RHS Bulletin No. 6.* Wisley, Surrey: RHS. www.rhs.org.uk/plants/documents/yellowdaisies04.pdf

Astilbe

Noblett, H. 2001. *Astilbe.* A Guide to the Identification of Cultivars and Common Species. Cumbria: Henry Noblett.

Aubrieta

1975. *International Registration Authority Checklist.* Weihenstephan, Germany: (Unpublished).

Bamboos

Ohrnberger, D. 1999. *The Bamboos of the World.* Amsterdam: Elsevier.

Begonia

American Begonia Society Astro Branch Begonia Data Base. Jan 2000. http://absastro.tripod.com/data.htm.

Ingles, J. 1990. *American Begonia Society Listing of Begonia Cultivars.* Revised Edition Buxton Checklist. American Begonia Society.

Thompson, M.L. & Thompson, E.J. 1981. *Begonias.* The Complete Reference Guide. New York: Times Books.

Berberidaceae

Stearn, W.T. & Shaw, J.M.H. 2002. *The Genus Epimedium and Other Herbaceous Berberidaceae including the Genus Podophyllum.* Kew: Royal Botanic Gardens.

Betula

Ashburner, K. & Schilling. T. 1985. *Betula utilis* and its Varieties. *The Plantsman* 7(2):116-125.

Ashburner, K.B. 1980. *Betula* – a Survey. *The Plantsman* 2(1):31-53.

Hunt, D. (ed.). 1993. *Betula: Proceedings of the IDS Betula Symposium 1992.* Richmond, Surrey: International Dendrology Society.

Boraginaceae

Bennett, M. 2003. *Pulmonarias and the Borage Family.* London: Batsford.

Bougainvillea

Gillis, W.T. 1976. Bougainvilleas of Cultivation (*Nyctaginaceae*). *Baileya* 20(1):34-41.

Iredell, J. 1990. *The Bougainvillea Grower's Handbook.* Brookvale, Australia: Simon & Schuster.

Iredell, J. 1994. *Growing Bougainvilleas.* London: Cassell.

MacDaniels, L.H. 1981. A Study of Cultivars in *Bougainvillea* (*Nyctaginaceae*). *Baileya* 21(2): 77-100.

Singh, B., Panwar, R.S., Voleti, S.R., Sharma, V.K. & Thakur, S. 1999. *The New International Bougainvillea Check List.* (2nd ed.). New Delhi: Indian Agricultural Research Institute.

Bromeliaceae

Beadle, D.A. 1991. *A Preliminary Listing of all the Known Cultivar and Grex Names for the Bromeliaceae.* Corpus Christi, Texas: Bromeliad Society.

Bromeliad Cultivar Registry Online Databases. Jan 2006. Bromeliad Society International http://fcbs.org/index1.html

Brugmansia

Haik, M. (comp.). Jan 2005. Brugmansia Database. American Brugmansia and Datura Society. www.abads.net/registry

Bulbs

Leeds, R. 2000. *The Plantfinder's Guide to Early Bulbs.* Newton Abbot, Devon: David & Charles.

Van Scheepen, J. (ed.). 1991. *International Checklist for Hyacinths and Miscellaneous Bulbs.* Hillegom, Netherlands: Royal General Bulbgrowers' Association (KAVB).

Buxus

Batdorf, L.R. 1995. *Boxwood Handbook. A Practical Guide to Knowing and Growing Boxwood.* Boyce, VA, USA: The American Boxwood Society.

Camellia

Trujillo, D. J. (ed.). 2002. *Camellia Nomenclature.* (24th revd ed.). Southern California Camellia Society.

Savige, T.J. (comp.). 1993. *The International Camellia Register.* The International Camellia Society. (2 vols).

Savige, T.J. (comp.). 1997. *The International Camellia Register.* Suppl. to vols 1 and 2. The International Camellia Society.

Campanula

Lewis, P. & Lynch, M. 1998. *Campanulas.* A Gardeners Guide. (2nd ed.). London: Batsford.

Lewis, P 2002. *Campanulas in the Garden.* Pershore, Worcs.: Hardy Plant Society.

Canna

Cooke, I. 2001. *The Gardener's Guide to Growing Cannas.* Newton Abbot, Devon: David & Charles.

Gray, J. & Grant, M. 2003. Canna: RHS Bulletin No 3. Wisley, Surrey: RHS. www.rhs.org.uk/plants/documents/canna03.pdf

Hayward, K. 2000. *Canna Handbook.* (Edition 1.01). Farnborough, Hants: Hart Canna.

Carnivorous Plants

Schlauer, J. (comp.). Jan 2006. Carnivorous Plant Database. www.omnisterra.com/bot/cp_home.cgi

Cercidiphyllum

Dosmann, M.S. 1999. Katsura: a Review of *Cercidiphyllum* in Cultivation and in the Wild. *The New Plantsman* 6(1):52-62.

Dosmann, M., Andrews, S., Del Tredici, P. & Li, J. 2003. Classification and Nomenclature of Weeping Katsuras. *The Plantsman* 2(1):21-27.

Chaenomeles

Weber, C. 1963. Cultivars in the Genus *Chaenomeles. Arnoldia (Jamaica Plain)* 23(3):17-75.

***Chrysanthemum* (*Dendranthema*)**

Brummitt, D. 1997. *Chrysanthemum* Once Again. *The Garden* (RHS) 122(9):662-663.

Gosling, S.G. (ed.). 1964. *British National Register of Chrysanthemums.* Whetstone, London: National Chrysanthemum Society.

National Chrysanthemum Society. 2000. *British National Register of Names of Chrysanthemums Amalgamated Edition 1964-1999.* Tamworth, Staffordshire: The National Chrysanthemum Society.

National Chrysanthemum Society UK Cultivar Database. Oct 2004. http://www.ncsuk.info/ncs-cultivardb.htm

Cistus

Demoly, J.-P. 2005. The identity of *Cistus* 'Greywood Pink' and related plants. *The Plantsman* 4(2):76-80.

Page, R.G. Jun 2005. Cistus and Halimium Website. www.cistuspage.org.uk

Citrus

Davies, F.S. & Albrigo, L.G. 1994. *Citrus.* Wallingford, Oxon: Cab International.

Saunt, J. 1990. *Citrus Varieties of the World.* An Illustrated Guide. Norwich: Sinclair

Clematis

Clematis on the Web. Jan 2006. www.clematis.hull.ac.uk

Grey-Wilson, C. 2000. *Clematis: the Genus.* London: Batsford

HelpMeFind Clematis. Dec 2005. www.helpmefind.com/clematis

Johnson, M. 2001. *The Genus Clematis.* Södertälje, Sweden: Magnus Johnsons Plantskola AB & Bengt Sundström.

Matthews, V. (comp.). 2002. *The International Clematis Register and Checklist 2002.* London: RHS.

Toomey, M. & Leeds, E. 2001. *An Illustrated Encyclopedia of Clematis.* Portland, Oregon: Timber Press.

Conifers

Farjon, A. 1998. *World Checklist and Bibliography of Conifers.* Kew: Royal Botanic Gardens.

Knees, S. Feb 2005. Complete List of Conifer Taxa Accepted for Registration. RHS. www.rhs.org.uk/research/registration_conifers_accepted.asp

Krüssmann, G. & Epp, M.E. (trans.). 1985. *Manual of Cultivated Conifers.* London: Batsford.

Lewis, J. & Leslie, A.C. 1987. *The International Conifer Register. Pt 1. Abies* to *Austrotaxus.* London: RHS.

Lewis, J. & Leslie, A.C. 1989. *The International Conifer Register. Pt 2. Belis* to *Pherosphaera,* excluding the Cypresses. London: RHS.

Lewis, J. & Leslie, A.C. 1992. *The International Conifer Register. Pt 3. The Cypresses.* London: RHS.

Lewis, J. & Leslie, A.C. 1998. *The International Conifer Register. Pt 4. Juniperus.* London: RHS.

den Ouden, P. & Boom, B.K. 1965. *Manual of Cultivated Conifers.* The Hague: Martinus Nijhof.

Welch, H.J. 1979. *Manual of Dwarf Conifers.* New York: Theophrastus.

Welch, H.J. 1991. *The Conifer Manual.* Vol. 1. Dordrecht, Netherlands: Kluwer Academic Publishers.

Welch, H.J. 1993. *The World Checklist of Conifers.* Bromyard, Herefordshire: Landsman's Bookshops Ltd.

Cornus

Cappiello, P. & Shadow, D. 2005. *Dogwoods.* Portland, Oregon: Timber Press.

Howard, R.A. 1961. Registration Lists of Cultivar Names in *Cornus L.. Arnoldia (Jamaica Plain)* 21(2):9-18.

Corydalis

Lidén, M. & Zetterlund, H. 1997. *Corydalis. A Gardener's Guide and a Monograph of the Tuberous Species.* Pershore, Worcs: Alpine Garden Society Publications Ltd.

Corylus

Crawford, M. 1995. *Hazelnuts: Production and Culture.* Dartington, Devon: Agroforestry Research Trust.

Cotoneaster

Fryer, J. & Hylmö, B. 1998. Seven New Species of *Cotoneaster* in Cultivation. *The New Plantsman* 5(3):132-144.

Fryer, J. & Hylmö, B. 2001. Captivating Cotoneasters. *The New Plantsman* 8(4): 227-238.

Fryer, J. 1996. Undervalued Versatility. *Cotoneaster. The Garden* (RHS) 121(11):709-715.

Crassulaceae

Rowley, G. 2003. *Crassula: A Grower's Guide.* Venegono Superiore, Italy: Cactus & Co.

Eggli, U. (ed.) 2003. *Illustrated Handbook of Succulent Plants.* Springer.

Crocosmia

Goldblatt, P., Manning, J.C. & Dunlop, G. 2004. *Crocosmia and Chasmanthe.* Portland, Oregon: Timber Press.

Crocus

Jacobsen, N., van Scheepen, J. & Ørgaard, M. 1997. The *Crocus chrysanthus – biflorus* Cultivars. *The New Plantsman* 4(1):6-38.

Mathew, B. 1982. *The Crocus. A Review of the Genus Crocus (Iridaceae).* London: Batsford.

Mathew, B. 2002. *Crocus* Up-date. *The Plantsman* 1(1):44-56.

Cyclamen

Clennett, C. Jan. 2003. Register of Cultivar Names. www.cyclamen.org/registrar_set.html

Grey-Wilson, C. 2003. *Cyclamen. A Guide for Gardeners, Horticulturists & Botanists.* London: Batsford.

Grey-Wilson, C. 2002 Sprenger's Alpine Cyclamen. *The Plantsman* 1(3):173-177.

Cypripedium

Cribb, P. 1997. *The Genus Cypripedium.* Portland, Oregon: Timber Press.

Dahlia

American Dahlia Society website. Oct 2003. www.dahlia.org

Bates, D. Dahlia Plant Finder 2006. www.dahliaworld.co.uk/availuk.htm

National Dahlia Society. 2003. *Classified Directory and Judging Rules.* (27th ed.) Aldershot, Hants: National Dahlia Society.

RHS & Hedge, R. (comps). 1969. *Tentative Classified List and International Register of Dahlia Names 1969.* (& Supplements 1-13). London: RHS.

Winchester Growers Ltd English National Dahlia Collection website. Jan 2006. www.wgltd.co.uk

Daphne

Brickell, C. & White, R. 2000. A Quartet of New Daphnes. *The New Plantsman* 7(1):6-18.

Brickell, C. 2000. *Daphne.* Pt 2: Henderson's Daphne. *The New Plantsman* 7(2):114-122.

Brickell, C.D. & Mathew, B. 1976. *Daphne. The Genus in the Wild and in Cultivation.* Woking, Surrey: Alpine Garden Society.

Grey-Wilson, C. (ed.). 2001. *The Smaller Daphnes. The Proceedings of 'Daphne 2000', a Conference held at the Royal Horticultural Society.* Pershore, Worcs: Alpine Garden Society Publications Ltd.

Delphinium

1949. *A Tentative Check-list of Delphinium Names.* London: RHS.

1970. *A Tentative Check-list of Delphinium Names.* Addendum to the 1949 tentative check-list of *Delphinium* names. London: RHS.

Leslie, A.C. 1995. The International Delphinium Register Supplement 1993-94. *The Delphinium Society Year Book 1995.*

Leslie, A.C. 1996. *The International Delphinium Register Cumulative Supplement 1970-1995.* London: RHS.

Leslie, A.C. 1996-2000. The International Delphinium Register Supplement 1994-99. *The Delphinium Society Year Book 1996-98.* London: RHS.

Dianthus

Galbally, J. & Galbally, E. 1997. *Carnations and Pinks for Garden and Greenhouse.* Portland, Oregon: Timber Press.

Leslie, A.C. *The International Dianthus Register.* 1983-2002. (2nd ed. & Supps 1-19). London: RHS.

Dierama

Hilliard, O.M. & Burtt, B.L. 1991. *Dierama. The Harebells of Africa.* Johannesburg; London: Acorn Books.

Dionysia

Grey-Wilson, C. 1989. *The Genus Dionysia.* Woking, Surrey: Alpine Garden Society.

Douglasia

Mitchell, B. 1999. Celebrating the Bicentenary of David Douglas: a Review of *Douglasia* in Cultivation. *The New Plantsman* 6(2):101-108.

Dracaena

Bos, J.J., Graven, P., Hetterscheid, W.L.A. & van de Wege, J.J. 1992. Wild and cultivated *Dracaena fragrans. Edinburgh J. Bot.* 49(3):311-331.

Episcia

Dates, J.D. 1993. *The Gesneriad Register 1993.* Check List of Names with Descriptions of Cultivated Plants in the Genera *Episcia* & *Alsobia.* Galesburg, Illinois: American Gloxinia & Gesneriad Society, Inc.

***Erica* (see also Heathers)**

Baker, H.A. & Oliver, E.G.H. 1967. *Heathers in Southern Africa.* Cape Town: Purnell.

Schumann, D., Kirsten, G. & Oliver, E.G.H. 1992. *Ericas of South Africa.* Vlaeberg, South Africa: Fernwood Press.

Erodium

Clifton, R. 1994. *Geranium Family Species Checklist. Pt 1 Erodium.* (4th ed.). The Geraniaceae Group.

Leslie, A.C. 1980. The Hybrid of *Erodium corsicum* With *Erodium reichardii. The Plantsman* 2:117-126.

Toomey, N., Cubey, J. & Culham, A. 2002. *Erodium × variabile. The Plantsman* 1(3): 166-172

Victor, D.X. (comp.). 2000. *Erodium: Register of Cultivar Names.* The Geraniaceae Group.

Erythronium

Mathew, B. 1992. A Taxonomic and Horticultural Review of *Erythronium* L. (*Liliaceae*). *J. Linn. Soc., Bot.* 109:453-471.

Mathew, B. 1998. The Genus *Erythronium. Bull. Alpine Gard. Soc. Gr. Brit.* 66(3):308-321.

Euonymus

Brown, N. 1996. Notes on Cultivated Species of *Euonymus. The New Plantsman* 3(4):238-243.

Lancaster, R.C. 1981. An Account of *Euonymus* in Cultivation and its Availability in Commerce. *The Plantsman* 3(3):133-166.

Lancaster, C.R. 1982. *Euonymus* in Cultivation – Addendum. *The Plantsman* 4:61-64, 253-254.

Euphorbia

Govaerts, R., Frodin, D.G. & Radcliffe-Smith, A. 2000. *World Checklist and Bibliography of Euphorbiaceae.* Kew: Royal Botanic Gardens.

Turner, R. 1995. *Euphorbias. A Gardeners' Guide.* London: Batsford.

Witton, D. 2000. *Euphorbias.* Pershore, Worcs: Hardy Plant Society.

Fagales

World Checklist and Bibliography Series: About the *Fagales.* Jan 2002. http://www.rbgkew.org.uk/wcb/aboutfag.html

Fagus

Dönig, G. 1994. *Die Park- und Gartenformen der Rotbuche – Fagus sylvatica L.* Erlangen, Germany: Verlag Gartenbild Heinz Hansmann.

Wyman, D. 1964. Registration List of Cultivar Names of *Fagus* L. *J. Arnold Arbor.* 24(1):1-8.

Fascicularia

Nelson, E.C. & Zizka, G. 1997. *Fascicularia* (*Bromeliaceae*): Which Species are Cultivated and Naturalized in Northwestern Europe. *The New Plantsman* 4(4):232-239.

Nelson, E.C., Zizka, G., Horres, R. & Weising, K. 1999. Revision of the Genus *Fascicularia* Mez (*Bromeliaceae*). *Botanical Journal of the Linnean Society* 129(4):315-332.

FERNS

Checklist of World Ferns. Oct 2001. http://homepages.caverock.net.nz/~bj/fern/

Johns, R.J. 1996. *Index Filicum.* Supplementum Sextum pro annis 1976-1990. Kew:Royal Botanic Gardens.

Johns, R.J. 1997. *Index Filicum.* Supplementum Septimum pro annis 1991-1995. Kew:Royal Botanic Gardens.

Jones, D.L. 1987. *Encyclopaedia of Ferns.* Melbourne, Australia: Lothian.

Kaye, R. 1968. *Hardy Ferns.* London: Faber & Faber

Rickard, M.H. 2000. *The Plantfinder's Guide to Garden Ferns.* Newton Abbot, Devon: David & Charles.

Rush, R. 1984. *A Guide to Hardy Ferns.* London: British Pteridological Society.

Forsythia

INRA Forsythia website. Dec 2000. www.angers.inra.fr/forsy/indexeng.html

Fragaria

Day, D. (ed.). 1993. *Grower Digest 3: Strawberries.* (Revd ed.). London: Nexus Business Communications.

Fritillaria

Clark, T. & Grey-Wilson, C. 2003. Crown Imperials. *The Plantsman* 2(1):33-47.

Mathew, B., et al. 2000. *Fritillaria* Issue. *Bot. Mag.* 17(3):145-185.

Pratt, K. & Jefferson-Brown, M. 1997. *The Gardener's Guide to Growing Fritillaries.* Newton Abbot: David & Charles.

Turrill, W.B. & Sealy, J.R. 1980. *Studies in the Genus Fritillaria (Liliaceae).* Hooker's Icones Plantarum Vol. 39 (1 & 2). Kew:Royal Botanic Gardens.

Fruit

Anon. 1997. *Catalogue of Cultivars in the United Kingdom National Fruit Collection.* Kent, UK: Brogdale Horticultural Trust.

Bowling, B.L. 2000. *The Berry Grower's Companion.* Portland, Oregon: Timber Press.

Hogg, R. 1884. *The Fruit Manual.* (5th ed.). London: Journal of Horticulture Office.

Index of the Bush Fruit Collection at the National Fruit Trials 1987. 1987. Faversham, Kent: MAFF.

Fuchsia

Bartlett, G. 1996. *Fuchsias – A Colour Guide.* Marlborough, Wilts: Crowood Press.

Boullemier, Leo.B. (comp.). 1991. *The Checklist of Species, Hybrids and Cultivars of the Genus Fuchsia.* London, New York, Sydney: Blandford Press.

Boullemier, Leo.B. (comp.). 1995. *Addendum No. 1 to the 1991 Checklist of Species, Hybrids and Cultivars of the Genus Fuchsia.* Dyfed, Wales: The British Fuchsia Society.

Goulding, E. 1995. *Fuchsias: The Complete Guide.* London: Batsford.

Johns, E.A. 1997. *Fuchsias of the 19th and Early 20th Century.* An Historical Checklist of Fuchsia Species & Cultivars, pre-1939. Kidderminster, Worcs: British Fuchsia Society

Stevens, R. Jan 2006. Find That Fuchsia. www.findthatfuchsia.info

Van Veen, G. Sept 2005. Gelderse Fuchsia Info-site. www.geldersefuchsia.info

Galanthus

Bishop, M., Davis, A. & Grimshaw, J. 2001. *Snowdrops. A monograph of cultivated Galanthus.* Maidenhead: Griffin Press.

Davis, A.P., Mathew, B. (ed.) & King, C. (ill.). 1999. *The Genus Galanthus. A Botanical Magazine Monograph.* Oregon: Timber Press.

Gentiana

Bartlett, M. 1975. *Gentians.* Dorset: Blandford Press.

Halda, J.J. 1996. *The Genus Gentiana.* Dobré, Czech Republic: Sen.

Wilkie, D. 1950. *Gentians.* (2nd ed. revised). London: Country Life.

Geranium

Armitage, J. 2005. Hardy Geraniums – Stage 1: RHS Bulletin No. 10. Wisley, Surrey: RHS. www.rhs.org.uk/plants/documents/geranium05.pdf

Bath, T. & Jones, J. 1994. *The Gardener's Guide to Growing Hardy Geraniums.* Newton Abbot, Devon: David & Charles.

Clifton, R.T.F. 1995. *Geranium Family Species Check List Pt 2.* Geranium. (4th ed. issue 2). Dover: The Geraniaceae Group.

Jones, J., et al. 2001. *Hardy Geraniums for the Garden.* (3rd ed., revised and enlarged). Pershore, Worcs: Hardy Plant Society.

Victor, D.X. 2004. *Register of Geranium Cultivar Names.* (2nd ed.). The Geraniaceae Group. www.hardygeraniums.com/register_of_cultivar_names.htm

Yeo, P.F. 2002. *Hardy Geraniums.* (3rd ed.). Kent: Croom Helm.

Gesneriaceae

American Gloxinia and Gesneriad Society. Listing of registered gesneriads. Sept 2003. www.aggs.org/ir_ges

Dates, J.D. 1986-1990. *The Gesneriad Register 1986-1987 & 1990.* Galesburg, Illinois: American Gloxinia & Gesneriad Society, Inc.

Gladiolus

British Gladiolus Society List of Cultivars Classified for Show Purposes 1994. Mayfield, Derbyshire: British Gladiolus Society.

1997-1998. British Gladiolus Society List of European Cultivars Classified for Exhibition Purposes 1997 & 1998. Mayfield, Derbyshire: British Gladiolus Society.

1997-1998. British Gladiolus Society List of New Zealand Cultivars Classified for Exhibition Purposes 1997 & 1998. Mayfield, Derbyshire: British Gladiolus Society.

1997-1998. British Gladiolus Society List of North American Cultivars Classified for Exhibition Purposes 1997 & 1998. Mayfield, Derbyshire: British Gladiolus Society.

Goldblatt, P. & Manning, J. 1998. *Gladiolus in Southern Africa.* Vlaeberg, South Africa: Fernwood Press.

Goldblatt, P. 1996. *Gladiolus in Tropical Africa.* Systematics Biology and Evolution. Oregon: Timber Press.

Lewis, G.J., Obermeyer, A.A. & Barnard, T.T. 1972. A Revision of the South African Species of *Gladiolus. J. S. African Bot.* (Supp. Vol. 10)

Gleditsia

Santamour, F.S. & McArdle, A.J. 1983. Checklist of Cultivars of Honeylocust (*Gleditsia triacanthos* L.). *J. Arboric.* 9:271-276.

Grevillea

Olde, P. & Marriott, N. 1995. *The Grevillea Book.* (3). Kenthurst, NSW: Kangaroo Press.

Haemanthus

Snijman, D. 1984. A Revision of the Genus *Haemanthus. J. S. African Bot.* (Supp. Vol. 12).

Hamamelis

Lane, C. 2005. *Witch Hazels.* Portland, Oregon: Timber Press.

Heathers

Nelson, E.C. Aug 2005. International Cultivar Registration Authority for Heathers. www.heathersociety.org.uk/registration.html

Hebe

Chalk, D. 1988. *Hebes and Parahebes.* Bromley, Kent: Christopher Helm (Publishers) Ltd.

Hutchins, G. 1997. *Hebes: Here and There.* A Monograph on the Genus *Hebe.* Caversham, Berks: Hutchins & Davies.

Metcalf, L.J. 2001. *International Register of Hebe Cultivars.* Canterbury, New Zealand: Royal New Zealand Institute of Horticulture (Inc.).

Hedera

McAllister, H. 1988. Canary and Algerian Ivies. *The Plantsman* 10(1):27-29.

McAllister, H.A. & Rutherford, A. 1990. *Hedera helix and H. hibernica* in the British Isles. *Watsonia* 18:7-15.

Rose, P.Q. 1996. *The Gardener's Guide to Growing Ivies.* Newton Abbot, Devon: David & Charles.

Rutherford, A., McAllister, H. & Mill, R.R. 1993. New Ivies from the Mediterranean Area and Macaronesia. *The Plantsman* 15(2):115-128.

Heliconia

Berry, F. & Kress, W.J. 1991. *Heliconia.* An Identification Guide. Washington: Smithsonian Institution Press.

Helleborus

Mathew, B. 1989. *Hellebores.* Woking: Alpine Garden Society.

Rice, G. & Strangman, E. 1993. *The Gardener's Guide to Growing Hellebores.* Newton Abbot, Devon: David & Charles.

Hemerocallis

AHS – Registered Daylily Database. Jan 2006. http://database.tinkersgardens.com

Baxter, G.J. (comp.). 2003. *Hemerocallis Cultivar Registrations 1890-2002.* (CD-ROM Version 2003a.) Jackson, Tennessee: American Hemerocallis Society.

Kitchingman, R.M. 1985. Some Species and Cultivars of *Hemerocallis. The Plantsman* 7(2):68-89.

Herbs

Page, M. & Stearn, W. *Culinary Herbs: A Wisley Handbook.* London: RHS.

Phillips, R. & Foy, N. 1990. *Herbs.* London: Pan Books Ltd.

Heuchera and* × *Heucherella

Heims, D. & Ware, G. 2005. *Heucheras and Heucherellas: Coral Bells and Foamy Bells.* Portland, Oregon: Timber Press.

Hibiscus

Noble, C. Jan 2005. Australian Hibiscus Society Official International Hibiscus Cross Check List and Register Database. www.australianhibiscus.com/database/register/boot.htm

Hippeastrum

Alfabetische Lijst van de in Nederland in Cultuur Zijnde Amaryllis (*Hippeastrum*) *Cultivars.* 1980. Hillegom, Netherlands: Koninklijke Algemeene Vereeniging Voor Bloembollencultur (KAVB).

Read, V.M. 2004. *Hippeastrum.* Portland, Oregon: RHS/Timber Press

Hosta

Hammelman, T. Mar 2001. Giboshi.com Hosta Database. www.giboshi.com

Hosta Library. Jan. 2003. www.hostalibrary.org

Grenfell, D. & Shadrack, M. 2004. *The Color Encyclopedia of Hostas.* Portland, Oregon: Timber Press.

Schmid, W.G. 1991. *The Genus Hosta.* London: Batsford.

Hyacinthaceae

Mathew, B. 2005. *Hardy Hyacinthaceae* Pt 1: *Muscari. The Plantsman* 4(1):40-53.

Mathew, B. 2005. *Hardy Hyacinthaceae* Pt 2: *Scilla, Chionodoxa* and × *Chinoscilla. The Plantsman* 4(2):110-121.

Hyacinthus

Clark, T. 2000. Focus on Plants: Treasures of the East (Hyacinths). *The Garden* (RHS) 125(9):672-675.

Stebbings, G. 1996. Heaven Scent. *The Garden* (RHS) 121(2):68-72.

Hydrangea

Dirr, M.A. 2004. *Hydrangeas for American Gardens.* Portland, Oregon: Timber Press.

Haworth-Booth, M. 1975. *The Hydrangeas.* London: Garden Book Club.

Van Gelderen, C.J. & Van Gelderen, D.M. 2004. *Encyclopedia of Hydrangeas.* Portland, Oregon: Timber Press.

Hypericum

Lancaster, R. & Robson, N. 1997. Focus on Plants: Bowls of Beauty. *The Garden* (RHS) 122(8):566-571.

Ilex

Andrews, S. 1983. Notes on Some *Ilex* × *altaclerensis* Clones. *The Plantsman* 5(2):65-81.

Andrews, S. 1984. More Notes on Clones of *Ilex* × *altaclerensis. The Plantsman* 6(3):157-166. Erratum vol.6 p.256.

Andrews, S. 1985. Holly Berries of a Varied Hue. *The Garden* (RHS) 110(11):518-522.

Andrews, S. 1994. Hollies with a Difference. *The Garden* (RHS) 119(12):580-583.

Dudley, T.R. & Eisenbeiss, G.K. 1973. *International Checklist of Cultivated Ilex.* Pt 1 *Ilex opaca.* Washington DC: United States Dept of Agriculture.

Dudley, T.R. & Eisenbeiss, G.K. 1992. *International Checklist of Cultivated Ilex.* Pt 2 *Ilex crenata.* Washington DC: United States Dept of Agriculture.

Galle, F.C. 1997. *Hollies: the Genus Ilex.* Portland, Oregon: Timber Press.

Iris

Hoog, M.H. 1980. Bulbous Irises . *The Plantsman* 2(3):141-64.

Mathew, B. 1981. *The Iris.* London: Batsford.

Mathew, B. 1993. The Spuria Irises. *The Plantsman* 15(1):14-25.

Service, N. 1990. *Iris unguicularis. The Plantsman* 12(1):1-9.

Stebbings, G. 1997. *The Gardener's Guide to Growing Iris.* Newton Abbot: David & Charles.

The Species Group of the British Iris Society, (ed.). 1997. *A Guide to Species Irises.* Their Identification and Cultivation. Cambridge: Cambridge University Press.

Jovibarba* see under *Sempervivum

Kalmia

Jaynes, R.A. 1997. *Kalmia. Mountain Laurel and Related Species.* Portland, Oregon: Timber Press.

Kniphofia

Grant-Downton, R. 1997. Notes on *Kniphofia thomsonii* in Cultivation and in the Wild. *The New Plantsman* 4(3):148-156.

Taylor, J. 1985. *Kniphofia* – a Survey. *The Plantsman* 7(3):129-160.

Kohleria

Dates, J.D. (ed.) & Batcheller, F.N. (comp.). 1985. *The Gesneriad Register 1985. Check List of Names with Descriptions of Cultivated Plants in the Genus Kohleria.* Lincoln Acres, California: American Gloxinia and Gesneriad Society, Inc.

Lachenalia

Duncan, G.D. 1988. *The Lachenalia Hand Book.* Kirstenbosch, South Africa: National Botanic Gardens.

Lantana

Howard, R.A. 1969. A Check List of Names Used in the Genus *Lantana. J. Arnold Arbor.* 29(11):73-109.

Lathyrus

Norton, S. 1996. *Lathyrus. Cousins of the Sweet Pea.* Surrey: NCCPG.

Lavandula

Upson, T. & Andrews, S. 2004. *The Genus Lavandula.* Kew: Royal Botanic Garden.

Legumes

ILDIS. International Legume Database and Information Service. Nov 2005. Version 8. www.ildis.org/LegumeWeb

Leptospermum

Check List of *Leptospermum* Cultivars. 1963. *J. Roy. New Zealand Inst. Hort.* 5(5):224-30.

Dawson, M. 1997. A History of *Leptospermum scoparium* in Cultivation – Discoveries from the Wild. *The New Plantsman* 4(1):51-59.

Dawson, M. 1997. A History of *Leptospermum scoparium* in Cultivation – Garden Selections. *The New Plantsman* 4(2):67-78.

Lewisia

Davidson, B.L.R. 2000. *Lewisias.* Portland, Oregon: Timber Press.

Elliott, R. 1978. *Lewisias.* Woking: Alpine Garden Society.

Mathew, B. 1989. *The Genus Lewisia.* Bromley, Kent: Christopher Helm.

Liliaceae sensu lato

Mathew, B. 1989. Splitting the *Liliaceae. The Plantsman* 11(2):89-105.

Lilium

Homick, M. Prideon. Feb 2005. www.prideon.com

Leslie, A.C. *The International Lily Register 1982-2002.* (3rd ed. & suppls 1-20). London: RHS.

Magnolia

Callaway, D.J. Oct 2005. Magnolia Cultivar Checklist. www.magnoliasociety.org/index.html

Frodin, D.G. & Govaerts, R. 1996. *World Checklist and Bibliography of Magnoliaceae.* Kew: Royal Botanic Garden.

Maianthemum

Cubey, J.J. 2005 *The Incorporation of Smilacina within Maianthemum. The Plantsman* N.S.4(4).

Malus

Brogdale National Apple Collection. 2004. http://www.webvalley.co.uk/brogdale/collectionapples.php

Crawford, M. 1994. *Directory of Apple Cultivars.* Devon: Agroforestry Research Trust.

Fiala, J.L. 1994. *Flowering Crabapples.* The genus *Malus.* Portland, Oregon: Timber Press.

Rouèche, A. Dec 2004. Les Crets Fruits et Pomologie. http://lescrets.free.fr

Smith, M.W.G. 1971. *National Apple Register of the United Kingdom.* London: MAFF

Spiers, V. 1996. *Burcombes, Queenies and Colloggetts.* St Dominic, Cornwall: West Brendon.

Meconopsis

Brickell, C. & Stevens, E. 2002. *Meconopsis* 'Lingholm'. *The New Plantsman* 1(2): 88-92.

Grey-Wilson, C. 1992. A Survey of the Genus *Meconopsis* in Cultivation. The Plantsman 14(1): 1-33.

Stevens, E. & Brickell, C. 2001. Problems with the Big Perennial Poppies. *The New Plantsman* 8(1):48-61.

Stevens, E. 2001. Further Observations on the Big Perennial Blue Poppies. *The New Plantsman* 8(2):105-111.

Miscanthus

Jones, L. 2004. Miscanthus: RHS Bulletin No. 7. Wisley, Surrey: RHS. www.rhs.org.uk/plant/documents/miscanthus04.pdf

Moraea

Goldblatt, P. 1986. *The Moraeas of Southern Africa.* Kirstenbosch, South Africa: National Botanic Gardens.

Musa

Germplasm available from INIBAP (list of accessions with genome groups). 2004. International Network for the Improvement of Banana and Plantain. www.inibap.org/index

Musalogue 2: Diversity in the Genus *Musa.* 2001. www.inibap.org/publications/musalogue2.pdf

Narcissus

Blanchard, J.W. 1990. *Narcissus – A Guide to Wild Daffodils.* Woking, Surrey: Alpine Garden Society.

Kington, S. (comp.). 1998. *The International Daffodil Register and Classified List 1998* (3rd ed. & Supps 1-5, 1998-2002). London: RHS. www.rhs.org.uk/research/registerpages/intro.asp

Nematanthus

Arnold, P. 1978. *The Gesneriad Register 1978.* Check List of *Nematanthus.* American Gloxinia and Gesneriad Society, Inc.

Nerium

Pagen, F.J.J. 1987. *Oleanders. Nerium L. and the Oleander Cultivars.* Wageningen, The Netherlands: Agricultural University Wageningen.

Nymphaea

International Water Lily Society. 1993. *Identification of Hardy Nymphaea.* Stapeley Water Gardens Ltd.

Knotts, K. & Sacher, R. (comps). 2000. *Provisional Check List of Names/Epithets of Nymphaea L.* Cocoa Beach, Florida: International Waterlily & Water Gardening Society.

Swindells, P. 1983. *Waterlilies.* London: Croom Helm.

Orchidaceae

Shaw, J.M.H. Dec 2005. The International Orchid Register. www.rhs.org.uk/plants/registration_orchids.asp

Origanum

Paton, A. 1994. Three Membranous-bracted Species of *Origanum. Kew Mag.* 11(3):109-117.

White, S. 1998. *Origanum. The Herb Marjoram and its Relatives.* Surrey: NCCPG.

Paeonia

HelpMeFind Peonies. Jan 2006. www.helpmefind.com/peony/index.html

Kessenich, G.M. 1976. *Peonies.* (Variety Check List Pts 1-3). American Peony Society.

Osti, G.L. 1999. *The Book of Tree Peonies.* Turin: Umberto Allemandi.

Page, M. 1997. *The Gardener's Guide to Growing Peonies.* Newton Abbott: David & Charles.

Rogers, A. 1995. *Peonies.* Portland, Oregon: Timber Press.

Wang, L., et al. 1998. *Chinese Tree Peony.* Beijing: China Forestry Publishing House.

Papaver

Grey-Wilson, C. 1998. Oriental Glories. *The Garden* (RHS) 123(5):320-325.

Grey-Wilson, C. 2000. *Poppies. The Poppy Family in the Wild and in Cultivation.* London: Batsford.

Passiflora

Vanderplank, J. 2002. *Passion Flowers.* (3rd ed.). London, England: Cassell.

Pelargonium

Abbott, P.G. 1994. *A Guide to Scented Geraniaceae.* Angmering, West Sussex: Hill Publicity Services.

Anon. 1978. *A Checklist and Register of Pelargonium Cultivar Names.* Pt 1 A-B. Australian Pelargonium Society.

Anon. 1985. *A Checklist and Register of Pelargonium Cultivar Names.* Pt 2: C-F. Australian Pelargonium Society.

Bagust, H. 1988. *Miniature and Dwarf Geraniums.* London: Christopher Helm.

Clifford, D. 1958. *Pelargoniums.* London: Blandford Press.

Clifton, R. 1999. *Geranium Family Species Checklist, Pt 4: Pelargonium.* The Geraniaceae Group.

Complete Copy of the Spalding Pelargonium Checklist. (Unpublished). USA.

Key, H. 2000. *1001 Pelargoniums.* London: Batsford.

Miller, D. 1996. *Pelargonium.* A Gardener's Guide to the Species and Cultivars and Hybrids. London: Batsford.

Pelargonium Palette: The Geranium and Pelargonium Society of Sydney Incorporated. Varieties – Alphabetical List. July 2000. www.elj.com/geranium/var/alphaind.htm

Van der Walt, J.J.A., et al. 1977. *Pelargoniums of South Africa.* (1-3). Kirstenbosch, South Africa: National Botanic Gardens.

Penstemon

Lindgren, D.T. & Davenport, B. 1992. List and description of named cultivars in the genus *Penstemon* (1992). University of Nebraska.

Nold, R. 1999. *Penstemons.* Portland, Oregon: Timber Press.

Way, D. & James, P. 1998. *The Gardener's Guide to Growing Penstemons.* Newton Abbott, Devon: David & Charles.

Phlomis

Mann Taylor, J. 1998. *Phlomis: The Neglected Genus.* Wisley: NCCPG.

Phlox

Harmer, J. & Elliott, J. 2001. *Phlox*. Pershore, Worcs: Hardy Plant Society.

Stebbings, G. 1999. Simply Charming. *The Garden* (RHS) 124(7):518-521.

Wherry, E.T. 1955. *The Genus Phlox.* Philadelphia, Pennsylvania: Morris Arboretum.

Phormium

Heenan, P.B. 1991. *Checklist of Phormium Cultivars.* Royal New Zealand Institute of Horticulture.

McBride-Whitehead, V. 1998. Phormiums of the Future. *The Garden* (RHS) 123(1):42-45.

Pieris

Bond, J. 1982. *Pieris* – a Survey. *The Plantsman* 4(2):65-75.

Wagenknecht, B.L. 1961. Registration Lists of Cultivar Names in the Genus *Pieris* D. Don. *Arnoldia (Jamaica Plain)* 21(8):47-50.

Plectranthus

Miller, D. & Morgan, N. 2000. Focus on Plants: A New Leaf. *The Garden* (RHS) 125(11):842-845.

Shaw, J.M.H. 1999. Notes on the Identity of Swedish Ivy and Other Cultivated *Plectranthus. The New Plantsman* 6(2):71-74.

Pleione

Cribb, P. & Butterfield, I. 1999. *The Genus Pleione.* (2nd ed.). Kew: Royal Botanic Gardens.

Shaw, J.M.H. (comp.). Oct 2002. Provisional List of *Pleione* Cultivars. RHS. www.rhs.org.co.uk/research/registerpages/Pleione_cv.PDF

Poaceae (Gramineae, grasses)

Clayton, W.D. & Renvoize, S.A. 1986. *Genera Graminum.* Grasses of the World. London: HMSO.

Darke, R. 1999. *The Colour Encyclopedia of Ornamental Grasses.* Sedges, Rushes, Restios, Cat-tails and Selected Bamboos. London: Weidenfeld & Nicolson.

Grounds, R. 1998. *The Plantfinder's Guide to Ornamental Grasses.* Newton Abott, Devon: David & Charles.

Ryves, T.B., Clement, E.J. & Foster, M.C.. 1996. *Alien Grasses of the British Isles.* London: Botanical Society of the British Isles.

Wood, T. 2002. *Garden Grasses, Rushes and Sedges.* (3rd ed.). Abingdon, Oxon: John Wood.

Polemonium

Nichol-Brown, D. 2000. *Polemonium.* Wisley: NCCPG.

Potentilla

Davidson, C.G., Enns, R.J. & Gobin, S. 1994. *A Checklist of Potentilla fruticosa: the Shrubby Potentillas.* Morden, Manitoba: Agriculture & Agri-Food Canada Research Centre. Data also on Plant Finder Reference Library professional version CD-ROM 1999/2000.

Miller, D.M. 2002. *Shrubby Potentilla: RHS Bulletin No 1.* Wisley, Surrey: RHS. www.rhs.org.uk/plants/documents/potentilla_report.pdf

Primula

Richards, J. 2002 (2nd ed.). *Primula.* London: Batsford.

Primula allionii

Archdale, B. & Richards, D. 1997. *Primula allionii Forms and Hybrids.* National Auricula & Primula Society, Midland & West Section.

***Primula auricula* hort.**

Baker, G. *Double Auriculas.* National Auricula & Primula Society, Midland & West Section.

Baker, G. & Ward, P. 1995. *Auriculas.* London: Batsford.

Hawkes, A. 1995. Striped Auriculas. National Auricula & Primula Society, Midland & West Section.

Nicholle, G. 1996. *Border Auriculas.* National Auricula & Primula Society, Midland & West Section.

Robinson, M.A. 2000. *Auriculas for Everyone.* How to Grow and Show Perfect Plants. Lewes, Sussex: Guild of Master Craftsmen Publications.

Telford, D. 1993. *Alpine Auriculas.* National Auricula & Primula Society, Midland & West Section.

Ward, P. 1991. *Show Auriculas.* National Auricula & Primula Society, Midland & West Section.

Proteaceae

International *Proteaceae* Register. July 2002. (7th ed.). http://www.nda.agric.za/docs/Protea2002/proteaceae_register.htm

Rebelo, T. 1995. *Proteas.* A Field Guide to the Proteas of Southern Africa. Vlaeberg: Fernwood Press/National Botanical Institute.

Sadie, J. (Comp.) 2000. *The International Protea Register*. Directorate Genetic Resources, NDA.

Prunus

1986. *Index of the Cherry Collection at the National Fruit Trials 1986.* Faversham, Kent: MAFF.

Brogdale National Plum Collection. 2004. http://www.webvalley.co.uk/brogdale/collectionplums.php

Crawford, M. 1996. *Plums.* Dartington, Devon: Agroforestry Research Trust.

Crawford, M. 1997. *Cherries: Production and Culture.* Dartington, Devon: Agroforestry Research Trust.

Jacobsen, A.L. 1992. *Purpleleaf Plums.* Portland, Oregon: Timber Press.
Jefferson, R.M. & Wain, K.K. 1984. *The Nomenclature of Cultivated Flowering Cherries (Prunus).* The Sato-Zakura Group. Washington DC: USDA.
Kuitert, W. 1999. *Japanese Flowering Cherries.* Portland, Oregon: Timber Press.
Pulmonaria
Hewitt, J. 1994. *Pulmonarias.* Pershore, Worcs: Hardy Plant Society.
Hewitt, J. 1999. Well Spotted. *The Garden* (RHS) 124(2):98-103.
Pyracantha
Egolf, D.R. & Andrick, A.O. 1995. *A Checklist of Pyracantha Cultivars.* Washington DC: Agricultural Research Service.
Pyrus
Crawford, M. 1996. *Directory of Pear Cultivars.* Totnes, Devon: Agroforestry Research Institute.
Parfitt, B. 1981. *Index of the Pear Collection at the National Fruit Trials.* Faversham, Kent: MAFF.
Smith, M.W.G. 1976. *Catalogue of the British Pear.* Faversham, Kent: MAFF.
Quercus
Miller, H.A. & Lamb, S.H. 1985. *Oaks of North America.* Happy Camp, California: Naturegraph Publishers.
Mitchell, A. 1994. The Lucombe Oaks. *The Plantsman* 15(4):216-224.
Rhododendron
Argent, G., Fairweather, C. & Walter, K. 1996. *Accepted Names in Rhododendron section Vireya.* Edinburgh: Royal Botanic Garden.
Argent, G., Bond, J., Chamberlain, D., Cox, P. & Hardy, A. 1997. *The Rhododendron Handbook 1998.* Rhododendron Species in Cultivation. London: RHS.
Chamberlain, D.F. & Rae, S.J. 1990. A Revision of *Rhododendron* IV. Subgenus *Tsutsusi. Edinburgh J. Bot.* 47(2).
Chamberlain, D.F. 1982. A Revision of *Rhododendron* II. Subgenus *Hymenanthes. Notes Roy. Bot. Gard. Edinburgh* 39(2).
Chamberlain, D., Hyam, R., Argent, G., Fairweather, G. & Walter, K.S. 1996. *The Genus Rhododendron.* Edinburgh:Royal Botanic Garden.
Cullen, J. 1980. A Revision of *Rhododendron* I. Subgenus *Rhododendron* sections *Rhododendron* and *Pogonanthum. Notes Roy. Bot. Gard. Edinburgh* 39(1).
Davidian, H.H. 1982-1992 *The Rhododendron Species* (Vols 1-4). London: Batsford.
Galle, F.C. 1985. *Azaleas.* Portland, Oregon: Timber Press.
Leslie, A. C. (comp.). 1980. *The Rhododendron Handbook 1980.* London: RHS.
Leslie, A.C. (Comp.) 2004. *The International Rhododendron Register and Checklist* (2nd ed.). London: RHS
Tamura, T. (ed.). 1989. *Azaleas in Kurume.* Kurume, Japan: International Azalea Festival '89.
Ribes
Crawford, M. 1997. *Currants and Gooseberries: Production and Culture.* Dartington, Devon: Agroforestry Research Trust.
Rosa
Beales, P., Cairns, T., et al. 1998. *Botanica's Rose: The Encyclopedia of Roses.* Hoo, Kent: Grange Books.
Cairns, T. (ed.). 2000. *Modern Roses XI. The World Encyclopedia of Roses.* London: Academic Press.
Dickerson, B.C. 1999. *The Old Rose Advisor.* Portland, Oregon: Timber Press.
Haw, S.G. 1996. Notes on Some Chinese and Himalayan Rose Species of Section *Pimpinellifoliae. The New Plantsman* 3(3): 143-146.
HelpMeFind Roses. Jan 2006. www.helpmefind.com/rose/index.html
McCann, S. 1985. *Miniature Roses.* Newton Abbot, Devon: David & Charles.
Quest-Ritson, C. 2003. *Climbing Roses of the World.* Portland, Oregon: Timber Press.
Quest-Ritson, C. & Quest-Ritson, B. 2003. *The Royal Horticultural Society Encyclopedia of Roses: The Definitive A-Z Guide.* London: Dorling Kindersley.
Thomas, G.S. 1995. *The Graham Stuart Thomas Rose Book.* London: John Murray.
Verrier, S. 1996. *Rosa Gallica.* Balmain, Australia: Florilegium.
Rosularia
Eggli, U. 1988. A Monographic Study of the Genus *Rosularia. Bradleya* (Suppl.) 6:1-118.
Rubiaceae
Govaerts, R. et al. 2005. *World Checklist & Bibliography of Rubiaceae (Draft Version).* www.kew.org/data/rubiaceae/index.htm
Saintpaulia
Goodship, G. 1987. *Saintpaulia Variety List.* Supplement. Slough, Bucks: Saintpaulia & Houseplant Society.
Moore, H.E. 1957. *African Violets, Gloxinias and Their Relatives.* A Guide to the Cultivated Gesneriads. New York: Macmillan.
Salix
Newsholme, C. 1992. *Willows.* The Genus *Salix.* London: Batsford.
Stott, K.G. 1971 *Willows for Amenity, Windbreaks and Other Uses.* Checklist of the Long Ashton Collection of Willows, with Notes on their Suitability for Various Purposes. Long Ashton Research Station: University of Bristol.
Salvia
Clebsch, B. 2003. *A Book of Salvias.* (2nd ed.). Portland, Oregon: Timber Press.
Compton, J. 1994. Mexican Salvias in Cultivation. *The Plantsman* 15(4):193-215.

Saxifraga

Bland, B. 2000. *Silver Saxifrages.* Pershore, Worcs: Alpine Garden Society.

Dashwood, M. & Bland, B. 2005. Silver Saxifrages: RHS Bulletin No 9. Wisley, Surrey: RHS. www.rhs.org.uk/plants/documents/saxifraga05.pdf

McGregor, M. Feb 2003. Saxbase. Saxifrage Society. www.saxifraga.org/plants/saxbase/default.asp

McGregor, M. 1995. *Saxifrages: The Complete Cultivars & Hybrids: International Register of Saxifrages.* (2nd ed.). Driffield, E. Yorks: Saxifrage Society.

Webb, D.A. & Gornall, R.J. 1989. *Saxifrages of Europe.* Bromley, Kent: Christopher Helm.

Sedum

Evans, R.L. 1983. *Handbook of Cultivated Sedums.* Motcombe, Dorset: Ivory Head Press.

Stephenson, R. 1994. *Sedum.* The Cultivated Stonecrops. Portland, Oregon: Timber Press.

Sempervivum

Diehm, H. Jan 2006. www.semperhorst.de

Miklánek, M. 2002. *The List of Cultivars: Sempervivum and Jovibarba v. 7.01.* Piešťany, Slovakia: M. Miklánek (private distribution).

Miklánek, M. 2000. *List of Cultivars: Sempervivum and Jovibarba* v. 15.1. http://miklanek.tripod.com/MCS/cv.html

Sinningia

Dates, J.D. 1988. *The Gesneriad Register 1988. Check List of Names with Descriptions of Cultivated Plants in the Genus Sinningia.* Galesburg, Illinois: American Gloxinia and Gesneriad Society, Inc.

Solenostemon

Pedley, W.K. & Pedley, R. 1974. *Coleus – A Guide to Cultivation and Identification.* Edinburgh: Bartholemew.

Sorbus

McAllister, H. 2005. *The Genus Sorbus: Mountain Ash and Other Rowans.* Kew: Royal Botanical Gardens.

Snyers d'Attenhoven, C. 1999. *Sorbus* Lombarts hybrids *Belgische Dendrologie*: 76-81. Belgium.

Wright, D. 1981. Sorbus – a Gardener's Evaluation. *The Plantsman* 3(2):65-98.

Spiraea

Miller, D.M. 2003. *Spiraea japonica with coloured leaves: RHS Bulletin No. 4.* Wisley, Surrey: Royal Horticultural Soceity. www.rhs.org.uk/plants/documents/spiraea03.pdf

Streptocarpus

Arnold, P. 1979. *The Gesneriad Register 1979: Check List of Streptocarpus.* Binghamton, New York: American Gloxinia & Gesneriad.

Dibleys Nurseries Online Catalogue. Oct 2005. www.dibleys.com.

Succulents

Eggli, U. (ed.) 2002. *Illustrated Handbook of Succulent Plants.* Heidelberg, Germany: Springer-Verlag.

Eggli, U. & Taylor, N. 1994. *List of Names of Succulent Plants other than Cacti Published 1950-92.* Kew: Royal Botanic Gardens.

Grantham, K. & Klaassen, P. 1999. *The Plantfinder's Guide to Cacti and Other Succulents.* Newton Abbot, Devon: David & Charles.

Jacobsen, H. 1973. *Lexicon of Succulent Plants.* London: Blandford.

Syringa

Vrugtman, F. 2000. *International Register of Cultivar Names in the Genus Syringa L. (Oleaceae).* (Contribution No. 91). Hamilton, Canada: Royal Botanic Gardens.

Tiliaceae

Wild, H. 1984. *Flora of Southern Africa 21 (1: Tiliaceae).* Pretoria: Botanical Research Institute, Dept of Agriculture.

Tillandsia

Kiff, L.F. 1991. *A Distributional Checklist of the Genus Tillandsia.* Encino, California: Botanical Diversions.

Trillium

Case, F.W.J. & Case, R.B. 1997. *Trilliums.* Portland, Oregon: Timber Press.

Jacobs, D.L. & Jacobs, R.L. 1997. *American Treasures.* Trilliums in Woodland Garden. Decatur, Georgia: Eco-Gardens.

Tulipa

van Scheepen, J. (ed.). 1996. *Classified List and International Register of Tulip Names.* Hillegom, The Netherlands: Koninklijke Algemeene Vereeniging Voor Bloembollencultuur.

Ulmus

Green, P.S. 1964. Registratration of Cultivar Names in *Ulmus. Arnoldia (Jamaica Plain)* 24:41-80.

Vaccinium

Trehane, J. 2004. *Blueberries, Cranberries and Other Vacciniums.* Portland, Oregon: Timber Press.

Vegetables

Official Journal of the European Communities. Common catalogue of varieties of vegetable species. (24th ed.). Nov 2005. http://europa.eu.int/eur-lex

Viola

Coombes, R.E. 2003. *Violets.* (2nd ed.). London: Batsford.

Fuller, R. 1990. *Pansies, Violas & Violettas.* The Complete Guide. Marlborough: The Crowood Press.

Perfect, E.J. 1996. *Armand Millet and his Violets.* High Wycombe: Park Farm Press.

Robinson, P.M. & Snocken, J. 2003. Checklist of the Cultivated Forms of the Genus *Viola* including the Register of Cultivars. American Violet Society. www.americanvioletsociety.org/Registry

Zambra, G.L. 1950. *Violets for Garden and Market.* (2nd ed.). London: Collingridge.

Vitis

Pearkes, G. 1989. *Vine Growing in Britain.* London: Dent.

Robinson, J. 1989. *Vines, Grapes and Wines.* London: Mitchell Beazley.

Watsonia

Goldblatt, P. 1989. *The Genus Watsonia.* A Systematic Monograph. South Africa: National Botanic Gardens.

Weigela

Howard, R.A. 1965. A Checklist of Cultivar Names in *Weigela. Arnoldia (Jamaica Plain)* 25:49-69.

Wisteria

Valder, P. 1995. *Wisterias.* A Comprehensive Guide. Balmain, Australia: Florilegium.

Yucca

Smith, C. 2004. *Yuccas: Giants among the Lilies.* NCCPG.

Zauschneria

Raven, P.H. 1977. Generic and Sectional Delimitation in *Onagraceae,* Tribe *Epilobieae. Ann. Missouri Bot. Gard.* 63(2):326-340.

Robinson, A. 2000. Focus on Plants: Piping Hot (*Zauschneria* Cultivars). *The Garden* (RHS) 125(9):698-699.

INTERNATIONAL PLANT FINDERS

AUSTRALIA

Hibbert, Margaret, (6th ed.) (2005), *The Aussie Plant Finder*. ISBN 1876314222. More than 35,000 plants from approx 400 specialist nurseries around Australia, with some 5,000 Australian plants listed. Published by Florilegium, 145 St. Johns Road, Glebe, NSW 2037, Australia. T +61 2 9571 8222, F +61 2 9571 8333. E-mail: florileg@tpg.com.au. Price Au$24.95.

NETHERLANDS

Terra/Lannoo (5th edition) *Plantenvinder voor de lage landen.* ISBN 90-5897-056-6. Approx. 50,000 plants and 150 nurseries. Orders: Terra/Lannoo Publishing, Postbus 614, 6800, AP Arnhem, Netherlands T +31 (0) 26-354 0310, F +31 (0) 26-443 4968. E-mail: info@terralannoo.nl; website: www.terralannoo.com Price €14.95.

UNITED KINGDOM

Pawsey, Angela (ed.). (24th ed.) 2006-2007. *Find that Rose!* Published May 2006. Lists approximately 3,450 varieties available in the U.K. with basic type, colour and fragrance. New varieties are highlighted and cross-referenced where applicable to alternative selling names. Includes standard roses. Details of around 60 growers/outlets, many offering mail order. How to find a rose with a particular Christian name or to celebrate a special event and where to see roses in bloom. For further information send S.A.E. to: 303 Mile End Road, Colchester, Essex CO4 5EA. To order send a cheque for £3.25 made out to *Find That Rose!* to the above address.

USA

Hill, Susan & Narizny, Susan (comp.) (2004), *The Plant Locator®: Western Region.* ISBN 0-88192-633-7. Directory of sources for plants (not seeds) available at retail and mail-order nurseries in 13 western states of the USA (California, Oregon, Washington, Idaho, Montana, Colorado, Wyoming, Utah, New Mexico, Arizona, Neveda, Alaska, and Hawaii) and British Columbia, Canada. Information on how to contact nurseries and purchase plants. Includes a common name/botanical name index. Co-published by Black-Eyed Susans Press. E-mail: susans@blackeyedsusanspress.com; website: www.blackeyedsusanspress.com and Timber Press. Price: UK £14.99, Europe €22.95, elsewhere US$19.95, plus postage. Order Online only from: www.timberpress.com

NURSERIES

THE FOLLOWING NURSERIES BETWEEN THEM STOCK AN UNRIVALLED CHOICE OF PLANTS. BEFORE MAKING A VISIT, PLEASE REMEMBER TO CHECK WITH THE NURSERY THAT THE PLANT YOU SEEK IS CURRENTLY AVAILABLE.

Nursery Codes and Symbols

The first letter of each nursery code represents the area of the country in which the nursery is situated.

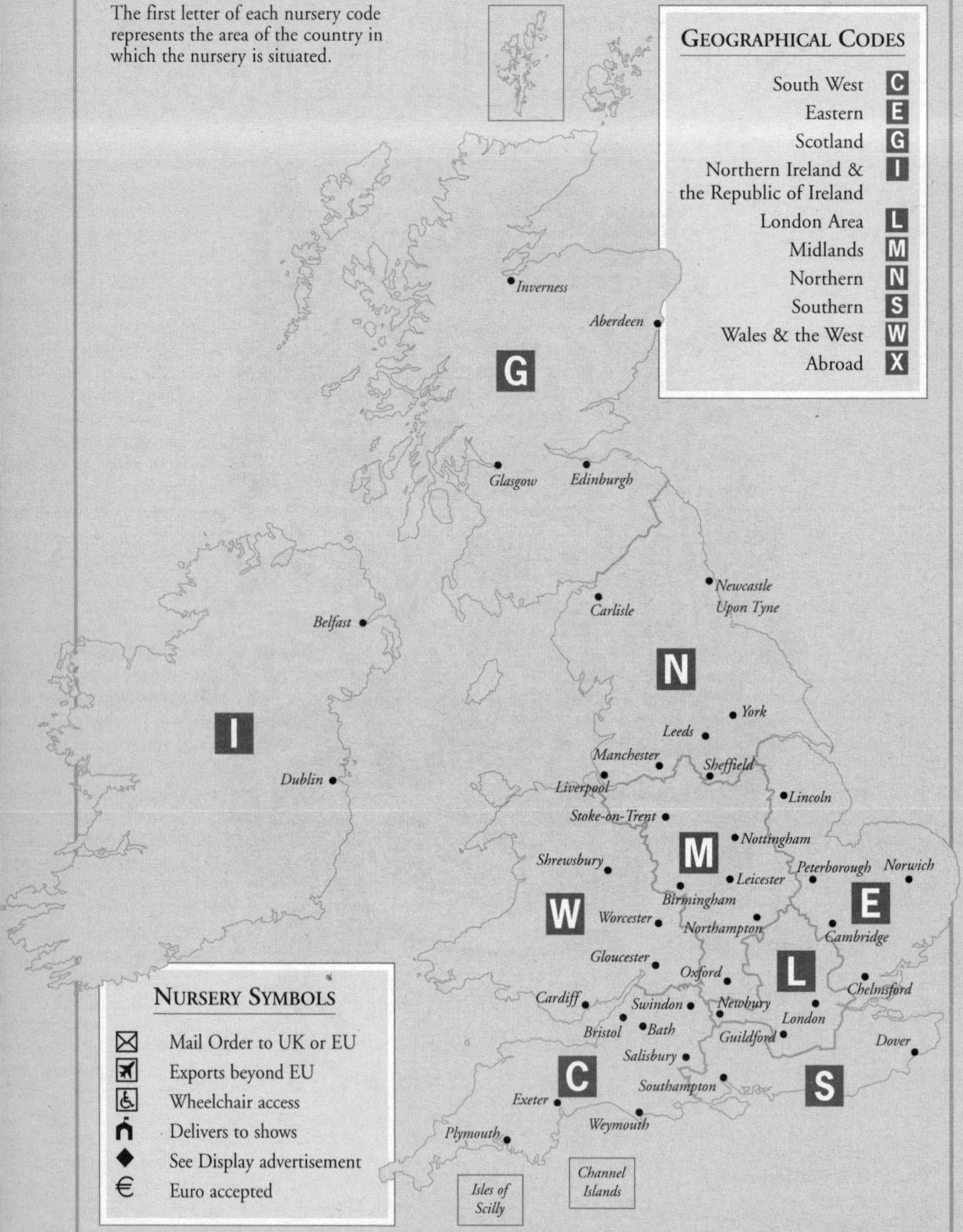

Geographical Codes

South West	C
Eastern	E
Scotland	G
Northern Ireland & the Republic of Ireland	I
London Area	L
Midlands	M
Northern	N
Southern	S
Wales & the West	W
Abroad	X

Nursery Symbols

- ⊠ Mail Order to UK or EU
- ✈ Exports beyond EU
- ♿ Wheelchair access
- Delivers to shows
- ◆ See Display advertisement
- € Euro accepted

USING THE THREE NURSERY LISTINGS

Your main reference from the Plant Directory is the Nursery Details by Code listing, which includes all relevant information for each nursery in order of nursery code. The Nursery Index by Name is an alphabetical list for those who know a nursery's name but not its code and wish to check its details in the main list. The Specialist Nurseries index is to aid those searching for a particular plant group.

1 NURSERY DETAILS BY CODE

Once you have found your plant in the Plant Directory, turn to this list to find out the name, address, opening times and other details of the nurseries whose codes accompany the plant.

KEY
- ✉ Mail order to UK or EU
- ✈ Exports beyond EU
- ♿ Wheelchair access
- Delivers to shows
- € Euro accepted
- ◆ See Display advertisement

Refer to the box at the base of each right-hand page for a key to the symbols

WHil **HILLVIEW HARDY PLANTS** ✉ ✈ € ♿ ◆
(off B4176), Worfield, Nr Bridgnorth,
Shropshire, WV15 5NT
Ⓣ (01746) 716454
Ⓕ (01746) 716454
Ⓔ hillview@onetel.net
Ⓦ www.hillviewhardyplants.com
Contact: Ingrid, John & Sarah Millington
Opening Times: 0900-1700 Mon-Sat Mar-mid Oct. At other times, please phone first.
Min Mail Order UK: £15.00 + p&p
Min Mail Order EU: £15.00 + p&p
Cat. Cost: 5 × 2nd class.
Credit Cards: All major credit/debit cards
Specialities: Choice herbaceous perennials incl. *Aquilegia, Astrantia, Auricula, Primula, Crocosmia, Eucomis, Ixia, Phlox, Schizostylis, Verbascum, Acanthus.* Nat Collection of *Acanthus.*
Notes: Also sells wholesale.
Map Ref: W, B4 **OS Grid Ref:** SO772969

A geographical code is followed by three letters reflecting the nursery's name

A brief summary of the plants available

Other information about the nursery

The map letter is followed by the map square in which the nursery is located

The Ordnance Survey national grid reference for use with OS maps

2 NURSERY INDEX BY NAME

If you seek a particular nursery, look it up in this alphabetical index. Note its code and turn to the Nursery Details by Code list for full information.

Highfield Hollies	SHHo
Hill Garth Nursery	SHGN
Hill House Nursery & Gardens	CHll
Hillview Hardy Plants	WHil
The Himalayan Garden Co.	**NHim**
Holden Clough Nursery	NHol
Holly Gate Cactus Nursery	SHol
Home Farm Plants	**CHFP**

3 SPECIALIST NURSERIES

A list of 32 categories under which nurseries have classified themselves if they exclusively, or predominantly, supply this range of plants.

DROUGHT TOLERANT

CKno, EAlp, ECha, EFam, EGln, EGoo, ETod, LIMB, LLWP, MAbb, MAga, MHrb, NMRc, SEND, SJoh, SKHP, SNew, SPhx, SSss, SSvw, WHil, XPep.

How to Use the Nursery Listings

The details given for each nursery have been compiled from information supplied to us in answer to a questionnaire. In some cases, because of constraints of space, the entries have been slightly abbreviated.

Nurseries are not charged for their entries and inclusion in no way implies a value judgement.

Nursery Details by Code (*page 796*)

Each nursery is allocated a code, for example GPoy. The first letter of each code indicates the main area of the country in which the nursery is situated. In this example, G=Scotland. The remaining three letters reflect the nursery's name, in this case Poyntzfield Herb Nursery.

In this main listing the nurseries are given in alphabetical order of codes for quick reference from the Plant Directory. All of the nurseries' details, such as address, opening times, mail order service etc., will be found here.

Opening Times

Although opening times have been published as submitted and where applicable, **it is always advisable, especially if travelling a long distance, to check with the nursery first**. The initials NGS indicate that the nursery is open under the National Gardens Scheme.

Mail Order - ⊠

Many nurseries provide a mail order service. **This is, however, often restricted to certain times of the year or to particular genera**. Please check the **Notes** section of each nursery's entry for any restrictions or special conditions.

In some cases, the mail order service extends to all members of the European Union. Where this is offered, the minimum charge to the EU will be noted in the Nursery entry.

Where **'No minimum charge'** (Nmc) is shown, please note that to send even one plant may involve the nursery in substantial postage and packing costs. Some nurseries may not be prepared to send tender or bulky plants.

Where a nursery offers a **mail order only** service, this will be noted under **Opening Times** in the nursery entry.

Export ✈

Export refers to mail order beyond the European Union. Nurseries that are prepared to consider exporting are indicated. However, there is usually a substantial minimum charge and, in addition, all the costs of Phytosanitary Certificates and Customs have to be met by the purchaser.

Catalogue Cost

Some nurseries offer their catalogue free, or for a few stamps, but a large (at least A5) stamped addressed envelope is always appreciated as well. Overseas customers should use an equivalent number of International Reply Coupons (IRCs) in place of stamps.

Increasingly, nurseries are finding it more cost effective to produce catalogues on the Internet rather than printing them. Many nurseries also offer an online mail order facility.

Wheelchair Access ♿

Nurseries are asked to indicate if their premises are suitable for wheelchair users. Where only partial access is indicated, this is noted in the Notes field and the nursery is not marked with the symbol.

The assessment of ease-of-access is entirely the responsibility of the individual nursery.

Specialities

Nurseries list here the plants or genera that they supply and any National Collections of plants they may hold. Please note that some nurseries may charge an entry fee to visit a National Collection. Always enquire before visiting.

Nurseries will also note here if they only have small quantities of individual plants available for sale or if they will propagate to order.

NOTES

In this section, you will find notes on any restrictions to mail order or export; on limited wheelchair access; or the nursery site address, if this differs from the office address; together with any other non-horticultural information.

DELIVERY TO SHOWS ⌂

Many nurseries will deliver pre-ordered plants to flower shows for collection by customers. These are indicated by a marquee symbol. Contact the nursery for details of shows they attend.

PAYMENT IN EUROS €

A number of UK nurseries have indicated that they will accept payment in Euros. You should, however, check with the nursery concerned before making such a payment, as some will only accept cash and some only cheques, whilst others will expect the purchaser to pay bank charges.

MAPS

If you wish to visit any of the nurseries you can find its approximate location on the relevant map (following p.919), unless the nursery has requested this is not shown. Nurseries are also encouraged to provide their Ordnance Survey national grid reference for use with OS publications such as the Land Ranger series.

NURSERY INDEX BY NAME (*page 910*)

For convenience, an alphabetical index of nurseries is included on p.910. This gives the names of all nurseries listed in the book in alphabetical order of nursery name together with their code.

SPECIALIST NURSERIES (*page 917*)

This list of nurseries is intended to help those with an interest in finding specialist categories of plant. Nurseries have been asked to classify themselves under one or more headings where this represents the type of plant they *predominantly* or *exclusively* have in stock. For example, if you wish to find a nursery specialising in ornamental grasses, look up 'Grasses' in the listing where you will find a list of nursery codes. Then turn to the Nursery Details by Code, for details of the nurseries.

Please note that not all nurseries shown here will have plants listed in the Plant Directory. This may be their choice or because the *RHS Plant Finder* does not list seeds or annuals and only terrestrial orchids and hardy cacti. For space reasons, it is rare to find a nursery's full catalogue listed in the Plant Directory.

In all cases, please ensure you ring to confirm the range available before embarking on a journey to the nursery.

The specialist plant groups listed in this edition are:

Acid-loving
Alpines/rock
Aquatics/marginals
Bamboos
British wild flowers
Bulbous plants
Cacti & succulents
Carnivorous
Chalk-loving
Climbers
Coastal
Conifers
Conservatory
Drought-tolerant
Ferns
Fruit
Grasses
Hedging
Herbs
Marginal/bog plants
Orchids
Organic
Ornamental trees
Peat-free
Period plants
Propagate to order
Roses
Seeds
Specimen-sized plants
Topiary
Tropical plants

Perennials and shrubs have been omitted as these are considered to be too general and serviced by a great proportion of the nurseries.

DELETED NURSERIES

Every year some nurseries ask to be removed from the book. This may be a temporary measure because they are moving, or it may be permanent due to closure, sale, retirement, or a change in the way in they trade. Occasionally, nurseries are unable to meet the closing date and will re-enter the book in the following edition. Some nurseries simply do not reply and, as we have no current information on them, they are deleted.

Please, never use an old edition

NURSERY DETAILS BY CODE

Please note that all these nurseries are listed in alphabetical order by their code. All nurseries are listed in alphabetical order by their name in the **Nursery Index by Name** on page 910.

SOUTH WEST

CAbb ABBOTSBURY SUB-TROPICAL GARDENS ⊠ ♿
Abbotsbury, Nr Weymouth, Dorset, DT3 4LA
Ⓣ (01305) 871344
Ⓕ (01305) 871344
Ⓔ info@abbotsburygardens.co.uk
Ⓦ www.abbotsburyplantsales.co.uk
Contact: David Sutton
Opening Times: 1000-1800 daily mid Mar-1st Nov. 1000-1500 Nov-mid Mar.
Min Mail Order UK: £10.00 + p&p
Cat. Cost: £2.00 + A4 sae + 42p stamp.
Credit Cards: Access Visa MasterCard Switch
Specialities: Less common & tender shrubs incl. palms, tree ferns, bamboos & plants from Australia, New Zealand & S. Africa.

CAbP ABBEY PLANTS ⊠ ♿
Chaffeymoor, Bourton, Gillingham, Dorset, SP8 5BY
Ⓣ (01747) 840841
Contact: K Potts
Opening Times: 1000-1300 & 1400-1700 Tue-Sat Mar-Nov. Dec-Feb by appt.
Min Mail Order UK: Nmc.
Cat. Cost: 2 × 2nd class.
Credit Cards: None
Specialities: Flowering trees & shrubs. Shrub roses incl. many unusual varieties. Limited stock.
Map Ref: C, B4 **OS Grid Ref:** ST762304

CAby THE ABBEY NURSERY ♿
Forde Abbey, Chard, Somerset, TA20 4LU
Ⓣ (01460) 220088
Ⓕ (01460) 220088
Ⓔ TheAbbeyNursery@btconnect.com
Contact: Peter Sims
Opening Times: 1000-1700 7 days, 1st Mar-31st Oct. Please phone first to check opening times in Mar.
Cat. Cost: None issued.
Credit Cards: All major credit/debit cards
Specialities: Hardy herbaceous perennials & grasses.
Map Ref: C, C4 **OS Grid Ref:** ST359052

CAgr AGROFORESTRY RESEARCH TRUST ⊠
46 Hunters Moon, Dartington, Totnes, Devon, TQ9 6JT
Ⓣ (01803) 840776
Ⓕ (01803) 840776
Ⓔ mail@agroforestry.co.uk
Ⓦ www.agroforestry.co.uk
Contact: Martin Crawford
Opening Times: Not open. Mail order only.
Min Mail Order UK: Nmc
Min Mail Order EU: Nmc
Cat. Cost: 4 × 1st class.
Credit Cards: MasterCardVisa
Specialities: Top & soft fruit, nut trees including *Castanea*, *Corylus*, *Juglans*, *Pinus*. Also seeds. Some plants in small quantities only.

CAni ANITA ALLEN ⊠
Shapcott Barton Estate, East Knowstone, South Molton, Devon, EX36 4EE
Ⓣ (01398) 341664
Ⓕ (01389) 341664
Contact: Anita Allen
Opening Times: By appt. only. Garden open under NGS.
Min Mail Order UK: Nmc.
Cat. Cost: 5 × 1st class.
Credit Cards: None
Specialities: Nat. Collection of *Leucanthemum superbum*. 70+ accurately named Shasta daisies, a few in very short supply. Also some hardy perennials & *Anthemis tinctoria* cultivars. Also 60+ cvs of *Buddleja davidii*.
Map Ref: C, B3 **OS Grid Ref:** SS846235

CArn **ARNE HERBS** ⊠ ✈ ⌂ € ♿
Limeburn Nurseries, Limeburn Hill, Chew Magna, Bristol, BS40 8QW
Ⓣ (01275) 333399
Ⓕ (01275) 333399
Ⓔ lyman@lyman-dixon.freeserve.co.uk
Ⓦ www.arneherbs.co.uk
Contact: A Lyman-Dixon & Jenny Thomas
Opening Times: Most times, please check first.
Min Mail Order UK: Nmc
Min Mail Order EU: Nmc
Cat. Cost: £3.75 UK, 10 × IRC refundable on first order. Or online.
Credit Cards: None
Specialities: Herbs, wildflowers & cottage flowers. Some in small quantities only, please see catalogue for details.
Notes: Will deliver to Farmers' Markets. Also sells wholesale.
Map Ref: C, A5 **OS Grid Ref:** ST563638

CAvo **AVON BULBS** ⊠ ⌂
Burnt House Farm, Mid-Lambrook, South Petherton, Somerset, TA13 5HE
Ⓣ (01460) 242177
Ⓕ (01460) 249025
Ⓔ info@avonbulbs.co.uk
Ⓦ www.avonbulbs.co.uk
Contact: C Ireland-Jones
Opening Times: Mail order only. Open Thu/Fri/Sat, mid-Sep to end Oct & mid-Feb to end Mar for collection of pre-booked orders.
Min Mail Order UK: £10.00 + p&p
Min Mail Order EU: £20.00 + p&p
Cat. Cost: 4 × 2nd class.
Credit Cards: Visa Access Switch MasterCard
Specialities: Some special snowdrops are only available in small quantities.
Notes: £1.00 handling charge for delivering plants to shows.
Map Ref: C, B5

CBcs **BURNCOOSE NURSERIES** ⊠ ✈ ⌂ ♿
Gwennap, Redruth, Cornwall, TR16 6BJ
Ⓣ (01209) 860316
Ⓕ (01209) 860011
Ⓔ burncoose@eclipse.co.uk
Ⓦ www.burncoose.co.uk
Contact: C H Williams
Opening Times: 0830-1700 Mon-Sat & 1100-1700 Sun.
Min Mail Order UK: Nmc
Min Mail Order EU: Individual quotations for EU sales.
Cat. Cost: £1.50 incl. p&p.
Credit Cards: Visa Access Switch
Specialities: Extensive range of over 3500 ornamental trees & shrubs and herbaceous. Rare & unusual *Magnolia*, *Rhododendron*. Conservatory plants. 30 acre garden.
Notes: Also sells wholesale.
Map Ref: C, D1 **OS Grid Ref:** SW742395

CBct **BARRACOTT PLANTS** ⊠ € ◆
Old Orchard, Calstock Road, Gunnislake, Cornwall, PL18 9AA
Ⓣ (01822) 832234
Ⓔ GEOFF@geoff63.freeserve.co.uk
Ⓦ www.barracottplants.co.uk
Contact: Geoff Turner, Thelma Watson
Opening Times: 0900-1700 Thu-Sat, Mar-end Sep. Other times by appt.
Min Mail Order UK: Nmc
Min Mail Order EU:
Cat. Cost: 2 × 1st class.
Credit Cards: None
Specialities: Herbaceous plants: shade-loving, foliage & form. *Acanthus*, *Astrantia*, *Bergenia*, *Convallaria*, *Ligularia*, *Liriope*, *Roscoea*, *Smilacina*, *Symphytum* & *Tricyrtis*.
Notes: Also sells wholesale.
Map Ref: C, C3 **OS Grid Ref:** SX436702

CBdn **BOWDEN HOSTAS** ⊠ ✈ ♿
Sticklepath, Okehampton, Devon, EX20 2NL
Ⓣ (01837) 840989
Ⓕ (01837) 851549
Ⓔ info@bowdenhostas.com
Ⓦ www.bowdenhostas.com
Contact: Tim Penrose
Opening Times: 1000-1600 Mon-Sat, 1st Mar to 30th Sep 2006.
Min Mail Order UK: Nmc
Min Mail Order EU: Nmc
Cat. Cost: Free.
Credit Cards: Visa Access EuroCard Switch
Specialities: *Hosta* only. Nat. Collection of modern hybrid *Hosta*.
Notes: Also sells wholesale.
Map Ref: C, C3 **OS Grid Ref:** SX640940

CBdw **BODWEN NURSERY** ⊠
Pothole, St Austell, Cornwall, PL26 7DW
Ⓣ (01726) 883855
Ⓔ sales@bodwen-nursery.co.uk
Ⓦ www.bodwen-nursery.co.uk
Contact: John Geraghty
Opening Times: Erratic. Essential to telephone in advance.

KEY
⊠ Mail order to UK or EU ⌂ Delivers to shows
✈ Exports beyond EU € Euro accepted
♿ Accessible by wheelchair ◆ See Display advertisement

C

Min Mail Order UK: Nmc
Cat. Cost: 2 × 2nd class.
Credit Cards: None
Specialities: Japanese maples. Some rarer cultivars available in small quantities only.
Notes: Also sells wholesale.
Map Ref: C, D2

CBel BELMONT HOUSE NURSERY ⊠ €
Little Horton, Devizes, Wiltshire, SN10 3LJ
Ⓣ (01380) 860510
Ⓔ rcottis@supanet.com
Contact: Gordon Cottis
Opening Times: By appt. only. Please phone.
Min Mail Order UK: £2.50
Cat. Cost: 2 × 2nd class.
Credit Cards: None
Specialities: *Helleborus* hybrids & true species, *Galanthus* & *Cyclamen*, some in small quantities only.
Notes: Mail order *Cyclamen* & *Galanthus* only, Nov-Feb.

CBen BENNETT'S WATER LILY FARM ⊠ ♿
Putton Lane, Chickerell, Weymouth, Dorset, DT3 4AF
Ⓣ (01305) 785150
Ⓕ (01305) 781619
Ⓔ JB@waterlily.co.uk
Ⓦ www.waterlily.co.uk
Contact: J Bennett
Opening Times: 1000-1700 Apr-Sep. Closed Mon & Sat.
Min Mail Order UK: Nmc + p&p
Min Mail Order EU: Nmc + p&p
Cat. Cost: Sae for price list
Credit Cards: Visa Access MasterCard Switch
Specialities: Aquatic plants. Nat. Collection of Water Lilies.
Notes: Mail order Apr-Sep only.
Map Ref: C, C5 **OS Grid Ref:** SY651797

CBgR BEGGAR'S ROOST PLANTS ⌂ ♿
Lilstock, Bridgwater, Somerset, TA5 1SU
Ⓣ (01278) 741519
Ⓕ (01278) 741519
Ⓔ nunnington@aol.com
Contact: Rosemary FitzGerald, Kate Harris
Opening Times: By appt. only.
Credit Cards: None
Specialities: Garden-worthy bulbs & herbaceous, emphasising species. Classic perennials, incl. *Salvia* & *Hemerocallis*. Winter interest plants. Small quantities only.
Map Ref: C, B4 **OS Grid Ref:** ST168450

CBig THE BIG GRASS CO. ⊠ ☒ ⌂ €
Hookhill Plantation, Woolfardisworthy East, Black Dog, Nr Crediton, Devon, EX17 4RX
Ⓣ (01363) 866146
Ⓕ (01363) 866146
Ⓔ alison@big-grass.com
Ⓦ www.big-grass.com
Contact: Alison & Scott Evans
Opening Times: Mail order only. Open by appt. only.
Min Mail Order UK: Nmc
Min Mail Order EU: Nmc
Cat. Cost: Now in CD format only. £2.50 by post.
Credit Cards: None
Specialities: Grasses & restios.
Notes: Also sells wholesale.
Map Ref: C, B3

CBnk M.T. BENNALLACK ⊠
(Office) Aintree, Green Park Way, Chillington, Kingsbridge, Devon, TQ7 2HY
Ⓣ (01548) 580381
Contact: M T Bennallack
Opening Times: By appt only Aug & Sept.
Min Mail Order UK: Nmc.
Cat. Cost: 3 × 1st class.
Credit Cards: None
Specialities: Nat. Collection of *Aster novi-belgii*.
Notes: Mail order Apr & May only. Nursery 9 miles from this address.

CBod BODMIN PLANT AND HERB NURSERY ♿
Laveddon Mill, Laninval Hill, Bodmin, Cornwall, PL30 5JU
Ⓣ (01208) 72837
Ⓕ (01208) 76491
Ⓔ bodminnursery@aol.com
Contact: Mark Lawlor
Opening Times: 0900-1700 Mon-Sat Nov-Mar, 0900-1800 Mon-Sat Apr-Oct. 1000-1600 Sun.
Credit Cards: All major credit/debit cards
Specialities: Herbs, herbaceous & grasses, hardy geraniums & coastal plants. Interesting shrubs, fruit & ornamental trees.
Map Ref: C, C2 **OS Grid Ref:** SX053659

CBow BOWLEY PLANTS ⌂ ◆
Church Farm, North End, Ashton Keynes, Nr Swindon, Wiltshire, SN6 6QR
Ⓣ (01285) 640352
Ⓜ 07855 524929
Ⓦ www.bowleyplants.co.uk
Contact: Piers Bowley
Opening Times: 1000-1600 Tue & Sat,

1300-1600 Sun, Mar-Oct incl.
Cat. Cost: 2 × 1st class.
Credit Cards: None
Specialities: Variegated plants & coloured foliage. Alpines, perennials. shrubs, ferns, grasses & herbs. Some varieties in small numbers.
Notes: Also sells wholesale.
Map Ref: C, A6 **OS Grid Ref:** SU043945

CBrd **BROADLEAS GARDENS LTD**
Broadleas, Devizes, Wiltshire, SN10 5JQ
Ⓣ (01380) 722035
Ⓕ (01380) 722970
Ⓔ broadleasgardens@btinternet.com
Contact: Lady Anne Cowdray
Opening Times: 1400-1800 Wed, Thu & Sun Apr-Oct.
Cat. Cost: 1 × 1st class.
Credit Cards: None
Specialities: General range.
Map Ref: C, A6

CBre **BREGOVER PLANTS** ⊠ ⌂
Hillbrooke, Middlewood, North Hill, Nr Launceston, Cornwall, PL15 7NN
Ⓣ (01566) 782661
Contact: Jennifer Bousfield
Opening Times: 1100-1700 Wed, Mar-mid Oct and by appt.
Min Mail Order UK: Nmc
Min Mail Order EU: Nmc
Cat. Cost: 3 × 1st class.
Credit Cards: None
Specialities: Unusual hardy perennials grown in small garden nursery. Available in small quantities only.
Notes: Mail order Oct-Mar only.
Map Ref: C, C2 **OS Grid Ref:** SX273752

CBrm **BRAMLEY LODGE GARDEN NURSERY** € ♿
Beech Tree Lane, Ipplepen, Newton Abbot, Devon, TQ12 5TW
Ⓣ (01803) 813265
Ⓔ blnursery@btopenworld.com
Ⓦ www.bramleylodge-nursery.co.uk
Contact: Susan Young
Opening Times: 1000-1600 Fri-Mon Mar-Jul, 1000-1600 Sun-Mon Aug-Oct. Phone for appt. at all other times.
Cat. Cost: 3 × 1st class.
Credit Cards: All major credit/debit cards
Specialities: Grasses. Also trees, shrubs, perennials & rock plants. Several small model themed gardens.
Map Ref: C, C3 **OS Grid Ref:** SX828673

CBrP **BROOKLANDS PLANTS** ⊠
25 Treves Road, Dorchester, Dorset, DT1 2HE
Ⓣ (01305) 265846
Ⓔ Ian@cycads.fsnet.co.uk
Contact: Ian Watt
Opening Times: By appt. for collection of plants only.
Min Mail Order UK: £25.00 + p&p
Min Mail Order EU: £25.00 + p&p
Cat. Cost: 2 × 2nd class.
Credit Cards: None
Specialities: Cycad nursery specialising in the more cold-tolerant species of *Encephalartos*, *Dioon*, *Macrozamia* & *Cycas*. Also hardy palms, *Agave*, *Yucca*, *Dasylirion*, *Restio* & bamboos. Some species available in small quantities only.
Map Ref: C, C5

CBur **BURNHAM NURSERIES** ⊠ ✈ ⌂ ♿
Forches Cross, Newton Abbot, Devon, TQ12 6PZ
Ⓣ (01626) 352233
Ⓕ (01626) 362167
Ⓔ mail@orchids.uk.com
Ⓦ www.orchids.uk.com
Contact: Any member of staff
Opening Times: 1000-1600 Mon-Sun.
Min Mail Order UK: Nmc
Min Mail Order EU: £100.00 + p&p
Cat. Cost: A4 sae + 47p stamp.
Credit Cards: Visa American Express MasterCard Maestro
Specialities: All types of orchid except British native types.
Notes: Please ask for details on export beyond EU.
Map Ref: C, C4

CCAT **CIDER APPLE TREES** ⊠ €
Kerian, Corkscrew Lane, Woolston, Nr North Cadbury, Somerset, BA22 7BP
Ⓣ (01963) 441101
Ⓦ www.ciderappletrees.co.uk
Contact: Mr J Dennis
Opening Times: By appt. only.
Min Mail Order UK: £9.50
Min Mail Order EU: £9.50
Cat. Cost: Free.
Credit Cards: None
Specialities: *Malus* (speciality standard trees).
Notes: Also sells wholesale.
Map Ref: C, B5

KEY
⊠ Mail order to UK or EU ⌂ Delivers to shows
✈ Exports beyond EU € Euro accepted
♿ Accessible by wheelchair ◆ See Display advertisement

C

CCCN **CROSS COMMON NURSERY** ⊠
The Lizard, Helston, Cornwall, TR12 7PD
Ⓣ (01326) 290722/290668
Ⓔ info@crosscommonnursery.co.uk
Ⓦ www.crosscommonnursery.co.uk
Contact: Suzy Bosustow
Opening Times: 1000-1700 7 days, Mar-mid Oct. Reduced hours in winter, please phone for appt.
Min Mail Order UK: Nmc
Cat. Cost: Online only.
Specialities: Tropical/sub-tropical, coastal plants & conservatory plants. Wide range of grapevines and citrus trees.
Notes: Credit cards only accepted for mail order & online sales.
Map Ref: C, D1 **OS Grid Ref:** SW704116

CCge **COTTAGE GARDEN PLANTS AND HERBS** ⌂
4 Lundy View, Northam, Bideford, Devon, EX39 1BE
Ⓣ (01237) 470370
Contact: Shirley Bennett
Opening Times: Ring for private visit. Sells at Devon NCCPG, plant sales & other markets.
Credit Cards: None
Specialities: Cottage garden plants, herbs and esp. hardy geraniums (200+ varieties available).
Notes: Lectures given on hardy geraniums & cottage garden plants and gardens.

CCha **CHAPEL FARM HOUSE NURSERY** € ♿
Halwill Junction,
Beaworthy, Devon,
EX21 5UF
Ⓣ (01409) 221594
Ⓕ (01409) 221594
Contact: Robin or Toshie Hull
Opening Times: 0900-1700 Tue-Sat, 1000-1600 Sun & B/hol Mons.
Cat. Cost: None issued.
Credit Cards: None
Specialities: Plants from Japan. Also herbaceous. Japanese garden design service offered.
Map Ref: C, C3

CChe **CHERRY TREE NURSERY** ♿
(Sheltered Work Opportunities), off New Road Roundabout, Northbourne, Bournemouth, Dorset, BH10 7DA
Ⓣ (01202) 593537 or (01202) 590840
Ⓕ (01202) 590626
Contact: Stephen Jailler
Opening Times: 0830-1530 Mon-Fri, 0900-1200 most Sats.
Cat. Cost: A4 sae + 66p stamp.
Credit Cards: None
Specialities: Hardy shrubs, perennials, climbers, grasses.
Notes: Also sells wholesale.
Map Ref: C, C6

CCol **COLD HARBOUR NURSERY** ⊠ ⌂
(Office) 28 Moor Road, Swanage, Dorset, BH19 1RG
Ⓣ (01929) 423520 evenings
Ⓔ coldharbournursery@hotmail.com
Ⓦ www.dorset-perennials.co.uk
Contact: Steve Saunders
Opening Times: 1000-1700 Tue-Fri & most w/ends 1st Mar-end Oct. Other times by appt.
Min Mail Order UK: £6.00 + p&p
Cat. Cost: 3 × 1st class.
Credit Cards: None
Specialities: Unusual herbaceous perennials incl. hardy geraniums, daylilies & grasses.
Notes: Nursery is at Bere Road (opp. Silent Woman Inn), Wareham.
Map Ref: C, C5

CCtw **CHURCHTOWN NURSERIES** ⊠ ⌂ ♿
Gulval, Penzance, Cornwall, TR18 3BE
Ⓣ (01736) 362626
Ⓕ (01736) 362626
Ⓔ Chris@churchtownnurseries.com
Ⓦ www.churchtownnurseries.co.uk
Contact: Chris or Fay Osborne
Opening Times: 1000-1700 Apr-Sep, 1000-1600 Oct-Mar or by appt.
Min Mail Order UK: £25.00 + p&p
Cat. Cost: 1st class sae for list.
Credit Cards: None
Specialities: Good, ever-increasing, range of shrubs, herbaceous & tender perennials & ornamental grasses incl. some more unusual.
Map Ref: C, D1 **OS Grid Ref:** SW486317

CCVN **CULM VIEW NURSERY** ⌂
Waterloo Farm, Clayhidon, Devon, EX15 3TN
Ⓣ (01823) 680698
Ⓔ plants@culmviewnursery.co.uk
Ⓦ www.culmviewnursery.co.uk
Contact: Brian & Alison Jacobs
Opening Times: By appt. only for collection.
Credit Cards: None
Specialities: Hebaceous perennials grown in peat-free compost.

CCVT **CHEW VALLEY TREES** ⊠
Winford Road, Chew Magna, Bristol, BS40 8QE
Ⓣ (01275) 333752
Ⓕ (01275) 333746

Ⓔ info@chewvalleytrees.co.uk
Ⓦ www.chewvalleytrees.co.uk
Contact: J Scarth
Opening Times: 0800-1700 Mon-Fri all year. 0900-1600 Sat, Sep-Jun. Closed Sun & B/hols.
Min Mail Order UK: Nmc
Cat. Cost: Free.
Credit Cards: All major credit/debit cards
Specialities: Native British & ornamental trees, shrubs, apple trees & hedging.
Notes: Partial wheelchair access. Max. plant height for mail order 2m incl. roots. Also sells wholesale.
Map Ref: C, A5 **OS Grid Ref:** ST558635

CDBb DORSET BLUEBERRY COMPANY ⊠ ⛫ ♿
(office) Littlemoors Farm, Ham Lane, Hampreston, Wimborne, Dorset, BH21 7LT
Ⓣ (01202) 891426
Ⓕ (01202) 874737
Ⓔ info@dorset-blueberry.co.uk
Ⓦ www.dorset-blueberry.co.uk
Contact: Jennifer Trehane or David Trehane
Opening Times: 1000-1630. Closed Xmas & New Year period.
Min Mail Order UK: £7.50 + p&p mainland Britain. Please enquire for islands, N Ireland & Rep. of Ireland.
Cat. Cost: 4 × 1st class.
Credit Cards: All major credit/debit cards
Specialities: Blueberries, cranberries & other *Vaccinium*.
Notes: New plant centre & shop. Tea room opening summer 2006.
Map Ref: C, C6

CDes DESIRABLE PLANTS ⊠ ⛫
(Office) Pentamar, Crosspark, Totnes, Devon, TQ9 5BQ
Ⓣ (01803) 864489 evenings
Ⓔ sutton.totnes@lineone.net
Ⓦ www.desirableplants.com
Contact: Dr J J & Mrs S A Sutton
Opening Times: Not open. Mail order only.
Min Mail Order UK: £15.00
Cat. Cost: 5 × 1st class.
Credit Cards: None
Specialities: Eclectic range of choice & interesting herbaceous plants by mail order.
Notes: Monthly retail event in Totnes, phone or see web for details. Nursery not at this address.

CDev DEVON VIOLET NURSERY ⊠ ⛫ €
10 Sunny Hill, Ottery St Mary, Devon, EX11 1DZ
Ⓣ (01404) 813701
Ⓔ hedgeland6@aol.com
Ⓦ www.sweetviolets.co.uk
Contact: Geoff Hedgeland
Opening Times: By appt. only.
Min Mail Order UK: £4.99
Min Mail Order EU: £6.99
Cat. Cost: 2 × 1st class.
Credit Cards: All major credit/debit cards
Specialities: Violets & Parma violets.
Notes: Also sells wholesale.
Map Ref: C, C4

CDHC DON HATCH CONIFERS ⊠ ♿
Combe Raleigh, Honiton, Devon, EX14 4TQ
Ⓣ (01404) 42981
Ⓕ (01404) 42167
Ⓔ sales@conifers.co.uk
Ⓦ www.conifers.co.uk
Contact: Chris Padget
Opening Times: Mail order only. Open by prior appt.
Min Mail Order UK: £40.00
Min Mail Order EU: £40.00
Cat. Cost: Conifer list £5.00 + p&p. Full catalogue online only.
Credit Cards: None
Specialities: Conifers & a limited range of Japanese maples. Peat-free cuttings.
Notes: Also sells wholesale.

CDMG DOCTON MILL GARDENS ♿
Lyme Bridge, Hartland, Devon, EX39 6EA
Ⓣ (01237) 441369
Ⓕ (01237) 441369
Ⓔ john@doctonmill.freeserve.co.uk
Ⓦ www.doctonmill.co.uk
Contact: John Borrett
Opening Times: 1000-1800 7 days, 1st Mar-31st Oct.
Credit Cards: All major credit/debit cards
Specialities: Most plants available in small quantities only.
Map Ref: C, B2

CDob SAMUEL DOBIE & SON ⊠
Long Road, Paignton, Devon, TQ4 7SX
Ⓣ 0870 112 3623
Ⓕ 0870 112 3624
Ⓦ www.dobies.co.uk
Contact: Customer Services
Opening Times: Not open. Mail order only. Phone line open 0830-1700 Mon-Fri (office). Also answerphone.

KEY
⊠ Mail order to UK or EU ⛫ Delivers to shows
✈ Exports beyond EU € Euro accepted
♿ Accessible by wheelchair ◆ See Display advertisement

C

Min Mail Order UK: Nmc
Cat. Cost: Free.
Credit Cards: Visa MasterCard Switch Delta
Specialities: Wide selection of popular flower & vegetable seeds. Also includes young plants, summer-flowering bulbs & garden sundries.
Notes: Mail order to UK & Rep. of Ireland only.

CDoC DUCHY OF CORNWALL ⊠ ◆
Cott Road, Lostwithiel, Cornwall, PL22 0HW
Ⓣ (01208) 872668
Ⓕ (01208) 872835
Ⓔ sales@duchynursery.co.uk
Ⓦ www.duchyofcornwallnursery.co.uk
Contact: Tracy Wilson
Opening Times: 0900-1700 Mon-Sat, 1000-1700 Sun & B/hols.
Min Mail Order UK: £14.00
Min Mail Order EU: Nmc
Cat. Cost: 8 × 1st class, CD catalogue 12 × 1st class.
Credit Cards: All major credit/debit cards
Specialities: Very wide range of garden plants incl. trees, shrubs, conifers, roses, perennials, fruit & half-hardy exotics.
Notes: Nursery partially available for wheelchair users.
Map Ref: C, C2 **OS Grid Ref:** SX112614

CDTJ DESERT TO JUNGLE ⊠ ♠ ♿
Henlade Garden Nursery, Lower Henlade, Taunton, Somerset, TA3 5NB
Ⓣ (01823) 443701
Ⓔ plants@deserttojungle.com
Ⓦ www.deserttojungle.com
Contact: Rob Gudge, Dave Root
Opening Times: 1000-1700 Tue-Sun, 1st Mar-31st Oct. Fri & Sat only Nov-Feb, or phone first.
Min Mail Order UK: Nmc
Cat. Cost: 1 × 1st class sae.
Credit Cards: Visa MasterCard Switch
Specialities: Exotic-looking plants giving a desert or jungle effect in the garden. Incl. *Canna*, aroids, succulents, tree ferns & bamboos.
Map Ref: C, B4 **OS Grid Ref:** ST273232

CDul DULFORD NURSERIES ⊠ ♿
Cullompton, Devon, EX15 2DG
Ⓣ (01884) 266361
Ⓕ (01884) 266663
Ⓔ dulford.nurseries@virgin.net
Ⓦ www.dulford-nurseries.co.uk
Contact: Paul & Mary Ann Rawlings
Opening Times: 0730-1630 Mon-Fri.
Min Mail Order UK: Nmc
Min Mail Order EU: Nmc
Cat. Cost: Free.
Credit Cards: All major credit/debit cards
Specialities: Native, ornamental & unusual trees & shrubs incl. oaks, maples, beech, birch, chestnut, ash, lime, *Sorbus* & pines.
Notes: Also sells wholesale.
Map Ref: C, C4 **OS Grid Ref:** SY062062

CDWL DORSET WATER LILIES ♠ ♿
Yeovil Road, Halstock, Yeovil, Somerset, BA22 9RR
Ⓣ (01935) 891668
Ⓕ (01935) 891946
Ⓔ dorsetwaterlily@tiscali.co.uk
Ⓦ www.dorsetwaterlily.co.uk
Contact: Richard Gallehawk
Opening Times: 0900-1600 Mon & Fri only, plus Sat in summer.
Cat. Cost: Free.
Credit Cards: None
Specialities: Hardy & tropical water lilies, lotus, marginal & bogside plants.
Notes: Pond design & construction service. Also sells wholesale.
Map Ref: C, C5 **OS Grid Ref:** ST543083

CElw ELWORTHY COTTAGE PLANTS ♠ ♿
Elworthy Cottage, Elworthy, Nr Lydeard St Lawrence, Taunton, Somerset, TA4 3PX
Ⓣ (01984) 656427
Ⓔ mike@elworthy-cottage.co.uk
Ⓦ www.elworthy-cottage.co.uk
Contact: Mrs J M Spiller
Opening Times: 1000-1630 Thu, Fri & Sat late Mar-end May, Thu only Jun-mid Oct. Also by appt.
Cat. Cost: 3 × 2nd class.
Credit Cards: None
Specialities: *Clematis* & unusual herbaceous plants esp. hardy geraniums, *Geum*, grasses, *Campanula*, *Crocosmia*, *Pulmonaria*, *Astrantia* & *Viola*. Some varieties only available in in small quantities.
Notes: Nursery on B3188, 5 miles north of Wiveliscombe, in centre of Elworthy village.
Map Ref: C, B4 **OS Grid Ref:** ST084349

CEnd ENDSLEIGH GARDENS ⊠ ♿ ◆
Milton Abbot, Tavistock, Devon, PL19 0PG
Ⓣ (01822) 870235
Ⓕ (01822) 870513
Ⓔ Treemail@endsleigh-gardens.com
Ⓦ www.endsleigh-gardens.com
Contact: Michael Taylor
Opening Times: 0800-1700 Mon-Sat. 1000-1700 Sun.

Min Mail Order UK: £12.00 + p&p
Cat. Cost: 2 × 1st class.
Credit Cards: Visa Access Switch MasterCard
Specialities: Choice & unusual trees & shrubs incl. *Acer* & *Cornus* cvs. Old apples & cherries. Wisteria. Grafting service.
Map Ref: C, C3

CEnt ENTWOOD FARM PLANTS
Harcombe, Lyme Regis, Dorset,
DT7 3RN
Ⓣ (01297) 444034
Contact: Jenny & Ivan Harding
Opening Times: 1000-1700 Wed-Sat, Mar-Oct. Other times, please phone first.
Cat. Cost: 3 × 1st class.
Credit Cards: None
Specialities: Perennials & grasses. Some shrubs & herbs. Interest in bamboos, *Digitalis* & plants suited to moisture-retentive soil. All stock propagated & grown at nursery, some in small quantities.
Map Ref: C, C4 **OS Grid Ref:** SY335953

CExc EXCLUSIVE PLANTS ⊠ €
Tretawn, High Cross, Constantine, Falmouth, Cornwall, TR11 5RE
Ⓜ 07775 811385
Ⓔ Pbonavia@lycos.co.uk
Ⓦ www.exclusiveplants.com
Contact: Paul Bonavia
Opening Times: Not open. Mail order only.
Min Mail Order UK: Nmc
Min Mail Order EU: £20 + p&p
Cat. Cost: 2 × 1st class.
Credit Cards: None
Specialities: Woodland plants.

CFee FEEBERS HARDY PLANTS ⊠ ♿ ◆
1 Feeber Cottage, Westwood,
Broadclyst, Nr Exeter, Devon,
EX5 3DQ
Ⓣ (01404) 822118
Ⓔ Feebers@onetel.com
Contact: Mrs E Squires
Opening Times: 1000-1700 Wed Mar-Jul & Sep-Oct. Sat & Sun by prior appt.
Min Mail Order UK: Nmc
Min Mail Order EU: Nmc
Cat. Cost: Sae + 36p stamp.
Credit Cards: None
Specialities: Plants for wet clay soils, alpines & hardy perennials incl. those raised by Amos Perry. Small quantities of plants held unless grown from seed.
Notes: Mail order ltd. Nursery accessible for wheelchairs in dry weather only.
Map Ref: C, C4

CFFs FLORAL FIREWORKS ⊠
Burnt House Farm, Mid Lambrook,
South Petherton, Somerset,
TA13 5HE
Ⓣ (01460) 249060
Ⓕ (01460) 249025
Ⓔ info@floralfireworks.co.uk
Ⓦ www.floralfireworks.co.uk
Contact: Charlie Pattisson
Opening Times: Not open. Mail order only. Orders can be collected by prior arrangement.
Min Mail Order UK: £10.00 + p&p
Min Mail Order EU: £20.00 + p&p
Cat. Cost: 4 × 2nd class.
Credit Cards: All major credit/debit cards
Specialities: Bulbs.

CFir FIR TREE FARM NURSERY ⊠ € ♿
Tresahor, Constantine, Falmouth, Cornwall,
TR11 5PL
Ⓣ (01326) 340593
Ⓔ plants@cornwallgardens.com
Ⓦ www.cornwallgardens.com
Contact: Glynn Wrapson & Sorcha Hitchcox
Opening Times: 1000-1700 Mon-Sat & 1100-1600 Sun, Feb-Sep. By appt. Oct-Jan.
Min Mail Order UK: £25.00 + p&p
Min Mail Order EU: £40.00 + p&p
Cat. Cost: 6 × 1st class.
Credit Cards: Visa Access Delta Switch
Specialities: Over 4000 varieties of cottage garden & rare perennials with many specialities. Also 80 varieties of *Clematis*.
Map Ref: C, D1

CFis MARGERY FISH GARDENS ♿
East Lambrook Manor, East Lambrook,
South Petherton, Somerset,
TA13 5HL
Ⓣ (01460) 240328
Ⓕ (01460) 242344
Ⓔ enquiries@eastlambrook.com
Ⓦ www.eastlambrook.com
Contact: Mark Stainer
Opening Times: 1000-1700 1st Feb-31st Oct 7 days.
Credit Cards: Visa Switch MasterCard
Specialities: Hardy geraniums, *Euphorbia*, *Helleborus* & herbaceous. Stock available in small quantities only. Major collection of hardy geraniums on site.
Map Ref: C, B5

KEY
⊠ Mail order to UK or EU — Delivers to shows
✈ Exports beyond EU — € Euro accepted
♿ Accessible by wheelchair — ◆ See Display advertisement

C

CFol **FOLLY GATE PLANTS** ♿
The Old Post Office, Folly Gate,
Nr Okehampton, Devon, EX20 3AF
Ⓣ (01837) 659164
Ⓔ perrylamb@hotmail.com
Contact: Sara Lamb
Opening Times: 1000-1700, Wed-Sun, Mar-Oct.
Cat. Cost: 2 × 1st class.
Specialities: Hardy herbaceous perennials, shrubs and grasses.
Map Ref: C, C3 **OS Grid Ref:** SX573978

CFul **THE RODNEY FULLER HELIANTHEMUM COLLECTION**
Coachman's Cottage, Higher Bratton
Seymour, Wincanton, Somerset,
BA9 8DA
Ⓣ (01963) 34480
Ⓔ coachmans@tinyworld.co.uk
Contact: Rodney Fuller
Opening Times: Open by appt. only.
Cat. Cost: 2 × 1st class.
Credit Cards: None
Specialities: *Helianthemum*. Nat. Collection holder. Stock available in very small quantities only.

CFwr **THE FLOWER BOWER** ⊠
Woodlands, Shurton, Stogursey,
Nr Bridgwater, Somerset, TA5 1QE
Ⓣ (01278) 732134
Ⓔ flower.bower@virgin.net
Contact: Sheila Tucker
Opening Times: Flexible opening times by appt. Please phone first.
Min Mail Order UK: £15.00 + p&p
Min Mail Order EU: £20.00 + p&p
Cat. Cost: 3 × 1st class.
Credit Cards: None
Specialities: Unusual perennials. *Anemone*, hardy geraniums, *Phlox*, grasses & ferns.
Notes: Mail order Mar onwards.
Map Ref: C, B4 **OS Grid Ref:** ST203442

CGHE **GARDEN HOUSE ENTERPRISES** ♿
The Garden House, Buckland Monachorum,
Yelverton, Devon, PL20 7LQ
Ⓕ (01822) 855358
Ⓦ www.thegardenhouse.org.uk
Contact: Ms Selman
Opening Times: 1030-1700 7 days 1st Mar-31st Oct.
Cat. Cost: 4 × 1st class.
Credit Cards: All major credit/debit cards
Specialities: Fortescue & Buckland plants. South African plants.
Map Ref: C, C3 **OS Grid Ref:** SX496683

CGra **GRAHAM'S HARDY PLANTS** ⊠ ♠ €
"Southcroft", North Road, Timsbury, Bath,
BA2 0JN
Ⓣ (01761) 472187
Ⓔ graplant@aol.com
Ⓦ www.members.aol.com/graplant
Contact: Graham Nicholls
Opening Times: Not open to the public. Mail order and show sales only.
Min Mail Order UK: £2.00 + p&p
Min Mail Order EU: £2.00 + p&p
Cat. Cost: 2 × 1st class or 2 × IRC.
Credit Cards: None
Specialities: North American alpines esp. *Lewisia*, *Eriogonum*, *Penstemon*, *Campanula*, *Kelseya*, *Phlox*.

CGro **C ♿ GROVES & SON LTD** ⊠ ♿
West Bay Road, Bridport, Dorset,
DT6 4BA
Ⓣ (01308) 422654
Ⓕ (01308) 420888
Ⓔ violets@grovesnurseries.co.uk
Ⓦ www.grovesnurseries.co.uk
Contact: Clive Groves
Opening Times: 0830-1700 Mon-Sat, 1030-1630 Sun.
Min Mail Order UK: Nmc
Min Mail Order EU: £15.00 + p&p
Cat. Cost: 2 × 1st class.
Credit Cards: Visa Switch MasterCard
Specialities: Nursery & garden centre specialising in Parma & hardy *Viola*. Nat. Collections of *Viola odorata* cvs & Parma Violets. Main display at nursery in Feb & Mar.
Notes: Mainly violets by mail order.
Map Ref: C, C5 **OS Grid Ref:** SY466918

CGrW **THE GREAT WESTERN GLADIOLUS NURSERY** ⊠ €
17 Valley View, Clutton, Bristol,
BS39 5SN
Ⓣ (01761) 452036
Ⓕ (01761) 452036
Ⓔ clutton.glads@btinternet.com
Ⓦ www.greatwesterngladiolus.co.uk
Contact: G F & J C Hazell
Opening Times: Mail order only. Open by appt. only.
Min Mail Order UK: Nmc
Min Mail Order EU: Nmc
Cat. Cost: 4 × 1st class (2 catalogues).
Credit Cards: None
Specialities: *Gladiolus* species & hybrids, corms & seeds. Other South African bulbous plants.
Notes: Also sells wholesale.

CHal **HALSWAY NURSERY** ⊠
Halsway, Nr Crowcombe, Taunton, Somerset, TA4 4BB
Ⓣ (01984) 618243
Contact: T A & D J Bushen
Opening Times: Most days, please phone first.
Min Mail Order UK: £2.00 + p&p
Cat. Cost: 2 × 1st class for list of *Coleus* & *Begonia* only.
Credit Cards: None
Specialities: *Coleus* & *Begonia* (excl. tuberous & winter-flowering). Good range of greenhouse & garden plants.
Map Ref: C, B4 **OS Grid Ref:** ST125383

CHar **WEST HARPTREE NURSERY** ⊠ €
Bristol Road, West Harptree, Bath, Somerset, BS40 6HG
Ⓣ (01761) 221370
Ⓕ (01761) 221989
Ⓔ bryn@harptreenursery.co.uk
Ⓦ www.harptreenursery.co.uk
Contact: Bryn & Helene Bowles
Opening Times: From 1000 Mon-Sun 7 days, 1st Mar-31st Oct.
Min Mail Order UK: Nmc
Min Mail Order EU: Nmc
Cat. Cost: Large sae for free names list.
Credit Cards: MasterCard Visa Maestro American Express Paypal
Specialities: Unusual herbaceous perennials & shrubs. Bulbs & grasses. Many AGM plants.
Notes: Also sells wholesale.
Map Ref: C, B5

CHby **THE HERBARY** ⊠ ✈ €
161 Chapel Street, Horningsham, Warminster, Wiltshire, BA12 7LU
Ⓣ (01985) 844442
Ⓔ info@beansandherbs.co.uk
Ⓦ www.beansandherbs.co.uk
Contact: Pippa Rosen
Opening Times: May-Oct by appt. only.
Min Mail Order UK: Nmc
Min Mail Order EU: Nmc
Cat. Cost: 4 × 1st class.
Credit Cards: None
Specialities: Culinary, medicinal & aromatic herbs organically grown.
Notes: Mail order all year for organic vegetable seed & large variety of organic bean & herb seed.
Map Ref: C, B5 **OS Grid Ref:** ST812414

CHew **HEWITT-COOPER CARNIVOROUS PLANTS** ⊠ ⌂ €
The Homestead, Glastonbury Road, West Pennard, Somerset, BA6 8NN
Ⓣ (01458) 835660
Ⓕ (01458) 832712
Ⓔ sales@hccarnivorousplants.co.uk
Ⓦ www.hccarnivorousplants.co.uk
Contact: Nigel Hewitt-Cooper
Opening Times: By appt.
Min Mail Order UK: £10.00 + p&p
Min Mail Order EU: £50.00
Cat. Cost: 1 × 1st class/1 × IRC.
Credit Cards: Visa MasterCard
Specialities: Carnivorous plants.
Notes: Mail order May-Nov. Credit cards not accepted for mail order.
Map Ref: C, B5

CHEx **HARDY EXOTICS** ⊠ ♿
Gilly Lane, Whitecross, Penzance, Cornwall, TR20 8BZ
Ⓣ (01736) 740660
Ⓕ (01736) 741101
Ⓔ contact@hardyexotics.co.uk
Ⓦ www.hardyexotics.co.uk
Contact: C Shilton/J Smith
Opening Times: 1000-1700 7 days Mar-Oct, 1000-1700 Mon-Sat Nov-Feb. Please phone first in winter months if travelling a long way.
Min Mail Order UK: £40 + carriage.
Cat. Cost: 4 × 1st class (no cheques).
Credit Cards: All major credit/debit cards
Specialities: Largest selection in the UK of trees, shrubs & herbaceous plants for tropical & desert effects. Hardy & half-hardy plants for gardens, patios & conservatories.
Map Ref: C, D1 **OS Grid Ref:** SW524345

CHFP **HOME FARM PLANTS** ♿
Devonshire Traditional Breed Centre, Downes, Crediton, Devon, EX17 3PL
Ⓣ (01363) 772430
Ⓕ (01363) 772462
Ⓔ info@homefarmplants.co.uk
Ⓦ www.homefarmplants.co.uk
Contact: Hazel Brandreth
Opening Times: 0930-1700 Mon-Fri, 1030-1630 Sat & Sun.
Cat. Cost: 3 × 1st class.
Credit Cards: All major credit/debit cards
Specialities: Hardy & unusual herbaceous perennials. Some stock in small quantities, phone to check.
Notes: The nursery is part of the Devonshire Traditional Breed Centre.
Map Ref: C, C3 **OS Grid Ref:** SX848998

KEY
⊠ Mail order to UK or EU ⌂ Delivers to shows
✈ Exports beyond EU € Euro accepted
♿ Accessible by wheelchair ◆ See Display advertisement

C

CHHB **HIDDEN HOUSE BULBS** ⊠ €
Tanqueray, Bilberry, St Austell, Cornwall, PL26 8QU
Ⓣ (01726) 852709
Ⓔ dawn@hiddenhousebulbs.com
Ⓦ www.hiddenhousebulbs.com
Contact: Dawn Molenkamp
Opening Times: Not open. Mail order only.
Min Mail Order UK: Nmc
Min Mail Order EU: Nmc
Cat. Cost: 4 × 1st class.
Credit Cards: Paypal
Specialities: Small nursery specialising in rare & unusual bulbs.
Notes: Euro notes only accepted. Also sells wholesale.

CHid **HIDDEN VALLEY NURSERY** €
Umberleigh, Devon, EX37 9BU
Ⓣ (01769) 560567
Ⓜ 07899 788789
Ⓔ lindleypla@tiscali.co.uk
Contact: Linda & Peter Lindley
Opening Times: Daylight hours, but please phone first.
Cat. Cost: 2 × 1st class.
Credit Cards: None
Specialities: Hardy perennials esp. shade lovers & Chatham Island forget-me-nots (*Myosotidium hortensia*).
Map Ref: C, B3 **OS Grid Ref:** SS567205

CHII **HILL HOUSE NURSERY & GARDENS** € ♿
Landscove, Nr Ashburton, Devon, TQ13 7LY
Ⓣ (01803) 762273
Ⓕ (01803) 762716
Ⓔ sacha@garden.506.fsnet.co.uk
Ⓦ www.hillhousenursery.co.uk
Contact: Raymond, Sacha & Matthew Hubbard
Opening Times: 1100-1700 7 days, all year. Open all B/hols incl. Easter Sun. Tearoom open 1st Mar-30th Sep.
Cat. Cost: None issued.
Credit Cards: Delta MasterCard Switch Visa
Specialities: 3000+ varieties of plants, most propagated on premises, many rare or unusual. The garden, open to the public, was laid out by Edward Hyams. Pioneers of glasshouse pests control by beneficial insects.
Map Ref: C, C3 **OS Grid Ref:** SX774664

CHrt **HORTUS NURSERY** ⊠ ♿
Shrubbery Bungalow, School Lane, Rousdon, Lyme Regis, Dorset, DT7 3XW
Ⓣ (01297) 44401
Ⓜ 07747 043997
Ⓕ (01297) 444019
Ⓔ plants@hortusnursery.com
Ⓦ www.hortusnursery.com
Contact: Marie-Elaine Houghton
Opening Times: 1000-1700 Wed-Sat, Mar-Oct. Other times by appt.
Min Mail Order UK: £15.00 + p&p
Cat. Cost: 2 × 1st class.
Credit Cards: None
Specialities: Ornamental grasses & perennials, particularly *Carex*, *Aster*, *Digitalis*, *Euphorbia*, *Geranium* & *Penstemon*. Garden open as nursery. Garden design & planting service.
Map Ref: C, C4 **OS Grid Ref:** SY296914

CHVG **HIDDEN VALLEY GARDENS** ♿
Treesmill, Nr Par, Cornwall, PL24 2TU
Ⓣ (01208) 873225
Ⓔ hiddenvalleygardens@yahoo.co.uk
Ⓦ www.hiddenvalleygardens.co.uk
Contact: Mrs P Howard
Opening Times: 1000-1800 7 days, 20th Mar-end Oct. Please phone for directions.
Cat. Cost: None issued.
Credit Cards: None
Specialities: Cottage garden plants, *Crocosmia*, *Iris sibirica* & many unusual perennials which can be seen growing in the garden. Some stock available in small quantities. Display garden. Garden open as nursery.
Map Ref: C, D2 **OS Grid Ref:** SX094567

CIri **THE IRIS GARDEN** ⊠ €
Yard House, Pilsdon, Bridport, Dorset, DT6 5PA
Ⓣ (01308) 868797
Ⓕ (01308) 868797
Ⓔ theirisgarden@aol.com
Ⓦ www.theirisgarden.co.uk
Contact: Clive Russell
Opening Times: Show garden open by appt. Please email or phone for details.
Min Mail Order UK: £15.00 + p&p
Min Mail Order EU: £25.00 + p&p
Cat. Cost: 8 × 1st class.
Credit Cards: All major credit/debit cards
Specialities: Modern bearded & beardless *Iris* from breeders in UK, USA, France, Italy & Australia. Nat. Collection of "Space Age" *Iris* applied for.
Notes: Orders for bearded iris & sibiricas must be received by end Jun & by end Aug for ensatas & spurias.
Map Ref: C, C5 **OS Grid Ref:** 424996

CJas **JASMINE COTTAGE GARDENS** ♿
26 Channel Road, Walton St Mary, Clevedon, Somerset, BS21 7BY
Ⓣ (01275) 871850
Ⓔ margaret@bologrew.demon.co.uk
Ⓦ www.bologrew.pwp.blueyonder.co.uk

Contact: Mr & Mrs M Redgrave
Opening Times: May to Sep, daily by appt. Garden open at the same times.
Cat. Cost: None issued.
Credit Cards: None
Specialities: *Rhodochiton*, *Asarina*, *Maurandya*, *Dicentra macrocapnos*, *Salvia*, *Solenopsis*, *Isotoma*, half-hardy geraniums.
Map Ref: C, A4 **OS Grid Ref:** ST405725

CKel KELWAYS LTD ⊠ ♠ € ♿
Langport, Somerset, TA10 9EZ
Ⓣ (01458) 250521
Ⓕ (01458) 253351
Ⓔ sales@kelways.co.uk
Ⓦ www.kelways.co.uk
Contact: Mr David Root
Opening Times: 0900-1700 Mon-Fri, 1000-1700 Sat, 1000-1600 Sun.
Min Mail Order UK: £4.00 + p&p
Min Mail Order EU: £8.00 + p&p
Cat. Cost: Free.
Credit Cards: Visa Access
Specialities: *Paeonia*, *Iris*, *Hemerocallis* & herbaceous perennials. Nat. Collection of *Paeonia lactiflora*.
Notes: Mail order for *Paeonia* & *Iris* only. Also sells wholesale.
Map Ref: C, B5 **OS Grid Ref:** ST434273

CKen KENWITH NURSERY (GORDON HADDOW) ⊠ ✈ € ♿ ◆
Blinsham, Nr Torrington, Beaford, Winkleigh, Devon, EX19 8NT
Ⓣ (01805) 603274
Ⓕ (01805) 603663
Ⓔ conifers@kenwith63.freeserve.co.uk
Ⓦ www.kenwithnursery.co.uk
Contact: Gordon Haddow
Opening Times: 1000-1630 Wed-Sat Nov-Feb & by appt. 1000-1630 Tue-Sat, Mar-Oct.
Min Mail Order UK: £10.00 + p&p
Min Mail Order EU: £50.00 + p&p
Cat. Cost: 3 × 1st class.
Credit Cards: Visa MasterCard
Specialities: All conifer genera. Grafting a speciality. Many new introductions to UK. Nat. Collection of Dwarf Conifers.
Map Ref: C, B3 **OS Grid Ref:** SS518160

CKno KNOLL GARDENS ⊠ ♠ ♿
Hampreston, Stapehill, Nr Wimborne, Dorset, BH21 7ND
Ⓣ (01202) 873931
Ⓕ (01202) 870842
Ⓔ enquiries@knollgardens.co.uk
Ⓦ www.knollgardens.co.uk
Contact: N R Lucas
Opening Times: 1000-1700 (or dusk if earlier) Wed-Sun. Closed from 18th Dec 2006, re-opening 1st Feb 2007.
Min Mail Order UK: Nmc
Cat. Cost: 9 × 2nd class or order online.
Credit Cards: Visa MasterCard
Specialities: Grasses (main specialism). Select perennials. Nat. Collections of *Pennisetum*, *Phygelius* & deciduous *Ceanothus*.
Notes: Also sells wholesale.
Map Ref: C, C6

CKob KOBAKOBA ⊠ ✈ ♠
2 High Street, Ashcott, Bridgwater, Somerset, TA7 9PL
Ⓣ (01458) 210700
Ⓜ 07870 624969
Ⓕ (01458) 210650
Ⓔ plants@kobakoba.co.uk
Ⓦ www.kobakoba.co.uk
Contact: Christine Smithee & David Constantine
Opening Times: Please phone for opening times.
Min Mail Order UK: Nmc
Min Mail Order EU: Nmc
Cat. Cost: 1 × 1st class for plant list or £3.50 for catalogue.
Credit Cards: Visa MasterCard Delta
Specialities: Plants for tropical effect incl. *Ensete*, *Musa*, *Hedychium*, *Curcuma* & other *Zingiberaceae*. Conservatory & greenhouse plants.
Map Ref: C, B5 **OS Grid Ref:** ST4237

CLAP LONG ACRE PLANTS ⊠ ♠ ♿
South Marsh, Charlton Musgrove, Nr Wincanton, Somerset, BA9 8EX
Ⓣ (01963) 32802
Ⓕ (01963) 32802
Ⓔ info@longacreplants.co.uk
Ⓦ www.longacreplants.co.uk
Contact: Nigel & Michelle Rowland
Opening Times: 1000-1300 & 1400-1700 Thu-Sat, Feb-Jun, Sep & Oct.
Min Mail Order UK: £25.00 + p&p
Min Mail Order EU: £50.00 + p&p
Cat. Cost: 3 × 1st class.
Credit Cards: Switch MasterCard Visa
Specialities: Ferns, lilies, woodland bulbs & perennials. Nat. Collection of *Asarum*.
Notes: Lilies only outside EU.
Map Ref: C, B5

KEY
⊠ Mail order to UK or EU ♠ Delivers to shows
✈ Exports beyond EU € Euro accepted
♿ Accessible by wheelchair ◆ See Display advertisement

C

CLnd LANDFORD TREES ⊠ €
Landford Lodge, Landford, Salisbury, Wiltshire, SP5 2EH
Ⓣ (01794) 390808
Ⓕ (01794) 390037
Ⓔ sales@landfordtrees.co.uk
Ⓦ www.landfordtrees.co.uk
Contact: C D Pilkington
Opening Times: 0800-1700 Mon-Fri.
Min Mail Order UK: Please enquire.
Min Mail Order EU: Please enquire.
Cat. Cost: Free.
Credit Cards: None
Specialities: Deciduous ornamental trees.
Notes: Mail order maximum size 120cms. Also sells wholesale.
Map Ref: C, B6 **OS Grid Ref:** SU247201

CLoc C ⊠ LOCKYER ⊠ ☒ ⌂ € ◆
Lansbury, 70 Henfield Road, Coalpit Heath, Bristol, BS36 2UZ
Ⓣ (01454) 772219
Ⓕ (01454) 772219
Ⓔ sales@lockyerfuchsias.co.uk
Ⓦ www.lockyerfuchsias.co.uk
Contact: C S Lockyer
Opening Times: 1000-1300, 1430-1700 most days, please ring.
Min Mail Order UK: 6 plants + p&p
Min Mail Order EU: £12.00 + p&p
Cat. Cost: 4 × 1st class.
Credit Cards: None
Specialities: *Fuchsia.*
Notes: Many Open Days & coach parties. Limited wheelchair access. Also sells wholesale.
Map Ref: C, A5

CLyd LYDFORD ALPINE NURSERY ⊠
2 Southern Cottages, Lydford, Okehampton, Devon, EX20 4BL
Ⓣ (01822) 820398
Contact: Julie & David Hatchett
Opening Times: By appt. only. Please ring for directions.
Min Mail Order UK: £10.00 + p&p
Cat. Cost: Sae for saxifrage list.
Credit Cards: None
Specialities: *Saxifraga.* Very wide range of choice & unusual alpines in small quantities.
Notes: Mail order *Saxifraga* only.
Map Ref: C, C3 **OS Grid Ref:** SX504830

CMac MACPENNYS NURSERIES ⊠
154 Burley Road, Bransgore, Christchurch, Dorset, BH23 8DB
Ⓣ (01425) 672348
Ⓕ (01425) 673917
Ⓔ office@macpennys.co.uk
Ⓦ www.macpennys.co.uk
Contact: T & V Lowndes
Opening Times: 0900-1700 Mon-Sat, 1100-1700 Sun. Closed Xmas & New Year.
Min Mail Order UK: Nmc
Cat. Cost: A4 sae with 4 × 1st class.
Credit Cards: All major credit/debit cards
Specialities: General. Plants available in small quantities only.
Notes: Mail order available Sep-Mar only. Nursery partially accessible for wheelchairs.
Map Ref: C, C6

CMCN MALLET COURT NURSERY ⊠ ☒ ⌂ € ♿
Curry Mallet, Taunton, Somerset, TA3 6SY
Ⓣ (01823) 481493
Ⓕ (01823) 481493
Ⓔ harris@malletcourt.freeserve.co.uk
Ⓦ www.malletcourt.co.uk
Contact: J G S & P M E Harris F.L.S.
Opening Times: 0930-1700 Mon-Fri summer, 0930-1600 winter. Sat & Sun by appt.
Min Mail Order UK: Nmc
Min Mail Order EU: Nmc
Cat. Cost: £1.50.
Credit Cards: All major credit/debit cards
Specialities: Maples, oaks, *Magnolia*, hollies & other rare and unusual plants including those from China & South Korea.
Notes: Mail order Oct-Mar only. Also sells wholesale.
Map Ref: C, B4

CMCo MEADOW COTTAGE PLANTS ⌂ € ♿
Pitt Hill, Ivybridge, Devon, PL21 0JJ
Ⓣ (01752) 894532
Ⓔ phil@pitthill.fsworld.co.uk
Contact: Mrs L P Hunt
Opening Times: By appt. only.
Cat. Cost: None issued.
Credit Cards: None
Specialities: Hardy geraniums, other hardy perennials, ornamental grasses and bamboos. Some varieties available in small numbers only. All plants grown in peat-free compost.
Notes: Also sells wholesale.
Map Ref: C, D3

CMdw MEADOWS NURSERY ⊠ ⌂
5 Rectory Cottages, Mells, Frome, Somerset, BA11 3PN
Ⓣ (01373) 812268
Ⓔ plants@meadowsnurserymells.co.uk
Contact: Sue Lees & Eddie Wheatley
Opening Times: 1000-1800 Wed-Sun 1st Feb-31st Oct & B/hols.

C

Min Mail Order UK: Nmc
Cat. Cost: 3 × 1st class.
Credit Cards: None
Specialities: Hardy perennials, shrubs & some conservatory plants. *Kniphofia*.
Map Ref: C, B5 **OS Grid Ref:** ST729492

CMea THE MEAD NURSERY ♿
Brokerswood, Nr Westbury, Wiltshire, BA13 4EG
Ⓣ (01373) 859990
Ⓦ www.themeadnursery.co.uk
Contact: Steve & Emma Lewis-Dale
Opening Times: 0900-1700 Wed-Sat & B/hols, 1200-1700 Sun, 1st Feb-10th Oct. Closed Easter Sun.
Cat. Cost: 5 × 1st class.
Credit Cards: All major credit/debit cards
Specialities: Perennials, alpines, pot-grown bulbs and grasses.
Map Ref: C, B5 **OS Grid Ref:** ST833517

CMen MENDIP BONSAI STUDIO ♿
Byways, Back Lane, Downside, Shepton Mallet, Somerset, BA4 4JR
Ⓣ (01749) 344274
Ⓕ (01749) 344274
Ⓔ jr.trott@ukonline.co.uk
Ⓦ www.mendipbonsai.co.uk
Contact: John Trott
Opening Times: By appt. only.
Cat. Cost: large sae for plant & workshop lists.
Credit Cards: MasterCard Visa
Specialities: Bonsai & garden stock. Acers, conifers, *Stewartia*. Many plants available in small numbers only.
Notes: Education classes, lectures, demonstrations & club talks on bonsai. Stockist of bonsai sundries.
Map Ref: C, B5

CMHG MARWOOD HILL GARDENS ♿
Barnstaple, Devon, EX31 4EB
Ⓣ (01271) 342528
Ⓔ malcolmpharoah@supanet.com
Ⓦ www.marwoodhillgarden.co.uk
Contact: Malcolm Pharoah
Opening Times: 1100-1630, 7 days.
Cat. Cost: 3 × 1st class.
Credit Cards: Visa Delta MasterCard Switch Solo
Specialities: Large range of unusual trees & shrubs. *Eucalyptus*, alpines, *Camellia*, *Astilbe*, bog plants & perennials. Nat. Collections of *Astilbe*, *Tulbaghia* & *Iris ensata*.
Map Ref: C, B3 **OS Grid Ref:** SS545375

CMil MILL COTTAGE PLANTS ⊠ ♿
The Mill, Henley Lane, Wookey, Somerset, BA5 1AP
Ⓣ (01749) 676966
Ⓔ millcottageplants@tiscali.co.uk
Ⓦ www.millcottageplants.co.uk
Contact: Sally Gregson
Opening Times: 1000-1800 Wed Mar-Sep or by appt. Phone for directions.
Min Mail Order UK: Nmc.
Min Mail Order EU: £20.00 + p&p
Cat. Cost: 4 × 1st class.
Credit Cards: All major credit/debit cards
Specialities: Rare *Hydrangea serrata* cvs, *H. aspera* cvs. Also *Papaver orientale*, *Arisaema*, *Tricyrtis*, *Epimedium*, ferns & grasses.
Map Ref: C, B5

CMMP M & M PLANTS ♿
Lloret, Chittlehamholt, Umberleigh, Devon, EX37 9PD
Ⓣ (01769) 540448
Ⓕ (01769) 540448
Ⓔ MMPlants@Chittlehamholt.freeserve.co.uk
Contact: Mr M Thorne
Opening Times: 0930-1730 Tue-Sat, Apr-Oct & 1000-1600 Tue-Fri, Nov-Mar. Sat by appt. Aug.
Cat. Cost: 3 × 1st class.
Credit Cards: None
Specialities: Perennials. We also carry a good range of alpines, shrubs, trees & roses.
Map Ref: C, B3

CNat NATURAL SELECTION ⊠ €
1 Station Cottages, Hullavington, Chippenham, Wiltshire, SN14 6ET
Ⓣ (01666) 837369
Ⓔ martin@worldmutation.demon.co.uk
Ⓦ www.worldmutation.demon.co.uk
Contact: Martin Cragg-Barber
Opening Times: Please phone first.
Min Mail Order UK: £9.00 + p&p
Cat. Cost: £1.00 or 5 × 2nd class.
Credit Cards: None
Specialities: Unusual British natives & others. Also seed. Only available in small quantities.
Map Ref: C, A5 **OS Grid Ref:** ST898828

CNCN NAKED CROSS NURSERIES ⊠ ♿
Waterloo Road, Corfe Mullen, Wimborne, Dorset, BH21 3SR
Ⓣ (01202) 693256

KEY
⊠ Mail order to UK or EU — Delivers to shows
✈ Exports beyond EU — € Euro accepted
♿ Accessible by wheelchair — ◆ See Display advertisement

C

Ⓕ (01202) 693259
Contact: Peter French
Opening Times: 0900-1700 7 days.
Min Mail Order UK: Nmc
Cat. Cost: 3 × 1st class.
Credit Cards: All major credit/debit cards
Specialities: Heathers.
Notes: Also sells wholesale.
Map Ref: C, C6

CNCS THE CHRYSANTHEMUM SOCIETY ⊠
Wood View, Hutton, Weston-super-Mare, Somerset, BS24 9RW
Ⓜ 07989 855339
Ⓔ TAPorter11@aol.com
Ⓦ www.ncsuk.info
Contact: Terry Porter
Opening Times: Not open. Mail order only.
Min Mail Order UK: Nmc.
Credit Cards: All major credit/debit cards
Specialities: Unusual varieties of *Chrysanthemum*. Only available in small quantities.

CNic NICKY'S ROCK GARDEN NURSERY ♿ €
Broadhayes, Stockland, Honiton, Devon, EX14 9EH
Ⓣ (01404) 881213
Ⓔ Dianabob.Dark@nickys.sagehost.co.uk
Contact: Diana & Bob Dark
Opening Times: 0900-dusk 7 days. Please phone first to check & for directions.
Credit Cards: None
Specialities: Plants for rock gardens, scree, troughs, banks, walls & front of border & dwarf shrubs. Many unusual. Plants propagated in small numbers. Ring to check availability before travelling.
Notes: Partial wheelchair access.
Map Ref: C, C4 **OS Grid Ref:** ST236027

CNMi NEWPORT MILLS NURSERY ⊠
Wrantage, Taunton, Somerset, TA3 6DJ
Ⓣ (01823) 490231
Ⓜ 07950 035668
Ⓕ (01823) 490231
Contact: John Barrington, Rachel Pettitt
Opening Times: By appt. only.
Min Mail Order UK: Nmc
Min Mail Order EU: Nmc
Cat. Cost: Free.
Credit Cards: None
Specialities: *Delphinium*. English scented varieties of perpetual flowering carnations. Some varieties only available in small quantities & propagated to order.
Notes: Mail order Apr-Sep for young delphiniums in 7cm pots. Dormant plants can be sent out in autumn/winter if requested.

COld THE OLD MILL HERBARY
Helland Bridge, Bodmin, Cornwall, PL30 4QR
Ⓣ (01208) 841206
Ⓔ oldmillherbary@aol.com
Ⓦ www.oldmillherbary.co.uk
Contact: Mrs B Whurr
Opening Times: 1000-1700 Thu-Tue 25th Mar-30th Sep. Closed Wed.
Cat. Cost: 6 × 1st class.
Credit Cards: None
Specialities: Culinary, medicinal & aromatic herbs.
Notes: Limited sales of medicinal herbs. Historical site in Area of Outstanding Natural Beauty. SSSI, SAC & AONB.
Map Ref: C, C2 **OS Grid Ref:** SX065717

COIW THE OLD WITHY GARDEN NURSERY ⊠
Grange Fruit Farm, Gweek, Helston, Cornwall, TR12 6BE
Ⓣ (01326) 221171
Ⓔ WithyNursery@fsbdial.co.uk
Contact: Sheila Chandler or Nick Chandler
Opening Times: 1000-1700 Wed-Mon, Feb-end Oct. 1000-1730 7 days, Apr-Sep.
Min Mail Order UK: £15.00
Cat. Cost: 4 × 1st class.
Credit Cards: Maestro MasterCard Visa Delta
Specialities: Cottage garden plants, perennials, some biennials & grasses. Some varieties in small quantities only.
Notes: Also sells wholesale.
Map Ref: C, D1 **OS Grid Ref:** SW688255

CPar PARKS PERENNIALS ♿
242 Wallisdown Road, Wallisdown, Bournemouth, Dorset, BH10 4HZ
Ⓣ (01202) 524464
Ⓔ parks.perennials@ntlworld.com
Contact: S. Parks
Opening Times: Apr-Oct most days, please phone first.
Cat. Cost: None issued.
Credit Cards: None
Specialities: Hardy herbaceous perennials.
Map Ref: C, C6

CPas PASSIFLORA (NATIONAL COLLECTION) ⊠ ☒ €
Lampley Road, Kingston Seymour, Clevedon, Somerset, BS21 6XS
Ⓣ (01934) 838895
Ⓜ 0776 834 0881
Ⓔ johnvanderplank@yahoo.co.uk

C

Contact: John Vanderplank
Opening Times: 0900-1700 7 days, 1st Aug-31st Aug. By appt. only rest of year.
Min Mail Order UK: £10.00 + p&p
Min Mail Order EU: £10.00 + p&p
Cat. Cost: 3 × 1st class.
Credit Cards: Visa Access EuroCard MasterCard
Specialities: *Passiflora*. Nat. Collection of over 200 species & cultivars. Scientific status. Brickell Award 2004.
Notes: Mail order seed only. Plants must be collected from nursery. Pre-ordered plants may be picked up from the nursery at any time. Also sells wholesale.
Map Ref: C, A4

CPbn **PENBORN GOAT FARM** ⊠ ♿
Penborn, Bounds Cross, Holsworthy, Devon, EX22 6LH
Ⓣ (01288) 381569
Contact: P R Oldfield
Opening Times: Not open. Mail order only.
Min Mail Order UK: £18.00
Cat. Cost: 2 × 1st class.
Credit Cards: None
Specialities: *Mentha*. Available in small quantities only.
Map Ref: C, C2

CPBP **PARHAM BUNGALOW PLANTS** ⊠ ⌂ €
Parham Lane, Market Lavington, Devizes, Wiltshire, SN10 4QA
Ⓣ (01380) 812605
Ⓔ jjs@pbplants.freeserve.co.uk
Contact: Mrs D E Sample
Opening Times: Please ring first.
Min Mail Order UK: Nmc
Min Mail Order EU: Nmc
Cat. Cost: Sae.
Credit Cards: None
Specialities: Alpines & dwarf shrubs.
Map Ref: C, B6

CPen **PENNARD PLANTS** ⊠ ✈ ⌂ €
3 The Gardens, East Pennard, Shepton Mallet, Somerset, BA4 6TU
Ⓣ (01749) 860039
Ⓕ 07043 017270
Ⓔ sales@pennardplants.com
Ⓦ www.pennardplants.com
Contact: Chris Smith
Opening Times: By appt. only.
Min Mail Order UK: Nmc
Min Mail Order EU: Nmc
Cat. Cost: 3 × 1st class.
Credit Cards: All major credit/debit cards
Specialities: Ornamental grasses, *Agapanthus*, *Crocosmia*, *Dierama* & South African bulbous plants.
Notes: Nursery at The Walled Garden at East Pennard.
Map Ref: C, B5

CPhi **ALAN PHIPPS CACTI** ⊠ €
62 Samuel White Road, Hanham, Bristol, BS15 3LX
Ⓣ (0117) 9607591
Ⓦ www.cactus-mall.com/alan-phipps/index.html
Contact: A Phipps
Opening Times: 10.00-1700 but prior phone call essential to ensure a greeting.
Min Mail Order UK: £5.00 + p&p
Min Mail Order EU: £20.00 + p&p
Cat. Cost: Sae or 2 × IRC (EC only).
Credit Cards: None
Specialities: *Mammillaria*, *Astrophytum* & *Ariocarpus*. Species & varieties will change with times. Ample quantities exist in spring. Limited range of *Agave*.
Notes: Euro accepted as cash only.
Map Ref: C, A5 **OS Grid Ref:** ST644717

CPHo **THE PALM HOUSE** ⊠
8 North Street, Ottery St Mary, Devon, EX11 1DR
Ⓣ (01404) 815450
Ⓔ george@thepalmhouse.co.uk
Ⓦ www.thepalmhouse.co.uk
Contact: George Gregory
Opening Times: Mail order only. Open by appt. only.
Min Mail Order UK: £15.00
Min Mail Order EU:
Cat. Cost: 2 × 1st class.
Credit Cards: All major credit/debit cards
Specialities: Palms.
Notes: Also sells wholesale.
Map Ref: C, C4 **OS Grid Ref:** SY098955

CPle **PLEASANT VIEW NURSERY** ⊠ ♿
Two Mile Oak, Nr Denbury, Newton Abbot, Devon, TQ12 6DG
Ⓣ (01803) 813388 answerphone
Contact: Mrs B D Yeo
Opening Times: 1000-1700 Wed-Fri mid Mar-end Sep (closed for lunch 1245-1330). Nursery will cease trading on 29th Sep 2006.
Min Mail Order UK: £20.00 + p&p

KEY
⊠ Mail order to UK or EU ⌂ Delivers to shows
✈ Exports beyond EU € Euro accepted
♿ Accessible by wheelchair ◆ See Display advertisement

C

Min Mail Order EU: £20.00 + p&p (Salvias only)
Cat. Cost: 3 × 2nd class or 2 × IRC.
Credit Cards: None
Specialities: *Salvia* & unusual shrubs for garden & conservatory.
Notes: Nursery off A381 at T.M. Oak Cross towards Denbury.
Map Ref: C, C3 **OS Grid Ref:** SX8368

CPLG Pine Lodge Gardens & Nursery ♿
Cuddra, Holmbush, St Austell, Cornwall, PL25 3RQ
Ⓣ (01726) 73500
Ⓕ (01726) 77370
Ⓔ gardens@pine-lodge.co.uk
Ⓦ www.pine-lodge.co.uk
Contact: Ray & Shirley Clemo
Opening Times: 1000-1700 7 days all year, except 24th/25th/26th Dec.
Cat. Cost: 6 × 2nd class.
Credit Cards: None
Specialities: Rare & unusual shrubs & herbaceous, some from seed collected on plant expeditions each year. Nat. Collection of *Grevillea*. All plants available in small quantities only.
Map Ref: C, D2 **OS Grid Ref:** SX045527

CPMA P M A Plant Specialities ⊠ ☒
Junker's Nursery Ltd., Lower Mead, West Hatch, Taunton, Somerset, TA3 5RN
Ⓣ (01823) 480774
Ⓕ (01823) 481046
Ⓔ karan@junker.co.uk
Ⓦ www.junker.co.uk
Contact: Karan or Nick Junker
Opening Times: Strictly by appt. only.
Min Mail Order UK: Nmc
Min Mail Order EU: Nmc
Cat. Cost: 6 × 2nd class.
Credit Cards: None
Specialities: Choice & unusual shrubs incl. grafted *Acer palmatum*, *Cornus*, *Magnolia* & wide range of *Daphne*. Small quantities of some hard to propagate plants, esp. daphnes. Reserve orders accepted. Planted areas to see how the plants look growing in "real world" conditions.
Notes: Partial wheelchair access. Also sells wholesale.
Map Ref: C, B4 **OS Grid Ref:** ST280203

CPne Pine Cottage Plants ⊠ ☒ ⌂ €
Pine Cottage, Fourways, Eggesford, Chulmleigh, Devon, EX18 7QZ
Ⓣ (01769) 580076
Ⓔ pcplants@supanet.com
Ⓦ www.pcplants.co.uk
Contact: Dick Fulcher
Opening Times: By appt. only. Special open weeks for *Agapanthus*, 1000-1800 daily, excl. Sun, 24th Jul-9th Sep 2006.
Min Mail Order UK: £20.00 + p&p
Min Mail Order EU: £20.00 + p&p
Cat. Cost: 4 × 1st class.
Credit Cards: Maestro MasterCard Visa
Specialities: Nat. Collection of *Agapanthus*. 150+ cvs available.
Notes: Mail order *Agapanthus* from Oct-Jun. Also sells wholesale.
Map Ref: C, B3 **OS Grid Ref:** SS6171

CPom Pomeroy Plants
Tower House, Pomeroy Lane, Wingfield, Trowbridge, Wiltshire, BA14 9LJ
Ⓣ (01225) 769551
Contact: Simon Young
Opening Times: Mar-Nov. Please phone first.
Cat. Cost: 2 × 1st class.
Credit Cards: None
Specialities: Hardy, mainly species, herbaceous perennials. Many unusual and often small numbers. Specialities *Allium*, *Salvia* & shade-lovers, esp. *Epimedium*.
Map Ref: C, B5 **OS Grid Ref:** ST817569

CPou Pounsley Plants ⊠ ⌂ € ♿
Pounsley Combe, Spriddlestone, Brixton, Plymouth, Devon, PL9 0DW
Ⓣ (01752) 402873
Ⓕ (01752) 402873
Ⓔ pou599@aol.com
Ⓦ www.pounsleyplants.com
Contact: Mrs Jane Hollow
Opening Times: Normally 1000-1700 Mon-Sat but please phone first.
Min Mail Order UK: £10.00 + p&p
Min Mail Order EU: £20.00 + p&p
Cat. Cost: 2 × 1st class.
Credit Cards: None
Specialities: Unusual herbaceous perennials & cottage plants. Selection of *Clematis* & old roses. Large selection of South African monocots.
Notes: Mail order Nov-Feb only. Also sells wholesale.
Map Ref: C, D3 **OS Grid Ref:** SX521538

CPrp Properplants.com ⊠ ☒ ⌂
Penknight, Edgcumbe Road, Lostwithiel, Cornwall, PL22 0JD
Ⓣ (01208) 872291
Ⓕ (01208) 872291

Ⓔ info@Properplants.com
Ⓦ www.ProperPlants.com
Contact: Sarah Wilks
Opening Times: 1000-1800 or dusk if earlier, Tue & B/hols mid-Mar to end-Sep & by appt.
Min Mail Order UK: Nmc
Min Mail Order EU: Nmc
Cat. Cost: 4 × 1st class.
Credit Cards: All major credit/debit cards
Specialities: Wide range of unusual & easy herbaceous perennials, ferns & grasses. Less common herbs.
Notes: Partially accessible for wheelchair users.
Map Ref: C, C2 **OS Grid Ref:** SX093596

CPSs PLANTS FOR THE SENSES ⊠
Corner Cottage, North Street, Dolton, Winkleigh, Devon, EX19 8QQ
Ⓣ (01805) 804467
Ⓔ michaelross@freenetname.co.uk
Contact: Michael Ross
Opening Times: Not open. Mail order only.
Min Mail Order UK: Nmc
Cat. Cost: 1 × 1st class.
Credit Cards: None
Specialities: Some emphasis on scented plants. Some stock in small quantities only.

CPuk PUKKA PLANTS ⊠ € ♿
Count House Farm, Treglisson, Wheal Alfred Road, Hayle, Cornwall, TR27 5JT
Ⓣ (01872) 271129
Ⓕ (01872) 271129
Ⓔ sktrevena@gmail.com
Ⓦ www.pukkaplants.co.uk
Contact: Colin Young
Opening Times: 0900-1700, Mon-Sat, closed Sun.
Min Mail Order UK: £5.00
Credit Cards: All major credit/debit cards
Specialities: Grasses.
Notes: Also sells wholesale.
Map Ref: C, D1 **OS Grid Ref:** SW369578

CQua QUALITY DAFFODILS ⊠ ✈ € ◆
14 Roscarrack Close, Falmouth, Cornwall, TR11 4PJ
Ⓣ (01326) 317959
Ⓕ (01326) 317959
Ⓔ rascamp@daffodils.uk.com
Ⓦ www.qualitydaffodils.co.uk
Contact: R A Scamp
Opening Times: Not open. Mail order only.
Min Mail Order UK: Nmc
Min Mail Order EU: Nmc
Cat. Cost: 3 × 1st class.
Credit Cards: All major credit/debit cards
Specialities: *Narcissus* hybrids & species. Some stocks are less than 100 bulbs.
Notes: Also sells wholesale.

CRea REALLY WILD FLOWERS ⊠ €
H V Horticulture Ltd, Spring Mead, Bedchester, Shaftesbury, Dorset, SP7 0JU
Ⓣ (01747) 811778
Ⓕ (01747) 811499
Ⓔ rwflowers@aol.com
Ⓦ www.reallywildflowers.co.uk
Contact: Grahame Dixie
Opening Times: Not open. Mail order only.
Min Mail Order UK: £40.00 + p&p
Min Mail Order EU: £100.00 + p&p
Cat. Cost: 3 × 1st class.
Credit Cards: None
Specialities: Wildflowers for grasslands, woodlands, wetlands & heaths. Seeds, orchids. Advisory & soil analysis services.
Notes: Also sells wholesale.

CRez REZARE NURSERIES
Rezare, Nr Treburley, Launceston, Cornwall, PL15 9NX
Ⓣ (01579) 370969
Ⓔ REZARENURSERIES@aol.com
Contact: Mel & Jim Gearing
Opening Times: 1000-1700, 7 days 1st Feb-end Oct. Other times by appt.
Cat. Cost: None issued.
Credit Cards: All major credit/debit cards
Specialities: Growers of a full & varied range of choice & unusual plants of the highest quality, incl. a good selection of herbaceous perennials, grasses, ferns, shrubs & trees.
Map Ref: C, C2

CRHN ROSELAND HOUSE NURSERY ⊠ ⋒
Chacewater, Truro, Cornwall, TR4 8QB
Ⓣ (01872) 560451
Ⓔ clematis@roselandhouse.co.uk
Ⓦ www.roselandhouse.co.uk
Contact: C R Pridham
Opening Times: 1300-1800 Tue & Wed, Apr-Sep. Other times by appt.
Min Mail Order UK: Nmc
Cat. Cost: 2 × 1st class.
Credit Cards: None
Specialities: Climbing & conservatory plants. Nat. Collection of *Clematis viticella* cvs. Garden open to the public.
Map Ref: C, D1 **OS Grid Ref:** SW752445

KEY
⊠ Mail order to UK or EU ⋒ Delivers to shows
✈ Exports beyond EU € Euro accepted
♿ Accessible by wheelchair ◆ See Display advertisement

C

CRob ROBERTS NURSERIES ⊠
East Allington, Totnes, Devon, TQ9 7QE
Ⓣ (01548) 521412
Ⓜ 07940 858778
Ⓕ (01548) 521533
Ⓔ info@conifersdirect.com
Ⓦ www.conifersdirect.com
Contact: W R Bartoszyn
Opening Times: By appt. only.
Min Mail Order UK: Nmc
Cat. Cost: 2 × 1st class.
Credit Cards: None
Specialities: Extensive range of hardy dwarf, ornamental conifers incl. old favourites, choice varieties & new introductions. A selected range of specimen shrubs & conifers in patio planters.
Notes: Also sells wholesale.
Map Ref: C, D3 **OS Grid Ref:** SX763495

CRWN THE REALLY WILD NURSERY ⊠ ☒ €
19 Hoopers Way, Torrington, Devon, EX38 7NS
Ⓣ (01805) 624739
Ⓕ (01805) 624739
Ⓔ thereallywildnursery@yahoo.co.uk
Ⓦ www.thereallywildnursery.co.uk
Contact: Kathryn Moore
Opening Times: Not open. Mail order only.
Min Mail Order UK: £10.00 + p&p
Min Mail Order EU: £20.00 + p&p
Cat. Cost: 3 × 1st class.
Specialities: Wildflowers, bulbs & seeds.
Notes: Mail order all year round, grown to order (plants in pots or plugs). Credit card payment accepted via Paypal online only. Also sells wholesale.

CSam SAMPFORD SHRUBS € ♿
Sampford Peverell, Tiverton, Devon, EX16 7EN
Ⓣ (01884) 821164
Ⓔ martin@samshrub.co.uk
Ⓦ www.samshrub.co.uk
Contact: M Hughes-Jones & S Proud
Opening Times: 0900-1700 Mon-Sat, 1000-1600 Sun, Feb-Jun. 0900-1700 (or dusk) Tue-Sat, Jul-Oct.
Cat. Cost: A5 sae + 35p stamp.
Credit Cards: All major credit/debit cards
Specialities: Large displays of *Pulmonaria* & *Crocosmia*. Nat. Collection of *Helenium*.
Notes: Mail order heleniums only, min. order £15.00 + p&p, despatched Mar.
Map Ref: C, B4 **OS Grid Ref:** ST043153

CSBt ST BRIDGET NURSERIES LTD ⊠ ♿
Old Rydon Lane, Exeter, Devon, EX2 7JY
Ⓣ (01392) 873672
Ⓕ (01392) 876710
Ⓔ info@stbridgetnurseries.co.uk
Ⓦ www.stbridgetnurseries.co.uk
Contact: Garden Centre Plant Advice
Opening Times: 0800-1700 Mon-Sat, 1030-1630 Sun, 0900-1700 Bank Hols. Closed Xmas Day, Boxing Day, New Year's Day & Easter Sun.
Min Mail Order UK: Nmc
Cat. Cost: Free.
Credit Cards: All major credit/debit cards
Specialities: Large general nursery, with two garden centres.
Notes: Mail order available between Nov & Mar.
Map Ref: C, C4 **OS Grid Ref:** SX955905

CSdC SHERWOOD COTTAGE €
Newton St Cyres, Exeter, Devon, EX5 5BT
Ⓣ (01392) 851589
Ⓔ vaughan.gallavan@connectfree.co.uk
Contact: Vaughan Gallavan
Opening Times: By appt. only. 1400-1700 Sun with Sherwood Gardens.
Cat. Cost: 2 × 1st class.
Credit Cards: None
Specialities: Magnolias, trees & shrubs. Nat. Collection of Knap Hill azaleas. Ghent & species deciduous azaleas. Sherwood Garden new Nat. Collection of *Magnolia*. Stock available in small quantities only.
Map Ref: C, C3

CSev LOWER SEVERALLS NURSERY ⊠ ♿
Crewkerne, Somerset, TA18 7NX
Ⓣ (01460) 73234
Ⓕ (01460) 76105
Ⓔ mary@lowerseveralls.co.uk
Ⓦ www.lowerseveralls.co.uk
Contact: Mary R Pring
Opening Times: 1000-1700 Tue, Wed, Fri, Sat, Mar-end Sep.
Min Mail Order UK: £20.00
Cat. Cost: 4 × 1st class.
Credit Cards: None
Specialities: Herbs, herbaceous.
Notes: Mail order perennials only.
Map Ref: C, B5 **OS Grid Ref:** ST457111

CSim SIMPSON'S SEEDS LTD ⊠ ♿
The Walled Garden Nursery, Horningsham, Warminster, Wiltshire, BA12 7NT
Ⓣ (01985) 845004
Ⓕ (01985) 845052
Ⓔ sales@simpsonsseeds.co.uk
Ⓦ www.simpsonsseeds.co.uk
Contact: Matthew Simpson
Opening Times: 1100-1700 Wed-Sun, Apr-May. 1100-1700 Tue-Fri & 1000-1300 Sat, rest of the year.

Min Mail Order UK: Nmc
Min Mail Order EU: Nmc
Credit Cards: Visa MasterCard Switch
Specialities: Large range of hardy perennials, ltd. quantities of each. Large range of seeds & vegetable plants. Specialities tomato & pepper.
Notes: Mail order catalogue currently only for seed & veg plants.
Map Ref: C, B5

CSli SLIPPS GARDEN CENTRE ♿
Butts Hill, Frome, Somerset,
BA11 1HR
Ⓣ (01373) 467013
Ⓕ (01373) 467013
Contact: James Hall
Opening Times: 0900-1730 Mon-Sat, 1000-1630 Sun.
Cat. Cost: None issued
Credit Cards: Visa Access MasterCard Delta Switch
Specialities: *Achillea*.
Notes: Also sells wholesale.
Map Ref: C, B5

CSna SNAPE COTTAGE ⊠
Chaffeymoor, Borton, Dorset,
SP8 5BY
Ⓣ (01747) 840330 (evenings only).
Ⓕ (01747) 840330
Ⓔ ianandangela@snapecottagegarden.co.uk
Ⓦ www.snapestakes.com
Contact: Mrs Angela Whinfield
Opening Times: 1030-1700, last 2 Suns in each month Feb-Aug incl. & every Thu May-Aug.
Min Mail Order UK: Nmc
Cat. Cost: Sae.
Credit Cards: None
Specialities: *Galanthus* & *Helleborus*. 'Old' forms of many popular garden plants. Plantsman's garden open same time as nursery. Stock available in small quantities.
Notes: Mail order *Galanthus* only. List issued in Mar.
Map Ref: C, B5 **OS Grid Ref:** ST762303

CSNP SECOND NATURE PLANT NURSERY ♿
Croft House, Aller, Somerset, TA10 0RA
Ⓣ (01458) 259190
Ⓔ allernursery@aol.com
Contact: Sarah Adamson
Opening Times: 0900-1700 Tue-Sat (closed Mon), 1000-1600 Sun.
Credit Cards: None
Specialities: Hardy perennials & unusual conservatory plants.
Map Ref: C, B4

CSpe SPECIAL PLANTS ⊠ ⌂ €
Hill Farm Barn, Greenways Lane, Cold Ashton, Chippenham, Wiltshire, SN14 8LA
Ⓣ (01225) 891686
Ⓔ derry@specialplants.net
Ⓦ www.specialplants.net
Contact: Derry Watkins
Opening Times: 1000-1700 7 days Mar-Oct. Other times please ring first to check.
Min Mail Order UK: £10.00 + p&p
Min Mail Order EU: £20.00 + p&p
Cat. Cost: 5 × 2nd class (sae only for seed list).
Credit Cards: All major credit/debit cards
Specialities: Tender perennials, *Mimulus*, *Pelargonium*, *Salvia*, *Streptocarpus*, hardy geraniums, *Anemone*, *Erysimum*, *Papaver*, *Viola* & grasses. Many varieties propagated in small numbers only. New introductions of S. African plants.
Notes: Mail order Sep-Mar only.
Map Ref: C, A5 **OS Grid Ref:** ST749726

CSPN SHERSTON PARVA NURSERY ⊠ ✈ ⌂ € ♿
Malmesbury Road, Sherston, Wiltshire,
SN16 0NX
Ⓣ (01666) 840348
Ⓜ 07887 814843
Ⓕ (01666) 840059
Ⓔ martin@sherstonparva.com
Ⓦ www.sherstonparva.com
Contact: Martin Rea
Opening Times: 1000-1700 7 days 1st Feb-31th Dec. Closed Jan.
Min Mail Order UK: Nmc
Min Mail Order EU: Nmc
Cat. Cost: Free.
Credit Cards: MasterCard Delta Visa Switch
Specialities: *Clematis*, wall shrubs & climbers.
Map Ref: C, A5

CSsd SUNNYSIDE PLANTS ⊠
Sunnyside, Leigh Road, Bradford-on-Avon, Wiltshire, BA15 2RQ
Ⓣ (01225) 862096
Ⓔ Filoman@fsmail.net
Contact: James Tracey
Opening Times: By prior arrangement only.
Min Mail Order UK: £6.00
Credit Cards: None
Specialities: Dry & lime-tolerant hardy plants. Smaller quantities of choice plants for

KEY
⊠ Mail order to UK or EU ⌂ Delivers to shows
✈ Exports beyond EU € Euro accepted
♿ Accessible by wheelchair ◆ See Display advertisement

C

damp or humus-rich conditions. Some plants available in small quantities only.
Notes: Mail order pre-arranged by phone.
Map Ref: C, A5 **OS Grid Ref:** ST832621

CSto **STONE LANE GARDENS** ⊠ ♿
Stone Farm, Chagford, Devon,
TQ13 8JU
Ⓣ (01647) 231311
Ⓔ orders@mythicgarden.eclipse.co.uk
Ⓦ www.mythicgarden.com
Contact: Kenneth Ashburner
Opening Times: Sculpture exhibition & garden open May-Sep. Charges apply. Nursery & arboretum open all year but please phone for appt.
Min Mail Order UK: Nmc
Cat. Cost: £2.00 or 6 × 1st class for descriptive catalogue.
Credit Cards: None
Specialities: Wide range of wild provenance *Betula* & *Alnus*. Interesting varieties of *Rubus*, *Sorbus* etc. Nat. Collection of Birch & Alder. Planting service available in West Country, details on request.
Notes: Also sells wholesale.
Map Ref: C, C3 **OS Grid Ref:** SX708908

CStu **STUCKEY'S ALPINES** ⌂
38 Phillipps Avenue, Exmouth, Devon,
EX8 3HZ
Ⓣ (01395) 273636
Ⓔ stuckeysalpines@aol.com
Contact: Roger & Brenda Stuckey
Opening Times: As NGS dates or by appt.
Cat. Cost: None issued.
Credit Cards: None
Specialities: Alpines in general. Hardy & half-hardy bulbs. NZ *Clematis* hybrids. Extensive choice of plants, many available only in small quantities.
Map Ref: C, C4

CSut **SUTTONS SEEDS** ⊠
Woodview Road, Paignton, Devon,
TQ4 7NG
Ⓣ 0870 220 2899
Ⓕ 0870 220 2265
Ⓦ www.suttons-seeds.co.uk
Contact: Customer Services
Opening Times: (Office) 0830-1700 Mon-Fri. Also answerphone.
Min Mail Order UK: Nmc
Min Mail Order EU: Nmc
Cat. Cost: Free.
Credit Cards: Visa MasterCard Switch Delta
Specialities: Over 1,000 varieties of flower & vegetable seed, bulbs, plants & sundries.

CSWC **SOUTH WEST CARNIVOROUS PLANTS** ⊠ ✈ ⌂
2 Rose Cottages, Culmstock, Cullompton,
Devon, EX15 3JJ
Ⓣ (01884) 841549
Ⓕ (01884) 841549
Ⓔ flytraps@littleshopofhorrors.co.uk
Ⓦ www.littleshopofhorrors.co.uk
Contact: Jenny Pearce & Alistair Pearce
Opening Times: By appt.
Min Mail Order UK: Nmc
Min Mail Order EU: Nmc
Cat. Cost: 2 × 2nd class.
Credit Cards: All major credit/debit cards
Specialities: *Cephalotus*, *Nepenthes*, *Dionaea*, *Drosera*, *Darlingtonia*, *Sarracenia*, *Pinguicula* & *Utricularia*. Specialists in hardy carnivorous plants & *Dionaea muscipula* cvs.
Map Ref: C, B4

CSWP **SONIA WRIGHT PLANTS** ⊠ ♿
Buckerfields Nursery, Ogbourne St George,
Marlborough, Wiltshire, SN8 1SG
Ⓣ (01672) 841065
Ⓕ (01672) 541047
Contact: Sonia Wright & Alison Duxbury
Opening Times: 1000-1800 Tue-Sat.
Min Mail Order UK: £15.00 primulas only
Min Mail Order EU: £15.00 primulas only
Cat. Cost: 4 × 1st class.
Credit Cards: All major credit/debit cards
Specialities: Barnhaven polyanthus & primroses. Grasses, grey-leaved plants, *Iris*, *Euphorbia*, *Penstemon*, old roses.
Notes: Mail order primroses only despatched autumn. Credit cards not accepted over the phone.
Map Ref: C, A6

CTca **TRECANNA NURSERY** ⊠ ⌂
Rose Farm, Latchley, Nr Gunnislake,
Cornwall, PL18 9AX
Ⓣ (01822) 834680
Ⓕ (01822) 834680
Ⓔ mark@trecanna.com
Ⓦ www.trecanna.com
Contact: Mark Wash
Opening Times: 1000-1700 Wed-Sat & B/hols all year. Closed Xmas Day & Boxing Day.
Min Mail Order UK: £12.00
Min Mail Order EU: £20.00
Cat. Cost: 2 × 1st class.
Credit Cards: None
Specialities: Hardy South African bulbs & plants. Extensive collections of less usual bulbs & perennials. *Crocosmia*, *Eucomis*, *Schizostylis* & *Sempervivum*.

Notes: Talks to garden societies, tours of the nursery. Partial wheelchair access.
Map Ref: C, C3 **OS Grid Ref:** SX247733

CTho THORNHAYES NURSERY ⊠
St Andrews Wood, Dulford,
Cullompton, Devon,
EX15 2DF
Ⓣ (01884) 266746
Ⓕ (01884) 266739
Ⓔ trees@thornhayes-nursery.co.uk
Ⓦ www.thornhayes-nursery.co.uk
Contact: K D Croucher
Opening Times: 0800-1600 Mon-Fri.
Min Mail Order UK: Nmc
Min Mail Order EU: Nmc
Credit Cards: None
Specialities: A broad range of forms of ornamental, amenity & fruit trees incl. West Country apple varieties.
Notes: Also sells wholesale.
Map Ref: C, C4

CTrC TREVENA CROSS NURSERIES ⊠ € ♿
Breage, Helston, Cornwall,
TR13 9PS
Ⓣ (01736) 763880
Ⓕ (01736) 762828
Ⓔ sales@trevenacross.co.uk
Ⓦ www.trevenacross.co.uk
Contact: Graham Jeffery, John Eddy
Opening Times: 0900-1700 Mon-Sat, 1030-1630 Sun.
Min Mail Order UK: Nmc
Cat. Cost: Online only.
Credit Cards: Access Visa Switch
Specialities: South African, Australian & New Zealand plants, incl. *Aloe*, *Protea*, tree ferns, palms, *Restio*, hardy succulents & wide range of other exotics.
Map Ref: C, D1 **OS Grid Ref:** SW614284

CTrG TREGOTHNAN NURSERY ⊠ ✈ € ♿
Estate Office, Tregothnan, Truro, Cornwall,
TR2 4AN
Ⓣ (01872) 520325
Ⓕ (01872) 520291
Ⓔ bigplants@tregothnan.co.uk
Ⓦ www.tregothnan.com
Contact: Jonathon Jones
Opening Times: By appt. for collection only.
Min Mail Order UK: £25.00
Min Mail Order EU: £500.00
Cat. Cost: Online only.
Credit Cards: MasterCard Visa Delta EuroCard
Specialities: Unusual & rare plants from own stock. Extra large specimens available for instant effect. Known wild origin plants.
Notes: English tea production & marketing. Also sells wholesale.

CTrh TREHANE CAMELLIA NURSERY ⊠ 🚚 € ♿
J Trehane & Sons Ltd, Stapehill Road,
Hampreston, Wimborne, Dorset, BH21 7ND
Ⓣ (01202) 873490
Ⓕ (01202) 873490
Ⓔ camellias@trehanenursery.co.uk
Ⓦ www.trehanenursery.co.uk
Contact: Lorraine or Jeanette
Opening Times: 0900-1630 Mon-Fri all year (excl. Xmas & New Year). 1000-1600 Sat-Sun in spring & by special appt.
Min Mail Order UK: Nmc
Min Mail Order EU: Nmc
Cat. Cost: £1.90 cat./book.
Credit Cards: All major credit/debit cards
Specialities: Extensive range of *Camellia* species, cultivars & hybrids. Many new introductions. Evergreen azaleas, *Pieris*, *Magnolia* & blueberries.
Notes: Also sells wholesale.
Map Ref: C, C6

CTri TRISCOMBE NURSERIES ⊠ ♿ ◆
West Bagborough, Nr Taunton, Somerset,
TA4 3HG
Ⓣ (01984) 618267
Ⓔ triscombe.nurseries2000@virgin.net
Ⓦ www.triscombenurseries.co.uk
Contact: S Parkman
Opening Times: 0900-1300 & 1400-1730 Mon-Sat. 1400-1730 Sun & B/hols.
Min Mail Order UK: Nmc
Cat. Cost: 2 × 1st class.
Credit Cards: None
Specialities: Trees, shrubs, roses, fruit, *Clematis*, herbaceous & rock plants.
Map Ref: C, B4

CTuc EDWIN TUCKER & SONS ⊠ ♿
Brewery Meadow, Stonepark, Ashburton,
Newton Abbot, Devon, TQ13 7DG
Ⓣ (01364) 652233
Ⓕ (01364) 654211
Ⓔ seeds@edwintucker.com
Ⓦ www.edwintucker.com
Contact: Geoff Penton
Opening Times: 0800-1700 Mon-Fri, 0800-1600 Sat.
Min Mail Order UK: Nmc

KEY
⊠ Mail order to UK or EU | 🚚 Delivers to shows
✈ Exports beyond EU | € Euro accepted
♿ Accessible by wheelchair | ◆ See Display advertisement

C

Min Mail Order EU: Nmc
Cat. Cost: Free.
Credit Cards: Visa MasterCard Switch
Specialities: Nearly 120 varieties of seed potatoes, incl. 50 organic varieties. Wide range of vegetables, flowers, green manures & sprouting seeds in packets. All not treated. Nearly 200 varieties of organically produced seeds.

CWan WANBOROUGH HERB NURSERY
Callas Hill, Wanborough, Swindon, Wiltshire, SN4 0AG
Ⓣ (01793) 790327 (answering machine)
Ⓔ Biggs@wanbherbnursery.fsnet.co.uk
Contact: Peter Biggs
Opening Times: 1000-1700 Tue-Fri (closed 1300-1400), w/ends 1000-1600, Mar-Oct. 1000-1600 (closed 1300-1400) Thu-Sun, Nov & Dec. Other times by appt.
Cat. Cost: 2 × 1st or A4 sae.
Credit Cards: None
Specialities: Herbs, herbaceous, esp. culinary. Available in small quantities only.
Map Ref: C, A6 **OS Grid Ref:** SU217828

CWat THE WATER GARDEN ⊠ ♿
Hinton Parva, Swindon, Wiltshire, SN4 0DH
Ⓣ (01793) 790558
Ⓕ (01793) 791298
Ⓔ mike@thewatergarden.co.uk
Ⓦ www.thewatergarden.co.uk
Contact: Mike & Anne Newman
Opening Times: 1000-1700 Wed-Sun.
Min Mail Order UK: £10.00 + p&p
Cat. Cost: 4 × 1st class.
Credit Cards: Visa Access Switch
Specialities: Water lilies, marginal & moisture plants, oxygenators & alpines.
Map Ref: C, A6

CWCL WESTCOUNTRY NURSERIES (INC. WESTCOUNTRY LUPINS) ⊠ ⌂ ♿ ◆
Donkey Meadow, Woolsery, Devon, EX39 5QH
Ⓣ (01237) 431111
Ⓕ (01237) 431111
Ⓔ info@westcountry-nurseries.co.uk
Ⓦ www.westcountry-nurseries.co.uk
Contact: Sarah Conibear
Opening Times: 1000-1600 7 days.
Min Mail Order UK: Nmc
Cat. Cost: 2 × 1st class + A5 sae for full colour cat.
Credit Cards: None. Nochex payment accepted online.
Specialities: *Lupinus*, *Lewisia*, *Hellebore*, cyclamen, acers, lavender, select perennials, grasses, ferns & climbers. Nat. Collection of Lupins.
Map Ref: C, B2 **OS Grid Ref:** SS3521

CWdb WOODBOROUGH GARDEN CENTRE LTD € ♿
Nursery Farm, Woodborough, Nr Pewsey, Wiltshire, SN9 5PF
Ⓣ (01672) 851249
Ⓕ (01672) 851465
Ⓔ clanparker@aol.com
Ⓦ www.woodboroughgardencentre.co.uk
Contact: Alison Parker
Opening Times: 0900-1700 Mon-Sat, 1100-1700 Sun.
Cat. Cost: None issued.
Credit Cards: All major credit/debit cards
Specialities: Wide range of shrubs, trees, herbaceous, alpines & herbs. Large selection of climbers esp. *Clematis*, & spring bulbs.
Notes: PYO fruit & daffodils.
Map Ref: C, A6 **OS Grid Ref:** SU119597

CWGN WALLED GARDEN NURSERY ⊠ ♿
Brinkworth House, Brinkworth, Nr Malmesbury, Wiltshire, SN16 9DQ
Ⓣ (01666) 826637
Ⓔ f.wescott@btintenet.com
Ⓦ www.clematis-nursery.co.uk
Contact: Fraser Wescott
Opening Times: 1000-1700, 7 days Mar-Oct. 1000-dusk, Mon-Fri Nov & Feb. Closed Dec & Jan.
Min Mail Order UK: £8.50
Cat. Cost: 3 × 1st class.
Credit Cards: All major credit/debit cards
Specialities: *Clematis* & climbers, with a selection of unusual perennials & shrubs.
Map Ref: C, A6 **OS Grid Ref:** SU002849

CWGr WINCHESTER GROWERS LTD. ⊠ ✈ ♿
Varfell Farm, Long Rock, Penzance, Cornwall, TR20 8AQ
Ⓣ (01736) 335851
Ⓕ (01736) 851033
Ⓔ dahlias@wgltd.co.uk
Ⓦ www.wgltd.co.uk
Contact: Sarah Thomas
Opening Times: 1300-1630 Thu, Fri & Sat, 13th Jul 2005-26th Aug 2006 incl. Open Day 1000-1600 Sun 20th Aug 2006.
Min Mail Order UK: Nmc
Min Mail Order EU: Nmc
Cat. Cost: Free.
Credit Cards: Visa Delta MasterCard Switch
Specialities: Nat. Collection of *Dahlia*. Due to large number of varieties, some stock available in small quantities only.
Notes: Also sells wholesale.
Map Ref: C, D1

C

CWib **WIBBLE FARM NURSERIES** ⊠ ✈ ⌂ ♿
Wibble Farm, West Quantoxhead,
Nr Taunton, Somerset,
TA4 4DD
Ⓣ (01984) 632303
Ⓕ (01984) 633168
Ⓔ sales@wibblefarmnurseries.co.uk
Ⓦ www.wibblefarmnurseries.co.uk
Contact: Mrs M L Francis
Opening Times: 0800-1700 Mon-Fri, 1000-1600 Sat. All year excl. B/hols.
Min Mail Order UK: Nmc
Min Mail Order EU: Nmc
Cat. Cost: 3 × 1st class.
Credit Cards: All major credit/debit cards
Specialities: Growers of a wide range of hardy plants, many rare & unusual.
Notes: Also sells wholesale.
Map Ref: C, B4

CWil **FERNWOOD NURSERY** ⊠ ✈ ⌂ € ♿
Peters Marland, Torrington, Devon,
EX38 8QG
Ⓣ (01805) 601446
Ⓔ hw@fernwood-nursery.co.uk
Ⓦ www.fernwood-nursery.co.uk
Contact: Howard Wills & Sally Wills
Opening Times: Any time by appt. Please phone first.
Min Mail Order UK: Nmc
Min Mail Order EU: Nmc
Cat. Cost: Sae for list.
Credit Cards: None
Specialities: Nat. Collections of *Sempervivum*, *Jovibarba*, *Rosularia* & *Phormium*.
Notes: Mail order for *Sempervivum*, *Jovibarba* & *Rosularia* only. 5 miles from RHS Rosemoor.
Map Ref: C, C3 **OS Grid Ref:** SS479133

CWiW **WINDRUSH WILLOW** ⊠ €
Higher Barn, Sidmouth Road,
Aylesbeare, Exeter, Devon,
EX5 2JJ
Ⓣ (01395) 233669
Ⓕ (01395) 233669
Ⓔ windrushw@aol.com
Ⓦ www.windrushwillow.com
Contact: Richard Kerwood
Opening Times: Mail order only. Open by appt.
Min Mail Order UK: Nmc
Min Mail Order EU: Nmc
Cat. Cost: 2 × 1st class.
Credit Cards: None
Specialities: *Salix*. Unrooted cuttings available Dec-Mar.
Notes: Also sells wholesale.

CWon **THE WONDER TREE** ⊠
35 Beaconsfield Road, Knowle, Bristol,
BS4 2JE
Ⓣ 0117 908 9057
Ⓜ 07989 333507
Ⓔ Kevin@wondertree.org.uk
Ⓦ www.wondertree.org.uk
Contact: Kevin Lindegaard
Opening Times: Not open. Mail order only.
Min Mail Order UK: £8.00
Cat. Cost: 2 × 1st class.
Credit Cards: None
Specialities: *Salix*.
Notes: Also sells wholesale.

CWoo **IAN AND ROSEMARY WOOD** ⊠
Newlands, 28 Furland Road, Crewkerne,
Somerset, TA18 8DD
Ⓣ (01460) 74630
Ⓔ eryth@wood31.waitrose.com
Contact: Ian and Rosemary Wood
Opening Times: By appt. only. Primarily mail order service. Enquiries welcomed to collect growing plants in season.
Min Mail Order UK: Nmc
Cat. Cost: 2 × 2nd class.
Credit Cards: None
Specialities: *Erythronium*, *Cyclamen* species & dwarf *Narcissus* species. Some species available in small quantities only, see catalogue.
Map Ref: C, B5

CWoW **WILL OF THE WISP PLANTS** ⊠ ⌂
(office) 5 Standards Road, Westonzoyland,
Bridgwater, Somerset, TA7 0EL
Ⓣ (01278) 691649 Ⓜ 07779 003998
Ⓕ (01278) 691649
Ⓔ mail@willofthewispplants.com
Contact: Jane East or Paul Coles
Opening Times: By appt. only.
Min Mail Order UK: Nmc.
Cat. Cost: 3 × 1st class.
Credit Cards: None
Specialities: Honeysuckle, *Clematis* & shrubs.
Notes: Nursery at Haygrass Nursery, Shoreditch Road, Taunton, TA3 7BS. Also sells wholesale.

CWri **NIGEL WRIGHT RHODODENDRONS** ♿
The Old Glebe, Eggesford, Chulmleigh,
Devon, EX18 7QU
Ⓣ (01769) 580632
Ⓔ wrightrhodos@aol.com

KEY		
	⊠ Mail order to UK or EU	⌂ Delivers to shows
	✈ Exports beyond EU	€ Euro accepted
	♿ Accessible by wheelchair	◆ See Display advertisement

C

Contact: Nigel Wright
Opening Times: By appt. only. 7 days.
Cat. Cost: 2 × 1st class.
Credit Cards: None
Specialities: *Rhododendron* & deciduous azaleas. 200 varieties field grown, root-balled, some potted. For collection only. Specialist grower. Free advice & planting plans.
Notes: Also sells wholesale.
Map Ref: C, B3 **OS Grid Ref:** SS6171

CWsd WILDSIDE NURSERY ⊠ ♿
Green Lane, Buckland Monachorum, Nr Yelverton, Devon, PL20 7NP
Ⓣ (01822) 855755
Ⓔ wildside.plants@virgin.net
Contact: Keith & Ros Wiley
Opening Times: 1000-1700 Wed-Sat, except Dec & Jan.
Min Mail Order UK: Nmc
Min Mail Order EU: £30.00
Cat. Cost: 2 × 1st class.
Credit Cards: All major credit/debit cards
Specialities: *Anemone nemorosa*, *Erythronium*, *Epimedium*, *Trillium*, *Rhodohypoxis* & unusual woodland plants.
Map Ref: C, C3 **OS Grid Ref:** 484681

CWSG WEST SOMERSET GARDEN CENTRE ⊠ ♿
Mart Road, Minehead, Somerset, TA24 5BJ
Ⓣ (01643) 703812
Ⓕ (01643) 706476
Ⓔ wsgc@btconnect.com
Ⓦ www.westsomersetgardencentre.co.uk
Contact: Mrs J K Shoulders
Opening Times: 0800-1700 Mon-Sat, 1000-1600 Sun.
Min Mail Order UK: Nmc
Cat. Cost: None issued.
Credit Cards: Access Visa Switch Solo
Specialities: Wide general range. *Ceanothus*.
Map Ref: C, B4

CWVF WHITE VEIL FUCHSIAS ⊠ ♿
Verwood Road, Three Legged Cross, Wimborne, Dorset, BH21 6RP
Ⓣ (01202) 813998
Contact: A. C. Holloway
Opening Times: 0900-1300 & 1400-1700 Mon-Fri Jan-Dec, & Sat Jan-Aug. 0900-1300 Sun Jan-Jul, closed Sun Aug, closed Sat & Sun Sep-Dec.
Min Mail Order UK: 8 plants
Cat. Cost: 4 × 1st class.
Credit Cards: None
Specialities: Fuchsias. Small plants grown from Jan-Apr. Available in small quantities only.
Map Ref: C, C6

EASTERN

EABi ALISON BILVERSTONE ⊠
22 Kings Street, Swaffham, Norfolk, PE37 7BU
Ⓣ (01760) 725026
Ⓔ kevinandhelen@greenfarmlane.freeserve.co.uk
Contact: Alison Bilverstone
Opening Times: Not open. Mail order only.
Min Mail Order UK: Nmc
Cat. Cost: Large sae.
Credit Cards: None
Specialities: *Achemene*, *Kohleria* & *Smithiantha* rhizomes, available Dec to mid-Apr. Stocked in small quantities.

EAlp THE ALPINE AND GRASS NURSERY ⊠
Northgate, Pinchbeck, Spalding, Lincolnshire, PE11 3TB
Ⓣ (01775) 640935
Ⓔ info@alpinesandgrasses.co.uk
Ⓦ www.alpinesandgrasses.co.uk
Contact: Hayley Merrison
Opening Times: Please telephone.
Min Mail Order UK: 15 plants.
Cat. Cost: Online only.
Credit Cards: None
Specialities: Alpines, rockery plants & ornamental grasses.
Notes: Also sells wholesale.
Map Ref: E, B1 **OS Grid Ref:** TF211262

EAmu AMULREE EXOTICS ⊠ ♿
The Turnpike, Norwich Road (B1113), Fundenhall, Norwich, Norfolk, NR16 1EL
Ⓣ (01508) 488101
Ⓕ (01508) 488101
Ⓔ SDG@exotica.fsbusiness.co.uk
Ⓦ www.turn-it-tropical.co.uk
Contact: S Gridley
Opening Times: 0930-1730 7 days spring-autumn, 1000-1630 7 days autumn-spring.
Min Mail Order UK: Nmc
Cat. Cost: 2 × 1st class.
Credit Cards: Visa MasterCard Electron Solo Switch
Specialities: Hardy & half-hardy plants for home, garden & conservatory. Palms, bamboos, bananas, tree ferns, cannas, gingers & much more.
Notes: Also sells wholesale.
Map Ref: E, B3 **OS Grid Ref:** DX123740

EAro **AROMAFOLIA** ⊠ ⌂
Barbers Farm, Leys Lane, Old Buckenham, Norfolk, NR17 1NT
Ⓣ (01953) 887713
Ⓔ enquiries@aromafolia.co.uk
Ⓦ www.aromafolia.co.uk
Contact: John Holden
Opening Times: 0930-1630 Thu-Sun & B/hols, Apr-Oct. Other times by appt.
Min Mail Order UK: £15.00
Cat. Cost: 3 × !st class.
Credit Cards: None
Specialities: Wide range of plants with aromatic foliage, incl. *Salvia*, *Monarda*, *Agastache*, *Nepeta*. All plants grown in peat-free compost. Some varieties only available in small quantities.
Map Ref: E,C3 **OS Grid Ref:** TM042913

EBak **B & H M BAKER**
Bourne Brook Nurseries, Greenstead Green, Halstead, Essex, CO9 1RJ
Ⓣ (01787) 476369 or 472900
Contact: B, HM and C Baker
Opening Times: 0800-1630 Mon-Fri, 0900-1200 & 1400-1630 Sat & Sun, Mar-30th Jun.
Cat. Cost: 2 × 1st class + 33p.
Credit Cards: MasterCard Delta Visa Switch
Specialities: *Fuchsia* & conservatory plants.
Notes: Also sells wholesale.
Map Ref: E, C2

EBee **BEECHES NURSERY** ⊠ ⌂ ♿
Village Centre, Ashdon, Saffron Walden, Essex, CB10 2HB
Ⓣ (01799) 584362
Ⓕ (01799) 584421
Ⓦ www.beechesnursery.co.uk
Contact: Alan Bidwell/Kevin Marsh
Opening Times: 0830-1700 Mon-Sat, 1000-1700 Sun & B/hols.
Min Mail Order UK: £10.00
Min Mail Order EU: £20.00
Cat. Cost: 6 × 2nd class herbaceous list.
Credit Cards: Visa Access MasterCard EuroCard Switch
Specialities: Herbaceous specialists & extensive range of other garden plants.
Notes: Mail order generally from Oct-Feb, Mar-Sep where conditions permit. Trees NOT available by mail order.
Map Ref: E, C2 **OS Grid Ref:** TL5842

EBla **BLACKSMITHS COTTAGE NURSERY** ⊠ ⌂ € ♿
Langmere Road, Langmere, Dickleburgh, Nr Diss, Norfolk, IP21 4QA
Ⓣ (01379) 740982
Ⓕ (01379) 741917
Ⓔ Blackcottnursery@aol.com
Ⓦ www.blackcottnursery.co.uk
Contact: Ben or Jill Potterton
Opening Times: 1000-1700 Thu-Sun, Mar-Oct. 1000-1700 Fri & Sat, Nov-Feb.
Min Mail Order UK: Nmc
Min Mail Order EU: Nmc
Cat. Cost: 3 × 1st class.
Credit Cards: All major credit/debit cards
Specialities: Over 2000 species grown. Large selection of shade plants. Large new display gardens.
Notes: Toilets & refreshments. Also sells wholesale.
Map Ref: E, C3

EBls **PETER BEALES ROSES** ⊠ ✈ ♿
London Road, Attleborough, Norfolk, NR17 1AY
Ⓣ (01953) 454707
Ⓕ (01953) 456845
Ⓔ sales@classicroses.co.uk
Ⓦ www.classicroses.co.uk
Contact: Customer Advisers
Opening Times: 0900-1700 Mon-Sat, 1000-1600 Sun & B/hols.
Min Mail Order UK: Nmc
Min Mail Order EU: Nmc
Cat. Cost: Free.
Credit Cards: All major credit/debit cards
Specialities: Old-fashioned roses & classic roses. Nat. Collection of Species Roses. Some stock available in small quantities only.
Map Ref: E, C3 **OS Grid Ref:** PM31612937

EBrs **BRESSINGHAM GARDENS (INCORP. VAN TUBERGEN UK)** ⊠ ♿
Bressingham, Diss, Norfolk, IP22 2AG
Ⓣ (01379) 688282
Ⓕ (01379) 687227
Ⓔ info@bressinghamgardens.com
Ⓦ www.bressinghamgardens.com
Contact: Fiona-Louise Tilden
Opening Times: Mail order 0900-1700 Mon-Fri. Gardens open daily 1030-1730 1st Apr-31st Oct.
Min Mail Order UK: Nmc
Min Mail Order EU: Nmc
Cat. Cost: Free on request.
Credit Cards: Maestro Visa Access MasterCard

KEY
⊠ Mail order to UK or EU — ⌂ Delivers to shows
✈ Exports beyond EU — € Euro accepted
♿ Accessible by wheelchair — ◆ See Display advertisement

Specialities: Bulbs, grafted conifers, grasses & perennials. Nat. Collection of *Miscanthus*.
Notes: Also sells wholesale.
Map Ref: E, C3 **OS Grid Ref:** TM071807

E

EBur JENNY BURGESS ✉ ♿
Alpine Nursery, Sisland, Norwich, Norfolk, NR14 6EF
Ⓣ (01508) 520724
Contact: Jenny Burgess
Opening Times: Any time by appt.
Min Mail Order UK: £5.00 + p&p
Min Mail Order EU: £10.00 + p&p
Cat. Cost: 3 × 1st class.
Credit Cards: None
Specialities: Alpines, *Sisyrinchium* & *Campanula*. Nat. Colection of *Sisyrinchium*.
Notes: Mail order for *Sisyrinchium* only.
Map Ref: E, B3

ECGP CAMBRIDGE GARDEN PLANTS ♿
The Lodge, Clayhithe Road, Horningsea, Cambridgeshire, CB5 9JD
Ⓣ (01223) 861370
Contact: Mrs Nancy Buchdahl
Opening Times: 1100-1730 Thu-Sun mid-Mar-31st Oct. Other times by appt.
Cat. Cost: 4 × 1st class.
Credit Cards: None
Specialities: Hardy perennials incl. wide range of *Geranium*, *Allium*, *Euphorbia*, *Penstemon*, *Digitalis*. Some shrubs, roses & *Clematis*.
Map Ref: E, C2 **OS Grid Ref:** TL497637

ECha THE BETH CHATTO GARDENS LTD ✉ ♿
Elmstead Market, Colchester, Essex, CO7 7DB
Ⓣ (01206) 822007
Ⓕ (01206) 825933
Ⓔ info@bethchatto.fsnet.co.uk
Ⓦ www.bethchatto.co.uk
Contact: Beth Chatto
Opening Times: 0900-1700 Mon-Sat 1st Mar-31st Oct. 0900-1600 Mon-Fri 1st Nov-1st Mar. Closed Sun.
Min Mail Order UK: £20.00
Min Mail Order EU: Ask for details.
Cat. Cos t: £3.00 incl. p&p.
Credit Cards: Visa Switch MasterCard
Specialities: Predominantly herbaceous. Many unusual for special situations.
Map Ref: E, D3 **OS Grid Ref:** TM069238

ECho CHOICE LANDSCAPES ✉ ✈ ⌂ € ♿
Priory Farm, 101 Salts Road, West Walton, Wisbech, Cambridgeshire, PE14 7EF
Ⓣ (01945) 585051
Ⓕ (01945) 580053
Ⓔ info@choicelandscapes.org
Ⓦ www.choicelandscapes.org
Contact: Michael Agg & Jillian Agg
Opening Times: 1000-1700 Tue-Sat 21st Feb-28th Oct 2006. Not open on show dates, please phone. Other times by appt.
Min Mail Order UK: £10.00
Min Mail Order EU: £10.00 + p&p
Cat. Cost: 6 × 1st class or 6 IRC.
Credit Cards: Maestro Visa MasterCard Solo
Specialities: Dwarf conifers, alpines, acers, rhododendrons, hostas, bulbs, pines & lilies.
Map Ref: E, B1

ECnt CANTS OF COLCHESTER ✉ ✈
Nayland Road, Mile End, Colchester, Essex, CO4 5EB
Ⓣ (01206) 844008
Ⓕ (01206) 855371
Ⓔ finder@cantsroses.co.uk
Ⓦ www.cantsroses.co.uk
Contact: Angela Pawsey
Opening Times: 0900-1300 & 1400-1630 Mon-Fri. Sat varied, please phone first. Sun closed.
Min Mail Order UK: Nmc
Min Mail Order EU: Nmc
Cat. Cost: Free.
Credit Cards: Visa MasterCard Delta Solo Switch
Specialities: Roses. Unstaffed rose field can be viewed dawn-dusk every day from end Jun-end Sep.
Notes: Mail order end Oct-end Mar only. Partial wheelchair access.
Map Ref: E, C3

ECot THE COTTAGE GARDEN € ♿
Langham Road, Boxted, Colchester, Essex, CO4 5HU
Ⓣ (01206) 272269
Ⓔ enquiries@thecottage-garden.co.uk
Ⓦ www.thecottage-garden.co.uk
Contact: Alison Smith
Opening Times: 0800-1700 7 days spring & summer. 0800-1700 Thu-Mon autumn/winter.
Cat. Cost: Free leaflet.
Credit Cards: Visa Access Connect Switch Delta
Specialities: 400 varieties of shrubs, 500 varieties of herbaceous. Huge range of trees, grasses, alpines, herbs, hedging, all home grown. Garden antiques.
Map Ref: E, C3 **OS Grid Ref:** TM003299

ECou COUNTY PARK NURSERY
Essex Gardens, Hornchurch, Essex, RM11 3BU
Ⓣ (01708) 445205
Ⓦ www.countyparknursery.co.uk

Contact: G Hutchins
Opening Times: 1000-1700 Mon-Sat excl. Wed, 1000-1700 Sun Mar-Oct. Nov-Feb by appt. only.
Cat. Cost: 3 × 1st class.
Credit Cards: None
Specialities: Alpines & rare and unusual plants from New Zealand, Tasmania & the Falklands. Nat. Collection of *Coprosma*. Many plants in small quantities only.
Map Ref: E, D2

ECre CREAKE PLANT CENTRE ♿
Nursery View, Leicester Road,
South Creake, Fakenham, Norfolk,
NR21 9PW
Ⓣ (01328) 823018
Contact: Mr T Harrison
Opening Times: 1000-1300 & 1400-1730 7 days excl. Xmas.
Cat. Cost: None issued.
Credit Cards: All major credit/debit cards
Specialities: Unusual shrubs, herbaceous, conservatory plants, old roses.
Map Ref: E, B1 **OS Grid Ref:** TF864353

ECrN CROWN NURSERY ⊠ ⛫ ♿
High Street, Ufford, Woodbridge, Suffolk,
IP13 6EL
Ⓣ (01394) 460755
Ⓕ (01394) 460142
Ⓔ enquiries@crown-nursery.co.uk
Ⓦ www.crown-nursery.co.uk
Contact: Anne Raymond
Opening Times: 0900-1700 (1600 in winter) Mon-Sat.
Min Mail Order UK: Nmc
Cat. Cost: 2 × 1st class.
Credit Cards: All major credit/debit cards
Specialities: Mature & semi-mature native, ornamental & fruit trees. Heritage fruit varieties.
Notes: Mail order for small/young stock only. Also sells wholesale.
Map Ref: E, C3 **OS Grid Ref:** TM292528

ECtt COTTAGE NURSERIES ⊠ ♿
Thoresthorpe, Alford, Lincolnshire,
LN13 0HX
Ⓣ (01507) 466968
Ⓕ (01507) 463409
Ⓔ bill@cottagenurseries.net
Ⓦ www.cottagenurseries.net
Contact: W H Denbigh
Opening Times: 0900-1700 7 days 1st Mar-31st Oct, 1000-1600 Thu-Sun Nov-Feb.
Min Mail Order UK: Nmc
Cat. Cost: 3 × 1st class.
Credit Cards: Visa MasterCard Maestro
Specialities: Hardy perennials. Wide general range.
Map Ref: E, A2 **OS Grid Ref:** TF423716

EDAr D'ARCY & EVEREST ⊠ ⛫ € ♿
(Office) PO Box 78, St Ives, Huntingdon,
Cambridgeshire, PE27 4UQ
Ⓣ (01480) 497672
Ⓜ 07715 374440/1
Ⓕ (01480) 466042
Ⓔ angela@darcyeverest.co.uk
Ⓦ www.darcyeverest.co.uk
Contact: Angela Whiting, Richard Oliver
Opening Times: By appt. only. Coach parties welcome by appt.
Min Mail Order UK: £10.00 + p&p
Min Mail Order EU: £10.00 + p&p
Cat. Cost: 6 × 1st class.
Credit Cards: None
Specialities: Alpines, herbs & selected perennials.
Notes: Nursery is at Pidley Sheep Lane (B1040), Somersham, Huntingdon.
Map Ref: E, C2 **OS Grid Ref:** TL533276

EDif DIFFERENT PLANTS ⛫ ♿
The Mellis Stud, Gate Farm, Cranley Green,
Eye, Suffolk, IP23 7NX
Ⓣ (01379) 870291
Contact: Fleur Waters
Opening Times: Sat-Thu by appt. only, closed Fri. Plant stall Eye market Fri 0900-1200.
Cat. Cost: 4 × 1st class.
Credit Cards: None
Specialities: *Mimulus aurantiacus* & hybrids, half-hardy bulbous/cormous perennials incl. *Dietes*, *Aristea*, *Cypella*, *Tigridia* & *Anomatheca laxa*. Bulbs may be available in small quantities only.
Map Ref: E, C3

EEls ELSWORTH HERBS ⊠ ♿
Avenue Farm Cottage, 31 Smith Street,
Elsworth, Cambridgeshire, CB3 8HY
Ⓣ (01954) 267414
Ⓕ (01954) 267414
Ⓔ john.twibell@btinternet.com
Contact: Drs J D & J M Twibell
Opening Times: By appt. only.
Min Mail Order UK: £10.00
Cat. Cost: 3 × 1st class.

KEY
⊠ Mail order to UK or EU ⛫ Delivers to shows
✈ Exports beyond EU € Euro accepted
♿ Accessible by wheelchair ◆ See Display advertisement

E

Credit Cards: None
Specialities: Nat. Collections of *Artemisia* (incl. *Seriphidium*) & *Nerium oleander*. Wide range of *Artemisia* & *Seriphidium*, *Nerium oleander*. Stock available in small quantities only. Orders may require propagation from Collection material, for which we are the primary reference source.
Map Ref: E, C2

EExo THE EXOTIC GARDEN COMPANY ⊠ ♿
Saxmundham Road, Aldeburgh, Nr Ipswich, Suffolk, IP15 5JD
Ⓣ (01728) 454456
Ⓕ (01473) 780651
Ⓦ www.theexoticgardenco.co.uk
Contact: Matthew Couchy
Opening Times: 1000-1700 Mon-Sat, 1000-1600 Sun.
Min Mail Order UK: Nmc
Cat. Cost: A4 sae.
Credit Cards: All major credit/debit cards
Specialities: Palms (hardy & half-hardy), bamboos, tree ferns & other exotics.
Map Ref: E, C3

EFam FAMECHECK REBLOOMING IRIS ⊠ ✈ € ♿
Hilltrees, Wandlebury Hill (A1307), Cambridge, Cambridgeshire, CB2 4AD
Ⓣ (01223) 243734 repeat ring after dark or leave phone number (not mobile).
Contact: Miss F Cook N.D.H.
Opening Times: 1500-1700 Mon-Fri, all year unless frost. Other times by appt. Please phone first, previous evening.
Min Mail Order UK: £5.00
Min Mail Order EU: £5.00
Cat. Cost: 4 × 1st class for list.
Credit Cards: None
Specialities: Daffodils, long-lasting & weatherproof cut-flower varieties. Bearded *Iris* & orange violets. Space Age & Reblooming Bearded *Iris*. Some only available in small quantities. About 1000 modern varieties, mostly imported. NCH status applied for daffodils & *Iris*.
Notes: Nursery between Cambridge Botanic Garden & Wandlebury Wildlife Park, next to Gogmagog Golf Course on A1307.
Map Ref: E, C2

EFer THE FERN NURSERY ⊠ ♿
Grimsby Road, Binbrook, Lincolnshire, LN8 6DH
Ⓣ (01472) 398092
Ⓔ richard@timm984.fsnet.co.uk
Ⓦ www.fernnursery.co.uk
Contact: R N Timm
Opening Times: 0900-1700 Sat & Sun Apr-Oct or by appt.
Min Mail Order UK: Nmc
Min Mail Order EU: Nmc
Cat. Cost: 2 × 1st class.
Credit Cards: None
Specialities: Ferns.
Notes: Only plants listed in the mail order part of the catalogue will be sent mail order. Also sells wholesale.
Map Ref: E, A1 **OS Grid Ref:** TF212942

EFEx FLORA EXOTICA ⊠ ✈ €
Pasadena, South-Green, Fingringhoe, Colchester, Essex, CO5 7DR
Ⓣ (01206) 729414
Contact: J Beddoes
Opening Times: Not open. Mail order only.
Min Mail Order UK: Nmc
Min Mail Order EU: Nmc
Cat. Cost: 4 × 1st class.
Credit Cards: None
Specialities: Exotica flora incl. orchids.

EFly THE FLY TRAP PLANTS ⊠ ⌂
10 Newton Close, Newton St. Faiths, Norwich, Norfolk, NR10 3LH
Ⓣ (01603) 710335
Ⓜ 07765 061629
Ⓕ (01603) 710335
Ⓔ sales@tftplants.co.uk
Ⓦ http://tftplants.co.uk
Contact: Pauline Steward
Opening Times: By appt. only.
Min Mail Order UK: Nmc
Cat. Cost: 1 × 1st class sae.
Credit Cards: None
Specialities: All kinds of carnivorous plants, such as *Sarracenia*, *Drosera*, *Pinguicula*, to the *Utricularia* aquatic plants.

EFul FULBROOKE NURSERY ⊠
Home Farm, Westley Waterless, Newmarket, Suffolk, CB8 0RG
Ⓣ (01638) 507124
Ⓕ (01638) 507124
Ⓔ bamboo@fulbrooke.co.uk
Ⓦ www.fulbrooke.co.uk
Contact: Paul Lazard
Opening Times: By appt. most times incl. w/ends.
Min Mail Order UK: £5.50 + p&p
Min Mail Order EU: £6.00 + p&p
Cat. Cost: 3 × 1st class.
Credit Cards: None
Specialities: Bamboos & grasses.
Map Ref: E, C2

EGFP GRANGE FARM PLANTS ⊠ ♿
Grange Farm, 38 Fishergate Road, Sutton St James, Spalding, Lincolnshire, PE12 0EZ
Ⓣ (01945) 440240
Ⓜ 07742 138760
Ⓕ (01945) 440355
Ⓔ ellis.family@tinyonline.co.uk
Contact: M C Ellis
Opening Times: Mail order only. Open by appt. only.
Min Mail Order UK: Nmc
Cat. Cost: 1 × 1st class.
Credit Cards: None
Specialities: Rare trees & shrubs, esp. *Juglans*, *Fraxinus*. Some species available in small quantities only.
Map Ref: E, B2 **OS Grid Ref:** TF3818

EGle GLEN CHANTRY €
Ishams Chase, Wickham Bishops, Essex, CM8 3LG
Ⓣ (01621) 891342
Ⓕ (01621) 891342
Ⓦ www.glenchantry.demon.co.uk
Contact: Sue Staines & Wol Staines
Opening Times: 1000-1600 Fri & Sat from 7th Apr-2nd Sep. Sae for details.
Cat. Cost: 5 × 1st class.
Credit Cards: None
Specialities: A wide & increasing range of perennials, many unusual.
Notes: Partial wheelchair access.
Map Ref: E, D2 **OS Grid Ref:** TM834133

EGln GLENHIRST CACTUS NURSERY ⊠ ✈
Station Road, Swineshead, Nr Boston, Lincolnshire, PE20 3NX
Ⓣ (01205) 820314
Ⓕ (01205) 820614
Ⓔ info@cacti4u.co.uk
Ⓦ www.cacti4u.co.uk
Contact: N C & S A Bell
Opening Times: Visitors welcome, but by telephone appt. only.
Min Mail Order UK: Nmc
Min Mail Order EU: Nmc
Cat. Cost: 2 × 1st class.
Credit Cards: Visa MasterCard Switch Solo Electron
Specialities: Extensive range of cacti & succulent plants & seeds, incl. Christmas cacti & orchid cacti. Hardy & half-hardy desert plants. Display gardens. Palms, *Cordyline*, *Phormium* & other hardy architectural plants.
Notes: Exports plants & seeds to EU, seeds only outside the EU. Will accept payment in euros online only.
Map Ref: E, B1 **OS Grid Ref:** TF245408

EGlv GLENVILLE NURSERIES ⊠ ◆
King John Bank, Walpole St Andrew, Wisbech, Cambridgeshire, PE14 7LD
Ⓣ (01945) 780020
Ⓕ (01945) 780078
Ⓔ brtowler@btopenworld.com
Ⓦ www.glenvillenurseries.co.uk
Contact: B R Towler
Opening Times: 1000-1600 Mon-Fri, Sat by arrangement, closed Sun.
Min Mail Order UK: £6.00 + p&p
Min Mail Order EU: £30.00 + p&p
Cat. Cost: 2 × 2nd class.
Credit Cards: MasterCard Switch Delta Visa
Specialities: Young flowering, ornamental & climbing shrubs. Also conifers.
Notes: Also sells wholesale.
Map Ref: E, B1 **OS Grid Ref:** TF487188

EGol GOLDBROOK PLANTS ⊠ ✈
Hoxne, Eye, Suffolk, IP21 5AN
Ⓣ (01379) 668770
Ⓕ (01379) 668770
Contact: Sandra Bond
Opening Times: 1000-1700 (or dusk if earlier) Thu-Sun Apr-Sep, Sat & Sun Oct-Mar or by appt. Closed Jan & during Hampton Court Flower Show.
Min Mail Order UK: £15.00 + p&p
Min Mail Order EU: £100.00 + p&p
Cat. Cost: 4 × 1st class.
Credit Cards: None
Specialities: Very large range of *Hosta* (1100+), *Hemerocallis*.
Map Ref: E, C3

EGoo ELISABETH GOODWIN NURSERIES ⊠ ∩ ♿
Elm Tree Farm, 1 Beeches Road, West Row, Bury St Edmunds, Suffolk, IP28 8NP
Ⓣ (01638) 713050
Ⓕ 0870 7053256
Ⓔ mail@e-g-n.co.uk
Ⓦ www.e-g-n.co.uk
Contact: Elisabeth Goodwin
Opening Times: By appt.
Min Mail Order UK: Nmc
Cat. Cost: Descriptive catalogue online.
Credit Cards: None
Specialities: Drought tolerant plants for both sun & shade esp. *Helianthemum*, *Sedum*, *Teucrium*, *Vinca*, grasses, *Aquilegia*, *Achillea*,

KEY
⊠ Mail order to UK or EU ∩ Delivers to shows
✈ Exports beyond EU € Euro accepted
♿ Accessible by wheelchair ◆ See Display advertisement

Agastache & *Onosma*. Some plants grown in ltd. quantities.
Notes: Also sells wholesale.
Map Ref: E, C2

E

EHea THE HEATHER SOCIETY ⊠ €
Denbeigh, All Saints Road,
Creeting St. Mary, Ipswich, Suffolk,
IP6 8PJ
Ⓣ (01449) 711220
Ⓕ (01449) 711220
Ⓔ heathers@zetnet.co.uk
Ⓦ www.heathersociety.org.uk
Contact: David & Anne Small
Opening Times: Not open.
Min Mail Order UK: Nmc for members.
Min Mail Order EU: Nmc for members.
Cat. Cost: 1 × 1st class.
Credit Cards: Visa MasterCard
Specialities: Heathers.
Notes: Mail order for Heather Society members within the EU, Apr only. One year's Membership UK £11.50, EC £12.50.

EHon HONEYSOME AQUATIC NURSERY ⊠
The Row, Sutton, Nr Ely, Cambridgeshire,
CB6 2PB
Ⓣ (01353) 778889
Ⓕ (01353) 777291
Contact: Mrs L S Bond
Opening Times: At all times by appt. only.
Min Mail Order UK: Nmc
Cat. Cost: 2 × 1st class.
Credit Cards: None
Specialities: Hardy aquatic, bog & marginal.
Notes: Also sells wholesale.
Map Ref: E, C2

EHrv HARVEYS GARDEN PLANTS ⊠ ✈ ♿ € ♿
Great Green, Thurston, Bury St Edmunds,
Suffolk, IP31 3SJ
Ⓣ (01359) 233363
Ⓕ (01359) 233363 & answerphone
Ⓔ admin@harveysgardenplants.co.uk
Ⓦ www.harveysgardenplants.co.uk
Contact: Roger Harvey
Opening Times: 0930-1630 Tue-Sat, 10th Jan-23rd Dec.
Min Mail Order UK: 6 plants + p&p
Min Mail Order EU: Please enquire.
Cat. Cost: 7 × 2nd class.
Credit Cards: All major credit/debit cards
Specialities: *Helleborus*, *Anemone*, *Epimedium*, *Euphorbia*, *Eryngium*, *Astrantia*, *Pulmonaria* & other herbaceous perennials. Woodland plants, heleniums. Nat. Collection of *Helenium* being set up with NCCPG.
Map Ref: E, C2 **OS Grid Ref:** 660939

EHul HULL FARM ⊠ ♿
Spring Valley Lane, Ardleigh,
Colchester, Essex,
CO7 7SA
Ⓣ (01206) 230045
Ⓕ (01206) 230820
Contact: J Fryer & Sons
Opening Times: 1000-1600 Mon-Sat, excl. Xmas.
Min Mail Order UK: £40.00 + p&p
Cat. Cost: 5 × 2nd class.
Credit Cards: MasterCard Visa
Specialities: Conifers, grasses.
Notes: Also sells wholesale.
Map Ref: E, C3 **OS Grid Ref:** GR043274

EJRN JOHN RAY NURSERY € ♿
36 Station Road, Braintree, Essex,
CM7 3QJ
Ⓜ 07866 296531
Ⓕ (01376) 322484
Contact: Brian James
Opening Times: 0900-1730 Sat, 1030-1630 Sun & B/Hol.
Cat. Cost: None issued.
Credit Cards: None
Specialities: *Pittosporum.*
Notes: Also sells wholesale.

EJWh JILL WHITE ⊠ ♿ ♿
St Davids', Recreation Way, Brightlingsea,
Essex, CO7 ONJ
Ⓣ (01206) 303547
Contact: Jill White
Opening Times: By appt. only.
Min Mail Order UK: Nmc
Cat. Cost: Sae.
Credit Cards: None
Specialities: *Cyclamen* species esp. *Cyclamen parviflorum. Cyclamen elegans*. Also seed.
Notes: Also sells wholesale.
Map Ref: E, D3

EKen KENWICK FARMHOUSE NURSERIES ⊠ ♿ ◆
Kenwick Road, Louth, Lincolnshire,
LN11 8NW
Ⓣ (01507) 606469
Ⓕ (01507) 606469
Ⓔ info@kenwicknursery.co.uk
Ⓦ www.kenwicknursery.co.uk
Contact: Janet Elmhirst
Opening Times: 0930-1700 (dusk in winter)Tue-Sat, closed Mon except B/hol. 1000-1600 Sun. Closed Jan.
Min Mail Order UK: £12.00
Cat. Cost: 2 × 1st class.
Credit Cards: None

Specialities: Hardy plants, grown in small quantities.
Notes: Mail order only if stock is available.
Map Ref: E, A2 **OS Grid Ref:** TF342853

EKMF **KATHLEEN MUNCASTER FUCHSIAS** ♿
18 Field Lane, Morton, Gainsborough, Lincolnshire, DN21 3BY
Ⓣ (01427) 612329
Ⓔ jim@smuncaster.freeserve.co.uk
Ⓦ www.kathleenmuncasterfuchsias.co.uk
Contact: Kathleen Muncaster
Opening Times: 1000-dusk Thu-Tue. After mid-Jun please phone to check.
Cat. Cost: 2 × 1st class.
Credit Cards: None
Specialities: *Fuchsia*. Nat. Collection of Hardy *Fuchsia* (full status).
Map Ref: E, A1

ELan **LANGTHORNS PLANTERY** ⊠ ♿
High Cross Lane West, Little Canfield, Dunmow, Essex, CM6 1TD
Ⓣ (01371) 872611
Ⓕ 0871 661 4093
Ⓔ info@langthorns.com
Ⓦ www.langthorns.com
Contact: E Cannon
Opening Times: 1000-1700 (or dusk if earlier) 7 days excl. Xmas fortnight.
Min Mail Order UK: Nmc
Cat. Cost: £1.50.
Credit Cards: Visa Access Switch MasterCard Delta
Specialities: Wide general range with many unusual plants.
Notes: Mail order 9cm perennials, 2 & 3 litre shrubs.
Map Ref: E, D2 **OS Grid Ref:** TL592204

ELar **LARKSPUR NURSERY** ⊠
Fourways, Dog Drove South, Holbeach Drove South, Spalding, Lincolnshire, PE12 0SD
Ⓣ (01406) 330830
Ⓔ info@larkspur-nursery.co.uk
Ⓦ www.larkspur-nursery.co.uk
Contact: Ashley Ramsbottom
Opening Times: Mail order only. Open by prior arrangement only.
Min Mail Order UK: Nmc
Cat. Cost: 2 × 1st class.
Credit Cards: None
Specialities: Delphiniums. Some varieties in small quantities. Order early to avoid disappointment.
Notes: Plants despatched from end April in 8cm pots. See website for details.

ELau **LAUREL FARM HERBS** ⊠ ♿
Main Road, Kelsale, Saxmundham, Suffolk, IP13 2RG
Ⓣ (01728) 668223
Ⓔ chris@laurelfarmherbs.co.uk
Ⓦ www.theherbfarm.co.uk
Contact: Chris Seagon
Opening Times: 1000-1700 Wed-Mon 1st Mar-31st Oct. 1000-1500 Wed-Fri, 15th Nov-28th Feb. All other times, please phone first.
Min Mail Order UK: 6 plants + p&p
Min Mail Order EU: 12 plants
Cat. Cost: Online only.
Credit Cards: Visa MasterCard Switch Delta
Specialities: Herbs esp. rosemary, thyme, lavender, mint, comfrey & sage.
Notes: Mail orders accepted by email, phone or post.
Map Ref: E, C3

ELon **LONG HOUSE PLANTS** ♿
The Long House, Church Road, Noak Hill, Romford, Essex, RM4 1LD
Ⓣ (01708) 371719
Ⓕ (01708) 346649
Contact: Tim Carter
Opening Times: 1000-1700 Fri, Sat, Sun & b/hols Mar-Oct.
Cat. Cost: 2 × 1st class.
Credit Cards: All major credit/debit cards
Specialities: Interesting range of choice shrubs, grasses & herbaceous perennials. Many unusual varieties.
Map Ref: E, D2 **OS Grid Ref:** TQ554194

EMac **FIRECREST (TREES & SHRUBS NURSERY)** ⊠ € ♿
Hall Road, Little Bealings, Woodbridge, Suffolk, IP13 6LU
Ⓣ (01473) 625937
Ⓕ (01473) 625937
Ⓔ mac@firecrest.org.uk
Ⓦ www.firecrest.org.uk
Contact: Mac McGregor
Opening Times: 0830-1700 Mon-Fri, 1230 Sat.
Min Mail Order UK: Nmc
Cat. Cost: 2 × 1st class (bare root only).
Credit Cards: None
Specialities: Trees & shrubs.
Notes: Also sells wholesale.

KEY
⊠ Mail order to UK or EU — Delivers to shows
✈ Exports beyond EU — € Euro accepted
♿ Accessible by wheelchair — ◆ See Display advertisement

E

EMal **MARSHALL'S MALMAISON**
Hullwood Barn, Shelley, Ipswich, Suffolk, IP7 5RE
Ⓣ (01473) 822400
Ⓔ marshalls.malmaisons@btinternet.com
Contact: J M Marshall
Opening Times: By appt. only.
Min Mail Order UK: £24.00 incl. p&p
Min Mail Order EU: £35.00 incl. p&p
Cat. Cost: 1st class sae.
Credit Cards: None
Specialities: Nat. Collection of Malmaison Carnations.
Notes: Also sells wholesale.
Map Ref: E,C3 **OS Grid Ref:** TM006394

EMan **MANOR NURSERY**
Thaxted Road, Wimbish, Saffron Walden, Essex, CB10 2UT
Ⓣ (01799) 513481
Ⓕ (01799) 513481
Contact: William Lyall
Opening Times: 0900-1700 summer. 0900-1600 winter. Closed Xmas.
Cat. Cost: 4 × 2nd class.
Credit Cards: Visa Access Switch EuroCard MasterCard
Specialities: Uncommon perennials, grasses, hardy geraniums, *Sedum* & cottage garden plants. Variegated & coloured foliage plants. Many newly introduced cultivars.
Map Ref: E, C2

EMar **LESLEY MARSHALL**
Uncommon Garden Plants, Islington Lodge Cottage, Tilney All Saints, King's Lynn, Norfolk, PE34 4SF
Ⓣ (01553) 765103
Ⓔ daylilies@tiscali.co.uk
Contact: Lesley & Peter Marshall
Opening Times: 0930-1800 Mon, Wed, Fri-Sun Apr-Sep.
Min Mail Order UK: Nmc
Cat. Cost: 3 × 1st class.
Credit Cards: None
Specialities: Uncommon garden plants, hardy perennials & plants for foliage effect. *Hemerocallis*. Some plants available in small quantities only.
Notes: Mail order daylilies only.
Map Ref: E, B1

EMcA **M MCARD (SEEDS)**
39 West Road, Pointon, Sleaford, Lincolnshire, NG34 0NA
Ⓣ (01529) 240765
Ⓕ (01529) 240765
Ⓔ seeds@smmcard.com
Ⓦ www.smmcard.com
Contact: Susan McArd
Opening Times: Not open. Mail order only.
Min Mail Order UK: Nmc
Min Mail Order EU: Nmc
Cat. Cost: 2 × 2nd class.
Credit Cards: None
Specialities: Unusual & giant vegetables esp. tree (Egyptian) onion. Seeds & plants.
Notes: Also sells wholesale.

EMFW **MICKFIELD WATERGARDEN CENTRE LTD**
Debenham Road, Mickfield, Stowmarket, Suffolk, IP14 5LP
Ⓣ (01449) 711336
Ⓕ (01449) 711018
Ⓔ mike@mickfield.co.uk
Ⓦ www.watergardenshop.co.uk
Contact: Mike Burch
Opening Times: 0930-1700 7 days.
Min Mail Order UK: Nmc
Min Mail Order EU: £25.00 + p&p
Cat. Cost: Free.
Credit Cards: Visa Access MasterCard Switch
Specialities: Hardy aquatics, *Nymphaea* & moisture lovers.
Notes: Also sells wholesale.
Map Ref: E, C3 **OS Grid Ref:** TM141616

EMic **MICKFIELD HOSTAS**
The Poplars, Mickfield, Stowmarket, Suffolk, IP14 5LH
Ⓣ (01449) 711576
Ⓕ (01449) 711576
Ⓔ mickfieldhostas@btconnect.com
Ⓦ www.mickfieldhostas.co.uk
Contact: Mr & Mrs R L C Milton
Opening Times: For specified dates see catalogue or website.
Min Mail Order UK: Nmc
Min Mail Order EU: Nmc
Cat. Cost: 4 × 1st class.
Credit Cards: Visa MasterCard
Specialities: *Hosta*, over 1000 varieties (some subject to availability) mostly from USA. New varieties become available during the season.
Map Ref: E, C3

EMil **MILL RACE GARDEN CENTRE**
New Road, Aldham, Colchester, Essex, CO6 3QT
Ⓣ (01206) 242521
Ⓕ (01206) 242073
Ⓔ admin@millracegardencentre.co.uk
Ⓦ www.millracegardencentre.co.uk
Contact: Steve Canham

Opening Times: 0900-1730 7 days.
Credit Cards: All major credit/debit cards
Specialities: Around 4000 varieties of plants always in stock.
Map Ref: E, C2 **OS Grid Ref:** TL918268

EMon MONKSILVER NURSERY ⊠ €
Oakington Road, Cottenham, Cambridgeshire, CB4 8TW
Ⓣ (01954) 251555
Ⓕ (01223) 309119
Ⓔ plants@monksilver.com
Ⓦ www.monksilver.com
Contact: Joe Sharman & Alan Leslie
Opening Times: 1000-1600 Fri & Sat 1st Mar-30th Jun, 23rd Sep & Fri & Sat Oct.
Min Mail Order UK: £15.00 + p&p
Min Mail Order EU: £30.00 + p&p
Cat. Cost: 8 × 1st class.
Credit Cards: None
Specialities: Herbaceous plants, grasses, *Anthemis*, *Arum*, *Helianthus*, *Lamium*, *Nepeta*, *Monarda*, *Salvia*, *Vinca*, sedges & variegated plants. Many NCCPG 'Pink Sheet' plants. Ferns.
Map Ref: E, C2 **OS Grid Ref:** TQ437665

EMui KEN MUIR LTD ⊠
Honeypot Farm, Rectory Road, Weeley Heath, Essex, CO16 9BJ
Ⓣ 0870 7479111
Ⓕ (01255) 831534
Ⓔ info@kenmuir.co.uk
Ⓦ www.kenmuir.co.uk
Contact: Ming Yang, Claire Higgins
Opening Times: 1000-1600.
Min Mail Order UK: Nmc
Cat. Cost: Free.
Credit Cards: Visa Access Switch
Specialities: Fruit.
Notes: Also sells wholesale.
Map Ref: E, D3

ENBC NORFOLK BAMBOO COMPANY ⊠
Vine Cottage, The Drift, Ingoldisthorpe, King's Lynn, Norfolk, PE31 6NW
Ⓣ (01485) 543935
Ⓕ (01485) 543314
Ⓔ Lewdyer@hotmail.com
Ⓦ www.norfolkbamboo.co.uk
Contact: Lewis Dyer
Opening Times: 1000-1800 Fri, Apr-Sep, or by appt.
Min Mail Order UK: £12.00 + p&p
Cat. Cost: 1 × 1st class sae for price list.
Credit Cards: None
Specialities: Bamboos.
Map Ref: E, B2 **OS Grid Ref:** TF683333

ENor NORFOLK LAVENDER ⊠ ✈ ♿
Caley Mill, Heacham, King's Lynn, Norfolk, PE31 7JE
Ⓣ (01485) 570384
Ⓕ (01485) 571176
Ⓔ admin@norfolk-lavender.co.uk
Ⓦ www.norfolk-lavender.co.uk
Contact: Henry Head
Opening Times: 0930-1700 7 days, Apr-Oct. 0930-1600 7 days, Nov-Mar.
Min Mail Order UK: £15.00 + p&p
Min Mail Order EU: £15.00 + p&p
Cat. Cost: Free.
Credit Cards: All major credit/debit cards
Specialities: Nat. Collection of *Lavandula*.
Map Ref: E, B2

ENot NOTCUTTS NURSERIES € ♿
Woodbridge, Suffolk, IP12 4AF
Ⓣ (01394) 445400
Ⓕ (01394) 445440
Ⓔ sales@notcutts.co.uk
Ⓦ www.notcutts.co.uk
Contact: Plant Adviser
Opening Times: Garden centres 0900-1800 Mon-Sat & 1030-1630 Sun. Check for local variations and late night openings.
Cat. Cost: £6.00 + £1.25
Credit Cards: Maestro Visa Access Connect
Specialities: Wide general range. Nat. Collection of *Hibiscus* (not available for public viewing during Woodbridge redevelopment).
Notes: Notcutts plants available from their 13 garden centres. Also sells wholesale.
Map Ref: E, C3 **OS Grid Ref:** TM268487

EOHP OLD HALL PLANTS ⊠ €
1 The Old Hall, Barsham, Beccles, Suffolk, NR34 8HB
Ⓣ (01502) 717475
Ⓔ info@oldhallplants.co.uk
Ⓦ www.oldhallplants.co.uk
Contact: Janet Elliott
Opening Times: By appt. only. Phone first.
Min Mail Order UK: Nmc
Min Mail Order EU: Nmc
Cat. Cost: 4 × 1st class.
Credit Cards: None
Specialities: A variety of rare herbs, house plants, *Plectranthus* & *Streptocarpus*.
Notes: Partial wheelchair access.
Map Ref: E, C3 **OS Grid Ref:** TM395904

KEY
⊠ Mail order to UK or EU — Delivers to shows
✈ Exports beyond EU — € Euro accepted
♿ Accessible by wheelchair — ◆ See Display advertisement

E

EOrn **Ornamental Conifers** ◆
22 Chapel Road, Terrington St Clement, King's Lynn, Norfolk, PE34 4ND
Ⓣ (01553) 828874
Ⓕ (01553) 828874
Ⓦ www.japanesegardenplants.co.uk/
Contact: Peter Rotchell
Opening Times: 0930-1700 Thu-Tue, closed Wed. Closed 20th Dec-2nd Feb.
Credit Cards: None
Specialities: Conifers.
Map Ref: E, B1

EPau **Paugers Plants** ♿
Bury Road, Depden, Bury St Edmunds, Suffolk, IP29 4BU
Ⓣ (01284) 850527
Ⓔ geraldinea@freenetname.co.uk
Ⓦ www.paugersplants.co.uk
Contact: Geraldine Arnold
Opening Times: 0900-1730 Wed-Sat, 1000-1700 Sun & B/hols, 1st Mar-30th Nov.
Cat. Cost: None issued.
Credit Cards: None
Specialities: Hardy shrubs & perennials in large or small quantities.
Notes: Also sells wholesale.
Map Ref: E, C2 **OS Grid Ref:** TL783568

EPem **Pembroke Farm Nursery** ⊠ € ♿
Pembroke Farm, Barway, Ely, Cambridgeshire, CB7 5UB
Ⓣ (01353) 722903
Ⓔ Pemcacti@aol.com/enquiries@cactiandsucculents.co.uk
Ⓦ www.cactiandsucculents.co.uk
Contact: Richard & Sheena Drane
Opening Times: Please phone or check website for opening times.
Min Mail Order UK: Nmc
Cat. Cost: 1 × 1st class.
Credit Cards: None
Specialities: Cacti & succulents incl. *Agave*, *Aloe* & *Sempervivum*. Many plants are available in small quantities only.
Notes: Also sells wholesale.
Map Ref: E, C2

EPfP **The Place for Plants** € ♿
East Bergholt Place, East Bergholt, Suffolk, CO7 6UP
Ⓣ (01206) 299224
Ⓕ (01206) 299224
Ⓔ sales@placeforplants.co.uk
Contact: Rupert & Sara Eley
Opening Times: 1000-1700 (or dusk if earlier) 7 days. Closed Easter Sun. Garden open Mar-Oct.
Cat. Cost: 2 × 1st class.
Credit Cards: All major credit/debit cards
Specialities: Wide range of specialist & popular plants. 15 acre mature garden.
Map Ref: E, C3

EPGN **Park Green Nurseries** ⊠
Wetheringsett, Stowmarket, Suffolk, IP14 5QH
Ⓣ (01728) 860139
Ⓕ (01728) 861277
Ⓔ nurseries@parkgreen.fsnet.co.uk
Ⓦ www.parkgreen.co.uk
Contact: Richard & Mary Ford
Opening Times: 1000-1600 Mon-Sat, 1 Mar-30 Sep.
Min Mail Order UK: Nmc
Min Mail Order EU: Nmc
Cat. Cost: 4 × 1st class.
Credit Cards: Visa MasterCard Delta Switch
Specialities: *Hosta*, ornamental grasses & herbaceous.
Notes: Mail order *Hosta* only.
Map Ref: E, C3 **OS Grid Ref:** TM136644

EPla **P W Plants** ⊠ ♿
Sunnyside, Heath Road, Kenninghall, Norfolk, NR16 2DS
Ⓣ (01953) 888212
Ⓕ (01953) 888212
Ⓔ pw@hardybamboo.com
Ⓦ www.hardybamboo.com
Contact: Paul Whittaker
Opening Times: Every Fri & last Sat in every month, plus all Sats Apr-Sep.
Min Mail Order UK: Nmc
Min Mail Order EU: Nmc
Cat. Cost: 5 × 1st class.
Credit Cards: All major credit/debit cards
Specialities: Bamboos, grasses, choice shrubs & perennials.
Notes: Does not deliver to Chelsea Show.
Map Ref: E, C3 **OS Grid Ref:** TM036846

EPot **Pottertons Nursery** ⊠ € ♿
Moortown Road, Nettleton, Caistor, Lincolnshire, LN7 6HX
Ⓣ (01472) 851714
Ⓕ (01472) 852580
Ⓔ sales@pottertons.co.uk
Ⓦ www.pottertons.co.uk
Contact: Robert Potterton
Opening Times: 0900-1600 7 days.
Min Mail Order UK: Nmc
Min Mail Order EU: Nmc
Cat. Cost: £2.00 in stamps.
Credit Cards: Maestro MasterCard Visa

Specialities: Alpines, dwarf bulbs & woodland plants. Hardy orchids & *Pleione*.
Map Ref: E, A1 **OS Grid Ref:** TA091001

EPPr **THE PLANTSMAN'S PREFERENCE** ⊠ ♠ ♿
(Office) Lynwood, Hopton Road, Garboldisham, Diss, Norfolk, IP22 2QN
Ⓣ (01953) 681439 (office)
Ⓜ (07799) 855559 (nursery)
Ⓔ info@plantpref.co.uk
Ⓦ www.plantpref.co.uk
Contact: Jenny & Tim Fuller
Opening Times: 0930-1700 Fri, Sat & Sun Mar-Oct. Other times by appt.
Min Mail Order UK: £15.00
Min Mail Order EU: £30.00
Cat. Cost: 4 × 1st class/IRCs or online.
Credit Cards: All major credit/debit cards
Specialities: Hardy geraniums (450), grasses & sedges (600+). Unusual & interesting perennials. Nat. Collection of *Molinia*.
Notes: Nursery is at Hall Farm, Church Road, South Lopham, Diss.
Map Ref: E, C3 **OS Grid Ref:** TM041819

EPts **POTASH NURSERY** ⊠ ♠ ♿
Cow Green, Bacton, Stowmarket, Suffolk, IP14 4HJ
Ⓣ (01449) 781671
Ⓔ enquiries@potashnursery.co.uk
Ⓦ www.potashnursery.co.uk
Contact: M W Clare
Opening Times: Pre-ordered plants can be collected by appt. only.
Min Mail Order UK: £12.00
Cat. Cost: 4 × 1st class.
Credit Cards: Visa Delta MasterCard
Specialities: *Fuchsia*.
Map Ref: E, C3 **OS Grid Ref:** TM0565NE

EPyc **PENNYCROSS PLANTS** ♠
Earith Road, Colne, Huntingdon, Cambridgeshire, PE28 3NL
Ⓣ (01487) 841520
Ⓔ plants@pennycross99.freeserve.co.uk
Contact: Janet M Buist
Opening Times: 1000-1600 Mon-Fri, 1st Mar-31st Oct by appt.
Credit Cards: None
Specialities: Hardy perennials. Salvias. Some plants available in ltd. quantities only.
Map Ref: E, C2 **OS Grid Ref:** TL378759

EQua **QUAYMOUNT NURSERY** ⊠ ♿
The Row, Wereham, King's Lynn, Norfolk, PE33 9AY
Ⓣ (01366) 500691
Ⓕ (01366) 500611
Ⓔ info@quaymountplants.co.uk
Ⓦ www.quaymountplants.co.uk
Contact: Paul Markwell
Opening Times: 0900-1700 (or dusk if earlier) Mon-Fri, 1000-1600 Sat & Sun. Closed Sun Dec & Jan.
Min Mail Order UK: Nmc
Cat. Cost: 2 × 1st class.
Credit Cards: All major credit/debit cards
Specialities: Wide range of specialist & popular plants.
Notes: Specimen plants collection only. Also sells wholesale.
Map Ref: E, B2 **OS Grid Ref:** TF679006

ERas **RASELL'S NURSERIES** ♿
Little Bytham, Grantham, Lincolnshire, NG33 4QY
Ⓣ (01780) 410345
Ⓕ (01780) 410475
Contact: Carole Wilson
Opening Times: 0900-1700 Mon-Sat, 1000-1600 Sun.
Cat. Cost: None issued.
Credit Cards: All major credit/debit cards
Map Ref: E, B1 **OS Grid Ref:** TF016178

ERCP **ROSE COTTAGE PLANTS** ⊠ ♠ ♿
Bay Tree Farm, Epping Green, Essex, CM16 6PU
Ⓣ (01992) 573775
Ⓕ (01992) 561198
Ⓔ anne@rosecottageplants.co.uk
Ⓦ www.rosecottageplants.co.uk
Contact: Anne & Jack Barnard
Opening Times: 1400-2000 (or dusk if earlier) Wed, Mar-Oct or by appt.
Min Mail Order UK: £20.00
Cat. Cost: Online only.
Credit Cards: All major credit/debit cards
Specialities: Bulbs.
Notes: Mail order bulbs only. Separate mail order catalogue available online from May.
Map Ref: E, B1 **OS Grid Ref:** TL435053

ERea **READS NURSERY** ⊠ ✈ ♿
Hales Hall, Loddon, Norfolk, NR14 6QW
Ⓣ (01508) 548395
Ⓕ (01508) 548040
Ⓔ plants@readsnursery.co.uk
Ⓦ www.readsnursery.co.uk
Contact: Stephen Read

KEY
⊠ Mail order to UK or EU ♠ Delivers to shows
✈ Exports beyond EU € Euro accepted
♿ Accessible by wheelchair ◆ See Display advertisement

E

Opening Times: 1000-1630 (dusk if earlier) Tue-Sat, 1100-1600 Sun & B/hols Easter-end Sep & by appt.
Min Mail Order UK: Nmc
Min Mail Order EU: £10.00 + p&p
Cat. Cost: 4 × 1st class.
Credit Cards: All major credit/debit cards
Specialities: Conservatory/greenhouse plants, flowering & fruiting. *Citrus*, figs grapevines. Unusual fruits & nuts. UK grown. Nat. Collections of *Citrus*, figs & grapevines. Some rarer plants in small quantities only.
Notes: Mostly accessible by wheelchair, some gravel paths.
Map Ref: E, B3 **OS Grid Ref:** TM369960

ERhR RHODES & ROCKLIFFE ⊠ ✈ €
2 Nursery Road, Nazeing, Essex, EN9 2JE
Ⓣ (01992) 451598 (office hours)
Ⓕ (01992) 440673
Ⓔ RRBegonias@aol.com
Contact: David Rhodes or John Rockliffe
Opening Times: By appt.
Min Mail Order UK: £2.50 + p&p
Min Mail Order EU: £5.00 + p&p
Cat. Cost: 2 × 1st class.
Credit Cards: None
Specialities: *Begonia* species & hybrids. Nat. Collection of *Begonia*. Plants propagated to order.
Notes: Mail order Apr-Sep only.
Map Ref: E, D2

ERob ROBIN SAVILL CLEMATIS SPECIALIST ⊠ ✈
(office) The Old Nursery, Butts Green Road, Sandon, Chelmsford, Essex, CM2 7RN
Ⓣ (01245) 224576
Ⓔ robinsavill@blueyonder.co.uk
Contact: Robin Savill
Opening Times: Visitors by appt. only.
Min Mail Order UK: 1 plant + p&p
Min Mail Order EU: 1 plant + p&p
Cat. Cost: £3.50.
Credit Cards: None
Specialities: Over 800 varieties of *Clematis* incl. many unusual species & cvs from around the world. Nat. Collection of *Clematis viticella*.
Notes: Nursery at The Garden Company, Mayes Lane, Sandon CM2 7RW. Also sells wholesale.
Map Ref: E, D2

ERod THE RODINGS PLANTERY ⊠ ✈ ⌂ €
Anchor Lane, Abbess Roding, Essex, CM5 0JW
Ⓣ (01279) 876421
Ⓕ (01279) 876421
Ⓔ janeandandy@therodingsplantery.co.uk
Contact: Jane & Andy Mogridge
Opening Times: By appt. only. Occasional open days, please phone for details.
Min Mail Order UK: £15.00 + p&p
Min Mail Order EU: £500.00 + p&p
Cat. Cost: 3 × 1st class.
Credit Cards: None
Specialities: *Bamboo*. Rare & unusual trees.
Map Ref: E, D2

ERom THE ROMANTIC GARDEN ⊠ ✈ € ♿ ◆
Swannington, Norwich, Norfolk, NR9 5NW
Ⓣ (01603) 261488
Ⓕ (01603) 864231
Ⓔ enquiries@romantic-garden-nursery.co.uk
Ⓦ www.romantic-garden-nursery.co.uk
Contact: John Powles/John Carrick
Opening Times: 1000-1700 Wed, Fri & Sat all year, plus B/Hol Mons.
Min Mail Order UK: £5.00 + p&p
Min Mail Order EU: £30.00 + p&p
Cat. Cost: 4 × 1st class.
Credit Cards: Visa Access American Express
Specialities: Half-hardy & conservatory. *Buxus* topiary, ornamental standards, large specimens. Hedging.
Notes: Also sells wholesale.
Map Ref: E, B3

ERos ROSEHOLME NURSERY ⊠ ✈ ♿
Roseholme Farm, Howsham, Market Rasen, Lincolnshire, LN7 6JZ
Ⓣ (01652) 678661
Ⓕ (01472) 852450
Ⓔ Pbcenterpr@aol.com
Contact: P B Clayton
Opening Times: Mail order only. By appt. for collection of orders.
Min Mail Order UK: Nmc
Min Mail Order EU: Nmc
Cat. Cost: 2 × 2nd class.
Credit Cards: None
Specialities: Underground lines: bulbs, corms, rhizomes & tubers (esp. *Crocus*, *Iris*).
Notes: Also sells wholesale.
Map Ref: E, A1 **OS Grid Ref:** TA042048

ERou ROUGHAM HALL NURSERIES ⊠ ✈ ⌂ € ◆
Ipswich Road, Rougham, Bury St Edmunds, Suffolk, IP30 9LZ
Ⓣ 0800 970 7516
Ⓕ (01359) 271149
Ⓔ hardyperennials@aol.com
Ⓦ www.roughamhallnurseries.co.uk
Contact: A A & K G Harbutt
Opening Times: 1000-1600 7 days. Closed from Xmas Day to New Year's Day.

Min Mail Order UK: Nmc
Min Mail Order EU: Nmc
Cat. Cost: Free.
Credit Cards: All major credit/debit cards
Specialities: Hardy perennials esp. *Aster* (n-a, n-b & species), *Delphinium*, *Hemerocallis*, *Iris*, *Kniphofia*, *Papaver* & *Phlox*. Nat. Collections of *Delphinium* & gooseberry.
Notes: *Delphinium* list available Apr-Jun. Despatch Jun-Aug. Also sells wholesale.
Map Ref: E, C2

ESCh SHEILA CHAPMAN CLEMATIS ⊠ ♠ ♿
c/o Coveney Nurseries Ltd, 160 Ongar Road, Abridge, Romford, Essex, RM4 1AA
Ⓣ (01708) 688090
Ⓕ (01708) 688090
Ⓔ sheilachapman@hotmail.com
Ⓦ www.sheilachapman.co.uk
Contact: Sheila Chapman
Opening Times: 0930-1700 (or dusk in winter) all year excl. Xmas week.
Min Mail Order UK: Nmc
Cat. Cost: 5 × 2nd class.
Credit Cards: All major credit/debit cards
Specialities: Over 600 varieties of *Clematis*.
Map Ref: E, D2 **OS Grid Ref:** TQ483969

ESgI SEAGATE IRISES ⊠ ✈ € ♿
A17 Long Sutton By-Pass, Long Sutton, Lincolnshire, PE12 9RX
Ⓣ (01406) 365138
Ⓕ (01406) 365447
Ⓔ Sales@irises.co.uk
Ⓦ www.irises.co.uk
Contact: Julian Browse or Wendy Browse
Opening Times: 1000-1700 daily May-Sep. Please phone for appt. Oct-Apr.
Min Mail Order UK: £30.00
Min Mail Order EU: Nmc. Carriage at cost.
Cat. Cost: £3.00 or 6 euros, no stamps pls.
Credit Cards: Maestro Visa MasterCard
Specialities: Different types of *Iris*, bearded, beardless & species hybrids with about 900 varieties in all, both historic & modern. Some only available in small quantities. Many container-grown available to callers.
Notes: Also sells wholesale.
Map Ref: E, B1 **OS Grid Ref:** TF437218

EShb SHRUBLAND PARK NURSERIES ⊠ ♠ € ◆
Coddenham, Ipswich, Suffolk, IP6 9QJ
Ⓣ (01473) 833187
Ⓜ 07890 527744
Ⓕ (01473) 832838
Ⓔ gill@shrublandparknurseries.co.uk
Ⓦ www.shrublandparknurseries.co.uk
Contact: Gill Stitt
Opening Times: 1000-1700 Wed-Sun, Mar-Sep. Oct-Feb, please ring first.
Min Mail Order UK: £10.00
Min Mail Order EU: £25.00
Cat. Cost: 3 × 1st class, free by email.
Credit Cards: All major credit/debit cards. Nochex/Paypal accepted for online payment.
Specialities: Hardy & tender perennials, conservatory plants, houseplants, succulents. Display beds in glasshouse & walled garden.
Notes: For directions phone or see website. Partial wheelchair access. Groups welcome.
Map Ref: E, C3 **OS Grid Ref:** TM128524

ESty STYLE ROSES ⊠ ♠ € ♿
10 Meridian Walk, Holbeach, Spalding, Lincolnshire, PE12 7NR
Ⓣ (01406) 424089
Ⓜ 07932 044093 or 07780 860415
Ⓕ (01406) 424089
Ⓔ styleroses@aol.com
Ⓦ www.styleroses.co.uk
Contact: Chris Styles, Margaret Styles
Opening Times: Vary, please phone.
Min Mail Order UK: Nmc
Min Mail Order EU: Nmc
Cat. Cost: Free.
Credit Cards: All major credit/debit cards
Specialities: Standard & bush roses.
Notes: Export subject to countries' plant health requirements, carriage & export certificates where required charged at cost. Also sells wholesale.
Map Ref: E, B1

ESul BRIAN & PEARL SULMAN ⊠ ♠ ♿
54 Kingsway, Mildenhall, Bury St Edmunds, Suffolk, IP28 7HR
Ⓣ (01638) 712297
Ⓕ (01638) 712297
Ⓔ pearl@sulmanspelargoniums.co.uk
Ⓦ www.sulmanspelargoniums.co.uk
Contact: Pearl Sulman
Opening Times: Mail order only. Not open except for Open Days 6th/7th May & 10th Jun 2006. Phone for information about 2007 dates.
Min Mail Order UK: £20.00
Cat. Cost: 4 × 1st class.
Credit Cards: Visa MasterCard
Specialities: *Pelargonium*. Some varieties only available in small quantities.
Map Ref: E, C2 **OS Grid Ref:** TL715747

KEY
⊠ Mail order to UK or EU ♠ Delivers to shows
✈ Exports beyond EU € Euro accepted
♿ Accessible by wheelchair ◆ See Display advertisement

E

ETho **Thorncroft Clematis Nursery** ⊠ ✈ ⌂ ♿
The Lings, Reymerston,
Norwich, Norfolk,
NR9 4QG
Ⓣ (01953) 850407
Ⓕ (01953) 851788
Ⓔ sales@thorncroft.co.uk
Ⓦ www.thorncroft.co.uk
Contact: Ruth P Gooch
Opening Times: 1000-1600 Tue-Sat all year, closed Sun & Mon. Open B/hol Mon.
Min Mail Order UK: Nmc
Min Mail Order EU: Nmc
Cat. Cost: 6 × 2nd class.
Credit Cards: Maestro MasterCard Solo Visa Delta
Specialities: *Clematis.*
Notes: Does not export to USA, Canada or Australia.
Map Ref: E, B3 **OS Grid Ref:** TG039062

ETod **Todd's Botanics** ⊠ ⌂ ♿
West Street, Coggeshall, Colchester, Essex, CO6 1NT
Ⓣ (01376) 561212
Ⓜ 07970 643711
Ⓕ (01376) 561212
Ⓔ info@toddsbotanics.co.uk
Ⓦ www.toddsbotanics.co.uk
Contact: Emma Macdonald
Opening Times: 0900-1700 Tue-Sun.
Min Mail Order UK: £20.00
Cat. Cost: 2 × 1st class.
Credit Cards: All major credit/debit cards
Specialities: Hardy exotics, herbaceous. Bamboos, olives, palms, ferns, grasses, *Canna* & *Hedychium.*
Notes: Also sells wholesale.
Map Ref: E, D2 **OS Grid Ref:** TL843224

EUnu **Unusual Herbs and Edibles** ⊠
23 Mill Lane, Wrentham,
Beccles, Suffolk,
NR34 7JQ
Ⓣ (01502) 675364
Ⓔ laurenrayner@aol.com
Ⓦ www.unusualherbsandedibles.co.uk
Contact: Lauren Rayner
Opening Times: By appt. only. Please email or phone first.
Min Mail Order UK: Nmc
Min Mail Order EU: Nmc
Cat. Cost: Online only.
Credit Cards: Credit card payment available online via Nochex & Paypal.
Specialities: Much stock available in small quantities only.

EWes **West Acre Gardens** ⌂ ♿
West Acre, King's Lynn, Norfolk, PE32 1UJ
Ⓣ (01760) 755562
Contact: J J Tuite
Opening Times: 1000-1700 7 days 1st Feb-30th Nov. Other times by appt.
Cat. Cost: None issued.
Credit Cards: Visa MasterCard Delta Switch
Specialities: Very wide selection of herbaceous & other garden plants incl. *Rhodohypoxis* & *Primula auricula.*
Map Ref: E, B1 **OS Grid Ref:** TF792182

EWin **Winter Flora Plant Centre** ♿
Hall Farm, Weston, Beccles, Suffolk,
NR34 8TT
Ⓣ (01502) 716810
Ⓜ 07771 882613
Ⓕ (01502) 716666
Ⓔ retail@goosegreennurseries.co.uk
Ⓦ www.goosegreennurseries.co.uk
Contact: Stephen Malster
Opening Times: 1000-1700 Mon-Sun all year. Ring for Xmas opening times.
Cat. Cost: Online only.
Credit Cards: All major credit/debit cards
Specialities: All plants grown in large quantities.
Notes: Also sells wholesale.
Map Ref: E, C3 **OS Grid Ref:** TM423878

EWld **Woodlands**
Peppin Lane, Fotherby, Louth, Lincolnshire, LN11 0UW
Ⓣ (01507) 603586
Ⓜ 07866 161864
Ⓔ annbobarmstrong@tesco.net
Contact: Ann Armstrong
Opening Times: Flexible, but please phone or email to avoid disappoinment.
Cat. Cost: None issued.
Credit Cards: None
Specialities: Small but interesting range of unusual plants, especially woodland and *Salvia*, all grown on the nursery in limited quantity.
Notes: Mature garden, art gallery & refreshments.
Map Ref: E, A2 **OS Grid Ref:** TF322918

EWll **The Walled Garden** ♿ ◆
Park Road, Benhall, Saxmundham, Suffolk, IP17 1JB
Ⓣ (01728) 602510
Ⓕ (01728) 602510
Ⓔ jim@thewalledgarden.co.uk
Ⓦ www.thewalledgarden.co.uk
Contact: Jim Mountain
Opening Times: 0930-1700 Tue-Sun Mar-Oct, Tue-Sat Nov-Feb.

Cat. Cost: 2 × 1st class.
Credit Cards: All major credit/debit cards
Specialities: Tender & hardy perennials, over 1000 varieties, & wall shrubs.
Map Ref: E, C3 **OS Grid Ref:** TM371613

EWsh **WESTSHORES NURSERIES** ⊠
82 West Street, Winterton,
Lincolnshire,
DN15 9QF
Ⓣ (01724) 733940
Ⓔ westshnur@aol.com
Ⓦ www.westshores.co.uk
Contact: Gail & John Summerfield
Opening Times: 0930-1800 (or dusk) w/ends & B/hols, 1st Mar-31st Oct. Other times by appt.
Min Mail Order UK: £15.00
Credit Cards: All major credit/debit cards
Specialities: Ornamental grasses & herbaceous perennials.
Map Ref: E, A1

EWTr **WALNUT TREE GARDEN NURSERY** ⊠ €
Flymoor Lane, Rocklands, Attleborough,
Norfolk, NR17 1BP
Ⓣ (01953) 488163
Ⓕ (01953) 483187
Ⓔ info@wtgn.co.uk
Ⓦ www.wtgn.co.uk
Contact: Jim Paine & Clare Billington
Opening Times: 0900-1800 Tue-Sun Feb-Nov & B/hols.
Min Mail Order UK: £30.00
Cat. Cost: 4 × 1st class.
Credit Cards: Visa MasterCard Switch Solo
Map Ref: E, B1 **OS Grid Ref:** TL978973

SCOTLAND

GAbr **ABRIACHAN NURSERIES** ⊠ 🛈 ♿
Loch Ness Side, Inverness, Inverness-shire,
IV3 8LA
Ⓣ (01463) 861232
Ⓕ (01463) 861232
Ⓔ info@lochnessgarden.com
Ⓦ www.lochnessgarden.com
Contact: Mr & Mrs D Davidson
Opening Times: 0900-1900 daily (dusk if earlier) Feb-Nov.
Min Mail Order UK: Nmc
Min Mail Order EU: Nmc
Cat. Cost: 4 × 1st class.
Credit Cards: None
Specialities: Herbaceous, *Primula*, *Helianthemum*, hardy geraniums, *Sempervivum* & *Primula auricula*.
Map Ref: G, B2 **OS Grid Ref:** NH571347

GBin **BINNY PLANTS** ⊠ €
West Lodge, Binny Estate, Ecclesmachen
Road, Nr Broxbourn, West Lothian,
EH52 6NL
Ⓣ (01506) 858931
Ⓕ (01506) 858155
Ⓔ binnyplants@aol.com
Ⓦ www.binnyplants.co.uk
Contact: Billy Carruthers
Opening Times: 1000-1700 7 days. Closed mid-Dec to mid-Jan.
Min Mail Order UK: Nmc
Min Mail Order EU: £25.00
Cat. Cost: £2.00 refundable on ordering.
Credit Cards: American Express Visa MasterCard Switch EuroCard
Specialities: Perennials incl. *Astilbe*, *Geranium*, *Hosta*, *Paeonia* & *Iris*. Plus large selection of grasses & ferns.
Notes: Mail order Oct-Mar only. Also sells wholesale.
Map Ref: G, C3

GBri **BRIDGE END NURSERIES** 🛈 ♿
Gretna Green, Dumfriesshire, DG16 5HN
Ⓣ (01461) 800612
Ⓕ (01461) 800612
Ⓔ enquiries@bridgendnurseries.co.uk
Ⓦ www.bridgendnurseries.co.uk
Contact: R Bird
Opening Times: 0930-1700 all year. Evenings by appt.
Cat. Cost: None issued.
Credit Cards: All major credit/debit cards
Specialities: Hardy cottage garden perennials. Many unusual & interesting varieties.
Map Ref: G, D3

GBuc **BUCKLAND PLANTS** ⊠ € ♿
Whinnieliggate, Kirkcudbright,
Kirkcudbrightshire, DG6 4XP
Ⓣ (01557) 331323
Ⓕ (01557) 331323
Ⓦ www.bucklandplants.co.uk
Contact: Rob or Dina Asbridge
Opening Times: 1000-1700 Thu-Sun 1st Mar-1st Nov.
Min Mail Order UK: £15.00 + p&p
Min Mail Order EU: £50.00 + p&p
Cat. Cost: 3 × 1st class.
Credit Cards: All major credit/debit cards
Specialities: A very wide range of scarce herbaceous & woodland plants incl. *Anemone*,

KEY
⊠ Mail order to UK or EU 🛈 Delivers to shows
✈ Exports beyond EU € Euro accepted
♿ Accessible by wheelchair ◆ See Display advertisement

G

Cardamine, Crocosmia, Erythronium, Helleborus, Lilium, Meconopsis, Primula, Tricyrtis & *Trillium.*
Map Ref: G, D2 **OS Grid Ref:** NX719524

G

GBut BUTTERWORTHS' ORGANIC NURSERY ⊠
Garden Cottage, Auchinleck Estate, Cumnock, Ayrshire, KA18 2LR
Ⓣ (01290) 551088
Ⓜ 07732 254300
Ⓔ butties@webage.co.uk
Ⓦ www.butterworthsorganicnursery.co.uk
Contact: John Butterworth
Opening Times: By appt. only.
Min Mail Order UK: £20.00
Cat. Cost: 2 × 1st class.
Credit Cards: None
Specialities: Fruit trees incl. Scottish apple varieties. Much of stock available in small quantities only. All stock certified organic.
Notes: Partially accessible for wheelchairs.

GCai CAIRNSMORE NURSERY ⊠ ♿
Chapmanton Road, Castle Douglas, Kirkcudbrightshire, DG7 2NU
Ⓣ (01556) 504819
Ⓜ 07980 176458
Ⓔ cairnsmorenursery@hotmail.com
Ⓦ www.cairnsmorenursery.co.uk
Contact: Valerie Smith
Opening Times: 1000-1700, Tue-Sat, Mar-Oct.
Min Mail Order UK: Nmc
Min Mail Order EU: Nmc
Cat. Cost: 4 × 1st class.
Credit Cards: Visa MasterCard
Specialities: Primulas for the garden and cold greenhouse, incl. auriculas. Heucheras and tiarellas.
Map Ref: G, D2 **OS Grid Ref:** NX756637

GCoc JAMES COCKER & SONS ⊠ ♿
Whitemyres, Lang Stracht, Aberdeen, Aberdeenshire, AB15 6XH
Ⓣ (01224) 313261
Ⓕ (01224) 312531
Ⓔ sales@roses.uk.com
Ⓦ www.roses.uk.com
Contact: Alec Cocker
Opening Times: 0900-1730 7 days.
Min Mail Order UK: Nmc
Min Mail Order EU: £5.40 + p&p
Cat. Cost: Free.
Credit Cards: Visa MasterCard Delta Switch Maestro
Specialities: Roses.
Notes: Also sells wholesale.
Map Ref: G, B3

GCra CRAIGIEBURN GARDEN ♿
Craigieburn House, Moffat, Dumfriesshire, DG10 9LF
Ⓣ (01683) 221250
Ⓕ (01683) 221250
Contact: Andrew & Janet Wheatcroft
Opening Times: 1030-1800 Fri, Sat, Sun, Easter-17 Oct 2004. Plus all English & Scottish public holidays. Other times by appt.
Cat. Cost: £1.00.
Credit Cards: None
Specialities: *Meconopsis* plants for damp gardens, herbaceous perennials.
Map Ref: G, D3

GCrs CHRISTIE'S NURSERY ⊠ ✈ € ♿
Downfield, Westmuir, Kirriemuir, Angus, DD8 5LP
Ⓣ (01575) 572977
Ⓕ (01575) 572977
Ⓔ ianchristie@btconnect.com
Ⓦ www.christiealpines.co.uk
Contact: Ian & Ann Christie
Opening Times: Closed to the public, except for Garden Open Days.
Min Mail Order UK: 5 plants + p&p
Min Mail Order EU: On request.
Cat. Cost: 3 × 1st class.
Credit Cards: All major credit/debit cards
Specialities: Alpines, esp. gentians, *Cassiope, Primula, Lewisia*, orchids, *Trillium* & ericaceous.
Map Ref: G, B3

GEdr EDROM NURSERIES ⊠ ♿
Coldingham, Eyemouth, Berwickshire, TD14 5TZ
Ⓣ (01890) 771386
Ⓕ (01890) 71387
Ⓔ info@edromnurseries.co.uk
Ⓦ www.edromnurseries.co.uk
Contact: Mr Terry Hunt
Opening Times: 0900-1700 Mon-Sun, 1 Mar-30 Sep. Other times by appt.
Min Mail Order UK: Nmc
Min Mail Order EU: £20.00
Cat. Cost: 3 × 2nd class. More plants listed online than in printed catalogue.
Credit Cards: Visa MasterCard
Specialities: *Trillium, Arisaema, Primula, Gentiana, Meconopsis, Anemone* & other alpines. *Fritillaria*, hardy orchids.
Map Ref: G, C3 **OS Grid Ref:** NT8866

GFai FAIRHOLM PLANTS ⊠
Fairholm, Larkhall, Lanarkshire, ML9 2UQ
Ⓣ (01698) 881671
Ⓕ (01698) 888135
Ⓔ fairholm.plants@stevenson-hamilton.co.uk

Contact: Mrs J M Hamilton
Opening Times: Apr-Oct by appt.
Min Mail Order UK: Nmc
Cat. Cost: 1 × 2nd class for descriptive list.
Credit Cards: None.
Specialities: *Abutilon* & unusual half-hardy perennials esp. South African. Nat. Collection of *Abutilon* cvs.
Notes: Mail order for young/small plants.
Map Ref: G, C2 **OS Grid Ref:** NS754515

GFor FORDMOUTH CROFT ORNAMENTAL GRASS NURSERY ⊠ ♿
Fordmouth Croft, Meikle Wartle, Inverurie, Aberdeenshire, AB51 5BE
Ⓣ (01467) 671519
Ⓔ Ann-Marie@fmcornamentalgrasses.co.uk
Ⓦ www.fmcornamentalgrasses.co.uk
Contact: Robert & Ann-Marie Grant
Opening Times: Mail order only. Open strictly by appt. only.
Min Mail Order UK: Nmc
Cat. Cost: 2 × 1st class.
Credit Cards: None
Specialities: Grasses, sedges, rushes. Small orders available.
Map Ref: G, B3 **OS Grid Ref:** NJ718302

GGar GARDEN COTTAGE NURSERY ⊠
Tournaig, Poolewe, Achnasheen, Ross-shire, IV22 2LH
Ⓣ (01445) 781777
Ⓔ sales@gcnursery.co.uk
Ⓦ www.gcnursery.co.uk
Contact: Ben Rushbrooke
Opening Times: 1030-1800 Mon-Sat mid Mar-mid Oct or by appt.
Min Mail Order UK: 5 plants + p&p
Cat. Cost: 4 × 2nd class.
Credit Cards: None
Specialities: A wide range of plants esp. those from the southern hemisphere, Asiatic primulas & plants for coastal gardens.
Map Ref: G, A2 **OS Grid Ref:** NG878835

GGGa GLENDOICK GARDENS LTD ⊠ ✈
Glencarse, Perth, Perthshire, PH2 7NS
Ⓣ (01738) 860205
Ⓕ (01738) 860630
Ⓔ sales@glendoick.com
Ⓦ www.glendoick.com
Contact: P A, E P & K N E Cox
Opening Times: 1000-1600 Mon-Fri only, mid-Apr to mid-Jun, otherwise by appt. 1400-1700 1st & 3rd Sun in May. Garden centre open 7 days.
Min Mail Order UK: £40.00 + p&p
Min Mail Order EU: £100.00 + p&p
Cat. Cost: £2.00 or £1.50 stamps
Credit Cards: Visa MasterCard Delta Switch JCB
Specialities: Rhododendrons, azaleas and ericaceous, *Primula* & *Meconopsis*. Plants from wild seed. Many catalogue plants available at garden centre. 3 Nat. Collections.
Notes: Wheelchair access to Garden Centre. Also sells wholesale.
Map Ref: G, C3

GGre GREENHEAD ROSES ⊠ ♿
Greenhead Nursery, Old Greenock Road, Inchinnan, Renfrew, Renfrewshire, PA4 9PH
Ⓣ (0141) 812 0121
Ⓕ (0141) 812 0121
Ⓔ greenheadnursery@aol.com
Contact: C N Urquhart
Opening Times: 1000-1700 7 days.
Min Mail Order UK: Nmc
Min Mail Order EU: Nmc
Cat. Cost: Sae.
Credit Cards: Visa Switch
Specialities: Roses. Wide general range, dwarf conifers, trees, heathers, rhododendrons & azaleas, shrubs, alpines, fruit, hardy herbaceous & spring & summer bedding.
Notes: Mail order available for bush roses throughout year. Also sells wholesale.
Map Ref: G, C2

GKev KEVOCK GARDEN PLANTS & FLOWERS ⊠ ✈ ⌂ €
16 Kevock Road, Lasswade, Midlothian, EH18 1HT
Ⓣ 0131 454 0660
Ⓜ 07811 321585
Ⓕ 0131 454 0660
Ⓔ info@kevockgarden.co.uk
Ⓦ www.kevockgarden.co.uk
Contact: Stella Rankin
Opening Times: Not open. Mail order only.
Min Mail Order UK: £20.00
Min Mail Order EU: £20.00
Cat. Cost: 4 × 1st class.
Credit Cards: Visa MasterCard Switch
Specialities: Chinese & Himalayan plants. *Primula*, *Meconopsis*, *Iris*, woodland plants.
Notes: Also sells wholesale.

GLld LOCHLANDS (HRB LTD) ⊠ ♿
Dundee Road, Forfar, Angus, DD8 1XF
Ⓣ (01307) 463621

KEY
⊠ Mail order to UK or EU ⌂ Delivers to shows
✈ Exports beyond EU € Euro accepted
♿ Accessible by wheelchair ◆ See Display advertisement

G

G

Ⓕ (01307) 469665
Ⓔ vandelft@btinternet.com
Ⓦ lochlands@btinternet.com
Contact: John van Delft
Opening Times: 0830-1730 Mon-Sat, 1030-1630 Sun.
Min Mail Order UK: £25.00
Cat. Cost: Free.
Credit Cards: All major credit/debit cards
Specialities: Camellias.
Notes: Also sells wholesale.
Map Ref: G, C3 **OS Grid Ref:** DD4548

GMac ELIZABETH MACGREGOR ⊠ ✈
Ellenbank, Tongland Road, Kirkcudbright, Dumfries & Galloway, DG6 4UU
Ⓣ (01557) 330620
Ⓕ (01557) 330620
Ⓔ elizabeth@violas.abel.co.uk
Contact: Elizabeth MacGregor
Opening Times: 1000-1700 Mon, Fri & Sat May-Sep, or please phone.
Min Mail Order UK: 6 plants £15.20 + p&p
Min Mail Order EU: £50.00 + p&p
Cat. Cost: 4 × 1st class or 5 × 2nd class.
Credit Cards: Visa MasterCard
Specialities: Violets, violas & violettas, old and new varieties. *Campanula*, *Geranium*, *Eryngium*, *Penstemon*, *Aster*, *Primula*, *Iris* & other unusual herbaceous.
Map Ref: G, D2

GMaP MACPLANTS
Berrybank Nursery, 5 Boggs Holdings, Pencaitland, East Lothian, EH34 5BA
Ⓣ (01875) 341179
Ⓕ (01875) 340842
Ⓔ sales@macplants.co.uk
Ⓦ www.macplants.co.uk
Contact: Claire McNaughton
Opening Times: 1030-1700, 7 days, Mar-end Jul.
Cat. Cost: 4 × 2nd class.
Credit Cards: MasterCard SwitchVisa
Specialities: Herbaceous perennials, alpines, hardy ferns, violas & grasses.
Notes: Nursery partially accessible to wheelchairs. Also sells wholesale.
Map Ref: G, C3 **OS Grid Ref:** NT447703

GPoy POYNTZFIELD HERB NURSERY ⊠ ✈ ♿
Nr Balblair, Black Isle, Dingwall, Ross-shire, IV7 8LX
Ⓣ (01381) 610352. Phone between 1200-1300 & 1800-1900 only.
Ⓕ (01381) 610352
Ⓔ info@poyntzfieldherbs.co.uk
Ⓦ www.poyntzfieldherbs.co.uk
Contact: Duncan Ross
Opening Times: 1300-1700 Mon-Sat 1st Mar-30th Sep, 1300-1700 Sun May-Aug.
Min Mail Order UK: £10.00 + p&p
Min Mail Order EU: £20.00 + p&p
Credit Cards: All major credit/debit cards
Specialities: Over 400 popular, unusual & rare herbs esp. medicinal. Also seeds.
Map Ref: G, B2 **OS Grid Ref:** NH711642

GQue QUERCUS GARDEN PLANTS ♿
Rankeilour Gardens, Rankeilour Estate, Springfield, Fife, KY15 5RE
Ⓣ (01337) 810444
Ⓕ (01337) 810444
Ⓔ colin@quercus.uk.net
Contact: Colin McBeath
Opening Times: 1000-1700 Sat-Wed, Mar-Oct. 1000-1600 Tues & Wed, 1000-1300 Sat, Nov-Mar.
Cat. Cost: 4 × 1st class.
Credit Cards: All major credit/debit cards
Specialities: Easy & unusual plants for contemporary Scottish gardens.
Notes: Delivery service available. Also sells wholesale.
Map Ref: G, C3 **OS Grid Ref:** NO330118

GQui QUINISH GARDEN NURSERY ⊠
Dervaig, Isle of Mull, Argyll, PA75 6QL
Ⓣ (01688) 400344
Ⓕ (01688) 400344
Ⓔ quinishplants@aol.com
Ⓦ www.Q-gardens.org
Contact: Nicholas Reed
Opening Times: By appt. only.
Min Mail Order UK: Nmc
Min Mail Order EU: Nmc
Cat. Cost: 2 × 1st class.
Credit Cards: None
Specialities: Choice garden shrubs & conservatory plants.
Map Ref: G, C1

GSki SKIPNESS PLANTS ⊠ ♿
The Gardens, Skipness, Nr Tarbert, Argyll, PA29 6XU
Ⓣ (01880) 760201
Ⓕ (01880) 760201
Ⓔ info@plants-scotland.co.uk
Ⓦ www.plants-scotland.co.uk
Contact: Bill & Joan McHugh
Opening Times: 0900-1800 Mon-Fri, 0900-1600 Sat-Sun end Mar-Oct.
Min Mail Order UK: Nmc
Min Mail Order EU: Nmc
Cat. Cost: £1.00.
Credit Cards: Visa MasterCard

Specialities: Unusual herbaceous perennials, shrubs, climbers & grasses.
Notes: Also sells wholesale.
Map Ref: G, C2

GTwe **J Tweedie Fruit Trees** ⊠
Maryfield Road Nursery, Nr Terregles, Dumfriesshire, DG2 9TH
Ⓣ (01387) 720880
Contact: John Tweedie
Opening Times: Please ring for times. Collections by appt.
Min Mail Order UK: Nmc
Cat. Cost: Sae.
Credit Cards: None
Specialities: Fruit trees & bushes. A wide range of old & new varieties.
Map Ref: G, D2

GUzu **Uzumara Orchids** ⊠ ✈ €
9 Port Henderson, Gairloch, Ross-shire, IV21 2AS
Ⓣ (01445) 741228
Ⓕ (01445) 741228
Ⓔ i.la_croix@virgin.net
Ⓦ www.uzumaraorchids.com
Contact: Mrs I F La Croix
Opening Times: Mail order only. Open by appt only.
Min Mail Order UK: Nmc
Min Mail Order EU: Nmc
Cat. Cost: Sae.
Credit Cards: None
Specialities: African & Madagascan orchids.

GWCH **Woodside Cottage Herbs** ⊠
Woodside Cottage, Longriggend, Airdrie, Lanarkshire, ML6 7RU
Ⓣ (01236) 843826
Ⓕ (01236) 842545
Ⓔ mail@herbscents.co.uk
Ⓦ www.herbscents.co.uk
Contact: Brenda Brown
Opening Times: Mail order only. Open by appt. only,
Min Mail Order UK: Minimum 10 plants.
Cat. Cost: 4 × 1st class.
Credit Cards: Visa MasterCard Switch Solo
Specialities: Herbs, wildflowers & hardy plants incl. shrubs, grasses & cottage garden flowers.

GWWP **The Weird and Wonderful Plant Co.** ⊠ € ♿
Fenton Barns, Drem, North Berwick, East Lothian, EH39 5BW
Ⓣ (01620) 850755
Ⓔ admin@weirdandwonderfulplant.co.uk
Ⓦ www.weirdandwonderfulplant.co.uk
Contact: Douglas Kerr
Opening Times: Beginning Mar-end Sep, 1100-1700 hours, 7 days.
Min Mail Order UK: Nmc.
Cat. Cost: 2 × 2nd class stamps.
Credit Cards: All major credit/debit cards
Specialities: Rare and unusual hardy perennials, especially 'black' flowered cultivars and old-fashioned varieties.
Notes: Year-round mail order available online. Also sells wholesale.
Map Ref: G, C3 **OS Grid Ref:** NT512817

N. Ireland & Republic

IArd **Ardcarne Garden Centre** € ♿
Ardcarne, Boyle, Co. Roscommon, Ireland
Ⓣ 00 353 (0)7196 67091
Ⓕ 00 353 (0)7196 67341
Ⓔ ardcarne@indigo.ie
Ⓦ www.ardcarnegc.com
Contact: James Wickham, Mary Frances Dwyer, Kirsty Ainge
Opening Times: 0900-1800 Mon-Sat, 1400-1800 Sun & B/hols.
Credit Cards: Access Visa American Express
Specialities: Coastal plants, native & unusual trees, specimen plants & semi-mature trees. Wide general range.
Map Ref: I, B1

IBal **Bali-hai Mail Order Nursery** ⊠ ✈ ⛺ € ♿
42 Largy Road, Carnlough, Ballymena, Co. Antrim, N. Ireland, BT44 0EZ
Ⓣ 028 2888 5289
Ⓕ 028 2888 5976
Ⓔ ianwscroggy@btopenworld.com
Ⓦ www.balihainursery.com
Contact: Mrs M E Scroggy
Opening Times: Mon-Sat by appt. only.
Min Mail Order UK: Nmc
Min Mail Order EU: Nmc
Cat. Cost: £3.00 cheque, made payable to Mrs M.E. Scroggy.
Credit Cards: None
Specialities: *Hosta, Phormium, Rhodohypoxis* & other perennials. Tree ferns.
Notes: Exports beyond EU restricted to bare root perennials, no grasses. Also sells wholesale.
Map Ref: I, A3

KEY
⊠ Mail order to UK or EU ⛺ Delivers to shows
✈ Exports beyond EU € Euro accepted
♿ Accessible by wheelchair ◆ See Display advertisement

I

IBlr **BALLYROGAN NURSERIES** ⊠ € ♿
The Grange, Ballyrogan, Newtownards, Co. Down, N. Ireland, BT23 4SD
Ⓣ (028) 9181 0451 (evenings)
Ⓔ gary.dunlop@btinternet.com
Contact: Gary Dunlop
Opening Times: Only open by appt.
Min Mail Order UK: £10.00 + p&p
Min Mail Order EU: £20.00 + p&p
Cat. Cost: 2 x 1st class.
Credit Cards: None
Specialities: Choice herbaceous. *Agapanthus, Celmisia, Crocosmia, Euphorbia, Meconopsis, Rodgersia, Iris, Dierama, Erythronium, Roscoea* & *Phormium.*
Notes: Also sells wholesale.
Map Ref: I, B3

IClo **CLONMEL GARDEN CENTRE** € ♿
Glenconnor House, Clonmel, Co. Tipperary, Ireland
Ⓣ 00 353 (0)52 23294
Ⓕ 00 353 (0)52 29196
Ⓔ clonmelgardencentre@eircom.net
Contact: Beth, Terry or Chris Hanna
Opening Times: 0900-1800 Mon-Sat, 1100-1800 Sun, 1000-1800 B/hols.
Credit Cards: Visa Access MasterCard Laser
Specialities: Wide general range with choice & unusual trees, shrubs & conifers in small quantities.
Notes: Situated in the grounds of a Georgian country house with extensive, mature gardens. Restaurant. Coach parties welcome. Also sells wholesale.
Map Ref: I, D2

ICro **CROCKNAFEOLA NURSERY** €
Killybegs, Co. Donegal, Ireland
Ⓣ 00 353 (0)74 97 51018
Ⓕ 00 353 (0)74 97 51095
Ⓔ crocknafeola@hotmail.com
Contact: Fionn McKenna
Opening Times: 0900-1800 Mon, Tue, Thu-Sat, closed Wed. 1200-1800 Sun.
Cat. Cost: None issued.
Credit Cards: None
Specialities: Bedding plants, herbaceous perennials, rhododendrons, plants for containers, roses, plus shrubs & hedging for coastal areas.
Map Ref: I, D2

IDee **DEELISH GARDEN CENTRE** ⊠ €
Skibbereen, Co. Cork, Ireland
Ⓣ 00 353 (0)28 21374
Ⓕ 00 353 (0)28 21374
Ⓔ deel@eircom.net
Ⓦ www.deelish.ie
Contact: Bill & Rain Chase
Opening Times: 1000-1300 & 1400-1800 Mon-Sat, 1400-1800 Sun.
Min Mail Order EU: 100 Euros + p&p (Ireland only).
Cat. Cost: Sae.
Credit Cards: Visa Access
Specialities: Unusual plants for the mild coastal climate of Ireland. Conservatory plants. Sole Irish agents for Chase Organic Seeds.
Notes: No mail order outside Ireland.
Map Ref: I, D1

IDic **DICKSON NURSERIES LTD** ⊠ ☒
Milecross Road, Newtownards, Co. Down, N. Ireland, BT23 4SS
Ⓣ (028) 9181 2206
Ⓕ (028) 9181 3366
Ⓔ mail@dickson-roses.co.uk
Ⓦ www.dickson-roses.co.uk
Contact: Linda Stewart
Opening Times: 0800-1230 & 1300-1700 Mon-Thu. 0800-1230 Fri. Closes at 1600 Mon-Thu Dec-Jan.
Min Mail Order UK: Nmc
Min Mail Order EU: £25.00 + p&p
Cat. Cost: Free.
Credit Cards: None
Specialities: Roses esp. modern Dickson varieties. Most varieties are available in small quantities only.
Notes: Also sells wholesale.
Map Ref: I, B3

IFoB **FIELD OF BLOOMS** ⊠ € ♿
Ballymackey, Lisnamoe, Nenagh, Co. Tipperary, Ireland
Ⓣ 067 29974 Ⓜ 08764 06044
Ⓔ guy2002@eircom.ie
Ⓦ www.nenagh.net/main/fieldofblooms.htm
Contact: Guy de Schrijver
Opening Times: Strictly by appt.
Min Mail Order UK: Nmc
Min Mail Order EU: Nmc
Cat. Cost: Free.
Credit Cards: None
Specialities: Hellebores, herbaceous, hardy perennials, ornamental grasses.
Map Ref: 1, C2

IGor **GORTKELLY CASTLE NURSERY** ⊠ €
Upperchurch, Thurles, Co. Tipperary, Ireland
Ⓣ 00 353 (0) 504 54441
Contact: Clare Beumer
Opening Times: Mail order only. Not open to the public.
Min Mail Order UK: Nmc
Min Mail Order EU: Nmc

Cat. Cost: 5 × 1st class (UK), 5 × 48c (Rep. of Ireland).
Credit Cards: None
Specialities: Choice perennials.
Map Ref: I, C2

IHer **HERITAGE BULBS** ⊠ € ◆
Tully Nally, Castle Meath, Co. Westmeath, Ireland
Ⓣ 353 44 62744
Ⓕ 353 44 62746
Ⓔ info@heritagebulbs.com
Ⓦ www.heritagebulbs.com
Contact: Alex Chisholm
Opening Times: Not open. Mail order only. Tullynally Castle Gardens open afternoons in Jun, Jul & Aug.
Min Mail Order UK: Nmc
Min Mail Order EU: Nmc
Cat. Cost: Free.
Credit Cards: MasterCard Visa
Specialities: Rare & historic bulbs (www.heritagebulbs.com) & native bulbs for naturalising (www.wildaboutbulbs.com).
Notes: Also sells wholesale.

ILad **LADYBIRD NURSERY** ⊠
32 Ballykeigle Road, off Moss Road, Nr Ballygowan, County Down, BT23 5SD
Ⓣ (028) 9752 8025
Ⓔ millarjoyce@hotmail.com
Ⓦ www.ladybirdgarden.co.uk
Also sells wholesale
Contact: Joyce Millar
Opening Times: 1400-1830 Thu & Fri, Apr-Sep. 1330-1700 1st Sun of each month. Other times, incl. evening & w/end visits, by appt. Please phone to arrange.
Min Mail Order UK: Nmc
Cat. Cost: 2 × 1st class or free by email.
Credit Cards: None
Specialities: Over 200 varieties of herbaceous perennials & grasses, beneficial for wildlife ranges. Some in small quanitites only.
Notes: Partial wheelchair access. Also sells wholesale.
Map Ref: I, B3 **OS Grid Ref:** J453633

ILis **LISDOONAN HERBS** ⊠ € ♿
98 Belfast Road, Saintfield, Co. Down, N. Ireland, BT24 7HF
Ⓣ (028) 9081 3624
Ⓔ b.pilcher@lisdoonanherbs.co.uk
Ⓦ www.lisdoonanherbs.co.uk
Contact: Barbara Pilcher
Opening Times: Wed & Sat am. For other times, please phone to check.
Min Mail Order UK: Nmc
Min Mail Order EU: Nmc
Cat. Cost: 2 × 1st class.
Credit Cards: None
Specialities: Aromatics, herbs, kitchen garden plants, period plants, some native species. Freshly cut herbs & salads. Some stock available in small quantities only. All peat-free.
Map Ref: I, B3 **OS Grid Ref:** J390624

IMGH **M G H NURSERIES** € ♿
50 Tullyhenan Road, Banbridge, Co. Down, N. Ireland, BT32 4EY
Ⓣ (028) 4062 2795
Contact: Miss M G Heslip
Opening Times: 1000-1800 Thu, Fri & Sat & B/Hol Mons.
Cat. Cost: 3 × 1st class
Credit Cards: None
Specialities: Grafted conifers, holly, maples, box, ornamental trees & flowering shrubs.
Map Ref: I, B3

IPen **PENINSULA PRIMULAS** ⊠ 🚚 €
72 Ballyeasborough Road, Kircubbin, Co. Down, N. Ireland, BT22 1AD
Ⓣ 028 4277 2193
Ⓔ Peninsula.Primulas@btinternet.com
Contact: Philip Bankhead
Opening Times: Mail order only. Not open.
Min Mail Order UK: Nmc
Min Mail Order EU: Nmc
Cat. Cost: Free.
Credit Cards: None
Specialities: Extensive selection of *Primula* species, plus auriculas.
Map Ref: I, B3

IPot **THE POTTING SHED** ⊠ 🚚 € ♿
Bolinaspick, Camolin, Enniscorthy, Co. Wexford, Ireland
Ⓣ 00 353 (0)5393 83629
Ⓕ 00 353 (0)5393 83663
Ⓔ sricher@iol.ie
Ⓦ www.camolinpottingshed.com
Contact: Susan Carrick
Opening Times: 1300-1800, Thu-Sun incl., Mar-Sep 2006. Other times by appt.
Min Mail Order UK: Nmc
Min Mail Order EU: Nmc
Cat. Cost: 3 × 1st class.
Credit Cards: MasterCard Visa
Specialities: Herbaceous & ornamental grasses.
Map Ref: I, C3

KEY		
	⊠ Mail order to UK or EU	🚚 Delivers to shows
	✈ Exports beyond EU	€ Euro accepted
	♿ Accessible by wheelchair	◆ See Display advertisement

I

IPPN **PERENNIAL PLANTS NURSERY** ⊠ €
Nr Ballymaloe, Barnabrow, Midleton, Co. Cork, Ireland
Ⓣ (00) 353 21 465 2122
Ⓕ (00) 353 21 465 2122
Ⓔ perennialplants@eircom.net
Contact: Sandy McCarthy
Opening Times: Please ring for times.
Min Mail Order UK: Nmc
Min Mail Order EU: Nmc
Cat. Cost: None issued.
Credit Cards: None
Specialities: Many unusual herbaceous, ornamental grasses, tender perennials. Some available in small quantities only.
Notes: Will accept payment in sterling.
Map Ref: I, D2 **OS Grid Ref:** W9568

IPPs **PEONY PASSIONS** ⊠ €
The Old School House, Bracknagh, Rathangan, Co. Kildare, Ireland
Ⓣ 00 353 (0)5786 29109
Ⓜ 00 353 (0)8724 48636
Ⓕ 00 353 (0)5786 29109
Ⓔ ciaran.flood@gmail.com
Ⓦ www.peonypassions.com
Contact: Ciaran Flood
Opening Times: Not open. Mail order only.
Min Mail Order UK: £20.00
Min Mail Order EU: £20.00
Cat. Cost: 2 × IRC.
Credit Cards: None
Specialities: Chinese tree peonies. *Paeonia suffruticosa* hybrids. *Paeonia rockii* varieties.
Map Ref: I, C2

IRhd **RINGHADDY DAFFODILS** ⊠ ☒ €
Ringhaddy Road, Killinchy, Newtownards, Co. Down, N. Ireland, BT23 6TU
Ⓣ (028) 9754 1007
Ⓕ (028) 9754 2276
Ⓔ ringdaff@nireland.com
Contact: Nial Watson
Opening Times: Mail order only. Not open.
Min Mail Order UK: £20.00 + p&p
Min Mail Order EU: £50.00 + p&p
Cat. Cost: £2.50 redeemable on order.
Credit Cards: None
Specialities: New daffodil varieties for exhibitors and hybridisers. Small stock of some varieties.

ISea **SEAFORDE GARDENS** ⊠ ☒ € ♿
Seaforde, Co. Down, N. Ireland, BT30 8PG
Ⓣ (028) 4481 1225
Ⓕ (028) 4481 1370
Ⓔ plants@seafordegardens.com
Ⓦ www.seafordegardens.com
Contact: P Forde
Opening Times: 1000-1700 Mon-Fri all year. 1000-1700 Sat & 1300-1800 Sun mid Feb-end Oct.
Min Mail Order UK: Nmc
Min Mail Order EU: Nmc
Cat. Cost: Free.
Credit Cards: None
Specialities: Over 600 varieties of self-propagated trees & shrubs. Nat. Collection of *Eucryphia*.
Notes: Also sells wholesale.
Map Ref: I, B3

ISsi **SEASIDE NURSERY** ⊠ € ♿
Claddaghduff, Co. Galway, Ireland
Ⓣ 00 353 (0)95 44687
Ⓕ 00 353 (0)95 44761
Ⓔ seaside@anu.ie
Ⓦ www.anu.ie/seaside/
Contact: Tom Dyck
Opening Times: 1000-1300 & 1400-1800 Mon-Sat, 1400-1800 Sun. Closed Sun 1st Nov-31st Mar.
Min Mail Order UK: Nmc
Min Mail Order EU: Nmc
Cat. Cost: 3.50 euros.
Credit Cards: Visa MasterCard
Specialities: Plants & hedging suitable for seaside locations. Rare plants originating from Australia & New Zealand esp. *Phormium*, *Astelia*.
Notes: Also sells wholesale.
Map Ref: I, B1

ITer **TERRA NOVA PLANTS** ⊠ €
Dromin, Kilmallock, Co. Limerick, Ireland
Ⓣ 00 353 (0)63 90744
Ⓔ terranovaplants@eircom.net
Ⓦ www.terranovaplants.com
Contact: Deborah Begley
Opening Times: Garden & nursery open by appt.
Min Mail Order UK: Nmc
Min Mail Order EU: Nmc
Cat. Cost: Online only.
Credit Cards: None
Specialities: Only bulbous aroids sent by mail order.
Map Ref: I, C2

ITim **TIMPANY NURSERIES & GARDENS** ⊠ ♿
77 Magheratimpany Road, Ballynahinch, Co. Down, N. Ireland, BT24 8PA
Ⓣ (028) 9756 2812
Ⓕ (028) 9756 2812
Ⓔ timpany@alpines.freeserve.co.uk
Ⓦ www.alpines.freeserve.co.uk
Contact: Susan Tindall
Opening Times: 1000-1730 Tue-Sat, Sun by appt. Closed Mon excl. B/hols.

Min Mail Order UK: Nmc
Min Mail Order EU: £30.00 + p&p
Cat. Cost: £1.50.
Credit Cards: Visa MasterCard
Specialities: *Celmisia*, *Androsace*, *Primula*, *Saxifraga*, *Helichrysum*, *Dianthus*, *Meconopsis*, *Cassiope*, *Rhodohypoxis*, *Cyclamen* & *Primula auricula*.
Notes: Also sells wholesale.
Map Ref: I, B3

London Area

LAma **Jacques Amand International** ✉ ✈ € ♿
The Nurseries, 145 Clamp Hill, Stanmore, Middlesex, HA7 3JS
Ⓣ (020) 8420 7110
Ⓕ (020) 8954 6784
Ⓔ bulbs@jacquesamand.co.uk
Ⓦ www.jacquesamand.com
Contact: John Amand & Stuart Chapman
Opening Times: 0900-1700 Mon-Fri, 1000-1400 Sat-Sun. Ltd. Sun opening in Dec & Jan.
Min Mail Order UK: Nmc
Min Mail Order EU: Nmc
Cat. Cost: 1 × 1st class.
Credit Cards: All major credit/debit cards
Specialities: Rare and unusual species bulbs esp. *Arisaema*, *Trillium*, *Fritillaria*, tulips.
Notes: Also sells wholesale.
Map Ref: L, B3

LAst **Asterby & Chalkcroft Nurseries** ♿
The Ridgeway, Blunham, Bedfordshire, MK44 3PH
Ⓣ (01767) 640148
Ⓕ (01767) 640667
Ⓔ sales@asterbyplants.co.uk
Ⓦ www.asterbyplants.co.uk
Contact: Simon & Eva Aldridge
Opening Times: 1000-1700 7 days. Closed Xmas & Jan.
Cat. Cost: 2 × 1st class.
Credit Cards: Visa MasterCard Switch
Specialities: Hardy shrubs & herbaceous. *Clematis* & trees.
Map Ref: L, A3 **OS Grid Ref:** TL151497

LAyl **Aylett Nurseries Ltd** ♿
North Orbital Road, St Albans, Hertfordshire, AL2 1DH
Ⓣ (01727) 822255
Ⓕ (01727) 823024
Ⓔ info@aylettnurseries.co.uk
Ⓦ www.aylettnurseries.co.uk
Contact: Roger S Aylett
Opening Times: 0830-1730 Mon-Fri, 0830-1700 Sat, 1030-1630 Sun.
Cat. Cost: Free.
Credit Cards: All major credit/debit cards
Specialities: *Dahlia*.
Notes: Trial grounds at Bowmans Farm nr Jct. 22 M25, at MacDonalds roundabout take B556 to Colney Heath on left hand side 500m. Also sells wholesale.

LBBr **Bell Bar Nursery** ✉ ♿
Linden Lodge, Bulls Lane, Bell Bar, Nr Hatfield, Hertfordshire, AL9 7BB
Ⓜ 077240 64629
Contact: Chris Genever
Opening Times: 0915-1645 Mon-Sat, 1000-1600 Sun, Apr-Oct. Other times by appt.
Min Mail Order UK: Nmc
Cat. Cost: 2 × 1st class.
Credit Cards: All major credit/debit cards
Specialities: Hardy perennials, grasses, bulbs, ferns & bamboos.
Notes: Also sells wholesale.
Map Ref: L, B4 **OS Grid Ref:** TL243053

LBee **Beechcroft Nursery** ♿
127 Reigate Road, Ewell, Surrey, KT17 3DE
Ⓣ (020) 8393 4265
Ⓕ (020) 8393 4265
Contact: C Kimber
Opening Times: 1000-1600 Mon-Sat, 1000-1400 Sun and B/hols. Closed Xmas-New Year week.
Cat. Cost: None issued.
Credit Cards: All major credit/debit cards
Specialities: Conifers & alpines.
Notes: Also sells wholesale.
Map Ref: L, C3

LBMP **Blooming Marvellous Plants** ⛫
Korketts Farm, Aylesbury Road, Shipton, Winslow, Buckinghamshire, MK18 3JL
Ⓜ 07963 747305
Ⓔ alex@bmplants.co.uk
Ⓦ www.bmplants.co.uk
Contact: Alex Ballance
Opening Times: 1000-1900 Thu, 1000-1700 Fri-Mon (closed Tue & Wed).
Credit Cards: All major credit/debit cards
Specialities: A mixture of unusual and familiar perennials, shrubs & grasses.

KEY
✉ Mail order to UK or EU ⛫ Delivers to shows
✈ Exports beyond EU € Euro accepted
♿ Accessible by wheelchair ◆ See Display advertisement

Notes: Located on the A413 just outside Winslow (if heading towards Aylesbury). Partial wheelchair access.
Map Ref: L, A2 **OS Grid Ref:** SP777271

LBuc **BUCKINGHAM NURSERIES** ⊠ ✈ € ♿ ◆
14 Tingewick Road, Buckingham, MK18 4AE
Ⓣ (01280) 822133
Ⓕ (01280) 815491
Ⓔ enquiries@buckingham-nurseries.co.uk
Ⓦ www.buckingham-nurseries.co.uk
Contact: R J & P L Brown
Opening Times: 0830-1730 (1800 in summer) Mon-Fri, 1000-1600 Sun. 0900-1800 Sat (0900-1900 in summer).
Min Mail Order UK: Nmc
Min Mail Order EU: Nmc
Cat. Cost: Free.
Credit Cards: Visa MasterCard Switch
Specialities: Bare rooted and container grown hedging. Trees, shrubs, herbaceous perennials, alpines, grasses & ferns.
Map Ref: L, A2 **OS Grid Ref:** SP675333

L

LBut **YAFFLES (FOMERLY BUTTERFIELDS NURSERY)** ⊠ ♿
Harvest Hill, Bourne End, Buckinghamshire, SL8 5JJ
Ⓣ (01628) 525455
Contact: I Butterfield
Opening Times: 0900-1300 & 1400-1700. Please phone beforehand in case we are attending shows.
Min Mail Order UK: Nmc
Min Mail Order EU: £30.00 + p&p
Cat. Cost: 2 × 2nd class.
Credit Cards: None
Specialities: Nat. Collection of *Pleione*. *Dahlia* for collection. Scientific Award 1999.
Notes: Only *Pleione* by mail order. Also sells wholesale.
Map Ref: L, B3

LChw **CHADWELL SEEDS** ⊠ ✈ €
81 Parlaunt Road, Slough, Berkshire, SL3 8BE
Ⓣ (01753) 542823
Ⓕ (01753) 542823
Ⓔ matthew.chadwell@btinternet.com
Contact: Chris Chadwell
Opening Times: Not open. Mail order only.
Min Mail Order UK: Nmc
Min Mail Order EU: Nmc
Cat. Cost: 3 × 2nd class.
Credit Cards: None
Specialities: Seed collecting expedition to the Himalayas. Separate general seed list of Japanese, N. American & Himalayan plants.

LCla **CLAY LANE NURSERY** ⊠ ⌂
3 Clay Lane, South Nutfield, Nr Redhill, Surrey, RH1 4EG
Ⓣ (01737) 823307
Ⓔ claylane.nursery@btinternet.com
Ⓦ www.claylane-fuchsias.co.uk
Contact: K W Belton
Opening Times: 1000-1700 Tue-Sun 1st Feb-30th Jun. Other times by appt. Please phone before travelling.
Min Mail Order UK: £6.00
Cat. Cost: 4 × 2nd class.
Credit Cards: None
Specialities: *Fuchsia*. Many varieties in small quantities only.
Notes: Mail order by telephone pre-arangement only.
Map Ref: L, C4

LCon **THE CONIFER GARDEN** ⊠ ⌂
Herons Mead, Little Missenden, Amersham, Buckinghamshire, HP7 0RA
Ⓣ (01494) 862086 (0900-1800 hrs)
Ⓕ (01494) 862086
Ⓔ sales@conifergarden.co.uk
Ⓦ www.conifergarden.co.uk
Contact: Mr & Mrs M P S Powell
Opening Times: Open by appt. only.
Min Mail Order UK: Nmc
Cat. Cost: 2 × 1st class for list only.
Credit Cards: None
Specialities: Conifers only, over 400 varieties always available.
Notes: Mail order to UK only, by overnight carrier.

LCro **CROCUS.CO.UK** ⊠
Nursery Court, London Road, Windlesham, Surrey, GU20 6LQ
Ⓣ 0870 787 1414 (order line)
Ⓕ 0870 787 1412
Ⓔ customerservices@crocus.co.uk
Ⓦ www.crocus.co.uk
Contact: Helen Sales
Opening Times: Not open. Mail order only. Order lines open 24hrs, 7 days.
Min Mail Order UK: Nmc
Cat. Cost: None issued.
Credit Cards: Visa MasterCard Solo Switch Delta

LDai **DAISY ROOTS** ⊠ ⌂
(office) 8 Gosselin Road, Bengeo, Hertford, Hertfordshire, SG14 3LG
Ⓣ (01992) 582401
Ⓕ (01992) 582401
Ⓔ anne@daisyroots.com

Ⓦ www.daisyroots.com
Contact: Anne Godfrey
Opening Times: 1000-1600 Fri & Sat Mar-Oct, or by appt.
Min Mail Order UK: Nmc
Cat. Cost: 4 × 1st class.
Credit Cards: None
Specialities: Ever-increasing range of choice & unusual perennials, particularly *Agastache, Anthemis, Centaurea, Digitalis, Erysimum, Salvia* & *Sedum.*
Notes: Nursery is at Jenningsbury, London Road, Hertford Heath.
Map Ref: L, B4

LDea DEREK LLOYD DEAN ⊠ ✈ ⌂
8 Lynwood Close, South Harrow,
Middlesex,
HA2 9PR
Ⓣ (020) 8864 0899
Ⓔ lloyddeancbtinternet.com
Ⓦ www.dereklloyddean.com
Contact: Derek Lloyd Dean
Opening Times: Not open. Mail order only.
Min Mail Order UK: £2.50 + p&p
Min Mail Order EU: £2.50 + p&p
Cat. Cost: 2 × 1st class.
Credit Cards: None
Specialities: Regal, angel, ivy & scented leaf *Pelargonium.* Nat. Collection of Angel *Pelargonium.*

LEdu EDULIS ⊠ ⌂ € ♿
(office) 1 Flowers Piece, Ashampstead,
Berkshire, RG8 8SG
Ⓣ (01635) 578113
Ⓕ (01635) 578113
Ⓔ edulis.nursery@virgin.net
Ⓦ www.edulis.co.uk
Contact: Paul Barney
Opening Times: By appt. only.
Min Mail Order UK: £10.00 + p&p
Min Mail Order EU: £50.00 + p&p
Cat. Cost: 6 × 1st class.
Credit Cards: None
Specialities: Unusual edibles, architectural plants, permaculture plants.
Notes: Nursery is at Bere Court Farm, Tidmarsh Lane, Pangbourne, RG8 8HT. Also sells wholesale.
Map Ref: L, B2 **OS Grid Ref:** SU615747

LFol FOLIAGE SCENTED & HERB PLANTS ♿
Walton Poor, Crocknorth Road, Ranmore Common, Dorking, Surrey, RH5 6SX
Ⓣ (01483) 282273
Ⓕ (01483) 282273
Contact: Mrs Prudence Calvert
Opening Times: Open during Apr-Sep, please phone for appt. if possible.
Cat. Cost: 3 × 2nd class.
Credit Cards: None
Specialities: Herbs, aromatic & scented plants.
Map Ref: L, C3

LFox FOXGROVE PLANTS ⊠ ⌂ ♿
Foxgrove, Enborne,
Nr Newbury, Berkshire,
RG14 6RE
Ⓣ (01635) 40554
Ⓕ (01635) 30555
Contact: Mrs Louise Peters
Opening Times: 1000-1300 & 1400-1600 Thu/Fri/Sat, mid-Jan to end-Oct. Other times by appt. only.
Min Mail Order UK: Nmc
Min Mail Order EU: Nmc
Cat. Cost: £1.00.
Credit Cards: None
Specialities: Hardy & unusual plants, incl. *Galanthus*, hellebores, grasses, *Penstemon*, alpines.
Notes: Mail order for *Galanthus* only.
Map Ref: L, C2

LFur FURZE PARK NURSERY ⊠
Furze Park Farm, Bycell Road,
Maids Moreton, Buckingham,
Buckinghamshire,
MK18 5AA
Ⓣ (01280) 821999
Ⓕ (01280) 821999
Contact: Lucy Hyde
Opening Times: 1000-1700 Thu-Sun, & B/hol Mons.
Min Mail Order UK: Nmc
Credit Cards: None
Specialities: Friendly & helpful nursery specialising in new & unusual hardy perennials, many woodlanders incl. Himalayan & Japanese *Arisaema*.

LGod GODLY'S ROSES ⊠ ♿
Redbourn, St Albans, Hertfordshire, AL3 7PS
Ⓣ (01582) 792255
Ⓕ (01582) 794267
Contact: Colin Godly
Opening Times: 0900-1700 summer, 7 days. 0900-dusk winter, 7 days. Closed Xmas & New Year's Day.

KEY
⊠ Mail order to UK or EU ⌂ Delivers to shows
✈ Exports beyond EU € Euro accepted
♿ Accessible by wheelchair ◆ See Display advertisement

L

Min Mail Order UK: Nmc
Min Mail Order EU: £4.50
Cat. Cost: Free.
Credit Cards: Visa American Express Switch MasterCard
Specialities: Roses.
Notes: Standard roses not sent mail order. Also sells wholesale.
Map Ref: L, B3 **OS Grid Ref:** TL096137

LHop **HOPLEYS PLANTS LTD** ⊠ ♿ ◆
High Street, Much Hadham, Hertfordshire, SG10 6BU
Ⓣ (01279) 842509
Ⓕ (01279) 843784
Ⓔ sales@hopleys.co.uk
Ⓦ www.hopleys.co.uk
Contact: Aubrey Barker
Opening Times: 0900-1700 Mon & Wed-Sat, 1400-1700 Sun. Closed Nov-Feb except by appt.
Min Mail Order UK: Nmc
Cat. Cost: 5 × 1st class.
Credit Cards: Visa Access Switch
Specialities: Wide range of hardy & half-hardy shrubs & perennials.
Notes: £2.00 charge for delivery to shows. Also sells wholesale.
Map Ref: L, A4 **OS Grid Ref:** TL428196

LHyd **HYDON NURSERIES** ⊠ € ◆
Clock Barn Lane, Hydon Heath, Godalming, Surrey, GU8 4AZ
Ⓣ (01483) 860252
Ⓕ (01483) 419937
Contact: A F George, Rodney Longhurst & Mrs A M George
Opening Times: 0930-1700 Mon-Sat (closed 12.45-1400), Feb-mid Jun & Oct-mid Nov. Other months 0930-1600 Mon-Fri, 0930-1300 Sat. Sun by appt.
Min Mail Order UK: Nmc
Min Mail Order EU: £25.00 + p&p
Cat. Cost: £2.00 or 7 × 1st class or 10 × 2nd class.
Credit Cards: None
Specialities: Large and dwarf *Rhododendron*, *yakushimanum* hybrids, azaleas (deciduous & evergreen), *Camellia* & other trees & shrubs. Specimen *Rhododendron*. Conservatory: scented tender rhododendrons & camellias.
Notes: Also sells wholesale.
Map Ref: L, C3

LIMB **I.M.B. PLANTS** ⊠
2 Ashdown Close, Giffard Park, Milton Keynes, Buckinghamshire, MK14 5PX
Ⓣ (01908) 618911
Ⓔ jackie.ridgway@u.genie.co.uk
Contact: Ian Brazier
Opening Times: Not open. Mail order only.
Min Mail Order UK: Nmc
Credit Cards: None
Specialities: Mainly helianthemums & *Phlox* but others available. All plants propagated in small quantities.

LLin **LINCLUDEN NURSERY** ⊠ € ♿
Shaftesbury Road, Bisley, Woking, Surrey, GU24 9EN
Ⓣ (01483) 797005
Ⓕ (01483) 797005
Ⓔ sales@lincludennursery.co.uk
Ⓦ www.lincludennursery.co.uk
Contact: Mr & Mrs K Hayward
Opening Times: 1000-1600 Tue-Sat all year excl. B/hols.
Min Mail Order UK: Nmc
Min Mail Order EU: Nmc
Cat. Cost: Printed catalogue free & online.
Credit Cards: Visa MasterCard Solo Switch
Specialities: Conifers, 400+ varieties & species: tall, short, miniature & hedging.
Map Ref: L, C3 **OS Grid Ref:** SU947596

LLWG **LILIES WATER GARDENS** ⊠ ♿
Broad Lane, Newdigate, Surrey, RH5 5AT
Ⓣ (01306) 631064
Ⓕ (01306) 631693
Ⓔ mail@clilieswatergardens.co.uk
Ⓦ www.lilieswatergardens.co.uk
Contact: Simon Harman
Opening Times: 0900-1700 Tues-Sat, 1st Mar-end Sep.
Min Mail Order UK: Nmc, but flat rate £10.00 delivery charge.
Cat. Cost: Online only.
Credit Cards: All major credit/debit cards
Specialities: *Nymphaea*, grasses, moist herbaceous, astilbes, primulas, marginal plants, bog-garden plants. (Tropical & semi-tropical frost-tender marginal & bog-garden plants.)
Map Ref: L, C3

LLWP **L W PLANTS** ⊠
23 Wroxham Way, Harpenden, Hertfordshire, AL5 4PP
Ⓣ (01582) 768467
Ⓔ lwplants@waitrose.com
Ⓦ www.thymus.co.uk
Contact: Mrs M Easter
Opening Times: 1000-1700 most days, but please phone first.
Min Mail Order UK: Nmc
Cat. Cost: A5 sae + 5 × 2nd class (loose).

Credit Cards: None
Specialities: Plants from a plantsman's garden, esp. *Geranium*, grasses, *Penstemon* & *Thymus*. Nat. Collections of *Thymus* (Scientific), *Hyssopus* & *Satureja*.
Notes: Mail order *Thymus* only.
Map Ref: L, B3 **OS Grid Ref:** TL141153

LMil MILLAIS NURSERIES ⊠ ♿
Crosswater Lane, Churt, Farnham, Surrey, GU10 2JN
Ⓣ (01252) 792698
Ⓕ (01252) 792526
Ⓔ sales@rhododendrons.co.uk
Ⓦ www.rhododendrons.co.uk
Contact: David Millais
Opening Times: 1000-1300 & 1400-1700 Mon-Fri. Sat spring & autumn. Daily in May and early Jun.
Min Mail Order UK: £30.00 + p&p
Min Mail Order EU: £60.00 + p&p
Cat. Cost: 4 × 1st class.
Credit Cards: All major credit/debit cards
Specialities: Rhododendrons, azaleas, magnolias & acers.
Notes: Mail order Oct-Mar only. Also sells wholesale.
Map Ref: L, C3 **OS Grid Ref:** SU856397

LMor MOREHAVENS ⊠ ♿
Sandpit Hill, Buckland Common, Tring, Hertfordshire, HP23 6NG
Ⓣ (01494) 758642
Ⓦ www.camomilelawns.co.uk
Contact: B Farmer
Opening Times: Mail order only. Open only for collection.
Min Mail Order UK: £15.95
Min Mail Order EU: £15.95 + p&p
Cat. Cost: Free.
Credit Cards: None
Specialities: *Camomile* 'Treneague'.
Notes: Also sells wholesale.
Map Ref: L, B3

LPal THE PALM CENTRE ⊠ € ♿
Ham Central Nursery, opposite Riverside Drive, Ham Street, Ham, Richmond, Surrey, TW10 7HA
Ⓣ (020) 8255 6191
Ⓕ (020) 8255 6192
Ⓔ mail@thepalmcentre.co.uk
Ⓦ www.thepalmcentre.co.uk
Contact: Martin Gibbons
Opening Times: 0900-1700 (dusk in winter) 7 days. Admin & Order Dept. 0900-1700 Mon-Fri.
Min Mail Order UK: £10.00 + p&p
Min Mail Order EU: £10.00 + p&p
Cat. Cost: Free.
Credit Cards: Visa MasterCard Switch
Specialities: Palms & cycads, exotic & sub-tropical, hardy, half-hardy & tropical. Seedlings to mature trees. Also bamboo, tree ferns & other exotics.
Notes: Also sells wholesale.
Map Ref: L, B3

LPan PANTILES PLANT & GARDEN CENTRE ⊠ ♿ ◆
Almners Road, Lyne, Chertsey, Surrey, KT16 0BJ
Ⓣ (01932) 872195
Ⓕ (01932) 874030
Ⓔ sales@pantiles-nurseries.co.uk
Ⓦ www.pantiles-nurseries.co.uk
Contact: Doug Hammond
Opening Times: 0900-1800 Mon-Sat, 1100-1700 Sun (summer). 0900-1700 Mon-Sat, 1000-1600 Sun (winter).
Min Mail Order UK: £100.00 + p&p
Min Mail Order EU: £100.00 + p&p
Cat. Cost: Free.
Credit Cards: Visa Switch MasterCard
Specialities: Large trees, shrubs, conifers & climbers in containers. Australasian & other unusual plants. Selection of tree ferns from New Zealand & Australia.
Notes: Also sells wholesale.
Map Ref: L, C3 **OS Grid Ref:** TQ0166

LPen PENSTEMONS BY COLOUR ⊠ €
Peterley Manor, Peterley, Prestwood, Great Missenden, Buckinghamshire, HP16 0HH
Ⓣ (01494) 866420
Ⓕ (01494) 866420
Ⓔ debra.hughes1@virgin.net
Contact: Debra Hughes
Opening Times: Any time by appt.
Min Mail Order UK: Nmc
Min Mail Order EU: Nmc
Cat. Cost: Free.
Credit Cards: None
Specialities: *Penstemon*.

LPio PIONEER NURSERY ⊠ € ♿
Baldock Lane, Willian, Letchworth, Hertfordshire, SG6 2AE
Ⓣ (01462) 675858
Ⓔ milly@pioneerplants.com

KEY
⊠ Mail order to UK or EU — Delivers to shows
Exports beyond EU — € Euro accepted
♿ Accessible by wheelchair — ◆ See Display advertisement

L

Ⓦ www.pioneerplants.com
Contact: Nick Downing
Opening Times: 0900-1700 Tue-Sat 1000-1600 Sun, Mar-Oct, 1000-1600 Tue-Sat Nov, Dec & Feb.
Min Mail Order UK: £15.00 + p&p
Min Mail Order EU: 30 euros
Cat. Cost: Free.
Credit Cards: MasterCard Visa
Specialities: *Salvia*, tender perennials. Wide range of hard-to-find perennials & bulbs. Species *Pelargonium*.
Notes: Also sells wholesale.
Map Ref: L, A3 **OS Grid Ref:** TL224307

L

LPJP **PJ'S PALMS AND EXOTICS** ⊠ €
41 Salcombe Road, Ashford, Middlesex, TW15 3BS
Ⓣ (01784) 250181
Contact: Peter Jenkins
Opening Times: Mail order only 1st Mar-30th Nov. Visits by arrangement.
Min Mail Order UK: Nmc
Min Mail Order EU: Nmc
Cat. Cost: 2 × 1st class.
Credit Cards: None
Specialities: Palms, bananas & other exotic foliage plants, hardy & half-hardy. *Trachycarpus wagnerianus* seeds available. Plants available in small quantities.
Notes: Also sells wholesale.
Map Ref: L, B3

LRav **RAVEN VALLEY PLANT NURSERY**
Mayfields, Whitmore Lane, Woking, Surrey, GU4 7QB
Ⓣ (01483) 234605
Ⓜ 07887 925945
Ⓔ ravenvalley@aol.com
Ⓦ www.plantexperience.co.uk
Contact: Maria & Terry Milton
Opening Times: 1100-1500 Thu & Fri. 1000-1600 (1700 in summer) Sat, Sun & B/hols. Closed Jan & Feb.
Cat. Cost: On floppy disc only, sae or email.
Credit Cards: None
Specialities: *Eucalyptus*, grasses, chillis, exotic hedging.
Notes: Also sells wholesale.
Map Ref: L, C3 **OS Grid Ref:** SU997544

LRHS **WISLEY PLANT CENTRE (RHS)** ♿ ◆
RHS Garden, Wisley, Woking, Surrey, GU23 6QB
Ⓣ (01483) 211113
Ⓕ (01483) 212372
Ⓔ wisleyplantcentre@rhs.org.uk
Ⓦ www.rhs.org.uk/wisleyplantcentre
Opening Times: 1000-1830 Mon-Sat, 1100-1700 Sun (summer). 1000-1700 Mon-Sat, 1000-1600 Sun (winter). Closed 25th-26th Dec & Easter Sun.
Cat. Cost: None issued
Credit Cards: All major credit/debit cards
Specialities: Very wide range, many rare & unusual.
Notes: Programme of free special events throughout the year. Ring or check website for details.
Map Ref: L, C3

LSee **SEEDS BY SIZE** ⊠ ✈ €
45 Crouchfield, Boxmoor, Hemel Hempstead, Hertfordshire, HP1 1PA
Ⓣ (01442) 251458
Ⓔ john-robert-size@seeds-by-size.co.uk
Ⓦ www.seeds-by-size.co.uk
Contact: John Robert Size
Opening Times: Not open, mail order only.
Min Mail Order UK: Nmc
Min Mail Order EU: Nmc
Cat. Cost: Online only.
Credit Cards: None
Specialities: 9000 varieties of flower, vegetable & herb seeds. 608 sweet peas, 684 pansies, 550 petunias, 258 *Impatiens*, 236 marigolds, 247 cabbages, 268 tomatoes, 130 cauliflowers, 210 herbs & 107 onions. 150 Oriental vegetables.
Notes: Cash only euro payments. Also sells wholesale.

LSiH **SINO-HIMALAYAN PLANT ASSOCIATION** ⊠
81 Parlaunt Road, Slough, Berkshire, SL3 8BE
Ⓣ (01753) 542823
Ⓕ (01753) 542823
Ⓔ matthew.chadwell@btinternet.com
Contact: Chris Chadwell
Opening Times: Mail order seed exchange only.
Min Mail Order UK: Nmc
Cat. Cost: None issued.
Credit Cards: None
Specialities:
Notes: Seed available for exchange to members. Please apply for membership. Euros accepted for membership fees only.

LSou **SOUTHON PLANTS** ⊠ ♿ ◆
Mutton Hill, Dormansland, Lingfield, Surrey, RH7 6NP
Ⓣ (01342) 870150
Ⓔ info@southonplants.com
Ⓦ www.southonplants.com

Contact: Mr Southon
Opening Times: 0900-1700 Mar-Oct, closed Wed in Nov. Dec & Jan please phone first.
Min Mail Order UK: Nmc. Please phone/email for details.
Cat. Cost: £2.00 or free online.
Credit Cards: All major credit/debit cards
Specialities: New & unusual hardy & tender perennials. Also hardy ferns, alpines, grasses, shrubs & climbers incl. many variegated plants.
Map Ref: L, C4

LSRN SPRING REACH NURSERY ⊠ ⋔ 🖘 ◆
Long Reach, Ockham, Guildford, Surrey, GU23 6PG
Ⓣ (01483) 284769
Ⓜ 07884 432666
Ⓕ (01483) 284769
Ⓔ n.hourhan@btopenworld.com
Contact: Nick Hourhan
Opening Times: 7 days. Mon-Sat 1000-1700, Sun 1030-1630.
Min Mail Order UK: £25.00
Cat. Cost: 2 × 1st class.
Credit Cards: All major credit/debit cards
Specialities: Shrubs, grasses, bamboos, climbers, perennials, trees & *Clematis*, chalk-loving plants, hedging, specimen plants, acid-loving plants, soft fruit & top fruit.
Notes: Not a mail order specialist but will do occasional orders by post. Also sells wholesale.
Map Ref: L, C3

LStr HENRY STREET NURSERY ⊠ 🖘
Swallowfield Road, Arborfield, Reading, Berkshire, RG2 9JY
Ⓣ (0118) 9761223
Ⓕ (0118) 9761417
Ⓔ info@henrystreet.co.uk
Ⓦ www.henrystreet.co.uk
Contact: Mr M C Goold
Opening Times: 0900-1730 Mon-Sat, 1030-1630 Sun.
Min Mail Order UK: Nmc
Min Mail Order EU: Nmc
Cat. Cost: Free.
Credit Cards: Visa Access Switch
Specialities: Roses.
Notes: Also sells wholesale.
Map Ref: L, C3

LToo TOOBEES EXOTICS ⊠ 🖘 €
(Office) 20 Inglewood, St Johns, Woking, Surrey, GU21 3HX
Ⓣ (01483) 722600
Ⓕ (01483) 751995
Ⓔ bbpotter@woking.plus.com

Ⓦ www.toobees-exotics.com
Contact: Bob Potter
Opening Times: Not open. Mail order & online shop only.
Min Mail Order UK: Nmc
Min Mail Order EU: Nmc
Cat. Cost: Sae
Specialities: South African & Madagascan succulents, many rare & unusual species, plus air plants, *Euphorbia* & *Pachypodium*.

LTwo TWO JAYS ALPINES
(Office) 35 Greenways, Luton, Bedfordshire, LU2 8BL
Ⓣ (01442) 864951
Ⓕ (01442) 864951
Ⓔ john.spokes@talk21.com
Contact: John Spokes
Opening Times: 1000-1700 or dusk if earlier, 7 days.
Cat. Cost: 3 × 2nd class.
Credit Cards: Visa MasterCard
Specialities: Large range of alpines, herbaceous, shrubs, many available in small quantities only.
Notes: Nursery is at Little Heath Farm, Little Heath Lane, Potten End, Berkhamsted, HP4 2RY.
Map Ref: L, A3

LVER THE VERNON GERANIUM NURSERY ⊠ 🖘
Cuddington Way, Cheam, Sutton, Surrey, SM2 7JB
Ⓣ (020) 8393 7616
Ⓕ (020) 8786 7437
Ⓔ mrgeranium@aol.com
Ⓦ www.geraniumsuk.com
Contact: Philip James & Liz Sims
Opening Times: 0930-1730 Mon-Sat, 1000-1600 Sun, 1st Mar-30th Jun.
Min Mail Order UK: Nmc
Min Mail Order EU: Nmc
Cat. Cost: £2.00 UK, £2.50 EU.
Credit Cards: All major credit/debit cards
Specialities: *Pelargonium* & *Fuchsia*.
Map Ref: L, C3 **OS Grid Ref:** TQ237615

LWoR WORLD OF ROSES ⊠
Briar Patch Nursery, Ickwell Road, Upper Caldecote, Bedfordshire, SG18 9BS
Ⓣ 08452 606888
Ⓕ (01767) 627634

K	⊠ Mail order to UK or EU	⋔	Delivers to shows
E	🖷 Exports beyond EU	€	Euro accepted
Y	🖘 Accessible by wheelchair	◆	See Display advertisement

Ⓔ enquiries@worldofroses.com
Ⓦ www.worldofroses.com
Contact: Claire Gill
Opening Times: Not open. Mail order only. Telephones open 0800-1700 Mon-Fri.
Min Mail Order UK: Nmc
Min Mail Order EU: Nmc
Cat. Cost: Free.
Credit Cards: All major credit/debit cards
Specialities: Roses. Gift roses, rose naming.
Notes: Mail order: bareroot, Oct-Mar; potted, Oct-July.
Map Ref: L, A3 **OS Grid Ref:** TL163458

L

MIDLANDS

MAbb ABBEY BROOK CACTUS NURSERY ⊠ ♿
Bakewell Road, Matlock, Derbyshire,
DE4 2QJ
Ⓣ (01629) 580306
Ⓕ (01629) 55852
Ⓔ brian@abbeybrook.freeserve.co.uk
Ⓦ www.abbeybrookcacti.com
Contact: Brian Fearn
Opening Times: 1300-1600 Wed/Thu/Fri. 1300-1700 Sat & Sun. (Closed Mon & Tue). May be closed some w/ends, check website for details.
Min Mail Order UK: Nmc
Min Mail Order EU: Nmc
Cat. Cost: Online only.
Credit Cards: Visa MasterCard
Specialities: Succulents and hardy cacti. *Agave*, *Sedum*, *Echeveria*, *Graptopetalum*, *Graptoveria*, *Pachyphytum*, *Echinopsis*, *Lobivia*, *Opuntia* & *Rebutia*. 6 Nat. Collections.
Notes: Mail order to EU *Echinopsis* only. Also sells wholesale.
Map Ref: M, B2

MACG ASHDALE COTTAGE GARDEN PLANTS ♿
204 Lambley Lane, Gedling,
Nottinghamshire, NG4 4PB
Ⓣ (0115) 966 6060
Ⓕ (0115) 966 6060
Contact: Stephen Mills
Opening Times: 0900-1700 Wed-Sun, Mar-Oct. Closed Nov-Feb.
Cat. Cost: None issued.
Credit Cards: All major credit/debit cards
Specialities: Wide range of rare and unusual herbaceous perennials.

MAco ACORN NURSERY ♿
Milton Road, Stadhampton, Oxfordshire,
OX44 7XX
Ⓣ (01865) 891663
Ⓔ alan@acornplants.co.uk
Ⓦ www.acornplants.co.uk
Contact: Alan Vincent
Opening Times: 0900-1700, closed Wed, Mar-Oct & Dec.
Cat. Cost: None issued.
Credit Cards: None
Notes: Also sells wholesale.
Map Ref: M, D3 **OS Grid Ref:** SU612997

MAga AGAVE NURSERY ⊠ ✈ ⌂ €
15 Sleetmoor Lane,
Somercotes, Derbyshire,
DE55 1RB
Ⓜ 01773 605843, 07814 787555, 07791 627358
Ⓔ jon@agavenursery.wanadoo.co.uk
Ⓦ www.agavenursery
Contact: Jon & Sue Dudek
Opening Times: Mail order only. Open by appt. only.
Min Mail Order UK: Nmc
Min Mail Order EU: Nmc
Cat. Cost: Free.
Credit Cards: None
Specialities: *Agave*, *Furcraea*, *Manfreda* & *Yucca*.
Notes: Also sells wholesale.
Map Ref: M, B2

MAJR A J ROBINSON ⊠
Sycamore Farm,
Foston, Derbyshire,
DE65 5PW
Ⓣ (01283) 815635
Ⓕ (01283) 815635
Contact: A J Robinson
Opening Times: By appt. for collection of plants only.
Min Mail Order UK: £13.00
Cat. Cost: 2 × 1st class for list.
Credit Cards: None
Specialities: Extensive collection of tender perennials. Salvias. Nat. Collection of *Argyranthemum*.
Notes: Mail order argyranthemums & heliotrope only.
Map Ref: M, B2

MArl ARLEY HALL NURSERY ♿
Arley Hall Nursery, Northwich, Cheshire,
CW9 6NA
Ⓣ (01565) 777479/777231
Ⓕ (01565) 777465
Contact: Jane Foster
Opening Times: 1100-1730 Tue-Sun, Easter-end Sep. Also B/hol Mons.
Cat. Cost: 4 × 1st class.
Credit Cards: All major credit/debit cards

Specialities: Wide range of herbaceous incl. many unusual varieties. Wide range of unusual pelargoniums.
Map Ref: M, A1 **OS Grid Ref:** SJ673808

MAsh **Ashwood Nurseries Ltd** ♿
Ashwood Lower Lane, Ashwood, Kingswinford, West Midlands, DY6 0AE
Ⓣ (01384) 401996
Ⓕ (01384) 401108
Ⓔ ashwoodnurs@btconnect.com
Ⓦ www.ashwood-nurseries.co.uk
Contact: Mark Warburton & Philip Baulk
Opening Times: 0900-1700 Mon-Sat & 0930-1700 Sun excl. Xmas & Boxing Day.
Min Mail Order UK: Nmc
Cat. Cost: 6 × 1st class.
Credit Cards: Visa Access MasterCard
Specialities: Large range of hardy plants & dwarf conifers. Nat. Collections of *Lewisia* & *Cyclamen* species. Hellebores, *Hepatica*, *Hydrangea* & *Salvia*.
Notes: Mail order seeds & special offers only.
Map Ref: M, C2 **OS Grid Ref:** SO865879

MAus **David Austin Roses Ltd** ☒ ✈ € ♿
Bowling Green Lane, Albrighton, Wolverhampton, WV7 3HB
Ⓣ (01902) 376300
Ⓕ (01902) 372142
Ⓔ retail@davidaustinroses.co.uk
Ⓦ www.davidaustinroses.com
Contact: Retail Dept
Opening Times: 0900-1700, 7 days.
Min Mail Order UK: Nmc
Min Mail Order EU: Nmc
Cat. Cost: Free.
Credit Cards: Switch Visa MasterCard Maestro Access
Specialities: Roses. Nat. Collection of English Roses.
Notes: Also sells wholesale.
Map Ref: M, B1

MAvo **Avondale Nursery** ⌂ ♿
(Office) 3 Avondale Road, Earlsdon, Coventry, Warwickshire, CV5 6DZ
Ⓣ (024) 766 73662
Ⓜ 07979 093096
Ⓕ (024) 766 73662
Ⓔ enquiries@avondalenursery.co.uk
Ⓦ www.avondalenursery.co.uk
Contact: Brian Ellis
Opening Times: 1000-1230, 1400-1700 Tue-Sun, Mar-Sep. Other times by appt.
Cat. Cost: 4 × 1st class.
Credit Cards: None
Specialities: Rare & unusual perennials esp. *Aster*, *Campanula*, *Eryngium*, *Leucanthemum*, *Geum*, *Crocosmia* & grasses. Display garden now open.
Notes: Nursery is at Russell's Nursery, Mill Hill, Baginton, Nr Coventry.
Map Ref: M, C2 **OS Grid Ref:** SP339751

MBar **Barncroft Nurseries** ☒ ♿
Dunwood Lane, Longsdon, Nr Leek, Stoke-on-Trent, Staffordshire, ST9 9QW
Ⓣ (01538) 384310
Ⓕ (01538) 384310
Ⓦ www.barncroftnurseries.com
Contact: S Warner
Opening Times: 0930-1730 or dusk if earlier Fri-Sun all year, plus Mon-Thu 0930-1730 Mar-Dec. Closed Xmas to New Year.
Min Mail Order UK: £20.00 + p&p
Cat. Cost: £2.50 incl. p&p.
Credit Cards: None
Specialities: Extensive range of over 2000 heathers, conifers, shrubs, trees, climbers, dwarf grasses & rhododendrons. Display garden containing 400 heather cvs.
Notes: Also sells wholesale.
Map Ref: M, B1 **OS Grid Ref:** SJ948552

MBec **Beechcroft Nurseries & Garden Centre** ♿ ◆
Madeley Road, Madeley Heath, Belbroughton, Stourbridge, West Midlands, DY9 9XA
Ⓣ (01562) 710358
Ⓕ (01562) 710507
Ⓔ mail@beechcroft.com
Ⓦ www.beechcroft.com
Contact: Paul Billingham
Opening Times: 0900-1730 Mon-Sat, 1100-1700 Sun. Close half-hour earlier in winter.
Cat. Cost: Free.
Credit Cards: All major credit/debit cards except American Express.
Specialities: Many unusual & hard to find plants. Shrubs, conifers, rhododendrons, azaleas, heathers, alpine & rockery plants, climbers & *Clematis*, outdoor ferns, wild-flowers & trees. Home-grown bedding & seasonal plants. Large range of herbaceous perennials & roses.
Notes: Set in beautiful countryside just minutes from the centre of Birmingham & M5 Jct 4.
Map Ref: M, C2 **OS Grid Ref:** SO951772

KEY
☒ Mail order to UK or EU ⌂ Delivers to shows
✈ Exports beyond EU € Euro accepted
♿ Accessible by wheelchair ◆ See Display advertisement

M

MBlu **BLUEBELL ARBORETUM & NURSERY** ⊠ ⌂ € ♿
Annwell Lane, Smisby, Nr Ashby de la Zouch, Derbyshire, LE65 2TA
Ⓣ (01530) 413700
Ⓕ (01530) 417600
Ⓔ sales@bluebellnursery.co.uk
Ⓦ www.bluebellnursery.co.uk
Contact: Robert & Suzette Vernon
Opening Times: 0900-1700 Mon-Sat & 1030-1630 Sun Mar-Oct, 0900-1600 Mon-Sat (not Sun) Nov-Feb. Closed 24th Dec-4th Jan & Easter Sun.
Min Mail Order UK: Nmc
Min Mail Order EU: Nmc
Cat. Cost: £1.50 + 3 × 1st class.
Credit Cards: Visa Access Switch
Specialities: Uncommon trees & shrubs. Display garden & arboretum.
Map Ref: M, B1

M

MBnl **BENSLEY NURSERIES** ⌂ ♿
(office) 7 Bramble Way, Kilburn, Derbyshire, DE56 0LH
Ⓣ (01332) 781961
Ⓜ 07929 720284
Ⓕ (01332) 690546
Ⓔ bensleynursery@yahoo.co.uk
Contact: Mairi Longdon
Opening Times: By appt. only.
Cat. Cost: 4 × 1st class.
Credit Cards: None
Specialities: Choice & unusual perennials esp. *Achillea*, *Geranium*, *Geum*, *Helenium*, *Heuchera*, *Pulmonaria*, grasses & ferns.
Notes: Nursery is at White Gables, Dale Road, Stanley, Derbyshire.
Map Ref: M, B2 **OS Grid Ref:** SK417398

MBNS **BARNSDALE GARDENS** ⊠ ⌂ ♿ ◆
Exton Avenue, Exton, Oakham, Rutland, LE15 8AH
Ⓣ (01572) 813200
Ⓕ (01572) 813346
Ⓔ office@barnsdalegardens.co.uk
Ⓦ www.barnsdalegardens.co.uk
Contact: Nick or Sue Hamilton
Opening Times: 0900-1700 Mar-May & Sep-Oct, 0900-1900 Jun-Aug, 1000-1600 Nov-Feb, 7 days. Closed 22nd & 25th Dec.
Min Mail Order UK: Nmc
Min Mail Order EU: Nmc
Cat. Cost: A5 + 5 × 1st class.
Credit Cards: All major credit/debit cards
Specialities: Wide range of choice & unusual garden plants. Over 140 varieties of *Penstemon*, over 200 varieties of *Hemerocallis*.
Map Ref: M, B3

MBPg **BARNFIELD PELARGONIUMS** ⊠ ⌂
Barnfield, Off Wilnecote Lane, Belgrave, Tamworth, Staffordshire, B77 2LF
Ⓣ (01827) 250123
Ⓕ (01827) 250123
Ⓔ brianandjenniewhite@hotmail.com
Contact: Jennie & Brian White
Opening Times: Open by appt. only.
Min Mail Order UK: £4.00
Min Mail Order EU: £6.50
Cat. Cost: 4 × 2nd class.
Credit Cards: None
Specialities: Over 200 varieties of scented leaf pelargoniums.

MBre **BRETBY NURSERIES** ♿
Bretby Lane, Burton-on-Trent, Staffordshire, DE15 0QS
Ⓣ (01283) 703355
Ⓕ (01283) 704035
Ⓔ bretby.nurseries@virgin.net
Ⓦ www.bretbynurseries.co.uk
Contact: Mrs S Lord
Opening Times: 0900-1700 Mon-Sat, 1030-1630 Sun.
Cat. Cost: Info. on request.
Credit Cards: All major credit/debit cards
Specialities: Wide range of shrubs.
Map Ref: M, B2

MBri **BRIDGEMERE NURSERIES** € ♿ ◆
Bridgemere, Nr Nantwich, Cheshire, CW5 7QB
Ⓣ (01270) 521100
Ⓕ (01270) 520215
Ⓔ info@bridgemere.co.uk
Ⓦ www.bridgemere.co.uk
Contact: Keith Atkey, Roger Pierce
Opening Times: 0900-1900 7 days, summer. 0900-1800 winter. Closed 25th & 26th Dec.
Cat. Cost: None issued
Credit Cards: Visa Access MasterCard Switch
Specialities: Huge range outdoor & indoor plants, many rare & unusual. Specimen shrubs.
Map Ref: M, B1 **OS Grid Ref:** SJ727435

MBrN **BRIDGE NURSERY** € ♿
Tomlow Road, Napton-on-the-Hill, Nr Rugby, Warwickshire, CV47 8HX
Ⓣ (01926) 812737
Ⓔ pmartino@beeb.net
Ⓦ www.Bridge-Nursery.co.uk
Contact: Christine Dakin & Philip Martino
Opening Times: 1000-1600 Fri-Sun 1st Feb-22nd Dec. Other times by appt.
Cat. Cost: 4 × 1st class.

Credit Cards: None
Specialities: Ornamental grasses, sedges & bamboos. Also range of shrubs & perennials. Display garden.
Notes: Also sells wholesale.
Map Ref: M, C2 **OS Grid Ref:** SP463625

MCCP COLLECTORS CORNER PLANTS ⊠ ♠
33 Rugby Road, Clifton-upon-Dunsmore, Rugby, Warwickshire, CV23 0DE
Ⓣ (01788) 571881
Contact: Pat Neesam
Opening Times: By appt. only.
Min Mail Order UK: £20.00
Cat. Cost: 6 × 1st class.
Credit Cards: None
Specialities: General range of choice herbaceous perennials, grasses, shrubs, palms, ferns & bamboos.
Map Ref: M, C3

MCoo COOL TEMPERATE ⊠ ✈
(office) 45 Stamford Street, Awsworth, Nottinghamshire, NG16 2QL
Ⓣ (0115) 916 2673
Ⓕ (0115) 916 2673
Ⓔ phil.corbett@cooltemperate.co.uk
Ⓦ www.cooltemperate.co.uk
Contact: Phil Corbett
Opening Times: 0900-1700, 7 days. Please ring/write first.
Min Mail Order UK: Nmc
Min Mail Order EU: Nmc
Cat. Cost: 3 × 1st class.
Credit Cards: None
Specialities: Tree fruit, soft fruit, nitrogen-fixers, hedging, own-root fruit trees. Many species available in small quantities only.
Notes: Nursery at Trinity Farm, Awsworth Lane, Cossall, Notts. Also sells wholesale.
Map Ref: M, B2 **OS Grid Ref:** SK482435

MCot COTON MANOR GARDEN
Guilsborough, Northampton, Northamptonshire, NN6 8RQ
Ⓣ (01604) 740219
Ⓕ (01604) 740838
Ⓔ pasleytyler@cotonmanor.fsnet.co.uk
Ⓦ www.cotonmanor.co.uk
Contact: Caroline Tait
Opening Times: 1200-1730 Tue-Sat, 1st April (or Easter if earlier) to 30th Sep. Also Sun Apr, May & B/hol w/ends. Other times in working hours by appt.
Cat. Cost: None issued.
Credit Cards: MasterCard Visa
Specialities: Wide-range of herbaceous perennials (3000+ varieties), some available in small quantities only. Also tender perennials & selected shrubs.
Notes: Garden open. Tea rooms. Garden School. Partial wheelchair access.
Map Ref: M, C3 **OS Grid Ref:** SP675715

MCri CRIN GARDENS ⊠
79 Partons Road, Kings Heath, Birmingham, B14 6TD
Ⓣ 0121 443 3815
Ⓕ 0121 443 3815
Ⓔ cringardens@tiscali.co.uk
Contact: M Milinkovic
Opening Times: Not open. Mail order only.
Min Mail Order UK: Nmc
Cat. Cost: 2 × 1st class
Credit Cards: None
Specialities: Lilies. Ltd. stock available on first come, first served basis.

MDKP D K PLANTS ♠
(Office) 19 Harbourne Road, Cheadle, Stoke on Trent, Staffordshire, ST10 1JU
Ⓣ (01538) 754460 (office)
Ⓜ 07779 545015 (nursery)
Ⓔ davidknoxc@aol.com
Contact: Dave Knox
Opening Times: 0900-2000 (or dusk if earlier) Mon-Tue & Thu-Fri. Other times by appt.
Cat. Cost: 4 × 1st class A4 sae + 46p 1st or 35p 2nd class.
Credit Cards: None
Specialities: Unusual hardy alpines & perennials. All grown on the nursery.
Notes: Nursery is at new roundabout across from Queen's Arms pub, Freehay Crossroads, Freehay, Cheadle, ST10 1TR.
Map Ref: M, B1

MDun DUNGE VALLEY GARDENS € ♿
Windgather Rocks, Kettleshulme, High Peak, Cheshire, SK23 7RF
Ⓣ (01663) 733787
Ⓕ (01663) 733787
Ⓔ plants@dungevalley.co.uk
Ⓦ www.dungevalley.co.uk
Contact: David Ketley
Opening Times: 1030-1700 Thu-Sun Mar & Apr, Tue-Sun May, Thu-Sun Jun, Jul & Aug. Open B/Hols. Otherwise by appt.
Cat. Cost: 2 × 1st class.
Credit Cards: All major credit/debit cards

KEY
⊠ Mail order to UK or EU ♠ Delivers to shows
✈ Exports beyond EU € Euro accepted
♿ Accessible by wheelchair ◆ See Display advertisement

M

Specialities: *Rhododendron* species & hybrids. Magnolias, acers, *Meconopsis*, trilliums, trees, shrubs & perennials, some rare & wild collected.
Notes: Also sells wholesale.
Map Ref: M, A2 **OS Grid Ref:** SJ989777

MEHN ELIZABETH HOUSE NURSERY ⌂ ♿
Weedon Lois, Towcester, Northamptonshire, NN12 8PN
Ⓣ (01327) 860056
Ⓕ (01327) 860779
Ⓔ elizabeth.house@andertontiger.com
Contact: Lindsey Cartwright
Opening Times: 1000-1700 Thu-Sat, Mar-Oct.
Cat. Cost: 2 × 1st class.
Credit Cards: None
Specialities: Wide range of hardy perennials.
Notes: Also sells wholesale.
Map Ref: M, C3 **OS Grid Ref:** SP604472

MFie FIELD HOUSE NURSERIES ⊠ € ♿
Leake Road, Gotham, Nottinghamshire, NG11 0JN
Ⓣ (0115) 9830278
Ⓕ (0115) 9831486
Ⓔ dlvwjw@field-house-alpines.fsbusiness.co.uk
Contact: Doug Lochhead & Valerie A Woolley
Opening Times: 0900-1600 Fri-Wed or by appt.
Min Mail Order UK: 4 plants.
Min Mail Order EU: £30.00
Cat. Cost: 4 × 1st or 4 × IRCs.
Credit Cards: Visa Access
Specialities: *Primula*, auriculas. 3 Nat. Collections of *Primula* and *P. auricula*.
Notes: Mail order for *Primula*, auriculas & seeds only.
Map Ref: M, B3

MFOX FOX COTTAGE PLANTS ⌂ ♿
Yew Tree Farm, Thatchers Lane, Tansley, Matlock, Derbyshire, DE4 5FD
Ⓣ (01629) 57493
Ⓜ 07787 963966
Ⓕ (01629) 57493
Ⓔ avril@yewtreefarm1.fslife.co.uk
Contact: Mrs Avril Buckley
Opening Times: 1200-1700 Wed-Sat, Feb-Sep, Nov-Oct by appt. Please ring to confirm.
Cat. Cost: 2 × 1st class.
Credit Cards: None
Specialities: Unusual hardy & tender perennials. Stock available in small quantities only.
Map Ref: M, C2 **OS Grid Ref:** SK324594

MGan GANDY'S (ROSES) LTD ⊠
North Kilworth, Nr Lutterworth, Leicestershire, LE17 6HZ
Ⓣ (01858) 880398
Ⓕ (01858) 880433
Ⓔ sales@gandys-roses.co.uk
Ⓦ www.gandys-roses.co.uk
Contact: Miss R D Gandy
Opening Times: 0900-1700 Mon-Sat.
Min Mail Order UK: Nmc
Min Mail Order EU: £25.00 + p&p
Cat. Cost: Free.
Credit Cards: All major credit/debit cards
Specialities: Wide range of rose varieties, hardy nursery stock & fruit.
Notes: Also sells wholesale.

MGol GOLDEN COTTAGE PLANTS ⊠
Golden Cottage, Scarcliffe Lanes, Upper Langwith, Mansfield, Nottinghamshire, NG20 9RQ
Ⓜ 07952 804077
Contact: C Coleman
Opening Times: By appt. only.
Min Mail Order UK: Nmc
Min Mail Order EU: Nmc
Cat. Cost: 1 × 1st class.
Credit Cards: None
Specialities: Ethnobotanical plants. Hardy, tropical & sub-tropical. All plants available in small quantities only, ie 2 plants/person/species.

MGos GOSCOTE NURSERIES LTD ♿ ◆
Syston Road, Cossington, Leicestershire, LE7 4UZ
Ⓣ (01509) 812121
Ⓕ (01509) 814231
Ⓔ sales@goscote.co.uk
Ⓦ www.goscote.co.uk
Contact: James Toone, Brian Phipps
Opening Times: 7 days, closed between Xmas & New Year.
Cat. Cost: Online only.
Credit Cards: Visa Access MasterCard Delta Switch
Specialities: Japanese maples, rhododendrons & azaleas, *Magnolia*, *Camellia*, *Pieris* & other *Ericaceae*. Ornamental trees & shrubs, conifers, fruit, heathers, alpines, *Clematis* & unusual climbers. Show Garden to visit.
Notes: Design & landscaping service available. Also sells wholesale.
Map Ref: M, B3 **OS Grid Ref:** SK602130

MHar HARTS GREEN NURSERY
89 Harts Green Road, Harborne, Birmingham, B17 9TZ
Ⓣ (0121) 427 5200

Contact: B Richardson
Opening Times: 1400-1730 Wed Apr-Jul. Other times, excl. Aug, by appt.
Cat. Cost: None issued.
Credit Cards: None
Specialities: Hardy perennials. Some in small quantities only.
Map Ref: M, C2 **OS Grid Ref:** SP030845

MHer THE HERB NURSERY ♿
Thistleton, Oakham, Rutland, LE15 7RE
Ⓣ (01572) 767658
Ⓕ (01572) 768021
Ⓦ www.herbnursery.co.uk
Contact: Peter Bench
Opening Times: 0900-1800 (or dusk) 7 days excl. Xmas-New Year.
Cat. Cost: A5 sae.
Credit Cards: None
Specialities: Herbs, wildflowers, cottage garden plants, scented-leaf pelargoniums. Especially *Thymus*, *Mentha*, *Lavandula*.
Map Ref: M, B3

MHom HOMESTEAD PLANTS ⊠
The Homestead, Normanton, Bottesford, Nottingham, NG13 0EP
Ⓣ (01949) 842745
Ⓕ (01949) 842745
Contact: Mrs S Palmer
Opening Times: By appt.
Min Mail Order UK: Nmc
Cat. Cost: 4 × 2nd class.
Credit Cards: None
Specialities: Unusual hardy & half-hardy perennials, especially *Paeonia* species. *Hosta*, *Jovibarba*, *Sempervivum* & *Heliotrope*. Drought-tolerant asters. Most available only in small quantities. Nat. Collection of *Heliotropium* cultivars.
Map Ref: M, B3 **OS Grid Ref:** SK812407

MHrb THE HERB GARDEN ♿
Kingston House Estate, Race Farm Lane, Kingston Bagpuize, Oxfordshire, OX13 5AU
Ⓣ (01865) 823101
Ⓕ (01865) 820159
Ⓔ vcjw37@yahoo.com
Ⓦ www.KingstonHerbGarden.co.uk
Contact: Val Williams
Opening Times: Phone for appt. or check website for details.
Cat. Cost: 2 × 1st class.
Credit Cards: None
Specialities: Small nursery specialising in the more unusual lavenders, herbs, dye plants, olive & citrus fruit trees according to season, displayed in a walled garden setting.
Map Ref: M, D2

MIDC IAN AND DEBORAH COPPACK ⊠ ♿
Woodside, Langley Road, Langley, Macclesfield, Cheshire, SK11 0DG
Ⓣ (01260) 253308
Ⓕ (01260) 253308
Ⓔ coppack@worldonline.co.uk
Contact: Ian & Deborah Coppack
Opening Times: 0900-1700 Mar-Sep.
Min Mail Order UK: Nmc
Cat. Cost: 2 × 1st class.
Credit Cards: None
Specialities: *Hosta.*
Notes: Also sells wholesale.
Map Ref: M, A2 **OS Grid Ref:** SJ938715

MJac JACKSON'S NURSERIES
Clifton Campville, Nr Tamworth, Staffordshire, B79 0AP
Ⓣ (01827) 373307
Contact: N Jackson
Opening Times: 0900-1800 Mon Wed-Sat, 1000-1700 Sun.
Cat. Cost: 2 × 1st class.
Credit Cards: None
Specialities: *Fuchsia.*
Notes: Also sells wholesale.
Map Ref: M, B1

MJnS JUNGLE SEEDS AND GARDENS ⊠
PO Box 45, Watlington SPDO, Oxfordshire, OX49 5YR
Ⓣ (01491) 614765
Ⓕ (01491) 612034
Ⓔ enquiry@junglegardens.co.uk
Ⓦ www.junglegardens.co.uk
Contact: Penny White
Opening Times: Mail order only. Open by appt. only to collect plants.
Min Mail Order UK: £11.99 plants. One plant only, £7.85.
Cat. Cost: 2 × 1st class.
Credit Cards: All major credit/debit cards
Specialities: Hardy, semi-hardy & conservatory exotics. Some items ltd. availability.

MJon C & K JONES ⊠ ✈ ♠ € ♿
Golden Fields Nurseries, Barrow Lane, Tarvin, Cheshire, CH3 8JF
Ⓣ (01829) 740663

KEY
⊠ Mail order to UK or EU — Delivers to shows
✈ Exports beyond EU — € Euro accepted
♿ Accessible by wheelchair — ◆ See Display advertisement

M

Ⓕ (01829) 741877
Ⓔ keith@ckjones.freeserve.co.uk
Ⓦ www.jonestherose.co.uk
Contact: Keith Jones
Opening Times: Office hours 0930-1600 Fri-Mon. 1st w/end in each month only & the Fri & Mon either side. Closed Jan & Feb.
Min Mail Order UK: 1 plant + p&p
Min Mail Order EU: Nmc.
Cat. Cost: £1.00.
Credit Cards: MasterCard Visa Maestro Electron Solo
Specialities: Roses.
Notes: Also sells wholesale.
Map Ref: M, B1

MKay **KAYES GARDEN NURSERY** ♿
1700 Melton Road, Rearsby, Leicestershire, LE7 4YR
Ⓣ (01664) 424578
Ⓔ hazelkaye.kgn@nascr.net
Contact: Hazel Kaye
Opening Times: 1000-1700 Tue-Sat & B/hols 1000-1200 Sun Mar-Oct. By appt. Nov, Dec & Feb. Closed Jan.
Cat. Cost: 2 × 1st class.
Credit Cards: None
Specialities: Herbaceous, climbers & aquatic plants. Grasses. Nat. Collection of *Tradescantia* Andersoniana Group.
Map Ref: M, B3 **OS Grid Ref:** SK648140

MLan **LANE END NURSERY** ♿
Old Cherry Lane, Lymm, Cheshire, WA13 0TA
Ⓣ (01925) 752618
Ⓔ rsawyer@onetel.net
Ⓦ www.laneendnursery.co.uk
Contact: I Sawyer
Opening Times: 0930-1730 Thu-Tue Feb-Dec.
Cat. Cost: None issued.
Credit Cards: None
Specialities: AGM plants with a wide range of choice & unusual shrubs, trees, perennials & ferns.
Notes: Nursery mostly accessible for wheelchair users.
Map Ref: M, A1 **OS Grid Ref:** SJ664850

MLBr **LEATHERBRITCHES KITCHEN GARDEN & NURSERY** ♿
(Office) 6 Sycamore Cottages, Parwich, Ashbourne, Derbyshire, DE6 1QL
Ⓣ (01335) 390571 answerphone
Ⓜ 07713 743295
Contact: Bill Whitfield
Opening Times: 1000-1700, 7 days (times vary in winter & poor weather).
Credit Cards: None
Specialities: Herbaceous, shrubs, alpines, bedding.
Notes: Nursery is situated opposite the Bentley Brook Inn, Bakewell Rd (A5056), Fenny Bentley, Ashbourne, DE6 1LF.
Map Ref: M, A2

MLea **LEA RHODODENDRON GARDENS LTD**
☒ ✈ ♿
Lea, Matlock, Derbyshire, DE4 5GH
Ⓣ (01629) 534380/534260
Ⓕ (01629) 534260
Ⓦ www.leagarden.co.uk
Contact: Peter Tye
Opening Times: 1000-1730 7 days 20 Mar-30 Jun. Out of season by appt.
Min Mail Order UK: £15.00 + p&p
Min Mail Order EU: £15.00 + p&p
Cat. Cost: 30p + sae.
Credit Cards: All major credit/debit cards
Specialities: Rhododendrons & azaleas.
Map Ref: M, B1 **OS Grid Ref:** SK324571

MLHP **LONGSTONE HARDY PLANTS NURSERY**
☒ ♿
(office) Stancil House, Barn Furlong, Great Longstone, Nr Bakewell, Derbyshire, DE45 1TR
Ⓣ (01629) 640136
Ⓜ 07762 083674
Ⓔ lucyinlongstone@hotmail.com
Ⓦ www.longstonehardyplants.co.uk
Contact: Lucy Wright
Opening Times: 1300-1700 Tue-Sat, 1st Apr-30th Sep. 1300-1700 Sat, Mar & Oct. Other times by appt.
Min Mail Order UK: Nmc
Cat. Cost: 2 × 1st class.
Credit Cards: None
Specialities: Specialist peat-free nursery displaying and producing all our own hardy perennials & shrubs, incl. many unusual varieties. Some stock available in small quantities only. Can propagate to order.
Notes: Nursery at Station Road 150 yds on right after turning onto it at the village green.
Map Ref: M, A2 **OS Grid Ref:** SK198717

MLLN **LODGE LANE NURSERY & GARDENS** ♿
Lodge Lane, Dutton, Nr Warrington, Cheshire, WA4 4HP
Ⓣ (01928) 713718
Ⓕ (01928) 713718
Ⓔ info@lodgelanenursery.co.uk
Ⓦ www.lodgelanenursery.co.uk
Contact: Jack Stewart

Opening Times: 1000-1700 Wed-Sun & B/hols, mid Mar-mid Sep. By appt. outside these dates.
Cat. Cost: 3 × 1st class.
Credit Cards: All major credit/debit cards
Specialities: Unusual perennials & shrubs incl. *Achillea*, *Allium*, *Astrantia*, *Campanula*, *Digitalis*, *Penstemon*, *Euphorbia*, *Geranium*, *Heuchera*, *Inula*, *Kniphofia*, *Nepeta*, *Papaver*, *Penstemon*, *Salvia* & ornamental grasses. Nat. Collection of *Inula*.
Map Ref: M, A1 **OS Grid Ref:** SJ586779

MLod LODGE FARM HERBS, PLANTS & WILDFLOWERS ⊠ ☗ € ♿
Case Lane, Fiveways, Hatton, Warwickshire, CV35 7JD
Ⓣ (01926) 484649
Ⓜ 07977 631368
Ⓕ (01926) 484649
Ⓔ lodgefarmplants@btinternet.com
Ⓦ www.lodgefarmplants.com
Contact: Janet Cook & Nick Cook
Opening Times: 1000-1700 Tue-Sun (closed Mon), Mar-end Oct. Please phone to check availability & for directions. Nov-Feb by appt. only, please phone first.
Min Mail Order UK: Nmc
Cat. Cost: 2 × 1st class.
Credit Cards: None
Specialities: Wildflowers, herbs and sensual plants. Vegetable plants, fruit, topiary. Native trees & hedging. Old-fashioned cottage garden plants. Wildflower seeds.
Notes: Will be at Malvern Spring Show & Gardeners World Live 2006. Also sells wholesale.
Map Ref: M, C2 **OS Grid Ref:** SP223700

MLul LULWORTH PLANTS ☗ ♿
28 Gladstone Street, Wigston Magna, Leicestershire, LE18 1AE
Ⓜ 07814 042889
Contact: Chris Huscroft
Opening Times: By appt. only.
Cat. Cost: Sae
Credit Cards: None
Specialities: *Arisaema*, plus small selection of shade-loving plants, small quantities only.
Map Ref: M, B3

MMHG MORTON HALL GARDENS ⊠ ☗ ♿
Morton Hall, Ranby, Retford, Nottinghamshire, DN22 8HW
Ⓣ (01777) 702530
Ⓔ gill@mortonhall.fsbusiness.co.uk
Contact: Gill McMaster
Opening Times: By appt.only
Min Mail Order UK: £5.00 + p&p
Cat. Cost: 3 × 1st class.
Credit Cards: None
Specialities: Shrubs & perennials.
Map Ref: M, A3

MMoz MOZART HOUSE NURSERY GARDEN ☗
84 Central Avenue, Wigston, Leicestershire, LE18 2AA
Ⓣ (0116) 288 9548
Contact: Des Martin
Opening Times: By appt. only.
Cat. Cost: 5 × 1st class.
Credit Cards: None
Specialities: Bamboo, ornamental grasses, rushes & sedges, ferns. Some stock available in small quantities.
Map Ref: M, C3

MMuc MUCKLESTONE NURSERIES ⊠ € ♿
Church Farm, Rock Lane, Mucklestone, Nr Market Drayton, Shropshire, TF9 4DN
Ⓣ (01630) 674242
Ⓜ 07985 425829
Ⓔ enquiries@botanyplants.com
Ⓦ www.botanyplants.com
Contact: Brian Watkins
Opening Times: Times may vary, please check first.
Min Mail Order UK: Nmc
Cat. Cost: Online only.
Credit Cards: Visa Switch MasterCard
Specialities: Plants for acid & damp soils of the north & western UK.
Notes: Also sells wholesale.
Map Ref: M, B2 **OS Grid Ref:** SJ728373

MNew NEWINGTON NURSERIES € ♿
Newington, Wallingford, Oxfordshire, OX10 7AW
Ⓣ (01865) 400533
Ⓔ plants@newington-nurseries.co.uk
Ⓦ www.newington-nurseries.co.uk
Contact: Mrs A T Hendry
Opening Times: 1000-1700 Tues-Sun Mar-Oct, 1000-1600 Tues-Sun Nov-Feb.
Cat. Cost: 2 × 1st class.
Credit Cards: Access MasterCard Visa Switch
Specialities: Unusual cottage garden plants, alpines, hardy exotics, conservatory plants & herbs. Nat. Collection of *Alocasia* (*Araceae*).
Notes: Also sells wholesale.
Map Ref: M, D3

KEY		
	⊠ Mail order to UK or EU	☗ Delivers to shows
	✈ Exports beyond EU	€ Euro accepted
	♿ Accessible by wheelchair	◆ See Display advertisement

M

MNFA **The Nursery Further Afield** ⊠ ♿
Evenley Road, Mixbury, Nr Brackley, Northamptonshire, NN13 5YR
Ⓣ (01280) 848808
Ⓕ (01280) 848539
Ⓔ sinclair@nurseryfurtherafield.co.uk
Ⓦ www.nurseryfurtherafield.co.uk
Contact: Gerald & Mary Sinclair
Opening Times: 1000-1700 Wed-Sat, mid-Mar-early Oct. Other times by appt.
Min Mail Order UK: Nmc
Cat. Cost: 2 × 1st class.
Credit Cards: None
Specialities: Worthwhile hardy perennials, many unusual. Large selection of *Geranium* & *Hemerocallis*. Nat. Collection of *Hemerocallis*.
Notes: Mail order for *Hemerocallis* only.
Map Ref: M, C3 **OS Grid Ref:** SP608344

M

MNHC **The National Herb Centre** ♿
Banbury Road, Warmington, Nr Banbury, Oxfordshire, OX17 1DF
Ⓣ (01295) 690999
Ⓕ (01295) 690034
Ⓦ www.herbcentre.co.uk
Contact: Nick Turner
Opening Times: 0900-1730 Mon-Sat, 1030-1700 Sun.
Credit Cards: All major credit/debit cards
Specialities: Herbs, culinary & medicinal. Extensive selection of rosemary, thyme & lavender, in particular.
Map Ref: M, C2 **OS Grid Ref:** SP413471

MNrw **Norwell Nurseries** ⊠ ♿ ◆
Woodhouse Road, Norwell, Newark, Nottinghamshire, NG23 6JX
Ⓣ (01636) 636337
Ⓔ wardha@aol.com
Contact: Dr Andrew Ward
Opening Times: 1000-1700 Mon, Wed-Fri & Sun (Wed-Mon May & Jun). By appt. Aug & 20th Oct-1st Mar.
Min Mail Order UK: £12.00 + p&p
Cat. Cost: 3 × 1st class.
Credit Cards: None
Specialities: A large collection of unusual & choice herbaceous perennials & alpines esp. *Penstemon*, hardy geraniums, *Geum*, cottage garden plants, *Hemerocallis*, grasses & woodland plants. Gardens open.
Notes: Also sells wholesale.
Map Ref: M, B3 **OS Grid Ref:** SK767616

MPes **Plantessential Ltd.** ⊠ ◆
29 Kingrove Avenue, Beeston, Nottinghamshire, NG9 4DQ
Ⓣ (0115) 877 6965
Ⓕ (0115) 877 6965
Ⓔ info@plantessential.com
Ⓦ www.plantessential.com
Contact: Stephen Pasek
Opening Times: Not open. Mail order only.
Min Mail Order UK: Nmc
Cat. Cost: Free.
Credit Cards: All major credit/debit cards
Specialities: Hardy garden ferns. Tropical ferns. *Cyclamen*, pelargoniums.
Notes: Payment: online secure credit card system, telephone/post by cheque. Sells at local farmers' markets (see website for details). Also sells wholesale.

MPet **Peter Grayson (Sweet Pea Seedsman)** ⊠ ✈
34 Glenthorne Close, Brampton, Chesterfield, Derbyshire, S40 3AR
Ⓣ (01246) 278503
Ⓕ (01246) 278503
Contact: Peter Grayson
Opening Times: Not open. Mail order only.
Min Mail Order UK: Nmc
Min Mail Order EU: Nmc
Cat. Cost: C5 sae, 1 × 2nd class.
Credit Cards: None
Specialities: *Lathyrus* species & cvs. Large collection of old-fashioned sweet peas & over 100 Spencer sweet peas incl. own cultivars and collection of old-fashioned cottage garden annuals & perennials.
Notes: Also sells wholesale.

MPhe **Phedar Nursery** ⊠ ✈ €
Bunkers Hill, Romiley, Stockport, Cheshire, SK6 3DS
Ⓣ (0161) 430 3772
Ⓕ (0161) 430 3772
Ⓔ mclewin@phedar.com
Ⓦ www.phedar.com
Contact: Will McLewin
Opening Times: Frequent esp. in spring but very irregular. Please phone to arrange appt.
Min Mail Order UK: Nmc
Min Mail Order EU: Nmc
Cat. Cost: 2 × A5 envelopes or address labels + 4 × 1st class
Credit Cards: None
Specialities: *Helleborus*, *Paeonia*. Limited stock of some rare items.
Notes: Non-EU exports subject to destination & on an ad hoc basic only. Please contact nursery for details. Also sells wholesale.
Map Ref: M, A2 **OS Grid Ref:** SJ936897

MPkF **PACKHORSE FARM NURSERY** ♠ ♿
Sandyford House, Lant Lane, Tansley, Matlock, Derbyshire, DE4 5FW
Ⓣ (01629) 57206 Ⓜ 07974 095752
Ⓕ (01629) 57206
Contact: Hilton W Haynes
Opening Times: 1000-1700 Tues & Wed, 1st Mar-31st Oct. Any other time by appt. only.
Cat. Cost: 2 × 1st class for plant list.
Credit Cards: None
Specialities: *Acer*, rare stock is limited in supply. Other more unusual hardy shrubs, trees & conifers.
Map Ref: M, B2 **OS Grid Ref:** SK322617

MPop **POPPIES NURSERY**
Ashby Pastures, Pasture Lane, Ashby Folville, Melton Mowbray, Leicestershire, LE14 2TT
Ⓣ (01664) 840894
Ⓔ robin_njones@lineone.net
Contact: Sheila Jones
Opening Times: By appt. only.
Cat. Cost: A4 sae.
Credit Cards: None
Specialities: Hardy perennials.

MPRe **PLANTS FOR ALL REASONS** ☒ ♿
Woodshoot Nurseries, King's Bromley, Burton-upon-Trent, Staffordshire, DE13 7HN
Ⓣ (01543) 472233
Ⓕ (01543) 472115
Ⓔ sales@plants-for-all-reasons.com
Ⓦ www.plants-for-all-reasons.com
Contact: Richard Flint
Opening Times: 0900-1700, 7 days.
Min Mail Order UK: £20.00 + p&p
Cat. Cost: 2 × 1st class.
Credit Cards: All major credit/debit cards
Specialities: *Phormium*, *Pittosporum*, *Tropaeolum*, *Daphne*, palms, *Agave*, *Acacia*, *Dicksonia*, citrus, olives & cordylines.
Notes: Also sells wholesale.
Map Ref: M, B2 **OS Grid Ref:** SK127164

MRav **RAVENSTHORPE NURSERY** ☒ ♿
6 East Haddon Road, Ravensthorpe, Northamptonshire, NN6 8ES
Ⓣ (01604) 770548
Ⓕ (01604) 770548
Ⓔ ravensthorpenursery@hotmail.com
Contact: Jean & Richard Wiseman
Opening Times: 1000-1800 (dusk if earlier) Tue-Sun. Also B/hol Mons.
Min Mail Order UK: Nmc
Min Mail Order EU: Nmc
Cat. Cost: None issued.
Credit Cards: Visa MasterCard
Specialities: Over 2,600 different trees, shrubs & perennials with many unusual varieties.
Notes: Search & delivery service for large orders, winter months only.
Map Ref: M, C3 **OS Grid Ref:** SP665699

MRea **REARSBY ROSES** ☒ ♠ ♿
Melton Road, Rearsby, Leicestershire, LE7 4YP
Ⓣ 0116 2601211
Ⓕ 0116 2640013
Contact: Mark Halford
Opening Times: 1000-1600 Mon, Fri & Sat. 1200-1600 Sun. Closed Tue, Wed, Thu. Please phone for confirmation as times may change. Seasonal variations apply.
Min Mail Order UK: Nmc
Cat. Cost: Free.
Credit Cards: All major credit/debit cards
Specialities: Roses. Rose root stocks (briars). Standard Roses. Presentation planters/baskets. New roses for you to name.
Notes: Also sells wholesale.
Map Ref: M, B3

MSal **SALLEY GARDENS** ☒ ✈ € ♿
32 Lansdowne Drive, West Bridgford, Nottinghamshire, NG2 7FJ
Ⓣ (0115) 9233878 evenings
Ⓜ 07811 703982
Ⓔ richienothavens@hotmail.com
Ⓦ www.thesalleygardens.co.uk
Contact: Richard Lewin
Opening Times: 0900-1700 Sun only, 1st Apr-30th Sep and by appt.
Min Mail Order UK: Nmc
Min Mail Order EU: Nmc
Cat. Cost: Sae.
Credit Cards: None
Specialities: Medicinal plants esp. from North America & China. Dye plants, herbs, spices, seeds. Some species available in small quanitities only.
Notes: Nursery is at Simkins Farm, Adbolton Lane, West Bridgford, Notts.
Map Ref: M, B3

MSGs **SHOWGLADS** ☒ €
105 Derby Road, Bramcote, Nottingham, NG9 3GZ
Ⓣ (0115) 925 5498
Ⓔ rogerbb@lineone.net
Ⓦ www.showglads.com
Contact: Roger Braithwaite

KEY
☒ Mail order to UK or EU ♠ Delivers to shows
✈ Exports beyond EU € Euro accepted
♿ Accessible by wheelchair ◆ See Display advertisement

Opening Times: Not open. Mail order only.
Min Mail Order UK: £4.00
Cat. Cost: 3 × 1st class.
Credit Cards: None
Specialities: *Gladiolus*.

MSSP S & S PERENNIALS ⊠
24 Main Street, Normanton Le Heath, Leicestershire, LE67 2TB
Ⓣ (01530) 262250
Contact: Shirley Pierce
Opening Times: Afternoons only, otherwise please phone.
Min Mail Order UK: Nmc
Cat. Cost: 2 × 1st class.
Credit Cards: None
Specialities: *Erythronium*, *Fritillaria*, hardy *Cyclamen*, dwarf *Narcissus* & *Anemone*. Stock available in small quantities only.
Map Ref: M, B1

M

MSte STEVENTON ROAD NURSERIES € ♿
Steventon Road, East Hanney, Wantage, Oxfordshire, OX12 0HS
Ⓣ (01235) 868828
Ⓕ (01235) 763670
Ⓔ johngraham.steventonroadnursery@virgin.net
Ⓦ www.steventonroadnurseries.co.uk
Contact: John Graham
Opening Times: 0900-1700 Mon-Fri, 1000-1700 Sat Mar-Nov. Winter by appt. Closed Sun.
Cat. Cost: 4 × 1st class.
Credit Cards: None
Specialities: Tender & hardy perennials.
Map Ref: M, D2

MSwo SWALLOWS NURSERY ⊠ ♿
Mixbury, Brackley, Northamptonshire, NN13 5RR
Ⓣ (01280) 847721
Ⓕ (01280) 848611
Ⓔ enq@swallowsnursery.co.uk
Ⓦ www.swallowsnursery.co.uk
Contact: Chris Swallow
Opening Times: 0900-1300 & 1400-1700 (earlier in winter) Mon-Fri, 0900-1300 Sat.
Min Mail Order UK: £15.00
Cat. Cost: 3 × 1st class (plus phone number).
Credit Cards: Visa MasterCard Switch
Specialities: Growing a wide range, particularly shrubs, trees, roses and heathers.
Notes: Trees not for mail order unless part of larger order. Nursery transport used where possible, esp. for trees. Also sells wholesale.
Map Ref: M, C3 **OS Grid Ref:** SP607336

MTho A & A THORP
Bungalow No 5, Main Street, Theddingworth, Leicestershire, LE17 6QZ
Ⓣ (01858) 880496
Contact: Anita & Andrew Thorp
Opening Times: 1000-1700.
Cat. Cost: 4 × 1st class.
Credit Cards: None
Specialities: Unusual plants or those in short supply.
Map Ref: M, C3

MTis TISSINGTON NURSERY ⌂ ♿
Tissington, Nr Ashbourne, Derbyshire, DE6 1RA
Ⓣ (01335) 390650
Ⓔ info@tissingtonnursery.co.uk
Ⓦ www.tissingtonnursery.co.uk
Contact: Mairi Longdon
Opening Times: 1000-1800 daily 1st Mar-30th Sep incl. Easter Sun & B/hols.
Cat. Cost: 3 × 1st class.
Credit Cards: Visa MasterCard
Specialities: Perennials, shrubs & climbers incl. unusual varieties. Some available in small quantities only.
Notes: Now under same ownership as Bensley Nurseries (MBnl) & offering same range of plants.
Map Ref: M, B1 **OS Grid Ref:** SK176521

MTPN SMART PLANTS ⊠ ⌂ ♿
Sandy Hill Lane, Off Overstone Road, Moulton, Northampton, NN3 7JB
Ⓣ (01604) 454106
Contact: Stuart Smart
Opening Times: 1000-1500 Thu & Fri, 1000-1700 Sat. Other times by appt.
Min Mail Order UK: Nmc
Cat. Cost: 3 × 1st class.
Credit Cards: None
Specialities: Wide range of herbaceous, alpines, shrubs, grasses, hardy geraniums, *Sempervivum* & succulents.
Map Ref: M, C3

MWar WARD FUCHSIAS ⊠
5 Pollen Close, Sale, Cheshire, M33 3LS
Ⓣ (0161) 282 7434
Contact: K Ward
Opening Times: 0930-1700 Tue-Sun Feb-Jun incl. B/hols.
Min Mail Order UK: Nmc
Cat. Cost: Free.
Credit Cards: None
Specialities: *Fuchsia*. Available in small quantities.
Map Ref: M, A2

MWat WATERPERRY GARDENS LTD ♿
Waterperry, Nr Wheatley, Oxfordshire, OX33 1JZ
Ⓣ (01844) 339226 or 339254
Ⓕ (01844) 339883
Ⓔ office@waterperrygardens.co.uk
Ⓦ www.waterperrygardens.co.uk
Contact: Mr R Jacobs
Opening Times: 0900-1730 summer. 0900-1700 winter.
Min Mail Order UK: Nmc
Cat. Cost: Online only.
Credit Cards: All major credit/debit cards
Specialities: General, plus Nat. Collection of *Saxifraga* (subsect. *Kabschia* & *Engleria*).
Map Ref: M, D3 **OS Grid Ref:** SP630064

MWea WEAR'S NURSERY ♿
(office) 84 Wantage Road, Wallingford, Oxfordshire, OX10 0LY
Ⓣ 07790 425284
Ⓕ (01491) 837803
Ⓦ www.wearsnursery.co.uk
Contact: David Wear
Opening Times: 1000-1700 Mon-Sat, Feb-Oct. 1000-1600 Sun (closed Sun in Aug). 1000-1600 Mon-Sat, Nov-Jan, please telephone first as may be closed on some days in winter.
Cat. Cost: Plant list online.
Credit Cards: None
Specialities: Unusual herbaceous varieties & shrubs. Large selection of *Geranium*. Some plants only available in small numbers.
Notes: Nursery sited at High Road, Brightwell cum Sotwell, Wallingford.
Map Ref: M, D3 **OS Grid Ref:** SU590910

MWgw WINGWELL NURSERY
Top Street, Wing, Oakham, Rutland, LE15 8SE
Ⓣ (01572) 737727
Ⓕ (01572) 737788
Ⓔ rosedejardin@btopenworld.com
Contact: Rose Dejardin
Opening Times: 1000-1700 daily Feb-Oct, or by appt.
Min Mail Order UK: Nmc
Cat. Cost: £1.00 for descriptive cat.
Credit Cards: All major credit/debit cards
Specialities: Herbaceous perennials.
Map Ref: M, B3 **OS Grid Ref:** SP892029

MWhe A D & N WHEELER 🛈
Pye Court, Willoughby, Rugby, Warwickshire, CV23 8BZ
Ⓣ (01788) 890341
Ⓕ (01788) 890341
Contact: Mrs N Wheeler
Opening Times: 1000-1630 7 days mid Feb-late Jun. Other times please phone for appt.
Cat. Cost: 3 × 1st class.
Credit Cards: None
Specialities: *Fuchsia*, *Pelargonium* & hardy geraniums.
Map Ref: M, C3

MWht WHITELEA NURSERY ⊠ ♿
Whitelea Lane, Tansley, Matlock, Derbyshire, DE4 5FL
Ⓣ (01629) 55010
Ⓔ whitelea@nursery-stock.freeserve.co.uk
Ⓦ www.uk-bamboos.co.uk
Contact: David Wilson
Opening Times: By appt.
Min Mail Order UK: No minimum charge
Cat. Cost: Online only. Price list available 2 × 1st class.
Credit Cards: None
Specialities: *Bamboo*, ivies. Substantial quantities of 45 cvs & species of bamboo, remainder stocked in small numbers only.
Notes: Also sells wholesale.
Map Ref: M, B1 **OS Grid Ref:** SK325603

MWrn WARREN HILLS NURSERY ⊠ 🛈 ♿
Warren Hills Cottage, Warren Hills Road, Coalville, Leicestershire, LE67 4UY
Ⓣ (01530) 812350
Ⓔ warrenhills@tinyworld.co.uk
Ⓦ www.warrenhills.co.uk
Contact: Bob Taylor
Opening Times: By appt. only, please phone. See NGS for open days.
Min Mail Order UK: £10.00 + p&p
Cat. Cost: 4 × 1st class.
Credit Cards: None
Specialities: *Astrantia*. Genuine hardy & unusual perennials. Nat. Collection of *Astrantia*.
Map Ref: M, B1 **OS Grid Ref:** SK459146

MWya WYATTS ⊠ 🛈 € ♿
Hill Barn Farm, Great Rollright, Chipping Norton, Oxfordshire, OX7 5SH
Ⓣ (01608) 684835 or 684990
Ⓔ wyatts@callnetuk.com
Ⓦ www.wyattscountry.com
Contact: John Wyatt or Christine Chittenden
Opening Times: 0900-1700 7 days 21st Oct-1st Mar, 0900-1800 2nd Mar-20th Oct.

KEY
⊠ Mail order to UK or EU — 🛈 Delivers to shows
✈ Exports beyond EU — € Euro accepted
♿ Accessible by wheelchair — ◆ See Display advertisement

M

Min Mail Order UK: £50.00
Cat. Cost: 2 × 1st class.
Credit Cards: MasterCard Switch Delta Visa
Specialities: Many unusual, rare & exotic plants, shrubs & trees incl. *Daphne, Euonymus, Viburnum, Magnolia, Clematis, Cornus* & *Acer*. Alpines, fruit trees & cane fruit. Please check availability list.
Map Ref: M, C2 **OS Grid Ref:** SP317313

MYeo YEOMANS' EXOTICS
2 Carrington Lane, Calverton, Nottingham, NG14 6HQ
Ⓣ 0115 965 4350
Ⓦ www.yeomansexotics.co.uk
Contact: Chris Yeomans
Opening Times: By appt. only Feb-Dec.
Min Mail Order UK: Nmc
Min Mail Order EU: Nmc
Cat. Cost: 1 × 1st class.
Credit Cards: None
Specialities: Carnivorous plants.
Notes: Mail order seeds only. Also sells wholesale.

M

NORTHERN

NAsh ASHTONS NURSERY GARDENS
Mythop Road, Lytham, Lytham St Annes, Lancashire, FY8 4JP
Ⓣ (01253) 736627/794808
Ⓕ (01253) 735311
Ⓔ sales@ashtons-lytham.co.uk
Ⓦ www.ashtons-lytham.co.uk
Contact: T M Ashton
Opening Times: 0900-1700 daily.
Cat. Cost: None issued.
Credit Cards: MasterCard Visa Switch Delta
Specialities: Herbaceous plants. Hardy shrubs.
Notes: Also sells wholesale.
Map Ref: N, D1

NBea BEAMISH CLEMATIS NURSERY €
Burntwood Cottage, Stoney Lane, Beamish, Co. Durham, DH9 0SJ
Ⓣ (0191) 370 0202
Ⓕ (0191) 370 0202
Ⓦ www.beamishclematisnursery.co.uk
Contact: Colin Brown or Jan Wilson
Opening Times: 0900-1700 Wed-Mon, closed Tue. Closed Easter Sun & Xmas week.
Cat. Cost: Online only.
Credit Cards: None
Specialities: *Clematis*, climbers, shrubs & ornamental trees.
Map Ref: N, B2 **OS Grid Ref:** NZ231535

NBee BEECHCROFT JUST TREES
Bongate, Appleby-in-Westmorland, Cumbria, CA16 6UE
Ⓣ (01768) 351201
Ⓕ (01768) 351201
Ⓔ souribrown4@hotmail.com
Contact: Roger Brown
Opening Times: 0900-1700 Tue-Sun, closed Mon.
Min Mail Order UK: Nmc
Cat. Cost: Sae for tree list.
Credit Cards: None
Specialities: Hardy field-grown trees.
Notes: Mail order trees Nov-Mar only. Formerly Beechcroft Nurseries.
Map Ref: N, C1

NBHF BOUNDARY HOUSE FARM
Holmeswood, Rufford, West Lancashire, L40 1UA
Ⓣ (01704) 821333
Ⓕ (01704) 821333
Contact: Linda Birchall
Opening Times: Fri & Sun, Apr-Sep. Phone first.
Credit Cards: None
Specialities: *Achillea*. Grasses.
Map Ref: N, D1 **OS Grid Ref:** SD4217SE

NBhm BEETHAM NURSERIES
Pool Darkin Lane, Beetham, Nr Milnthorpe, Cumbria, LA7 7AP
Ⓣ (01539) 563630
Ⓕ (01539) 564487
Contact: S & L Abbit
Opening Times: 0900-1730 summer, 0900-1730 winter.
Cat. Cost: None issued.
Credit Cards: Visa American Express Switch
Specialities: Comprehensive range of trees, shrubs & herbaceous plants. Many unusual varieties.
Map Ref: N, C1

NBid BIDE-A-WEE COTTAGE GARDENS
Stanton, Netherwitton, Morpeth, Northumberland, NE65 8PR
Ⓣ (01670) 772238
Ⓕ (01670) 772238
Ⓔ bideaweecg@aol.com
Ⓦ www.bideawee.co.uk
Contact: Mark Robson
Opening Times: 1330-1700 Sat & Wed, 22nd Apr-26th Aug 2006.
Min Mail Order UK: £20.00
Cat. Cost: 3 × 1st class.
Credit Cards: All major credit/debit cards

Specialities: Unusual herbaceous perennials, *Primula*, ferns, grasses. Nat. Collection of *Centaurea*.
Map Ref: N, B2 **OS Grid Ref:** NZ132900

NBir **BIRKHEADS SECRET GARDENS & NURSERY** ⊠ ♿
Nr Causey Arch, Sunniside, Newcastle upon Tyne, NE16 5EL
Ⓣ (01207) 232262
Ⓜ 07778 447920
Ⓕ (01207) 232262
Ⓔ birkheads.nursery@virgin.net
Ⓦ www.birkheadsnursery.co.uk
Contact: Mrs Christine Liddle
Opening Times: 1000-1700 daily (except Mon) Mar-mid-Oct. Groups by appt.
Min Mail Order UK: Nmc
Cat. Cost: None issued.
Credit Cards: All major credit/debit cards
Specialities: Hardy herbaceous perennials, grasses, bulbs & herbs. *Allium*, *Campanula*, *Digitalis*, *Euphorbia*, *Geranium*, *Primula*. Max. 30 of any plant propagated each year.
Notes: Mail order Nov-Feb only. Orders taken all year for winter deliveries.
Map Ref: N, B2 **OS Grid Ref:** NZ220569

NBlu **BLUNDELL'S NURSERIES** ♿
68 Southport New Road, Tarleton, Preston, Lancashire, PR4 6HY
Ⓣ (01772) 815442
Ⓔ jerplusjeff@aol.com
Contact: Any member of staff
Opening Times: 0900-1700 daily. Closed Dec-Feb.
Cat. Cost: None issued.
Credit Cards: None
Specialities: Trees, shrubs, incl. topiary & large specimens, conifers. Perennials, alpines, ferns, heathers, herbs, hanging basket/bedding/ conservatory plants, aquatics, hedging, roses. Garden design service available.
Notes: Also sells wholesale.
Map Ref: N, D1

NBPC **THE BARN PLANT CENTRE & GIFT SHOP** ♿
The Square, Scorton, Preston, Lancashire, PR3 1AU
Ⓣ (01524) 793533
Ⓕ (01524) 793533
Ⓔ sales@plantsandgifts.co.uk
Ⓦ www.plantsandgifts.co.uk
Contact: Neil Anderton, Judith Graham
Opening Times: 0900-1700 Mon-Sat, 1000-1800 Sun.
Cat. Cost: 2 1st class.
Credit Cards: All major credit/debit cards
Specialities: 600 varieties of perennials.
Map Ref: N, C1 **OS Grid Ref:** GR501487

NBPN **BLACK PLANTS NURSERY** ⊠
35 Longfield Road, Crookes, Sheffield, S10 1QW
Ⓣ (0114) 268 1700
Ⓔ k@karenplatt.co.uk
Ⓦ www.blackplants.co.uk
Contact: Karen Platt
Opening Times: Not open. Mail order only.
Min Mail Order UK: 6 plants
Min Mail Order EU: 6 plants
Cat. Cost: 3 × 1st class.
Credit Cards: None
Specialities: All black or dark flowered & foliage plants. Over 2,750 plants.
Map Ref: N, D2

NBre **BREEZY KNEES NURSERIES** ♿
Common Lane, Warthill, York,YO19 5XS
Ⓣ (01904) 488800
Contact: Any member of staff
Opening Times: 0930-1700 7 days, 15th March-15th Sep.
Credit Cards: All major credit/debit cards
Specialities: Very wide range of perennials from popular favourites to something decidedly different.
Map Ref: N, C3 **OS Grid Ref:** SE675565

NBro **BROWNTHWAITE HARDY PLANTS** ⊠ ♿
Fell Yeat, Casterton, Kirkby Lonsdale, Lancashire, LA6 2JW
Ⓣ (015242) 71340 (after 1800).
Contact: Chris Benson
Opening Times: Tue-Sun 1st Apr-30th Sep.
Min Mail Order UK: Nmc
Cat. Cost: 3 × 1st class sae for catalogue. Sae for *P. auricula* mail order list, also ltd *Iris* list.
Credit Cards: None
Specialities: Herbaceous perennials & grasses incl. *Geranium*, *Hosta*, *Iris*, especially *I. ensata* & *I. sibirica*, *Heucherella*, *Tiarella*, *Primula auricula* & *P. sieboldii*.
Map Ref: N, C1 **OS Grid Ref:** SD632794

NBtw **BRAITHWELL NURSERIES** € ♿
2 Holywell Cottages, Braithwell, Rotherham, South Yorkshire, S66 7AB
Ⓣ (01709) 812093
Contact: Philip Yardley

KEY
⊠ Mail order to UK or EU — Delivers to shows
✈ Exports beyond EU — € Euro accepted
♿ Accessible by wheelchair — ◆ See Display advertisement

M

Opening Times: 1000-1800 Mar-Nov, times vary Dec-Feb, please phone first. Closed Xmas & New Year.
Cat. Cost: None issued.
Credit Cards: None
Specialities: Wide range incl. shrubs, perennials, grasses, climbers, alpines, bamboos, palms, agave. Many seasonal plants. Some available in small quantities only.
Notes: Nursery on B6427 between Braithwell & Maltby.
Map Ref: N, D2 **OS Grid Ref:** SK535938

NCGa CATH'S GARDEN PLANTS ⊠ ♿
The Walled Garden, Heaves Hotel, Levens, Nr Kendal, Cumbria, LA8 8EF
Ⓣ (01539) 561126
Ⓕ (01539) 561126
Ⓔ cath@cathsgardenplants.fsbusiness.co.uk
Ⓦ www.cathsgardenplants.co.uk
Contact: Bob Sanderson
Opening Times: 1030-1630 Mon-Fri all year, except Xmas & New Year weeks. 1030-1700 Sat & Sun, Mar-Oct.
Min Mail Order UK: Nmc
Min Mail Order EU: £25.00
Cat. Cost: 4 × 1st class.
Credit Cards: All major credit/debit cards
Specialities: Wide variety of perennials, incl. uncommon varieties & selections of grasses, ferns, shrubs & climbing plants.
Notes: Also sells wholesale.
Map Ref: N, C1 **OS Grid Ref:** SD497867

NChi CHIPCHASE CASTLE NURSERY ⊠ ♿
Chipchase Castle, Wark, Hexham, Northumberland, NE48 3NT
Ⓣ (01434) 230083
Ⓔ Joyali-chipchase@hotmail.com
Ⓦ www.chipchaseplants.co.uk
Contact: Joyce Hunt & Alison Jones
Opening Times: 1000-1700 Thu-Sun & B/hol Mons Easter (or 1st Apr)-mid Oct.
Min Mail Order UK: Nmc
Min Mail Order EU: Nmc
Cat. Cost: A5 sae for list
Credit Cards: All major credit/debit cards
Specialities: Unusual herbaceous esp. *Erodium*, *Eryngium*, *Geranium* & *Viola*. Some plants only available in small quantities.
Notes: Suitable for accompanied wheelchair users.
Map Ref: N, B2 **OS Grid Ref:** NY880758

NChl CHILTERN SEEDS ⊠ € ◆
Bortree Stile, Ulverston, Cumbria, LA12 7PB
Ⓣ (01229) 581137 (24 hrs)
Ⓕ (01229) 584549
Ⓔ info@chilternseeds.co.uk
Ⓦ www.chilternseeds.co.uk
Opening Times: Mail order only. Normal office hours, Mon-Fri.
Min Mail Order UK: Nmc
Min Mail Order EU: Nmc
Cat. Cost: 3 × 2nd class.
Credit Cards: All major credit/debit cards
Specialities: Over 4,500 items of all kinds - wildflowers, trees, shrubs, cacti, annuals, houseplants, vegetables & herbs.

NCiC CICELY'S COTTAGE GARDEN PLANTS ⊠
43 Elmers Green, Skelmersdale, Lancashire, WN8 6SG
Ⓣ (01695) 720790
Ⓔ maureen.duncan@ic24.net
Contact: Maureen Duncan
Opening Times: Please phone to avoid disappointment as opening times vary.
Min Mail Order UK: Nmc
Cat. Cost: Free plant list.
Credit Cards: None
Specialities: Hardy, half-hardy & tender perennials incl. *Penstemon*. Traditional & unusual cottage garden plants & pelargoniums. Stock available in small quantities.
Map Ref: N, D1

NCob COBBLE HEY GARDENS ♿
Off Hobbs Lane, Claughton-on-Brock, Garstang, Nr Preston, Lancashire, PR3 0QN
Ⓣ (01995) 602643
Ⓕ (01995) 602643
Ⓔ cobblehey@aol.com
Ⓦ www.cobblehey.co.uk
Contact: Edwina Miller
Opening Times: 1030-1630 w/ends only 1st Apr-30th Sep 2006.
Credit Cards: All major credit/debit cards
Specialities: Wide range of unusual plants grown on hill farm at over 600ft. Specialises in *Phlox paniculata* & geraniums (Nat. Collection status applied for).
Map Ref: N, C1

NCot COTTAGE GARDEN PLANTS ⊠ €
1 Sycamore Close, Whitehaven, Cumbria, CA28 6LE
Ⓣ (01946) 695831
Ⓔ expressplants@aol.com
Ⓦ www.cottagegardenplants.com
Contact: Mrs J Purkiss
Opening Times: Mail order only. Open by appt. For garden, consult local press & radio for charity openings.
Min Mail Order UK: Nmc
Min Mail Order EU: Nmc

Cat. Cost: 3 × 1st class sae.
Credit Cards: None
Specialities: Hardy perennials incl. *Crocosmia*, *Geranium*, *Primula*, *Schizostylis* & bog plants. Small quantities only.
Map Ref: N, C1

NCro CROSTON CACTUS ⊠ ⛺ € ♿
43 Southport Road, Eccleston, Chorley, Lancashire, PR7 6ET
Ⓣ (01257) 452555
Ⓔ sales@croston-cactus.co.uk
Ⓦ www.CROSTON-CACTUS.CO.UK
Contact: John Henshaw
Opening Times: 0930-1700 by appt. only.
Min Mail Order UK: £5.00 + p&p
Min Mail Order EU: £10.00 + p&p
Cat. Cost: 2 × 1st or 2 × IRCs.
Credit Cards: None
Specialities: Mexican cacti, *Echeveria* hybrids & some bromeliads & *Tillandsia*. Some items held in small quantities only.
Map Ref: N, D1

NDlv DALESVIEW NURSERY ⊠ ♿
24 Braithwaite Edge Road, Keighley, West Yorkshire, BD22 6RA
Ⓣ (01535) 606531
Ⓔ nursery@dalesviewnursery.co.uk
Ⓦ www.dalesviewnursery.co.uk
Contact: David Ellis & Eileen Morgan
Opening Times: 1000-1700 Wed-Sun & B/hols, Feb-Oct. Nov-Jan by appt., please telephone.
Min Mail Order UK: Nmc
Min Mail Order EU: Nmc
Cat. Cost: Plant list online.
Credit Cards: None
Specialities: Dwarf *Hebe*, *Saxifraga*, *Primula*, *Rhododendron*, *Fuchsia* & conifers.
Notes: Also sells wholesale.
Map Ref: N, C2

NDov DOVE COTTAGE NURSERY & GARDEN ♿
23 Shibden Hall Road, Halifax, West Yorkshire, HX3 9XA
Ⓣ (01422) 203553
Ⓔ info@dovecottagenursery.co.uk
Ⓦ www.dovecottagenursery.co.uk
Contact: Stephen & Kim Rogers
Opening Times: 1000-1700 Wed-Sun & B/hols Mar-Oct.
Cat. Cost: Free.
Credit Cards: All major credit/debit cards
Specialities: *Helleborus* & selected perennials & grasses for naturalistic planting.
Notes: Also sells wholesale.
Map Ref: N, D2 **OS Grid Ref:** SE115256

NEgg EGGLESTON HALL GARDENS €
Eggleston, Barnard Castle, Co. Durham, DL12 0AG
Ⓣ (01833) 650115
Ⓕ (01833) 650971
Ⓔ mbhock@btinternet.com
Ⓦ www.egglestonhallgardens.co.uk
Contact: Malcolm Hockham, Gordon Long
Opening Times: 1000-1700 7 days.
Min Mail Order UK: £12.95
Cat. Cost: Online only.
Credit Cards: All major credit/debit cards
Specialities: Rare & unusual plants with particular emphasis on flower arranging.
Notes: Mail order for *Celmisia spectabilis* only, Sep-Mar. Also sells wholesale.
Map Ref: N, C2 **OS Grid Ref:** NY997233

N

NEqu EQUATORIAL PLANT CO. ⊠ ✈ ⛺ €
7 Gray Lane, Barnard Castle, Co. Durham, DL12 8PD
Ⓣ (01833) 690519
Ⓕ (01833) 690519
Ⓔ equatorialplants@teesdaleonline.co.uk
Ⓦ www.equatorialplants.com
Contact: Dr Richard Warren
Opening Times: By appt. only.
Min Mail Order UK: Nmc
Min Mail Order EU: Nmc
Cat. Cost: Free.
Credit Cards: Visa Access
Specialities: Laboratory-raised orchids only.
Notes: Also sells wholesale.

NFir FIR TREES PELARGONIUM NURSERY ⊠ ⛺ ♿
Stokesley, Middlesbrough, Cleveland, TS9 5LD
Ⓣ (01642) 713066
Ⓕ (01642) 713066
Ⓔ mark@firtreespelargoniums.co.uk
Ⓦ www.firtreespelargoniums.co.uk
Contact: Helen Bainbridge
Opening Times: 1000-1600 7 days 1st Apr-31st Aug, 1000-1600 Mon-Fri 1st Sep-31st Mar.
Min Mail Order UK: £3.50 + p&p
Cat. Cost: 4 × 1st class or £1.00 coin.
Credit Cards: MasterCard Visa Switch
Specialities: All types of *Pelargonium* - fancy leaf, regal, decorative regal, oriental regal, angel, miniature, zonal, ivy leaf, stellar, scented, dwarf, unique, golden stellar & species. Also dieramas.
Map Ref: N, C2

KEY
⊠ Mail order to UK or EU ⛺ Delivers to shows
✈ Exports beyond EU € Euro accepted
♿ Accessible by wheelchair ◆ See Display advertisement

NGBl **GARDEN BLOOMS**
(office) The Ridings, Netherfield Drive, Guiseley, West Yorkshire, LS20 9DF
Ⓣ (01943) 875295 (after 1900 hours)
Ⓜ 07970 669354
Ⓕ 0870 0528148
Ⓔ info@gardenblooms.co.uk
Ⓦ www.gardenblooms.co.uk
Contact: Liz Webster
Opening Times: 1200-1600 Sat, Sun & B/hols, 25th Mar-25th Jun, but please check before travelling.
Cat. Cost: 2 × 1st class or free online.
Credit Cards: None
Specialities: Hardy perennials. Available in small quantities only.
Notes: Nursery at Carlton Lane, East Carlton, Yeadon, LS19 7BE.
Map Ref: N, D2 **OS Grid Ref:** SE213430

N

NGby **GILBEY'S PLANTS** ⊠ € ♿
The Walled Garden, Cemetery Road, Thirsk, North Yorkshire, YO7 4DA
Ⓣ (01765) 689927 or (01845) 525285
Ⓕ (01765) 688272
Ⓔ gilbeyplants@aol.com
Contact: Giles N Gilbey
Opening Times: 1000-1700 Mon-Sat (closed Sun) 1st Mar-1st Oct. Winter by appt. only.
Min Mail Order UK: Nmc
Min Mail Order EU: Nmc
Cat. Cost: 4 × 1st class.
Credit Cards: All major credit/debit cards
Specialities: Unusual hardy perennials & ferns.
Notes: Mail order Oct-Mar only. Also sells wholesale.
Map Ref: N, C2

NGdn **GARDEN HOUSE NURSERY** ♿
The Square, Dalston, Carlisle, Cumbria, CA5 7LL
Ⓣ (01228) 710297
Ⓔ david@gardenhousenursery.co.uk
Ⓦ www.gardenhousenursery.co.uk
Contact: David Hickson
Opening Times: 0900-1700 7 days Mar-Oct.
Cat. Cost: Plant list online only.
Credit Cards: None
Specialities: *Geranium*, *Hosta*, *Hemerocallis*, *Iris*, grasses & bamboos.
Notes: Also sells wholesale.
Map Ref: N, B1 **OS Grid Ref:** NY369503

NGHP **GREEN GARDEN HERBS** ⊠ ♿
13 West Bank, Carlton, North Yorkshire, DN14 9PZ
Ⓣ (01405) 860708
Ⓔ info@greengardenherbs.co.uk
Ⓦ www.greengardenherbs.co.uk
Contact: Sarah Clark
Opening Times: 1000-1700 Wed-Mon, Mar-Sep. Other times by appt.
Min Mail Order UK: £10.00
Min Mail Order EU: £10.00
Cat. Cost: Free with sae or online.
Credit Cards: All major credit/debit cards
Specialities: Herbs, aromatic, culinary, medicinal & ornamental, incl. *Salvia*, *Monarda*, *Thymus* & wide selection of *Lavandula*. Plants & seed available.
Notes: Also sells wholesale.
Map Ref: N, D3 **OS Grid Ref:** SE626242

NHal **HALLS OF HEDDON** ⊠ ✈ ♿
(Office) West Heddon Nurseries, Heddon-on-the-Wall, Northumberland, NE15 0JS
Ⓣ (01661) 852445
Ⓕ (01661) 852398
Ⓔ orders@hallsofheddon.co.uk
Ⓦ www.hallsofheddon.co.uk
Contact: David Hall
Opening Times: 0900-1700 Mon-Sat 1000-1700 Sun.
Min Mail Order UK: Nmc
Min Mail Order EU: £25.00 + p&p
Cat. Cost: 3 × 2nd class.
Credit Cards: MasterCard Visa Switch Delta
Specialities: *Chrysanthemum* & *Dahlia*. Wide range of herbaceous.
Notes: Mail order *Dahlia* & *Chrysanthemum* only. EU & export *Dahlia* tubers only. Also sells wholesale.
Map Ref: N, B2

NHar **HARTSIDE NURSERY GARDEN** ⊠ ✈
Nr Alston, Cumbria, CA9 3BL
Ⓣ (01434) 381372
Ⓕ (01434) 381372
Ⓔ Hartside@macunlimited.net
Ⓦ www.hartsidenursery.co.uk
Contact: S L & N Huntley
Opening Times: 1130-1630 Mon-Fri, 1230-1600 Sat, Sun & B/hols, mid Mar-31st Oct. All other times & winter by appt.
Min Mail Order UK: Nmc
Min Mail Order EU: £50.00 + p&p
Cat. Cost: 4 × 1st class or 3 × IRC.
Credit Cards: All major credit/debit cards
Specialities: Alpines grown at altitude of 1100 feet in Pennines. *Primula*, ferns, *Gentian* & *Meconopsis*.
Map Ref: N, B1

NHaw **THE HAWTHORNES NURSERY** ⊠ ♿
Marsh Road, Hesketh Bank, Nr Preston, Lancashire, PR4 6XT

Ⓣ (01772) 812379
Ⓦ www.hawthornes-nursery.co.uk
Contact: Irene & Richard Hodson
Opening Times: 0900-1800 7 days 1st Mar-30th Jun, Thu-Sun July-Oct. Gardens open for NGS.
Min Mail Order UK: £10.00
Cat. Cost: 5 × 1st class.
Credit Cards: None
Specialities: *Clematis*, honeysuckle, choice selection of shrub & climbing roses, extensive range of perennials, mostly on display in the garden. Nat. Collection *Clematis viticella*.
Map Ref: N, D1

NHer HERTERTON HOUSE GARDEN NURSERY
Hartington, Cambo, Morpeth, Northumberland, NE61 4BN
Ⓣ (01670) 774278
Contact: Mrs M Lawley & Mr Frank Lawley
Opening Times: 1330-1730 Mon Wed Fri-Sun 1st Apr-end Sep. (Earlier or later in the year weather permitting.)
Cat. Cost: None issued.
Credit Cards: None
Specialities: Country garden flowers.
Map Ref: N, B2

NHim THE HIMALAYAN GARDEN CO. ⊠ ⛫ € ♿
The Hutts, Grewelthorpe, Ripon, Yorkshire, HG4 3DA
Ⓣ (01765) 658009
Ⓕ (01765) 658912
Ⓔ info@himalayangarden.com
Ⓦ www.himalayangarden.com
Contact: Peter Roberts
Opening Times: By appt. only.
Min Mail Order UK: £20.00
Min Mail Order EU: £50.00
Cat. Cost: Free.
Credit Cards: All major credit/debit cards
Specialities: Rare and unusual species & hybrid rhododendrons, azaleas, magnolias & *Cornus*, as well as other Himalayan plants.
Notes: Also sells wholesale.
Map Ref: N, C2 **OS Grid Ref:** 774212

NHol HOLDEN CLOUGH NURSERY ⊠ ✈ ⛫ ♿ ◆
Holden, Bolton-by-Bowland, Clitheroe, Lancashire, BB7 4PF
Ⓣ (01200) 447615
Ⓕ (01200) 447197
Ⓔ enquiries@holdencloughnursery.co.uk
Ⓦ www.holdencloughnursery.co.uk
Contact: P J Foley
Opening Times: 0900-1630 Mon-Fri Mar-Oct & B/hol Mons, 0900-1630 Sat all year. Closed 25th Dec-1st Jan 2007 & Good Fri. Other times by appt. only.
Min Mail Order UK: Nmc
Min Mail Order EU: Nmc
Cat. Cost: 4 × 1st class.
Credit Cards: MasterCard Visa Delta
Specialities: Large general list incl. *Crocosmia*, *Primula*, *Saxifraga*, *Sempervivum*, *Jovibarba*, *Astilbe*, grasses, *Hosta*, heathers & *Rhododendron*.
Notes: Seasonal mail order on some items. Also sells wholesale.
Map Ref: N, C2 **OS Grid Ref:** SD773496

NHor HORN'S GARDEN CENTRE ♿
Dixon Estate, Shotton Colliery, Co. Durham, DH6 2PX
Ⓣ (0191) 526 2987
Ⓕ (0191) 526 2889
Contact: G Horn & Theresa Horn
Opening Times: 0900-1730 Mon-Sat 1000-1600 Sun, all year excl. Easter Mon.
Cat. Cost: 3 × 1st class.
Credit Cards: All major credit/debit cards
Specialities: *Fuchsia*, *Solenostemon*. Wide range of trees, shrubs & perennials.
Map Ref: N, B2

NHoy HOYLAND PLANT CENTRE ⊠ ✈ ⛫ ♿
54 Greenside Lane, Hoyland, Barnsley, Yorkshire, S74 9PZ
Ⓣ (01226) 744466
Ⓜ 07717 182169
Ⓕ (01226) 744466
Ⓔ hickman@hoyland13.freeserve.co.uk
Ⓦ www.somethingforthegarden.co.uk
Contact: Steven Hickman
Opening Times: All year round by appt. only.
Min Mail Order UK: Nmc
Min Mail Order EU: Nmc
Cat. Cost: 4 × 1st class.
Credit Cards: None
Specialities: *Agapanthus* & *Tulbaghia*. 400+ cvs. Nat. Collection status applied for. Some cvs available in small numbers only.
Notes: Also sells wholesale.
Map Ref: N, D2 **OS Grid Ref:** SE372010

NLan LANDLIFE WILDFLOWERS LTD ⊠ ♿
National Wildflower Centre, Court Hey Park, Liverpool, L16 3NA
Ⓣ (0151) 737 1819
Ⓕ (0151) 737 1820

KEY
⊠ Mail order to UK or EU ⛫ Delivers to shows
✈ Exports beyond EU € Euro accepted
♿ Accessible by wheelchair ◆ See Display advertisement

N

Ⓔ gill@landlife.org.uk
Ⓦ www.wildflower.org.uk
Contact: Gillian Watson
Opening Times: 1000-1700, 7 days, 1 Apr-30 Sep only.
Min Mail Order UK: £30.00 (plants), nmc for seeds.
Cat. Cost: Sae + 2 × 2nd class.
Credit Cards: Visa Delta Access Switch Solo
Specialities: Wild herbaceous plants & seeds.
Notes: Cafe & shop. Visitor centre, admission charge. Also sells wholesale.
Map Ref: N, D1

N

NLAp LANESIDE ALPINES ⊠ ♠ ♿
74 Croston Road, Garstang, Preston, Lancashire, PR3 1HR
Ⓣ (01995) 605537
Ⓜ 0794 6659661
Ⓔ jcrhutch@aol.com
Ⓦ www.lanesidealpines.com
Contact: Jeff Hutchings
Opening Times: 0930-1630 Thu-Sat, 1st Mar-30th Sep. 1000-1600 Sun.
Min Mail Order UK: Nmc
Cat. Cost: Sae.
Specialities: Wide range of alpines and rare plants plus over 50 species of hardy orchids.
Notes: Mail order for orchids & a limited range of alpines. Also tufa, Toresa & Shap grit from the nursery.
Map Ref: N, D1

NLar LARCH COTTAGE NURSERIES ⊠ € ♿ ◆
Melkinthorpe, Penrith, Cumbria, CA10 2DR
Ⓣ (01931) 712404
Ⓕ (01931) 712727
Ⓔ plants@larchcottage.co.uk
Ⓦ www.larchcottagenurseries.com
Contact: Joanne McCullock/Peter Stott
Opening Times: Daily from 1000-1730.
Min Mail Order UK: Nmc
Min Mail Order EU: Nmc
Cat. Cost: £3.50.
Credit Cards: Visa Access Switch Delta Solo
Specialities: Unusual & old-fashioned perennials. Rare & dwarf conifers. Unusual shrubs & trees.
Notes: Terraced restaurant & art gallery.
Map Ref: N, C1 **OS Grid Ref:** NY315602

NLLv LEEDS LAVENDER ⊠
at Greenscapes Nursery, Brandon Crescent, Shadwell, Leeds, LS17 9JH
Ⓣ (0113) 2892922
Ⓦ www.leedslavender.co.uk
Contact: Ruth Dorrington
Opening Times: 1000-1630, Mon-Fri, 1000-1700 Sat & Sun all year round, or by appt.
Min Mail Order UK: Nmc
Cat. Cost: 2 × 1st class.
Credit Cards: None
Specialities: *Lavandula*. Limited numbers of particular varieties available at certain times, especially at end of summer.
Notes: Wheelchair access difficult in some areas. Also sells wholesale.
Map Ref: N, D2

NMen MENDLE NURSERY ⊠ ♠ ♿
Holme, Scunthorpe, Lincolnshire, DN16 3RF
Ⓣ (01724) 850864
Ⓔ annearnshaw@lineone.net
Ⓦ www.mendlenursery.com
Contact: Mrs A Earnshaw
Opening Times: 1000-1600 Tue-Sun.
Min Mail Order UK: Nmc
Min Mail Order EU: Nmc
Cat. Cost: 3 × 1st class.
Credit Cards: All major credit/debit cards
Specialities: Many unusual alpines esp. *Saxifraga* & *Sempervivum*.
Map Ref: N, D3 **OS Grid Ref:** SE925070

NMin MINIATURE BULBS UK ⊠ ♠ € ◆
The Warren Estate, 9 Greengate Drive, Knaresborough, North Yorkshire, HG5 9EN
Ⓣ (01423) 542819
Ⓕ (01423) 542819
Ⓦ www.miniaturebulbs.co.uk
Contact: Ivor Fox
Opening Times: Not open. Mail order only.
Min Mail Order UK: Nmc
Min Mail Order EU: Nmc
Cat. Cost: 1 × 1st class.
Credit Cards: None
Specialities: Rare & unusual miniature bulbs, incl. *Narcissus*, *Tulipa*, *Iris*, *Crocus*, *Fritillaria* & others. Spring bulb list sent out in April. Some stock in small quantities.
Map Ref: N, C2 **OS Grid Ref:** SE3558SW

NMir MIRES BECK NURSERY ⊠ ♿
Low Mill Lane, North Cave, Brough, East Riding, Yorkshire, HU15 2NR
Ⓣ (01430) 421543
Ⓔ admin@miresbeck.co.uk
Ⓦ www.miresbeck.co.uk
Contact: Irene Tinklin & Martin Rowland
Opening Times: 1000-1600 Wed-Sat 1st Mar-30th Sep. 1000-1500 Wed-Fri 1st Oct-30th Nov & by appt.
Min Mail Order UK: Nmc
Min Mail Order EU: Nmc

Cat. Cost: 3 × 1st class.
Credit Cards: None
Specialities: Wildflower plants of Yorkshire provenance.
Notes: Mail order for wildflower plants, plugs & seeds only. Also sells wholesale.
Map Ref: N, D3 **OS Grid Ref:** SE889316

NMoo **MOOR MONKTON NURSERIES** ⊠ ♿
Moor Monkton, York Road, Nr York, Yorkshire, YO26 8JJ
Ⓣ (01904) 738770
Ⓕ (01904) 738770
Ⓔ sales@bamboo-uk.co.uk
Ⓦ www.bamboo-uk.co.uk
Contact: Peter Owen
Opening Times: 0900-1700.
Min Mail Order UK: Nmc
Cat. Cost: 5 × 2nd class or email for details.
Credit Cards: None
Specialities: Bamboos, palms, ferns, unusual trees, shrubs & perennials.
Notes: Mail order for bamboo only.
Map Ref: N, C2

NMRc **MILLRACE NURSERY** ♿
84 Selby Road, Garforth, Leeds, LS25 1LP
Ⓣ (0113) 286 9233
Ⓕ (0113) 286 9908
Ⓔ carol@millrace-plants.co.uk
Ⓦ www.millrace-plants.co.uk
Contact: C Carthy
Opening Times: 1000-1700 Tue, Thu-Sun, Mar-May & Tue, Thu-Sat Jun-Sep.
Cat. Cost: 4 × 1st class.
Credit Cards: None
Specialities: Unusual perennials, especially drought-resistant, incl. hardy geraniums, alliums, campanulas, penstemnons, potentillas & veronicas. Some plants in small quantities only.
Map Ref: N, D2

NMyG **MARY GREEN** ⊠ ⌂ ♿
The Walled Garden, Hornby, Lancaster, Lancashire, LA2 8LD
Ⓣ (01524) 221989
Ⓜ 07778 910348
Ⓕ (01524) 221989
Ⓔ Marygreenplants@aol.com
Contact: Mary Green
Opening Times: By appt. only.
Min Mail Order UK: £10.00
Cat. Cost: 4 × 1st class.
Credit Cards: None
Specialities: Hostas, astilbes, ferns & other shade-loving perennials.
Map Ref: N, C1 **OS Grid Ref:** SD588688

NNew **NEWTON HILL ALPINES** ♿
335 Leeds Road, Wakefield, West Yorkshire, WF1 2JH
Ⓣ (01924) 377056
Ⓔ newtalp@aol.com
Contact: Sheena Vigors
Opening Times: 0900-1700 Fri-Wed all year. Closed Thu. Please phone first.
Cat. Cost: 2 × 1st class.
Credit Cards: None
Specialities: Alpines esp. *Saxifraga*, also *Erica*, conifers & dwarf shrubs.
Notes: Also sells wholesale.
Map Ref: N, D2 **OS Grid Ref:** SE328229

NNor **NORCROFT NURSERIES** ⊠ ♿
Roadends, Intack, Southwaite, Carlisle, Cumbria, CA4 0LH
Ⓣ (016974) 73933
Ⓜ 07789 050633
Ⓕ (016974) 73969
Ⓔ stellaandkeithbell@sbell44.fsnet.co.uk
Contact: Keith Bell
Opening Times: Every afternoon excl. Mon but open B/hols.
Min Mail Order UK: Nmc
Cat. Cost: 2 × 2nd class.
Credit Cards: None
Specialities: Hardy herbaceous, ornamental grasses, hostas, *Lilium*, *Hemerocallis*, *Penstemon*.
Notes: Also sells wholesale.
Map Ref: N, B1 **OS Grid Ref:** NY474433

NOaD **OAK DENE NURSERIES** ⊠ ⌂
10 Back Lane West, Royston, Barnsley, South Yorkshire, S71 4SB
Ⓣ (01226) 722253
Contact: J Foster or G Foster
Opening Times: 0900-1800 1st Apr-30th Sep, 1000-1600 1st Oct-31st Mar. (Closed 1230-1330.)
Min Mail Order UK: Phone for details.
Min Mail Order EU: Phone for details.
Cat. Cost: None issued.
Credit Cards: None
Specialities: Cacti, succulents & South African *Lachenalia* bulbs.
Notes: Also sells wholesale.
Map Ref: N, D2

NOak **OAK TREE NURSERY** ⊠ ⌂ ♿
Mill Lane, Barlow, Selby, North Yorkshire, YO8 8EY

KEY		
	⊠ Mail order to UK or EU	⌂ Delivers to shows
	✈ Exports beyond EU	€ Euro accepted
	♿ Accessible by wheelchair	◆ See Display advertisement

N

Ⓣ (01757) 618409
Ⓔ gill.plowes@tesco.net
Contact: Gill Plowes
Opening Times: By appt. only.
Min Mail Order UK: £10.00 + p&p
Cat. Cost: 2 × 1st class.
Credit Cards: None
Specialities: Cottage garden plants, grasses & ferns.

NOrc **ORCHARD HOUSE NURSERY**
Orchard House, Wormald Green, Nr Harrogate, North Yorkshire, HG3 3NQ
Ⓣ (01765) 677541
Ⓕ (01765) 677541
Contact: Mr B M Corner
Opening Times: 0800-1630 Mon-Fri.
Cat. Cost: Retail catalogue available at nursery.
Credit Cards: None
Specialities: Herbaceous perennials, ferns, grasses, water plants & unusual cottage garden plants.
Notes: Also sells wholesale.
Map Ref: N, C2

N

NPal **THE PALM FARM** ⊠ € ♿
Thornton Hall Gardens, Station Road, Thornton Curtis, Nr Ulceby, Humberside, DN39 6XF
Ⓣ (01469) 531232
Ⓕ (01469) 531232
Ⓔ bill@palmfarm.fsbusiness.co.uk
Ⓦ www.thepalmfarm.com
Contact: W W Spink
Opening Times: 1400-1700 7 days.
Min Mail Order UK: £11.00 + p&p
Min Mail Order EU: £25.00 + p&p
Cat. Cost: 1 × 2nd class.
Credit Cards: None
Specialities: Hardy & half-hardy palms, unusual trees, shrubs & conservatory plants. Some plants available only in small quantities.
Notes: Euro payment accepted only if purchaser pays bank commission. Mail order only if small enough to go by post (min. charge £12.50 p&p) or large enough to go by Palletline (min. charge £35.00 p&p). Also sells wholesale.
Map Ref: N, D3 **OS Grid Ref:** TA100183

NPen **PENTON MILL RHODODENDRONS** ⊠ ⌂ €
Penton, Carlisle, Cumbria, CA6 5QU
Ⓣ (01228) 577336
Ⓕ (01228) 577336
Ⓔ info@pentonmill.com
Ⓦ www.pentonmill.com
Contact: Amanda Cullen
Opening Times: Vary, due to off-site working. Please phone first.
Min Mail Order UK: Nmc
Min Mail Order EU: £50.00
Cat. Cost: 6 × 1st class.
Credit Cards: None
Specialities: Rhododendrons & azaleas. Some stock available in small quantities only.
Map Ref: N, B1 **OS Grid Ref:** NY434764

NPer **PERRY'S PLANTS** ♿
The River Garden, Sleights, Whitby, North Yorkshire, YO21 1RR
Ⓣ (01947) 810329
Ⓔ perry@rivergardens.fsnet.co.uk
Contact: Pat & Richard Perry
Opening Times: 1000-1700 mid-March to Oct.
Cat. Cost: Large A4 sae.
Credit Cards: None
Specialities: *Lavatera*, *Malva*, *Erysimum*, *Euphorbia*, *Anthemis*, *Osteospermum* & *Hebe*. Uncommon hardy & container plants & aquatic plants.
Map Ref: N, C3 **OS Grid Ref:** NZ869082

NPol **POLEMONIUM PLANTERY** ⊠ ⌂ ♿
28 Sunnyside Terrace, Trimdon Grange, Trimdon Station, Co. Durham, TS29 6HF
Ⓣ (01429) 881529
Ⓔ DANDD@Polemonium.co.uk
Ⓦ www.polemonium.co.uk
Contact: David or Dianne Nichol-Brown
Opening Times: By appt. only.
Min Mail Order UK: £10.00
Cat. Cost: Sae for list.
Credit Cards: None
Specialities: Nat. Collection of *Polemonium* & related genera, plus some rare North American plants. The Collection holds scientific status.
Notes: Also sells wholesale.
Map Ref: N, B2 **OS Grid Ref:** NZ369353

NPri **PRIMROSE COTTAGE NURSERY** ♿ ◆
Ringway Road, Moss Nook, Wythenshawe, Manchester, M22 5WF
Ⓣ (0161) 437 1557
Ⓕ (0161) 499 9932
Ⓔ info@primrosecottagenursery.co.uk
Ⓦ www.primrosecottagenursery.co.uk
Contact: Caroline Dumville
Opening Times: 0900-1730 Mon-Sat, 0930-1730 Sun (summer). 0900-1700 Mon-Sat, 0930-1700 Sun (winter).
Cat. Cost: 1 × 1st class.
Credit Cards: All major credit/debit cards
Specialities: Hardy herbaceous perennials,

alpines, herbs, roses, patio & hanging basket plants. Shrubs.
Notes: Coffee shop open daily.
Map Ref: N, D2

NPro **PROUDPLANTS** ⌂ ♿
East of Eden Nurseries, Ainstable, Carlisle, Cumbria, CA4 9QN
Ⓣ (01768) 896604
Ⓕ (01768) 896604
Ⓔ rogereastofeden@hotmail.com
Contact: Roger Proud
Opening Times: 0900-1800 7 days Mar-Nov. Other times by appt.
Cat. Cost: None issued.
Credit Cards: None
Specialities: Interesting & unusual shrubs, perennials & alpines, esp. dwarf & ground cover plants.
Map Ref: N, B1 **OS Grid Ref:** HA1336186

NRar **RARER PLANTS** ♿
Ashfield House, Austfield Lane, Monk Fryston, Leeds, LS25 5EH
Ⓣ (01977) 682263
Contact: Anne Watson
Opening Times: Feb, Mar. By appt. only.
Cat. Cost: Sae.
Credit Cards: None
Specialities: *Helleborus.*
Map Ref: N, D2

NRib **RIBBLESDALE NURSERIES** ♿
Newsham Hall Lane, Woodplumpton, Preston, Lancashire, PR4 0AS
Ⓣ (01772) 863081
Ⓕ (01772) 861884
Contact: Mr & Mrs Dunnett
Opening Times: 0900-1800 Mon-Sat Apr-Sep, 0900-1700 Mon-Sat Oct-Mar. 1030-1630 Sun.
Credit Cards: Visa MasterCard Delta Switch
Specialities: Trees, shrubs & perennials. Conifers, hedging, alpines, fruit, climbers, herbs, aquatics, ferns & wildflowers.
Map Ref: N, D1 **OS Grid Ref:** SD515351

NRnb **RAINBOW PLANTS** ⊠ ⌂ ♿
Springvale Nursery, Springvale, Penistone, Sheffield, Yorkshire, S36 6HJ
Ⓜ 07798 691853
Ⓕ (01226) 280256
Ⓔ BRIAN@cockerline.force9.co.uk
Contact: Brian Cockerline
Opening Times: 0900-1700 Mon-Fri.
Min Mail Order UK: Nmc.
Cat. Cost: 2 × 1st class.
Credit Cards: None
Notes: Also sells wholesale.

NRob ♿ **ROBINSON & SONS LTD** ⊠ ✈ ⌂ € ♿
Sunny Bank, Forton, Nr Preston, Lancashire, PR3 0BN
Ⓣ (01524) 791210
Ⓕ (01524) 791933
Ⓔ info@mammothonion.co.uk
Ⓦ www.mammothonion.co.uk
Contact: Miss Robinson
Opening Times: 0900-1700 7 days Mar-Jun, 0800-1700 Mon-Fri Jul-Feb.
Min Mail Order UK: Nmc
Min Mail Order EU: Nmc
Cat. Cost: Free.
Credit Cards: Visa Access American Express Switch
Specialities: Mammoth vegetable seed. Onions, leeks, tomatoes & beans. Range of vegetable plants in the spring.
Notes: Also sells wholesale.

NRya **RYAL NURSERY** ⊠ ⌂ ♿
East Farm Cottage, Ryal, Northumberland, NE20 0SA
Ⓣ (01661) 886562
Ⓕ (01661) 886918
Ⓔ alpines@ryal.freeserve.co.uk
Contact: R F Hadden
Opening Times: 1000-1600 Sun Mar-Jul & other times by appt.
Min Mail Order UK: £10.00 + p&p
Min Mail Order EU: £10.00 + p&p
Cat. Cost: Sae.
Credit Cards: None
Specialities: Alpine & woodland plants. Mainly available in small quantities only.
Notes: Also sells wholesale.
Map Ref: N, B2 **OS Grid Ref:** NZ015744

NSco **SCOTT'S WILDFLOWERS** ⊠ ♿
Swallow Hill Barn, 31 Common Side, Distington, Workington, Cumbria, CA14 4PU
Ⓣ (01946) 830486
Ⓔ scotts.wildflowers@virgin.net
Ⓦ www.scottswildflowers.co.uk
Contact: Ted Scott
Opening Times: 1000-1600 Mar-Oct, 1130-1500 Nov-Feb, 7 days.
Min Mail Order UK: £10.40 + £4.50 p&p
Cat. Cost: 3 × 1st class.
Specialities: Native British wildflowers, including aquatics.
Notes: Also sells wholesale.
Map Ref: N, C1

KEY
⊠ Mail order to UK or EU ⌂ Delivers to shows
✈ Exports beyond EU € Euro accepted
♿ Accessible by wheelchair ◆ See Display advertisement

N

NScw SCAWSBY HALL NURSERIES ⊠ ♿
Barnsley Road, Scawsby, Doncaster, South Yorkshire, DN5 7UB
Ⓣ (01302) 782585
Ⓕ (01302) 783434
Ⓔ mail@scawsbyhallnurseries.co.uk
Ⓦ www.scawsbyhallnurseries.co.uk
Contact: David Lawson
Opening Times: 0930-1700 Mon-Sat 1100-1700 Sun.
Min Mail Order UK: Nmc
Cat. Cost: None issued.
Credit Cards: Maestro Visa MasterCard Solo
Specialities: A wide range of herbaceous perennials, hardy trees, shrubs & indoor plants. Some indoor & aquatic plants in small quantities only.
Map Ref: N, D3 **OS Grid Ref:** SE542049

N

NSfd SPRINGFIELD NURSERIES ⊠
Back Gisburn Road, Blacko, Nr Nelson, Lancashire, BB9 6LT
Ⓣ (01282) 690518
Ⓕ (01282) 690518
Ⓔ yvonneholden@tiscali.co.uk
Contact: Peter & Yvonne Holden
Opening Times: Not open. Mail order only.
Min Mail Order UK: Nmc
Cat. Cost: 2 × 1st class.
Credit Cards: None
Specialities: *Campanulaceae* family.
Notes: Mail order seeds & plants. Also sells wholesale.

NShi SHIRLEY'S PLANTS ⊠
6 Sandheys Drive, Churchtown, Southport, Merseyside, PR9 9PQ
Ⓣ (01704) 213048
Ⓜ 07951 834066
Ⓦ www.stbegonias.com
Contact: Shirley & Terry Tasker
Opening Times: By appt. only.
Min Mail Order UK: Nmc
Cat. Cost: 2 × 1st class.
Credit Cards: None
Specialities: Nat. Collection of *Begonia* species & hybrids.
Map Ref: N, D1 **OS Grid Ref:** SD355183

NSla SLACK TOP NURSERIES ⊠ €
Hebden Bridge, West Yorkshire, HX7 7HA
Ⓣ (01422) 845348
Ⓦ www.slacktopnurseries.co.uk
Contact: M R or R Mitchell
Opening Times: 1000-1700 Wed-Sun 1st Mar-30th Sep & B/hol Mons 1st Mar-30th Sep.
Min Mail Order UK: £30.00
Cat. Cost: Sae.
Credit Cards: None
Specialities: Alpine & rockery plants. *Celmisia semi-cordata, Gentiana, Saxifraga, Primula, Hepatica, Paeonia* & *Pulsatilla.*
Notes: Suitable for wheelchairs but 2 steps at entrance. Also sells wholesale.
Map Ref: N, D2 **OS Grid Ref:** SD977286

NSpr SPRINGWOOD PLEIONES ⊠ ⊠ € ♿
8 Tredgold Avenue, Leeds, LS16 9BU
Ⓣ (0113) 230 1158
Ⓔ simon@pleiones.com
Ⓦ www.pleiones.com
Contact: Simon Redshaw
Opening Times: By appt. only.
Min Mail Order UK: £3.00 + p&p
Min Mail Order EU: £3.00 + p&p
Cat. Cost: 1 × 1st class.
Credit Cards: None
Specialities: *Pleione.*
Map Ref: N, D2 **OS Grid Ref:** SE256429

NSRo SCENTED ROSES ⊠ ♿
Stewart Hill Cottage, Nr Hesket Newmarket, Cumbria, CA7 8HX
Ⓣ (01768) 484172
Ⓕ (01768) 484172
Contact: Iain Billot
Opening Times: 1300-1700 Thu-Sun May to mid-Jul. Jul-May by arrangement.
Min Mail Order UK: Nmc
Cat. Cost: Free.
Credit Cards: None
Specialities: Roses. Carefully selected to survive in a wet, cold climate, such as Cumbria. Ramblers & climbers a speciality.
Notes: Also sells wholesale.
Map Ref: N, B1 **OS Grid Ref:** NY365354

NSti STILLINGFLEET LODGE NURSERIES ⊠ ♿
Stillingfleet, North Yorkshire, YO19 6HP
Ⓣ (01904) 728506
Ⓕ (01904) 728506
Ⓔ vanessa.cook@still-lodge.freeserve.co.uk
Ⓦ www.stillingfleetlodgenurseries.co.uk
Contact: Vanessa Cook
Opening Times: 1000-1600 Tue Wed Fri & Sat 1st Apr-18th Oct. Closed Sat in Aug.
Min Mail Order UK: Nmc
Cat. Cost: 10 × 2nd class.
Credit Cards: None
Specialities: Foliage & unusual perennials. Hardy geraniums, *Pulmonaria,* variegated plants & grasses. Nat. Collection of *Pulmonaria.*
Notes: Mail order Nov-mid Mar only.
Map Ref: N, C2

NSum SUMMERDALE GARDEN NURSERY ⊠
Summerdale House, Cow Brow, Lupton, Carnforth, Lancashire, LA6 1PE
Ⓣ (01539) 567210
Ⓔ sheals@btinternet.com
Contact: Abi Sheals
Opening Times: 1000-1600 Fri-Mon (closed Tue-Thu) 1st Feb-31st Oct. Nov-Jan, open by appt. only.
Min Mail Order UK: Nmc
Cat. Cost: 4 × 1st class.
Credit Cards: None
Specialities: Wide variety of pernnials, large collection of *Primula*. Many moist and shade-loving plants incl. *Meconopsis* & hellebores.
Map Ref: N, C1 **OS Grid Ref:** SD545819

NTHB TAVISTOCK HERB NURSERY ⊠ ♠
Tavistock, Preston Old Road, Clifton, Lancashire, PR4 0ZA
Ⓣ (01772) 683505
Ⓕ (01772) 683505
Ⓔ tavistockherbs@themail.co.uk
Contact: Mrs C Jones
Opening Times: By appt. only.
Min Mail Order UK: Nmc
Cat. Cost: 3 × 1st class.
Credit Cards: None
Specialities: Herbs & wildflowers.
Notes: Main nursery at Garstang Road, Barton, near Preston, Lancs. Also sells wholesale.
Map Ref: N, D1

NVic THE VICARAGE GARDEN ⊠ ♿
Carrington, Manchester, M31 4AG
Ⓣ (0161) 775 2750
Ⓔ info@vicaragebotanicalgardens.co.uk
Ⓦ www.vicaragebotanicalgardens.co.uk
Contact: Paul Haine
Opening Times: 0900-1700 Mon-Sat, closed Thu. 1000-1630 Sun all year.
Min Mail Order UK: Nmc
Cat. Cost: 2 × 2nd class for list
Credit Cards: All major credit/debit cards
Specialities: Herbaceous, alpines, grasses, ferns. Free admission to 7 acre gardens.
Map Ref: N, D2 **OS Grid Ref:** SJ729926

NWCA WHITE COTTAGE ALPINES ⊠ ♠ ♿ ◆
Sunnyside Nurseries, Hornsea Road, Sigglesthorne, East Yorkshire, HU11 5QL
Ⓣ (01964) 542692
Ⓕ (01964) 542692
Ⓔ plants@whitecottagealpines.co.uk
Ⓦ www.whitecottagealpines.co.uk
Contact: Sally E Cummins
Opening Times: 1000-1700 (or dusk) Thu-Sun & B/hol Mon 1 Mar-30 Sep. If travelling far, please phone first. In winter by appt. only.
Min Mail Order UK: Nmc.
Min Mail Order EU: £15.00 + p&p by card only.
Cat. Cost: 4 × 1st class.
Credit Cards: Visa MasterCard Switch
Specialities: Alpines & rock plants. 500+ species incl. American, dwarf *Salix* & *Helichrysum*, also increasing range of *Penstemon*.
Notes: Euro payments by card only.
Map Ref: N, C3

NWea WEASDALE NURSERIES LTD. ⊠
Newbiggin-on-Lune, Kirkby Stephen, Cumbria, CA17 4LX
Ⓣ (01539) 623246
Ⓕ (01539) 623277
Ⓔ sales@weasdale.com
Ⓦ www.weasdale.com
Contact: Andrew Forsyth
Opening Times: 0830-1730 Mon-Fri. Closed w/ends, B/hols, Xmas through to the New Year.
Min Mail Order UK: Nmc
Min Mail Order EU: Nmc
Cat. Cost: £2.00 or 7 × 1st class. £2.00 by debit card, £2.50 by credit card.
Credit Cards: All major credit/debit cards
Specialities: Hardy forest trees, hedging, broadleaved & conifers. Specimen trees & shrubs grown at 850 feet (260 metre) elevation.
Notes: Mail order a speciality. Mail order Nov-Apr only.
Map Ref: N, C1

NWit D S WITTON ⊠
26 Casson Drive, Harthill, Sheffield, Yorkshire, S26 7WA
Ⓣ (01909) 771366
Ⓕ (01909) 771366
Ⓔ donshardyeuphorbias@btopenworld.com
Ⓦ www.euphorbias.co.uk
Contact: Don Witton
Opening Times: By appt. only.
Min Mail Order UK: Nmc
Cat. Cost: 1 × 1st class + sae.
Credit Cards: None
Specialities: Nat. Collection of Hardy *Euphorbia*. Over 130 varieties.
Notes: Mail order seed & plants, Oct-Feb.
Map Ref: N, D2 **OS Grid Ref:** SK494812

KEY
⊠ Mail order to UK or EU ♠ Delivers to shows
✈ Exports beyond EU € Euro accepted
♿ Accessible by wheelchair ◆ See Display advertisement

N

NZep ZEPHYRWUDE IRISES ⊠
48 Blacker Lane, Crigglestone, Wakefield, West Yorkshire, WF4 3EW
Ⓣ (01924) 252101
Ⓜ 07813 978165
Ⓔ zephyrwude@aol.com
Ⓦ http://zephyrwude.co.uk
Contact: Richard L Brook
Opening Times: Mail order only. Viewing by appt. May-early June, peak late May. Phone 0900-2300.
Min Mail Order UK: Nmc
Min Mail Order EU: Nmc
Cat. Cost: Free.
Credit Cards: None
Specialities: Bearded *Iris*, 1970s-80s hybrids only. Mainly 12" dwarf & intermediate, a few tall.
Notes: Main despatch season Aug-Oct.
Map Ref: N, D2 **OS Grid Ref:** SE302161

N

SOUTHERN

SAdn ASHDOWN FOREST GARDEN CENTRE & NURSERY ♿
Duddleswell, Ashdown Forest, Nr Uckfield, East Sussex, TN22 3JP
Ⓣ (01825) 712300
Ⓦ www.ashdownforestgardencentre.co.uk
Contact: Victoria Falletti
Opening Times: 0900-1730 winter, 0900-1800 summer.
Credit Cards: All major credit/debit cards
Specialities: Ornamental grasses, *Lavandula*, fuchsias.
Notes: Also sells wholesale.
Map Ref: S, C4 **OS Grid Ref:** TQ468283

SAga AGAR'S NURSERY € ♿
Agars Lane, Hordle, Lymington, Hampshire, SO41 0FL
Ⓣ (01590) 683703
Contact: Diana Tombs, Debbie Ursell
Opening Times: 1000-1700 Fri-Wed (closed Thu) Mar-Sep, 1000-1600 Fri-Mon (closed Tue-Thu) Feb & Oct-Dec, or by appt.
Credit Cards: None
Specialities: *Penstemon* & *Salvia*. Also wide range of hardy plants incl. hardy & tender shrubs, climbers & herbaceous.
Map Ref: S, D2

SAin AINSWORTH DISPLAYS ⊠ ⌂
5 Kentidge Road, Waterlooville, Hampshire, PO7 5NH
Ⓣ (023) 92 255057
Ⓔ Britishpalms@ntlworld.com
Contact: Mark Ainsworth
Opening Times: Not open. Mail order only.
Min Mail Order UK: £10.00 + p&p
Cat. Cost: 2 × 1st class for price list.
Credit Cards: Visa MasterCard
Specialities: Palm trees. Available in small quantities & in one size only.
Notes: Also sells wholesale.

SAll ALLWOOD BROS ⊠ ⌂ ♿
London Road, Hassocks, West Sussex, BN6 9NB
Ⓣ (01273) 844229
Ⓕ (01273) 846022
Ⓔ info@allwoodbros.co.uk
Ⓦ www.allwoodbros.co.uk
Contact: David James or Emma
Opening Times: Office: 0900-1630 Mon-Fri. Answer machine all other times. Nursery: 7 days, 1st Mar-30th Jun.
Min Mail Order UK: Nmc
Min Mail Order EU: Nmc
Cat. Cost: 2 × 1st class.
Credit Cards: Access,Visa MasterCardSwitch
Specialities: *Dianthus* incl. hardy border carnations, pinks, perpetual & *D. allwoodii*, some available as seed. Certain lavender varieties.
Notes: Exports seed only.
Map Ref: S, D4 **OS Grid Ref:** TQ303170

SAPC ARCHITECTURAL PLANTS (CHICHESTER) LTD ⊠ ⌂ € ♿ ◆
Lidsey Road Nursery, Westergate, Nr Chichester, West Sussex, PO20 6SU
Ⓣ (01243) 545008
Ⓕ (01243) 545009
Ⓔ chichester@architecturalplants.com
Ⓦ www.architecturalplants.com
Contact: Christine Shaw
Opening Times: 1000-1600 Sun-Fri all year. Closed Sat & B/hol Mons. Open Good Fri.
Min Mail Order UK: Nmc
Min Mail Order EU: £150.00 + p&p
Cat. Cost: Free.
Credit Cards: All major credit/debit cards
Specialities: Architectural plants & hardy exotics esp. rare evergreen broadleaved trees & seaside exotics, spiky plants, yuccas/agaves.
Notes: Second nursery near Horsham, Code SArc. Also sells wholesale.
Map Ref: S, D3

SApp APPLE COURT ⊠ €
Hordle Lane, Hordle, Lymington, Hampshire, S041 0HU
Ⓣ (01590) 642130
Ⓕ (01590) 644220
Ⓔ applecourt@btinternet.com

Ⓦ www.applecourt.com
Contact: Angela & Charles Meads
Opening Times: 1000-1700 Fri, Sat, Sun & B/hol 1st Mar-31st Oct. Closed Nov-Feb.
Min Mail Order UK: Nmc
Min Mail Order EU: Nmc
Cat. Cost: 4 × 1st class.
Credit Cards: All major credit/debit cards
Specialities: *Hemerocallis*, *Hosta*, grasses & ferns.
Map Ref: S, D2 **OS Grid Ref:** SZ270941

SArc ARCHITECTURAL PLANTS ⊠ € ♿ ◆
Cooks Farm, Nuthurst, Horsham, West Sussex, RH13 6LH
Ⓣ (01403) 891772
Ⓕ (01403) 891056
Ⓔ enquiries@architecturalplants.com
Ⓦ www.architecturalplants.com
Contact: Christine Shaw
Opening Times: 0900-1700 Mon-Sat, closed Sun.
Min Mail Order UK: Nmc
Min Mail Order EU: £150.00 + p&p
Cat. Cost: Free.
Credit Cards: All major credit/debit cards
Specialities: Architectural plants & hardy exotics & rare broadleaved trees, bamboos & spiky plants.
Notes: Second nursery near Chichester, code SAPC. Also sells wholesale.
Map Ref: S, C3

SBai STEVEN BAILEY LTD ⊠ ♿
Silver Street, Sway, Lymington, Hampshire, SO41 6ZA
Ⓣ (01590) 682227
Ⓕ (01590) 683765
Ⓔ info@steven-bailey.co.uk
Ⓦ www.steven-bailey.co.uk
Contact: Stef Bailey
Opening Times: 1000-1600 all year.
Min Mail Order UK: Nmc
Min Mail Order EU: Nmc
Credit Cards: Visa MasterCard Switch
Specialities: Carnations, pinks, *Alstroemeria* & penstemons.
Notes: Mail order *Alstroemeria* & carnations only. Also sells wholesale.
Map Ref: S, D2 **OS Grid Ref:** SZ284958

SBch BIRCHWOOD PLANTS
(office) 10 Westering, Romsey, Hampshire, SO51 7LY
Ⓣ (01794) 502192
Ⓔ lesleybaker@lycos.co.uk
Ⓦ www.birchwoodplants.co.uk
Contact: Lesley Baker
Opening Times: By appt. at nursery only for collection of plants. Plants available at Mottisfont Abbey (NT) but ring first to check availability.
Cat. Cost: Free by email or 5 × 1st class.
Credit Cards: None
Specialities: Wide range of plants, mainly herbaceous, many unusual. Good selection of salvias, geraniums, grasses & herbs, also good range for bees & butterflies. Some stock available in small quantities only.
Notes: Nursery at Gardener's Lane, Nr Romsey, SO51 6AD. Mottisfont accessible for wheelchairs.
Map Ref: S, D2 **OS Grid Ref:** SU333190

SBHP BLEAK HILL PLANTS ♿
Braemoor, Bleak Hill, Harbridge, Ringwood, Hampshire, BH24 3PX
Ⓣ (01425) 652983
Ⓔ tracey_netherway@btopenworld.com
Contact: Tracy Netherway
Opening Times: 0900-1800, Mon, Tue, Fri, Sat & 1000-1600 Sun, Mar-Oct. Closed Wed & Thu.
Cat. Cost: 2 x1st class.
Credit Cards: None
Specialities: Hardy & half-hardy herbaceous perennials. Stock available in small quantities.
Map Ref: S, D1 **OS Grid Ref:** SU132111

SBla BLACKTHORN NURSERY € ♿
Kilmeston, Alresford, Hampshire, SO24 0NL
Ⓣ (01962) 771796
Ⓕ (01962) 771071
Contact: A R & S B White
Opening Times: Every 2nd & 4th Fri & Sat (closed Sun), Jan-Mar & Sep only. 0900-1700 8th/9th & 22nd/23rd Sep 2006. 1000-1600 12th/13th & 26th/27th Jan, 9th/10th & 23rd/24th Feb, 9th/10th & 23rd/24th Mar 2007.
Cat. Cost: 3 × 1st class for plant list.
Credit Cards: None
Specialities: Alpines, *Daphne*, *Epimedium*, *Helleborus*, *Hepatica* & spring woodlanders.
Map Ref: S, C2 **OS Grid Ref:** SU590264

SBLw BRIAN LEWINGTON ⊠ ♿
(office) 9 Meadow Rise, Horam, Heathfield, East Sussex, TN21 0LZ
Ⓣ (01435) 810124
Ⓕ (01435) 810124

KEY
⊠ Mail order to UK or EU — Delivers to shows
✈ Exports beyond EU — € Euro accepted
♿ Accessible by wheelchair — ◆ See Display advertisement

S

Ⓔ BHLewington@aol.com
Ⓦ www.treesandhedges.co.uk
Contact: Brian Lewington
Opening Times: 0800-1700 Sat. Other times by appt. only .
Min Mail Order UK: Nmc
Specialities: Larger size trees and hedging.
Notes: Nursery is at Leverett Farm, Dallington, Nr Heathfield, Sussex. Also sells wholesale.
Map Ref: S, D4 **OS Grid Ref:** TQ578172

SBmr BLACKMOOR NURSERIES ⊠ ♿
Blackmoor Estate, Blackmoor, Liss, Hampshire, GU33 6BS
Ⓣ (01420) 473576
Ⓕ (01420) 487813
Ⓔ jonmunday@blackmoor.co.uk
Ⓦ www.blackmoor.co.uk
Contact: Jon Munday
Opening Times: 0730-1600.
Min Mail Order UK: Nmc
Cat. Cost: None issued.
Credit Cards: All major credit/debit cards
Specialities: Fruit trees, soft fruit & ornamental trees.
Notes: Also sells wholesale.

SBod BODIAM NURSERY ⊠ ♿
Cowfield Cottage, Bodiam, Robertsbridge, East Sussex, TN32 5RA
Ⓣ (01580) 830811
Ⓕ (01580) 831989
Ⓔ contact@bodiamnursery.com
Ⓦ www.bodiamnursery.co.uk
Contact: Danielle Seymour
Opening Times: 1000-1700 7 days. Closed Mon & Fri Dec & Jan.
Min Mail Order UK: £5.00
Cat. Cost: None issued.
Credit Cards: Visa MasterCard Solo JCB
Specialities: Herbaceous perennials, grasses, conifers, *Camellia* & climbers. Acers. Shrubs, trees.
Map Ref: S, C5

SBra J BRADSHAW & SON ⊠ ♿ ◆
Busheyfield Nursery, Herne, Herne Bay, Kent, CT6 7LJ
Ⓣ (01227) 375415
Ⓕ (01227) 375415
Contact: D J Bradshaw & Martin Bradshaw
Opening Times: 1000-1700 Tue-Sun 1st Mar-31st Oct & B/hol Mons. Other times by appt. only.
Min Mail Order UK: 2 plants + p&p
Cat. Cost: 2 × 1st class.
Credit Cards: Visa MasterCard Switch
Specialities: *Clematis*, *Lonicera*, other climbers & wall shrubs.
Notes: Also sells wholesale.
Map Ref: S, C5 **OS Grid Ref:** TR174646

SBri BRICKWALL COTTAGE NURSERY ♿
1 Brickwall Cottages, Frittenden, Cranbrook, Kent, TN17 2DH
Ⓣ (01580) 852425
Ⓔ suemartin@brickcot.fsnet.co.uk
Contact: Sue Martin
Opening Times: By appt. only.
Credit Cards: None
Specialities: Hardy perennials. Stock available in small quantities only. *Geum*, *Potentilla* (herbaceous).
Map Ref: S, C5 **OS Grid Ref:** TQ815410

SBrm BRAMBLY HEDGE ⊠
Mill Lane, Sway, Hampshire, SO41 8LN
Ⓣ (01590) 683570
Contact: Kim Williams
Opening Times: By appt. only for 2006.
Min Mail Order UK: Nmc
Cat. Cost: 9"× 7" sae.
Credit Cards: None
Specialities: Nat. Collection of *Streptocarpus*. Available in small quantities only.
Notes: Mail order Mar-Sep.
Map Ref: S, D2 **OS Grid Ref:** SZ294973

SCac CACTI & SUCCULENTS ⊠
Hammerfield, Crockham Hill, Edenbridge, Kent, TN8 6RR
Ⓣ (01732) 866295
Contact: Geoff Southon
Opening Times: Flexible. Please phone first.
Min Mail Order UK: Nmc.
Cat. Cost: None issued.
Credit Cards: None
Specialities: *Echeveria* & related genera & hybrids. *Agave*, haworthias, aloes, gasterias, crassulas. Large range of plants available in small quantities.

SCam CAMELLIA GROVE NURSERY ⊠ ⊠ € ♿
Market Garden, Lower Beeding, West Sussex, RH13 6PP
Ⓣ (01403) 891143
Ⓕ (01403) 891336
Ⓔ rhs20@camellia-grove.com
Ⓦ www.camellia-grove.com
Contact: Chris Loder
Opening Times: 1000-1600 Mon-Sat, please phone first so we can give you our undivided attention.
Min Mail Order UK: Nmc
Min Mail Order EU: £100.00 +p&p

Cat. Cost: 2 × 1st class.
Credit Cards: Switch MasterCard Visa
Specialities: Camellias & azaleas.
Notes: Also sells wholesale.
Map Ref: S, C3

SChF CHARLESHURST FARM NURSERY ✉ ⌂
Loxwood Road, Plaistow,
Billingshurst, West Sussex,
RH14 0NY
Ⓣ (01403) 752273
Ⓜ 07736 522788
Ⓔ Charleshurstfarm@aol.com
Contact: Clive Mellor
Opening Times: Normally 0800-1700 Fri, Sat, Sun, Feb-Oct, but please ring first before travelling.
Min Mail Order UK: Nmc
Cat. Cost: 2 × 1st class.
Credit Cards: None
Specialities: Shrubs including some more unusual species. Good range of daphnes & Japanese maples.
Map Ref: S, C3 **OS Grid Ref:** TQ01308591

SChr JOHN CHURCHER ✉ ✈
47 Grove Avenue, Portchester, Fareham, Hampshire, PO16 9EZ
Ⓣ (023) 9232 6740
Ⓕ (023) 9232 6740
Ⓔ John@plants-palms.freeserve.co.uk
Contact: John Churcher
Opening Times: By appt. only. Please phone or email.
Min Mail Order UK: Nmc
Min Mail Order EU: Nmc
Cat. Cost: None issued.
Credit Cards: None
Specialities: Hardy *Opuntia*, *Aeonium*, *Agave*, *Aloe*, *Canna*, *Hedychium*, plus hardy bananas, palms, tree ferns & echiums for the exotic Mediterranean garden.
Map Ref: S, D2 **OS Grid Ref:** SU614047

SCmr CROMAR NURSERY ✉ ♿
39 Livesey Street, North Pole, Wateringbury, Maidstone, Kent, ME18 5BQ
Ⓣ (01622) 812380
Ⓔ CromarNursery@aol.com
Ⓦ www.cromarnursery.co.uk
Contact: Debra & Martin Cronk
Opening Times: 0930-1700 daily except Wed.
Min Mail Order UK: Nmc
Cat. Cost: 2 × 1st class.
Credit Cards: All major credit/debit cards
Specialities: Ornamental & fruit trees.
Map Ref: S, C4 **OS Grid Ref:** TQ697547

SCnR COLIN ROBERTS ✉
Tragumna, Morgay Wood Lane,
Three Oaks, Guestling,
East Sussex,
TN35 4NF
Ⓜ 07718 029909
Contact: Colin Roberts
Opening Times: Not open. Mail order only.
Min Mail Order UK: £20.00
Cat. Cost: 2 × 1st class.
Credit Cards: None
Specialities: Dwarf bulbs & woodland plants incl. many rare & unusual, in small numbers.

SCog COGHURST CAMELLIAS ✉ ⌂ € ♿
Ivy House Lane, Near Three Oaks,
Hastings, East Sussex,
TN35 4NP
Ⓣ (01424) 756228
Ⓕ (01424) 428944
Ⓔ rotherview@btinternet.com
Ⓦ www.rotherview.com
Contact: R Bates & W Bates
Opening Times: 0930-1600 7 days.
Min Mail Order UK: Nmc
Min Mail Order EU: Nmc
Cat. Cost: 4 × 1st class.
Credit Cards: All major credit/debit cards
Specialities: *Camellia.*
Notes: Nursery is on the same site as Rotherview Nursery. Also sells wholesale.
Map Ref: S, D5

SCoo COOLING'S NURSERIES LTD ♿
Rushmore Hill, Knockholt,
Sevenoaks, Kent,
TN14 7NN
Ⓣ (01959) 532269
Ⓕ (01959) 534092
Ⓔ Plantfinder@coolings.co.uk
Ⓦ www.coolings.co.uk
Contact: Mark Reeve & Dan Short
Opening Times: 0900-1700 Mon-Sat & 1000-1630 Sun.
Cat. Cost: None issued.
Credit Cards: All major credit/debit cards except American Express.
Specialities: Large range of perennials, conifers & bedding plants. Many unusual shrubs & trees.
Notes: Third generation family business. Coffee shop. Display garden.
Map Ref: S, C4 **OS Grid Ref:** TK477610

KEY
✉ Mail order to UK or EU ⌂ Delivers to shows
✈ Exports beyond EU € Euro accepted
♿ Accessible by wheelchair ◆ See Display advertisement

S

SCrf **CROFTERS NURSERIES** € ♿
Church Hill, Charing Heath, Near Ashford, Kent, TN27 0BU
Ⓣ (01233) 712798
Ⓕ (01233) 712798
Ⓔ crofters.nursery1@virgin.net
Contact: John & Sue Webb
Opening Times: 1000-1700. Closed Sun-Tue. Please check first.
Cat. Cost: 3 × 1st class.
Credit Cards: None
Specialities: Fruit, ornamental trees & conifers. Old apple varieties. Small number of *Prunus serrula* with grafted ornamental heads.
Map Ref: S, C5 **OS Grid Ref:** TQ923493

SDay **A LA CARTE DAYLILIES** ⊠ € ◆
Little Hermitage, St Catherine's Down, Nr Ventnor, Isle of Wight, PO38 2PD
Ⓣ (01983) 730512
Ⓦ www.alacartedaylilies.co.uk
Contact: Jan & Andy Wyers
Opening Times: Mail order only. Open by appt. only. Difficult to find, on an unmade private road.
Min Mail Order UK: Nmc
Min Mail Order EU: Nmc
Cat. Cost: 3 × 1st class.
Credit Cards: None
Specialities: *Hemerocallis*. Nat. Collections of Miniature & Small Flowered *Hemerocallis* & Large Flowered *Hemerocallis* (post-1960 award-winning cultivars).
Notes: Also sells wholesale.
Map Ref: S, D2 **OS Grid Ref:** SZ499787

SDea **DEACON'S NURSERY** ⊠ ✈ € ◆
Moor View, Godshill, Isle of Wight, PO38 3HW
Ⓣ (01983) 840750 (24 hrs) or (01983) 522243
Ⓕ (01983) 523575
Ⓔ deacons.nursery@btopenworld.com
Ⓦ www.deaconsnurseryfruits.co.uk
Contact: G D & B H W Deacon
Opening Times: 0800-1600 Mon-Fri May-Sep, 0800-1700 Mon-Fri 0800-1200 Sat Oct-Apr.
Min Mail Order UK: Nmc
Min Mail Order EU: Nmc
Cat. Cost: Free.
Credit Cards: All major credit/debit cards
Specialities: Over 300 varieties of apple, old & new, pears, plums, gages, damsons, cherries. Modern soft fruit, grapes, hops, nuts & family trees.
Notes: Also sells wholesale.
Map Ref: S, D2

SDix **GREAT DIXTER NURSERIES** ⊠ ♿
Northiam, Rye, East Sussex, TN31 6PH
Ⓣ (01797) 253107
Ⓕ (01797) 252879
Ⓔ nursery@greatdixter.co.uk
Ⓦ www.greatdixter.co.uk
Contact: K Leighton
Opening Times: 0900-1230 & 1330-1700 Mon-Fri, 0900-1200 Sat all year. Also 1400-1700 Sat, Sun & B/hols Apr-Oct.
Min Mail Order UK: Nmc
Min Mail Order EU: Nmc
Cat. Cost: 4 × 1st class.
Credit Cards: All major credit/debit cards
Specialities: *Clematis*, shrubs and plants. Gardens open.
Notes: Plants dispatched Sep-Mar only.
Map Ref: S, C5

SDnm **DENMANS GARDEN, (JOHN BROOKES LTD)** ♿
Denmans Lane, Fontwell, West Sussex, BN18 0SU
Ⓣ (01243) 542808
Ⓕ (01243) 544064
Ⓔ denmans@denmans-garden.co.uk
Ⓦ www.denmans-garden.co.uk
Contact: Claudia Murphy
Opening Times: 0900-1700 (dusk in winter) 7 days all year, except 25th & 26th Dec & 1st Jan.
Cat. Cost: None issued.
Credit Cards: Visa MasterCard
Specialities: Rare and unusual plants.
Map Ref: S, D3 **OS Grid Ref:** SU944070

SDow **DOWNDERRY NURSERY** ⊠ ✈ ⌂ € ♿
Pillar Box Lane, Hadlow, Nr Tonbridge, Kent, TN11 9SW
Ⓣ (01732) 810081
Ⓕ (01732) 811398
Ⓔ info@downderry-nursery.co.uk
Ⓦ www.downderry-nursery.co.uk
Contact: Dr S J Charlesworth
Opening Times: 1000-1700 Tue-Sun 1st May-31st Oct & B/Hols. Other times by appt.
Min Mail Order UK: Nmc
Min Mail Order EU: Nmc
Cat. Cost: 3 × 1st class.
Credit Cards: Delta MasterCard Maestro Visa
Specialities: Nat. Collections of *Lavandula* and *Rosmarinus*.
Map Ref: S, C4 **OS Grid Ref:** TQ625521

SDry **DRYSDALE GARDEN EXOTICS** ⊠ ♿
Bowerwood Road, Fordingbridge, Hampshire, SP6 1BN
Ⓣ (01425) 653010

Contact: David Crampton
Opening Times: 0930-1730 Wed-Fri, 1000-1730 Sun. Closed 24th Dec-2nd Jan incl.
Min Mail Order UK: £10.00 + p&p
Min Mail Order EU: £15.00 + p&p
Cat. Cost: 3 × 1st class.
Credit Cards: None
Specialities: Plants for exotic & foliage effect. Plants for Mediterranean gardens. Nat. Collection of Bamboos.
Map Ref: S, D1

SDys DYSONS NURSERIES ⊠ ♿
Great Comp Garden, Platt, Sevenoaks, Kent, TN15 8QS
Ⓣ (01732) 886154
Ⓔ dysonsnurseries@aol.com
Ⓦ www.greatcomp.co.uk
Contact: William T Dyson
Opening Times: 1100-1730 7 days 1st Apr-31st Oct. Other times by appt.
Min Mail Order UK: £9.00 + p&p
Cat. Cost: 2 × 1st class.
Credit Cards: None
Specialities: Salvias, especially New World species and cultivars.
Notes: Also sells wholesale.
Map Ref: S, C4

SECG THE ENGLISH COTTAGE GARDEN NURSERY ⊠ ⛟
Eggarton Cottages, Eggarton Lane, Godmersham, Kent, CT4 7DY
Ⓣ (01227) 730242
Ⓕ (01227) 730242
Ⓔ enquiries@englishplants.co.uk
Ⓦ www.englishplants.co.uk
Contact: Teresa Sinclair
Opening Times: 7 days, please phone first.
Min Mail Order UK: £10.00
Cat. Cost: Free.
Credit Cards: MasterCard Visa Solo Electron Switch
Specialities: Small nursery offering variety of traditional cottage garden plants, wildflowers & herbs. Some wildflowers available in small quantities only. Also native hedging, meadow & wildflower seed.
Notes: Plants can be ordered & paid for online. Availability regularly updated on website. Also sells wholesale.
Map Ref: S, C5

SEND EAST NORTHDOWN FARM ⊠ € ♿ ◆
Margate, Kent, CT9 3TS
Ⓣ (01843) 862060
Ⓕ (01843) 860206
Ⓔ friend.northdown@ukonline.co.uk
Ⓦ www.botanyplants.com
Contact: Louise & William Friend
Opening Times: 0900-1700 Mon-Sat, 1000-1700 Sun all year. Closed Xmas week & Easter Sun.
Min Mail Order UK: Nmc
Cat. Cost: Online only.
Credit Cards: Visa Switch MasterCard
Specialities: Chalk & coast-loving plants.
Map Ref: S, B6

SEWo ENGLISH WOODLANDS ⊠
Burrow Nursery, Cross in Hand, Heathfield, East Sussex, TN21 0UG
Ⓣ (01435) 862992
Ⓕ (01435) 867742
Ⓔ michael@ewburrownursery.co.uk
Ⓦ www.ewburrownursery.co.uk
Contact: Michael Hardcastle
Opening Times: 8000-1700 Mon-Sat. Closed Sun.
Min Mail Order UK: £25.00
Cat. Cost: 4 × 1st class.
Credit Cards: All major credit/debit cards
Specialities: Trees.
Notes: Also sells wholesale.
Map Ref: S, C4 **OS Grid Ref:** TQ557122

SFam FAMILY TREES ⊠ ♿
Sandy Lane, Shedfield, Hampshire, SO32 2HQ
Ⓣ (01329) 834812
Contact: Philip House
Opening Times: 0930-1230 Wed & Sat mid Oct-end Apr.
Min Mail Order UK: £16.00
Min Mail Order EU: Nmc
Cat. Cost: Free.
Credit Cards: None
Specialities: Fruit & ornamental trees. Trained fruit tree specialists: standards, espaliers, cordons. Other trees, old- fashioned & climbing roses, evergreens. Trees, except evergreens, sold bare-rooted.
Map Ref: S, D2

SFgr FIRGROVE PLANTS ⊠
24 Wykeham Field, Wickham, Fareham, Hampshire, PO17 5AB
Ⓣ (01329) 835206 after 1900 hours.
Ⓔ jenny@firgroveplants.demon.co.uk
Ⓦ www.firgroveplants.demon.co.uk
Contact: Jenny MacKinnon

KEY
⊠ Mail order to UK or EU — ⛟ Delivers to shows
✈ Exports beyond EU — € Euro accepted
♿ Accessible by wheelchair — ◆ See Display advertisement

S

Opening Times: Not open. Mail order only.
Min Mail Order UK: £7.00
Cat. Cost: Sae.
Specialities: Wide range of houseleeks & smaller range of other alpines in small quantities.
Notes: Houseleeks by mail order Apr-mid Oct.

SGar GARDEN PLANTS ⊠ ♠
Windy Ridge, Victory Road, St Margarets-at-Cliffe, Dover, Kent, CT15 6HF
Ⓣ (01304) 853225
Ⓔ GardenPlants@GardenPlants-nursery.co.uk
Ⓦ www.GardenPlants-nursery.co.uk
Contact: Teresa Ryder & David Ryder
Opening Times: 1000-1730 summer, 1000-1700 winter. Closed Tues.
Min Mail Order UK: Nmc
Cat. Cost: 2 × 1st class + A5 sae.
Credit Cards: None
Specialities: Unusual perennials, *Penstemon* & *Salvia*. Plantsman's garden open to view.
Notes: Map essential for first visit. Also sells wholesale.
Map Ref: S, C6 **OS Grid Ref:** TR358464

SGFT THE GARDEN FRUIT TREE COMPANY LTD ⊠ ♠ €
The Nursery, New Place Farm,
Wingham Lane, Ickham, Kent, CT3 1RA
Ⓣ (01227) 721110
Ⓜ 07795 608134
Ⓕ 0870 051 4893
Ⓔ enquiries@gardenfruittree.co.uk
Ⓦ www.gardenfruittree.co.uk
Contact: Alan Bicker
Opening Times: 0700-1800 daily.
Min Mail Order UK: Nmc
Min Mail Order EU: Nmc
Cat. Cost: Free.
Credit Cards: All major credit/debit cards
Specialities: Container-grown trained fruit trees, grapevines, and soft fruit plants. Espaliers, fans, cordons, stepovers, pyramids & goblets. Grapes as double-guyot and cordons.
Notes: Also sells wholesale.
Map Ref: S, C6 **OS Grid Ref:** TR222578

SHaC HART CANNA ⊠ € ♿
27 Guildford Road West, Farnborough, Hampshire, GU14 6PS
Ⓣ (01252) 514421
Ⓕ (01252) 378821
Ⓔ plants@hartcanna.com
Ⓦ www.hartcanna.com
Contact: Keith Hayward
Opening Times: Visitors by arrangement.
Min Mail Order UK: Nmc
Min Mail Order EU: Nmc
Cat. Cost: Free.
Credit Cards: All major credit/debit cards
Specialities: *Canna*. Nat. Collection of *Canna*.
Notes: Also sells wholesale.
Map Ref: S, C3

SHar HARDY'S COTTAGE GARDEN PLANTS ⊠ ♠ ♿
Priory Lane Nursery, Freefolk Priors, Whitchurch, Hampshire, RG28 7NJ
Ⓣ (01256) 896533
Ⓕ (01256) 896572
Ⓔ info@hardys-plants.co.uk
Ⓦ www.hardys-plants.co.uk
Contact: Rosy Hardy
Opening Times: 1000-1700 7 days 1st Mar-31st Oct.
Min Mail Order UK: Nmc
Cat. Cost: 10 × 1st class.
Credit Cards: Visa Access Electron Switch Solo
Specialities: Wide range of herbaceous perennials incl. *Heuchera*, *Penstemon*, *Salvia*, *Verbascum* & *Viola* .
Notes: A charge of £2.00 is made for delivery of pre-ordered plants to shows. Also sells wholesale.
Map Ref: S, C2

SHBN HIGH BANKS NURSERIES ♿
Slip Mill Road, Hawkhurst, Kent, TN18 5AD
Ⓣ (01580) 754492
Ⓕ (01580) 754450
Contact: Jeremy Homewood
Opening Times: 0800-1700 (1630 in winter) daily.
Cat. Cost: £1.50 in stamps + A4 sae.
Credit Cards: All major credit/debit cards
Specialities: Wide general range with many unusual plants. Minimum of 250,000 plants on site at any one time. Many unusual plants. Open ground stock limited between Nov and Feb.
Notes: Also sells wholesale.
Map Ref: S, C5

SHDw HIGHDOWN NURSERY ⊠ ☒ ♠ €
New Hall Lane, Small Dole, Nr Henfield, West Sussex, BN5 9YH
Ⓣ (01273) 492976
Ⓕ (01273) 492976
Ⓔ highdown.herbs@btopenworld.com
Contact: A G & J H Shearing
Opening Times: 0900-1700 7 days.
Min Mail Order UK: £10.00 + p&p
Min Mail Order EU: £10.00 + p&p
Cat. Cost: 3 × 1st class.

Credit Cards: Visa MasterCard Delta JCB, EuroCard
Specialities: Herbs. Grasses.
Notes: Partial wheelchair access. Also sells wholesale.
Map Ref: S, D3

SHdy HARDY ORCHIDS ⊠ ⌂
Pitcot Lane, Owslebury, Winchester, Hampshire, SO21 1LR
Ⓣ (01962) 777372
Ⓕ (01962) 777664
Ⓔ orchids@hardyorchids.co.uk
Ⓦ www.hardyorchids.co.uk
Contact: Claudia Whales
Opening Times: Mail order only. Open by appt. only.
Min Mail Order UK: £15.00 + p&p
Min Mail Order EU: £15.00 + p&p
Cat. Cost: 2 × 1st class.
Credit Cards: All major credit/debit cards
Specialities: Hardy orchids. *Dactylorhiza, Pleione, Anacamptis, Orchis, Ophrys, Epipactis, Cypripedium, Bletilla, Gymnadenia, Himantoglossum* & *Platanthera*.
Notes: Also sells wholesale.

SHea HEASELANDS GARDEN NURSERY €
The Old Lodge, Isaacs Lane, Haywards Heath, West Sussex, RH16 4SA
Ⓣ (01444) 458084
Ⓕ (01444) 458084
Ⓔ headgardener@heaselands.wanadoo.co.uk
Contact: Stephen Harding
Opening Times: 0800-1700, Mon-Fri, but please phone first. W/ends by appt. only.
Cat. Cost: Sae.
Credit Cards: None
Specialities: *Rhododendron* hybrids and deciduous azaleas, home-produced from cuttings. Some in small quantities. Nat. Collection of Mollis Azaleas & Knaphill/Exbury Azaleas.
Notes: Also sells wholesale.
Map Ref: S, C4 **OS Grid Ref:** TQ3122

SHFr SUE HARTFREE
25 Crouch Hill Court, Lower Halstow, Nr Sittingbourne, Kent, ME9 7EJ
Ⓣ (01795) 842426
Ⓕ (01795) 841034
Ⓔ sue@thegardendesigners.co.uk
Ⓦ www.thegardendesigners.co.uk
Contact: Sue Hartfree
Opening Times: Any time by appt. Please phone first.
Cat. Cost: Plant list online.
Credit Cards: None
Specialities: Rare & unusual plants for the garden & conservatory incl. many varieties of *Salvia*. Some plants available in small quantities but can be propagated to order. Garden design service available.
Map Ref: S, C5 **OS Grid Ref:** TQ860672

SHGN HILL GARTH NURSERY ♿
Woodgreen Road, Godshill, Fordingbridge, Hampshire, SP6 2LP
Ⓣ (01425) 657619
Ⓕ (01425) 657619
Contact: Mrs S J Giddins
Opening Times: 0930-1700 Thu & Sun, Mar-end Oct.
Cat. Cost: None issued.
Credit Cards: None
Specialities: Small nursery offering a range of rare, unusual & traditional hardy perennials, shrubs & trees. Some stock may be limited.
Map Ref: S, D1

SHHo HIGHFIELD HOLLIES ⊠ ◆
Highfield Farm, Hatch Lane, Liss, Hampshire, GU33 7NH
Ⓣ (01730) 892372
Ⓕ (01730) 894853
Ⓔ louise@highfieldhollies.com
Ⓦ www.highfieldhollies.com
Contact: Mrs Louise Bendall Duck
Opening Times: By appt.
Min Mail Order UK: £30.00
Cat. Cost: £3.50 for illustrated cat.
Credit Cards: None
Specialities: 150+ species & cultivars *Ilex* incl. specimen trees, hedging & topiary. Some in short supply.
Map Ref: S, C3 **OS Grid Ref:** SU787276

SHmp HAMPSHIRE CARNIVOROUS PLANTS ⊠ ✈ ⌂ €
Ya-Mayla, Allington Lane, West End, Southampton, Hampshire, SO30 3HQ
Ⓣ (023) 8047 3314
Ⓜ 07703 258296
Ⓕ (023) 8047 3314
Ⓔ matthew@msoper.freesave.co.uk
Ⓦ www.hampshire-carnivorous-plants.co.uk
Contact: Matthew Soper
Opening Times: Mail order only. Open by appt. only.
Min Mail Order UK: Nmc
Min Mail Order EU: £50.00 + p&p

KEY
⊠ Mail order to UK or EU ⌂ Delivers to shows
✈ Exports beyond EU € Euro accepted
♿ Accessible by wheelchair ◆ See Display advertisement

Cat. Cost: 2 × 2nd class.
Credit Cards: Visa MasterCard
Specialities: Carnivorous plants esp. *Nepenthes*, *Heliamphora*, *Sarracenia*, *Pinguicula* & *Utricularia*.
Notes: Also sells wholesale.

SHol HOLLY GATE CACTUS NURSERY ⊠ € ♿
Billingshurst Road, Ashington, West Sussex, RH20 3BB
Ⓣ (01903) 892 930
Ⓔ info@hollygatecactus.co.uk
Ⓦ www.hollygatecactus.co.uk
Contact: David Dickinson
Opening Times: 0900-1700 7 days Feb-Oct, 0900-1600 Nov-Jan.
Min Mail Order UK: £10.00 + p&p
Min Mail Order EU: £10.00 + p&p
Cat. Cost: 2 × 1st class.
Credit Cards: All major credit/debit cards
Specialities: Cacti & succulents, plants & seeds. World-famous cactus & succulent garden.
Notes: Also sells wholesale.
Map Ref: S, D3 **OS Grid Ref:** TQ133175

S

SHom HOME PLANTS
52 Dorman Ave North, Aylesham, Canterbury, Kent, CT3 3BW
Ⓣ (01304) 841746
Ⓔ homeplants@supanet.com
Contact: Stuart & Sue Roycroft
Opening Times: By appt. only, please phone first.
Cat. Cost: Sae for list.
Credit Cards: None
Specialities: *Phygelius* & unusual South African hardy plants. Limited stock, please phone first.

SHyH HYDRANGEA HAVEN ⊠ ☒ ♠ € ♿
Market Garden, Lower Beeding, West Sussex, RH13 6PP
Ⓣ (01403) 892580
Ⓕ (01403) 891336
Ⓔ rhspf@hydrangea-haven.com
Ⓦ www.hydrangea-haven.com
Contact: Chris Loder
Opening Times: 1000-1600 Mon-Sat, please phone first, so we can give you our undivided attention.
Min Mail Order UK: Nmc
Min Mail Order EU: £100.00 + p&p
Cat. Cost: 2 × 1st class.
Credit Cards: Switch MasterCard Visa
Specialities: *Hydrangea* .
Notes: Also sells wholesale.
Map Ref: S, C3

SIde IDEN CROFT HERBS ⊠ ♿ ◆
Frittenden Road, Staplehurst, Kent, TN12 0DH
Ⓣ (01580) 891432
Ⓕ (01580) 892416
Ⓔ idencroftherbs@yahoo.co.uk
Ⓦ www.herbs-uk.com
Contact: Tracey Pearman
Opening Times: 0900-1700 Mon-Sat & 1100-1700 Sun & B/hols during summer. Open all winter with reduced hours, please phone to confirm prior to visit.
Min Mail Order UK: £10.00
Min Mail Order EU: £25.00
Cat. Cost: 2 × 1st class for descriptive list.
Credit Cards: All major credit/debit cards
Specialities: Herbs, aromatic & wildflower plants & plants for bees & butterflies. Nat. Collections of *Mentha*, *Nepeta* & *Origanum*.
Notes: Wheelchairs available at nursery. Exports seed only.
Map Ref: S, C5

SIFN IAN FITZROY NURSERYMAN ⊠ ♠
(Office) Beeches Farm Lane, off Smithers Lane, Cowden, Kent, TN8 7LA
Ⓣ (01342) 851179
Ⓕ (01342) 851179
Ⓔ ian@ianfitzroy.com
Ⓦ www.ianfitzroy.com
Contact: Ian FitzRoy
Opening Times: Mail order only. Open by appt. only.
Min Mail Order UK: Nmc
Min Mail Order EU: Nmc
Cat. Cost: 4 × 1st class.
Credit Cards: SwitchVisaMasterCard
Specialities: Japanese maples. Rare and unusual grafted trees and shrubs. *Ginkgo*, *Betula* & *Carpinus*.
Notes: Nursery is at Scarlets, Smithers Lane, Cowden, Kent. Also sells wholesale.
Map Ref: S, C4

SImb IMBERHORNE LANE NURSERY ⊠ €
Imberhorne Lane, East Grinstead, West Sussex, RH19 1TZ
Ⓣ (01342) 321175
Ⓕ (01342) 317477
Ⓔ gardenexpert@btinternet.com
Ⓦ www.camelliasonline.co.uk
Contact: Michael Dongray
Opening Times: 0900-1645, 7 days.
Min Mail Order UK: £10.00
Cat. Cost: 3 × 1st class.
Credit Cards: All major credit/debit cards
Specialities: 300 varieties of *Camellia* plus

extensive range of shrubs & herbaceous. 66 varieties of Chinese tree peony (*Paeonia suffruticosa*).
Map Ref: S, C4 **OS Grid Ref:** TQ377373

SIng **W E Th. Ingwersen Ltd** ⛺
Birch Farm Nursery, Gravetye, East Grinstead, West Sussex, RH19 4LE
Ⓣ (01342) 810236
Ⓔ info@ingwersen.co.uk
Ⓦ www.ingwersen.co.uk
Contact: M P & M R Ingwersen
Opening Times: 0900-1600 daily excl. Sun & B/hols, Mar-Sep. 0900-1600 Mon-Fri Oct-Feb.
Cat. Cost: 2 × 1st class.
Credit Cards: None
Specialities: Very wide range of hardy plants, mostly alpines. Also seed.
Notes: Wheelchair accessible with assistance.
Map Ref: S, C4

SIri **Iris of Sissinghurst** ⊠ ⛺ € ♿ ◆
Plummers Farmhouse, Biddenden Road, Sissinghurst, Kent, TN17 2JP
Ⓣ (01622) 831511
Ⓔ irisofs@aol.com
Ⓦ www.irisofsissinghurst.com
Contact: Margaret Roberts
Opening Times: Contact nursery or see website.
Min Mail Order UK: Nmc
Min Mail Order EU: Nmc
Cat. Cost: 2 × 1st class.
Credit Cards: None
Specialities: *Iris*, short, intermediate & tall bearded, *ensata*, *sibirica* & many species.
Map Ref: S, C5 **OS Grid Ref:** TQ796375

SJoh **Vic Johnstone and Claire Wilson** €
43 Winchester Street, Whitchurch, Hampshire, RG28 7AJ
Ⓣ (01256) 893144
Contact: Vic Johnstone, Claire Wilson
Opening Times: By appt. Please telephone first.
Cat. Cost: 2 × 1st class.
Credit Cards: None
Specialities: Nat. Collection of *Verbascum*. *Verbascum* only. Stock available in small quantities.
Map Ref: S, C2 **OS Grid Ref:** SU463478

SJoo **Jooles Plants** ⊠ ⛺ ♿
Spring Hill Nurseries, Shirley Holmes, Boldre, Lymington, Hampshire, SO41 8NL
Ⓣ (01590) 670581
Ⓜ 07973 291062
Ⓕ (01590) 670581
Ⓔ cruella@joolesplants.fsnet.co.uk
Ⓦ www.heucheraholics.com
Contact: Julie Burton
Opening Times: 1000-1600 Wed-Sat. Please phone first.
Min Mail Order UK: Nmc
Cat. Cost: 2 × 1st class.
Specialities: Heucheras, heucherellas & tiarellas. Foliage plants. Lavenders. Alpines.
Map Ref: S, D2 **OS Grid Ref:** SZ310934

SKee **Keepers Nursery** ⊠
Gallants Court, Gallants Lane, East Farleigh, Maidstone, Kent, ME15 0LE
Ⓣ (01622) 726465
Ⓕ 0870 705 2145
Ⓔ info@keepers-nursery.co.uk
Ⓦ www.keepers-nursery.co.uk
Contact: Hamid Habibi
Opening Times: All reasonable hours by appt.
Min Mail Order UK: Nmc
Cat. Cost: Online only.
Credit Cards: All major credit/debit cards
Specialities: Old & unusual top fruit varieties. Top fruit propagated to order.
Map Ref: S, C4

SKHP **Kevin Hughes Plants** ⊠ ✈ ⛺ €
Springhill Nurseries, Shirley Holmes, Boldre, Lymington, Hampshire, SO41 8NL
Ⓣ 07720 718671
Ⓕ (01590) 679506
Ⓔ kevin@hughes83.fsnet.co.uk
Ⓦ www.kevinhughesplants.com
Contact: Kevin Hughes
Opening Times: 1000-1700 Wed-Sat, 1st Mar-31st Oct. Other times by appt. only.
Min Mail Order UK: £20.00
Min Mail Order EU: £20.00
Cat. Cost: 3 × 1st class.
Credit Cards: None
Specialities: Choice & desirable shrubs, herbaceous, ferns. Specialities incl. legumes, *Magnolia*, *Trillium* (Nat. Collection status applied for), Mediterranean & deer-resistant plants.
Notes: Mail order only between Oct & Feb.
Map Ref: S, D2 **OS Grid Ref:** SZ310980

KEY
⊠ Mail order to UK or EU ⛺ Delivers to shows
✈ Exports beyond EU € Euro accepted
♿ Accessible by wheelchair ◆ See Display advertisement

S

SLan **LANGLEY BOXWOOD NURSERY LTD.** ⊠ ✈ € ♿ ◆
Langley Lane, Rake, Nr Liss, Hampshire, GU33 7JN
Ⓣ (01730) 894467
Ⓕ (01730) 894703
Ⓔ sales@boxwood.co.uk
Ⓦ www.boxwood.co.uk
Contact: Russell Coates
Opening Times: 0900-1630 Mon-Fri, 1000-1600 Sat. Please phone for directions.
Min Mail Order UK: Nmc
Min Mail Order EU: Nmc
Cat. Cost: 4 × 1st class.
Credit Cards: All major credit/debit cards
Specialities: *Buxus* species, cultivars & hedging. Good range of topiary, *Taxus*, and 'character-pruned' specimens. Nat. Collection of *Buxus*. Evergreen topiary & hedging.
Notes: Also sells wholesale.
Map Ref: S, C3 **OS Grid Ref:** SU812290

S

SLau **THE LAURELS NURSERY** ⊠ €
Benenden, Cranbrook, Kent, TN17 4JU
Ⓣ (01580) 240463
Ⓕ (01580) 240463
Ⓦ www.thelaurelsnursery.co.uk
Contact: Peter or Sylvia Kellett
Opening Times: 0800-1600 Mon-Fri, 0900-1200 Sat, Sun by appt. only.
Min Mail Order UK: £20.00
Cat. Cost: Free.
Credit Cards: None
Specialities: Open ground & container ornamental trees, shrubs & climbers incl. birch, beech & *Wisteria*.
Notes: Mail order of small *Wisteria* only. Also sells wholesale.
Map Ref: S, C5 **OS Grid Ref:** TQ815313

SLay **LAYHAM GARDEN CENTRE & NURSERY** ⊠ ♿
Lower Road, Staple, Nr Canterbury, Kent, CT3 1LH
Ⓣ (01304) 813267
Ⓕ (01304) 814007
Ⓔ layham@gcstaple.fsnet.co.uk
Contact: Ellen Wessel
Opening Times: 0900-1700 7 days.
Min Mail Order UK: Nmc
Min Mail Order EU: £25.00 + p&p
Cat. Cost: Free.
Credit Cards: Visa Switch MasterCard
Specialities: Roses, herbaceous, shrubs, trees & hedging plants.
Notes: Also sells wholesale.
Map Ref: S, C6 **OS Grid Ref:** TR276567

SLBF **LITTLE BROOK FUCHSIAS** ♿
Ash Green Lane West, Ash Green, Nr Aldershot, Hampshire, GU12 6HL
Ⓣ (01252) 329731
Ⓔ carol.gubler@business.ntl.com
Ⓦ www.littlebrookfuchsias.co.uk
Contact: Carol Gubler
Opening Times: 0900-1700 Wed-Sun 1st Jan-2nd Jul.
Cat. Cost: 50p + sae.
Credit Cards: None
Specialities: Fuchsias, old & new.
Map Ref: S, C3

SLdr **LODER PLANTS** ⊠ ✈ ⌂ € ♿
Market Garden, Lower Beeding, West Sussex, RH13 6PP
Ⓣ (01403) 891412
Ⓕ (01403) 891336
Ⓔ rhspf@rhododendrons.com
Ⓦ www.rhododendrons.com
Contact: Chris Loder
Opening Times: 1000-1600 Mon-Sat, please ring first.
Min Mail Order UK: Nmc
Min Mail Order EU: £100.00 + p&p
Cat. Cost: 2 × 1st class.
Credit Cards: Switch MasterCard Visa
Specialities: Rhododendrons & azaleas in all sizes. *Camellia* & *Hydrangea*.
Notes: Also sells wholesale.
Map Ref: S, C3

SLim **LIME CROSS NURSERY** ♿ ◆
Herstmonceux, Hailsham, East Sussex, BN27 4RS
Ⓣ (01323) 833229
Ⓕ (01323) 833944
Ⓔ LimeCross@aol.com
Ⓦ www.Limecross.co.uk
Contact: Jonathan Tate, Anita Green
Opening Times: 0830-1700 Mon-Sat & 1000-1600 Sun.
Cat. Cost: 3 × 1st class.
Credit Cards: Visa MasterCard Delta Switch
Specialities: Conifers, trees & shrubs, climbers.
Notes: Also sells wholesale.
Map Ref: S, D4 **OS Grid Ref:** TQ642125

SLon **LONGSTOCK PARK NURSERY** ♿
Longstock, Stockbridge, Hampshire, SO20 6EH
Ⓣ (01264) 810894
Ⓕ (01264) 810924
Ⓔ longstocknursery@leckfordestate.co.uk
Ⓦ www.longstocknursery.co.uk
Contact: Peter Moore

Opening Times: 0830-1630 Mon-Sat all year excl. Xmas & New Year, & 1100-1700 Sun Mar-Oct, 1000-1600 Sun, Nov-Feb.
Cat. Cost: None issued. 1 × 1st class for lists of *Buddleja*, *Penstemon*, roses or fruit, or can be emailed.
Credit Cards: All major credit/debit cards
Specialities: A wide range, over 2000 varieties, of trees, shrubs, perennials, climbers, aquatics & ferns. Nat. Collections of *Buddleja* & *Clematis viticella*.
Map Ref: S, C2 **OS Grid Ref:** SO365389

SLPl LANDSCAPE PLANTS ⊠ ✈ ♿
Cattamount, Grafty Green, Maidstone, Kent, ME17 2AP
Ⓣ (01622) 850245
Ⓕ (01622) 858063
Ⓔ landscapeplants@aol.com
Contact: Tom La Dell
Opening Times: 0800-1600 Mon-Fri, by appt. only.
Min Mail Order UK: £100.00 + p&p
Min Mail Order EU: £200.00 + p&p
Cat. Cost: 2 × 1st class.
Credit Cards: None
Specialities: Garden & landscape shrubs & perennials.
Notes: Also sells wholesale.
Map Ref: S, C5 **OS Grid Ref:** TQ772468

SMac MACGREGORS PLANTS FOR SHADE ⊠
Carters Clay Road, Lockerley, Romsey, Hampshire, SO51 0GL
Ⓣ (01794) 340256
Ⓔ plants@macgregors-shadeplants.co.uk
Ⓦ www.macgregors-shadeplants.co.uk
Contact: Irene & Stuart Bowron
Opening Times: By appt. only. Please phone before travelling to make arrangements.
Min Mail Order UK: Nmc
Cat. Cost: Online only.
Credit Cards: MasterCard Visa
Specialities: All types of shade plants & other less usual shrubs & perennials. Ltd. stock of rarer plants.
Notes: Mail order usually restricted to small numbers sent by 24hr carrier. Other arrangements by negotiation. Also sells wholesale.
Map Ref: S, C2 **OS Grid Ref:** SU308239

SMad MADRONA NURSERY ⊠ ⌂ € ♿
Pluckley Road, Bethersden, Kent, TN26 3DD
Ⓣ (01233) 820100
Ⓕ (01233) 820091
Ⓔ madrona@fsmail.net
Ⓦ www.madrona.co.uk
Contact: Liam MacKenzie
Opening Times: 1000-1700 Sat-Tue 11th Mar-29th Oct. Closed 5th-18th Aug.
Min Mail Order UK: Nmc
Cat. Cost: Free.
Credit Cards: All major credit/debit cards
Specialities: Unusual shrubs, conifers & perennials. Eryngiums, *Pseudopanax*.
Map Ref: S, C5 **OS Grid Ref:** TQ918419

SMDP MARCUS DANCER PLANTS ⌂ ♿
Kilcreggan, Alderholt Road, Sandleheath, Fordingbridge, Hampshire, SP6 1PT
Ⓣ (01425) 652747
Ⓔ marcus.dancer@btopenworld.com
Contact: Marcus Dancer
Opening Times: By appointment only.
Cat. Cost: 2 × 1st class.
Credit Cards: None
Specialities: Wide range of *Clematis*, smaller range of *Daphne*. Some varieties available in small quantities only.
Map Ref: S, D1

SMeo MEON VALLEY PLANTS ⌂ ♿
Broadhanger Farm, Froxfield, Nr Petersfield, Hampshire, GU32 1DW
Ⓜ 07818 088019
Ⓔ info@meonvalleyplants.co.uk
Ⓦ www.meonvalleyplants.co.uk
Contact: Camilla Moreton
Opening Times: 1000-1700 Fri & Sat, 10th Mar-14th Oct 2006 and by appt.
Cat. Cost: 2 × 1st class for list.
Credit Cards: None
Specialities: Unusual bulbs, perennials & grasses. Many plants produced in small quantities.
Map Ref: S, C2 **OS Grid Ref:** SU713259

SMer MERRYFIELD NURSERIES (CANTERBURY) LTD ⊠ ♿
Stodmarsh Road, Canterbury, Kent, CT3 4AP
Ⓣ (01227) 462602
Ⓔ merry1field@tiscali.co.uk
Contact: Mrs A Downs
Opening Times: 0930-1730 Tue-Sat, 1000-1700 Sun B/hol Mons.
Min Mail Order UK: £10.00 + p&p
Cat. Cost: 2 × 1st class.

KEY
⊠ Mail order to UK or EU ⌂ Delivers to shows
✈ Exports beyond EU € Euro accepted
♿ Accessible by wheelchair ◆ See Display advertisement

S

Credit Cards: All major credit/debit cards
Specialities: Wide range of shrubs, conifers, herbaceous, many unusual.
Map Ref: S, C5

S

SMHy MARCHANTS HARDY PLANTS € ♿
2 Marchants Cottages, Mill Lane, Laughton, East Sussex, BN8 6AJ
Ⓣ (01323) 811737
Ⓕ (01323) 811737
Contact: Graham Gough
Opening Times: 0930-1730 Wed-Sat, 22nd Mar-28th Oct 2006.
Cat. Cost: 6 × 2nd class.
Specialities: Uncommon herbaceous perennials. *Agapanthus*, *Kniphofia*, *Sedum*, choice grasses, *Miscanthus*, *Molinia*.
Map Ref: S, D4 **OS Grid Ref:** TQ506119

SMrm MERRIMENTS GARDENS ♿
Hawkhurst Road, Hurst Green, East Sussex, TN19 7RA
Ⓣ (01580) 860666
Ⓕ (01580) 860324
Ⓔ alanasharp@beeb.net
Ⓦ www.merriments.co.uk
Contact: Alana Sharp
Opening Times: 0930-1730 Mon-Sat, 1030-1730 Sun (or dusk in winter).
Cat. Cost: Online only.
Credit Cards: Visa Access American Express
Specialities: Unusual shrubs. Tender & hardy perennials.
Map Ref: S, C4

SNew NEW FOREST PALMS & EXOTICS € ♿
Pauls Lane, Sway, Lymington, Hampshire, SO41 6BR
Ⓣ (01590) 683864
Ⓜ 07870 483972
Ⓕ (01590) 681244
Ⓔ Paulsnursery@farmersweekly.net
Ⓦ www.newforestpalms.co.uk
Contact: F R Toyne
Opening Times: 1000-1700 Tue-Sun Mar-Oct. 1000-1500 Tue-Sun Nov-Feb. Closed Mon. Closed Jan.
Cat. Cost: 2 × 1st class.
Credit Cards: All major credit/debit cards
Specialities: Ornamental grasses & plants for the Mediterranean look, incl. bamboos, tree ferns. Topiary, large specimen shrubs.
Notes: Free delivery within 10 miles for orders over £100. Also sells wholesale.
Map Ref: S, D2 **OS Grid Ref:** SZ292978

SNin NINESPRINGS NURSERY ⌂ € ♿
The Weir, Whitchurch, Hampshire, RG28 7RA
Ⓣ (01256) 892837
Ⓔ graham@gyrdan.demon.co.uk
Contact: Graham Burgess
Credit Cards: None
Specialities: Aquatic, emergent and marginal plants. *Gunnera manicata*, *Lysichiton*, *Iris laevigata* as well as other waterside plants. Design advice on water features.
Notes: Also sells wholesale.
Map Ref: S, C2

SOWG THE OLD WALLED GARDEN ⊠ ⌂ € ♿
Oxonhoath, Hadlow, Kent, TN11 9SS
Ⓣ (01732) 810012
Ⓕ (01732) 810856
Ⓔ HeatherAngrave@aol.com
Ⓦ www.theoldwalledgarden.co.uk
Contact: John & Heather Angrave
Opening Times: 0900-1700 Mon-Sat. Sun by appt.
Min Mail Order UK: Nmc
Cat. Cost: 4 × 1st class.
Credit Cards: All major credit/debit cards
Specialities: Many rare & unusual shrubs. Wide range of conservatory plants esp. Australian. Nat. Collection of *Callistemon*.
Notes: Also sells wholesale.
Map Ref: S, C4

SPad PADDOCK PLANTS ⊠ ⌂
The Paddock, Upper Toothill Road, Rownhams, Southampton, Hampshire, SO16 8AL
Ⓣ (023) 8073 9912
Ⓔ rob@paddockplants.co.uk
Ⓦ www.paddockplants.co.uk
Contact: Robert Courtney
Opening Times: By appt. only. Please telephone in advance.
Min Mail Order UK: Nmc
Cat. Cost: Free.
Credit Cards: None
Specialities: Family-run nursery offering interesting range of perennials, grasses, ferns & shrubs, incl. some more unusual varieties. Some varieties grown in small quantities.
Notes: Online descriptive catalogue & ordering. Local delivery by our own transport.

SPav PAVILION PLANTS ⊠ ⌂
18 Pavilion Road, Worthing, West Sussex, BN14 7EF
Ⓣ (01903) 821338 Ⓜ 07881 876037
Ⓔ rewrew18@hotmail.com
Contact: Andrew Muggeridge

Opening Times: Please phone for details.
Min Mail Order UK: Nmc
Cat. Cost: 4 × 1st class.
Credit Cards: None
Specialities: Perennials and bulbs.
Notes: Also sells wholesale.
Map Ref: S, D3

SPer PERRYHILL NURSERIES LTD ⊠ ♠ ♿
Hartfield, East Sussex, TN7 4JP
Ⓣ (01892) 770377
Ⓕ (01892) 770929
Ⓔ sales@perryhillnurseries.co.uk
Ⓦ www.perryhillnurseries.co.uk
Contact: P J Chapman
Opening Times: 0900-1700 7 days 1st Mar-31st Oct. 0900-1630 1st Nov-28th Feb.
Min Mail Order UK: Nmc
Cat. Cost: £2.00 or online.
Credit Cards: Visa Access MasterCard Switch
Specialities: Wide range of trees, shrubs, conifers, *Rhododendron* etc. Over 1300 herbaceous varieties, over 500 rose varieties.
Notes: Will deliver to small number of non-RHS shows. Mail order despatch depends on size & weight of plants.
Map Ref: S, C4 **OS Grid Ref:** TQ480375

SPet PETTET'S NURSERY ⊠ ♠ € ♿
Poison Cross, Eastry, Sandwich, Kent, CT13 0EA
Ⓣ (01304) 613869
Ⓕ (01304) 613869
Ⓔ terry@pettetsnursery.fsnet.co.uk
Ⓦ www.pettetsnursery.co.uk
Contact: T & E H P Pettet
Opening Times: 0900-1700 daily Mar-Jul. 1000-1600 Aug-Oct weekdays only.
Min Mail Order UK: £10.00
Min Mail Order EU: £20.00
Credit Cards: None
Specialities: Climbers, shrubs, herbaceous perennials, alpines, pelargoniums, fuchsias.
Notes: Mail order Oct-Mar only. Also sells wholesale.
Map Ref: S, C6

SPhx PHOENIX PERENNIAL PLANTS ♠ € ♿
Paice Lane, Medstead, Alton, Hampshire, GU34 5PR
Ⓣ (01420) 560695
Ⓕ (01420) 563640
Ⓔ GreenFarmPlants.Marina.Christopher@Care4free.net
Contact: Marina Christopher
Opening Times: 1000-1800 Thu, Fri & Sat, 23rd Mar-21st Oct 2006.
Cat. Cost: 4 × 1st class.
Credit Cards: All major credit/debit cards
Specialities: Perennials, many uncommon. *Sanguisorba, Thalictrum, Achillea, Eryngium, Monarda, Phlox, Verbascum*, centaureas, bulbs, grasses & late-flowering perenials.
Notes: Co-located with Select Seeds SSss.
Map Ref: S, C2 **OS Grid Ref:** SU657362

SPin JOHN AND LYNSEY'S PLANTS
2 Hillside Cottages, Trampers Lane, North Boarhunt, Fareham, Hampshire, PO17 6DA
Ⓣ (01329) 832786
Contact: Mrs Lynsey Pink
Opening Times: By appt. only. Open under NGS Sun 13th Aug & Sun 17 Sep 06.
Cat. Cost: None issued.
Credit Cards: None
Specialities: Mainly *Salvia* with a wide range of other unusual perennials. Stock available in small quantities only, we will be happy to propagate to order. Nat. Collection of *Salvia* species. Garden design & consultation service also available.
Map Ref: S, D2 **OS Grid Ref:** SU603109

SPla PLAXTOL NURSERIES ⊠ ♿
The Spoute, Plaxtol, Sevenoaks, Kent, TN15 0QR
Ⓣ (01732) 810550
Ⓕ (01732) 810149
Ⓔ info@plaxtol-nurseries.co.uk
Ⓦ www.plaxtol-nurseries.co.uk
Contact: Alan Harvey
Opening Times: 1000-1700 7 days. Closed 2 weeks from Xmas Eve.
Min Mail Order UK: Nmc
Min Mail Order EU: £30.00 + p&p
Cat. Cost: 2 × 1st class.
Credit Cards: All major credit/debit cards
Specialities: Hardy shrubs & herbaceous esp. for flower arrangers. Old-fashioned roses, ferns & climbers.
Map Ref: S, C4 **OS Grid Ref:** TQ611535

SPlb PLANTBASE € ♿
Lamberhurst Vineyard, Lamberhurst Down, Lamberhurst, Kent, TN3 8ER
Ⓣ (01892) 891453
Ⓔ graham@plantbase.freeserve.co.uk
Ⓦ www.lamberhurstvineyards.com
Contact: Graham Blunt
Opening Times: 1000-1700 7 days Mar-Oct.
Cat. Cost: 2 × 1st class.

KEY
⊠ Mail order to UK or EU ♠ Delivers to shows
✈ Exports beyond EU € Euro accepted
♿ Accessible by wheelchair ◆ See Display advertisement

S

Credit Cards: Visa Switch Access MasterCard Delta
Specialities: Wide range of alpines, perennials, shrubs, climbers, waterside plants, herbs, Australasian shrubs & South African plants.
Map Ref: S, C5

SPoG THE POTTED GARDEN NURSERY
Ashford Road, Bearsted, Maidstone, Kent, ME14 4NH
Ⓣ (01622) 737801
Ⓕ (01622) 632459
Ⓔ pottedgarden@btconnect.com
Ⓦ www.thepottedgarden.co.uk
Contact: Any staff member
Opening Times: 0900-1730 (dusk in winter) 7 days. Xmas period opening times on website or answerphone. (Closed Xmas Day & Boxing Day.)
Credit Cards: All major credit/debit cards
Notes: Mail order not available. Nursery partially accessible for wheelchair users.
Map Ref: S, C5

SPol POLLIE'S PERENNIALS AND DAYLILY NURSERY ⊠
Lodore, Mount Pleasant Lane, Sway, Lymington, Hampshire, SO41 8LS
Ⓣ (01590) 682577
Ⓕ (01590) 682577
Ⓔ terry@maasz.fsnet.co.uk
Ⓦ www.polliesdaylilies.co.uk
Contact: Pollie Maasz
Opening Times: 0930-1730 w/ends only during the daylily season mid-May to mid-Aug. Other times by appt. only.
Min Mail Order UK: £5.00
Cat. Cost: 2 × 1st class.
Credit Cards: None
Specialities: *Hemerocallis*, also less commonly available hardy perennials. Stock available in small quantities only. Nat. Collection of Spider & Unusual Form *Hemerocallis*. 1200 different cvs can be viewed, late Jun-mid Sep.
Notes: Mail order, daylilies only. Nursery partially accessible for wheelchair users.
Map Ref: S, D2

SPop POPS PLANTS ⊠ ⊠ ♿ €
Pops Cottage, Barford Lane, Downton, Salisbury, Wiltshire, SP5 3PZ
Ⓣ (01725) 511421
Ⓔ mail@popsplants
Ⓦ www.popsplants.com
Contact: G Dawson or L Roberts
Opening Times: By appt. only.
Min Mail Order UK: Nmc
Min Mail Order EU: Nmc
Cat. Cost: £2.00 for colour brochure.
Credit Cards: Credit cards accepted online only.
Specialities: *Primula auricula*. Some varieties in ltd. numbers. Nat. Collection of Show, Alpine & Double Auriculas.

SPur PURE PLANTS
Blackboys Nursery, Blackboys, Uckfield, East Sussex, TN22 5LS
Ⓣ (01825) 890858
Ⓕ (01825) 890878
Ⓦ www.pureplants.com
Contact: Brian Fidler
Opening Times: 0900-1700 Tue-Sat. Closed Sun & Mon except B/hol Sun 1000-1600 & B/hol Mon 0900-1700.
Cat. Cost: 2 × 1st class.
Credit Cards: All major credit/debit cards
Specialities: Trees, shrubs, herbaceous, grasses & ferns. Many unusual varieties offered.
Map Ref: S, C4 **OS Grid Ref:** TQ515206

SReu G REUTHE LTD ⊠
Crown Point Nursery, Sevenoaks Road, Ightham, Nr Sevenoaks, Kent, TN15 0HB
Ⓣ (01732) 810694
Ⓕ (01732) 862166
Contact: C & P Tomlin
Opening Times: 0900-1600 Mon-Sat (closed Wed). 1000-1600 Sun & B/hols Apr & May only, occasionally in Jun, please check. Closed Jan, Jul & Aug.
Min Mail Order UK: £30.00 + p&p
Min Mail Order EU: £500.00
Cat. Cost: £2.00.
Credit Cards: Visa Access
Specialities: Rhododendrons & azaleas, trees, shrubs & climbers.
Notes: Mail order certain plants only to EU.

SRGP ROSIE'S GARDEN PLANTS ⊠ ⊠ ♿
Rochester Road, Aylesford, Kent, ME20 7EB
Ⓣ (01622) 715777
Ⓜ 07740 696277
Ⓕ (01622) 715777
Ⓔ JC Aviolet@aol.com
Ⓦ www.rosiesgardenplants.biz
Contact: J C Aviolet
Opening Times: Mail order & shows only. Closed for 4-acre redevelopment. Ring or check website for details.
Min Mail Order UK: Nmc
Min Mail Order EU: Nmc
Cat. Cost: 2 × 1st class.
Credit Cards: Visa MasterCard Switch

Specialities: Hardy geraniums, *Buddleja* & *Aster*. 'Named' herbaceous & shrubs.
Map Ref: S, C4 **OS Grid Ref:** TQ7460

SRiF **RIVERSIDE FUCHSIAS** ⊠ ✈ ⌂ € ♿
Gravel Road, Sutton-at-Hone, Dartford, Kent, DA4 9HQ
Ⓣ (01322) 863891
Ⓕ (01322) 863891
Ⓔ riverside_fuchsias@btopenworld.com
Ⓦ www.riversidefuchsias.pwp.blueyonder.co.uk/
Contact: George & Nellie Puddefoot
Opening Times: 0900-1700, Tue, Wed, Fri, Sat & Sun.
Min Mail Order UK: £1.50 per plant, 10 plants min. order.
Min Mail Order EU: 3 euros
Cat. Cost: 3 × 1st class.
Credit Cards: All major credit/debit cards
Specialities: *Fuchsia*. Nat. Collection holder.
Notes: Also sells wholesale.
Map Ref: S, B4

SRiv **RIVER GARDEN NURSERIES** ⊠ ⌂ € ♿
Troutbeck, Otford, Sevenoaks, Kent, TN14 5PH
Ⓣ (01959) 525588
Ⓕ (01959) 525810
Ⓔ box@river-garden.co.uk
Ⓦ www.river-garden.co.uk
Contact: Jenny Alban Davies
Opening Times: By appt. only.
Min Mail Order UK: £10.00 + p&p
Min Mail Order EU: £50.00 + p&p
Cat. Cost: 2 × 1st class.
Credit Cards: All major credit/debit cards
Specialities: *Buxus* species, cultivars & hedging. *Buxus* topiary.
Notes: Also sells wholesale.
Map Ref: S, C4 **OS Grid Ref:** TQ523593

SRkn **RAPKYNS NURSERY** ⌂ ♿
(Office) Brinkwells, School Lane, Hadlow Down, East Sussex, TN22 4HY
Ⓣ (01825) 830065
Ⓜ 07771 916933
Ⓕ (01825) 830065
Contact: Fiona Moore, Steven Moore
Opening Times: 1000-1700 Tue, Thu & Fri, Mar-Oct incl.
Cat. Cost: 2 × 1st class.
Credit Cards: None
Specialities: Unusual shrubs, perennials & climbers. Azaleas, campanulas, *Ceanothus*, geraniums, lavenders, lobelias, *Clematis*, penstemons & grasses. New collections of *Phormium*, *Phygelius*, *Agastache*, *Anemone*, *Heuchera*, *Heucherella* & *Salvias*.
Notes: Nursery at Scotsford Farm, Street End Lane, Broad Oak. Heathfield, TN21 8UB. Also sells wholesale.
Map Ref: S, C4 **OS Grid Ref:** TQ604248

SRms **RUMSEY GARDENS** ⊠ ♿ ◆
117 Drift Road, Clanfield, Waterlooville, Hampshire, PO8 0PD
Ⓣ (023) 9259 3367
Ⓔ info@rumsey-gardens.co.uk
Ⓦ www.rumsey-gardens.co.uk
Contact: Mrs M A Giles
Opening Times: 0900-1700 Mon-Sat & 1000-1700 Sun & B/hols. Closed Sun Nov-Feb.
Min Mail Order UK: Nmc
Cat. Cost: Online only.
Credit Cards: Visa MasterCard Switch
Specialities: Wide general range. Herbaceous, alpines, heathers & ferns. Nat. & International Collection of *Cotoneaster*.
Map Ref: S, D2

SRos **ROSEWOOD DAYLILIES** ⊠
70 Deansway Avenue, Sturry, Nr Canterbury, Kent, CT2 0NN
Ⓣ (01227) 711071
Ⓕ (01227) 711071
Ⓔ Rosewoodgdns@aol.com
Contact: Chris Searle
Opening Times: By appt. only. Please phone.
Min Mail Order UK: Nmc
Cat. Cost: 2 × 1st class.
Credit Cards: None
Specialities: *Hemerocallis*, mainly newer American varieties. *Agapanthus*.
Map Ref: S, C5

SRot **ROTHERVIEW NURSERY** ⊠ ⌂ € ♿
Ivy House Lane, Three Oaks, Hastings, East Sussex, TN35 4NP
Ⓣ (01424) 756228
Ⓕ (01424) 428944
Ⓔ rotherview@btinternet.com
Ⓦ www.rotherview.com
Contact: Ray Bates
Opening Times: 1000-1700 Mar-Oct, 1000-1530 Nov-Feb, 7 days.
Min Mail Order UK: £10.00 + p&p
Min Mail Order EU: £20.00 + p&p
Cat. Cost: 4 × 1st class.
Credit Cards: All major credit/debit cards

KEY
⊠ Mail order to UK or EU ⌂ Delivers to shows
✈ Exports beyond EU € Euro accepted
♿ Accessible by wheelchair ◆ See Display advertisement

S

Specialities: Alpines.
Notes: Nursery is on same site as Coghurst Camellias. Also sells wholesale.
Map Ref: S, D5

SSea SEALE NURSERIES ♿ ◆
Seale Lane, Seale, Farnham, Surrey, GU10 1LD
Ⓣ (01252) 782410
Ⓔ plants@sealenurseries.demon.co.uk
Contact: David & Catherine May
Opening Times: 1000-1600 Tue-Sat incl. Other times by appt. Closed 25th Dec-mid Jan.
Cat. Cost: None issued.
Credit Cards: Visa Switch Access Delta
Specialities: Roses & *Pelargonium*. Some varieties in short supply, please phone first.
Map Ref: S, C3 **OS Grid Ref:** SU887477

S

SSpi SPINNERS GARDEN € ♿
School Lane, Boldre, Lymington, Hampshire, SO41 5QE
Ⓣ (01590) 673347
Contact: Peter Chappell
Opening Times: 1000-1700 Tue-Sat. By appt. Dec & Jan.
Cat. Cost: Sae for plant list.
Credit Cards: None
Specialities: Less common trees & shrubs esp. *Acer*, *Magnolia*, species & lace-cap *Hydrangea*. Bog & woodland plants, especially trilliums.
Map Ref: S, D2 **OS Grid Ref:** SZ323981

SSss SELECT SEEDS ⊠ ⌂ € ♿
Paice Lane, Medstead, Nr Alton, Hampshire, GU34 5PR
Ⓣ (01420) 560695
Ⓕ (01420) 563640
Ⓔ GreenFarmPlants.Marina.Christopher@Care4free.net
Contact: Marina Christopher
Opening Times: Not open. Mail order only.
Min Mail Order UK: £10.00
Cat. Cost: 3 × 1st class.
Credit Cards: All major credit/debit cards
Specialities: Seeds. *Aconitum*, *Eryngium*, *Thalictrum*, *Sanguisorba* & *Angelica*.
Notes: Co-located with Phoenix Perennial Plants SPhx.
Map Ref: S, C2 **OS Grid Ref:** SU657362

SSta STARBOROUGH NURSERY ⊠ ♿
Starborough Road, Marsh Green, Edenbridge, Kent, TN8 5RB
Ⓣ (01732) 865614
Ⓕ (01732) 862166
Contact: C & P Tomlin
Opening Times: 0900-1600 Mon-Sat (closed Wed & Sun). Closed Jan, Jul & Aug.
Min Mail Order UK: £30.00 + p&p
Min Mail Order EU: £500.00
Cat. Cost: £2.00
Credit Cards: Visa Access
Specialities: Rare and unusual shrubs especially *Daphne*, *Acer*, rhododendrons & azaleas, *Magnolia* & *Hamamelis*.
Notes: Certain plants only to EU.

SSth SOUTHEASE PLANTS ♿
Corner Cottage, Southease, Nr Lewes, East Sussex, BN7 3HX
Ⓣ (01273) 513681
Ⓜ 07791 856206
Ⓕ (01273) 513681
Contact: Adrian Orchard
Opening Times: 1100-1700 Wed-Sat, 1400-1700 Sun & by appt.
Cat. Cost: 2 × 1st class.
Credit Cards: None
Specialities: A small nursery concentrating on hellebores, species & hybrids, grown on the nursery from seed collected from selected plants or obtained from specialist growers. Ltd. quantities.
Map Ref: S, D4 **OS Grid Ref:** TQ422052

SSvw SOUTHVIEW NURSERIES ⊠ ⌂
Chequers Lane, Eversley Cross, Hook, Hampshire, RG27 0NT
Ⓣ (0118) 9732206
Ⓕ (0118) 9736160
Ⓔ Mark@Trenear.freeserve.co.uk
Ⓦ www.southviewnurseries.co.uk
Contact: Mark & Elaine Trenear
Opening Times: Mail order only. Orders for collection by prior arrangement.
Min Mail Order UK: Nmc
Cat. Cost: Free.
Credit Cards: None
Specialities: Unusual hardy plants, specialising in old-fashioned pinks & period plants. Nat. Collection of Old Pinks. Collection open in June. Please ring for details.
Notes: Orders by prior arrangement only.
Map Ref: S, C3

SSwd SPRINGWOOD NURSERY ⊠ ⌂
5 Southview Drive, Uckfield, East Sussex, TN22 1TA
Ⓣ 07760 152587
Ⓔ springwood.nurserysx@tiscali.co.uk
Ⓦ http://SpringwoodNurserySussex.co.uk
Contact: Kevin Clift

Opening Times: Not open. Mail order only. Open by appt. only.
Min Mail Order UK: Nmc
Credit Cards: None
Specialities: *Hedychium*. Some plants available in small quantities.
Notes: Also sells wholesale.

STes TEST VALLEY NURSERY ⊠ ♠ €
Stockbridge Road, Timsbury, Romsey, Hampshire, SO51 0NG
Ⓣ (01794) 368881
Ⓔ julia@testvalleynursery.co.uk
Ⓦ www.testvalleynursery.co.uk
Contact: Julia Benn
Opening Times: 1000-1700 Tue-Sun Mar-Oct, or by appt.
Min Mail Order UK: Nmc.
Cat. Cost: 3 × 1st class.
Credit Cards: All major credit/debit cards
Specialities: Large range of herbaceous perennials, incl. unusual & new varieties. Some varieties available in small quantities only. Phone first to avoid disappointment.
Notes: Mail order Oct-Mar only.
Map Ref: S, C2

STil TILE BARN NURSERY ⊠ ✈ ♠ €
Standen Street, Iden Green, Benenden, Kent, TN17 4LB
Ⓣ (01580) 240221
Ⓕ (01580) 240221
Ⓔ tilebarn.nursery@virgin.net
Ⓦ www.tilebarn-cyclamen.co.uk
Contact: Peter Moore
Opening Times: 0900-1700 Wed-Sat.
Min Mail Order UK: £10.00 + p&p
Min Mail Order EU: £25.00 + p&p
Cat. Cost: Sae.
Credit Cards: None
Specialities: *Cyclamen* species.
Notes: Also sells wholesale.
Map Ref: S, C5 **OS Grid Ref:** TQ805301

STop SUSSEX TOPIARY ⊠ ♿ ◆
Naldretts Lane, Bucks Green, Horsham, West Sussex, RH12 3BU
Ⓣ (01403) 823131
Ⓜ 07811 467743
Ⓔ sussextopiary.freeserve.co.uk
Ⓦ www. sussextopiary.freeserve.co.uk
Contact: Denis De Ambrosi
Opening Times: Please ring before visiting.
Min Mail Order UK: £5.00
Min Mail Order EU: Nmc
Cat. Cost: 2 × 1st class.
Credit Cards: None
Specialities: Specimen plants, trainers, hedging, box species.
Notes: Also sells wholesale.
Map Ref: S, C3 **OS Grid Ref:** TQ082329

STre PETER TRENEAR ⊠ ♿
Chantreyland, Chequers Lane, Eversley Cross, Hampshire, RG27 0NX
Ⓣ (0118) 9732300
Ⓔ peter@babytrees.co.uk
Ⓦ www.babytrees.co.uk
Contact: Peter Trenear
Opening Times: 0900-1630 Mon-Sat.
Min Mail Order UK: £5.00 + p&p
Cat. Cost: 1 × 1st class.
Credit Cards: None
Specialities: Trees, shrubs, conifers, bonsai & *Pinus*.
Map Ref: S, C3 **OS Grid Ref:** SU795612

STrG TERRACE GARDENER ⊠ ♠ €
Meadow View, Hildenbrook Farm, Riding Lane, Hildenbrook, Kent, TN11 9JN
Ⓣ (01732) 832762
Ⓔ johan@terracegardener.com
Ⓦ www.terracegardener.co.uk
Contact: Johan Hall
Opening Times: Not open. Mail order only. Telephone orders 0900-1700 Mon-Fri.
Min Mail Order UK: Nmc
Cat. Cost: Free.
Credit Cards: All major credit/debit cards
Specialities: Mediterranean trees & plants. Container gardening.

SVic VICTORIANA NURSERY GARDENS ⊠ ✈ ♿
Challock, Ashford, Kent, TN25 4DG
Ⓣ (01233) 740529
Ⓕ (01233) 740030
Ⓔ info@victoriana.ws
Ⓦ www.victoriana.ws
Contact: Stephen Shirley
Opening Times: 0930-1630 (or dusk) Mon-Fri, 1030-1630 Sat. (1030-1630 Sun in summer months.)
Min Mail Order UK: Nmc
Cat. Cost: Free or online.
Credit Cards: Delta MasterCard Visa Switch
Specialities: *Fuchsia*, 600+ varieties. Also veg plants, seeds, fruit trees & bushes.
Notes: Exports beyond EC at cost.
Map Ref: S, C5

KEY		
	⊠ Mail order to UK or EU	♠ Delivers to shows
	✈ Exports beyond EU	€ Euro accepted
	♿ Accessible by wheelchair	◆ See Display advertisement

S

SVil **THE VILLAGE NURSERIES** ◆
Sinnocks, West Chiltington, Pulborough, West Sussex, RH20 2JX
Ⓣ (01798) 813040
Ⓕ (01798) 817240
Ⓔ petermanfield@aol.com
Ⓦ www.village-nurseries.co.uk
Contact: Peter Manfield
Opening Times: 0900-1800 or dusk, 7 days.
Cat. Cost: None issued.
Credit Cards: All major credit/debit cards
Specialities: Extensive selection of hardy perennials, plus wide range of seasonal patio & bedding plants.
Map Ref: S, D3 **OS Grid Ref:** TQ095182

SWal **WALLACE PLANTS**
Lewes Road Nursery, Lewes Road, Laughton, East Sussex, BN8 6BN
Ⓣ (01323) 811729
Ⓔ sjk@wallaceplants.fsnet.co.uk
Contact: Simon Wallace
Opening Times: 0930-1800 7 days, incl. b/hols, Mar-Sep, 0930-1600 Oct-Feb.
Cat. Cost: 3 × 1st class.
Credit Cards: None
Specialities: Ornamental grasses, hebes, hardy fuchsias, salvias, penstemons, unusual plants.
Map Ref: S, D4 **OS Grid Ref:** TQ513126

SWat **WATER MEADOW NURSERY**
Cheriton, Nr Alresford, Hampshire, SO24 0QB
Ⓣ (01962) 771895
Ⓕ (01962) 771895
Ⓔ plantaholic@onetel.com
Ⓦ www.plantaholic.co.uk
Contact: Mrs Sandy Worth
Opening Times: 1000-1700 Wed-Sat Mar-Jul or by appt.
Min Mail Order UK: £10.00 + p&p
Min Mail Order EU: £50.00 + p&p
Cat. Cost: 6 × 1st class or £2.00 cheque.
Credit Cards: Visa MasterCard
Specialities: Water lilies, extensive water garden plants, unusual herbaceous perennials, aromatic herbs & wildflowers. New Super Poppy range. Nat. Collection of *Papaver orientale* Group.
Notes: Mail order by 24 hour courier service only. Also sells wholesale.
Map Ref: S, C2

SWCr **WYCH CROSS NURSERIES**
Wych Cross, Forest Row, East Sussex, RH18 5JW
Ⓣ (01342) 822705
Ⓕ (01342) 825329
Ⓔ roses@wychcross.co.uk
Ⓦ www.wychcross.co.uk
Contact: J Paisley
Opening Times: 0900-1730 Mon-Sat.
Cat. Cost: Free.
Credit Cards: All major credit/debit cards
Specialities: Roses.
Map Ref: S, C4 **OS Grid Ref:** TQ42133190

SWvt **WOLVERTON PLANTS LTD** ◆
Wolverton Common, Tadley, Hampshire, RG26 5RU
Ⓣ (01635) 298453
Ⓕ (01635) 299075
Ⓔ Julian@wolvertonplants.co.uk
Ⓦ www.wolvertonplants.co.uk
Contact: Julian Jones
Opening Times: 0900-1800 (or dusk Nov-Feb), 7 days. Closed Xmas/New Year.
Cat. Cost: Online only.
Credit Cards: All major credit/debit cards
Notes: Also sells wholesale.
Map Ref: S, C2 **OS Grid Ref:** SU555589

WALES AND THE WEST

WAbb **ABBEY DORE COURT GARDEN**
Abbey Dore Court, Abbey Dore, Herefordshire, HR2 0AD
Ⓣ (01981) 240419
Ⓕ (01981) 240419
Ⓦ www.abbeydorecourt.co.uk
Contact: Mrs C Ward
Opening Times: 1100-1730 1st Apr-30th Sep. Closed Mon, Wed & Fri. Open B/hol Mons.
Cat. Cost: None issued.
Credit Cards: None
Specialities: Mainly hardy perennials, many unusual, which may be seen growing in the garden. *Astrantia*, *Crocosmia*, *Helleborus*, *Paeonia*, *Pulmonaria* & *Sedum*.
Map Ref: W, C4 **OS Grid Ref:** SO388308

WAbe **ABERCONWY NURSERY**
Graig, Glan Conwy, Colwyn Bay, Conwy, LL28 5TL
Ⓣ (01492) 580875
Contact: Dr & Mrs K G Lever
Opening Times: 1000-1700 Tue-Sun mid-Feb-mid-Oct.
Cat. Cost: 2 × 2nd class.
Credit Cards: Visa MasterCard
Specialities: Alpines, including specialist varieties, esp. autumn gentians, *Saxifraga* & dwarf ericaceous. Shrubs & woodland plants incl. *Helleborus* & smaller ferns.
Map Ref: W, A3 **OS Grid Ref:** SH799744

WAct ACTON BEAUCHAMP ROSES ⊠ ✈
Acton Beauchamp, Worcestershire, WR6 5AE
Ⓣ (01531) 640433
Ⓕ (01531) 640802
Ⓔ enquiries@actonbeaurose.co.uk
Ⓦ www.actonbeaurose.co.uk
Contact: Lindsay Bousfield
Opening Times: 1400-1700 Wed-Sun Apr-Oct, 1000-1700 B/hol Mon. 1400-1700 Thu-Sat, Nov-Mar.
Min Mail Order UK: Nmc
Min Mail Order EU: Nmc
Cat. Cost: 3 × 1st class.
Credit Cards: Switch Solo Visa MasterCard
Specialities: Species roses, old roses, modern shrub, English, climbers, ramblers & ground-cover roses.
Map Ref: W, C4 **OS Grid Ref:** SO683492

WAln L A ALLEN ⊠
Windy Ridge, Cerrigwibber, Llandrindod Wells, Powys, LD1 5NY
Ⓔ les@fidalgo.freeserve.co.uk
Contact: L A Allen
Opening Times: By prior appt.
Min Mail Order UK: Nmc
Min Mail Order EU: Nmc
Cat. Cost: 4 × 1st class.
Credit Cards: None
Specialities: Nat. Collection of *Primula auricula*. Type: alpine auricula, show edged, show self, doubles, stripes. Surplus plants from the Collection so available in small quantities. Occasionally only 1 or 2 available of some cvs.
Notes: Also sells wholesale.

WAul AULDEN FARM ⊠ ♠ ♿
Aulden, Leominster, Herefordshire, HR6 0JT
Ⓣ (01568) 720129
Ⓔ pf@auldenfarm.co.uk
Ⓦ www.auldenfarm.co.uk
Contact: Alun & Jill Whitehead
Opening Times: 1000-1700 Tue & Thu Apr-Aug. Other times by appt. Please phone.
Min Mail Order UK: Nmc
Min Mail Order EU: £20.00
Cat. Cost: 2 × 1st class.
Credit Cards: Credit card payments can be made by Paypal.
Specialities: Hardy herbaceous perennials, with a special interest in *Hemerocallis* & *Iris*.
Notes: Ltd. mail order for *Hemerocallis* & *Iris* only.
Map Ref: W, C4 **OS Grid Ref:** SO462548

WBGC BURFORD GARDEN COMPANY ♿
Burford House Gardens, Tenbury Wells, Worcestershire, WR15 8HQ
Ⓣ (01584) 810777
Ⓕ (01584) 810673
Ⓔ info@burford.co.uk
Ⓦ www.burford.co.uk
Opening Times: 0900-1800 7 days. Gardens close at dusk if earlier.
Credit Cards: Visa Access Switch
Specialities: *Clematis* and herbaceous, trees & shrubs. Nat. Collection of *Clematis*.
Map Ref: W, C4

WBIS BRITISH IRIS SOCIETY ⊠
Aulden Farm, Aulden, Leominster, Herefordshire, HR6 0JT
Ⓣ (01568) 720129
Ⓔ alun@britishirissociety.org.uk
Ⓦ www.britishirissociety.org.uk
Contact: Alun Whitehead
Min Mail Order UK: Nmc
Min Mail Order EU: Nmc
Cat. Cost: Plant list free but membership required.
Credit Cards: None
Specialities: *Iris*.
Notes: Plants available to members. Please apply for membership.

WBod BODNANT GARDEN NURSERY LTD ⊠ ♿
Tal-y-Cafn, Colwyn Bay, Caernarfonshire, LL28 5RE
Ⓣ (01492) 650731
Ⓕ (01492) 650863
Ⓔ sales@bodnant-plants.co.uk
Ⓦ www.bodnant-plants.co.uk
Contact: Stephen Dixon
Opening Times: All year.
Min Mail Order UK: Nmc
Cat. Cost: £2.50 cost refundable with 1st order.
Credit Cards: Visa MasterCard Switch Connect
Specialities: *Rhododendron*, *Camellia*, *Magnolia*. Wide range of unusual trees and shrubs.
Map Ref: W, A3 **OS Grid Ref:** SH809723

WBor BORDERVALE PLANTS ♠ ♿
Nantyderi, Sandy Lane, Ystradowen, Cowbridge, Vale of Glamorgan, CF71 7SX
Ⓣ (01446) 774036

KEY
⊠ Mail order to UK or EU ♠ Delivers to shows
✈ Exports beyond EU € Euro accepted
♿ Accessible by wheelchair ◆ See Display advertisement

W

Ⓦ www.bordervale.co.uk
Contact: Claire E Jenkins
Opening Times: 1000-1700 Fri-Sun & B/hols mid Mar-mid Oct. Other times by appt.
Cat. Cost: 2 × 1st class large sae or online.
Credit Cards: None
Specialities: Unusual herbaceous perennials, trees & shrubs, as well as cottage garden plants, many displayed in the 2 acre garden.
Notes: Garden open for NGS & Red Cross. See website for details.
Map Ref: W, D3 **OS Grid Ref:** ST022776

WBou BOUTS COTTAGE NURSERIES ⊠ ⌂ €
Bouts Lane, Inkberrow, Worcestershire, WR7 4HP
Ⓣ (01386) 792923
Ⓦ www.boutsviolas.co.uk
Contact: M & S Roberts
Opening Times: Not open to the public.
Min Mail Order UK: Nmc
Min Mail Order EU: Nmc
Cat. Cost: 1st class sae.
Credit Cards: None
Specialities: *Viola*.

W

WBrE BRON EIFION NURSERY ⊠
Bron Eifion, Criccieth, Caernarfonshire, LL52 0SA
Ⓣ (01766) 522890
Ⓔ gardencottage@onetel.com
Contact: Suzanne Evans
Opening Times: 1000-dusk 7 days 1st Mar-31st Oct. 1st Nov-29th Feb by appt. only.
Min Mail Order UK: £30.00 + p&p
Min Mail Order EU: £50.00 + p&p
Cat. Cost: 4 × 2nd class.
Credit Cards: None
Specialities: *Kalmia*, *Daphne*, *Embothrium*, plants for coastal regions & wide and interesting range of hardy plants.
Map Ref: W, B2

WBrk BROCKAMIN PLANTS ⌂ ♿
Brockamin, Old Hills, Callow End, Worcestershire, WR2 4TQ
Ⓣ (01905) 830370
Ⓔ dickstonebrockamin@tinyworld.co.uk
Contact: Margaret Stone
Opening Times: By appt. only.
Cat. Cost: Free.
Credit Cards: None
Specialities: Hardy perennials, especially hardy geraniums and some asters. Stock available in small quantities only.
Map Ref: W, C5 **OS Grid Ref:** SO830488

WBuc BUCKNELL NURSERIES ⊠
Bucknell, Shropshire, SY7 0EL
Ⓣ (01547) 530606
Ⓕ (01547) 530699
Contact: A N Coull
Opening Times: 0800-1700 Mon-Fri & 1000-1300 Sat.
Min Mail Order UK: Nmc
Cat. Cost: Free.
Credit Cards: None
Specialities: Bare-rooted hedging conifers & forest trees.
Notes: Also sells wholesale.
Map Ref: W, C4 **OS Grid Ref:** SO356736

WBVN BANWY VALLEY NURSERY ⊠ ♿
Foel, Llangadfan, Nr Welshpool, Powys, SY21 0PT
Ⓣ (01938) 820281
Ⓕ (01938) 820281
Ⓔ syd@banwnursery.co.uk
Ⓦ www.banwnursery.co.uk
Contact: Syd Luck
Opening Times: 1000-1700 Tue-Sun. Open B/hols.
Min Mail Order UK: Nmc
Cat. Cost: 2 × 1st class or via email.
Credit Cards: All major credit/debit cards
Specialities: Perennials, shrubs, incl. climbers, ornamental & fruit trees. Ever-expanding range of magnolias & rhododendrons. All grown on the nursery.
Notes: Large specimens not available by mail order.
Map Ref: W, B3 **OS Grid Ref:** SH993107

WCAu CLAIRE AUSTIN HARDY PLANTS ⊠ ☒ € ♿ ◆
The Stone House, Cramp Pool, Shifnal, Shropshire, TF11 8PE
Ⓣ (01952) 463700
Ⓕ (01952) 463111
Ⓔ enquiries@claireaustin-hardyplants.co.uk
Ⓦ www.claireaustin-hardyplants.co.uk
Contact: Claire Austin
Opening Times: 1000-1600 7 days, 1st Mar-30th Sep. Oct-Feb w/days by appt.
Min Mail Order UK: Nmc
Min Mail Order EU: £50.00 + p&p
Cat. Cost: UK £3.50, Europe 5 euros .
Credit Cards: MasterCard Visa Switch
Specialities: *Paeonia*, *Iris*, *Hemerocallis* & hardy plants. Nat. Collections of Bearded *Iris* & Hybrid Herbaceous *Paeonia*.
Notes: Exports tree peonies only beyond EU.
Map Ref: W, B4

WCel **CELYN VALE EUCALYPTUS NURSERIES** ⊠ ✈
Carrog, Corwen, Merioneth, LL21 9LD
Ⓣ (01490) 430671
Ⓕ (01490) 430671
Ⓔ info@eucalyptus.co.uk
Ⓦ www.eucalyptus.co.uk
Contact: Andrew McConnell & Paul Yoxall
Opening Times: 0900-1600 Mon-Fri Jan-Nov. For other days, please phone first.
Min Mail Order UK: 3 plants + p&p
Min Mail Order EU: 3 plants + p&p
Cat. Cost: 2 × 1st class.
Credit Cards: All major credit/debit cards
Specialities: Hardy *Eucalyptus* & *Acacia*.
Notes: Also sells wholesale.
Map Ref: W, A3 **OS Grid Ref:** SJ116452

WCFE **CHARLES F ELLIS & SON** €
(Office) Barn House, Wormington, Nr Broadway, Worcestershire, WR12 7NL
Ⓣ (01386) 584077 (nursery)
Ⓕ (01386) 584491
Ⓦ www.ellisplants.co.uk
Contact: Charles Ellis
Opening Times: 1000-1600 7 days 1st Apr-30th Sep.
Cat. Cost: None issued.
Credit Cards: None
Specialities: Wide range of more unusual shrubs, conifers & climbers.
Notes: Nursery is at Oak Piece Farm Nursery, Stanton, near Broadway.
Map Ref: W, C5

WChG **CHENNELS GATE GARDENS & NURSERY** ♿
Eardisley, Herefordshire, HR3 6LT
Ⓣ (01544) 327288
Contact: Mark Dawson
Opening Times: 1000-1700 7 days Mar-Oct.
Cat. Cost: None issued.
Credit Cards: None
Specialities: Interesting & unusual cottage garden plants, grasses, hedging & shrubs.

WCLn **COUNTRY LANE NURSERIES** ⌂ ♿
Plwmp, Llandysul, Ceredigion, SA44 6HU
Ⓣ (01239) 851015
Ⓜ 07976 411884
Ⓕ (01239) 858921
Ⓔ Theresa.Glover@btinternet.com
Contact: Theresa Glover
Opening Times: 1000-1700 Wed-Sun, Easter-end of Sep. Other times please phone first.
Cat. Cost: 2 × 1st sae for plant list.
Specialities: Good range of unusual hardy perennials and shrubs, incl. large range of moisture-loving & bog plants.
Notes: Home-reared, pure-breed poultry & waterfowl to view & for sale. Also sells plants wholesale.
Map Ref: W, C2 **OS Grid Ref:** SN3658

WCot **COTSWOLD GARDEN FLOWERS** ⊠ ⌂ €
Sands Lane, Badsey, Evesham, Worcestershire, WR11 7EZ
Ⓣ nursery (01386) 833849 or mail order (01386) 422829
Ⓕ nursery (01386) 49844
Ⓔ info@cgf.net
Ⓦ www.cgf.net
Contact: Bob Brown/Vicky Parkhouse
Opening Times: 0900-1730 Mon-Fri all year. 1000-1730 Sat & Sun Mar-Sep. Sat & Sun Oct-Feb by appt.
Min Mail Order UK: Nmc
Min Mail Order EU: Nmc
Cat. Cost: £1.50 or 6 × 1st class.
Credit Cards: MasterCard Access Visa Switch
Specialities: A very wide range of easy & unusual perennials. Nat. Collection of *Lysimachia*.
Notes: Also sells wholesale.
Map Ref: W, C5 **OS Grid Ref:** SP077426

WCra **CRANESBILL NURSERY** ⊠ ♿
White Cottage, Stock Green, Nr Redditch, Worcestershire, B96 6SZ
Ⓣ (01386) 792414
Ⓕ (01386) 792280
Ⓔ cranesbilluk@aol.com
Ⓦ www.cranesbillnursery.com
Contact: Mrs S M Bates
Opening Times: 1000-1700 19th Mar-30th Sep. Closed Wed & Thu. Aug by appt. only. Open most w/ends.
Min Mail Order UK: Nmc
Min Mail Order EU: Nmc
Cat. Cost: 4 × 1st class.
Credit Cards: All major credit/debit cards
Specialities: Hardy geraniums & other herbaceous plants.
Map Ref: W, C5

WCru **CRÛG FARM PLANTS** ♿
Griffith's Crossing, Nr Caernarfon, Gwynedd, LL55 1TU
Ⓣ (01248) 670232
Ⓔ bleddyn&sue@crug-farm.co.uk

KEY		
	⊠ Mail order to UK or EU	⌂ Delivers to shows
	✈ Exports beyond EU	€ Euro accepted
	♿ Accessible by wheelchair	◆ See Display advertisement

W

Ⓦ www.crug-farm.co.uk
Contact: B and S Wynn-Jones
Opening Times: 1000-1800 Thu-Sun last Sat Feb-last Sun Sep, plus B/hols.
Cat. Cost: 3 × 2nd class or online.
Credit Cards: Visa Access Delta MasterCard
Specialities: Shade plants, climbers, hardy geraniums, *Pulmonaria*, rare shrubs, *Tropaeolum*, herbaceous & bulbous incl. self-collected new introductions from the Far East. Nat. Collections of *Coriaria*, *Paris* & *Polygonatum*.
Map Ref: W, A2 **OS Grid Ref:** SH509652

WCwm CWMRHAIADR NURSERY ⊠
Glaspwll, Machynlleth, Montgomeryshire, SY20 8UB
Ⓣ (01654) 702223
Ⓕ (01654) 702223
Ⓔ glynne.jones@btinternet.com
Contact: Glynne Jones
Opening Times: By appt. only. Please phone. Garden open under NGS & to nursery visitors.
Min Mail Order UK: Nmc
Cat. Cost: Sae for list.
Credit Cards: None
Specialities: *Acer* species. Rhododendrons.
Notes: Mail order Nov & Mar only & small plants (less than 18 inches in height).
Map Ref: W, B3

W

WDib DIBLEY'S NURSERIES ⊠ ♿ € ◆
Llanelidan, Ruthin, Denbighshire, LL15 2LG
Ⓣ (01978) 790677
Ⓕ (01978) 790668
Ⓔ sales@dibleys.com
Ⓦ www.dibleys.com
Contact: R Dibley
Opening Times: 1000-1700 7 days Mar-Oct.
Min Mail Order UK: Nmc
Min Mail Order EU: Nmc
Cat. Cost: Free.
Credit Cards: Visa Access Switch Electron Solo
Specialities: *Streptocarpus*, *Columnea*, *Solenostemon* & other gesneriads & *Begonia*. Nat. Collection of *Streptocarpus*.
Notes: Also sells wholesale.
Map Ref: W, A3

WDyf DYFFRYN NURSERIES ⊠ € ♿
Home Farm, Dyffryn, Cardiff, CF5 6JU
Ⓣ (02920) 592085
Ⓕ (02920) 593462
Ⓔ sales@dyffryn-nurseries.co.uk
Ⓦ www.dyffryn-nurseries.co.uk
Contact: Victoria Hardaker
Opening Times: 0800-1600 Mon-Fri, 1100-1600 Sat & Sun.
Min Mail Order UK: £25.00
Min Mail Order EU: £25.00
Cat. Cost: Information on request.
Credit Cards: MasterCard Access Switch Delta Visa
Specialities: Native & exotic mature, hardy specimen & architectural plants.
Notes: Also sells wholesale.
Map Ref: W, D3

WDyG DYFFRYN GWYDDNO NURSERY
Dyffryn Farm, Lampeter Velfrey, Narberth, Pembrokeshire, SA67 8UN
Ⓣ (01834) 861684
Ⓔ sally.polson@virgin.net
Ⓦ www.pembrokeshireplants.co.uk
Contact: Mrs S L Polson
Opening Times: By appt. only. Bamboo collection open by appt. in aid of NGS.
Credit Cards: None
Specialities: Eclectic, yet wide-ranging, from tender salvias & grasses to bog. Peat-free & principled. Bamboos. Plants available in small quantities only.
Notes: Also sells wholesale.
Map Ref: W, D2 **OS Grid Ref:** SR138148

WEas EASTGROVE COTTAGE GARDEN NURSERY ♿
Sankyns Green, Nr Shrawley, Little Witley, Worcestershire, WR6 6LQ
Ⓣ (01299) 896389
Ⓦ www.eastgrove.co.uk
Contact: Malcolm & Carol Skinner
Opening Times: 1400-1700 Thu, Fri, Sat 13th Apr-29th Jul & B/hol Sun & Mon. Closed throughout Aug. 1400-1700 Thu, Fri, Sat 7th Sep-14th Oct.
Cat. Cost: Online only.
Credit Cards: None
Specialities: Unique cottage garden & arboretum. Many varieties of *Viola*, *Iris*, *Dianthus* & *Aquilegia*, plus a wide range of old favourites & many unusual plants.
RHS Partnership garden. Extra 2 acres of arboretum 2005.
Map Ref: W, C5 **OS Grid Ref:** SO795644

WEll ELLWOOD PENSTEMONS ⊠
Ellwood House, Fern Road, Ellwood, Coleford, Gloucestershire, GL16 7LY
Ⓣ (01594) 833839
Ⓔ Yvonne193@btinternet.com
Contact: Yvonne Shorthouse
Opening Times: Visitors very welcome at most times Mon-Sat Jun-Oct, please phone

first. Special open days 28th/29th Jul 2006. Also open under NGS 3rd, 7th, 10th, 19th, 21st, 24th Aug &1st Sep 2006.
Min Mail Order UK: Nmc
Cat. Cost: 3 × 1st class.
Credit Cards: None
Specialities: Penstemons. Will propagate to order. Stock ltd. as propagated on site. Personal visit strongly recommended.
Notes: Mail order very limited.
Map Ref: W, D4 **OS Grid Ref:** SO591082

WEve EVERGREEN CONIFER CENTRE ⊠ ♿ ◆
Tenbury Road, Rock, Nr Kidderminster, Worcestershire, DY14 9RB
Ⓣ (01299) 266581
Ⓕ (01299) 266755
Ⓔ brian@evergreen-conifers.co.uk
Ⓦ www.evergreen-conifers.co.uk
Contact: Mr B Warrington
Opening Times: 0900-1650 Mon-Sat (closed Sun) Oct-Mar. Also closed Mon, Apr-Sep.
Min Mail Order UK: Nmc
Cat. Cost: 4 × 1st class for list.
Credit Cards: All major credit/debit cards
Specialities: Conifers mainly but also heathers, trees, evergreen shrubs.
Notes: Mail order for conifers only.
Map Ref: W, C4 **OS Grid Ref:** SO731737

WFar FARMYARD NURSERIES ⊠ ✈ ♿ ◆
Llandysul, Ceridigion, SA44 4RL
Ⓣ (01559) 363389 or (01267) 220259
Ⓕ (01559) 362200
Ⓔ richard@farmyardnurseries.co.uk
Ⓦ www.farmyardnurseries.co.uk
Contact: Richard Bramley
Opening Times: 1000-1700 7 days excl. Xmas, Boxing & New Year's Day.
Min Mail Order UK: Nmc
Min Mail Order EU: Nmc
Cat. Cost: 4 × 1st class.
Credit Cards: Visa Switch MasterCard
Specialities: Excellent general range esp. *Helleborus*, *Hosta*, *Tricyrtis* & *Schizostylis*, plus shrubs, trees, climbers, alpines & esp. herbaceous. Nat. Collection of *Tricyrtis*.
Notes: Also sells wholesale.
Map Ref: W, C2 **OS Grid Ref:** SN421406

WFFs FABULOUS FUCHSIAS
The Martins, Stanley Hill, Bosbury, Nr Ledbury, Herefordshire, HR8 1HE
Ⓣ (01531) 640298
Ⓔ afuchsia@excite.com
Contact: Angela Thompson
Opening Times: By appt. only. Sells at local plant fairs.
Cat. Cost: 3 × 1st class.
Credit Cards: None
Specialities: *Fuchsia*: hardy, bush, trailing, species, triphyllas, unusual varieties, many available in small quantities only.

WFib FIBREX NURSERIES LTD ⊠ ✈ ⌂
Honeybourne Road, Pebworth, Stratford-on-Avon, Warwickshire, CV37 8XP
Ⓣ (01789) 720788
Ⓕ (01789) 721162
Ⓔ sales@fibrex.co.uk
Ⓦ www.fibrex.co.uk
Contact: U Key-Davis & R L Godard-Key
Opening Times: 0900-1700 Mon-Fri 1st Apr-30th Sep. 0900-1600 Mon-Fri 1st Oct-31st Mar. 1030-1600 Sat & Sun 18th Feb-30th Jul. Closed last 2 weeks Dec & 1st week Jan. Closed Easter Sun & Aug B/hol Mon.
Min Mail Order UK: £10.00 + p&p
Min Mail Order EU: £20.00 + p&p
Cat. Cost: 2 × 1st class.
Credit Cards: Switch MasterCard Visa
Specialities: *Hedera*, ferns, *Pelargonium* & *Helleborus*. Nat. Collections of *Pelargonium* & *Hedera*. Plant collections subject to time of year, please check by phone.
Notes: Restricted wheelchair access. Also sells wholesale.

WFoF FLOWERS OF THE FIELD
Field Farm, Weobley, Herefordshire, HR4 8QJ
Ⓣ (01544) 318262
Ⓕ (01544) 318262
Ⓔ flowerofthefield@tesco.net
Contact: Kathy Davies
Opening Times: 0900-1900 7 days.
Cat. Cost: 2 × 1st class.
Credit Cards: None
Specialities: Traditional & unusual perennials, grasses, shrubs, trees & herbs. Oriental lilies & freesias for cutting.
Notes: Nursery partially accessible for wheelchairs. Also sells wholesale.
Map Ref: W, C4

WGer FRON GOCH GARDEN CENTRE ♿
Pant Road, Llanfaglan, Caernarfon, Carnarfonshire, LL54 5RL
Ⓣ (01286) 672212
Ⓕ (01286) 678912
Ⓔ info@frongoch-gardencentre.co.uk

KEY		
	⊠ Mail order to UK or EU	⌂ Delivers to shows
	✈ Exports beyond EU	€ Euro accepted
	♿ Accessible by wheelchair	◆ See Display advertisement

W

Ⓦ www.frongoch-gardencentre.co.uk
Contact: R A & Mrs V Williams
Opening Times: 0900-1800 Mon-Sat, 1030-1630 Sun all year.
Cat. Cost: None issued.
Credit Cards: All major credit/debit cards
Specialities: Wide range of trees, shrubs, conifers & herbaceous perennials, ferns & grasses; emphasis on plants for coastal & damp sites.
Map Ref: W, A2

WGob THE GOBBETT NURSERY ⊠
Farlow, Kidderminster, Worcestershire, DY14 8TD
Ⓣ (01746) 718647
Ⓕ (01746) 718647
Ⓔ christine.link@lineone.net
Ⓦ www.thegobbettnursery.co.uk
Contact: C H Link
Opening Times: 1030-1700, Mon-Sat.
Min Mail Order UK: £10.00
Cat. Cost: 3 × 1st class.
Credit Cards: None
Specialities: *Syringa*, *Magnolia*. Some varieties available in small quantities only.
Map Ref: W, B4 **OS Grid Ref:** SO648811

WGor GORDON'S NURSERY ⊠ ♿
1 Cefnpennar Cottages, Cefnpennar, Mountain Ash, Mid-Glamorgan, CF45 4EE
Ⓣ (01443) 474593
Ⓕ (01443) 475835
Ⓔ sales@gordonsnursery.co.uk
Ⓦ www.gordonsnursery.co.uk
Contact: D A Gordon
Opening Times: 1000-1800 7 days Mar-Jun. 1000-1700 7 days Jul-Oct. 1100-1600 weekends only Nov & Feb. Closed Dec-Jan.
Min Mail Order UK: Nmc
Cat. Cost: 3 × 1st class.
Credit Cards: All major credit/debit cards
Specialities: Shrubs, perennials, alpines & dwarf conifers.
Notes: Mail order only available in some cases, please check for conditions in catalogue.
Map Ref: W, D3 **OS Grid Ref:** SO037012

WGwG GWYNFOR GROWERS ⊠ € ♿
Gwynfor, Pontgarreg, Llangranog, Llandysul, Ceredigion, SA44 6AU
Ⓣ (01239) 654151
Ⓔ info@gwynfor.co.uk
Ⓦ www.gwynfor.co.uk
Contact: Steve & Angie Hipkin
Opening Times: 1000-dusk Wed, Thu & Sun, all year round.
Min Mail Order UK: Nmc
Cat. Cost: 4 × 1st class, free by email.
Credit Cards: None
Specialities: Plants to intrigue & delight the gardener, incl. heritage Welsh apple varieties, scented shrubs & ground cover.
Notes: Plants also available at Aberystwyth & Lampeter Farmers' Markets.
Map Ref: W, C2 **OS Grid Ref:** SN331536

WGWT GRAFTED WALNUT TREES ⊠ € ♿
The Manse, Capel Isaac, Llandeilo, Carmarthenshire, SA19 7TN
Ⓣ (01558) 669043
Ⓔ sales@graftedwalnuts.co.uk
Ⓦ www.graftedwalnuts.co.uk
Contact: Pete Wignall
Opening Times: 0900-1800 Mon-Fri. Nursery visits by appt. only.
Min Mail Order UK: Nmc
Min Mail Order EU: Nmc
Cat. Cost: 3 × 1st class.
Credit Cards: None
Specialities: Grafted walnut trees incl. nut-bearing varieties of English walnut, ornamental forms of English & black walnut, minor species & hybrids. Ltd. supply of ornamental varieties.
Notes: Mail order available Nov-Feb, collect or special delivery all year. Also sells wholesale.
Map Ref: W, C3 **OS Grid Ref:** SN580266

WHal HALL FARM NURSERY ⊠ €
Vicarage Lane, Kinnerley, Nr Oswestry, Shropshire, SY10 8DH
Ⓣ (01691) 682135
Ⓕ (01691) 682135
Ⓔ hallfarmnursery@ukonline.co.uk
Ⓦ www.hallfarmnursery.co.uk
Contact: Christine & Nick Ffoulkes-Jones
Opening Times: 1000-1700 Tue-Sat 1st Mar-7th Oct 2006. Winter by appt.
Min Mail Order UK: £20.00
Cat. Cost: 4 × 1st class.
Credit Cards: Visa MasterCard Electron Maestro
Specialities: Unusual herbaceous plants, grasses, bog plants & pool marginals, late-flowering perennials, foliage plants.
Notes: Nursery partially accessible for wheelchairs.
Map Ref: W, B4 **OS Grid Ref:** SJ333209

WHar HARLEY NURSERY ♿
Harley, Shropshire, SY5 6LP
Ⓣ (01952) 510241
Ⓕ (01952) 510570
Ⓔ Harleynursery@hotmail.com

W

Contact: Duncan Murphy, Moira Murphy & Nicholas Murphy
Opening Times: 0900-1730 Mon-Sat, 1000-1700 Sun & B/hols. Winter hours 0900-1700 Sun & B/hols.
Cat. Cost: 2 × 1st class.
Credit Cards: All major credit/debit cards
Specialities: Wide range of ornamental & fruit trees. Own grown shrubs, climbers, wide range of hedging plants year round. Conservation & wildlife plants & native trees a speciality.
Map Ref: W, B4

WHCG HUNTS COURT GARDEN & NURSERY ♿
North Nibley, Dursley,
Gloucestershire,
GL11 6DZ
Ⓣ (01453) 547440
Ⓕ (01453) 549944
Ⓔ keith@huntscourt.fsnet.co.uk
Contact: T K & M M Marshall
Opening Times: 0900-1230 & 1345-1700 Tue-Sat excl. Aug, nursery & garden. Also by appt. See NGS for Sun openings.
Cat. Cost: 5 × 2nd class.
Credit Cards: None
Specialities: Old roses species & climbers. Hardy geraniums, *Penstemon* & unusual shrubs.
Map Ref: W, D4

WHCr HERGEST CROFT GARDENS ♿
Kington, Herefordshire, HR5 3EG
Ⓣ (01544) 230160
Ⓕ (01544) 232031
Ⓔ gardens@hergest.co.uk
Ⓦ www.hergest.co.uk
Contact: Stephen Lloyd
Opening Times: 1230-1730 7 days Apr-Oct, 1200-1800 7 days May-Jun.
Cat. Cost: None issued.
Credit Cards: All major credit/debit cards
Specialities: *Acer*, *Betula* & unusual woody plants.

WHen HENLLYS LODGE PLANTS ♿
Henllys Lodge, Beaumaris, Anglesey, Gwynedd, LL58 8HU
Ⓣ (01248) 810106
Ⓔ cranesbill@hugheslane.freeserve.co.uk
Contact: Mrs E Lane
Opening Times: 1100-1700 Mon, Tue, Sat, Sun & by appt. Apr-Oct.
Cat. Cost: None issued.
Credit Cards: None
Specialities: Hardy geraniums, ground cover & cottage style perennials.
Map Ref: W, A3 **OS Grid Ref:** SH601773

WHer THE HERB GARDEN & HISTORICAL PLANT NURSERY ✉
Ty Capel Pensarn, Pentre Berw, Anglesey, Gwynedd, LL60 6LG
Ⓣ (01248) 422208
Ⓜ 07751 583958
Ⓕ (01248) 422208
Ⓦ www.HistoricalPlants.co.uk
Contact: Corinne & David Tremaine-Stevenson
Opening Times: By appt. only.
Min Mail Order UK: £15.00 + p&p
Min Mail Order EU: £50.00 + p&p sterling only.
Cat. Cost: List £2.50.
Credit Cards: None
Specialities: Rarer herbs, rare natives & wild-flowers; rare & unusual & historical perennials & old roses.
Map Ref: W, A2

WHil HILLVIEW HARDY PLANTS ✉ ✈ ⛺ € ♿ ◆
(off B4176), Worfield, Nr Bridgnorth, Shropshire, WV15 5NT
Ⓣ (01746) 716454
Ⓕ (01746) 716454
Ⓔ hillview@onetel.net
Ⓦ www.hillviewhardyplants.com
Contact: Ingrid, John & Sarah Millington
Opening Times: 0900-1700 Mon-Sat Mar-mid Oct. At other times, please phone first.
Min Mail Order UK: £15.00 + p&p
Min Mail Order EU: £15.00 + p&p
Cat. Cost: 5 × 2nd class.
Credit Cards: All major credit/debit cards
Specialities: Choice herbaceous perennials incl. *Aquilegia*, *Astrantia*, *Auricula*, *Primula*, *Crocosmia*, *Eucomis*, *Ixia*, *Phlox*, *Schizostylis*, *Verbascum*, *Acanthus*. Nat Collection of *Acanthus*.
Notes: Also sells wholesale.
Map Ref: W, B4 **OS Grid Ref:** SO772969

WHlf HAYLOFT PLANTS ✉
Manor Farm, Pensham, Pershore, Worcestershire, WR10 3HB
Ⓣ (01386) 554440
Ⓕ (01386) 553833
Ⓔ info@hayloftplants.co.uk
Ⓦ www.hayloftplants.co.uk
Contact: Yvonne Walker
Opening Times: Not open. Mail order only.

KEY
✉ Mail order to UK or EU ⛺ Delivers to shows
✈ Exports beyond EU € Euro accepted
♿ Accessible by wheelchair ◆ See Display advertisement

Min Mail Order UK: Nmc
Min Mail Order EU: Nmc
Cat. Cost: Free.
Credit Cards: All major credit/debit cards

WHoo **Hoo House Nursery** € ♿ ◆
Hoo House, Gloucester Road, Tewkesbury, Gloucestershire, GL20 7DA
Ⓣ (01684) 293389
Ⓕ (01684) 293389
Ⓔ nursery@hoohouse.co.uk
Ⓦ www.hoohouse.plus.com
Contact: Robin & Julie Ritchie
Opening Times: 1000-1700 Mon-Sat, 1100-1700 Sun.
Cat. Cost: 3 × 1st class.
Credit Cards: None
Specialities: Wide range of herbaceous & alpines - many unusual, incl. *Aster*, *Papaver*, *Geranium* & *Penstemon*. Nat. Collections of *Platycodon* & *Gentiana asclepiadea* cvs.
Notes: Also sells wholesale.
Map Ref: W, C5 **OS Grid Ref:** SO893293

W

WHrl **Harrells Hardy Plants** ⊠
(Office) 15 Coxlea Close, Evesham, Worcestershire, WR11 4JS
Ⓣ (01386) 443077
Ⓕ (01386) 443852
Ⓔ enicklin@evesham11.fsnet.co.uk
Ⓦ www.harrellshardyplants.co.uk
Contact: Liz Nicklin & Kate Phillips
Opening Times: 1000-1200 Sun Mar-Nov. Other times by appt. Please phone.
Min Mail Order UK: Nmc.
Cat. Cost: 3 × 1st class.
Credit Cards: None
Specialities: Now developing display gardens to showcase wide range of hardy plants, many unusual.
Notes: Nursery located off Rudge Rd, Evesham. Please phone for directions or see catalogue. Partial wheelchair access. Mail order Nov-Mar only.
Map Ref: W, C5 **OS Grid Ref:** SP033443

WIvy **Ivycroft Plants** ⊠ € ♿
Upper Ivington, Leominster, Herefordshire, HR6 0JN
Ⓣ (01568) 720344
Ⓔ rogerandsue@ivycroft.freeserve.co.uk
Ⓦ www.ivycroft.freeserve.co.uk
Contact: Roger Norman
Opening Times: 0900-1600 Thu Feb, Wed & Thu Mar-Sep. Other times by appt., please phone.
Min Mail Order UK: Nmc
Min Mail Order EU: Nmc
Cat. Cost: 2 × 1st class.
Credit Cards: None
Specialities: *Cyclamen*, *Galanthus*, *Salix*, alpines, herbaceous & ferns.
Notes: Mail order Feb/Mar *Galanthus* & *Salix* only.
Map Ref: W, C4 **OS Grid Ref:** SO464562

WJas **Paul Jasper Trees** ⊠
The Lighthouse, Bridge Street, Leominster, Herefordshire, HR6 8DX
Ⓕ (01568) 616499 for orders.
Ⓔ enquiries@jaspertrees.co.uk
Ⓦ www.jaspertrees.co.uk
Contact: Paul Jasper
Opening Times: Not open. Mail order only.
Min Mail Order UK: £40.00 + p&p
Cat. Cost: Online only.
Credit Cards: None
Specialities: Full range of fruit & ornamental trees. Over 100 modern and traditional apple varieties + 220 others all direct from the grower. Many unusual varieties of *Malus domestica*.
Notes: See photogallery on website. Also sells wholesale.

WJek **Jekka's Herb Farm** ⊠ ⌂ ♿
Rose Cottage, Shellards Lane, Alveston, Bristol, BS35 3SY
Ⓣ (01454) 418878
Ⓕ (01454) 411988
Ⓔ farm@jekkasherbfarm.com
Ⓦ www.jekkasherbfarm.com
Contact: Jekka McVicar
Opening Times: 4 times a year. Please check website for dates.
Min Mail Order UK: £15 plants
Min Mail Order EU: Seeds only to the EU.
Cat. Cost: 4 × 1st class.
Credit Cards: Visa MasterCard Delta Switch Maestro
Specialities: Culinary, medicinal, aromatic, decorative herbs. Soil Association licensed herb farm.
Map Ref: W, D4

WKif **Kiftsgate Court Gardens** ♿
Kiftsgate Court, Chipping Camden, Gloucestershire, GL55 6LW
Ⓣ (01386) 438777
Ⓕ (01386) 438777
Ⓔ kiftsgte@aol.com
Ⓦ www.kiftsgate.co.uk
Contact: Mrs J Chambers
Opening Times: 1200-1800 Sat-Wed, May, Jun & Jul. 1400-1800 Sun, Mon-Wed, Apr, Aug, Sep.

Cat. Cost: None issued.
Credit Cards: None
Specialities: Small range of unusual plants.
Map Ref: W, C5 **OS Grid Ref:** SP170430

WKin KINGSTONE COTTAGE PLANTS ⊠ ♿
Weston-under-Penyard, Ross-on-Wye, Herefordshire, HR9 7PH
Ⓣ (01989) 565267
Ⓦ www.hoohouse.plus.com/Kingstone/KingFrames.htm
Contact: Mr M Hughes
Opening Times: By appt. and as under NGS.
Min Mail Order UK: Nmc
Min Mail Order EU: Nmc
Cat. Cost: 2 × 1st class
Credit Cards: None
Specialities: Nat. Collection of *Dianthus*.
Map Ref: W, C4 **OS Grid Ref:** 24563

WLav THE LAVENDER GARDEN ⊠ ń €
Ashcroft Nurseries, Nr Ozleworth, Kingscote, Tetbury, Gloucestershire, GL8 8YF
Ⓣ (01453) 860356 or 549286
Ⓜ 07837 582943
Ⓔ Andrew007Bullock@aol.com
Ⓦ www.TheLavenderG.co.uk
Contact: Andrew Bullock
Opening Times: 1100-1700 Sat & Sun. Weekdays variable, please phone. 1st Nov-1st Mar by appt. only.
Min Mail Order UK: £50.00 + p&p
Min Mail Order EU: £50.00 + p&p
Cat. Cost: 2 × 1st class.
Credit Cards: None
Specialities: *Lavandula*, *Buddleja*, plants to attract butterflies. Herbs, wildflowers. Nat. Collection of *Buddleja*.
Notes: Also sells wholesale.
Map Ref: W, D5 **OS Grid Ref:** ST798948

WLeb LEBA ORCHARD - GREEN'S LEAVES ⊠ ń ♿
Lea Bailey, Nr Ross-on-Wye, Herefordshire, HR9 5TY
Ⓣ (01989) 750303
Contact: Paul Green
Opening Times: By appt. only, w/ends preferred.
Min Mail Order UK: £10.00 + p&p
Cat. Cost: 4 × 2nd class.
Credit Cards: None
Specialities: Ornamental grasses, sedges & phormiums. Increasing range of rare & choice shrubs, also some perennials.
Notes: Also sells wholesale.
Map Ref: W, C4

WLin LINGEN NURSERY AND GARDEN ⊠ ń
Lingen, Nr Bucknell, Shropshire, SY7 0DY
Ⓣ (01544) 267720
Ⓕ (01544) 267720
Ⓔ kim&maggie@lingen.freeserve.co.uk
Ⓦ www.lingennursery.co.uk
Contact: Kim W Davis
Opening Times: 1200-1700 Mon-Sat. Closed Sun (except b/hols).
Min Mail Order UK: £15.00
Min Mail Order EU: £20.00 + p&p
Cat. Cost: 3 × 1st class.
Credit Cards: All major credit/debit cards
Specialities: Alpines, rock plants, herbaceous esp. *Androsace*, *Aquilegia*, *Campanula*, *Iris*, *Primula*, auriculas & *Penstemon*. Nat. Collection of Herbaceous *Campanula* & housing *Iris sibirica*. Many available in small quantities only.
Notes: Partially accessible for wheelchair users with help. Also sells wholesale.
Map Ref: W, C4 **OS Grid Ref:** SO366669

W

WMAq MEREBROOK WATER PLANTS ⊠ ♿
Merebrook Farm, Hanley Swan, Worcestershire, WR8 0DX
Ⓣ (01684) 310950
Ⓔ enquiries@pondplants.co.uk
Ⓦ www.pondplants.co.uk
Contact: Roger Kings & Biddi Kings
Opening Times: 1000-1600 1st Apr-31st Jul. Aug-Mar by appt.
Min Mail Order UK: Nmc
Min Mail Order EU: £25.00
Cat. Cost: Free or Online.
Credit Cards: All major credit/debit cards
Specialities: *Nymphaea* & other aquatic plants. International Waterlily & Water Gardening Soc. accredited collection. Extensive display gardens open to the public (no charge).
Map Ref: W, C5 **OS Grid Ref:** SO802425

WMnd MYND HARDY PLANTS ⊠
Delbury Hall Estate, Diddlebury, Craven Arms, Shropshire, SY7 9DH
Ⓜ 07812 689155
Ⓕ (01547) 530459
Ⓔ sales@myndplants.co.uk
Ⓦ www.myndplants.co.uk
Contact: Steve Adams
Opening Times: 1000-1700 Mon, Wed-Sat, closed Tues, 1100-1700 Sun, Mar-end Sep. Other times phone for appt.
Min Mail Order UK: £10.00 + p&p
Min Mail Order EU: £10.00 + p&p
Cat. Cost: 4 × 2nd class.

Credit Cards: Visa MasterCard
Specialities: Herbaceous plants.
Notes: Also sells wholesale.
Map Ref: W, B4 **OS Grid Ref:** SO510852

WMoo Moorland Cottage Plants ⊠ ♿
Rhyd-y-Groes, Brynberian,
Crymych, Pembrokeshire,
SA41 3TT
Ⓣ (01239) 891363
Ⓔ jenny@moorlandcottageplants.co.uk
Ⓦ www.moorlandcottageplants.co.uk
Contact: Jennifer Matthews
Opening Times: 1030-1730 daily excl. Wed end Feb-end Sep. Display garden open for NGS from mid-May.
Min Mail Order UK: See cat. for details.
Cat. Cost: 4 × 1st class.
Credit Cards: None
Specialities: Traditional & unusual hardy perennials. Many garden-worthy rarities. Cottage garden plants; ferns & many shade plants; moisture lovers; ornamental grasses & bamboos; colourful ground cover.
Map Ref: W, C2 **OS Grid Ref:** SN091343

WMou Mount Pleasant Trees €
Rockhampton, Berkeley,
Gloucestershire,
GL13 9DU
Ⓣ (01454) 260348
Contact: P & G Locke
Opening Times: By appt. only.
Cat. Cost: 3 × 2nd class.
Credit Cards: None
Specialities: Wide range of trees for forestry, hedging, woodlands & gardens esp. *Populus*, *Platanus* & *Salix*.
Notes: Also sells wholesale.

WNor Norfields ⊠ €
Llangwm Arboretum,
Usk, Monmouthshire,
NP15 1NQ
Ⓣ (01291) 650306
Ⓕ (01291) 650577
Ⓔ andrew@norfields.co.uk
Ⓦ www.Norfields.co.uk
Contact: Andrew Norfield
Opening Times: Not open.
Min Mail Order UK: £3.00 + p&p
Min Mail Order EU: £3.00 + p&p
Cat. Cost: 3 × 1st class.
Credit Cards: None
Specialities: Wide range of tree seedlings for growing on. *Acer*, *Betula*, *Stewartia* & pre-treated seed.
Notes: Also sells wholesale.

WOFF Old Fashioned Flowers ⊠
Cleeway, Eardington, Bridgnorth, Shropshire, WV16 5JT
Ⓣ (01746) 766909
Ⓔ jand.cm@virgin.net
Contact: John Snocken
Opening Times: By appt. only.
Min Mail Order UK: Nmc
Min Mail Order EU: Nmc
Cat. Cost: 2 × 1st class.
Credit Cards: None
Specialities: Show pansies, fancy pansies & exhibition violas. Bedding violas, pinks, auriculas, chrysanthemums, dahlias, violets & species *Viola*. Nat. Collection of Florists' Violas & Pansies.
Map Ref: W, B4 **OS Grid Ref:** 723907

WOld Old Court Nurseries ⊠ € ♿
Colwall, Nr Malvern, Worcestershire,
WR13 6QE
Ⓣ (01684) 540416
Ⓔ picton@dircon.co.uk
Ⓦ www.autumnasters.co.uk
Contact: Paul & Meriel Picton
Opening Times: 1100-1700 Fri-Sun May-Oct, 7 days 1st week Sep-2nd week Oct.
Min Mail Order UK: Nmc
Min Mail Order EU: Nmc
Cat. Cost: 1 × 1st class.
Credit Cards: None
Specialities: Nat. Collection of Michaelmas Daisies. Herbaceous perennials.
Notes: Mail order for *Aster* only.
Map Ref: W, C4 **OS Grid Ref:** SO759430

WOrn Ornamental Tree Nurseries ⊠ ♿
Broomy Hill Gardens, Cobnash, Kingsland, Herefordshire, HR6 9QZ
Ⓣ (01568) 708016
Ⓕ (01568) 709022
Ⓔ enquiries@ornamental-trees.co.uk
Ⓦ www.ornamental-trees.co.uk
Contact: Russell Mills
Opening Times: 0900-1800 Mon-Sat. 1000-1600 Sun.
Min Mail Order UK: £9.95
Cat. Cost: 3 × 1st class.
Credit Cards: All major credit/debit cards
Specialities: Ornamental trees. Fruit trees.
Notes: Also sells wholesale.
Map Ref: W, C4

WOut Out of the Common Way ⊠
(Office) Penhyddgan, Boduan, Pwllheli, Gwynedd, LL53 8YH
Ⓣ (01758) 721577 (Office): (01407) 720431 (Nursery)

W

Ⓔ penhyddgan@tiscali.co.uk
Contact: Joanna Davidson (nursery) Margaret Mason (office & mail order)
Opening Times: By arrangement.
Min Mail Order UK: Nmc
Min Mail Order EU: Nmc
Cat. Cost: A5 sae 35p.
Credit Cards: None
Specialities: Labiates, esp. *Nepeta* & *Salvia*. *Aster*, *Geranium* & *Crocosmia*. Some plants propagated in small quantities only. Will propagate salvias to order.
Notes: Nursery is at Pandy Treban, Bryngwran, Anglesey. Partially accessible for wheelchairs.
Map Ref: W, A2 **OS Grid Ref:** SH370778

WOVN THE OLD VICARAGE NURSERY ⊠
Lucton, Leominster, Herefordshire, HR6 9PN
Ⓣ (01568) 780538
Ⓕ (01568) 780818
Contact: Mrs R M Flake
Opening Times: Most days. Please phone first if making a special journey.
Min Mail Order UK: Nmc
Cat. Cost: None issued.
Credit Cards: None
Specialities: Roses: old roses; climbers & ramblers; species & ground cover. *Euphorbia* & half-hardy *Salvia*.
Map Ref: W, C4

WPat CHRIS PATTISON ⊠ € ♿
Brookend, Pendock, Gloucestershire, GL19 3PL
Ⓣ (01531) 650480
Ⓕ (01531) 650480
Ⓔ cp@chrispattison.fsnet.co.uk
Ⓦ www.chrispattison.fsnet.co.uk
Contact: Chris Pattison
Opening Times: 0900-1700 Mon-Fri. W/ends by appt. only.
Min Mail Order UK: £10.00 +p&p
Cat. Cost: 3 × 1st class.
Credit Cards: None
Specialities: Choice, rare shrubs & alpines. Grafted stock esp. Japanese maples & *Liquidambar*. Wide range of *Viburnum*, *Phormium* & dwarf willows.
Notes: Mail order Nov-Feb only. Also sells wholesale.
Map Ref: W, C5 **OS Grid Ref:** SO781327

WPBF P & B FUCHSIAS ⊠ ♠ € ♿
Maes y Gwaelod, Penclawdd Road, Penclawdd, Swansea, West Glamorgan, SA4 3RB
Ⓣ (01792) 851669
Ⓔ sales@gower-fuchsias.co.uk
Ⓦ www.gower-fuchsias.co.uk
Contact: Paul Fisher
Opening Times: 0900-1800 7 days 1 Mar-30 Sep.
Min Mail Order UK: £9.00 (6 plants @ £1.50 incl. P&P)
Cat. Cost: 3 × 1st class.
Credit Cards: None
Specialities: Fuchsias. Hybrid & species.
Notes: Cuttings only available Mar-May. Very ltd. quantities of each.
Map Ref: W, D3

WPen PENPERGWM PLANTS ♿
Penpergwm Lodge, Abergavenny, Monmonthshire, NP7 9AS
Ⓣ (01873) 840422/840208
Ⓕ (01873) 840422/840208
Ⓔ boyle@penpergwm.co.uk
Ⓦ www.penplants.com
Contact: Mrs J Kerr/Mrs S Boyle
Opening Times: 30th Mar-24th Sep 2006, Thu-Sun 1400-1800.
Cat. Cost: 2 × 1st class.
Credit Cards: None
Specialities: Hardy perennials.
Map Ref: W, D4 **OS Grid Ref:** SO335104

W

WPer PERHILL NURSERIES ⊠ € ♿
Worcester Road, Great Witley, Worcestershire, WR6 6JT
Ⓣ (01299) 896329
Ⓕ (01299) 896990
Ⓔ PerhillP@aol.com
Ⓦ www.perhillplants.co.uk
Contact: Duncan Straw
Opening Times: 0900-1700 Mon-Sat, 1000-1600 Sun, 1st Feb-31st Jul. 0900-1700 Mon-Fri, 1st Aug-31st Jan.
Min Mail Order UK: Nmc
Min Mail Order EU: £10.00
Cat. Cost: 6 × 2nd class.
Credit Cards: All major credit/debit cards
Specialities: 2500+ varieties of rare, unusual alpines & herbaceous perennials incl. *Penstemon*, *Campanula*, *Salvia*, *Thymus*, herbs, *Veronica*.
Notes: Also sells wholesale.
Map Ref: W, C4 **OS Grid Ref:** SO763656

WPGP PAN-GLOBAL PLANTS ♿
The Walled Garden, Frampton Court, Frampton-on-Severn, Gloucestershire, GL2 7EX
Ⓣ (01452) 741641
Ⓜ 07801 275138
Ⓕ (01453) 768858

KEY		
	⊠ Mail order to UK or EU	♠ Delivers to shows
	✈ Exports beyond EU	€ Euro accepted
	♿ Accessible by wheelchair	◆ See Display advertisement

Ⓔ info@panglobalplants.com
Ⓦ www.panglobalplants.com
Contact: Nick Macer
Opening Times: 1100-1700 Wed-Sun 1st Feb-31st Oct. Also B/hols. Closed 2nd Sun in Sep. Winter months by appt., please phone first.
Cat. Cost: 6 × 1st class.
Credit Cards: Maestro MasterCard Visa Solo Delta
Specialities: A plantsman's nursery offering a wide selection of rare & desirable trees, shrubs, herbaceous, bamboos, exotics, climbers, ferns etc. Specialities incl. *Magnolia, Hydrangea* & *Bamboo*.
Map Ref: W, D5

WPic THE PICTON CASTLE TRUST NURSERY ♿
Picton Castle, Haverfordwest, Pembrokeshire, SA62 4AS
Ⓣ (01437) 751326
Ⓕ (01437) 751326
Ⓔ pct@pictoncastle.freeserve.co.uk
Ⓦ www.pictoncastle.co.uk
Contact: D L Pryse Lloyd
Opening Times: 1030-1700 7 days except Mon Apr-Sep. Other times by arrangement.
Cat. Cost: 1 × 1st class.
Credit Cards: None
Specialities: *Rhododendron*. Myrtle and relatives. Woodland & unusual shrubs. Nursery attached to 40 acre woodland garden.
Map Ref: W, D2 **OS Grid Ref:** SN011135

W

WPnn THE PERENNIAL NURSERY
Rhosygilwen, Llanrhian Road, St Davids, Pembrokeshire, SA62 6DB
Ⓣ (01437) 721954
Ⓕ (01437) 721954
Ⓔ philipasymons@tesco.net
Contact: Mrs Philipa Symons
Opening Times: 1030-1730 Mar-Oct. Nov-Feb by appt.
Credit Cards: All major credit/debit cards
Specialities: Herbaceous perennials & alpines. Tender perennials. Coastal plants. Herbs.
Notes: Cafe.
Map Ref: W, C1 **OS Grid Ref:** SM775292

WPnP PENLAN PERENNIALS ⊠ ✈ ṅ € ♿
Penlan Farm, Penrhiwpal, Llandysul, Ceredigion, SA44 5QH
Ⓣ (01239) 851244
Ⓕ (01239) 851244
Ⓔ rcain@penlanperennials.co.uk
Ⓦ www.penlanperennials.co.uk
Contact: Richard & Jane Cain
Opening Times: 0930-1730 Wed-Sun Mar-Sep & B/hols. Oct-Feb by appt.
Min Mail Order UK: Nmc
Min Mail Order EU: Nmc
Cat. Cost: 4 × 2nd class or free online.
Credit Cards: All major credit/debit cards
Specialities: Aquatic, marginal & bog plants. Shade-loving & woodland perennials, ferns & grasses, all grown peat-free.
Notes: Mail order all year, next day delivery. Secure online web ordering.
Map Ref: W, C2 **OS Grid Ref:** SN344457

WPrP PRIME PERENNIALS ⊠ ṅ €
Llety Moel, Rhos-y-Garth, Llanilar, Nr Aberystwyth, Ceredigion, SY23 4SG
Ⓣ (01974) 241505
Ⓜ 07891 333656
Ⓔ liz@prime-perennials.co.uk
Ⓦ www.prime-perennials.co.uk
Contact: Elizabeth Powney
Opening Times: Open by appt. only.
Min Mail Order UK: £12.00
Min Mail Order EU: £12.00
Cat. Cost: 4 × 1st class.
Credit Cards: None
Specialities: Specialist growers of rare, unusual & obscure perennials, ferns, bulbs & grasses. Special emphasis on South African *Tulbaghia*. Some stock in small quanitites but can be grown to order. Nursery 650ft above sea level.
Notes: Mail order all year.
Map Ref: W, C3

WPtf PANTYFOD GARDEN NURSERY ⊠ ♿
Llandewi Brefi, Tregaron, Ceredigion, SY25 6PE
Ⓣ (01570) 493564
Ⓕ (01570) 493585
Ⓔ sales@pantyfodgarden.co.uk
Ⓦ www.pantyfodgarden.co.uk
Contact: Susan Rowe
Opening Times: 1300-1800 15th Apr-10th Sep 2006, weekends and B/hols only.
Min Mail Order UK: Nmc
Min Mail Order EU: Nmc
Cat. Cost: A5 sae, 47p stamp. Also online.
Credit Cards: None
Specialities: Hardy geraniums, unusual hardy perennials, black plants, woodland plants, plants for moist soil, all grown largely peat-free. Some plants are in small quantities. Nursery at 950ft with spectacular views.
Map Ref: W, C3 **OS Grid Ref:** SN654540

WRai RAILS END NURSERY ♿
Back Lane, Ashton under Hill, Evesham, Worcestershire, WR11 7RG
Ⓣ (01386) 881884
Ⓕ (01386) 881407

Ⓔ salski@quinweb.net
Ⓦ www.ashtonunderhill.org.uk/business/railsend
Contact: Sally Skinner
Opening Times: 1000-1700 7 days, mid-Feb-end Oct. Nov-Jan by appt. only.
Cat. Cost: Free. Also online.
Credit Cards: All major credit/debit cards
Specialities: Family-run nursery, specialising in hardy herbaceous perennials, with an extending range of the unusual. All stock in small quantities.
Notes: Partially accessible for wheelchair users.
Map Ref: W, C5 **OS Grid Ref:** SO999375

WRHF RED HOUSE FARM ♿
Flying Horse Lane, Bradley Green,
Nr Redditch, Worcestershire, B96 6QT
Ⓣ (01527) 821269
Ⓕ (01527) 821674
Ⓔ contact@redhousefarmgardenandnursery.co.uk
Ⓦ www.redhousefarmgardenandnursery.co.uk
Contact: Mrs Maureen Weaver
Opening Times: 0900-1700 Mon-Sat all year. 1000-1700 Sun & B/Hols.
Cat. Cost: 2 × 1st class.
Credit Cards: None
Specialities: Cottage garden perennials.
Map Ref: W, C5 **OS Grid Ref:** SO986623

WRic RICKARD'S HARDY FERNS LTD ⊠ ⌂ €
Carreg y Fedwen, Sling, Tregarth, Nr Bangor,
Caernarfonshire, LL57 4RP
Ⓣ (01248) 602944 or (01286) 677641
Ⓕ (01248) 600385
Ⓔ rickardshardy@freeuk.co.uk
Ⓦ www.rickardshardyferns.co.uk
Contact: Richard Hayward
Opening Times: 1000-1700 Mon-Fri, 1100-1700 Sat & Sun Mar-Oct. 1000-1700 Nov-Mar by appt. only.
Min Mail Order UK: £20.00 + p&p
Min Mail Order EU: £50.00 + p&p
Cat. Cost: 5 × 1st class or 6 × 2nd class.
Credit Cards: None
Specialities: Ferns, incl. tree ferns. Some available in small quantities only.
Notes: UK customers order with ltd. cheque. EU customers confirm availability before ordering. Rare items in ltd. numbers, year-round availability not guaranteed.
Map Ref: W, A3 **OS Grid Ref:** GR592667

WRos ROSEMARY'S FARMHOUSE NURSERY ♿
Llwyn-y-moel-gau, Llanfihangel, Llanfyllin,
Montgomeryshire, SY22 5JE
Ⓣ (01691) 648196
Ⓕ (01691) 648196
Ⓔ rosemary@farmhouse-nursery.fsnet.co.uk
Contact: Rosemary Pryce
Opening Times: 1000-1700 most days all year, but advisable to phone to confirm.
Cat. Cost: None issued.
Credit Cards: None
Specialities: Unusual perennials & ornamental grasses. Hardy geraniums. The garden is planted as display & to encourage wildlife, butterflies & many birds.
Map Ref: W, B3 **OS Grid Ref:** SJ083149

WRou ROUALEYN NURSERIES ⌂ ♿
Trefriw, Conwy, LL27 0SX
Ⓣ (01492) 640548
Ⓕ (01492) 640548
Ⓔ roualeyn@beeb.net
Contact: Doug Jones
Opening Times: 1000-1700 weekdays 1st Mar-31st Aug, 1000-1600 Sat, Sun & B/hols.
Cat. Cost: 2 × 1st class.
Credit Cards: None
Specialities: Fuchsias, incl. species.
Map Ref: W, A3 **OS Grid Ref:** SH632778

WSel THE SELSLEY HERB NURSERY ⌂ ♿
Hayhedge Lane, Bisley, Stroud,
Gloucestershire, GL6 7AN
Ⓣ (01452) 770073
Ⓕ (01452) 770073
Ⓔ selsleyherbs@btconnect.com
Ⓦ www.selsleyherbs.co.uk
Contact: Rob Wimperis
Opening Times: 1000-1700 Tue-Sat, 1400-1700 Sun & B/hols Mar-Oct. Nov-Feb variable, please phone to check.
Cat. Cost: 4 × 1st class.
Credit Cards: MasterCard Visa
Specialities: Culinary, aromatic & medicinal herbs & selected garden plants.
Map Ref: W, D5 **OS Grid Ref:** SO058906

WSFF SAITH FFYNNON FARM ⊠ ⌂ € ♿
Whitford, Holywell, Flintshire, CH8 9EQ
Ⓣ (01352) 711198
Ⓕ (01352) 716777
Ⓔ jan@7wells.org
Ⓦ www.northwalesbutterflies.org.uk
Contact: Jan Miller
Opening Times: By appt. only.
Min Mail Order UK: Nmc
Min Mail Order EU: Nmc
Cat. Cost: 2 × 1st class.
Credit Cards: None
Specialities: Plants and seeds to attract butterflies and moths. Nat. Collection status for *Eupatorium* applied for. Stock available in small quantities unless ordered well in advance.

Notes: Profits go to Butterfly Conservation. Also sells wholesale.
Map Ref: W, A3 **OS Grid Ref:** SJ154775

WSHC STONE HOUSE COTTAGE NURSERIES ♿
Stone, Nr Kidderminster, Worcestershire, DY10 4BG
Ⓣ (01562) 69902
Ⓔ louisa@shcn.co.uk
Ⓦ www.shcn.co.uk
Contact: L N Arbuthnott
Opening Times: 1000-1700 Wed-Sat. By appt. only mid Sep-Mar.
Cat. Cost: Sae.
Credit Cards: None
Specialities: Small general range esp. wall shrubs, climbers & unusual plants.
Map Ref: W, C5 **OS Grid Ref:** SO863750

WShi SHIPTON BULBS ⊠ €
Y Felin, Henllan Amgoed, Whitland, Carmarthenshire, SA34 0SL
Ⓣ (01994) 240125
Ⓕ (01994) 241180
Ⓔ bluebell@zoo.co.uk
Ⓦ www.bluebellbulbs.co.uk
Contact: John Shipton & Alison Foot
Opening Times: By appt. only.
Min Mail Order UK: Nmc
Min Mail Order EU: Nmc
Cat. Cost: Sae.
Credit Cards: None
Specialities: Native British bulbs, & bulbs & plants for naturalising.
Map Ref: W, D2 **OS Grid Ref:** SN188207

WSpi SPINNEYWELL NURSERY ⊠ ◆
Waterlane, Oakridge, Bisley, Gloucestershire, GL6 7PH
Ⓣ (01452) 770151
Ⓕ (01452) 770151
Ⓔ spinneywellsales@btconnect.com
Ⓦ www.spinneywellplants.co.uk
Contact: Wendy Asher
Opening Times: 1000-1500 Mon-Sat, spring, summer, autumn. 1000-1500 Mon-Fri, winter.
Min Mail Order UK: £10.00 + p&p
Min Mail Order EU: £30.00 + p&p
Cat. Cost: Online or 6 × 1st class for plant list.
Credit Cards: All major credit/debit cards
Specialities: *Buxus*, *Taxus* & unusual herbaceous & shrubs. Hellebores, euphorbias, *Ceanothus*, hardy geraniums.
Notes: Plant sourcing service available. Also sells wholesale.
Map Ref: W, D5 **OS Grid Ref:** SO9204

WSPU PERSHORE COLLEGE OF HORTICULTURE ♿
Specialist Plant Unit & Plant Centre, Avonbank, Pershore, Worcestershire, WR10 3JP
Ⓣ (01386) 561385
Ⓕ (01386) 551108
Contact: Jo Yates (Plant Centre)
Opening Times: (Plant Centre) 0900-1700 Mon-Sat, 1030-1630 Sun.
Cat. Cost: £1.00.
Credit Cards: Visa Access
Specialities: Nat. Collection of *Penstemon*. Open for viewing 0830-1630 Mon-Fri.
Notes: Also sells wholesale.
Map Ref: W, C5

WSSs SHROPSHIRE SARRACENIAS ⊠ ✈ ⌂ € ♿
5 Field Close, Malinslee, Telford, Shropshire, TF4 2EH
Ⓣ (01952) 501598
Ⓔ mike@carnivorousplants.uk.com
Ⓦ www.carnivorousplants.uk.com
Contact: Mike King
Opening Times: By appt. only.
Min Mail Order UK: Nmc
Min Mail Order EU: Nmc
Cat. Cost: 2 × 1st class.
Credit Cards: None
Specialities: *Sarracenia*. *Dionaea muscipula* & forms. Some stock available in small quantities only. Nat. Collections of *Sarracenia* & *Dionaea*.
Map Ref: W, B4 **OS Grid Ref:** SJ689085

WSuV SUNNYBANK VINE NURSERY ⊠ ✈
King Street, Ewyas Harold, Herefordshire, HR2 OEE
Ⓣ (01981) 240256
Ⓔ vinenursery@hotmail.com
Ⓦ vinenursery.netfirms.com
Contact: B R Edwards
Opening Times: Not open. Mail order only.
Min Mail Order UK: £8.00 incl. p&p
Min Mail Order EU: £10.00 incl. p&p
Cat. Cost: Sae.
Credit Cards: None
Specialities: Vines. Nat. Collection of *Vitis vinifera* (hardy, incl. dessert & wine).
Notes: EU sales by arrangement. Also sells wholesale.
Map Ref: W, C4

WTan TAN-Y-LLYN NURSERIES
Meifod, Powys, SY22 6YB
Ⓣ (01938) 500370
Ⓔ callumjohnston@tanyllyn.the-nursery.co.uk
Ⓦ www.tanyllyn.the-nursery.co.uk
Contact: Callum Johnston

Opening Times: 1000-1700 Tue-Fri Mar-Jun and at other times by appt.
Cat. Cost: 2 × 1st class.
Credit Cards: None
Specialities: Herbs, alpines, perennials.
Notes: Also sells wholesale.
Map Ref: W, B3 **OS Grid Ref:** SJ167125

WTel TELLING AND COATES ⊠
64A Church Street, Charlton Kings, Cheltenham, Gloucestershire, GL53 8AS
Ⓣ (01242) 514472
Ⓔ tellingandcoates@freeola.net
Ⓦ www.tellingandcoates.freeola.net
Contact: John Coates
Opening Times: 0830-1300 & 1400-1730 Mon, Fri & Sat, or by appt. on other days.
Min Mail Order UK: Nmc
Cat. Cost: 3 × 1st class or 4 × 2nd class.
Credit Cards: None
Specialities: A traditional hardy plant nursery offering a wide range of shrubs, climbers, heathers, alpines & herbaceous plants at reasonable prices.
Map Ref: W, C5 **OS Grid Ref:** SO966205

WThu THUYA ALPINE NURSERY ⊠ ⛺
Glebelands, Hartpury, Gloucestershire, GL19 3BW
Ⓣ (01452) 700548
Contact: S W Bond
Opening Times: 1000-dusk Sat & Bank hol. 1100-dusk Sun, Weekdays appt. advised.
Min Mail Order UK: £4.00 + p&p
Min Mail Order EU: £10.00 + p&p
Cat. Cost: 4 × 2nd class.
Credit Cards: None
Specialities: Wide and changing range including rarities, available in smallish numbers.
Notes: Partially accessible for wheelchair users.
Map Ref: W, C5

WTin TINPENNY PLANTS ♿
Tinpenny Farm, Fiddington, Tewkesbury, Gloucestershire, GL20 7BJ
Ⓣ (01684) 292668
Ⓔ plants@tinpenny.plus.com
Contact: Elaine Horton
Opening Times: 1200-1700 Tue-Thu or by appt.
Cat. Cost: None issued.
Credit Cards: None
Specialities: Wide range of hardy garden-worthy plants esp. *Helleborus*, *Iris* & *Sempervivum*. Will propagate to order rare plants from own stock. Small quantities only of some plants.
Map Ref: W, C5 **OS Grid Ref:** SO919318

WTMC TIR MAB CYNAN NURSERY ⊠ ♿
Brithdir, Dolgellau, Caernarfonshire, LL40 2RW
Ⓣ (01341) 450339
Ⓕ (01341) 450339
Ⓦ www.tirmabcynan.nursery@btopenworld.com
Contact: Jim Haunch
Opening Times: 1000-1700, 7 days, Easter-1 Sep. Other times by appt.
Min Mail Order UK: £10.00
Cat. Cost: None issued.
Credit Cards: None
Specialities: Hardy geraniums, *Hemerocallis*, hostas, ferns, *Iris*, a wide range of hardy perennials & sought after plants. Nat. Collection of *Geranium phaeum* cvs.
Notes: Also sells wholesale.
Map Ref: W, B3

WVaB VALDUCCI BRUGMANSIAS ⊠ € ♿
61 Green Lane, Bayston Hill, Shrewsbury, Shropshire, SY3 0NR
Ⓣ 07921 368968
Ⓕ (01743) 871199
Ⓔ valbros@btconnect.com
Contact: Luigi Valducci
Opening Times: 1000-1600 by appt. only.
Min Mail Order UK: Nmc
Credit Cards: None
Specialities: Brugmansias.
Notes: Main nursery site at Meole Brace Garden Club, Vicarage Road, Shrewsbury.

WViv VIV MARSH POSTAL PLANTS ⊠
Walford Heath, Shrewsbury, Shropshire, SY4 2HT
Ⓣ (01939) 291475
Ⓔ mail@PostalPlants.co.uk
Ⓦ www.PostalPlants.co.uk
Contact: Mr Viv Marsh
Opening Times: Selected w/ends in spring & autumn. Please phone for details.
Min Mail Order UK: £30.00 plant value
Cat. Cost: 5 × 1st class (£1 refund on first order). Also online.
Credit Cards: Visa MasterCard Switch
Specialities: Specialists in *Alstroemeria*.
Notes: Also sells wholesale.
Map Ref: W, B4 **OS Grid Ref:** SJ446198

KEY
⊠ Mail order to UK or EU ⛺ Delivers to shows
✈ Exports beyond EU € Euro accepted
♿ Accessible by wheelchair ◆ See Display advertisement

WWeb **Webbs of Wychbold** € ◆
Wychbold, Droitwich,
Worcestershire,
WR9 0DG
Ⓣ (01527) 860000
Ⓕ (01527) 861284
Ⓔ gardenplants@webbsofwychbold.co.uk
Ⓦ www.webbsofwychbold.co.uk
Contact: Garden Plants Dept.
Opening Times: 0900-1800 Mon-Fri winter. 0900-2000 Mon-Fri summer. 0900-1800 Sat & 1030-1630 Sun all year. Closed Xmas Day, Boxing Day & Easter Sun.
Cat. Cost: None issued.
Credit Cards: Visa Access American Express
Specialities: Hardy trees & shrubs, climbers, conifers, alpines, heathers, herbaceous, herbs, roses, fruit & aquatics. Nat. Collection of Shrubby *Potentilla*.
Notes: Also sells wholesale.
Map Ref: W, C5

WWFP **Whitehall Farmhouse Plants** ⊠
Sevenhampton, Cheltenham,
Gloucestershire,
GL54 5TL
Ⓣ (01242) 820772
Ⓜ 07711 021034
Ⓕ (01242) 821226
Ⓔ info@wfplants.co.uk
Contact: Victoria Logue
Opening Times: By appt. only.
Min Mail Order UK: Nmc
Cat. Cost: 2 × 1st class.
Credit Cards: None
Specialities: A small nursery producing a range of interesting & easy hardy perennials for the garden. Some plants held in small quantities only.
Map Ref: W, C5 **OS Grid Ref:** SP018229

WWHy **Welsh Holly** ⊠ € ♿
Llyn-y-gors, Tenby Road,
St Clears, Carmarthenshire,
SA33 4JP
Ⓣ (01994) 231789
Ⓕ (01994) 231789
Ⓔ info@welsh-holly.co.uk
Ⓦ www.welsh-holly.co.uk
Contact: Philip Lanc
Opening Times: By appt. only.
Min Mail Order UK: Nmc
Min Mail Order EU: Nmc
Cat. Cost: 2 × 1st class.
Credit Cards: None
Specialities: Hollies. Ltd. stock of less common plants.
Notes: Also sells wholesale.

WWll **West Wales Willows** ⊠ ✈ ♿
Martinique Farm, Wolf's Castle,
Haverfordwest, Pembrokeshire, SA62 5DY
Ⓣ (01437) 741714
Ⓕ (01437) 741714
Ⓔ info@westwaleswillows.co.uk
Ⓦ www.westwaleswillows.co.uk
Contact: Billa Schleicher & David Clark
Opening Times: Mail order only. Not open except on Open Day in Oct or by appt.
Min Mail Order UK: £5.00
Min Mail Order EU: £5.00
Cat. Cost: Online only.
Credit Cards: Visa MasterCard
Specialities: Willows. Some in small quantities only.

WWlt **Wollerton Old Hall Garden** ♿
Wollerton, Market Drayton, Shropshire,
TF9 3NA
Ⓣ (01630) 685760
Ⓕ (01630) 685583
Ⓔ info@wollertonoldhallgarden.com
Ⓦ www.wollertonoldhallgarden.com
Contact: Mr John Jenkins
Opening Times: 1200-1700 Fri, Sun & B/hols Easter-end Sep.
Cat. Cost: None issued.
Credit Cards: All major credit/debit cards
Specialities: Perennials, hardy & half-hardy.
Map Ref: W, B4 **OS Grid Ref:** SJ624296

WWpP **Waterpump Plants** ⊠
Waterpump Farm, Ryeford, Ross-on-Wye,
Herefordshire, HR9 7PU
Ⓣ (01989) 750177
Ⓔ liz.sugden2@btinternet.com
Contact: Mrs E Sugden
Opening Times: Open under the NGS scheme. Order collection service available.
Min Mail Order UK: £15.00
Cat. Cost: 4 × 1st class.
Credit Cards: None
Specialities: Hardy geraniums & heleniums. Small nursery with limited stock, will propagate to order.
Map Ref: W, C4 **OS Grid Ref:** SO642226

WWst **Westonbirt Plants** ⊠ ✈ €
9 Westonbirt Close, Worcester, WR5 3RX
Ⓣ (01905) 350429 (answerphone)
Ⓔ office@westonbirtplants.co.uk
Ⓦ www.westonbirtplants.co.uk
Contact: Garry Dickerson
Opening Times: Not open. Mail order only.
Min Mail Order UK: Nmc
Min Mail Order EU: Nmc
Cat. Cost: 3 × 1st class.

Credit Cards: None
Specialities: *Iris*, *Fritillaria*, *Erythronium*, particular interest in Juno *Iris* species. *Crocus*, *Corydalis*, *Lilium*, *Arisaema*, *Trillium*, *Arum* & tulip species. Woodland plants & hardy orchids, esp. *Calanthe* & *Cypripedium*. Many rare plants in ltd. numbers.

Abroad

XBlo TABLE BAY VIEW NURSERY ⊠ ☒ €
(Office) 60 Molteno Road, Oranjezicht,
Cape Town 8001, South Africa
Ⓣ 00 27 21 683 5108
Ⓕ 00 27 21 683 5108
Ⓔ info@tablebayviewnursery.co.za
Contact: Terence Bloch
Opening Times: Mail order only. No personal callers.
Min Mail Order UK: £15.00 + p&p
Min Mail Order EU: £15.00
Cat. Cost: £3.40 (postal order).
Credit Cards: None
Specialities: Tropical & sub-tropical ornamental & fruiting plants.
Notes: Due to high local bank charges, can no longer accept foreign bank cheques, only undated postal orders.

XBTW B & T WORLD SEEDS ⊠ ☒ €
Paguignan, 34210 Aigues-Vives, France
Ⓣ 00 33 (0) 4689 12963
Ⓕ 00 33 (0) 4689 13039
Ⓔ le@b-and-t-world-seeds.com
Ⓦ www.b-and-t-world-seeds.com
Contact: Lesley Sleigh
Opening Times: Not open. Mail order only.
Min Mail Order UK: £14.00 inc. carriage
Min Mail Order EU: £14.00 inc. carriage
Cat. Cost: £10 Europe, £14 elsewhere.
Credit Cards: Visa MasterCard
Specialities: Master list contains over 30,000 items. 700 sub-lists available.
Notes: Exports seed only. Catalogue/botanical reference system available on CD Rom. SeedyRom™ catalogue £20 worldwide. Also sells wholesale.

XFro FROSCH EXCLUSIVE PERENNIALS ⊠ ☒ €
Lindener Str. 5, D-83623 Dietramszell-Lochen, Germany
Ⓣ 00 49 172 842 2050
Ⓕ 00 49 8027 9049975
Ⓔ info@cypripedium.de
Ⓦ www.cypripedium.de
Contact: Michael Weinert
Opening Times: Not open. Mail order only. Orders taken between 0700-2200 hours.
Min Mail Order UK: £350.00 + p&p
Min Mail Order EU: £350.00 + p&p
Cat. Cost: None issued.
Credit Cards: None
Specialities: *Cypripedium* hybrids. Hardy orchids.
Notes: Also sells wholesale.

XIsg ISGRANNATORPS TRÄDGÅRD ⊠ €
Kristianstad, Sweden
Ⓣ 00 46 44 229595
Ⓔ krook.c4@swipnet.se
Ⓦ www.isgrannatorpstradgard.se
Contact: Mats Krook
Opening Times: By appt. only, 1st Apr-1st Nov.
Min Mail Order UK: £25.00
Min Mail Order EU: £25.00
Cat. Cost: Plant list free.
Credit Cards: None
Specialities: Ornamental grasses.

XPde PÉPINIÈRE DE L'ÎLE ⊠ €
Keranroux, 22870,
Ile de Brehat, France
Ⓣ 00 33 (0)2 96 20 03 84
Ⓜ 0686 128609
Ⓕ 00 33 (0)2 96 20 03 84
Ⓔ contact@pepiniere-brehat.com
Ⓦ www.pepiniere-brehat.com
Contact: Laurence Blasco & Charles Blasco
Opening Times: 1400-1800 spring & summer. Other times by appt. incl. Aug.
Min Mail Order UK: Nmc
Min Mail Order EU: Nmc
Cat. Cost: 4 Euros.
Credit Cards: None
Specialities: *Agapanthus* & *Echium*. Plants from South Africa.

XPep PÉPINIÈRE FILIPPI ⊠ €
RN 113, 34140 Meze, France
Ⓣ 00 33 (0)4 67 43 88 69
Ⓕ 00 33 (0)4 67 43 84 59
Ⓔ olivier.filippi@wanadoo.fr
Ⓦ www.jardin-sec.com
Contact: Olivier Filippi
Opening Times: 0900-1200 & 1330-1730 Mon-Fri, 0900-1200 Sat, Sep-Jun. Closed Sun & B/hols. 0830-1200 Mon-Sat, Jul-Aug.
Min Mail Order UK: 30 Euros
Min Mail Order EU: 30 Euros
Cat. Cost: 10 Euros or online.
Credit Cards: Visa MasterCard
Specialities: *Cistus* and botanical range of mediterranean plants. CCVS French Nat. Collections of *Cistus* & *Nerium*.
Notes: Also sells wholesale.

NURSERY INDEX BY NAME

Nurseries that are included in the *RHS Plant Finder* for the first time this year (or have been reintroduced) are marked in **bold type**. Full details of the nurseries will be found in **Nursery Details by Code** on page 796. For a key to the geographical codes, see the start of **Nurseries**.

A La Carte Daylilies	SDay
Abbey Brook Cactus Nursery	**MAbb**
Abbey Dore Court Garden	WAbb
The Abbey Nursery	CAby
Abbey Plants	CAbP
Abbotsbury Sub-Tropical Gardens	CAbb
Aberconwy Nursery	WAbe
Abriachan Nurseries	GAbr
Acorn Nursery	**MAco**
Acton Beauchamp Roses	WAct
Agar's Nursery	SAga
Agave Nursery	MAga
Agroforestry Research Trust	CAgr
Ainsworth Displays	SAin
Anita Allen	CAni
L A Allen	WAln
Allwood Bros	SAll
The Alpine and Grass Nursery	**EAlp**
Jacques Amand International	**LAma**
Amulree Exotics	EAmu
Apple Court	**SApp**
Architectural Plants	SArc
Architectural Plants (Chichester) Ltd	SAPC
Ardcarne Garden Centre	IArd
Arley Hall Nursery	MArl
Arne Herbs	CArn
Aromafolia	EAro
Ashdale Cottage Garden Plants	MACG
Ashdown Forest Garden Centre & Nursery	SAdn
Ashtons Nursery Gardens	NAsh
Ashwood Nurseries Ltd	MAsh
Asterby & Chalkcroft Nurseries	LAst
Aulden Farm	WAul
Claire Austin Hardy Plants	WCAu
David Austin Roses Ltd	MAus
Avon Bulbs	CAvo
Avondale Nursery	MAvo
Aylett Nurseries Ltd	LAyl
B & T World Seeds	XBTW
Steven Bailey Ltd	SBai
B & H M Baker	EBak
Bali-hai Mail Order Nursery	IBal
Ballyrogan Nurseries	IBlr
Banwy Valley Nursery	WBVN
The Barn Plant Centre & Gift Shop	NBPC
Barncroft Nurseries	MBar
Barnfield Pelargoniums	MBPg
Barnsdale Gardens	MBNS
Barracott Plants	CBct
Peter Beales Roses	**EBls**
Beamish Clematis Nursery	NBea
Beechcroft Nursery	LBee
Beechcroft Just Trees	NBee
Beechcroft Nurseries & Garden Centre	**MBec**
Beeches Nursery	EBee
Beetham Nurseries	NBhm
Beggar's Roost Plants	CBgR
Bell Bar Nursery	LBBr
Belmont House Nursery	CBel
M.T. Bennallack	**CBnk**
Bennett's Water Lily Farm	CBen
Bensley Nurseries	MBnl
Bide-A-Wee Cottage Gardens	NBid
The Big Grass Co.	CBig
Alison Bilverstone	**EABi**
Binny Plants	GBin
Birchwood Plants	SBch
Birkheads Secret Gardens & Nursery	NBir
Black Plants Nursery	**NBPN**
Blackmoor Nurseries	**SBmr**
Blacksmiths Cottage Nursery	EBla
Blackthorn Nursery	SBla
Bleak Hill Plants	**SBHP**
Blooming Marvellous Plants	LBMP
Bluebell Arboretum & Nursery	MBlu
Blundell's Nurseries	NBlu
Bodiam Nursery	SBod
Bodmin Plant and Herb Nursery	CBod
Bodnant Garden Nursery Ltd	**WBod**

Bodwen Nursery	CBdw
Bordervale Plants	WBor
Boundary House Farm	NBHF
Bouts Cottage Nurseries	WBou
Bowden Hostas	**CBdn**
Bowley Plants	CBow
J Bradshaw & Son	SBra
Braithwell Nurseries	NBtw
Brambly Hedge	SBrm
Bramley Lodge Garden Nursery	CBrm
Breezy Knees Nurseries	NBre
Bregover Plants	CBre
Bressingham Gardens (incorp. Van Tubergen UK)	EBrs
Bretby Nurseries	**MBre**
Brickwall Cottage Nursery	SBri
Bridge End Nurseries	GBri
Bridge Nursery	MBrN
Bridgemere Nurseries	MBri
British Iris Society	**WBIS**
Broadleas Gardens Ltd	CBrd
Brockamin Plants	WBrk
Bron Eifion Nursery	WBrE
Brooklands Plants	CBrP
Brownthwaite Hardy Plants	NBro
Buckingham Nurseries	LBuc
Buckland Plants	GBuc
Bucknell Nurseries	WBuc
Burford Garden Company	WBGC
Jenny Burgess	EBur
Burncoose Nurseries	CBcs
Burnham Nurseries	CBur
Butterworths' Organic Nursery	GBut
Cacti & Succulents	SCac
Cairnsmore Nursery	GCai
Cambridge Garden Plants	ECGP
Camellia Grove Nursery	SCam
Cants of Colchester	ECnt
Cath's Garden Plants	NCGa
Celyn Vale Eucalyptus Nurseries	WCel
Chadwell Seeds	LChw
Chapel Farm House Nursery	CCha
Sheila Chapman Clematis	ESCh
Charleshurst Farm Nursery	**SChF**
The Beth Chatto Gardens Ltd	ECha
Chennels Gate Gardens & Nursery	WChG
Cherry Tree Nursery	**CChe**
Chew Valley Trees	CCVT
Chiltern Seeds	NChl
Chipchase Castle Nursery	NChi
Choice Landscapes	ECho
Christie's Nursery	GCrs
The Chrysanthemum Society	**CNCS**
John Churcher	SChr
Churchtown Nurseries	CCtw
Cicely's Cottage Garden Plants	NCiC
Cider Apple Trees	CCAT
Clay Lane Nursery	LCla
Clonmel Garden Centre	**IClo**
Cobble Hey Gardens	NCob
James Cocker & Sons	GCoc
Coghurst Camellias	SCog
Cold Harbour Nursery	CCol
Collectors Corner Plants	MCCP
The Conifer Garden	LCon
Cool Temperate	MCoo
Cooling's Nurseries Ltd	SCoo
Ian and Deborah Coppack	MIDC
Coton Manor Garden	**MCot**
Cotswold Garden Flowers	WCot
Cottage Garden Plants and Herbs	CCge
Cottage Garden Plants	NCot
The Cottage Garden	ECot
Cottage Nurseries	ECtt
Country Lane Nurseries	WCLn
County Park Nursery	ECou
Craigieburn Garden	**GCra**
Cranesbill Nursery	WCra
Creake Plant Centre	ECre
Crin Gardens	MCri
Crocknafeola Nursery	ICro
Crocus.co.uk	**LCro**
Crofters Nurseries	SCrf
Cromar Nursery	**SCmr**
Cross Common Nursery	CCCN
Croston Cactus	NCro
Crown Nursery	ECrN
Crûg Farm Plants	WCru
Culm View Nursery	CCVN
Cwmrhaiadr Nursery	WCwm
D K Plants	MDKP
Daisy Roots	LDai
Dalesview Nursery	NDlv
D'Arcy & Everest	EDAr
Deacon's Nursery	SDea
Derek Lloyd Dean	LDea
Deelish Garden Centre	IDee
Denmans Garden, (John Brookes Ltd)	SDnm
Desert to Jungle	CDTJ
Desirable Plants	CDes
Devon Violet Nursery	CDev
Dibley's Nurseries	WDib
Dickson Nurseries Ltd	IDic
Different Plants	EDif
Samuel Dobie & Son	CDob
Docton Mill Gardens	CDMG
Don Hatch Conifers	CDHC
Dorset Blueberry Company	CDBb
Dorset Water Lilies	CDWL
Dove Cottage Nursery & Garden	NDov
Downderry Nursery	SDow
Drysdale Garden Exotics	**SDry**
Duchy of Cornwall	CDoC
Dulford Nurseries	CDul
Dunge Valley Gardens	MDun
Dyffryn Gwyddno Nursery	WDyG

Dyffryn Nurseries	WDyf
Dysons Nurseries	SDys
East Northdown Farm	SEND
Eastgrove Cottage Garden Nursery	WEas
Edrom Nurseries	GEdr
Edulis	LEdu
Eggleston Hall Gardens	NEgg
Elizabeth House Nursery	MEHN
Charles F Ellis & Son	WCFE
Ellwood Penstemons	**WEll**
Elsworth Herbs	EEls
Elworthy Cottage Plants	CElw
Endsleigh Gardens	CEnd
The English Cottage Garden Nursery	SECG
English Woodlands	**SEWo**
Entwood Farm Plants	CEnt
Equatorial Plant Co.	NEqu
Evergreen Conifer Centre	WEve
Exclusive Plants	**CExc**
The Exotic Garden Company	EExo
Fabulous Fuchsias	**WFFs**
Fairholm Plants	GFai
Famecheck Reblooming Iris	EFam
Family Trees	SFam
Farmyard Nurseries	WFar
Feebers Hardy Plants	CFee
The Fern Nursery	EFer
Fernwood Nursery	CWil
Fibrex Nurseries Ltd	WFib
Field House Nurseries	MFie
Field of Blooms	IFoB
Fir Tree Farm Nursery	CFir
Fir Trees Pelargonium Nursery	NFir
Firecrest (Trees & Shrubs Nursery)	**EMac**
Firgrove Plants	**SFgr**
Margery Fish Gardens	CFis
Ian FitzRoy Nurseryman	SIFN
Flora Exotica	EFEx
Floral Fireworks	CFFs
The Flower Bower	CFwr
Flowers of the Field	WFoF
The Fly Trap Plants	EFly
Foliage Scented & Herb Plants	LFol
Folly Gate Plants	CFol
Fordmouth Croft Ornamental Grass Nursery	**GFor**
Fox Cottage Plants	MFOX
Foxgrove Plants	LFox
Fron Goch Garden Centre	WGer
Frosch Exclusive Perennials	XFro
Fulbrooke Nursery	EFul
The Rodney Fuller Helianthemum Collection	CFul
Furze Park Nursery	**LFur**
Gandy's (Roses) Ltd	MGan
Garden Blooms	**NGBl**
Garden Cottage Nursery	GGar
The Garden Fruit Tree Company Ltd	**SGFT**
Garden House Nursery	NGdn
Garden House Enterprises	**CGHE**
Garden Plants	SGar
Gilbey's Plants	NGby
Glen Chantry	EGle
Glendoick Gardens Ltd	GGGa
Glenhirst Cactus Nursery	EGln
Glenville Nurseries	EGlv
The Gobbett Nursery	WGob
Godly's Roses	LGod
Goldbrook Plants	EGol
Golden Cottage Plants	MGol
Elisabeth Goodwin Nurseries	EGoo
Gordon's Nursery	WGor
Gortkelly Castle Nursery	IGor
Goscote Nurseries Ltd	MGos
Grafted Walnut Trees	WGWT
Graham's Hardy Plants	CGra
Grange Farm Plants	EGFP
Peter Grayson (Sweet Pea Seedsman)	MPet
Great Dixter Nurseries	SDix
The Great Western Gladiolus Nursery	CGrW
Green Garden Herbs	NGHP
Mary Green	NMyG
Greenhead Roses	GGre
C W Groves & Son Ltd	CGro
Gwynfor Growers	WGwG
Hall Farm Nursery	WHal
Halls of Heddon	NHal
Halsway Nursery	CHal
Hampshire Carnivorous Plants	SHmp
Hardy Exotics	CHEx
Hardy Orchids	SHdy
Hardy's Cottage Garden Plants	SHar
Harley Nursery	WHar
Harrells Hardy Plants	WHrl
Hart Canna	SHaC
Sue Hartfree	SHFr
Harts Green Nursery	MHar
Hartside Nursery Garden	NHar
Harveys Garden Plants	EHrv
The Hawthornes Nursery	NHaw
Hayloft Plants	WHlf
Heaselands Garden Nursery	**SHea**
The Heather Society	EHea
Henllys Lodge Plants	WHen
Henry Street Nursery	LStr
The Herb Garden	MHrb
The Herb Garden & Historical Plant Nursery	WHer
The Herb Nursery	MHer
The Herbary	CHby
Hergest Croft Gardens	WHCr
Heritage Bulbs	**IHer**
Herterton House Garden Nursery	NHer
Hewitt-Cooper Carnivorous Plants	CHew
Hidden House Bulbs	**CHHB**
Hidden Valley Gardens	CHVG

Hidden Valley Nursery	**CHid**
High Banks Nurseries	SHBN
Highdown Nursery	SHDw
Highfield Hollies	SHHo
Hill Garth Nursery	SHGN
Hill House Nursery & Gardens	CHll
Hillview Hardy Plants	WHil
The Himalayan Garden Co.	**NHim**
Holden Clough Nursery	NHol
Holly Gate Cactus Nursery	SHol
Home Farm Plants	**CHFP**
Home Plants	SHom
Homestead Plants	MHom
Honeysome Aquatic Nursery	EHon
Hoo House Nursery	WHoo
Hopleys Plants Ltd	LHop
Horn's Garden Centre	NHor
Hortus Nursery	CHrt
Hoyland Plant Centre	**NHoy**
Kevin Hughes Plants	**SKHP**
Hull Farm	EHul
Hunts Court Garden & Nursery	WHCG
Hydon Nurseries	LHyd
Hydrangea Haven	SHyH
I.M.B. Plants	**LIMB**
Iden Croft Herbs	SIde
Imberhorne Lane Nursery	**SImb**
W E Th. Ingwersen Ltd	SIng
The Iris Garden	CIri
Iris of Sissinghurst	SIri
Isgrannatorps Trädgård	**XIsg**
Ivycroft Plants	WIvy
Jackson's Nurseries	MJac
Jasmine Cottage Gardens	CJas
Paul Jasper Trees	WJas
Jekka's Herb Farm	WJek
John and Lynsey's Plants	SPin
John Ray Nursery	EJRN
Vic Johnstone and Claire Wilson	SJoh
C & K Jones	MJon
Jooles Plants	**SJoo**
Jungle Seeds and Gardens	MJnS
Kayes Garden Nursery	MKay
Keepers Nursery	SKee
Kelways Ltd	CKel
Kenwick Farmhouse Nurseries	EKen
Kenwith Nursery (Gordon Haddow)	CKen
Kevock Garden Plants & Flowers	GKev
Kiftsgate Court Gardens	WKif
Kingstone Cottage Plants	WKin
Knoll Gardens	CKno
Kobakoba	CKob
L W Plants	LLWP
Ladybird Nursery	**ILad**
Landford Trees	CLnd
Landlife Wildflowers Ltd	NLan
Landscape Plants	SLPl
Lane End Nursery	MLan
Laneside Alpines	NLAp
Langley Boxwood Nursery Ltd	SLan
Langthorns Plantery	ELan
Larch Cottage Nurseries	NLar
Larkspur Nursery	**ELar**
Laurel Farm Herbs	ELau
The Laurels Nursery	SLau
The Lavender Garden	WLav
Layham Garden Centre & Nursery	SLay
Lea Rhododendron Gardens Ltd	MLea
Leatherbritches Kitchen Garden & Nursery	**MLBr**
Leba Orchard - Green's Leaves	WLeb
Leeds Lavender	NLLv
Brian Lewington	SBLw
Lilies Water Gardens	**LLWG**
Lime Cross Nursery	SLim
Lincluden Nursery	LLin
Lingen Nursery and Garden	WLin
Lisdoonan Herbs	ILis
Little Brook Fuchsias	SLBF
Lochlands (HRB Ltd)	GLld
C S Lockyer	CLoc
Loder Plants	SLdr
Lodge Farm Herbs, Plants & Wildflowers	MLod
Lodge Lane Nursery & Gardens	MLLN
Long Acre Plants	CLAP
Long House Plants	**ELon**
Longstock Park Nursery	SLon
Longstone Hardy Plants Nursery	MLHP
Lower Severalls Nursery	CSev
Lulworth Plants	MLul
Lydford Alpine Nursery	CLyd
M & M Plants	CMMP
M G H Nurseries	IMGH
S M McArd (Seeds)	EMcA
Elizabeth MacGregor	GMac
MacGregors Plants for Shade	SMac
Macpennys Nurseries	CMac
Macplants	GMaP
Madrona Nursery	SMad
Mallet Court Nursery	CMCN
Manor Nursery	EMan
Marchants Hardy Plants	SMHy
Marcus Dancer Plants	SMDP
Lesley Marshall	EMar
Marshall's Malmaison	EMal
Marwood Hill Gardens	CMHG
The Mead Nursery	CMea
Meadow Cottage Plants	CMCo
Meadows Nursery	CMdw
Mendip Bonsai Studio	CMen
Mendle Nursery	NMen
Meon Valley Plants	SMeo
Merebrook Water Plants	WMAq
Merriments Gardens	SMrm
Merryfield Nurseries (Canterbury) Ltd	SMer
Mickfield Hostas	EMic

Mickfield Watergarden Centre Ltd	EMFW
Mill Cottage Plants	CMil
Mill Race Garden Centre	EMil
Millais Nurseries	LMil
Millrace Nursery	NMRc
Miniature Bulbs UK	**NMin**
Mires Beck Nursery	NMir
Monksilver Nursery	EMon
Moor Monkton Nurseries	NMoo
Moorland Cottage Plants	WMoo
Morehavens	LMor
Morton Hall Gardens	MMHG
Mount Pleasant Trees	WMou
Mozart House Nursery Garden	MMoz
Mucklestone Nurseries	MMuc
Ken Muir Ltd	EMui
Kathleen Muncaster Fuchsias	EKMF
Mynd Hardy Plants	WMnd
Naked Cross Nurseries	CNCN
The National Herb Centre	MNHC
Natural Selection	CNat
New Forest Palms & Exotics	SNew
Newington Nurseries	MNew
Newport Mills Nursery	CNMi
Newton Hill Alpines	NNew
Nicky's Rock Garden Nursery	CNic
Ninesprings Nursery	**SNin**
Norcroft Nurseries	NNor
Norfields	WNor
Norfolk Bamboo Company	ENBC
Norfolk Lavender	ENor
Norwell Nurseries	MNrw
Notcutts Nurseries	ENot
The Nursery Further Afield	MNFA
Oak Dene Nurseries	NOaD
Oak Tree Nursery	NOak
Old Court Nurseries	WOld
Old Fashioned Flowers	WOFF
Old Hall Plants	EOHP
The Old Mill Herbary	COld
The Old Vicarage Nursery	WOVN
The Old Walled Garden	SOWG
The Old Withy Garden Nursery	COlW
Orchard House Nursery	NOrc
Ornamental Conifers	EOrn
Ornamental Tree Nurseries	WOrn
Out of the Common Way	WOut
P & B Fuchsias	WPBF
PJ's Palms and Exotics	LPJP
P M A Plant Specialities	CPMA
P W Plants	EPla
Packhorse Farm Nursery	MPkF
Paddock Plants	**SPad**
The Palm Centre	LPal
The Palm Farm	NPal
The Palm House	CPHo
Pan-Global Plants	WPGP
Pantiles Plant & Garden Centre	LPan
Pantyfod Garden Nursery	WPtf
Parham Bungalow Plants	CPBP
Park Green Nurseries	EPGN
Parks Perennials	CPar
Passiflora (National Collection)	CPas
Chris Pattison	WPat
Paugers Plants	**EPau**
Pavilion Plants	SPav
Pembroke Farm Nursery	EPem
Penborn Goat Farm	CPbn
Peninsula Primulas	**IPen**
Penlan Perennials	WPnP
Pennard Plants	CPen
Pennycross Plants	EPyc
Penpergwm Plants	**WPen**
Penstemons by Colour	LPen
Penton Mill Rhododendrons	NPen
Peony Passions	IPPs
Pépinière de L'île	XPde
Pépinière Filippi	XPep
The Perennial Nursery	WPnn
Perennial Plants Nursery	IPPN
Perhill Nurseries	WPer
Perry's Plants	NPer
Perryhill Nurseries Ltd	SPer
Pershore College of Horticulture	WSPU
Pettet's Nursery	SPet
Phedar Nursery	MPhe
Alan Phipps Cacti	CPhi
Phoenix Perennial Plants	SPhx
The Picton Castle Trust Nursery	WPic
Pine Cottage Plants	CPne
Pine Lodge Gardens & Nursery	CPLG
Pioneer Nursery	**LPio**
The Place for Plants	EPfP
Plantbase	SPlb
Plantessential Ltd	**MPes**
Plants For All Reasons	MPRe
Plants for the Senses	CPSs
The Plantsman's Preference	EPPr
Plaxtol Nurseries	SPla
Pleasant View Nursery	CPle
Polemonium Plantery	NPol
Pollie's Perennials and Daylily Nursery	SPol
Pomeroy Plants	CPom
Poppies Nursery	**MPop**
Pops Plants	SPop
Potash Nursery	EPts
The Potted Garden Nursery	SPoG
Pottertons Nursery	EPot
The Potting Shed	IPot
Pounsley Plants	CPou
Poyntzfield Herb Nursery	GPoy
Prime Perennials	WPrP
Primrose Cottage Nursery	NPri
Properplants.com	CPrp
ProudPlants	NPro
Pukka Plants	**CPuk**

Pure Plants	SPur
Quality Daffodils	CQua
Quaymount Nursery	**EQua**
Quercus Garden Plants	GQue
Quinish Garden Nursery	GQui
Rails End Nursery	WRai
Rainbow Plants	NRnb
Rapkyns Nursery	SRkn
Rarer Plants	NRar
Rasell's Nurseries	**ERas**
Raven Valley Plant Nursery	LRav
Ravensthorpe Nursery	MRav
Reads Nursery	ERea
Really Wild Flowers	CRea
The Really Wild Nursery	CRWN
Rearsby Roses	MRea
Red House Farm	WRHF
G Reuthe Ltd	SReu
Rezare Nurseries	CRez
Rhodes & Rockliffe	ERhR
Ribblesdale Nurseries	NRib
Rickard's Hardy Ferns Ltd	**WRic**
Ringhaddy Daffodils	IRhd
River Garden Nurseries	SRiv
Riverside Fuchsias	**SRiF**
Colin Roberts	SCnR
Roberts Nurseries	CRob
A J Robinson	MAJR
W Robinson & Sons Ltd	NRob
The Rodings Plantery	ERod
The Romantic Garden	ERom
Rose Cottage Plants	**ERCP**
Roseholme Nursery	ERos
Roseland House Nursery	CRHN
Rosemary's Farmhouse Nursery	WRos
Rosewood Daylilies	SRos
Rosie's Garden Plants	SRGP
Rotherview Nursery	SRot
Roualeyn Nurseries	WRou
Rougham Hall Nurseries	ERou
Rumsey Gardens	SRms
Ryal Nursery	NRya
S & S Perennials	MSSP
St Bridget Nurseries Ltd	CSBt
Saith Ffynnon Farm	WSFF
Salley Gardens	MSal
Sampford Shrubs	CSam
Robin Savill Clematis Specialist	ERob
Scawsby Hall Nurseries	NScw
Scented Roses	NSRo
Scott's Wildflowers	NSco
Seaforde Gardens	ISea
Seagate Irises	ESgI
Seale Nurseries	SSea
Seaside Nursery	ISsi
Second Nature Plant Nursery	**CSNP**
Seeds by Size	LSee
Select Seeds	SSss

The Selsley Herb Nursery	WSel
Sherston Parva Nursery	CSPN
Sherwood Cottage	CSdC
Shipton Bulbs	WShi
Shirley's Plants	NShi
Showglads	MSGs
Shropshire Sarracenias	WSSs
Shrubland Park Nurseries	EShb
Simpson's Seeds Ltd	CSim
Sino-Himalayan Plant Association	LSiH
Skipness Plants	GSki
Slack Top Nurseries	NSla
Slipps Garden Centre	CSli
Smart Plants	MTPN
Snape Cottage	CSna
South West Carnivorous Plants	CSWC
Southease Plants	SSth
Southon Plants	LSou
Southview Nurseries	SSvw
Special Plants	CSpe
Spinners Garden	SSpi
Spinneywell Nursery	**WSpi**
Spring Reach Nursery	LSRN
Springfield Nurseries	NSfd
Springwood Nursery	**SSwd**
Springwood Pleiones	NSpr
Starborough Nursery	SSta
Steventon Road Nurseries	MSte
Stillingfleet Lodge Nurseries	NSti
Stone House Cottage Nurseries	WSHC
Stone Lane Gardens	CSto
Stuckey's Alpines	CStu
Style Roses	ESty
Brian & Pearl Sulman	ESul
Summerdale Garden Nursery	**NSum**
Sunnybank Vine Nursery	WSuV
Sunnyside Plants	**CSsd**
Sussex Topiary	STop
Suttons Seeds	CSut
Swallows Nursery	MSwo
Table Bay View Nursery	XBlo
Tan-y-Llyn Nurseries	WTan
Tavistock Herb Nursery	NTHB
Telling and Coates	WTel
Terra Nova Plants	ITer
Terrace Gardener	**STrG**
Test Valley Nursery	STes
Thorncroft Clematis Nursery	ETho
Thornhayes Nursery	CTho
A & A Thorp	MTho
Thuya Alpine Nursery	WThu
Tile Barn Nursery	STil
Timpany Nurseries & Gardens	ITim
Tinpenny Plants	WTin
Tir Mab Cynan Nursery	WTMC
Tissington Nursery	MTis
Todd's Botanics	**ETod**
Toobees Exotics	LToo

SPECIALIST NURSERIES

Nurseries have classified themselves under the following headings where they *exclusively* or *predominantly* supply this range of plants. Plant groups are set out in alphabetical order. Refer to **Nursery Details by Code** on page 796 for details of the nurseries whose codes are listed under the plant group which interests you. See page 793 for a fuller explanation.

ACID LOVING PLANTS

CBcs, CBig, CCha, CDBb, CMen, CWCL, CWri, EHea, EPot, GCrs, GGGa, GLld, IMGH, IPen, LHyd, LMil, MBar, MCri, MGos, MLea, MMuc, NDlv, NHar, NHim, NLAp, NPen, SBmr, SBrw, SCam, SCog, SHea, SImb, SLdr, SOWG, SReu, SRot, SSta, WAbe, WBod, WCru, WThu.

ALPINE/ROCK PLANTS

CBrm, CCha, CFul, CGra, CHHB, CLyd, CMMP, CNic, CPBP, CPMA, CStu, CWat, CWil, CWon, EAlp, EBur, ECho, ECot, EDAr, EEls, EPot, ETow, GCrs, GEdr, GFle, IBal, IHer, IPen, LIMB, MACG, MCri, NBro, NDlv, NHar, NJOw, NLAp, NMin, NNew, NPol, NRya, NSla, NWCA, SAll, SCog, SHdy, SIng, SKHP, SPop, SRot, WAbe, WGor, WHoo, WLin, WThu, WWst, XFro.

AQUATIC PLANTS

CBen, CWat, EMFW, LLWG, LNCo, NMRc, NSco, SLon, SNin, SWat, WMAq, WPnP, WRic.

BAMBOOS

CDTJ, EAmu, EExo, EFul, ENBC, EPla, ETod, GBin, LEdu, MBrN, MJnS, MMoz, MMuc, MWht, NGdn, NMoo, NPal, SAPC, SArc, SDry, SImb, SNew, WDyG, WPGP.

BRITISH WILD FLOWERS

CArn, CDev, CNic, COld, CRea, CTuc, GPoy, GWCH, MHer, MLod, MYeo, NLan, NMir, NSco, NTHB, SECG, SHdy, SIde, SWat, WHer, WLav, WSFF, WShi.

BULBOUS PLANTS

CAvo, CFFs, CGrW, CHHB, CPne, CQua, CStu, CTca, ECho, EFam, EMui, EPot, ERCP, ERos, GCrs, GEdr, IHer, MCri, MSSP, NFir, NMin, NOaD, WHil, WPrP, WShi, WWst, XBlo.

CACTI & SUCCULENTS

CDTJ, CPhi, CWil, EGln, EShb, LSou, LToo, MAbb, MAga, NCro, NOaD, SChr, SHol.

CARNIVOROUS PLANTS

CHew, CSWC, EFly, MYeo, SHmp, WSSs.

CHALK-LOVING PLANTS

CRea, CSev, CSpe, EFam, EGoo, LSRN, NLan, SAll, SEND, SJoh, SPhx, SSvw.

CLIMBERS

CRHN, CSPN, CTri, CWGN, ELan, ERob, ESCh, ETho, LFol, LSRN, MBlu, MGos, NBea, NSti, SBra, SDea, SImb, SLau, SLim, SMDP, WBGC, WCru, WFib, WSHC, WSpi.

COASTAL PLANTS

CBig, CBod, CCCN, CMHG, CTrC, GGar, IBal, ISsi, SAPC, SChr, SDea, SDry, SEND, WBod, WPnn.

CONIFERS

CDHC, CKen, CLnd, CMen, CRob, CTho, ECho, EHul, EOrn, LCon, LLin, MACG, MBar, MPkF, NHim, SCrf, SLim, WDyf, WEve, WGor, WMou, WThu.

CONSERVATORY PLANTS

CBcs, CBrP, CCCN, CHHB, CKob, CPne, CRHN, CSpe, EABi, EBak, EBls, EEls, EOHP, ERea, EShb, ESul, GFai, LExo, LHyd, MAbb, MAga, MNew, NFir, NMin, SDnm, SHaC, SOWG, WDib, WRic, XBlo.

DROUGHT TOLERANT

CKno, EAlp, ECha, EFam, EGln, EGoo, ETod, LIMB, LLWP, MAbb, MAga, MHrb, NMRc, SEND, SJoh, SKHP, SNew, SPhx, SSss, SSvw, WHil, XPep.

FERNS

CFwr, CLAP, CRWN, CTrC, ECha, EExo, EFer, EMon, GBin, IBal, MMoz, MPes, NHar, NMoo, NMyG, SApp, SArc, SHmp, WAbe, WFib, WMoo, WPnP, WRic.

FRUIT

CAgr, CCAT, CCVT, CDBb, CTho, CTri, ECrN, EMui, ERea, EUnu, GBut, GTwe, LBuc, LEdu, MCoo, MLod, SBmr, SCrf, SDea, SFam, SGFT, SKee, WBuc, WHar, WJas, WSuV, XBlo.

GRASSES

CBig, CBod, CBrm, CFwr, CKno, CMMP, CPuk, EAlp,

ECha, EFul, EGle, EHul, ELan, EMon, EPla, EPPr, EPyc, EWsh, GBin, GFor, IFoB, LEdu, LFox, LLWG, LLWP, LSRN, MBar, MBrN, MMoz, MNrw, NBea, NBro, NGdn, NOak, NSti, SApp, SDnm, SHDw, SMHy, SPhx, SSss, SWal, WHal, WLeb, WMoo, WPGP, WPrP, XIsg.

HEDGING

CCVT, CLnd, CTrG, CTri, ECrN, EMac, ERom, IClo, IMGH, ISsi, LBuc, LCon, MCoo, MHrb, NBee, SBLw, SHHo, SLan, SRiv, STop, WAct, WBuc, WEve, WHar, WLav, WMou, WOrn, WSpi, WWeb, WWHy.

HERBS

CArn, CBod, CCha, CHby, COld, CPbn, CSev, CWan, ECot, ELau, ENor, EOHP, EUnu, GPoy, GWCH, ILis, LFol, LLWP, LMor, MHer, MHrb, MLod, NGHP, NLLv, NTHB, SECG, SHDw, SIde, SWat, WJek, WLav, WSel.

MARGINAL/BOG PLANTS

CBen, CDWL, CLAP, CMHG, COld, CWat, CWon, EFly, EHon, EMFW, GGar, IPen, LLWG, MMuc, MYeo, NCot, NMRc, SHaC, WHal, WMoo, WPnP, WShi.

ORCHIDS

CBur, EFEx, GEdr, GUzu, LBut, MNew, NEqu, NLAp, NSla, NSpr, SHdy, WHer, WWst, XFro.

ORGANIC

CBdw, CBgR, CHby, CTca, CTuc, EFer, EPla, GBut, GPoy, ILis, LEdu, LLWP, MLod, MYeo, NPol, NSRo, NTHB, SECG, SNin, SOWG, SPol, WGwG, WGWT, WJek, WPnP, WSFF, WShi.

ORNAMENTAL TREES

CBcs, CBdw, CCAT, CCVT, CDul, CEnd, CLnd, CMen, CMMP, CPMA, CSto, CTho, CTri, CWon, ECot, ECrN, EGFP, ELan, EMac, EMui, ERom, IMGH, LBuc, LHyd, LPan, MBlu, MGos, MPkF, NBea, NBee, NHim, NPal, SBLw, SBmr, SCrf, SGFT, SHBN, SHHo, SLan, SLau, SLim, SLon, SSta, WBod, WBuc, WDyf, WEve, WHar, WHCr, WJas, WMou, WNor, WOrn, WPGP, WWHy.

PALMS

CKob, CPHo, CTrC, EAmu, EExo, EGln, ETod, NMoo, NPal, SAin, SAPC, SArc, SChr, SDry, SNew.

PEAT FREE

CAgr, CBgR, CCVN, CElw, CHby, CKob, CLAP, CMdw, CMea, CNic, CPen, CPom, CRHN, CRWN, CSam, CSNP, CSsd, CTca, CTho, CWan, CWon, EAro, EBla, ECrN, EDsa, EGoo, ELau, EMal, EPts, ERea, GPoy, ILis, LEdu, LLWP, MBNS, MCri, MEHN, MLHP, MLod, MMoz, MPhe, MWgw, NBid, NGby, NLan, NPol, NSco, NSRo, SBch, SECG, SMDP, SNin, SRiF, STes, WDyG, WGWT, WHoo, WJek, WPic, WPnP, WPrP, WSFF, WShi, WSpi.

PERIOD PLANTS

CArn, CKel, CSev, CSna, CTca, CWGr, EBls, EKMF, EMFP, ERob, GBut, IHer, ILis, IPPs, LMil, SAll, SPop, SSvw, WAct, WHer, WJas, WOFF, WSpi.

PROPAGATE TO ORDER

CArn, CBig, CBnk, CCAT, CDTJ, CElw, CKel, CKob, CMen, CPne, CTrC, CWan, CWCL, CWGr, CWon, CWVF, EAlp, EBla, EBls, ECho, ECrN, ECtt, EEls, EFer, EGFP, EOHP, EPla, EPyc, EQua, ERea, ERhR, EShb, GBut, GFai, GQue, GWWP, ILis, IPPN, LHyd, LLWP, LMil, MBNS, MLHP, MLod, MMoz, MYeo, NBPN, NChi, NCot, NCro, NLLv, NPol, NRya, NShi, NTHB, SAga, SBch, SCam, SDea, SECG, SGFT, SHDw, SHea, SHyH, SKee, SLau, SLdr, SLon, SMDP, SPol, SPop, SRiF, SRiv, SSea, SWat, WEll, WFFs, WHer, WHil, WJek, WLav, WOFF, WOrn, WPBF, WPic, WPrP, WSFF, WSSs, WTin, WVaB, WWHy, WWpP, XBlo.

ROSES

CPou, EBls, ECnt, ESty, GCoc, IDic, LFol, LGod, LWoR, MAus, MGan, MMat, MRea, NSRo, SDnm, SLay, SLon, SSea, SWCr, WAct, WHCG.

SEED

CDob, CHby, CKno, CRea, CSpe, CSut, CTuc, EABi, EMcA, GPoy, LExo, LSee, MJnS, MPet, NChl, NGHP, NLan, NPol, NRob, SECG, SIde, SSss, WHen, WJek, WNor

SPECIMEN SIZED PLANTS

CBdn, CDBb, CDTJ, CKel, CPMA, CPne, CSto, CTho, CTrC, CTrG, CWon, EAmu, EBla, ECho, ECot, ECrN, EExo, EFer, EKMF, ELau, ENBC, EPla, EQua, ERea, EShb, ETod, GLld, IMGH, IPPs, LBuc, LHyd, LMil, LPan, LSRN, MAbb, MAga, MBar, MBrN, MGos, MLea, MMoz, MMuc, MNew, MPhe, MYeo, NCro, NHim, NMin, NPol, NRob, SAPC, SBLw, SBrw, SCam, SDry, SEND, SFam, SGFT, SHdy, SHea, SHHo, SHmp, SHyH, SImb, SLan, SLdr, SLon, SNew, SNin, SReu, SRiF, SSta, STop, SWat, WBuc, WDyf, WEve, WHer, WJek, WOrn, WPat, WRic, WSpi, WWeb.

TOPIARY

ERom, LPan, SHHo, SLan, SRiv, STop, WDyf, WWeb.

TROPICAL PLANTS

CCCN, CDTJ, CKob, CPuk, EAmu, ERea, EUnu, ISsi, LExo, MJnS, MNew, MPes, SHaC, SKHP, SOWG, WCru, WDib, WHil, XBlo.

INDEX MAP

The maps on the following pages show the approximate location of the nurseries whose details are listed in this directory.

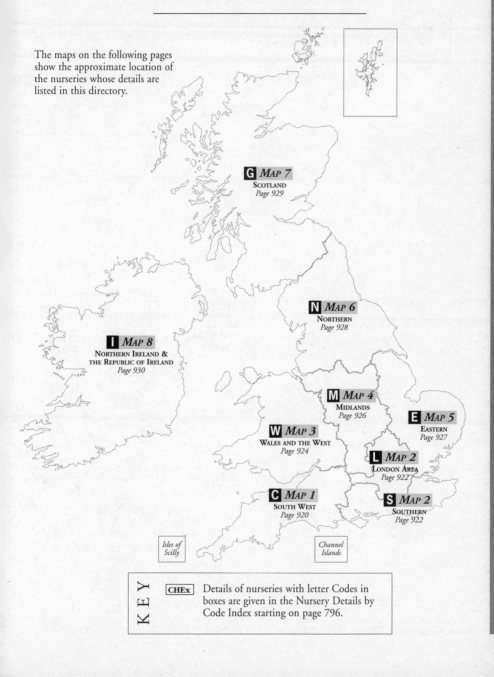

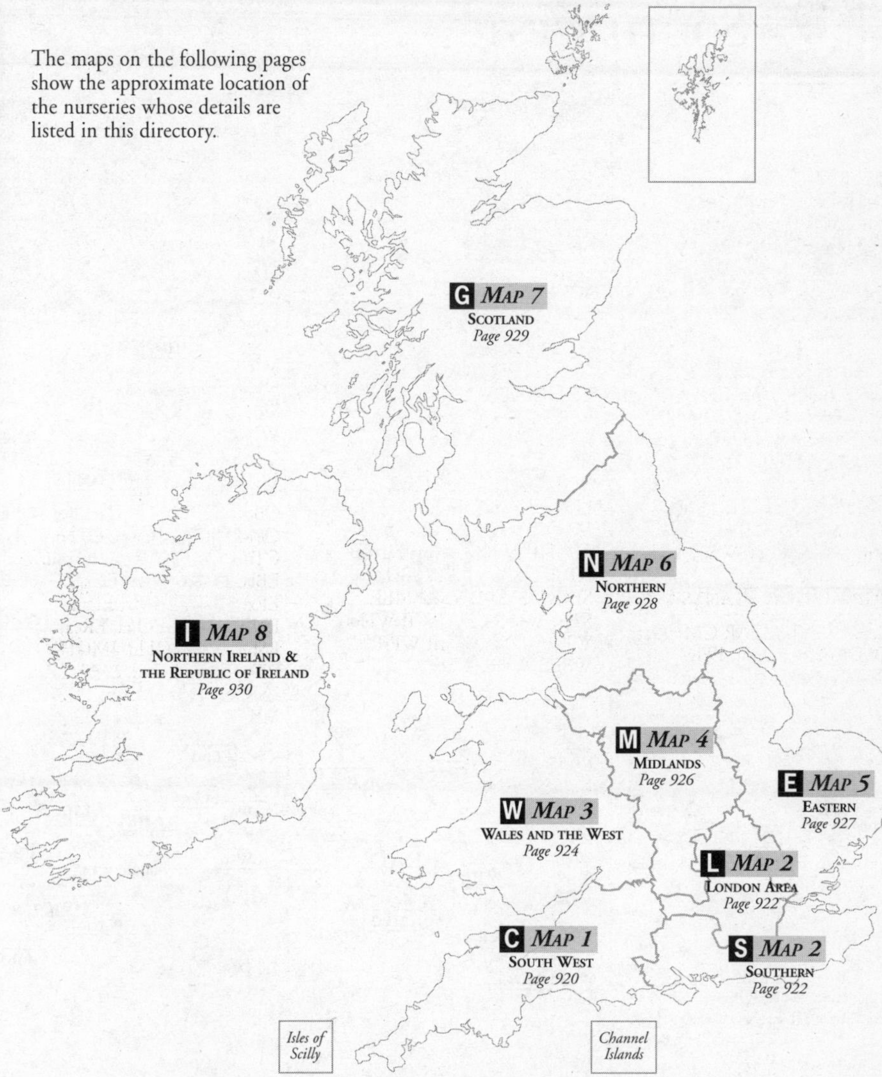

KEY

CHEx Details of nurseries with letter Codes in boxes are given in the Nursery Details by Code Index starting on page 796.

1
2
3
A
B
C
D
C
MAP ONE
SOUTH WEST
Llanelli
M4
Neath
Swansea
Port Talb
Bridge
Ilfracombe
Combe Martin
CMHG
Barnstaple
CAni
Bideford
CHid
CMMP
CDMG
CWCL
CPne
CBig
CKen
CWri
A39
A377
CHFP
Bude
CWil
CPbn
CCha
CFol
CSdC
CSto
Okehampton
CLyd
CBdn
Launceston
CBre
CEnd
CPle
COld
CRez
Tavistock
Newton Abbot
Wadebridge
CBct
CTca
CGHE
CHll
CBod
Bodmin
Liskeard
CDoC
CWsd
CBrm
Newquay
CPrp
Plymouth
A38
A30
CMCo
CHVG
St Austell
CPou
CRHN
CPLG
CRob
Truro
CBdw
St Ives
CPuk
Redruth
CHEx
Camborne
CBcS
CTrC
CCtw
Helston
Falmouth
Penzance
CWGr
CFir
COIW
CCCN
1
2
3

4
5
6
A
B
C
D
Stroud
Cirencester
M5
CSPN
CBow
CWGN
Swindon
CWat
CLoc
M4
Newport
CARDIFF
Pontypool
Cwmbran
Bristol
CPhi
CSpe
CNat
CWan
CJas
Clevedon
Chippenham
Marlborough
CSWP
Newbury
CSsd
Calne
CWdb
CPas
Weston
Super
Mare
CArn
CCVT
Bath
Trowbridge
Melksham
Devizes
CBrd
CHar
CPom
CPBP
Burnham on Sea
CMdw
CWSG
CFwr
CMil
CMen
Frome
Minehead
CWib
Wells
CSli
CMea
Warminster
Andover
CHew
CSim
Williton
CBgR
CKob
CHby
A36
CHal
CTri
Bridgwater
Glastonbury
CSna
CElw
CSNP
CPen
CAbP
Salisbury
Wincanton
CKel
CLAP
Taunton
CMCN
A303
CDJT
CFis
CCAT
Shaftesbury
M3
CSam
CAvo
CLnd
Wellington
CSWC
CPMA
Yeovil
Southampton
CWoo
A354
Tiverton
Chard
CSev
Ringwood
Blandford Forum
CTho
CNic
CDBb
CWVF
CDul
CDWL
CKno
CTrh
Lymington
Honiton
CAby
CFee
CIri
Winborne Minster
CChe
CMac
Exeter
CEnt
Bridport
Bournemouth
CDev
Lyme Regis
A35
Dorchester
CNCN
CSBt
CPHo
CBrP
CCol
Poole
CPar
CHrt
CGro
CStu
CBen
Exmouth
Weymouth
Dawlish
CBur
Teignmouth
Torquay
Paignton
Brixham

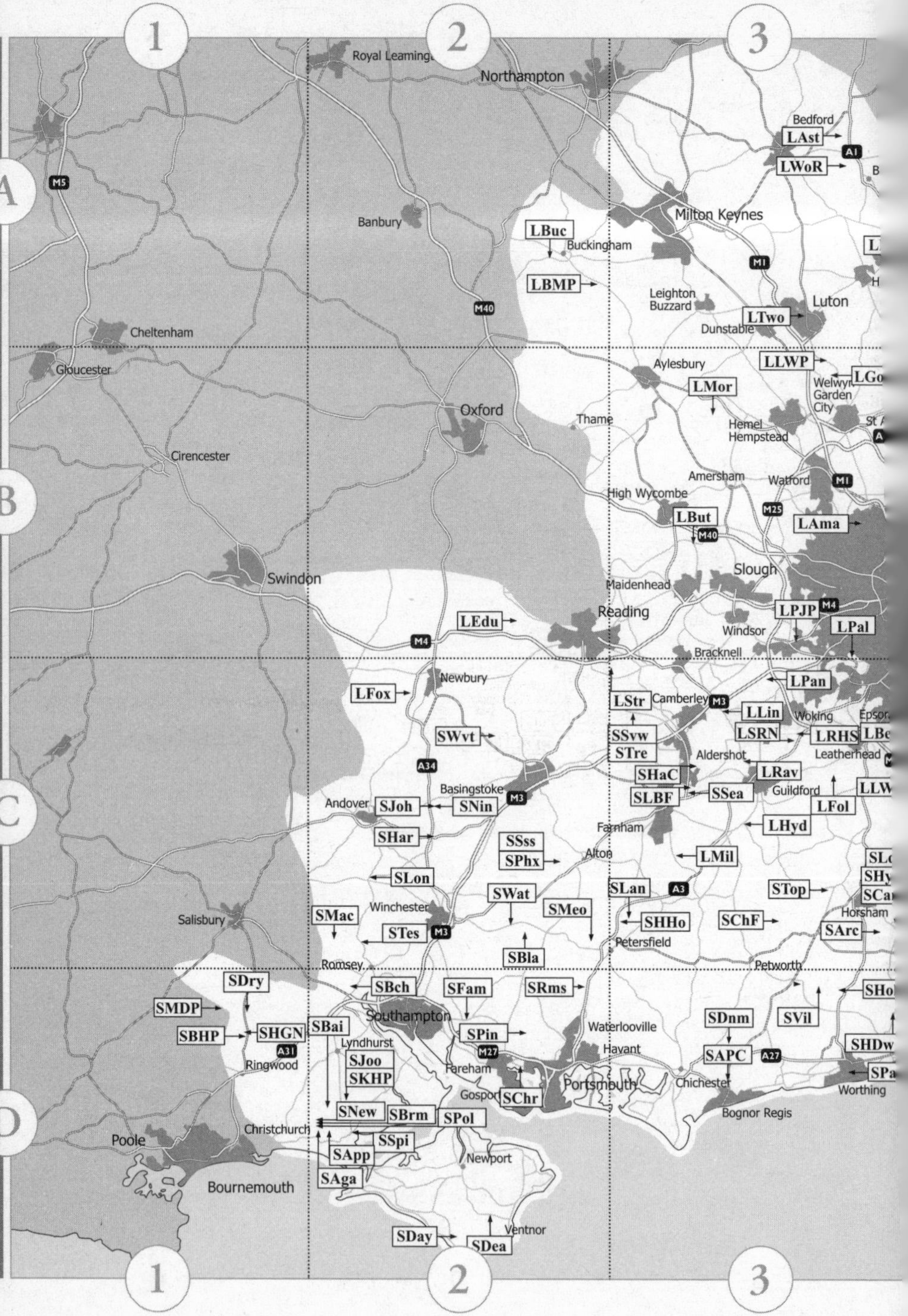
1
2
3
A
B
C
D
Royal Leaming
Northampton
Bedford
LAst
A1
LWoR
M5
Banbury
Milton Keynes
LBuc
Buckingham
M1
LBMP
Leighton Buzzard
Luton
M40
LTwo
Dunstable
Cheltenham
Gloucester
Aylesbury
LLWP
LMor
Welwyn Garden City
Oxford
Thame
Hemel Hempstead
Cirencester
Amersham
Watford
M1
High Wycombe
M25
LBut
M40
LAma
Swindon
Slough
Maidenhead
Reading
LPJP
M4
LEdu
LPal
Windsor
M4
Bracknell
Newbury
LPan
LFox
LStr
Camberley
M3
LLin
Woking
SSvw
STre
LSRN
LRHS
SWvt
Aldershot
Leatherhead
A34
SHaC
LRav
Basingstoke
SLBF
SSea
Guildford
Andover
SJoh
SNin
M3
LFol
Farnham
LHyd
SHar
SSss
SPhx
Alton
LMil
SLon
SLan
A3
STop
SWat
Winchester
SMeo
SMac
SHHo
SChF
Horsham
Salisbury
STes
M3
SArc
SBla
Petersfield
Romsey
Petworth
SDry
SBch
SFam
SRms
SMDP
Southampton
SVil
SDnm
SBHP
SHGN
SBai
SPin
Waterlooville
A31
Lyndhurst
M27
Havant
SAPC
A27
SHDw
Ringwood
SJoo
SKHP
Fareham
Portsmouth
Chichester
Worthing
Gosport
SChr
SNew
SBrm
SPol
Bognor Regis
Christchurch
SSpi
Poole
SApp
Newport
SAga
Bournemouth
SDay
Ventnor
SDea
1
2
3

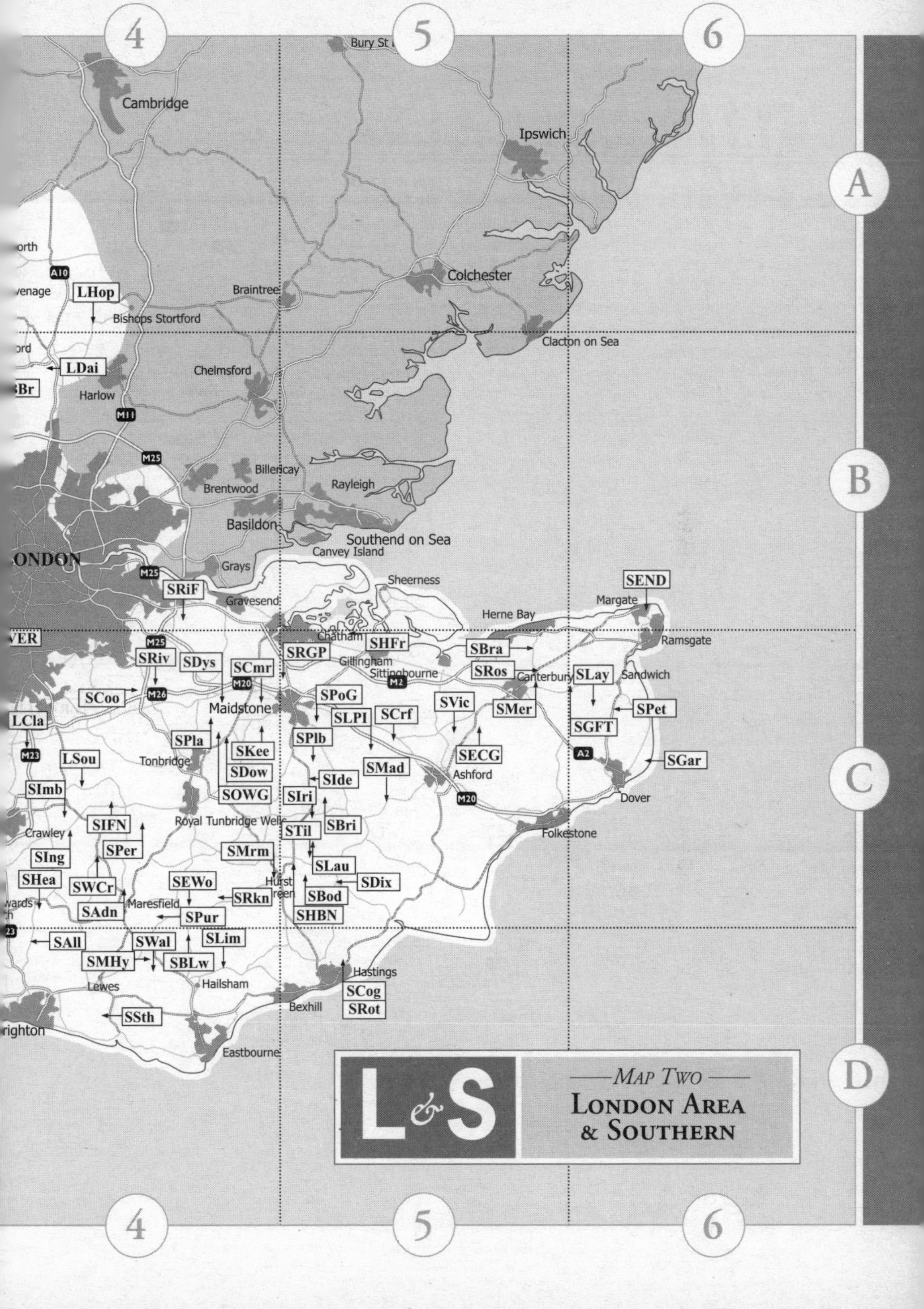
4
5
6
A
B
C
D
Cambridge
Ipswich
Colchester
Braintree
Bishops Stortford
Clacton on Sea
Chelmsford
Harlow
Billericay
Brentwood
Rayleigh
Basildon
Southend on Sea
Canvey Island
Grays
Gravesend
Sheerness
Herne Bay
Margate
Ramsgate
Chatham
Gillingham
Sittingbourne
Canterbury
Sandwich
Maidstone
Tonbridge
Ashford
Dover
Folkestone
Royal Tunbridge Wells
Crawley
Maresfield
Hailsham
Lewes
Hastings
Bexhill
Eastbourne
A10
M11
M25
M20
M26
M2
M23
A2
LHop
LDai
SRiF
SEND
SRiv
SDys
SCmr
SRGP
SHFr
SBra
SRos
SLay
SCoo
SPoG
SLPI
SCrf
SVic
SMer
SPet
SGFT
LCla
SPla
SKee
SPlb
SMad
SECG
SGar
LSou
SDow
SIde
SImb
SOWG
SIri
SIFN
SBri
STil
SPer
SMrm
SIng
SLau
SHea
SWCr
SEWo
SDix
SRkn
SBod
SAdn
SPur
SHBN
SAll
SWal
SLim
SMHy
SBLw
SCog
SRot
SSth
L&S
MAP TWO
LONDON AREA & SOUTHERN

1
2
3
A
B
C
D
W
MAP THREE
WALES & THE WEST
WOut
WHen
Llandudno
WSFF
A55
WAbe
WBod
WHer
Bangor
WRic
WRou
WCru
A470
WGer
Caernarvon
A5
Betws-y-coed
WDib
A5
WCel
WBrE
Porthmadog
A470
A494
Dolgellau
WRos
WTan
WTMC
WBVN
A470
A458
Machynlleth
WCwm
Aberystwyth
A44
Llangurig
A483
WPrP
A487
A470
WPtf
Builth Wells
A470
WGwG
WCLn
Cardigan
WPnP
WMoo
WFar
A483
Llandovery
Fishguard
WGWT
WPnn
St David's
Llandeilo
WPic
WShi
Carmarthen
Haverfordwest
A40
St Clears
WDyG
A48
Merthyr Tydfil
Milford Haven
Pembroke Dock
Tenby
WGor
Llanelli
Neath
WPBF
Swansea
Port Talbot
WBor
Bridgend
WDyf
Barry
1
2
3

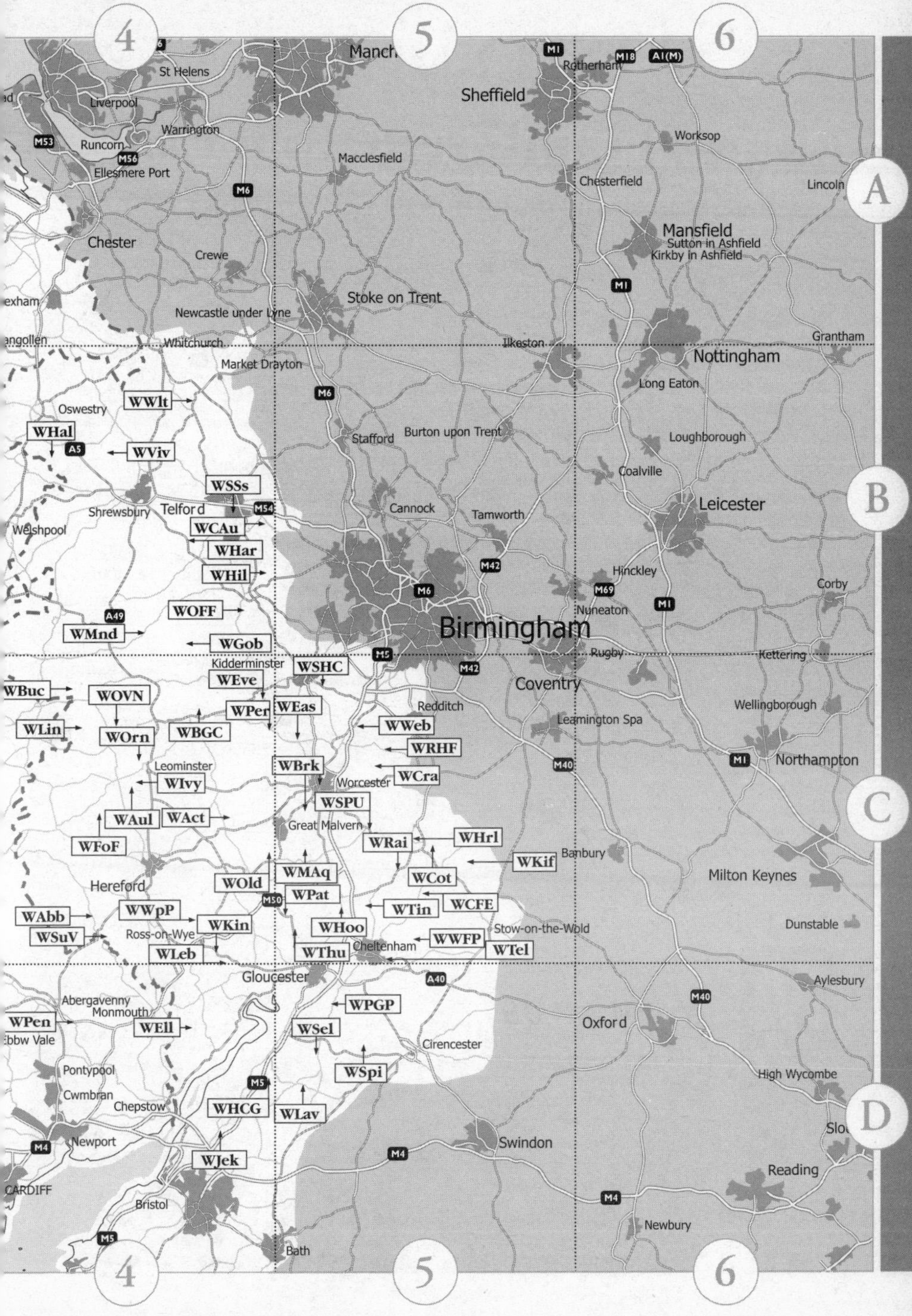
4
5
6
A
B
C
D
Manch
St Helens
Liverpool
Warrington
Runcorn
M53
M56
Ellesmere Port
M6
Chester
Crewe
exham
Newcastle under Lyne
angollen
Whitchurch
Macclesfield
Stoke on Trent
M1
Rotherham
M18
A1(M)
Sheffield
Worksop
Chesterfield
Lincoln
Mansfield
Sutton in Ashfield
Kirkby in Ashfield
Ilkeston
Grantham
Nottingham
Long Eaton
Loughborough
Coalville
Leicester
Hinckley
M69
Nuneaton
Corby
Birmingham
Rugby
Kettering
Coventry
Wellingborough
Leamington Spa
M40
Northampton
Banbury
Milton Keynes
Dunstable
Stow-on-the-Wold
Aylesbury
Oxford
High Wycombe
Slo
Swindon
M4
Reading
Newbury
Market Drayton
Oswestry
WWlt
WHal
A5
WViv
Stafford
Burton upon Trent
WSSs
Shrewsbury
Telford
M54
Welshpool
WCAu
WHar
Cannock
Tamworth
M42
WHil
M6
WOFF
A49
WMnd
WGob
Kidderminster
WSHC
M5
WEve
WBuc
WOVN
WPer
WEas
Redditch
WLin
WOrn
WBGC
WWeb
WRHF
Leominster
WIvy
WBrk
Worcester
WCra
WSPU
WAul
WAct
Great Malvern
WHrl
WFoF
WRai
WKif
WMAq
WOld
WCot
Hereford
M50
WPat
WCFE
WTin
WAbb
WWpP
WKin
WHoo
WSuV
Ross-on-Wye
WWFP
WTel
WLeb
WThu
Cheltenham
Gloucester
A40
Abergavenny
Monmouth
WPGP
WPen
WEll
Ebbw Vale
WSel
Cirencester
Pontypool
WSpi
M5
Cwmbran
Chepstow
WHCG
WLav
M4
Newport
WJek
CARDIFF
Bristol
M5
Bath

MAP FOUR
MIDLANDS
M
1
2
3
A
B
C
D
Blackpool
Preston
Lytham St. Anne's
Keighley
Nelson
Burnley
Accrington
Blackburn
Darwen
Bradford
Halifax
Brighouse
Leeds
Pudsey
Batley
Wakefield
Castleford
Kingston upon Hull
Southport
Dewsbury
Huddersfield
Scunthorpe
Wigan
Skelmersdale
Leigh
MANCHESTER
Barnsley
Doncaster
Crosby
Litherland
Bootle
Liverpool
St. Helens
Wallasey
Birkenhead
Bebington
Warrington
Widnes
Runcorn
Rotherham
SHEFFIELD
Worksop
Knutsford
Buxton
Chesterfield
Lincoln
Macclesfield
Chester
Crewe
Mansfield
Sutton in Ashfield
Kirkby in Ashfield
Newark-on-Trent
Wrexham
Nantwich
Newcastle under Lyne
Ashbourne
Nottingham
Stoke on Trent
Ilkeston
Grantham
Derby
Long Eaton
Burton upon Trent
Stafford
Loughborough
Melton Mowbray
Shrewsbury
Coalville
Telford
Cannock
Tamworth
Leicester
Uppingham
Peterborough
Hinckley
Birmingham
Nuneaton
Corby
Coventry
Kidderminster
Rugby
Kettering
Leamington Spa
Wellingborough
Redditch
Warwick
Worcester
Northampton
Great Malvern
Bedford
Banbury
Hereford
Milton Keynes
Letchworth
Chipping Norton
Leighton Buzzard
Woodstock
Dunstable
Aylesbury
Burford
Oxford
Hemel Hempstead
St. Albans
Pontypool
Cwmbran
Faringdon
Watford
High Wycombe
Newport
Wallingford
Swindon
Maidenhead
Slough
CARDIFF
Bristol
Reading
Windsor
Bath
Newbury
Bracknell
Staines
Leatherhead
Trowbridge
Woking
Epsom
M6
M66
M62
M18
M1
A1(M)
M56
M53
A6
M6
A1
A50
M54
A5
M42
M69
M40
M5
M4
M25
A40
A34
MWar
MLan
MPhe
MMHG
MIDC
MDun
MLLN
MArl
MLHP
MJon
MAbb
MFOX
MNrw
MBar
MLea
MPkF
MLBr
MWht
MDKP
MAga
MTis
MBri
MCoo
MHom
MMuc
MAJR
MBnl
MSal
MBlu
MFie
MBre
MRea
MHer
MPRe
MKay
MBNS
MJac
MGos
MSSP
MLul
MAus
MWgw
MWrn
MAsh
MMoz
MTho
MHar
MRav
MCot
MBec
MAvo
MTPN
MLod
MCCP
MBrN
MWhe
MNHC
MEHN
MSwo
MWya
MNFA
MWat
MAco
MHrb
MWea
MNew

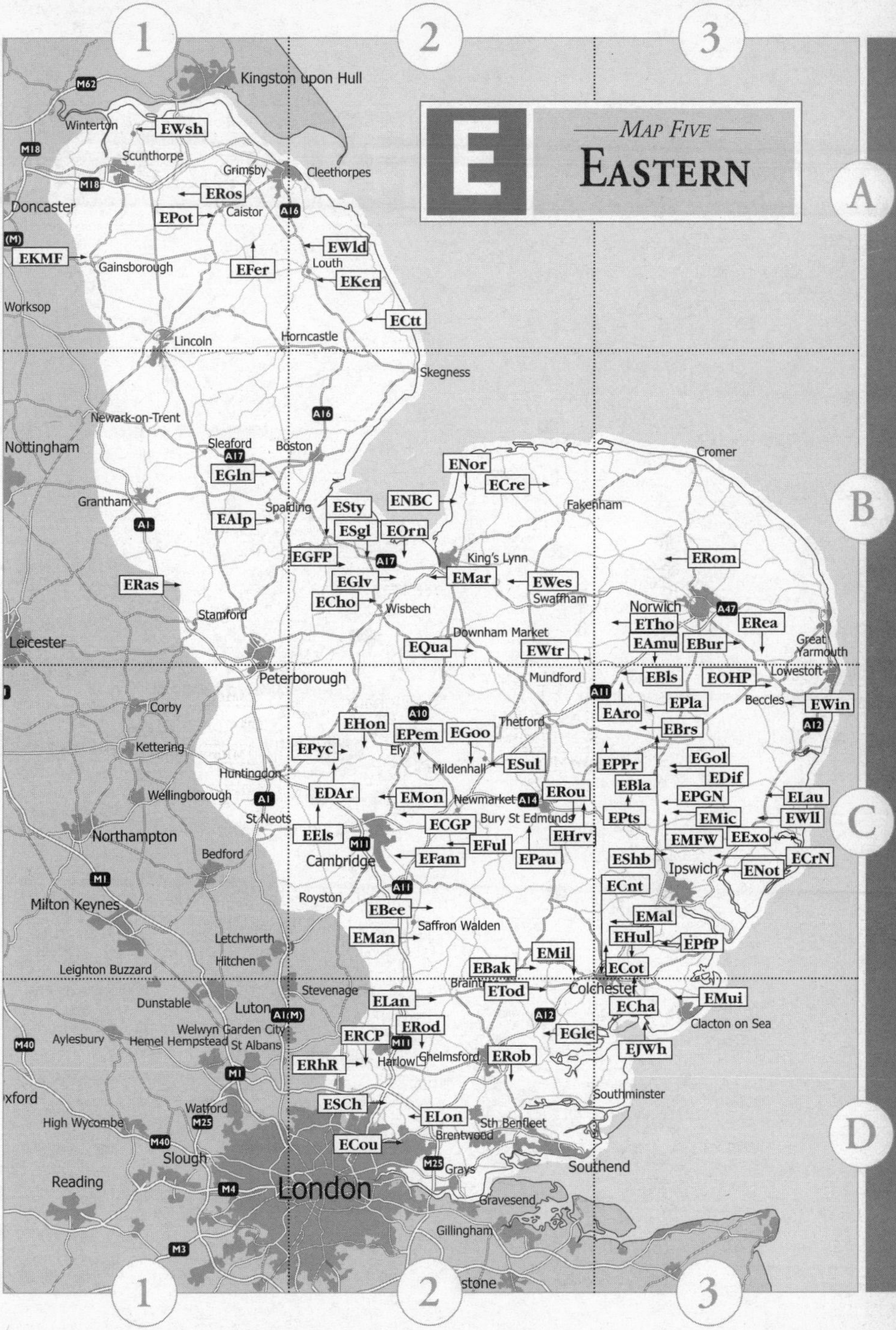

E
MAP FIVE
EASTERN
1
2
3
A
B
C
D
Kingston upon Hull
Winterton
EWsh
Scunthorpe
Grimsby
Cleethorpes
Doncaster
ERos
EPot
Caistor
EWld
EKMF
Gainsborough
EFer
Louth
EKen
Worksop
ECtt
Lincoln
Horncastle
Skegness
Newark-on-Trent
Nottingham
Sleaford
Boston
Cromer
ENor
EGln
ECre
Grantham
ENBC
Spalding
ESty
Fakenham
EAlp
ESgl
EOrn
EGFP
King's Lynn
ERom
EGlv
EMar
EWes
ERas
Swaffham
ECho
Wisbech
Norwich
Stamford
ETho
ERea
Downham Market
EAmu
EBur
Leicester
EQua
EWtr
Great Yarmouth
Peterborough
Mundford
EBls
EOHP
Lowestoft
Corby
EPla
Beccles
EWin
EAro
EHon
EPem
EGoo
Thetford
EBrs
Kettering
EPyc
Ely
EGol
Mildenhall
ESul
EPPr
EDif
Huntingdon
EBla
EDAr
EMon
Newmarket
ERou
EPGN
ELau
Wellingborough
St Neots
ECGP
Bury St Edmunds
EPts
EMic
EWll
Northampton
EEls
EHrv
EMFW
EExo
Bedford
EFul
EShb
ECrN
Cambridge
EFam
EPau
Ipswich
ENot
Milton Keynes
ECnt
Royston
EBee
Saffron Walden
EMal
Letchworth
EMan
EHul
EPfP
Hitchen
EMil
Leighton Buzzard
EBak
ECot
Stevenage
ETod
Colchester
Dunstable
ELan
EMui
Luton
ECha
Welwyn Garden City
ERod
Clacton on Sea
Aylesbury
Hemel Hempstead
St Albans
ERCP
EGle
Harlow
Chelmsford
ERob
EJWh
ERhR
Southminster
xford
Watford
ESCh
High Wycombe
ELon
Sth Benfleet
Brentwood
ECou
Slough
Grays
Southend
Reading
London
Gravesend
Gillingham
stone
M62
M18
(M)
A16
A17
A1
A10
A11
A12
A14
A47
M11
M1
A1(M)
M40
M25
M4
M3

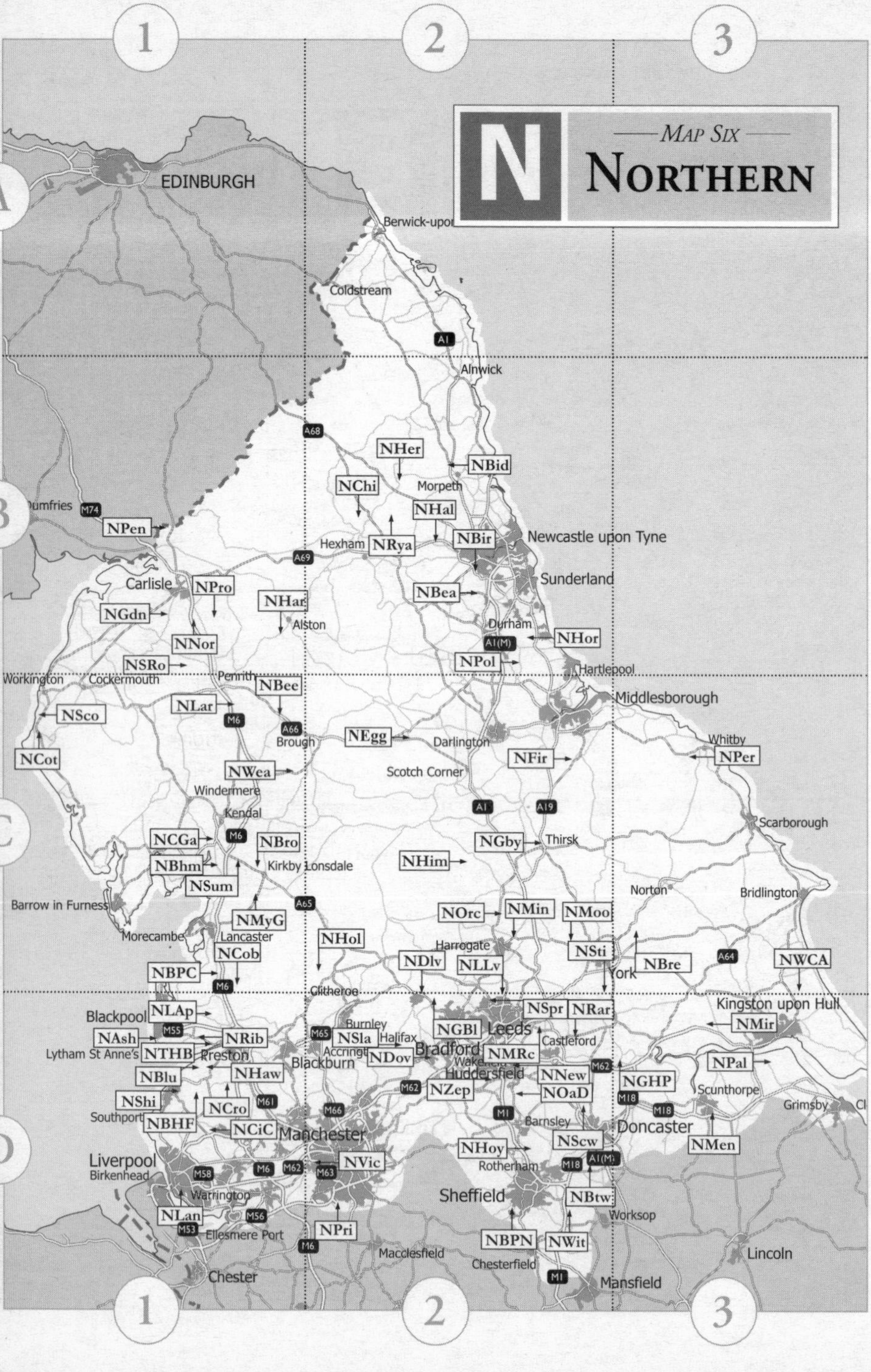
N
MAP SIX
NORTHERN
1
2
3
A
B
C
D
EDINBURGH
Berwick-upon
Coldstream
A1
Alnwick
A68
NHer
NBid
NChi
Morpeth
NHal
Dumfries
M74
NPen
Hexham
NRya
NBir
Newcastle upon Tyne
A69
Sunderland
Carlisle
NPro
NHar
NBea
NGdn
Alston
Durham
NHor
NNor
A1(M)
NPol
NSRo
Hartlepool
Workington
Cockermouth
Penrith
NBee
Middlesborough
NLar
NSco
M6
A66
Brough
NEgg
Darlington
Whitby
NCot
NFir
NPer
NWea
Scotch Corner
Windermere
Kendal
A1
A19
Scarborough
NCGa
M6
NBro
NGby
Thirsk
NBhm
Kirkby Lonsdale
NHim
NSum
Barrow in Furness
A65
Norton
Bridlington
NOrc
NMin
NMoo
NMyG
Morecambe
Lancaster
NHol
Harrogate
NCob
NSti
NDlv
NLLv
NBre
A64
NWCA
NBPC
York
M6
Clitheroe
Blackpool
NLAp
NSpr
NRar
Kingston upon Hull
M55
Burnley
NGBl
Leeds
NMir
NAsh
NRib
M65
NSla
Halifax
Castleford
Lytham St Anne's
NTHB
Preston
Accrington
NDov
Bradford
NMRc
Wakefield
NPal
M62
Blackburn
Huddersfield
NNew
NBlu
NHaw
NGHP
M62
NZep
NOaD
Scunthorpe
NShi
M61
M18
Grimsby
M18
NCro
Southport
M66
M1
NBHF
NCiC
Manchester
Barnsley
Doncaster
NHoy
NScw
NMen
Liverpool
NVic
Birkenhead
M58
M6
M62
M63
Rotherham
M18
A1(M)
Warrington
Sheffield
NBtw
NLan
M56
Worksop
M53
Ellesmere Port
NPri
M6
NBPN
NWit
Macclesfield
Lincoln
Chesterfield
Chester
M1
Mansfield
1
2
3

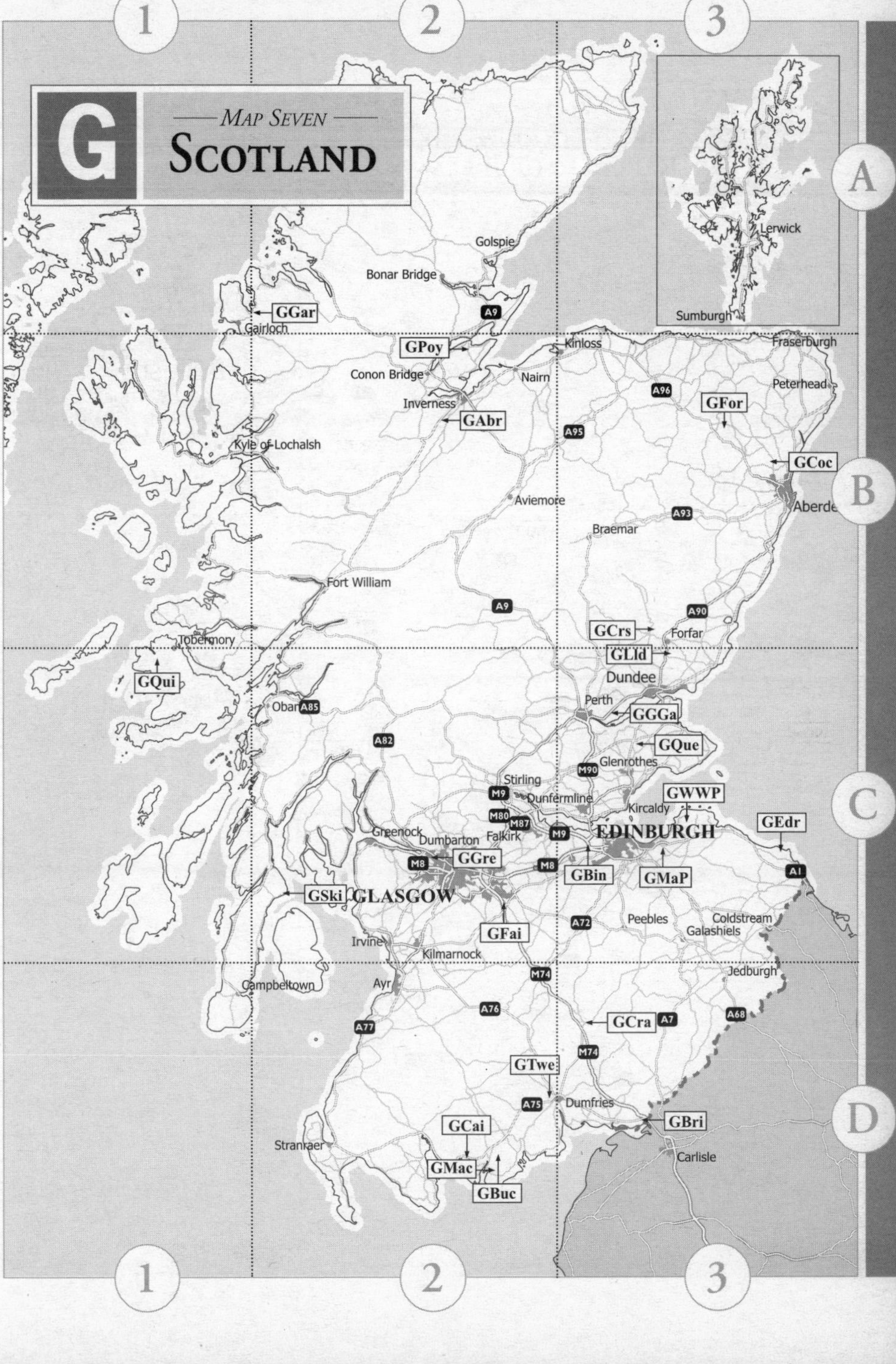

1
2
3
G
MAP SEVEN
SCOTLAND
A
B
C
D
Lerwick
Sumburgh
Golspie
Bonar Bridge
A9
GGar
Gairloch
GPoy
Kinloss
Fraserburgh
Conon Bridge
Nairn
Peterhead
A96
Inverness
GAbr
GFor
A95
Kyle of Lochalsh
GCoc
Aviemore
Aberde
A93
Braemar
Fort William
A9
A90
GCrs
Forfar
Tobermory
GLld
Dundee
GQui
Perth
GGGa
Oban
A85
A82
GQue
Glenrothes
M90
Stirling
GWWP
M9
Dunfermline
Kircaldy
GEdr
M80
M87
Greenock
Dumbarton
Falkirk
M9
EDINBURGH
M8
GGre
M8
GBin
GMaP
A1
GSki
GLASGOW
A72
Peebles
Coldstream
GFai
Galashiels
Irvine
Kilmarnock
Jedburgh
M74
Campbeltown
Ayr
A76
GCra
A7
A68
A77
M74
GTwe
A75
Dumfries
GBri
GCai
Stranraer
Carlisle
GMac
GBuc

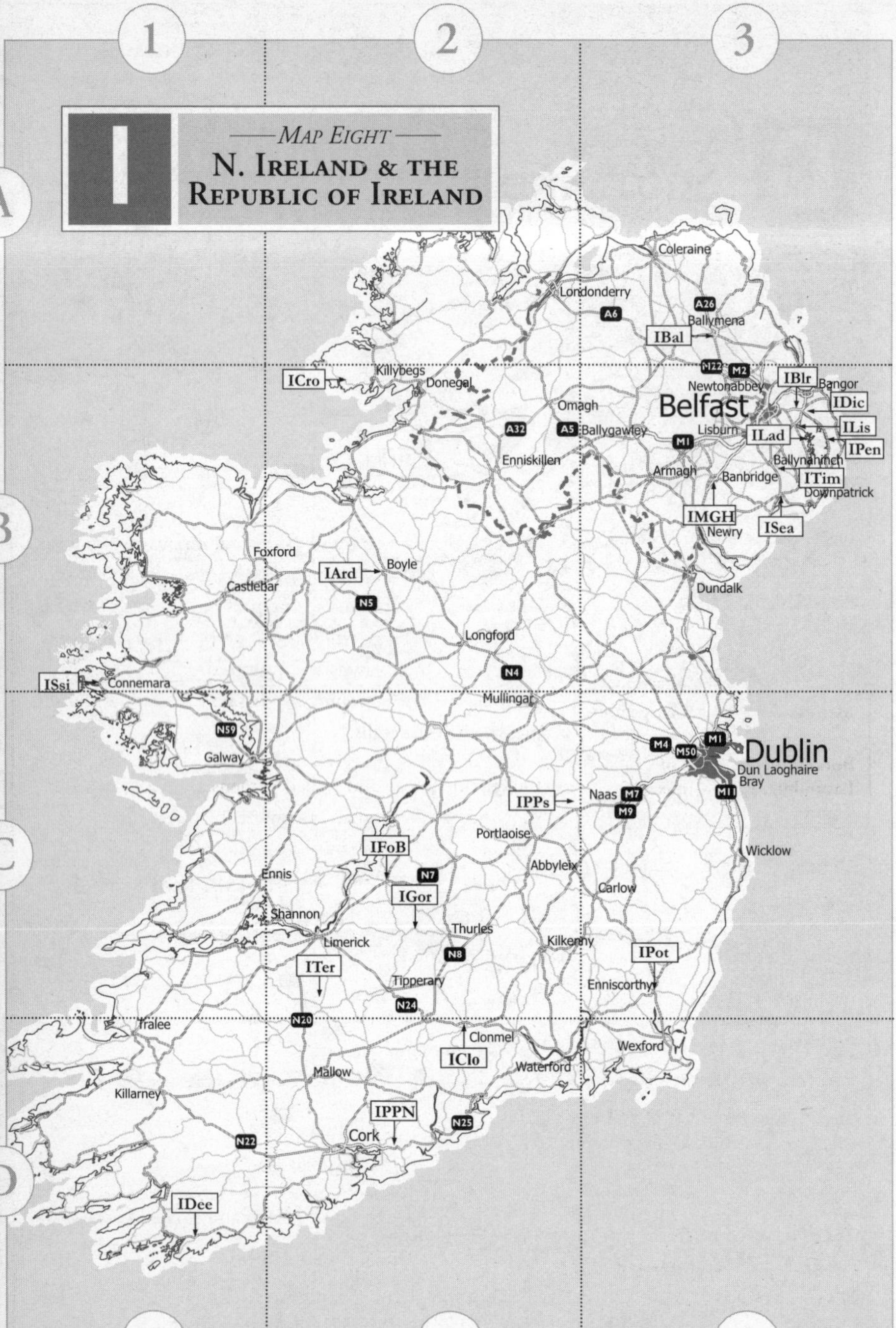
1
2
3
A
B
C
D
I
MAP EIGHT
N. IRELAND & THE REPUBLIC OF IRELAND
Coleraine
Londonderry
A26
A6
Ballymena
IBal
N22
M2
ICro
Killybegs
Donegal
IBlr
Bangor
Newtonabbey
Belfast
IDic
Omagh
A32
A5
Ballygawley
Lisburn
ILad
ILis
M1
IPen
Enniskillen
Ballynahinch
Armagh
Banbridge
ITim
Downpatrick
IMGH
Newry
ISea
Foxford
IArd
Boyle
Castlebar
N5
Dundalk
Longford
ISsi
Connemara
N4
Mullingar
N59
M1
M4
M50
Dublin
Galway
Dun Laoghaire
Bray
IPPs
Naas
M7
M11
M9
Portlaoise
IFoB
Wicklow
Abbyleix
N7
Ennis
IGor
Carlow
Shannon
Thurles
Limerick
Kilkenny
N8
ITer
IPot
Tipperary
Enniscorthy
N24
Tralee
N20
Clonmel
Wexford
IClo
Waterford
Mallow
Killarney
IPPN
N25
Cork
N22
IDee
1
2
3

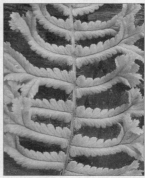

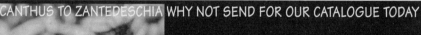

INDEX OF ADVERTISERS

RHS Show Awards 2005

RHS Plant Finder nurseries who were awarded RHS medals at the three major RHS Shows in 2005

Chelsea Gold

Jacques Amand International
Ashwood Nurseries Ltd
David Austin Roses Ltd
Avon Bulbs
Peter Beales Roses
Bowden Hostas
Burncoose Nurseries
Dibley's Nurseries
Downderry Nursery
Fernwood Nursery
Hall Farm Nursery
Hampshire Carnivorous Plants
Hardy's Cottage Garden Plants
Jekka's Herb Farm
Ken Muir Ltd
Knoll Gardens
Norfields
Notcutts Nurseries
P W Plants
Romantic Garden Nursery
Roualeyn Nurseries

Chelsea Silver Gilt

Ainsworth Displays
Burnham Nurseries
Sheila Chapman Clematis
Choice Landscapes
D'Arcy & Everest
Harveys Garden Plants
Hewitt-Cooper Carnivorous Plants
Kelways Ltd
Millais Nurseries
Pops Plants
Potash Nursery
Pottertons Nursery
Rhodes & Rockliffe
Rickard's Hardy Ferns Ltd
Rougham Hall Nurseries
Brian & Pearl Sulman
Thorncroft Clematis Nursery
Trevena Cross Nurseries
Westcountry Nurseries

Chelsea Silver

The Big Grass Co.
Fibrex Nurseries
Foxgrove Plants
C S Lockyer
Mallet Court Nursery
Newington Nurseries
Rotherview Nursery

Chelsea Silver Knightian

W Robinson & Son (Seeds & Plants)

Chelsea Bronze

Hopleys Plants
Pennard Plants

Chelsea Bronze Grenfell

David Austin Roses Ltd

Hampton Court Gold

Dibley's Nurseries
Downderry Nursery (& **Tudor Rose Award**)
Fir Trees Pelargonium Nursery
Goldbrook Plants
Hampshire Carnivorous Plants
Hardy's Cottage Garden Plants
Harts Green Nursery
Jekka's Herb Farm
Kobakoba
C S Lockyer
Mendip Bonsai Studio
Norfields
Park Green Nurseries
Potash Nursery
Roualeyn Nurseries
South West Carnivorous Plants
Brian & Pearl Sulman
Toobees Exotics
Trevena Cross

Hampton Court Silver-Gilt

Jacques Amand International
Burncoose Nurseries
Sheila Chapman Clematis
Choice Landscapes
Culm View Nursery
Dysons Nurseries

Edrom Nurseries
Foxgrove Plants
Harveys Garden Plants
Long Acre Plants
P W Plants
Rickard's Hardy Ferns Ltd
Thorncroft Clematis Nursery
Winchester Growers

HAMPTON COURT SILVER

Ainsworth Displays
Avon Bulbs
Blacksmiths Cottage Nursery
Burnham Nurseries
Churchtown Nurseries
Derek Lloyd Dean
Fernwood Nursery
Fibrex Nurseries Ltd
Hopleys Plants
Mill Cottage Plants
Pine Cottage Plants
Rotherview Nursery
Rougham Hall Nurseries
Southview Nurseries

HAMPTON COURT SILVER KNIGHTIAN

Highdown Nursery

HAMPTON COURT BRONZE

Allwood Bros
W E Th. Ingwersen Ltd
Ken Muir Ltd

HAMPTON COURT FESTIVAL OF ROSES GOLD

David Austin Roses Ltd
Henry Street Nursery

HAMPTON COURT FESTIVAL OF ROSES SILVER-GILT

Claire Austin Hardy Plants

HAMPTON COURT FESTIVAL OF ROSES SILVER

Peter Beales Roses
C & K Jones
Notcutts Nurseries
Seale Nurseries
Style Roses

HAMPTON COURT PLANT HERITAGE GOLD

Dibley's Nurseries

HAMPTON COURT PLANT HERITAGE SILVER LINDLEY

Downderry Nursery
Pine Cottage Plants

HAMPTON COURT PLANT HERITAGE BRONZE LINDLEY

The Old Walled Garden
Southview Nurseries

Tir Mab Cynan Nursery
Warren Hills Nursery
Winchester Growers Ltd

TATTON GOLD

Bluebell Arboretum & Nursery
Bowden Hostas
Croston Cactus
Dibley's Nurseries
Edrom Nurseries
Fernwood Nursery
Fir Trees Pelargonium Nursery
Foxgrove Plants
Hall Farm Nursery
Hampshire Carnivorous Plants
Hardy's Cottage Garden Plants
Kobakoba
Jekka's Herb Farm
Long Acre Plants
Elizabeth MacGregor
Mendip Bonsai Studio (& **Best Exhibit in Floral Marquees**)
Norfields
Oak Tree Nursery
Potash Nursery
Roualeyn Nurseries
South West Carnivorous Plants

TATTON SILVER-GILT

Ainsworth Displays
Burncoose Nurseries
Cairnsmore Nursery
Cath's Garden Plants
D'Arcy & Everest
Fibrex Nurseries Ltd
Holden Clough Nusery
Mary Green Hostas
Park Green Nurseries
Packhorse Farm Nursery
Proudplants
Shirley's Plants
Brian & Pearl Sulman

TATTON SILVER-GILT KNIGHTIAN

W Robinson & Sons Ltd

TATTON SILVER

Bridge End Nursery
Hartside Nursery Garden
Mallet Court Nursery
Mickfield Hostas
Rougham Hall Nurseries
Springfield Nurseries

TATTON BRONZE

Morton Hall Gardens

TATTON BRONZE KNIGHTIAN

Tavistock Herb Nursery

The HARDY PLANT SOCIETY

MEMBERSHIP APPLICATION FOR 2006

The Annual Subscriptions are:
Single **£13.00** per year (one member)
Joint **£15.00** per year (two members at the same address)

• Subscriptions are renewable annually on **1 January**.
• Subscriptions of members joining after 1 October are valid until the end of the following year.
• Overseas members are requested to pay in pounds sterling by International Money Order or by credit card. An optional charge of £10.00 is made for airmail postage outside Western Europe of all literature, if preferred.

Please fill in the details in BLOCK CAPITALS, tear off this form and send it with your payment to the Administrator or telephone the Administrator with details of your credit card.

Please tick the type of membership required

☐ Single £13.00 per year (one member)
☐ Joint £15.00 per year (two members at one address)
☐ Airmail postage £10.00 per year (optional for members outside Western Europe)

NAME/S ....

ADDRESS ....

....

.... POST CODE ....

TELEPHONE NUMBER ....

E-mail ....

I enclose a cheque/postal order* payable to **THE HARDY PLANT SOCIETY** (in pounds sterling ONLY) for £ ....

OR
Please debit my Visa/Master Card* by the sum of £ ....
(* delete as required)

CARD NUMBER ☐☐☐☐ ☐☐☐☐ ☐☐☐☐ ☐☐☐☐

EXPIRY DATE ☐☐☐☐

Name as embossed on card ....

Signature ....

Please print your name and address clearly, tear out the page and send it to The Administrator at the address overleaf

The Hardy Plant Society is a Registered Charity, number 208080

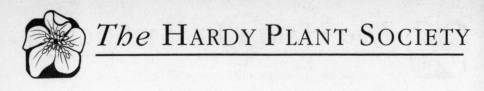

National Council for the Conservation of Plants & Gardens

Membership Application Form

Please complete and detach this form enclosing your payment and send to: Membership, NCCPG, The Stable Courtyard, Wisley Garden, Woking, Surrey GU23 6QP.

PLANT HER[…] NCCPG

How to Join

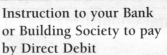

By post: complete form and send to theabove address

On line: www.nccpg.com

Annual Subscription Rates

(please tick relevant boxes)

- ☐ Individual UK **£20**
- ☐ Joint UK **£34** (two people at same address)
- ☐ Student (up to age 25 in full time education) **£5**
- ☐ Gardening clubs and non-commercial groups **£30**
- ☐ Corporate **£55**
- ☐ Friend ________ **(min £100)**

  Friends make annual donations in support of our work (in addition to the membership fee)
- ☐ Please send me information on legacies
- ☐ Please send me information on becoming a Collection Holder
- ☐ I would like to make an additional donation of ________ towards the conservation work of NCCPG

Please complete in CAPITALS

Title ____ First Name ________

Last Name ________

Date of Birth ________

Address ________

____

________ Postcode ________

Daytime Telephone ________

Email ________

giftaid it

Gift Aid Declaration: Are you a UK taxpayer? If you are, we can claim 28% from the government on your subscription at no extra cost to you.

☐ I would like the National Council for the Conservation of Plants & Gardens to reclaim the tax on any membership subscription or donation that I make/have made since 6th April 2000 and all subscriptions and donations I make in the future, until I notify you otherwise. I have paid an amount of UK income tax or capital gains tax equal to any tax reclaimed. (Remember that if you receive a company pension, income tax may well be paid at source.)

Instruction to your Bank or Building Society to pay by Direct Debit

DIRECT Debit

Please fill in the form and send to:
Membership, NCCPG, The Stable Courtyard, Wisley Garden, Woking, Surrey GU23 6QP.

Originators Identification Num[…]

9 7 4 2 1 2

Name and full postal address of your Bank or Building Socie[…]

To: The Manager ________ Bank/Building Socie[…]

Address ________

____

____

Postcode ________

Name(s) of Account Holder ________

Branch Sort Code ☐☐☐☐☐☐

Bank/Building Society account number ☐☐☐☐☐☐☐☐

Reference No. (NCCPG use only) ☐☐☐☐☐☐

Instruction to your Bank or Building Society
Please pay the NCCPG Direct Debits from the account detailed in the instructi[…] subject to the safeguards assured by the Direct Debit Guarantee. I understa[…] that this instruction may remain with the NCCPG and if so, details will be pass[…] electronically to my Bank/Building Society.

Signature(s) ________

Date / /

Banks and Building Societies may not accept Direct Debit Instructions for some types of accou[…]

Payment by Credit or Debit card (Excluding American Express/Diners)

Card No: ________

Issue No *(Switch only)* ☐☐ Security code ☐☐☐

Start Date ☐☐ / ☐☐ Expiry Date ☐☐ / ☐☐

Bank Name ________

Name on Card ________

Signature ________ Date ________

Payment by cheque: Please make sterling cheques payable to **NCCPG**.

Data Protection Act: Records for each member are kept at NCCPG National Office and by local Group Membership Secretaries. Under no circumstances are membership records used for purpose[…] other than those connected to the legitimate activities of The National Council for the Conservation of Plants & Gardens. Registered charity number: 1004009.

National Council for the Conservation of Plants and Gardens

The Stable Courtyard, Wisley Garden, Woking, Surrey GU23 6QP. **T** 01483 211465 **F** 01483 212404 **E** membership@nccpg.org.uk **W** www.nccpg.com

Company Registration No. 2222953. Registered charity No.1004009